# List of Elements with Their Symbols and Atomic Weights

| Element | Symbol | Atomic Number | Atomic Weight |
|---|---|---|---|
| Actinium | Ac | 89 | 227.03[a] |
| Aluminum | Al | 13 | 26.981538 |
| Americium | Am | 95 | 243.06[a] |
| Antimony | Sb | 51 | 121.760 |
| Argon | Ar | 18 | 39.948 |
| Arsenic | As | 33 | 74.92160 |
| Astatine | At | 85 | 209.99[a] |
| Barium | Ba | 56 | 137.327 |
| Berkelium | Bk | 97 | 247.07[a] |
| Beryllium | Be | 4 | 9.012182 |
| Bismuth | Bi | 83 | 208.98038 |
| Bohrium | Bh | 107 | 264.12[a] |
| Boron | B | 5 | 10.811 |
| Bromine | Br | 35 | 79.904 |
| Cadmium | Cd | 48 | 112.411 |
| Calcium | Ca | 20 | 40.078 |
| Californium | Cf | 98 | 251.08[a] |
| Carbon | C | 6 | 12.0107 |
| Cerium | Ce | 58 | 140.116 |
| Cesium | Cs | 55 | 132.90545 |
| Chlorine | Cl | 17 | 35.453 |
| Chromium | Cr | 24 | 51.9961 |
| Cobalt | Co | 27 | 58.933200 |
| Copernicium | Cn | 112 | 285 |
| Copper | Cu | 29 | 63.546 |
| Curium | Cm | 96 | 247.07[a] |
| Darmstadtium | Ds | 110 | 281.15[a] |
| Dubnium | Db | 105 | 262.11[a] |
| Dysprosium | Dy | 66 | 162.50 |
| Einsteinium | Es | 99 | 252.08[a] |
| Erbium | Er | 68 | 167.259 |
| Europium | Eu | 63 | 151.964 |
| Fermium | Fm | 100 | 257.10[a] |
| Fluorine | F | 9 | 18.9984032 |
| Francium | Fr | 87 | 223.02[a] |
| Gadolinium | Gd | 64 | 157.25 |
| Gallium | Ga | 31 | 69.723 |
| Germanium | Ge | 32 | 72.64 |
| Gold | Au | 79 | 196.96655 |

| Element | Symbol | Atomic Number | Atomic Weight |
|---|---|---|---|
| Hafnium | Hf | 72 | 178.49 |
| Hassium | Hs | 108 | 269.13[a] |
| Helium | He | 2 | 4.002602[a] |
| Holmium | Ho | 67 | 164.93032 |
| Hydrogen | H | 1 | 1.00794 |
| Indium | In | 49 | 114.818 |
| Iodine | I | 53 | 126.90447 |
| Iridium | Ir | 77 | 192.217 |
| Iron | Fe | 26 | 55.845 |
| Krypton | Kr | 36 | 83.80 |
| Lanthanum | La | 57 | 138.9055 |
| Lawrencium | Lr | 103 | 262.11[a] |
| Lead | Pb | 82 | 207.2 |
| Lithium | Li | 3 | 6.941 |
| Lutetium | Lu | 71 | 174.967 |
| Magnesium | Mg | 12 | 24.3050 |
| Manganese | Mn | 25 | 54.938049 |
| Meitnerium | Mt | 109 | 268.14[a] |
| Mendelevium | Md | 101 | 258.10[a] |
| Mercury | Hg | 80 | 200.59 |
| Molybdenum | Mo | 42 | 95.94 |
| Neodymium | Nd | 60 | 144.24 |
| Neon | Ne | 10 | 20.1797 |
| Neptunium | Np | 93 | 237.05[a] |
| Nickel | Ni | 28 | 58.6934 |
| Niobium | Nb | 41 | 92.90638 |
| Nitrogen | N | 7 | 14.0067 |
| Nobelium | No | 102 | 259.10[a] |
| Osmium | Os | 76 | 190.23 |
| Oxygen | O | 8 | 15.9994 |
| Palladium | Pd | 46 | 106.42 |
| Phosphorus | P | 15 | 30.973761 |
| Platinum | Pt | 78 | 195.078 |
| Plutonium | Pu | 94 | 244.06[a] |
| Polonium | Po | 84 | 208.98[a] |
| Potassium | K | 19 | 39.0983 |
| Praseodymium | Pr | 59 | 140.90765 |
| Promethium | Pm | 61 | 145[a] |
| Protactinium | Pa | 91 | 231.03588 |
| Radium | Ra | 88 | 226.03[a] |

| Element | Symbol | Atomic Number | Atomic Weight |
|---|---|---|---|
| Radon | Rn | 86 | 222.02[a] |
| Rhenium | Re | 75 | 186.207[a] |
| Rhodium | Rh | 45 | 102.90550 |
| Roentgenium | Rg | 111 | 272.15[a] |
| Rubidium | Rb | 37 | 85.4678 |
| Ruthenium | Ru | 44 | 101.07 |
| Rutherfordium | Rf | 104 | 261.11[a] |
| Samarium | Sm | 62 | 150.36 |
| Scandium | Sc | 21 | 44.955910 |
| Seaborgium | Sg | 106 | 266[a] |
| Selenium | Se | 34 | 78.96 |
| Silicon | Si | 14 | 28.0855 |
| Silver | Ag | 47 | 107.8682 |
| Sodium | Na | 11 | 22.989770 |
| Strontium | Sr | 38 | 87.62 |
| Sulfur | S | 16 | 32.065 |
| Tantalum | Ta | 73 | 180.9479 |
| Technetium | Tc | 43 | 98[a] |
| Tellurium | Te | 52 | 127.60 |
| Terbium | Tb | 65 | 158.92534 |
| Thallium | Tl | 81 | 204.3833 |
| Thorium | Th | 90 | 232.0381 |
| Thulium | Tm | 69 | 168.93421 |
| Tin | Sn | 50 | 118.710 |
| Titanium | Ti | 22 | 47.867 |
| Tungsten | W | 74 | 183.84 |
| Uranium | U | 92 | 238.02891 |
| Vanadium | V | 23 | 50.9415 |
| Xenon | Xe | 54 | |
| Ytterbium | Yb | 70 | |
| Yttrium | Y | 39 | |
| Zinc | Zn | 30 | |
| Zirconium | Zr | 40 | |
| *b | | 113 | |
| *b | | 114 | |
| *b | | 115 | |
| *b | | 116 | |
| *b | | 117 | |
| *b | | 118 | |

[a]Mass of longest-lived or most important isotope.
[b]The names of elements 113 and above have not yet been decided.

# CHEMISTRY

## THE CENTRAL SCIENCE CHEMISTRY

## SECOND CUSTOM EDITION

THEODORE L. BROWN
H. EUGENE LeMAY, JR.
BRUCE E. BURSTEN
CATHERINE J. MURPHY
PATRICK M. WOODWARD

Taken from:

*Chemistry: The Central Science,* Twelfth Edition
by Theodore L. Brown, H. Eugene LeMay, Jr., Bruce E. Burstsen,
Catherine J. Murphy, and Patrick M. Woodward

Cover Art: Courtesy of Vincent J. Catalano, University of Nevada-Reno.

The cover shows the multimetallic core of an inorganic transition metal complex synthesized in Professor Vincent Catalano's research laboratory at the University of Nevada-Reno.

Taken from:

*Chemistry: The Central Science,* Twelfth Edition
by Theodore L. Brown, H. Eugene LeMay, Jr.,
Bruce E. Bursten, Catherine J. Murphy, and Patrick M. Woodward
Copyright © 2012, 2009, 2006, 2003, 2000, 1997, 1994, 1991, 1988, 1985, 1981, 1977
by Pearson Education, Inc.
Publishing as Pearson Prentice Hall
Glenview, Illinois 60025

Pearson Learning Solutions, 501 Boylston Street, Suite 900, Boston, MA 02116
A Pearson Education Company
www.pearsoned.com

Printed in the United States of America

1 2 3 4 5 6 7 8 9 10 V357 16 15 14 13 12 11

000200010270763513

NLS

Dear Student:

In this course you will be using MasteringChemistry®, an online tutorial and homework program that accompanies your textbook. If you have joined a MasteringChemistry course before and can still log in: Save time by following the guide for joining another course (available from www.masteringchemistry.com > Tours & Training > Getting Started) instead of this page.

## What You Need:

✓ A valid email address

✓ A student access code
(Comes in the Student Access Code Card/Kit that may have been packaged with your new textbook or that may be available separately in your school's bookstore. Otherwise, you can purchase access online at www.masteringchemistry.com.)

✓ The ZIP or other postal code for your school: **89557**

✓ A Course ID: _____ (Provided by your instructor)

## 1. Register

● Go to www.masteringchemistry.com and click Students under Register .

● To register using the student access code inside the MasteringChemistry Student Access Code Card/Kit, select Yes, I have an access code . Click Continue .

–OR– Purchase access online: Select No, I need to purchase access online now . Select your textbook, whether you want access to the eText, and click Continue . Follow the on-screen instructions to purchase access using a credit card. The purchase path includes registration, but the process is a bit different from the steps printed here.

● License Agreement and Privacy Policy: Click I Accept to indicate that you have read and agree to the license agreement and privacy policy.

● Select the appropriate option under "Do you have a Pearson Education account?" Continue to give the requested information until you complete the process. The Confirmation & Summary page confirms your registration. This information will also be emailed to you for your records. You can either click Log In Now or return to www.masteringchemistry.com later.

## 2. Log In

● Go to www.masteringchemistry.com.

● Enter your Login Name and Password that you specified during registration and click Log In .

## 3. Join Your Instructor's Online Course and/or Open Self-Study Resources

Upon first login, you'll be asked to do one or more of the following:

● Join a Course by entering the MasteringChemistry Course ID provided by your instructor. If you don't have a Course ID now, you can return to join the MasteringChemistry course later. When you join a course, you may also be asked for a Student ID (follow on-screen instructions).

● Explore the Study Area or Launch Your eText , if these resources are available for your textbook.

## To Access MasteringChemistry Again Later

Simply go to www.masteringchemistry.com, enter your Login Name and Password, and click Log In .

After you have joined a course: You can open any assignments from the Assignments Due Soon area or from the Assignments page. For self-study, click eText or Study Area , if these options are available.

## Support

Access Customer Support at http://www.masteringchemistry.com/support, where you will find:

● System Requirements

● Answers to Frequently Asked Questions

● Registration Tips & Tricks video

● Additional contact information for Customer Support, including Live Chat

ALWAYS LEARNING                                                                    PEARSON

*To our students,
whose enthusiasm and curiosity
have often inspired us,
and whose questions and suggestions
have sometimes taught us.*

# BRIEF CONTENTS

# CONTENTS

## 2  ATOMS, MOLECULES, AND IONS   38

# 3 STOICHIOMETRY: CALCULATIONS WITH CHEMICAL FORMULAS AND EQUATIONS  76

# 4 REACTIONS IN AQUEOUS SOLUTION   114

# 5 THERMOCHEMISTRY   158

# 6 ELECTRONIC STRUCTURE OF ATOMS   206

# 7 PERIODIC PROPERTIES OF THE ELEMENTS 248

# 8 BASIC CONCEPTS OF CHEMICAL BONDING 288

# 9 MOLECULAR GEOMETRY AND BONDING THEORIES 330

# 10 GASES  382

# 11 LIQUIDS AND INTERMOLECULAR FORCES  424

# 12 SOLIDS AND MODERN MATERIALS  462

# 13 PROPERTIES OF SOLUTIONS  512

# 14 CHEMICAL KINETICS 556

# 15 CHEMICAL EQUILIBRIUM 610

# 16 ACID–BASE EQUILIBRIA 650

# 17 ADDITIONAL ASPECTS OF AQUEOUS EQUILIBRIA 702

# 18 CHEMISTRY OF THE ENVIRONMENT 748

# 19 CHEMICAL THERMODYNAMICS 784

# 20 ELECTROCHEMISTRY 826

# 21 NUCLEAR CHEMISTRY  874

# 22 CHEMISTRY OF THE NONMETALS 916

# 23 TRANSITION METALS AND COORDINATION CHEMISTRY 962

# Appendices

# CHEMICAL APPLICATIONS AND ESSAYS

# PREFACE

## TO THE INSTRUCTOR

### Philosophy

The cover of this new edition of *Chemistry: The Central Science* features a striking illustration of the structure of graphene, a recently discovered form of carbon. As we began preparing the previous edition in 2006, single-layer graphene was virtually unknown. The extraordinary properties of graphene, and its promise for future applications, has already resulted in a Nobel Prize. An understanding of the structure and many of the properties of graphene is well within the reach of an undergraduate student of general chemistry. Through such examples, it is possible to demonstrate in a general chemistry course that chemistry is a dynamic science in continuous development. New research leads to new applications of chemistry in other fields of science and in technology. In addition, environmental and economic concerns bring about changes in the place of chemistry in society. Our textbook reflects this dynamic, changing character. We hope that it also conveys the excitement that scientists experience in making new discoveries that contribute to our understanding of the physical world.

New ideas about how to teach chemistry are constantly being developed, and many of them are reflected in how our textbook is organized and in the ways in which topics are presented. This edition incorporates a number of new methodologies to assist students, including use of the Internet, computer-based classroom tools, Web-based tools, particularly MasteringChemistry®, and more effective means of testing.

As authors, we want this text to be a central, indispensable learning tool for students. It can be carried everywhere and used at any time. It is the one place students can go to obtain the information needed for learning, skill development, reference, and test preparation. At the same time, the text provides the background in modern chemistry that students need to serve their professional interests and, as appropriate, to prepare for more advanced chemistry courses.

If the text is to be effective in supporting your role as teacher, it must be addressed to the students. We have done our best to keep our writing clear and interesting and the book attractive and well illustrated. The book has numerous in-text study aids for students, including carefully placed descriptions of problem-solving strategies. Together we have logged many years of teaching experience. We hope this is evident in our pacing, choice of examples, and the kinds of study aids and motivational tools we have employed. Because we believe that students are more enthusiastic about learning chemistry when they see its importance to their own goals and interests, we have highlighted many important applications of chemistry in everyday life. We hope you make use of this material.

A textbook is only as useful to students as the instructor permits it to be. This book is replete with features that can help students learn and that can guide them as they acquire both conceptual understanding and problem-solving skills. But the text and all the supplementary materials provided to support its use must work in concert with you, the instructor. There is a great deal for the students to use here, too much for all of it to be absorbed by any one student. You will be the guide to the best use of the book. Only with your active help will the students be able to utilize most effectively all that the text and its supplements offer. Students care about grades, of course, and with encouragement they will also become interested in the subject matter and care about learning. Please consider emphasizing features of the book that can enhance student appreciation of chemistry, such as the ***Chemistry Put to Work*** and ***Chemistry and Life*** boxes that show how chemistry impacts modern life and its relationship to health and life processes. Learn to use, and urge students to use, the rich Internet resources available. Emphasize conceptual understanding and place less emphasis on simple manipulative, algorithmic problem solving.

## What's New in This Edition?

A great many changes have been made in producing this twelfth edition. The entire art program for the text has been reworked, and new features connected with the art have been introduced.

- Nearly every figure in the book has undergone some modification, and hundreds of figures have been entirely redone.
- A systematic effort has been made to move information that was contained in figure captions directly into the figures.
- Explanatory labels have been employed extensively in figures to guide the student in understanding the art.
- In several important places, art has been modified to convey the notion of progression in time, as in a reaction. See, for instance, Figures 4.4 and 14.27.
- New designs have been employed to more closely integrate photographic materials into figures that convey chemical principles, as in Figure 2.21.
- A new feature called **Go Figure** has been added to about 40% of the figures. This feature asks the student a question that can be answered by examining the figure. It tests whether the student has in fact examined the figure and understands its primary message. Answers to the **Go Figure** questions are provided in the back of the text.
- New end-of-chapter exercises have been added, and many of those carried over from the eleventh edition have been significantly revised. Results from analysis of student responses to MasteringChemistry, the online homework program connected with the text, have been used to eliminate questions that did not appear to be functioning well and to assess the degree to which instructors have used the end-of-chapter materials. On the basis of these analyses, many exercises have been revised or eliminated.
- Chapter introductions have been redesigned to enhance the student's exposure to the aims of the chapter and its contents.
- The presentation of hybrid orbitals in Chapter 9 and elsewhere has been rewritten to limit the treatment to $s$ and $p$ orbitals, based on theoretical work indicating that $d$ orbital participation in hybridization is not significant.
- The treatment of condensed phases, liquids and solids, has been reorganized into two chapters that contain much new material. Chapter 11 deals with liquids and intermolecular forces, while Chapter 12 deals with solids, starting from the basics of crystal structures and covering a broad range of materials (including metals, semiconductors, polymers, and nanomaterials) in a cohesive manner.
- Chapter 18 on the Chemistry of the Environment has been substantially revised to focus on how human activities affect Earth's atmosphere and water, and to enlarge the coverage of the green chemistry initiative.
- The treatment of metals, Chapter 23 of the eleventh edition, has been reorganized and augmented. Structure and bonding in metals and alloys are now covered in Chapter 12 (Solids and Modern Materials), and other parts of Chapter 23 have been combined with material from Chapter 24 of the eleventh edition to form a new chapter, Transition Metals and Coordination Chemistry. Material covering occurrences and production of metals that was not widely used by instructors has been eliminated.

Throughout the text, the writing has been improved by enhancing the clarity and flow of ideas while achieving an economy of words. Thus, despite the addition of new features, the length of the text has not changed significantly.

## Organization and Contents

The first five chapters give a largely macroscopic, phenomenological view of chemistry. The basic concepts introduced—such as nomenclature, stoichiometry, and thermochemistry—provide necessary background for many of the laboratory experiments usually performed in general chemistry. We believe that an early introduction to thermochemistry is desirable because so much of our understanding of chemical processes is based on considerations of energy changes. Thermochemistry is also important when we come to a discussion of bond enthalpies. We believe we have produced an effective, balanced approach to teaching thermodynamics in general chemistry, as well as providing students with an introduction to some of the global issues involving energy production and consumption. It is no easy matter to walk the narrow pathway between—on the one hand—trying to teach too much at too high a level and—on the other hand—resorting to oversimplifications. As with the book as a whole, the emphasis has been on imparting *conceptual* understanding, as opposed to presenting equations into which students are supposed to plug numbers.

The next four chapters (Chapters 6–9) deal with electronic structure and bonding. We have largely retained our presentation of atomic orbitals. For more advanced students, **Closer Look** boxes in Chapters 6 and 9 deal with radial probability functions and the phases of orbitals. Our approach of placing this latter discussion in a Closer Look box in Chapter 9 enables those who wish to cover this topic to do so, while others may wish to bypass it. In treating this topic and others in Chapters 7 and 9 we have materially enhanced the accompanying figures to more effectively bring home their central messages.

The focus of the text then changes (Chapters 10–13) to the next level of the organization of matter, examining the states of matter. Chapters 10 and 11 deal with gases, liquids, and intermolecular forces, much as in earlier editions. Chapter 12, however, is now devoted to solids, presenting an enlarged and more contemporary view of the solid state as well as of modern materials. This change is appropriate, given the ever-increasing importance of solid-state materials in solar energy, illumination, and electronics. Chapter 12 provides an opportunity to show how abstract chemical bonding concepts impact real-world applications. The modular organization of the chapter allows you to tailor your coverage to focus on materials (semiconductors, polymers, nanomaterials, and so forth) that are most relevant to your students and your own interests. Chapter 13 treats the formation and properties of solutions in much the same manner as the previous edition.

The next several chapters examine the factors that determine the speed and extent of chemical reactions: kinetics (Chapter 14), equilibria (Chapters 15–17), thermodynamics (Chapter 19), and electrochemistry (Chapter 20). Also in this section is a chapter on environmental chemistry (Chapter 18), in which the concepts developed in preceding chapters are applied to a discussion of the atmosphere and hydrosphere. This chapter has been revised to focus more sharply on the impacts of human activities on Earth's water and atmosphere and on green chemistry.

After a discussion of nuclear chemistry (Chapter 21), the book ends with three survey chapters. Chapter 22, on nonmetals, has been consolidated slightly from the eleventh edition. Chapter 23 now deals with the chemistry of transition metals, including coordination compounds, and the last chapter deals with the chemistry of organic compounds and elementary biochemical themes. These final four chapters are developed in a parallel fashion and can be treated in any order.

Our chapter sequence provides a fairly standard organization, but we recognize that not everyone teaches all the topics in just the order we have chosen. We have therefore made sure that instructors can make common changes in teaching sequence with no loss in student comprehension. In particular, many instructors prefer to introduce gases (Chapter 10) after stoichiometry (Chapter 3) rather than with states of matter. The chapter on gases has been written to permit this change with *no* disruption in the flow of material. It is also possible to treat balancing redox equations (Sections 20.1 and 20.2) earlier, after the introduction of redox reactions in Section 4.4. Finally, some instructors like to cover organic chemistry (Chapter 24) right after bonding (Chapters 8 and 9). This, too, is a largely seamless move.

We have brought students into greater contact with descriptive organic and inorganic chemistry by integrating examples throughout the text. You will find pertinent and relevant examples of "real" chemistry woven into all the chapters to illustrate principles and applications. Some chapters, of course, more directly address the "descriptive" properties of elements and their compounds, especially Chapters 4, 7, 11, 18, and 22–24. We also in-corporate descriptive organic and inorganic chemistry in the end-of-chapter exercises.

## Changes in This Edition

The **What's New in This Edition** on page xxvii details changes made throughout the new edition. Beyond a mere listing, however, it is worth dwelling on the general goals we set in formulating the twelfth edition. *Chemistry: The Central Science* has traditionally been valued for its clarity of writing, its scientific accuracy and currency, its strong end-of-chapter exercises, and its consistency in level of coverage. In making changes, we have made sure not to compromise these characteristics, and we have also continued to employ an open, clean design in the layout of the book.

The major systemic change in the new edition involves the art program. It is widely recognized that contemporary students rely more on visual learning materials than in the past, yet for the most part textbook art has not evolved greatly in response other than a greater use of molecular art. In this edition, with the help of a strong editorial development team, we have redone a large portion of the figures with the aim of in-creasing their power as teaching tools. What can we do to encourage students to study a figure, and how can we help them learn from it? The first step has been to incorporate elements that direct attention to the figure's major features. The flow from one impor-tant aspect to the next, particularly involving processes occurring over time, has been emphasized through new layouts and through the use of both visual and textual cues, as in Figures 2.15, 4.3, 4.9, and 14.17. Our aim is to draw the student into a more careful and thoughtful viewing through extensive use of explanatory labels and other devices. A new feature called **Go Figure**, analogous to the **Give It Some Thought** exercises we pioneered in the tenth edition, directs attention to the art and provides an opportunity for students to judge whether they have really absorbed the content of the figure. We have also found new and more effective ways to show trends and relationships in figures involving presentations of data, as in Figures 7.6, 8.8, and 8.15.

We have continued to use the **What's Ahead** overview at the opening of each chapter, introduced in the ninth edition. *Concept links* ( ∞ ) continue to provide easy-to-see cross-references to pertinent material covered earlier in the text. The essays titled *Strategies in Chemistry*, which provide advice to students on problem solving and "thinking like a chemist," continue to be an important feature. The **Give It Some Thought** exercises that we introduced in the tenth edition have proved to be very popu-lar, and we have continued to refine their use. These informal, sharply focused questions give students opportunities to test whether they are "getting it" as they read along.

We have continued to emphasize conceptual exercises in the end-of-chapter exer-cise materials. The **Visualizing Concepts** exercise category has been continued in this edition. These exercises are designed to facilitate concept understanding through use of models, graphs, and other visual materials. They precede the regular end-of-chapter exercises and are identified in each case with the relevant chapter section number. The **Integrative Exercises**, which give students the opportunity to solve problems that integrate concepts from the present chapter with those of previous chapters, have been continued. The importance of integrative problem solving is highlighted by the **Sample Integrative Exercise** that ends each chapter beginning with Chapter 4. In gen-eral, we have included more conceptual end-of-chapter exercises and have made sure that there is a good representation of somewhat more difficult exercises to provide a better mix in terms of topic and level of difficulty. The results from student use of MasteringChemistry have enabled us to more reliably evaluate the effectiveness of our end-of-chapter exercises and make changes accordingly.

New essays in our well-received *Chemistry Put to Work* and *Chemistry and Life* series emphasize world events, scientific discoveries, and medical breakthroughs that have occurred since publication of the eleventh edition. We maintain our focus on the positive aspects of chemistry without neglecting the problems that can arise in an increasingly technological world. Our goal is to help students appreciate the real-world perspective of chemistry and the ways in which chemistry affects their lives.

# TO THE STUDENT

*Chemistry: The Central Science,* **Twelfth Edition,** has been written to introduce you to modern chemistry. As authors, we have, in effect, been engaged by your instructor to help you learn chemistry. Based on the comments of students and instructors who have used this book in its previous editions, we believe that we have done that job well. Of course, we expect the text to continue to evolve through future editions. We invite you to write to tell us what you like about the book so that we will know where we have helped you most. Also, we would like to learn of any shortcomings so that we might further improve the book in subsequent editions. Our addresses are given at the end of the Preface.

## Advice for Learning and Studying Chemistry

Learning chemistry requires both the assimilation of many concepts and the development of analytical skills. In this text we have provided you with numerous tools to help you succeed in both tasks. If you are going to succeed in your chemistry course, you will have to develop good study habits. Science courses, and chemistry in particular, make different demands on your learning skills than do other types of courses. We offer the following tips for success in your study of chemistry:

**Don't fall behind!** As the course moves along, new topics will build on material already presented. If you don't keep up in your reading and problem solving, you will find it much harder to follow the lectures and discussions on current topics. Experienced teachers know that students who read the relevant sections of the text *before* coming to a class learn more from the class and retain greater recall. "Cramming" just before an exam has been shown to be an ineffective way to study any subject, chemistry included. So now you know. How important to you in this competitive world is a good grade in chemistry?

**Focus your study.** The amount of information you will be expected to learn can sometimes seem overwhelming. It is essential to recognize those concepts and skills that are particularly important. Pay attention to what your instructor is emphasizing. As you work through the **Sample Exercises** and homework assignments, try to see what general principles and skills they employ. Use the **What's Ahead** feature at the beginning of each chapter to help orient yourself to what is important in each chapter. A single reading of a chapter will simply not be enough for successful learning of chapter concepts and problem-solving skills. You will need to go over assigned materials more than once. Don't skip the **Give It Some Thought** and **Go Figure** features, **Sample Exercises**, and **Practice Exercises**. They are your guides to whether you are learning the material. The **Key Skills** and **Key Equations** at the end of the chapter should help you focus your study.

**Keep good lecture notes.** Your lecture notes will provide you with a clear and concise record of what your instructor regards as the most important material to learn. Using your lecture notes in conjunction with this text is the best way to determine which material to study.

**Skim topics in the text before they are covered in lecture.** Reviewing a topic before lecture will make it easier for you to take good notes. First read the **What's Ahead** points and the end-of-chapter **Summary**; then quickly read through the chapter, skipping Sample Exercises and supplemental sections. Paying attention to the titles of sections and subsections gives you a feeling for the scope of topics. Try to avoid thinking that you must learn and understand everything right away.

**After lecture, carefully read the topics covered in class.** As you read, pay attention to the concepts presented and to the application of these concepts in the Sample

Exercises. Once you think you understand a Sample Exercise, test your understanding by working the accompanying Practice Exercise.

**Learn the language of chemistry.** As you study chemistry, you will encounter many new words. It is important to pay attention to these words and to know their meanings or the entities to which they refer. Knowing how to identify chemical substances from their names is an important skill; it can help you avoid painful mistakes on examinations. For example, "chlorine" and "chloride" refer to very different things.

**Attempt the assigned end-of-chapter exercises.** Working the exercises selected by your instructor provides necessary practice in recalling and using the essential ideas of the chapter. You cannot learn merely by observing; you must be a participant. In particular, try to resist checking the *Student-Solutions Manual* (if you have one) until you have made a sincere effort to solve the exercise yourself. If you get stuck on an exercise, however, get help from your instructor, your teaching assistant, or another student. Spending more than 20 minutes on a single exercise is rarely effective unless you know that it is particularly challenging.

**Use online resources.** Some things are more easily learned by discovery, and others are best shown in three dimensions. If your instructor has included MasteringChemistry with your book, take advantage of the unique tools it provides to get the most out of your time in chemistry.

The bottom line is to work hard, study effectively, and use the tools available to you, including this textbook. We want to help you learn more about the world of chemistry and why chemistry is the central science. If you really learn chemistry, you can be the life of the party, impress your friends and parents, and . . . well, also pass the course with a good grade.

# ACKNOWLEDGMENTS

The production of a textbook is a team effort requiring the involvement of many people besides the authors who contributed hard work and talent to bring this edition to life. Although their names don't appear on the cover of the book, their creativity, time, and support have been instrumental in all stages of its development and production.

Each of us has benefited greatly from discussions with colleagues and from correspondence with instructors and students both here and abroad. Colleagues have also helped immensely by reviewing our materials, sharing their insights, and providing suggestions for improvements. On this edition we were particularly blessed with an exceptional group of accuracy checkers who read through our materials looking for both technical inaccuracies and typographical errors.

## Twelfth Edition Reviewers

| | |
|---|---|
| Rebecca Barlag | Ohio University |
| Hafed, Bascal | University of Findlay |
| Donald Bellew | University of New Mexico |
| Elzbieta Cook | Louisiana State University |
| Robert Dunn | University of Kansas |
| Michael Hay | Pennsylvania State University |
| Carl Hoeger | University of California at San Diego |
| Kathryn Rowberg | Purdue University at Calumet |
| Lewis Silverman | University of Missouri at Columbia |
| Clyde Webster | University of California at Riverside |
| Troy Wood | University of Buffalo |

## Twelfth Edition Accuracy Reviewers

| | |
|---|---|
| Rebecca Barlag | Ohio University |
| Kelly Beefus | Anoka-Ramsey Community College |
| Louis J. Kirschenbaum | University of Rhode Island |
| Barbara Mowery | York College |
| Maria Vogt | Bloomfield College |

## Twelth Edition Focus Group Participants

| | |
|---|---|
| Robert Carter | University of Massachusetts at Boston Harbor |
| Tom Clayton | Knox College |
| Elzbieta Cook | Louisiana State University |
| Debra Feakes | Texas State University at San Marcos |
| Robert Gellert | Glendale Community College |
| John Gorden | Auburn University |
| Thomas J. Greenbowe | Iowa State University |
| Kingston Jesudoss | Iowa State University |
| Daniela Kohen | Carleton University |
| Sergiy Kryatov | Tufts University |
| Jeff McVey | Texas State University at San Marcos |
| Michael Seymour | Hope College |
| Matthew Stoltzfus | The Ohio State University |

## MasteringChemistry® Summit Participants

| | |
|---|---|
| Phil Bennett | Santa Fe Community College |
| Jo Blackburn | Richland College |
| John Bookstaver | St. Charles Community College |
| David Carter | Angelo State University |
| Doug Cody | Nassau Community College |
| Tom Dowd | Harper College |
| Palmer Graves | Florida International University |
| Margie Haak | Oregon State University |
| Brad Herrick | Colorado School of Mines |
| Jeff Jenson | University of Findlay |
| Jeff McVey | Texas State University at San Marcos |
| Gary Michels | Creighton University |
| Bob Pribush | Butler University |
| Al Rives | Wake Forest University |
| Joel Russell | Oakland University |
| Greg Szulczewski | University of Alabama, Tuscaloosa |
| Matt Tarr | University of New Orleans |
| Dennis Taylor | Clemson University |
| Harold Trimm | Broome Community College |
| Emanuel Waddell | University of Alabama, Huntsville |
| Kurt Winklemann | Florida Institute of Technology |
| Klaus Woelk | University of Missouri, Rolla |
| Steve Wood | Brigham Young University |

## Reviewers of Previous Editions of *Chemistry: The Central Science*

| | |
|---|---|
| S.K. Airee | University of Tennessee |
| John J. Alexander | University of Cincinnati |
| Robert Allendoerfer | SUNY Buffalo |
| Patricia Amateis | Virginia Polytechnic Institute and State University |
| Sandra Anderson | University of Wisconsin |
| John Arnold | University of California |
| Socorro Arteaga | El Paso Community College |
| Margaret Asirvatham | University of Colorado |
| Todd L. Austell | University of North Carolina, Chapel Hill |
| Melita Balch | University of Illinois at Chicago |
| Rosemary Bartoszek-Loza | The Ohio State University |
| Boyd Beck | Snow College |
| Amy Beilstein | Centre College |
| Victor Berner | New Mexico Junior College |
| Narayan Bhat | University of Texas, Pan American |
| Merrill Blackman | United States Military Academy |
| Salah M. Blaih | Kent State University |
| James A. Boiani | SUNY Geneseo |
| Leon Borowski | Diablo Valley College |
| Simon Bott | University of Houston |
| Kevin L. Bray | Washington State University |
| Daeg Scott Brenner | Clark University |
| Gregory Alan Brewer | Catholic University of America |
| Karen Brewer | Virginia Polytechnic Institute and State University |
| Edward Brown | Lee University |
| Gary Buckley | Cameron University |
| Carmela Byrnes | Texas A&M University |
| B. Edward Cain | Rochester Institute of Technology |

| | |
|---|---|
| Kim Calvo | University of Akron |
| Donald L. Campbell | University of Wisconsin |
| Gene O. Carlisle | Texas A&M University |
| Elaine Carter | Los Angeles City College |
| Robert Carter | University of Massachusetts |
| Ann Cartwright | San Jacinto Central College |
| David L. Cedeño | Illinois State University |
| Dana Chatellier | University of Delaware |
| Stanton Ching | Connecticut College |
| Paul Chirik | Cornell University |
| William Cleaver | University of Vermont |
| Beverly Clement | Blinn College |
| Robert D. Cloney | Fordham University |
| John Collins | Broward Community College |
| Edward Werner Cook | Tunxis Community Technical College |
| Elzbieta Cook | Louisiana State University |
| Enriqueta Cortez | South Texas College |
| Thomas Edgar Crumm | Indiana University of Pennsylvania |
| Dwaine Davis | Forsyth Tech Community College |
| Ramón López de la Vega | Florida International University |
| Nancy De Luca | University of Massachusetts, Lowell North Campus |
| Angel de Dios | Georgetown University |
| John M. DeKorte | Glendale Community College |
| Daniel Domin | Tennessee State University |
| James Donaldson | University of Toronto |
| Bill Donovan | University of Akron |
| Stephen Drucker | University of Wisconsin-Eau Claire |
| Ronald Duchovic | Indiana University-Purdue University at Fort Wayne |
| David Easter | Southwest Texas State University |
| Joseph Ellison | United States Military Academy |
| George O. Evans II | East Carolina University |
| James M. Farrar | University of Rochester |
| Gregory M. Ferrence | Illinois State University |
| Clark L. Fields | University of Northern Colorado |
| Jennifer Firestine | Lindenwood University |
| Jan M. Fleischner | College of New Jersey |
| Paul A. Flowers | University of North Carolina at Pembroke |
| Michelle Fossum | Laney College |
| Roger Frampton | Tidewater Community College |
| Joe Franek | University of Minnesota |
| David Frank | California State University |
| Cheryl B. Frech | University of Central Oklahoma |
| Ewa Fredette | Moraine Valley College |
| Kenneth A. French | Blinn College |
| Karen Frindell | Santa Rosa Junior College |
| John I. Gelder | Oklahoma State University |
| Paul Gilletti | Mesa Community College |
| Peter Gold | Pennsylvania State University |
| Eric Goll | Brookdale Community College |
| James Gordon | Central Methodist College |
| Thomas J. Greenbowe | Iowa State University |
| Michael Greenlief | University of Missouri |
| Eric P. Grimsrud | Montana State University |
| John Hagadorn | University of Colorado |
| Randy Hall | Louisiana State University |
| John M. Halpin | New York University |
| Marie Hankins | University of Southern Indiana |
| Robert M. Hanson | St. Olaf College |
| Daniel Haworth | Marquette University |
| Inna Hefley | Blinn College |
| David Henderson | Trinity College |
| Paul Higgs | Barry University |
| Carl A. Hoeger | University of California, San Diego |
| Gary G. Hoffman | Florida International University |
| Deborah Hokien | Marywood University |
| Robin Horner | Fayetteville Tech Community College |
| Roger K. House | Moraine Valley College |
| Michael O. Hurst | Georgia Southern University |
| William Jensen | South Dakota State University |
| Janet Johannessen | County College of Morris |
| Milton D. Johnston, Jr. | University of South Florida |
| Andrew Jones | Southern Alberta Institute of Technology |
| Booker Juma | Fayetteville State University |
| Ismail Kady | East Tennessee State University |
| Siam Kahmis | University of Pittsburgh |
| Steven Keller | University of Missouri |
| John W. Kenney | Eastern New Mexico University |
| Neil Kestner | Louisiana State University |
| Leslie Kinsland | University of Louisiana |
| Louis J. Kirschenbaum | University of Rhode Island |
| Donald Kleinfelter | University of Tennessee, Knoxville |
| David Kort | George Mason University |
| George P. Kreishman | University of Cincinnati |
| Paul Kreiss | Anne Arundel Community College |
| Manickham Krishnamurthy | Howard University |
| Brian D. Kybett | University of Regina |
| William R. Lammela | Nazareth College |
| John T. Landrum | Florida International University |
| Richard Langley | Stephen F. Austin State University |
| N. Dale Ledford | University of South Alabama |
| Ernestine Lee | Utah State University |
| David Lehmpuhl | University of Southern Colorado |
| Robley J. Light | Florida State University |
| Donald E. Linn, Jr. | Indiana University-Purdue University Indianapolis |
| David Lippmann | Southwest Texas State |
| Patrick Lloyd | Kingsborough Community College |
| Encarnacion Lopez | Miami Dade College, Wolfson |
| Arthur Low | Tarleton State University |
| Gary L. Lyon | Louisiana State University |
| Preston J. MacDougall | Middle Tennessee State University |
| Jeffrey Madura | Duquesne University |
| Larry Manno | Triton College |
| Asoka Marasinghe | Moorhead State University |
| Earl L. Mark | ITT Technical Institute |
| Pamela Marks | Arizona State University |
| Albert H. Martin | Moravian College |
| Przemyslaw Maslak | Pennsylvania State University |
| Hilary L. Maybaum | ThinkQuest, Inc. |
| Armin Mayr | El Paso Community College |
| Marcus T. McEllistrem | University of Wisconsin |
| Craig McLauchlan | Illinois State University |
| William A. Meena | Valley College |
| Joseph Merola | Virginia Polytechnic Institute and State University |
| Stephen Mezyk | California State University |
| Eric Miller | San Juan College |
| Gordon Miller | Iowa State University |
| Shelley Minteer | Saint Louis University |
| Massoud (Matt) Miri | Rochester Institute of Technology |
| Mohammad Moharerrzadeh | Bowie State University |
| Tracy Morkin | Emory University |
| Barbara Mowery | Yorktown, VA |
| Kathleen E. Murphy | Daemen College |
| Kathy Nabona | Austin Community College |
| Robert Nelson | Georgia Southern University |
| Al Nichols | Jacksonville State University |

| | | | |
|---|---|---|---|
| Ross Nord | Eastern Michigan University | Kathy Thrush Shaginaw | Villanova University |
| Jessica Orvis | Georgia Southern University | Susan M. Shih | College of DuPage |
| Mark Ott | Jackson Community College | David Shinn | University of Hawaii at Hilo |
| Jason Overby | College of Charleston | Vince Sollimo | Burlington Community College |
| Robert H. Paine | Rochester Institute of Technology | David Soriano | University of Pittsburgh-Bradford |
| Robert T. Paine | University of New Mexico | Eugene Stevens | Binghamton University |
| Sandra Patrick | Malaspina University College | James Symes | Cosumnes River College |
| Mary Jane Patterson | Brazosport College | Iwao Teraoka | Polytechnic University |
| Tammi Pavelec | Lindenwood University | Kathy Thrush | Villanova University |
| Albert Payton | Broward Community College | Domenic J. Tiani | University of North Carolina, Chapel Hill |
| Christopher J. Peeples | University of Tulsa | Edmund Tisko | University of Nebraska at Omaha |
| Kim Percell | Cape Fear Community College | Richard S. Treptow | Chicago State University |
| Gita Perkins | Estrella Mountain Community College | Michael Tubergen | Kent State University |
| Richard Perkins | University of Louisiana | Claudia Turro | The Ohio State University |
| Nancy Peterson | North Central College | James Tyrell | Southern Illinois University |
| Robert C. Pfaff | Saint Joseph's College | Michael J. Van Stipdonk | Wichita State University |
| John Pfeffer | Highline Community College | Philip Verhalen | Panola College |
| Lou Pignolet | University of Minnesota | Ann Verner | University of Toronto at Scarborough |
| Bernard Powell | University of Texas | Edward Vickner | Gloucester County Community College |
| Jeffrey A. Rahn | Eastern Washington University | John Vincent | University of Alabama |
| Steve Rathbone | Blinn College | Maria Vogt | Bloomfield College |
| Scott Reeve | Arkansas State University | Tony Wallner | Barry University |
| John Reissner | University of North Carolina | Lichang Wang | Southern Illinois University |
| Helen Richter | University of Akron | Thomas R. Webb | Auburn University |
| Thomas Ridgway | University of Cincinnati | Karen Weichelman | University of Louisiana-Lafayette |
| Mark G. Rockley | Oklahoma State University | Paul G. Wenthold | Purdue University |
| Lenore Rodicio | Miami Dade College | Laurence Werbelow | New Mexico Institute of Mining and Technology |
| Amy L. Rogers | College of Charleston | | |
| Jimmy R. Rogers | University of Texas at Arlington | Wayne Wesolowski | University Of Arizona |
| Steven Rowley | Middlesex Community College | Sarah West | University of Notre Dame |
| James E. Russo | Whitman College | Linda M. Wilkes | University at Southern Colorado |
| Theodore Sakano | Rockland Community College | Charles A. Wilkie | Marquette University |
| Michael J. Sanger | University of Northern Iowa | Darren L. Williams | West Texas A&M University |
| Jerry L. Sarquis | Miami University | Troy Wood | SUNY Buffalo |
| James P. Schneider | Portland Community College | Thao Yang | University of Wisconsin |
| Mark Schraf | West Virginia University | David Zax | Cornell University |
| Gray Scrimgeour | University of Toronto | Dr. Susan M. Zirpoli | Slippery Rock University |
| Paula Secondo | Western Connecticut State University | | |

We would also like to express our gratitude to our many team members at Pearson Prentice Hall whose hard work, imagination, and commitment have contributed so greatly to the final form of this edition: Nicole Folchetti, our former Editor in Chief, brought energy and imagination not only to this edition but to earlier ones as well; Terry Haugen, our Chemistry Editor, for many fresh ideas and his unflagging enthusiasm, continuous encouragement, and support; Jennifer Hart, our Project Editor, who very effectively coordinated the scheduling and tracked the multidimensional deadlines that come with a project of this magnitude; Erin Gardner, our marketing manager, for her energy, enthusiam, and creative promotion of our text; Irene Nunes, our Development Editor, whose diligence and careful attention to detail were invaluable to this revision, especially in keeping us on task in terms of consistency and student understanding; Donna Mulder, our Copy Editor, for her keen eye; Greg Gambino, our Art Developmental Editor, who managed the complex task of bringing our sketches into final form and who contributed so many great ideas to the new art program; Shari Toron, our Project Manager, who managed the complex responsibilities of bringing the design, photos, artwork, and writing together with efficiency and good cheer. The Pearson Prentice Hall team is a first-class operation.

There are many others who also deserve special recognition, including the following: Eric Schrader, our photo researcher, who was so effective in finding photos to bring chemistry to life for students, and Roxy Wilson (University of Illinois), who so ably coordinated the difficult job of working out solutions to the end-of-chapter exercises. We thank Dr. Jannik C. Meyer of the University of Ulm, Germany, for providing us with a high resolution image of graphene used in the cover design.

Finally, we wish to thank our families and friends for their love, support, encouragement, and patience as we brought this twelfth edition to completion.

Theodore L. Brown
*Department of Chemistry*
*University of Illinois*
*at Urbana-Champaign*
*Urbana, IL 61801*
*tlbrown@illinois.edu*
or *tlbrown1@earthlink.net*

H. Eugene LeMay, Jr.
*Department of Chemistry*
*University of Nevada*
*Reno, NV 89557*
*lemay@unr.edu*

Bruce E. Bursten
*College of Arts and Sciences*
*University of Tennessee*
*Knoxville, TN 37996*
*bbursten@utk.edu*

Catherine J. Murphy
*Department of Chemistry*
*University of Illinois*
*at Urbana-Champaign*
*Urbana, IL 61801*
*murphycj@illinois.edu.*

Patrick M. Woodward
*Department of Chemistry*
*The Ohio State University*
*Columbus, OH 43210*
*woodward@chemistry.*
*ohio-state.edu*

# LIST OF RESOURCES

## For Students

### MasteringChemistry® (http://www.masteringchemistry.com)

MasteringChemistry is the most effective, widely used online tutorial, homework and assessment system for chemistry. It helps instructors maximize class time with customizable, easy-to-assign, and automatically graded assessments that motivate students to learn outside of class and arrive prepared for lecture. These assessments can easily be customized and personalized by instructors to suit their individual teaching style. The powerful gradebook provides unique insight into student and class performance even before the first test. As a result, instructors can spend class time where students need it most.

### Pearson eText

The integration of Pearson eText within MasteringChemistry gives students with eTexts easy access to the electronic text when they are logged into Mastering Chemistry. Pearson eText pages look exactly like the printed text, offering powerful new functionality for students and instructors. Users can create notes, highlight text in different colors, create bookmarks, zoom, view in single-page or two-page view, and more.

### Student's Guide (0-321-70458-4)

Prepared by James C. Hill of California State University. This book assists students through the text material with chapter overviews, learning objectives, a review of key terms, as well as self-tests with answers and explanations. This edition also features MCAT practice questions.

### Solutions to Red Exercises (0-321-70548-3)

Prepared by Roxy Wilson of the University of Illinois, Urbana-Champaign. Full solutions to all the red-numbered exercises in the text are provided. (Short answers to red exercises are found in the appendix of the text.)

### Solutions to Black Exercises (0-321-70501-7)

Prepared by Roxy Wilson of the University of Illinois, Urbana-Champaign. Full solutions to all the black-numbered exercises in the text are provided.

### Laboratory Experiments (0-321-70502-5)

Prepared by John H. Nelson and Kenneth C. Kemp, both of the University of Nevada, with contributions by Matthew Stoltzfus of The Ohio State University. This manual contains 43 finely tuned experiments chosen to introduce students to basic lab techniques and to illustrate core chemical principles. This new edition has been revised to correlate more tightly with the text and now includes GIST questions and section references to the text. You can also customize these labs through Catalyst, our custom database program. For more information, visit *http://www.pearsoncustom.com/custom-library/*

## For Instructors

### Solutions to Exercises (0-321-70500-9)

Prepared by Roxy Wilson of the University of Illinois, Urbana-Champaign. This manual contains all end-of-chapter exercises in the text. With an instructor's permission, this manual may be made available to students.

### Instructor's Resource Center on CD-DVD (0-321-70503-3)

This resource provides an integrated collection of resources to help instructors make efficient and effective use of their time. This DVD features all artwork from the text, including figures and tables in PDF format for high-resolution printing, as well as four prebuilt PowerPoint™ presentations. The first presentation contains the images embedded within PowerPoint slides. The second includes a complete lecture outline that is modifiable by the user. The final two presentations contain worked "in-chapter" sample exercises and questions to be used with Classroom Response Systems. This DVD also contains movies, animations, and electronic files of the Instructor's Resource Manual, as well as the Test Item File.

### Printed Testbank (0-321-70497-5)

Prepared by Joseph P. Laurino of the University of Tampa. The Test Item File now provides a selection of more than 4000 test questions with 300 new questions in the twelfth edition and 200 additional algorithmic questions.

### Instructor's Resource Manual (0-321-70499-1)

Prepared by Linda Brunauer of Santa Clara University and Elzbieta Cook of Louisiana State University. Organized by chapter, this manual offers detailed lecture outlines and complete descriptions of all available lecture demonstrations, interactive media assets, common student misconceptions, and more.

### Transparencies (0-321-70498-3)

Approximately 275 full-color transparencies put principles into visual perspective and save you time when preparing lectures.

### Annotated Instructor's Edition to Laboratory Experiments (0-321-71197-1)

Prepared by John H. Nelson and Kenneth C. Kemp, both of the University of Nevada, with contributions by Matthew Stoltzfus of The Ohio State University. This AIE combines the full student lab manual with appendices covering the proper disposal of chemical waste, safety instructions for the lab, descriptions of standard lab equipment, answers to questions, and more.

### WebCT Test Item File (IRC download only)

978-0-321-70506-8 / 0-321-70506-8

### Blackboard Test Item File (IRC download only)

978-0-321-70507-5 / 0-321-70507-6

**THEODORE L. BROWN** received his Ph.D. from Michigan State University in 1956. Since then, he has been a member of the faculty of the University of Illinois, Urbana-Champaign, where he is now Professor of Chemistry, Emeritus. He served as Vice Chancellor for Research, and Dean of The Graduate College, from 1980 to 1986, and as Founding Director of the Arnold and Mabel Beckman Institute for Advanced Science and Technology from 1987 to 1993. Professor Brown has been an Alfred P. Sloan Foundation Research Fellow and has been awarded a Guggenheim Fellowship. In 1972 he was awarded the American Chemical Society Award for Research in Inorganic Chemistry and received the American Chemical Society Award for Distinguished Service in the Advancement of Inorganic Chemistry in 1993. He has been elected a Fellow of the American Association for the Advancement of Science, the American Academy of Arts and Sciences, and the American Chemical Society.

**H. EUGENE LEMAY, JR.,** received his B.S. degree in Chemistry from Pacific Lutheran University (Washington) and his Ph.D. in Chemistry in 1966 from the University of Illinois, Urbana-Champaign. He then joined the faculty of the University of Nevada, Reno, where he is currently Professor of Chemistry, Emeritus. He has enjoyed Visiting Professorships at the University of North Carolina at Chapel Hill, at the University College of Wales in Great Britain, and at the University of California, Los Angeles. Professor LeMay is a popular and effective teacher, who has taught thousands of students during more than 40 years of university teaching. Known for the clarity of his lectures and his sense of humor, he has received several teaching awards, including the University Distinguished Teacher of the Year Award (1991) and the first Regents' Teaching Award given by the State of Nevada Board of Regents (1997).

**BRUCE E. BURSTEN** received his Ph.D. in Chemistry from the University of Wisconsin in 1978. After two years as a National Science Foundation Postdoctoral Fellow at Texas A&M University, he joined the faculty of The Ohio State University, where he rose to the rank of Distinguished University Professor. In 2005, he moved to the University of Tennessee, Knoxville, as Distinguished Professor of Chemistry and Dean of the College of Arts and Sciences. Professor Bursten has been a Camille and Henry Dreyfus Foundation Teacher-Scholar and an Alfred P. Sloan Foundation Research Fellow, and he is a Fellow of both the American Association for the Advancement of Science and the American Chemical Society. At Ohio State he has received the University Distinguished Teaching Award in 1982 and 1996, the Arts and Sciences Student Council Outstanding Teaching Award in 1984, and the University Distinguished Scholar Award in 1990. He received the Spiers Memorial Prize and Medal of the Royal Society of Chemistry in 2003, and the Morley Medal of the Cleveland Section of the American Chemical Society in 2005. He was President of the American Chemical Society for 2008. In addition to his teaching and service activities, Professor Bursten's research program focuses on compounds of the transition-metal and actinide elements.

**CATHERINE J. MURPHY** received two B.S. degrees, one in Chemistry and one in Biochemistry, from the University of Illinois, Urbana-Champaign, in 1986. She received her Ph.D. in Chemistry from the University of Wisconsin in 1990. She was a National Science Foundation and National Institutes of Health Postdoctoral Fellow at the California Institute of Technology from 1990 to 1993. In 1993, she joined the faculty of the University of South Carolina, Columbia, becoming the Guy F. Lipscomb Professor of Chemistry in 2003. In 2009 she moved to the University of Illinois, Urbana-Champaign, as the Peter C. and Gretchen Miller Markunas Professor of Chemistry. Professor Murphy has been honored for both research and teaching as a Camille Dreyfus Teacher-Scholar, an Alfred P. Sloan Foundation Research Fellow, a Cottrell Scholar of the Research Corporation, a National Science Foundation CAREER Award winner, and a subsequent NSF Award for Special Creativity. She has also received a USC Mortar Board Excellence in Teaching Award, the USC Golden Key Faculty Award for Creative Integration of Research and Undergraduate Teaching, the USC Michael J. Mungo Undergraduate Teaching Award, and the USC Outstanding Undergraduate Research Mentor Award. Since 2006, Professor Murphy has served as a Senior Editor for the Journal of Physical Chemistry. In 2008 she was elected a Fellow of the American Association for the Advancement of Science. Professor Murphy's research program focuses on the synthesis and optical properties of inorganic nanomaterials, and on the local structure and dynamics of the DNA double helix.

**PATRICK M. WOODWARD** received B.S. degrees in both Chemistry and Engineering from Idaho State University in 1991. He received a M.S. degree in Materials Science and a Ph.D. in Chemistry from Oregon State University in 1996. He spent two years as a postdoctoral researcher in the Department of Physics at Brookhaven National Laboratory. In 1998, he joined the faculty of the Chemistry Department at The Ohio State University where he currently holds the rank of Professor. He has enjoyed visiting professorships at the University of Bordeaux in France and the University of Sydney in Australia. Professor Woodward has been an Alfred P. Sloan Foundation Research Fellow and a National Science Foundation CAREER Award winner. He currently serves as an Associate Editor to the Journal of Solid State Chemistry and as the director of the Ohio REEL program, an NSF-funded center that works to bring authentic research experiments into the laboratories of first- and second-year chemistry classes in 15 colleges and universities across the state of Ohio. Professor Woodward's research program focuses on understanding the links between bonding, structure, and properties of solid-state inorganic functional materials.

# A GUIDE TO USING THIS TEXT

■ *Chemistry: The Central Science* has been the leader in general chemistry for decades. Now, its unrivaled problems, scientific accuracy, and clarity have been upheld and are woven seamlessly with each new feature. The **Twelfth Edition** is this text's most ambitious revision to date; every word and piece of art has been scrutinized for effectiveness by all five authors, and many revisions are based on student performance data gathered through MasteringChemistry.®

## Visualizing concepts makes chemistry accessible

Chemistry is by nature an abstract subject. First, it relies on a symbolic language based on chemical formulas and equations. Second, it is based on the behavior of atoms and molecules—particles far too small to see. By presenting chemistry visually, the authors help you to "see" the chemistry you need to learn and increase your success in the course.

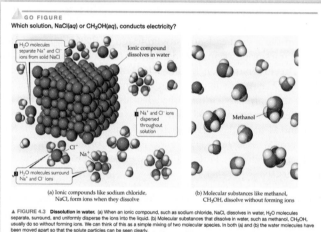

Twelfth Edition

**Molecular Illustrations**

**Molecular Illustrations** are computer-generated renditions of molecules and materials that represent matter visually at the atomic level. These drawings help you visualize molecules in three dimensions, and enhance your understanding of molecular architecture.

Eleventh Edition

▲ FIGURE 4.1  Cenote formation.

Twelfth Edition

## Multi-Focus Graphics

To help you develop a more complete understanding of the topic presented, **Multi-Focus Graphics** provide macroscopic, microscopic, and symbolic perspectives to portray various chemical concepts. The Twelfth Edition adds to these graphics an intermediate process that shows you where chemistry is occurring in problem solving.

▲ Figure 4.1  **Limestone cave.** When $CO_2$ dissolves in water, the resulting solution is slightly acidic. Limestone caves are formed by the dissolving action of this acidic solution acting on $CaCO_3$ in the limestone.

Eleventh Edition

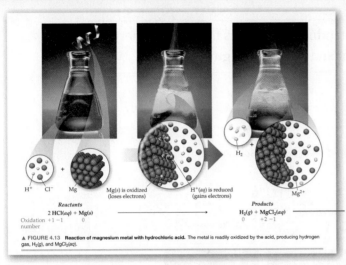

▲ FIGURE 4.13 **Reaction of magnesium metal with hydrochloric acid.** The metal is readily oxidized by the acid, producing hydrogen gas, $H_2(g)$, and $MgCl_2(aq)$.

Reactants
$$2\ HCl(aq) + Mg(s)$$
Oxidation  $+1$  $-1$     $0$
number

$H^+$  $Cl^-$  $Mg$

$Mg(s)$ is oxidized (loses electrons)

$H^+(aq)$ is reduced (gains electrons)

Products
$$H_2(g) + MgCl_2(aq)$$
$0$     $+2$  $-1$

$H_2$  $Mg^{2+}$

Macro to Micro Art
These illustrations offer three parts: a macroscopic image (what you can see with your eyes); a molecular image (what the molecules are doing); and a symbolic representation (how chemists represent the process with symbols and equations).

A new intermediate step has been added, showing where chemistry occurs in the problem-solving process.

## A focus on relevance makes chemistry meaningful

Chemistry occurs all around us, throughout every day. Recognizing the importance of chemistry in your daily life can improve your understanding of chemical concepts.

### CHEMISTRY PUT TO WORK

#### Antacids

Your stomach secretes acids to help digest foods. These acids, which include hydrochloric acid, contain about 0.1 mol of $H^+$ per liter of solution. The stomach and digestive tract are normally protected from the corrosive effects of stomach acid by a mucosal lining. Holes can develop in this lining, however, allowing the acid to attack the underlying tissue, causing painful damage. These holes, known as ulcers, can be caused by the secretion of excess acids or by a weakness in the digestive lining. Studies indicate, however, that many ulcers are caused by bacterial infection. Between 10 and 20% of Americans suffer from ulcers at some point in their lives. Many

others experience occasional indigestion or heartburn due to digestive acids entering the esophagus.

We can address the problem of excess stomach acid in two ways: (1) removing the excess acid or (2) decreasing the production of acid. Substances that remove excess acid are called *antacids*, whereas those that decrease acid production are called *acid inhibitors*. ◀ FIGURE 4.10 shows several common over-the-counter antacids, which usually contain hydroxide, carbonate, or bicarbonate ions (▼ TABLE 4.4). Antiulcer drugs, such as Tagamet® and Zantac®, are acid inhibitors. They act on acid-producing cells in the lining of the stomach. Formulations that control acid in this way are now available as over-the-counter drugs.

*RELATED EXERCISE:* 4.95

▲ FIGURE 4.10 **Antacids.** These products all serve as acid-neutralizing agents in the stomach.

| TABLE 4.4 • Some Common Antacids | |
| --- | --- |
| **Commercial Name** | **Acid-Neutralizing Agents** |
| Alka-Seltzer® | $NaHCO_3$ |
| Amphojel® | $Al(OH)_3$ |
| Di-Gel® | $Mg(OH)_2$ and $CaCO_3$ |
| Milk of Magnesia | $Mg(OH)_2$ |
| Maalox® | $Mg(OH)_2$ and $Al(OH)_3$ |
| Mylanta® | $Mg(OH)_2$ and $Al(OH)_3$ |
| Rolaids® | $NaAl(OH)_2CO_3$ |
| Tums® | $CaCO_3$ |

Chemistry Put to Work and Chemistry and Life
Chemistry's connection to world events, scientific discoveries, and medical breakthroughs are showcased in **Chemistry and Life** and **Chemistry Put to Work** features throughout the text.

### CHEMISTRY AND LIFE

#### DRINKING TOO MUCH WATER CAN KILL YOU

For a long time dehydration was considered a potential danger for people engaged in extended vigorous activity. Thus, athletes were encouraged to drink lots of water while engaged in active sport. The trend toward extensive hydration has spread throughout society, so that today many people carry water bottles everywhere and dutifully keep well hydrated.

In some circumstances, however, drinking too much water is a greater danger than not drinking enough. Excess water consumption can lead to *hyponatremia*, a condition in which the concentration of sodium ion in the blood is too low. In the past decade at least four marathon runners have died from hyponatremia-related trauma, and dozens more have become seriously ill. For example, a first-time

marathoner named Hillary Bellamy, running in the Marine Corps marathon in 2003, collapsed near mile 22 and died the next day. One physician who treated her said that she died from hyponatremia-induced brain swelling, the result of drinking too much water before and during the race.

The normal blood sodium level is 135 to 145 m$M$ *(millimolar)*. When that level drops to 125 m$M$, dizziness and confusion set in. A concentration below 120 m$M$ can be critical. Dangerously low levels can occur in any active athlete who is sweating out salt ($NaCl$) at the same time that excessive amounts of $NaCl$-free water are being drunk to compensate for water loss. The condition affects women more than men because of differences in body composition and patterns of metabolism. Drinking a sport drink that contains some electrolytes helps to prevent hyponatremia.

*RELATED EXERCISES:* 4.63, 4.64

# CONCEPTUAL UNDERSTANDING BRINGS CHEMISTRY TO LIFE

The authors help you achieve a deeper understanding of concepts through a variety of learning aids, including **Give it Some Thought** and **NEW! Go Figure** questions.

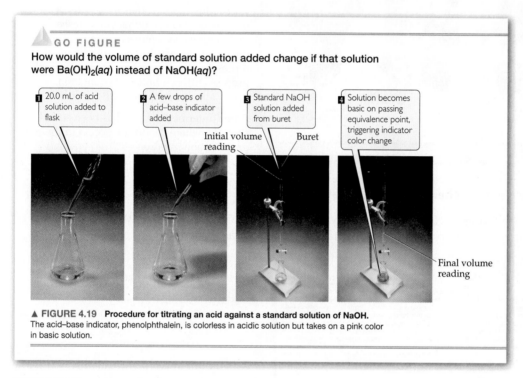

**GO FIGURE**

How would the volume of standard solution added change if that solution were Ba(OH)$_2$(aq) instead of NaOH(aq)?

1 20.0 mL of acid solution added to flask

2 A few drops of acid–base indicator added

3 Standard NaOH solution added from buret

4 Solution becomes basic on passing equivalence point, triggering indicator color change

Initial volume reading

Buret

Final volume reading

▲ **FIGURE 4.19** **Procedure for titrating an acid against a standard solution of NaOH.** The acid–base indicator, phenolphthalein, is colorless in acidic solution but takes on a pink color in basic solution.

**NEW! Go Figure questions**
**Go Figure questions** encourage you to stop and analyze the artwork in the text, for conceptual understanding. "Voice Balloons" in selected figures help you break down and understand the components of the image. These questions are also available in MasteringChemistry.

 **GIVE IT SOME THOUGHT**
What is the principal reason we must consider the uncertainty principle when discussing electrons and other subatomic particles but not when discussing our macroscopic world?

**Give It Some Thought (GIST) questions**
These informal, sharply focused exercises give you opportunities to test whether you are "getting it" as you read along. We've increased the number of GIST questions in the Twelfth Edition.

A consistent problem-solving process is incorporated throughout, so you'll always know where to go when solving problems.

**Analyze/Plan/Solve/Check**
This four-step problem-solving method helps you understand what you are being asked to solve, to plan how you will solve each problem, to work your way through the solution, and to check your answers. This method is introduced in Chapter 3 and reinforced throughout the book.

**Dual-Column Problem-Solving Strategies**
Found in Selected Sample Exercises, these strategies explain the thought process involved in each step of a mathematical calculation using a unique layout for clarity. They help you develop a conceptual understanding of those calculations.

---

**SAMPLE EXERCISE 5.6** | **Measuring $\Delta H$ Using a Coffee-Cup Calorimeter**

When a student mixes 50 mL of 1.0 $M$ HCl and 50 mL of 1.0 $M$ NaOH in a coffee-cup calorimeter, the temperature of the resultant solution increases from 21.0 °C to 27.5 °C. Calculate the enthalpy change for the reaction in kJ/mol HCl, assuming that the calorimeter loses only a negligible quantity of heat, that the total volume of the solution is 100 mL, that its density is 1.0 g/mL, and that its specific heat is 4.18 J/g-K.

**SOLUTION**

**Analyze** Mixing solutions of HCl and NaOH results in an acid–base reaction:

$$HCl(aq) + NaOH(aq) \longrightarrow H_2O(l) + NaCl(aq)$$

We need to calculate the heat produced per mole of HCl, given the temperature increase of the solution, the number of moles of HCl and NaOH involved, and the density and specific heat of the solution.

**Plan** The total heat produced can be calculated using Equation 5.23. The number of moles of HCl consumed in the reaction must be calculated from the volume and molarity of this substance, and this amount is then used to determine the heat produced per mol HCl.

**Solve**

| | |
|---|---|
| Because the total volume of the solution is 100 mL, its mass is | $(100\ \text{mL})(1.0\ \text{g/mL}) = 100\ \text{g}$ |
| The temperature change is | $\Delta T = 27.5\ °\text{C} - 21.0\ °\text{C} = 6.5\ °\text{C} = 6.5\ \text{K}$ |
| Using Equation 5.23, we have | $q_{rxn} = -C_s \times m \times \Delta T$ |
| | $= -(4.18\ \text{J/g-K})(100\ \text{g})(6.5\ \text{K}) = -2.7 \times 10^3\ \text{J} = -2.7\ \text{kJ}$ |
| Because the process occurs at constant pressure, | $\Delta H = q_P = -2.7\ \text{kJ}$ |
| To express the enthalpy change on a molar basis, we use the fact that the number of moles of HCl is given by the product of the volume (50 mL = 0.050 L) and concentration (1.0 $M$ = 1.0 mol/L) of the HCl solution: | $(0.050\ \text{L})(1.0\ \text{mol/L}) = 0.050\ \text{mol}$ |
| Thus, the enthalpy change per mole of HCl is | $\Delta H = -2.7\ \text{kJ}/0.050\ \text{mol} = -54\ \text{kJ/mol}$ |

**Check** $\Delta H$ is negative (exothermic), which is expected for the reaction of an acid with a base and evidenced by the fact that the reaction causes the temperature of the solution to increase. The magnitude of the molar enthalpy change seems reasonable.

**PRACTICE EXERCISE**
When 50.0 mL of 0.100 $M$ AgNO$_3$ and 50.0 mL of 0.100 $M$ HCl are mixed in a constant-pressure calorimeter, the temperature of the mixture increases from 22.30 °C to 23.11 °C. The temperature increase is caused by the following reaction:

$$AgNO_3(aq) + HCl(aq) \longrightarrow AgCl(s) + HNO_3(aq)$$

Calculate $\Delta H$ for this reaction in kJ/mol AgNO$_3$, assuming that the combined solution has a mass of 100.0 g and a specific heat of 4.18 J/g °C.
*Answer:* $-68,000\ \text{J/mol} = -68\ \text{kJ/mol}$

---

**STRATEGIES IN CHEMISTRY**

**PROBLEM SOLVING**

Practice is the key to success in solving problems. As you practice, you can improve your skills by following these steps:

**Step 1: Analyze the problem.** Read the problem carefully. What does it say? Draw a picture or diagram that will help you to visualize the problem. Write down both the data you are given and the quantity you need to obtain (the unknown).

**Step 2: Develop a plan for solving the problem.** Consider a possible path between the given information and the unknown. What principles or equations relate the known data to the unknown?

Recognize that some data may not be given explicitly in the problem; you may be expected to know certain quantities (such as Avogadro's number) or look them up in tables (such as atomic weights). Recognize also that your plan may involve either a single step or a series of steps with intermediate answers.

**Step 3: Solve the problem.** Use the known information and suitable equations or relationships to solve for the unknown. Dimensional analysis ∞ (Section 1.6) is a useful tool for solving a great number of problems. Be careful with significant figures, signs, and units.

**Step 4: Check the solution.** Read the problem again to make sure you have found all the solutions asked for in the problem. Does your answer make sense? That is, is the answer outrageously large or small or is it in the ballpark? Finally, are the units and significant figures correct?

**Strategies in Chemistry**
**Strategies in Chemistry** teach ways to analyze information and organize thoughts, helping to improve your problem-solving and critical-thinking abilities.

# UPDATED END-OF-CHAPTER MATERIALS BOOST YOUR COMPREHENSION

Unique to the Twelfth Edition, the end-of-chapter materials have been updated and streamlined based on student performance data gathered through MasteringChemistry. Only content that has proven to increase student comprehension of fundamental concepts has been retained.

## CHAPTER SUMMARY AND KEY TERMS

**INTRODUCTION AND SECTION 3.1** The study of the quantitative relationships between chemical formulas and chemical equations is known as **stoichiometry**. One of the important concepts of stoichiometry is the law of conservation of mass, which states that the total mass of the products of a chemical reaction is the same as the total mass of the reactants. The same numbers of atoms of each type are present before and after a chemical reaction. A balanced **chemical equation** shows equal numbers of atoms of each element on each side of the equation. Equations are balanced by placing coefficients in front of the chemical formulas for the **reactants** and **products** of a reaction, *not* by changing the subscripts in chemical formulas.

**SECTION 3.2** Among the reaction types described in this chapter are (1) **combination reactions**, in which two reactants combine to form one product; (2) **decomposition reactions**, in which a single reactant forms two or more products; and (3) **combustion reactions** in oxygen, in which a hydrocarbon or related compound reacts with $O_2$ to form $CO_2$ and $H_2O$.

**SECTION 3.3** Much quantitative information can be determined from chemical formulas and balanced chemical equations by using atomic weights. The **formula weight** of a compound equals the sum of the atomic weights of the atoms in its formula. If the formula is a molecular formula, the formula weight is also called the **molecular weight**. Atomic weights and formula weights can be used to determine the elemental composition of a compound.

**SECTION 3.4** A mole of any substance is **Avogadro's number** ($6.02 \times 10^{23}$) of formula units of that substance. The mass of a **mole** of atoms, molecules, or ions (the **molar mass**) equals the formula weight of that material expressed in grams. The mass of one molecule of $H_2O$, for example, is 18 amu, so the mass of 1 mol of $H_2O$ is 18 g. That is, the molar mass of $H_2O$ is 18 g/mol.

**SECTION 3.5** The empirical formula of any substance can be determined from its percent composition by calculating the relative number of moles of each atom in 100 g of the substance. If the substance is molecular in nature, its molecular formula can be determined from the empirical formula if the molecular weight is also known.

**SECTIONS 3.6 AND 3.7** The mole concept can be used to calculate the relative quantities of reactants and products in chemical reactions. The coefficients in a balanced equation give the relative numbers of moles of the reactants and products. To calculate the number of grams of a product from the number of grams of a reactant, first convert grams of reactant to moles of reactant. Then use the coefficients in the balanced equation to convert the number of moles of reactant to moles of product. Finally, convert moles of product to grams of product.

A **limiting reactant** is completely consumed in a reaction. When it is used up, the reaction stops, thus limiting the quantities of products formed. The **theoretical yield** of a reaction is the quantity of product calculated to form when all of the limiting reactant reacts. The actual yield of a reaction is always less than the theoretical yield. The **percent yield** compares the actual and theoretical yields.

Summary with Key Terms
These list all of the chapter's boldfaced items, organized by section in order of appearance, with page references. Definitions are found in the Glossary.

Key Equations
The **Key Equations** section lists each of the key equations and important quantitative relationships from the chapter.

## KEY EQUATIONS

- $E_{el} = \dfrac{\kappa Q_1 Q_2}{d}$   [8.4]   The potential energy of two interacting charges

- $\mu = Qr$   [8.11]   The dipole moment of two charges of equal magnitude but opposite sign, separated by a distance $r$

- $\Delta H_{rxn} = \Sigma(\text{bond enthalpies of bonds broken}) - \Sigma(\text{bond enthalpies of bonds formed})$   [8.12]   The enthalpy change as a function of bond enthalpies for reactions involving gas-phase molecules

## KEY SKILLS

- Write Lewis symbols for atoms and ions. (Section 8.1)
- Understand lattice energy and be able to arrange compounds in order of increasing lattice energy based on the charges and sizes of the ions involved. (Section 8.2)
- Use atomic electron configurations and the octet rule to write Lewis structures for molecules to determine their electron distribution. (Section 8.3)
- Use electronegativity differences to identify nonpolar covalent, polar covalent, and ionic bonds. (Section 8.4)
- Calculate charge separation in diatomic molecules based on the experimentally measured dipole moment and bond distance. (Section 8.4)
- Calculate formal charges from Lewis structures and use those formal charges to identify the dominant Lewis structure for a molecule or ion. (Section 8.5)
- Recognize molecules where resonance structures are needed to describe the bonding. (Section 8.6)
- Recognize exceptions to the octet rule and draw accurate Lewis structures even when the octet rule is not obeyed. (Section 8.7)
- Understand the relationship between bond type (single, double, and triple), bond strength (or enthalpy), and bond length. (Section 8.8)
- Use bond enthalpies to estimate enthalpy changes for reactions involving gas-phase reactants and products. (Section 8.8)

Key Skills
The **Key Skills** section in each chapter lists the fundamental concepts you should comprehend.

## VISUALIZING CONCEPTS

**4.1** Which of the following schematic drawings best describes a solution of $Li_2SO_4$ in water (water molecules not shown for simplicity)? [Section 4.1]

    (a)          (b)          (c)

**4.2** Aqueous solutions of three different substances, AX, AY, and AZ, are represented by the three accompanying diagrams. Identify each substance as a strong electrolyte, weak electrolyte, or nonelectrolyte. [Section 4.1]

    (a)          (b)          (c)

**4.3** Use the molecular representations shown here to classify each compound as either a nonelectrolyte, a weak electrolyte, or a strong electrolyte. [Sections 4.1 and 4.3]

    (a)          (b)          (c)

See inside back cover for element color scheme.

**4.4** A 0.1 $M$ solution of acetic acid, $CH_3COOH$, causes the light-bulb in the apparatus of Figure 4.2 to glow about as brightly as a 0.001 $M$ solution of HBr. How do you account for this fact? [Section 4.1]

**4.5** You are presented with a white solid and told that due to careless labeling it is not clear if the substance is barium chloride, lead chloride, or zinc chloride. When you transfer the solid to a beaker and add water, the solid dissolves to give a clear solution. Next a $Na_2SO_4(aq)$ solution is added and a white precipitate forms. What is the identity of the unknown white solid? [Section 4.2]

**4.6** We have seen that ions in aqueous solution are stabilized by the attractions between the ions and the water molecules. Why then do some pairs of ions in solution form precipitates? [Section 4.2]

**4.7** Which of the following ions will *always* be a spectator ion in a precipitation reaction? (a) $Cl^-$, (b) $NO_3^-$, (c) $NH_4^+$, (d) $S^{2-}$, (e) $SO_4^{2-}$. Explain briefly. [Section 4.2]

**4.8** The labels have fallen off three bottles containing powdered samples of metals; one contains zinc, one lead, and the other platinum. You have three solutions at your disposal: 1 $M$ sodium nitrate, 1 $M$ nitric acid, and 1 $M$ nickel nitrate. How could you use these solutions to determine the identities of each metal powder? [Section 4.4]

**4.9** Explain how a redox reaction involves electrons in the same way that a neutralization reaction involves protons. [Sections 4.3 and 4.4]

**4.10** If you want to double the concentration of a solution, how could you do it? [Section 4.5]

---

## EXERCISES

### VISUALIZING CONCEPTS

**8.1** For each of these Lewis symbols, indicate the group in the periodic table in which the element X belongs: [Section 8.1]

(a) $\cdot \dot{X} \cdot$    (b) $\cdot \ddot{X} \cdot$    (c) $: \ddot{X} \cdot$

**8.2** Illustrated are four ions—A, B, X, and Y— showing their relative ionic radii. The ions shown in red carry positive charges: a

    A      B      X      Y

---

### INTEGRATIVE EXERCISES

**6.97** Microwave ovens use microwave radiation to heat food. The energy of the microwaves is absorbed by water molecules in food and then transferred to other components of the food. **(a)** Suppose that the microwave radiation has a wavelength of 11.2 cm. How many photons are required to heat 200 mL of coffee from 23 °C to 60 °C? **(b)** Suppose the microwave's power is 900 W (1 Watt = 1 joule-second). How long would you have to heat the coffee in part (a)?

**6.98** The stratospheric ozone ($O_3$) layer helps to protect us from harmful ultraviolet radiation. It does so by absorbing ultraviolet light and falling apart into an $O_2$ molecule and an oxygen atom, a process known as photodissociation.

$$O_3(g) \longrightarrow O_2(g) + O(g)$$

Use the data in Appendix C to calculate the enthalpy change for this reaction. What is the maximum wavelength a photon can have if it is to possess sufficient energy to cause this dissociation? In what portion of the spectrum does this wavelength occur?

---

### ADDITIONAL EXERCISES

**6.75** Consider the two waves shown here, which we will consider to represent two electromagnetic radiations:
**(a)** What is the wavelength of wave A? Of wave B?
**(b)** What is the frequency of wave A? Of wave B?
**(c)** Identify the regions of the electromagnetic spectrum to which waves A and B belong.

A

B

$1.6 \times 10^{-7}$ m

---

[4.114] The newest US standard for arsenate in drinking water, mandated by the Safe Drinking Water Act, required that by January 2006, public water supplies must contain no greater than 10 parts per billion (ppb) arsenic. If this arsenic is present as arsenate, $AsO_4^{3-}$, what mass of sodium arsenate would be present in a 1.00-L sample of drinking water that just meets the standard? Parts per billion is defined on a mass basis as

$$ppb = \frac{g \text{ solute}}{g \text{ solution}} \times 10^9.$$

---

## Visualizing Concepts

**Visualizing Concepts** exercises begin the end-of-chapter exercises and ask you to consider concepts through the use of models, graphs, and other visual materials. These help you develop a conceptual understanding of the key ideas in the chapter. Additional conceptual exercises are found among the end-of-chapter exercises.

## Exercises

**End-of-Chapter Exercises** are grouped by topic and presented in matched pairs based on data gathered from MasteringChemistry, giving you multiple opportunities to test each concept.

## Integrative Exercises

Included among the exercises at the end of Chapters 3-24, **Integrative Exercises** connect concepts for the current chapter with those from previous chapters. These help you gain a deeper understanding of how chemistry fits together and serve as an overall review of key concepts.

## Bracketed Challenge Problems

The Bracketed Challenge Problems have been revised for the Twelfth Edition, based on student performance data gathered through MasteringChemistry reflecting the difficulty of the problem.

## Additional Exercises

Additional Exercises follow the paired exercises and are not categorized, because many of these exercises draw on multiple concepts from within the chapter.

# PERSONALIZED COACHING AND FEEDBACK AT YOUR FINGERTIPS

## Mastering CHEMISTRY®

MasteringChemistry is the most effective, widely used online tutorial, homework and assessment system for chemistry. It helps instructors maximize class time with customizable, easy-to-assign, and automatically graded assessments that motivate students to learn outside of class and arrive prepared for lecture. These assessments can easily be customized and personalized by instructors to suit their individual teaching style. To learn more, visit **www.masteringchemistry.com**

### Student Tutorials
MasteringChemistry is the only system to provide instantaneous feedback specific to the most-common wrong answers. Students can submit an answer and receive immediate, error-specific feedback. Simpler sub-problems—"hints"—are provided upon request.

### Gradebook
MasteringChemistry is the only system to capture the step-by-step work of each student in class, including wrong answers submitted, hints requested, and time taken on every step. This data powers an unprecedented gradebook.

### Student Performance Snapshot
This screen provides your favorite weekly diagnostics. With a single click, charts summarize the most difficult problems, vulnerable students, grade distribution, and even score improvement over the course.

# EXTEND LEARNING
# BEYOND THE CLASSROOM

## Pearson eText

The eText gives students access to the text whenever and wherever they can access the Internet. The eText pages look exactly like the printed text, and include powerful interactive and customization features.

Students can:

- Create notes, highlight text in different colors, create book marks, zoom, click hyperlinked words and phrases to view definitions, and view in single-page or two-page format.

- Link directly to associated media files, enabling them to view an animation as they read the text.

- Perform a full-text search and save or export notes.

Instructors can share their notes and highlights with students, and can also hide chapters that they do not want students to read.

## NEW! Visualizations

These new tutorials enable you to make connections between real-life phenomena and the underlying chemistry that explains such phenomena. The tutorials increase your understanding of chemistry and clearly illustrate cause-and-effect relationships.

## NEW! Reading Quizzes

Chapter-specific quizzes and activities focus on important, hard-to-grasp chemistry concepts.

# WHAT'S AHEAD

**HUBBLE SPACE TELESCOPE IMAGE** of the Omega Nebula, a 15-light-year-wide expanding remnant of a star's supernova explosion. The orange filaments are the tattered remains of the star and consist mostly of hydrogen, the simplest and most plentiful element in the universe. Hydrogen occurs as molecules in cool regions of the nebula, as atoms in hotter regions, and as ions in the hottest regions. The processes that occur within stars are responsible for creating other chemical elements from hydrogen.

**1.5 UNCERTAINTY IN MEASUREMENT**
We observe that the uncertainty inherent in all measured quantities is expressed by the number of *significant figures* used to report the quantity. Significant figures are also used to express the uncertainty associated with calculations involving measured quantities.

**1.6 DIMENSIONAL ANALYSIS**
We recognize that units as well as numbers are carried through calculations and that obtaining correct units for the result of a calculation is an important way to check whether the calculation is correct.

# INTRODUCTION: MATTER AND MEASUREMENT

**HAVE YOU EVER WONDERED** why the stars shine? Or why leaves change color in the fall or how a battery generates electricity? Have you ever wondered why keeping foods cold slows their spoilage and how our bodies use food to maintain life? Chemistry answers these questions as well as countless others.

**Chemistry** is the study of matter and the changes that matter undergoes. One of the joys of learning chemistry is seeing how chemical principles operate in all aspects of our lives, from everyday activities like cooking dinner to more complex processes like the development of drugs to cure cancer. Chemical principles also operate in the far reaches of our galaxy (chapter-opening photograph) as well as within and around us.

This first chapter provides an overview of what chemistry is about and what chemists do. The preceding "What's Ahead" list gives an overview of the chapter organization and of some of the ideas we will consider. As you study, keep in mind that the chemical facts and concepts you are asked to learn are not ends in themselves; they are tools to help you better understand the world around you.

# 1.1 | THE STUDY OF CHEMISTRY

Before traveling to an unfamiliar city, you might look at a map to get some sense of where you are heading. Because chemistry may be unfamiliar to you, it's useful to get a general idea of what lies ahead before you embark on your journey. In fact, you might even ask why you are taking the trip.

## The Atomic and Molecular Perspective of Chemistry

Chemistry is the study of the properties and behavior of matter. **Matter** is the physical material of the universe; it is anything that has mass and occupies space. A **property** is any characteristic that allows us to recognize a particular type of matter and to distinguish it from other types. This book, your body, the air you are breathing, and the clothes you are wearing are all samples of matter. Countless experiments have shown that the tremendous variety of matter in our world is due to combinations of only about 100 substances called **elements**. As we proceed through this text, we will seek to relate the properties of matter to its composition, that is, to the particular elements it contains.

Chemistry also provides a background for understanding the properties of matter in terms of **atoms**, the almost infinitesimally small building blocks of matter. Each element is composed of a unique kind of atom. We will see that the properties of matter relate to both the kinds of atoms the matter contains (*composition*) and to the arrangements of these atoms (*structure*).

In **molecules**, two or more atoms are joined together in specific shapes. Throughout this text you will see molecules represented using colored spheres to show how the atoms are connected (▼ FIGURE 1.1). The color provides a convenient way to distinguish between atoms of different elements. For example, notice that the molecules of ethanol and ethylene glycol in Figure 1.1 have different compositions and structures. Ethanol contains one oxygen atom, depicted by one red sphere. In contrast, ethylene glycol contains two oxygen atoms.

Even apparently minor differences in the composition or structure of molecules can cause profound differences in properties. Ethanol, for example, is the alcohol in

GO FIGURE

**How many carbon atoms are in one aspirin molecule?**

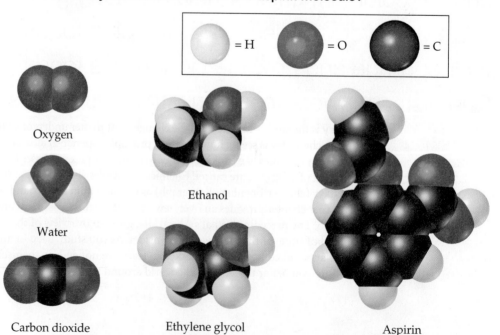

Oxygen

Water

Carbon dioxide

Ethanol

Ethylene glycol

Aspirin

▲ FIGURE 1.1 **Molecular models.** The white, black, and red spheres represent atoms of hydrogen, carbon, and oxygen, respectively.

beverages such as beer and wine, whereas ethylene glycol is a viscous liquid used as automobile antifreeze. The properties of these two substances differ in many ways, as do their biological activities. Ethanol is consumed throughout the world, but you should *never* consume ethylene glycol because it is highly toxic. One of the challenges chemists undertake is to alter the composition or structure of molecules in a controlled way, creating new substances with different properties.

Every change in the observable world—from boiling water to the changes that occur as our bodies combat invading viruses—has its basis in the world of atoms and molecules. Thus, as we proceed with our study of chemistry, we will find ourselves thinking in two realms: the *macroscopic* realm of ordinary-sized objects (*macro* = large) and the *submicroscopic* realm of atoms and molecules. We make our observations in the macroscopic world, but in order to understand that world, we must visualize how atoms and molecules behave at the submicroscopic level. Chemistry is the science that seeks to understand the properties and behavior of matter by studying the properties and behavior of atoms and molecules.

### GIVE IT SOME THOUGHT

a. Approximately how many elements are there?
b. What submicroscopic particles are the building blocks of matter?

## Why Study Chemistry?

Chemistry greatly impacts our daily lives. Indeed, chemistry lies near the heart of many matters of public concern: improvement of health care, conservation of natural resources, protection of the environment, and provision of our daily needs for food, clothing, and shelter. Using chemistry, we have discovered pharmaceutical chemicals that enhance health and prolong lives. We have increased food production through the use of fertilizers and pesticides, and we have developed plastics and other materials used in almost every facet of our lives, from electronics to sporting equipment to building construction. Unfortunately, some chemicals can harm our health or the environment. As educated citizens and consumers, it is in our best interest to understand the profound effects, both positive and negative, that chemicals have on our lives and to strike an informed balance about their uses.

Most of you are studying chemistry, however, not merely to satisfy your curiosity or to become more informed consumers or citizens but also because it is an essential part of your curriculum. Your major might be chemistry, but it could be biology, engineering, pharmacy, agriculture, geology, or some other field. Why do so many subjects share an essential tie to chemistry? The answer is that chemistry is the *central science,* central to a fundamental understanding of other sciences and technologies. For example, our interactions with the material world raise basic questions about the materials around us. What are their compositions and properties? How do they interact with us and with our environment? How, why, and when do materials undergo change? These questions are important whether the material is part of a solar cell, a pigment used by a Renaissance painter, or a living creature (▼ FIGURE 1.2).

(a)                     (b)                     (c)

◀ FIGURE 1.2
**Chemistry helps us understand the world around us.**
(a) Solar cells are made of silicon. (b) A Renaissance painting, *Young Girl Reading,* by Vittore Carpaccio (1472–1526), uses pigments that keep their color for years.
(c) The light from this firefly is the result of a chemical reaction within the animal.

By studying chemistry, you will learn to use the powerful language and ideas that have evolved to describe and enhance our understanding of matter. Furthermore, an understanding of chemistry provides powerful insights into other areas of modern science, technology, and engineering.

# CHEMISTRY PUT TO WORK

## Chemistry and the Chemical Industry

**Chemistry is all around us.** Many people are familiar with household chemicals such as those shown in ► FIGURE 1.3, but few realize the size and importance of the chemical industry. Worldwide sales of chemicals and related products manufactured in the United States total approximately $550 billion annually. The chemical industry employs more than 10% of all scientists and engineers and is a major contributor to the US economy.

Vast amounts of chemicals are produced each year and serve as raw materials for a variety of uses, including the manufacture and processing of metals, plastics, fertilizers, pharmaceuticals, fuels, paints, adhesives, pesticides, synthetic fibers, and microprocessor chips. ▼ TABLE 1.1 lists the top eight chemicals produced in the United States.

**Who are chemists, and what do they do?** People who have degrees in chemistry hold a variety of positions in industry, government, and academia. Those in industry work as laboratory chemists, developing new products (research and development), analyzing materials (quality control), or assisting customers in using products (sales and service). Those with more experience or training may work as managers or company directors. Chemists are important members of the scientific workforce in government (the National Institutes of Health, Department of Energy, and Environmental Protection Agency all employ chemists) and at universities. A chemistry degree is also good preparation for careers in teaching, medicine, biomedical research, information science, environmental work, technical sales, work with government regulatory agencies, and patent law.

Fundamentally, chemists do three things: (1) make new types of matter: materials, substances, or combinations of substances with

► FIGURE 1.3
**Common household chemicals.**

desired properties; (2) measure the properties of matter; and (3) develop models that explain and/or predict the properties of matter. One chemist, for example, may spend years working in the laboratory to discover new drugs. Another may concentrate on the development of new instrumentation to measure properties of matter at the atomic level. Other chemists may use existing materials and methods to understand how pollutants are transported in the environment or how drugs are processed in the body. Yet another chemist will develop theory, write computer code, or run computer simulations to understand how molecules move and react on very fast time scales. The collective chemical enterprise is a rich mix of all of these activities.

**TABLE 1.1 • The Top Eight Chemicals Produced by the US Chemical Industry in 2008[a]**

| Rank | Chemical | Formula | 2008 Production (Billions of Pounds) | Principal End Uses |
|------|----------|---------|--------------------------------------|--------------------|
| 1 | Sulfuric acid | $H_2SO_4$ | 71 | Fertilizers, chemical manufacturing |
| 2 | Ethylene | $C_2H_4$ | 50 | Plastics, antifreeze |
| 3 | Lime | $CaO$ | 44 | Paper, cement, steel |
| 4 | Propylene | $C_3H_6$ | 33 | Plastics |
| 5 | Ammonia | $NH_3$ | 21 | Fertilizers |
| 6 | Chlorine | $Cl_2$ | 21 | Bleaches, plastics, water purification |
| 7 | Phosphoric acid | $H_3PO_4$ | 20 | Fertilizers |
| 8 | Sodium hydroxide | $NaOH$ | 16 | Aluminum production, soap |

[a]Most data from *Chemical and Engineering News*, July 6, 2009, pp. 53, 56. Data on lime from U.S. Geological Survey.

# 1.2 | CLASSIFICATIONS OF MATTER

Let's begin our study of chemistry by examining some fundamental ways in which matter is classified. Two principal ways of classifying matter are according to physical state (gas, liquid, or solid) and according to composition (element, compound, or mixture).

## States of Matter

A sample of matter can be a gas, a liquid, or a solid. These three forms, called the **states of matter**, differ in some of their observable properties. A **gas** (also known as *vapor*) has no fixed volume or shape; rather, it conforms to the volume and shape of its container. A gas can be compressed to occupy a smaller volume, or it can expand to occupy a larger one. A **liquid** has a distinct volume independent of its container but has no specific shape. It assumes the shape of the portion of the container it occupies. A **solid** has both a definite shape and a definite volume. Neither liquids nor solids can be compressed to any appreciable extent.

The properties of the states of matter can be understood on the molecular level (▶ **FIGURE 1.4**). In a gas the molecules are far apart and moving at high speeds, colliding repeatedly with one another and with the walls of the container. Compressing a gas decreases the amount of space between molecules and increases the frequency of collisions between molecules but does not alter the size or shape of the molecules. In a liquid the molecules are packed closely together but still move rapidly. The rapid movement allows the molecules to slide over one another; thus, a liquid pours easily. In a solid the molecules are held tightly together, usually in definite arrangements in which the molecules can wiggle only slightly in their otherwise fixed positions. Thus, the distances between molecules are similar in the liquid and solid states, but the two states differ in how free the molecules are to move around. Changes in temperature and/or pressure can lead to conversion from one state of matter to another, illustrated by such familiar processes as ice melting or water vapor condensing.

## Pure Substances

Most forms of matter we encounter—the air we breathe (a gas), the gasoline we burn in our cars (a liquid), and the sidewalk we walk on (a solid)—are not chemically pure. We can, however, separate these forms of matter into pure substances. A **pure substance** (usually referred to simply as a *substance*) is matter that has distinct properties and a composition that does not vary from sample to sample. Water and table salt (sodium chloride), the primary components of seawater, are examples of pure substances.

All substances are either elements or compounds. **Elements** are substances that cannot be decomposed into simpler substances. On the molecular level, each element is composed of only one kind of atom [▶ **FIGURE 1.5**(a and b)]. **Compounds** are substances composed of two or more elements; they contain two or more kinds of atoms [Figure 1.5(c)]. Water, for example, is a compound composed of two elements: hydrogen and oxygen. Figure 1.5(d) shows a mixture of substances. **Mixtures** are combinations of two or more substances in which each substance retains its chemical identity.

## Elements

Currently, 118 elements are known, though they vary widely in abundance. For example, only five elements—oxygen, silicon, aluminum, iron, and calcium—account for over 90% of Earth's crust (including oceans and atmosphere) and only three—oxygen,

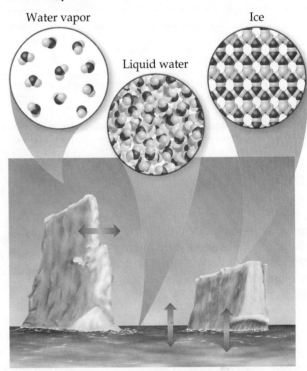

**▲ GO FIGURE**

**In which form of water are the water molecules farthest apart?**

Water vapor          Liquid water          Ice

**▲ FIGURE 1.4   The three physical states of water—water vapor, liquid water, and ice.** We see the liquid and solid states but cannot see the gas (vapor) state. When we look at steam or clouds, we see tiny droplets of liquid water dispersed in the atmosphere. The red arrows show that the three states of matter interconvert.

**How do the molecules of a compound differ from the molecules of an element?**

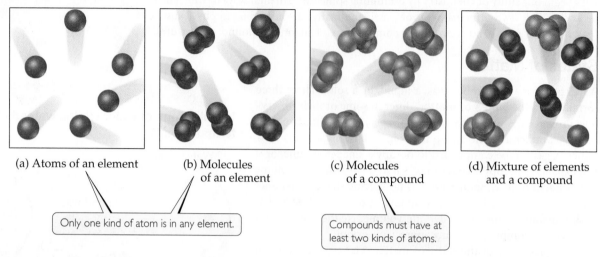

(a) Atoms of an element   (b) Molecules of an element   (c) Molecules of a compound   (d) Mixture of elements and a compound

Only one kind of atom is in any element.

Compounds must have at least two kinds of atoms.

▲ FIGURE 1.5   **Molecular comparison of elements, compounds, and mixtures.**

**Can you name two significant differences between the elemental composition of Earth's crust and the elemental composition of the human body?**

Earth's crust

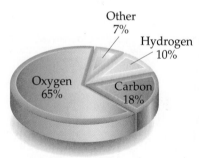

Human body

▲ FIGURE 1.6   **Relative abundances of elements.** Elements in percent by mass in Earth's crust (including oceans and atmosphere) and the human body.

carbon, and hydrogen—account for over 90% of the mass of the human body (◀ FIGURE 1.6).

▼ TABLE 1.2 lists some common elements, along with the chemical *symbols* used to denote them. The symbol for each element consists of one or two letters, with the first letter capitalized. These symbols are derived mostly from the English names of the elements, but sometimes they are derived from a foreign name instead (last column in Table 1.2). You will need to know these symbols and learn others as we encounter them in the text.

All of the known elements and their symbols are listed on the front inside cover of this text in a table known as the *periodic table*. In the periodic table the elements are arranged in columns so that closely related elements are grouped together. We describe the periodic table in more detail in Section 2.5 and consider the periodically repeating properties of the elements in Chapter 7.

## Compounds

Most elements can interact with other elements to form compounds. For example, when hydrogen gas burns in oxygen gas, the elements hydrogen and oxygen combine to form the compound water. Conversely, water can be decomposed into its elements by passing an electrical current through it (▶ FIGURE 1.7). Pure water, regardless of its source, consists of 11% hydrogen and 89% oxygen by mass. This

| TABLE 1.2 • Some Common Elements and Their Symbols | | | | | |
|---|---|---|---|---|---|
| Carbon | C | Aluminum | Al | Copper | Cu (from *cuprum*) |
| Fluorine | F | Bromine | Br | Iron | Fe (from *ferrum*) |
| Hydrogen | H | Calcium | Ca | Lead | Pb (from *plumbum*) |
| Iodine | I | Chlorine | Cl | Mercury | Hg (from *hydrargyrum*) |
| Nitrogen | N | Helium | He | Potassium | K (from *kalium*) |
| Oxygen | O | Lithium | Li | Silver | Ag (from *argentum*) |
| Phosphorus | P | Magnesium | Mg | Sodium | Na (from *natrium*) |
| Sulfur | S | Silicon | Si | Tin | Sn (from *stannum*) |

**What is the connection between the relative gas volumes collected in the two tubes and the relative number of gas molecules in the tubes?**

Oxygen gas, O₂

Water, H₂O

Hydrogen gas, H₂

◀ **FIGURE 1.7**
**Electrolysis of water.**
Water decomposes into its component elements, hydrogen and oxygen, when an electrical current is passed through it. The volume of hydrogen, collected in the right test tube, is twice the volume of oxygen.

macroscopic composition corresponds to the molecular composition, which consists of two hydrogen atoms combined with one oxygen atom:

Hydrogen atom

(written H)

Oxygen atom

(written O)

Water molecule

(written H₂O)

The elements hydrogen and oxygen themselves exist naturally as diatomic (two-atom) molecules:

Oxygen molecule          (written O₂)

Hydrogen molecule          (written H₂)

As seen in ▼ **TABLE 1.3**, the properties of water bear no resemblance to the properties of its component elements. Hydrogen, oxygen, and water are each a unique substance, a consequence of the uniqueness of their respective molecules.

**TABLE 1.3 • Comparison of Water, Hydrogen, and Oxygen**

|  | **Water** | **Hydrogen** | **Oxygen** |
|---|---|---|---|
| State[a] | Liquid | Gas | Gas |
| Normal boiling point | 100 °C | −253 °C | −183 °C |
| Density[a] | 1000 g/L | 0.084 g/L | 1.33 g/L |
| Flammable | No | Yes | No |

[a]At room temperature and atmospheric pressure.

The observation that the elemental composition of a compound is always the same is known as the **law of constant composition** (or the **law of definite proportions**). French chemist Joseph Louis Proust (1754–1826) first stated the law in about 1800. Although this law has been known for 200 years, the belief persists among some people that a fundamental difference exists between compounds prepared in the laboratory and the corresponding compounds found in nature. However, a pure compound has the same composition and properties regardless of its source. Both chemists and nature must use the same elements and operate under the same natural laws. When two materials differ in composition or properties, either they are composed of different compounds or they differ in purity.

 GIVE IT SOME THOUGHT

Hydrogen, oxygen, and water are all composed of molecules. What is it about a molecule of water that makes it a compound, whereas hydrogen and oxygen are elements?

## Mixtures

Most of the matter we encounter consists of mixtures of different substances. Each substance in a mixture retains its chemical identity and properties. In contrast to a pure substance, which by definition has a fixed composition, the composition of a mixture can vary. A cup of sweetened coffee, for example, can contain either a little sugar or a lot. The substances making up a mixture are called *components* of the mixture.

Some mixtures do not have the same composition, properties, and appearance throughout. Rocks and wood, for example, vary in texture and appearance in any typical sample. Such mixtures are *heterogeneous* [▼ **FIGURE 1.8**(a)]. Mixtures that are uniform throughout are *homogeneous*. Air is a homogeneous mixture of nitrogen, oxygen, and smaller amounts of other gases. The nitrogen in air has all the properties of pure nitrogen because both the pure substance and the mixture contain the same nitrogen molecules. Salt, sugar, and many other substances dissolve in water to form homogeneous mixtures [Figure 1.8(b)]. Homogeneous mixtures are also called **solutions**. Although the term *solution* conjures an image of a liquid, solutions can be solids, liquids, or gases.

▶ **FIGURE 1.9** summarizes the classification of matter into elements, compounds, and mixtures.

(a)                                                    (b)

▲ **FIGURE 1.8**   **Mixtures.** (a) Many common materials, including rocks, are heterogeneous mixtures. This photograph of granite shows a heterogeneous mixture of silicon dioxide and other metal oxides. (b) Homogeneous mixtures are called solutions. Many substances, including the blue solid shown here [copper(II) sulfate], dissolve in water to form solutions.

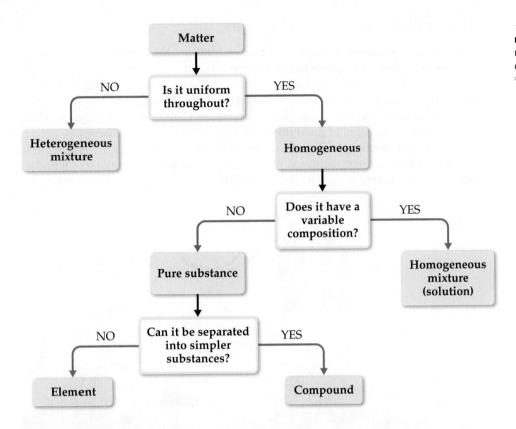

◄ **FIGURE 1.9  Classification of matter.** All pure matter is classified ultimately as either an element or a compound.

---

| **SAMPLE EXERCISE 1.1** | **Distinguishing among Elements, Compounds, and Mixtures** |
|---|---|

"White gold" contains gold and a "white" metal, such as palladium. Two samples of white gold differ in the relative amounts of gold and palladium they contain. Both samples are uniform in composition throughout. Use Figure 1.9 to classify white gold.

**SOLUTION**

Because the material is uniform throughout, it is homogeneous. Because its composition differs for the two samples, it cannot be a compound. Instead, it must be a homogeneous mixture.

**PRACTICE EXERCISE**

Aspirin is composed of 60.0% carbon, 4.5% hydrogen, and 35.5% oxygen by mass, regardless of its source. Use Figure 1.9 to classify aspirin.

***Answer:*** It is a compound because it has constant composition and can be separated into several elements.

---

# 1.3 | PROPERTIES OF MATTER

Every substance has unique properties. For example, the properties listed in Table 1.3 allow us to distinguish hydrogen, oxygen, and water from one another. The properties of matter can be categorized as physical or chemical. **Physical properties** can be observed without changing the identity and composition of the substance. These properties include color, odor, density, melting point, boiling point, and hardness. **Chemical properties** describe the way a substance may change, or *react,* to form other substances. A common chemical property is flammability, the ability of a substance to burn in the presence of oxygen.

Some properties, such as temperature and melting point, are **intensive properties**. They do not depend on the amount of sample being examined and are particularly useful in chemistry because many intensive properties can be used to *identify* substances. **Extensive properties** depend on the amount of sample, with two examples being mass and volume. Extensive properties relate to the *amount* of substance present.

## Physical and Chemical Changes

The changes substances undergo are either physical or chemical. During a **physical change**, a substance changes its physical appearance but not its composition. (That is, it is the same substance before and after the change.) The evaporation of water is a physical change. When water evaporates, it changes from the liquid state to the gas state, but it is still composed of water molecules, as depicted in Figure 1.4. All **changes of state** (for example, from liquid to gas or from liquid to solid) are physical changes.

In a **chemical change** (also called a **chemical reaction**), a substance is transformed into a chemically different substance. When hydrogen burns in air, for example, it undergoes a chemical change because it combines with oxygen to form water (▼ **FIGURE 1.10**).

▶ FIGURE 1.10   **A chemical reaction.**

Burn

H₂          O₂                              H₂O

Chemical changes can be dramatic. In the account that follows, Ira Remsen, author of a popular chemistry text published in 1901, describes his first experiences with chemical reactions. The chemical reaction that he observed is shown in ▼ **FIGURE 1.11**.

▲ FIGURE 1.11   **The chemical reaction between a copper penny and nitric acid.** The dissolved copper produces the blue-green solution; the reddish brown gas produced is nitrogen dioxide.

While reading a textbook of chemistry, I came upon the statement "nitric acid acts upon copper," and I determined to see what this meant. Having located some nitric acid, I had only to learn what the words "act upon" meant. In the interest of knowledge I was even willing to sacrifice one of the few copper cents then in my possession. I put one of them on the table, opened a bottle labeled "nitric acid," poured some of the liquid on the copper, and prepared to make an observation. But what was this wonderful thing which I beheld? The cent was already changed, and it was no small change either. A greenish-blue liquid foamed and fumed over the cent and over the table. The air became colored dark red. How could I stop this? I tried by picking the cent up and throwing it out the window. I learned another fact: nitric acid acts upon fingers. The pain led to another unpremeditated experiment. I drew my fingers across my trousers and discovered nitric acid acts upon trousers. That was the most impressive experiment I have ever performed. I tell of it even now with interest. It was a revelation to me. Plainly the only way to learn about such remarkable kinds of action is to see the results, to experiment, to work in the laboratory.

## ◢ GIVE IT SOME THOUGHT

Which of these changes are physical and which are chemical? Explain.
a. Plants make sugar from carbon dioxide and water.
b. Water vapor in the air forms frost.
c. A goldsmith melts a nugget of gold and pulls it into a wire.

## Separation of Mixtures

We can separate a mixture into its components by taking advantage of differences in their properties. For example, a heterogeneous mixture of iron filings and gold filings could be sorted by color into iron and gold. A less tedious approach would be to use a magnet to attract the iron filings, leaving the gold ones behind. We can also take advantage of an important chemical difference between these two metals: Many acids dissolve iron but not gold. Thus, if we put our mixture into an appropriate acid, the acid would dissolve the iron and the solid gold would be left behind. The two could then be separated by *filtration* (▼ FIGURE 1.12). We would have to use other chemical reactions, which we will learn about later, to transform the dissolved iron back into metal.

An important method of separating the components of a homogeneous mixture is *distillation*, a process that depends on the different abilities of substances to form gases.

**▲ FIGURE 1.12 Separation by filtration.** A mixture of a solid and a liquid is poured through filter paper. The liquid passes through the paper while the solid remains on the paper.

For example, if we boil a solution of salt and water, the water evaporates, forming a gas, and the salt is left behind. The gaseous water can be converted back to a liquid on the walls of a condenser, as shown in ▼ FIGURE 1.13.

▶ FIGURE 1.13 **Distillation.** Apparatus for separating a sodium chloride solution (salt water) into its components.

The differing abilities of substances to adhere to the surfaces of solids can also be used to separate mixtures. This ability is the basis of *chromatography* (literally, "the writing of colors"), a technique shown in ▼ FIGURE 1.14.

▲ FIGURE 1.14   **Separation of ink into components by paper chromatography.**

# 1.4 | UNITS OF MEASUREMENT

Many properties of matter are *quantitative*, that is, associated with numbers. When a number represents a measured quantity, the units of that quantity must be specified. To say that the length of a pencil is 17.5 is meaningless. Expressing the number with its units, 17.5 centimeters (cm), properly specifies the length. The units used for scientific measurements are those of the **metric system**.

The metric system, developed in France during the late eighteenth century, is used as the system of measurement in most countries. The United States has traditionally used the English system, although use of the metric system has become more common (◀ FIGURE 1.15).

▶ FIGURE 1.15 **Metric units.** Metric measurements are increasingly common in the United States, as exemplified by the volume printed on this soda can in both English units (fluid ounces, fl oz) and metric units (milliliters, mL).

# A CLOSER LOOK

## THE SCIENTIFIC METHOD

Although two scientists rarely approach the same problem in exactly the same way, they use guidelines for the practice of science known as the **scientific method**. As ▶ FIGURE 1.16 shows, we begin by collecting information, or *data,* by observation and experiment. The ultimate goal, however, is not collecting data but rather finding a pattern or sense of order in our observations and understanding the origin of this order.

As we gather more data, we may see patterns that lead us to a *tentative explanation,* or **hypothesis**, that guides us in planning further experiments. A key feature of a good hypothesis is that it proposes a mechanism that underlies our observations and can be used to make predictions about new experiments. If a hypothesis is sufficiently general and repeatedly effective in predicting results of future experiments, it is called a theory. A **theory** *is an explanation of the general causes of certain phenomena, with considerable evidence or facts to support it.* For example, Einstein's theory of relativity was a revolutionary way of thinking about space and time. It was more than just a hypothesis because it could be used to make predictions that could be tested experimentally. The results of these experiments were generally in agreement with Einstein's predictions and were not explainable by earlier theories.

In spite of the landmark achievements of Einstein's theory, scientists can never say the theory is "proven." A theory that has excellent predictive power today may not work as well in the future as more data and improved scientific equipment are developed. Thus, science is always a work in progress.

Eventually, we may be able to tie together a great number of observations in a **scientific law**, which is *a concise verbal statement or mathematical equation that summarizes a broad variety of observations and experiences.* We tend to think of scientific laws as the basic rules under which nature operates. However, it is not so much that matter obeys these laws, but rather that these laws describe the behavior of matter. As we proceed through this text, we will rarely have the opportunity to discuss the doubts, conflicts, clashes of personalities, and revolutions of perception that have led to our present scientific ideas. You need to be aware that just because we can spell out the results of science so concisely and neatly in textbooks does not mean scientific progress is smooth, certain, and predictable. Some of the ideas we present in this text took centuries to develop and involved many scientists. We gain our view of the natural world by standing on the shoulders of the scientists who came before us. Take advantage of this view. As you study, exercise your imagination. Don't be afraid to ask daring questions when they occur to you. You may be fascinated by what you discover!

*RELATED EXERCISE:* 1.58

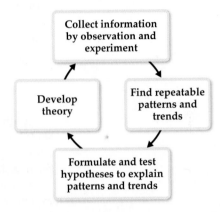

▲ FIGURE 1.16 **The scientific method.** This general approach to solving problems involves making observations, confirming that they are reproducible, seeking patterns in the observations, formulating hypotheses to explain the observations, and testing these hypotheses by further experiments. Hypotheses that withstand such tests and prove themselves useful in explaining and predicting behavior become known as theories.

# SI Units

In 1960 an international agreement was reached specifying a particular choice of metric units for use in scientific measurements. These preferred units are called **SI units**, after the French *Système International d'Unités.* This system has seven *base units* from which all other units are derived (▼ TABLE 1.4). In this chapter we will consider the base units for length, mass, and temperature.

**TABLE 1.4 • SI Base Units**

| Physical Quantity | Name of Unit | Abbreviation |
| --- | --- | --- |
| Mass | Kilogram | kg |
| Length | Meter | m |
| Time | Second | s or sec |
| Temperature | Kelvin | K |
| Amount of substance | Mole | mol |
| Electric current | Ampere | A or amp |
| Luminous intensity | Candela | cd |

| TABLE 1.5 • Prefixes Used in the Metric System and with SI Units | | | |
|---|---|---|---|
| **Prefix** | **Abbreviation** | **Meaning** | **Example** |
| Peta | P | $10^{15}$ | 1 petawatt (PW) $= 1 \times 10^{15}$ watts[a] |
| Tera | T | $10^{12}$ | 1 terawatt (TW) $= 1 \times 10^{12}$ watts |
| Giga | G | $10^{9}$ | 1 gigawatt (GW) $= 1 \times 10^{9}$ watts |
| Mega | M | $10^{6}$ | 1 megawatt (MW) $= 1 \times 10^{6}$ watts |
| Kilo | k | $10^{3}$ | 1 kilowatt (kW) $= 1 \times 10^{3}$ watts |
| Deci | d | $10^{-1}$ | 1 deciwatt (dW) $= 1 \times 10^{-1}$ watt |
| Centi | c | $10^{-2}$ | 1 centiwatt (cW) $= 1 \times 10^{-2}$ watt |
| Milli | m | $10^{-3}$ | 1 milliwatt (mW) $= 1 \times 10^{-3}$ watt |
| Micro | $\mu$[b] | $10^{-6}$ | 1 microwatt ($\mu$W) $= 1 \times 10^{-6}$ watt |
| Nano | n | $10^{-9}$ | 1 nanowatt (nW) $= 1 \times 10^{-9}$ watt |
| Pico | p | $10^{-12}$ | 1 picowatt (pW) $= 1 \times 10^{-12}$ watt |
| Femto | f | $10^{-15}$ | 1 femtowatt (fW) $= 1 \times 10^{-15}$ watt |
| Atto | a | $10^{-18}$ | 1 attowatt (aW) $= 1 \times 10^{-18}$ watt |
| Zepto | z | $10^{-21}$ | 1 zeptowatt (zW) $= 1 \times 10^{-21}$ watt |

[a]The watt (W) is the SI unit of power, which is the rate at which energy is either generated or consumed. The SI unit of energy is the joule (J); $1 \text{ J} = 1 \text{ kg} \cdot \text{m}^2/\text{s}^2$ and $1 \text{ W} = 1 \text{ J/s}$.
[b]Greek letter mu, pronounced "mew."

With SI units, prefixes are used to indicate decimal fractions or multiples of various units. For example, the prefix *milli-* represents a $10^{-3}$ fraction, one-thousandth, of a unit: A milligram (mg) is $10^{-3}$ gram (g), a millimeter (mm) is $10^{-3}$ meter (m), and so forth. ▲ TABLE 1.5 presents the prefixes commonly encountered in chemistry. In using SI units and in working problems throughout this text, you must be comfortable using exponential notation. If you are unfamiliar with exponential notation or want to review it, refer to Appendix A.1.

Although non–SI units are being phased out, some are still commonly used by scientists. Whenever we first encounter a non–SI unit in the text, the SI unit will also be given. The relations between the non–SI and SI units we will use most frequently in this text appear on the back inside cover. We will discuss how to convert from one to the other in Section 1.6.

◢ GIVE IT SOME THOUGHT

Which quantity is the smallest: 1 mg, 1 $\mu$g, or 1 pg?

## Length and Mass

The SI base unit of *length* is the meter, a distance slightly longer than a yard. **Mass*** is a measure of the amount of material in an object. The SI base unit of mass is the kilogram (kg), which is equal to about 2.2 pounds (lb). This base unit is unusual because it uses a prefix, *kilo-*, instead of the word *gram* alone. We obtain other units for mass by adding prefixes to the word *gram*.

**SAMPLE EXERCISE 1.2** Using SI Prefixes

What is the name of the unit that equals (**a**) $10^{-9}$ gram, (**b**) $10^{-6}$ second, (**c**) $10^{-3}$ meter?

**SOLUTION**

We can find the prefix related to each power of ten in Table 1.5: (**a**) nanogram, ng, (**b**) microsecond, $\mu$s, (**c**) millimeter, mm.

***Mass and weight are often incorrectly thought to be the same. The weight of an object is the force that is exerted on its mass by gravity. In space, where gravitational forces are very weak, an astronaut can be weightless, but he or she cannot be massless. The astronaut's mass in space is the same as it is on Earth.

## Temperature

*Temperature,* a measure of the hotness or coldness of an object, is a physical property that determines the direction of heat flow. Heat always flows spontaneously from a substance at higher temperature to one at lower temperature. Thus, we feel the influx of heat when we touch a hot object, and we know that the object is at a higher temperature than our hand.

The temperature scales commonly employed in science are the Celsius and Kelvin scales. The **Celsius scale** was originally based on the assignment of 0 °C to the freezing point of water and 100 °C to its boiling point at sea level (▼ **FIGURE 1.17**).

The **Kelvin scale** is the SI temperature scale, and the SI unit of temperature is the *kelvin* (K). Zero on the Kelvin scale is the lowest attainable temperature, −273.15 °C, referred to as *absolute zero*. The Celsius and Kelvin scales have equal-sized units—that is, a kelvin is the same size as a degree Celsius. Thus, the Kelvin and Celsius scales are related according to

$$K = °C + 273.15 \qquad\qquad [1.1]$$

The freezing point of water, 0 °C, is 273.15 K (Figure 1.17). Notice that we do not use a degree sign (°) with temperatures on the Kelvin scale.

The common temperature scale in the United States is the *Fahrenheit scale,* which is not generally used in science. Water freezes at 32 °F and boils at 212 °F. The Fahrenheit and Celsius scales are related according to

$$°C = \frac{5}{9}(°F - 32) \quad \text{or} \quad °F = \frac{9}{5}(°C) + 32 \qquad\qquad [1.2]$$

GO FIGURE

True or false: The "size" of a degree on the Celsius scale is the same as the "size" of a degree on the Kelvin scale.

◀ **FIGURE 1.17  Comparison of the Kelvin, Celsius, and Fahrenheit temperature scales.**

**How many 1-L bottles are required to contain 1 m³ of liquid?**

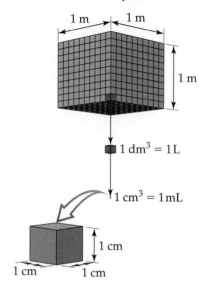

▲ **FIGURE 1.18  Volume relationships.**
The volume occupied by a cube 1 m on each edge is one cubic meter, 1 m³. Each cubic meter contains 1000 dm³. One liter is the same volume as one cubic decimeter, 1 L = 1 dm³. Each cubic decimeter contains 1000 cubic centimeters, 1 dm³ = 1000 cm³. One cubic centimeter equals one milliliter, 1 cm³ = 1 mL.

---

**SAMPLE EXERCISE 1.3  Converting Units of Temperature**

A weather forecaster predicts the temperature will reach 31 °C. What is this temperature (**a**) in K, (**b**) in °F?

**SOLUTION**

(**a**) Using Equation 1.1, we have K = 31 + 273 = 304 K.

(**b**) Using Equation 1.2, we have $°F = \dfrac{9}{5}(31) + 32 = 56 + 32 = 88 \,°F$.

**PRACTICE EXERCISE**

Ethylene glycol, the major ingredient in antifreeze, freezes at −11.5 °C. What is the freezing point in (**a**) K, (**b**) °F?
**Answers:**  (**a**) 261.7 K, (**b**) 11.3 °F

## Derived SI Units

The SI base units are used to obtain *derived units*. To do so, we use the defining equation for the quantity, substituting the appropriate base units. For example, speed is defined as the ratio of distance traveled to elapsed time. Thus, the SI unit for speed—m/s, read "meters per second"—is a derived unit, the SI unit for distance (length), m, divided by the SI unit for time, s. Two common derived units in chemistry are those for volume and density.

## Volume

The *volume* of a cube is its length cubed, (length)³. Thus, the derived SI unit of volume is the SI unit of length, m, raised to the third power. The cubic meter, m³, is the volume of a cube that is 1 m on each edge (◀ **FIGURE 1.18**). Smaller units, such as cubic centimeters, cm³ (sometimes written cc), are frequently used in chemistry. Another volume unit used in chemistry is the *liter* (L), which equals a cubic decimeter, dm³, and is slightly larger than a quart. (The liter is the first metric unit we have encountered that is *not* an SI unit.) There are 1000 milliliters (mL) in a liter, and 1 mL is the same volume as 1 cm³: 1 mL = 1 cm³. The devices used most frequently in chemistry to measure volume are illustrated in ▼ **FIGURE 1.19**.

These deliver **variable** volumes    Pipet **delivers** a **specific** volume    Volumetric flask **contains** a specific volume

▲ **FIGURE 1.19  Common volumetric glassware.**

Syringes, burets, and pipets deliver amounts of liquids with more precision than graduated cylinders. Volumetric flasks are used to contain specific volumes of liquid.

 **GIVE IT SOME THOUGHT**

Which of the following quantities represents volume measurements: $15\,m^2$; $2.5 \times 10^2\,m^3$; $5.77\,L/s$? How do you know?

## Density

**Density** is defined as the amount of mass in a unit volume of a substance:

$$\text{Density} = \frac{\text{mass}}{\text{volume}} \qquad\qquad [1.3]$$

The densities of solids and liquids are commonly expressed in either grams per cubic centimeter $(g/cm^3)$ or grams per milliliter $(g/mL)$. The densities of some common substances are listed in ▶ **TABLE 1.6**. It is no coincidence that the density of water is 1.00 g/mL; the gram was originally defined as the mass of 1 mL of water at a specific temperature. Because most substances change volume when they are heated or cooled, densities are temperature dependent, and so temperature should be specified when reporting densities. If no temperature is reported, we assume 25 °C, close to normal room temperature.

The terms *density* and *weight* are sometimes confused. A person who says that iron weighs more than air generally means that iron has a higher density than air—1 kg of air has the same mass as 1 kg of iron, but the iron occupies a smaller volume, thereby giving it a higher density. If we combine two liquids that do not mix, the less dense liquid will float on the denser liquid.

**TABLE 1.6 • Densities of Selected Substances at 25 °C**

| Substance | Density $(g/cm^3)$ |
|---|---|
| Air | 0.001 |
| Balsa wood | 0.16 |
| Ethanol | 0.79 |
| Water | 1.00 |
| Ethylene glycol | 1.09 |
| Table sugar | 1.59 |
| Table salt | 2.16 |
| Iron | 7.9 |
| Gold | 19.32 |

---

**SAMPLE EXERCISE 1.4**   **Determining Density and Using Density to Determine Volume or Mass**

(a) Calculate the density of mercury if $1.00 \times 10^2$ g occupies a volume of $7.36\,cm^3$.
(b) Calculate the volume of 65.0 g of liquid methanol (wood alcohol) if its density is 0.791 g/mL.
(c) What is the mass in grams of a cube of gold (density $= 19.32\,g/cm^3$) if the length of the cube is 2.00 cm?

**SOLUTION**

(a) We are given mass and volume, so Equation 1.3 yields

$$\text{Density} = \frac{\text{mass}}{\text{volume}} = \frac{1.00 \times 10^2\,g}{7.36\,cm^3} = 13.6\,g/cm^3$$

(b) Solving Equation 1.3 for volume and then using the given mass and density gives

$$\text{Volume} = \frac{\text{mass}}{\text{density}} = \frac{65.0\,g}{0.791\,g/mL} = 82.2\,mL$$

(c) We can calculate the mass from the volume of the cube and its density. The volume of a cube is given by its length cubed:

$$\text{Volume} = (2.00\,cm)^3 = (2.00)^3\,cm^3 = 8.00\,cm^3$$

Solving Equation 1.3 for mass and substituting the volume and density of the cube, we have

$$\text{Mass} = \text{volume} \times \text{density} = (8.00\,cm^3)(19.32\,g/cm^3) = 155\,g$$

**PRACTICE EXERCISE**

(a) Calculate the density of a 374.5-g sample of copper if it has a volume of $41.8\,cm^3$. (b) A student needs 15.0 g of ethanol for an experiment. If the density of ethanol is 0.789 g/mL, how many milliliters of ethanol are needed? (c) What is the mass, in grams, of 25.0 mL of mercury (density $= 13.6\,g/mL$)?

**Answers: (a)** $8.96\,g/cm^3$, **(b)** 19.0 mL, **(c)** 340 g

# CHEMISTRY PUT TO WORK

## Chemistry in the News

Because chemistry is so central to our lives, reports on matters of chemical significance appear in the news nearly every day. Some reports tell of breakthroughs in the development of new pharmaceuticals, materials, and processes. Others deal with energy, environmental, and public safety issues. As you study chemistry, you will develop the skills to better understand the importance of chemistry in your life. Here are summaries of a few recent stories in which chemistry plays a role.

### Biofuels Reality Check

With the Energy Policy Act of 2005, the US Congress gave a big push to fuels derived from biomass (plants or algae) as a renewable alternative to gasoline. The 2005 act was followed by the Energy Independence and Security Act of 2007, which required that 9.0 billion gallons of renewable fuel be used in gasoline in 2008, 11.1 billion gallons in 2009, and 36 billion gallons by 2022. The United States currently consumes about 140 billion gallons of gasoline per year.

Ethanol derived from corn currently dominates the alternatives, with 40% of all gasoline now containing some ethanol. A blend of 10% ethanol and 90% gasoline, called E10, is the most common blend because it can be used in virtually all vehicles. Blends of 85% ethanol and 15% gasoline, called E85, are also available but can be used only with specially modified engines (▶ FIGURE 1.20).

However, using a food crop to produce transportation fuel may not be the best long-term solution for the energy problem. In 2006, researchers at the University of Minnesota calculated that "even dedicating all US corn and soybean production to biofuels would meet only 12% of gasoline and 6% of diesel demand." The conversion of a much wider range of plant material, using a much greater fraction of available plant matter, into fuels will be necessary to improve these numbers substantially. Because the most abundant plant material, cellulose, does not readily convert to ethanol, a great deal of research will be needed to solve this challenging problem. Meanwhile, it is worth reflecting that a 3% improvement in vehicle fuel efficiency would displace more gasoline use than the entire 2006 US ethanol production. An alternative to ethanol relies on coaxing microorganisms to produce molecules that can be used as fuel. In 2009, ExxonMobil

◀ FIGURE 1.20   A gasoline pump that dispenses E85, a mixture of 85% ethanol and 15% gasoline.

Research and Engineering Company partnered with a start-up company, Synthetic Genomics, to find strains of photosynthetic algae that will efficiently produce oils and hydrocarbons from sunlight and carbon dioxide.

### Advances in Solar Energy

In the 1970s, at the height of the oil crisis, there was a burst of research on renewable energy, including solar energy. After the oil crisis passed and gasoline was once again cheap and readily available, solar energy research was less of a priority. With the more recent increase in gasoline prices and a greater realization that the burning of fossil fuels contributes to global warming, solar energy research is again in vogue. The amount of solar radiation reaching Earth every day is enormous, and if we could harness it efficiently, our energy needs could be easily met. Solar panels like those shown in Figure 1.2a are about 10% efficient in converting light directly into electricity. However, storage of solar energy remains a vigorous area of research:

## 1.5 | UNCERTAINTY IN MEASUREMENT

Two kinds of numbers are encountered in scientific work: *exact numbers* (those whose values are known exactly) and *inexact numbers* (those whose values have some uncertainty). Most of the exact numbers we will encounter in this book have defined values. For example, there are exactly 12 eggs in a dozen, exactly 1000 g in a kilogram, and exactly 2.54 cm in an inch. The number 1 in any conversion factor, such as $1\,m = 100\,cm$ or $1\,kg = 2.2046\,lb$, is an exact number. Exact numbers can also result from counting objects. For example, we can count the exact number of marbles in a jar or the exact number of people in a classroom.

Numbers obtained by measurement are always *inexact*. The equipment used to measure quantities always has inherent limitations (equipment errors), and there are differences in how different people make the same measurement (human errors). Suppose ten students with ten balances are to determine the mass of the same dime. The ten

How can we capture solar energy for use when the Sun is not shining? One potential answer is to store the energy in chemical bonds. One promising new material, first reported in 2008, is a cobalt-containing compound that can convert water into oxygen with sunlight. Hydrogen can also be generated in sunlight from water but using a different compound to facilitate the reaction. Electricity can then be produced by combining the hydrogen and oxygen in a fuel cell.

### Important Antibiotic Modified to Combat Bacterial Resistance

Vancomycin is an antibiotic of last resort—used only when other antibacterial agents are ineffective. Some bacteria have developed resistance to vancomycin, causing researchers to modify the molecular structure of the substance to make it more effective in killing bacteria. This approach was based on the knowledge that vancomycin works by binding to a protein that is essential to forming bacterial cell walls. Researchers have synthesized a vancomycin analog in which a CO group has been converted to a $CH_2$ group (▼ FIGURE 1.21). This modification increases the compound's binding affinity in the cell walls of vancomycin-resistant bacteria, making the analog 100 times more active than vancomycin against vancomycin-resistant bacteria.

### Replacing the Lightbulb through Chemistry

If you want to save the world from global warming, you can start by replacing incandescent lightbulbs. In 2001 approximately 22% of all electricity generated in the United States was used for lighting. This surprisingly high number is due in part to the fact that incandescent lights convert only 5% of the energy supplied to them into visible light and last only 1000 hours on average. Compact fluorescent lamps are more efficient (20% of their output energy is converted into visible light) and last longer (up to 15,000 hours), but they contain mercury, which is toxic and creates disposal problems. A promising replacement bulb is the light-emitting diode (LED). Red LEDs were first made in 1962. As a result of subsequent increases in efficiency and development of other colors, LEDs are now used in traffic lights, car taillights, and a host of electronics applications. These "solid state" devices do not contain mercury, can achieve efficiencies as high as 50%, and hold the promise of longer lifetimes (red LEDs last up to 100,000 hours). With advances in research and development, costs are coming down to the point that some small cities are replacing their streetlights with white LEDs (▼ FIGURE 1.22).

▲ FIGURE 1.22  **LED lighting.** Ann Arbor, Michigan, has replaced incandescent streetlights with white LEDs. The city estimates the change will save $100,000 per year and reduce annual greenhouse gas emissions by 267 tons.

▲ FIGURE 1.21  **Comparing CO and CH₂ groups.** The molecule on the left contains a CO group, and the one on the right contains a $CH_2$ group. This subtle difference is similar to how the structure of the much more complex vancomycin molecule was modified.

measurements will probably vary slightly for various reasons. The balances might be calibrated slightly differently, and there might be differences in how each student reads the mass from the balance. Remember: *Uncertainties always exist in measured quantities.*

 GIVE IT SOME THOUGHT

Which of the following is an inexact quantity:
a. the number of people in your chemistry class,
b. the mass of a penny,
c. the number of grams in a kilogram?

## Precision and Accuracy

The terms *precision* and *accuracy* are often used in discussing the uncertainties of measured values. **Precision** is a measure of how closely individual measurements agree with one another. **Accuracy** refers to how closely individual measurements agree with the

GO FIGURE

**How would the darts be positioned on the target for the case of "good accuracy, poor precision"?**

Good accuracy
Good precision

Poor accuracy
Good precision

Poor accuracy
Poor precision

▲ **FIGURE 1.23** **Precision and accuracy.**

correct, or "true," value. The dart analogy in ◄ **FIGURE 1.23** illustrates the difference between these two concepts.

In the laboratory we often perform several "trials" of an experiment and average the results. The precision of the measurements is often expressed in terms of the *standard deviation* (Appendix A.5), which reflects how much the individual measurements differ from the average. We gain confidence in our measurements if we obtain nearly the same value each time—that is, the standard deviation is small. Figure 1.23 reminds us, however, that precise measurements can be inaccurate. For example, if a very sensitive balance is poorly calibrated, the masses we measure will be consistently either high or low. They will be inaccurate even if they are precise.

## Significant Figures

Suppose you determine the mass of a dime on a balance capable of measuring to the nearest 0.0001 g. You could report the mass as $2.2405 \pm 0.0001$ g. The $\pm$ notation (read "plus or minus") expresses the magnitude of the uncertainty of your measurement. In much scientific work we drop the $\pm$ notation with the understanding that *there is always some uncertainty in the last digit reported for any measured quantity*.

▼ **FIGURE 1.24** shows a thermometer with its liquid column between two scale marks. We can read the certain digits from the scale and estimate the uncertain one. Seeing that the liquid is between the 25 °C and 30 °C marks, we estimate the temperature to be 27 °C, being uncertain of the second digit of our measurement.

All digits of a measured quantity, including the uncertain one, are called **significant figures**. A measured mass reported as 2.2 g has two significant figures, whereas one reported as 2.2405 g has five significant figures. The greater the number of significant figures, the greater the certainty implied for the measurement.

| **SAMPLE EXERCISE 1.5** | **Relating Significant Figures to the Uncertainty of a Measurement** |
| --- | --- |

What difference exists between the measured values 4.0 g and 4.00 g?

### SOLUTION

The value 4.0 has two significant figures, whereas 4.00 has three. This difference implies that the 4.0 has more uncertainty. A mass reported as 4.0 g indicates that the uncertainty is in the first decimal place. Thus, the mass might be anything between 3.9 and 4.1 g, which we can represent as $4.0 \pm 0.1$ g. A mass reported as 4.00 g indicates that the uncertainty is in the second decimal place. Thus, the mass might be anything between 3.99 and 4.01 g, which we can represent as $4.00 \pm 0.01$ g. (Without further information, we cannot be sure whether the difference in uncertainties of the two measurements reflects the precision or the accuracy of the measurement.)

▶ **FIGURE 1.24** **Uncertainty and significant figures in a measurement.**

To determine the number of significant figures in a reported measurement, read the number from left to right, counting the digits starting with the first digit that is not zero. *In any measurement that is properly reported, all nonzero digits are significant.* Because zeros can be used either as part of the measured value or merely to locate the decimal point, they may or may not be significant:

1. Zeros *between* nonzero digits are always significant—1005 kg (four significant figures); 7.03 cm (three significant figures).

2. Zeros *at the beginning* of a number are never significant; they merely indicate the position of the decimal point—0.02 g (one significant figure); 0.0026 cm (two significant figures).

3. Zeros *at the end* of a number are significant if the number contains a decimal point—0.0200 g (three significant figures); 3.0 cm (two significant figures).

A problem arises when a number ends with zeros but contains no decimal point. In such cases, it is normally assumed that the zeros are not significant. Exponential notation (Appendix A.1) can be used to indicate whether end zeros are significant. For example, a mass of 10,300 g can be written to show three, four, or five significant figures depending on how the measurement is obtained:

"MY GOODNESS, IT'S 12:15:0936420175! TIME FOR LUNCH."

| | |
|---|---|
| $1.03 \times 10^4$ g | (three significant figures) |
| $1.030 \times 10^4$ g | (four significant figures) |
| $1.0300 \times 10^4$ g | (five significant figures) |

In these numbers all the zeros to the right of the decimal point are significant (rules 1 and 3). (The exponential term $10^4$ does not add to the number of significant figures.)

---

**SAMPLE EXERCISE 1.6**   **Determining the Number of Significant Figures in a Measurement**

How many significant figures are in each of the following numbers (assume that each number is a measured quantity): (a) 4.003, (b) $6.023 \times 10^{23}$, (c) 5000?

**SOLUTION**

(a) Four; the zeros are significant figures. (b) Four; the exponential term does not add to the number of significant figures. (c) One; we assume that the zeros are not significant when there is no decimal point shown. If the number has more significant figures, a decimal point should be employed or the number written in exponential notation. Thus, 5000. has four significant figures, whereas $5.00 \times 10^3$ has three.

**PRACTICE EXERCISE**

How many significant figures are in each of the following measurements: (a) 3.549 g, (b) $2.3 \times 10^4$ cm, (c) 0.00134 m$^3$?
*Answers:* (a) four, (b) two, (c) three

## Significant Figures in Calculations

When carrying measured quantities through calculations, *the least certain measurement limits the certainty of the calculated quantity and thereby determines the number of significant figures in the final answer. The final answer should be reported with only one uncertain digit.* To keep track of significant figures in calculations, we will make frequent use of two rules, one for addition and subtraction, and another for multiplication and division.

1. *For addition and subtraction*, the result has the same number of decimal places as the measurement with the fewest decimal places. When the result contains more than the correct number of significant figures, it must be rounded off. Consider the following example in which the uncertain digits appear in color:

| | | |
|---|---|---|
| This number limits | 20.42 | ← two decimal places |
| the number of significant | 1.322 | ← three decimal places |
| figures in the result → | 83.1 | ← one decimal place |
| | 104.842 | ← round off to one decimal place (104.8) |

We report the result as 104.8 because 83.1 has only one decimal place.

2. *For multiplication and division*, the result contains the same number of significant figures as the measurement with the fewest significant figures. When the result contains more than the correct number of significant figures, it must be rounded off. For example, the area of a rectangle whose measured edge lengths are 6.221 cm and 5.2 cm should be reported as 32 $cm^2$ even though a calculator shows the product to have more digits:

$$\text{Area} = (6.221 \text{ cm})(5.2 \text{ cm}) = 32.3492 \text{ cm}^2 \Rightarrow \text{round off to } 32 \text{ cm}^2$$

because 5.2 has two significant figures.

*Notice that for addition and subtraction, decimal places are counted in determining how many digits to report in an answer, whereas for multiplication and division, significant figures are counted in determining how many digits to report.*

In determining the final answer for a calculated quantity, *exact numbers* are assumed to have an infinite number of significant figures. Thus, when we say, "There are 12 inches in 1 foot," the number 12 is exact, and we need not worry about the number of significant figures in it.

In *rounding off numbers,* look at the leftmost digit to be removed:

- If the leftmost digit removed is less than 5, the preceding number is left unchanged. Thus, rounding 7.248 to two significant figures gives 7.2.
- If the leftmost digit removed is 5 or greater, the preceding number is increased by 1. Rounding 4.735 to three significant figures gives 4.74, and rounding 2.376 to two significant figures gives 2.4.*

---

**SAMPLE EXERCISE 1.7** | **Determining the Number of Significant Figures in a Calculated Quantity**

The width, length, and height of a small box are 15.5 cm, 27.3 cm, and 5.4 cm, respectively. Calculate the volume of the box, using the correct number of significant figures in your answer.

**SOLUTION**

In reporting the volume, we can show only as many significant figures as given in the dimension with the fewest significant figures, that for the height (two significant figures):

$$\text{Volume} = \text{width} \times \text{length} \times \text{height}$$
$$= (15.5 \text{ cm})(27.3 \text{ cm})(5.4 \text{ cm}) = 2285.01 \text{ cm}^3 \Rightarrow 2.3 \times 10^3 \text{ cm}^3$$

A calculator used for this calculation shows 2285.01, which we must round off to two significant figures. Because the resulting number is 2300, it is best reported in exponential notation, $2.3 \times 10^3$, to clearly indicate two significant figures.

---

*Your instructor may want you to use a slight variation on the rule when the leftmost digit to be removed is exactly 5, with no following digits or only zeros following. One common practice is to round up to the next higher number if that number will be even and down to the next lower number otherwise. Thus, 4.7350 would be rounded to 4.74, and 4.7450 would also be rounded to 4.74.

It takes 10.5 s for a sprinter to run 100.00 m. Calculate her average speed in meters per second, and express the result to the correct number of significant figures.
*Answer:* 9.52 m/s (three significant figures)

**SAMPLE EXERCISE 1.8** | **Determining the Number of Significant Figures in a Calculated Quantity**

A gas at 25 °C fills a container whose volume is $1.05 \times 10^3$ cm$^3$. The container plus gas has a mass of 837.6 g. The container, when emptied of all gas, has a mass of 836.2 g. What is the density of the gas at 25 °C?

**SOLUTION**

To calculate the density, we must know both the mass and the volume of the gas. The mass of the gas is just the difference in the masses of the full and empty container:

$$(837.6 - 836.2) \text{ g} = 1.4 \text{ g}$$

In subtracting numbers, we determine the number of significant figures in our result by counting decimal places in each quantity. In this case each quantity has one decimal place. Thus, the mass of the gas, 1.4 g, has one decimal place.

Using the volume given in the question, $1.05 \times 10^3$ cm$^3$, and the definition of density, we have

$$\text{Density} = \frac{\text{mass}}{\text{volume}} = \frac{1.4 \text{ g}}{1.05 \times 10^3 \text{ cm}^3}$$

$$= 1.3 \times 10^{-3} \text{ g/cm}^3 = 0.0013 \text{ g/cm}^3$$

In dividing numbers, we determine the number of significant figures in our result by counting the number of significant figures in each quantity. There are two significant figures in our answer, corresponding to the smaller number of significant figures in the two numbers that form the ratio. Notice that in this example, following the rules for determining significant figures gives an answer containing only two significant figures, even though each of the measured quantities contained at least three significant figures.

**PRACTICE EXERCISE**

To how many significant figures should the mass of the container be measured (with and without the gas) in Sample Exercise 1.8 for the density to be calculated to three significant figures?
*Answer:* five (For the difference in the two masses to have three significant figures, there must be two decimal places in the masses of the filled and empty containers. Therefore, each mass must be measured to five significant figures.)

When a calculation involves two or more steps and you write answers for intermediate steps, retain at least one nonsignificant digit for the intermediate answers. This procedure ensures that small errors from rounding at each step do not combine to affect the final result. When using a calculator, you may enter the numbers one after another, rounding only the final answer. Accumulated rounding-off errors may account for small differences among results you obtain and answers given in the text for numerical problems.

# 1.6 | DIMENSIONAL ANALYSIS

Throughout the text we use **dimensional analysis** in solving problems. In this approach, units are multiplied together, divided into each other, or "canceled." Using dimensional analysis helps ensure that solutions to problems yield the proper units. Moreover, it provides a systematic way of solving many numerical problems and of checking solutions for possible errors.

The key to using dimensional analysis is the correct use of conversion factors to change one unit into another. A **conversion factor** is a fraction whose numerator and denominator are the same quantity expressed in different units. For example, 2.54 cm and 1 in. are the same length, 2.54 cm = 1 in. This relationship allows us to write two conversion factors:

$$\frac{2.54 \text{ cm}}{1 \text{ in.}} \quad \text{and} \quad \frac{1 \text{ in.}}{2.54 \text{ cm}}$$

We use the first factor to convert inches to centimeters. For example, the length in centimeters of an object that is 8.50 in. long is

Number of centimeters = (8.50 in.) $\dfrac{2.54 \text{ cm}}{1 \text{ in.}}$ = 21.6 cm

Desired unit

Given unit

The unit inches in the denominator of the conversion factor cancels the unit inches in the given data (8.50 *inches*). The unit centimeters in the numerator of the conversion factor becomes the unit of the final answer. Because the numerator and denominator of a conversion factor are equal, multiplying any quantity by a conversion factor is equivalent to multiplying by the number 1 and so does not change the intrinsic value of the quantity. The length 8.50 in. is the same as the length 21.6 cm.

In general, we begin any conversion by examining the units of the given data and the units we desire. We then ask ourselves what conversion factors we have available to take us from the units of the given quantity to those of the desired one. When we multiply a quantity by a conversion factor, the units multiply and divide as follows:

$$\text{Given unit} \times \dfrac{\text{desired unit}}{\text{given unit}} = \text{desired unit}$$

If the desired units are not obtained in a calculation, an error must have been made somewhere. Careful inspection of units often reveals the source of the error.

---

### SAMPLE EXERCISE 1.9    Converting Units

If a woman has a mass of 115 lb, what is her mass in grams? (Use the relationships between units given on the back inside cover of the text.)

#### SOLUTION

Because we want to change from pounds to grams, we look for a relationship between these units of mass. From the back inside cover we have 1 lb = 453.6 g. To cancel pounds and leave grams, we write the conversion factor with grams in the numerator and pounds in the denominator:

$$\text{Mass in grams} = (115 \text{ lb}) \left( \dfrac{453.6 \text{ g}}{1 \text{ lb}} \right) = 5.22 \times 10^4 \text{ g}$$

The answer can be given to only three significant figures, the number of significant figures in 115 lb. The process we have used is diagrammed in the margin.

#### PRACTICE EXERCISE

By using a conversion factor from the back inside cover, determine the length in kilometers of a 500.0-mi automobile race.
***Answer:*** 804.7 km

Given:    lb

Use    $\dfrac{453.6 \text{ g}}{1 \text{ lb}}$

Find:    g

---

# STRATEGIES IN CHEMISTRY

### ESTIMATING ANSWERS

A friend once remarked cynically that calculators let you get the wrong answer more quickly. He was implying that unless you have the correct strategy for solving a problem and have punched in the correct numbers, the answer will be incorrect. If you learn to *estimate* answers, however, you will be able to check whether the answers to your calculations are reasonable.

The idea is to make a rough calculation using numbers that are rounded off in such a way that the arithmetic can be done without a calculator. This approach is often referred to as making a "ballpark" estimate, meaning that although it does not give an exact answer, it gives one that is roughly the right size. By using dimensional analysis and by estimating answers, we can readily check the reasonableness of our answers to calculations.

⚠️ **GIVE IT SOME THOUGHT**

How do we determine how many digits to use in conversion factors, such as the one between pounds and grams in Sample Exercise 1.9?

## Using Two or More Conversion Factors

It is often necessary to use several conversion factors in solving a problem. As an example, let's convert the length of an 8.00-m rod to inches. The table on the back inside cover does not give the relationship between meters and inches. It *does*, however, give the relationship between centimeters and inches (1 in. = 2.54 cm). From our knowledge of SI prefixes, we know that $1 \, cm = 10^{-2} \, m$. Thus, we can convert step by step, first from meters to centimeters and then from centimeters to inches:

Combining the given quantity (8.00 m) and the two conversion factors, we have

$$\text{Number of inches} = (8.00 \, \cancel{m})\left(\frac{1 \, \cancel{cm}}{10^{-2} \, \cancel{m}}\right)\left(\frac{1 \, \text{in.}}{2.54 \, \cancel{cm}}\right) = 315 \, \text{in.}$$

The first conversion factor is used to cancel meters and convert the length to centimeters. Thus, meters are written in the denominator and centimeters in the numerator. The second conversion factor is used to cancel centimeters and convert the length to inches, so it has centimeters in the denominator and inches, the desired unit, in the numerator.

Note that you could have used 100 cm = 1 m as a conversion factor as well in the second parentheses. As long as you follow your units and cancel them properly to obtain the desired units, you are likely to be successful in your calculations.

---

**SAMPLE EXERCISE 1.10** | **Converting Units Using Two or More Conversion Factors**

The average speed of a nitrogen molecule in air at 25 °C is 515 m/s. Convert this speed to miles per hour.

### SOLUTION

To go from the given units, m/s, to the desired units, mi/hr, we must convert meters to miles and seconds to hours. From our knowledge of SI prefixes we know that $1 \, km = 10^3 \, m$. From the relationships given on the back inside cover of the book, we find that 1 mi = 1.6093 km.

Thus, we can convert m to km and then convert km to mi. From our knowledge of time we know that 60 s = 1 min and 60 min = 1 hr. Thus, we can convert s to min and then convert min to hr. The overall process is

Applying first the conversions for distance and then those for time, we can set up one long equation in which unwanted units are canceled:

$$\text{Speed in mi/hr} = \left(515 \, \frac{\cancel{m}}{\cancel{s}}\right)\left(\frac{1 \, \cancel{km}}{10^3 \, \cancel{m}}\right)\left(\frac{1 \, \text{mi}}{1.6093 \, \cancel{km}}\right)\left(\frac{60 \, \cancel{s}}{1 \, \cancel{min}}\right)\left(\frac{60 \, \cancel{min}}{1 \, hr}\right)$$

$$= 1.15 \times 10^3 \, \text{mi/hr}$$

Our answer has the desired units. We can check our calculation, using the estimating procedure described in the "Strategies in Chemistry" box. The given speed is about 500 m/s. Dividing by 1000 converts m to km, giving 0.5 km/s. Because 1 mi is about 1.6 km, this speed corresponds to $0.5/1.6 = 0.3$ mi/s. Multiplying by 60 gives about $0.3 \times 60 = 20$ mi/min. Multiplying again by 60 gives $20 \times 60 = 1200$ mi/hr. The approximate solution (about 1200 mi/hr) and the detailed solution (1150 mi/hr) are reasonably close. The answer to the detailed solution has three significant figures, corresponding to the number of significant figures in the given speed in m/s.

**PRACTICE EXERCISE**

A car travels 28 mi per gallon of gasoline. How many kilometers per liter will it go?

***Answer:*** 12 km/L

## Conversions Involving Volume

The conversion factors previously noted convert from one unit of a given measure to another unit of the same measure, such as from length to length. We also have conversion factors that convert from one measure to a different one. The density of a substance, for example, can be treated as a conversion factor between mass and volume. Suppose we want to know the mass in grams of 2 cubic inches ($2.00\text{ in.}^3$) of gold, which has a density of $19.3\text{ g/cm}^3$. The density gives us the conversion factor:

$$\frac{19.3\text{ g}}{1\text{ cm}^3} \quad \text{and} \quad \frac{1\text{ cm}^3}{19.3\text{ g}}$$

Because we want a mass in grams, we use the first factor, which has mass in grams in the numerator. To use this factor, however, we must first convert cubic inches to cubic centimeters. The relationship between $\text{in.}^3$ and $\text{cm}^3$ is not given on the back inside cover, but the relationship between inches and centimeters is given: $1\text{ in.} = 2.54\text{ cm}$ (exactly). Cubing both sides of this equation gives $(1\text{ in.})^3 = (2.54\text{ cm})^3$, from which we write the desired conversion factor:

$$\frac{(2.54\text{ cm})^3}{(1\text{ in.})^3} = \frac{(2.54)^3\text{ cm}^3}{(1)^3\text{ in.}^3} = \frac{16.39\text{ cm}^3}{1\text{ in.}^3}$$

Notice that both the numbers and the units are cubed. Also, because 2.54 is an exact number, we can retain as many digits of $(2.54)^3$ as we need. We have used four, one more than the number of digits in the density ($19.3\text{ g/cm}^3$). Applying our conversion factors, we can now solve the problem:

$$\text{Mass in grams} = (2.00\text{ in.}^3)\left(\frac{16.39\text{ cm}^3}{1\text{ in.}^3}\right)\left(\frac{19.3\text{ g}}{1\text{ cm}^3}\right) = 633\text{ g}$$

The procedure is diagrammed here. The final answer is reported to three significant figures, the same number of significant figures as in $2.00\text{ in.}^3$ and 19.3 g.

Given: **in.³** → Use $\left(\dfrac{2.54\text{ cm}}{1\text{ in.}}\right)^3$ → **cm³** → Use $\dfrac{19.3\text{ g}}{1\text{ cm}^3}$ → Find: **g**

**SAMPLE EXERCISE 1.11** Converting Volume Units

Earth's oceans contain approximately $1.36 \times 10^9\text{ km}^3$ of water. Calculate the volume in liters.

**SOLUTION**

From the back inside cover, we find $1\text{ L} = 10^{-3}\text{ m}^3$, but there is no relationship listed involving $\text{km}^3$. From our knowledge of SI prefixes, however, we know $1\text{ km} = 10^3\text{ m}$ and we can use this relationship between lengths to write the desired conversion factor between volumes:

$$\left(\frac{10^3\text{ m}}{1\text{ km}}\right)^3 = \frac{10^9\text{ m}^3}{1\text{ km}^3}$$

Thus, converting from km$^3$ to m$^3$ to L, we have

$$\text{Volume in liters} = (1.36 \times 10^9 \text{ km}^3)\left(\frac{10^9 \text{ m}^3}{1 \text{ km}^3}\right)\left(\frac{1 \text{L}}{10^{-3} \text{ m}^3}\right) = 1.36 \times 10^{21} \text{ L}$$

**PRACTICE EXERCISE**

If the volume of an object is reported as 5.0 ft$^3$, what is the volume in cubic meters?
***Answer:*** 0.14 m$^3$

# STRATEGIES IN CHEMISTRY

## THE IMPORTANCE OF PRACTICE

If you have ever played a musical instrument or participated in athletics, you know that the keys to success are practice and discipline. You cannot learn to play a piano merely by listening to music, and you cannot learn how to play basketball merely by watching games on television. Likewise, you cannot learn chemistry by merely watching your instructor do it. Simply reading this book, listening to lectures, or reviewing notes will not usually be sufficient when exam time comes around. Your task is not only to understand how someone else does chemistry but also to be able to do it yourself. That takes practice on a regular basis, and anything that you have to do on a regular basis requires self-discipline until it becomes a habit.

Throughout the book, we have provided sample exercises in which the solutions are shown in detail. A practice exercise, for which only the answer is given, accompanies each sample exercise. It is important that you use these exercises as learning aids. End-of-chapter exercises provide additional questions to help you understand the material in the chapter. A review of basic mathematics is given in Appendix A.

The practice exercises in this text and the homework assignments given by your instructor provide the minimal practice that you will need to succeed in your chemistry course. Only by working all the assigned problems will you face the full range of difficulty and coverage that your instructor expects you to master for exams. There is no substitute for a determined and perhaps lengthy effort to work problems on your own. If you are stuck on a problem, however, ask for help from your instructor, a teaching assistant, a tutor, or a fellow student. Spending an inordinate amount of time on a single exercise is rarely effective unless you know that it is particularly challenging and requires extensive thought and effort.

**SAMPLE EXERCISE 1.12**  **Conversions Involving Density**

What is the mass in grams of 1.00 gal of water? The density of water is 1.00 g/mL.

**SOLUTION**

Before we begin solving this exercise, we note the following:

1. We are given 1.00 gal of water (the known, or given, quantity) and asked to calculate its mass in grams (the unknown).

2. We have the following conversion factors either given, commonly known, or available on the back inside cover of the text:

$$\frac{1.00 \text{ g water}}{1 \text{ mL water}} \qquad \frac{1 \text{ L}}{1000 \text{ mL}} \qquad \frac{1 \text{ L}}{1.057 \text{ qt}} \qquad \frac{1 \text{ gal}}{4 \text{ qt}}$$

The first of these conversion factors must be used as written (with grams in the numerator) to give the desired result, whereas the last conversion factor must be inverted in order to cancel gallons:

$$\text{Mass in grams} = (1.00 \text{ gal})\left(\frac{4 \text{ qt}}{1 \text{ gal}}\right)\left(\frac{1 \text{ L}}{1.057 \text{ qt}}\right)\left(\frac{1000 \text{ mL}}{1 \text{ L}}\right)\left(\frac{1.00 \text{ g}}{1 \text{ mL}}\right)$$

$$= 3.78 \times 10^3 \text{ g water}$$

The unit of our final answer is appropriate, and we've taken care of our significant figures. We can further check our calculation by estimating. We can round 1.057 off to 1. Then focusing on the numbers that do not equal 1 gives $4 \times 1000 = 4000$ g, in agreement with the detailed calculation.

You should also use common sense to assess the reasonableness of your answer. In this case we know that most people can lift a gallon of milk with one hand, although it would be tiring to carry it around all day. Milk is mostly water and will have a density not too different from that of water. Therefore, we might estimate that a gallon of water has mass that is more than 5 lb but less than 50 lb. The mass we have calculated, 3.78 kg × 2.2 lb/kg = 8.3 lb, is thus reasonable as an order-of-magnitude estimate.

**PRACTICE EXERCISE**

The density of benzene is 0.879 g/mL. Calculate the mass in grams of 1.00 qt of benzene.

*Answer:* 832 g

## STRATEGIES IN CHEMISTRY

### THE FEATURES OF THIS BOOK

To help you understand chemistry, this book includes features that help you organize your thoughts. At the beginning of each chapter, "What's Ahead," which outlines the chapter by section, will prepare you for the material in the chapter. At the end of each chapter, the Summary, Key Terms, Key Skills, and Key Equations will help you remember what you have learned and prepare you for quizzes and exams.

During the course of the chapter, there are "speed bumps" to prompt you to think about what you have just read. The "Give It Some Thought" features are embedded in the text after a key concept; the "Go Figure" features are associated with artwork and ask you to interpret a concept visually. Sample Exercises, with worked-out solutions and answers, and Practice Exercises, which provide only the answer, test your problem-solving skills in chemistry.

At the end of each chapter is a series of exercises, again to test your problem-solving skills in chemistry. Your instructor will very likely assign some of these end-of-chapter exercises as homework. The first few exercises called "Visualizing Concepts" are meant to test how well you understand a concept without plugging a lot of numbers into a formula. The other exercises are divided into sections that reflect the order of the material in the chapter. These exercises are grouped in pairs, with the answers given in the back of the book to

the odd-numbered exercises, as indicated by the red exercise numbers. An exercise with a [bracket] around its number means that it is more challenging. Additional Exercises appear after the regular exercises; the chapter sections that they cover are not identified, and they are not paired. Integrative Exercises, which start appearing in Chapter 3, are problems that require skills learned in previous chapters.

Throughout the book you will occasionally find little blue link [ ∞ ] symbols. These "concept links" tell you in which section of the book this concept is first discussed in case you wish to turn to that section and review it.

Throughout the book boxed essays highlight the importance of chemistry to our everyday lives. The "Chemistry and Life" boxes focus on biological and environmental aspects of chemistry. The "Chemistry Put to Work" boxes illustrate the large industrial role chemistry plays in modern society. "Strategies in Chemistry" boxes, like this one, are meant to help you think about the material you are learning. Finally, boxes entitled "A Closer Look" provide in-depth coverage of a key chemical concept.

Many chemical databases are available, usually through your school. The *CRC Handbook of Chemistry and Physics* is the standard reference for many types of data and is available in libraries. The *Merck Index* is a standard reference for the properties of many small organic compounds, especially ones of biological interest. WebElements (http://www.webelements.com) is a good Web site for looking up the properties of the elements.

## CHAPTER SUMMARY AND KEY TERMS

**INTRODUCTION AND SECTION 1.1**    **Chemistry** is the study of the composition, structure, properties, and changes of **matter**. The composition of matter relates to the kinds of **elements** it contains. The structure of matter relates to the ways the **atoms** of these elements are arranged. A **property** is any characteristic that gives a sample of matter its unique identity. A **molecule** is an entity composed of two or more atoms with the atoms attached to one another in a specific way.

**SECTION 1.2**    Matter exists in three physical states, **gas, liquid**, and **solid**, which are known as the **states of matter**. There are two kinds of **pure substances: elements** and **compounds**. Each element has a single kind of atom and is represented by a chemical symbol consisting of

one or two letters, with the first letter capitalized. Compounds are composed of two or more elements joined chemically. The **law of constant composition**, also called the **law of definite proportions**, states that the elemental composition of a pure compound is always the same. Most matter consists of a mixture of substances. **Mixtures** have variable compositions and can be either homogeneous or heterogeneous; homogeneous mixtures are called **solutions**.

**SECTION 1.3**    Each substance has a unique set of **physical properties** and **chemical properties** that can be used to identify it. During a **physical change**, matter does not change its composition. **Changes of state** are physical changes. In a **chemical change (chemical**

reaction) a substance is transformed into a chemically different substance. **Intensive properties** are independent of the amount of matter examined and are used to identify substances. **Extensive properties** relate to the amount of substance present. Differences in physical and chemical properties are used to separate substances.

The **scientific method** is a dynamic process used to answer questions about our physical world. Observations and experiments lead to **scientific laws**, general rules that summarize how nature behaves. Observations also lead to tentative explanations or **hypotheses**. As a hypothesis is tested and refined, a **theory** may be developed that can predict the results of future observations and experiments.

**SECTION 1.4** Measurements in chemistry are made using the **metric system**. Special emphasis is placed on **SI units**, which are based on the meter, the kilogram, and the second as the basic units of length, **mass**, and time, respectively. SI units use prefixes to indicate fractions or multiples of base units. The SI temperature scale is the **Kelvin scale**, although the **Celsius scale** is frequently used as well. **Density** is an important property that equals mass divided by volume.

**SECTION 1.5** All measured quantities are inexact to some extent. The **precision** of a measurement indicates how closely different measurements of a quantity agree with one another. The **accuracy** of a measurement indicates how well a measurement agrees with the accepted or "true" value. The **significant figures** in a measured quantity include one estimated digit, the last digit of the measurement. The significant figures indicate the extent of the uncertainty of the measurement. Certain rules must be followed so that a calculation involving measured quantities is reported with the appropriate number of significant figures.

**SECTION 1.6** In the **dimensional analysis** approach to problem solving, we keep track of units as we carry measurements through calculations. The units are multiplied together, divided into each other, or canceled like algebraic quantities. Obtaining the proper units for the final result is an important means of checking the method of calculation. When converting units and when carrying out several other types of problems, **conversion factors** can be used. These factors are ratios constructed from valid relations between equivalent quantities.

## KEY SKILLS

- Distinguish among elements, compounds, and mixtures. (Section 1.2)
- Memorize symbols of common elements. (Section 1.2)
- Memorize common metric prefixes. (Section 1.4)
- Use significant figures, scientific notation, and SI units in calculations. (Section 1.5)
- Use dimensional analysis in calculations. (Section 1.6)

## KEY EQUATIONS

- $K = °C + 273.15$    [1.1]    Converting between Celsius (°C) and Kelvin (K) temperature scales

- $°C = \dfrac{5}{9}(°F - 32)$  or  $°F = \dfrac{9}{5}(°C) + 32$   [1.2]    Converting between Celsius (°C) and Fahrenheit (°F) temperature scales

- $\text{Density} = \dfrac{\text{mass}}{\text{volume}}$    [1.3]    Definition of density

# EXERCISES

## VISUALIZING CONCEPTS

1.1 Which of the following figures represents **(a)** a pure element, **(b)** a mixture of two elements, **(c)** a pure compound, **(d)** a mixture of an element and a compound? (More than one picture might fit each description.) [Section 1.2]

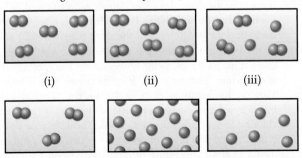

|     |      |       |
|-----|------|-------|
| (i) | (ii) | (iii) |
| (iv) | (v) | (vi)  |

1.2 Does the following diagram represent a chemical or physical change? How do you know? [Section 1.3]

**1.3** Describe the separation method(s) involved in brewing a cup of coffee. [Section 1.3]

**1.4** Identify each of the following as measurements of length, area, volume, mass, density, time, or temperature: **(a)** 25 ps, **(b)** 374.2 mg, **(c)** 77 K, **(d)** 100,000 km$^2$, **(e)** 1.06 μm, **(f)** 16 nm$^2$, **(g)** −78 °C, **(h)** 2.56 g/cm$^3$, **(i)** 28 cm$^3$. [Section 1.4]

**1.5** **(a)** Three spheres of equal size are composed of aluminum (density = 2.70 g/cm$^3$), silver (density = 10.49 g/cm$^3$), and nickel (density = 8.90 g/cm$^3$). List the spheres from lightest to heaviest. **(b)** Three cubes of equal mass are composed of gold (density = 19.32 g/cm$^3$), platinum (density = 21.45 g/cm$^3$), and lead (density = 11.35 g/cm$^3$). List the cubes from smallest to largest. [Section 1.4]

**1.6** The following dartboards illustrate the types of errors often seen when one measurement is repeated several times. The bull's-eye represents the "true value," and the darts represent the experimental measurements. Which board best represents each of the following scenarios: **(a)** measurements both accurate and precise, **(b)** measurements precise but inaccurate, **(c)** measurements imprecise but yielding an accurate average? [Section 1.5]

(i)                    (ii)                    (iii)

**1.7** **(a)** What is the length of the pencil in the following figure if the ruler reads in centimeters? How many significant figures are there in this measurement? **(b)** An automobile speedometer with circular scales reading both miles per hour and kilometers per hour is shown. What speed is indicated, in both units? How many significant figures are in the measurements? [Section 1.5]

**1.8** **(a)** How many significant figures should be reported for the volume of the metal bar shown here? **(b)** If the mass of the bar is 104.72 g, how many significant figures should be reported when its density is determined using the calculated volume? [Section 1.5]

2.5 cm

1.25 cm

5.30 cm

**1.9** When you convert units, how do you decide which part of the conversion factor is in the numerator and which is in the denominator? [Section 1.6]

**1.10** Show the steps to convert the speed of sound, 344 meters per second, into miles per hour. [Section 1.6]

# CLASSIFICATION AND PROPERTIES OF MATTER (sections 1.2 and 1.3)

**1.11** Classify each of the following as a pure substance or a mixture. If a mixture, indicate whether it is homogeneous or heterogeneous: **(a)** rice pudding, **(b)** seawater, **(c)** magnesium, **(d)** crushed ice.

**1.12** Classify each of the following as a pure substance or a mixture. If a mixture, indicate whether it is homogeneous or heterogeneous: **(a)** air, **(b)** tomato juice, **(c)** iodine crystals, **(d)** sand.

**1.13** Give the chemical symbol or name for the following elements, as appropriate: **(a)** sulfur, **(b)** gold, **(c)** potassium, **(d)** chlorine, **(e)** copper, **(f)** U, **(g)** Ni, **(h)** Na, **(i)** Al, **(j)** Si.

**1.14** Give the chemical symbol or name for each of the following elements, as appropriate: **(a)** carbon, **(b)** nitrogen, **(c)** titanium, **(d)** zinc, **(e)** iron, **(f)** P, **(g)** Ca, **(h)** He, **(i)** Pb, **(j)** Ag.

**1.15** A solid white substance A is heated strongly in the absence of air. It decomposes to form a new white substance B and a gas C. The gas has exactly the same properties as the product obtained when carbon is burned in an excess of oxygen. Based on these observations, can we determine whether solids A and B and gas C are elements or compounds? Explain your conclusions for each substance.

**1.16** You are hiking in the mountains and find a shiny gold nugget. It might be the element gold, or it might be "fool's gold," which is a nickname for iron pyrite, $FeS_2$. What kinds of experiments could be done to determine if the shiny nugget is really gold?

**1.17** In the process of attempting to characterize a substance, a chemist makes the following observations: The substance is a silvery white, lustrous metal. It melts at 649 °C and boils at 1105 °C. Its density at 20 °C is 1.738 g/cm$^3$. The substance burns in air, producing an intense white light. It reacts with chlorine to give a brittle white solid. The substance can be pounded into thin sheets or drawn into wires. It is a good conductor of electricity. Which of these characteristics are physical properties, and which are chemical properties?

**1.18** Read the following description of the element zinc and indicate which are physical properties and which are chemical properties. Zinc is a silver-gray–colored metal that melts at 420 °C. When zinc granules are added to dilute sulfuric acid, hydrogen is given off and the metal dissolves. Zinc has a hardness on the Mohs scale of 2.5 and a density of 7.13 g/cm³ at 25 °C. It reacts slowly with oxygen gas at elevated temperatures to form zinc oxide, ZnO.

**1.19** Label each of the following as either a physical process or a chemical process: **(a)** rusting of a metal can, **(b)** boiling a cup of water, **(c)** pulverizing an aspirin, **(d)** digesting a candy bar, **(e)** exploding of nitroglycerin.

**1.20** A match is lit and held under a cold piece of metal. The following observations are made: **(a)** The match burns. **(b)** The metal gets warmer. **(c)** Water condenses on the metal. **(d)** Soot (carbon) is deposited on the metal. Which of these occurrences are due to physical changes, and which are due to chemical changes?

**1.21** Suggest a method of separating each of the following mixtures into two components: **(a)** sugar and sand, **(b)** oil and vinegar.

**1.22** Three beakers contain clear, colorless liquids. One beaker contains pure water, another contains salt water, and another contains sugar water. How can you tell which beaker is which? (No tasting allowed!)

# UNITS AND MEASUREMENT (section 1.4)

**1.23** What exponential notation do the following abbreviations represent: **(a)** d, **(b)** c, **(c)** f, **(d)** $\mu$, **(e)** M, **(f)** k, **(g)** n, **(h)** m, **(i)** p?

**1.24** Use appropriate metric prefixes to write the following measurements without use of exponents: **(a)** $2.3 \times 10^{-10}$ L, **(b)** $4.7 \times 10^{-6}$ g, **(c)** $1.85 \times 10^{-12}$ m, **(d)** $16.7 \times 10^{6}$ s; **(e)** $15.7 \times 10^{3}$ g, **(f)** $1.34 \times 10^{-3}$ m, **(g)** $1.84 \times 10^{2}$ cm.

**1.25** Make the following conversions: **(a)** 72 °F to °C, **(b)** 216.7 °C to °F, **(c)** 233 °C to K, **(d)** 315 K to °F, **(e)** 2500 °F to K, **(f)** 0 K to °F.

**1.26** **(a)** The temperature on a warm summer day is 87 °F. What is the temperature in °C? **(b)** Many scientific data are reported at 25 °C. What is this temperature in kelvins and in degrees Fahrenheit? **(c)** Suppose that a recipe calls for an oven temperature of 400 °F. Convert this temperature to degrees Celsius and to kelvins. **(d)** Liquid nitrogen boils at 77 K. Convert this temperature to degrees Fahrenheit and to degrees Celsius.

**1.27** **(a)** A sample of tetrachloroethylene, a liquid used in dry cleaning that is being phased out because of its potential to cause cancer, has a mass of 40.55 g and a volume of 25.0 mL at 25 °C. What is its density at this temperature? Will tetrachloroethylene float on water? (Materials that are less dense than water will float.) **(b)** Carbon dioxide ($CO_2$) is a gas at room temperature and pressure. However, carbon dioxide can be put under pressure to become a "supercritical fluid" that is a much safer dry-cleaning agent than tetrachloroethylene. At a certain pressure, the density of supercritical $CO_2$ is 0.469 g/cm³. What is the mass of a 25.0-mL sample of supercritical $CO_2$ at this pressure?

**1.28** **(a)** A cube of osmium metal 1.500 cm on a side has a mass of 76.31 g at 25 °C. What is its density in g/cm³ at this temperature? **(b)** The density of titanium metal is 4.51 g/cm³ at 25 °C. What mass of titanium displaces 125.0 mL of water at 25 °C? **(c)** The density of benzene at 15 °C is 0.8787 g/mL. Calculate the mass of 0.1500 L of benzene at this temperature.

**1.29** **(a)** To identify a liquid substance, a student determined its density. Using a graduated cylinder, she measured out a 45-mL sample of the substance. She then measured the mass of the sample, finding that it weighed 38.5 g. She knew that the substance had to be either isopropyl alcohol (density 0.785 g/mL) or toluene (density 0.866/mL). What are the calculated density and the probable identity of the substance? **(b)** An experiment requires 45.0 g of ethylene glycol, a liquid whose density is 1.114 g/mL. Rather than weigh the sample on a balance, a chemist chooses to dispense the liquid using a graduated cylinder. What volume of the liquid should he use? **(c)** A cubic piece of metal measures 5.00 cm on each edge. If the metal is nickel, whose density is 8.90 g/cm³, what is the mass of the cube?

**1.30** **(a)** After the label fell off a bottle containing a clear liquid believed to be benzene, a chemist measured the density of the liquid to verify its identity. A 25.0-mL portion of the liquid had a mass of 21.95 g. A chemistry handbook lists the density of benzene at 15 °C as 0.8787 g/mL. Is the calculated density in agreement with the tabulated value? **(b)** An experiment requires 15.0 g of cyclohexane, whose density at 25 °C is 0.7781 g/mL. What volume of cyclohexane should be used? **(c)** A spherical ball of lead has a diameter of 5.0 cm. What is the mass of the sphere if lead has a density of 11.34 g/cm³? (The volume of a sphere is $(4/3)\pi r^3$ where $r$ is the radius.)

**1.31** In the year 2007, an estimated amount of 31 billion tons of carbon dioxide ($CO_2$) was emitted worldwide due to fossil fuel combustion and cement production. Express this mass of $CO_2$ in grams without exponential notation, using an appropriate metric prefix.

**1.32** Silicon for computer chips is grown in large cylinders called "boules" that are 300 mm in diameter and 2 m in height. The density of silicon is 2.33 g/cm³. Silicon wafers for making integrated circuits are sliced from a 2.0 m boule and are typically 0.75 mm thick and 300 mm in diameter. **(a)** How many wafers can be cut from a single boule? **(b)** What is the mass of a silicon wafer? (The volume of a cylinder is given by $\pi r^2 h$, where $r$ is the radius and $h$ is its height.)

# UNCERTAINTY IN MEASUREMENT (section 1.5)

**1.33** Indicate which of the following are exact numbers: **(a)** the mass of a piece of paper, **(b)** the volume of a cup of coffee, **(c)** the number of inches in a mile, **(d)** the number of ounces in a pound, **(e)** the number of microseconds in a week, **(f)** the number of pages in this book.

**1.34** Indicate which of the following are exact numbers: **(a)** the mass of a 32-oz can of coffee, **(b)** the number of students in your chemistry class, **(c)** the temperature of the surface of the sun, **(d)** the mass of a postage stamp, **(e)** the number of milliliters in a cubic meter of water, **(f)** the average height of students in your school.

**1.35** What is the number of significant figures in each of the following measured quantities? (a) 601 kg, (b) 0.054 s, (c) 6.3050 cm, (d) 0.0105 L, (e) $7.0500 \times 10^{-3}$ m³, (f) 400 g.

**1.36** Indicate the number of significant figures in each of the following measured quantities: (a) 3.774 km, (b) 205 m², (c) 1.700 cm, (d) 350.00 K, (e) 307.080 g, (f) $1.3 \times 10^3$ m/s.

**1.37** Round each of the following numbers to four significant figures, and express the result in standard exponential notation: (a) 102.53070, (b) 656,980, (c) 0.008543210, (d) 0.000257870, (e) −0.0357202.

**1.38** (a) The diameter of Earth at the equator is 7926.381 mi. Round this number to three significant figures, and express it in standard exponential notation. (b) The circumference of Earth through the poles is 40,008 km. Round this number to four significant figures, and express it in standard exponential notation.

**1.39** Carry out the following operations, and express the answers with the appropriate number of significant figures.
(a) 14.3505 + 2.65
(b) 952.7 − 140.7389
(c) $(3.29 \times 10^4)(0.2501)$
(d) 0.0588/0.677

**1.40** Carry out the following operations, and express the answer with the appropriate number of significant figures.
(a) 320.5 − (6104.5/2.3)
(b) $[(285.3 \times 10^5) - (1.200 \times 10^3)] \times 2.8954$
(c) $(0.0045 \times 20,000.0) + (2813 \times 12)$
(d) $863 \times [1255 - (3.45 \times 108)]$

**1.41** You weigh an object on a balance and read the mass in grams according to the picture. How many significant figures are in this measurement?

**1.42** You have a graduated cylinder that contains a liquid (see photograph). Write the volume of the liquid, in milliliters, using the proper number of significant figures.

# DIMENSIONAL ANALYSIS (section 1.6)

**1.43** Using your knowledge of metric units, English units, and the information on the back inside cover, write down the conversion factors needed to convert (a) mm to nm, (b) mg to kg, (c) km to ft, (d) in.³ to cm³.

**1.44** Using your knowledge of metric units, English units, and the information on the back inside cover, write down the conversion factors needed to convert (a) $\mu$m to mm, (b) ms to ns, (c) mi to km, (d) ft³ to L.

**1.45** (a) A bumblebee flies with a ground speed of 15.2 m/s. Calculate its speed in km/h. (b) The lung capacity of the blue whale is $5.0 \times 10^3$ L. Convert this volume into gallons. (c) The Statue of Liberty is 151 ft tall. Calculate its height in meters. (d) Bamboo can grow up to 60.0 cm/day. Convert this growth rate into inches per hour.

**1.46** (a) The speed of light in a vacuum is $2.998 \times 10^8$ m/s. Calculate its speed in miles per hour. (b) The Sears Tower in Chicago is 1454 ft tall. Calculate its height in meters. (c) The Vehicle Assembly Building at the Kennedy Space Center in Florida has a volume of 3,666,500 m³. Convert this volume to liters and express the result in standard exponential notation. (d) An individual suffering from a high cholesterol level in her blood has 242 mg of cholesterol per 100 mL of blood. If the total blood volume of the individual is 5.2 L, how many grams of total blood cholesterol does the individual's body contain?

**1.47** Perform the following conversions: (a) 5.00 days to s, (b) 0.0550 mi to m, (c) $1.89/gal to dollars per liter, (d) 0.510 in./ms to km/hr, (e) 22.50 gal/min to L/s, (f) 0.02500 ft³ to cm³.

**1.48** Carry out the following conversions: (a) 0.105 in. to mm, (b) 0.650 qt to mL, (c) 8.75 $\mu$m/s to km/hr, (d) 1.955 m³ to yd³, (e) $3.99/lb to dollars per kg, (f) 8.75 lb/ft³ to g/mL.

**1.49** (a) How many liters of wine can be held in a wine barrel whose capacity is 31 gal? (b) The recommended adult dose of Elixophyllin®, a drug used to treat asthma, is 6 mg/kg of body mass. Calculate the dose in milligrams for a 185-lb person. (c) If an automobile is able to travel 400 km on 47.3 L of gasoline, what is the gas mileage in miles per gallon? (d) A pound of coffee beans yields 50 cups of coffee (4 cups = 1 qt). How many milliliters of coffee can be obtained from 1 g of coffee beans?

**1.50** (a) If an electric car is capable of going 225 km on a single charge, how many charges will it need to travel from Seattle, Washington, to San Diego, California, a distance of 1257 mi, assuming that the trip begins with a full charge? (b) If a migrating loon flies at an average speed of 14 m/s, what is its average speed in mi/hr? (c) What is the engine piston displacement in liters of an engine whose displacement is listed as 450 in.³? (d) In March 1989 the *Exxon Valdez* ran aground and spilled 240,000 barrels of crude petroleum off the coast of Alaska. One barrel of petroleum is equal to 42 gal. How many liters of petroleum were spilled?

1.51 The density of air at ordinary atmospheric pressure and 25 °C is 1.19 g/L. What is the mass, in kilograms, of the air in a room that measures 14.5 ft × 16.5 ft × 8.0 ft?

1.52 The concentration of carbon monoxide in an urban apartment is 48 $\mu$g/m$^3$. What mass of carbon monoxide in grams is present in a room measuring 11.0 ft × 11.5 ft × 20.5 ft?

1.53 By using estimation techniques, arrange these items in order from shortest to longest: a 57-cm length of string, a 14-in.-long shoe, and a 1.1-m length of pipe.

1.54 By using estimation techniques, determine which of the following is the heaviest and which is the lightest: a 5-lb bag of potatoes, a 5-kg bag of sugar, or 1 gal of water (density = 1.0 g/mL).

1.55 Gold can be hammered into extremely thin sheets called gold leaf. An architect wants to cover a 100 ft × 82 ft ceiling with gold leaf that is five-millionths of an inch thick. The density of gold is 19.32 g/cm$^3$, and gold costs $953 per troy ounce (1 troy ounce = 31.1034768 g). How much will it cost the architect to buy the necessary gold?

1.56 A copper refinery produces a copper ingot weighing 150 lb. If the copper is drawn into wire whose diameter is 7.50 mm, how many feet of copper can be obtained from the ingot? The density of copper is 8.94 g/cm$^3$. (Assume that the wire is a cylinder whose volume $V = \pi r^2 h$, where $r$ is its radius and $h$ is its height or length.)

# ADDITIONAL EXERCISES

1.57 (a) Classify each of the following as a pure substance, a solution, or a heterogeneous mixture: a gold coin, a cup of coffee, a wood plank. (b) What ambiguities are there in answering part (a) from the descriptions given?

1.58 (a) What is the difference between a hypothesis and a theory? (b) Explain the difference between a theory and a scientific law. Which addresses how matter behaves, and which addresses why it behaves that way?

1.59 A sample of ascorbic acid (vitamin C) is synthesized in the laboratory. It contains 1.50 g of carbon and 2.00 g of oxygen. Another sample of ascorbic acid isolated from citrus fruits contains 6.35 g of carbon. How many grams of oxygen does it contain? Which law are you assuming in answering this question?

1.60 Two students determine the percentage of lead in a sample as a laboratory exercise. The true percentage is 22.52%. The students' results for three determinations are as follows:
1. 22.52, 22.48, 22.54
2. 22.64, 22.58, 22.62

(a) Calculate the average percentage for each set of data, and state which set is the more accurate based on the average. (b) Precision can be judged by examining the average of the deviations from the average value for that data set. (Calculate the average value for each data set; then calculate the average value of the absolute deviations of each measurement from the average.) Which set is more precise?

1.61 Is the use of significant figures in each of the following statements appropriate? Why or why not? (a) Apple sold 22,727,000 iPods during the last three months of 2008. (b) New York City receives 49.7 inches of rain, on average, per year. (c) In the United States, 0.621% of the population has the surname Brown. (d) You calculate your grade point average to be 3.87562.

1.62 What type of quantity (for example, length, volume, density) do the following units indicate: (a) mL, (b) cm$^2$, (c) mm$^3$, (d) mg/L, (e) ps, (f) nm, (g) K?

1.63 Give the derived SI units for each of the following quantities in base SI units: (a) acceleration = distance/time$^2$, (b)

force = mass × acceleration, (c) work = force × distance, (d) pressure = force/area, (e) power = work/time, (f) velocity = distance/time, (g) energy = mass × (velocity)$^2$.

1.64 The distance from Earth to the Moon is approximately 240,000 mi. (a) What is this distance in meters? (b) The peregrine falcon has been measured as traveling up to 350 km/hr in a dive. If this falcon could fly to the Moon at this speed, how many seconds would it take? (c) The speed of light is $3.00 \times 10^8$ m/s. How long does it take for light to travel from Earth to the Moon and back again? (d) Earth travels around the Sun at an average speed of 29.783 km/s. Convert this speed to miles per hour.

1.65 The US quarter has a mass of 5.67 g and is approximately 1.55 mm thick. (a) How many quarters would have to be stacked to reach 575 ft, the height of the Washington Monument? (b) How much would this stack weigh? (c) How much money would this stack contain? (d) The US National Debt Clock showed the outstanding public debt to be $11,687,233,914,811.11 on August 19, 2009. How many stacks like the one described would be necessary to pay off this debt?

1.66 In the United States, water used for irrigation is measured in acre-feet. An acre-foot of water covers an acre to a depth of exactly 1 ft. An acre is 4840 yd$^2$. An acre-foot is enough water to supply two typical households for 1.00 yr. (a) If desalinated water costs $1950 per acre-foot, how much does desalinated water cost per liter? (b) How much would it cost one household per day if it were the only source of water?

1.67 Suppose you decide to define your own temperature scale using the freezing point (13 °C) and boiling point (360 °C) of oleic acid, the main component of olive oil. If you set the freezing point of oleic acid as 0 °O and the boiling point as 100 °O, what is the freezing point of water on this new scale?

1.68 The liquid substances mercury (density = 13.6 g/mL), water (1.00 g/mL), and cyclohexane (0.778 g/mL) do not form a solution when mixed but separate in distinct layers. Sketch how the liquids would position themselves in a test tube.

**1.69** Two spheres of equal volume are placed on the scales as shown. Which one is more dense?

**1.70** Water has a density of 0.997 g/cm$^3$ at 25 °C; ice has a density of 0.917 g/cm$^3$ at −10 °C. **(a)** If a soft-drink bottle whose volume is 1.50 L is completely filled with water and then frozen to −10 °C, what volume does the ice occupy? **(b)** Can the ice be contained within the bottle?

**1.71** A 32.65-g sample of a solid is placed in a flask. Toluene, in which the solid is insoluble, is added to the flask so that the total volume of solid and liquid together is 50.00 mL. The solid and toluene together weigh 58.58 g. The density of toluene at the temperature of the experiment is 0.864 g/mL. What is the density of the solid?

**1.72** A thief plans to steal a gold sphere with a radius of 28.9 cm from a museum. If the gold has a density of 19.3 g/cm$^3$, what is the mass of the sphere in pounds? [The volume of a sphere is $V = (4/3)\pi r^3$.] Is the thief likely to be able to walk off with the gold sphere unassisted?

**1.73** Automobile batteries contain sulfuric acid, which is commonly referred to as "battery acid." Calculate the number of grams of sulfuric acid in 1.00 gallon of battery acid if the solution has a density of 1.28 g/mL and is 38.1% sulfuric acid by mass.

**1.74** A 40-lb container of peat moss measures 14 × 20 × 30 in. A 40-lb container of topsoil has a volume of 1.9 gal. **(a)** Calculate the average densities of peat moss and topsoil in units of g/cm$^3$. Would it be correct to say that peat moss is "lighter" than topsoil? Explain. **(b)** How many bags of peat moss are needed to cover an area measuring 15.0 ft × 20.0 ft to a depth of 3.0 in.?

**1.75** A package of aluminum foil contains 50 ft$^2$ of foil, which weighs approximately 8.0 oz. Aluminum has a density of 2.70 g/cm$^3$. What is the approximate thickness of the foil in millimeters?

**1.76** The total power used by humans worldwide is approximately 15 TW (terawatts). Sunlight striking Earth provides 1.336 kW per square meter (assuming no clouds). The surface area of Earth is approximately 197,000,000 square miles. How much of Earth's surface would we need to cover with solar energy collectors to power the planet for use by all humans? Assume that the solar energy collectors can only convert 10% of the available sunlight into useful power.

**1.77** A 15.0-cm long cylindrical glass tube, sealed at one end, is filled with ethanol. The mass of ethanol needed to fill the tube is found to be 11.86 g. The density of ethanol is 0.789 g/mL. Calculate the inner diameter of the tube in centimeters.

**1.78** Gold is alloyed (mixed) with other metals to increase its hardness in making jewelry. **(a)** Consider a piece of gold jewelry that weighs 9.85 g and has a volume of 0.675 cm$^3$. The jewelry contains only gold and silver, which have densities of 19.3 g/cm$^3$ and 10.5 g/cm$^3$, respectively. If the total volume of the jewelry is the sum of the volumes of the gold and silver that it contains, calculate the percentage of gold (by mass) in the jewelry. **(b)** The relative amount of gold in an alloy is commonly expressed in units of carats. Pure gold is 24 carat, and the percentage of gold in an alloy is given as a percentage of this value. For example, an alloy that is 50% gold is 12 carat. State the purity of the gold jewelry in carats.

**1.79** Chromatography (Figure 1.14) is a simple but reliable method for separating a mixture into its constituent substances. You have a mixture of two vegetable dyes, one red and one blue, that you are trying to separate. You try two different chromatography procedures and achieve the separations shown in the figure. Which procedure worked better? Can you suggest a method to quantify how good or poor the separation was?

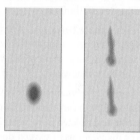

**1.80** You are assigned the task of separating a desired granular material with a density of 3.62 g/cm$^3$ from an undesired granular material that has a density of 2.04 g/cm$^3$. You want to do this by shaking the mixture in a liquid in which the heavier material will fall to the bottom and the lighter material will float. A solid will float on any liquid that is more dense. Using the Internet or a handbook of chemistry, find the densities of the following substances: carbon tetrachloride, hexane, benzene, and diiodomethane. Which of these liquids will serve your purpose, assuming no chemical interaction between the liquid and the solids?

**1.81** In 2009, a team from Northwestern University and Western Washington University reported the preparation of a new "spongy" material composed of nickel, molybdenum, and sulfur that excels at removing mercury from water. The density of this new material is 0.20 g/cm$^3$, and its surface area is 1242 m$^2$ per gram of material. **(a)** Calculate the volume of a 10.0-mg sample of this material. **(b)** Calculate the surface area for a 10.0-mg sample of this material. **(c)** A 10.0-mL sample of contaminated water had 7.748 mg of mercury in it. After treatment with 10.0 mg of the new spongy material, 0.001 mg of mercury remained in the contaminated water. What percentage of the mercury was removed from the water? **(d)** What is the final mass of the spongy material after the exposure to mercury?

**1.82** The concepts of accuracy and precision are not always easy to grasp. Here are two sets of studies: **(a)** The mass of a secondary weight standard is determined by weighing it on a very precise balance under carefully controlled laboratory conditions. The average of 18 different weight measurements is taken as the weight of the standard. **(b)** A group of 10,000 males between the ages of 50 and 55 is surveyed to ascertain a relationship between calorie intake and blood cholesterol level. The survey questionnaire is quite detailed, asking the respondents about what they eat, smoke, drink, and so on. The results are reported as showing that for men of comparable lifestyles, there is a 40% chance of the blood cholesterol level being above 230 mg/dL for those who consume more than 40 calories per gram of body weight per day, as compared with those who consume fewer than 30 calories per gram of body weight per day.

Discuss and compare these two studies in terms of the precision and accuracy of the result in each case. How do the two studies differ in ways that affect the accuracy and precision of the results? What makes for high precision and accuracy in any given study? In each of these studies, what factors might not be controlled that could affect the accuracy and precision? What steps can be taken generally to attain higher precision and accuracy?

**A COLLECTION OF UNCUT DIAMONDS.**
Diamond is one of the crystalline forms of carbon. Pure diamonds are clear and colorless. Small levels of impurities or defects cause diamond to have color—nitrogen produces yellow, whereas boron produces blue.

2

# ATOMS, MOLECULES, AND IONS

**LOOK AROUND AT THE GREAT** variety of colors, textures, and other properties in the materials that surround you—the colors in a garden, the texture of the fabric in your clothes, the solubility of sugar in a cup of coffee, or the transparency and beauty of a diamond. The materials in our world exhibit a striking and seemingly infinite variety of properties, but how do we understand and explain them? What makes diamonds transparent and hard, whereas table salt is brittle and dissolves in water? Why does paper burn, and why does water quench fires? The structure and behavior of atoms are key to understanding both the physical and chemical properties of matter.

Although the materials in our world vary greatly in their properties, everything is formed from only about 100 elements and, therefore, from only about 100 chemically different kinds of atoms. In a sense, the atoms are like the 26 letters of the English alphabet that join in different combinations to form the immense number of words in our language. But what rules govern the ways in which atoms combine? How do the properties of a substance relate to the kinds of atoms it contains? Indeed, what is an atom like, and what makes the atoms of one element different from those of another?

In this chapter we examine the basic structure of atoms and discuss the formation of molecules and ions, thereby providing a foundation for exploring chemistry more deeply in later chapters.

# 2.1 | THE ATOMIC THEORY OF MATTER

Philosophers from the earliest times speculated about the nature of the fundamental "stuff" from which the world is made. Democritus (460–370 BC) and other early Greek philosophers described the material world as made up of tiny indivisible particles they called *atomos*, meaning "indivisible or uncuttable." Later, however, Plato and Aristotle formulated the notion that there can be no ultimately indivisible particles, and the "atomic" view of matter faded for many centuries during which Aristotelean philosophy dominated Western culture.

The notion of **atoms** reemerged in Europe during the seventeenth century. As chemists learned to measure the amounts of elements that reacted with one another to form new substances, the ground was laid for an atomic theory that linked the idea of elements with the idea of atoms. That theory came from the work of John Dalton during the period from 1803 to 1807. Dalton's atomic theory was based on the four postulates given in ▼ FIGURE 2.1.

Dalton's theory explains several laws of chemical combination that were known during his time, including the *law of constant composition* ∞ (Section 1.2),* based on postulate 4:

> In a given compound, the relative numbers and kinds of atoms are constant.

It also explains the *law of conservation of mass*, based on postulate 3:

> The total mass of materials present after a chemical reaction is the same as the total mass present before the reaction.

A good theory explains known facts and predicts new ones. Dalton used his theory to deduce the *law of multiple proportions*:

> If two elements A and B combine to form more than one compound, the masses of B that can combine with a given mass of A are in the ratio of small whole numbers.

**Dalton's Atomic Theory**

1. Each element is composed of extremely small particles called atoms.

   ● An atom of the element oxygen          ● An atom of the element nitrogen

2. All atoms of a given element are identical, but the atoms of one element are different from the atoms of all other elements.

   ●●● Oxygen          ●●● Nitrogen

3. Atoms of one element cannot be changed into atoms of a different element by chemical reactions; atoms are neither created nor destroyed in chemical reactions.

   Oxygen ● ⊘→ ● Nitrogen

4. Compounds are formed when atoms of more than one element combine; a given compound always has the same relative number and kind of atoms.

   ● + ● ⟶ ●●
   N     O        NO
   └─ Elements ─┘   └ Compound ┘

▶ **FIGURE 2.1  Dalton's atomic theory.** John Dalton (1766–1844), the son of a poor English weaver, began teaching at age 12. He spent most of his years in Manchester, where he taught both grammar school and college. His lifelong interest in meteorology led him to study gases, then chemistry, and eventually atomic theory. Despite his humble beginnings, Dalton gained a strong scientific reputation during his lifetime.

*The short chainlike symbol that precedes the section reference indicates a link to ideas presented earlier in the text.

We can illustrate this law by considering water and hydrogen peroxide, both of which consist of the elements hydrogen and oxygen. In forming water, 8.0 g of oxygen combine with 1.0 g of hydrogen. In forming hydrogen peroxide, 16.0 g of oxygen combine with 1.0 g of hydrogen. Thus, the ratio of the mass of oxygen per gram of hydrogen in the two compounds is 2:1. Using Dalton's atomic theory, we conclude that hydrogen peroxide contains twice as many atoms of oxygen per hydrogen atom as does water.

 **GIVE IT SOME THOUGHT**

Compound A contains 1.333 g of oxygen per gram of carbon, whereas compound B contains 2.666 g of oxygen per gram of carbon.
a. What chemical law do these data illustrate?
b. If compound A has an equal number of oxygen and carbon atoms, what can we conclude about the composition of compound B?

# 2.2 | THE DISCOVERY OF ATOMIC STRUCTURE

Dalton based his conclusions about atoms on chemical observations made in the laboratory. Neither he nor those who followed him during the century after his work was published had any direct evidence for the existence of atoms. Today, however, we can measure the properties of individual atoms and even provide images of them (▶ FIGURE 2.2).

As scientists developed methods for probing the nature of matter, the supposedly indivisible atom began to show signs of a more complex structure, and today we know that the atom is composed of **subatomic particles**. Before we summarize the current model, we briefly consider a few of the landmark discoveries that led to that model. We will see that the atom is composed in part of electrically charged particles, some with a positive charge and some with a negative charge. As we discuss the development of our current model of the atom, keep in mind this fact: *Particles with the same charge repel one another, whereas particles with unlike charges attract one another.*

▲ FIGURE 2.2 **An image of the surface of silicon.** The image was obtained by a technique called scanning tunneling microscopy. The color was added to the image by computer to help distinguish its features. Each purple sphere is a silicon atom.

## Cathode Rays and Electrons

During the mid-1800s, scientists began to study electrical discharge through a glass tube pumped almost empty of air (▼ FIGURE 2.3). When a high voltage was applied to the electrodes in the tube, radiation was produced between the electrodes. This radiation, called **cathode rays**, originated at the negative electrode and traveled to the positive electrode. Although the rays could not be seen, their presence was detected because they cause certain materials to *fluoresce*, or to give off light.

 **GO FIGURE**

**How do we know that the cathode rays travel from cathode to anode?**

(a) Electrons move from the cathode (negative electrode) to the anode (positive electrode). The tube contains a glass screen (set diagonally to the electron beam) that fluoresces, showing the path of the cathode rays.

(b) The rays are deflected by a magnet.

◀ FIGURE 2.3 **Cathode-ray tube.**

## GO FIGURE

**If no magnetic field were applied, would you expect the electron beam to be deflected upward or downward by the electric field?**

▶ **FIGURE 2.4 Cathode-ray tube with perpendicular magnetic and electric fields.** The cathode rays (electrons) originate at the cathode and are accelerated toward the anode, which has a hole in its center. A narrow beam of electrons passes through the hole and travels to the fluorescent screen. The strengths of the electric and magnetic fields are adjusted so their effects cancel each other allowing the beam to travel a straight path.

▲ **FIGURE 2.5 Millikan's oil-drop experiment used to measure the charge of the electron.** Small drops of oil were allowed to fall between electrically charged plates. The drops picked up extra electrons as a result of irradiation by X-rays and so became negatively charged. Millikan measured how varying the voltage between the plates affected the rate of fall. From these data he calculated the negative charge on the drops. Because the charge on any drop was always some integral multiple of $1.602 \times 10^{-19}$ C, Millikan deduced this value to be the charge of a single electron.

Experiments showed that cathode rays are deflected by electric or magnetic fields in a way consistent with their being a stream of negative electrical charge. The British scientist J. J. Thomson (1856–1940) observed that cathode rays are the same regardless of the identity of the cathode material. In a paper published in 1897, Thomson described cathode rays as streams of negatively charged particles. His paper is generally accepted as the "discovery" of what became known as the *electron*.

Thomson constructed a cathode-ray tube having a hole in the anode through which a beam of electrons passed. Electrically charged plates and a magnet were positioned perpendicular to the electron beam, and a fluorescent screen was located at one end (▲ **FIGURE 2.4**). The electric field deflected the rays in one direction, and the magnetic field deflected them in the opposite direction. Thomson adjusted the strengths of the fields so that the effects balanced each other, allowing the electrons to travel in a straight path to the screen. Knowing the strengths that resulted in the straight path made it possible to calculate a value of $1.76 \times 10^8$ coulombs per gram for the ratio of the electron's electrical charge to its mass.*

Once the charge-to-mass ratio of the electron was known, measuring either quantity allowed scientists to calculate the other. In 1909, Robert Millikan (1868–1953) of the University of Chicago succeeded in measuring the charge of an electron by performing the experiment described in ◀ **FIGURE 2.5**. He then calculated the mass of the electron by using his experimental value for the charge, $1.602 \times 10^{-19}$ C, and Thomson's charge-to-mass ratio, $1.76 \times 10^8$ C/g:

$$\text{Electron mass} = \frac{1.602 \times 10^{-19} \text{ C}}{1.76 \times 10^8 \text{ C/g}} = 9.10 \times 10^{-28} \text{ g}$$

*The coulomb (C) is the SI unit for electrical charge.

This result agrees well with the currently accepted value for the electron mass, $9.10938 \times 10^{-28}$ g. This mass is about 2000 times smaller than that of hydrogen, the lightest atom.

## Radioactivity

In 1896 the French scientist Henri Becquerel (1852–1908) discovered that a compound of uranium spontaneously emits high-energy radiation. This spontaneous emission of radiation is called **radioactivity**. At Becquerel's suggestion, Marie Curie (▶ FIGURE 2.6) and her husband, Pierre, began experiments to isolate the radioactive components of the compound.

Further study of radioactivity, principally by the British scientist Ernest Rutherford (▶ FIGURE 2.7), revealed three types of radiation: alpha ($\alpha$), beta ($\beta$), and gamma ($\gamma$). The paths of $\alpha$ and $\beta$ radiation are bent by an electric field, although in opposite directions; $\gamma$ radiation is unaffected by the field (▼ FIGURE 2.8).

Rutherford showed that $\alpha$ and $\beta$ rays consist of fast-moving particles. In fact, $\beta$ particles are high-speed electrons and can be considered the radioactive equivalent of cathode rays. They are attracted to a positively charged plate. The $\alpha$ particles have a positive charge and are attracted to a negative plate. In units of the charge of the electron, $\beta$ particles have a charge of $1-$ and $\alpha$ particles a charge of $2+$. Each $\alpha$ particle has a mass about 7400 times that of an electron. Gamma radiation is high-energy radiation similar to X-rays; it does not consist of particles and carries no charge.

## The Nuclear Model of the Atom

With growing evidence that the atom is composed of smaller particles, attention was given to how the particles fit together. During the early 1900s, Thomson reasoned that because electrons contribute only a very small fraction of an atom's mass they probably were responsible for an equally small fraction of the atom's size. He proposed that the atom consisted of a uniform positive sphere of matter in which the electrons were embedded like raisins in a pudding or seeds in a watermelon (▶ FIGURE 2.9). This *plum-pudding model,* named after a traditional English dessert, was very short-lived.

In 1910, Rutherford was studying the angles at which $\alpha$ particles were deflected, or *scattered,* as they passed through a thin sheet of gold foil (▶ FIGURE 2.10). He discovered that almost all the particles passed directly through the foil without deflection, with a few particles deflected about 1 degree, consistent with Thomson's plum-pudding model. For the sake of completeness, Rutherford suggested that Ernest Marsden, an undergraduate student working in the laboratory, look for scattering at large angles. To everyone's surprise, a small amount of scattering was observed at large angles, with some particles scattered back in the direction from which they had come. The explanation for these results was not immediately obvious, but they were clearly inconsistent with Thomson's plum-pudding model.

▲ FIGURE 2.6   **Marie Sklodowska Curie (1867–1934).** When Marie Curie presented her doctoral thesis, it was described as the greatest single contribution of any doctoral thesis in the history of science. In 1903 Henri Becquerel, Maire Curie, and her husband, Pierre, were jointly awarded the Nobel Prize in Physics for their pioneering work on radioactivity (a term she introduced). In 1911 Marie Curie won a second Nobel Prize, this time in chemistry for her discovery of the elements polonium and radium.

▲ FIGURE 2.7   **Ernest Rutherford (1871–1937).** In 1895, Rutherford was awarded a position at Cambridge University in England, where he worked with J. J. Thomson. In 1898 he moved to McGill University in Montreal, where he did the research on radioactivity that led to his 1908 Nobel Prize in Chemistry. In 1907 Rutherford returned to England as a faculty member at Manchester University, where in 1910 he performed his famous $\alpha$-particle scattering experiments. In 1992 his native New Zealand honored him by putting his likeness on their $100 currency note.

◢ **GO FIGURE**

**Which of the three kinds of radiation shown consists of electrons? Why are these rays deflected to a greater extent than the others?**

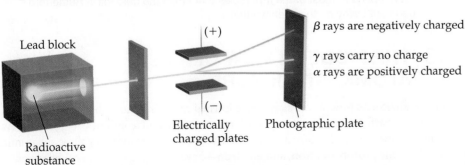

▲ FIGURE 2.8   **Behavior of alpha ($\alpha$), beta ($\beta$), and gamma ($\gamma$) rays in an electric field.**

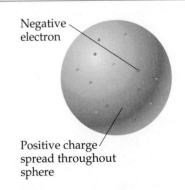

▲ FIGURE 2.9   **J. J. Thomson's plum-pudding model of the atom.** Ernest Rutherford proved this model wrong.

▲GO FIGURE

**What is the charge on the particles that form the beam?**

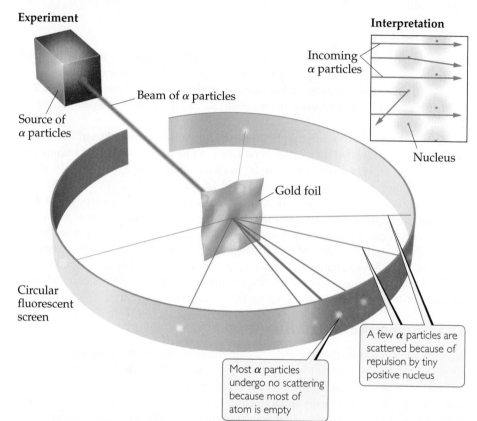

**Experiment**

Source of
α particles

Beam of α particles

Gold foil

Circular
fluorescent
screen

Most α particles
undergo no scattering
because most of
atom is empty

A few α particles are
scattered because of
repulsion by tiny
positive nucleus

**Interpretation**

Incoming
α particles

Nucleus

▶ **FIGURE 2.10 Rutherford's α-scattering experiment.** When α particles pass through a gold foil, most pass through undeflected but some are scattered, a few at very large angles. According to the plum-pudding model of the atom, the particles should experience only very minor deflections. The nuclear model of the atom explains why a few α particles are deflected at large angles. For clarity, the nuclear atom is shown here as a colored sphere, but most of the space around the nucleus is empty except for the tiny electrons moving around.

Rutherford explained the results by postulating the **nuclear model** of the atom, a model in which most of the mass of each gold atom and all of its positive charge reside in a very small, extremely dense region that he called the **nucleus**. He postulated further that most of the volume of an atom is empty space in which electrons move around the nucleus. In the α-scattering experiment, most of the particles passed through the foil unscattered because they did not encounter the minute nucleus of any gold atom. Occasionally, however, an α particle came close to a gold nucleus. The repulsion between the highly positive charge of the gold nucleus and the positive charge of the α particle was then strong enough to deflect the particle, as shown in Figure 2.10.

Subsequent experiments led to the discovery of positive particles (*protons*) and neutral particles (*neutrons*) in the nucleus. Protons were discovered in 1919 by Rutherford and neutrons in 1932 by British scientist James Chadwick (1891–1972). Thus, the atom is composed of electrons, protons, and neutrons.

▲ **GIVE IT SOME THOUGHT**

What happens to most of the α particles that strike the gold foil in Rutherford's experiment? Why do they behave that way?

## 2.3 | THE MODERN VIEW OF ATOMIC STRUCTURE

Since Rutherford's time, as physicists have learned more and more about atomic nuclei, the list of particles that make up nuclei has grown and continues to increase. As chemists, however, we can take a simple view of the atom because only three subatomic particles—the **proton**, **neutron**, and **electron**—have a bearing on chemical behavior.

As noted earlier, the charge of an electron is $-1.602 \times 10^{-19}$ C. That of a proton is equal in magnitude, $+1.602 \times 10^{-19}$ C. The quantity $1.602 \times 10^{-19}$ C is called the

**electronic charge**. For convenience, the charges of atomic and subatomic particles are usually expressed as multiples of this charge rather than in coulombs. Thus, the charge of the electron is 1− and that of the proton is 1+. Neutrons are electrically neutral (which is how they received their name). *Every atom has an equal number of electrons and protons, so atoms have no net electrical charge.*

Protons and neutrons reside in the tiny nucleus of the atom. The vast majority of an atom's volume is the space in which the electrons reside (▶ **FIGURE 2.11**). The electrons are attracted to the protons in the nucleus by the electrostatic force that exists between particles of opposite electrical charge. In later chapters we will see that the strength of the attractive forces between electrons and nuclei can be used to explain many of the differences among different elements.

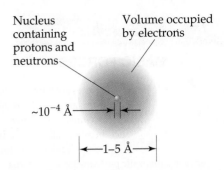

▲ **FIGURE 2.11 The structure of the atom.** A cloud of rapidly moving electrons occupies most of the volume of the atom. The nucleus occupies a tiny region at the center of the atom and is composed of the protons and neutrons. The nucleus contains virtually all the mass of the atom.

### ⚠ GIVE IT SOME THOUGHT

a. If an atom has 15 protons, how many electrons does it have?
b. Where do the protons reside in an atom?

Atoms have extremely small masses. The mass of the heaviest known atom, for example, is approximately $4 \times 10^{-22}$ g. Because it would be cumbersome to express such small masses in grams, we use the **atomic mass unit** (amu),* where 1 amu = $1.66054 \times 10^{-24}$ g. A proton has a mass of 1.0073 amu, a neutron 1.0087 amu, and an electron $5.486 \times 10^{-4}$ amu (▼ **TABLE 2.1**). Because it takes 1836 electrons to equal the mass of one proton or one neutron, the nucleus contains most of the mass of an atom.

Most atoms have diameters between $1 \times 10^{-10}$ m and $5 \times 10^{-10}$ m. A convenient non–SI unit of length used for atomic dimensions is the **angstrom** (Å), where $1 \text{ Å} = 1 \times 10^{-10}$ m. Thus, atoms have diameters of approximately 1−5 Å. The diameter of a chlorine atom, for example, is 200 pm, or 2.0 Å.

---

### SAMPLE EXERCISE 2.1 | Atomic Size

The diameter of a US dime is 17.9 mm, and the diameter of a silver atom is 2.88 Å. How many silver atoms could be arranged side by side across the diameter of a dime?

#### SOLUTION

The unknown is the number of silver (Ag) atoms. Using the relationship 1 Ag atom = 2.88 Å as a conversion factor relating number of atoms and distance, we start with the diameter of the dime, first converting this distance into angstroms and then using the diameter of the Ag atom to convert distance to number of Ag atoms:

$$\text{Ag atoms} = (17.9 \text{ mm})\left(\frac{10^{-3} \text{ m}}{1 \text{ mm}}\right)\left(\frac{1 \text{ Å}}{10^{-10} \text{ m}}\right)\left(\frac{1 \text{ Ag atom}}{2.88 \text{ Å}}\right) = 6.22 \times 10^{7} \text{Ag atoms}$$

That is, 62.2 million silver atoms could sit side by side across a dime!

#### PRACTICE EXERCISE

The diameter of a carbon atom is 1.54 Å. **(a)** Express this diameter in picometers. **(b)** How many carbon atoms could be aligned side by side across the width of a pencil line that is 0.20 mm wide?

***Answers:*** **(a)** 154 pm, **(b)** $1.3 \times 10^{6}$ C atoms

---

The diameter of an atomic nucleus is approximately $10^{-4}$ Å, only a small fraction of the diameter of the atom as a whole. You can appreciate the relative sizes of the atom and its nucleus by imagining that if the hydrogen atom were as large as a football stadium,

### TABLE 2.1 · Comparison of the Proton, Neutron, and Electron

| Particle | Charge | Mass (amu) |
|---|---|---|
| Proton | Positive (1+) | 1.0073 |
| Neutron | None (neutral) | 1.0087 |
| Electron | Negative (1−) | $5.486 \times 10^{-4}$ |

*The SI abbreviation for the atomic mass unit is u. We will use the more common abbreviation amu.

## A CLOSER LOOK

### BASIC FORCES

Four basic forces are known in nature: (1) gravitational, (2) electromagnetic, (3) strong nuclear, and (4) weak nuclear. *Gravitational forces* are attractive forces that act between all objects in proportion to their masses. Gravitational forces between atoms or between subatomic particles are so small that they are of no chemical significance.

*Electromagnetic forces* are attractive or repulsive forces that act between either electrically charged or magnetic objects. Electric forces are important in understanding the chemical behavior of atoms. The magnitude of the electric force between two charged particles is given by *Coulomb's law*: $F = kQ_1Q_2/d^2$, where $Q_1$ and $Q_2$ are the magnitudes of the charges on the two particles, $d$ is the distance between their centers, and $k$ is a constant determined by the units for $Q$ and $d$. A negative value for the force indicates attraction, whereas a positive value indicates repulsion.

All nuclei except those of hydrogen atoms contain two or more protons. Because like charges repel, electrical repulsion would cause the protons to fly apart if the *strong nuclear force* did not keep them together. This force acts between subatomic particles, as in the nucleus. At this distance, the attractive strong nuclear force is stronger than the positive–positive repulsive electric force and holds the nucleus together.

The *weak nuclear force* is weaker than the electric force but stronger than the gravitational force. We are aware of its existence only because it shows itself in certain types of radioactivity.

*RELATED EXERCISE: 2.88*

the nucleus would be the size of a small marble. Because the tiny nucleus carries most of the mass of the atom in such a small volume, it has an incredibly high density—on the order of $10^{13}$–$10^{14}$ g/cm$^3$. A matchbox full of material of such density would weigh over 2.5 billion tons!

An illustration of the atom that incorporates the features we have just discussed is shown in Figure 2.11. The electrons play the major role in chemical reactions. The significance of representing the region containing the electrons as an indistinct cloud will become clear in later chapters when we consider the energies and spatial arrangements of the electrons.

## Atomic Numbers, Mass Numbers, and Isotopes

What makes an atom of one element different from an atom of another element is that the atoms of each element have a *characteristic number of protons*. Indeed, the number of protons in an atom of any particular element is called that element's **atomic number**. Because an atom has no net electrical charge, the number of electrons it contains must equal the number of protons. All atoms of carbon, for example, have six protons and six electrons, whereas all atoms of oxygen have eight protons and eight electrons. Thus, carbon has atomic number 6, and oxygen has atomic number 8. The atomic number of each element is listed with the name and symbol of the element on the inside front cover of the text.

Atoms of a given element can differ in the number of neutrons they contain and, consequently, in mass. For example, most atoms of carbon have six neutrons, although some have more and some have less. The symbol $^{12}_{6}\text{C}$ (read "carbon twelve," carbon-12) represents the carbon atom containing six protons and six neutrons. The atomic number is shown by the subscript; the superscript, called the **mass number**, is the number of protons plus neutrons in the atom:

Mass number (number of protons plus neutrons)

$$^{12}_{6}\text{C} \longleftarrow \text{Symbol of element}$$

Atomic number (number of protons or electrons)

Because all atoms of a given element have the same atomic number, the subscript is redundant and is often omitted. Thus, the symbol for carbon-12 can be represented simply as $^{12}\text{C}$. As one more example of this notation, carbon atoms that contain six protons and eight neutrons have mass number 14, are represented as $^{14}_{6}\text{C}$ or $^{14}\text{C}$, and are referred to as carbon-14.

**TABLE 2.2 • Some Isotopes of Carbon***

| Symbol | Number of Protons | Number of Electrons | Number of Neutrons |
|--------|-------------------|---------------------|--------------------|
| $^{11}C$ | 6 | 6 | 5 |
| $^{12}C$ | 6 | 6 | 6 |
| $^{13}C$ | 6 | 6 | 7 |
| $^{14}C$ | 6 | 6 | 8 |

*Almost 99% of the carbon found in nature is $^{12}C$.

Atoms with identical atomic numbers but different mass numbers (that is, same number of protons but different numbers of neutrons) are called **isotopes** of one another. Several isotopes of carbon are listed in ▲ TABLE 2.2. We will generally use the notation with superscripts only when referring to a particular isotope of an element.

---

**SAMPLE EXERCISE 2.2**  **Determining the Number of Subatomic Particles in Atoms**

How many protons, neutrons, and electrons are in (a) an atom of $^{197}Au$, (b) an atom of strontium-90?

**SOLUTION**

(a) The superscript 197 is the mass number (protons + neutrons). According to the list of elements given on the inside front cover, gold has atomic number 79. Consequently, an atom of $^{197}Au$ has 79 protons, 79 electrons, and $197 - 79 = 118$ neutrons. (b) The atomic number of strontium (listed on inside front cover) is 38. Thus, all atoms of this element have 38 protons and 38 electrons. The strontium-90 isotope has $90 - 38 = 52$ neutrons.

**PRACTICE EXERCISE**

How many protons, neutrons, and electrons are in (a) a $^{138}Ba$ atom, (b) an atom of phosphorus-31?
**Answer:**   (a) 56 protons, 56 electrons, and 82 neutrons, (b) 15 protons, 15 electrons, and 16 neutrons

---

**SAMPLE EXERCISE 2.3**  **Writing Symbols for Atoms**

Magnesium has three isotopes with mass numbers 24, 25, and 26. (a) Write the complete chemical symbol (superscript and subscript) for each. (b) How many neutrons are in an atom of each isotope?

**SOLUTION**

(a) Magnesium has atomic number 12, so all atoms of magnesium contain 12 protons and 12 electrons. The three isotopes are therefore represented by $^{24}_{12}Mg$, $^{25}_{12}Mg$, and $^{26}_{12}Mg$. (b) The number of neutrons in each isotope is the mass number minus the number of protons. The numbers of neutrons in an atom of each isotope are therefore 12, 13, and 14, respectively.

**PRACTICE EXERCISE**

Give the complete chemical symbol for the atom that contains 82 protons, 82 electrons, and 126 neutrons.
**Answer:** $^{208}_{82}Pb$

---

# 2.4 | ATOMIC WEIGHTS

Atoms are small pieces of matter, so they have mass. In this section we discuss the mass scale used for atoms and introduce the concept of *atomic weights*.

## The Atomic Mass Scale

Scientists of the nineteenth century were aware that atoms of different elements have different masses. They found, for example, that each 100.0 g of water contains 11.1 g of hydrogen and 88.9 g of oxygen. Thus, water contains $88.9/11.1 = 8$ times as much oxygen, by mass, as hydrogen. Once scientists understood that water contains two hydrogen atoms for each oxygen atom, they concluded that an oxygen atom must have $2 \times 8 = 16$ times as much mass as a hydrogen atom. Hydrogen, the lightest atom, was arbitrarily assigned a relative mass of 1 (no units). Atomic masses of other elements were at first determined relative to this value. Thus, oxygen was assigned an atomic mass of 16.

Today we can determine the masses of individual atoms with a high degree of accuracy. For example, we know that the $^1$H atom has a mass of $1.6735 \times 10^{-24}$ g and the $^{16}$O atom has a mass of $2.6560 \times 10^{-23}$ g. As we noted in Section 2.3, it is convenient to use the *atomic mass unit* (amu) when dealing with these extremely small masses:

$$1 \text{ amu} = 1.66054 \times 10^{-24} \text{ g and } 1 \text{ g} = 6.02214 \times 10^{23} \text{ amu}$$

The atomic mass unit is presently defined by assigning a mass of exactly 12 amu to an atom of the $^{12}$C isotope of carbon. In these units, an $^1$H atom has a mass of 1.0078 amu and an $^{16}$O atom has a mass of 15.9949 amu.

## Atomic Weight

Most elements occur in nature as mixtures of isotopes. We can determine the *average atomic mass* of an element, usually called the element's **atomic weight**, by using the masses of its isotopes and their relative abundances:

$$\text{Atomic weight} = \sum [(\text{isotope mass}) \times (\text{fractional isotope abundance})]$$

$$\text{over all isotopes of the element} \quad [2.1]$$

Naturally occurring carbon, for example, is composed of 98.93% $^{12}$C and 1.07% $^{13}$C. The masses of these isotopes are 12 amu (exactly) and 13.00335 amu, respectively, making the atomic weight of carbon

$$(0.9893)(12 \text{ amu}) + (0.0107)(13.00335 \text{ amu}) = 12.01 \text{ amu}$$

The atomic weights of the elements are listed in both the periodic table and the table of elements inside the front cover of this text.

 **GIVE IT SOME THOUGHT**

A particular atom of chromium has a mass of 52.94 amu, whereas the atomic weight of chromium is 51.99 amu. Explain the difference in the two masses.

**SAMPLE EXERCISE 2.4** | **Calculating the Atomic Weight of an Element from Isotopic Abundances**

Naturally occurring chlorine is 75.78% $^{35}$Cl (atomic mass 34.969 amu) and 24.22% $^{37}$Cl (atomic mass 36.966 amu). Calculate the atomic weight of chlorine.

**SOLUTION**

We can calculate the atomic weight by multiplying the abundance of each isotope by its atomic mass and summing these products. Because 75.78% = 0.7578 and 24.22% = 0.2422, we have

$$\text{Atomic weight} = (0.7578)(34.969 \text{ amu}) + (0.2422)(36.966 \text{ amu})$$
$$= 26.50 \text{ amu} + 8.953 \text{ amu}$$
$$= 35.45 \text{ amu}$$

This answer makes sense: The atomic weight, which is actually the average atomic mass, is between the masses of the two isotopes and is closer to the value of $^{35}$Cl, the more abundant isotope.

**PRACTICE EXERCISE**

Three isotopes of silicon occur in nature: $^{28}$Si (92.23%), atomic mass 27.97693 amu; $^{29}$Si (4.68%), atomic mass 28.97649 amu; and $^{30}$Si (3.09%), atomic mass 29.97377 amu. Calculate the atomic weight of silicon.
*Answer:* 28.09 amu

## A CLOSER LOOK

### THE MASS SPECTROMETER

The most accurate means for determining atomic weights is provided by the **mass spectrometer** (▼ FIGURE 2.12). A gaseous sample is introduced at *A* and bombarded by a stream of high-energy electrons at *B*. Collisions between the electrons and the atoms or molecules of the gas produce positively charged particles that are then accelerated toward a negatively charged grid (*C*). After the particles pass through the grid, they encounter two slits that allow only a narrow beam of particles to pass. This beam then passes between the poles of a magnet, which deflects the particles into a curved path. For particles with the same charge, the extent of deflection depends on mass—the more massive the particle, the less the deflection. The particles are thereby separated according to their masses. By changing the strength of the magnetic field or the accelerating voltage on the grid, charged particles of various masses can be selected to enter the detector.

A graph of the intensity of the detector signal versus particle atomic mass is called a *mass spectrum* (▼ FIGURE 2.13). Analysis of a mass spectrum gives both the masses of the charged particles reaching the detector and their relative abundances, which are obtained from the signal intensities. Knowing the atomic mass and the abundance of each isotope allows us to calculate the atomic weight of an element, as shown in Sample Exercise 2.4.

Mass spectrometers are used extensively today to identify chemical compounds and analyze mixtures of substances. Any molecule that loses electrons can fall apart, forming an array of positively charged fragments. The mass spectrometer measures the masses of these fragments, producing a chemical "fingerprint" of the molecule and providing clues about how the atoms were connected in the original molecule. Thus, a chemist might use this technique to determine the molecular structure of a newly synthesized compound or to identify a pollutant in the environment.

*RELATED EXERCISES:* 2.33, 2.34, 2.35(b), 2.36, 2.92, and 2.93

▲ **FIGURE 2.12  A mass spectrometer.** Cl atoms are introduced at *A* and are ionized to form Cl⁺ ions, which are then directed through a magnetic field. The paths of the ions of the two Cl isotopes diverge as they pass through the field.

▲ **FIGURE 2.13  Mass spectrum of atomic chlorine.** The fractional abundances of the isotopes $^{35}Cl$ and $^{37}Cl$ are indicated by the relative signal intensities of the beams reaching the detector of the mass spectrometer.

## 2.5 | THE PERIODIC TABLE

As the list of known elements expanded during the early 1800s, attempts were made to find patterns in chemical behavior. These efforts culminated in the development of the periodic table in 1869. We will have much to say about the periodic table in later chapters, but it is so important and useful that you should become acquainted with it now. You will quickly learn that *the periodic table is the most significant tool that chemists use for organizing and remembering chemical facts.*

Many elements show strong similarities to one another. The elements lithium (Li), sodium (Na), and potassium (K) are all soft, very reactive metals, for example. The elements helium (He), neon (Ne), and argon (Ar) are all very nonreactive gases. If the elements are arranged in order of increasing atomic number, their chemical and physical properties show a repeating, or *periodic,* pattern. For example, each of the soft, reactive metals—lithium, sodium, and potassium—comes immediately after one of the nonreactive gases—helium, neon, and argon—as shown in ▶ FIGURE 2.14.

**GO FIGURE**

If F is a reactive nonmetal, which other element or elements shown here do
you expect to also be a reactive nonmetal?

▶ **FIGURE 2.14** **Arranging elements**
**by atomic number reveals a periodic**
**pattern of properties.** This pattern is the
basis of the periodic table.

The arrangement of elements in order of increasing atomic number, with elements
having similar properties placed in vertical columns, is known as the **periodic table**
(▼ **FIGURE 2.15**). The table shows the atomic number and atomic symbol for each element, and the atomic weight is often given as well, as in this typical entry for potassium:

You may notice slight variations in periodic tables from one book to another or between
those in the lecture hall and in the text. These are simply matters of style, or they might
concern the particular information included. There are no fundamental differences.

▲ **FIGURE 2.15** **Periodic table of the elements.**

The horizontal rows of the periodic table are called **periods**. The first period consists of only two elements, hydrogen (H) and helium (He). The second and third periods consist of eight elements each. The fourth and fifth periods contain 18 elements. The sixth period has 32 elements, but for it to fit on a page, 14 of these elements (atomic numbers 57–70) appear at the bottom of the table. The seventh period is incomplete, but it also has 14 of its members placed in a row at the bottom of the table.

The vertical columns are **groups**. The way in which the groups are labeled is somewhat arbitrary. Three labeling schemes are in common use, two of which are shown in Figure 2.15. The top set of labels, which have A and B designations, is widely used in North America. Roman numerals, rather than Arabic ones, are often employed in this scheme. Group 7A, for example, is often labeled VIIA. Europeans use a similar convention that numbers the columns from 1A through 8A and then from 1B through 8B, thereby giving the label 7B (or VIIB) instead of 7A to the group headed by fluorine (F). In an effort to eliminate this confusion, the International Union of Pure and Applied Chemistry (IUPAC) has proposed a convention that numbers the groups from 1 through 18 with no A or B designations, as shown in Figure 2.15. We will use the traditional North American convention with Arabic numerals and the letters A and B.

Elements in a group often exhibit similarities in physical and chemical properties. For example, the "coinage metals"—copper (Cu), silver (Ag), and gold (Au)—belong to group 1B. These elements are less reactive than most metals, which is why they are used throughout the world to make coins. Many other groups in the periodic table also have names, listed in ▼ TABLE 2.3.

We will learn in Chapters 6 and 7 that elements in a group have similar properties because they have the same arrangement of electrons at the periphery of their atoms. However, we need not wait until then to make good use of the periodic table; after all, chemists who knew nothing about electrons developed the table! We can use the table, as they intended, to correlate behaviors of elements and to help us remember many facts. The color code of Figure 2.15 shows that, except for hydrogen, all the elements on the left and in the middle of the table are **metallic elements**, or **metals**. All the metallic elements share characteristic properties, such as luster and high electrical and heat conductivity, and all of them except mercury (Hg) are solid at room temperature. The metals are separated from the **nonmetallic elements**, or **nonmetals**, by a stepped line that runs from boron (B) to astatine (At). (Note that hydrogen, although on the left side of the table, is a nonmetal.) At room temperature some of the nonmetals are gaseous, some are solid, and one is liquid. Nonmetals generally differ from the metals in appearance (▶ FIGURE 2.16) and in other physical properties. Many of the elements that lie along the line that separates metals from nonmetals have properties that fall between those of metals and those of nonmetals. These elements are often referred to as **metalloids**.

🛆 GIVE IT SOME THOUGHT

Chlorine is a halogen (Table 2.3). Locate this element in the periodic table.
a. What is its symbol?
b. In which period and in which group is the element located?
c. What is its atomic number?
d. Is it a metal or nonmetal?

▲ FIGURE 2.16  **Examples of metals (top) and nonmetals (bottom).**

| Group | Name | Elements |
|---|---|---|
| **TABLE 2.3 • Names of Some Groups in the Periodic Table** | | |
| 1A | Alkali metals | Li, Na, K, Rb, Cs, Fr |
| 2A | Alkaline earth metals | Be, Mg, Ca, Sr, Ba, Ra |
| 6A | Chalcogens | O, S, Se, Te, Po |
| 7A | Halogens | F, Cl, Br, I, At |
| 8A | Noble gases (or rare gases) | He, Ne, Ar, Kr, Xe, Rn |

# A CLOSER LOOK

## GLENN SEABORG AND SEABORGIUM

Prior to 1940 the periodic table ended at uranium, element number 92. Since that time, no scientist has had a greater effect on the periodic table than Glenn Seaborg (▶ FIGURE 2.17). In 1940 Seaborg, Edwin McMillan, and coworkers at the University of California, Berkeley, succeeded in isolating plutonium (Pu) as a product of the reaction between uranium and neutrons. We will talk about reactions of this type, called *nuclear reactions,* in Chapter 21.

Between 1944 and 1958, Seaborg and his coworkers also identified various products of nuclear reactions as being the elements having atomic numbers 95 through 102. All these elements are radioactive and are not found in nature; they can be synthesized only via nuclear reactions. For their efforts in identifying the elements beyond uranium (the *transuranium* elements), McMillan and Seaborg shared the 1951 Nobel Prize in Chemistry.

From 1961 to 1971, Seaborg served as the chairman of the US Atomic Energy Commission (now the Department of Energy). In this position he had an important role in establishing international treaties to limit the testing of nuclear weapons. Upon his return to Berkeley, he was part of the team that in 1974 first identified element number 106. In 1994, to honor Seaborg's many contributions to the discovery of new elements, the American Chemical Society proposed that element number 106 be named seaborgium (Sg). After several years of controversy about whether an element should be named

◀ FIGURE 2.17 **Glenn Seaborg (1912–1999).** Seaborg at Berkeley in 1941 measuring radiation produced by plutonium.

after a living person, the IUPAC officially adopted the name in 1997. Seaborg became the first person to have an element named after him while he was alive.

*RELATED EXERCISE:* 2.95

---

**SAMPLE EXERCISE 2.5** | **Using the Periodic Table**

Which two of these elements would you expect to show the greatest similarity in chemical and physical properties: B, Ca, F, He, Mg, P?

**SOLUTION**

Elements in the same group of the periodic table are most likely to exhibit similar properties. We therefore expect Ca and Mg to be most alike because they are in the same group (2A, the alkaline earth metals).

**PRACTICE EXERCISE**

Locate Na (sodium) and Br (bromine) in the periodic table. Give the atomic number of each and classify each as metal, metalloid, or nonmetal.

**Answer:** Na, atomic number 11, is a metal; Br, atomic number 35, is a nonmetal.

---

## 2.6 | MOLECULES AND MOLECULAR COMPOUNDS

Even though the atom is the smallest representative sample of an element, only the noble-gas elements are normally found in nature as isolated atoms. Most matter is composed of molecules or ions. We examine molecules here and ions in Section 2.7.

### Molecules and Chemical Formulas

Several elements are found in nature in molecular form—two or more of the same type of atom bound together. For example, most of the oxygen in air consists of molecules that contain two oxygen atoms. As we saw in Section 1.2, we represent this molecular oxygen by the **chemical formula** $O_2$ (read "oh two"). The subscript tells us that two oxygen atoms are present in each molecule. A molecule made up of two atoms is called a **diatomic molecule**.

Oxygen also exists in another molecular form known as *ozone*. Molecules of ozone consist of three oxygen atoms, making the chemical formula $O_3$. Even though "normal" oxygen ($O_2$) and ozone ($O_3$) are both composed only of oxygen atoms, they exhibit very different chemical and physical properties. For example, $O_2$ is essential for life, but $O_3$ is toxic; $O_2$ is odorless, whereas $O_3$ has a sharp, pungent smell.

The elements that normally occur as diatomic molecules are hydrogen, oxygen, nitrogen, and the halogens ($H_2$, $O_2$, $N_2$, $F_2$, $Cl_2$, $Br_2$, and $I_2$). Except for hydrogen, these diatomic elements are clustered on the right side of the periodic table.

Compounds composed of molecules contain more than one type of atom and are called **molecular compounds**. A molecule of the compound methane, for example, consists of one carbon atom and four hydrogen atoms and is therefore represented by the chemical formula $CH_4$. Lack of a subscript on the C indicates one atom of C per methane molecule. Several common molecules of both elements and compounds are shown in ▶ **FIGURE 2.18**. Notice how the composition of each substance is given by its chemical formula. Notice also that these substances are composed only of nonmetallic elements. *Most molecular substances we will encounter contain only nonmetals.*

## Molecular and Empirical Formulas

Chemical formulas that indicate the actual numbers of atoms in a molecule are called **molecular formulas**. (The formulas in Figure 2.18 are molecular formulas.) Chemical formulas that give only the relative number of atoms of each type in a molecule are called **empirical formulas**. The subscripts in an empirical formula are always the smallest possible whole-number ratios. The molecular formula for hydrogen peroxide is $H_2O_2$, for example, whereas its empirical formula is HO. The molecular formula for ethylene is $C_2H_4$, and its empirical formula is $CH_2$. For many substances, the molecular formula and the empirical formula are identical, as in the case of water, $H_2O$.

Whenever we know the molecular formula of a compound, we can determine its empirical formula. The converse is not true, however. If we know the empirical formula of a substance, we cannot determine its molecular formula unless we have more information. So why do chemists bother with empirical formulas? As we will see in Chapter 3, certain common methods of analyzing substances lead to the empirical formula only. Once the empirical formula is known, additional experiments can give the information needed to convert the empirical formula to the molecular one. In addition, there are substances that do not exist as isolated molecules. For these substances, we must rely on empirical formulas.

Hydrogen, $H_2$

Oxygen, $O_2$

Water, $H_2O$

Hydrogen peroxide, $H_2O_2$

Carbon monoxide, CO

Carbon dioxide, $CO_2$

Methane, $CH_4$

Ethylene, $C_2H_4$

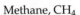

▲ **FIGURE 2.18  Molecular models.** Notice how the chemical formulas of these simple molecules correspond to their compositions.

---

**SAMPLE EXERCISE 2.6**  **Relating Empirical and Molecular Formulas**

Write the empirical formulas for **(a)** glucose, a substance also known as either blood sugar or dextrose, molecular formula $C_6H_{12}O_6$; **(b)** nitrous oxide, a substance used as an anesthetic and commonly called laughing gas, molecular formula $N_2O$.

**SOLUTION**

**(a)** The subscripts of an empirical formula are the smallest whole-number ratios. The smallest ratios are obtained by dividing each subscript by the largest common factor, in this case 6. The resultant empirical formula for glucose is $CH_2O$.

**(b)** Because the subscripts in $N_2O$ are already the lowest integral numbers, the empirical formula for nitrous oxide is the same as its molecular formula, $N_2O$.

**PRACTICE EXERCISE**

Give the empirical formula for *diborane*, whose molecular formula is $B_2H_6$.

*Answer:* $BH_3$

**What advantage does a ball-and-stick model have over a space-filling model?**

$CH_4$

Molecular formula

Structural formula

Dashed wedge is bond behind page

Solid line is bond in plane of page

Wedge is bond out of page

Perspective drawing

Ball-and-stick model

Space-filling model

△ **FIGURE 2.19** **Different representations of the methane ($CH_4$) molecule.** Structural formulas, perspective drawings, ball-and-stick models, and space-filling models correspond to the molecular formula, and each helps us visualize the ways atoms are attached to each other.

# Picturing Molecules

The molecular formula of a substance summarizes the composition of the substance but does not show how the atoms are joined together in the molecule. A **structural formula** shows which atoms are attached to which, as in the following examples:

Water          Hydrogen peroxide          Methane

The atoms are represented by their chemical symbols, and lines are used to represent the bonds that hold the atoms together.

A structural formula usually does not depict the actual geometry of the molecule, that is, the actual angles at which atoms are joined together. A structural formula can be written as a *perspective drawing* (◀ **FIGURE 2.19**), however, to give some sense of three-dimensional shape.

Scientists also rely on various models to help visualize molecules. *Ball-and-stick models* show atoms as spheres and bonds as sticks. This type of model has the advantage of accurately representing the angles at which the atoms are attached to one another in the molecule (Figure 2.19). Sometimes the chemical symbols of the elements are superimposed on the balls, but often the atoms are identified simply by color.

A *space-filling model* depicts what the molecule would look like if the atoms were scaled up in size (Figure 2.19). These models show the relative sizes of the atoms, but the angles between atoms, which help define their molecular geometry, are often more difficult to see than in ball-and-stick models. As in ball-and-stick models, the identities of the atoms are indicated by color, but they may also be labeled with the element's symbol.

△ **GIVE IT SOME THOUGHT**

The structural formula for ethane is

$$H-\underset{\underset{H}{|}}{\overset{\overset{H}{|}}{C}}-\underset{\underset{H}{|}}{\overset{\overset{H}{|}}{C}}-H$$

a. What is the molecular formula for ethane?
b. What is its empirical formula?
c. Which kind of molecular model would most clearly show the angles between atoms?

# 2.7 | IONS AND IONIC COMPOUNDS

The nucleus of an atom is unchanged by chemical processes, but some atoms can readily gain or lose electrons. If electrons are removed from or added to an atom, a charged particle called an **ion** is formed. An ion with a positive charge is a **cation** (pronounced CAT-ion); a negatively charged ion is an **anion** (AN-ion).

To see how ions form, consider the sodium atom, which has 11 protons and 11 electrons. This atom easily loses one electron. The resulting cation has 11 protons and 10 electrons, which means it has a net charge of 1+.

$11p^+$    $11e^-$        $11p^+$    $10e^-$

Loses an electron

Na atom                Na$^+$ ion

The net charge on an ion is represented by a superscript. The superscripts $+$, $2+$, and $3+$, for instance, mean a net charge resulting from the *loss* of one, two, and three electrons, respectively. The superscripts $-$, $2-$, and $3-$ represent net charges resulting from the *gain* of one, two, and three electrons, respectively. Chlorine, with 17 protons and 17 electrons, for example, can gain an electron in chemical reactions, producing the $Cl^-$ ion:

In general, metal atoms tend to lose electrons to form cations and nonmetal atoms tend to gain electrons to form anions. Thus, ionic compounds tend to be composed of metals bonded with nonmetals, as in NaCl.

---

**SAMPLE EXERCISE 2.7**    **Writing Chemical Symbols for Ions**

Give the chemical symbol, including superscript indicating mass number, for **(a)** the ion with 22 protons, 26 neutrons, and 19 electrons; **(b)** the ion of sulfur that has 16 neutrons and 18 electrons.

**SOLUTION**

**(a)** The number of protons is the atomic number of the element. A periodic table or list of elements tells us that the element with atomic number 22 is titanium (Ti). The mass number (protons plus neutrons) of this isotope of titanium is $22 + 26 = 48$. Because the ion has three more protons than electrons, it has a net charge of $3+$: $^{48}Ti^{3+}$.

**(b)** The periodic table tells us that sulfur (S) has an atomic number of 16. Thus, each atom or ion of sulfur contains 16 protons. We are told that the ion also has 16 neutrons, meaning the mass number is $16 + 16 = 32$. Because the ion has 16 protons and 18 electrons, its net charge is $2-$ and the ion symbol is $^{32}S^{2-}$.

In general, we will focus on the net charges of ions and ignore their mass numbers unless the circumstances dictate that we specify a certain isotope.

**PRACTICE EXERCISE**

How many protons, neutrons, and electrons does the $^{79}Se^{2-}$ ion possess?

**Answer:** 34 protons, 45 neutrons, and 36 electrons

---

In addition to simple ions such as $Na^+$ and $Cl^-$, there are **polyatomic ions**, such as $NH_4^+$ (ammonium ion) and $SO_4^{2-}$ (sulfate ion). These latter ions consist of atoms joined as in a molecule, but they have a net positive or negative charge. We consider polyatomic ions in Section 2.8.

It is important to realize that the chemical properties of ions are very different from the chemical properties of the atoms from which the ions are derived. Although a given atom and its ion may be essentially the same (plus or minus a few electrons), the behavior of the ion is very different from that of its associated atom.

## Predicting Ionic Charges

Many atoms gain or lose electrons to end up with the same number of electrons as the noble gas closest to them in the periodic table. Noble-gas elements are chemically non-reactive and form very few compounds. We might deduce that this is because their electron arrangements are very stable. Nearby elements can obtain these same stable arrangements by losing or gaining electrons. For example, the loss of one electron from an atom of sodium leaves it with the same number of electrons as in a neon atom (10). Similarly, when chlorine gains an electron, it ends up with 18, the same number of electrons as in argon. We will use this simple observation to explain the formation of ions until Chapter 8, where we discuss chemical bonding.

**SAMPLE EXERCISE 2.8**   **Predicting Ionic Charge**

Predict the charge expected for the most stable ion of barium and the most stable ion of oxygen.

**SOLUTION**

We will assume that these elements form ions that have the same number of electrons as the nearest noble-gas atom. From the periodic table, we see that barium has atomic number 56. The nearest noble gas is xenon, atomic number 54. Barium can attain a stable arrangement of 54 electrons by losing two electrons, forming the $Ba^{2+}$ cation.

Oxygen has atomic number 8. The nearest noble gas is neon, atomic number 10. Oxygen can attain this stable electron arrangement by gaining two electrons, forming the $O^{2-}$ anion.

**PRACTICE EXERCISE**

Predict the charge expected for the most stable ion of (**a**) aluminum and (**b**) fluorine.

*Answer:* (**a**) 3+, (**b**) 1−

The periodic table is very useful for remembering ionic charges, especially those of elements on the left and right sides of the table. As ▼ **FIGURE 2.20** shows, the charges of these ions relate in a simple way to their positions in the table: The group 1A elements (alkali metals) form 1+ ions, the group 2A elements (alkaline earths) form 2+ ions, the group 7A elements (halogens) form 1− ions, and the group 6A elements form 2− ions. (Many of the other groups do not lend themselves to such simple rules.)

## Ionic Compounds

A great deal of chemical activity involves the transfer of electrons from one substance to another. ▶ **FIGURE 2.21** shows that when elemental sodium is allowed to react with elemental chlorine, an electron transfers from a sodium atom to a chlorine atom, forming a $Na^+$ ion and a $Cl^-$ ion. Because objects of opposite charge attract, the $Na^+$ and the $Cl^-$ ions bind together to form the compound sodium chloride (NaCl). Sodium chloride, which we know better as common table salt, is an example of an **ionic compound**, a compound made up of cations and anions.

We can often tell whether a compound is ionic (consisting of ions) or molecular (consisting of molecules) from its composition. In general, cations are metal ions and anions are nonmetal ions. Consequently, *ionic compounds are generally combinations of metals and nonmetals,* as in NaCl. In contrast, *molecular compounds are generally composed of nonmetals only,* as in $H_2O$.

**GO FIGURE**

The most common ions for silver, zinc, and scandium are $Ag^+$, $Zn^{2+}$, and $Sc^{3+}$. Locate the boxes in which you would place these ions in this table. Which of these ions have the same number of electrons as a noble-gas element?

▶ **FIGURE 2.20   Predictable charges of some common ions.** Notice that the red stepped line that divides metals from nonmetals also separates cations from anions. Hydrogen forms both 1+ and 1− ions.

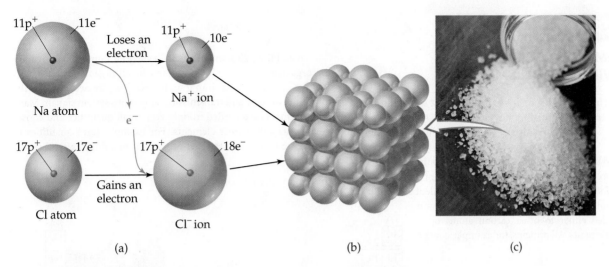

▲ **FIGURE 2.21    Formation of an ionic compound.** (a) The transfer of an electron from a Na atom to a Cl atom leads to the formation of a $Na^+$ ion and a $Cl^-$ ion. (b) Arrangement of these ions in solid sodium chloride, NaCl. (c) A sample of sodium chloride crystals.

---

**SAMPLE EXERCISE 2.9    Identifying Ionic and Molecular Compounds**

Which of these compounds would you expect to be ionic: $N_2O$, $Na_2O$, $CaCl_2$, $SF_4$?

**SOLUTION**

We predict that $Na_2O$ and $CaCl_2$ are ionic compounds because they are composed of a metal combined with a nonmetal. We predict (correctly) that $N_2O$ and $SF_4$ are molecular compounds because they are composed entirely of nonmetals.

**PRACTICE EXERCISE**

Which of these compounds are molecular: $CBr_4$, FeS, $P_4O_6$, $PbF_2$?
**Answer:** $CBr_4$ and $P_4O_6$

---

The ions in ionic compounds are arranged in three-dimensional structures, as Figure 2.21(b) shows for NaCl. Because there is no discrete "molecule" of NaCl, we are able to write only an empirical formula for this substance. This is true for most other ionic compounds.

We can write the empirical formula for an ionic compound if we know the charges of the ions. This is true because chemical compounds are always electrically neutral. Consequently, the ions in an ionic compound always occur in such a ratio that the total positive charge equals the total negative charge. Thus, there is one $Na^+$ to one $Cl^-$ (giving NaCl), one $Ba^{2+}$ to two $Cl^-$ (giving $BaCl_2$), and so forth.

As you consider these and other examples, you will see that if the charges on the cation and anion are equal, the subscript on each ion is 1. If the charges are not equal, the charge on one ion (without its sign) will become the subscript on the other ion. For example, the ionic compound formed from Mg (which forms $Mg^{2+}$ ions) and N (which forms $N^{3-}$ ions) is $Mg_3N_2$:

$$Mg^{2+} \quad N^{3-} \longrightarrow Mg_3N_2$$

▲ **GIVE IT SOME THOUGHT**

Why don't we write the formula for the compound formed by $Ca^{2+}$ and $O^{2-}$ as $Ca_2O_2$?

# CHEMISTRY AND LIFE

## ELEMENTS REQUIRED BY LIVING ORGANISMS

The colored regions of ▶ FIGURE 2.22 shows the elements essential to life. More than 97% of the mass of most organisms is made up of just six of these elements—oxygen, carbon, hydrogen, nitrogen, phosphorus, and sulfur. Water is the most common compound in living organisms, accounting for at least 70% of the mass of most cells. In the solid components of cells, carbon is the most prevalent element by mass. Carbon atoms are found in a vast variety of organic molecules, bonded either to other carbon atoms or to atoms of other elements. All proteins, for example, contain the group

$$
\begin{array}{c}
\quad\ \overset{\displaystyle O}{\|} \\
-N-C- \\
\ \ | \\
\ \ R
\end{array}
$$

which occurs repeatedly in the molecules. (R is either an H atom or a combination of atoms, such as $CH_3$.)

In addition, 23 more elements have been found in various living organisms. Five are ions required by all organisms: $Ca^{2+}$, $Cl^-$, $Mg^{2+}$, $K^+$, and $Na^+$. Calcium ions, for example, are necessary for the formation of bone and transmission of nervous system signals. Many other elements are needed in only very small quantities and consequently are called *trace* elements. For example, trace quantities of copper are required in the diet of humans to aid in the synthesis of hemoglobin.

*RELATED EXERCISE:* 2.96

⬜ 6 most abundant essential elements    ⬜ 5 next most abundant essential elements    ⬛ elements needed only in trace quantities

▲ FIGURE 2.22   **Elements essential to life.**

# STRATEGIES IN CHEMISTRY

## PATTERN RECOGNITION

Someone once said that drinking at the fountain of knowledge in a chemistry course is like drinking from a fire hydrant. Indeed, the pace can sometimes seem brisk. More to the point, however, we can drown in the facts if we do not see the general patterns. The value of recognizing patterns and learning rules and generalizations is that they free us from having to learn (or trying to memorize) many individual facts. The patterns, rules, and generalizations tie ideas together so that we do not get lost in the details.

Many students struggle with chemistry because they do not see how different topics relate to one another so they treat every idea and problem as being unique instead of as an example or application of a general rule, procedure, or relationship. You can avoid this pitfall by remembering the following.

Notice the structure of the topic you are studying. Pay attention to trends and rules given to summarize a large body of information. Notice, for example, how atomic structure helps us understand the existence of isotopes (as Table 2.2 shows) and how the periodic table helps us remember ionic charges (as Figure 2.20 shows).

You may surprise yourself by observing patterns that are not explicitly spelled out yet. Perhaps you have noticed certain trends in chemical formulas, for instance. Moving across the periodic table from element 11 (Na), we find that the elements form compounds with F having the following compositions: NaF, $MgF_2$, and $AlF_3$. Does this trend continue? Do $SiF_4$, $PF_5$, and $SF_6$ exist? Indeed they do. If you have noticed trends like this from the scraps of information you have seen so far, then you are ahead of the game and have prepared yourself for some topics we will address in later chapters.

| SAMPLE EXERCISE 2.10 | Using Ionic Charge to Write Empirical Formulas for Ionic Compounds |
| --- | --- |

Write the empirical formula of the compound formed by (a) $Al^{3+}$ and $Cl^-$ ions, (b) $Al^{3+}$ and $O^{2-}$ ions, (c) $Mg^{2+}$ and $NO_3^-$ ions.

### SOLUTION

(a) Three $Cl^-$ ions are required to balance the charge of one $Al^{3+}$ ion, making the formula $AlCl_3$.

(b) Two $Al^{3+}$ ions are required to balance the charge of three $O^{2-}$ ions. That is, the total positive charge is 6+, and the total negative charge is 6−. The formula is $Al_2O_3$.

**(c)** Two $NO_3^-$ ions are needed to balance the charge of one $Mg^{2+}$, yielding $Mg(NO_3)_2$. Note that the formula for the polyatomic ion, $NO_3^-$, must be enclosed in parentheses so that it is clear that the subscript 2 applies to all the atoms of that ion.

### PRACTICE EXERCISE

Write the empirical formula for the compound formed by **(a)** $Na^+$ and $PO_4^{3-}$, **(b)** $Zn^{2+}$ and $SO_4^{2-}$, **(c)** $Fe^{3+}$ and $CO_3^{2-}$.

***Answers:*** **(a)** $Na_3PO_4$, **(b)** $ZnSO_4$, **(c)** $Fe_2(CO_3)_3$

# 2.8 | NAMING INORGANIC COMPOUNDS

The names and chemical formulas of compounds are essential vocabulary in chemistry. The system used in naming substances is called **chemical nomenclature**, from the Latin words *nomen* (name) and *calare* (to call).

There are more than 50 million known chemical substances. Naming them all would be a hopelessly complicated task if each had a name independent of all others. Many important substances that have been known for a long time, such as water ($H_2O$) and ammonia ($NH_3$), do have traditional names (called *common names*). For most substances, however, we rely on a set of rules that leads to an informative and unique name for each substance, a name based on the composition of the substance.

The rules for chemical nomenclature are based on the division of substances into categories. The major division is between organic and inorganic compounds. *Organic compounds* contain carbon and hydrogen, often in combination with oxygen, nitrogen, or other elements. All others are *inorganic compounds*. Early chemists associated organic compounds with plants and animals and inorganic compounds with the nonliving portion of our world. Although this distinction is no longer pertinent, the classification between organic and inorganic compounds continues to be useful. In this section we consider the basic rules for naming three categories of inorganic compounds: ionic compounds, molecular compounds, and acids.

## Names and Formulas of Ionic Compounds

Recall from Section 2.7 that ionic compounds usually consist of metal ions combined with nonmetal ions. The metals form the cations, and the nonmetals form the anions.

1. Cations

   **a.** *Cations formed from metal atoms have the same name as the metal:*

   | | | |
   |---|---|---|
   | $Na^+$ sodium ion | $Zn^{2+}$ zinc ion | $Al^{3+}$ aluminum ion |

   **b.** *If a metal can form cations with different charges, the positive charge is indicated by a Roman numeral in parentheses following the name of the metal:*

   | | |
   |---|---|
   | $Fe^{2+}$ iron(II) ion | $Cu^+$ copper(I) ion |
   | $Fe^{3+}$ iron(III) ion | $Cu^{2+}$ copper(II) ion |

   Ions of the same element that have different charges have different properties, such as different colors (▶ **FIGURE 2.23**).

   Most metals that form cations with different charges are *transition metals*, elements that occur in the middle of the periodic table, from group 3B to group 2B. The metals that form only one cation (only one possible charge) are those of group 1A and group 2A, as well as $Al^{3+}$ (group 3A) and two transition-metal ions: $Ag^+$ (group 1B) and $Zn^{2+}$ (group 2B). Charges are not expressed when naming these ions. However, if there is any doubt in your mind whether a metal forms more than one cation, use a Roman numeral to indicate the charge. It is never wrong to do so, even though it may be unnecessary.

▲ **FIGURE 2.23 Different ions of the same element have different properties.** Both substances shown are compounds of iron. The substance on the left is $Fe_3O_4$, which contains $Fe^{2+}$ and $Fe^{3+}$ ions. The substance on the right is $Fe_2O_3$, which contains $Fe^{3+}$ ions.

An older method still widely used for distinguishing between differently charged ions of a metal uses the endings *-ous* and *-ic* added to the root of the element's Latin name:

| | | | | |
|---|---|---|---|---|
| $Fe^{2+}$ | ferrous ion | | $Cu^+$ | cuprous ion |
| $Fe^{3+}$ | ferric ion | | $Cu^{2+}$ | cupric ion |

Although we will only rarely use these older names in this text, you might encounter them elsewhere.

**c.** *Cations formed from nonmetal atoms have names that end in* -ium:

| | | | |
|---|---|---|---|
| $NH_4^+$ | ammonium ion | $H_3O^+$ | hydronium ion |

These two ions are the only ions of this kind that we will encounter frequently in the text.

The names and formulas of some common cations are shown in ▼ TABLE 2.4 and on the back inside cover of the text. The ions on the left side in Table 2.4 are the monatomic ions that do not have more than one possible charge. Those on the right side are either polyatomic cations or cations with more than one possible charge. The $Hg_2^{2+}$ ion is unusual because, even though it is a metal ion, it is not monatomic. It is called the mercury(I) ion because it can be thought of as two $Hg^+$ ions bound together. The cations that you will encounter most frequently are shown in boldface. You should learn these cations first.

### ▲ GIVE IT SOME THOUGHT

**a.** Why is CrO named using a Roman numeral, chromium(II) oxide, whereas CaO is named without a Roman numeral, calcium oxide?

**b.** What does the *-ium* ending on the name ammonium ion tell you about the composition of the ion?

**TABLE 2.4 • Common Cations***

| Charge | Formula | Name | Formula | Name |
|---|---|---|---|---|
| 1+ | **$H^+$** | **hydrogen ion** | $NH_4^+$ | **ammonium ion** |
| | $Li^+$ | lithium ion | $Cu^+$ | copper(I) or cuprous ion |
| | **$Na^+$** | **sodium ion** | | |
| | **$K^+$** | **potassium ion** | | |
| | $Cs^+$ | cesium ion | | |
| | **$Ag^+$** | **silver ion** | | |
| 2+ | **$Mg^{2+}$** | **magnesium ion** | $Co^{2+}$ | cobalt(II) or cobaltous ion |
| | **$Ca^{2+}$** | **calcium ion** | **$Cu^{2+}$** | **copper(II)** or cupric ion |
| | $Sr^{2+}$ | strontium ion | **$Fe^{2+}$** | **iron(II)** or ferrous ion |
| | $Ba^{2+}$ | barium ion | $Mn^{2+}$ | manganese(II) or manganous ion |
| | **$Zn^{2+}$** | **zinc ion** | $Hg_2^{2+}$ | mercury(I) or mercurous ion |
| | $Cd^{2+}$ | cadmium ion | **$Hg^{2+}$** | **mercury(II)** or mercuric ion |
| | | | $Ni^{2+}$ | nickel(II) or nickelous ion |
| | | | **$Pb^{2+}$** | **lead(II)** or plumbous ion |
| | | | $Sn^{2+}$ | tin(II) or stannous ion |
| 3+ | **$Al^{3+}$** | **aluminum ion** | $Cr^{3+}$ | chromium(III) or chromic ion |
| | | | **$Fe^{3+}$** | **iron(III)** or ferric ion |

*The ions we use most often in this course are in boldface. Learn them first.

2. Anions

   a. *The names of monatomic anions are formed by replacing the ending of the name of the element with -ide:*

   | | | |
   |---|---|---|
   | $H^-$   hydride ion | $O^{2-}$   oxide ion | $N^{3-}$   nitride ion |

   A few polyatomic anions also have names ending in *-ide*:

   | | | |
   |---|---|---|
   | $OH^-$   hydroxide ion | $CN^-$   cyanide ion | $O_2{}^{2-}$   peroxide ion |

   b. *Polyatomic anions containing oxygen have names ending in either* -ate *or* -ite *and are called* **oxyanions**. The *-ate* is used for the most common or representative oxyanion of an element, and *-ite* is used for an oxyanion that has the same charge but one O atom fewer:

   | | |
   |---|---|
   | $NO_3{}^-$   nitrate ion | $SO_4{}^{2-}$   sulfate ion |
   | $NO_2{}^-$   nitrite ion | $SO_3{}^{2-}$   sulfite ion |

   Prefixes are used when the series of oxyanions of an element extends to four members, as with the halogens. The prefix *per-* indicates one more O atom than the oxyanion ending in *-ate*; *hypo-* indicates one O atom fewer than the oxyanion ending in *-ite*:

   | | |
   |---|---|
   | $ClO_4{}^-$ | perchlorate ion (one more O atom than chlorate) |
   | **$ClO_3{}^-$** | **chlorate ion** |
   | $ClO_2{}^-$ | chlorite ion (one O atom fewer than chlorate) |
   | $ClO^-$ | hypochlorite ion (one O atom fewer than chlorite) |

   These rules are summarized in ▼ **FIGURE 2.24**.

◢ GIVE IT SOME THOUGHT

What information is conveyed by the endings *-ide, -ate,* and *-ite* in the name of an anion?

▶ **FIGURE 2.25** can help you remember the charge and number of oxygen atoms in the various oxyanions. Notice that C and N, both period 2 elements, have only three O atoms each, whereas the period 3 elements P, S, and Cl have four O atoms each. Beginning at the lower right in Figure 2.25, note that ionic charge increases from right to left, from 1− for $ClO_4{}^-$ to 3− for $PO_4{}^{3-}$. In the second period the charges also increase from right to left, from 1− for $NO_3{}^-$ to 2− for $CO_3{}^{2-}$. Notice also that although each of the anions in Figure 2.25 ends in *-ate*, the $ClO_4{}^-$ ion also has a *per-* prefix.

◢ GO FIGURE

Name the anion obtained by removing one oxygen atom from the perbromate ion, $BrO_4{}^-$.

| | |
|---|---|
| Simple anion | _____ide<br>(chloride, $Cl^-$) |

Oxyanions

| per_____ate<br>(perchlorate, $ClO_4{}^-$) | +O atom ← | _____ate<br>(chlorate, $ClO_3{}^-$) | −O atom → | _____ite<br>(chlorite, $ClO_2{}^-$) | −O atom → | hypo_____ite<br>(hypochlorite, $ClO^-$) |
|---|---|---|---|---|---|---|

Common or representative oxyanion

▲ **FIGURE 2.24   Procedure for naming anions.** The first part of the element's name, such as "chlor" for chlorine or "sulf" for sulfur, goes in the blank.

▲ **FIGURE 2.25  Common oxyanions.** The composition and charges of common oxyanions are related to their location in the periodic table.

△ **GIVE IT SOME THOUGHT**

Predict the formulas for the borate ion and silicate ion, assuming they contain a single B and Si atom, respectively, and follow the trends shown in Figure 2.25.

---

**SAMPLE EXERCISE 2.11**   **Determining the Formula of an Oxyanion from Its Name**

Based on the formula for the sulfate ion, predict the formula for **(a)** the selenate ion and **(b)** the selenite ion. (Sulfur and selenium are both in group 6A and form analogous oxyanions.)

**SOLUTION**

**(a)** The sulfate ion is $SO_4^{2-}$. The analogous selenate ion is therefore $SeO_4^{2-}$.
**(b)** The ending *-ite* indicates an oxyanion with the same charge but one O atom fewer than the corresponding oxyanion that ends in *-ate*. Thus, the formula for the selenite ion is $SeO_3^{2-}$.

**PRACTICE EXERCISE**

The formula for the bromate ion is analogous to that for the chlorate ion. Write the formula for the hypobromite and bromite ions.
**Answer:** $BrO^-$ and $BrO_2^-$

**c.** *Anions derived by adding $H^+$ to an oxyanion are named by adding as a prefix the word* hydrogen *or* dihydrogen, *as appropriate:*

| | | | |
|---|---|---|---|
| $CO_3^{2-}$ | carbonate ion | $PO_4^{3-}$ | phosphate ion |
| $HCO_3^-$ | hydrogen carbonate ion | $H_2PO_4^-$ | dihydrogen phosphate ion |

Notice that each $H^+$ added reduces the negative charge of the parent anion by one. An older method for naming some of these ions uses the prefix *bi-*. Thus, the $HCO_3^-$ ion is commonly called the bicarbonate ion, and $HSO_4^-$ is sometimes called the bisulfate ion.

The names and formulas of the common anions are listed in ▶ **TABLE 2.5** and on the back inside cover of the text. Those anions whose names end in *-ide* are listed on the left portion of Table 2.5, and those whose names end in *-ate* are listed on the right. The most common of these ions are shown in boldface. You should learn names and formulas of these anions first. The formulas of the ions whose names end with *-ite* can be derived from those ending in *-ate* by removing an O atom. Notice the location of the monatomic ions in the periodic table. Those of group 7A always have a 1− charge ($F^-$, $Cl^-$, $Br^-$, and $I^-$), and those of group 6A have a 2− charge ($O^{2-}$ and $S^{2-}$).

**3. Ionic Compounds**

*Names of ionic compounds consist of the cation name followed by the anion name:*

| | |
|---|---|
| $CaCl_2$ | calcium chloride |
| $Al(NO_3)_3$ | aluminum nitrate |
| $Cu(ClO_4)_2$ | copper(II) perchlorate (or cupric perchlorate) |

In the chemical formulas for aluminum nitrate and copper(II) perchlorate, parentheses followed by the appropriate subscript are used because the compounds contain two or more polyatomic ions.

---

**SAMPLE EXERCISE 2.12** | **Determining the Names of Ionic Compounds from Their Formulas**

Name the ionic compounds (**a**) $K_2SO_4$, (**b**) $Ba(OH)_2$, (**c**) $FeCl_3$.

**SOLUTION**

In naming ionic compounds, it is important to recognize polyatomic ions and to determine the charge of cations with variable charge.

(**a**) The cation is $K^+$, the potassium ion, and the anion is $SO_4^{2-}$, the sulfate ion, making the name potassium sulfate. (If you thought the compound contained $S^{2-}$ and $O^{2-}$ ions, you failed to recognize the polyatomic sulfate ion.)

(**b**) The cation is $Ba^{2+}$, the barium ion, and the anion is $OH^-$, the hydroxide ion: barium hydroxide.

(**c**) You must determine the charge of Fe in this compound because an iron atom can form more than one cation. Because the compound contains three chloride ions, $Cl^-$, the cation must be $Fe^{3+}$, the iron(III), or ferric, ion. Thus, the compound is iron(III) chloride or ferric chloride.

**PRACTICE EXERCISE**

Name the ionic compounds (**a**) $NH_4Br$, (**b**) $Cr_2O_3$, (**c**) $Co(NO_3)_2$.
**Answers:** (**a**) ammonium bromide, (**b**) chromium(III) oxide, (**c**) cobalt(II) nitrate

---

**TABLE 2.5 • Common Anions**[*]

| Charge | Formula | Name | Formula | Name |
|---|---|---|---|---|
| 1− | $H^-$ | hydride ion | $CH_3COO^-$ (or $C_2H_3O_2^-$) | acetate ion |
| | $F^-$ | **fluoride ion** | $ClO_3^-$ | chlorate ion |
| | $Cl^-$ | **chloride ion** | $ClO_4^-$ | **perchlorate ion** |
| | $Br^-$ | **bromide ion** | $NO_3^-$ | **nitrate ion** |
| | $I^-$ | **iodide ion** | $MnO_4^-$ | permanganate ion |
| | $CN^-$ | cyanide ion | | |
| | $OH^-$ | **hydroxide ion** | | |
| 2− | $O^{2-}$ | **oxide ion** | $CO_3^{2-}$ | **carbonate ion** |
| | $O_2^{2-}$ | peroxide ion | $CrO_4^{2-}$ | chromate ion |
| | $S^{2-}$ | **sulfide ion** | $Cr_2O_7^{2-}$ | dichromate ion |
| | | | $SO_4^{2-}$ | **sulfate ion** |
| 3− | $N^{3-}$ | nitride ion | $PO_4^{3-}$ | **phosphate ion** |

*The ions we use most often are in boldface. Learn them first.

---

**SAMPLE EXERCISE 2.13** | **Determining the Formulas of Ionic Compounds from Their Names**

Write the chemical formulas for (**a**) potassium sulfide, (**b**) calcium hydrogen carbonate, (**c**) nickel(II) perchlorate.

**SOLUTION**

In going from the name of an ionic compound to its chemical formula, you must know the charges of the ions to determine the subscripts.

(**a**) The potassium ion is $K^+$, and the sulfide ion is $S^{2-}$. Because ionic compounds are electrically neutral, two $K^+$ ions are required to balance the charge of one $S^{2-}$ ion, giving $K_2S$ for the empirical formula.

**(b)** The calcium ion is $Ca^{2+}$. The carbonate ion is $CO_3^{2-}$, so the hydrogen carbonate ion is $HCO_3^-$. Two $HCO_3^-$ ions are needed to balance the positive charge of $Ca^{2+}$, giving $Ca(HCO_3)_2$.

**(c)** The nickel(II) ion is $Ni^{2+}$. The perchlorate ion is $ClO_4^-$. Two $ClO_4^-$ ions are required to balance the charge on one $Ni^{2+}$ ion, giving $Ni(ClO_4)_2$.

**PRACTICE EXERCISE**
Give the chemical formulas for **(a)** magnesium sulfate, **(b)** silver sulfide, **(c)** lead(II) nitrate.
**Answers:** (a) $MgSO_4$, (b) $Ag_2S$, (c) $Pb(NO_3)_2$

## Names and Formulas of Acids

Acids are an important class of hydrogen-containing compounds, and they are named in a special way. For our present purposes, an *acid* is a substance whose molecules yield hydrogen ions ($H^+$) when dissolved in water. When we encounter the chemical formula for an acid at this stage of the course, it will be written with H as the first element, as in HCl and $H_2SO_4$.

An acid is composed of an anion connected to enough $H^+$ ions to neutralize, or balance, the anion's charge. Thus, the $SO_4^{2-}$ ion requires two $H^+$ ions, forming $H_2SO_4$. The name of an acid is related to the name of its anion, as summarized in ▼ **FIGURE 2.26**.

1. *Acids containing anions whose names end in -ide are named by changing the -ide ending to -ic, adding the prefix* hydro- *to this anion name, and then following with the word* acid:

| Anion | Corresponding Acid |
|---|---|
| $Cl^-$ (chloride) | HCl (hydrochloric acid) |
| $S^{2-}$ (sulfide) | $H_2S$ (hydrosulfuric acid) |

2. *Acids containing anions whose names end in -ate or -ite are named by changing -ate to -ic and -ite to -ous and then adding the word* acid. *Prefixes in the anion name are retained in the name of the acid:*

| Anion | Corresponding Acid |
|---|---|
| $ClO_4^-$ (perchlorate) | $HClO_4$ (perchloric acid) |
| $ClO_3^-$ (chlorate) | $HClO_3$ (chloric acid) |
| $ClO_2^-$ (chlorite) | $HClO_2$ (chlorous acid) |
| $ClO^-$ (hypochlorite) | HClO (hypochlorous acid) |

▶ **FIGURE 2.26 How anion names and acid names relate.** The prefixes *per-* and *hypo-* are retained in going from the anion to the acid.

▲ GIVE IT SOME THOUGHT

Name the acid obtained by adding $H^+$ to the iodate ion, $IO_3^-$.

---

**SAMPLE EXERCISE 2.14** **Relating the Names and Formulas of Acids**

Name the acids (**a**) HCN, (**b**) $HNO_3$, (**c**) $H_2SO_4$, (**d**) $H_2SO_3$.

**SOLUTION**

(**a**) The anion from which this acid is derived is $CN^-$, the cyanide ion. Because this ion has an -ide ending, the acid is given a *hydro-* prefix and an *-ic* ending: hydrocyanic acid. Only water solutions of HCN are referred to as hydrocyanic acid. The pure compound, which is a gas under normal conditions, is called hydrogen cyanide. Both hydrocyanic acid and hydrogen cyanide are *extremely* toxic.

(**b**) Because $NO_3^-$ is the nitrate ion, $HNO_3$ is called nitric acid (the *-ate* ending of the anion is replaced with an *-ic* ending in naming the acid).

(**c**) Because $SO_4^{2-}$ is the sulfate ion, $H_2SO_4$ is called sulfuric acid.

(**d**) Because $SO_3^{2-}$ is the sulfite ion, $H_2SO_3$ is sulfurous acid (the *-ite* ending of the anion is replaced with an *-ous* ending).

**PRACTICE EXERCISE**

Give the chemical formulas for (**a**) hydrobromic acid, (**b**) carbonic acid.

**Answers:** (**a**) HBr, (**b**) $H_2CO_3$

---

## Names and Formulas of Binary Molecular Compounds

The procedures used for naming *binary* (two-element) molecular compounds are similar to those used for naming ionic compounds:

1. *The name of the element farther to the left in the periodic table (closest to the metals) is usually written first.* An exception occurs when the compound contains oxygen and chlorine, bromine, or iodine (any halogen except fluorine), in which case oxygen is written last.

2. *If both elements are in the same group, the lower one is named first.*

3. *The name of the second element is given an* -ide *ending.*

4. *Greek prefixes* (▶ TABLE 2.6) are used to indicate the number of atoms of each element. The prefix *mono-* is never used with the first element. When the prefix ends in *a* or *o* and the name of the second element begins with a vowel, the *a* or *o* of the prefix is often dropped.

The following examples illustrate these rules:

| | | | |
|---|---|---|---|
| $Cl_2O$ | dichlorine monoxide | $NF_3$ | nitrogen trifluoride |
| $N_2O_4$ | dinitrogen tetroxide | $P_4S_{10}$ | tetraphosphorus decasulfide |

Rule 4 is necessary because we cannot predict formulas for most molecular substances the way we can for ionic compounds. Molecular compounds that contain hydrogen and one other element are an important exception, however. These compounds can be treated as if they were neutral substances containing $H^+$ ions and anions. Thus, you can predict that the substance named hydrogen chloride has the formula HCl, containing one $H^+$ to balance the charge of one $Cl^-$. (The name hydrogen chloride is used only for the pure compound; water solutions of HCl are called hydrochloric acid.) Similarly, the formula for hydrogen sulfide is $H_2S$ because two $H^+$ are needed to balance the charge on $S^{2-}$.

**TABLE 2.6** • **Prefixes Used in Naming Binary Compounds Formed between Nonmetals**

| Prefix | Meaning |
|---|---|
| *Mono-* | *1* |
| *Di-* | *2* |
| *Tri-* | *3* |
| *Tetra-* | *4* |
| *Penta-* | *5* |
| *Hexa-* | *6* |
| *Hepta-* | *7* |
| *Octa-* | *8* |
| *Nona-* | *9* |
| *Deca-* | *10* |

| SAMPLE EXERCISE 2.15 | Relating the Names and Formulas of Binary Molecular Compounds |
|---|---|

Name the compounds (a) $SO_2$, (b) $PCl_5$, (c) $Cl_2O_3$.

**SOLUTION**

The compounds consist entirely of nonmetals, so they are molecular rather than ionic. Using the prefixes in Table 2.6, we have (a) sulfur dioxide, (b) phosphorus pentachloride, and (c) dichlorine trioxide.

**PRACTICE EXERCISE**

Give the chemical formulas for (a) silicon tetrabromide, (b) disulfur dichloride.

*Answers:*  (a) $SiBr_4$, (b) $S_2Cl_2$

# 2.9 | SOME SIMPLE ORGANIC COMPOUNDS

The study of compounds of carbon is called **organic chemistry**, and as noted earlier, compounds that contain carbon and hydrogen, often in combination with oxygen, nitrogen, or other elements, are called *organic compounds*. We will examine organic compounds in Chapter 24, but here we present a brief introduction to some of the simplest organic compounds.

## Alkanes

Compounds that contain only carbon and hydrogen are called **hydrocarbons**. In the simplest class of hydrocarbons, **alkanes**, each carbon is bonded to four other atoms. The three smallest alkanes are methane ($CH_4$), ethane ($C_2H_6$), and propane ($C_3H_8$). The structural formulas of these three alkanes are as follows:

Methane            Ethane            Propane

Although hydrocarbons are binary molecular compounds, they are not named like the binary inorganic compounds discussed in Section 2.8. Instead, each alkane has a name that ends in *-ane*. The alkane with four carbons is called *butane*. For alkanes with five or more carbons, the names are derived from prefixes like those in Table 2.6. An alkane with eight carbon atoms, for example, is *octane* ($C_8H_{18}$), where the *octa-* prefix for eight is combined with the *-ane* ending for an alkane.

## Some Derivatives of Alkanes

Other classes of organic compounds are obtained when one or more hydrogen atoms in an alkane are replaced with *functional groups*, which are specific groups of atoms. An **alcohol**, for example, is obtained by replacing an H atom of an alkane with an —OH group. The name of the alcohol is derived from that of the alkane by adding an *-ol* ending:

Methanol            Ethanol            1-Propanol

Alcohols have properties that are very different from the properties of the alkanes from which the alcohols are obtained. For example, methane, ethane, and propane are all colorless gases under normal conditions, whereas methanol, ethanol, and propanol are colorless liquids. We will discuss the reasons for these differences in Chapter 11.

The prefix "1" in the name 1-propanol indicates that the replacement of H with OH has occurred at one of the "outer" carbon atoms rather than the "middle" carbon atom. A different compound, called either 2-propanol or isopropyl alcohol, is obtained when the OH functional group is attached to the middle carbon atom (▶ **FIGURE 2.27**).

Compounds with the same molecular formula but different arrangements of atoms are called **isomers**. There are many different kinds of isomers, as we will discover later in this book. What we have here with 1-propanol and 2-propanol are *structural isomers,* compounds having the same molecular formula but different structural formulas.

OH group on end carbon

1-Propanol

### ⚠ GIVE IT SOME THOUGHT

Draw the structural formulas of the two isomers of butane, $C_4H_{10}$.

Much of the richness of organic chemistry is possible because organic compounds can form long chains of carbon–carbon bonds. The series of alkanes that begins with methane, ethane, and propane and the series of alcohols that begins with methanol, ethanol, and propanol can both be extended for as long as we desire, in principle. The properties of alkanes and alcohols change as the chains get longer. Octanes, which are alkanes with eight carbon atoms, are liquids under normal conditions. If the alkane series is extended to tens of thousands of carbon atoms, we obtain *polyethylene,* a solid substance that is used to make thousands of plastic products, such as plastic bags, food containers, and laboratory equipment.

OH group on middle carbon

2-Propanol

▲ **FIGURE 2.27** **The two forms (isomers) of propanol.**

---

| SAMPLE EXERCISE 2.16 | Writing Structural and Molecular Formulas for Hydrocarbons |

Assuming the carbon atoms in *pentane* are in a linear chain, write **(a)** the structural formula and **(b)** the molecular formula for this alkane.

#### SOLUTION

**(a)** Alkanes contain only carbon and hydrogen, and each carbon is attached to four other atoms. The name pentane contains the prefix *penta-* for five (Table 2.6), and we are told that the carbons are in a linear chain. If we then add enough hydrogen atoms to make four bonds to each carbon, we obtain the structural formula

$$
\begin{array}{ccccc}
\text{H} & \text{H} & \text{H} & \text{H} & \text{H} \\
| & | & | & | & | \\
\text{H}\!-\!\text{C}\!-\!\text{C}\!-\!\text{C}\!-\!\text{C}\!-\!\text{C}\!-\!\text{H} \\
| & | & | & | & | \\
\text{H} & \text{H} & \text{H} & \text{H} & \text{H}
\end{array}
$$

This form of pentane is often called *n*-pentane, where the *n*- stands for "normal" because all five carbon atoms are in one line in the structural formula.

**(b)** Once the structural formula is written, we determine the molecular formula by counting the atoms present. Thus, *n*-pentane has the molecular formula $C_5H_{12}$.

#### PRACTICE EXERCISE

**(a)** What is the molecular formula of butane, the alkane with four carbons? **(b)** What are the name and molecular formula of an alcohol derived from butane?

***Answers:*** **(a)** $C_4H_{10}$, **(b)** butanol, $C_4H_{10}O$ or $C_4H_9OH$

---

# CHAPTER SUMMARY AND KEY TERMS

**SECTIONS 2.1 AND 2.2** **Atoms** are the basic building blocks of matter. They are the smallest units of an element that can combine with other elements. Atoms are composed of even smaller particles, called **subatomic particles.** Some of these subatomic particles are charged and follow the usual behavior of charged particles: Particles with the same charge repel one another, whereas particles with unlike charges are attracted to one another. We considered some of the important experiments that led to the discovery and characterization of subatomic particles. Thomson's experiments on the behavior of

**cathode rays** in magnetic and electric fields led to the discovery of the electron and allowed its charge-to-mass ratio to be measured. Millikan's oil-drop experiment determined the charge of the electron. Becquerel's discovery of **radioactivity,** the spontaneous emission of radiation by atoms, gave further evidence that the atom has a substructure. Rutherford's studies of how thin metal foils scatter $\alpha$ particles led to the **nuclear model** of the atom, showing that the atom has a dense, positively charged **nucleus.**

**SECTION 2.3**    Atoms have a nucleus that contains **protons** and **neutrons; electrons** move in the space around the nucleus. The magnitude of the charge of the electron, $1.602 \times 10^{-19}$ C, is called the **electronic charge**. The charges of particles are usually represented as multiples of this charge—an electron has a $1-$ charge, and a proton has a $1+$ charge. The masses of atoms are usually expressed in terms of **atomic mass units** ($1$ amu $= 1.66054 \times 10^{-24}$ g). The dimensions of atoms are often expressed in units of **angstroms** ($1$ Å $= 10^{-10}$ m).

Elements can be classified by **atomic number**, the number of protons in the nucleus of an atom. All atoms of a given element have the same atomic number. The **mass number** of an atom is the sum of the numbers of protons and neutrons. Atoms of the same element that differ in mass number are known as **isotopes**.

**SECTION 2.4**    The atomic mass scale is defined by assigning a mass of exactly 12 amu to a $^{12}$C atom. The **atomic weight** (average atomic mass) of an element can be calculated from the relative abundances and masses of that element's isotopes. The **mass spectrometer** provides the most direct and accurate means of experimentally measuring atomic (and molecular) weights.

**SECTION 2.5**    The **periodic table** is an arrangement of the elements in order of increasing atomic number. Elements with similar properties are placed in vertical columns. The elements in a column are known as a **group**. The elements in a horizontal row are known as a **period**. The **metallic elements** (**metals**), which comprise the majority of the elements, dominate the left side and the middle of the table; the **nonmetallic elements** (**nonmetals**) are located on the upper right side. Many of the elements that lie along the line that separates metals from nonmetals are **metalloids**.

**SECTION 2.6**    Atoms can combine to form **molecules**. Compounds composed of molecules (**molecular compounds**) usually contain only nonmetallic elements. A molecule that contains two atoms is called a **diatomic molecule**. The composition of a substance is given by its **chemical formula**. A molecular substance can be represented by its **empirical formula**, which gives the relative numbers of atoms of each kind. It is usually represented by its **molecular formula**, however, which gives the actual numbers of each type of atom in a molecule.

**Structural formulas** show the order in which the atoms in a molecule are connected. Ball-and-stick models and space-filling models are often used to represent molecules.

**SECTION 2.7**    Atoms can either gain or lose electrons, forming charged particles called **ions**. Metals tend to lose electrons, becoming positively charged ions (**cations**). Nonmetals tend to gain electrons, forming negatively charged ions (**anions**). Because **ionic compounds** are electrically neutral, containing both cations and anions, they usually contain both metallic and nonmetallic elements. Atoms that are joined together, as in a molecule, but carry a net charge are called **polyatomic ions**. The chemical formulas used for ionic compounds are empirical formulas, which can be written readily if the charges of the ions are known. The total positive charge of the cations in an ionic compound equals the total negative charge of the anions.

**SECTION 2.8**    The set of rules for naming chemical compounds is called **chemical nomenclature**. We studied the systematic rules used for naming three classes of inorganic substances: ionic compounds, acids, and binary molecular compounds. In naming an ionic compound, the cation is named first and then the anion. Cations formed from metal atoms have the same name as the metal. If the metal can form cations of differing charges, the charge is given using Roman numerals. Monatomic anions have names ending in -*ide*. Polyatomic anions containing oxygen and another element (**oxyanions**) have names ending in -*ate* or -*ite*.

**SECTION 2.9**    **Organic chemistry** is the study of compounds that contain carbon. The simplest class of organic molecules is the **hydrocarbons**, which contain only carbon and hydrogen. Hydrocarbons in which each carbon atom is attached to four other atoms are called **alkanes**. Alkanes have names that end in -*ane*, such as methane and ethane. Other organic compounds are formed when an H atom of a hydrocarbon is replaced with a functional group. An **alcohol**, for example, is a compound in which an H atom of a hydrocarbon is replaced by an OH functional group. Alcohols have names that end in -*ol*, such as methanol and ethanol. Compounds with the same molecular formula but a different bonding arrangement of their constituent atoms are called **isomers**.

# KEY SKILLS

- Describe the basic postulates of Dalton's atomic theory. (Section 2.1)
- Describe the key experiments that led to the discovery of electrons and to the nuclear model of the atom. (Section 2.2)
- Describe the structure of the atom in terms of protons, neutrons, and electrons. (Section 2.3)
- Describe the electrical charge and relative masses of protons, neutrons, and electrons. (Section 2.3)
- Use chemical symbols together with atomic number and mass number to express the subatomic composition of isotopes. (Section 2.3)
- Understand how atomic weights relate to the masses of individual atoms and to their natural abundances. (Section 2.4)
- Describe how elements are organized in the periodic table by atomic number and by similarities in chemical behavior, giving rise to periods and groups. (Section 2.5)
- Describe the locations of metals and nonmetals in the periodic table. (Section 2.5)
- Distinguish between molecular substances and ionic substances in terms of their composition. (Sections 2.6 and 2.7)
- Distinguish between empirical formulas and molecular formulas. (Section 2.6)
- Describe how molecular formulas and structural formulas are used to represent the compositions of molecules. (Section 2.6)
- Explain how ions are formed by the gain or loss of electrons and be able to use the periodic table to predict the charges of common ions. (Section 2.7)
- Write the empirical formulas of ionic compounds, given the charges of their component ions. (Section 2.7)
- Write the name of an ionic compound given its chemical formula, or write the chemical formula given its name. (Section 2.8)
- Name or write chemical formulas for binary inorganic compounds and for acids. (Section 2.8)
- Identify organic compounds and name simple alkanes and alcohols. (Section 2.9)

# EXERCISES

## VISUALIZING CONCEPTS

These exercises are intended to probe your understanding of key concepts rather than your ability to utilize formulas and perform calculations. Exercises with red exercise numbers have answers in the back of the book.

2.1 A charged particle is caused to move between two electrically charged plates, as shown here.

(a) Why does the path of the charged particle bend? (b) What is the sign of the electrical charge on the particle? (c) As the charge on the plates is increased, would you expect the bending to increase, decrease, or stay the same? (d) As the mass of the particle is increased while the speed of the particles remains the same, would you expect the bending to increase, decrease, or stay the same? [Section 2.2]

2.2 The following diagram is a representation of 20 atoms of a fictitious element, which we will call nevadium (Nv). The red spheres are $^{293}$Nv, and the blue spheres are $^{295}$Nv. (a) Assuming that this sample is a statistically representative sample of the element, calculate the percent abundance of each element. (b) If the mass of $^{293}$Nv is 293.15 amu and that of $^{295}$Nv is 295.15 amu, what is the atomic weight of Nv? [Section 2.4]

2.3 Four of the boxes in the following periodic table are colored. Which of these are metals and which are nonmetals? Which one is an alkaline earth metal? Which one is a noble gas? [Section 2.5]

2.4 Does the following drawing represent a neutral atom or an ion? Write its complete chemical symbol including mass number, atomic number, and net charge (if any). [Sections 2.3 and 2.7]

— 16 protons + 16 neutrons
— 18 electrons

2.5 Which of the following diagrams most likely represents an ionic compound, and which represents a molecular one? Explain your choice. [Sections 2.6 and 2.7]

(i)

(ii)

2.6 Write the chemical formula for the following compound. Is the compound ionic or molecular? Name the compound. [Sections 2.6 and 2.8]

2.7 Five of the boxes in the following periodic table are colored. Predict the charge on the ion associated with each of these elements. [Section 2.7]

2.8 The following diagram represents an ionic compound in which the red spheres represent cations and blue spheres represent anions. Which of the following formulas is consistent with the drawing: KBr, $K_2SO_4$, $Ca(NO_3)_2$, $Fe_2(SO_4)_3$? Name the compound. [Sections 2.7 and 2.8]

These exercises are divided into sections that deal with specific topics in the chapter. The exercises are grouped in pairs, with the answers given in the back of the book to the odd-numbered exercises, as indicated by the red exercise numbers. Those exercises whose numbers appear in brackets are more challenging than the nonbracketed exercises.

# ATOMIC THEORY AND THE DISCOVERY OF ATOMIC STRUCTURE (sections 2.1–2.2)

**2.9** How does Dalton's atomic theory account for the fact that when 1.000 g of water is decomposed into its elements, 0.111 g of hydrogen and 0.889 g of oxygen are obtained regardless of the source of the water?

**2.10** Hydrogen sulfide is composed of two elements: hydrogen and sulfur. In an experiment, 6.500 g of hydrogen sulfide is fully decomposed into its elements. **(a)** If 0.384 g of hydrogen is obtained in this experiment, how many grams of sulfur must be obtained? **(b)** What fundamental law does this experiment demonstrate? **(c)** How is this law explained by Dalton's atomic theory?

**2.11** A chemist finds that 30.82 g of nitrogen will react with 17.60 g, 35.20 g, 70.40 g, or 88.00 g of oxygen to form four different compounds. **(a)** Calculate the mass of oxygen per gram of nitrogen in each compound. **(b)** How do the numbers in part (a) support Dalton's atomic theory?

**2.12** In a series of experiments, a chemist prepared three different compounds that contain only iodine and fluorine and determined the mass of each element in each compound:

| Compound | Mass of Iodine (g) | Mass of Fluorine (g) |
|----------|--------------------|--------------------|
| 1 | 4.75 | 3.56 |
| 2 | 7.64 | 3.43 |
| 3 | 9.41 | 9.86 |

**(a)** Calculate the mass of fluorine per gram of iodine in each compound. **(b)** How do the numbers in part (a) support the atomic theory?

**2.13** Summarize the evidence used by J. J. Thomson to argue that cathode rays consist of negatively charged particles.

**2.14** An unknown particle is caused to move between two electrically charged plates, as illustrated in Figure 2.8. Its path is deflected by a smaller magnitude in the opposite direction from that of a beta particle. What can you conclude about the charge and mass of this unknown particle?

**2.15** How did Rutherford interpret the following observations made during his α-particle scattering experiments? **(a)** Most α particles were not appreciably deflected as they passed through the gold foil. **(b)** A few α particles were deflected at very large angles. **(c)** What differences would you expect if beryllium foil were used instead of gold foil in the α-particle scattering experiment?

**2.16** Millikan determined the charge on the electron by studying the static charges on oil drops falling in an electric field (Figure 2.5). A student carried out this experiment using several oil drops for her measurements and calculated the charges on the drops. She obtained the following data:

| Droplet | Calculated Charge (C) |
|---------|------------------------|
| A | $1.60 \times 10^{-19}$ |
| B | $3.15 \times 10^{-19}$ |
| C | $4.81 \times 10^{-19}$ |
| D | $6.31 \times 10^{-19}$ |

**(a)** What is the significance of the fact that the droplets carried different charges? **(b)** What conclusion can the student draw from these data regarding the charge of the electron? **(c)** What value (and to how many significant figures) should she report for the electronic charge?

# MODERN VIEW OF ATOMIC STRUCTURE; ATOMIC WEIGHTS (sections 2.3–2.4)

**2.17** The radius of an atom of gold (Au) is about 1.35 Å. **(a)** Express this distance in nanometers (nm) and in picometers (pm). **(b)** How many gold atoms would have to be lined up to span 1.0 mm? **(c)** If the atom is assumed to be a sphere, what is the volume in $cm^3$ of a single Au atom?

**2.18** An atom of rhodium (Rh) has a diameter of about $2.7 \times 10^{-8}$ cm. **(a)** What is the radius of a rhodium atom in angstroms (Å) and in meters (m)? **(b)** How many Rh atoms would have to be placed side by side to span a distance of 6.0 μm? **(c)** If you assume that the Rh atom is a sphere, what is the volume in $m^3$ of a single atom?

**2.19** Answer the following questions without referring to Table 2.1: **(a)** What are the main subatomic particles that make up the atom? **(b)** What is the relative charge (in multiples of the electronic charge) of each of the particles? **(c)** Which of the particles is the most massive? **(d)** Which is the least massive?

**2.20** Determine whether each of the following statements is true or false. If false, correct the statement to make it true: **(a)** The nucleus has most of the mass and comprises most of the volume of an atom. **(b)** Every atom of a given element has the same number of protons. **(c)** The number of electrons in an atom equals the number of neutrons in the atom. **(d)** The protons in the nucleus of the helium atom are held together by a force called the strong nuclear force.

**2.21** **(a)** Define atomic number and mass number. **(b)** Which of these can vary without changing the identity of the element?

**2.22** **(a)** Which two of the following are isotopes of the same element: $^{31}_{16}X$, $^{31}_{15}X$, $^{32}_{16}X$? **(b)** What is the identity of the element whose isotopes you have selected?

**2.23** How many protons, neutrons, and electrons are in the following atoms: **(a)** $^{40}Ar$, **(b)** $^{65}Zn$, **(c)** $^{70}Ga$, **(d)** $^{80}Br$, **(e)** $^{184}W$, **(f)** $^{243}Am$?

**2.24** Each of the following isotopes is used in medicine. Indicate the number of protons and neutrons in each isotope: (a) phosphorus-32, (b) chromium-51, (c) cobalt-60, (d) technetium-99, (e) iodine-131, (f) thallium-201.

**2.25** Fill in the gaps in the following table, assuming each column represents a neutral atom.

| Symbol | $^{52}Cr$ | | | | |
|---|---|---|---|---|---|
| Protons | | 25 | | | 82 |
| Neutrons | | 30 | 64 | | |
| Electrons | | | 48 | 86 | |
| Mass no. | | | | 222 | 207 |

**2.26** Fill in the gaps in the following table, assuming each column represents a neutral atom.

| Symbol | $^{65}Zn$ | | | | |
|---|---|---|---|---|---|
| Protons | | 38 | | | 92 |
| Neutrons | | 58 | 49 | | |
| Electrons | | | 38 | 36 | |
| Mass no. | | | | 81 | 235 |

**2.27** Write the correct symbol, with both superscript and subscript, for each of the following. Use the list of elements inside the front cover as needed: (a) the isotope of platinum that contains 118 neutrons, (b) the isotope of krypton with mass number 84, (c) the isotope of arsenic with mass number 75, (d) the isotope of magnesium that has an equal number of protons and neutrons.

**2.28** One way in which Earth's evolution as a planet can be understood is by measuring the amounts of certain isotopes in rocks. One quantity recently measured is the ratio of $^{129}Xe$ to $^{130}Xe$ in some minerals. In what way do these two isotopes differ from one another? In what respects are they the same?

**2.29** (a) What isotope is used as the standard in establishing the atomic mass scale? (b) The atomic weight of boron is reported as 10.81, yet no atom of boron has the mass of 10.81 amu. Explain.

**2.30** (a) What is the mass in amu of a carbon-12 atom? (b) Why is the atomic weight of carbon reported as 12.011 in the table of elements and the periodic table in the front inside cover of this text?

**2.31** Only two isotopes of copper occur naturally, $^{63}Cu$ (atomic mass = 62.9296 amu; abundance 69.17%) and $^{65}Cu$ (atomic mass = 64.9278 amu; abundance 30.83%). Calculate the atomic weight (average atomic mass) of copper.

**2.32** Rubidium has two naturally occurring isotopes, rubidium-85 (atomic mass = 84.9118 amu; abundance = 72.15%) and rubidium-87 (atomic mass = 86.9092 amu; abundance = 27.85%). Calculate the atomic weight of rubidium.

**2.33** (a) In what fundamental way is mass spectrometry related to Thomson's cathode-ray experiments (Figure 2.4)? (b) What are the labels on the axes of a mass spectrum? (c) To measure the mass spectrum of an atom, the atom must first lose one or more electrons. Why is this so?

**2.34** (a) The mass spectrometer in Figure 2.12 has a magnet as one of its components. What is the purpose of the magnet? (b) The atomic weight of Cl is 35.5 amu. However, the mass spectrum of Cl (Figure 2.13) does not show a peak at this mass. Explain. (c) A mass spectrum of phosphorus (P) atoms shows only a single peak at a mass of 31. What can you conclude from this observation?

**2.35** Naturally occurring magnesium has the following isotopic abundances:

| Isotope | Abundance | Atomic mass (amu) |
|---|---|---|
| $^{24}Mg$ | 78.99 % | 23.98504 |
| $^{25}Mg$ | 10.00 % | 24.98584 |
| $^{26}Mg$ | 11.01 % | 25.98259 |

(a) What is the average atomic mass of Mg? (b) Sketch the mass spectrum of Mg.

**2.36** Mass spectrometry is more often applied to molecules than to atoms. We will see in Chapter 3 that the *molecular weight* of a molecule is the sum of the atomic weights of the atoms in the molecule. The mass spectrum of $H_2$ is taken under conditions that prevent decomposition into H atoms. The two naturally occurring isotopes of hydrogen are $^1H$ (atomic mass = 1.00783 amu; abundance 99.9885%) and $^2H$ (atomic mass = 2.01410 amu; abundance 0.0115%). (a) How many peaks will the mass spectrum have? (b) Give the relative atomic masses of each of these peaks. (c) Which peak will be the largest and which the smallest?

# THE PERIODIC TABLE; MOLECULES AND IONS (sections 2.5–2.7)

**2.37** For each of the following elements, write its chemical symbol, locate it in the periodic table, give its atomic number, and indicate whether it is a metal, metalloid, or nonmetal: (a) chromium, (b) helium, (c) phosphorus, (d) zinc, (e) magnesium, (f) bromine, (g) arsenic.

**2.38** Locate each of the following elements in the periodic table; give its name and atomic number, and indicate whether it is a metal, metalloid, or nonmetal: (a) Li, (b) Sc, (c) Ge, (d) Yb, (e) Mn, (f) Sb, (g) Xe.

**2.39** For each of the following elements, write its chemical symbol, determine the name of the group to which it belongs (Table 2.3), and indicate whether it is a metal, metalloid, or nonmetal: (a) potassium, (b) iodine, (c) magnesium, (d) argon, (e) sulfur.

**2.40** The elements of group 4A show an interesting change in properties moving down the group. Give the name and chemical symbol of each element in the group and label it as a nonmetal, metalloid, or metal.

**2.41** What can we tell about a compound when we know the empirical formula? What additional information is conveyed by the molecular formula? By the structural formula? Explain in each case.

**2.42** Two compounds have the same empirical formula. One substance is a gas, whereas the other is a viscous liquid. How is it possible for two substances with the same empirical formula to have markedly different properties?

**2.43** Write the empirical formula corresponding to each of the following molecular formulas: (a) $Al_2Br_6$, (b) $C_8H_{10}$, (c) $C_4H_8O_2$, (d) $P_4O_{10}$, (e) $C_6H_4Cl_2$, (f) $B_3N_3H_6$.

**2.44** Determine the molecular and empirical formulas of the following: **(a)** the organic solvent *benzene*, which has six carbon atoms and six hydrogen atoms; **(b)** the compound *silicon tetrachloride*, which has a silicon atom and four chlorine atoms and is used in the manufacture of computer chips; **(c)** the reactive substance *diborane*, which has two boron atoms and six hydrogen atoms; **(d)** the sugar called *glucose*, which has six carbon atoms, twelve hydrogen atoms, and six oxygen atoms.

**2.45** How many hydrogen atoms are in each of the following: **(a)** $C_2H_5OH$, **(b)** $Ca(CH_3COO)_2$, **(c)** $(NH_4)_3PO_4$?

**2.46** How many of the indicated atoms are represented by each chemical formula: **(a)** carbon atoms in $C_2H_5COOCH_3$, **(b)** oxygen atoms in $Ca(ClO_4)_2$, **(c)** hydrogen atoms in $(NH_4)_2HPO_4$?

**2.47** Write the molecular and structural formulas for the compounds represented by the following molecular models:

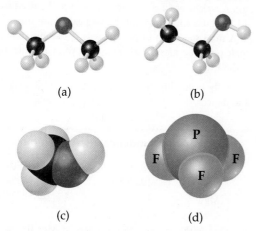

(a)  (b)

(c)  (d)

**2.48** Write the molecular and structural formulas for the compounds represented by the following models:

(a)  (b)

(c)  (d)

**2.49** Fill in the gaps in the following table:

| Symbol | $^{59}Co^{3+}$ | | | |
|---|---|---|---|---|
| Protons | | 34 | 76 | 80 |
| Neutrons | | 46 | 116 | 120 |
| Electrons | | 36 | | 78 |
| Net charge | | | 2+ | |

**2.50** Fill in the gaps in the following table:

| Symbol | $^{31}P^{3-}$ | | | |
|---|---|---|---|---|
| Protons | | 34 | 50 | |
| Neutrons | | 45 | 69 | 118 |
| Electrons | | | 46 | 76 |
| Net charge | | 2− | | 3+ |

**2.51** Each of the following elements is capable of forming an ion in chemical reactions. By referring to the periodic table, predict the charge of the most stable ion of each: **(a)** Mg, **(b)** Al, **(c)** K, **(d)** S, **(e)** F.

**2.52** Using the periodic table, predict the charges of the ions of the following elements: **(a)** Ga, **(b)** Sr, **(c)** As, **(d)** Br, **(e)** Se.

**2.53** Using the periodic table to guide you, predict the chemical formula and name of the compound formed by the following elements: **(a)** Ga and F, **(b)** Li and H, **(c)** Al and I, **(d)** K and S.

**2.54** The most common charge associated with scandium in its compounds is 3+. Indicate the chemical formulas you would expect for compounds formed between scandium and **(a)** iodine, **(b)** sulfur, **(c)** nitrogen.

**2.55** Predict the chemical formula for the ionic compound formed by **(a)** $Ca^{2+}$ and $Br^-$, **(b)** $K^+$ and $CO_3^{2-}$, **(c)** $Al^{3+}$ and $CH_3COO^-$, **(d)** $NH_4^+$ and $SO_4^{2-}$, **(e)** $Mg^{2+}$ and $PO_4^{3-}$.

**2.56** Predict the chemical formulas of the compounds formed by the following pairs of ions: **(a)** $Cr^{3+}$ and $Br^-$, **(b)** $Fe^{3+}$ and $O^{2-}$, **(c)** $Hg_2^{2+}$ and $CO_3^{2-}$, **(d)** $Ca^{2+}$ and $ClO_3^-$, **(e)** $NH_4^+$ and $PO_4^{3-}$.

**2.57** Complete the table by filling in the formula for the ionic compound formed by each pair of cations and anions, as shown for the first pair.

| Ion | $K^+$ | $NH_4^+$ | $Mg^{2+}$ | $Fe^{3+}$ |
|---|---|---|---|---|
| $Cl^-$ | KCl | | | |
| $OH^-$ | | | | |
| $CO_3^{2-}$ | | | | |
| $PO_4^{3-}$ | | | | |

**2.58** Complete the table by filling in the formula for the ionic compound formed by each pair of cations and anions, as shown for the first pair.

| Ion | $Na^+$ | $Ca^{2+}$ | $Fe^{2+}$ | $Al^{3+}$ |
|---|---|---|---|---|
| $O^{2-}$ | $Na_2O$ | | | |
| $NO_3^-$ | | | | |
| $SO_4^{2-}$ | | | | |
| $AsO_4^{3-}$ | | | | |

**2.59** Predict whether each of the following compounds is molecular or ionic: **(a)** $B_2H_6$, **(b)** $CH_3OH$, **(c)** $LiNO_3$, **(d)** $Sc_2O_3$, **(e)** CsBr, **(f)** NOCl, **(g)** $NF_3$, **(h)** $Ag_2SO_4$.

**2.60** Which of the following are ionic, and which are molecular? **(a)** $PF_5$, **(b)** NaI, **(c)** $SCl_2$, **(d)** $Ca(NO_3)_2$, **(e)** $FeCl_3$, **(f)** LaP, **(g)** $CoCO_3$, **(h)** $N_2O_4$.

# NAMING INORGANIC COMPOUNDS; ORGANIC MOLECULES
## (sections 2.8–2.9)

**2.61** Give the chemical formula for (a) chlorite ion, (b) chloride ion, (c) chlorate ion, (d) perchlorate ion, (e) hypochlorite ion.

**2.62** Selenium, an element required nutritionally in trace quantities, forms compounds analogous to sulfur. Name the following ions: (a) $SeO_4^{2-}$, (b) $Se^{2-}$, (c) $HSe^-$, (d) $HSeO_3^-$.

**2.63** Give the names and charges of the cation and anion in each of the following compounds: (a) $CaO$, (b) $Na_2SO_4$, (c) $KClO_4$, (d) $Fe(NO_3)_2$, (e) $Cr(OH)_3$.

**2.64** Give the names and charges of the cation and anion in each of the following compounds: (a) $CuS$, (b) $Ag_2SO_4$, (c) $Al(ClO_3)_3$, (d) $Co(OH)_2$, (e) $PbCO_3$.

**2.65** Name the following ionic compounds: (a) $Li_2O$, (b) $FeCl_3$, (c) $NaClO$, (d) $CaSO_3$, (e) $Cu(OH)_2$, (f) $Fe(NO_3)_2$, (g) $Ca(CH_3COO)_2$, (h) $Cr_2(CO_3)_3$, (i) $K_2CrO_4$, (j) $(NH_4)_2SO_4$.

**2.66** Name the following ionic compounds: (a) $KCN$, (b) $NaBrO_2$, (c) $Sr(OH)_2$, (d) $CoS$, (e) $Fe_2(CO_3)_3$, (f) $Cr(NO_3)_3$, (g) $(NH_4)_2SO_3$, (h) $NaH_2PO_4$, (i) $KMnO_4$, (j) $Ag_2Cr_2O_7$.

**2.67** Write the chemical formulas for the following compounds: (a) aluminum hydroxide, (b) potassium sulfate, (c) copper(I) oxide, (d) zinc nitrate, (e) mercury(II) bromide, (f) iron(III) carbonate, (g) sodium hypobromite.

**2.68** Give the chemical formula for each of the following ionic compounds: (a) sodium phosphate, (b) zinc nitrate, (c) barium bromate, (d) iron(II) perchlorate, (e) cobalt(II) hydrogen carbonate, (f) chromium(III) acetate, (g) potassium dichromate.

**2.69** Give the name or chemical formula, as appropriate, for each of the following acids: (a) $HBrO_3$, (b) $HBr$, (c) $H_3PO_4$, (d) hypochlorous acid, (e) iodic acid, (f) sulfurous acid.

**2.70** Provide the name or chemical formula, as appropriate, for each of the following acids: (a) hydroiodic acid, (b) chloric acid, (c) nitrous acid, (d) $H_2CO_3$, (e) $HClO_4$, (f) $CH_3COOH$.

**2.71** Give the name or chemical formula, as appropriate, for each of the following binary molecular substances: (a) $SF_6$, (b) $IF_5$, (c) $XeO_3$, (d) dinitrogen tetroxide, (e) hydrogen cyanide, (f) tetraphosphorus hexasulfide.

**2.72** The oxides of nitrogen are very important components in urban air pollution. Name each of the following compounds: (a) $N_2O$, (b) $NO$, (c) $NO_2$, (d) $N_2O_5$, (e) $N_2O_4$.

**2.73** Write the chemical formula for each substance mentioned in the following word descriptions (use the front inside cover to find the symbols for the elements you don't know). (a) Zinc carbonate can be heated to form zinc oxide and carbon dioxide. (b) On treatment with hydrofluoric acid, silicon dioxide forms silicon tetrafluoride and water. (c) Sulfur dioxide reacts with water to form sulfurous acid. (d) The substance phosphorus trihydride, commonly called phosphine, is a toxic gas. (e) Perchloric acid reacts with cadmium to form cadmium(II) perchlorate. (f) Vanadium(III) bromide is a colored solid.

**2.74** Assume that you encounter the following sentences in your reading. What is the chemical formula for each substance mentioned? (a) Sodium hydrogen carbonate is used as a deodorant. (b) Calcium hypochlorite is used in some bleaching solutions. (c) Hydrogen cyanide is a very poisonous gas. (d) Magnesium hydroxide is used as a cathartic. (e) Tin(II) fluoride has been used as a fluoride additive in toothpastes. (f) When cadmium sulfide is treated with sulfuric acid, fumes of hydrogen sulfide are given off.

**2.75** (a) What is a hydrocarbon? (b) Butane is the alkane with a chain of four carbon atoms. Write a structural formula for this compound and determine its molecular and empirical formulas.

**2.76** (a) What ending is used for the names of alkanes? (b) Hexane is an alkane whose structural formula has all its carbon atoms in a straight chain. Draw the structural formula for this compound and determine its molecular and empirical formulas. (*Hint:* You might need to refer to Table 2.6.)

**2.77** (a) What is a functional group? (b) What functional group characterizes an alcohol? (c) With reference to Exercise 2.75, write a structural formula for 1-butanol, the alcohol derived from butane, by making a substitution on one of the carbon atoms.

**2.78** (a) What do ethane and ethanol have in common? (b) How does 1-propanol differ from propane?

**2.79** Chloropropane is a compound derived from propane by substituting Cl for H on one of the carbon atoms. (a) Draw the structural formulas for the two isomers of chloropropane. (b) Suggest names for these two compounds.

**2.80** Draw the structural formulas for three isomers of pentane, $C_5H_{12}$.

# ADDITIONAL EXERCISES

These exercises are not divided by category, although they are roughly in the order of the topics in the chapter. They are not paired.

**2.81** Suppose a scientist repeats the Millikan oil-drop experiment but reports the charges on the drops using an unusual (and imaginary) unit called the *warmomb* (wa). The scientist obtains the following data for four of the drops:

(a) If all the droplets were the same size, which would fall most slowly through the apparatus? (b) From these data, what is the best choice for the charge of the electron in warmombs?

| Droplet | Calculated Charge (wa) |
| --- | --- |
| A | $3.84 \times 10^{-8}$ |
| B | $4.80 \times 10^{-8}$ |
| C | $2.88 \times 10^{-8}$ |
| D | $8.64 \times 10^{-8}$ |

(c) Based on your answer to part (b), how many electrons are there on each of the droplets? (d) What is the conversion factor between warmombs and coulombs?

**2.82** The natural abundance of $^3$He is 0.000137%. **(a)** How many protons, neutrons, and electrons are in an atom of $^3$He? **(b)** Based on the sum of the masses of their subatomic particles, which is expected to be more massive, an atom of $^3$He or an atom of $^3$H (which is also called *tritium*)? **(c)** Based on your answer to part (b), what would need to be the precision of a mass spectrometer that is able to differentiate between peaks that are due to $^3$He$^+$ and $^3$H$^+$?

**2.83** A cube of gold that is 1.00 cm on a side has a mass of 19.3 g. A single gold atom has a mass of 197.0 amu. **(a)** How many gold atoms are in the cube? **(b)** From the information given, estimate the diameter in Å of a single gold atom. **(c)** What assumptions did you make in arriving at your answer for part (b)?

**2.84** The diameter of a rubidium atom is 4.95 Å. We will consider two different ways of placing the atoms on a surface. In arrangement A, all the atoms are lined up with one another to form a square grid. Arrangement B is called a *close-packed* arrangement because the atoms sit in the "depressions" formed by the previous row of atoms:

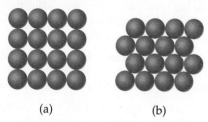

(a)                    (b)

**(a)** Using arrangement A, how many Rb atoms could be placed on a square surface that is 1.0 cm on a side? **(b)** How many Rb atoms could be placed on a square surface that is 1.0 cm on a side, using arrangement B? **(c)** By what factor has the number of atoms on the surface increased in going to arrangement B from arrangement A? If extended to three dimensions, which arrangement would lead to a greater density for Rb metal?

**2.85** **(a)** Assuming the dimensions of the nucleus and atom shown in Figure 2.11, what fraction of the *volume* of the atom is taken up by the nucleus? **(b)** Using the mass of the proton from Table 2.1 and assuming its diameter is $1.0 \times 10^{-15}$ m, calculate the density of a proton in g/cm$^3$.

**2.86** Identify the element represented by each of the following symbols and give the number of protons and neutrons in each: **(a)** $^{74}_{33}$X, **(b)** $^{127}_{53}$X, **(c)** $^{152}_{63}$X, **(d)** $^{209}_{83}$X.

**2.87** The element oxygen has three naturally occurring isotopes, with 8, 9, and 10 neutrons in the nucleus, respectively. **(a)** Write the full chemical symbols for these three isotopes. **(b)** Describe the similarities and differences between the three kinds of atoms of oxygen.

**2.88** Use Coulomb's law, $F = kQ_1Q_2/d^2$, to calculate the electric force on an electron ($Q = -1.6 \times 10^{-19}$ C) exerted by a single proton if the particles are $0.53 \times 10^{-10}$ m apart. The constant $k$ in Coulomb's law is $9.0 \times 10^9$ N·m$^2$/C$^2$. (The unit abbreviated N is the newton, the SI unit of force.)

**2.89** The element lead (Pb) consists of four naturally occurring isotopes with atomic masses 203.97302, 205.97444, 206.97587, and 207.97663 amu. The relative abundances of these four iso-

topes are 1.4, 24.1, 22.1, and 52.4%, respectively. From these data, calculate the atomic weight of lead.

**2.90** Gallium (Ga) consists of two naturally occurring isotopes with masses of 68.926 and 70.925 amu. **(a)** How many protons and neutrons are in the nucleus of each isotope? Write the complete atomic symbol for each, showing the atomic number and mass number. **(b)** The average atomic mass of Ga is 69.72 amu. Calculate the abundance of each isotope.

**2.91** Using a suitable reference such as the *CRC Handbook of Chemistry and Physics* or http://www.webelements.com, look up the following information for nickel: **(a)** the number of known isotopes, **(b)** the atomic masses (in amu) and **(c)** the natural abundances of the five most abundant isotopes.

**2.92** There are two different isotopes of bromine atoms. Under normal conditions, elemental bromine consists of Br$_2$ molecules, and the mass of a Br$_2$ molecule is the sum of the masses of the two atoms in the molecule. The mass spectrum of Br$_2$ consists of three peaks:

| Mass (amu) | Relative Size |
|---|---|
| 157.836 | 0.2569 |
| 159.834 | 0.4999 |
| 161.832 | 0.2431 |

**(a)** What is the origin of each peak (of what isotopes does each consist)? **(b)** What is the mass of each isotope? **(c)** Determine the average molecular mass of a Br$_2$ molecule. **(d)** Determine the average atomic mass of a bromine atom. **(e)** Calculate the abundances of the two isotopes.

**2.93** It is common in mass spectrometry to assume that the mass of a cation is the same as that of its parent atom. **(a)** Using data in Table 2.1, determine the number of significant figures that must be reported before the difference in mass of $^1$H and $^1$H$^+$ is significant. **(b)** What percentage of the mass of an $^1$H atom does the electron represent?

**2.94** From the following list of elements—Ar, H, Ga, Al, Ca, Br, Ge, K, O—pick the one that best fits each description. Use each element only once: **(a)** an alkali metal, **(b)** an alkaline earth metal, **(c)** a noble gas, **(d)** a halogen, **(e)** a metalloid, **(f)** a nonmetal listed in group 1A, **(g)** a metal that forms a 3+ ion, **(h)** a nonmetal that forms a 2− ion, **(i)** an element that resembles aluminum.

**2.95** The first atoms of seaborgium (Sg) were identified in 1974. The longest-lived isotope of Sg has a mass number of 266. **(a)** How many protons, electrons, and neutrons are in an $^{266}$Sg atom? **(b)** Atoms of Sg are very unstable, and it is therefore difficult to study this element's properties. Based on the position of Sg in the periodic table, what element should it most closely resemble in its chemical properties?

**2.96** The explosion of an atomic bomb releases many radioactive isotopes, including strontium-90. Considering the location of strontium in the periodic table, suggest a reason for the fact that this isotope is particularly harmful to humans.

**2.97** From the molecular structures shown here, identify the one that corresponds to each of the following species: (a) chlorine gas, (b) propane, (c) nitrate ion, (d) sulfur trioxide, (e) methyl chloride, $CH_3Cl$.

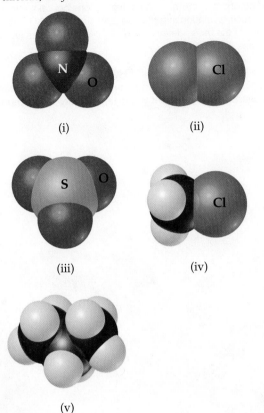

**2.98** Name each of the following oxides. Assuming that the compounds are ionic, what charge is associated with the metallic element in each case? (a) NiO, (b) $MnO_2$, (c) $Cr_2O_3$, (d) $MoO_3$.

**2.99** Fill in the blanks in the following table:

| Cation | Anion | Formula | Name |
|---|---|---|---|
| | | | Lithium oxide |
| $Fe^{2+}$ | $PO_4^{3-}$ | | |
| | | $Al_2(SO_4)_3$ | |
| | | | Copper(II) nitrate |
| $Cr^{3+}$ | $I^-$ | | |
| | | $MnClO_2$ | |
| | | | Ammonium carbonate |
| | | | Zinc perchlorate |

**2.100** Iodic acid has the molecular formula $HIO_3$. Write the formulas for the following: (a) the iodate anion, (b) the periodate anion, (c) the hypoiodite anion, (d) hypoiodous acid, (e) periodic acid.

**2.101** Elements in the same group of the periodic table often form oxyanions with the same general formula. The anions are also named in a similar fashion. Based on these observations, suggest a chemical formula or name, as appropriate, for each of the following ions: (a) $BrO_4^-$, (b) $SeO_3^{2-}$, (c) arsenate ion, (d) hydrogen tellurate ion.

**2.102** Carbonic acid occurs in carbonated beverages. When allowed to react with lithium hydroxide it produces lithium carbonate. Lithium carbonate is used to treat depression and bipolar disorder. Write chemical formulas for carbonic acid, lithium hydroxide, and lithium carbonate.

**2.103** Give the chemical names of each of the following familiar compounds: (a) NaCl (table salt), (b) $NaHCO_3$ (baking soda), (c) NaOCl (in many bleaches), (d) NaOH (caustic soda), (e) $(NH_4)_2CO_3$ (smelling salts), (f) $CaSO_4$ (plaster of Paris).

**2.104** Many familiar substances have common, unsystematic names. For each of the following, give the correct systematic name: (a) saltpeter, $KNO_3$; (b) soda ash, $Na_2CO_3$; (c) lime, CaO; (d) muriatic acid, HCl; (e) Epsom salts, $MgSO_4$; (f) milk of magnesia, $Mg(OH)_2$.

**2.105** Because many ions and compounds have very similar names, there is great potential for confusing them. Write the correct chemical formulas to distinguish between (a) calcium sulfide and calcium hydrogen sulfide, (b) hydrobromic acid and bromic acid, (c) aluminum nitride and aluminum nitrite, (d) iron(II) oxide and iron(III) oxide, (e) ammonia and ammonium ion, (f) potassium sulfite and potassium bisulfite, (g) mercurous chloride and mercuric chloride, (h) chloric acid and perchloric acid.

**2.106** The compound *cyclohexane* is an alkane in which six carbon atoms form a ring. The partial structural formula of the compound is as follows:

(a) Complete the structural formula for cyclohexane. (b) Is the molecular formula for cyclohexane the same as that for *n*-hexane, in which the carbon atoms are in a straight line? If possible, comment on the source of any differences. (c) Propose a structural formula for *cyclohexanol*, the alcohol derived from cyclohexane.

# WHAT'S AHEAD

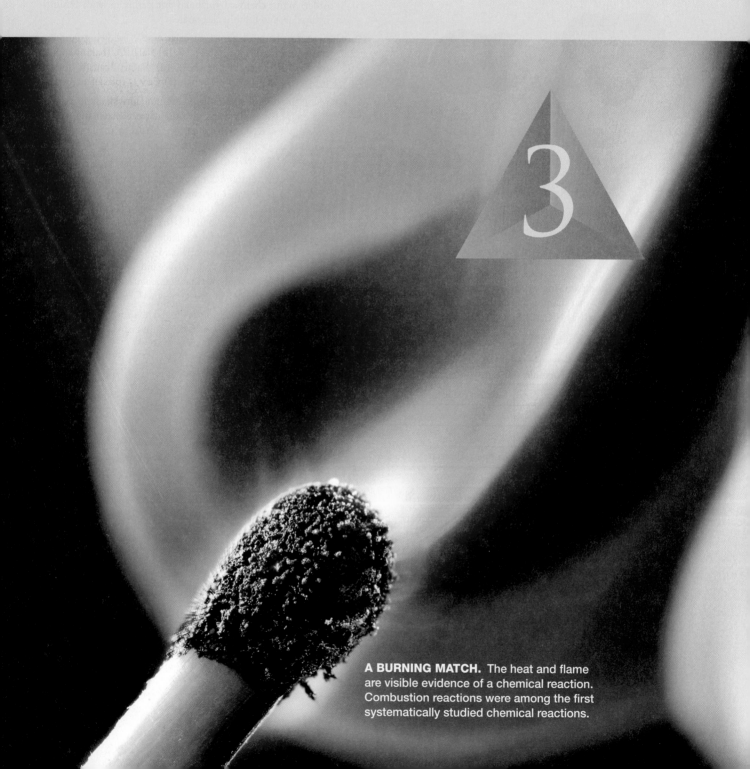

**A BURNING MATCH.** The heat and flame are visible evidence of a chemical reaction. Combustion reactions were among the first systematically studied chemical reactions.

**3.6 QUANTITATIVE INFORMATION FROM BALANCED EQUATIONS**

We use the quantitative information inherent in chemical formulas and equations together with the mole concept to predict the amounts of substances consumed or produced in chemical reactions.

**3.7 LIMITING REACTANTS**

We recognize that one reactant may be used up before others in a chemical reaction. This is the *limiting reactant*. The reaction stops, leaving some excess starting material.

# STOICHIOMETRY: CALCULATIONS WITH CHEMICAL FORMULAS AND EQUATIONS

**YOU POUR VINEGAR INTO** a glass of water containing baking soda and bubbles form. You strike a match and use the flame to light a candle. You heat sugar in a pan and it turns brown. The bubbles, flame, and color change are visual evidence that something is happening.

To an experienced eye, these visual changes indicate a chemical change, or chemical reaction. Some chemical changes are simple; others are complex. Some are dramatic; some are very subtle. Even as you sit reading this chapter, chemical changes are occurring in your body. Those occurring in your eyes and brain, for example, allow you to see these words and think about them. Although not as obvious as those we see

▲ **FIGURE 3.1 Antoine Lavoisier (1734–1794).** The science career of Lavoisier, who conducted many important studies on combustion reactions, was cut short by the French Revolution. Guillotined in 1794 during the Reign of Terror, he is generally considered the father of modern chemistry because he conducted carefully controlled experiments and used quantitative measurements.

in the laboratory, the chemical changes taking place in our bodies are nevertheless remarkable for how they allow us to function.

In this chapter we explore some important aspects of chemical change. Our focus will be both on the use of chemical formulas to represent reactions and on the quantitative information we can obtain about the amounts of substances involved in reactions. **Stoichiometry** (pronounced stoy-key-OM-uh-tree) is the area of study that examines the quantities of substances consumed and produced in chemical reactions. Stoichiometry (Greek *stoicheion,* "element," and *metron,* "measure") provides an essential set of tools widely used in chemistry, including such diverse applications as measuring ozone concentrations in the atmosphere and assessing different processes for converting coal into gaseous fuels.

Stoichiometry is built on an understanding of atomic masses ∞ (Section 2.4), chemical formulas, and the law of conservation of mass. ∞ (Section 2.1) The French nobleman and scientist Antoine Lavoisier (◄ **FIGURE 3.1**) discovered this important chemical law during the late 1700s. Lavoisier stated the law in this eloquent way: "We may lay it down as an incontestable axiom that, in all the operations of art and nature, nothing is created; an equal quantity of matter exists both before and after the experiment. Upon this principle, the whole art of performing chemical experiments depends." With the advent of Dalton's atomic theory, chemists came to understand the basis for this law: *Atoms are neither created nor destroyed during a chemical reaction.* The changes that occur during any reaction merely rearrange the atoms. The same collection of atoms is present both before and after the reaction.

# 3.1 | CHEMICAL EQUATIONS

We represent chemical reactions by **chemical equations**. When the gas hydrogen ($H_2$) burns, for example, it reacts with oxygen ($O_2$) in the air to form water ($H_2O$). We write the chemical equation for this reaction as

$$2\,H_2 + O_2 \longrightarrow 2\,H_2O \qquad\qquad [3.1]$$

We read the + sign as "reacts with" and the arrow as "produces." The chemical formulas to the left of the arrow represent the starting substances, called **reactants**. The chemical formulas to the right of the arrow represent substances produced in the reaction, called **products**. The numbers in front of the formulas, called *coefficients,* indicate the relative numbers of molecules of each kind involved in the reaction. (As in algebraic equations, *the coefficient 1 is usually not written.*)

Because atoms are neither created nor destroyed in any reaction, a chemical equation must have an equal number of atoms of each element on each side of the arrow. When this condition is met, the equation is *balanced.* On the right side of Equation 3.1, for example, there are two molecules of $H_2O$, each composed of two atoms of hydrogen and one atom of oxygen (◄ **FIGURE 3.2**). Thus, 2 $H_2O$ (read "two molecules of water") contains $2 \times 2 = 4$ H atoms and $2 \times 1 = 2$ O atoms. Notice that *the number of atoms is obtained by multiplying each subscript in a chemical formula by the coefficient for the formula.* Because there are four H atoms and two O atoms on each side of the equation, the equation is balanced.

⚠ **GIVE IT SOME THOUGHT**
How many atoms of Mg, O, and H are represented by the notation 3 $Mg(OH)_2$?

## Balancing Equations

Once we know the formulas of the reactants and products in a reaction, we can write an unbalanced equation. We then balance the equation by determining the coefficients that provide equal numbers of each type of atom on the two sides of the equation. For most purposes, a balanced equation should contain the smallest possible whole-number coefficients.

Reactants                     Products

$2\,H_2 + O_2 \longrightarrow 2\,H_2O$

▲ **FIGURE 3.2 A balanced chemical equation.**

⚠️ GO FIGURE

**What is the difference in atom count between the notation $CO_2$ and the notation 2 CO?**

$H_2O$

Changing coefficient changes amount → $2 H_2O$ — 2 molecules water (contain 4 H atoms and 2 O atoms)

Changing subscript changes composition and identity → $H_2O_2$ — 1 molecule hydrogen peroxide (contains 2 H atoms and 2 O atoms)

▲ **FIGURE 3.3** The difference between changing subscripts and changing coefficients in chemical equations.

In balancing an equation, you need to understand the difference between coefficients and subscripts. As ▲ **FIGURE 3.3** illustrates, changing a subscript in a formula—from $H_2O$ to $H_2O_2$, for example—changes the identity of the substance. The substance $H_2O_2$, hydrogen peroxide, is quite different from the substance $H_2O$, water. *Never change subscripts when balancing an equation.* In contrast, placing a coefficient in front of a formula changes only the *amount* of the substance and not its *identity*. Thus, $2 H_2O$ means two molecules of water, $3 H_2O$ means three molecules of water, and so forth.

To illustrate the process of balancing an equation, consider the reaction that occurs when methane ($CH_4$), the principal component of natural gas, burns in air to produce carbon dioxide gas ($CO_2$) and water vapor ($H_2O$) (▼ **FIGURE 3.4**). Both products contain oxygen atoms that come from $O_2$ in the air. Thus, $O_2$ is a reactant, and the unbalanced equation is

$$CH_4 + O_2 \longrightarrow CO_2 + H_2O \quad \text{(unbalanced)} \qquad [3.2]$$

It is usually best to balance first those elements that occur in the fewest chemical formulas in the equation. In our example, C appears in only one reactant ($CH_4$) and one product ($CO_2$). The same is true for H ($CH_4$ and $H_2O$). Notice, however, that O appears in one reactant ($O_2$) and two products ($CO_2$ and $H_2O$). So, let's begin with C. Because one molecule of $CH_4$ contains the same number of C atoms (one) as one molecule of $CO_2$ the coefficients for these substances *must* be the same in the balanced equation. Therefore, we start by choosing the coefficient 1 (unwritten) for both $CH_4$ and $CO_2$.

**Reactants** **Products**

$CH_4$ $O_2$ $CO_2$ and $H_2O$

▲ **FIGURE 3.4** Methane reacts with oxygen in a Bunsen burner.

$$CH_4 \quad + \quad 2\,O_2 \quad \longrightarrow \quad CO_2 \quad + \quad 2\,H_2O$$

1 C, 4 H, 4 O                    1 C, 4 H, 4 O

▲ **FIGURE 3.5** **Balanced chemical equation for the combustion of $CH_4$.**

Next we focus on H. Because $CH_4$ contains four H atoms and $H_2O$ contains two H atoms, we balance the H atoms by placing the coefficient 2 in front of $H_2O$. There are then four H atoms on each side of the equation:

$$CH_4 + O_2 \longrightarrow CO_2 + 2\,H_2O \quad \text{(unbalanced)} \qquad [3.3]$$

Finally, a coefficient 2 in front of $O_2$ balances the equation by giving four O atoms on each side ($2 \times 2$ left, $2 + 2 \times 1$ right):

$$CH_4 + 2\,O_2 \longrightarrow CO_2 + 2\,H_2O \quad \text{(balanced)} \qquad [3.4]$$

The molecular view of the balanced equation is shown in ◄ **FIGURE 3.5**.

---

**SAMPLE EXERCISE 3.1** | **Interpreting and Balancing Chemical Equations**

The following diagram represents a chemical reaction in which the red spheres are oxygen atoms and the blue spheres are nitrogen atoms. (**a**) Write the chemical formulas for the reactants and products. (**b**) Write a balanced equation for the reaction. (**c**) Is the diagram consistent with the law of conservation of mass?

**SOLUTION**

(**a**) The left box, which represents reactants, contains two kinds of molecules, those composed of two oxygen atoms ($O_2$) and those composed of one nitrogen atom and one oxygen atom (NO). The right box, which represents products, contains only molecules composed of one nitrogen atom and two oxygen atoms ($NO_2$).

(**b**) The unbalanced chemical equation is

$$O_2 + NO \longrightarrow NO_2 \quad \text{(unbalanced)}$$

An inventory of atoms on each side of the equation shows that there are one N and three O on the left side of the arrow and one N and two O on the right. To balance O we must increase the number of O atoms on the right while keeping the coefficients for NO and $NO_2$ equal. Sometimes we need to go back and forth several times from one side of an equation to the other, changing coefficients first on one side of the equation and then the other until it is balanced. In our present case, we can increase the number of O atoms by placing the coefficient 2 in front of $NO_2$:

$$O_2 + NO \longrightarrow 2\,NO_2 \quad \text{(unbalanced)}$$

That gives two N atoms and four O atoms on the right, so we go back to the left side. Placing the coefficient 2 in front of NO balances both N and O:

$$O_2 + 2\,NO \longrightarrow 2\,NO_2 \text{ (balanced)}$$

2 N, 4 O          2 N, 4 O

(**c**) The reactants box contains four $O_2$ and eight NO. Thus, the molecular ratio is one $O_2$ for each two NO, as required by the balanced equation. The products box contains eight $NO_2$, which means the number of $NO_2$ product molecules equals the number of NO reactant molecules, as the balanced equation requires.

There are eight N atoms in the eight NO molecules in the reactants box. There are also $4 \times 2 = 8$ O atoms in the $O_2$ molecules and eight O atoms in the NO molecules, giving a total of 16 O atoms. In the products box, we find eight N atoms and $8 \times 2 = 16$ O atoms in the eight $NO_2$ molecules. Because there are equal numbers of N and O atoms in the two boxes, the drawing is consistent with the law of conservation of mass.

**PRACTICE EXERCISE**

In the following diagram, the white spheres represent hydrogen atoms and the blue spheres represent nitrogen atoms.

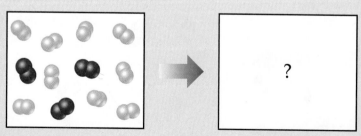

To be consistent with the law of conservation of mass, how many $NH_3$ molecules should be shown in the right (products) box?

***Answer:*** Six $NH_3$ molecules

## Indicating the States of Reactants and Products

Symbols indicating the physical state of each reactant and product are often shown in chemical equations. We use the symbols $(g)$, $(l)$, $(s)$, and $(aq)$ for gas, liquid, solid, and aqueous (water) solution, respectively. Thus, Equation 3.4 can be written

$$CH_4(g) + 2\,O_2(g) \longrightarrow CO_2(g) + 2\,H_2O(g) \qquad [3.5]$$

Sometimes the conditions under which the reaction proceeds appear above or below the reaction arrow. The symbol $\Delta$ (Greek uppercase delta) above the arrow indicates addition of heat.

---

**SAMPLE EXERCISE 3.2**   **Balancing Chemical Equations**

Balance the equation

$$Na(s) + H_2O(l) \longrightarrow NaOH(aq) + H_2(g)$$

**SOLUTION**

Begin by counting each kind of atom on the two sides of the arrow. There are one Na, one O, and two H on the left side, and one Na, one O, and three H on the right. To increase the number of H atoms on the left, let's try placing the coefficient 2 in front of $H_2O$:

Although beginning this way does not balance H, it does increase the number of reactant H atoms, which we need to do. (Also, adding the coefficient 2 on $H_2O$ unbalances O, but we will take care of that after we balance H.) Now that we have 2 $H_2O$ on the left, we balance H by putting the coefficient 2 in front of NaOH:

Balancing H in this way brings O into balance, but now Na is unbalanced, with one Na on the left and two on the right. To rebalance Na, we put the coefficient 2 in front of the reactant:

$$Na(s) + 2\,H_2O(l) \longrightarrow NaOH(aq) + H_2(g)$$

$$Na(s) + 2\,H_2O(l) \longrightarrow 2\,NaOH(aq) + H_2(g)$$

$$2\,Na(s) + 2\,H_2O(l) \longrightarrow 2\,NaOH(aq) + H_2(g)$$

We now have two Na atoms, four H atoms, and two O atoms on each side. The equation is balanced.

**Comment** Notice that we moved back and forth, placing a coefficient in front of $H_2O$, then NaOH, and finally Na. In balancing equations, we often find ourselves following this pattern of moving back and forth from one side of the arrow to the other, placing coefficients first in front of a formula on one side and then in front of a formula on the other side until the equation is balanced. You can always tell if you have balanced your equation correctly by checking that the number of atoms of each element is the same on the two sides of the arrow.

**PRACTICE EXERCISE**

Balance these equations by providing the missing coefficients:

**(a)** __ Fe$(s)$ + __ O$_2(g)$ $\longrightarrow$ __ Fe$_2$O$_3(s)$
**(b)** __ C$_2$H$_4(g)$ + __ O$_2(g)$ $\longrightarrow$ __ CO$_2(g)$ + __ H$_2$O$(g)$
**(c)** __ Al$(s)$ + __ HCl$(aq)$ $\longrightarrow$ __ AlCl$_3(aq)$ + __ H$_2(g)$

**Answers:**  **(a)** 4, 3, 2; **(b)** 1, 3, 2, 2; **(c)** 2, 6, 2, 3

---

# 3.2 | SOME SIMPLE PATTERNS OF CHEMICAL REACTIVITY

In this section we examine three types of reactions that we see frequently throughout this chapter: combination reactions, decomposition reactions, and combustion reactions. Our first reason for examining these reactions is to become better acquainted with chemical reactions and their balanced equations. Our second reason is to consider how we might predict the products of some of these reactions knowing only their reactants. The key to predicting the products formed by a given combination of reactants is recognizing general patterns of chemical reactivity. Recognizing a pattern of reactivity for a class of substances gives you a broader understanding than merely memorizing a large number of unrelated reactions.

## Combination and Decomposition Reactions

In **combination reactions** two or more substances react to form one product (▼ TABLE 3.1). For example, magnesium metal burns brilliantly in air to produce magnesium oxide (▼ FIGURE 3.6):

$$2\,Mg(s) + O_2(g) \longrightarrow 2\,MgO(s) \qquad\qquad [3.6]$$

This reaction is used to produce the bright flame generated by flares and some fireworks.

A combination reaction between a metal and a nonmetal, as in Equation 3.6, produces an ionic solid. Recall that the formula of an ionic compound can be determined from the charges of its ions. ∞ (Section 2.7) When magnesium reacts with oxygen, the magnesium loses electrons and forms the magnesium ion, $Mg^{2+}$. The oxygen gains electrons and forms the oxide ion, $O^{2-}$. Thus, the reaction product is MgO.

You should be able to recognize when a reaction is a combination reaction and to predict the products when the reactants are a metal and a nonmetal.

**TABLE 3.1 • Combination and Decomposition Reactions**

**Combination Reactions**

| | |
|---|---|
| $A + B \longrightarrow C$<br>$C(s) + O_2(g) \longrightarrow CO_2(g)$<br>$N_2(g) + 3\,H_2(g) \longrightarrow 2\,NH_3(g)$<br>$CaO(s) + H_2O(l) \longrightarrow Ca(OH)_2(s)$ | Two or more reactants combine to form a single product. Many elements react with one another in this fashion to form compounds. |

**Decomposition Reactions**

| | |
|---|---|
| $C \longrightarrow A + B$<br>$2\,KClO_3(s) \longrightarrow 2\,KCl(s) + 3\,O_2(g)$<br>$PbCO_3(s) \longrightarrow PbO(s) + CO_2(g)$<br>$Cu(OH)_2(s) \longrightarrow CuO(s) + H_2O(l)$ | A single reactant breaks apart to form two or more substances. Many compounds react this way when heated. |

▼ FIGURE 3.6 **Combustion of magnesium metal in air, a combination reaction.**

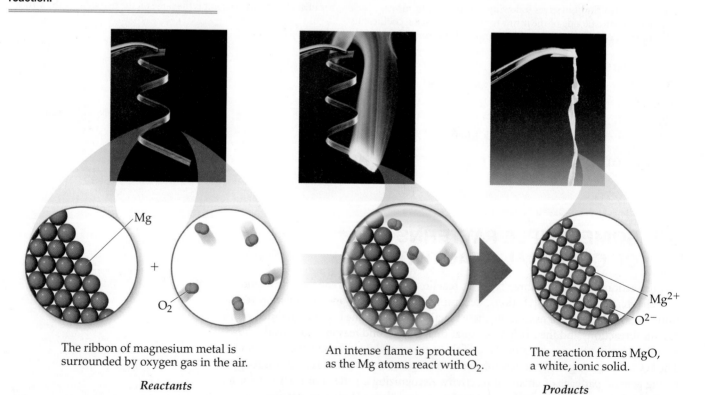

The ribbon of magnesium metal is surrounded by oxygen gas in the air.

An intense flame is produced as the Mg atoms react with $O_2$.

The reaction forms MgO, a white, ionic solid.

*Reactants*

$2\,Mg(s) + O_2(g)$   ⟶   *Products*    $2\,MgO(s)$

Mg

$O_2$

$Mg^{2+}$

$O^{2-}$

GIVE IT SOME THOUGHT

When Na and S undergo a combination reaction, what is the chemical formula of the product?

In a **decomposition reaction** one substance undergoes a reaction to produce two or more other substances (Table 3.1). For example, many metal carbonates decompose to form metal oxides and carbon dioxide when heated:

$$CaCO_3(s) \xrightarrow{\Delta} CaO(s) + CO_2(g) \qquad [3.7]$$

Decomposition of $CaCO_3$ is an important commercial process. Limestone or seashells, which are both primarily $CaCO_3$, are heated to prepare CaO, known as lime or quicklime. About $2 \times 10^{10}$ kg (20 million tons) of CaO is used in the United States each year, principally in making glass, in obtaining iron from its ores, and in making mortar to bind bricks.

The decomposition of sodium azide ($NaN_3$) rapidly releases $N_2(g)$, so this reaction is used to inflate safety air bags in automobiles (▶ **FIGURE 3.7**):

$$2\,NaN_3(s) \longrightarrow 2\,Na(s) + 3\,N_2(g) \qquad [3.8]$$

The system is designed so that an impact ignites a detonator cap, which in turn causes $NaN_3$ to decompose explosively. A small quantity of $NaN_3$ (about 100 g) forms a large quantity of gas (about 50 L).

▲ **FIGURE 3.7   Decomposition of sodium azide, NaN₃(s), is used to inflate automobile air bags.**

---

| **SAMPLE EXERCISE 3.3** | **Writing Balanced Equations for Combination and Decomposition Reactions** |

Write a balanced equation for **(a)** the combination reaction between lithium metal and fluorine gas and **(b)** the decomposition reaction that occurs when solid barium carbonate is heated (two products form, a solid and a gas).

**SOLUTION**

**(a)** With the exception of mercury, all metals are solids at room temperature. Fluorine occurs as a diatomic molecule. Thus, the reactants are Li(s) and $F_2(g)$. The product will be composed of a metal and a nonmetal, so we expect it to be an ionic solid. Lithium ions have a 1+ charge, $Li^+$, whereas fluoride ions have a 1− charge, $F^-$. Thus, the chemical formula for the product is LiF. The balanced chemical equation is

$$2\,Li(s) + F_2(g) \longrightarrow 2\,LiF(s)$$

**(b)** The chemical formula for barium carbonate is $BaCO_3$. As noted in the text, many metal carbonates decompose to metal oxides and carbon dioxide when heated. In Equation 3.7, for example, $CaCO_3$ decomposes to form CaO and $CO_2$. Thus, we expect $BaCO_3$ to decompose to BaO and $CO_2$. Barium and calcium are both in group 2A in the periodic table, which further suggests they react in the same way:

$$BaCO_3(s) \longrightarrow BaO(s) + CO_2(g)$$

**PRACTICE EXERCISE**

Write a balanced equation for **(a)** solid mercury(II) sulfide decomposing into its component elements when heated and **(b)** aluminum metal combining with oxygen in the air.

***Answers:*** **(a)** $HgS(s) \longrightarrow Hg(l) + S(s)$, **(b)** $4\,Al(s) + 3\,O_2(g) \longrightarrow 2\,Al_2O_3(s)$

---

## Combustion Reactions

**Combustion reactions** are rapid reactions that produce a flame. Most combustion reactions we observe involve $O_2$ from air as a reactant. Equation 3.5 illustrates a general class of reactions involving the burning, or combustion, of hydrocarbons (compounds that contain only carbon and hydrogen, such as $CH_4$ and $C_2H_4$). ∞ (Section 2.9)

Hydrocarbons combusted in air react with $O_2$ to form $CO_2$ and $H_2O$.* The number of molecules of $O_2$ required and the number of molecules of $CO_2$ and $H_2O$ formed

---

*When there is an insufficient quantity of $O_2$ present, carbon monoxide (CO) is produced along with $CO_2$; this is called incomplete combustion. If the $O_2$ quantity is severely restricted, the fine particles of carbon we call soot are produced. Complete combustion produces only $CO_2$ and $H_2O$. Unless stated to the contrary, we will always take combustion to mean complete combustion.

◣ GO FIGURE

In what ways are the reactions depicted in Figures 3.4 and 3.8 alike?

▲ FIGURE 3.8 **Propane burning in air.** Liquid propane in the tank, $C_3H_8$, vaporizes and mixes with air as it escapes through the nozzle. The combustion reaction of $C_3H_8$ and $O_2$ produces a blue flame.

depend on the composition of the hydrocarbon, which acts as the fuel in the reaction. For example, the combustion of propane ($C_3H_8$, ◀ FIGURE 3.8), a gas used for cooking and home heating, is described by the equation

$$C_3H_8(g) + 5\,O_2(g) \longrightarrow 3\,CO_2(g) + 4\,H_2O(g) \qquad [3.9]$$

The state of the water in this reaction, $H_2O(g)$ or $H_2O(l)$, depends on the reaction conditions. Water vapor, $H_2O(g)$, is formed at high temperature in an open container.

Combustion of oxygen-containing derivatives of hydrocarbons, such as $CH_3OH$, also produces $CO_2$ and $H_2O$. The rule that hydrocarbons and their oxygen-containing derivatives form $CO_2$ and $H_2O$ when they burn in air summarizes the behavior of about 3 million compounds. Many substances that our bodies use as energy sources, such as the sugar glucose ($C_6H_{12}O_6$), react with $O_2$ to form $CO_2$ and $H_2O$. In our bodies, however, the reactions take place in a series of intermediate steps that occur at body temperature. These reactions that involve intermediate steps are described as *oxidation reactions* instead of combustion reactions.

---

**SAMPLE EXERCISE 3.4** | **Writing Balanced Equations for Combustion Reactions**

Write the balanced equation for the reaction that occurs when methanol, $CH_3OH(l)$, is burned in air.

**SOLUTION**

When any compound containing C, H, and O is combusted, it reacts with the $O_2(g)$ in air to produce $CO_2(g)$ and $H_2O(g)$. Thus, the unbalanced equation is

$$CH_3OH(l) + O_2(g) \longrightarrow CO_2(g) + H_2O(g)$$

The C atoms are balanced, one on each side of the arrow. Because $CH_3OH$ has four H atoms, we place the coefficient 2 in front of $H_2O$ to balance the H atoms:

$$CH_3OH(l) + O_2(g) \longrightarrow CO_2(g) + 2\,H_2O(g)$$

Adding this coefficient balances H but gives four O atoms in the products. Because there are only three O atoms in the reactants, we are not finished. We can place the coefficient $\frac{3}{2}$ in front of $O_2$ to give four O atoms in the reactants ($\frac{3}{2} \times 2 = 3$ O atoms in $\frac{3}{2}\,O_2$):

$$CH_3OH(l) + \tfrac{3}{2}\,O_2(g) \longrightarrow CO_2(g) + 2\,H_2O(g)$$

Although this equation is balanced, it is not in its most conventional form because it contains a fractional coefficient. However, multiplying through by 2 removes the fraction and keeps the equation balanced:

$$2\,CH_3OH(l) + 3\,O_2(g) \longrightarrow 2\,CO_2(g) + 4\,H_2O(g)$$

**PRACTICE EXERCISE**

Write the balanced equation for the reaction that occurs when ethanol, $C_2H_5OH(l)$, burns in air.

***Answer:*** $C_2H_5OH(l) + 3\,O_2(g) \longrightarrow 2\,CO_2(g) + 3\,H_2O(g)$

---

# 3.3 | FORMULA WEIGHTS

Chemical formulas and chemical equations both have a *quantitative* significance in that the subscripts in formulas and the coefficients in equations represent precise quantities. The formula $H_2O$ indicates that a molecule of this substance (water) contains exactly two atoms of hydrogen and one atom of oxygen. Similarly, the coefficients in a balanced chemical equation indicate the relative quantities of reactants and products. But how do we relate the numbers of atoms or molecules to the amounts we measure in the laboratory? Although we cannot directly count atoms or molecules, we can indirectly determine their numbers if we know their masses. Therefore, before we can pursue the quantitative aspects of chemical formulas and equations, we must examine the masses of atoms and molecules.

## Formula and Molecular Weights

The **formula weight** of a substance is the sum of the atomic weights of the atoms in the chemical formula of the substance. Using atomic weights, we find, for example, that the formula weight of sulfuric acid ($H_2SO_4$) is 98.1 amu:*

$$FW \text{ of } H_2SO_4 = 2(AW \text{ of } H) + (AW \text{ of } S) + 4(AW \text{ of } O)$$
$$= 2(1.0 \text{ amu}) + 32.1 \text{ amu} + 4(16.0 \text{ amu})$$
$$= 98.1 \text{ amu}$$

For convenience, we have rounded off the atomic weights to one decimal place, a practice we will follow in most calculations in this book.

If the chemical formula is the chemical symbol of an element, such as Na, the formula weight equals the atomic weight of the element, in this case 23.0 amu. If the chemical formula is that of a molecule, the formula weight is also called the **molecular weight**. The molecular weight of glucose ($C_6H_{12}O_6$), for example, is

$$MW \text{ of } C_6H_{12}O_6 = 6(12.0 \text{ amu}) + 12(1.0 \text{ amu}) + 6(16.0 \text{ amu}) = 180.0 \text{ amu}$$

Because ionic substances exist as three-dimensional arrays of ions (see Figure 2.21), it is inappropriate to speak of molecules of these substances. Instead, we speak of *formula units*. The formula unit of NaCl, for instance, consists of one $Na^+$ ion and one $Cl^-$ ion. Thus, the formula weight of NaCl is defined as the mass of one formula unit:

$$FW \text{ of } NaCl = 23.0 \text{ amu} + 35.5 \text{ amu} = 58.5 \text{ amu}$$

---

**SAMPLE EXERCISE 3.5** | **Calculating Formula Weights**

Calculate the formula weight of (a) sucrose, $C_{12}H_{22}O_{11}$ (table sugar), and (b) calcium nitrate, $Ca(NO_3)_2$.

**SOLUTION**

(a) By adding the atomic weights of the atoms in sucrose, we find the formula weight to be 342.0 amu:

$$12 \text{ C atoms} = 12(12.0 \text{ amu}) = 144.0 \text{ amu}$$
$$22 \text{ H atoms} = 22(1.0 \text{ amu}) = 22.0 \text{ amu}$$
$$11 \text{ O atoms} = 11(16.0 \text{ amu}) = \underline{176.0 \text{ amu}}$$
$$342.0 \text{ amu}$$

(b) If a chemical formula has parentheses, the subscript outside the parentheses is a multiplier for all atoms inside. Thus, for $Ca(NO_3)_2$ we have

$$1 \text{ Ca atom} = 1(40.1 \text{ amu}) = 40.1 \text{ amu}$$
$$2 \text{ N atoms} = 2(14.0 \text{ amu}) = 28.0 \text{ amu}$$
$$6 \text{ O atoms} = 6(16.0 \text{ amu}) = \underline{96.0 \text{ amu}}$$
$$164.1 \text{ amu}$$

**PRACTICE EXERCISE**

Calculate the formula weight of (a) $Al(OH)_3$ and (b) $CH_3OH$.
**Answers:** (a) 78.0 amu, (b) 32.0 amu

---

## Percentage Composition from Chemical Formulas

Chemists must sometimes calculate the *percentage composition* of a compound—that is, the percentage by mass contributed by each element in the substance. Forensic chemists, for example, will measure the percentage composition of an unknown powder and compare it with the percentage compositions for sugar, salt, or cocaine to identify the powder.

Calculating the percentage composition of any element in a substance is straightforward if the chemical formula is known. The calculation depends on the formula weight of the substance, the atomic weight of the element of interest, and the number of atoms of that element in the chemical formula:

$$\% \text{ composition of element} = \frac{\left(\begin{array}{c}\text{number of atoms} \\ \text{of element}\end{array}\right)\left(\begin{array}{c}\text{atomic weight} \\ \text{of element}\end{array}\right)}{\text{formula weight of substance}} \times 100\% \quad [3.10]$$

*The abbreviation AW is used for atomic weight, FW for formula weight, and MW for molecular weight.

**SAMPLE EXERCISE 3.6** | **Calculating Percentage Composition**

Calculate the percentage of carbon, hydrogen, and oxygen (by mass) in $C_{12}H_{22}O_{11}$.

**SOLUTION**

Let's examine this question using the problem-solving steps in the accompanying "Strategies in Chemistry: Problem Solving" essay.

**Analyze** We are given a chemical formula and asked to calculate the percentage by mass of each element.

**Plan** We use Equation 3.10, obtaining our atomic weights from a periodic table. We know the denominator in Equation 3.10, the formula weight of $C_{12}H_{22}O_{11}$, from Sample Exercise 3.5. We must use that value in three calculations, one for each element.

**Solve**

$$\%C = \frac{(12)(12.0\ \text{amu})}{342.0\ \text{amu}} \times 100\% = 42.1\%$$

$$\%H = \frac{(22)(1.0\ \text{amu})}{342.0\ \text{amu}} \times 100\% = 6.4\%$$

$$\%O = \frac{(11)(16.0\ \text{amu})}{342.0\ \text{amu}} \times 100\% = 51.5\%$$

**Check** Our calculated percentages must add up to 100%, which they do. We could have used more significant figures for our atomic weights, giving more significant figures for our percentage composition, but we have adhered to our suggested guideline of rounding atomic weights to one digit beyond the decimal point.

**PRACTICE EXERCISE**

Calculate the percentage of nitrogen, by mass, in $Ca(NO_3)_2$.
*Answer:* 17.1%

# 3.4 | AVOGADRO'S NUMBER AND THE MOLE

Even the smallest samples we deal with in the laboratory contain enormous numbers of atoms, ions, or molecules. For example, a teaspoon of water (about 5 mL) contains $2 \times 10^{23}$ water molecules, a number so large it almost defies comprehension. Chemists therefore have devised a counting unit for describing such large numbers of atoms or molecules.

In everyday life we use such familiar counting units as dozen (12 objects) and gross (144 objects). In chemistry the counting unit for numbers of atoms, ions, or molecules in a laboratory-size sample is the **mole**, abbreviated mol.* One mole is the amount of matter that contains as many objects (atoms, molecules, or whatever other objects we are considering) as the number of atoms in exactly 12 g of isotopically pure $^{12}C$. From experiments, scientists have determined this number to be $6.0221421 \times 10^{23}$, which we will usually round to $6.02 \times 10^{23}$. Scientists call this value **Avogadro's number**, $N_A$, in honor

# STRATEGIES IN CHEMISTRY

## PROBLEM SOLVING

Practice is the key to success in solving problems. As you practice, you can improve your skills by following these steps:

**Step 1: Analyze the problem.** Read the problem carefully. What does it say? Draw a picture or diagram that will help you to visualize the problem. Write down both the data you are given and the quantity you need to obtain (the unknown).

**Step 2: Develop a plan for solving the problem.** Consider a possible path between the given information and the unknown. What principles or equations relate the known data to the unknown?

Recognize that some data may not be given explicitly in the problem; you may be expected to know certain quantities (such as Avogadro's number) or look them up in tables (such as atomic weights). Recognize also that your plan may involve either a single step or a series of steps with intermediate answers.

**Step 3: Solve the problem.** Use the known information and suitable equations or relationships to solve for the unknown. Dimensional analysis ∞ (Section 1.6) is a useful tool for solving a great number of problems. Be careful with significant figures, signs, and units.

**Step 4: Check the solution.** Read the problem again to make sure you have found all the solutions asked for in the problem. Does your answer make sense? That is, is the answer outrageously large or small or is it in the ballpark? Finally, are the units and significant figures correct?

---

*The term *mole* comes from the Latin word *moles*, meaning "a mass." The term *molecule* is the diminutive of this word and means "a small mass."

of the Italian scientist Amedeo Avogadro (1776–1856), and it is often cited with units of reciprocal moles, $6.02 \times 10^{23} \text{ mol}^{-1}$. The unit (read as either "inverse mole" or "per mole") reminds us that there are $6.02 \times 10^{23}$ objects per one mole. A mole of atoms, a mole of molecules, or a mole of anything else all contain Avogadro's number of objects:

$$1 \text{ mol } {}^{12}\text{C atoms} = 6.02 \times 10^{23} \, {}^{12}\text{C atoms}$$

$$1 \text{ mol } H_2O \text{ molecules} = 6.02 \times 10^{23} \, H_2O \text{ molecules}$$

$$1 \text{ mol } NO_3^- \text{ ions} = 6.02 \times 10^{23} \, NO_3^- \text{ ions}$$

Avogadro's number is so large that it is difficult to imagine. Spreading $6.02 \times 10^{23}$ marbles over Earth's surface would produce a layer about 3 miles thick. Avogadro's number of pennies placed side by side in a straight line would encircle Earth 300 trillion ($3 \times 10^{14}$) times.

---

**SAMPLE EXERCISE 3.7    Estimating Numbers of Atoms**

Without using a calculator, arrange these samples in order of increasing numbers of carbon atoms: 12 g $^{12}$C, 1 mol $C_2H_2$, $9 \times 10^{23}$ molecules of $CO_2$.

**SOLUTION**

**Analyze** We are given amounts of three substances expressed in grams, moles, and number of molecules and asked to arrange the samples in order of increasing numbers of C atoms.

**Plan** To determine the number of C atoms in each sample, we must convert 12 g $^{12}$C, 1 mol $C_2H_2$, and $9 \times 10^{23}$ molecules $CO_2$ to numbers of C atoms. To make these conversions, we use the definition of mole and Avogadro's number.

**Solve** One mole is defined as the amount of matter that contains as many units of the matter as there are C atoms in exactly 12 g of $^{12}$C. Thus, 12 g of $^{12}$C contains 1 mol of C atoms = $6.02 \times 10^{23}$ C atoms. One mol of $C_2H_2$ contains $6 \times 10^{23}$ $C_2H_2$ molecules. Because

there are two C atoms in each molecule, this sample contains $12 \times 10^{23}$ C atoms. Because each $CO_2$ molecule contains one C atom, the $CO_2$ sample contains $9 \times 10^{23}$ C atoms. Hence, the order is 12 g $^{12}$C ($6 \times 10^{23}$ C atoms) $< 9 \times 10^{23}$ $CO_2$ molecules ($9 \times 10^{23}$ C atoms) $< 1$ mol $C_2H_2$ ($12 \times 10^{23}$ C atoms).

**Check** We can check our results by comparing numbers of moles of C atoms in the samples because the number of moles is proportional to the number of atoms. Thus, 12 g of $^{12}$C is 1 mol C; 1 mol of $C_2H_2$ contains 2 mol C, and $9 \times 10^{23}$ molecules of $CO_2$ contain 1.5 mol C, giving the same order as stated previously.

**PRACTICE EXERCISE**

Without using a calculator, arrange these samples in order of increasing number of O atoms: 1 mol $H_2O$, 1 mol $CO_2$, $3 \times 10^{23}$ molecules $O_3$.

**Answer:** 1 mol $H_2O$ ($6 \times 10^{23}$ O atoms) $< 3 \times 10^{23}$ molecules $O_3$ ($9 \times 10^{23}$ O atoms) $< 1$ mol $CO_2$ ($12 \times 10^{23}$ O atoms)

---

**SAMPLE EXERCISE 3.8    Converting Moles to Number of Atoms**

Calculate the number of H atoms in 0.350 mol of $C_6H_{12}O_6$.

**SOLUTION**

**Analyze** We are given the amount of a substance (0.350 mol) and its chemical formula $C_6H_{12}O_6$. The unknown is the number of H atoms in the sample.

**Plan** Avogadro's number provides the conversion factor between number of moles of $C_6H_{12}O_6$ and number of molecules of $C_6H_{12}O_6$: 1 mol $C_6H_{12}O_6$ = $6.02 \times 10^{23}$ molecules $C_6H_{12}O_6$. Once we know the number of molecules of $C_6H_{12}O_6$, we can use the chemical formula, which tells us that each molecule of $C_6H_{12}O_6$ contains 12 H atoms. Thus, we convert moles of $C_6H_{12}O_6$ to molecules of $C_6H_{12}O_6$ and then determine the number of atoms of H from the number of molecules of $C_6H_{12}O_6$:

$$\text{Moles } C_6H_{12}O_6 \longrightarrow \text{molecules } C_6H_{12}O_6 \longrightarrow \text{atoms H}$$

**Solve**

$$\text{H atoms} = (0.350 \text{ mol } C_6H_{12}O_6)\left(\frac{6.02 \times 10^{23} \text{ molecules } C_6H_{12}O_6}{1 \text{ mol } C_6H_{12}O_6}\right)$$

$$\times \left(\frac{12 \text{ H atoms}}{1 \text{ molecule } C_6H_{12}O_6}\right) = 2.53 \times 10^{24} \text{ H atoms}$$

**Check** We can do a ballpark calculation: First, $0.35(6 \times 10^{23})$ is about $2 \times 10^{23}$ molecules of $C_6H_{12}O_6$, and each one of these molecules contains 12 H atoms. So $12(2 \times 10^{23})$ gives $24 \times 10^{23} = 2.4 \times 10^{24}$ H atoms, which agrees with our result. Because we were asked for the number of H atoms, the units of our answer are correct. The given data had three significant figures, so our answer has three significant figures.

**PRACTICE EXERCISE**

How many oxygen atoms are in **(a)** 0.25 mol $Ca(NO_3)_2$ and **(b)** 1.50 mol of sodium carbonate?

**Answers:** **(a)** $9.0 \times 10^{23}$, **(b)** $2.71 \times 10^{24}$

How many H₂O molecules are in a 9.00-g sample of water?

Single molecule

Laboratory-size sample

Avogadro's number of molecules (6.02 × 10²³)

1 molecule H₂O
(18.0 amu)

1 mol H₂O
(18.0 g)

▲ FIGURE 3.9 **Comparing the mass of 1 molecule and 1 mol of H₂O.** Both masses have the same number but different units (atomic mass units and grams). Expressing both masses in grams indicates their huge difference: 1 molecule H₂O has a mass of $2.99 \times 10^{-23}$ g whereas 1 mol H₂O has a mass of 18.0 g.

## Molar Mass

A dozen is the same number, 12, whether we have a dozen eggs or a dozen elephants. Clearly, however, a dozen eggs does not have the same mass as a dozen elephants. Similarly, a mole is always the *same number* ($6.02 \times 10^{23}$), but 1-mol samples of different substances have *different masses*. Compare, for example, 1 mol of $^{12}$C and 1 mol of $^{24}$Mg. A single $^{12}$C atom has a mass of 12 amu, whereas a single $^{24}$Mg atom is twice as massive, 24 amu (to two significant figures). Because a mole of anything always contains the same number of particles, a mole of $^{24}$Mg must be twice as massive as a mole of $^{12}$C. Because a mole of $^{12}$C has a mass of 12 g (by definition), a mole of $^{24}$Mg must have a mass of 24 g. This example illustrates a general rule relating the mass of an atom to the mass of Avogadro's number (1 mol) of these atoms: *The atomic weight of an element in atomic mass units is numerically equal to the mass in grams of 1 mol of that element.* For example,

Cl has an atomic weight of 35.5 amu $\Rightarrow$ 1 mol Cl has a mass of 35.5 g

Au has an atomic weight of 197 amu $\Rightarrow$ 1 mol Au has a mass of 197 g

For other kinds of substances, the same numerical relationship exists between formula weight and mass of one mole of a substance:

H₂O has a formula weight of 18.0 amu  $\Rightarrow$ 1 mol H₂O has a mass of 18.0 g

(◀ FIGURE 3.9)

$NO_3^-$ has a formula weight of 62.0 amu $\Rightarrow$ 1 mol $NO_3^-$ has a mass of 62.0 g

NaCl has a formula weight of 58.5 amu $\Rightarrow$ 1 mol NaCl has a mass of 58.5 g

 GIVE IT SOME THOUGHT

**a.** Which has more mass, a mole of water (H₂O) or a mole of glucose ($C_6H_{12}O_6$)?
**b.** Which contains more molecules, a mole of water or a mole of glucose?

The mass in grams of one mole of a substance (that is, the mass in grams per mole) is called the **molar mass** of the substance. *The molar mass in grams per mole of any substance is numerically equal to its formula weight in atomic mass units.* For NaCl, for example, the formula weight is 58.5 amu and the molar mass is 58.5 g/mol. Mole relationships for several other substances are shown in ▼ TABLE 3.2, and ▶ FIGURE 3.10 shows 1-mol quantities of three common substances.

The entries in Table 3.2 for N and N₂ point out the importance of stating the chemical form of a substance when using the mole concept. Suppose you read that 1 mol of nitrogen is produced in a particular reaction. You might interpret this statement to mean 1 mol of nitrogen atoms (14.0 g). Unless otherwise stated, however, what is

**TABLE 3.2 • Mole Relationships**

| Name of Substance | Formula | Formula Weight (amu) | Molar Mass (g/mol) | Number and Kind of Particles in One Mole |
|---|---|---|---|---|
| Atomic nitrogen | N | 14.0 | 14.0 | $6.02 \times 10^{23}$ N atoms |
| Molecular nitrogen | N₂ | 28.0 | 28.0 | $\begin{cases} 6.02 \times 10^{23} \text{ N}_2 \text{ molecules} \\ 2(6.02 \times 10^{23}) \text{ N atoms} \end{cases}$ |
| Silver | Ag | 107.9 | 107.9 | $6.02 \times 10^{23}$ Ag atoms |
| Silver ions | Ag⁺ | 107.9* | 107.9 | $6.02 \times 10^{23}$ Ag⁺ ions |
| Barium chloride | BaCl₂ | 208.2 | 208.2 | $\begin{cases} 6.02 \times 10^{23} \text{ BaCl}_2 \text{ formula units} \\ 6.02 \times 10^{23} \text{ Ba}^{2+} \text{ ions} \\ 2(6.02 \times 10^{23}) \text{ Cl}^- \text{ ions} \end{cases}$ |

*Recall that the electron has negligible mass; thus, ions and atoms have essentially the same mass.

1 mol $O_2(g)$ has a mass of 32.0 g

1 mol $H_2O(l)$ has a mass of 18.0 g

1 mol NaCl($s$) has a mass of 58.45 g

▲ **FIGURE 3.10   One mole each of a solid (NaCl), a liquid (H₂O), and a gas (O₂).** In each case, the mass in grams of 1 mol—that is, the molar mass—is numerically equal to the formula weight in atomic mass units. Each of these samples contains $6.02 \times 10^{23}$ formula units.

probably meant is 1 mol of nitrogen molecules, $N_2$ (28.0 g), because $N_2$ is the most common chemical form of the element. To avoid ambiguity, it is important to state explicitly the chemical form being discussed. Using the chemical formula—N or $N_2$, for instance—avoids ambiguity.

---

**SAMPLE EXERCISE 3.9**   **Calculating Molar Mass**

What is the molar mass of glucose, $C_6H_{12}O_6$?

**SOLUTION**

**Analyze**  We are given a chemical formula and asked to determine its molar mass.

**Plan**  Because the molar mass of any substance is numerically equal to its formula weight, we first determine the formula weight of glucose by adding the atomic weights of its component atoms. The formula weight will have units of amu, whereas the molar mass has units of g/mol.

**Solve**  Our first step is to determine the formula weight of glucose:

$$6 \text{ C atoms} = 6(12.0 \text{ amu}) = 72.0 \text{ amu}$$
$$12 \text{ H atoms} = 12(1.0 \text{ amu}) = 12.0 \text{ amu}$$
$$6 \text{ O atoms} = 6(16.0 \text{ amu}) = \underline{96.0 \text{ amu}}$$
$$180.0 \text{ amu}$$

Because glucose has a formula weight of 180.0 amu, 1 mol of this substance ($6.02 \times 10^{23}$ molecules) has a mass of 180.0 g. In other words, $C_6H_{12}O_6$ has a molar mass of 180.0 g/mol.

**Check**  A magnitude below 250 seems reasonable based on the earlier examples we have encountered, and grams per mole is the appropriate unit for the molar mass.

**Comment**  Glucose, also known as blood sugar, is found in nature in honey and fruits. Other sugars used as food are converted into glucose in the stomach or liver before the body uses them as energy sources. Because glucose requires no conversion, it is often given intravenously to patients who need immediate nourishment.

**PRACTICE EXERCISE**

Calculate the molar mass of $Ca(NO_3)_2$.

**Answer:**  164.1 g/mol

## CHEMISTRY AND LIFE

### GLUCOSE MONITORING

Over 20 million Americans have diabetes, and globally the number approaches 172 million. Diabetes is a metabolic disorder in which the body either cannot produce or cannot properly use the hormone insulin. One signal that a person is diabetic is that the concentration of glucose in the blood is higher than normal. Therefore, people who are diabetic need to measure their blood glucose concentrations regularly. Untreated diabetes can cause severe complications such as blindness and loss of limbs.

The body converts most of the food we eat into glucose. After digestion, glucose is delivered to cells via the blood. Cells need glucose to live, and insulin must be present in order for glucose to enter the cells. Normally, the body adjusts the concentration of insulin automatically, in concert with the glucose concentration after eating. However, in a diabetic person, either little or no insulin is produced (Type 1 diabetes) or insulin is produced but the cells cannot take it up properly (Type 2 diabetes). The result is that the blood glucose concentration is too high. People normally have a range of 70–120 mg glucose per deciliter of blood. A person who has not eaten for 8 hours or more is diagnosed as diabetic if his or her glucose level is 126 mg/dL or higher.

Glucose meters work by the introduction of blood from a person, usually by a prick of the finger, onto a small strip of paper that contains chemicals that react with glucose. Insertion of the strip into a small battery-operated reader gives the glucose concentration (▼ FIGURE 3.11). The mechanism of the readout varies from one monitor to another—it may be a measurement of a small electrical current or measurement of light produced in a chemical reaction. Depending on the reading on any given day, a diabetic person may need to receive an injection of insulin or simply stop eating sweets for a while.

▲ **FIGURE 3.11   Glucose meter.**

## Interconverting Masses and Moles

Conversions of mass to moles and of moles to mass are frequently encountered in calculations using the mole concept. These calculations are simplified using dimensional analysis, as shown in Sample Exercises 3.10 and 3.11.

---

**SAMPLE EXERCISE 3.10   Converting Grams to Moles**

Calculate the number of moles of glucose ($C_6H_{12}O_6$) in 5.380 g of $C_6H_{12}O_6$.

### SOLUTION

**Analyze** We are given the number of grams of a substance and its chemical formula and asked to calculate the number of moles.

**Plan** The molar mass of a substance provides the factor for converting grams to moles. The molar mass of $C_6H_{12}O_6$ is 180.0 g/mol (Sample Exercise 3.9).

**Solve** Using 1 mol $C_6H_{12}O_6$ = 180.0 g $C_6H_{12}O_6$ to write the appropriate conversion factor, we have

$$\text{Moles } C_6H_{12}O_6 = (5.380 \text{ g } C_6H_{12}O_6)\left(\frac{1 \text{ mol } C_6H_{12}O_6}{180.0 \text{ g } C_6H_{12}O_6}\right) = 0.02989 \text{ mol } C_6H_{12}O_6$$

**Check** Because 5.380 g is less than the molar mass, an answer less than one mole is reasonable. The unit mol is appropriate. The original data had four significant figures, so our answer has four significant figures.

### PRACTICE EXERCISE

How many moles of sodium bicarbonate ($NaHCO_3$) are in 508 g of $NaHCO_3$?
**Answer:** 6.05 mol $NaHCO_3$

---

**SAMPLE EXERCISE 3.11   Converting Moles to Grams**

Calculate the mass, in grams, of 0.433 mol of calcium nitrate.

### SOLUTION

**Analyze** We are given the number of moles and the name of a substance and asked to calculate the number of grams in the sample.

**Plan** To convert moles to grams, we need the molar mass, which we can calculate using the chemical formula and atomic weights.

**Solve** Because the calcium ion is $Ca^{2+}$ and the nitrate ion is $NO_3^-$, calcium nitrate is $Ca(NO_3)_2$. Adding the atomic weights of the elements in the compound gives a formula weight of 164.1 amu. Using 1 mol $Ca(NO_3)_2$ = 164.1 g $Ca(NO_3)_2$ to write the appropriate conversion factor, we have

$$\text{Grams } Ca(NO_3)_2 = (0.433 \text{ mol } Ca(NO_3)_2)\left(\frac{164.1 \text{ g } Ca(NO_3)_2}{1 \text{ mol } Ca(NO_3)_2}\right) = 71.1 \text{ g } Ca(NO_3)_2$$

**Check** The number of moles is less than 1, so the number of grams must be less than the molar mass, 164.1 g. Using rounded numbers to estimate, we have $0.5 \times 150 = 75$ g, which means the magnitude of our answer is reasonable. Both the units (g) and the number of significant figures (3) are correct.

**PRACTICE EXERCISE**
What is the mass, in grams, of **(a)** 6.33 mol of $NaHCO_3$ and **(b)** $3.0 \times 10^{-5}$ mol of sulfuric acid?

***Answers:*** **(a)** 532 g, **(b)** $2.9 \times 10^{-3}$ g

## Interconverting Masses and Numbers of Particles

The mole concept provides the bridge between mass and number of particles. To illustrate how this bridge works, let's calculate the number of copper atoms in an old copper penny. Such a penny has a mass of about 3 g, and we assume it is 100% copper:

$$\text{Cu atoms} = (3 \text{ g Cu})\left(\frac{1 \text{ mol Cu}}{63.5 \text{ g Cu}}\right)\left(\frac{6.02 \times 10^{23} \text{ Cu atoms}}{1 \text{ mol Cu}}\right)$$

$$= 3 \times 10^{22} \text{ Cu atoms}$$

We have rounded our answer to one significant figure because we used only one significant figure for the mass of the penny. Notice how dimensional analysis ∞ (Section 1.6) provides a straightforward route from grams to numbers of atoms. The molar mass and Avogadro's number are used as conversion factors to convert grams to moles and then moles to atoms. Notice also that our answer is a very large number. Any time you calculate the number of atoms, molecules, or ions in an ordinary sample of matter, you can expect the answer to be very large. In contrast, the number of moles in a sample will usually be small, often less than 1.

The general procedure for interconverting mass and number of formula units (atoms, molecules, ions, or whatever else is represented by the chemical formula) is summarized in ▼ **FIGURE 3.12**.

**GO FIGURE**
What number would you use to convert (a) moles of $CH_4$ to grams of $CH_4$ and (b) number of molecules of $CH_4$ to moles of $CH_4$?

▲ **FIGURE 3.12  Procedure for interconverting mass and number of formula units.** The number of moles of the substance is central to the calculation. Thus, the mole concept can be thought of as the bridge between the mass of a sample in grams and the number of formula units contained in the sample.

**SAMPLE EXERCISE 3.12** | **Calculating Numbers of Molecules and Atoms from Mass**

(a) How many glucose molecules are in 5.23 g of $C_6H_{12}O_6$? (b) How many oxygen atoms are in this sample?

**SOLUTION**

**Analyze** We are given the number of grams and the chemical formula and asked to calculate (a) the number of molecules and (b) the number of O atoms in the sample.

**(a) Plan** The strategy for determining the number of molecules in a given quantity of a substance is summarized in Figure 3.12. We must convert 5.23 g to moles of $C_6H_{12}O_6$ and then convert moles to molecules of $C_6H_{12}O_6$. The first conversion uses the molar mass of $C_6H_{12}O_6$, 180.0 g, and the second conversion uses Avogadro's number.

**Solve** Molecules $C_6H_{12}O_6$

$$= (5.23 \text{ g } C_6H_{12}O_6)\left(\frac{1 \text{ mol } C_6H_{12}O_6}{180.0 \text{ g } C_6H_{12}O_6}\right)\left(\frac{6.02 \times 10^{23} \text{ molecules } C_6H_{12}O_6}{1 \text{ mol } C_6H_{12}O_6}\right)$$

$$= 1.75 \times 10^{22} \text{ molecules } C_6H_{12}O_6$$

**Check** Because the mass we began with is less than a mole, there should be fewer than $6.02 \times 10^{23}$ molecules in the sample, which means the magnitude of our answer is reasonable. We can make a ballpark estimate of the answer: $5/200 = 2.5 \times 10^{-2}$ mol; $2.5 \times 10^{-2} \times 6 \times 10^{23} = 15 \times 10^{21} = 1.5 \times 10^{22}$ molecules. The units (molecules) and significant figures (three) are appropriate.

**(b) Plan** To determine the number of O atoms, we use the fact that there are six O atoms in each $C_6H_{12}O_6$ molecule. Thus, multiplying the number of molecules we calculated in (a) by the factor (6 atoms O/1 molecule $C_6H_{12}O_6$) gives the number of O atoms.

**Solve**

$$\text{Atoms O} = (1.75 \times 10^{22} \text{ molecules } C_6H_{12}O_6)\left(\frac{6 \text{ atoms O}}{1 \text{ molecule } C_6H_{12}O_6}\right)$$

$$= 1.05 \times 10^{23} \text{ atoms O}$$

**Check** The answer is 6 times as large as the answer to part (a), exactly what it should be. The number of significant figures (three) and the units (atoms O) are correct.

**PRACTICE EXERCISE**

(a) How many nitric acid molecules are in 4.20 g of $HNO_3$? (b) How many O atoms are in this sample?
**Answers:** (a) $4.01 \times 10^{22}$ molecules $HNO_3$, (b) $1.20 \times 10^{23}$ atoms O

# 3.5 | EMPIRICAL FORMULAS FROM ANALYSES

As we learned in Section 2.6, the empirical formula for a substance tells us the relative number of atoms of each element in the substance. The empirical formula $H_2O$ shows that water contains two H atoms for each O atom. This ratio also applies on the molar level: 1 mol of $H_2O$ contains 2 mol of H atoms and 1 mol of O atoms. Conversely, *the ratio of the numbers of moles of all elements in a compound gives the subscripts in the compound's empirical formula.* Thus, the mole concept provides a way of calculating empirical formulas.

Mercury and chlorine, for example, combine to form a compound that is 73.9% mercury and 26.1% chlorine by mass. Thus, if we had a 100.0-g sample of the compound, it would contain 73.9 g of mercury and 26.1 g of chlorine. (Samples of any size can be used in problems of this type, but we will generally use 100.0 g to simplify the calculation of mass from percentage.) Using atomic weights to get molar masses, we can calculate the number of moles of each element in the sample:

$$(73.9 \text{ g } Hg)\left(\frac{1 \text{ mol Hg}}{200.6 \text{ g } Hg}\right) = 0.368 \text{ mol Hg}$$

$$(26.1 \text{ g } Cl)\left(\frac{1 \text{ mol Cl}}{35.5 \text{ g } Cl}\right) = 0.735 \text{ mol Cl}$$

GO FIGURE

How do you calculate the mole ratio of each element in any compound?

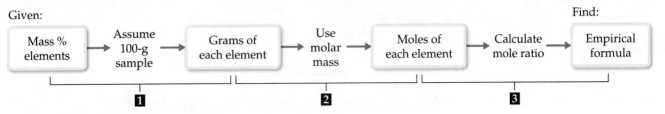

▲ **FIGURE 3.13  Procedure for calculating an empirical formula from percentage composition.** The key step in the calculation is step 2, determining the number of moles of each element in the compound.

We then divide the larger number of moles by the smaller number to obtain the Cl:Hg mole ratio:

$$\frac{\text{moles of Cl}}{\text{moles of Hg}} = \frac{0.735 \text{ mol Cl}}{0.368 \text{ mol Hg}} = \frac{1.99 \text{ mol Cl}}{1 \text{ mol Hg}}$$

Because of experimental errors, calculated values for a mole ratio may not be whole numbers, as in the calculation here. The number 1.99 is very close to 2, however, and so we can confidently conclude that the empirical formula for the compound is $HgCl_2$. The empirical formula is correct because its subscripts are the smallest integers that express the *ratio* of atoms present in the compound. ∞ (Section 2.6).

The general procedure for determining empirical formulas is outlined in ▲ **FIGURE 3.13**.

GIVE IT SOME THOUGHT

What is the mole ratio of nitrogen to hydrogen in $N_2H_4$?

---

**SAMPLE EXERCISE 3.13**   **Calculating an Empirical Formula**

Ascorbic acid (vitamin C) contains 40.92% C, 4.58% H, and 54.50% O by mass. What is the empirical formula of ascorbic acid?

**SOLUTION**

**Analyze**  We are to determine the empirical formula of a compound from the mass percentages of its elements.

**Plan**  The strategy for determining the empirical formula involves the three steps given in Figure 3.13.

**Solve**

1.  For simplicity, we assume we have exactly 100 g of material (although any other mass could also be used). In 100 g of ascorbic acid, we have

    40.92 g C, 4.58 g H, and 54.50 g O.

2.  We calculate the number of moles of each element:

    $$\text{Moles C} = (40.92 \text{ g C})\left(\frac{1 \text{ mol C}}{12.01 \text{ g C}}\right) = 3.407 \text{ mol C}$$

    $$\text{Moles H} = (4.58 \text{ g H})\left(\frac{1 \text{ mol H}}{1.008 \text{ g H}}\right) = 4.54 \text{ mol H}$$

    $$\text{Moles O} = (54.50 \text{ g O})\left(\frac{1 \text{ mol O}}{16.00 \text{ g O}}\right) = 3.406 \text{ mol O}$$

3.  We determine the simplest whole-number ratio of moles by dividing each number of moles by the smallest number of moles:

    $$\text{C:} \frac{3.407}{3.406} = 1.000 \quad \text{H:} \frac{4.54}{3.406} = 1.33 \quad \text{O:} \frac{3.406}{3.406} = 1.000$$

    The ratio for H is too far from 1 to attribute the difference to experimental error; in fact, it is quite close to $1\frac{1}{3}$. This suggests we should multiply the ratios by 3 to obtain whole numbers:

    $$\text{C:H:O} = 3(1{:}1.33{:}1) = 3{:}4{:}3$$

    Thus, the empirical formula is

    $$C_3H_4O_3$$

**Check** It is reassuring that the subscripts are moderate-size whole numbers. Also, calculating the percentage composition of $C_3H_8O$ gives values very close to the original percentages.

**PRACTICE EXERCISE**

A 5.325-g sample of methyl benzoate, a compound used in the manufacture of perfumes, contains 3.758 g of carbon, 0.316 g of hydrogen, and 1.251 g of oxygen. What is the empirical formula of this substance?

**Answer:** $C_4H_4O$

## Molecular Formulas from Empirical Formulas

We can obtain a molecular formula for any compound from its empirical formula if we know either the molecular weight or the molar mass of the compound. *The subscripts in the molecular formula of a substance are always whole-number multiples of the subscripts in its empirical formula.* ∞ (Section 2.6) This multiple can be found by dividing the molecular weight by the empirical formula weight:

$$\text{Whole-number multiple} = \frac{\text{molecular weight}}{\text{empirical formula weight}} \qquad [3.11]$$

In Sample Exercise 3.13, for example, the empirical formula of ascorbic acid was determined to be $C_3H_4O_3$. This means the empirical formula weight is 3(12.0 amu) + 4(1.0 amu) + 3(16.0 amu) = 88.0 amu. The experimentally determined molecular weight is 176 amu. Thus, we find the whole-number multiple that converts the empirical formula to the molecular formula by dividing:

$$\text{Whole-number multiple} = \frac{\text{molecular weight}}{\text{empirical formula weight}} = \frac{176 \text{ amu}}{88.0 \text{ amu}} = 2$$

Consequently, we multiply the subscripts in the empirical formula by this multiple, giving the molecular formula: $C_6H_8O_6$.

---

**SAMPLE EXERCISE 3.14** | **Determining a Molecular Formula**

Mesitylene, a hydrocarbon found in crude oil, has an empirical formula of $C_3H_4$ and an experimentally determined molecular weight of 121 amu. What is its molecular formula?

**SOLUTION**

**Analyze** We are given an empirical formula and a molecular weight and asked to determine a molecular formula.

**Plan** The subscripts in a compound's molecular formula are whole-number multiples of the subscripts in its empirical formula. We find the appropriate multiple by using Equation 3.11.

**Solve** The formula weight of the empirical formula $C_3H_4$ is

$$3(12.0 \text{ amu}) + 4(1.0 \text{ amu}) = 40.0 \text{ amu}$$

Next, we use this value in Equation 3.11:

$$\text{Whole-number multiple} = \frac{\text{molecular weight}}{\text{empirical formula weight}} = \frac{121}{40.0} = 3.02$$

Only whole-number ratios make physical sense because molecules contain whole atoms. The 3.02 in this case could result from a small experimental error in the molecular weight. We therefore multiply each subscript in the empirical formula by 3 to give the molecular formula: $C_9H_{12}$.

**Check** We can have confidence in the result because dividing molecular weight by empirical formula weight yields nearly a whole number.

**PRACTICE EXERCISE**

Ethylene glycol, used in automobile antifreeze, is 38.7% C, 9.7% H, and 51.6% O by mass. Its molar mass is 62.1 g/mol. **(a)** What is the empirical formula of ethylene glycol? **(b)** What is its molecular formula?

**Answers:** **(a)** $CH_3O$, **(b)** $C_2H_6O_2$

# Combustion Analysis

One technique for determining empirical formulas in the laboratory is *combustion analysis,* commonly used for compounds containing principally carbon and hydrogen.

When a compound containing carbon and hydrogen is completely combusted in an apparatus such as that shown in ▶ FIGURE 3.14, the carbon is converted to $CO_2$ and the hydrogen is converted to $H_2O$. ∞ (Section 3.2) The amounts of $CO_2$ and $H_2O$ produced are determined by measuring the mass increase in the $CO_2$ and $H_2O$ absorbers. From the masses of $CO_2$ and $H_2O$ we can calculate the number of moles of C and H in the original sample and thereby the empirical formula. If a third element is present in the compound, its mass can be determined by subtracting the measured masses of C and H from the original sample mass.

Mass gained by each absorber corresponds to mass of $CO_2$ or $H_2O$ produced

▲ **FIGURE 3.14  Apparatus for combustion analysis.**

---

**SAMPLE EXERCISE 3.15**  |  **Determining an Empirical Formula by Combustion Analysis**

Isopropyl alcohol, sold as rubbing alcohol, is composed of C, H, and O. Combustion of 0.255 g of isopropyl alcohol produces 0.561 g of $CO_2$ and 0.306 g of $H_2O$. Determine the empirical formula of isopropyl alcohol.

## SOLUTION

**Analyze** We are told that isopropyl alcohol contains C, H, and O atoms and given the quantities of $CO_2$ and $H_2O$ produced when a given quantity of the alcohol is combusted. We must determine the empirical formula for isopropyl alcohol, a task that requires us to calculate the number of moles of C, H, and O in the sample.

**Plan** We can use the mole concept to calculate grams of C in the $CO_2$ and grams of H in the $H_2O$. These masses are the masses of C and H in the alcohol before combustion. The mass of O in the compound equals the mass of the original sample minus the sum of the C and H masses. Once we have the C, H, and O masses, we can proceed as in Sample Exercise 3.13.

## Solve

To calculate the mass of C from the measured mass of $CO_2$, we first use the molar mass of $CO_2$, 44.0 g/mol, to convert grams of $CO_2$ to moles of $CO_2$. Because each $CO_2$ molecule has only one C atom, there is 1 mol of C atoms per mole of $CO_2$ molecules. This fact allows us to convert moles of $CO_2$ to moles of C. Finally, we use the molar mass of C, 12.0 g, to convert moles of C to grams of C:

$$\text{Grams C} = (0.561 \text{ g CO}_2)\left(\frac{1 \text{ mol CO}_2}{44.0 \text{ g CO}_2}\right)\left(\frac{1 \text{ mol C}}{1 \text{ mol CO}_2}\right)\left(\frac{12.0 \text{ g C}}{1 \text{ mol C}}\right) = 0.153 \text{ g C}$$

The calculation for determining H mass from $H_2O$ mass is similar, although we must remember that there are 2 mol of H atoms per 1 mol of $H_2O$ molecules:

$$\text{Grams H} = (0.306 \text{ g H}_2O)\left(\frac{1 \text{ mol H}_2O}{18.0 \text{ g H}_2O}\right)\left(\frac{2 \text{ mol H}}{1 \text{ mol H}_2O}\right)\left(\frac{1.01 \text{ g H}}{1 \text{ mol H}}\right) = 0.0343 \text{ g H}$$

The mass of the sample, 0.255 g, is the sum of the masses of C, H, and O. Thus, the O mass is

$$\text{Mass of O} = \text{mass of sample} - (\text{mass of C} + \text{mass of H})$$
$$= 0.255 \text{ g} - (0.153 \text{ g} + 0.0343 \text{ g}) = 0.068 \text{ g O}$$

The number of moles of C, H, and O in the sample is therefore

$$\text{Moles C} = (0.153 \text{ g C})\left(\frac{1 \text{ mol C}}{12.0 \text{ g C}}\right) = 0.0128 \text{ mol C}$$

$$\text{Moles H} = (0.0343 \text{ g H})\left(\frac{1 \text{ mol H}}{1.01 \text{ g H}}\right) = 0.0340 \text{ mol H}$$

$$\text{Moles O} = (0.068 \text{ g O})\left(\frac{1 \text{ mol O}}{16.0 \text{ g O}}\right) = 0.0043 \text{ mol O}$$

To find the empirical formula, we must compare the relative number of moles of each element in the sample. We determine relative number of moles by dividing each of our calculated number of moles by the smallest number:

$$\text{C: } \frac{0.0128}{0.0043} = 3.0 \quad \text{H: } \frac{0.0340}{0.0043} = 7.9 \quad \text{O: } \frac{0.0043}{0.0043} = 1.0$$

The first two numbers are very close to the whole numbers 3 and 8, giving the empirical formula

$C_3H_8O$.

**Check**  The subscripts work out to be moderate-size whole numbers, as expected.

**PRACTICE EXERCISE**

(a) Caproic acid, responsible for the odor of dirty socks, is composed of C, H, and O atoms. Combustion of a 0.225-g sample of this compound produces 0.512 g $CO_2$ and 0.209 g $H_2O$. What is the empirical formula of caproic acid? (b) Caproic acid has a molar mass of 116 g/mol. What is its molecular formula?

**Answers:**  (a) $C_3H_6O$, (b) $C_6H_{12}O_2$

 **GIVE IT SOME THOUGHT**

In Sample Exercise 3.15, how do you explain the fact that the values in our calculated C:H:O ratio are 3.0:7.9:1.0 rather than exact integers 3:8:1?

## 3.6 | QUANTITATIVE INFORMATION FROM BALANCED EQUATIONS

The coefficients in a chemical equation represent the relative numbers of molecules in a reaction. The mole concept allows us to convert this information to the masses of the substances in the reaction. For instance, the coefficients in the balanced equation

$$2\,H_2(g) + O_2(g) \longrightarrow 2\,H_2O(l) \qquad [3.12]$$

indicate that two molecules of $H_2$ react with one molecule of $O_2$ to form two molecules of $H_2O$. It follows that the relative numbers of moles are identical to the relative numbers of molecules:

| $2\,H_2(g)$ | + | $O_2(g)$ | $\longrightarrow$ | $2\,H_2O(l)$ |
|:---:|:---:|:---:|:---:|:---:|
| 2 molecules | | 1 molecule | | 2 molecules |
| $2(6.02 \times 10^{23}$ molecules) | | $1(6.02 \times 10^{23}$ molecules) | | $2(6.02 \times 10^{23}$ molecules) |
| 2 mol | | 1 mol | | 2 mol |

We can generalize this observation to all balanced chemical equations: *The coefficients in a balanced chemical equation indicate both the relative numbers of molecules (or formula units) in the reaction and the relative numbers of moles.* ▼ **FIGURE 3.15** shows how this result corresponds to the law of conservation of mass.

The quantities 2 mol $H_2$, 1 mol $O_2$, and 2 mol $H_2O$ given by the coefficients in Equation 3.12 are called *stoichiometrically equivalent quantities*. The relationship between these quantities can be represented as

$$2\text{ mol }H_2 \,\hat{=}\, 1\text{ mol }O_2 \,\hat{=}\, 2\text{ mol }H_2O$$

where the $\hat{=}$ symbol means "is stoichiometrically equivalent to." Stoichiometric relations such as these can be used to convert between quantities of reactants and products

| Chemical equation: | $2\,H_2(g)$ | + | $O_2(g)$ | $\longrightarrow$ | $2\,H_2O(l)$ |
|---|:---:|:---:|:---:|:---:|:---:|
| **Molecular interpretation:** | 2 molecules $H_2$ | | 1 molecule $O_2$ | | 2 molecules $H_2O$ |
| **Mole-level interpretation:** | 2 mol $H_2$ | | 1 mol $O_2$ | | 2 mol $H_2O$ |

Convert to grams (using molar masses)

| 4.0 g $H_2$ | 32.0 g $O_2$ | 36.0 g $H_2O$ |

▶ **FIGURE 3.15  Interpreting a balanced chemical equation quantitatively.**

Notice the conservation of mass ·······
(4.0 g + 32.0 g = 36.0 g)

in a chemical reaction. For example, the number of moles of $H_2O$ produced from 1.57 mol of $O_2$ is

$$\text{Moles } H_2O = (1.57 \text{ mol } O_2)\left(\frac{2 \text{ mol } H_2O}{1 \text{ mol } O_2}\right) = 3.14 \text{ mol } H_2O$$

## GIVE IT SOME THOUGHT

When 1.57 mol $O_2$ reacts with $H_2$ to form $H_2O$, how many moles of $H_2$ are consumed in the process?

As an additional example, consider the combustion of butane ($C_4H_{10}$), the fuel in disposable general-purpose lighters:

$$2 C_4H_{10}(l) + 13 O_2(g) \longrightarrow 8 CO_2(g) + 10 H_2O(g) \qquad [3.13]$$

Let's calculate the mass of $CO_2$ produced when 1.00 g of $C_4H_{10}$ is burned. The coefficients in Equation 3.13 tell us how the amount of $C_4H_{10}$ consumed is related to the amount of $CO_2$ produced: 2 mol $C_4H_{10} \mathrel{\widehat{=}}$ 8 mol $CO_2$. To use this stoichiometric relationship, we must convert grams of $C_4H_{10}$ to moles using the molar mass of $C_4H_{10}$, 58.0 g/mol:

$$\text{Moles } C_4H_{10} = (1.00 \text{ g } C_4H_{10})\left(\frac{1 \text{ mol } C_4H_{10}}{58.0 \text{ g } C_4H_{10}}\right)$$

$$= 1.72 \times 10^{-2} \text{ mol } C_4H_{10}$$

We then use the stoichiometric factor from the balanced equation to calculate moles of $CO_2$:

$$\text{Moles } CO_2 = (1.72 \times 10^{-2} \text{ mol } C_4H_{10})\left(\frac{8 \text{ mol } CO_2}{2 \text{ mol } C_4H_{10}}\right)$$

$$= 6.88 \times 10^{-2} \text{ mol } CO_2$$

Finally, we use the molar mass of $CO_2$, 44.0 g/mol, to calculate the $CO_2$ mass in grams:

$$\text{Grams } CO_2 = (6.88 \times 10^{-2} \text{ mol } CO_2)\left(\frac{44.0 \text{ g } CO_2}{1 \text{ mol } CO_2}\right)$$

$$= 3.03 \text{ g } CO_2$$

This conversion sequence involves three steps, as illustrated in ▼ FIGURE 3.16. These three conversions can be combined in a single equation:

$$\text{Grams } CO_2 = (1.00 \text{ g } C_4H_{10})\left(\frac{1 \text{ mol } C_4H_{10}}{58.0 \text{ g } C_4H_{10}}\right)\left(\frac{8 \text{ mol } CO_2}{2 \text{ mol } C_4H_{10}}\right)\left(\frac{44.0 \text{ g } CO_2}{1 \text{ mol } CO_2}\right)$$

$$= 3.03 \text{ g } CO_2$$

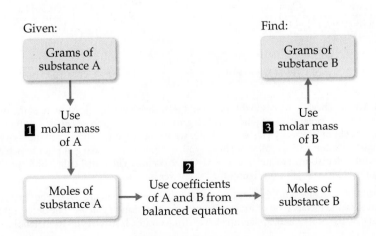

◀ FIGURE 3.16 Procedure for calculating amounts of reactants consumed or products formed in a reaction. The number of grams of a reactant consumed or product formed can be calculated in three steps, starting with the number of grams of any reactant or product. Notice how molar masses and the coefficients in the balanced equation are used.

To calculate the amount of $O_2$ consumed in the reaction of Equation 3.13, we again rely on the coefficients in the balanced equation for our stoichiometric factor: 2 mol $C_4H_{10}$ ≏ 13 mol $O_2$:

$$\text{Grams } O_2 = (1.00 \text{ g } C_4H_{10})\left(\frac{1 \text{ mol } C_4H_{10}}{58.0 \text{ g } C_4H_{10}}\right)\left(\frac{13 \text{ mol } O_2}{2 \text{ mol } C_4H_{10}}\right)\left(\frac{32.0 \text{ g } O_2}{1 \text{ mol } O_2}\right)$$

$$= 3.59 \text{ g } O_2$$

⚠ **GIVE IT SOME THOUGHT**

If 20.00 g of a compound reacts completely with 30.00 g of another compound in a combination reaction, how many grams of product are formed?

---

**SAMPLE EXERCISE 3.16** **Calculating Amounts of Reactants and Products**

Determine how many grams of water are produced in the oxidation of 1.00 g of glucose, $C_6H_{12}O_6$:

$$C_6H_{12}O_6(s) + 6 O_2(g) \longrightarrow 6 CO_2(g) + 6 H_2O(l)$$

**SOLUTION**

**Analyze** We are given the mass of a reactant and must determine the mass of a product in the given reaction.

**Plan** The general strategy, as outlined in Figure 3.16, requires three steps:
1. Convert grams of $C_6H_{12}O_6$ to moles using the molar mass of $C_6H_{12}O_6$.
2. Convert moles of $C_6H_{12}O_6$ to moles of $H_2O$ using the stoichiometric relationship 1 mol $C_6H_{12}O_6$ ≏ 6 mol $H_2O$.
3. Convert moles of $H_2O$ to grams using the molar mass of $H_2O$.

**Solve**

1. $\text{Moles } C_6H_{12}O_6 = (1.00 \text{ g } C_6H_{12}O_6)\left(\dfrac{1 \text{ mol } C_6H_{12}O_6}{180.0 \text{ g } C_6H_{12}O_6}\right)$

2. $\text{Moles } H_2O = (1.00 \text{ g } C_6H_{12}O_6)\left(\dfrac{1 \text{ mol } C_6H_{12}O_6}{180.0 \text{ g } C_6H_{12}O_6}\right)\left(\dfrac{6 \text{ mol } H_2O}{1 \text{ mol } C_6H_{12}O_6}\right)$

3. $\text{Grams } H_2O = (1.00 \text{ g } C_6H_{12}O_6)\left(\dfrac{1 \text{ mol } C_6H_{12}O_6}{180.0 \text{ g } C_6H_{12}O_6}\right)\left(\dfrac{6 \text{ mol } H_2O}{1 \text{ mol } C_6H_{12}O_6}\right)\left(\dfrac{18.0 \text{ g } H_2O}{1 \text{ mol } H_2O}\right)$

$$= 0.600 \text{ g } H_2O$$

The steps can be summarized in a diagram like that in Figure 3.16:

**Check** We can check how reasonable our result is by doing a ballpark estimate of the mass of $H_2O$. Because the molar mass of glucose is 180 g/mol, 1 gram of glucose equals 1/180 mol. Because one mole of glucose yields 6 mol $H_2O$, we would have 6/180 = 1/30 mol $H_2O$. The molar mass of water is 18 g/mol, so we have 1/30 × 18 = 6/10 = 0.6 g of $H_2O$, which agrees with the full calculation. The units, grams $H_2O$, are correct. The initial data had three significant figures, so three significant figures for the answer is correct.

**Comment** An average adult ingests 2 L of water daily and eliminates 2.4 L. The "extra" 0.4 L is produced in the metabolism of foodstuffs, such as oxidation of glucose. The desert rat (kangaroo rat), on the other hand, apparently never drinks water. It survives on its metabolic water.

---

**SAMPLE EXERCISE 3.17** | **Calculating Amounts of Reactants and Products**

Solid lithium hydroxide is used in space vehicles to remove the carbon dioxide gas exhaled by astronauts. The hydroxide reacts with the carbon dioxide to form solid lithium carbonate and liquid water. How many grams of carbon dioxide can be absorbed by 1.00 g of lithium hydroxide?

**SOLUTION**

**Analyze** We are given a verbal description of a reaction and asked to calculate the number of grams of one reactant that reacts with 1.00 g of another.

**Plan** The verbal description of the reaction can be used to write a balanced equation:

$$2\, LiOH(s) + CO_2(g) \longrightarrow Li_2CO_3(s) + H_2O(l)$$

We are given the mass in grams of LiOH and asked to calculate the mass in grams of $CO_2$. We can accomplish this task by using the three conversion steps in Figure 3.16. The conversion of step 1 requires the molar mass of LiOH $(6.94 + 16.00 + 1.01 = 23.95$ g/mol). The conversion of step 2 is based on a stoichiometric relationship from the balanced chemical equation: 2 mol LiOH $\hateq$ 1 mol $CO_2$. For the step 3 conversion, we use the molar mass of $CO_2$: $12.01 + 2(16.00) = 44.01$ g/mol.

**Solve**

$$(1.00 \text{ g LiOH})\left(\frac{1 \text{ mol LiOH}}{23.95 \text{ g LiOH}}\right)\left(\frac{1 \text{ mol CO}_2}{2 \text{ mol LiOH}}\right)\left(\frac{44.01 \text{ g CO}_2}{1 \text{ mol CO}_2}\right) = 0.919 \text{ g CO}_2$$

**Check** Notice that 23.95 g LiOH/mol $\approx$ 24 g LiOH/mol, that 24 g LiOH/mol $\times$ 2 mol LiOH = 48 g LiOH, and (44 g $CO_2$/mol)/(48 g LiOH) is slightly less than 1. Thus, the magnitude of our answer, 0.919 g $CO_2$, is reasonable based on the amount of starting LiOH. The significant figures and units are also appropriate.

**PRACTICE EXERCISE**

Propane, $C_3H_8$ (Figure 3.8), is a common fuel used for cooking and home heating. What mass of $O_2$ is consumed in the combustion of 1.00 g of propane?

**Answer:** 3.64 g

---

# 3.7 | LIMITING REACTANTS

Suppose you wish to make several sandwiches using one slice of cheese and two slices of bread for each. Using Bd = bread, Ch = cheese, and $Bd_2Ch$ = sandwich, the recipe for making a sandwich can be represented like a chemical equation:

$$2\, Bd + Ch \longrightarrow Bd_2Ch$$

If you have 10 slices of bread and 7 slices of cheese, you can make only 5 sandwiches and will have 2 slices of cheese left over. The amount of bread available limits the number of sandwiches.

An analogous situation occurs in chemical reactions when one reactant is used up before the others. The reaction stops as soon as any reactant is totally consumed, leaving the excess reactants as leftovers. Suppose, for example, we have a mixture of 10 mol $H_2$ and 7 mol $O_2$, which react to form water:

$$2\, H_2(g) + O_2(g) \longrightarrow 2\, H_2O(g)$$

Because 2 mol $H_2$ $\hateq$ 1 mol $O_2$, the number of moles of $O_2$ needed to react with all the $H_2$ is

$$\text{Moles } O_2 = (10 \text{ mol H}_2)\left(\frac{1 \text{ mol O}_2}{2 \text{ mol H}_2}\right) = 5 \text{ mol O}_2$$

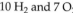

▲ **GO FIGURE**

**If $O_2$ had been the limiting reactant, how many moles of $H_2O$ would have formed?**

Before reaction

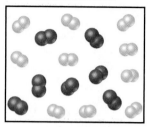

10 $H_2$ and 7 $O_2$

After reaction

10 $H_2O$ and 2 $O_2$ (no $H_2$ molecules)

▲ **FIGURE 3.17 Limiting reactant.** Because $H_2$ is completely consumed, it is the limiting reactant. Because some $O_2$ is left over after the reaction is complete, $O_2$ is the excess reactant. The amount of $H_2O$ formed depends on the amount of limiting reactant, $H_2$.

Because 7 mol $O_2$ is available at the start of the reaction, 7 mol $O_2$ − 5 mol $O_2$ = 2 mol $O_2$ is present when all the $H_2$ is consumed.

The reactant that is completely consumed in a reaction is called the **limiting reactant** because it determines, or limits, the amount of product formed. The other reactants are sometimes called *excess reactants*. In our example, shown in ◄ **FIGURE 3.17**, $H_2$ is the limiting reactant, which means that once all the $H_2$ has been consumed, the reaction stops. The excess reactant is $O_2$; some is left over when the reaction stops.

There are no restrictions on the starting amounts of reactants in any reaction. Indeed, many reactions are carried out using an excess of one reactant. The quantities of reactants consumed and products formed, however, are restricted by the quantity of the limiting reactant. For example, when a combustion reaction takes place in the open air, oxygen is plentiful and is therefore the excess reactant. If you run out of gasoline while driving, the car stops because the gasoline is the limiting reactant in the combustion reaction that moves the car.

Before we leave the example illustrated in Figure 3.17, let's summarize the data:

|  | $2 H_2(g)$ | $+$ | $O_2(g)$ | $\longrightarrow$ | $2 H_2O(g)$ |
|---|---|---|---|---|---|
| Initial quantities: | 10 mol | | 7 mol | | 0 mol |
| Change (reaction): | −10 mol | | −5 mol | | +10 mol |
| Final quantities: | 0 mol | | 2 mol | | 10 mol |

The second line in the table (Change) summarizes the amounts of reactants consumed (where this consumption is indicated by the minus signs) and the amount of the product formed (indicated by the plus sign). These quantities are restricted by the quantity of the limiting reactant and depend on the coefficients in the balanced equation. The mole ratio $H_2:O_2:H_2O = 10:5:10$ conforms to the ratio of the coefficients in the balanced equation, 2:1:2. The final quantities, which depend on the initial quantities and their changes, are found by adding the initial quantity and change quantity for each column. None of the limiting reactant ($H_2$) remains at the end of the reaction. What remains is 2 mol $O_2$ (excess reactant) and 10 mol $H_2O$ (product).

---

**SAMPLE EXERCISE 3.18** Calculating the Amount of Product Formed from a Limiting Reactant

The most important commercial process for converting $N_2$ from the air into nitrogen-containing compounds is based on the reaction of $N_2$ and $H_2$ to form ammonia ($NH_3$):

$$N_2(g) + 3 H_2(g) \longrightarrow 2 NH_3(g)$$

How many moles of $NH_3$ can be formed from 3.0 mol of $N_2$ and 6.0 mol of $H_2$?

**SOLUTION**

**Analyze** We are asked to calculate the number of moles of product, $NH_3$, given the quantities of each reactant, $N_2$ and $H_2$, available in a reaction. This is a limiting reactant problem.

**Plan** If we assume one reactant is completely consumed, we can calculate how much of the second reactant is needed. By comparing the calculated quantity of the second reactant with the amount available, we can determine which reactant is limiting. We then proceed with the calculation, using the quantity of the limiting reactant.

**Solve**

The number of moles of $H_2$ needed for complete consumption of 3.0 mol of $N_2$ is:

$$\text{Moles } H_2 = (3.0 \text{ mol } N_2)\left(\frac{3 \text{ mol } H_2}{1 \text{ mol } N_2}\right) = 9.0 \text{ mol } H_2$$

Because only 6.0 mol $H_2$ is available, we will run out of $H_2$ before the $N_2$ is gone, which tells us that $H_2$ is the limiting reactant. Therefore, we use the quantity of $H_2$ to calculate the quantity of $NH_3$ produced:

$$\text{Moles } NH_3 = (6.0 \text{ mol } H_2)\left(\frac{2 \text{ mol } NH_3}{3 \text{ mol } H_2}\right) = 4.0 \text{ mol } NH_3$$

**Comment** The table on the right summarizes this example:

| | $N_2(g)$ | + | $3 H_2(g)$ | $\longrightarrow$ | $2 NH_3(g)$ |
|---|---|---|---|---|---|
| Initial quantities: | 3.0 mol | | 6.0 mol | | 0 mol |
| Change (reaction): | −2.0 mol | | −6.0 mol | | +4.0 mol |
| Final quantities: | 1.0 mol | | 0 mol | | 4.0 mol |

Notice that we can calculate not only the number of moles of $NH_3$ formed but also the number of moles of each reactant remaining after the reaction. Notice also that although the initial number of moles of $H_2$ is greater than the final number of moles of $N_2$, the $H_2$ is nevertheless the limiting reactant because of its larger coefficient in the balanced equation.

**Check** The Change row of the summary table shows that the mole ratio of reactants consumed and product formed, 2:6:4, conforms to the coefficients in the balanced equation, 1:3:2. Because $H_2$ is the limiting reactant, it is completely consumed in the reaction, leaving 0 mol at the end. Because 6.0 mol $H_2$ has two significant figures, our answer has two significant figures.

### PRACTICE EXERCISE

(a) When 1.50 mol of Al and 3.00 mol of $Cl_2$ combine in the reaction $2 Al(s) + 3 Cl_2(g) \longrightarrow 2 AlCl_3(s)$, which is the limiting reactant? (b) How many moles of $AlCl_3$ are formed? (c) How many moles of the excess reactant remain at the end of the reaction?

*Answers:* (a) Al, (b) 1.50 mol, (c) 0.75 mol $Cl_2$

---

**SAMPLE EXERCISE 3.19** | **Calculating the Amount of Product Formed from a Limiting Reactant**

The reaction

$$2 H_2(g) + O_2(g) \longrightarrow 2 H_2O(g)$$

is used to produce electricity in a hydrogen fuel cell. Suppose a fuel cell contains 150 g of $H_2(g)$ and 1500 g of $O_2(g)$ (each measured to two significant figures). How many grams of water can form?

### SOLUTION

**Analyze** We are asked to calculate the amount of a product, given the amounts of two reactants, so this is a limiting reactant problem.

**Plan** To identify the limiting reactant, we can calculate the number of moles of each reactant and compare their ratio with the ratio of coefficients in the balanced equation. We then use the quantity of the limiting reactant to calculate the mass of water that forms.

**Solve** From the balanced equation, we have the stoichiometric relations

$$2 \text{ mol } H_2 \simeq 1 \text{ mol } O_2 \simeq 2 \text{ mol } H_2O$$

Using the molar mass of each substance, we calculate the number of moles of each reactant:

$$\text{Moles } H_2 = (150 \text{ g } H_2)\left(\frac{1 \text{ mol } H_2}{2.00 \text{ g } H_2}\right) = 75 \text{ mol } H_2$$

$$\text{Moles } O_2 = (1500 \text{ g } O_2)\left(\frac{1 \text{ mol } O_2}{32.0 \text{ g } O_2}\right) = 47 \text{ mol } O_2$$

The coefficients in the balanced equation indicate that the reaction requires 2 mol of $H_2$ for every 1 mol of $O_2$. Therefore, for all the $O_2$ to completely react, we would need $2 \times 47 = 94$ mol of $H_2$. Since there are only 75 mol of $H_2$, all of the $O_2$ cannot react, so it is the excess reactant, and $H_2$ must be the limiting reactant. (Notice that the limiting reactant is not merely the one present in the lowest amount.)

We use the given quantity of $H_2$ (the limiting reactant) to calculate the quantity of water formed. We could begin this calculation with the given $H_2$ mass, 150 g, but we can save a step by starting with the moles of $H_2$, 75 mol, we just calculated:

$$\text{Grams } H_2O = (75 \text{ mol } H_2)\left(\frac{2 \text{ mol } H_2O}{2 \text{ mol } H_2}\right)\left(\frac{18.0 \text{ g } H_2O}{1 \text{ mol } H_2O}\right)$$

$$= 1400 \text{ g } H_2O = 1.4 \times 10^2 \text{ g } H_2O \text{ (two significant figures)}$$

**Check** The magnitude of the answer seems reasonable based on the amounts of the reactants. The units are correct, and the number of significant figures (two) corresponds to those in the values given in the problem statement.

**Comment** The quantity of the limiting reactant, $H_2$, can also be used to determine the quantity of $O_2$ used:

$$\text{Grams } O_2 = (75 \text{ mol } H_2)\left(\frac{1 \text{ mol } O_2}{2 \text{ mol } H_2}\right)\left(\frac{32.0 \text{ g } O_2}{1 \text{ mol } O_2}\right)$$

$$= 1.2 \times 10^3 \text{ g } H_2O$$

The mass of $O_2$ remaining at the end of the reaction equals the starting amount minus the amount consumed:

$$1500 \text{ g} - 1200 \text{ g} = 300 \text{ g}.$$

**PRACTICE EXERCISE**

When a 2.00-g strip of zinc metal is placed in an aqueous solution containing 2.50 g of silver nitrate, the reaction is

$$Zn(s) + 2\,AgNO_3(aq) \longrightarrow 2\,Ag(s) + Zn(NO_3)_2(aq)$$

**(a)** Which reactant is limiting? **(b)** How many grams of Ag form? **(c)** How many grams of $Zn(NO_3)_2$ form? **(d)** How many grams of the excess reactant are left at the end of the reaction?
*Answers:* **(a)** $AgNO_3$, **(b)** 1.59 g, **(c)** 1.39 g, **(d)** 1.52 g Zn

## Theoretical Yields

The quantity of product calculated to form when all of a limiting reactant is consumed is called the **theoretical yield**. The amount of product actually obtained, called the *actual yield*, is almost always less than (and can never be greater than) the theoretical yield. There are many reasons for this difference. Part of the reactants may not react, for example, or they may react in a way different from that desired (side reactions). In addition, it is not always possible to recover all of the product from the reaction mixture. The **percent yield** of a reaction relates actual and theoretical yields:

$$\text{Percent yield} = \frac{\text{actual yield}}{\text{theoretical yield}} \times 100\% \qquad [3.14]$$

**SAMPLE EXERCISE 3.20** | **Calculating Theoretical Yield and Percent Yield**

Adipic acid, $H_2C_6H_8O_4$, used to produce nylon, is made commercially by a reaction between cyclohexane ($C_6H_{12}$) and $O_2$:

$$2\,C_6H_{12}(l) + 5\,O_2(g) \longrightarrow 2\,H_2C_6H_8O_4(l) + 2\,H_2O(g)$$

**(a)** Assume that you carry out this reaction with 25.0 g of cyclohexane and that cyclohexane is the limiting reactant. What is the theoretical yield of adipic acid? **(b)** If you obtain 33.5 g of adipic acid, what is the percent yield for the reaction?

**SOLUTION**

**Analyze** We are given a chemical equation and the quantity of the limiting reactant (25.0 g of $C_6H_{12}$). We are asked to calculate the theoretical yield of a product $H_2C_6H_8O_4$ and the percent yield if only 33.5 g of product is obtained.

**Plan**

**(a)** The theoretical yield, which is the calculated quantity of adipic acid formed, can be calculated using the sequence of conversions shown in Figure 3.16.
**(b)** The percent yield is calculated by using Equation 3.14 to compare the given actual yield (33.5 g) with the theoretical yield.

**Solve**

**(a)** The theoretical yield is

$$\text{Grams } H_2C_6H_8O_4 = (25.0 \text{ g } C_6H_{12})\left(\frac{1 \text{ mol } C_6H_{12}}{84.0 \text{ g } C_6H_{12}}\right)\left(\frac{2 \text{ mol } H_2C_6H_8O_4}{2 \text{ mol } C_6H_{12}}\right)\left(\frac{146.0 \text{ g } H_2C_6H_8O_4}{1 \text{ mol } H_2C_6H_8O_4}\right)$$

$$= 43.5 \text{ g } H_2C_6H_8O_4$$

**(b)** Percent yield = $\dfrac{\text{actual yield}}{\text{theoretical yield}} \times 100\% = \dfrac{33.5 \text{ g}}{43.5 \text{ g}} \times 100\% = 77.0\%$

**Check** We can check our answer in (a) by doing a ballpark calculation. From the balanced equation we know that each mole of cyclohexane gives 1 mol adipic acid. We have $25/84 \approx 25/75 = 0.3$ mol hexane, so we expect 0.3 mol adipic acid, which equals about $0.3 \times 150 = 45$ g, about the same magnitude as the 43.5 g obtained in the more detailed calculation given previously. In addition, our answer has the appropriate units and significant figures. In (b) the answer is less than 100%, as it must be from the definition of percent yield.

## PRACTICE EXERCISE

Imagine you are working on ways to improve the process by which iron ore containing $Fe_2O_3$ is converted into iron:

$$Fe_2O_3(s) + 3\,CO(g) \longrightarrow 2\,Fe(s) + 3\,CO_2(g)$$

**(a)** If you start with 150 g of $Fe_2O_3$ as the limiting reactant, what is the theoretical yield of Fe?
**(b)** If your actual yield is 87.9 g, what is the percent yield?
*Answers:* **(a)** 105 g Fe, **(b)** 83.7%

# STRATEGIES IN CHEMISTRY

## HOW TO TAKE A TEST

At about this time in your study of chemistry, you are likely to face your first hour-long examination. The best way to prepare is to study, do homework diligently, and get help from the instructor on any material that is unclear or confusing. (See the advice for learning and studying chemistry presented in the preface of the book.) We present here some general guidelines for taking tests.

Depending on the nature of your course, the exam could consist of a variety of different types of questions.

1. **Multiple-choice questions** In large-enrollment courses, the most common kind of test question is the multiple-choice question. You are given the problem and presented with four or five answers from which you must select the correct one. The first thing to realize is that the instructor has written the question so that at first glance all the answers appear to be correct. (There would be little point in offering choices you could tell were wrong even without knowing much about the concept being tested.) Thus, you should not jump to the conclusion that because one of the choices looks correct, it must be correct.

If a multiple-choice question involves a calculation, do the calculation, check your work, and *only then* compare your answer with the choices. If you find a match, you have probably found the correct answer. Keep in mind, though, that your instructor has anticipated the most common errors you might make in solving a given problem and has probably listed the incorrect answers resulting from those errors. Always double-check your reasoning and use dimensional analysis to arrive at the correct numeric answer and the correct units.

In multiple-choice questions that do not involve calculations, if you are not sure of the correct choice, eliminate all the choices you know for sure to be incorrect. The reasoning you use in eliminating incorrect choices will help you in reasoning about which of the remaining choices is correct.

2. **Calculations in which you must show your work** In questions of this kind, you may receive partial credit even if you do not arrive at the correct answer, depending on whether the instructor can follow your line of reasoning. It is important, therefore, to be neat and organized in your calculations. Pay particular attention to what information is given and to what your unknown is. Think about how you can get from the given information to your unknown.

You may want to write a few words or a diagram on the test paper to indicate your approach. Then write out your calculations as neatly as you can. Show the units for every number you write down, and use dimensional analysis as much as you can, showing how units cancel.

3. **Questions requiring drawings** Questions of this kind will come later in the course, but it is useful to talk about them here. (You should review this box before each exam to remind yourself of good exam-taking practices.) Be sure to label your drawing as completely as possible.

4. **Other types of questions** Other exam questions you might encounter include true-false questions and ones in which you are given a list and asked to indicate which members of the list match some criterion given in the question. Often students answer such questions incorrectly because, in their haste, they misunderstand the nature of the question. Whatever the form of the question, ask yourself this: What is the instructor testing here? What material am I supposed to know that this question covers?

Finally, if you find that you simply do not understand how to arrive at a reasoned response to a question, do not linger over the question. Put a check next to it and go on to the next one. If time permits, you can come back to the unanswered questions, but lingering over a question when nothing is coming to mind is wasting time you may need to finish the exam.

# CHAPTER SUMMARY AND KEY TERMS

**INTRODUCTION AND SECTION 3.1** The study of the quantitative relationships between chemical formulas and chemical equations is known as **stoichiometry**. One of the important concepts of stoichiometry is the law of conservation of mass, which states that the total mass of the products of a chemical reaction is the same as the total mass of the reactants. The same numbers of atoms of each type are present before and after a chemical reaction. A balanced **chemical equation** shows equal numbers of atoms of each element on each side of the equation. Equations are balanced by placing coefficients in front of the chemical formulas for the **reactants** and **products** of a reaction, *not* by changing the subscripts in chemical formulas.

**SECTION 3.2** Among the reaction types described in this chapter are (1) **combination reactions**, in which two reactants combine to form one product; (2) **decomposition reactions**, in which a single reactant forms two or more products; and (3) **combustion reactions** in oxygen, in which a hydrocarbon or related compound reacts with $O_2$ to form $CO_2$ and $H_2O$.

**SECTION 3.3** Much quantitative information can be determined from chemical formulas and balanced chemical equations by using atomic weights. The **formula weight** of a compound equals the sum of the atomic weights of the atoms in its formula. If the formula is a molecular formula, the formula weight is also called the **molecular weight**. Atomic weights and formula weights can be used to determine the elemental composition of a compound.

**SECTION 3.4** A mole of any substance is **Avogadro's number** $(6.02 \times 10^{23})$ of formula units of that substance. The mass of a **mole** of atoms, molecules, or ions (the **molar mass**) equals the formula weight of that material expressed in grams. The mass of one molecule of $H_2O$, for example, is 18 amu, so the mass of 1 mol of $H_2O$ is 18 g. That is, the molar mass of $H_2O$ is 18 g/mol.

**SECTION 3.5** The empirical formula of any substance can be determined from its percent composition by calculating the relative number of moles of each atom in 100 g of the substance. If the substance is molecular in nature, its molecular formula can be determined from the empirical formula if the molecular weight is also known.

**SECTIONS 3.6 AND 3.7** The mole concept can be used to calculate the relative quantities of reactants and products in chemical reactions. The coefficients in a balanced equation give the relative numbers of moles of the reactants and products. To calculate the number of grams of a product from the number of grams of a reactant, first convert grams of reactant to moles of reactant. Then use the coefficients in the balanced equation to convert the number of moles of reactant to moles of product. Finally, convert moles of product to grams of product.

A **limiting reactant** is completely consumed in a reaction. When it is used up, the reaction stops, thus limiting the quantities of products formed. The **theoretical yield** of a reaction is the quantity of product calculated to form when all of the limiting reactant reacts. The actual yield of a reaction is always less than the theoretical yield. The **percent yield** compares the actual and theoretical yields.

# KEY SKILLS

- Balance chemical equations. (Section 3.1)
- Predict the products of simple combination, decomposition, and combustion reactions. (Section 3.2)
- Calculate formula weights. (Section 3.3)
- Convert grams to moles and moles to grams using molar masses. (Section 3.4)
- Convert number of molecules to moles and moles to number of molecules using Avogadro's number. (Section 3.4)
- Calculate the empirical and molecular formulas of a compound from percentage composition and molecular weight. (Section 3.5)
- Calculate amounts, in grams or moles, of reactants and products for a reaction. (Section 3.6)
- Calculate the percent yield of a reaction. (Section 3.7)

# KEY EQUATIONS

- $$\% \text{ element} = \frac{\left(\begin{array}{c}\text{number of atoms}\\\text{of that element}\end{array}\right)\left(\begin{array}{c}\text{atomic weight}\\\text{of element}\end{array}\right)}{(\text{formula weight of compound})} \times 100\%$$   [3.10]

   This is the formula to calculate the mass percentage of each element in a compound. The sum of all the percentages of all the elements in a compound should add up to 100%.

- $$\% \text{ yield} = \frac{(\text{actual yield})}{(\text{theoretical yield})} \times 100\%$$   [3.14]

   This is the formula to calculate the percent yield of a reaction. The percent yield can never be more than 100%.

# EXERCISES

## VISUALIZING CONCEPTS

**3.1** The reaction between reactant A (blue spheres) and reactant B (red spheres) is shown in the following diagram:

Based on this diagram, which equation best describes the reaction? [Section 3.1]

(a) $A_2 + B \longrightarrow A_2B$

(b) $A_2 + 4B \longrightarrow 2AB_2$

(c) $2A + B_4 \longrightarrow 2AB_2$

(d) $A + B_2 \longrightarrow AB_2$

**3.2** Under appropriate experimental conditions, $H_2$ and CO undergo a combination reaction to form $CH_3OH$. The following drawing represents a sample of $H_2$. Make a corresponding drawing of the CO needed to react completely with the $H_2$. How did you arrive at the number of CO molecules in your drawing? [Section 3.2]

**3.3** The following diagram represents the collection of elements formed by a decomposition reaction. (a) If the blue spheres represent N atoms and the red ones represent O atoms, what was the empirical formula of the original compound? (b) Could you draw a diagram representing the molecules of the compound that had been decomposed? Why or why not? [Section 3.2]

**3.4** The following diagram represents the collection of $CO_2$ and $H_2O$ molecules formed by complete combustion of a hydrocarbon. What is the empirical formula of the hydrocarbon? [Section 3.2]

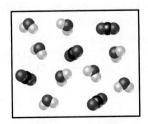

**3.5** Glycine, an amino acid used by organisms to make proteins, is represented by the following molecular model.

(a) Write its molecular formula.

(b) Determine its molar mass.

(c) Calculate the mass of 3 moles of glycine.

(d) Calculate the percent nitrogen by mass in glycine. [Sections 3.3 and 3.5]

**3.6** The following diagram represents a high-temperature reaction between $CH_4$ and $H_2O$. Based on this reaction, how many moles of each product can be obtained starting with 4.0 mol $CH_4$? [Section 3.6]

**3.7** Nitrogen ($N_2$) and hydrogen ($H_2$) react to form ammonia ($NH_3$). Consider the mixture of $N_2$ and $H_2$ shown in the accompanying diagram. The blue spheres represent N, and the white ones represent H. Draw a representation of the product mixture, assuming that the reaction goes to completion. How did you arrive at your representation? What is the limiting reactant in this case? [Section 3.7]

**3.8** Nitrogen monoxide and oxygen react to form nitrogen dioxide. Consider the mixture of NO and $O_2$ shown in the accompanying diagram. The blue spheres represent N, and the red ones represent O. (a) Draw a representation of the product mixture, assuming that the reaction goes to completion. What is the limiting reactant in this case? (b) How many $NO_2$ molecules would you draw as products if the reaction had a percent yield of 75%? [Section 3.7]

# BALANCING CHEMICAL EQUATIONS (section 3.1)

**3.9** **(a)** What scientific principle or law is used in the process of balancing chemical equations? **(b)** In balancing equations, why should you not change subscripts in chemical formulas? **(c)** How would you write out liquid water, water vapor, aqueous sodium chloride, and solid sodium chloride in chemical equations?

**3.10** **(a)** What is the difference between adding a subscript 2 to the end of the formula for CO to give $CO_2$ and adding a coefficient in front of the formula to give 2 CO? **(b)** Is the following chemical equation, as written, consistent with the law of conservation of mass?

$$3\ Mg(OH)_2(s) + 2\ H_3PO_4(aq) \longrightarrow$$
$$Mg_3(PO_4)_2(s) + 6\ H_2O(l)$$

Why or why not?

**3.11** Balance the following equations:
**(a)** $CO(g) + O_2(g) \longrightarrow CO_2(g)$
**(b)** $N_2O_5(g) + H_2O(l) \longrightarrow HNO_3(aq)$
**(c)** $CH_4(g) + Cl_2(g) \longrightarrow CCl_4(l) + HCl(g)$
**(d)** $Al_4C_3(s) + H_2O(l) \longrightarrow Al(OH)_3(s) + CH_4(g)$
**(e)** $C_5H_{10}O_2(l) + O_2(g) \longrightarrow CO_2(g) + H_2O(g)$
**(f)** $Fe(OH)_3(s) + H_2SO_4(aq) \longrightarrow$
$$Fe_2(SO_4)_3(aq) + H_2O(l)$$
**(g)** $Mg_3N_2(s) + H_2SO_4(aq) \longrightarrow$
$$MgSO_4(aq) + (NH_4)_2SO_4(aq)$$

**3.12** Balance the following equations:
**(a)** $Li(s) + N_2(g) \longrightarrow Li_3N(s)$
**(b)** $TiCl_4(l) + H_2O(l) \longrightarrow TiO_2(s) + HCl(aq)$
**(c)** $NH_4NO_3(s) \longrightarrow N_2(g) + O_2(g) + H_2O(g)$

**(d)** $Ca_3P_2(s) + H_2O(l) \longrightarrow Ca(OH)_2(aq) + PH_3(g)$
**(e)** $Al(OH)_3(s) + H_2SO_4(aq) \longrightarrow Al_2(SO_4)_3(aq) + H_2O(l)$
**(f)** $AgNO_3(aq) + Na_2CO_3(aq) \longrightarrow$
$$Ag_2NO_3(s) + Na_2CO_3(aq)$$
**(g)** $C_2H_5NH_2(g) + O_2(g) \longrightarrow$
$$CO_2(g) + H_2O(g) + N_2(g)$$

**3.13** Write balanced chemical equations to correspond to each of the following descriptions: **(a)** Solid calcium carbide, $CaC_2$, reacts with water to form an aqueous solution of calcium hydroxide and acetylene gas, $C_2H_2$. **(b)** When solid potassium chlorate is heated, it decomposes to form solid potassium chloride and oxygen gas. **(c)** Solid zinc metal reacts with sulfuric acid to form hydrogen gas and an aqueous solution of zinc sulfate. **(d)** When liquid phosphorus trichloride is added to water, it reacts to form aqueous phosphorous acid, $H_3PO_3(aq)$, and aqueous hydrochloric acid. **(e)** When hydrogen sulfide gas is passed over solid hot iron(III) hydroxide, the resultant reaction produces solid iron(III) sulfide and gaseous water.

**3.14** Write balanced chemical equations to correspond to each of the following descriptions: **(a)** When sulfur trioxide gas reacts with water, a solution of sulfuric acid forms. **(b)** Boron sulfide, $B_2S_3(s)$, reacts violently with water to form dissolved boric acid, $H_3BO_3$, and hydrogen sulfide gas. **(c)** Phosphine, $PH_3(g)$, combusts in oxygen gas to form water vapor and solid tetraphosphorus decaoxide. **(d)** When solid mercury(II) nitrate is heated, it decomposes to form solid mercury(II) oxide, gaseous nitrogen dioxide, and oxygen. **(e)** Copper metal reacts with hot concentrated sulfuric acid solution to form aqueous copper(II) sulfate, sulfur dioxide gas, and water.

# PATTERNS OF CHEMICAL REACTIVITY (section 3.2)

**3.15** **(a)** When the metallic element sodium combines with the nonmetallic element bromine, $Br_2(l)$, how can you determine the chemical formula of the product? How do you know whether the product is a solid, liquid, or gas at room temperature? Write the balanced chemical equation for the reaction. **(b)** When a hydrocarbon burns in air, what reactant besides the hydrocarbon is involved in the reaction? What products are formed? Write a balanced chemical equation for the combustion of benzene, $C_6H_6(l)$, in air.

**3.16** **(a)** Determine the chemical formula of the product formed when the metallic element aluminum combines with the nonmetallic element bromine, $Br_2$. Write the balanced chemical equation for the reaction. **(b)** What products form when a compound containing C, H, and O is completely combusted in air? Write a balanced chemical equation for the combustion of acetone, $C_3H_6O(l)$, in air.

**3.17** Write a balanced chemical equation for the reaction that occurs when **(a)** $Mg(s)$ reacts with $Cl_2(g)$; **(b)** barium carbonate decomposes into barium oxide and carbon dioxide gas when heated; **(c)** the hydrocarbon styrene, $C_8H_8(l)$, is combusted in air; **(d)** dimethylether, $CH_3OCH_3(g)$, is combusted in air.

**3.18** Write a balanced chemical equation for the reaction that occurs when **(a)** calcium metal undergoes a combination reaction with $O_2(g)$; **(b)** copper(II) hydroxide decomposes into copper(II) oxide and water when heated; **(c)** heptane, $C_7H_{16}(l)$, burns in air; **(d)** methyl tert-butyl ether, $C_5H_{12}O(l)$, burns in air.

**3.19** Balance the following equations and indicate whether they are combination, decomposition, or combustion reactions:
**(a)** $C_3H_6(g) + O_2(g) \longrightarrow CO_2(g) + H_2O(g)$
**(b)** $NH_4NO_3(s) \longrightarrow N_2O(g) + H_2O(g)$
**(c)** $C_5H_6O(l) + O_2(g) \longrightarrow CO_2(g) + H_2O(g)$
**(d)** $N_2(g) + H_2(g) \longrightarrow NH_3(g)$
**(e)** $K_2O(s) + H_2O(l) \longrightarrow KOH(aq)$

**3.20** Balance the following equations and indicate whether they are combination, decomposition, or combustion reactions:
**(a)** $PbCO_3(s) \longrightarrow PbO(s) + CO_2(g)$
**(b)** $C_2H_4(g) + O_2(g) \longrightarrow CO_2(g) + H_2O(g)$
**(c)** $Mg(s) + N_2(g) \longrightarrow Mg_3N_2(s)$
**(d)** $C_7H_8O_2(l) + O_2(g) \longrightarrow CO_2(g) + H_2O(g)$
**(e)** $Al(s) + Cl_2(g) \longrightarrow AlCl_3(s)$

# FORMULA WEIGHTS (section 3.3)

**3.21** Determine the formula weights of each of the following compounds: **(a)** nitric acid, $HNO_3$; **(b)** $KMnO_4$; **(c)** $Ca_3(PO_4)_2$; **(d)** quartz, $SiO_2$; **(e)** gallium sulfide, **(f)** chromium(III) sulfate, **(g)** phosphorus trichloride.

**3.22** Determine the formula weights of each of the following compounds: **(a)** nitrous oxide, $N_2O$, known as laughing gas and used as an anesthetic in dentistry; **(b)** benzoic acid, $HC_7H_5O_2$, a substance used as a food preservative; **(c)** $Mg(OH)_2$, the active ingredient in milk of magnesia; **(d)** urea, $(NH_2)_2CO$, a compound used as a nitrogen fertilizer; **(e)** isopentyl acetate, $CH_3CO_2C_5H_{11}$, responsible for the odor of bananas.

**3.23** Calculate the percentage by mass of oxygen in the following compounds: **(a)** morphine, $C_{17}H_{19}NO_3$; **(b)** codeine, $C_{18}H_{21}NO_3$ **(c)** cocaine, $C_{17}H_{21}NO_4$; **(d)** tetracycline, $C_{22}H_{24}N_2O_8$; **(e)** digitoxin, $C_{41}H_{64}O_{13}$; **(f)** vancomycin, $C_{66}H_{75}Cl_2N_9O_{24}$.

**3.24** Calculate the percentage by mass of the indicated element in the following compounds: **(a)** carbon in acetylene, $C_2H_2$, a gas used in welding; **(b)** hydrogen in ascorbic acid, $HC_6H_7O_6$, also known as vitamin C; **(c)** hydrogen in ammonium sulfate, $(NH_4)_2SO_4$, a substance used as a nitrogen fertilizer; **(d)** platinum in $PtCl_2(NH_3)_2$, a chemotherapy agent called cisplatin; **(e)** oxygen in the female sex hormone estradiol, $C_{18}H_{24}O_2$; **(f)** carbon in capsaicin, $C_{18}H_{27}NO_3$, the compound that gives the hot taste to chili peppers.

**3.25** Based on the following structural formulas, calculate the percentage of carbon by mass present in each compound:

**(a)** Benzaldehyde (almond fragrance)

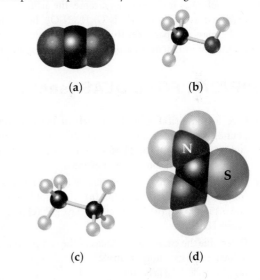

**(b)** Vanillin (vanilla flavor)

**(c)** Isopentyl acetate (banana flavor)

**3.26** Calculate the percentage of carbon by mass in each of the compounds represented by the following models:

**(a)**    **(b)**

**(c)**    **(d)**

# AVOGADRO'S NUMBER AND THE MOLE (section 3.4)

**3.27** **(a)** What is Avogadro's number, and how is it related to the mole? **(b)** What is the relationship between the formula weight of a substance and its molar mass?

**3.28** **(a)** What is the mass, in grams, of a mole of $^{12}C$? **(b)** How many carbon atoms are present in a mole of $^{12}C$?

**3.29** Without doing any detailed calculations (but using a periodic table to give atomic weights), rank the following samples in order of increasing number of atoms: 0.50 mol $H_2O$, 23 g Na, $6.0 \times 10^{23}$ $N_2$ molecules.

**3.30** Without doing any detailed calculations (but using a periodic table to give atomic weights), rank the following samples in order of increasing number of atoms: $9.0 \times 10^{23}$ molecules of $H_2O_2$, 2.0 mol $CH_4$, 16 g $O_2$.

**3.31** What is the mass, in kilograms, of an Avogadro's number of people, if the average mass of a person is 160 lb? How does this compare with the mass of Earth, $5.98 \times 10^{24}$ kg?

**3.32** If Avogadro's number of pennies is divided equally among the 300 million men, women, and children in the United States,

how many dollars would each receive? How does this compare with the gross domestic product (GDP) of the United States, which was $14.4 trillion in 2008? (The GDP is the total market value of the nation's goods and services.)

**3.33** Calculate the following quantities:
**(a)** mass, in grams, of 0.105 mole of sucrose ($C_{12}H_{22}O_{11}$)
**(b)** moles of $Zn(NO_3)_2$ in 143.50 g of this substance
**(c)** number of molecules in $1.0 \times 10^{-6}$ mol $CH_3CH_2OH$
**(d)** number of N atoms in 0.410 mol $NH_3$

**3.34** Calculate the following quantities:
**(a)** mass, in grams, of $1.50 \times 10^{-2}$ mol of CdS
**(b)** number of moles of $NH_4Cl$ in 86.6 g of this substance
**(c)** number of molecules in $8.447 \times 10^{-2}$ mol $C_6H_6$
**(d)** number of O atoms in $6.25 \times 10^{-3}$ mol $Al(NO_3)_3$

**3.35** **(a)** What is the mass, in grams, of $2.50 \times 10^{-3}$ mol of ammonium phosphate?
**(b)** How many moles of chloride ions are in 0.2550 g of aluminum chloride?

**(c)** What is the mass, in grams, of $7.70 \times 10^{20}$ molecules of caffeine, $C_8H_{10}N_4O_2$?

**(d)** What is the molar mass of cholesterol if 0.00105 mol has a mass of 0.406 g?

**3.36 (a)** What is the mass, in grams, of 1.223 mol of iron(III) sulfate?

**(b)** How many moles of ammonium ions are in 6.955 g of ammonium carbonate?

**(c)** What is the mass, in grams, of $1.50 \times 10^{21}$ molecules of aspirin, $C_9H_8O_4$?

**(d)** What is the molar mass of diazepam (Valium®) if 0.05570 mol has a mass of 15.86 g?

**3.37** The molecular formula of allicin, the compound responsible for the characteristic smell of garlic, is $C_6H_{10}OS_2$. **(a)** What is the molar mass of allicin? **(b)** How many moles of allicin are present in 5.00 mg of this substance? **(c)** How many molecules of allicin are in 5.00 mg of this substance? **(d)** How many S atoms are present in 5.00 mg of allicin?

**3.38** The molecular formula of aspartame, the artificial sweetener marketed as NutraSweet®, is $C_{14}H_{18}N_2O_5$. **(a)** What is the molar mass of aspartame? **(b)** How many moles of aspartame are present in 1.00 mg of aspartame? **(c)** How many molecules

of aspartame are present in 1.00 mg of aspartame? **(d)** How many hydrogen atoms are present in 1.00 mg of aspartame?

**3.39** A sample of glucose, $C_6H_{12}O_6$, contains $1.250 \times 10^{21}$ carbon atoms. **(a)** How many atoms of hydrogen does it contain? **(b)** How many molecules of glucose does it contain? **(c)** How many moles of glucose does it contain? **(d)** What is the mass of this sample in grams?

**3.40** A sample of the male sex hormone testosterone, $C_{19}H_{28}O_2$, contains $3.88 \times 10^{21}$ hydrogen atoms. **(a)** How many atoms of carbon does it contain? **(b)** How many molecules of testosterone does it contain? **(c)** How many moles of testosterone does it contain? **(d)** What is the mass of this sample in grams?

**3.41** The allowable concentration level of vinyl chloride, $C_2H_3Cl$, in the atmosphere in a chemical plant is $2.0 \times 10^{-6}$ g/L. How many moles of vinyl chloride in each liter does this represent? How many molecules per liter?

**3.42** At least 25 $\mu$g of tetrahydrocannabinol (THC), the active ingredient in marijuana, is required to produce intoxication. The molecular formula of THC is $C_{21}H_{30}O_2$. How many moles of THC does this 25 $\mu$g represent? How many molecules?

# EMPIRICAL FORMULAS (section 3.5)

**3.43** Give the empirical formula of each of the following compounds if a sample contains **(a)** 0.0130 mol C, 0.0390 mol H, and 0.0065 mol O; **(b)** 11.66 g iron and 5.01 g oxygen; **(c)** 40.0% C, 6.7% H, and 53.3% O by mass.

**3.44** Determine the empirical formula of each of the following compounds if a sample contains **(a)** 0.104 mol K, 0.052 mol C, and 0.156 mol O; **(b)** 5.28 g Sn and 3.37 g F; **(c)** 87.5% N and 12.5% H by mass.

**3.45** Determine the empirical formulas of the compounds with the following compositions by mass:
**(a)** 10.4% C, 27.8% S, and 61.7% Cl
**(b)** 21.7% C, 9.6% O, and 68.7% F
**(c)** 32.79% Na, 13.02% Al, and the remainder F

**3.46** Determine the empirical formulas of the compounds with the following compositions by mass:
**(a)** 55.3% K, 14.6% P, and 30.1% O
**(b)** 24.5% Na, 14.9% Si, and 60.6% F
**(c)** 62.1% C, 5.21% H, 12.1% N, and the remainder O

**3.47** A compound whose empirical formula is $XF_3$ consists of 65% F by mass. What is the atomic mass of X?

**3.48** The compound $XCl_4$ contains 75.0% Cl by mass. What is the element X?

**3.49** What is the molecular formula of each of the following compounds?
**(a)** empirical formula $CH_2$, molar mass = 84 g/mol
**(b)** empirical formula $NH_2Cl$, molar mass = 51.5 g/mol

**3.50** What is the molecular formula of each of the following compounds?
**(a)** empirical formula $HCO_2$, molar mass = 90.0 g/mol
**(b)** empirical formula $C_2H_4O$, molar mass = 88 g/mol

**3.51** Determine the empirical and molecular formulas of each of the following substances:
**(a)** Styrene, a compound substance used to make Styrofoam® cups and insulation, contains 92.3% C and 7.7% H by mass and has a molar mass of 104 g/mol.

**(b)** Caffeine, a stimulant found in coffee, contains 49.5% C, 5.15% H, 28.9% N, and 16.5% O by mass and has a molar mass of 195 g/mol.

**(c)** Monosodium glutamate (MSG), a flavor enhancer in certain foods, contains 35.51% C, 4.77% H, 37.85% O, 8.29% N, and 13.60% Na, and has a molar mass of 169 g/mol.

**3.52** Determine the empirical and molecular formulas of each of the following substances:
**(a)** Ibuprofen, a headache remedy, contains 75.69% C, 8.80% H, and 15.51% O by mass, and has a molar mass of 206 g/mol.
**(b)** Cadaverine, a foul-smelling substance produced by the action of bacteria on meat, contains 58.55% C, 13.81% H, and 27.40% N by mass; its molar mass is 102.2 g/mol.
**(c)** Epinephrine (adrenaline), a hormone secreted into the bloodstream in times of danger or stress, contains 59.0% C, 7.1% H, 26.2% O, and 7.7% N by mass; its MW is about 180 amu.

**3.53 (a)** Combustion analysis of toluene, a common organic solvent, gives 5.86 mg of $CO_2$ and 1.37 mg of $H_2O$. If the compound contains only carbon and hydrogen, what is its empirical formula? **(b)** Menthol, the substance we can smell in mentholated cough drops, is composed of C, H, and O. A 0.1005-g sample of menthol is combusted, producing 0.2829 g of $CO_2$ and 0.1159 g of $H_2O$. What is the empirical formula for menthol? If menthol has a molar mass of 156 g/mol, what is its molecular formula?

**3.54 (a)** The characteristic odor of pineapple is due to ethyl butyrate, a compound containing carbon, hydrogen, and oxygen. Combustion of 2.78 mg of ethyl butyrate produces 6.32 mg of $CO_2$ and 2.58 mg of $H_2O$. What is the empirical formula of the compound? **(b)** Nicotine, a component of tobacco, is composed of C, H, and N. A 5.250-mg sample of nicotine was combusted, producing 14.242 mg of $CO_2$ and 4.083 mg of

$H_2O$. What is the empirical formula for nicotine? If nicotine has a molar mass of $160 \pm 5$ g/mol, what is its molecular formula?

**3.55** Valproic acid, used to treat seizures and bipolar disorder, is composed of C, H, and O. A 0.165-g sample is combusted in an apparatus such as that shown in Figure 3.14. The gain in mass of the $H_2O$ absorber is 0.166 g, whereas that of the $CO_2$ absorber is 0.403 g. What empirical formula for valproic acid do these results indicate? Is this empirical formula consistent with the molecular model shown here?

**3.56** Propenoic acid, as shown here,

is a reactive organic liquid used in the manufacture of plastics, coatings, and adhesives. An unlabeled container is thought to contain this acid. A 0.2033-g sample is combusted in an apparatus such as that shown in Figure 3.14. The gain in mass of the $H_2O$ absorber is 0.102 g, whereas that of the $CO_2$ absorber is 0.374 g. Is this analysis consistent with the contents of the container being propenoic acid?

**3.57** Washing soda, a compound used to prepare hard water for washing laundry, is a hydrate, which means that a certain number of water molecules are included in the solid structure. Its formula can be written as $Na_2CO_3 \cdot xH_2O$, where $x$ is the number of moles of $H_2O$ per mole of $Na_2CO_3$. When a 2.558-g sample of washing soda is heated at 25 °C, all the water of hydration is lost, leaving 0.948 g of $Na_2CO_3$. What is the value of $x$?

**3.58** Epsom salts, a strong laxative used in veterinary medicine, is a hydrate, which means that a certain number of water molecules are included in the solid structure. The formula for Epsom salts can be written as $MgSO_4 \cdot xH_2O$, where $x$ indicates the number of moles of $H_2O$ per mole of $MgSO_4$. When 5.061 g of this hydrate is heated to 250 °C, all the water of hydration is lost, leaving 2.472 g of $MgSO_4$. What is the value of $x$?

# CALCULATIONS BASED ON CHEMICAL EQUATIONS (section 3.6)

**3.59** Why is it essential to use balanced chemical equations when determining the quantity of a product formed from a given quantity of a reactant?

**3.60** What parts of balanced chemical equations give information about the relative numbers of moles of reactants and products involved in a reaction?

**3.61** Hydrofluoric acid, HF($aq$), cannot be stored in glass bottles because compounds called silicates in the glass are attacked by the HF($aq$). Sodium silicate ($Na_2SiO_3$), for example, reacts as follows:

$$Na_2SiO_3(s) + 8\,HF(aq) \longrightarrow$$
$$H_2SiF_6(aq) + 2\,NaF(aq) + 3\,H_2O(l)$$

**(a)** How many moles of HF are needed to react with 0.300 mol of $Na_2SiO_3$?

**(b)** How many grams of NaF form when 0.500 mol of HF reacts with excess $Na_2SiO_3$?

**(c)** How many grams of $Na_2SiO_3$ can react with 0.800 g of HF?

**3.62** The reaction between potassium superoxide, $KO_2$, and $CO_2$,

$$4\,KO_2 + 2\,CO_2 \longrightarrow 2\,K_2CO_3 + 3\,O_2$$

is used as a source of $O_2$ and absorber of $CO_2$ in self-contained breathing equipment used by rescue workers.

**(a)** How many moles of $O_2$ are produced when 0.400 mol of $KO_2$ reacts in this fashion?

**(b)** How many grams of $KO_2$ are needed to form 7.50 g of $O_2$?

**(c)** How many grams of $CO_2$ are used when 7.50 g of $O_2$ are produced?

**3.63** Several brands of antacids use $Al(OH)_3$ to react with stomach acid, which contains primarily HCl:

$$Al(OH)_3(s) + HCl(aq) \longrightarrow AlCl_3(aq) + H_2O(l)$$

**(a)** Balance this equation.

**(b)** Calculate the number of grams of HCl that can react with 0.500 g of $Al(OH)_3$.

**(c)** Calculate the number of grams of $AlCl_3$ and the number of grams of $H_2O$ formed when 0.500 g of $Al(OH)_3$ reacts.

**(d)** Show that your calculations in parts (b) and (c) are consistent with the law of conservation of mass.

**3.64** An iron ore sample contains $Fe_2O_3$ together with other substances. Reaction of the ore with CO produces iron metal:

$$Fe_2O_3(s) + CO(g) \longrightarrow Fe(s) + CO_2(g)$$

**(a)** Balance this equation.
**(b)** Calculate the number of grams of CO that can react with 0.350 kg of $Fe_2O_3$.
**(c)** Calculate the number of grams of Fe and the number of grams of $CO_2$ formed when 0.350 kg of $Fe_2O_3$ reacts.
**(d)** Show that your calculations in parts (b) and (c) are consistent with the law of conservation of mass.

**3.65** Aluminum sulfide reacts with water to form aluminum hydroxide and hydrogen sulfide. **(a)** Write the balanced chemical equation for this reaction. **(b)** How many grams of aluminum hydroxide are obtained from 14.2 g of aluminum sulfide?

**3.66** Calcium hydride reacts with water to form calcium hydroxide and hydrogen gas. **(a)** Write a balanced chemical equation for the reaction. **(b)** How many grams of calcium hydride are needed to form 4.500 g of hydrogen?

**3.67** Automotive air bags inflate when sodium azide, $NaN_3$, rapidly decomposes to its component elements:

$$2\,NaN_3(s) \longrightarrow 2\,Na(s) + 3\,N_2(g)$$

**(a)** How many moles of $N_2$ are produced by the decomposition of 1.50 mol of $NaN_3$?
**(b)** How many grams of $NaN_3$ are required to form 10.0 g of nitrogen gas?
**(c)** How many grams of $NaN_3$ are required to produce 10.0 $ft^3$ of nitrogen gas, about the size of an automotive air bag, if the gas has a density of 1.25 g/L?

**3.68** The complete combustion of octane, $C_8H_{18}$, the main component of gasoline, proceeds as follows:

$$2\,C_8H_{18}(l) + 25\,O_2(g) \longrightarrow 16\,CO_2(g) + 18\,H_2O(g)$$

**(a)** How many moles of $O_2$ are needed to burn 1.50 mol of $C_8H_{18}$?
**(b)** How many grams of $O_2$ are needed to burn 10.0 g of $C_8H_{18}$?
**(c)** Octane has a density of 0.692 g/mL at 20 °C. How many grams of $O_2$ are required to burn 15.0 gal of $C_8H_{18}$ (the capacity of an average fuel tank)?

**(d)** How many grams of $CO_2$ are produced when 15.0 gal of $C_8H_{18}$ are combusted?

**3.69** A piece of aluminum foil 1.00 cm square and 0.550 mm thick is allowed to react with bromine to form aluminum bromide.

**(a)** How many moles of aluminum were used? (The density of aluminum is 2.699 $g/cm^3$.) **(b)** How many grams of aluminum bromide form, assuming the aluminum reacts completely?

**3.70** Detonation of nitroglycerin proceeds as follows:

$$4\,C_3H_5N_3O_9(l) \longrightarrow$$
$$12\,CO_2(g) + 6\,N_2(g) + O_2(g) + 10\,H_2O(g)$$

**(a)** If a sample containing 2.00 mL of nitroglycerin (density = 1.592 g/mL) is detonated, how many total moles of gas are produced? **(b)** If each mole of gas occupies 55 L under the conditions of the explosion, how many liters of gas are produced? **(c)** How many grams of $N_2$ are produced in the detonation?

# LIMITING REACTANTS (section 3.7)

**3.71** **(a)** Define the terms *limiting reactant* and *excess reactant*. **(b)** Why are the amounts of products formed in a reaction determined only by the amount of the limiting reactant? **(c)** Why should you base your choice of which compound is the limiting reactant on its number of initial moles, not on its initial mass in grams?

**3.72** **(a)** Define the terms *theoretical yield*, *actual yield*, and *percent yield*. **(b)** Why is the actual yield in a reaction almost always less than the theoretical yield? **(c)** Can a reaction ever have 110% actual yield?

**3.73** A manufacturer of bicycles has 4815 wheels, 2305 frames, and 2255 handlebars. **(a)** How many bicycles can be manufactured using these parts? **(b)** How many parts of each kind are left over? **(c)** Which part limits the production of bicycles?

**3.74** A bottling plant has 126,515 bottles with a capacity of 355 mL, 108,500 caps, and 48,775 L of beverage. **(a)** How many bottles

can be filled and capped? **(b)** How much of each item is left over? **(c)** Which component limits the production?

**3.75** Sodium hydroxide reacts with carbon dioxide as follows:

$$2\,NaOH(s) + CO_2(g) \longrightarrow Na_2CO_3(s) + H_2O(l)$$

Which is the limiting reactant when 1.85 mol NaOH and 1.00 mol $CO_2$ are allowed to react? How many moles of $Na_2CO_3$ can be produced? How many moles of the excess reactant remain after the completion of the reaction?

**3.76** Aluminum hydroxide reacts with sulfuric acid as follows:

$$2\,Al(OH)_3(s) + 3\,H_2SO_4(aq) \longrightarrow$$
$$Al_2(SO_4)_3(aq) + 6\,H_2O(l)$$

Which is the limiting reactant when 0.500 mol $Al(OH)_3$ and 0.500 mol $H_2SO_4$ are allowed to react? How many moles of $Al_2(SO_4)_3$ can form under these conditions? How many moles of the excess reactant remain after the completion of the reaction?

**3.77** The fizz produced when an Alka-Seltzer® tablet is dissolved in water is due to the reaction between sodium bicarbonate ($NaHCO_3$) and citric acid ($H_3C_6H_5O_7$):

$$3\,NaHCO_3(aq) + H_3C_6H_5O_7(aq) \longrightarrow$$
$$3\,CO_2(g) + 3\,H_2O(l) + Na_3C_6H_5O_7(aq)$$

In a certain experiment 1.00 g of sodium bicarbonate and 1.00 g of citric acid are allowed to react. **(a)** Which is the limiting reactant? **(b)** How many grams of carbon dioxide form? **(c)** How many grams of the excess reactant remain after the limiting reactant is completely consumed?

**3.78** One of the steps in the commercial process for converting ammonia to nitric acid is the conversion of $NH_3$ to $NO$:

$$4\,NH_3(g) + 5\,O_2(g) \longrightarrow 4\,NO(g) + 6\,H_2O(g)$$

In a certain experiment, 2.00 g of $NH_3$ reacts with 2.50 g of $O_2$ **(a)** Which is the limiting reactant? **(b)** How many grams of $NO$ and of $H_2O$ form? **(c)** How many grams of the excess reactant remain after the limiting reactant is completely consumed? **(d)** Show that your calculations in parts (b) and (c) are consistent with the law of conservation of mass.

**3.79** Solutions of sodium carbonate and silver nitrate react to form solid silver carbonate and a solution of sodium nitrate. A solution containing 3.50 g of sodium carbonate is mixed with one containing 5.00 g of silver nitrate. How many grams of sodium

carbonate, silver nitrate, silver carbonate, and sodium nitrate are present after the reaction is complete?

**3.80** Solutions of sulfuric acid and lead(II) acetate react to form solid lead(II) sulfate and a solution of acetic acid. If 5.00 g of sulfuric acid and 5.00 g of lead(II) acetate are mixed, calculate the number of grams of sulfuric acid, lead(II) acetate, lead(II) sulfate, and acetic acid present in the mixture after the reaction is complete.

**3.81** When benzene ($C_6H_6$) reacts with bromine ($Br_2$), bromobenzene ($C_6H_5Br$) is obtained:

$$C_6H_6 + Br_2 \longrightarrow C_6H_5Br + HBr$$

**(a)** When 30.0 g of benzene reacts with 65.0 g of bromine, what is the theoretical yield of bromobenzene? **(b)** If the actual yield of bromobenzene is 42.3 g, what is the percentage yield?

**3.82** When ethane ($C_2H_6$) reacts with chlorine ($Cl_2$), the main product is $C_2H_5Cl$, but other products containing Cl, such as $C_2H_4Cl_2$, are also obtained in small quantities. The formation of these other products reduces the yield of $C_2H_5Cl$. **(a)** Calculate the theoretical yield of $C_2H_5Cl$ when 125 g of $C_2H_6$ reacts with 255 g of $Cl_2$, assuming that $C_2H_6$ and $Cl_2$ react only to form $C_2H_2Cl$ and HCl. **(b)** Calculate the percent yield of $C_2H_5Cl$ if the reaction produces 206 g of $C_2H_5Cl$.

**3.83** Hydrogen sulfide is an impurity in natural gas that must be removed. One common removal method is called the Claus process, which relies on the reaction:

$$8\,H_2S(g) + 4\,O_2(g) \longrightarrow S_8(l) + 8\,H_2O(g)$$

Under optimal conditions the Claus process gives 98% yield of $S_8$ from $H_2S$. If you started with 30.0 grams of $H_2S$ and 50.0 grams of $O_2$, how many grams of $S_8$ would be produced, assuming 98% yield?

**3.84** When hydrogen sulfide gas is bubbled into a solution of sodium hydroxide, the reaction forms sodium sulfide and water. How many grams of sodium sulfide are formed if 1.25 g of hydrogen sulfide is bubbled into a solution containing 2.00 g of sodium hydroxide, assuming that the sodium sulfide is made in 92.0% yield?

# ADDITIONAL EXERCISES

**3.85** Write the balanced chemical equations for **(a)** the complete combustion of acetic acid ($CH_3COOH$), the main active ingredient in vinegar; **(b)** the decomposition of solid calcium hydroxide into solid calcium(II) oxide (lime) and water vapor; **(c)** the combination reaction between nickel metal and chlorine gas.

**3.86** If 1.5 mol $C_2H_5OH$, 1.5 mol $C_3H_8$, and 1.5 mol $CH_3CH_2COCH_3$ are completely combusted in oxygen, which produces the largest number of moles of $H_2O$? Which produces the least? Explain.

**3.87** The effectiveness of nitrogen fertilizers depends on both their ability to deliver nitrogen to plants and the amount of nitrogen they can deliver. Four common nitrogen-containing fertilizers are ammonia, ammonium nitrate, ammonium sulfate, and urea [$(NH_2)_2CO$]. Rank these fertilizers in terms of the mass percentage nitrogen they contain.

**3.88** **(a)** The molecular formula of acetylsalicylic acid (aspirin), one of the most common pain relievers, is $C_9H_8O_4$. How many moles of $C_9H_8O_4$ are in a 0.500-g tablet of aspirin? **(b)** How

many molecules of $C_9H_8O_4$ are in this tablet? **(c)** How many carbon atoms are in the tablet?

**3.89** Very small crystals composed of 1000 to 100,000 atoms, called quantum dots, are being investigated for use in electronic devices.
   **(a)** A quantum dot was made of solid silicon in the shape of a sphere, with a diameter of 4 nm. Calculate the mass of the quantum dot, using the density of silicon ($2.3\ g/cm^3$).
   **(b)** How many silicon atoms are in the quantum dot?
   **(c)** The density of germanium is $5.325\ g/cm^3$. If you made a 4-nm quantum dot of germanium, how many Ge atoms would it contain? Assume the dot is spherical.

**3.90** **(a)** One molecule of the antibiotic penicillin G has a mass of $5.342 \times 10^{-21}$ g. What is the molar mass of penicillin G? **(b)** Hemoglobin, the oxygen-carrying protein in red blood cells, has four iron atoms per molecule and contains 0.340% iron by mass. Calculate the molar mass of hemoglobin.

**3.91** Serotonin is a compound that conducts nerve impulses in the brain. It contains 68.2 mass percent C, 6.86 mass percent H, 15.9 mass percent N, and 9.08 mass percent O. Its molar mass is 176 g/mol. Determine its molecular formula.

**3.92** The koala dines exclusively on eucalyptus leaves. Its digestive system detoxifies the eucalyptus oil, a poison to other animals. The chief constituent in eucalyptus oil is a substance called eucalyptol, which contains 77.87% C, 11.76% H, and the remainder O. (a) What is the empirical formula for this substance? (b) A mass spectrum of eucalyptol shows a peak at about 154 amu. What is the molecular formula of the substance?

**3.93** Vanillin, the dominant flavoring in vanilla, contains C, H, and O. When 1.05 g of this substance is completely combusted, 2.43 g of $CO_2$ and 0.50 g of $H_2O$ are produced. What is the empirical formula of vanillin?

**[3.94]** An organic compound was found to contain only C, H, and Cl. When a 1.50-g sample of the compound was completely combusted in air, 3.52 g of $CO_2$ was formed. In a separate experiment the chlorine in a 1.00-g sample of the compound was converted to 1.27 g of AgCl. Determine the empirical formula of the compound.

**[3.95]** A compound, $KBrO_x$, where $x$ is unknown, is analyzed and found to contain 52.92% Br. What is the value of $x$?

**[3.96]** An element X forms an iodide ($XI_3$) and a chloride ($XCl_3$). The iodide is quantitatively converted to the chloride when it is heated in a stream of chlorine:

$$2 XI_3 + 3 Cl_2 \longrightarrow 2 XCl_3 + 3 I_2$$

If 0.5000 g of $XI_3$ is treated, 0.2360 g of $XCl_3$ is obtained. (a) Calculate the atomic weight of the element X. (b) Identify the element X.

**3.97** A method used by the U.S. Environmental Protection Agency (EPA) for determining the concentration of ozone in air is to pass the air sample through a "bubbler" containing sodium iodide, which removes the ozone according to the following equation:

$$O_3(g) + 2 NaI(aq) + H_2O(l) \longrightarrow$$
$$O_2(g) + I_2(s) + 2 NaOH(aq)$$

(a) How many moles of sodium iodide are needed to remove $5.95 \times 10^{-6}$ mol of $O_3$? (b) How many grams of sodium iodide are needed to remove 1.3 mg of $O_3$?

**3.98** A chemical plant uses electrical energy to decompose aqueous solutions of NaCl to give $Cl_2$, $H_2$, and NaOH:

$$2 NaCl(aq) + 2 H_2O(l) \longrightarrow$$
$$2 NaOH(aq) + H_2(g) + Cl_2(g)$$

If the plant produces $1.5 \times 10^6$ kg (1500 metric tons) of $Cl_2$ daily, estimate the quantities of $H_2$ and NaOH produced.

**3.99** The fat stored in a camel's hump is a source of both energy and water. Calculate the mass of $H_2O$ produced by metabolism of 1.0 kg of fat, assuming the fat consists entirely of tristearin ($C_{57}H_{110}O_6$), a typical animal fat, and assuming that during metabolism, tristearin reacts with $O_2$ to form only $CO_2$ and $H_2O$.

**[3.100]** When hydrocarbons are burned in a limited amount of air, both CO and $CO_2$ form. When 0.450 g of a particular hydrocarbon was burned in air, 0.467 g of CO, 0.733 g of $CO_2$, and 0.450 g of $H_2O$ were formed. (a) What is the empirical formula of the compound? (b) How many grams of $O_2$ were used in the reaction? (c) How many grams would have been required for complete combustion?

**3.101** A mixture of $N_2(g)$ and $H_2(g)$ reacts in a closed container to form ammonia, $NH_3(g)$. The reaction ceases before either reactant has been totally consumed. At this stage 3.0 mol $N_2$, 3.0 mol $H_2$, and 3.0 mol $NH_3$ are present. How many moles of $N_2$ and $H_2$ were present originally?

**[3.102]** A mixture containing $KClO_3$, $K_2CO_3$, $KHCO_3$, and KCl was heated, producing $CO_2$, $O_2$, and $H_2O$ gases according to the following equations:

$$2 KClO_3(s) \longrightarrow 2 KCl(s) + 3 O_2(g)$$
$$2 KHCO_3(s) \longrightarrow K_2O(s) + H_2O(g) + 2 CO_2(g)$$
$$K_2CO_3(s) \longrightarrow K_2O(s) + CO_2(g)$$

The KCl does not react under the conditions of the reaction. If 100.0 g of the mixture produces 1.80 g of $H_2O$, 13.20 g of $CO_2$, and 4.00 g of $O_2$, what was the composition of the original mixture? (Assume complete decomposition of the mixture.)

**3.103** When a mixture of 10.0 g of acetylene ($C_2H_2$); and 10.0 g of oxygen ($O_2$) is ignited, the resultant combustion reaction produces $CO_2$ and $H_2O$. (a) Write the balanced chemical equation for this reaction. (b) Which is the limiting reactant? (c) How many grams of $C_2H_2$, $O_2$, $CO_2$, and $H_2O$ are present after the reaction is complete?

**3.104** Aspirin ($C_9H_8O_4$) is produced from salicylic acid ($C_7H_6O_3$) and acetic anhydride ($C_4H_6O_3$):

$$C_7H_6O_3 + C_4H_6O_3 \longrightarrow C_9H_8O_4 + HC_2H_3O_2$$

(a) How much salicylic acid is required to produce $1.5 \times 10^2$ kg of aspirin, assuming that all of the salicylic acid is converted to aspirin? (b) How much salicylic acid would be required if only 80% of the salicylic acid is converted to aspirin? (c) What is the theoretical yield of aspirin if 185 kg of salicylic acid is allowed to react with 125 kg of acetic anhydride? (d) If the situation described in part (c) produces 182 kg of aspirin, what is the percentage yield?

# INTEGRATIVE EXERCISES

These exercises require skills from earlier chapters as well as skills from the present chapter.

**3.105** Consider a sample of calcium carbonate in the form of a cube measuring 2.005 in. on each edge. If the sample has a density of 2.71 $g/cm^3$, how many oxygen atoms does it contain?

**3.106** (a) You are given a cube of silver metal that measures 1.000 cm on each edge. The density of silver is 10.5 $g/cm^3$. How many atoms are in this cube? (b) Because atoms are spherical, they cannot occupy all of the space of the cube. The silver atoms pack in the solid in such a way that 74% of the volume of the solid is actually filled with the silver atoms. Calculate the volume of a single silver atom. (c) Using the volume of a silver atom and the formula for the volume of a sphere, calculate the radius in angstroms of a silver atom.

**3.107** (a) If an automobile travels 225 mi with a gas mileage of 20.5 mi/gal, how many kilograms of $CO_2$ are produced? Assume that the gasoline is composed of octane, $C_8H_{18}(l)$, whose density is 0.69 g/mL. (b) Repeat the calculation for a truck that has a gas mileage of 5 mi/gal.

**3.108** ∞ Section 2.9 introduced the idea of structural isomerism, with 1-propanol and 2-propanol as examples. Determine which of these properties would distinguish these two substances: (a) boiling point; (b) combustion analysis results; (c) molecular weight; (d) density at a given temperature and pressure. You can check on the properties of these two compounds in *Wolfram Alpha* (*http://www.wolframalpha.com/*) or the *CRC Handbook of Chemistry and Physics*.

**3.109** A particular coal contains 2.5% sulfur by mass. When this coal is burned at a power plant, the sulfur is converted into sulfur dioxide gas, which is a pollutant. To reduce sulfur dioxide emissions, calcium oxide (lime) is used. The sulfur dioxide reacts with calcium oxide to form solid calcium sulfite. (a) Write the balanced chemical equation for the reaction. (b) If the coal is burned in a power plant that uses 2000 tons of coal per day, what mass of calcium oxide is required daily to eliminate the sulfur dioxide? (c) How many grams of calcium sulfite are produced daily by this power plant?

**3.110** Copper is an excellent electrical conductor widely used in making electric circuits. In producing a printed circuit board for the electronics industry, a layer of copper is laminated on a plastic board. A circuit pattern is then printed on the board using a chemically resistant polymer. The board is then exposed to a chemical bath that reacts with the exposed copper, leaving the desired copper circuit, which has been protected by the overlaying polymer. Finally, a solvent removes the polymer. One reaction used to remove the exposed copper from the circuit board is

$$Cu(s) + Cu(NH_3)_4Cl_2(aq) + 4\,NH_3(aq) \longrightarrow$$
$$2\,Cu(NH_3)_4Cl(aq)$$

A plant needs to produce 5000 circuit boards, each with a surface area measuring 2.0 in. × 3.0 in. The boards are covered with a 0.65-mm layer of copper. In subsequent processing, 85% of the copper is removed. Copper has a density of 8.96 $g/cm^3$. Calculate the masses of $Cu(NH_3)_4Cl_2$ and $NH_3$ needed to produce the circuit boards, assuming that the reaction used gives a 97% yield.

**3.111** Hydrogen cyanide, HCN, is a poisonous gas. The lethal dose is approximately 300 mg HCN per kilogram of air when inhaled. (a) Calculate the amount of HCN that gives the lethal dose in a small laboratory room measuring 12 × 15 × 8.0 ft. The density of air at 26 °C is 0.00118 $g/cm^3$. (b) If the HCN is formed by reaction of NaCN with an acid such as $H_2SO_4$, what mass of NaCN gives the lethal dose in the room?

$$2\,NaCN(s) + H_2SO_4(aq) \longrightarrow Na_2SO_4(aq) + 2\,HCN(g)$$

(c) HCN forms when synthetic fibers containing Orlon® or Acrilan® burn. Acrilan® has an empirical formula of $CH_2CHCN$, so HCN is 50.9% of the formula by mass. A rug measures 12 × 15 ft and contains 30 oz of Acrilan® fibers per square yard of carpet. If the rug burns, will a lethal dose of HCN be generated in the room? Assume that the yield of HCN from the fibers is 20% and that the carpet is 50% consumed.

**3.112** The source of oxygen that drives the internal combustion engine in an automobile is air. Air is a mixture of gases, principally $N_2$ (~79%) and $O_2$ (~20%). In the cylinder of an automobile engine, nitrogen can react with oxygen to produce nitric oxide gas, NO. As NO is emitted from the tailpipe of the car, it can react with more oxygen to produce nitrogen dioxide gas. (a) Write balanced chemical equations for both reactions. (b) Both nitric oxide and nitrogen dioxide are pollutants that can lead to acid rain and global warming; collectively, they are called "$NO_x$" gases. In 2007, the United States emitted an estimated 22 million tons of nitrogen dioxide into the atmosphere. How many grams of nitrogen dioxide is this? (c) The production of $NO_x$ gases is an unwanted side reaction of the main engine combustion process that turns octane, $C_8H_{18}$, into $CO_2$ and water. If 85% of the oxygen in an engine is used to combust octane and the remainder used to produce nitrogen dioxide, calculate how many grams of nitrogen dioxide would be produced during the combustion of 500 grams of octane.

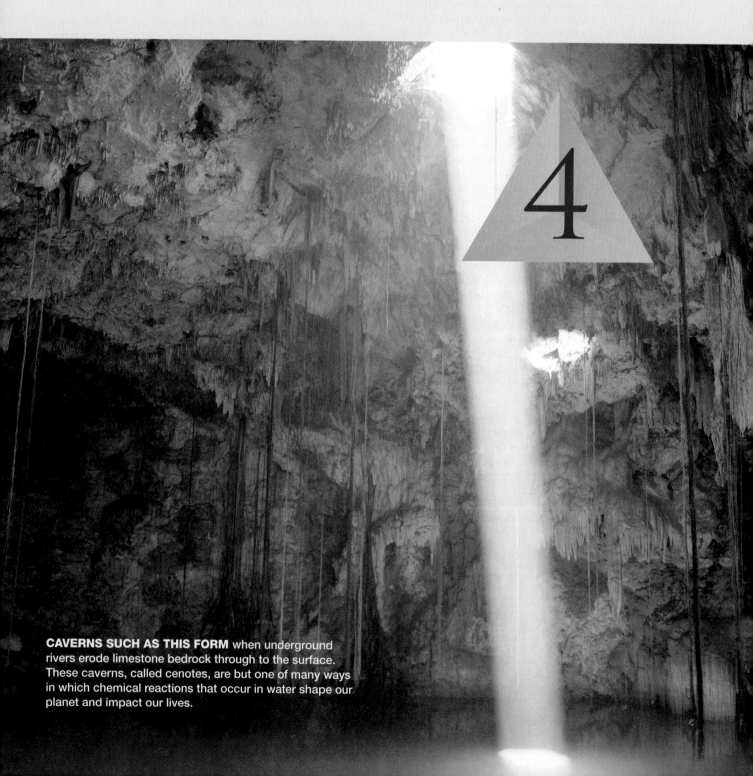

# WHAT'S AHEAD

**4.1 GENERAL PROPERTIES OF AQUEOUS SOLUTIONS**
We begin by examining whether substances dissolved in water exist as ions, molecules, or a mixture of the two.

**4.2 PRECIPITATION REACTIONS**
We identify reactions in which soluble reactants yield an insoluble product.

**4.3 ACIDS, BASES, AND NEUTRALIZATION REACTIONS**
We explore reactions in which protons, $H^+$ ions, are transferred from one reactant to another.

**4.4 OXIDATION-REDUCTION REACTIONS**
We examine reactions in which electrons are transferred from one reactant to another.

**CAVERNS SUCH AS THIS FORM** when underground rivers erode limestone bedrock through to the surface. These caverns, called cenotes, are but one of many ways in which chemical reactions that occur in water shape our planet and impact our lives.

4.5 CONCENTRATIONS OF SOLUTIONS
We learn how the amount of a compound dissolved in a given volume of a solution can be expressed as a *concentration*. Concentration can be defined in a number of ways, the most commonly used being moles of compound per liter of solution (*molarity*).

4.6 SOLUTION STOICHIOMETRY
AND CHEMICAL ANALYSIS
We see how the concepts of stoichiometry and concentration can be used to calculate amounts or concentrations of substances in solution through a process called *titration*.

# REACTIONS IN AQUEOUS SOLUTION

**WATER COVERS NEARLY TWO-THIRDS** of our planet, and this simple substance has been the key to much of Earth's evolutionary history. Life almost certainly originated in water, and the need for water by all forms of life has helped determine diverse biological structures.

Given the importance of water for life, it should come as no surprise that development of civilizations has been closely tied to reliable sources of fresh water. During the first millennium, Mayan civilization was one of the most advanced on Earth. Mayan city-states covered much of the Yucatan peninsula in what is now easternmost Mexico. The northern half of the peninsula is a flat shelf of land composed largely of carbonate rocks, such as limestone. Because there are no rivers and very few lakes, the Mayans depended on sinkholes called *cenotes*, for their fresh water (▶ FIGURE 4.1).

Chemical reactions that occur in water are responsible for creation of cenotes. When carbon dioxide, $CO_2$, dissolves in water, the resulting solution is slightly acidic and reacts with $CaCO_3$ in the limestone:

$$CaCO_3(s) + H_2O(l) + CO_2(aq) \longrightarrow Ca(HCO_3)_2(aq) \qquad [4.1]$$

A solution in which water is the dissolving medium is called an **aqueous solution**. In this chapter we examine chemical reactions that take place in aqueous solutions. In addition, we extend the concepts of stoichiometry learned in Chapter 3 by considering how solution concentrations are expressed and used.

**115**

1 Atmospheric $CO_2$ dissolves in groundwater, forming $H^+$ and $HCO_3^-$

2 Acidic water reacts with $CaCO_3$, dissolving limestone and forming a cenote

▲ **FIGURE 4.1 Cenote formation.**

# 4.1 | GENERAL PROPERTIES OF AQUEOUS SOLUTIONS

A *solution* is a homogeneous mixture of two or more substances. ∞ (Section 1.2) The substance present in the greatest quantity is usually called the **solvent**, and the other substances are called **solutes**; they are said to be *dissolved in* the solvent. When a small amount of sodium chloride (NaCl) is dissolved in a large quantity of water, for example, water is the solvent and sodium chloride is the solute.

## Electrolytic Properties

At a young age we learn not to bring electrical devices into the bathtub so as not to electrocute ourselves. That's a useful lesson because most of the water you encounter in daily life is electrically conducting. Pure water, however, is a very poor conductor of electricity. The conductivity of bathwater originates from the substances dissolved in the water, not from the water itself.

Not all substances that dissolve in water make the resulting solution conducting. Imagine preparing two aqueous solutions—one by dissolving a teaspoon of table salt (sodium chloride) in a cup of water and the other by dissolving a teaspoon of table sugar (sucrose) in a cup of water (▶ **FIGURE 4.2**). Both solutions are clear and colorless, but they possess very different electrical conductivities: the salt solution is a good conductor of electricity, whereas the sugar solution is not.

In order for the bulb in the device of Figure 4.2 to light up, there must be a current (that is, a *flow* of electrically charged particles) between two electrodes immersed in the solution. The conductivity of pure water is not sufficient to complete the electrical circuit and light the bulb. The situation changes when ions are present in solution because the ions carry electrical charge from one electrode to the other, completing the circuit. Thus, the conductivity of NaCl solutions indicates the presence of ions. The lack of conductivity of sucrose solutions indicates the absence of ions. When NaCl dissolves in water, the solution contains $Na^+$ and $Cl^-$ ions, each surrounded by water molecules. When sucrose ($C_{12}H_{22}O_{11}$) dissolves in water, the solution contains only neutral sucrose molecules surrounded by water molecules.

Pure water,
**H₂O(l)**
*does not conduct electricity*

Sucrose solution,
**C₁₂H₂₂O₁₁(aq)**
*Nonelectrolyte
does not conduct electricity*

Sodium chloride solution,
**NaCl(aq)**
*Electrolyte
conducts electricity*

◀ **FIGURE 4.2**
**Electrical conductivities of water and two aqueous solutions.**

A substance (such as NaCl) whose aqueous solutions contain ions is called an **electrolyte**. A substance (such as $C_{12}H_{22}O_{11}$) that does not form ions in solution is called a **nonelectrolyte**. The different classifications of NaCl and $C_{12}H_{22}O_{11}$ arise largely because NaCl is ionic, whereas $C_{12}H_{22}O_{11}$ is molecular.

## Ionic Compounds in Water

Recall from Figure 2.21 that solid NaCl consists of an orderly arrangement of $Na^+$ and $Cl^-$ ions. When NaCl dissolves in water, each ion separates from the solid structure and disperses throughout the solution [▼ **FIGURE 4.3**(a)]. The ionic solid *dissociates* into its component ions as it dissolves.

---

**⚠ GO FIGURE**

**Which solution, NaCl(aq) or CH₃OH(aq), conducts electricity?**

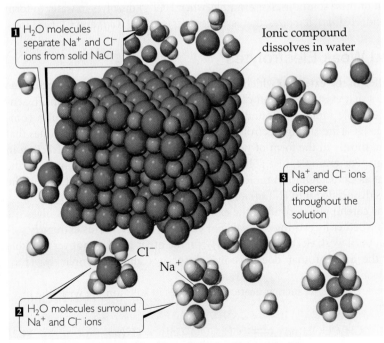

**1** H₂O molecules separate Na⁺ and Cl⁻ ions from solid NaCl

Ionic compound dissolves in water

**3** Na⁺ and Cl⁻ ions disperse throughout the solution

Cl⁻   Na⁺

**2** H₂O molecules surround Na⁺ and Cl⁻ ions

(a) Ionic compounds like sodium chloride, NaCl, form ions when they dissolve

Methanol

(b) Molecular substances like methanol, CH₃OH, dissolve without forming ions

▲ **FIGURE 4.3   Dissolution in water.** (a) When an ionic compound, such as sodium chloride, NaCl, dissolves in water, H₂O molecules separate, surround, and uniformly disperse the ions into the liquid. (b) Molecular substances that dissolve in water, such as methanol, CH₃OH, usually do so without forming ions. We can think of this as a simple mixing of two molecular species. In both (a) and (b) the water molecules have been moved apart so that the solute particles can be seen clearly.

Water is a very effective solvent for ionic compounds. Although $H_2O$ is an electrically neutral molecule, the O atom is rich in electrons and has a partial negative charge, denoted by $\delta^-$. Each H atom has a partial positive charge, denoted by $\delta^+$. Cations are attracted by the negative end of $H_2O$, and anions are attracted by the positive end.

As an ionic compound dissolves, the ions become surrounded by $H_2O$ molecules, as shown in Figure 4.3(a). The ions are said to be *solvated*. In chemical equations, we denote solvated ions by writing them as $Na^+(aq)$ and $Cl^-(aq)$, where $aq$ is an abbreviation for "aqueous."  (Section 3.1) **Solvation** helps stabilize the ions in solution and prevents cations and anions from recombining. Furthermore, because the ions and their shells of surrounding water molecules are free to move about, the ions become dispersed uniformly throughout the solution.

We can usually predict the nature of the ions in a solution of an ionic compound from the chemical name of the substance. Sodium sulfate $(Na_2SO_4)$, for example, dissociates into sodium ions $(Na^+)$ and sulfate ions $(SO_4{}^{2-})$. You must remember the formulas and charges of common ions (Tables 2.4 and 2.5) to understand the forms in which ionic compounds exist in aqueous solution.

### GIVE IT SOME THOUGHT

What dissolved species are present in a solution of
a. KCN,
b. NaClO₄?

## Molecular Compounds in Water

When a molecular compound dissolves in water, the solution usually consists of intact molecules dispersed throughout the solution. Consequently, most molecular compounds are nonelectrolytes. As we have seen, table sugar (sucrose) is a nonelectrolyte. As another example, a solution of methanol $(CH_3OH)$ in water consists entirely of $CH_3OH$ molecules dispersed in the water [Figure 4.3(b)].

A few molecular substances have aqueous solutions that contain ions. Acids are the most important of these solutions. For example, when $HCl(g)$ dissolves in water to form hydrochloric acid, $HCl(aq)$, it *ionizes*; that is, it dissociates into $H^+(aq)$ and $Cl^-(aq)$ ions.

## Strong and Weak Electrolytes

Electrolytes differ in the extent to which they conduct electricity. **Strong electrolytes** are those solutes that exist in solution completely or nearly completely as ions. Essentially all water-soluble ionic compounds (such as NaCl) and a few molecular compounds (such as HCl) are strong electrolytes. **Weak electrolytes** are those solutes that exist in solution mostly in the form of neutral molecules with only a small fraction in the form of ions. For example, in a solution of acetic acid $(CH_3COOH)$ most of the solute is present as $CH_3COOH(aq)$ molecules. Only a small fraction (about 1%) of the $CH_3COOH$ has dissociated into $H^+(aq)$ and $CH_3COO^-(aq)$ ions.*

We must be careful not to confuse the extent to which an electrolyte dissolves (its solubility) with whether it is strong or weak. For example, $CH_3COOH$ is extremely soluble in water but is a weak electrolyte. $Ca(OH)_2$, on the other hand, is not very soluble in water, but the amount that does dissolve dissociates almost completely. Thus, $Ca(OH)_2$ is a strong electrolyte.

When a weak electrolyte, such as acetic acid, ionizes in solution, we write the reaction in the form

$$CH_3COOH(aq) \rightleftharpoons CH_3COO^-(aq) + H^+(aq) \qquad [4.2]$$

The half-arrows pointing in opposite directions mean that the reaction is significant in both directions. At any given moment some $CH_3COOH$ molecules are ionizing to

---

*The chemical formula of acetic acid is sometimes written $HC_2H_3O_2$ so that the formula looks like that of other common acids such as HCl. The formula $CH_3COOH$ conforms to the molecular structure of acetic acid, with the acidic H on the O atom at the end of the formula.

form $H^+$ and $CH_3COO^-$ ions but $H^+$ and $CH_3COO^-$ ions are recombining to form $CH_3COOH$. The balance between these opposing processes determines the relative numbers of ions and neutral molecules. This balance produces a state of **chemical equilibrium** in which the relative numbers of each type of ion or molecule in the reaction are constant over time. Chemists use half-arrows pointing in opposite directions to represent the ionization of weak electrolytes and a single arrow to represent the ionization of strong electrolytes. Because HCl is a strong electrolyte, we write the equation for the ionization of HCl as

$$HCl(aq) \longrightarrow H^+(aq) + Cl^-(aq) \qquad [4.3]$$

The absence of a left-pointing arrow indicates that the $H^+$ and $Cl^-$ ions have no tendency to recombine to form HCl molecules.

In the following sections we will look at how a compound's composition lets us predict whether it is a strong electrolyte, weak electrolyte, or nonelectrolyte. For the moment, you need only to remember that *water-soluble ionic compounds are strong electrolytes*. Ionic compounds can usually be identified by the presence of both metals and nonmetals [for example, NaCl, $FeSO_4$, and $Al(NO_3)_3$]. Ionic compounds containing the ammonium ion, $NH_4^+$ [for example, $NH_4Br$ and $(NH_4)_2CO_3$], are exceptions to this rule of thumb.

 **GIVE IT SOME THOUGHT**

Which solute will cause the lightbulb in Figure 4.2 to glow most brightly, $CH_3OH$, NaOH, or $CH_3COOH$?

---

**SAMPLE EXERCISE 4.1** | **Relating Relative Numbers of Anions and Cations to Chemical Formulas**

The accompanying diagram represents an aqueous solution of either $MgCl_2$, KCl, or $K_2SO_4$. Which solution does the drawing best represent?

**SOLUTION**

**Analyze** We are asked to associate the charged spheres in the diagram with ions present in a solution of an ionic substance.

**Plan** We examine each ionic substance given to determine the relative numbers and charges of its ions. We then correlate these ionic species with the ones shown in the diagram.

**Solve** The diagram shows twice as many cations as anions, consistent with the formulation $K_2SO_4$.

**Check** Notice that the net charge in the diagram is zero, as it must be if it is to represent an ionic substance.

**PRACTICE EXERCISE**

If you were to draw diagrams representing aqueous solutions of (**a**) $NiSO_4$, (**b**) $Ca(NO_3)_2$, (**c**) $Na_3PO_4$, (**d**) $Al_2(SO_4)_3$, how many anions would you show if each diagram contained six cations?

*Answers:* (**a**) 6, (**b**) 12, (**c**) 2, (**d**) 9

---

# 4.2 | PRECIPITATION REACTIONS

▶ **FIGURE 4.4** shows two clear solutions being mixed. One solution contains potassium iodide, KI, dissolved in water and the other contains lead nitrate, $Pb(NO_3)_2$, dissolved in water. The reaction between these two solutes produces a water-insoluble yellow solid. Reactions that result in the formation of an insoluble product are called **precipitation reactions**. A **precipitate** is an insoluble solid formed by a reaction in solution. In Figure 4.4 the precipitate is lead iodide ($PbI_2$), a compound that has a very low solubility in water:

$$Pb(NO_3)_2(aq) + 2 KI(aq) \longrightarrow PbI_2(s) + 2 KNO_3(aq) \qquad [4.4]$$

The other product of this reaction, potassium nitrate ($KNO_3$), remains in solution.

**Which ions remain in solution after PbI₂ precipitation is complete?**

▲ **FIGURE 4.4   A precipitation reaction.**

Precipitation reactions occur when pairs of oppositely charged ions attract each other so strongly that they form an insoluble ionic solid. To predict whether certain combinations of ions form insoluble compounds, we must consider some guidelines concerning the solubilities of common ionic compounds.

## Solubility Guidelines for Ionic Compounds

The **solubility** of a substance at a given temperature is the amount of the substance that can be dissolved in a given quantity of solvent at the given temperature. In our discussions, any substance with a solubility less than 0.01 mol/L will be referred to as *insoluble*. In those cases the attraction between the oppositely charged ions in the solid is too great for the water molecules to separate the ions to any significant extent; the substance remains largely undissolved.

Unfortunately, there are no rules based on simple physical properties such as ionic charge to guide us in predicting whether a particular ionic compound will be soluble. Experimental observations, however, have led to guidelines for predicting solubility for ionic compounds. For example, experiments show that all common ionic compounds that contain the nitrate anion, $NO_3^-$, are soluble in water. ▶ **TABLE 4.1** summarizes the solubility guidelines for common ionic compounds. The table is organized according to the anion in the compound, but it also reveals many important facts about cations. Note that *all common ionic compounds of the alkali metal ions (group 1A of the periodic table) and of the ammonium ion ($NH_4^+$) are soluble in water.*

**TABLE 4.1 • Solubility Guidelines for Common Ionic Compounds in Water**

| Soluble Ionic Compounds | | Important Exceptions |
|---|---|---|
| Compounds containing | $NO_3^-$ | None |
| | $CH_3COO^-$ | None |
| | $Cl^-$ | Compounds of $Ag^+$, $Hg_2^{2+}$, and $Pb^{2+}$ |
| | $Br^-$ | Compounds of $Ag^+$, $Hg_2^{2+}$, and $Pb^{2+}$ |
| | $I^-$ | Compounds of $Ag^+$, $Hg_2^{2+}$, and $Pb^{2+}$ |
| | $SO_4^{2-}$ | Compounds of $Sr^{2+}$, $Ba^{2+}$, $Hg_2^{2+}$, and $Pb^{2+}$ |

| Insoluble Ionic Compounds | | Important Exceptions |
|---|---|---|
| Compounds containing | $S^{2-}$ | Compounds of $NH_4^+$, the alkali metal cations, $Ca^{2+}$, $Sr^{2+}$, and $Ba^{2+}$ |
| | $CO_3^{2-}$ | Compounds of $NH_4^+$ and the alkali metal cations |
| | $PO_4^{3-}$ | Compounds of $NH_4^+$ and the alkali metal cations |
| | $OH^-$ | Compounds of $NH_4^+$, the alkali metal cations, $Ca^{2+}$, $Sr^{2+}$, and $Ba^{2+}$ |

**SAMPLE EXERCISE 4.2** | **Using Solubility Rules**

Classify these ionic compounds as soluble or insoluble in water: (a) sodium carbonate, $Na_2CO_3$, (b) lead sulfate, $PbSO_4$.

**SOLUTION**

**Analyze** We are given the names and formulas of two ionic compounds and asked to predict whether they are soluble or insoluble in water.

**Plan** We can use Table 4.1 to answer the question. Thus, we need to focus on the anion in each compound because the table is organized by anions.

**Solve**

(a) According to Table 4.1, most carbonates are insoluble. But carbonates of the alkali metal cations (such as sodium ion) are an exception to this rule and are soluble. Thus, $Na_2CO_3$ is soluble in water.

(b) Table 4.1 indicates that although most sulfates are water soluble, the sulfate of $Pb^{2+}$ is an exception. Thus, $PbSO_4$ is insoluble in water.

**PRACTICE EXERCISE**

Classify the following compounds as soluble or insoluble in water: (a) cobalt(II) hydroxide, (b) barium nitrate, (c) ammonium phosphate.

*Answers:* (a) insoluble, (b) soluble, (c) soluble

To predict whether a precipitate forms when we mix aqueous solutions of two strong electrolytes, we must (1) note the ions present in the reactants, (2) consider the possible cation–anion combinations, and (3) use Table 4.1 to determine if any of these combinations is insoluble. For example, will a precipitate form when solutions of $Mg(NO_3)_2$ and NaOH are mixed? Both substances are soluble ionic compounds and strong electrolytes. Mixing the solutions first produces a solution containing $Mg^{2+}$, $NO_3^-$, $Na^+$, and $OH^-$ ions. Will either cation interact with either anion to form an insoluble compound? Knowing from Table 4.1 that $Mg(NO_3)_2$ and NaOH are both soluble in water, our only possibilities are $Mg^{2+}$ with $OH^-$ and $Na^+$ with $NO_3^-$. From Table 4.1 we see that hydroxides are generally insoluble. Because $Mg^{2+}$ is not an exception, $Mg(OH)_2$ is insoluble and thus forms a precipitate. $NaNO_3$, however, is soluble, so $Na^+$ and $NO_3^-$ remain in solution. The balanced equation for the precipitation reaction is

$$Mg(NO_3)_2(aq) + 2\,NaOH(aq) \longrightarrow Mg(OH)_2(s) + 2\,NaNO_3(aq) \quad [4.5]$$

## Exchange (Metathesis) Reactions

Notice in Equation 4.5 that the reactant cations exchange anions—$Mg^{2+}$ ends up with $OH^-$, and $Na^+$ ends up with $NO_3^-$. The chemical formulas of the products are based on the charges of the ions—two $OH^-$ ions are needed to give a neutral compound with $Mg^{2+}$, and one $NO_3^-$ ion is needed to give a neutral compound with $Na^+$. ∞ (Section 2.7) *The equation can be balanced only after the chemical formulas of the products have been determined.*

Reactions in which cations and anions appear to exchange partners conform to the general equation

$$AX + BY \longrightarrow AY + BX \qquad [4.6]$$

*Example:* $\qquad AgNO_3(aq) + KCl(aq) \longrightarrow AgCl(s) + KNO_3(aq)$

Such reactions are called either **exchange reactions** or **metathesis reactions** (meh-TATH-eh-sis, Greek for "to transpose"). Precipitation reactions conform to this pattern, as do many neutralization reactions between acids and bases, as we will see in Section 4.3.

To complete and balance the equation for a metathesis reaction, we follow these steps:

1. Use the chemical formulas of the reactants to determine which ions are present.

2. Write the chemical formulas of the products by combining the cation from one reactant with the anion of the other, using the ionic charges to determine the subscripts in the chemical formulas.

3. Check the water solubilities of the products. For a precipitation reaction to occur, at least one product must be insoluble in water.

4. Balance the equation.

---

**SAMPLE EXERCISE 4.3** | **Predicting a Metathesis Reaction**

(a) Predict the identity of the precipitate that forms when aqueous solutions of $BaCl_2$ and $K_2SO_4$ are mixed. (b) Write the balanced chemical equation for the reaction.

**SOLUTION**

**Analyze** We are given two ionic reactants and asked to predict the insoluble product that they form.

**Plan** We need to write the ions present in the reactants and exchange the anions between the two cations. Once we have written the chemical formulas for these products, we can use Table 4.1 to determine which is insoluble in water. Knowing the products also allows us to write the equation for the reaction.

**Solve**

(a) The reactants contain $Ba^{2+}$, $Cl^-$, $K^+$, and $SO_4^{2-}$ ions. Exchanging the anions gives us $BaSO_4$ and $KCl$. According to Table 4.1, most compounds of $SO_4^{2-}$ are soluble but those of $Ba^{2+}$ are not. Thus, $BaSO_4$ is insoluble and will precipitate from solution. KCl is soluble.

(b) From part (a) we know the chemical formulas of the products, $BaSO_4$ and KCl. The balanced equation is

$$BaCl_2(aq) + K_2SO_4(aq) \longrightarrow BaSO_4(s) + 2\,KCl(aq)$$

**PRACTICE EXERCISE**

(a) What compound precipitates when aqueous solutions of $Fe_2(SO_4)_3$ and LiOH are mixed? (b) Write a balanced equation for the reaction. (c) Will a precipitate form when solutions of $Ba(NO_3)_2$ and KOH are mixed?

***Answers:*** (a) $Fe(OH)_3$, (b) $Fe_2(SO_4)_3(aq) + 6\,LiOH(aq) \longrightarrow 2\,Fe(OH)_3(s) + 3\,Li_2SO_4(aq)$, (c) no (both possible products, $Ba(OH)_2$ and $KNO_3$, are water soluble)

---

## Ionic Equations

In writing equations for reactions in aqueous solution, it is often useful to indicate whether the dissolved substances are present predominantly as ions or as molecules. Let's reconsider the precipitation reaction between $Pb(NO_3)_2$ and 2 KI:

$$Pb(NO_3)_2(aq) + 2\,KI(aq) \longrightarrow PbI_2(s) + 2\,KNO_3(aq)$$

An equation written in this fashion, showing the complete chemical formulas of reactants and products, is called a **molecular equation** because it shows chemical formulas without indicating ionic character. Because $Pb(NO_3)_2$, KI, and $KNO_3$ are all water-soluble ionic compounds and therefore strong electrolytes, we can write the equation in a form that indicates which species exist as ions in the solution:

$$Pb^{2+}(aq) + 2\,NO_3^-(aq) + 2\,K^+(aq) + 2\,I^-(aq) \longrightarrow$$
$$PbI_2(s) + 2\,K^+(aq) + 2\,NO_3^-(aq) \qquad [4.7]$$

An equation written in this form, with all soluble strong electrolytes shown as ions, is called a **complete ionic equation**.

Notice that $K^+(aq)$ and $NO_3^-(aq)$ appear on both sides of Equation 4.7. Ions that appear in identical forms on both sides of a complete ionic equation, called **spectator ions**, play no direct role in the reaction. When spectator ions are omitted from the equation (they cancel out like algebraic quantities), we are left with the **net ionic equation**, which is one that includes only the ions and molecules directly involved in the reaction:

$$Pb^{2+}(aq) + 2\,I^-(aq) \longrightarrow PbI_2(s) \qquad [4.8]$$

Because charge is conserved in reactions, the sum of the ionic charges must be the same on both sides of a balanced net ionic equation. In this case the 2+ charge of the cation and the two 1− charges of the anions add to zero, the charge of the electrically neutral product. *If every ion in a complete ionic equation is a spectator, no reaction occurs.*

### GIVE IT SOME THOUGHT

Which ions, if any, are spectator ions in the reaction $AgNO_3(aq) + NaCl(aq) \longrightarrow AgCl(s) + NaNO_3(aq)$?

Net ionic equations illustrate the similarities between various reactions involving electrolytes. For example, Equation 4.8 expresses the essential feature of the precipitation reaction between any strong electrolyte containing $Pb^{2+}(aq)$ and any strong electrolyte containing $I^-(aq)$: The ions combine to form a precipitate of $PbI_2$. Thus, a net ionic equation demonstrates that more than one set of reactants can lead to the same net reaction. For example, aqueous solutions of KI and $MgI_2$ share many chemical similarities because both contain $I^-$ ions. Either solution when mixed with a $Pb(NO_3)_2$ solution produces $PbI_2(s)$. The complete ionic equation, on the other hand, identifies the actual reactants that participate in a reaction.

The following steps summarize the procedure for writing net ionic equations:

1. Write a balanced molecular equation for the reaction.
2. Rewrite the equation to show the ions that form in solution when each soluble strong electrolyte dissociates into its ions. *Only strong electrolytes dissolved in aqueous solution are written in ionic form.*
3. Identify and cancel spectator ions.

---

**SAMPLE EXERCISE 4.4**    **Writing a Net Ionic Equation**

Write the net ionic equation for the precipitation reaction that occurs when aqueous solutions of calcium chloride and sodium carbonate are mixed.

### SOLUTION

**Analyze** Our task is to write a net ionic equation for a precipitation reaction, given the names of the reactants present in solution.

**Plan** We write the chemical formulas of the reactants and products and then determine which product is insoluble. We then write and balance the molecular equation. Next, we write each soluble strong electrolyte as separated ions to obtain the complete ionic equation. Finally, we eliminate the spectator ions to obtain the net ionic equation.

**Solve** Calcium chloride is composed of calcium ions, $Ca^{2+}$, and chloride ions, $Cl^-$; hence, an aqueous solution of the substance is $CaCl_2(aq)$. Sodium carbonate is composed of $Na^+$ ions and $CO_3^{2-}$ ions; hence, an aqueous solution of the compound is $Na_2CO_3(aq)$. In the molecular

▲ **FIGURE 4.5** **Vinegar and lemon juice are common household acids. Ammonia and baking soda (sodium bicarbonate) are common household bases.**

equations for precipitation reactions, the anions and cations appear to exchange partners. Thus, we put $Ca^{2+}$ and $CO_3^{2-}$ together to give $CaCO_3$ and $Na^+$ and $Cl^-$ together to give $NaCl$. According to the solubility guidelines in Table 4.1, $CaCO_3$ is insoluble and $NaCl$ is soluble. The balanced molecular equation is

$$CaCl_2(aq) + Na_2CO_3(aq) \longrightarrow CaCO_3(s) + 2\,NaCl(aq)$$

In a complete ionic equation, *only* dissolved strong electrolytes (such as soluble ionic compounds) are written as separate ions. As the $(aq)$ designations remind us, $CaCl_2$, $Na_2CO_3$, and $NaCl$ are all dissolved in the solution. Furthermore, they are all strong electrolytes. $CaCO_3$ is an ionic compound, but it is not soluble. We do not write the formula of any insoluble compound as its component ions. Thus, the complete ionic equation is

$$Ca^{2+}(aq) + 2\,Cl^-(aq) + 2\,Na^+(aq) + CO_3^{2-}(aq) \longrightarrow$$
$$CaCO_3(s) + 2\,Na^+(aq) + 2\,Cl^-(aq)$$

$Cl^-$ and $Na^+$ are spectator ions. Canceling them gives the following net ionic equation:

$$Ca^{2+}(aq) + CO_3^{2-}(aq) \longrightarrow CaCO_3(s)$$

**Check** We can check our result by confirming that both the elements and the electric charge are balanced. Each side has one Ca, one C, and three O, and the net charge on each side equals 0.

**Comment** If none of the ions in an ionic equation is removed from solution or changed in some way, all ions are spectator ions and a reaction does not occur.

**PRACTICE EXERCISE**
Write the net ionic equation for the precipitation reaction that occurs when aqueous solutions of silver nitrate and potassium phosphate are mixed.

***Answer:*** $3\,Ag^+(aq) + PO_4^{3-}(aq) \longrightarrow Ag_3PO_4(s)$

# 4.3 | ACIDS, BASES, AND NEUTRALIZATION REACTIONS

Many acids and bases are industrial and household substances (◀ **FIGURE 4.5**), and some are important components of biological fluids. Hydrochloric acid, for example, is an important industrial chemical and the main constituent of gastric juice in your stomach. Acids and bases are also common electrolytes.

## Acids

Hydrochloric acid, HCl

Nitric acid, $HNO_3$

| | |
|---|---|
| | H |
| | Cl |
| | N |
| | O |
| | C |

Acetic acid, $CH_3COOH$

▲ **FIGURE 4.6** **Molecular models of three common acids.**

As noted in Section 2.8, **acids** are substances that ionize in aqueous solution to form hydrogen ions $H^+(aq)$. Because a hydrogen atom consists of a proton and an electron, $H^+$ is simply a proton. Thus, acids are often called *proton donors*. Molecular models of three common acids are shown in ◀ **FIGURE 4.6.**

Protons in aqueous solution are solvated by water molecules, just as other cations are [Figure 4.3(a)]. In writing chemical equations involving protons in water, therefore, we write $H^+(aq)$.

Molecules of different acids ionize to form different numbers of $H^+$ ions. Both HCl and $HNO_3$ are *monoprotic* acids, yielding one $H^+$ per molecule of acid. Sulfuric acid, $H_2SO_4$, is a *diprotic* acid, one that yields two $H^+$ per molecule of acid. The ionization of $H_2SO_4$ and other diprotic acids occurs in two steps:

$$H_2SO_4(aq) \longrightarrow H^+(aq) + HSO_4^-(aq) \qquad [4.9]$$

$$HSO_4^-(aq) \rightleftharpoons H^+(aq) + SO_4^{2-}(aq) \qquad [4.10]$$

Although $H_2SO_4$ is a strong electrolyte, only the first ionization (Equation 4.9) is complete. Thus, aqueous solutions of sulfuric acid contain a mixture of $H^+(aq)$, $HSO_4^-(aq)$, and $SO_4^{2-}(aq)$.

The molecule $CH_3COOH$ (acetic acid) that we have mentioned frequently is the primary component in vinegar. Acetic acid has four hydrogens, as Figure 4.6 shows, but only one of them, the H in the COOH group, is ionized in water. The three other hydrogens are bound to carbon and do not break their C—H bonds in water.

⧨ GIVE IT SOME THOUGHT

The structural formula of citric acid, a main component of citrus fruits, is

$$\begin{array}{c} \text{H} \\ | \\ \text{H}-\text{C}-\text{COOH} \\ | \\ \text{HO}-\text{C}-\text{COOH} \\ | \\ \text{H}-\text{C}-\text{COOH} \\ | \\ \text{H} \end{array}$$

How many $H^+(aq)$ can be generated by each citric acid molecule dissolved in water?

▲ **FIGURE 4.7   Hydrogen ion transfer.** An $H_2O$ molecule acts as a proton donor (acid), and $NH_3$ acts as a proton acceptor (base). Only a fraction of the $NH_3$ molecules react with $H_2O$. Consequently, $NH_3$ is a weak electrolyte.

## Bases

**Bases** are substances that accept (react with) $H^+$ ions. Bases produce hydroxide ions ($OH^-$) when they dissolve in water. Ionic hydroxide compounds, such as NaOH, KOH, and $Ca(OH)_2$, are among the most common bases. When dissolved in water, they dissociate into ions, introducing $OH^-$ ions into the solution.

Compounds that do not contain $OH^-$ ions can also be bases. For example, ammonia ($NH_3$) is a common base. When added to water, it accepts an $H^+$ ion from a water molecule and thereby produces an $OH^-$ ion (▶ **FIGURE 4.7**):

$$NH_3(aq) + H_2O(l) \rightleftharpoons NH_4^+(aq) + OH^-(aq) \qquad [4.11]$$

Ammonia is a weak electrolyte because only about 1% of the $NH_3$ forms $NH_4^+$ and $OH^-$ ions.

## Strong and Weak Acids and Bases

Acids and bases that are strong electrolytes (completely ionized in solution) are **strong acids** and **strong bases**. Those that are weak electrolytes (partly ionized) are **weak acids** and **weak bases**. When reactivity depends only on $H^+(aq)$ concentration, strong acids are more reactive than weak acids. The reactivity of an acid, however, can depend on the anion as well as on $H^+(aq)$ concentration. For example, hydrofluoric acid (HF) is a weak acid (only partly ionized in aqueous solution), but it is very reactive and vigorously attacks many substances, including glass. This reactivity is due to the combined action of $H^+(aq)$ and $F^-(aq)$.

▼ **TABLE 4.2** lists the strong acids and bases we are most likely to encounter. You need to commit this information to memory in order to correctly identify strong electrolytes and write net ionic equations. The brevity of this list tells us that most acids are weak. (For $H_2SO_4$, as we noted earlier, only the first proton completely ionizes.) The only common strong bases are the common soluble metal hydroxides. Most other metal hydroxides are insoluble in water. The most common weak base is $NH_3$, which reacts with water to form $OH^-$ ions (Equation 4.11).

| **TABLE 4.2 • Common Strong Acids and Bases** | |
|---|---|
| **Strong Acids** | **Strong Bases** |
| Hydrochloric, HCl | Group 1A metal hydroxides [LiOH, NaOH, KOH, RbOH, CsOH] |
| Hydrobromic, HBr | Heavy group 2A metal hydroxides [$Ca(OH)_2$, $Sr(OH)_2$, $Ba(OH)_2$] |
| Hydroiodic, HI | |
| Chloric, $HClO_3$ | |
| Perchloric, $HClO_4$ | |
| Nitric, $HNO_3$ | |
| Sulfuric, $H_2SO_4$ | |

▲ **GIVE IT SOME THOUGHT**

Why isn't $Al(OH)_3$ classified as a strong base?

---

**SAMPLE EXERCISE 4.5** | **Comparing Acid Strengths**

The following diagrams represent aqueous solutions of acids HX, HY, and HZ, with water molecules omitted for clarity. Rank the acids from strongest to weakest.

HX

HY

HZ

**SOLUTION**

**Analyze** We are asked to rank three acids from strongest to weakest, based on schematic drawings of their solutions.

**Plan** We can determine the relative numbers of uncharged molecular species in the diagrams. The strongest acid is the one with the most $H^+$ ions and fewest undissociated molecules in solution. The weakest acid is the one with the largest number of undissociated molecules.

**Solve** The order is HY > HZ > HX. HY is a strong acid because it is totally ionized (no HY molecules in solution), whereas both HX and HZ are weak acids, whose solutions consist of a mixture of molecules and ions. Because HZ contains more $H^+$ ions and fewer molecules than HX, it is a stronger acid.

**PRACTICE EXERCISE**

Imagine a diagram showing 10 $Na^+$ ions and 10 $OH^-$ ions. If this solution were mixed with the one pictured above for HY, what species would be present in a diagram that represents the combined solutions after any possible reaction?

**Answer:** The diagram would show 10 $Na^+$ ions, 2 $OH^-$ ions, 8 $Y^-$ ions, and 8 $H_2O$ molecules.

---

## Identifying Strong and Weak Electrolytes

If we remember the common strong acids and bases (Table 4.2) and also remember that $NH_3$ is a weak base, we can make reasonable predictions about the electrolytic strength of a great number of *water-soluble* substances. ▼ **TABLE 4.3** summarizes our observations about electrolytes. To classify a soluble substance as strong electrolyte, weak electrolyte, or nonelectrolyte, we work our way down and across this table. We first ask whether the substance is ionic or molecular. If it is ionic, it is a strong electrolyte. The second column of Table 4.3 tells us that all ionic compounds are strong electrolytes. If the substance is molecular, we ask whether it is an acid or a base. (It is an acid if it either has H first in the chemical formula or contains a COOH group.) If it is an acid, we use Table 4.2 to determine whether it is a strong or weak electrolyte: All strong acids are strong electrolytes, and all weak acids are weak electrolytes. If an acid is not listed in Table 4.2, it is probably a weak acid and therefore a weak electrolyte.

**TABLE 4.3** • **Summary of the Electrolytic Behavior of Common Soluble Ionic and Molecular Compounds**

|  | Strong Electrolyte | Weak Electrolyte | Nonelectrolyte |
|---|---|---|---|
| **Ionic** | All | None | None |
| **Molecular** | Strong acids (see Table 4.2) | Weak acids, weak bases | All other compounds |

If our substance is a base, we use Table 4.2 to determine whether it is a strong base. $NH_3$ is the only molecular base that we consider in this chapter, and Table 4.3 tells us it is a weak electrolyte. Finally, any molecular substance that we encounter in this chapter that is not an acid or $NH_3$ is probably a nonelectrolyte.

---

**SAMPLE EXERCISE 4.6** | **Identifying Strong, Weak, and Nonelectrolytes**

Classify these dissolved substances as strong, weak, or nonelectrolyte: $CaCl_2$, $HNO_3$, $C_2H_5OH$ (ethanol), HCOOH (formic acid), KOH.

### SOLUTION

**Analyze** We are given several chemical formulas and asked to classify each substance as a strong electrolyte, weak electrolyte, or nonelectrolyte.

**Plan** The approach we take is outlined in Table 4.3. We can predict whether a substance is ionic or molecular based on its composition. As we saw in Section 2.7, most ionic compounds we encounter in this text are composed of a metal and a nonmetal, whereas most molecular compounds are composed only of nonmetals.

**Solve** Two compounds fit the criteria for ionic compounds: $CaCl_2$ and KOH. Because Table 4.3 tells us that all ionic compounds are strong electrolytes, that is how we classify these two substances. The three remaining compounds are molecular. Two, $HNO_3$ and HCOOH, are acids. Nitric acid, $HNO_3$, is a common strong acid, as shown in Table 4.2, and therefore is a strong electrolyte. Because most acids are weak acids, our best guess would be that HCOOH is a weak acid (weak electrolyte). This is correct. The remaining molecular compound, $C_2H_5OH$, is neither an acid nor a base, so it is a nonelectrolyte.

**Comment** Although $C_2H_5OH$ has an OH group, it is not a metal hydroxide and so not a base. Rather, it is a member of a class of organic compounds that have C—OH bonds, which are known as alcohols. ⬭ (Section 2.9) Organic compounds containing the COOH group are called carboxylic acids (Chapter 16). Molecules that have this group are weak acids.

### PRACTICE EXERCISE

Consider solutions in which 0.1 mol of each of the following compounds is dissolved in 1 L of water: $Ca(NO_3)_2$ (calcium nitrate), $C_6H_{12}O_6$ (glucose), $NaCH_3COO$ (sodium acetate), and $CH_3COOH$ (acetic acid). Rank the solutions in order of increasing electrical conductivity, based on the fact that the greater the number of ions in solution, the greater the conductivity.

**Answers:** $C_6H_{12}O_6$ (nonelectrolyte) < $CH_3COOH$ (weak electrolyte, existing mainly in the form of molecules with few ions) < $NaCH_3COO$ (strong electrolyte that provides two ions, $Na^+$ and $CH_3COO^-$) < $Ca(NO_3)_2$ (strong electrolyte that provides three ions, $Ca^{2+}$ and $2 NO_3^-$)

---

## Neutralization Reactions and Salts

The properties of acidic solutions are quite different from those of basic solutions. Acids have a sour taste, whereas bases have a bitter taste.* Acids change the colors of certain dyes in a way that differs from the way bases affect the same dyes. This is the principle behind the indicator known as litmus paper (▶ **FIGURE 4.8**). In addition, acidic and basic solutions differ in chemical properties in several other important ways that we explore in this chapter and in later chapters.

When a solution of an acid and a solution of a base are mixed, a **neutralization reaction** occurs. The products of the reaction have none of the characteristic properties of either the acidic solution or the basic solution. For example, when hydrochloric acid is mixed with a solution of sodium hydroxide, the reaction is

$$HCl(aq) + NaOH(aq) \longrightarrow H_2O(l) + NaCl\ (aq) \qquad [4.12]$$
$$\text{(acid)} \qquad \text{(base)} \qquad\qquad \text{(water)} \qquad \text{(salt)}$$

Base turns litmus paper blue

Acid turns litmus paper red

▲ **FIGURE 4.8 Litmus paper.** Litmus paper is coated with dyes that change color in response to exposure to either acids or bases.

---

*Tasting chemical solutions is not a good practice. However, we have all had acids such as ascorbic acid (vitamin C), acetylsalicylic acid (aspirin), and citric acid (in citrus fruits) in our mouths, and we are familiar with their characteristic sour taste. Soaps, which are basic, have the characteristic bitter taste of bases.

Water and table salt, NaCl, are the products of the reaction. By analogy to this reaction, the term **salt** has come to mean any ionic compound whose cation comes from a base (for example, $Na^+$ from NaOH) and whose anion comes from an acid (for example, $Cl^-$ from HCl). In general, *a neutralization reaction between an acid and a metal hydroxide produces water and a salt.*

Because HCl, NaOH, and NaCl are all water-soluble strong electrolytes, the complete ionic equation associated with Equation 4.12 is

$$H^+(aq) + Cl^-(aq) + Na^+(aq) + OH^-(aq) \longrightarrow$$
$$H_2O(l) + Na^+(aq) + Cl^-(aq) \quad [4.13]$$

Therefore, the net ionic equation is

$$H^+(aq) + OH^-(aq) \longrightarrow H_2O(l) \quad [4.14]$$

Equation 4.14 summarizes the main feature of the neutralization reaction between any strong acid and any strong base: $H^+(aq)$ and $OH^-(aq)$ ions combine to form $H_2O$.

▼ **FIGURE 4.9** shows the neutralization reaction between hydrochloric acid and the water-insoluble base $Mg(OH)_2$:

*Molecular equation:*

$$Mg(OH)_2(s) + 2\,HCl(aq) \longrightarrow MgCl_2(aq) + 2\,H_2O(l) \quad [4.15]$$

*Net ionic equation:*

$$Mg(OH)_2(s) + 2\,H^+(aq) \longrightarrow Mg^{2+}(aq) + 2\,H_2O(l) \quad [4.16]$$

Notice that the $OH^-$ ions (this time in a solid reactant) and $H^+$ ions combine to form $H_2O$. Because the ions exchange partners, neutralization reactions between acids and metal hydroxides are metathesis reactions.

---

GO FIGURE

**Adding just a few drops of hydrochloric acid would not be sufficient to dissolve all the $Mg(OH)_2(s)$. Why not?**

*Reactants*
**$Mg(OH)_2(s) + 2\,HCl(aq)$**

$H^+(aq)$ combines with
hydroxide ions in $Mg(OH)_2(s)$,
forming $H_2O(l)$

*Products*
**$MgCl_2(aq) + 2\,H_2O(l)$**

▲ **FIGURE 4.9  Neutralization reaction between $Mg(OH)_2(s)$ and hydrochloric acid.** Milk of magnesia is a suspension of water-insoluble magnesium hydroxide, $Mg(OH)_2(s)$, in water. When sufficient hydrochloric acid, $HCl(aq)$, is added a reaction ensues that leads to an aqueous solution containing $Mg^{2+}(aq)$ and $Cl^-(aq)$ ions.

**SAMPLE EXERCISE 4.7**   **Writing Chemical Equations for a Neutralization Reaction**

For the reaction between aqueous solutions of acetic acid ($CH_3COOH$) and barium hydroxide, $Ba(OH)_2$, write **(a)** the balanced molecular equation, **(b)** the complete ionic equation, **(c)** the net ionic equation.

## SOLUTION

**Analyze** We are given the chemical formulas for an acid and a base and asked to write a balanced molecular equation, a complete ionic equation, and a net ionic equation for their neutralization reaction.

**Plan** As Equation 4.12 and the italicized statement that follows it indicate, neutralization reactions form two products, $H_2O$ and a salt. We examine the cation of the base and the anion of the acid to determine the composition of the salt.

**Solve**

**(a)** The salt contains the cation of the base $(Ba^{2+})$ and the anion of the acid $(CH_3COO^-)$. Thus, the salt formula is $Ba(CH_3COO)_2$. According to Table 4.1, this compound is soluble in water. The unbalanced molecular equation for the neutralization reaction is

$$CH_3COOH(aq) + Ba(OH)_2(aq) \longrightarrow H_2O(l) + Ba(CH_3COO)_2(aq)$$

To balance this equation, we must provide two molecules of $CH_3COOH$ to furnish the two $CH_3COO^-$ ions and to supply the two $H^+$ ions needed to combine with the two $OH^-$ ions of the base. The balanced molecular equation is

$$2\ CH_3COOH(aq) + Ba(OH)_2(aq) \longrightarrow$$
$$2\ H_2O(l) + Ba(CH_3COO)_2(aq)$$

**(b)** To write the complete ionic equation, we identify the strong electrolytes and break them into ions. In this case $Ba(OH)_2$ and $Ba(CH_3COO)_2$ are both water-soluble ionic compounds and hence strong electrolytes. Thus, the complete ionic equation is

$$2\ CH_3COOH(aq) + Ba^{2+}(aq) + 2\ OH^-(aq) \longrightarrow$$
$$2\ H_2O(l) + Ba^{2+}(aq) + 2\ CH_3COO^-(aq)$$

**(c)** Eliminating the spectator ion, $Ba^{2+}$, and simplifying coefficients gives the net ionic equation:

$$2\ CH_3COOH(aq) + 2\ OH^-(aq) \longrightarrow 2\ H_2O(l) + 2\ CH_3COO^-(aq)$$
$$CH_3COOH(aq) + OH^-(aq) \longrightarrow H_2O(l) + CH_3COO^-(aq)$$

**Check** We can determine whether the molecular equation is balanced by counting the number of atoms of each kind on both sides of the arrow (10 H, 6 O, 4 C, and 1 Ba on each side). However, it is often easier to check equations by counting groups: There are

2 $CH_3COO$ groups, as well as 1 Ba, and 4 additional H atoms and 2 additional O atoms on each side of the equation. The net ionic equation checks out because the numbers of each kind of element and the net charge are the same on both sides of the equation.

## PRACTICE EXERCISE

For the reaction of phosphorous acid ($H_3PO_3$) and potassium hydroxide (KOH), write **(a)** the balanced molecular equation and **(b)** the net ionic equation.

*Answers:* **(a)** $H_3PO_3(aq) + 3\ KOH(aq) \longrightarrow 3\ H_2O(l) + K_3PO_3(aq)$,
**(b)** $H_3PO_3(aq) + 3\ OH^-(aq) \longrightarrow 3\ H_2O(l) + PO_3^{3-}(aq)$. ($H_3PO_3$ is a weak acid and therefore a weak electrolyte, whereas KOH, a strong base, and $K_3PO_3$, an ionic compound, are strong electrolytes.)

# Neutralization Reactions with Gas Formation

Many bases besides $OH^-$ react with $H^+$ to form molecular compounds. Two of these that you might encounter in the laboratory are the sulfide ion and the carbonate ion. Both of these anions react with acids to form gases that have low solubilities in water. Hydrogen sulfide ($H_2S$), the substance that gives rotten eggs their foul odor, forms when an acid such as $HCl(aq)$ reacts with a metal sulfide such as $Na_2S$:

*Molecular equation:*

$$2\ HCl(aq) + Na_2S(aq) \longrightarrow H_2S(g) + 2\ NaCl(aq) \qquad [4.17]$$

*Net ionic equation:*

$$2\ H^+(aq) + S^{2-}(aq) \longrightarrow H_2S(g) \qquad [4.18]$$

Carbonates and bicarbonates react with acids to form $CO_2(g)$. Reaction of $CO_3^{2-}$ or $HCO_3^-$ with an acid first gives carbonic acid ($H_2CO_3$). For example, when hydrochloric acid is added to sodium bicarbonate, the reaction is

$$HCl(aq) + NaHCO_3(aq) \longrightarrow NaCl(aq) + H_2CO_3(aq) \qquad [4.19]$$

Carbonic acid is unstable. If present in solution in sufficient concentrations, it decomposes to $H_2O$ and $CO_2$, which escapes from the solution as a gas:

$$H_2CO_3(aq) \longrightarrow H_2O(l) + CO_2(g) \qquad [4.20]$$

The overall reaction is summarized by the equations

*Molecular equation:*

$$HCl(aq) + NaHCO_3(aq) \longrightarrow NaCl(aq) + H_2O(l) + CO_2(g) \qquad [4.21]$$

*Net ionic equation:*

$$H^+(aq) + HCO_3^-(aq) \longrightarrow H_2O(l) + CO_2(g) \qquad [4.22]$$

Both $NaHCO_3(s)$ and $Na_2CO_3(s)$ are used as neutralizers in acid spills, either salt is added until the fizzing caused by $CO_2(g)$ formation stops. Sometimes sodium bicarbonate is used as an antacid to soothe an upset stomach. In that case the $HCO_3^-$ reacts with stomach acid to form $CO_2(g)$.

 GIVE IT SOME THOUGHT

By analogy to examples given in the text, predict what gas forms when $Na_2SO_3(s)$ reacts with $HCl(aq)$.

## CHEMISTRY PUT TO WORK

### Antacids

Your stomach secretes acids to help digest foods. These acids, which include hydrochloric acid, contain about 0.1 mol of $H^+$ per liter of solution. The stomach and digestive tract are normally protected from the corrosive effects of stomach acid by a mucosal lining. Holes can develop in this lining, however, allowing the acid to attack the underlying tissue, causing painful damage. These holes, known as ulcers, can be caused by the secretion of excess acids or by a weakness in the digestive lining. Studies indicate, however, that many ulcers are caused by bacterial infection. Between 10 and 20% of Americans suffer from ulcers at some point in their lives. Many others experience occasional indigestion or heartburn due to digestive acids entering the esophagus.

We can address the problem of excess stomach acid in two ways: (1) removing the excess acid or (2) decreasing the production of acid. Substances that remove excess acid are called *antacids*, whereas those that decrease acid production are called *acid inhibitors*. ◀ FIGURE 4.10 shows several common over-the-counter antacids, which usually contain hydroxide, carbonate, or bicarbonate ions (▼ TABLE 4.4). Antiulcer drugs, such as Tagamet® and Zantac®, are acid inhibitors. They act on acid-producing cells in the lining of the stomach. Formulations that control acid in this way are now available as over-the-counter drugs.

*RELATED EXERCISE: 4.95*

▲ **FIGURE 4.10  Antacids.** These products all serve as acid-neutralizing agents in the stomach.

**TABLE 4.4 • Some Common Antacids**

| Commercial Name | Acid-Neutralizing Agents |
| --- | --- |
| Alka-Seltzer® | $NaHCO_3$ |
| Amphojel® | $Al(OH)_3$ |
| Di-Gel® | $Mg(OH)_2$ and $CaCO_3$ |
| Milk of Magnesia | $Mg(OH)_2$ |
| Maalox® | $Mg(OH)_2$ and $Al(OH)_3$ |
| Mylanta® | $Mg(OH)_2$ and $Al(OH)_3$ |
| Rolaids® | $NaAl(OH)_2CO_3$ |
| Tums® | $CaCO_3$ |

# 4.4 | OXIDATION-REDUCTION REACTIONS

In precipitation reactions, cations and anions come together to form an insoluble ionic compound. In neutralization reactions, $H^+$ ions and $OH^-$ ions come together to form $H_2O$ molecules. Now let's consider a third kind of reaction, one in which electrons are transferred from one reactant to another. Such reactions are called either **oxidation-reduction reactions** or **redox reactions**. In this chapter we concentrate on redox reactions where one of the reactants is a metal in its elemental form.

## Oxidation and Reduction

One of the most familiar redox reactions is *corrosion* of a metal (▼ FIGURE 4.11). In some instances corrosion is limited to the surface of the metal, with the green coating that forms on copper roofs and statues being one such case. In other instances the corrosion goes deeper, eventually compromising the structural integrity of the metal. Iron rusting is an important example.

Corrosion is the conversion of a metal into a metal compound by a reaction between the metal and some substance in its environment. When a metal corrodes, each metal atom loses electrons and so forms a cation, which can combine with an anion to form an ionic compound. The green coating on the Statue of Liberty contains $Cu^{2+}$ combined with carbonate and hydroxide anions, rust contains $Fe^{3+}$ combined with oxide and hydroxide anions, and silver tarnish contains $Ag^+$ combined with sulfide anions.

When an atom, ion, or molecule becomes more positively charged (that is, when it loses electrons), we say that it has been oxidized. *Loss of electrons by a substance is called* **oxidation**. The term *oxidation* is used because the first reactions of this sort to be studied were reactions with oxygen. Many metals react directly with $O_2$ in air to form metal oxides. In these reactions the metal loses electrons to oxygen, forming an ionic compound of the metal ion and oxide ion. The familiar example of rusting involves the reaction between iron metal and oxygen in the presence of water. In this process Fe is *oxidized* (loses electrons) to form $Fe^{3+}$.

The reaction between iron and oxygen tends to be relatively slow, but other metals, such as the alkali and alkaline earth metals, react quickly upon exposure to air. ▶ FIGURE 4.12 shows how the bright metallic surface of calcium tarnishes as CaO forms in the reaction

$$2\,Ca(s) \,+\, O_2(g) \,\longrightarrow\, 2\,CaO(s) \qquad [4.23]$$

In this reaction Ca is oxidized to $Ca^{2+}$ and neutral $O_2$ is transformed to $O^{2-}$ ions. When an atom, ion, or molecule becomes more negatively charged (gains electrons), we say that it is *reduced*. *The gain of electrons by a substance is called* **reduction**. When one reactant loses electrons (that is, when it is *oxidized*), another reactant must gain them. In other words, oxidation of one substance must be accompanied by reduction of some other substance.

(a)

(b)

(c)

▲ FIGURE 4.11   **Familiar corrosion products.** (a) A green coating forms when copper is oxidized. (b) Rust forms when iron corrodes. (c) A black tarnish forms as silver corrodes.

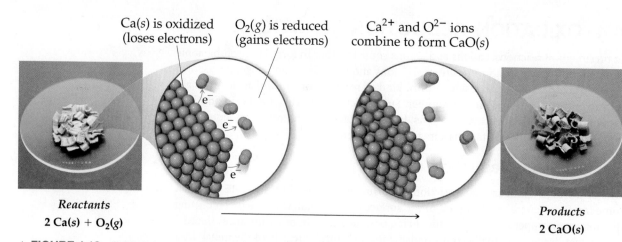

Ca(*s*) is oxidized
(loses electrons)

O$_2$(*g*) is reduced
(gains electrons)

Ca$^{2+}$ and O$^{2-}$ ions
combine to form CaO(*s*)

*Reactants*

**2 Ca(*s*) + O$_2$(*g*)**

*Products*

**2 CaO(*s*)**

▲ **FIGURE 4.12   Oxidation of calcium metal by molecular oxygen.** The oxidation involves transfer of electrons from the calcium metal to the O$_2$, leading to formation of CaO.

## Oxidation Numbers

Before we can identify an oxidation-reduction reaction, we must have a bookkeeping system—a way of keeping track of electrons gained by the substance being reduced and electrons lost by the substance being oxidized. The concept of oxidation numbers (also called *oxidation states*) was devised as a way of doing this. Each atom in a neutral substance or ion is assigned an **oxidation number**. For monatomic ions the oxidation number is the same as the charge. For neutral molecules and polyatomic ions, the oxidation number of a given atom is a hypothetical charge. This charge is assigned by artificially dividing up the electrons among the atoms in the molecule or ion. We use the following rules for assigning oxidation numbers:

1. *For an atom in its **elemental form**, the oxidation number is always zero.* Thus, each H atom in the H$_2$ molecule has an oxidation number of 0 and each P atom in the P$_4$ molecule has an oxidation number of 0.

2. *For any **monatomic ion** the oxidation number equals the ionic charge.* Thus, K$^+$ has an oxidation number of +1, S$^{2-}$ has an oxidation number of −2, and so forth. In ionic compounds the alkali metal ions (group 1A) always have a 1+ charge and therefore an oxidation number of +1. The alkaline earth metals (group 2A) are always +2, and aluminum (group 3A) is always +3 in ionic compounds. (In writing oxidation numbers we will write the sign before the number to distinguish them from the actual electronic charges, which we write with the number first.)

3. ***Nonmetals** usually have negative oxidation numbers, although they can sometimes be positive:*

   (a) *The oxidation number of **oxygen** is usually −2 in both ionic and molecular compounds.* The major exception is in compounds called peroxides, which contain the O$_2{}^{2-}$ ion, giving each oxygen an oxidation number of −1.

   (b) *The oxidation number of **hydrogen** is usually +1 when bonded to nonmetals and −1 when bonded to metals.*

   (c) *The oxidation number of **fluorine** is −1 in all compounds.* The other **halogens** have an oxidation number of −1 in most binary compounds. When combined with oxygen, as in oxyanions, however, they have positive oxidation states.

4. ***The sum of the oxidation numbers** of all atoms in a neutral compound is zero. The sum of the oxidation numbers in a polyatomic ion equals the charge of the ion.* For example, in the hydronium ion H$_3$O$^+$ the oxidation number of each hydrogen is +1 and that of oxygen is −2. Thus, the sum of the oxidation numbers is $3(+1) + (−2) = +1$, which equals the net charge of the ion. This rule is useful in obtaining the oxidation number of one atom in a compound or ion if you know the oxidation numbers of the other atoms, as illustrated in Sample Exercise 4.8.

It's important to remember that in every oxidation-reduction reaction, the oxidation numbers of at least two atoms must change. The oxidation number increases for any atom that is oxidized and decreases for any atom that is reduced.

## ▲ GIVE IT SOME THOUGHT

What is the oxidation number of nitrogen (a) in aluminum nitride, AlN, and (b) in nitric acid, $HNO_3$?

---

**SAMPLE EXERCISE 4.8** | **Determining Oxidation Numbers**

Determine the oxidation number of sulfur in (a) $H_2S$, (b) $S_8$, (c) $SCl_2$, (d) $Na_2SO_3$, (e) $SO_4^{2-}$.

### SOLUTION

**Analyze** We are asked to determine the oxidation number of sulfur in two molecular species, in the elemental form, and in two substances containing ions.

**Plan** In each species the sum of oxidation numbers of all the atoms must equal the charge on the species. We will use the rules outlined previously to assign oxidation numbers.

**Solve**
(a) When bonded to a nonmetal, hydrogen has an oxidation number of $+1$ (rule 3b). Because the $H_2S$ molecule is neutral, the sum of the oxidation numbers must equal zero (rule 4). Letting $x$ equal the oxidation number of S, we have $2(+1) + x = 0$. Thus, S has an oxidation number of $-2$.

(b) Because this is an elemental form of sulfur, the oxidation number of S is 0 (rule 1).

(c) Because this is a binary compound, we expect chlorine to have an oxidation number of $-1$ (rule 3c). The sum of the oxidation numbers must equal zero (rule 4). Letting $x$ equal the oxidation number of S, we have $x + 2(-1) = 0$. Consequently, the oxidation number of S must be $+2$.

(d) Sodium, an alkali metal, always has an oxidation number of $+1$ in its compounds (rule 2). Oxygen has a common oxidation state of $-2$ (rule 3a). Letting $x$ equal the oxidation number of S, we have $2(+1) + x + 3(-2) = 0$. Therefore, the oxidation number of S in this compound is $+4$.

(e) The oxidation state of O is $-2$ (rule 3a). The sum of the oxidation numbers equals $-2$, the net charge of the $SO_4^{2-}$ ion (rule 4). Thus, we have $x + 4(-2) = -2$. From this relation we conclude that the oxidation number of S in this ion is $+6$.

**Comment** These examples illustrate that the oxidation number of a given element depends on the compound in which it occurs. The oxidation numbers of sulfur, as seen in these examples, range from $-2$ to $+6$.

### PRACTICE EXERCISE

What is the oxidation state of the boldfaced element in (a) $\mathbf{P}_2O_5$, (b) $Na\mathbf{H}$, (c) $\mathbf{Cr}_2O_7^{2-}$, (d) $\mathbf{Sn}Br_4$, (e) $Ba\mathbf{O}_2$?
*Answers:* (a) $+5$, (b) $-1$, (c) $+6$, (d) $+4$, (e) $-1$

---

## Oxidation of Metals by Acids and Salts

The reaction between a metal and either an acid or a metal salt conforms to the general pattern

$$A + BX \longrightarrow AX + B \qquad\qquad [4.24]$$

*Examples:*
$$Zn(s) + 2\,HBr(aq) \longrightarrow ZnBr_2(aq) + H_2(g)$$

$$Mn(s) + Pb(NO_3)_2(aq) \longrightarrow Mn(NO_3)_2(aq) + Pb(s)$$

These reactions are called **displacement reactions** because the ion in solution is *displaced* (replaced) through oxidation of an element.

▲ **FIGURE 4.13** **Reaction of magnesium metal with hydrochloric acid.** The metal is readily oxidized by the acid, producing hydrogen gas, $H_2(g)$, and $MgCl_2(aq)$.

Many metals undergo displacement reactions with acids, producing salts and hydrogen gas. For example, magnesium metal reacts with hydrochloric acid to form magnesium chloride and hydrogen gas (▲ **FIGURE 4.13**):

$$Mg(s) + 2\,HCl(aq) \longrightarrow MgCl_2(aq) + H_2(g) \qquad [4.25]$$

Oxidation number    0        +1  −1        +2  −1        0

The oxidation number of Mg changes from 0 to +2, an increase that indicates the atom has lost electrons and has therefore been oxidized. The oxidation number of $H^+$ in the acid decreases from +1 to 0, indicating that this ion has gained electrons and has therefore been reduced. Chlorine has an oxidation number of −1 both before and after the reaction, indicating that it is neither oxidized nor reduced. In fact the $Cl^-$ ions are spectator ions, dropping out of the net ionic equation:

$$Mg(s) + 2\,H^+(aq) \longrightarrow Mg^{2+}(aq) + H_2(g) \qquad [4.26]$$

Metals can also be oxidized by aqueous solutions of various salts. Iron metal, for example, is oxidized to $Fe^{2+}$ by aqueous solutions of $Ni^{2+}$ such as $Ni(NO_3)_2(aq)$:

*Molecular equation:*    $Fe(s) + Ni(NO_3)_2(aq) \longrightarrow Fe(NO_3)_2(aq) + Ni(s)$    [4.27]

*Net ionic equation:*    $Fe(s) + Ni^{2+}(aq) \longrightarrow Fe^{2+}(aq) + Ni(s)$    [4.28]

The oxidation of Fe to $Fe^{2+}$ in this reaction is accompanied by the reduction of $Ni^{2+}$ to Ni. Remember: *Whenever one substance is oxidized, another substance must be reduced.*

**SAMPLE EXERCISE 4.9** | **Writing Equations for Oxidation-Reduction Reactions**

Write the balanced molecular and net ionic equations for the reaction of aluminum with hydrobromic acid.

### SOLUTION

**Analyze** We must write two equations—molecular and net ionic—for the redox reaction between a metal and an acid.

**Plan** Metals react with acids to form salts and $H_2$ gas. To write the balanced equations, we must write the chemical formulas for the two reactants and then determine the formula of the salt, which is composed of the cation formed by the metal and the anion of the acid.

**Solve** The reactants are Al and HBr. The cation formed by Al is $Al^{3+}$, and the anion from hydrobromic acid is $Br^-$. Thus, the salt formed in the reaction is $AlBr_3$. Writing the reactants and products and then balancing the equation gives the molecular equation:

$$2\,Al(s) + 6\,HBr(aq) \longrightarrow 2\,AlBr_3(aq) + 3\,H_2(g)$$

Both HBr and $AlBr_3$ are soluble strong electrolytes. Thus, the complete ionic equation is

$$2\,Al(s) + 6\,H^+(aq) + 6\,Br^-(aq) \longrightarrow 2\,Al^{3+}(aq) + 6\,Br^-(aq) + 3\,H_2(g)$$

Because $Br^-$ is a spectator ion, the net ionic equation is

$$2\,Al(s) + 6\,H^+(aq) \longrightarrow 2\,Al^{3+}(aq) + 3\,H_2(g)$$

**Comment** The substance oxidized is the aluminum metal because its oxidation state changes from 0 in the metal to +3 in the cation, thereby increasing in oxidation number. The $H^+$ is reduced because its oxidation state changes from +1 in the acid to 0 in $H_2$.

### PRACTICE EXERCISE

**(a)** Write the balanced molecular and net ionic equations for the reaction between magnesium and cobalt(II) sulfate. **(b)** What is oxidized and what is reduced in the reaction?

*Answers:* **(a)** $Mg(s) + CoSO_4(aq) \longrightarrow MgSO_4(aq) + Co(s)$;
$Mg(s) + Co^{2+}(aq) \longrightarrow Mg^{2+}(aq) + Co(s)$, **(b)** Mg is oxidized and $Co^{2+}$ is reduced.

## The Activity Series

Can we predict whether a certain metal will be oxidized either by an acid or by a particular salt? This question is of practical importance as well as chemical interest. According to Equation 4.27, for example, it would be unwise to store a solution of nickel nitrate in an iron container because the solution would dissolve the container. When a metal is oxidized, it forms various compounds. Extensive oxidation can lead to the failure of metal machinery parts or the deterioration of metal structures.

Different metals vary in the ease with which they are oxidized. Zn is oxidized by aqueous solutions of $Cu^{2+}$, for example, but Ag is not. Zn, therefore, loses electrons more readily than Ag; that is, Zn is easier to oxidize than Ag.

A list of metals arranged in order of decreasing ease of oxidation, such as ▶ **TABLE 4.5**, is called an **activity series**. The metals at the top of the table, such as the alkali metals and the alkaline earth metals, are most easily oxidized; that is, they react most readily to form compounds. They are called the *active metals*. The metals at the bottom of the activity series, such as the transition elements from groups 8B and 1B, are very stable and form compounds less readily. These metals, which are used to make coins and jewelry, are called *noble metals* because of their low reactivity.

The activity series can be used to predict the outcome of reactions between metals and either metal salts or acids. *Any metal on the list can be oxidized by the ions of elements below it.* For example, copper is above silver in the series. Thus, copper metal is oxidized by silver ions:

$$Cu(s) + 2\,Ag^+(aq) \longrightarrow Cu^{2+}(aq) + 2\,Ag(s) \qquad [4.29]$$

**TABLE 4.5 • Activity Series of Metals in Aqueous Solution**

| Metal | Oxidation Reaction |
|---|---|
| Lithium | $Li(s) \longrightarrow Li^+(aq) + e^-$ |
| Potassium | $K(s) \longrightarrow K^+(aq) + e^-$ |
| Barium | $Ba(s) \longrightarrow Ba^{2+}(aq) + 2e^-$ |
| Calcium | $Ca(s) \longrightarrow Ca^{2+}(aq) + 2e^-$ |
| Sodium | $Na(s) \longrightarrow Na^+(aq) + e^-$ |
| Magnesium | $Mg(s) \longrightarrow Mg^{2+}(aq) + 2e^-$ |
| Aluminum | $Al(s) \longrightarrow Al^{3+}(aq) + 3e^-$ |
| Manganese | $Mn(s) \longrightarrow Mn^{2+}(aq) + 2e^-$ |
| Zinc | $Zn(s) \longrightarrow Zn^{2+}(aq) + 2e^-$ |
| Chromium | $Cr(s) \longrightarrow Cr^{3+}(aq) + 3e^-$ |
| Iron | $Fe(s) \longrightarrow Fe^{2+}(aq) + 2e^-$ |
| Cobalt | $Co(s) \longrightarrow Co^{2+}(aq) + 2e^-$ |
| Nickel | $Ni(s) \longrightarrow Ni^{2+}(aq) + 2e^-$ |
| Tin | $Sn(s) \longrightarrow Sn^{2+}(aq) + 2e^-$ |
| Lead | $Pb(s) \longrightarrow Pb^{2+}(aq) + 2e^-$ |
| Hydrogen | $H_2(g) \longrightarrow 2H^+(aq) + 2e^-$ |
| Copper | $Cu(s) \longrightarrow Cu^{2+}(aq) + 2e^-$ |
| Silver | $Ag(s) \longrightarrow Ag^+(aq) + e^-$ |
| Mercury | $Hg(l) \longrightarrow Hg^{2+}(aq) + 2e^-$ |
| Platinum | $Pt(s) \longrightarrow Pt^{2+}(aq) + 2e^-$ |
| Gold | $Au(s) \longrightarrow Au^{3+}(aq) + 3e^-$ |

Ease of oxidation increases →

The oxidation of copper to copper ions is accompanied by the reduction of silver ions to silver metal. The silver metal is evident on the surface of the copper wire in ▶ **FIGURE 4.14**. The copper(II) nitrate produces a blue color in the solution, as can be seen most clearly in the photograph on the right of Figure 4.14.

### GIVE IT SOME THOUGHT

Does a reaction occur (a) when an aqueous solution of $NiCl_2(aq)$ is added to a test tube containing strips of metallic zinc, and (b) when $NiCl_2(aq)$ is added to a test tube containing $Zn(NO_3)_2(aq)$?

Only metals above hydrogen in the activity series are able to react with acids to form $H_2$. For example, Ni reacts with $HCl(aq)$ to form $H_2$:

$$Ni(s) + 2HCl(aq) \longrightarrow NiCl_2(aq) + H_2(g) \qquad [4.30]$$

Because elements below hydrogen in the activity series are not oxidized by $H^+$, Cu does not react with $HCl(aq)$. Interestingly, copper does react with nitric acid, as shown in Figure 1.11, but the reaction is not oxidation of Cu by $H^+$ ions. Instead, the metal is oxidized to $Cu^{2+}$ by the nitrate ion, accompanied by the formation of brown nitrogen dioxide, $NO_2(g)$:

$$Cu(s) + 4HNO_3(aq) \longrightarrow Cu(NO_3)_2(aq) + 2H_2O(l) + 2NO_2(g) \quad [4.31]$$

As the copper is oxidized in this reaction, $NO_3^-$, where the oxidation number of nitrogen is $+5$, is reduced to $NO_2$, where the oxidation number of nitrogen is $+4$. We will examine reactions of this type in Chapter 20.

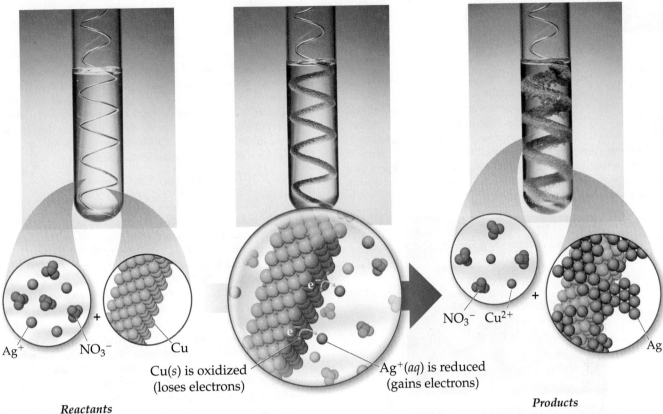

Ag$^+$   NO$_3^-$   +   Cu

Cu(s) is oxidized
(loses electrons)

Ag$^+$(aq) is reduced
(gains electrons)

NO$_3^-$   Cu$^{2+}$   +   Ag

*Reactants*
**2 AgNO$_3$(aq) + Cu(s)**

*Products*
**Cu(NO$_3$)$_2$(aq) + 2 Ag(s)**

▲ **FIGURE 4.14** **Reaction of copper metal with silver ion.** When copper metal is placed in a solution of silver nitrate, a redox reaction forms silver metal and a blue solution of copper(II) nitrate.

---

**SAMPLE EXERCISE 4.10** **Determining When an Oxidation-Reduction Reaction Can Occur**

Will an aqueous solution of iron(II) chloride oxidize magnesium metal? If so, write the balanced molecular and net ionic equations for the reaction.

**SOLUTION**

**Analyze** We are given two substances—an aqueous salt, FeCl$_2$, and a metal, Mg—and asked if they react with each other.

**Plan** A reaction occurs if the reactant that is a metal in its elemental form (Mg) is located above the reactant that is a metal in its oxidized form (Fe$^{2+}$) in Table 4.5. If the reaction occurs, the Fe$^{2+}$ ion in FeCl$_2$ is reduced to Fe, and the Mg is oxidized to Mg$^{2+}$.

**Solve** Because Mg is above Fe in the table, the reaction occurs. To write the formula for the salt produced in the reaction, we must remember the charges on common ions. Magnesium is always present in compounds as Mg$^{2+}$; the chloride ion is Cl$^-$. The magnesium salt formed in the reaction is MgCl$_2$, meaning the balanced molecular equation is

$$Mg(s) + FeCl_2(aq) \longrightarrow MgCl_2(aq) + Fe(s)$$

Both FeCl$_2$ and MgCl$_2$ are soluble strong electrolytes and can be written in ionic form, which shows us that Cl$^-$ is a spectator ion in the reaction. The net ionic equation is

$$Mg(s) + Fe^{2+}(aq) \longrightarrow Mg^{2+}(aq) + Fe(s)$$

The net ionic equation shows that Mg is oxidized and Fe$^{2+}$ is reduced in this reaction.

**Check** Note that the net ionic equation is balanced with respect to both charge and mass.

**PRACTICE EXERCISE**

Which of the following metals will be oxidized by Pb(NO$_3$)$_2$: Zn, Cu, Fe?

**Answer:** Zn and Fe

# A CLOSER LOOK

## THE AURA OF GOLD

Throughout history, people have cherished gold, fought for it, and even died for it.

The physical and chemical properties of gold make it special. First, its intrinsic beauty and rarity make it precious. Second, it is soft and can be easily formed into jewelry, coins, and other objects. Third, it is one of the least active metals (Table 4.5). It is not oxidized in air and does not react with water (▼ **FIGURE 4.15**), with basic solutions, or with most acidic solutions.

▲ **FIGURE 4.15 The chemical inertness of gold.** Two, stamped, weighed, and priced (in the 1800's) gold bars recently recovered from a steamship that sank off the coast of Central America in 1857.

Many of the early studies on gold arose from *alchemy*, in which people attempted to turn cheap metals, such as lead, into gold. Alchemists discovered that gold can be dissolved in a 3:1 mixture of concentrated hydrochloric and nitric acids, known as aqua regia ("royal water"). The action of the nitric acid on gold is similar to that on copper (Equation 4.31) in that the nitrate ion, rather than $H^+$, oxidizes the metal to $Au^{3+}$. The $Cl^-$ ions interact with $Au^{3+}$ to form highly stable $AuCl_4^-$ ions. The net ionic equation is

$$Au(s) + NO_3^-(aq) + 4\,H^+(aq) + 4\,Cl^-(aq) \longrightarrow$$
$$AuCl_4^-(aq) + 2\,H_2O(l) + NO(g)$$

All the gold ever mined would fit in a cube 21 m on a side and weighing about $1.6 \times 10^8$ kg. More than 90% of this amount has been produced since the 1848 California gold rush. Annual worldwide production of gold is about $2.4 \times 10^6$ kg. By contrast 16,000 times more aluminum, over $3.97 \times 10^{10}$ kg, are produced annually.

Roughly three-quarters of gold production goes to make jewelry, where it is often alloyed with other metals. Approximately 12% of gold production is used to meet a variety of industrial applications, most notably in electronic devices where its excellent conductivity and corrosion resistance make it a valuable component. A typical touch-tone telephone contains 33 gold-plated contacts. Gold is also used in computers and other microelectronic devices where fine gold wire is used to link components.

Because of its resistance to corrosion, gold is an ideal metal for dental crowns and caps, which accounts for about 3% of the annual use of the element. The pure metal is too soft to use in dentistry, so it is combined with other metals to form alloys.

*RELATED EXERCISE:* 4.91

# STRATEGIES IN CHEMISTRY

## ANALYZING CHEMICAL REACTIONS

In this chapter you have been introduced to a great number of chemical reactions. A major difficulty students face in trying to master material of this sort is gaining a "feel" for what happens when chemicals react. In fact, you might marvel at the ease with which your professor or teaching assistant can figure out the results of a chemical reaction. One of our goals in this textbook is to help you become more adept at predicting the outcomes of reactions. The key to gaining this "chemical intuition" is understanding how to categorize reactions.

Attempting to memorize individual reactions would be a futile task. It is far more fruitful to recognize patterns to determine the general category of a reaction, such as metathesis or oxidation-reduction. Thus, when you are faced with the challenge of predicting the outcome of a chemical reaction, ask yourself the following questions:

- What are the reactants?
- Are they electrolytes or nonelectrolytes?
- Are they acids and bases?
- If the reactants are electrolytes, will metathesis produce a precipitate? Water? A gas?
- If metathesis cannot occur, can the reactants engage in an oxidation-reduction reaction? This requires that there be both a reactant that can be oxidized and a reactant that can be reduced.

By asking questions such as these, you should be able to predict what happens during the reaction. You might not always be entirely correct, but if you keep your wits about you, you will not be far off. As you gain experience, you will begin to look for reactants that might not be immediately obvious, such as water from the solution or oxygen from the atmosphere.

One of the greatest tools available to chemists is experimentation. If you perform an experiment in which two solutions are mixed, you can make observations that help you understand what is happening. For example, using Table 4.1 to predict whether a precipitate will form is not nearly as exciting as seeing the precipitate form, as in Figure 4.4. Careful observations in the laboratory portion of the course will make your lecture material easier to master.

# 4.5 | CONCENTRATIONS OF SOLUTIONS

Scientists use the term **concentration** to designate the amount of solute dissolved in a given quantity of solvent or quantity of solution. The greater the amount of solute dissolved in a certain amount of solvent, the more concentrated the resulting solution. In chemistry we often need to express the concentrations of solutions quantitatively.

## Molarity

**Molarity** (symbol $M$) expresses the concentration of a solution as the number of moles of solute in a liter of solution (soln):

$$\text{Molarity} = \frac{\text{moles solute}}{\text{volume of solution in liters}} \qquad [4.32]$$

A 1.00 molar solution (written 1.00 $M$) contains 1.00 mol of solute in every liter of solution. ▼ **FIGURE 4.16** shows the preparation of 250.0 mL of a 1.00 $M$ solution of $CuSO_4$. The molarity of the solution is $(0.250 \text{ mol } CuSO_4)/(0.250 \text{ L soln}) = 1.00 \, M$.

### ⚠ GIVE IT SOME THOUGHT

Which is more concentrated, a solution prepared by dissolving 21.0 g of NaF (0.500 mol) in enough water to make 500 mL of solution or a solution prepared by dissolving 10.5 g (0.250 mol) of NaF in enough water to make 100 mL of solution?

1 Weigh out 39.9 g (0.250 mol) $CuSO_4$

2 Put $CuSO_4$ (solute) into 250-mL volumetric flask; add water and swirl to dissolve solute

3 Add water until solution just reaches calibration mark on neck of flask

◀ **FIGURE 4.16** Preparing 0.250 L of a 1.00 $M$ solution of $CuSO_4$.

---

**SAMPLE EXERCISE 4.11** | **Calculating Molarity**

Calculate the molarity of a solution made by dissolving 23.4 g of sodium sulfate ($Na_2SO_4$) in enough water to form 125 mL of solution.

### SOLUTION

**Analyze** We are given the number of grams of solute (23.4 g), its chemical formula ($Na_2SO_4$), and the volume of the solution (125 mL) and asked to calculate the molarity of the solution.

**Plan** We can calculate molarity using Equation 4.32. To do so, we must convert the number of grams of solute to moles and the volume of the solution from milliliters to liters.

**Solve** The number of moles of $Na_2SO_4$ is obtained by using its molar mass:

$$\text{Moles } Na_2SO_4 = (23.4 \text{ g } Na_2SO_4)\left(\frac{1 \text{ mol } Na_2SO_4}{142 \text{ g } Na_2SO_4}\right) = 0.165 \text{ mol } Na_2SO_4$$

Converting the volume of the solution to liters:

$$\text{Liters soln} = (125 \text{ mL})\left(\frac{1 \text{ L}}{1000 \text{ mL}}\right) = 0.125 \text{ L}$$

Thus, the molarity is

$$\text{Molarity} = \frac{0.165 \text{ mol } Na_2SO_4}{0.125 \text{ L soln}} = 1.32 \frac{\text{mol } Na_2SO_4}{\text{L soln}} = 1.32 \text{ } M$$

**Check** Because the numerator is only slightly larger than the denominator, it is reasonable for the answer to be a little over 1 $M$. The units (mol/L) are appropriate for molarity, and three signifi- cant figures are appropriate for the answer because each of the initial pieces of data had three significant figures.

**PRACTICE EXERCISE**

Calculate the molarity of a solution made by dissolving 5.00 g of glucose ($C_6H_{12}O_6$) in sufficient water to form exactly 100 mL of solution.
*Answer:* 0.278 $M$

## Expressing the Concentration of an Electrolyte

When an ionic compound dissolves, the relative concentrations of the ions in the solu- tion depend on the chemical formula of the compound. For example, a 1.0 $M$ solution of NaCl is 1.0 $M$ in $Na^+$ ions and 1.0 $M$ in $Cl^-$ ions, and a 1.0 $M$ solution of $Na_2SO_4$ is 2.0 $M$ in $Na^+$ ions and 1.0 $M$ in $SO_4^{2-}$ ions. Thus, the concentration of an electrolyte solution can be specified either in terms of the compound used to make the solution (1.0 $M$ $Na_2SO_4$) or in terms of the ions in the solution (2.0 $M$ $Na^+$ and 1.0 $M$ $SO_4^{2-}$).

**SAMPLE EXERCISE 4.12** | **Calculating Molar Concentrations of Ions**

What is the molar concentration of each ion present in a 0.025 $M$ aqueous solution of calcium nitrate?

**SOLUTION:**

**Analyze** We are given the concentration of the ionic compound used to make the solution and asked to determine the concentrations of the ions in the solution.

**Plan** We can use the subscripts in the chemical formula of the compound to determine the relative ion concentrations.

**Solve** Calcium nitrate is composed of calcium ions ($Ca^{2+}$) and nitrate ions ($NO_3^-$), so its chemical formula is $Ca(NO_3)_2$. Because there are two $NO_3^-$ ions for each $Ca^{2+}$ ion, each mole of $Ca(NO_3)_2$ that dissolves dissociates into 1 mol of $Ca^{2+}$ and 2 mol of $NO_3^-$. Thus, a solution that is 0.025 $M$ in $Ca(NO_3)_2$ is 0.025 $M$ in $Ca^{2+}$ and $2 \times 0.025 M = 0.050 M$ in $NO_3^-$:

$$\frac{\text{mol } NO_3^-}{L} = \left(\frac{0.025 \text{ mol } Ca(NO_3)_2}{L}\right)\left(\frac{2 \text{ mol } NO_3^-}{1 \text{ mol } Ca(NO_3)_2}\right) = 0.050 \text{ } M$$

**Check** The concentration of $NO_3^-$ ions is twice that of $Ca^{2+}$ ions, as the subscript 2 after the $NO_3^-$ in the chemical formula $Ca(NO_3)_2$ suggests it should be.

**PRACTICE EXERCISE**

What is the molar concentration of $K^+$ ions in a 0.015 $M$ solution of potassium carbonate?
*Answer:* 0.030 $M$

## Interconverting Molarity, Moles, and Volume

If we know any two of the three quantities in Equation 4.32, we can calculate the third. For example, if we know the molarity of an $HNO_3$ solution to be 0.200 $M$, which means 0.200 mol of $HNO_3$ per liter of solution, we can calculate the number of moles of solute in a given volume, say 2.0 L. Molarity therefore is a conversion factor between volume of solution and moles of solute:

$$\text{Moles } HNO_3 = (2.0 \text{ L soln})\left(\frac{0.200 \text{ mol } HNO_3}{1 \text{ L soln}}\right) = 0.40 \text{ mol } HNO_3$$

To illustrate the conversion of moles to volume, let's calculate the volume of 0.30 $M$ $HNO_3$ solution required to supply 2.0 mol of $HNO_3$:

$$\text{Liters soln} = (2.0 \text{ mol } HNO_3)\left(\frac{1 \text{ L soln}}{0.30 \text{ mol } HNO_3}\right) = 6.7 \text{ L soln}$$

In this case we must use the reciprocal of molarity in the conversion: Liters = moles $\times$ $1/M$ = moles $\times$ liters/mole.

---

**SAMPLE EXERCISE 4.13**  **Using Molarity to Calculate Grams of Solute**

How many grams of $Na_2SO_4$ are required to make 0.350 L of 0.500 $M$ $Na_2SO_4$?

**SOLUTION**

**Analyze** We are given the volume of the solution (0.350 L), its concentration (0.500 $M$), and the identity of the solute $Na_2SO_4$ and asked to calculate the number of grams of the solute in the solution.

**Plan** We can use the definition of molarity (Equation 4.32) to determine the number of moles of solute, and then convert moles to grams using the molar mass of the solute.

$$M_{Na_2SO_4} = \frac{\text{moles } Na_2SO_4}{\text{liters soln}}$$

**Solve** Calculating the moles of $Na_2SO_4$ using the molarity and volume of solution gives

$$M_{Na_2SO_4} = \frac{\text{moles } Na_2SO_4}{\text{liters soln}}$$

$$\text{Moles } Na_2SO_4 = \text{liters soln} \times M_{Na_2SO_4}$$

$$= (0.350 \text{ L soln})\left(\frac{0.500 \text{ mol } Na_2SO_4}{1 \text{ L soln}}\right)$$

$$= 0.175 \text{ mol } Na_2SO_4$$

Because each mole of $Na_2SO_4$ has a mass of 142 g, the required number of grams of $Na_2SO_4$ is

$$\text{Grams } Na_2SO_4 = (0.175 \text{ mol } Na_2SO_4)\left(\frac{142 \text{ g } Na_2SO_4}{1 \text{ mol } Na_2SO_4}\right) = 24.9 \text{ g } Na_2SO_4$$

**Check** The magnitude of the answer, the units, and the number of significant figures are all appropriate.

**PRACTICE EXERCISE**

(a) How many grams of $Na_2SO_4$ are there in 15 mL of 0.50 $M$ $Na_2SO_4$? (b) How many milliliters of 0.50 $M$ $Na_2SO_4$ solution are needed to provide 0.038 mol of this salt?
**Answers:** (a) 1.1 g, (b) 76 mL

---

# Dilution

Solutions used routinely in the laboratory are often purchased or prepared in concentrated form (called *stock solutions*). Solutions of lower concentrations can then be obtained by adding water, a process called **dilution**.*

Let's see how we can prepare a dilute solution from a concentrated one. Suppose we want to prepare 250.0 mL (that is, 0.2500 L) of 0.100 $M$ $CuSO_4$ solution by diluting a 1.00 $M$ $CuSO_4$ stock solution. The main point to remember is that when solvent is added to a solution, the number of moles of solute remains unchanged:

$$\text{Moles solute before dilution} = \text{moles solute after dilution} \qquad [4.33]$$

---

*In diluting a concentrated acid or base, the acid or base should be added to water and then further diluted by adding more water. Adding water directly to concentrated acid or base can cause spattering because of the intense heat generated.

Because we know both the volume (250 mL) and the concentration (0.100 mol/L) of the dilute solution, we can calculate the number of moles of $CuSO_4$ it contains:

$$\text{Moles } CuSO_4 \text{ in dilute soln} = (0.2500 \text{ L soln})\left(\frac{0.100 \text{ mol } CuSO_4}{\text{L soln}}\right)$$

$$= 0.0250 \text{ mol } CuSO_4$$

The volume of stock solution needed to provide 0.0250 mol $CuSO_4$ is therefore:

$$\text{Liters of conc soln} = (0.0250 \text{ mol } CuSO_4)\left(\frac{1 \text{ L soln}}{1.00 \text{ mol } CuSO_4}\right) = 0.0250 \text{ L}$$

▼ **FIGURE 4.17** shows the dilution carried out in the laboratory. Notice that the diluted solution is less intensely colored than the concentrated one.

▲ **GIVE IT SOME THOUGHT**

How is the molarity of a 0.50 $M$ KBr solution changed when water is added to double its volume?

In laboratory situations, calculations of this sort are often made with an equation derived by remembering that the number of moles of solute is the same in both the concentrated and dilute solutions and that moles = molarity × liters:

$$\text{Moles solute in conc soln} = \text{moles solute in dilute soln}$$

$$M_{conc} \times V_{conc} = M_{dil} \times V_{dil} \qquad [4.34]$$

Although we derived Equation 4.34 in terms of liters, any volume unit can be used as long as it is used on both sides of the equation. For example, in the calculation we did for the $CuSO_4$ solution, we have

$$(1.00\ M)(V_{conc}) = (0.100\ M)(250.\ \text{mL})$$

Solving for $V_{conc}$ gives $V_{conc} = 25.0$ mL as before.

**1** Draw 25.0 mL of 1.00 $M$ stock solution into pipet

**2** Add concentrated solution in pipet to 250–mL volumetric flask

**3** Dilute with water until solution reaches calibration mark on neck of flask and mix to create 0.100 $M$ solution

▲ **FIGURE 4.17**   **Preparing 250 mL of 0.100 $M$ $CuSO_4$ by dilution of 1.00 $M$ $CuSO_4$.**

# CHEMISTRY AND LIFE

## DRINKING TOO MUCH WATER CAN KILL YOU

For a long time dehydration was considered a potential danger for people engaged in extended vigorous activity. Thus, athletes were encouraged to drink lots of water while engaged in active sport. The trend toward extensive hydration has spread throughout society, so that today many people carry water bottles everywhere and dutifully keep well hydrated.

In some circumstances, however, drinking too much water is a greater danger than not drinking enough. Excess water consumption can lead to *hyponatremia*, a condition in which the concentration of sodium ion in the blood is too low. In the past decade at least four marathon runners have died from hyponatremia-related trauma, and dozens more have become seriously ill. For example, a first-time marathoner named Hillary Bellamy, running in the Marine Corps marathon in 2003, collapsed near mile 22 and died the next day. One physician who treated her said that she died from hyponatremia-induced brain swelling, the result of drinking too much water before and during the race.

The normal blood sodium level is 135 to 145 m*M* *(millimolar)*. When that level drops to 125 m*M*, dizziness and confusion set in. A concentration below 120 m*M* can be critical. Dangerously low levels can occur in any active athlete who is sweating out salt (NaCl) at the same time that excessive amounts of NaCl-free water are being drunk to compensate for water loss. The condition affects women more than men because of differences in body composition and patterns of metabolism. Drinking a sport drink that contains some electrolytes helps to prevent hyponatremia.

*RELATED EXERCISES:* 4.63, 4.64

---

**SAMPLE EXERCISE 4.14**   **Preparing a Solution by Dilution**

How many milliliters of 3.0 *M* $H_2SO_4$ are needed to make 450 mL of 0.10 *M* $H_2SO_4$?

### SOLUTION

**Analyze** We need to dilute a concentrated solution. We are given the molarity of a more concentrated solution (3.0 *M*) and the volume and molarity of a more dilute one containing the same solute (450 mL of 0.10 *M* solution). We must calculate the volume of the concentrated solution needed to prepare the dilute solution.

**Plan** We can calculate the number of moles of solute, $H_2SO_4$, in the dilute solution and then calculate the volume of the concentrated solution needed to supply this amount of solute. Alternatively, we can directly apply Equation 4.34. Let's compare the two methods.

**Solve** Calculating the moles of $H_2SO_4$ in the dilute solution:

$$\text{Moles } H_2SO_4 \text{ in dilute solution} = (0.450 \text{ L soln})\left(\frac{0.10 \text{ mol } H_2SO_4}{1 \text{ L soln}}\right)$$
$$= 0.045 \text{ mol } H_2SO_4$$

Calculating the volume of the concentrated solution that contains 0.045 mol $H_2SO_4$:

$$\text{L conc soln} = (0.045 \text{ mol } H_2SO_4)\left(\frac{1 \text{ L soln}}{3.0 \text{ mol } H_2SO_4}\right) = 0.015 \text{ L soln}$$

Converting liters to milliliters gives 15 mL.
If we apply Equation 4.34, we get the same result:

$$(3.0 \, M)(V_{conc}) = (0.10 \, M)(450 \text{ mL})$$
$$(V_{conc}) = \frac{(0.10 \, M)(450 \text{ mL})}{3.0 \, M} = 15 \text{ mL}$$

Either way, we see that if we start with 15 mL of 3.0 *M* $H_2SO_4$ and dilute it to a total volume of 450 mL, the desired 0.10 *M* solution will be obtained.

**Check** The calculated volume seems reasonable because a small volume of concentrated solution is used to prepare a large volume of dilute solution.

**Comment** The first approach can also be used to find the final concentration when two solutions of different concentrations are mixed, whereas the second approach, using Equation 4.34, can be used only for diluting a concentrated solution with pure solvent.

### PRACTICE EXERCISE

**(a)** What volume of 2.50 *M* lead(II) nitrate solution contains 0.0500 mol of $Pb^{2+}$? **(b)** How many milliliters of 5.0 *M* $K_2Cr_2O_7$ solution must be diluted to prepare 250 mL of 0.10 *M* solution? **(c)** If 10.0 mL of a 10.0 *M* stock solution of NaOH is diluted to 250 mL, what is the concentration of the resulting stock solution?

*Answers:* **(a)** 0.0200 L = 20.0 mL, **(b)** 5.0 mL, **(c)** 0.40 *M*

# 4.6 | SOLUTION STOICHIOMETRY AND CHEMICAL ANALYSIS

In Chapter 3 we learned that given the chemical equation for a reaction and the amount of one reactant consumed in the reaction, you can calculate the quantities of other reactants and products. In this section we extend this concept to reactions involving solutions.

Recall that the coefficients in a balanced equation give the relative number of moles of reactants and products. ∞ (Section 3.6) To use this information, we must convert the masses of substances involved in a reaction into moles. When dealing with pure substances, as we were in Chapter 3, we use molar mass to convert between grams and moles of the substances. This conversion is not valid when working with a solution because both solute and solvent contribute to its mass. However, if we know the solute concentration, we can use molarity and volume to determine the number of moles (moles solute = $M \times V$). ▼ **FIGURE 4.18** summarizes this approach to using stoichiometry for the reaction between a pure substance and a solution.

---

**SAMPLE EXERCISE 4.15** | **Using Mass Relations in a Neutralization Reaction**

How many grams of $Ca(OH)_2$ are needed to neutralize 25.0 mL of 0.100 $M$ $HNO_3$?

**SOLUTION**

**Analyze** The reactants are an acid, $HNO_3$, and a base, $Ca(OH)_2$. The volume and molarity of $HNO_3$ are given, and we are asked how many grams of $Ca(OH)_2$ are needed to neutralize this quantity of $HNO_3$.

**Plan** Following the steps outlined by the green arrows in Figure 4.18, we use the molarity and volume of the $HNO_3$ solution (substance B in Figure 4.18) to calculate the number of moles of $HNO_3$. We then use the balanced equation to relate moles of $HNO_3$ to moles of $Ca(OH)_2$ (substance A). Finally, we use the molar mass to convert moles to grams of $Ca(OH)_2$:

$$V_{HNO_3} \times M_{HNO_3} \Rightarrow \text{mol } HNO_3 \Rightarrow \text{mol } Ca(OH)_2 \Rightarrow \text{g } Ca(OH)_2$$

**Solve** The product of the molar concentration of a solution and its volume in liters gives the number of moles of solute:

$$\text{Moles } HNO_3 = V_{HNO_3} \times M_{HNO_3} = (0.0250 \text{ L})\left(\frac{0.100 \text{ mol } HNO_3}{\text{L}}\right)$$

$$= 2.50 \times 10^{-3} \text{ mol } HNO_3$$

---

◄ **FIGURE 4.18** **Procedure for solving stoichiometry problems involving reactions between a pure substance A and a solution containing a known concentration of substance B.** Starting from a known mass of substance A, we follow the red arrows to determine either the volume of the solution containing B (if the molarity of B is known) or the molarity of the solution containing B (if the volume of B is known). Starting from either a known volume or known molarity of the solution containing B, we follow the green arrows to determine the mass of substance A.

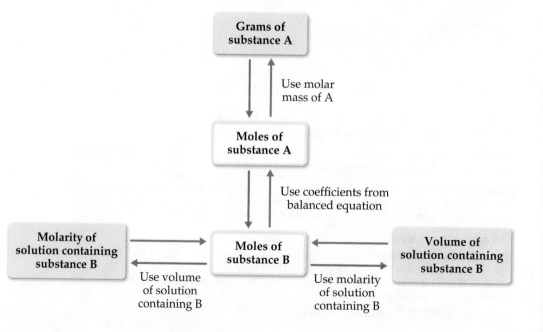

Because this is a neutralization reaction, $HNO_3$ and $Ca(OH)_2$ react to form $H_2O$ and the salt containing $Ca^{2+}$ and $NO_3^-$:

$$2\ HNO_3(aq) + Ca(OH)_2(s) \longrightarrow 2\ H_2O(l) + Ca(NO_3)_2(aq)$$

Thus, 2 mol $HNO_3 \simeq$ mol $Ca(OH)_2$. Therefore,

$$\text{Grams } Ca(OH)_2 = (2.50 \times 10^{-3}\ \text{mol } HNO_3)\left(\frac{1\ \text{mol } Ca(OH)_2}{2\ \text{mol } HNO_3}\right)\left(\frac{74.1\ \text{g } Ca(OH)_2}{1\ \text{mol } Ca(OH)_2}\right)$$

$$= 0.0926\ \text{g } Ca(OH)_2$$

**Check** The answer is reasonable because a small volume of dilute acid requires only a small amount of base to neutralize it.

**PRACTICE EXERCISE**

**(a)** How many grams of NaOH are needed to neutralize 20.0 mL of 0.150 $M$ $H_2SO_4$ solution?
**(b)** How many liters of 0.500 $M$ HCl($aq$) are needed to react completely with 0.100 mol of $Pb(NO_3)_2(aq)$, forming a precipitate of $PbCl_2(s)$?

**Answers:** **(a)** 0.240 g, **(b)** 0.400 L

## Titrations

To determine the concentration of a particular solute in a solution, chemists often carry out a **titration**, which involves combining a solution where the solute concentration is not known with a reagent solution of known concentration, called a **standard solution**. Just enough standard solution is added to completely react with the solute in the solution of unknown concentration. The point at which stoichiometrically equivalent quantities are brought together is known as the **equivalence point**.

Titrations can be conducted using neutralization, precipitation, or oxidation-reduction reactions. ▼ **FIGURE 4.19** illustrates a typical neutralization titration, one between a HCl solution of unknown concentration and a NaOH solution we know to have a concentration of 0.100 $M$ (our standard solution). To determine the HCl concentration, we first add a specific volume of the HCl solution, 20.0 mL in this example, to a flask. Next

△ **GO FIGURE**

How would the volume of standard solution added change if that solution were $Ba(OH)_2(aq)$ instead of NaOH($aq$)?

**1** 20.0 mL of acid solution added to flask

**2** A few drops of acid–base indicator added

**3** Standard NaOH solution added from buret

**4** Solution becomes basic on passing equivalence point, triggering indicator color change

Initial volume reading

Buret

Final volume reading

▲ **FIGURE 4.19  Procedure for titrating an acid against a standard solution of NaOH.**
The acid–base indicator, phenolphthalein, is colorless in acidic solution but takes on a pink color in basic solution.

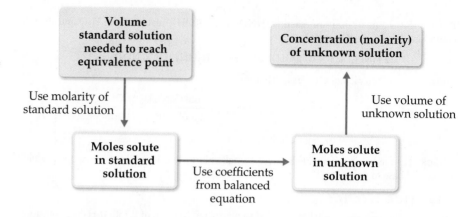

a few drops of an acid–base indicator are added. The acid–base indicator is a dye that changes color on passing the equivalence point.* For example, the dye phenolphthalein is colorless in acidic solution but pink in basic solution. The standard solution is then slowly added until the solution turns pink, telling us that the neutralization reaction between HCl and NaOH is complete. The standard solution is added from a *buret* so that we can accurately determine the added volume of NaOH solution. Knowing the volumes of both solutions and the concentration of the standard solution we can calculate the concentration of the unknown solution as diagrammed in ▲ FIGURE 4.20.

---

**SAMPLE EXERCISE 4.16** | **Determining Solution Concentration by an Acid–Base Titration**

One commercial method used to peel potatoes is to soak them in a NaOH solution for a short time, then remove them and spray off the peel. The NaOH concentration is normally 3 to 6 $M$, and the solution must be analyzed periodically. In one such analysis, 45.7 mL of 0.500 $M$ $H_2SO_4$ is required to neutralize 20.0 mL of NaOH solution. What is the concentration of the NaOH solution?

**SOLUTION**

**Analyze** We are given the volume (45.7 mL) and molarity (0.500 $M$) of an $H_2SO_4$ solution (the standard solution) that reacts completely with 20.0 mL of NaOH solution. We are asked to calculate the molarity of the NaOH solution.

**Plan** Following the steps of Figure 4.20, we use the $H_2SO_4$ volume and molarity to calculate the number of moles of $H_2SO_4$. Then we can use this quantity and the balanced equation for the reaction to calculate moles of NaOH. Finally, we can use moles of NaOH and the NaOH volume to calculate NaOH molarity.

**Solve** The number of moles of $H_2SO_4$ is the product of the volume and molarity of this solution:

$$\text{Moles } H_2SO_4 = (45.7 \text{ mL soln})\left(\frac{1 \text{ L soln}}{1000 \text{ mL soln}}\right)\left(\frac{0.500 \text{ mol } H_2SO_4}{\text{L soln}}\right)$$

$$= 2.28 \times 10^{-2} \text{ mol } H_2SO_4$$

Acids react with metal hydroxides to form water and a salt. Thus, the balanced equation for the neutralization reaction is

$$H_2SO_4(aq) + 2 \text{ NaOH}(aq) \longrightarrow 2 \text{ H}_2O(l) + Na_2SO_4(aq)$$

According to the balanced equation, 1 mol $H_2SO_4 \simeq 2$ mol NaOH. Therefore,

$$\text{Moles NaOH} = (2.28 \times 10^{-2} \text{ mol } H_2SO_4)\left(\frac{2 \text{ mol NaOH}}{1 \text{ mol } H_2SO_4}\right)$$

$$= 4.56 \times 10^{-2} \text{ mol NaOH}$$

---

*More precisely, the color change of an indicator signals the end point of the titration, which if the proper indicator is chosen lies very near the equivalence point. Acid–base titrations are discussed in more detail in Section 17.3.

Knowing the number of moles of NaOH in 20.0 mL of solution allows us to calculate the molarity of this solution:

$$\text{Molarity NaOH} = \frac{\text{mol NaOH}}{\text{L soln}} = \left(\frac{4.56 \times 10^{-2} \text{ mol NaOH}}{20.0 \text{ mL soln}}\right)\left(\frac{1000 \text{ mL soln}}{1 \text{ L soln}}\right)$$

$$= 2.28 \frac{\text{mol NaOH}}{\text{L soln}} = 2.28 \ M$$

### PRACTICE EXERCISE

What is the molarity of an NaOH solution if 48.0 mL neutralizes 35.0 mL of 0.144 $M$ $H_2SO_4$?

*Answer:*  0.210 $M$

---

| SAMPLE EXERCISE 4.17 | Determining the Quantity of Solute by Titration |

The quantity of $Cl^-$ in a municipal water supply is determined by titrating the sample with $Ag^+$. The precipitation reaction taking place during the titration is

$$Ag^+(aq) + Cl^-(aq) \longrightarrow AgCl(s)$$

The end point in this type of titration is marked by a change in color of a special type of indicator. (a) How many grams of chloride ion are in a sample of the water if 20.2 mL of 0.100 $M$ $Ag^+$ is needed to react with all the chloride in the sample? (b) If the sample has a mass of 10.0 g, what percent $Cl^-$ does it contain?

### SOLUTION

**Analyze**  We are given the volume (20.2 mL) and molarity (0.100 $M$) of a solution of $Ag^+$ and the chemical equation for reaction of this ion with $Cl^-$. We are asked to calculate the number of grams of $Cl^-$ in the sample and the mass percent of $Cl^-$ in the sample.

**(a) Plan**  We can use the procedure outlined by the green arrows in Figure 4.18. We begin by using the volume and molarity of $Ag^+$ to calculate the number of moles of $Ag^+$ used in the titration. We then use the balanced equation to determine the moles of $Cl^-$ in the sample and from that the grams of $Cl^-$.

**Solve**

$$\text{Moles Ag}^+ = (20.2 \text{ mL soln})\left(\frac{1 \text{ L soln}}{1000 \text{ mL soln}}\right)\left(\frac{0.100 \text{ mol Ag}^+}{\text{L soln}}\right)$$

$$= 2.02 \times 10^{-3} \text{ mol Ag}^+$$

From the balanced equation we see that 1 mol $Ag^+ \simeq 1$ mol $Cl^-$. Using this information and the molar mass of Cl, we have

$$\text{Grams Cl}^- = (2.02 \times 10^{-3} \text{ mol Ag}^+)\left(\frac{1 \text{ mol Cl}^-}{1 \text{ mol Ag}^+}\right)\left(\frac{35.5 \text{ g Cl}^-}{\text{mol Cl}^-}\right)$$

$$= 7.17 \times 10^{-2} \text{ g Cl}^-$$

**(b) Plan**  To calculate the percentage of $Cl^-$ in the sample, we compare the number of grams of $Cl^-$ in the sample, $7.17 \times 10^{-2}$ g, with the original mass of the sample, 10.0 g.

**Solve**

$$\text{Percent Cl}^- = \frac{7.17 \times 10^{-2} \text{ g}}{10.0 \text{ g}} \times 100\% = 0.717\% \text{ Cl}^-$$

**Comment**  Chloride ion is one of the most common ions in water and sewage. Ocean water contains 1.92% $Cl^-$. Whether water containing $Cl^-$ tastes salty depends on the other ions present. If the only accompanying ions are $Na^+$, a salty taste may be detected with as little as 0.03% $Cl^-$.

## PRACTICE EXERCISE

A sample of an iron ore is dissolved in acid, and the iron is converted to $Fe^{2+}$. The sample is then titrated with 47.20 mL of 0.02240 $M$ $MnO_4^-$ solution. The oxidation-reduction reaction that occurs during titration is

$$MnO_4^-(aq) + 5\,Fe^{2+}(aq) + 8\,H^+(aq) \longrightarrow Mn^{2+}(aq) + 5\,Fe^{3+}(aq) + 4\,H_2O(l)$$

**(a)** How many moles of $MnO_4^-$ were added to the solution? **(b)** How many moles of $Fe^{2+}$ were in the sample? **(c)** How many grams of iron were in the sample? **(d)** If the sample had a mass of 0.8890 g, what is the percentage of iron in the sample?
*Answers:* **(a)** $1.057 \times 10^{-3}$ mol $MnO_4^-$, **(b)** $5.286 \times 10^{-3}$ mol $Fe^{2+}$, **(c)** 0.2952 g, **(d)** 33.21%

---

**SAMPLE INTEGRATIVE EXERCISE** Putting Concepts Together

*Note: Integrative exercises require skills from earlier chapters as well as ones from the present chapter.*

A sample of 70.5 mg of potassium phosphate is added to 15.0 mL of 0.050 $M$ silver nitrate, resulting in the formation of a precipitate. **(a)** Write the molecular equation for the reaction. **(b)** What is the limiting reactant in the reaction? **(c)** Calculate the theoretical yield, in grams, of the precipitate that forms.

## SOLUTION

**(a)** Potassium phosphate and silver nitrate are both ionic compounds. Potassium phosphate contains $K^+$ and $PO_4^{3-}$ ions, so its chemical formula is $K_3PO_4$. Silver nitrate contains $Ag^+$ and $NO_3^-$ ions, so its chemical formula is $AgNO_3$. Because both reactants are strong electrolytes, the solution contains $K^+$, $PO_4^{3-}$, $Ag^+$, and $NO_3^-$ ions before the reaction occurs. According to the solubility guidelines in Table 4.1, $Ag^+$ and $PO_4^{3-}$ form an insoluble compound, so $Ag_3PO_4$ will precipitate from the solution. In contrast, $K^+$ and $NO_3^-$ will remain in solution because $KNO_3$ is water soluble. Thus, the balanced molecular equation for the reaction is

$$K_3PO_4(aq) + 3\,AgNO_3(aq) \longrightarrow Ag_3PO_4(s) + 3\,KNO_3(aq)$$

**(b)** To determine the limiting reactant, we must examine the number of moles of each reactant. ∞ (Section 3.7) The number of moles of $K_3PO_4$ is calculated from the mass of the sample using the molar mass as a conversion factor. ∞ (Section 3.4) The molar mass of $K_3PO_4$ is $3(39.1) + 31.0 + 4(16.0) = 212.3$ g/mol. Converting milligrams to grams and then to moles, we have

$$(70.5 \text{ mg K}_3\text{PO}_4)\left(\frac{10^{-3} \text{ g K}_3\text{PO}_4}{1 \text{ mg K}_3\text{PO}_4}\right)\left(\frac{1 \text{ mol K}_3\text{PO}_4}{212.3 \text{ g K}_3\text{PO}_4}\right) = 3.32 \times 10^{-4} \text{ mol K}_3\text{PO}_4$$

We determine the number of moles of $AgNO_3$ from the volume and molarity of the solution. (Section 4.5) Converting milliliters to liters and then to moles, we have

$$(15.0 \text{ mL})\left(\frac{10^{-3} \text{ L}}{1 \text{ mL}}\right)\left(\frac{0.050 \text{ mol AgNO}_3}{\text{L}}\right) = 7.5 \times 10^{-4} \text{ mol AgNO}_3$$

Comparing the amounts of the two reactants, we find that there are $(7.5 \times 10^{-4})/(3.32 \times 10^{-4}) = 2.3$ times as many moles of $AgNO_3$ as there are moles of $K_3PO_4$. According to the balanced equation, however, 1 mol $K_3PO_4$ requires 3 mol $AgNO_3$. Thus, there is insufficient $AgNO_3$ to consume the $K_3PO_4$, and $AgNO_3$ is the limiting reactant.

**(c)** The precipitate is $Ag_3PO_4$, whose molar mass is $3(107.9) + 31.0 + 4(16.0) = 418.7$ g/mol. To calculate the number of grams of $Ag_3PO_4$ that could be produced in this reaction (the theoretical yield), we use the number of moles of the limiting reactant, converting mol $AgNO_3 \Rightarrow$ mol $Ag_3PO_4 \Rightarrow$ g $Ag_3PO_4$. We use the coefficients in the balanced equation to convert moles of $AgNO_3$ to moles $Ag_3PO_4$, and we use the molar mass of $Ag_3PO_4$ to convert the number of moles of this substance to grams.

$$(7.5 \times 10^{-4} \text{ mol AgNO}_3)\left(\frac{1 \text{ mol Ag}_3\text{PO}_4}{3 \text{ mol AgNO}_3}\right)\left(\frac{418.7 \text{ g Ag}_3\text{PO}_4}{1 \text{ mol Ag}_3\text{PO}_4}\right) = 0.10 \text{ g Ag}_3\text{PO}_4$$

The answer has only two significant figures because the quantity of $AgNO_3$ is given to only two significant figures.

# CHAPTER SUMMARY AND KEY TERMS

**INTRODUCTION AND SECTION 4.1** Solutions in which water is the dissolving medium are called **aqueous solutions**. The component of the solution that is present in the greatest quantity is the **solvent**. The other components are **solutes**.

Any substance whose aqueous solution contains ions is called an **electrolyte**. Any substance that forms a solution containing no ions is a **nonelectrolyte**. Electrolytes that are present in solution entirely as ions are **strong electrolytes**, whereas those that are present partly as ions and partly as molecules are **weak electrolytes**. Ionic compounds dissociate into ions when they dissolve, and they are strong electrolytes. The solubility of ionic substances is made possible by **solvation**, the interaction of ions with polar solvent molecules. Most molecular compounds are nonelectrolytes, although some are weak electrolytes, and a few are strong electrolytes. When representing the ionization of a weak electrolyte in solution, half-arrows in both directions are used, indicating that the forward and reverse reactions can achieve a chemical balance called a **chemical equilibrium**.

**SECTION 4.2** **Precipitation reactions** are those in which an insoluble product, called a **precipitate**, forms. Solubility guidelines help determine whether or not an ionic compound will be soluble in water. (The **solubility** of a substance is the amount that dissolves in a given quantity of solvent.) Reactions such as precipitation reactions, in which cations and anions appear to exchange partners, are called **exchange reactions**, or **metathesis reactions**.

Chemical equations can be written to show whether dissolved substances are present in solution predominantly as ions or molecules. When the complete chemical formulas of all reactants and products are used, the equation is called a **molecular equation**. A **complete ionic equation** shows all dissolved strong electrolytes as their component ions. In a **net ionic equation**, those ions that go through the reaction unchanged (**spectator ions**) are omitted.

**SECTION 4.3** Acids and bases are important electrolytes. **Acids** are proton donors; they increase the concentration of $H^+(aq)$ in aqueous solutions to which they are added. **Bases** are proton acceptors; they increase the concentration of $OH^-(aq)$ in aqueous solutions. Those acids and bases that are strong electrolytes are called **strong acids** and **strong bases**, respectively. Those that are weak electrolytes are **weak acids** and **weak bases**. When solutions of acids and bases are mixed, a neutralization reaction occurs. The **neutralization reaction** between an acid and a metal hydroxide produces water and a **salt**. Gases can also be formed as a result of neutralization reactions. The reaction of a sulfide with an acid forms $H_2S(g)$; the reaction between a carbonate and an acid forms $CO_2(g)$.

**SECTION 4.4** **Oxidation** is the loss of electrons by a substance, whereas **reduction** is the gain of electrons by a substance. **Oxidation numbers** keep track of electrons during chemical reactions and are assigned to atoms using specific rules. The oxidation of an element results in an increase in its oxidation number, whereas reduction is accompanied by a decrease in oxidation number. Oxidation is always accompanied by reduction, giving **oxidation-reduction**, or **redox**, **reactions**.

Many metals are oxidized by $O_2$, acids, and salts. The redox reactions between metals and acids as well as those between metals and salts are called **displacement reactions**. The products of these displacement reactions are always an element ($H_2$ or a metal) and a salt. Comparing such reactions allows us to rank metals according to their ease of oxidation. A list of metals arranged in order of decreasing ease of oxidation is called an **activity series**. Any metal on the list can be oxidized by ions of metals (or $H^+$) below it in the series.

**SECTION 4.5** The **concentration** of a solution expresses the amount of a solute dissolved in the solution. One of the common ways to express the concentration of a solute is in terms of molarity. The **molarity** of a solution is the number of moles of solute per liter of solution. Molarity makes it possible to interconvert solution volume and number of moles of solute. Solutions of known molarity can be formed either by weighing out the solute and diluting it to a known volume or by the **dilution** of a more concentrated solution of known concentration (a stock solution). Adding solvent to the solution (the process of dilution) decreases the concentration of the solute without changing the number of moles of solute in the solution ($M_{conc} \times V_{conc} = M_{dil} \times V_{dil}$).

**SECTION 4.6** In the process called **titration**, we combine a solution of known concentration (a **standard solution**) with a solution of unknown concentration to determine the unknown concentration or the quantity of solute in the unknown. The point in the titration at which stoichiometrically equivalent quantities of reactants are brought together is called the **equivalence point**. An indicator can be used to show the end point of the titration, which coincides closely with the equivalence point.

# KEY SKILLS

- Recognize compounds as acids or bases, and as strong, weak, or nonelectrolytes. (Sections 4.1 and 4.3)
- Recognize reactions by type and be able to predict the products of simple acid–base, precipitation, and redox reactions. (Sections 4.2–4.4)
- Be able to calculate molarity and use it to convert between moles of a substance in solution and volume of the solution. (Section 4.5)
- Understand how to carry out a dilution to achieve a desired solution concentration. (Section 4.5)
- Understand how to perform and interpret the results of a titration. (Section 4.6)

# KEY EQUATIONS

- $\text{Molarity} = \dfrac{\text{moles solute}}{\text{volume of solution in liters}}$   [4.32]   Molarity is the most commonly used unit of concentration in chemistry.

- $M_{conc} \times V_{conc} = M_{dil} \times V_{dil}$   [4.34]   When adding solvent to a concentrated solution to make a dilute solution, molarities and volumes of both concentrated and dilute solutions can be calculated if three of the quantities are known.

# EXERCISES

## VISUALIZING CONCEPTS

**4.1** Which of the following schematic drawings best describes a solution of $Li_2SO_4$ in water (water molecules not shown for simplicity)? [Section 4.1]

(a)

(b)

(c)

**4.2** Aqueous solutions of three different substances, AX, AY, and AZ, are represented by the three accompanying diagrams. Identify each substance as a strong electrolyte, weak electrolyte, or non-electrolyte. [Section 4.1]

AX

(a)

AY

(b)

AZ

(c)

**4.3** Use the molecular representations shown here to classify each compound as either a nonelectrolyte, a weak electrolyte, or a strong electrolyte (see inside back cover for element color scheme). [Sections 4.1 and 4.3]

(a)

(b)

(c)

**4.4** A 0.1 $M$ solution of acetic acid, $CH_3COOH$, causes the light-bulb in the apparatus of Figure 4.2 to glow about as brightly as a 0.001 $M$ solution of HBr. How do you account for this fact? [Section 4.1]

**4.5** You are presented with a white solid and told that due to care-less labeling it is not clear if the substance is barium chloride, lead chloride, or zinc chloride. When you transfer the solid to a beaker and add water, the solid dissolves to give a clear solution. Next a $Na_2SO_4(aq)$ solution is added and a white precipitate forms. What is the identity of the unknown white solid? [Section 4.2]

**4.6** We have seen that ions in aqueous solution are stabilized by the attractions between the ions and the water molecules. Why then do some pairs of ions in solution form precipitates? [Section 4.2]

**4.7** Which of the following ions will *always* be a spectator ion in a precipitation reaction? (a) $Cl^-$, (b) $NO_3^-$, (c) $NH_4^+$, (d) $S^{2-}$, (e) $SO_4^{2-}$. Explain briefly. [Section 4.2]

**4.8** The labels have fallen off three bottles containing powdered samples of metals; one contains zinc, one lead, and the other platinum. You have three solutions at your disposal: 1 $M$ sodium nitrate, 1 $M$ nitric acid, and 1 $M$ nickel nitrate. How could you use these solutions to determine the identities of each metal powder? [Section 4.4]

**4.9** Explain how a redox reaction involves electrons in the same way that a neutralization reaction involves protons. [Sections 4.3 and 4.4]

**4.10** If you want to double the concentration of a solution, how could you do it? [Section 4.5]

## GENERAL PROPERTIES OF AQUEOUS SOLUTIONS (section 4.1)

**4.11** When asked what causes electrolyte solutions to conduct electricity, a student responds that it is due to the movement of electrons through the solution. Is the student correct? If not, what is the correct response?

**4.12** When methanol, $CH_3OH$, is dissolved in water, a nonconducting solution results. When acetic acid, $CH_3COOH$, dissolves in water, the solution is weakly conducting and acidic in nature. Describe what happens upon dissolution in the two cases, and account for the different results.

**4.13** We have learned in this chapter that many ionic solids dissolve in water as strong electrolytes, that is, as separated ions in solution. What properties of water facilitate this process? Would you expect ionic compounds to be soluble in elemental liquids like bromine or mercury, just as they are in water? Explain.

**4.14** What does it mean to say that ions are solvated when an ionic substance dissolves in water?

**4.15** Specify what ions are present in solution upon dissolving each of the following substances in water: (a) $ZnCl_2$, (b) $HNO_3$, (c) $(NH_4)_2SO_4$, (d) $Ca(OH)_2$.

**4.16** Specify what ions are present upon dissolving each of the following substances in water: (a) $MgI_2$, (b) $Al(NO_3)_3$, (c) $HClO_4$, (d) $NaCH_3COO$.

**4.17** Formic acid, HCOOH, is a weak electrolyte. What solute particles are present in an aqueous solution of this compound? Write the chemical equation for the ionization of HCOOH.

**4.18** Acetone, $CH_3COCH_3$, is a nonelectrolyte; hypochlorous acid, HClO, is a weak electrolyte; and ammonium chloride, $NH_4Cl$, is a strong electrolyte. (a) What are the solute particles present in aqueous solutions of each compound? (b) If 0.1 mol of each compound is dissolved in solution, which one contains 0.2 mol of solute particles, which contains 0.1 mol of solute particles, and which contains somewhere between 0.1 and 0.2 mol of solute particles?

# PRECIPITATION REACTIONS (section 4.2)

**4.19** Using solubility guidelines, predict whether each of the following compounds is soluble or insoluble in water: **(a)** $MgBr_2$, **(b)** $PbI_2$, **(c)** $(NH_4)_2CO_3$, **(d)** $Sr(OH)_2$, **(e)** $ZnSO_4$.

**4.20** Predict whether each of the following compounds is soluble in water: **(a)** $AgI$, **(b)** $Na_2CO_3$, **(c)** $BaCl_2$, **(d)** $Al(OH)_3$, **(e)** $Zn(CH_3COO)_2$.

**4.21** Will precipitation occur when the following solutions are mixed? If so, write a balanced chemical equation for the reaction. **(a)** $Na_2CO_3$ and $AgNO_3$, **(b)** $NaNO_3$ and $NiSO_4$, **(c)** $FeSO_4$ and $Pb(NO_3)_2$.

**4.22** Identify the precipitate (if any) that forms when the following solutions are mixed, and write a balanced equation for each reaction. **(a)** $NaCH_3COO$ and $HCl$, **(b)** $KOH$ and $Cu(NO_3)_2$, **(c)** $Na_2S$ and $CdSO_4$.

**4.23** Name the spectator ions in any reactions that may be involved when each of the following pairs of solutions are mixed.
**(a)** $Na_2CO_3(aq)$ and $MgSO_4(aq)$
**(b)** $Pb(NO_3)_2(aq)$ and $Na_2S(aq)$
**(c)** $(NH_4)_3PO_4(aq)$ and $CaCl_2(aq)$

**4.24** Write balanced net ionic equations for the reactions that occur in each of the following cases. Identify the spectator ion or ions in each reaction.

**(a)** $Cr_2(SO_4)_3(aq) + (NH_4)_2CO_3(aq) \longrightarrow$
**(b)** $Ba(NO_3)_2(aq) + K_2SO_4(aq) \longrightarrow$
**(c)** $Fe(NO_3)_2(aq) + KOH(aq) \longrightarrow$

**4.25** Separate samples of a solution of an unknown salt are treated with dilute solutions of HBr, $H_2SO_4$, and NaOH. A precipitate forms in all three cases. Which of the following cations could the solution contain: $K^+$, $Pb^{2+}$, $Ba^{2+}$?

**4.26** Separate samples of a solution of an unknown ionic compound are treated with dilute $AgNO_3$, $Pb(NO_3)_2$, and $BaCl_2$. Precipitates form in all three cases. Which of the following could be the anion of the unknown salt: $Br^-$, $CO_3^{2-}$, $NO_3^-$?

**4.27** You know that an unlabeled bottle contains a solution of one of the following: $AgNO_3$, $CaCl_2$, or $Al_2(SO_4)_3$. A friend suggests that you test a portion of the solution with $Ba(NO_3)_2$ and then with NaCl solutions. Explain how these two tests together would be sufficient to determine which salt is present in the solution.

**4.28** Three solutions are mixed together to form a single solution. One contains 0.2 mol $Pb(CH_3COO)_2$, the second contains 0.1 mol $Na_2S$, and the third contains 0.1 mol $CaCl_2$. **(a)** Write the net ionic equations for the precipitation reaction or reactions that occur. **(b)** What are the spectator ions in the solution?

# ACIDS, BASES, AND NEUTRALIZATION REACTIONS (section 4.3)

**4.29** Which of the following solutions has the largest concentration of solvated protons: **(a)** 0.2 *M* LiOH, **(b)** 0.2 *M* HI, **(c)** 1.0 *M* methyl alcohol ($CH_3OH$)? Explain

**4.30** Which of the following solutions is the most basic? **(a)** 0.6 *M* $NH_3$, **(b)** 0.150 *M* KOH, **(c)** 0.100 *M* $Ba(OH)_2$. Explain.

**4.31** What is the difference between **(a)** a monoprotic acid and a diprotic acid, **(b)** a weak acid and a strong acid, **(c)** an acid and a base?

**4.32** Explain the following observations: **(a)** $NH_3$ contains no $OH^-$ ions, and yet its aqueous solutions are basic; **(b)** HF is called a weak acid, and yet it is very reactive; **(c)** although sulfuric acid is a strong electrolyte, an aqueous solution of $H_2SO_4$ contains more $HSO_4^-$ ions than $SO_4^{2-}$ ions.

**4.33** Is there any correlation between the anions that form when each of the strong acids in Table 4.2 dissociates and the anions that normally form soluble ionic compounds (Table 4.1)? Which anions if any are exceptions to the general trend?

**4.34** What is the relationship between the solubility rules in Table 4.1 and the list of strong bases in Table 4.2? Another way of asking this question is, why is $Cd(OH)_2$, for example, not listed as a strong base in Table 4.2?

**4.35** Label each of the following substances as an acid, base, salt, or none of the above. Indicate whether the substance exists in aqueous solution entirely in molecular form, entirely as ions, or as a mixture of molecules and ions. **(a)** HF, **(b)** acetonitrile, $CH_3CN$, **(c)** $NaClO_4$, **(d)** $Ba(OH)_2$.

**4.36** An aqueous solution of an unknown solute is tested with litmus paper and found to be acidic. The solution is weakly conducting compared with a solution of NaCl of the same concentration.

Which of the following substances could the unknown be: KOH, $NH_3$, $HNO_3$, $KClO_2$, $H_3PO_3$, $CH_3COCH_3$ (acetone)?

**4.37** Classify each of the following substances as a nonelectrolyte, weak electrolyte, or strong electrolyte in water: **(a)** $H_2SO_3$, **(b)** $C_2H_5OH$ (ethanol), **(c)** $NH_3$, **(d)** $KClO_3$, **(e)** $Cu(NO_3)_2$.

**4.38** Classify each of the following aqueous solutions as a nonelectrolyte, weak electrolyte, or strong electrolyte: **(a)** $LiClO_4$, **(b)** $HClO$, **(c)** $CH_3CH_2CH_2OH$ (propanol), **(d)** $HClO_3$, **(e)** $CuSO_4$, **(f)** $C_{12}H_{22}O_{11}$ (sucrose).

**4.39** Complete and balance the following molecular equations, and then write the net ionic equation for each:
**(a)** $HBr(aq) + Ca(OH)_2(aq) \longrightarrow$
**(b)** $Cu(OH)_2(s) + HClO_4(aq) \longrightarrow$
**(c)** $Al(OH)_3(s) + HNO_3(aq) \longrightarrow$

**4.40** Write the balanced molecular and net ionic equations for each of the following neutralization reactions:
**(a)** Aqueous acetic acid is neutralized by aqueous barium hydroxide.
**(b)** Solid chromium(III) hydroxide reacts with nitrous acid.
**(c)** Aqueous nitric acid and aqueous ammonia react.

**4.41** Write balanced molecular and net ionic equations for the following reactions, and identify the gas formed in each: **(a)** solid cadmium sulfide reacts with an aqueous solution of sulfuric acid; **(b)** solid magnesium carbonate reacts with an aqueous solution of perchloric acid.

**4.42** Because the oxide ion is basic, metal oxides react readily with acids. **(a)** Write the net ionic equation for the following reaction:

$$FeO(s) + 2\ HClO_4(aq) \longrightarrow Fe(ClO_4)_2(aq) + H_2O(l)$$

**(b)** Based on the equation in part (a), write the net ionic equation for the reaction that occurs between NiO(s) and an aqueous solution of nitric acid.

**4.43** Magnesium carbonate, magnesium oxide, and magnesium hydroxide are all white solids that react with acidic solutions. **(a)** Write a balanced molecular equation and a net ionic equation for the reaction that occurs when each substance reacts with a hydrochloric acid solution. **(b)** By observing the reactions in part (a) could you distinguish any of the three

magnesium substances from the other two? If so how? **(c)** If excess HCl(aq) is added, would the clear solutions left behind after the reaction is complete contain the same or different ions in each case?

**4.44** As $K_2O$ dissolves in water, the oxide ion reacts with water molecules to form hydroxide ions. Write the molecular and net ionic equations for this reaction. Based on the definitions of acid and base, what ion is the base in this reaction? What is the acid? What is the spectator ion in the reaction?

# OXIDATION-REDUCTION REACTIONS (section 4.4)

**4.45** Define oxidation and reduction in terms of **(a)** electron transfer and **(b)** oxidation numbers.

**4.46** Can oxidation occur without oxygen? Can oxidation occur without reduction?

**4.47** Which region of the periodic table shown here contains the most readily oxidized elements? Which region contains the least readily oxidized?

**4.48** Determine the oxidation number of sulfur in each of the following substances: **(a)** barium sulfate, $BaSO_4$, **(b)** sulfurous acid, $H_2SO_3$, **(c)** strontium sulfide, SrS, **(d)** hydrogen sulfide, $H_2S$. **(e)** Based on these compounds what is the range of oxidation numbers seen for sulfur? Is there any relationship between the range of accessible oxidation states and sulfur's position on the periodic table?

**4.49** Determine the oxidation number for the indicated element in each of the following substances: **(a)** S in $SO_2$, **(b)** C in $COCl_2$, **(c)** Mn in $KMnO_4$, **(d)** Br in HBrO, **(e)** As in $As_4$, **(f)** O in $K_2O_2$.

**4.50** Determine the oxidation number for the indicated element in each of the following compounds: **(a)** Co in $LiCoO_2$, **(b)** Al in $NaAlH_4$, **(c)** C in $CH_3OH$ (methanol), **(d)** N in GaN, **(e)** Cl in $HClO_2$, **(f)** Cr in $BaCrO_4$.

**4.51** Which element is oxidized and which is reduced in the following reactions?
**(a)** $N_2(g) + 3 H_2(g) \longrightarrow 2 NH_3(g)$
**(b)** $3 Fe(NO_3)_2(aq) + 2 Al(s) \longrightarrow$
$3 Fe(s) + 2 Al(NO_3)_3(aq)$
**(c)** $Cl_2(aq) + 2 NaI(aq) \longrightarrow I_2(aq) + 2 NaCl(aq)$
**(d)** $PbS(s) + 4 H_2O_2(aq) \longrightarrow PbSO_4(s) + 4 H_2O(l)$

**4.52** Which of the following are redox reactions? For those that are, indicate which element is oxidized and which is reduced. For those that are not, indicate whether they are precipitation or neutralization reactions.
**(a)** $P_4(s) + 10 HClO(aq) + 6 H_2O(l) \longrightarrow$
$4 H_3PO_4(aq) + 10 HCl(aq)$
**(b)** $Br_2(l) + 2 K(s) \longrightarrow 2 KBr(s)$

**(c)** $CH_3CH_2OH(l) + 3 O_2(g) \longrightarrow 3 H_2O(l) + 2 CO_2(g)$
**(d)** $ZnCl_2(aq) + 2 NaOH(aq) \longrightarrow Zn(OH)_2(s) + 2 NaCl(aq)$

**4.53** Write balanced molecular and net ionic equations for the reactions of **(a)** manganese with dilute sulfuric acid, **(b)** chromium with hydrobromic acid, **(c)** tin with hydrochloric acid, **(d)** aluminum with formic acid, HCOOH.

**4.54** Write balanced molecular and net ionic equations for the reactions of **(a)** hydrochloric acid with nickel, **(b)** dilute sulfuric acid with iron, **(c)** hydrobromic acid with magnesium, **(d)** acetic acid, $CH_3COOH$, with zinc.

**4.55** Using the activity series (Table 4.5), write balanced chemical equations for the following reactions. If no reaction occurs, simply write NR. **(a)** Iron metal is added to a solution of copper(II) nitrate; **(b)** zinc metal is added to a solution of magnesium sulfate; **(c)** hydrobromic acid is added to tin metal; **(d)** hydrogen gas is bubbled through an aqueous solution of nickel(II) chloride; **(e)** aluminum metal is added to a solution of cobalt(II) sulfate.

**4.56** Using the activity series (Table 4.5), write balanced chemical equations for the following reactions. If no reaction occurs, simply write NR. **(a)** Nickel metal is added to a solution of copper(II) nitrate; **(b)** a solution of zinc nitrate is added to a solution of magnesium sulfate; **(c)** hydrochloric acid is added to gold metal; **(d)** chromium metal is immersed in an aqueous solution of cobalt(II) chloride; **(e)** hydrogen gas is bubbled through a solution of silver nitrate.

**4.57** The metal cadmium tends to form $Cd^{2+}$ ions. The following observations are made: (i) When a strip of zinc metal is placed in $CdCl_2(aq)$, cadmium metal is deposited on the strip. (ii) When a strip of cadmium metal is placed in $Ni(NO_3)_2(aq)$, nickel metal is deposited on the strip. **(a)** Write net ionic equations to explain each of the preceding observations. **(b)** What can you conclude about the position of cadmium in the activity series? **(c)** What experiments would you need to perform to locate more precisely the position of cadmium in the activity series?

**4.58** **(a)** Use the following reactions to prepare an activity series for the halogens:
$Br_2(aq) + 2 NaI(aq) \longrightarrow 2 NaBr(aq) + I_2(aq)$
$Cl_2(aq) + 2 NaBr(aq) \longrightarrow 2 NaCl(aq) + Br_2(aq)$
**(b)** Relate the positions of the halogens in the periodic table with their locations in this activity series. **(c)** Predict whether a reaction occurs when the following reagents are mixed: $Cl_2(aq)$ and KI(aq); $Br_2(aq)$ and LiCl(aq).

# CONCENTRATIONS OF SOLUTIONS (section 4.5)

**4.59** (a) Is the concentration of a solution an intensive or an extensive property? (b) What is the difference between 0.50 mol HCl and 0.50 $M$ HCl?

**4.60** (a) Suppose you prepare 500 mL of a 0.10 $M$ solution of some salt and then spill some of it. What happens to the concentration of the solution left in the container? (b) Suppose you prepare 500 mL of a 0.10 $M$ aqueous solution of some salt and let it sit out, uncovered, for a long time, and some water evaporates. What happens to the concentration of the solution left in the container? (c) A certain volume of a 0.50 $M$ solution contains 4.5 g of a salt. What mass of the salt is present in the same volume of a 2.50 $M$ solution?

**4.61** (a) Calculate the molarity of a solution that contains 0.175 mol $ZnCl_2$ in exactly 150 mL of solution. (b) How many moles of HCl are present in 35.0 mL of a 4.50 $M$ solution of nitric acid? (c) How many milliliters of 6.00 $M$ NaOH solution are needed to provide 0.325 mol of NaOH?

**4.62** (a) Calculate the molarity of a solution made by dissolving 12.5 grams of $Na_2CrO_4$ in enough water to form exactly 550 mL of solution. (b) How many moles of KBr are present in 150 mL of a 0.275 $M$ solution? (c) How many milliliters of 6.1 $M$ HCl solution are needed to obtain 0.100 mol of HCl?

**4.63** The average adult human male has a total blood volume of 5.0 L. If the concentration of sodium ion in this average individual is 0.135 $M$, what is the mass of sodium ion circulating in the blood?

**4.64** A person suffering from hyponatremia has a sodium ion concentration in the blood of 0.118 $M$ and a total blood volume of 4.6 L. What mass of sodium chloride would need to be added to the blood to bring the sodium ion concentration up to 0.138 $M$, assuming no change in blood volume?

**4.65** The concentration of alcohol ($CH_3CH_2OH$) in blood, called the "blood alcohol concentration" or BAC, is given in units of grams of alcohol per 100 mL of blood. The legal definition of intoxication, in many states of the United States, is that the BAC is 0.08 or higher. What is the concentration of alcohol, in terms of molarity, in blood if the BAC is 0.08?

**4.66** The average adult male has a total blood volume of 5.0 L. After drinking a few beers, he has a BAC of 0.10 (see Exercise 4.65). What mass of alcohol is circulating in his blood?

**4.67** Calculate (a) the number of grams of solute in 0.250 L of 0.175 $M$ KBr, (b) the molar concentration of a solution containing 14.75 g of $Ca(NO_3)_2$ in 1.375 L, (c) the volume of 1.50 $M$ $Na_3PO_4$ in milliliters that contains 2.50 g of solute.

**4.68** (a) How many grams of solute are present in 15.0 mL of 0.736 $M$ $K_2Cr_2O_7$? (b) If 14.00 g of $(NH_4)_2SO_4$ is dissolved in enough water to form 250 mL of solution, what is the molarity of the solution? (c) How many milliliters of 0.0455 $M$ $CuSO_4$ contain 3.65 g of solute?

**4.69** (a) Which will have the highest concentration of potassium ion: 0.20 $M$ KCl, 0.15 $M$ $K_2CrO_4$, or 0.080 $M$ $K_3PO_4$? (b) Which will contain the greater number of moles of potassium ion: 30.0 mL of 0.15 $M$ $K_2CrO_4$ or 25.0 mL of 0.080 $M$ $K_3PO_4$?

**4.70** In each of the following pairs, indicate which has the higher concentration of $I^-$ ion: (a) 0.10 $M$ $BaI_2$ or 0.25 $M$ KI solution, (b) 100 mL of 0.10 $M$ KI solution or 200 mL of 0.040 $M$ $ZnI_2$ solution, (c) 3.2 $M$ HI solution or a solution made by dissolving 145 g of NaI in water to make 150 mL of solution.

**4.71** Indicate the concentration of each ion or molecule present in the following solutions: (a) 0.25 $M$ $NaNO_3$, (b) $1.3 \times 10^{-2}$ $M$ $MgSO_4$, (c) 0.0150 $M$ $C_6H_{12}O_6$, (d) a mixture of 45.0 mL of 0.272 $M$ NaCl and 65.0 mL of 0.0247 $M$ $(NH_4)_2CO_3$. Assume that the volumes are additive.

**4.72** Indicate the concentration of each ion present in the solution formed by mixing (a) 42.0 mL of 0.170 $M$ NaOH and 37.6 mL of 0.400 $M$ NaOH, (b) 44.0 mL of 0.100 $M$ and $Na_2SO_4$ and 25.0 mL of 0.150 $M$ KCl, (c) 3.60 g KCl in 75.0 mL of 0.250 $M$ $CaCl_2$ solution. Assume that the volumes are additive.

**4.73** (a) You have a stock solution of 14.8 $M$ $NH_3$. How many milliliters of this solution should you dilute to make 1000.0 mL of 0.250 $M$ $NH_3$? (b) If you take a 10.0-mL portion of the stock solution and dilute it to a total volume of 0.500 L, what will be the concentration of the final solution?

**4.74** (a) How many milliliters of a stock solution of 6.0 $M$ $HNO_3$ would you have to use to prepare 110 mL of 0.500 $M$ $HNO_3$? (b) If you dilute 10.0 mL of the stock solution to a final volume of 0.250 L, what will be the concentration of the diluted solution?

**4.75** (a) Starting with solid sucrose, $C_{12}H_{22}O_{11}$, describe how you would prepare 250 mL of a 0.250 $M$ sucrose solution. (b) Describe how you would prepare 350.0 mL of 0.100 $M$ $C_{12}H_{22}O_{11}$ starting with 3.00 L of 1.50 $M$ $C_{12}H_{22}O_{11}$.

**4.76** (a) How would you prepare 175.0 mL of 0.150 $M$ $AgNO_3$ solution starting with pure $AgNO_3$? (b) An experiment calls for you to use 100 mL of 0.50 $M$ $HNO_3$ solution. All you have available is a bottle of 3.6 $M$ $HNO_3$. How would you prepare the desired solution?

**4.77** Pure acetic acid, known as glacial acetic acid, is a liquid with a density of 1.049 g/mL at 25 °C. Calculate the molarity of a solution of acetic acid made by dissolving 20.00 mL of glacial acetic acid at 25 °C in enough water to make 250.0 mL of solution.

**4.78** Glycerol, $C_3H_8O_3$, is a substance used extensively in the manufacture of cosmetics, foodstuffs, antifreeze, and plastics. Glycerol is a water-soluble liquid with a density of 1.2656 g/mL at 15 °C. Calculate the molarity of a solution of glycerol made by dissolving 50.000 mL glycerol at 15 °C in enough water to make 250.00 mL of solution.

# SOLUTION STOICHIOMETRY AND CHEMICAL ANALYSIS (section 4.6)

**4.79** What mass of KCl is needed to precipitate the silver ions from 15.0 mL of 0.200 $M$ $AgNO_3$ solution?

**4.80** What mass of NaOH is needed to precipitate the $Cd^{2+}$ ions from 35.0 mL of 0.500 $M$ $Cd(NO_3)_2$ solution?

**4.81** (a) What volume of 0.115 $M$ $HClO_4$ solution is needed to neutralize 50.00 mL of 0.0875 $M$ NaOH? (b) What volume of 0.128 $M$ HCl is needed to neutralize 2.87 g of $Mg(OH)_2$? (c) If 25.8 mL of $AgNO_3$ is needed to precipitate all the $Cl^-$ ions in a

785-mg sample of KCl (forming AgCl), what is the molarity of the $AgNO_3$ solution? **(d)** If 45.3 mL of 0.108 $M$ HCl solution is needed to neutralize a solution of KOH, how many grams of KOH must be present in the solution?

**4.82** **(a)** How many milliliters of 0.120 $M$ HCl are needed to completely neutralize 50.0 mL of 0.101 $M$ $Ba(OH)_2$ solution? **(b)** How many milliliters of 0.125 $M$ $H_2SO_4$ are needed to neutralize 0.200 g of NaOH? **(c)** If 55.8 mL of $BaCl_2$ solution is needed to precipitate all the sulfate ion in a 752-mg sample of $Na_2SO_4$, what is the molarity of the solution? **(d)** If 42.7 mL of 0.208 $M$ HCl solution is needed to neutralize a solution of $Ca(OH)_2$, how many grams of $Ca(OH)_2$ must be in the solution?

**4.83** Some sulfuric acid is spilled on a lab bench. You can neutralize the acid by sprinkling sodium bicarbonate on it and then mopping up the resultant solution. The sodium bicarbonate reacts with sulfuric acid as follows:

$$2\,NaHCO_3(s) + H_2SO_4(aq) \longrightarrow$$
$$Na_2SO_4(aq) + 2\,H_2O(l) + 2\,CO_2(g)$$

Sodium bicarbonate is added until the fizzing due to the formation of $CO_2(g)$ stops. If 27 mL of 6.0 $M$ $H_2SO_4$ was spilled, what is the minimum mass of $NaHCO_3$ that must be added to the spill to neutralize the acid?

**4.84** The distinctive odor of vinegar is due to acetic acid, $CH_3COOH$, which reacts with sodium hydroxide in the following fashion:

$$CH_3COOH(aq) + NaOH(aq) \longrightarrow$$
$$H_2O(l) + NaC_2H_3O_2(aq)$$

If 3.45 mL of vinegar needs 42.5 mL of 0.115 $M$ NaOH to reach the equivalence point in a titration, how many grams of acetic acid are in a 1.00-qt sample of this vinegar?

**4.85** A 4.36-g sample of an unknown alkali metal hydroxide is dissolved in 100.0 mL of water. An acid–base indicator is added and the resulting solution is titrated with 2.50 $M$ HCl($aq$) solution. The indicator changes color signaling that the equivalence point has been reached after 17.0 mL of the hydrochloric acid solution has been added. **(a)** What is the molar mass of the metal hydroxide? **(b)** What is the identity of the alkali metal cation: $Li^+$, $Na^+$, $K^+$, $Rb^+$, or $Cs^+$?

**4.86** An 8.65-g sample of an unknown group 2A metal hydroxide is dissolved in 85.0 mL of water. An acid–base indicator is added and the resulting solution is titrated with 2.50 $M$ HCl($aq$) solution. The indicator changes color signaling that the equivalence point has been reached after 56.9 mL of the hydrochloric acid solution has been added. **(a)** What is the molar mass of the metal hydroxide? **(b)** What is the identity of the metal cation: $Ca^{2+}$, $Sr^{2+}$, $Ba^{2+}$?

**4.87** A solution of 100.0 mL of 0.200 $M$ KOH is mixed with a solution of 200.0 mL of 0.150 $M$ $NiSO_4$. **(a)** Write the balanced chemical equation for the reaction that occurs. **(b)** What precipitate forms? **(c)** What is the limiting reactant? **(d)** How many grams of this precipitate form? **(e)** What is the concentration of each ion that remains in solution?

**4.88** A solution is made by mixing 15.0 g of $Sr(OH)_2$ and 55.0 mL of 0.200 $M$ $HNO_3$. **(a)** Write a balanced equation for the reaction that occurs between the solutes. **(b)** Calculate the concentration of each ion remaining in solution. **(c)** Is the resultant solution acidic or basic?

**4.89** A 0.5895-g sample of impure magnesium hydroxide is dissolved in 100.0 mL of 0.2050 $M$ HCl solution. The excess acid then needs 19.85 mL of 0.1020 $M$ NaOH for neutralization. Calculate the percent by mass of magnesium hydroxide in the sample, assuming that it is the only substance reacting with the HCl solution.

**4.90** A 1.248-g sample of limestone rock is pulverized and then treated with 30.00 mL of 1.035 $M$ HCl solution. The excess acid then requires 11.56 mL of 1.010 $M$ NaOH for neutralization. Calculate the percent by mass of calcium carbonate in the rock, assuming that it is the only substance reacting with the HCl solution.

# ADDITIONAL EXERCISES

**4.91** Gold is one of the few metals that can be obtained by panning, where a simple pan is used to separate gold from other deposits found in or near a stream bed. What two properties of gold make it possible to find gold, but not metals like copper, silver, lead, and aluminum, by panning?

**4.92** The accompanying photo shows the reaction between a solution of $Cd(NO_3)_2$ and one of $Na_2S$. What is the identity of the precipitate? What ions remain in solution? Write the net ionic equation for the reaction.

**4.93** Suppose you have a solution that might contain any or all of the following cations: $Ni^{2+}$, $Ag^+$, $Sr^{2+}$, and $Mn^{2+}$. Addition of HCl solution causes a precipitate to form. After filtering off the precipitate, $H_2SO_4$ solution is added to the resulting solution and another precipitate forms. This is filtered off, and a solution of NaOH is added to the resulting solution. No precipitate is observed. Which ions are present in each of the precipitates? Which of the four ions listed above must be absent from the original solution?

**4.94** You choose to investigate some of the solubility guidelines for two ions not listed in Table 4.1, the chromate ion ($CrO_4^{2-}$) and the oxalate ion ($C_2O_4^{2-}$). You are given 0.01 $M$ solutions (A, B, C, D) of four water-soluble salts:

| Solution | Solute | Color of Solution |
| --- | --- | --- |
| A | $Na_2CrO_4$ | Yellow |
| B | $(NH_4)_2C_2O_4$ | Colorless |
| C | $AgNO_3$ | Colorless |
| D | $CaCl_2$ | Colorless |

When these solutions are mixed, the following observations are made:

| Expt Number | Solutions Mixed | Result |
| --- | --- | --- |
| 1 | A + B | No precipitate, yellow solution |
| 2 | A + C | Red precipitate forms |
| 3 | A + D | Yellow precipitate forms |
| 4 | B + C | White precipitate forms |
| 5 | B + D | White precipitate forms |
| 6 | C + D | White precipitate forms |

**(a)** Write a net ionic equation for the reaction that occurs in each of the experiments. **(b)** Identify the precipitate formed, if any, in each of the experiments.

**4.95** Antacids are often used to relieve pain and promote healing in the treatment of mild ulcers. Write balanced net ionic equations for the reactions between the HCl($aq$) in the stomach and each of the following substances used in various antacids: **(a)** $Al(OH)_3(s)$, **(b)** $Mg(OH)_2(s)$, **(c)** $MgCO_3(s)$, **(d)** $NaAl(CO_3)(OH)_2(s)$, **(e)** $CaCO_3(s)$.

**[4.96]** The commercial production of nitric acid involves the following chemical reactions:

$$4 NH_3(g) + 5 O_2(g) \longrightarrow 4 NO(g) + 6 H_2O(g)$$
$$2 NO(g) + O_2(g) \longrightarrow 2 NO_2(g)$$
$$3 NO_2(g) + H_2O(l) \longrightarrow 2 HNO_3(aq) + NO(g)$$

**(a)** Which of these reactions are redox reactions? **(b)** In each redox reaction identify the element undergoing oxidation and the element undergoing reduction.

**4.97** Consider the following reagents: zinc, copper, mercury (density 13.6 g/mL), silver nitrate solution, nitric acid solution. **(a)** Given a 500-mL Erlenmeyer flask and a balloon can you combine two or more of the foregoing reagents to initiate a chemical reaction that will inflate the balloon? Write a balanced chemical equation to represent this process. What is the identity of the substance that inflates the balloon? **(b)** What is the theoretical yield of the substance that fills the balloon? **(c)** Can you combine two or more of the foregoing reagents to initiate a chemical reaction that will produce metallic silver? Write a balanced chemical equation to represent this process. What ions are left behind in solution? **(d)** What is the theoretical yield of silver?

35.0 g Zn    42.0 g Cu    6.55 mL Hg

150 mL of 0.750 $M$ $AgNO_3(aq)$    150 mL of 3.00 $M$ $HNO_3(aq)$

**[4.98]** Lanthanum metal forms cations with a charge of 3+. Consider the following observations about the chemistry of lanthanum: When lanthanum metal is exposed to air, a white solid (compound A) is formed that contains lanthanum and one other element. When lanthanum metal is added to water, gas bubbles are observed and a different white solid (compound B) is formed. Both A and B dissolve in hydrochloric acid to give a clear solution. When either of these solutions is evaporated, a soluble white solid (compound C) remains. If compound C is dissolved in water and sulfuric acid is added, a white precipitate (compound D) forms. **(a)** Propose identities for the substances A, B, C, and D. **(b)** Write net ionic equations for all the reactions described. **(c)** Based on the preceding observations, what can be said about the position of lanthanum in the activity series (Table 4.5)?

**4.99** A 35.0-mL sample of 1.00 $M$ KBr and a 60.0-mL sample of 0.600 $M$ KBr are mixed. The solution is then heated to evaporate water until the total volume is 50.0 mL. What is the molarity of the KBr in the final solution?

**4.100** Using modern analytical techniques, it is possible to detect sodium ions in concentrations as low as 50 pg/mL. What is this detection limit expressed in **(a)** molarity of $Na^+$, **(b)** $Na^+$ ions per cubic centimeter?

**4.101** Hard water contains $Ca^{2+}$, $Mg^{2+}$, and $Fe^{2+}$, which interfere with the action of soap and leave an insoluble coating on the insides of containers and pipes when heated. Water softeners replace these ions with $Na^+$. **(a)** If 1500 L of hard water contains 0.020 $M$ $Ca^{2+}$ and 0.0040 $M$ $Mg^{2+}$, how many moles of $Na^+$ are needed to replace these ions? **(b)** If the sodium is added to the water softener in the form of NaCl, how many grams of sodium chloride are needed?

**4.102** Tartaric acid, $H_2C_4H_4O_6$, has two acidic hydrogens. The acid is often present in wines and precipitates from solution as the wine ages. A solution containing an unknown concentration of the acid is titrated with NaOH. It requires 24.65 mL of 0.2500 $M$ NaOH solution to titrate both acidic protons in 50.00 mL of the tartaric acid solution. Write a balanced net ionic equation for the neutralization reaction, and calculate the molarity of the tartaric acid solution.

**4.103** **(a)** A strontium hydroxide solution is prepared by dissolving 10.45 g of $Sr(OH)_2$ in water to make 50.00 mL of solution. What is the molarity of this solution? **(b)** Next the strontium hydroxide solution prepared in part (a) is used to titrate a nitric acid solution of unknown concentration. Write a balanced chemical equation to represent the reaction between strontium hydroxide and nitric acid solutions. **(c)** If 23.9 mL of the strontium hydroxide solution was needed to neutralize a 31.5 mL aliquot of the nitric acid solution, what is the concentration (molarity) of the acid?

**[4.104]** A solid sample of $Zn(OH)_2$ is added to 0.350 L of 0.500 $M$ aqueous HBr. The solution that remains is still acidic. It is then titrated with 0.500 $M$ NaOH solution, and it takes 88.5 mL of the NaOH solution to reach the equivalence point. What mass of $Zn(OH)_2$ was added to the HBr solution?

# INTEGRATIVE EXERCISES

**4.105** Suppose you have 5.00 g of powdered magnesium metal, 1.00 L of 2.00 $M$ potassium nitrate solution, and 1.00 L of 2.00 $M$ silver nitrate solution. **(a)** Which one of the solutions will react with the magnesium powder? **(b)** What is the net ionic equation that describes this reaction? **(c)** What volume of solution is needed to completely react with the magnesium? **(d)** What is the molarity of the $Mg^{2+}$ ions in the resulting solution?

**4.106** **(a)** By titration, 15.0 mL of 0.1008 $M$ sodium hydroxide is needed to neutralize a 0.2053-g sample of an organic acid. What is the molar mass of the acid if it is monoprotic? **(b)** An elemental analysis of the acid indicates that it is composed of 5.89% H, 70.6% C, and 23.5% O by mass. What is its molecular formula?

**4.107** A 3.455-g sample of a mixture was analyzed for barium ion by adding a small excess of sulfuric acid to an aqueous solution of the sample. The resultant reaction produced a precipitate of barium sulfate, which was collected by filtration, washed, dried, and weighed. If 0.2815 g of barium sulfate was obtained, what was the mass percentage of barium in the sample?

**4.108** A tanker truck carrying $5.0 \times 10^3$ kg of concentrated sulfuric acid solution tips over and spills its load. If the sulfuric acid is 95.0% $H_2SO_4$ by mass and has a density of 1.84 g/mL, how many kilograms of sodium carbonate must be added to neutralize the acid?

**4.109** A sample of 5.53 g of $Mg(OH)_2$ is added to 25.0 mL of 0.200 $M$ $HNO_3$. **(a)** Write the chemical equation for the reaction that occurs. **(b)** Which is the limiting reactant in the reaction? **(c)** How many moles of $Mg(OH)_2$, $HNO_3$, and $Mg(NO_3)_2$ are present after the reaction is complete?

**4.110** A sample of 1.50 g of lead(II) nitrate is mixed with 125 mL of 0.100 $M$ sodium sulfate solution. **(a)** Write the chemical equation for the reaction that occurs. **(b)** Which is the limiting reactant in the reaction? **(c)** What are the concentrations of all ions that remain in solution after the reaction is complete?

**[4.111]** The average concentration of bromide ion in seawater is 65 mg of bromide ion per kg of seawater. What is the molarity of the bromide ion if the density of the seawater is 1.025 g/mL?

**[4.112]** The mass percentage of chloride ion in a 25.00-mL sample of seawater was determined by titrating the sample with silver nitrate, precipitating silver chloride. It took 42.58 mL of 0.2997 $M$ silver nitrate solution to reach the equivalence point in the titration. What is the mass percentage of chloride ion in the seawater if its density is 1.025 g/mL?

**4.113** The arsenic in a 1.22-g sample of a pesticide was converted to $AsO_4^{3-}$ by suitable chemical treatment. It was then titrated using $Ag^+$ to form $Ag_3AsO_4$ as a precipitate. **(a)** What is the oxidation state of As in $AsO_4^{3-}$? **(b)** Name $Ag_3AsO_4$ by analogy to the corresponding compound containing phosphorus in place of arsenic. **(c)** If it took 25.0 mL of 0.102 $M$ $Ag^+$ to reach the equivalence point in this titration, what is the mass percentage of arsenic in the pesticide?

**[4.114]** The newest US standard for arsenate in drinking water, mandated by the Safe Drinking Water Act, required that by January 2006, public water supplies must contain no greater than 10 parts per billion (ppb) arsenic. If this arsenic is present as arsenate, $AsO_4^{3-}$, what mass of sodium arsenate would be present in a 1.00-L sample of drinking water that just meets the standard? Parts per billion is defined on a mass basis as

$$ppb = \frac{g\ solute}{g\ solution} \times 10^9.$$

[4.115] Federal regulations set an upper limit of 50 parts per million (ppm) of $NH_3$ in the air in a work environment [that is, 50 molecules of $NH_3(g)$ for every million molecules in the air]. Air from a manufacturing operation was drawn through a solution containing $1.00 \times 10^2$ mL of 0.0105 $M$ HCl. The $NH_3$ reacts with HCl as follows:

$$NH_3(aq) + HCl(aq) \longrightarrow NH_4Cl(aq)$$

After drawing air through the acid solution for 10.0 min at a rate of 10.0 L/min, the acid was titrated. The remaining acid needed 13.1 mL of 0.0588 $M$ NaOH to reach the equivalence point. (a) How many grams of $NH_3$ were drawn into the acid solution? (b) How many ppm of $NH_3$ were in the air? (Air has a density of 1.20 g/L and an average molar mass of 29.0 g/mol under the conditions of the experiment.) (c) Is this manufacturer in compliance with regulations?

# WHAT'S AHEAD

### 5.1 THE NATURE OF ENERGY
We begin by considering the nature of *energy* and the forms it takes, notably *kinetic energy* and *potential energy*. We discuss the units used in measuring energy and the fact that energy can be used to do *work* or to transfer *heat*. To study energy changes, we focus on a particular part of the universe, which we call the *system*. Everything else is called the *surroundings*.

### 5.2 THE FIRST LAW OF THERMODYNAMICS
We then explore the *first law of thermodynamics*: Energy cannot be created or destroyed but can be transformed from one form to another or transferred between systems and surroundings. The energy possessed by a system is called its *internal energy*. Internal energy is a *state function,* a quantity whose value depends only on the current state of a system, not on how the system came to be in that state.

### 5.3 ENTHALPY
Next, we encounter a state function called *enthalpy* that is useful because the change in enthalpy measures the quantity of heat energy gained or lost by a system in a process occurring under constant pressure.

**BIOENERGY**. The sugars in sugarcane, produced from $CO_2$, $H_2O$, and sunshine via photosynthesis, can be converted into ethanol, which is used as an alternative to gasoline. In certain climates, such as that in Brazil, the sugarcane crop replenishes itself rapidly, making cane-based ethanol a *sustainable* fuel source.

5

# THERMO-CHEMISTRY

**CHANCES ARE YOU'VE HEARD THE** word *energy* today, perhaps in one of your courses, in the news, in conversation, or possibly in all these instances. Our modern society depends on energy for its existence. The issues surrounding energy—its sources, production, distribution, and consumption—pervade a lot of our

conversation, from science to politics to economics to environmental issues. The production of energy is a major factor in the growth of national economies, especially rapidly developing countries such as China, India, and Brazil. The chapter-opening photograph highlights the efforts in Brazil to use their bountiful and fast-growing sugarcane crop as a source of ethanol. A major part of the Brazilian economy has depended on the use of ethanol instead of petroleum-based fuels in transportation and industry.

With the exception of the energy from the Sun, most of the energy used in our daily lives comes from chemical reactions. The combustion of gasoline, the production of electricity from coal, the heating of homes by natural gas, and the use of batteries to power electronic devices are all examples of how chemistry is used to produce energy. In addition, chemical reactions provide the energy that sustains living systems. Plants, such as the sugarcane in the chapter-opening photograph, use solar energy to carry out photosynthesis, allowing them to grow. The plants in turn provide food from which we humans derive the energy needed to move, maintain body temperature, and carry out all other bodily functions. What exactly is energy, though, and what principles are involved in its production, consumption, and transformation from one form to another?

In this chapter we begin to explore energy and its changes. We are motivated not only by the impact of energy on so many aspects of our daily lives but also by the fact that if we are to properly understand chemistry, we must understand the energy changes that accompany chemical reactions.

The study of energy and its transformations is known as **thermodynamics** (Greek: *thérme-*, "heat"; *dy'namis*, "power"). This area of study began during the Industrial Revolution in order to develop the relationships among heat, work, and fuels in steam engines. In this chapter we will examine the relationships between chemical reactions and energy changes that involve heat. This portion of thermodynamics is called **thermochemistry**. We will discuss additional aspects of thermodynamics in Chapter 19.

# 5.1 | THE NATURE OF ENERGY

The concept of matter has always been easy to grasp because matter can be seen and touched. By contrast, although the concept of energy is a familiar one, it is challenging to deal with in a precise way. **Energy** is commonly defined as *the capacity to do work or transfer heat.* This definition requires us to understand the concepts of work and heat. **Work** is *the energy used to cause an object to move against a force,* and **heat** is *the energy used to cause the temperature of an object to increase* (◀ FIGURE 5.1). Let's begin our study of thermochemistry by examining the ways in which matter can possess energy and how that energy can be transferred from one piece of matter to another.

## Kinetic Energy and Potential Energy

Objects, whether they are baseballs or molecules, can possess **kinetic energy**, the energy of *motion*. The magnitude of the kinetic energy, $E_k$, of an object depends on its mass, $m$, and speed, $v$:

$$E_k = \tfrac{1}{2} mv^2 \tag{5.1}$$

We see that the kinetic energy of an object increases as its speed increases. For example, a car moving at 55 miles per hour (mph) has greater kinetic energy than it does at 25 mph. For a given speed the kinetic energy increases with increasing mass. Thus, a large truck traveling at 55 mph has greater kinetic energy than a small sedan traveling at the same speed because the truck has the greater mass. In chemistry, we are interested in the kinetic energy of atoms and molecules. Although too small to be seen, these particles have mass and are in motion and, therefore, possess kinetic energy.

All other kinds of energy—the energy stored in a stretched spring, in a weight held above your head, or in a chemical bond, for example—are potential energy. An object has **potential energy** by virtue of its position relative to other objects. Potential energy is, in essence, the "stored" energy that arises from the attractions and repulsions an object experiences in relation to other objects.

We are all familiar with instances in which potential energy is converted into kinetic energy. For example, think of a cyclist poised at the top of a hill (▶ FIGURE 5.2). Because of the attractive force of gravity, the potential energy of the cyclist and her bicycle is greater at the top of the hill than at the bottom. As a result, the bicycle easily moves down the hill with increasing speed. As it does so, the potential energy initially stored in it is converted into kinetic energy. The potential energy decreases as the bicycle rolls down the hill, but its kinetic energy increases as the speed increases (Equation 5.1).

We will soon see that this interconversion of energy, with one form decreasing while the other increases, is the first cornerstone of thermodynamics.

Gravitational forces play a negligible role in the ways that atoms and molecules interact with one another. Forces that arise from electrical charges are more important when dealing with atoms and molecules. One of the most important forms of potential energy in chemistry is *electrostatic potential energy,* $E_{el}$, which arises from the interactions between charged particles. This energy is proportional to the electrical charges on the

GO FIGURE

**Why is a pitcher able to throw a baseball faster than he could throw a bowling ball?**

Work done by pitcher on ball to make ball move

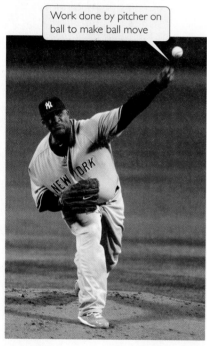

(a)

Heat added by burner to water makes water temperature rise

(b)

▲ FIGURE 5.1 **Work and heat, two forms of energy.** (a) *Work* is energy used to cause an object to move. (b) *Heat* is energy used to cause the temperature of an object to increase.

▲ **GO FIGURE**

**Suppose the bicyclist is coasting (not pedaling) at constant speed on a flat road and begins to go up a hill. If she does not start pedaling, what happens to her speed? Why?**

High potential energy,
zero kinetic energy

Decreasing potential energy,
increasing kinetic energy

◄ **FIGURE 5.2   Potential energy and kinetic energy.** The potential energy initially stored in the motionless bicycle at the top of the hill is converted to kinetic energy as the bicycle moves down the hill and loses potential energy.

two interacting objects, $Q_1$ and $Q_2$, and inversely proportional to the distance, $d$, separating them:

$$E_{el} = \frac{\kappa Q_1 Q_2}{d} \qquad [5.2]$$

Here $\kappa$ is simply a constant of proportionality, $8.99 \times 10^9$ J-m/C$^2$. [C is the coulomb, a unit of electrical charge ∞ (Section 2.2), and J is the joule, a unit of energy we will discuss soon.] At the molecular level, the electrical charges $Q_1$ and $Q_2$ are typically on the order of magnitude of the charge of the electron ($1.60 \times 10^{-19}$ C).

Equation 5.2 shows that the electrostatic potential energy goes to zero as $d$ becomes infinite; in other words, the zero of electrostatic potential energy is defined as infinite separation of the charged particles. ▼ **FIGURE 5.3** illustrates how $E_{el}$ behaves for

▲ **GO FIGURE**

**A positively charged particle and a negatively charged particle are initially far apart. What happens to their electrostatic potential energy as they are brought closer together?**

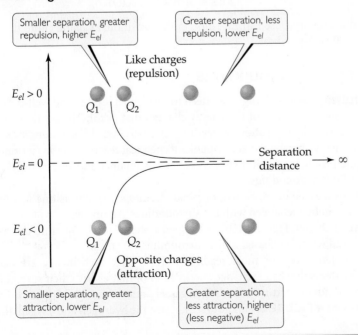

Smaller separation, greater
repulsion, higher $E_{el}$

Greater separation, less
repulsion, lower $E_{el}$

Like charges
(repulsion)

$E_{el} > 0$

$Q_1$   $Q_2$

$E_{el} = 0$

Separation
distance   ∞

$E_{el} < 0$

$Q_1$   $Q_2$

Opposite charges
(attraction)

Smaller separation, greater
attraction, lower $E_{el}$

Greater separation,
less attraction, higher
(less negative) $E_{el}$

◄ **FIGURE 5.3   Electrostatic potential energy.** At finite separation distances for two charged particles, $E_{el}$ is positive for like charges and negative for opposite charges. As the particles move farther apart, their electrostatic potential energy approaches zero.

charges of the same and different sign. When $Q_1$ and $Q_2$ have the same sign (for example, both positive), the two charged particles repel each other, and a repulsive force pushes them apart. In this case, $E_{el}$ is positive, and the potential energy decreases as the particles move farther and farther apart. When $Q_1$ and $Q_2$ have opposite signs, the particles attract each other, and an attractive force pulls them toward each other. In this case, $E_{el}$ is negative, and the potential energy increases (becomes less negative) as the particles move apart.

These trends in electrostatic potential energy are used often in chemistry, as we will see later in the text.

One of our goals in chemistry is to relate the energy changes seen in the macroscopic world to the kinetic or potential energy of substances at the molecular level. Many substances—fuels, for example—release *chemical energy* when they react, energy due to the potential energy stored in the arrangements of their atoms. The energy a substance possesses because of its temperature (its *thermal energy*) is associated with the kinetic energy of the molecules in the substance.

 **GIVE IT SOME THOUGHT**

When the cyclist and bicycle in Figure 5.2 come to a stop at the bottom of the hill, (a) is the potential energy the same as it was at the top of the hill? (b) Is the kinetic energy the same as it was at the top of the hill?

## Units of Energy

The SI unit for energy is the **joule** (pronounced "jool"), J, in honor of James Joule (1818–1889), a British scientist who investigated work and heat: $1\,J = 1\,kg\text{-}m^2/s^2$. Equation 5.1 shows that a mass of 2 kg moving at a speed of 1 m/s possesses a kinetic energy of 1 J:

$$E_k = \tfrac{1}{2} mv^2 = \tfrac{1}{2}(2\,kg)(1\,m/s)^2 = 1\,kg\text{-}m^2/s^2 = 1\,J$$

Because a joule is not a large amount of energy, we often use *kilojoules* (kJ) in discussing the energies associated with chemical reactions.

Traditionally, energy changes accompanying chemical reactions have been expressed in calories, a non–SI unit still widely used in chemistry, biology, and biochemistry. A **calorie** (cal) was originally defined as the amount of energy required to raise the temperature of 1 g of water from 14.5 °C to 15.5 °C. A calorie is now defined in terms of the joule:

$$1\,cal = 4.184\,J\ (exactly)$$

A related energy unit used in nutrition is the nutritional *Calorie* (note the capital C): 1 Cal = 1000 cal = 1 kcal.

## System and Surroundings

When analyzing energy changes, we need to focus on a limited and well-defined part of the universe to keep track of the energy changes that occur. The portion we single out for study is called the **system**; everything else is called the **surroundings**. When we study the energy change that accompanies a chemical reaction in the laboratory, the reactants and products constitute the system. The container and everything beyond it are considered the surroundings.

Systems may be open, closed, or isolated. An *open* system is one in which matter and energy can be exchanged with the surroundings. An uncovered pot of boiling water on a stove, such as in Figure 5.1(b), is an open system: Heat comes into the system from the stove, and water is released to the surroundings as steam.

The systems we can most readily study in thermochemistry are called *closed systems*—systems that can exchange energy but not matter with their surroundings. For example, consider a mixture of hydrogen gas, $H_2$, and oxygen gas, $O_2$, in a cylinder fitted with a piston (◄ **FIGURE 5.4**). The system is just the hydrogen and oxygen; the cylinder,

▲ **GO FIGURE**

If the piston is pulled upward so that it sits halfway between the position shown and the top of the cylinder, is the system still closed?

Energy can enter or leave system as heat or as work done on piston

Matter can not enter or leave system

Surroundings = cylinder, piston, and everything beyond

System = $H_2(g)$ and $O_2(g)$

▲ **FIGURE 5.4** A closed system.

piston, and everything beyond them (including us) are the surroundings. If the gases react to form water, energy is liberated:

$$2\,H_2(g) + O_2(g) \longrightarrow 2\,H_2O(g) + energy$$

Although the chemical form of the hydrogen and oxygen atoms in the system is changed by this reaction, the system has not lost or gained mass, which means it has not exchanged any matter with its surroundings. However, it can exchange energy with its surroundings in the form of *work* and *heat*.

An *isolated* system is one in which neither energy nor matter can be exchanged with the surroundings. An insulated thermos containing hot coffee approximates an isolated system. We know, however, that the coffee eventually cools, so it is not perfectly isolated.

 **GIVE IT SOME THOUGHT**

Is a human being an isolated, closed, or open system?

## Transferring Energy: Work and Heat

Figure 5.1 illustrates the two ways we experience energy changes in our everyday lives—in the form of work and in the form of heat. In Figure 5.1(a) work is done as energy is transferred from the pitcher's arm to the ball, directing it toward the plate at high speed. In Figure 5.1(b) energy is transferred in the form of heat. Causing the motion of an object against a force and causing a temperature change are the two general ways that energy can be transferred into or out of a system.

A **force** is any push or pull exerted on an object. We define work, $w$, as the energy transferred when a force moves an object. The magnitude of this work equals the product of the force, $F$, and the distance, $d$, the object moves:

$$w = F \times d \qquad\qquad [5.3]$$

We perform work, for example, when we lift an object against the force of gravity. If we define the object as the system, then we—as part of the surroundings—are performing work on that system, transferring energy to it.

The other way in which energy is transferred is as heat. *Heat* is the energy transferred from a hotter object to a colder one. A combustion reaction, such as the burning of natural gas illustrated in Figure 5.1(b), releases the chemical energy stored in the molecules of the fuel. ⚬ (Section 3.2) If we define the substances involved in the reaction as the system and everything else as the surroundings, we find that the released energy causes the temperature of the system to increase. Energy in the form of heat is then transferred from the hotter system to the cooler surroundings.

---

**SAMPLE EXERCISE 5.1** **Describing and Calculating Energy Changes**

A bowler lifts a 5.4-kg (12-lb) bowling ball from ground level to a height of 1.6 m (5.2 ft) and then drops it. **(a)** What happens to the potential energy of the ball as it is raised? **(b)** What quantity of work, in J, is used to raise the ball? **(c)** After the ball is dropped, it gains kinetic energy. If all the work done in part (b) has been converted to kinetic energy by the time the ball strikes the ground, what is the ball's speed just before it hits the ground? (Note: The force due to gravity is $F = m \times g$, where $m$ is the mass of the object and $g$ is the gravitational constant; $g = 9.8\ m/s^2$.)

**SOLUTION**

**Analyze** We need to relate the potential energy of the bowling ball to its position relative to the ground. We then need to establish the relationship between work and the change in the ball's potential energy. Finally, we need to connect the change in potential energy when the ball is dropped with the kinetic energy attained by the ball.

**Plan** We can calculate the work done in lifting the ball by using Equation 5.3: $w = F \times d$. The kinetic energy of the ball just before it hits the ground equals its initial potential energy. We can use the kinetic energy and Equation 5.1 to calculate the speed, $v$, just before impact.

**Solve**

**(a)** Because the ball is raised above the ground, its potential energy relative to the ground increases.

**(b)** The ball has a mass of 5.4 kg and is lifted 1.6 m. To calculate the work performed to raise the ball, we use Equation 5.3 and $F = m \times g$ for the force that is due to gravity:

$$w = F \times d = m \times g \times d = (5.4 \text{ kg})(9.8 \text{ m/s}^2)(1.6 \text{ m}) = 85 \text{ kg-m}^2/\text{s}^2 = 85 \text{ J}$$

Thus, the bowler has done 85 J of work to lift the ball to a height of 1.6 m.

**(c)** When the ball is dropped, its potential energy is converted to kinetic energy. We assume that the kinetic energy just before the ball hits the ground is equal to the work done in part (b), 85 J:

$$E_k = \tfrac{1}{2} mv^2 = 85 \text{ J} = 85 \text{ kg-m}^2/\text{s}^2$$

We can now solve this equation for $v$:

$$v^2 = \left(\frac{2E_k}{m}\right) = \left(\frac{2(85 \text{ kg-m}^2/\text{s}^2)}{5.4 \text{ kg}}\right) = 31.5 \text{ m}^2/\text{s}^2$$

$$v = \sqrt{31.5 \text{ m}^2/\text{s}^2} = 5.6 \text{ m/s}$$

**Check** Work must be done in (b) to increase the potential energy of the ball, which is in accord with our experience. The units are appropriate in (b) and (c). The work is in units of J and the speed in units of m/s. In (c) we carry an additional digit in the intermediate calculation involving the square root, but we report the final value to only two significant figures, as appropriate.

**Comment** A speed of 1 m/s is roughly 2 mph, so the bowling ball has a speed greater than 10 mph just before impact.

**PRACTICE EXERCISE**

What is the kinetic energy, in J, of **(a)** an Ar atom moving at a speed of 650 m/s, **(b)** a mole of Ar atoms moving at 650 m/s? (*Hint:* 1 amu = $1.66 \times 10^{-27}$ kg.)

**Answers:** **(a)** $1.4 \times 10^{-20}$ J, **(b)** $8.4 \times 10^3$ J

## 5.2 | THE FIRST LAW OF THERMODYNAMICS

We have seen that the potential energy of a system can be converted into kinetic energy, and vice versa. We have also seen that energy can be transferred back and forth between a system and its surroundings in the forms of work and heat. All of these conversions and transfers proceed in accord with one of the most important observations in science: Energy can be neither created nor destroyed. Any energy that is lost by a system must be gained by the surroundings, and vice versa. This important observation—that *energy is conserved*—is known as the **first law of thermodynamics**. To apply this law quantitatively, let's first define the energy of a system more precisely.

### Internal Energy

We will use the first law of thermodynamics to analyze energy changes in chemical systems. In order to do so, we must consider all the sources of kinetic and potential energy in the system we are studying. We define the **internal energy**, $E$, of a system as the sum of *all* the kinetic and potential energies of the components of the system. For the system in Figure 5.4, for example, the internal energy includes not only the motions and interactions of the $H_2$ and $O_2$ molecules but also the motions and interactions of the nuclei and electrons. We generally do not know the numerical value of a system's internal energy. In thermodynamics, we are mainly concerned with the *change* in $E$ (and, as we shall see, changes in other quantities as well) that accompanies a change in the system.

Imagine that we start with a system with an initial internal energy $E_{initial}$. The system then undergoes a change, which might involve work being done or heat being transferred. After the change, the final internal energy of the system is $E_{final}$. We define

**What is the value of $\Delta E$ if $E_{final}$ equals $E_{initial}$?**

Energy lost to surroundings, internal energy of system decreases, $\Delta E$ negative

Energy gained from surroundings, internal energy of system increases, $\Delta E$ positive

◀ **FIGURE 5.5  Changes in internal energy.**

the *change* in internal energy, denoted $\Delta E$ (read "delta E"),* as the difference between $E_{final}$ and $E_{initial}$:

$$\Delta E = E_{final} - E_{initial} \qquad [5.4]$$

We generally can't determine the actual values of $E_{final}$ and $E_{initial}$ for any system of practical interest. Nevertheless, one of the beautiful aspects of the first law of thermodynamics is that we need only the value of $\Delta E$ in order to apply the law. We can often determine the value of $\Delta E$ even though we don't know the specific values of $E_{final}$ and $E_{initial}$.

Thermodynamic quantities such as $\Delta E$ have three parts: (1) a number and (2) a unit, which together give the magnitude of the change, and (3) a sign that gives the direction. A *positive* value of $\Delta E$ results when $E_{final} > E_{initial}$, indicating that the system has gained energy from its surroundings. A *negative* value of $\Delta E$ results when $E_{final} < E_{initial}$, indicating that the system has lost energy to its surroundings. Notice that we are taking the point of view of the system rather than that of the surroundings in discussing the energy changes. We need to remember, however, that any increase in the energy of the system is accompanied by a decrease in the energy of the surroundings, and vice versa. These features of energy changes are summarized in ▲ **FIGURE 5.5.**

In a chemical reaction, the initial state of the system refers to the reactants and the final state refers to the products. In the reaction

$$2\ H_2(g) + O_2(g) \longrightarrow 2\ H_2O(l)$$

for instance, the initial state is the $2\ H_2(g) + O_2(g)$ and the final state is the $2\ H_2O(l)$. When hydrogen and oxygen form water at a given temperature, the system loses energy to the surroundings. Because energy is lost from the system, the internal energy of the products (final state) is less than that of the reactants (initial state), and $\Delta E$ for the process is negative. Thus, the *energy diagram* in ▶ **FIGURE 5.6** shows that the internal energy of the mixture of $H_2$ and $O_2$ is greater than that of the $H_2O$ produced in the reaction.

## Relating $\Delta E$ to Heat and Work

As we noted in Section 5.1, a system may exchange energy with its surroundings in two general ways: as heat or as work. The internal energy of a system changes in magnitude as heat is added to or removed from the system or as work is done on or by the system. If we think of internal energy as the system's bank account of energy, we see that deposits or withdrawals can be made either in increments of heat or in increments of

**The internal energy for Mg(s) and $Cl_2(g)$ is greater than that of $MgCl_2(s)$. Sketch an energy diagram that represents the reaction $MgCl_2(s) \longrightarrow Mg(s) + Cl_2(g)$.**

$E_{initial}$ greater than $E_{final}$, energy released from system to surrounding during reaction, $\Delta E < 0$

▲ **FIGURE 5.6  Energy diagram for the reaction $2\ H_2(g) + O_2(g) \longrightarrow 2\ H_2O(l)$.**

*The symbol $\Delta$ is commonly used to denote *change*. For example, a change in height, $h$, can be represented by $\Delta h$.

▲ GO FIGURE

Suppose a system receives a "deposit" of work from the surroundings and loses a "withdrawal" of heat to the surroundings. Can we determine the sign of $\Delta E$ for this process?

System is interior of vault

▶ **FIGURE 5.7 Sign conventions for heat and work.** Heat, $q$, gained by a system and work, $w$, done on a system are both positive quantities, corresponding to "deposits" of internal energy into the system. Conversely, heat transferred from the system to the surroundings and work done by the system on the surroundings are both "withdrawals" of internal energy from the system.

Energy deposited into system
$\Delta E > 0$

Energy withdrawn from system
$\Delta E < 0$

work. Deposits increase the energy of the system (positive $\Delta E$), whereas withdrawals decrease the energy of the system (negative $\Delta E$).

We can use these ideas to write a useful algebraic expression of the first law of thermodynamics. When a system undergoes any chemical or physical change, the accompanying change in internal energy, $\Delta E$, is the sum of the heat added to or liberated from the system, $q$, and the work done on or by the system, $w$:

$$\Delta E = q + w \qquad [5.5]$$

*When heat is added to a system or work is done on a system, its internal energy increases.* Therefore, when heat is transferred to the system from the surroundings, $q$ has a positive value. Adding heat to the system is like making a deposit to the energy account—the energy of the system increases (▲ FIGURE 5.7). Likewise, when work is done on the system by the surroundings, $w$ has a positive value. Conversely, both the heat lost by the system to the surroundings and the work done by the system on the surroundings have negative values; that is, they lower the internal energy of the system. They are energy withdrawals and lower the amount of energy in the system's account.

The sign conventions for $q$, $w$, and $\Delta E$ are summarized in ▼ TABLE 5.1. Notice that any energy entering the system as either heat or work carries a positive sign.

**TABLE 5.1 • Sign Conventions for $q$, $w$, and $\Delta E$**

| | | |
|---|---|---|
| For $q$ | + means system *gains* heat | − means system *loses* heat |
| For $w$ | + means work done *on* system | − means work done *by* system |
| For $\Delta E$ | + means *net gain* of energy by system | − means *net loss* of energy by system |

| SAMPLE EXERCISE 5.2 | Relating Heat and Work to Changes of Internal Energy |

Gases A($g$) and B($g$) are confined in a cylinder-and-piston arrangement like that in Figure 5.4 and react to form a solid product C($s$): A($g$) + B($g$) $\longrightarrow$ C($s$). As the reaction occurs, the system loses 1150 J of heat to the surroundings. The piston moves downward as the gases react to form a solid. As the volume of the gas decreases under the constant pressure of the atmosphere, the surroundings do 480 J of work on the system. What is the change in the internal energy of the system?

**SOLUTION**

**Analyze** The question asks us to determine $\Delta E$, given information about $q$ and $w$.

**Plan** We first determine the signs of $q$ and $w$ (Table 5.1) and then use Equation 5.5, $\Delta E = q + w$, to calculate $\Delta E$.

**Solve** Heat is transferred from the system to the surroundings, and work is done on the system by the surroundings, so $q$ is negative and $w$ is positive: $q = -1150$ J and $w = 480$ kJ. Thus,

$$\Delta E = q + w = (-1150 \text{ J}) + (480 \text{ J}) = -670 \text{ J}$$

The negative value of $\Delta E$ tells us that a net quantity of 670 J of energy has been transferred from the system to the surroundings.

**Comment** You can think of this change as a decrease of 670 J in the net value of the system's energy bank account (hence, the negative sign); 1150 J is withdrawn in the form of heat while 480 J is deposited in the form of work. Notice that as the volume of the gases decreases, work is being done *on* the system *by* the surroundings, resulting in a deposit of energy.

**PRACTICE EXERCISE**

Calculate the change in the internal energy for a process in which a system absorbs 140 J of heat from the surroundings and does 85 J of work on the surroundings.

*Answer:* +55 J

## Endothermic and Exothermic Processes

Because transfer of heat to and from the system is central to our discussion in this chapter, we have some special terminology to indicate the direction of transfer. When a process occurs in which the system absorbs heat, the process is called **endothermic** (*endo-* means "into"). During an endothermic process, such as the melting of ice, heat flows *into* the system from its surroundings [▶ FIGURE 5.8(a)]. If we, as part of the surroundings, touch a container in which ice is melting, the container feels cold to us because heat has passed from our hand to the container.

A process in which the system loses heat is called **exothermic** (*exo-* means "out of"). During an exothermic process, such as the combustion of gasoline, heat *exits* or flows *out* of the system into the surroundings [Figure 5.8(b)].

 GIVE IT SOME THOUGHT

When $H_2(g)$ and $O_2(g)$ react to form $H_2O(l)$, heat is released to the surroundings. Consider the reverse reaction, namely, the formation of $H_2(g)$ and $O_2(g)$ from $H_2O(l)$: $2 H_2O(l) \longrightarrow 2 H_2(g) + O_2(g)$. Is this reaction exothermic or endothermic? (*Hint:* Refer to Figure 5.6)

## State Functions

Although we usually have no way of knowing the precise value of the internal energy of a system, $E$, it does have a fixed value for a given set of conditions. The conditions that influence internal energy include the temperature and pressure. Furthermore, the internal energy of a system is proportional to the total quantity of matter in the system because energy is an extensive property. ∞ (Section 1.3)

Suppose we define our system as 50 g of water at 25 °C (▶ FIGURE 5.9). The system could have reached this state by cooling 50 g of water from 100 °C to 25 °C or by melting 50 g of ice and subsequently warming the water to 25 °C. The internal energy of

▶ **FIGURE 5.8 Endothermic and exothermic reactions.** (a) When ammonium thiocyanate and barium hydroxide octahydrate are mixed at room temperature, the temperature drops. (b) The reaction of powdered aluminum with $Fe_2O_3$ (the thermite reaction) proceeds vigorously, releasing heat and forming $Al_2O_3$ and molten iron.

**System:** reactants + products

**Surroundings:** solvent, initially at room temperature

Heat flows from surroundings into system (endothermic reaction), temperature of surroundings drops, thermometer reads temperature well below room temperature

(a)

**System:** reactants

**Surroundings:** air around reactants

Heat flows (violently) from system into surroundings (exothermic reaction), temperature of surroundings increases

(b)

▶ **FIGURE 5.9 Internal energy, *E*, a state function.** Any state function depends only on the present state of the system and not on the path by which the system arrived at that state.

50 g $H_2O(l)$ 100 °C

Initially hot water cools to water at 25 °C; once this temperature is reached, system has internal energy E

50 g $H_2O(l)$ 25 °C

Ice warms up to water at 25 °C; once this temperature is reached, system has internal energy E

50 g $H_2O(s)$ 0 °C

the water at 25 °C is the same in either case. Internal energy is an example of a **state function**, a property of a system that is determined by specifying the system's condition, or state (in terms of temperature, pressure, and so forth). *The value of a state function depends only on the present state of the system, not on the path the system took to reach that state.* Because *E* is a state function, $\Delta E$ depends only on the initial and final states of the system, not on how the change occurs.

An analogy may help you understand the difference between quantities that are state functions and those that are not. Suppose you drive from Chicago, which is 596 ft above sea level, to Denver, which is 5280 ft above sea level. No matter which route you take, the altitude change is 4684 ft. The distance you travel, however, depends on your route. Altitude is analogous to a state function because the change in altitude is independent of the path taken. Distance traveled is not a state function.

Some thermodynamic quantities, such as *E*, are state functions. Other quantities, such as *q* and *w*, are not. This means that, although $\Delta E = q + w$ does not depend on how the change occurs, the specific amounts of heat and work produced depend on the way in which the change occurs, analogous to the choice of travel route between Chicago and Denver. Nevertheless, if changing the path by which a system goes from an initial state to a final state increases the value of *q*, that path change will also decrease the value of *w* by exactly the same amount. The result is that $\Delta E$ is the same for the two paths.

We can illustrate this principle using a flashlight battery as our system. As the battery is discharged, its internal energy decreases as the energy stored in the battery is released to the surroundings. In ▶ **FIGURE 5.10**, we consider two possible ways of discharging the battery at constant temperature. If a wire shorts out the battery, no work is accomplished because nothing is moved against a force. All the energy lost from the battery is in the form of heat. (The wire gets warmer and releases heat to the surroundings.) If the battery is used to make a motor turn, the discharge produces work. Some heat is released, but not as much as when the battery is shorted out. We see that the magnitudes of $q$ and $w$ must be different for these two cases. If the initial and final states of the battery are identical in the two cases, however, then $\Delta E = q + w$ must be the same in both cases because $\Delta E$ is a state function. Remember: $\Delta E$ depends only on the initial and final states of the system, not on the specific path taken from the initial to the final state.

### GIVE IT SOME THOUGHT

In what ways is the balance in your checkbook a state function?

## 5.3 | ENTHALPY

The chemical and physical changes that occur around us, such as photosynthesis in the leaves of a plant, evaporation of water from a lake, or a reaction in an open beaker in a laboratory, occur under the essentially constant pressure of Earth's atmosphere.* These changes can result in the release or absorption of heat and can be accompanied by work done by or on the system. In exploring these changes, we have a number of experimental means to measure the flow of heat into and out of the system, and we therefore focus much of our discussion on what we can learn from the heat flow. (Of course, in order to apply the first law of thermodynamics to these processes, we still need to account for any work that accompanies the process.)

A system that consists of a gas confined to a container can be characterized by several different properties. Among the most important are the *pressure* of the gas, $P$, and the *volume* of the container, $V$. Like internal energy $E$, both $P$ and $V$ are state functions—they depend only on the current state of the system and not on the path taken to that state.

We can combine these three state functions—$E$, $P$, and $V$—to define a new state function called **enthalpy** (from the Greek *enthalpein*, "to warm"). This new function is particularly useful for discussing heat flow in processes that occur under constant (or nearly constant) pressure. Enthalpy, which we denote by the symbol $H$, is defined as the internal energy plus the product of the pressure and volume of the system:

$$H = E + PV \qquad [5.6]$$

### GIVE IT SOME THOUGHT

Given the definition of enthalpy in Equation 5.6, why must $H$ be a state function?

You might be asking yourself why it is convenient to define a new function $H$. To answer that question, recall from Equation 5.5 that $\Delta E$ involves not only the heat $q$ added to or removed from the system but also the work $w$ done by or on the system. Most commonly, the only kind of work produced by chemical or physical changes open to the atmosphere is the mechanical work associated with a change in volume. For example, when the reaction of zinc metal with hydrochloric acid solution,

$$Zn(s) + 2\,H^+(aq) \longrightarrow Zn^{2+}(aq) + H_2(g) \qquad [5.7]$$

### GO FIGURE

If the battery is defined as the system, what is the sign on $w$ in part (b)?

▲ **FIGURE 5.10  Internal energy is a state function, but heat and work are not.** (a) A battery shorted out by a wire loses energy to the surroundings only as heat; no work is performed. (b) A battery discharged through a motor loses energy as work (to make the fan turn) and also loses some energy as heat. The value of $\Delta E$ is the same for both processes even though the values of $q$ and $w$ in (a) are different from those in (b).

---

*You are probably familiar with the notion of atmospheric pressure from a previous course in chemistry. We will discuss it in detail in Chapter 10. Here we need realize only that the atmosphere exerts a pressure on the surface of Earth that is nearly constant.

▲ **GO FIGURE**

If the amount of zinc used in the reaction is increased, will more work be done by the system? Is there additional information you need in order to answer this question?

Increase in volume means system does pressure-volume work

Piston

H$_2$ gas plus original atmosphere

Zn($s$)

HCl($aq$)    Zn($s$)    HCl($aq$)

$$Zn(s) + 2\,H^+(aq) \longrightarrow Zn^{2+}(aq) + H_2(g)$$

▲ **FIGURE 5.11    A system that does work on its surroundings.**

is run at constant pressure in the apparatus illustrated in ▲ **FIGURE 5.11**, the piston moves up or down to maintain a constant pressure in the vessel. If we assume for simplicity that the piston has no mass, the pressure in the apparatus is the same as atmospheric pressure. As the reaction proceeds, H$_2$ gas forms, and the piston rises. The gas within the flask is thus doing work on the surroundings by lifting the piston against the force of atmospheric pressure.

The work involved in the expansion or compression of gases is called **pressure-volume work** (or *P-V* work). When pressure is constant in a process, as in our preceding example, the sign and magnitude of the pressure-volume work are given by

$$w = -P\,\Delta V \qquad [5.8]$$

where *P* is pressure and $\Delta V = V_{final} - V_{initial}$ is the change in volume of the system. The negative sign in Equation 5.8 is necessary to conform to the sign conventions of Table 5.1. The pressure *P* is always either a positive number or zero. If the volume of the system expands, then $\Delta V$ is positive as well. Because the expanding system does work on the surroundings, *w* is negative—energy leaves the system as work. Notice that if the gas is compressed, $\Delta V$ is negative (the volume decreases), and Equation 5.8 indicates that *w* is positive, meaning work is done on the system by the surroundings. The "A Closer Look" box discusses pressure-volume work in detail, but all you need to keep in mind for now is Equation 5.8, which applies to processes occurring at constant pressure.

 **GIVE IT SOME THOUGHT**

If a system does not change its volume during the course of a process, does it do pressure-volume work?

Let's now return to our discussion of enthalpy. When a change occurs at constant pressure, the change in enthalpy, $\Delta H$, is given by the relationship

$$\Delta H = \Delta(E + PV)$$
$$= \Delta E + P\Delta V \quad \text{(constant pressure)} \qquad [5.9]$$

That is, the change in enthalpy equals the change in internal energy plus the product of the constant pressure times the change in volume.

Recall that $\Delta E = q + w$ (Equation 5.5) and that the work involved in the expansion or compression of a gas is $w = -P\,\Delta V$ (at constant pressure). Substituting $-w$ for $P\,\Delta V$ and $q + w$ for $\Delta E$ into Equation 5.9, we have

$$\Delta H = \Delta E + P\,\Delta V = (q_P + w) - w = q_P \qquad [5.10]$$

The subscript $P$ on $q$ indicates that the process occurs at constant pressure. Thus, *the change in enthalpy equals the heat $q_P$ gained or lost at constant pressure*. Because $q_P$ is something we can either measure or readily calculate and because so many physical and chemical changes of interest to us occur at constant pressure, enthalpy is a more useful function for most reactions than is internal energy. In addition, for most reactions the difference in $\Delta H$ and $\Delta E$ is small because $P\,\Delta V$ is small.

When $\Delta H$ is positive (that is, when $q_P$ is positive), the system has gained heat from the surroundings (Table 5.1), which means the process is endothermic. When $\Delta H$ is negative, the system has released heat to the surroundings, which means the process is exothermic. To continue the bank analogy of Figure 5.7, under constant pressure an endothermic process deposits energy in the system in the form of heat and an exothermic process withdraws energy in the form of heat (▶ FIGURE 5.12).

Because $H$ is a state function, $\Delta H$ (which equals $q_P$) depends only on the initial and final states of the system, not on how the change occurs. At first glance this statement might seem to contradict our discussion in Section 5.2, in which we said that $q$ is *not* a state function. There is no contradiction, however, because the relationship between $\Delta H$ and $q_P$ has the special limitations that only $P$-$V$ work is involved and that the pressure is constant.

 **GIVE IT SOME THOUGHT**

What common laboratory measuring device will we likely always use in experiments that measure enthalpy changes?

Constant pressure maintained in system

$\Delta H > 0$ (Endothermic)
Heat gain

(a)

$\Delta H < 0$ (Exothermic)
Heat loss

(b)

$\Delta H$ is amount of heat that flows into or out of system under constant pressure

▲ FIGURE 5.12 **Endothermic and exothermic processes.** (a) An endothermic process ($\Delta H > 0$) deposits heat into the system. (b) An exothermic process ($\Delta H < 0$) withdraws heat from the system.

**SAMPLE EXERCISE 5.3**   **Determining the Sign of $\Delta H$**

Indicate the sign of the enthalpy change, $\Delta H$, in these processes carried out under atmospheric pressure and indicate whether each process is endothermic or exothermic: **(a)** An ice cube melts; **(b)** 1 g of butane ($C_4H_{10}$) is combusted in sufficient oxygen to give complete combustion to $CO_2$ and $H_2O$.

**SOLUTION**

**Analyze** Our goal is to determine whether $\Delta H$ is positive or negative for each process. Because each process occurs at constant pressure, the enthalpy change equals the quantity of heat absorbed or released, $\Delta H = q_P$.

**Plan** We must predict whether heat is absorbed or released by the system in each process. Processes in which heat is absorbed are endothermic and have a positive sign for $\Delta H$; those in which heat is released are exothermic and have a negative sign for $\Delta H$.

**Solve** In (a) the water that makes up the ice cube is the system. The ice cube absorbs heat from the surroundings as it melts, so $\Delta H$ is positive and the process is endothermic. In (b) the system is the 1 g of butane and the oxygen required to combust it. The combustion of butane in oxygen gives off heat, so $\Delta H$ is negative and the process is exothermic.

**PRACTICE EXERCISE**

Molten gold poured into a mold solidifies at atmospheric pressure. With the gold defined as the system, is the solidification an exothermic or endothermic process?

**Answer:** In order to solidify, the gold must cool to below its melting temperature. It cools by transferring heat to its surroundings. The air around the sample would feel hot because heat is transferred to it from the molten gold, meaning the process is exothermic.

You may notice that solidification of a liquid is the reverse of the melting we analyzed in the exercise. As we will see, reversing the direction of a process changes the sign of the heat transferred.

## A CLOSER LOOK

### ENERGY, ENTHALPY, AND *P-V* WORK

In chemistry we are interested mainly in two types of work: electrical work and mechanical work done by expanding gases. We focus here on the latter, called pressure-volume, or *P-V*, work. Expanding gases in the cylinder of an automobile engine do *P-V* work on the piston; this work eventually turns the wheels. Expanding gases from an open reaction vessel do *P-V* work on the atmosphere. This work accomplishes nothing in a practical sense, but we must keep track of all work, useful or not, when monitoring energy changes in a system.

Let's consider a gas confined to a cylinder with a movable piston of cross-sectional area *A* (▼ **FIGURE 5.13**). A downward force *F* acts on the piston. The *pressure, P,* on the gas is the force per area: $P = F/A$. We assume that the piston is massless and that the only pressure acting on it is the *atmospheric pressure* that is due to Earth's atmosphere, which we assume to be constant.

System does work $w = -P\Delta V$ on surroundings as gas expands, pushing piston up distance $\Delta h$

$P = F/A$      $P = F/A$

$\Delta h$    $\Delta V$

Volume change

Gas enclosed in cylinder

Initial state    Cross-sectional area = *A*    Final state

▲ **FIGURE 5.13 Pressure-volume work.** The amount of work done by the system on the surroundings is $w = -P\Delta V$.

Suppose the gas expands and the piston moves a distance $\Delta h$. From Equation 5.3, the magnitude of the work done by the system is

$$\text{Magnitude of work} = \text{force} \times \text{distance} = F \times \Delta h \quad [5.11]$$

We can rearrange the definition of pressure, $P = F/A$, to $F = P \times A$. The volume change, $\Delta V$, resulting from the movement of the piston is the product of the cross-sectional area of the piston and the distance it moves: $\Delta V = A \times \Delta h$. Substituting into Equation 5.11 gives

$$\text{Magnitude of work} = F \times \Delta h = P \times A \times \Delta h$$
$$= P \times \Delta V$$

Because the system (the confined gas) does work on the surroundings, the work is a negative quantity:

$$w = -P\,\Delta V \quad [5.12]$$

Now, if *P-V* work is the only work that can be done, we can substitute Equation 5.12 into Equation 5.5 to give

$$\Delta E = q + w = q - P\,\Delta V \quad [5.13]$$

When a reaction is carried out in a constant-volume container ($\Delta V = 0$), therefore, the heat transferred equals the change in internal energy:

$$\Delta E = q - P\Delta V = q - P(0) = q_V \quad \text{(constant volume)} \;[5.14]$$

The subscript *V* indicates that the volume is constant.

Most reactions are run under constant pressure, so that Equation 5.13 becomes

$$\Delta E = q_P - P\,\Delta V$$
$$q_P = \Delta E + P\,\Delta V \quad \text{(constant pressure)} \quad [5.15]$$

We see from Equation 5.9 that the right side of Equation 5.15 is the enthalpy change under constant-pressure conditions. Thus, $\Delta H = q_P$, as we saw in Equation 5.10.

In summary, the change in internal energy is equal to the heat gained or lost at constant volume, and the change in enthalpy is equal to the heat gained or lost at constant pressure. The difference between $\Delta E$ and $\Delta H$ is the amount of *P-V* work done by the system when the process occurs at constant pressure, $-P\,\Delta V$. The volume change accompanying many reactions is close to zero, which makes $P\,\Delta V$ and, therefore, the difference between $\Delta E$ and $\Delta H$ small. Under most circumstances, it is generally satisfactory to use $\Delta H$ as the measure of energy changes during most chemical processes.

*RELATED EXERCISES:* 5.35, 5.36, 5.37, 5.38

## 5.4 | ENTHALPIES OF REACTION

Because $\Delta H = H_{\text{final}} - H_{\text{initial}}$, the enthalpy change for a chemical reaction is given by

$$\Delta H = H_{\text{products}} - H_{\text{reactants}} \quad [5.16]$$

The enthalpy change that accompanies a reaction is called either the **enthalpy of reaction** or the *heat of reaction* and is sometimes written $\Delta H_{\text{rxn}}$, where "rxn" is a commonly used abbreviation for "reaction."

When we give a numerical value for $\Delta H_{\text{rxn}}$, we must specify the reaction involved. For example, when 2 mol $H_2(g)$ burn to form 2 mol $H_2O(g)$ at a constant pressure, the system releases 483.6 kJ of heat. We can summarize this information as

$$2\,H_2(g) + O_2(g) \longrightarrow 2\,H_2O(g) \qquad \Delta H = -483.6 \text{ kJ} \quad [5.17]$$

◀ **FIGURE 5.14  Exothermic reaction of hydrogen with oxygen.** When a mixture of $H_2(g)$ and $O_2(g)$ is ignited to form $H_2O(g)$, the resultant explosion produces a ball of flame. Because the system releases heat to the surroundings, the reaction is exothermic as indicated in the enthalpy diagram.

$$2 H_2(g) + O_2(g) \longrightarrow 2 H_2O(g)$$

The negative sign for $\Delta H$ tells us that this reaction is exothermic. Notice that $\Delta H$ is reported at the end of the balanced equation, without explicitly specifying the amounts of chemicals involved. In such cases the coefficients in the balanced equation represent the number of moles of reactants and products producing the associated enthalpy change. Balanced chemical equations that show the associated enthalpy change in this way are called *thermochemical equations*.

The exothermic nature of this reaction is also shown in the *enthalpy diagram* in ▲ **FIGURE 5.14**. Notice that the enthalpy of the reactants is greater (more positive) than the enthalpy of the products. Thus, $\Delta H = H_{products} - H_{reactants}$ is negative.

⚠ GIVE IT SOME THOUGHT

If the reaction to form water were written $H_2(g) + \frac{1}{2} O_2(g) \longrightarrow H_2O(g)$, would you expect the same value of $\Delta H$ as in Equation 5.17? Why or why not?

The reaction of hydrogen with oxygen is highly exothermic and occurs rapidly once it starts. It can occur with explosive violence, as demonstrated by the explosions of the German airship *Hindenburg* in 1937 (▼ **FIGURE 5.15**) and the U.S. space shuttle *Challenger* in 1986.

◀ **FIGURE 5.15  The burning of the hydrogen-filled airship *Hindenburg*.** This tragedy, in Lakehurst, New Jersey, on May 6, 1937, led to the discontinuation of hydrogen as a buoyant gas in such craft. Modern-day airships are filled with helium, which is not as buoyant as hydrogen but is not flammable.

▲ **FIGURE 5.16** $\Delta H$ **for a reverse reaction.** Reversing a reaction changes the sign but not the magnitude of the enthalpy change: $\Delta H_2 = -\Delta H_1$.

The following guidelines are helpful when using thermochemical equations and enthalpy diagrams:

1. **Enthalpy is an extensive property.** The magnitude of $\Delta H$ is proportional to the amount of reactant consumed in the process. For example, 890 kJ of heat is produced when 1 mol of $CH_4$ is burned in a constant-pressure system:

$$CH_4(g) + 2 O_2(g) \longrightarrow CO_2(g) + 2 H_2O(l) \qquad \Delta H = -890 \text{ kJ} \qquad [5.18]$$

Because the combustion of 1 mol of $CH_4$ with 2 mol of $O_2$ releases 890 kJ of heat, the combustion of 2 mol of $CH_4$ with 4 mol of $O_2$ releases twice as much heat, 1780 kJ.

2. **The enthalpy change for a reaction is equal in magnitude, but opposite in sign, to $\Delta H$ for the reverse reaction.** For example, $\Delta H$ for the reverse of Equation 5.18 is +890 kJ:

$$CO_2(g) + 2 H_2O(l) \longrightarrow CH_4(g) + 2 O_2(g) \qquad \Delta H = +890 \text{ kJ} \qquad [5.19]$$

When we reverse a reaction, we reverse the roles of the products and the reactants. From Equation 5.16, we see that reversing the products and reactants leads to the same magnitude of $\Delta H$ but a change in sign (◄ **FIGURE 5.16**).

3. **The enthalpy change for a reaction depends on the states of the reactants and products.** If the product in Equation 5.18 were $H_2O(g)$ instead of $H_2O(l)$, $\Delta H_{rxn}$ would be $-802$ kJ instead of $-890$ kJ. Less heat would be available for transfer to the surroundings because the enthalpy of $H_2O(g)$ is greater than that of $H_2O(l)$. One way to see this is to imagine that the product is initially liquid water. The liquid water must be converted to water vapor, and the conversion of 2 mol $H_2O(l)$ to 2 mol $H_2O(g)$ is an endothermic process that absorbs 88 kJ:

$$2 H_2O(l) \longrightarrow 2 H_2O(g) \qquad \Delta H = +88 \text{ kJ} \qquad [5.20]$$

Thus, it is important to specify the states of the reactants and products in thermochemical equations. In addition, we will generally assume that the reactants and products are both at the same temperature, 25 °C, unless otherwise indicated.

---

**SAMPLE EXERCISE 5.4** | **Relating $\Delta H$ to Quantities of Reactants and Products**

How much heat is released when 4.50 g of methane gas is burned in a constant-pressure system? (Use the information given in Equation 5.18.)

**SOLUTION**

**Analyze** Our goal is to use a thermochemical equation to calculate the heat produced when a specific amount of methane gas is combusted. According to Equation 5.18, 890 kJ is released by the system when 1 mol $CH_4$ is burned at constant pressure.

**Plan** Equation 5.18 provides us with a stoichiometric conversion factor: (1 mol $CH_4 \simeq -890$ kJ). Thus, we can convert moles of $CH_4$ to kJ of energy. First, however, we must convert grams of $CH_4$ to moles of $CH_4$. Thus, the conversion sequence is grams $CH_4$ (given) $\rightarrow$ moles $CH_4$ $\rightarrow$ kJ (unknown to be found).

**Solve** By adding the atomic weights of C and 4 H, we have 1 mol $CH_4 = 16.0$ $CH_4$. We can use the appropriate conversion factors to convert grams of $CH_4$ to moles of $CH_4$ to kilojoules:

$$\text{Heat} = (4.50 \text{ g } CH_4)\left(\frac{1 \text{ mol } CH_4}{16.0 \text{ g } CH_4}\right)\left(\frac{-890 \text{ kJ}}{1 \text{ mol } CH_4}\right) = -250 \text{ kJ}$$

The negative sign indicates that the system released 250 kJ into the surroundings.

**PRACTICE EXERCISE**

Hydrogen peroxide can decompose to water and oxygen by the reaction

$$2 H_2O_2(l) \longrightarrow 2 H_2O(l) + O_2(g) \qquad \Delta H = -196 \text{ kJ}$$

Calculate the quantity of heat released when 5.00 g of $H_2O_2(l)$ decomposes at constant pressure.
**Answer:** $-14.4$ kJ

# STRATEGIES IN CHEMISTRY

## USING ENTHALPY AS A GUIDE

If you hold a brick in the air and let it go, you know what happens: It falls as the force of gravity pulls it toward Earth. A process that is thermodynamically favored to happen, such as a brick falling to the ground, is called a *spontaneous* process. A spontaneous process can be either fast or slow; the rate at which processes occur is not governed by thermodynamics.

Chemical processes can be thermodynamically favored, or spontaneous, too. By spontaneous, however, we do not mean that the reaction will form products without any intervention. That can be the case, but often some energy must be imparted to get the process started. The enthalpy change in a reaction gives one indication as to whether the reaction is likely to be spontaneous. The combustion of $H_2(g)$ and $O_2(g)$, for example, is highly exothermic:

$$H_2(g) + \tfrac{1}{2} O_2(g) \longrightarrow H_2O(g) \qquad \Delta H = -242 \text{ kJ}$$

Hydrogen gas and oxygen gas can exist together in a volume indefinitely without noticeable reaction occurring. Once the reaction is initiated, however, energy is rapidly transferred from the system (the reactants) to the surroundings as heat. The system thus loses enthalpy by transferring the heat to the surroundings. (Recall that the first law of thermodynamics tells us that the total energy of the system plus the surroundings does not change; energy is conserved.)

Enthalpy change is not the only consideration in the spontaneity of reactions, however, nor is it a foolproof guide. For example, even though ice melting is an endothermic process,

$$H_2O(s) \longrightarrow H_2O(l) \qquad \Delta H = +6.01 \text{ kJ}$$

this process is spontaneous at temperatures above the freezing point of water (0 °C). The reverse process, water freezing, is spontaneous at temperatures below 0 °C. Thus, we know that ice at room temperature melts and water put into a freezer at −20 °C turns into ice. Both processes are spontaneous under different conditions even though they are the reverse of one another. In Chapter 19 we will address the spontaneity of processes more fully. We will see why a process can be spontaneous at one temperature but not at another, as is the case for the conversion of water to ice.

Despite these complicating factors, you should pay attention to the enthalpy changes in reactions. As a general observation, when the enthalpy change is large, it is the dominant factor in determining spontaneity. Thus, reactions for which $\Delta H$ is *large* and *negative* tend to be spontaneous. Reactions for which $\Delta H$ is *large* and *positive* tend to be spontaneous only in the reverse direction.

*RELATED EXERCISES:* 5.47, 5.48

In many situations we will find it valuable to know the sign and magnitude of the enthalpy change associated with a given chemical process. As we see in the following sections, $\Delta H$ can be either determined directly by experiment or calculated from known enthalpy changes of other reactions.

# 5.5 | CALORIMETRY

The value of $\Delta H$ can be determined experimentally by measuring the heat flow accompanying a reaction at constant pressure. Typically, we can determine the magnitude of the heat flow by measuring the magnitude of the temperature change the heat flow produces. The measurement of heat flow is **calorimetry**; a device used to measure heat flow is a **calorimeter**.

## Heat Capacity and Specific Heat

The more heat an object gains, the hotter it gets. All substances change temperature when they are heated, but the magnitude of the temperature change produced by a given quantity of heat varies from substance to substance. The temperature change experienced by an object when it absorbs a certain amount of heat is determined by its **heat capacity**, denoted $C$. The heat capacity of an object is the amount of heat required to raise its temperature by 1 K (or 1 °C). The greater the heat capacity, the greater the heat required to produce a given increase in temperature.

For pure substances the heat capacity is usually given for a specified amount of the substance. The heat capacity of one mole of a substance is called its **molar heat capacity**, $C_m$. The heat capacity of one gram of a substance is called its *specific heat capacity*, or merely its **specific heat**. The specific heat, $C_s$, of a substance can be determined experimentally by

**Is the process shown in the figure endothermic or exothermic?**

▲ FIGURE 5.17 **Specific heat of water.**

measuring the temperature change, $\Delta T$, that a known mass $m$ of the substance undergoes when it gains or loses a specific quantity of heat $q$:

$$\text{Specific heat} = \frac{\text{(quantity of heat transferred)}}{\text{(grams of substance)} \times \text{(temperature change)}}$$

$$C_s = \frac{q}{m \times \Delta T} \qquad [5.21]$$

For example, 209 J is required to increase the temperature of 50.0 g of water by 1.00 K. Thus, the specific heat of water is

$$C_s = \frac{209 \text{ J}}{(50.0 \text{ g})(1.00 \text{ K})} = 4.18 \text{ J/g-K}$$

A temperature change in kelvins is equal in magnitude to the temperature change in degrees Celsius: $\Delta T$ in $K = \Delta T$ in °C. ∞ (Section 1.4) Therefore, this specific heat for water can also be reported as 4.18 J/g-°C.

Because the specific heat values for a given substance can vary slightly with temperature, the temperature is often precisely specified. The 4.18 J/g-K value we use here for water, for instance, is for water initially at 14.5 °C (◀ FIGURE 5.17). Water's specific heat at this temperature is used to define the calorie at the value given in Section 5.1: 1 cal = 4.184 J exactly.

When a sample absorbs heat (positive $q$), its temperature increases (positive $\Delta T$). Rearranging Equation 5.21, we get

$$q = C_s \times m \times \Delta T \qquad [5.22]$$

Thus, we can calculate the quantity of heat a substance gains or loses by using its specific heat together with its measured mass and temperature change.

▼ TABLE 5.2 lists the specific heats of several substances. Notice that the specific heat of liquid water is higher than those of the other substances listed. The high specific heat of water affects Earth's climate because it makes the temperatures of the oceans relatively resistant to change.

GIVE IT SOME THOUGHT

Which substance in Table 5.2 undergoes the greatest temperature change when the same mass of each substance absorbs the same quantity of heat?

| TABLE 5.2 • Specific Heats of Some Substances at 298 K | | | |
|---|---|---|---|
| **Elements** | | **Compounds** | |
| **Substance** | **Specific Heat (J/g-K)** | **Substance** | **Specific Heat (J/g-K)** |
| $N_2(g)$ | 1.04 | $H_2O(l)$ | 4.18 |
| $Al(s)$ | 0.90 | $CH_4(g)$ | 2.20 |
| $Fe(s)$ | 0.45 | $CO_2(g)$ | 0.84 |
| $Hg(l)$ | 0.14 | $CaCO_3(s)$ | 0.82 |

**SAMPLE EXERCISE 5.5** **Relating Heat, Temperature Change, and Heat Capacity**

**(a)** How much heat is needed to warm 250 g of water (about 1 cup) from 22 °C (about room temperature) to 98 °C (near its boiling point)? **(b)** What is the molar heat capacity of water?

**SOLUTION**

**Analyze** In part **(a)** we must find the quantity of heat ($q$) needed to warm the water, given the mass of water ($m$), its temperature change ($\Delta T$), and its specific heat ($C_s$). In part **(b)** we must calculate the molar heat capacity (heat capacity per mole, $C_m$) of water from its specific heat (heat capacity per gram).

**Plan** (a) Given $C_s$, $m$, and $\Delta T$, we can calculate the quantity of heat, $q$, using Equation 5.22. (b) We can use the molar mass of water and dimensional analysis to convert from heat capacity per gram to heat capacity per mole.

**Solve**

(a) The water undergoes a temperature change of

$$\Delta T = 98\,°C - 22\,°C = 76\,°C = 76\,K$$

Using Equation 5.22, we have

$$q = C_s \times m \times \Delta T$$
$$= (4.18\,J/g\text{-}K)(250\,g)(76\,K) = 7.9 \times 10^4\,J$$

(b) The molar heat capacity is the heat capacity of one mole of substance. Using the atomic weights of hydrogen and oxygen, we have

$$1\,mol\,H_2O = 18.0\,g\,H_2O$$

From the specific heat given in part (a), we have

$$C_m = \left(4.18\,\frac{J}{g\text{-}K}\right)\left(\frac{18.0\,g}{1\,mol}\right) = 75.2\,J/mol\text{-}K$$

**PRACTICE EXERCISE**

(a) Large beds of rocks are used in some solar-heated homes to store heat. Assume that the specific heat of the rocks is 0.82 J/g-K. Calculate the quantity of heat absorbed by 50.0 kg of rocks if their temperature increases by 12.0 °C. (b) What temperature change would these rocks undergo if they emitted 450 kJ of heat?

**Answers:** (a) $4.9 \times 10^5$ J, (b) 11 K decrease = 11 °C decrease

# Constant-Pressure Calorimetry

The techniques and equipment employed in calorimetry depend on the nature of the process being studied. For many reactions, such as those occurring in solution, it is easy to control pressure so that $\Delta H$ is measured directly. Although the calorimeters used for highly accurate work are precision instruments, a simple "coffee-cup" calorimeter (▶ FIGURE 5.18) is often used in general chemistry laboratories to illustrate the principles of calorimetry. Because the calorimeter is not sealed, the reaction occurs under the essentially constant pressure of the atmosphere.

Imagine adding two aqueous solutions, each containing a reactant, to a coffee-cup calorimeter. Once mixed, the reactants can react to form products. In this case there is no physical boundary between the system and the surroundings. The reactants and products of the reaction are the system, and the water in which they are dissolved is part of the surroundings. (The calorimeter apparatus is also part of the surroundings.) If we assume that the calorimeter is perfectly insulated, then any heat released or absorbed by the reaction will raise or lower the temperature of the water in the solution. Thus, we measure the temperature change of the solution and assume that any changes are due to heat transferred from the reaction to the water (for an exothermic process) or transferred from the water to the reaction (endothermic). In other words, by monitoring the temperature of the solution, we are seeing the flow of heat between the system (the reactants and products in the solution) and the surroundings (the water that forms the bulk of the solution).

For an exothermic reaction, heat is "lost" by the reaction and "gained" by the water in the solution, so the temperature of the solution rises. The opposite occurs for an endothermic reaction: Heat is gained by the reaction and lost by the water in the solution, and the temperature of the solution decreases. The heat gained or lost by the solution, $q_{soln}$, is therefore equal in magnitude but opposite in sign to the heat absorbed or released by the reaction, $q_{rxn}$: $q_{soln} = -q_{rxn}$. The value of $q_{soln}$ is readily calculated from the mass of the solution, its specific heat, and the temperature change:

$$q_{soln} = (\text{specific heat of solution}) \times (\text{grams of solution}) \times \Delta T = -q_{rxn} \quad [5.23]$$

For dilute aqueous solutions we usually assume that the specific heat of the solution is the same as that of water, 4.18 J/g-K.

Equation 5.23 makes it possible to calculate $q_{rxn}$ from the temperature change of the solution in which the reaction occurs. A temperature increase ($\Delta T > 0$) means the reaction is exothermic ($q_{rxn} < 0$).

▲ GO FIGURE

Propose a reason for why two Styrofoam® cups are often used instead of just one.

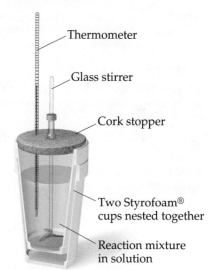

Thermometer

Glass stirrer

Cork stopper

Two Styrofoam® cups nested together

Reaction mixture in solution

▲ FIGURE 5.18 **Coffee-cup calorimeter.** This simple apparatus is used to measure temperature changes of reactions at constant pressure.

| SAMPLE EXERCISE 5.6 | Measuring ΔH Using a Coffee-Cup Calorimeter |
|---|---|

When a student mixes 50 mL of 1.0 $M$ HCl and 50 mL of 1.0 $M$ NaOH in a coffee-cup calorimeter, the temperature of the resultant solution increases from 21.0 °C to 27.5 °C. Calculate the enthalpy change for the reaction in kJ/mol HCl, assuming that the calorimeter loses only a negligible quantity of heat, that the total volume of the solution is 100 mL, that its density is 1.0 g/mL, and that its specific heat is 4.18 J/g-K.

### SOLUTION

**Analyze** Mixing solutions of HCl and NaOH results in an acid–base reaction:

$$HCl(aq) + NaOH(aq) \longrightarrow H_2O(l) + NaCl(aq)$$

We need to calculate the heat produced per mole of HCl, given the temperature increase of the solution, the number of moles of HCl and NaOH involved, and the density and specific heat of the solution.

**Plan** The total heat produced can be calculated using Equation 5.23. The number of moles of HCl consumed in the reaction must be calculated from the volume and molarity of this substance, and this amount is then used to determine the heat produced per mol HCl.

**Solve**

Because the total volume of the solution is 100 mL, its mass is

$$(100 \text{ mL})(1.0 \text{ g/mL}) = 100 \text{ g}$$

The temperature change is

$$\Delta T = 27.5 \text{ °C} - 21.0 \text{ °C} = 6.5 \text{ °C} = 6.5 \text{ K}$$

Using Equation 5.23, we have

$$q_{rxn} = -C_s \times m \times \Delta T$$
$$= -(4.18 \text{ J/g-K})(100 \text{ g})(6.5 \text{ K}) = -2.7 \times 10^3 \text{ J} = -2.7 \text{ kJ}$$

Because the process occurs at constant pressure,

$$\Delta H = q_P = -2.7 \text{ kJ}$$

To express the enthalpy change on a molar basis, we use the fact that the number of moles of HCl is given by the product of the volume (50 mL = 0.050 L) and concentration (1.0 $M$ = 1.0 mol/L) of the HCl solution:

$$(0.050 \text{ L})(1.0 \text{ mol/L}) = 0.050 \text{ mol}$$

Thus, the enthalpy change per mole of HCl is

$$\Delta H = -2.7 \text{ kJ}/0.050 \text{ mol} = -54 \text{ kJ/mol}$$

**Check** ΔH is negative (exothermic), which is expected for the reaction of an acid with a base and evidenced by the fact that the reaction causes the temperature of the solution to increase. The magnitude of the molar enthalpy change seems reasonable.

### PRACTICE EXERCISE

When 50.0 mL of 0.100 $M$ AgNO$_3$ and 50.0 mL of 0.100 $M$ HCl are mixed in a constant-pressure calorimeter, the temperature of the mixture increases from 22.30 °C to 23.11 °C. The temperature increase is caused by the following reaction:

$$AgNO_3(aq) + HCl(aq) \longrightarrow AgCl(s) + HNO_3(aq)$$

Calculate ΔH for this reaction in kJ/mol AgNO$_3$, assuming that the combined solution has a mass of 100.0 g and a specific heat of 4.18 J/g °C.

**Answer:** −68,000 J/mol = −68 kJ/mol

## Bomb Calorimetry (Constant-Volume Calorimetry)

An important type of reaction studied using calorimetry is combustion, in which a compound reacts completely with excess oxygen. ∞ (Section 3.2) Combustion reactions are most accurately studied using a **bomb calorimeter** (▶ FIGURE 5.19). The substance to be studied is placed in a small cup within an insulated sealed vessel called a *bomb*. The bomb, which is designed to withstand high pressures, has an inlet valve for adding oxygen and electrical leads. After the sample has been placed in the bomb, the bomb is sealed and pressurized with oxygen. It is then placed in the calorimeter and covered with an accurately measured quantity of water. The combustion reaction is initiated by passing an electrical current through a fine wire in contact with the sample. When the wire becomes sufficiently hot, the sample ignites.

The heat released when combustion occurs is absorbed by the water and the various components of the calorimeter (which all together make up the surroundings), causing the water temperature to rise. The change in water temperature caused by the reaction is measured very precisely.

To calculate the heat of combustion from the measured temperature increase, we must know the total heat capacity of the calorimeter, $C_{cal}$. This quantity is determined by combusting a sample that releases a known quantity of heat and measuring the temperature change. For example, combustion of exactly 1 g of benzoic acid, $C_6H_5COOH$, in a bomb calorimeter produces 26.38 kJ of heat. Suppose 1.000 g of benzoic acid is combusted in a calorimeter, leading to a temerature increase of 4.857 °C. The heat capacity of the calorimeter is then $C_{cal}$ = 26.38 kJ/4.857 °C = 5.431 kJ/°C. Once we know $C_{cal}$, we can measure temperature changes produced by other reactions, and from these we can calculate the heat evolved in the reaction, $q_{rxn}$:

$$q_{rxn} = -C_{cal} \times \Delta T \qquad\qquad [5.24]$$

Measurements made with a bomb calorimeter are generally more precise than those made with a coffee-cup calorimeter.

△ **GO FIGURE**

**Why is a stirrer used in calorimeters?**

▲ **FIGURE 5.19  Bomb calorimeter.**

---

**SAMPLE EXERCISE 5.7**  **Measuring $q_{rxn}$ Using a Bomb Calorimeter**

The combustion of methylhydrazine ($CH_6N_2$), a liquid rocket fuel, produces $N_2(g)$, $CO_2(g)$, and $H_2O(l)$:

$$2\ CH_6N_2(l) + 5\ O_2(g) \longrightarrow 2\ N_2(g) + 2\ CO_2(g) + 6\ H_2O(l)$$

When 4.00 g of methylhydrazine is combusted in a bomb calorimeter, the temperature of the calorimeter increases from 25.00 °C to 39.50 °C. In a separate experiment the heat capacity of the calorimeter is measured to be 7.794 kJ/°C. Calculate the heat of reaction for the combustion of a mole of $CH_6N_2$.

**SOLUTION**

**Analyze** We are given a temperature change and the total heat capacity of the calorimeter. We are also given the amount of reactant combusted. Our goal is to calculate the enthalpy change per mole for combustion of the reactant.

**Plan** We will first calculate the heat evolved for the combustion of the 4.00-g sample. We will then convert this heat to a molar quantity.

**Solve**

For combustion of the 4.00-g sample of methylhydrazine, the temperature change of the calorimeter is

$$\Delta T = (39.50\ °C - 25.00\ °C) = 14.50\ °C$$

We can use $\Delta T$ and the value for $C_{cal}$ to calculate the heat of reaction (Equation 5.24):

$$q_{rxn} = -C_{cal} \times \Delta T = -(7.794\ kJ/°C)(14.50\ °C) = -113.0\ kJ$$

We can readily convert this value to the heat of reaction for a mole of $CH_6N_2$:

$$\left(\frac{-113.0\ kJ}{4.00\ g\ CH_6N_2}\right) \times \left(\frac{46.1\ g\ CH_6N_2}{1\ mol\ CH_6N_2}\right) = -1.30 \times 10^3\ kJ/mol\ CH_6N_2$$

**Check** The units cancel properly, and the sign of the answer is negative as it should be for an exothermic reaction. The magnitude of the answer seems reasonable.

**PRACTICE EXERCISE**

A 0.5865-g sample of lactic acid ($HC_3H_5O_3$) is burned in a calorimeter whose heat capacity is 4.812 kJ/°C. The temperature increases from 23.10 °C to 24.95 °C. Calculate the heat of combustion of lactic acid (a) per gram and (b) per mole.

**Answers: (a)** −15.2 kJ/g, **(b)** −1370 kJ/mol

---

Because reactions in a bomb calorimeter are carried out at constant volume, the heat transferred corresponds to the change in internal energy, $\Delta E$, rather than the change in enthalpy, $\Delta H$ (Equation 5.14). For most reactions, however, the difference between $\Delta E$ and $\Delta H$ is very small. For the reaction discussed in Sample Exercise 5.7, for example, the difference between $\Delta E$ and $\Delta H$ is about 1 kJ/mol—a difference of less than 0.1%. It is possible to correct the measured heat changes to obtain $\Delta H$ values, and these form the basis of the tables of enthalpy used in the following sections. We need not concern ourselves with how these small corrections are made.

# CHEMISTRY AND LIFE

## THE REGULATION OF BODY TEMPERATURE

For most of us, being asked the question "Are you running a fever?" was one of our first introductions to medical diagnosis. Indeed, a deviation in body temperature of only a few degrees indicates something amiss. In the laboratory you may have observed how difficult it is to maintain a solution at a constant temperature. Yet our bodies maintain a near-constant temperature in spite of widely varying weather, levels of physical activity, and periods of high metabolic activity (such as after a meal).

Maintaining a near-constant temperature is one of the primary physiological functions of the human body. Normal body temperature generally ranges from 35.8 °C to 37.2 °C (96.5 °F to 99 °F). This very narrow range is essential to proper muscle function and to control of the rates of the biochemical reactions in the body. You will learn more about the effects of temperature on reaction rates in Chapter 14.

The portion of the human brain stem called the *hypothalamus* regulates body temperature—in essence, the hypothalamus acts as a thermostat for the body. When body temperature rises above the normal range, the hypothalamus triggers mechanisms to lower the temperature. It likewise triggers mechanisms to increase the temperature if body temperature drops too low.

To understand how the body's heating and cooling mechanisms operate, we can view the body as a thermodynamic system. The body increases its internal energy content by ingesting foods from the surroundings. The foods, such as glucose ($C_6H_{12}O_6$), are metabolized—a process that is essentially controlled oxidation to $CO_2$ and $H_2O$:

$$C_6H_{12}O_6(s) + 6\,O_2(g) \longrightarrow 6\,CO_2(g) + 6\,H_2O(l)$$
$$\Delta H = -2803 \text{ kJ}$$

Roughly 40% of the energy produced is ultimately used to do work in the form of muscle contractions and nerve cell activities. The remainder is released as heat, part of which is used to maintain body temperature. When the body produces too much heat, as in times of heavy physical exertion, it dissipates the excess to the surroundings.

Heat is transferred from the body to its surroundings primarily by *radiation, convection,* and *evaporation.* Radiation is the direct loss of heat from the body to cooler surroundings, much as a hot stovetop radiates heat to its surroundings. Convection is heat loss by virtue of heating air that is in contact with the body. The heated air rises and is replaced with cooler air, and the process continues. Warm clothing, which usually consists of insulating layers of material with "dead air" in between, decreases convective heat loss in cold weather. Evaporative cooling occurs when perspiration is generated at the skin surface by the sweat glands (▶ FIGURE 5.20). Heat is removed from the body as the perspiration evaporates into the surroundings. Perspira-

▲ **FIGURE 5.20** **Perspiration!**

tion is predominantly water, so the process is the endothermic conversion of liquid water into water vapor:

$$H_2O(l) \longrightarrow H_2O(g) \qquad \Delta H = +44.0 \text{ kJ}$$

The speed with which evaporative cooling occurs decreases as the atmospheric humidity increases, which is why we feel more sweaty and uncomfortable on hot, humid days.

When the hypothalamus senses that body temperature has risen too high, it increases heat loss from the body in two principal ways. First, it increases blood flow near the skin surface, which allows for increased radiational and convective cooling. The reddish, "flushed" appearance of a hot individual is the result of this increased subsurface blood flow. Second, the hypothalamus stimulates secretion of perspiration from the sweat glands, which increases evaporative cooling. During extreme activity, the amount of liquid secreted as perspiration can be as high as 2 to 4 liters per hour. As a result, the body's water supply must be replenished during these periods. If the body loses too much liquid through perspiration, it will no longer be able to cool itself and blood volume decreases, which can lead to either *heat exhaustion* or the more serious and potentially fatal *heat stroke,* during which the body temperature can rise to as high as 41 °C to 45 °C (106 °F to 113 °F). However, replenishing water without replenishing the electrolytes lost during perspiration can also lead to serious problems, as pointed out in the "Chemistry and Life" box in Section 4.5.

When body temperature drops too low, the hypothalamus decreases blood flow to the skin surface, thereby decreasing heat loss. It also triggers small involuntary contractions of the muscles; the biochemical reactions that generate the energy to do this work also generate heat for the body. When these contractions get large enough—as when the body feels a chill—a *shiver* results. If the body is unable to maintain a temperature above 35 °C (95 °F), the very dangerous condition called *hypothermia* can result.

The ability of the human body to maintain its temperature by "tuning" the amount of heat it transfers to and from its surroundings is truly remarkable. If you take courses in human anatomy and physiology, you will see many other applications of thermochemistry and thermodynamics to the ways in which the human body works.

# 5.6 | HESS'S LAW

It is often possible to calculate the $\Delta H$ for a reaction from the tabulated $\Delta H$ values of other reactions. Thus, it is not necessary to make calorimetric measurements for all reactions.

Because enthalpy is a state function, the enthalpy change, $\Delta H$, associated with any chemical process depends only on the amount of matter that undergoes change and on the nature of the initial state of the reactants and the final state of the products. This means that whether a particular reaction is carried out in one step or in a series of steps, the sum of the enthalpy changes associated with the individual steps must be the same as the enthalpy change associated with the one-step process. As an example, combustion of methane gas, $CH_4(g)$, to form $CO_2(g)$ and $H_2O(l)$ can be thought of as occurring in one step, as represented on the left in ▶ **FIGURE 5.21**, or in two steps, as represented on the right in Figure 5.21: (1) combustion of $CH_4(g)$ to form $CO_2(g)$ and $H_2O(g)$ and (2) condensation of $H_2O(g)$ to form $H_2O(l)$. The enthalpy change for the overall process is the sum of the enthalpy changes for these two steps:

$$CH_4(g) + 2\,O_2(g) \longrightarrow CO_2(g) + 2\,H_2O(g) \qquad \Delta H = -802 \text{ kJ}$$

(Add) $\qquad 2\,H_2O(g) \longrightarrow 2\,H_2O(l) \qquad \Delta H = -\;88 \text{ kJ}$

$$\overline{CH_4(g) + 2\,O_2(g) + 2\,H_2O(g) \longrightarrow CO_2(g) + 2\,H_2O(l) + 2\,H_2O(g)}$$

$$\Delta H = -890 \text{ kJ}$$

The net equation is

$$CH_4(g) + 2\,O_2(g) \longrightarrow CO_2(g) + 2\,H_2O(l) \qquad \Delta H = -890 \text{ kJ}$$

**Hess's law** states that *if a reaction is carried out in a series of steps, $\Delta H$ for the overall reaction equals the sum of the enthalpy changes for the individual steps.* The overall enthalpy change for the process is independent of the number of steps and independent of the path by which the reaction is carried out. This law is a consequence of the fact that enthalpy is a state function. We can therefore calculate $\Delta H$ for any process as long as we find a route for which $\Delta H$ is known for each step. This means that a relatively small number of experimental measurements can be used to calculate $\Delta H$ for a vast number of reactions.

Hess's law provides a useful means of calculating energy changes that are difficult to measure directly. For instance, it is impossible to measure directly the enthalpy for the combustion of carbon to form carbon monoxide. Combustion of 1 mol of carbon with 0.5 mol of $O_2$ produces both CO and $CO_2$, leaving some carbon unreacted. However, solid carbon and carbon monoxide can both be completely burned in $O_2$ to produce $CO_2$. We can therefore use the enthalpy changes of these reactions to calculate the heat of combustion of carbon.

 GIVE IT SOME THOUGHT

What effect do these changes have on $\Delta H$ for a reaction:
a. reversing the reaction,
b. multiplying the coefficients of the equation for the reaction by 2?

 GO FIGURE

**What process corresponds to the −88 kJ enthalpy change?**

▲ **FIGURE 5.21 Enthalpy diagram for combustion of 1 mol of methane.** The enthalpy change of the one-step reaction equals the sum of the enthalpy changes of the reaction run in two steps: −890 kJ = −802 kJ + (−88 kJ).

---

**SAMPLE EXERCISE 5.8** | **Using Hess's Law to Calculate $\Delta H$**

The enthalpy of reaction for the combustion of C to $CO_2$ is −393.5 kJ/mol C, and the enthalpy for the combustion of CO to $CO_2$ is −283.0 kJ/mol CO:

(1) $\qquad C(s) + O_2(g) \longrightarrow CO_2(g) \qquad \Delta H = -393.5 \text{ kJ}$

(2) $\qquad CO(g) + \frac{1}{2}O_2(g) \longrightarrow CO_2(g) \qquad \Delta H = -283.0 \text{ kJ}$

Using these data, calculate the enthalpy for the combustion of C to CO:

(3) $\qquad C(s) + \frac{1}{2}O_2(g) \longrightarrow CO(g) \qquad \Delta H = ?$

## SOLUTION

**Analyze** We are given two thermochemical equations, and our goal is to combine them in such a way as to obtain the third equation and its enthalpy change.

**Plan** We will use Hess's law. In doing so, we first note the numbers of moles of substances among the reactants and products in the target equation, (3). We then manipulate equations (1) and (2) to give the same number of moles of these substances, so that when the resulting equations are added, we obtain the target equation. At the same time, we keep track of the enthalpy changes, which we add.

**Solve** To use equations (1) and (2), we arrange them so that $C(s)$ is on the reactant side and $CO(g)$ is on the product side of the arrow, as in the target reaction, equation (3). Because equation (1) has $C(s)$ as a reactant, we can use that equation just as it is. We need to turn equation (2) around, however, so that $CO(g)$ is a product. Remember that when reactions are turned around, the sign of $\Delta H$ is reversed. We arrange the two equations so that they can be added to give the desired equation:

$$C(s) + O_2(g) \longrightarrow CO_2(g) \qquad\qquad \Delta H = -393.5 \text{ kJ}$$
$$\underline{CO_2(g) \longrightarrow CO(g) + \tfrac{1}{2}O_2(g) \qquad\qquad -\Delta H = \phantom{-}283.0 \text{ kJ}}$$
$$C(s) + \tfrac{1}{2}O_2(g) \longrightarrow CO(g) \qquad\qquad \Delta H = -110.5 \text{ kJ}$$

When we add the two equations, $CO_2(g)$ appears on both sides of the arrow and therefore cancels out. Likewise, $\tfrac{1}{2}O_2(g)$ is eliminated from each side.

## PRACTICE EXERCISE

Carbon occurs in two forms, graphite and diamond. The enthalpy of the combustion of graphite is $-393.5$ kJ/mol, and that of diamond is $-395.4$ kJ/mol:

$$C(graphite) + O_2(g) \longrightarrow CO_2(g) \qquad \Delta H = -393.5 \text{ kJ}$$
$$C(diamond) + O_2(g) \longrightarrow CO_2(g) \qquad \Delta H = -395.4 \text{ kJ}$$

Calculate $\Delta H$ for the conversion of graphite to diamond:

$$C(graphite) \longrightarrow C(diamond) \qquad \Delta H = ?$$

*Answer:* $+1.9$ kJ

---

**SAMPLE EXERCISE 5.9** | **Using Three Equations with Hess's Law to Calculate $\Delta H$**

Calculate $\Delta H$ for the reaction

$$2 C(s) + H_2(g) \longrightarrow C_2H_2(g)$$

given the following chemical equations and their respective enthalpy changes:

$$C_2H_2(g) + \tfrac{5}{2}O_2(g) \longrightarrow 2 CO_2(g) + H_2O(l) \qquad \Delta H = -1299.6 \text{ kJ}$$
$$C(s) + O_2(g) \longrightarrow CO_2(g) \qquad \Delta H = -393.5 \text{ kJ}$$
$$H_2(g) + \tfrac{1}{2}O_2(g) \longrightarrow H_2O(l) \qquad \Delta H = -285.8 \text{ kJ}$$

## SOLUTION

**Analyze** We are given a chemical equation and asked to calculate its $\Delta H$ using three chemical equations and their associated enthalpy changes.

**Plan** We will use Hess's law, summing the three equations or their reverses and multiplying each by an appropriate coefficient so that they add to give the net equation for the reaction of interest. At the same time, we keep track of the $\Delta H$ values, reversing their signs if the reactions are reversed and multiplying them by whatever coefficient is employed in the equation.

**Solve** Because the target equation has $C_2H_2$ as a product, we turn the first equation around; the sign of $\Delta H$ is therefore changed. The desired equation has $2 C(s)$ as a reactant, so we multiply the second equation and its $\Delta H$ by 2. Because the target equation has $H_2$ as a reactant, we keep the third equation as it is. We then add the three equations and their enthalpy changes in accordance with Hess's law:

$$2 CO_2(g) + H_2O(l) \longrightarrow C_2H_2(g) + \tfrac{5}{2}O_2(g) \qquad \Delta H = 1299.6 \text{ kJ}$$
$$2 C(s) + 2 O_2(g) \longrightarrow 2 CO_2(g) \qquad \Delta H = -787.0 \text{ kJ}$$
$$\underline{H_2(g) + \tfrac{1}{2}O_2(g) \longrightarrow H_2O(l) \qquad \Delta H = -285.8 \text{ kJ}}$$
$$2 C(s) + H_2(g) \longrightarrow C_2H_2(g) \qquad \Delta H = 226.8 \text{ kJ}$$

When the equations are added, there are $2 CO_2$, $\frac{5}{2} O_2$, and $H_2O$ on both sides of the arrow. These are canceled in writing the net equation.

**Check** The procedure must be correct because we obtained the correct net equation. In cases like this you should go back over the numerical manipulations of the $\Delta H$ values to ensure that you did not make an inadvertent error with signs.

**PRACTICE EXERCISE**

Calculate $\Delta H$ for the reaction

$$NO(g) + O(g) \longrightarrow NO_2(g)$$

given the following information:

$$NO(g) + O_3(g) \longrightarrow NO_2(g) + O_2(g) \qquad \Delta H = -198.9 \text{ kJ}$$
$$O_3(g) \longrightarrow \tfrac{3}{2} O_2(g) \qquad \Delta H = -142.3 \text{ kJ}$$
$$O_2(g) \longrightarrow 2 O(g) \qquad \Delta H = 495.0 \text{ kJ}$$

*Answer:* $-304.1$ kJ

The key point of these examples is that $H$ is a state function, so *for a particular set of reactants and products, $\Delta H$ is the same whether the reaction takes place in one step or in a series of steps.* We reinforce this point by giving one more example of an enthalpy diagram and Hess's law. Again we use combustion of methane to form $CO_2$ and $H_2O$, our reaction from Figure 5.21. This time we envision a different two-step path, with the initial formation of CO, which is then combusted to $CO_2$ (▶ **FIGURE 5.22**). Even though the two-step path is different from that in Figure 5.21, the overall reaction again has $\Delta H_1 = -890$ kJ. Because $H$ is a state function, both paths *must* produce the same value of $\Delta H$. In Figure 5.22, that means $\Delta H_1 = \Delta H_2 + \Delta H_3$. We will soon see that breaking up reactions in this way allows us to derive the enthalpy changes for reactions that are hard to carry out in the laboratory.

## 5.7 | ENTHALPIES OF FORMATION

We can use the methods just discussed to calculate enthalpy changes for a great many reactions from tabulated $\Delta H$ values. For example, extensive tables exist of *enthalpies of vaporization* ($\Delta H$ for converting liquids to gases), *enthalpies of fusion* ($\Delta H$ for melting solids), *enthalpies of combustion* ($\Delta H$ for combusting a substance in oxygen), and so forth. A particularly important process used for tabulating thermochemical data is the formation of a compound from its constituent elements. The enthalpy change associated with this process is called the **enthalpy of formation** (or *heat of formation*), $\Delta H_f$, where the subscript $f$ indicates that the substance has been *formed* from its constituent elements.

The magnitude of any enthalpy change depends on the temperature, pressure, and state (gas, liquid, or solid crystalline form) of the reactants and products. To compare enthalpies of different reactions, we must define a set of conditions, called a *standard state*, at which most enthalpies are tabulated. The standard state of a substance is its pure form at atmospheric pressure (1 atm) and the temperature of interest, which we usually choose to be 298 K (25 °C).* The **standard enthalpy change** of a reaction is defined as the enthalpy change when all reactants and products are in their standard states. We denote a standard enthalpy change as $\Delta H°$, where the superscript ° indicates standard-state conditions.

The **standard enthalpy of formation** of a compound, $\Delta H_f°$, is the change in enthalpy for the reaction that forms one mole of the compound from its elements with all substances in their standard states:

If: elements (in standard state) $\longrightarrow$ compound (1 mol in standard state)
Then: $\Delta H = \Delta H_f°$

**GO FIGURE**

Suppose the overall reaction were modified to produce $2 H_2O(g)$ rather than $2 H_2O(l)$. Would any of the values of $\Delta H$ in the diagram stay the same?

▲ **FIGURE 5.22  Enthalpy diagram illustrating Hess's law.** The net reaction is the same as in Figure 5.21, but here we imagine different reactions in our two-step version. As long as we can write a series of equations that add up to the equation we need, and as long as we know a value for $\Delta H$ for all intermediate reactions, we can calculate the overall $\Delta H$.

*The definition of the standard state for gases has been changed to 1 bar (1 atm = 1.013 bar), a slightly lower pressure than 1 atm. For most purposes, this change makes very little difference in the standard enthalpy changes.

## TABLE 5.3 • Standard Enthalpies of Formation, $\Delta H_f^\circ$, at 298 K

| Substance | Formula | $\Delta H_f^\circ$ (kJ/mol) | Substance | Formula | $\Delta H_f^\circ$ (kJ/mol) |
|---|---|---|---|---|---|
| Acetylene | $C_2H_2(g)$ | 226.7 | Hydrogen chloride | $HCl(g)$ | −92.30 |
| Ammonia | $NH_3(g)$ | −46.19 | Hydrogen fluoride | $HF(g)$ | −268.60 |
| Benzene | $C_6H_6(l)$ | 49.0 | Hydrogen iodide | $HI(g)$ | 25.9 |
| Calcium carbonate | $CaCO_3(s)$ | −1207.1 | Methane | $CH_4(g)$ | −74.80 |
| Calcium oxide | $CaO(s)$ | −635.5 | Methanol | $CH_3OH(l)$ | −238.6 |
| Carbon dioxide | $CO_2(g)$ | −393.5 | Propane | $C_3H_8(g)$ | −103.85 |
| Carbon monoxide | $CO(g)$ | −110.5 | Silver chloride | $AgCl(s)$ | −127.0 |
| Diamond | $C(s)$ | 1.88 | Sodium bicarbonate | $NaHCO_3(s)$ | −947.7 |
| Ethane | $C_2H_6(g)$ | −84.68 | Sodium carbonate | $Na_2CO_3(s)$ | −1130.9 |
| Ethanol | $C_2H_5OH(l)$ | −277.7 | Sodium chloride | $NaCl(s)$ | −410.9 |
| Ethylene | $C_2H_4(g)$ | 52.30 | Sucrose | $C_{12}H_{22}O_{11}(s)$ | −2221 |
| Glucose | $C_6H_{12}O_6(s)$ | −1273 | Water | $H_2O(l)$ | −285.8 |
| Hydrogen bromide | $HBr(g)$ | −36.23 | Water vapor | $H_2O(g)$ | −241.8 |

We usually report $\Delta H_f^\circ$ values at 298 K. If an element exists in more than one form under standard conditions, the most stable form of the element is usually used for the formation reaction. For example, the standard enthalpy of formation for ethanol, $C_2H_5OH$, is the enthalpy change for the reaction

$$2\,C(graphite) + 3\,H_2(g) + \tfrac{1}{2}\,O_2(g) \longrightarrow C_2H_5OH(l) \quad \Delta H_f^\circ = -277.7\ \text{kJ} \quad [5.25]$$

The elemental source of oxygen is $O_2$, not O or $O_3$, because $O_2$ is the stable form of oxygen at 298 K and atmospheric pressure. Similarly, the elemental source of carbon is graphite and not diamond because graphite is the more stable (lower-energy) form at 298 K and atmospheric pressure (see Practice Exercise 5.8). Likewise, the most stable form of hydrogen under standard conditions is $H_2(g)$, so this is used as the source of hydrogen in Equation 5.25.

The stoichiometry of formation reactions always indicates that one mole of the desired substance is produced, as in Equation 5.25. As a result, standard enthalpies of formation are reported in kJ/mol of the substance being formed. Some values are given in ▲ TABLE 5.3, and a more extensive table is provided in Appendix C.

By definition, *the standard enthalpy of formation of the most stable form of any element is zero* because there is no formation reaction needed when the element is already in its standard state. Thus, the values of $\Delta H_f^\circ$ for C(graphite), $H_2(g)$, $O_2(g)$, and the standard states of other elements are zero by definition.

 **GIVE IT SOME THOUGHT**

Ozone, $O_3(g)$, is a form of elemental oxygen produced during electrical discharge. Is $\Delta H_f^\circ$ for $O_3(g)$ necessarily zero?

---

**SAMPLE EXERCISE 5.10** **Equations Associated with Enthalpies of Formation**

For which of these reactions at 25 °C does the enthalpy change represent a standard enthalpy of formation? For each that does not, what changes are needed to make it an equation whose $\Delta H$ is an enthalpy of formation?

(a) $2\,Na(s) + \tfrac{1}{2}\,O_2(g) \longrightarrow Na_2O(s)$

(b) $2\,K(l) + Cl_2(g) \longrightarrow 2\,KCl(s)$

(c) $C_6H_{12}O_6(s) \longrightarrow 6\,C(diamond) + 6\,H_2(g) + 3\,O_2(g)$

**SOLUTION**

**Analyze** The standard enthalpy of formation is represented by a reaction in which each reactant is an element in its standard state and the product is one mole of the compound.

**Plan** We need to examine each equation to determine (1) whether the reaction is one in which one mole of substance is formed from the elements, and (2) whether the reactant elements are in their standard states.

**Solve** In (a) 1 mol $Na_2O$ is formed from the elements sodium and oxygen in their proper states, solid Na and $O_2$ gas, respectively. Therefore, the enthalpy change for reaction (a) corresponds to a standard enthalpy of formation.

In (b) potassium is given as a liquid. It must be changed to the solid form, its standard state at room temperature. Furthermore, two moles of product are formed, so the enthalpy change for the reaction as written is twice the standard enthalpy of formation of $KCl(s)$. The equation for the formation reaction of 1 mol of $KCl(s)$ is

$$K(s) + \tfrac{1}{2} Cl_2(g) \longrightarrow KCl(s)$$

Reaction (c) does not form a substance from its elements. Instead, a substance decomposes to its elements, so this reaction must be reversed. Next, the element carbon is given as diamond, whereas graphite is the standard state of carbon at room temperature and 1 atm pressure. The equation that correctly represents the enthalpy of formation of glucose from its elements is

$$6\, C(graphite) + 6\, H_2(g) + 3\, O_2(g) \longrightarrow C_6H_{12}O_6(s)$$

**PRACTICE EXERCISE**
Write the equation corresponding to the standard enthalpy of formation of liquid carbon tetrachloride ($CCl_4$).
**Answer:** $C(graphite) + 2\, Cl_2(g) \longrightarrow CCl_4(l)$

## Using Enthalpies of Formation to Calculate Enthalpies of Reaction

We can use Hess's law and tabulations of $\Delta H_f^\circ$ values, such as those in Table 5.3 and Appendix C, to calculate the standard enthalpy change for any reaction for which we know the $\Delta H_f^\circ$ values for all reactants and products. For example, consider the combustion of propane gas, $C_3H_8(g)$, to $CO_2(g)$ and $H_2O(l)$ under standard conditions:

$$C_3H_8(g) + 5\, O_2(g) \longrightarrow 3\, CO_2(g) + 4\, H_2O(l)$$

We can write this equation as the sum of three formation equations:

| | | |
|---|---|---|
| $C_3H_8(g) \longrightarrow 3\, C(s) + 4\, H_2(g)$ | $\Delta H_1 = -\Delta H_f^\circ [C_3H_8(g)]$ | [5.26] |
| $3\, C(s) + 3\, O_2(g) \longrightarrow 3\, CO_2(g)$ | $\Delta H_2 = 3\Delta H_f^\circ [CO_2(g)]$ | [5.27] |
| $4\, H_2(g) + 2\, O_2(g) \longrightarrow 4\, H_2O(l)$ | $\Delta H_3 = 4\Delta H_f^\circ [H_2O(l)]$ | [5.28] |
| $C_3H_8(g) + 5\, O_2(g) \longrightarrow 3\, CO_2(g) + 4\, H_2O(l)$ | $\Delta H_{rxn}^\circ = \Delta H_1 + \Delta H_2 + \Delta H_3$ | [5.29] |

(Note that it is sometimes useful to add subscripts to the enthalpy changes, as we have done here, to keep track of the associations between reactions and their $\Delta H$ values.)

Notice that we have used Hess's law to write the standard enthalpy change for Equation 5.29 as the sum of the enthalpy changes for Equations 5.26 through 5.28. We can use values from Table 5.3 to calculate $\Delta H_{rxn}^\circ$:

$$\begin{aligned}
\Delta H_{rxn}^\circ &= \Delta H_1 + \Delta H_2 + \Delta H_3 \\
&= -\Delta H_f^\circ [C_3H_8(g)] + 3\Delta H_f^\circ [CO_2(g)] + 4\Delta H_f^\circ [H_2O(l)] \\
&= -(-103.85\ kJ) + 3(-393.5\ kJ) + 4(-285.8\ kJ) = -2220\ kJ \quad [5.30]
\end{aligned}$$

▶ **FIGURE 5.23**, an enthalpy diagram for Equation 5.29, shows our propane combustion reaction broken down to the three reactions. Several aspects of this calculation depend on the guidelines we discussed in Section 5.4.

1. **Decomposition.** Equation 5.26 is the reverse of the formation reaction for $C_3H_8(g)$, so the enthalpy change for this decomposition reaction is the negative of the $\Delta H_f^\circ$ value for the propane formation reaction: $-\Delta H_f^\circ [C_3H_8(g)]$.

3 C (*graphite*) + 4 H$_2$(*g*) + 5 O$_2$(*g*)

Elements

❶ Decomposition to elements

$\Delta H_1 = +103.85$ kJ

C$_3$H$_8$(*g*) + 5 O$_2$(*g*)

Reactants

❷ Formation of 3 CO$_2$

$\Delta H_2 = -1181$ kJ

3 CO$_2$(*g*) + 4 H$_2$(*g*) + 2 O$_2$(*g*)

❸ Formation of 4 H$_2$O

$\Delta H_3 = -1143$ kJ

$\Delta H^\circ_{rxn} = -2220$ kJ

3 CO$_2$(*g*) + 4 H$_2$O(*l*)

Products

Enthalpy

Blue arrow shows direct route to products CO$_2$(*g*) and H$_2$O(*l*)

Green arrows show multi-step route to same products

▲ **FIGURE 5.23**   **Enthalpy diagram for propane combustion.**

2. **Formation of CO$_2$.** Equation 5.27 is the formation reaction for 3 mol of CO$_2$(*g*). Because enthalpy is an extensive property, the enthalpy change for this step is $3\Delta H^\circ_f$ [CO$_2$(*g*)].

3. **Formation of H$_2$O.** The enthalpy change for Equation 5.28, formation of 4 mol of H$_2$O, is $4\Delta H^\circ_f$ [H$_2$O(*l*)]. The reaction specifies that H$_2$O(*l*) is produced, so be careful to use the value of $\Delta H^\circ_f$ for H$_2$O(*l*) and not the value for H$_2$O(*g*).

Note that in this analysis we assume that the stoichiometric coefficients in the balanced equation represent moles. For Equation 5.29, therefore, $\Delta H^\circ_{rxn} = -2220$ kJ represents the enthalpy change for the reaction of 1 mol C$_3$H$_8$ and 5 mol O$_2$ to form 3 mol CO$_2$ and 4 mol H$_2$O. The product of the number of moles and the enthalpy change in kJ/mol has the units kJ: (number of moles) $\times$ ($\Delta H^\circ_f$ in kJ/mol) = kJ. We therefore report $\Delta H^\circ_{rxn}$ in kJ.

We can break down any reaction into formation reactions as we have done here. When we do, we obtain the general result that the standard enthalpy change of a reaction is the sum of the standard enthalpies of formation of the products minus the standard enthalpies of formation of the reactants:

$$\Delta H^\circ_{rxn} = \Sigma n\Delta H^\circ_f(\text{products}) - \Sigma m\Delta H^\circ_f(\text{reactants}) \qquad [5.31]$$

The symbol $\Sigma$ (sigma) means "the sum of," and $n$ and $m$ are the stoichiometric coefficients of the relevant chemical equation. The first term on the right in Equation 5.31 represents the formation reactions of the products, which are written in the "forward" direction in the chemical equation, that is, elements reacting to form products. This term is analogous to Equations 5.27 and 5.28. The second term on the right in Equation 5.31 represents the reverse of the formation reactions of the reactants, analogous to Equation 5.26, which is why this term is preceded by a minus sign.

---

**SAMPLE EXERCISE 5.11** | **Calculating an Enthalpy of Reaction from Enthalpies of Formation**

(a) Calculate the standard enthalpy change for the combustion of 1 mol of benzene, $C_6H_6(l)$, to $CO_2(g)$ and $H_2O(l)$. (b) Compare the quantity of heat produced by combustion of 1.00 g propane with that produced by 1.00 g benzene.

**SOLUTION**

**Analyze** (a) We are given a reaction [combustion of $C_6H_6(l)$ to form $CO_2(g)$ and $H_2O(l)$] and asked to calculate its standard enthalpy change, $\Delta H°$. (b) We then need to compare the quantity of heat produced by combustion of 1.00 g $C_6H_6$ with that produced by 1.00 g $C_3H_8$, whose combustion was treated previously in the text. (See Equations 5.29 and 5.30.)

**Plan** (a) We need to write the balanced equation for the combustion of $C_6H_6$. We then look up $\Delta H_f°$ values in Appendix C or in Table 5.3 and apply Equation 5.31 to calculate the enthalpy change for the reaction. (b) We use the molar mass of $C_6H_6$ to change the enthalpy change per mole to that per gram. We similarly use the molar mass of $C_3H_8$ and the enthalpy change per mole calculated in the text previously to calculate the enthalpy change per gram of that substance.

**Solve**

(a) We know that a combustion reaction involves $O_2(g)$ as a reactant. Thus, the balanced equation for the combustion reaction of 1 mol $C_6H_6(l)$ is

$$C_6H_6(l) + \tfrac{15}{2} O_2(g) \longrightarrow 6\,CO_2(g) + 3\,H_2O(l)$$

We can calculate $\Delta H°$ for this reaction by using Equation 5.31 and data in Table 5.3. Remember to multiply the $\Delta H_f°$ value for each substance in the reaction by that substance's stoichiometric coefficient. Recall also that $\Delta H_f° = 0$ for any element in its most stable form under standard conditions, so $\Delta H_f°[O_2(g)] = 0$:

$$\begin{aligned}\Delta H_{rxn}° &= [6\Delta H_f°(CO_2) + 3\Delta H_f°(H_2O)] - [\Delta H_f°(C_6H_6) + \tfrac{15}{2}\Delta H_f°(O_2)]\\ &= [6(-393.5\text{ kJ}) + 3(-285.8\text{ kJ})] - [(49.0\text{ kJ}) + \tfrac{15}{2}(0\text{ kJ})]\\ &= (-2361 - 857.4 - 49.0)\text{ kJ}\\ &= -3267\text{ kJ}\end{aligned}$$

(b) From the example worked in the text, $\Delta H° = -2220$ kJ for the combustion of 1 mol of propane. In part (a) of this exercise we determined that $\Delta H° = -3267$ kJ for the combustion of 1 mol benzene. To determine the heat of combustion per gram of each substance, we use the molar masses to convert moles to grams:

$C_3H_8(g)$:   $(-2220\text{ kJ/mol})(1\text{ mol}/44.1\text{ g}) = -50.3\text{ kJ/g}$
$C_6H_6(l)$:   $(-3267\text{ kJ/mol})(1\text{ mol}/78.1\text{ g}) = -41.8\text{ kJ/g}$

**Comment** Both propane and benzene are hydrocarbons. As a rule, the energy obtained from the combustion of a gram of hydrocarbon is between 40 and 50 kJ.

**PRACTICE EXERCISE**

Use Table 5.3 to calculate the enthalpy change for the combustion of 1 mol of ethanol:

$$C_2H_5OH(l) + 3\,O_2(g) \longrightarrow 2\,CO_2(g) + 3\,H_2O(l)$$

*Answer:* −1367 kJ

---

**SAMPLE EXERCISE 5.12** | **Calculating an Enthalpy of Formation Using an Enthalpy of Reaction**

The standard enthalpy change for the reaction $CaCO_3(s) \longrightarrow CaO(s) + CO_2(g)$ is 178.1 kJ. Use Table 5.3 to calculate the standard enthalpy of formation of $CaCO_3(s)$.

**SOLUTION**

**Analyze** Our goal is to obtain $\Delta H_f°[CaCO_3(s)]$.

**Plan** We begin by writing the expression for the standard enthalpy change for the reaction:

$$\Delta H_{rxn}° = \Delta H_f°[CaO(s)] + \Delta H_f°[CO_2(g)] - \Delta H_f°[CaCO_3(s)]$$

**Solve** Inserting the given $\Delta H_{rxn}°$ and the known $\Delta H_f°$ values from Table 5.3 or Appendix C, we have

$$178.1 = -635.5\text{ kJ} - 393.5\text{ kJ} - \Delta H_f°[CaCO_3(s)]$$

Solving for $\Delta H_f°[CaCO_3(s)]$ gives

$$\Delta H_f°[CaCO_3(s)] = -1207.1\text{ kJ/mol}$$

**Check** We expect the enthalpy of formation of a stable solid such as calcium carbonate to be negative, as obtained.

**PRACTICE EXERCISE**

Given the following standard enthalpy change, use the standard enthalpies of formation in Table 5.3 to calculate the standard enthalpy of formation of $CuO(s)$:

$$CuO(s) + H_2(g) \longrightarrow Cu(s) + H_2O(l) \qquad \Delta H° = -129.7\text{ kJ}$$

*Answer:* −156.1 kJ/mol

# 5.8 | FOODS AND FUELS

Most chemical reactions used for the production of heat are combustion reactions. The energy released when one gram of any substance is combusted is the **fuel value** of the substance. The fuel value of any food or fuel can be measured by calorimetry.

## Foods

Most of the energy our bodies need comes from carbohydrates and fats. The carbohydrates known as starches are decomposed in the intestines into glucose, $C_6H_{12}O_6$. Glucose is soluble in blood, and in the human body it is known as blood sugar. It is transported by the blood to cells where it reacts with $O_2$ in a series of steps, eventually producing $CO_2(g)$, $H_2O(l)$, and energy:

$$C_6H_{12}O_6(s) + 6\,O_2(g) \longrightarrow 6\,CO_2(g) + 6\,H_2O(l) \qquad \Delta H° = -2803 \text{ kJ}$$

Because carbohydrates break down rapidly, their energy is quickly supplied to the body. However, the body stores only a very small amount of carbohydrates. The average fuel value of carbohydrates is 17 kJ/g (4 kcal/g).*

Like carbohydrates, fats produce $CO_2$ and $H_2O$ when metabolized. The reaction of tristearin, $C_{57}H_{110}O_6$, a typical fat, is

$$2\,C_{57}H_{110}O_6(s) + 163\,O_2(g) \longrightarrow 114\,CO_2(g) + 110\,H_2O(l) \quad \Delta H° = -75{,}520 \text{ kJ}$$

The body uses the chemical energy from foods to maintain body temperature (see the "Chemistry and Life" box in Section 5.5), to contract muscles, and to construct and repair tissues. Any excess energy is stored as fats. Fats are well suited to serve as the body's energy reserve for at least two reasons: (1) They are insoluble in water, which facilitates storage in the body, and (2) they produce more energy per gram than either proteins or carbohydrates, which makes them efficient energy sources on a mass basis. The average fuel value of fats is 38 kJ/g (9 kcal/g).

The combustion of carbohydrates and fats in a bomb calorimeter gives the same products as when they are metabolized in the body. The metabolism of proteins produces less energy than combustion in a calorimeter because the products are different. Proteins contain nitrogen, which is released in the bomb calorimeter as $N_2$. In the body this nitrogen ends up mainly as urea, $(NH_2)_2CO$. Proteins are used by the body mainly as building materials for organ walls, skin, hair, muscle, and so forth. On average, the metabolism of proteins produces 17 kJ/g (4 kcal/g), the same as for carbohydrates.

Fuel values for some common foods are shown in ▼ TABLE 5.4. Labels on packaged foods show the amounts of carbohydrate, fat, and protein contained in an average serving, as well as the amount of energy supplied by a serving (◄ FIGURE 5.24).

## GO FIGURE

Which value would change most if this label were for skim milk instead of whole milk: grams of fat, grams of total carbohydrate, or grams of protein?

▲ **FIGURE 5.24    Nutrition label for whole milk.**

### TABLE 5.4 • Compositions and Fuel Values of Some Common Foods

|  | Approximate Composition (% by mass) | | | Fuel Value | |
|---|---|---|---|---|---|
|  | **Carbohydrate** | **Fat** | **Protein** | **kJ/g** | **kcal/g (Cal/g)** |
| Carbohydrate | 100 | — | — | 17 | 4 |
| Fat | — | 100 | — | 38 | 9 |
| Protein | — | — | 100 | 17 | 4 |
| Apples | 13 | 0.5 | 0.4 | 2.5 | 0.59 |
| Beer[†] | 1.2 | — | 0.3 | 1.8 | 0.42 |
| Bread | 52 | 3 | 9 | 12 | 2.8 |
| Cheese | 4 | 37 | 28 | 20 | 4.7 |
| Eggs | 0.7 | 10 | 13 | 6.0 | 1.4 |
| Fudge | 81 | 11 | 2 | 18 | 4.4 |
| Green beans | 7.0 | — | 1.9 | 1.5 | 0.38 |
| Hamburger | — | 30 | 22 | 15 | 3.6 |
| Milk (whole) | 5.0 | 4.0 | 3.3 | 3.0 | 0.74 |
| Peanuts | 22 | 39 | 26 | 23 | 5.5 |

[†]Beer typically contains 3.5% ethanol, which has fuel value.

*Although fuel values represent the heat *released* in a combustion reaction, fuel values are reported as positive numbers.

The amount of energy our bodies require varies considerably, depending on such factors as weight, age, and muscular activity. About 100 kJ per kilogram of body mass per day is required to keep the body functioning at a minimal level. An average 70-kg (154-lb) person expends about 800 kJ/hr when doing light work, and strenuous activity often requires 2000 kJ/hr or more. When the fuel value, or caloric content, of the food we ingest exceeds the energy we expend, our body stores the surplus as fat.

◢ GIVE IT SOME THOUGHT

Which releases the greatest amount of energy per gram when metabolized: carbohydrates, proteins, or fats?

### SAMPLE EXERCISE 5.13  Comparing Fuel Values

Celery contains carbohydrates in the form of starch and cellulose, which have essentially the same fuel values when combusted in a bomb calorimeter. When we eat celery, however, our bodies receive fuel value from the starch only. What can we conclude about the difference between starch and cellulose as foods?

#### SOLUTION

If cellulose does not provide fuel value, we must conclude that it is not converted in the body into $CO_2$ and $H_2O$, as starch is. A slight but critical difference in the structures of starch and cellulose explains why only starch is broken down into glucose in the body. Cellulose passes through without undergoing significant chemical change. It serves as fiber, or roughage, in the diet but provides no caloric value.

#### PRACTICE EXERCISE

The nutrition label on a bottle of canola oil indicates that 10 g of the oil has a fuel value of 86 kcal. A similar label on a bottle of pancake syrup indicates that 60 mL (about 60 g) has a fuel value of 200 kcal. Account for the difference.

**Answer:** The oil has a fuel value of 8.6 kcal/g, whereas the syrup has a fuel value of about 3.3 kcal/g. The higher fuel value for the canola oil arises because the oil is essentially pure fat, whereas the syrup is a solution of sugars (carbohydrates) in water. The oil has a higher fuel value per gram; in addition, the syrup is diluted by water.

### SAMPLE EXERCISE 5.14  Estimating the Fuel Value of a Food from Its Composition

**(a)** A 28-g (1-oz) serving of a popular breakfast cereal served with 120 mL of skim milk provides 8 g protein, 26 g carbohydrates, and 2 g fat. Using the average fuel values of these substances, estimate the fuel value (caloric content) of this serving. **(b)** A person of average weight uses about 100 Cal/mi when running or jogging. How many servings of this cereal provide the fuel value requirements to run 3 mi?

#### SOLUTION

**(a) Analyze** The fuel value of the serving will be the sum of the fuel values of the protein, carbohydrates, and fat.

**Plan** We are given the masses of the protein, carbohydrates, and fat contained in a serving. We can use the data in Table 5.4 to convert these masses to their fuel values, which we can sum to get the total fuel value.

**Solve**

$$(8 \text{ g protein})\left(\frac{17 \text{ kJ}}{1 \text{ g protein}}\right) + (26 \text{ g carbohydrate})\left(\frac{17 \text{ kJ}}{1 \text{ g carbohydrate}}\right) +$$
$$(2 \text{ g fat})\left(\frac{38 \text{ kJ}}{1 \text{ g fat}}\right) = 650 \text{ kJ (to two significant figures)}$$

This corresponds to 160 kcal:

$$(650 \text{ kJ})\left(\frac{1 \text{ kcal}}{4.18 \text{ kJ}}\right) = 160 \text{ kcal}$$

Recall that the dietary Calorie is equivalent to 1 kcal. Thus, the serving provides 160 Cal.

**(b) Analyze** Here we are faced with the reverse problem, calculating the quantity of food that provides a specific fuel value.

**Plan** The problem statement provides a conversion factor between Calories and miles. The answer to part (a) provides us with a conversion factor between servings and Calories.

**Solve** We can use these factors in a straightforward dimensional analysis to determine the number of servings needed, rounded to the nearest whole number:

$$\text{Servings} = (3 \text{ mi})\left(\frac{100 \text{ Cal}}{1 \text{ mi}}\right)\left(\frac{1 \text{ serving}}{160 \text{ Cal}}\right) = 2 \text{ servings}$$

**PRACTICE EXERCISE**

(a) Dry red beans contain 62% carbohydrate, 22% protein, and 1.5% fat. Estimate the fuel value of these beans. (b) During a very light activity, such as reading or watching television, the average adult expends about 7 kJ/min. How many minutes of such activity can be sustained by the energy provided by a serving of chicken noodle soup containing 13 g protein, 15 g carbohydrate, and 5 g fat?
*Answers:* (a) 15 kJ/g, (b) 100 min

## Fuels

During the complete combustion of fuels, carbon is converted to $CO_2$ and hydrogen is converted to $H_2O$, both of which have large negative enthalpies of formation. Consequently, the greater the percentage of carbon and hydrogen in a fuel, the higher its fuel value. In ▼ TABLE 5.5, for example, compare the compositions and fuel values of bituminous coal and wood. The coal has a higher fuel value because of its greater carbon content.

In 2008 the United States consumed $1.05 \times 10^{17}$ kJ of energy. This value corresponds to an average daily energy consumption per person of $9.4 \times 10^5$ kJ, roughly 100 times greater than the per capita food-energy needs. Although the population of the United States is only about 4.5% of the world's population, the United States accounts for nearly 20% of the world's total energy consumption. ◄ FIGURE 5.25 illustrates the sources of this energy.

Coal, petroleum, and natural gas, which are the world's major sources of energy, are known as **fossil fuels**. All have formed over millions of years from the decomposition of plants and animals and are being depleted far more rapidly than they are being formed.

**Natural gas** consists of gaseous hydrocarbons, compounds of hydrogen and carbon. It contains primarily methane ($CH_4$), with small amounts of ethane ($C_2H_6$), propane ($C_3H_8$), and butane ($C_4H_{10}$). We determined the fuel value of propane in Sample Exercise 5.11. **Petroleum** is a liquid composed of hundreds of compounds, most of which are hydrocarbons, with the remainder being chiefly organic compounds containing sulfur, nitrogen, or oxygen. **Coal**, which is solid, contains hydrocarbons of high molecular weight as well as compounds containing sulfur, oxygen, or nitrogen. Coal is the most abundant

Nuclear (8.5%)  Renewable energy (7.4%)
Petroleum (37.6%)
Coal (22.6%)
Natural gas (24.0%)

▲ **FIGURE 5.25 Energy consumption in the United States.** In 2008 the United States consumed a total of $1.05 \times 10^{17}$ kJ of energy.

| TABLE 5.5 • Fuel Values and Compositions of Some Common Fuels | | | | |
|---|---|---|---|---|
| | **Approximate Elemental Composition (mass %)** | | | |
| | **C** | **H** | **O** | **Fuel Value (kJ/g)** |
| Wood (pine) | 50 | 6 | 44 | 18 |
| Anthracite coal (Pennsylvania) | 82 | 1 | 2 | 31 |
| Bituminous coal (Pennsylvania) | 77 | 5 | 7 | 32 |
| Charcoal | 100 | 0 | 0 | 34 |
| Crude oil (Texas) | 85 | 12 | 0 | 45 |
| Gasoline | 85 | 15 | 0 | 48 |
| Natural gas | 70 | 23 | 0 | 49 |
| Hydrogen | 0 | 100 | 0 | 142 |

fossil fuel; current reserves are projected to last for well over 100 years at current consumption rates. However, the use of coal presents a number of problems.

Coal is a complex mixture of substances, and it contains components that cause air pollution. When coal is combusted, the sulfur it contains is converted mainly to sulfur dioxide, $SO_2$, a troublesome air pollutant. Because coal is a solid, recovery from its underground deposits is expensive and often dangerous. Furthermore, coal deposits are not always close to locations of high-energy use, so there are often substantial shipping costs.

Fossil fuels release energy in combustion reactions, which ideally produce only $CO_2$ and $H_2O$. The production of $CO_2$ has become a major issue that involves science and public policy because of concerns that increasing concentrations of atmospheric $CO_2$ are causing global climate changes. In December 2009 the United Nations held a Climate Change Conference in Copenhagen, Denmark, that attracted about 15,000 participants from nearly 200 countries, including many government leaders. Much of the discussion at this conference involved the impact of atmospheric $CO_2$ and ways in which alternative energy sources could be implemented. We will discuss the environmental aspects of atmospheric $CO_2$ in Chapter 18.

 GIVE IT SOME THOUGHT

Much current research is directed toward using hydrogen gas, $H_2(g)$, as a fuel. What intrinsic advantage does hydrogen as a fuel have with respect to the current climate-change debate?

## Other Energy Sources

*Nuclear energy* is the energy released in either the splitting or the fusion (combining) of atomic nuclei. Nuclear power is currently used to produce about 21% of the electric power in the United States and makes up about 8.5% of the total U.S. energy production (Figure 5.25). Nuclear energy is, in principle, free of the polluting emissions that are a major problem with fossil fuels. However, nuclear power plants produce radioactive waste products, and their use has therefore been controversial. We will discuss issues related to the production of nuclear energy in Chapter 21.

Fossil fuels and nuclear energy are *nonrenewable* sources of energy—they are limited resources that we are consuming at a much greater rate than they can be regenerated. Eventually these fuels will be expended, although estimates vary greatly as to when this will occur. Because nonrenewable energy sources will eventually be used up, a great deal of research is being conducted on **renewable energy sources**, sources that are essentially inexhaustible. Renewable energy sources include *solar energy* from the Sun, *wind energy* harnessed by windmills, *geothermal energy* from the heat stored inside Earth, *hydroelectric energy* from flowing rivers, and *biomass energy* from crops and biological waste matter. Currently, renewable sources provide about 7.4% of the U.S. annual energy consumption, with hydroelectric and biomass sources the major contributors.

Fulfilling our future energy needs will depend on developing technology to harness solar energy with greater efficiency. Solar energy is the world's largest energy source. On a clear day about 1 kJ of solar energy reaches each square meter of Earth's surface every second. The average solar energy falling on only 0.1% of U.S. land area is equivalent to all the energy this nation currently uses. Harnessing this energy is difficult because it is dilute (that is, distributed over a wide area) and varies with time of day and weather conditions. The effective use of solar energy will depend on the development of some means of storing and distributing it. Any practical means for doing this will almost certainly involve an endothermic chemical process that can be later reversed to release heat. One such reaction is

$$CH_4(g) + H_2O(g) + \text{heat} \longleftrightarrow CO(g) + 3\,H_2(g)$$

This reaction proceeds in the forward direction at high temperatures, which can be obtained in a solar furnace. The CO and $H_2$ formed in the reaction could then be stored and allowed to react later, with the heat released being put to useful work.

# CHEMISTRY PUT TO WORK

## The Scientific and Political Challenges of Biofuels

One of the biggest challenges facing us in the twenty-first century is production of abundant sources of energy, both food and fuels. World population more than doubled from 1960 to 2000, from about 3 billion to more than 6 billion people. It continues to grow at a rate of about 750 million per decade—at the end of 2009, the global population was about 6.8 billion people. A growing world population puts greater demands on the global food supply, especially in Asia and Africa, which together make up more than 75% of the world population.

A growing population also increases demands on the production of fuels for transportation, industry, electricity, heating, and cooling. Further, many of the most populous nations, such as China and India, have seen dramatic increases in the quality of life among their citizens. As these countries have modernized, their per capita consumption of energy—for automobiles, new industries, modern housing, and technology advances—has increased significantly. In China, for instance, per capita energy consumption roughly doubled between 1990 and 2010 (although it is still less than 20% of U.S. per capita energy consumption).

Global fuel energy consumption in 2009 was more than $5 \times 10^{17}$ kJ, a staggeringly large number that is projected to grow to more than $7 \times 10^{17}$ kJ by 2030. More than 80% of current energy requirements comes from combustion of nonrenewable fossil fuels, especially petroleum. Depletion has generally increased the cost of petroleum-based fuels. In addition, the exploration of new petroleum sources often involves environmentally sensitive regions, such as the Arctic National Wildlife Refuge. Thus, increasing the supplies of petroleum becomes a major political and economic issue.

Global dependence on petroleum is in large part because it provides liquid fuels, such as gasoline, that are critical to supplying transportation needs. One of the most promising—but controversial—alternatives to petroleum-based fuels is *biofuels,* liquid fuels derived from biological matter. The most common approach to producing biofuels is to transform plant sugars and other carbohydrates into combustible liquids. The energy stored in the carbohydrates produced in photosynthesis (Equation 5.32) is higher than the energy in $H_2O$ and $CO_2$; thus, photosynthesis is a way to "store" solar energy in plants.

The most commonly produced biofuel is *bioethanol,* which is ethanol ($C_2H_5OH$) made from fermentation of plant carbohydrates. The fuel value of ethanol is about two-thirds that of gasoline and is therefore comparable to that of coal (Table 5.5). The United States and Brazil dominate bioethanol production, together supplying 85% of the world's total.

In the United States, nearly all the bioethanol currently produced is made from yellow feed corn (▶ FIGURE 5.26). Glucose ($C_6H_{12}O_6$) in the corn is converted to ethanol and $CO_2$:

$$C_6H_{12}O_6(s) \longrightarrow 2\,C_2H_5OH(l) + 2\,CO_2(g) \qquad \Delta H = 15.8 \text{ KJ}$$

Notice that this reaction is *anaerobic*—it does not involve $O_2(g)$—and that the enthalpy change is positive and much smaller in magnitude than for most combustion reactions. Other carbohydrates can be converted to ethanol in similar fashion.

Producing bioethanol from corn is controversial for two main reasons. First, growing and transporting corn are both energy-intensive processes, and growing it requires the use of fertilizers. It is estimated that the *energy return* on corn-based bioethanol is only 34%—that is, for each 1.00 J of energy expended to produce the corn, 1.34 J of energy is produced in the form of bioethanol. Second, the use of corn as a starting material for making bioethanol competes with its use as an important component of the food chain (the so-called "food versus fuel" debate). In particular, the diversion of corn crops to bioethanol production has led to higher prices for food, including beef (corn is used as feed for cattle). Much current research focuses on the formation of bioethanol from *cellulosic* plants, plants that contain the complex carbohydrate cellulose. Cellulose is not readily metabolized (Sample Exercise 5.13) and so does not compete with the food supply. However, the chemistry for converting cellulose to ethanol is much more complex than that for converting corn. Cellulosic bioethanol could be produced from very fast growing nonfood plants, such as prairie grasses and switchgrass, which readily renew themselves without the use of fertilizers.

As shown in the chapter-opening photograph, the Brazilian bioethanol industry uses sugarcane as its feedstock. Sugarcane grows much faster than corn and without the need for fertilizers or tending. Because of these differences, the energy return for sugarcane is much higher than the energy return for corn. It is estimated that for each 1.0 J of energy expended in growing and processing sugarcane, 8.0 J of energy is produced as bioethanol. Because the climate in Brazil is ideal for growing cane, the Brazilian government started investing in the 1970s in ways to utilize sugarcane as a major fuel source.

Other biofuels that are also becoming a major part of the world economy include *biodiesel,* a substitute for petroleum-derived diesel fuel. Biodiesel is typically produced from crops that have a high oil content, such as soybeans and canola. It can also be produced from animal fats and waste vegetable oil from the food and restaurant industry.

Biofuels are combusted in the presence of $O_2(g)$ to produce $CO_2(g)$, $H_2O(g)$, and energy in the form of heat, much as hydrocarbon fuels do. Because $CO_2(g)$ is a product, the use of biofuels is part of the international debate about carbon dioxide and climate change. We will discuss this issue further in Chapter 18.

*RELATED EXERCISES:*
5.89, 5.90, 5.111, 5.119

▲ FIGURE 5.26 **Corn, a source of food and bioethanol.** The sugars in the kernels of feed corn can be used as food or as a feedstock for fermentation to ethanol.

Plants utilize solar energy in *photosynthesis,* the reaction in which the energy of sunlight is used to convert $CO_2$ and $H_2O$ into carbohydrates and $O_2$. One common photosynthetic reaction produces the sugar glucose:

$$6\,CO_2(g) + 6\,H_2O(l) + \text{sunlight} \longrightarrow C_6H_{12}O_6(s) + 6\,O_2(g) \qquad [5.32]$$

In essence, photosynthesis is the reverse of combustion in that $CO_2$ and $H_2O$ are consumed and $O_2$ and an organic molecule are produced. Photosynthesis is an important part of Earth's ecosystem because it replenishes atmospheric $O_2$, produces an energy-rich molecule that can be used as fuel, and consumes some atmospheric $CO_2$.

Perhaps the most direct way to use the Sun's energy is to convert it directly into electricity in photovoltaic devices, sometimes called *solar cells*. The efficiencies of such devices have increased dramatically during the past few years. Photovoltaics are vital to the generation of power for space vehicles, such as the International Space Station research facility currently orbiting Earth. Technological advances have led to solar panels that last longer and produce electricity with greater efficiency at steadily decreasing unit cost. Indeed, the future of solar energy is, like the Sun itself, very bright.

## SAMPLE INTEGRATIVE EXERCISE   Putting Concepts Together

Trinitroglycerin, $C_3H_5N_3O_9$ (usually referred to simply as nitroglycerin), has been widely used as an explosive. Alfred Nobel used it to make dynamite in 1866. Rather surprisingly, it also is used as a medication, to relieve angina (chest pains resulting from partially blocked arteries to the heart) by dilating the blood vessels. At 1 atm pressure and 25 °C, the enthalpy of decomposition of trinitroglycerin to form nitrogen gas, carbon dioxide gas, liquid water, and oxygen gas is $-1541.4$ kJ/mol. **(a)** Write a balanced chemical equation for the decomposition of trinitroglycerin. **(b)** Calculate the standard heat of formation of trinitroglycerin. **(c)** A standard dose of trinitroglycerin for relief of angina is 0.60 mg. If the sample is eventually oxidized in the body (not explosively, though!) to nitrogen gas, carbon dioxide gas, and liquid water, what number of calories is released? **(d)** One common form of trinitroglycerin melts at about 3 °C. From this information and the formula for the substance, would you expect it to be a molecular or ionic compound? Explain. **(e)** Describe the various conversions of forms of energy when trinitroglycerin is used as an explosive to break rockfaces in highway construction.

### SOLUTION

**(a)** The general form of the equation we must balance is

$$C_3H_5N_3O_9(l) \longrightarrow N_2(g) + CO_2(g) + H_2O(l) + O_2(g)$$

We go about balancing in the usual way. To obtain an even number of nitrogen atoms on the left, we multiply the formula for $C_3H_5N_3O_9$ by 2, which gives us 3 mol of $N_2$, 6 mol of $CO_2$ and 5 mol of $H_2O$. Everything is balanced except for oxygen. We have an odd number of oxygen atoms on the right. We can balance the oxygen by adding $\frac{1}{2}$ mol of $O_2$ on the right:

$$2\,C_3H_5N_3O_9(l) \longrightarrow 3\,N_2(g) + 6\,CO_2(g) + 5\,H_2O(l) + \tfrac{1}{2}\,O_2(g)$$

We multiply through by 2 to convert all coefficients to whole numbers:

$$4\,C_3H_5N_3O_9(l) \longrightarrow 6\,N_2(g) + 12\,CO_2(g) + 10\,H_2O(l) + O_2(g)$$

(At the temperature of the explosion, water is a gas. The rapid expansion of the gaseous products creates the force of an explosion.)

**(b)** The heat of formation is the enthalpy change in the balanced chemical equation:

$$3\,C(s) + \tfrac{3}{2}\,N_2(g) + \tfrac{5}{2}\,H_2(g) + \tfrac{9}{2}\,O_2(g) \longrightarrow C_3H_5N_3O_9(l) \qquad \Delta H_f^\circ = ?$$

We can obtain the value of $\Delta H_f^\circ$ by using the equation for the heat of decomposition of trinitroglycerin:

$$4\,C_3H_5N_3O_9(l) \longrightarrow 6\,N_2(g) + 12\,CO_2(g) + 10\,H_2O(l) + O_2(g)$$

The enthalpy change in this reaction is $4(-1541.4$ kJ$) = -6165.6$ kJ. [We need to multiply by 4 because there are 4 mol of $C_3H_5N_3O_9(l)$ in the balanced equation.] This enthalpy change is given by the sum of the heats of formation of the products minus the heats of formation of the reactants, each multiplied by its coefficient in the balanced equation:

$$-6165.6\text{ kJ} = \left\{ 6\Delta H_f^\circ[N_2(g)] + 12\Delta H_f^\circ[CO_2(g)] + 10\Delta H_f^\circ[H_2O(l)] + \Delta H_f^\circ[O_2(g)] \right\}$$

$$-4\Delta H_f^\circ\,[C_3H_5N_3O_9(l)]$$

The $\Delta H_f^\circ$ values for $N_2(g)$ and $O_2(g)$ are zero, by definition. We look up the values for $H_2O(l)$ and $CO_2(g)$ in Table 5.3 and find that

$$-6165.6 \text{ kJ} = 12(-393.5 \text{ kJ}) + 10(-285.8 \text{ kJ}) - 4\Delta H_f^\circ[C_3H_5N_3O_9(l)]$$

$$\Delta H_f^\circ[C_3H_5N_3O_9(l)] = -353.6 \text{ kJ/mol}$$

**(c)** We know that on oxidation 1 mol of $C_3H_5N_3O_9(l)$ yields 1541.4 kJ. We need to calculate the number of moles of $C_3H_5N_3O_9(l)$ in 0.60 mg:

$$(0.60 \times 10^{-3} \text{ g } C_3H_5N_3O_9)\left(\frac{1 \text{ mol } C_3H_5N_3O_9}{227 \text{ g } C_3H_5N_3O_9}\right)\left(\frac{1541.4 \text{ kJ}}{1 \text{ mol } C_3H_5N_3O_9}\right) = 4.1 \times 10^{-3} \text{ kJ}$$
$$= 4.1 \text{ J}$$

**(d)** Because trinitroglycerin melts below room temperature, we expect that it is a molecular compound. With few exceptions, ionic substances are generally hard, crystalline materials that melt at high temperatures. ⟶ (Sections 2.6 and 2.7) Also, the molecular formula suggests that it is likely to be a molecular substance. All the elements of which it is composed are nonmetals.

**(e)** The energy stored in trinitroglycerin is chemical potential energy. When the substance reacts explosively, it forms substances such as carbon dioxide, water, and nitrogen gas, which are of lower potential energy. In the course of the chemical transformation, energy is released in the form of heat; the gaseous reaction products are very hot. This very high heat energy is transferred to the surroundings; the gases expand against the surroundings, which may be solid materials. Work is done in moving the solid materials and imparting kinetic energy to them. For example, a chunk of rock might be impelled upward. It has been given kinetic energy by transfer of energy from the hot, expanding gases. As the rock rises, its kinetic energy is transformed into potential energy. Eventually, it again acquires kinetic energy as it falls to Earth. When it strikes Earth, its kinetic energy is converted largely to thermal energy, though some work may be done on the surroundings as well.

# CHAPTER SUMMARY AND KEY TERMS

**INTRODUCTION AND SECTION 5.1** **Thermodynamics** is the study of energy and its transformations. In this chapter we have focused on **thermochemistry**, the transformations of energy—especially heat—during chemical reactions.

An object can possess energy in two forms: (1) **kinetic energy** is the energy due to the motion of the object, and (2) **potential energy** is the energy that an object possesses by virtue of its position relative to other objects. An electron in motion near a proton, for example, has kinetic energy because of its motion and potential energy because of its electrostatic attraction to the proton. The SI unit of energy is the **joule** (J): $1 \text{ J} = 1 \text{ kg-m}^2/\text{s}^2$. Another common energy unit is the **calorie** (cal), which was originally defined as the quantity of energy necessary to increase the temperature of 1 g of water by 1 °C: $1 \text{ cal} = 4.184 \text{ J}$.

When we study thermodynamic properties, we define a specific amount of matter as the **system**. Everything outside the system is the **surroundings**. When we study a chemical reaction, the system is generally the reactants and products. A closed system can exchange energy, but not matter, with the surroundings. Energy can be transferred between the system and the surroundings as work or heat. **Work** is the energy expended to move an object against a **force**. **Heat** is the energy that is transferred from a hotter object to a colder one. **Energy** is the capacity to do work or to transfer heat.

**SECTION 5.2** The **internal energy** of a system is the sum of all the kinetic and potential energies of its component parts. The internal energy of a system can change because of energy transferred between the system and the surroundings. According to the **first law of thermodynamics**, the change in the internal energy of a system, $\Delta E$, is the sum of the heat, $q$, transferred into or out of the system and the work, $w$, done on or by the system: $\Delta E = q + w$. Both $q$ and $w$ have a sign that indicates the direction of energy transfer. When heat is transferred

from the surroundings to the system, $q > 0$. Likewise, when the surroundings do work on the system, $w > 0$. In an **endothermic** process the system absorbs heat from the surroundings; in an **exothermic** process the system releases heat to the surroundings.

The internal energy, $E$, is a **state function**. The value of any state function depends only on the state or condition of the system and not on the details of how it came to be in that state. The heat, $q$, and the work, $w$, are not state functions; their values depend on the particular way by which a system changes its state.

**SECTIONS 5.3 AND 5.4** When a gas is produced or consumed in a chemical reaction occurring at constant pressure, the system may perform **pressure-volume (P-V) work** against the prevailing pressure of the surroundings. For this reason, we define a new state function called **enthalpy**, $H$, which is related to energy: $H = E + PV$. In systems where only pressure-volume work is involved, the change in the enthalpy of a system, $\Delta H$, equals the heat gained or lost by the system at constant pressure: $\Delta H = q_p$ (the subscript $p$ denotes constant pressure). For an endothermic process, $\Delta H > 0$; for an exothermic process, $\Delta H < 0$.

In a chemical process, the **enthalpy of reaction** is the enthalpy of the products minus the enthalpy of the reactants: $\Delta H_{rxn} = H$ (products) $- H$ (reactants). Enthalpies of reaction follow some simple rules: (1) The enthalpy of reaction is proportional to the amount of reactant that reacts. (2) Reversing a reaction changes the sign of $\Delta H$. (3) The enthalpy of reaction depends on the physical states of the reactants and products.

**SECTION 5.5** The amount of heat transferred between the system and the surroundings is measured experimentally by **calorimetry**. A **calorimeter** measures the temperature change accompanying a process. The temperature change of a calorimeter depends on its **heat**

**capacity**, the amount of heat required to raise its temperature by 1 K. The heat capacity for one mole of a pure substance is called its **molar heat capacity**; for one gram of the substance, we use the term **specific heat**. Water has a very high specific heat, 4.18 J/g-K. The amount of heat, $q$, absorbed by a substance is the product of its specific heat ($C_s$), its mass, and its temperature change: $q = C_s \times m \times \Delta T$.

If a calorimetry experiment is carried out under a constant pressure, the heat transferred provides a direct measure of the enthalpy change of the reaction. Constant-volume calorimetry is carried out in a vessel of fixed volume called a **bomb calorimeter**. Bomb calorimeters are used to measure the heat evolved in combustion reactions. The heat transferred under constant-volume conditions is equal to $\Delta E$. Corrections can be applied to $\Delta E$ values to yield enthalpies of combustion.

**SECTION 5.6**  Because enthalpy is a state function, $\Delta H$ depends only on the initial and final states of the system. Thus, the enthalpy change of a process is the same whether the process is carried out in one step or in a series of steps. **Hess's law** states that if a reaction is carried out in a series of steps, $\Delta H$ for the reaction will be equal to the sum of the enthalpy changes for the steps. We can therefore calculate $\Delta H$ for any process, as long as we can write the process as a series of steps for which $\Delta H$ is known.

**SECTION 5.7**  The **enthalpy of formation**, $\Delta H_f$, of a substance is the enthalpy change for the reaction in which the substance is formed from its constituent elements. The **standard enthalpy change** of a reaction, $\Delta H°$, is the enthalpy change when all reactants and products are at 1 atm pressure and a specific temperature, usually 298 K (25 °C). Combining these ideas, the **standard enthalpy of formation**, $\Delta H_f°$, of a substance is the change in enthalpy for the reaction that forms one mole of the substance from its elements in their most stable form with all reactants and products at 1 atm pressure and usually 298 K. For any element in its most stable state at 298 K and 1 atm pressure, $\Delta H_f° = 0$. The standard enthalpy change for any reaction can be readily calculated from the standard enthalpies of formation of the reactants and products in the reaction:

$$\Delta H_{rxn}° = \Sigma n \Delta H_f°(\text{products}) - \Sigma m \Delta H_f°(\text{reactants})$$

**SECTION 5.8**  The **fuel value** of a substance is the heat released when one gram of the substance is combusted. Different types of foods have different fuel values and differing abilities to be stored in the body. The most common fuels are hydrocarbons that are found as **fossil fuels**, such as **natural gas**, **petroleum**, and **coal**. Coal is the most abundant fossil fuel, but the sulfur present in most coals causes air pollution. **Renewable energy sources** include solar energy, wind energy, biomass, and hydroelectric energy. Nuclear power does not utilize fossil fuels but does create controversial waste-disposal problems. The challenge of providing energy for the world has significant political and social implications in the areas of food supply and the environment.

# KEY SKILLS

- Interconvert energy units. (Section 5.1)
- Distinguish between the system and the surroundings in thermodynamics. (Section 5.1)
- State the first law of thermodynamics. (Section 5.2)
- Understand the concept of a state function and be able to give examples. (Section 5.2)
- Express the relationships among the quantities $q$, $w$, $\Delta E$, and $\Delta H$. Learn their sign conventions, including how the signs of $q$ and $\Delta H$ relate to whether a process is exothermic or endothermic. (Sections 5.2 and 5.3)
- Use thermochemical equations to relate the amount of heat energy transferred in reactions at constant pressure ($\Delta H$) to the amount of substance involved in the reaction. (Section 5.4)
- Calculate the heat transferred in a process from temperature measurements together with heat capacities or specific heats (calorimetry). (Section 5.5)
- Use Hess's law to determine enthalpy changes for reactions. (Section 5.6)
- Use standard enthalpies of formation to calculate $\Delta H°$ for reactions. (Section 5.7)

# KEY EQUATIONS

- $E_k = \frac{1}{2}mv^2$      [5.1]      Kinetic energy
- $\Delta E = E_{final} - E_{initial}$      [5.4]      The change in internal energy
- $\Delta E = q + w$      [5.5]      Relates the change in internal energy to heat and work (the first law of thermodynamics)
- $w = -P \Delta V$      [5.8]      The work done by an expanding gas at constant pressure
- $\Delta H = \Delta E + P \Delta V = q_P$      [5.10]      Enthalpy change at constant pressure
- $q = C_s \times m \times \Delta T$      [5.22]      Heat gained or lost based on specific heat, mass, and temperature change
- $\Delta H_{rxn}° = \Sigma n \Delta H_f°(\text{products}) - \Sigma m \Delta H_f°(\text{reactants})$      [5.31]      Standard enthalpy change of a reaction

# EXERCISES

## VISUALIZING CONCEPTS

**5.1** Imagine a book that is falling from a shelf. At a particular moment during its fall, the book has a kinetic energy of 24 J and a potential energy with respect to the floor of 47 J. **(a)** How does the book's kinetic energy and its potential energy change as it continues to fall? **(b)** What is its total kinetic energy at the instant just before it strikes the floor? **(c)** If a heavier book fell from the same shelf, would it have the same kinetic energy when it strikes the floor? [Section 5.1]

**5.2** The accompanying photo shows a pipevine swallowtail caterpillar climbing up a twig. **(a)** As the caterpillar climbs, its potential energy is increasing. What source of energy has been used to effect this change in potential energy? **(b)** If the caterpillar is the system, can you predict the sign of $q$ as the caterpillar climbs? **(c)** Does the caterpillar do work in climbing the twig? Explain. **(d)** Does the amount of work done in climbing a 12-inch section of the twig depend on the speed of the caterpillar's climb? **(e)** Does the change in potential energy depend on the caterpillar's speed of climb? [Section 5.1]

**5.3** Consider the accompanying energy diagram. **(a)** Does this diagram represent an increase or decrease in the internal energy of the system? **(b)** What sign is given to $\Delta E$ for this process? **(c)** If there is no work associated with the process, is it exothermic or endothermic? [Section 5.2]

**5.4** The contents of the closed box in each of the following illustrations represent a system, and the arrows show the changes to the system during some process. The lengths of the arrows represent the relative magnitudes of $q$ and $w$. **(a)** Which of these processes is endothermic? **(b)** For which of these processes, if any, is $\Delta E < 0$? **(c)** For which process, if any, does the system experience a net gain in internal energy? [Section 5.2]

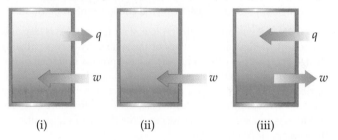

(i)          (ii)          (iii)

**5.5** Imagine that you are climbing a mountain. **(a)** Is the distance you travel to the top a state function? Why or why not? **(b)** Is the change in elevation between your base camp and the peak a state function? Why or why not? [Section 5.2]

**5.6** The diagram shows four states of a system, each with different internal energy, $E$. **(a)** Which of the states of the system has the greatest internal energy? **(b)** In terms of the $\Delta E$ values, write two expressions for the difference in internal energy between State A and State B. **(c)** Write an expression for the difference in energy between State C and State D. **(d)** Suppose there is another state of the system, State E, and that its energy relative to State A is $\Delta E = \Delta E_1 + \Delta E_4$. Where would State E be on the diagram? [Section 5.2]

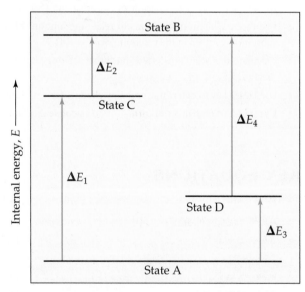

**5.7** You may have noticed that when you compress the air in a bicycle pump, the body of the pump gets warmer. **(a)** Assuming the pump and the air in it comprise the system, what is the sign of $w$ when you compress the air? **(b)** What is the sign of $q$ for this process? **(c)** Based on your answers to parts (a) and (b), can you determine the sign of $\Delta E$ for compressing the air in the pump? If not, what would you expect for the sign of $\Delta E$? What is your reasoning? [Section 5.2]

**5.8** In the accompanying cylinder diagram a chemical process occurs at constant temperature and pressure. (a) Is the sign of $w$ indicated by this change positive or negative? (b) If the process is endothermic, does the internal energy of the system within the cylinder increase or decrease during the change and is $\Delta E$ positive or negative? [Sections 5.2 and 5.3]

**5.9** Imagine a container placed in a tub of water, as depicted in the accompanying diagram. (a) If the contents of the container are the system and heat is able to flow through the container walls, what qualitative changes will occur in the temperatures of the system and in its surroundings? What is the sign of $q$ associated with each change? From the system's perspective, is the process exothermic or endothermic? (b) If neither the volume nor the pressure of the system changes during the process, how is the change in internal energy related to the change in enthalpy? [Sections 5.2 and 5.3]

**5.10** The gas-phase reaction shown, between $N_2$ and $O_2$, was run in an apparatus designed to maintain a constant pressure. (a) Write a balanced chemical equation for the reaction depicted and predict whether $w$ is positive, negative, or zero. (b) Using data from Appendix C, determine $\Delta H$ for the formation of one mole of the product. Why is this enthalpy change called the enthalpy of formation of the involved product? [Sections 5.3 and 5.7]

**5.11** Consider the two diagrams that follow. (a) Based on (i), write an equation showing how $\Delta H_A$ is related to $\Delta H_B$ and $\Delta H_C$. How do both diagram (i) and your equation relate to the fact that enthalpy is a state function? (b) Based on (ii), write an equation relating $\Delta H_Z$ to the other enthalpy changes in the diagram. (c) How do these diagrams relate to Hess's law? [Section 5.6]

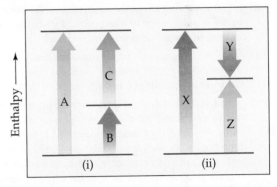

**5.12** Consider the conversion of compound A into compound B: A $\longrightarrow$ B. For both compounds A and B, $\Delta H_f^\circ > 0$. (a) Sketch an enthalpy diagram for the reaction that is analogous to Figure 5.23. (b) Suppose the overall reaction is exothermic. What can you conclude? [Section 5.7]

# THE NATURE OF ENERGY (section 5.1)

**5.13** In what two ways can an object possess energy? How do these two ways differ from one another?

**5.14** Suppose you toss a tennis ball upward. (a) Does the kinetic energy of the ball increase or decrease as it moves higher? (b) What happens to the potential energy of the ball as it moves higher? (c) If the same amount of energy were imparted to a ball the same size as a tennis ball but of twice the mass, how high would it go in comparison to the tennis ball? Explain your answers.

**5.15** (a) Calculate the kinetic energy in joules of a 1200-kg automobile moving at 18 m/s. (b) Convert this energy to calories. (c) What happens to this energy when the automobile brakes to a stop?

**5.16** (a) A baseball weighs 5.13 oz. What is the kinetic energy in joules of this baseball when it is thrown by a major-league pitcher at 95.0 mph? (b) By what factor will the kinetic energy change if the speed of the baseball is decreased to 55.0 mph? (c) What happens to the kinetic energy when the baseball is caught by the catcher? (d) What careful experimental measurement could (in principle) be made to confirm your answer to (c)?

**5.17** The use of the British thermal unit (Btu) is common in much engineering work. A Btu is the amount of heat required to raise the temperature of 1 lb of water by 1 °F. Calculate the number of joules in a Btu.

**5.18** A watt is a measure of power (the rate of energy change) equal to 1 J/s. (a) Calculate the number of joules in a kilowatt-hour. (b) An adult person radiates heat to the surroundings at about the same rate as a 100-watt electric incandescent lightbulb. What is the total amount of energy in kcal radiated to the surroundings by an adult in 24 hours?

**5.19** (a) What is meant by the term *system* in thermodynamics? (b) What is a *closed system*? (c) What do we call the part of the universe that is not part of the system?

**5.20** In a thermodynamic study a scientist focuses on the properties of a solution in an apparatus as illustrated. A solution is continuously flowing into the apparatus at the top and out at the bottom, such that the amount of solution in the apparatus is constant with time. (a) Is the solution in the apparatus a closed system, open system, or isolated system? Explain your choice. (b) If it is not a closed system, what could be done to make it a closed system?

**5.21** (a) What is work? (b) How do we determine the amount of work done, given the force associated with the work?

**5.22** (a) What is heat? (b) Under what conditions is heat transferred from one object to another?

**5.23** Identify the force present and explain whether work is being performed in the following cases: (a) You lift a pencil off the top of a desk. (b) A spring is compressed to half its normal length.

**5.24** Identify the force present and explain whether work is done when (a) a positively charged particle moves in a circle at a fixed distance from a negatively charged particle; (b) an iron nail is pulled off a magnet.

# THE FIRST LAW OF THERMODYNAMICS (section 5.2)

**5.25** (a) State the first law of thermodynamics. (b) What is meant by the *internal energy* of a system? (c) By what means can the internal energy of a closed system increase?

**5.26** (a) Write an equation that expresses the first law of thermodynamics in terms of heat and work. (b) Under what conditions will the quantities $q$ and $w$ be negative numbers?

**5.27** Calculate $\Delta E$ and determine whether the process is endothermic or exothermic for the following cases: (a) $q = 0.763$ kJ and $w = -840$ J; (b) a system releases 66.1 kJ of heat to its surroundings while the surroundings do 44.0 kJ of work on the system; (c) the system absorbs 7.25 kJ of heat from the surroundings while its volume remains constant (assume that only $P\text{-}V$ work can be done).

**5.28** For the following processes, calculate the change in internal energy of the system and determine whether the process is endothermic or exothermic: (a) A balloon is cooled by removing 0.655 kJ of heat. It shrinks on cooling, and the atmosphere does 382 J of work on the balloon. (b) A 100.0-g bar of gold is heated from 25 °C to 50 °C during which it absorbs 322 J of heat. Assume the volume of the gold bar remains constant. (c) The surroundings do 1.44 kJ of work compressing gas in a perfectly insulated cylinder.

**5.29** A gas is confined to a cylinder fitted with a piston and an electrical heater, as shown here:

Suppose that current is supplied to the heater so that 100 J of energy is added. Consider two different situations. In case (1) the piston is allowed to move as the energy is added. In case (2) the piston is fixed so that it cannot move. (a) In which case does the gas have the higher temperature after addition of the electrical energy? Explain. (b) What can you say about the values of $q$ and $w$ in each case? (c) What can you say about the relative values of $\Delta E$ for the system (the gas in the cylinder) in the two cases?

**5.30** Consider a system consisting of two oppositely charged spheres hanging by strings and separated by a distance $r_1$, as shown in the accompanying illustration. Suppose they are separated to a larger distance $r_2$, by moving them apart along a track. (a) What change, if any, has occurred in the potential energy of the system? (b) What effect, if any, does this process have on the value of $\Delta E$? (c) What can you say about $q$ and $w$ for this process?

**5.31** (a) What is meant by the term *state function*? (b) Give an example of a quantity that is a state function and one that is not. (c) Is the volume of the system a state function? Why or why not?

**5.32** Indicate which of the following is independent of the path by which a change occurs: (a) the change in potential energy when a book is transferred from table to shelf, (b) the heat evolved when a cube of sugar is oxidized to $CO_2(g)$ and $H_2O(g)$, (c) the work accomplished in burning a gallon of gasoline.

# ENTHALPY (sections 5.3 and 5.4)

**5.33** **(a)** Why is the change in enthalpy usually easier to measure than the change in internal energy? **(b)** $H$ is a state function, but $q$ is not a state function. Explain. **(c)** For a given process at constant pressure, $\Delta H$ is positive. Is the process endothermic or exothermic?

**5.34** **(a)** Under what condition will the enthalpy change of a process equal the amount of heat transferred into or out of the system? **(b)** During a constant-pressure process, the system releases heat to the surroundings. Does the enthalpy of the system increase or decrease during the process? **(c)** In a constant-pressure process, $\Delta H = 0$. What can you conclude about $\Delta E$, $q$, and $w$?

**5.35** You are given $\Delta H$ for a process that occurs at constant pressure. What additional information do you need to determine $\Delta E$ for the process?

**5.36** Suppose that the gas-phase reaction $2\,NO(g) + O_2(g) \longrightarrow 2\,NO_2(g)$ were carried out in a constant-volume container at constant temperature. Would the measured heat change represent $\Delta H$ or $\Delta E$? If there is a difference, which quantity is larger for this reaction? Explain.

**5.37** A gas is confined to a cylinder under constant atmospheric pressure, as illustrated in Figure 5.4. When the gas undergoes a particular chemical reaction, it absorbs 824 J of heat from its surroundings and has 0.65 kJ of $P$-$V$ work done on it by its surroundings. What are the values of $\Delta H$ and $\Delta E$ for this process?

**5.38** A gas is confined to a cylinder under constant atmospheric pressure, as illustrated in Figure 5.4. When 0.49 kJ of heat is added to the gas, it expands and does 214 J of work on the surroundings. What are the values of $\Delta H$ and $\Delta E$ for this process?

**5.39** The complete combustion of ethanol, $C_2H_5OH(l)$, to form $H_2O(g)$ and $CO_2(g)$ at constant pressure releases 1235 kJ of heat per mole of $C_2H_5OH$. **(a)** Write a balanced thermochemical equation for this reaction. **(b)** Draw an enthalpy diagram for the reaction.

**5.40** The decomposition of *slaked lime*, $Ca(OH)_2(s)$, into *lime*, $CaO(s)$, and $H_2O(g)$ at constant pressure requires the addition of 109 kJ of heat per mole of $Ca(OH)_2$. **(a)** Write a balanced thermochemical equation for the reaction. **(b)** Draw an enthalpy diagram for the reaction.

**5.41** Ozone, $O_3(g)$, is a form of elemental oxygen that is important in the absorption of ultraviolet radiation in the stratosphere. It decomposes to $O_2(g)$ at room temperature and pressure according to the following reaction:

$$2\,O_3(g) \longrightarrow 3\,O_2(g) \qquad \Delta H = -284.6\ \text{kJ}$$

**(a)** What is the enthalpy change for this reaction per mole of $O_3(g)$? **(b)** Which has the higher enthalpy under these conditions, $2\,O_3(g)$ or $3\,O_2(g)$?

**5.42** Without referring to tables, predict which of the following has the higher enthalpy in each case: **(a)** 1 mol $CO_2(s)$ or 1 mol $CO_2(g)$ at the same temperature, **(b)** 2 mol of hydrogen atoms or 1 mol of $H_2$, **(c)** 1 mol $H_2(g)$ and 0.5 mol $O_2(g)$ at 25 °C or 1 mol $H_2O(g)$ at 25 °C, **(d)** 1 mol $N_2(g)$ at 100 °C or 1 mol $N_2(g)$ at 300 °C.

**5.43** Consider the following reaction:

$$2\,Mg(s) + O_2(g) \longrightarrow 2\,MgO(s) \qquad \Delta H = -1204\ \text{kJ}$$

**(a)** Is this reaction exothermic or endothermic? **(b)** Calculate the amount of heat transferred when 3.55 g of $Mg(s)$ reacts at constant pressure. **(c)** How many grams of MgO are produced during an enthalpy change of $-234$ kJ? **(d)** How many kilojoules of heat are absorbed when 40.3 g of $MgO(s)$ is decomposed into $Mg(s)$ and $O_2(g)$ at constant pressure?

**5.44** Consider the following reaction:

$$2\,CH_3OH(g) \longrightarrow 2\,CH_4(g) + O_2(g) \qquad \Delta H = +252.8\ \text{kJ}$$

**(a)** Is this reaction exothermic or endothermic? **(b)** Calculate the amount of heat transferred when 24.0 g of $CH_3OH(g)$ is decomposed by this reaction at constant pressure. **(c)** For a given sample of $CH_3OH$, the enthalpy change during the reaction is 82.1 kJ. How many grams of methane gas are produced? **(d)** How many kilojoules of heat are released when 38.5 g of $CH_4(g)$ reacts completely with $O_2(g)$ to form $CH_3OH(g)$ at constant pressure?

**5.45** When solutions containing silver ions and chloride ions are mixed, silver chloride precipitates:

$$Ag^+(aq) + Cl^-(aq) \longrightarrow AgCl(s) \qquad \Delta H = -65.5\ \text{kJ}$$

**(a)** Calculate $\Delta H$ for production of 0.450 mol of AgCl by this reaction. **(b)** Calculate $\Delta H$ for the production of 9.00 g of AgCl. **(c)** Calculate $\Delta H$ when $9.25 \times 10^{-4}$ mol of AgCl dissolves in water.

**5.46** At one time, a common means of forming small quantities of oxygen gas in the laboratory was to heat $KClO_3$:

$$2\,KClO_3(s) \longrightarrow 2\,KCl(s) + 3\,O_2(g) \qquad \Delta H = -89.4\ \text{kJ}$$

For this reaction, calculate $\Delta H$ for the formation of **(a)** 1.36 mol of $O_2$ and **(b)** 10.4 g of KCl. **(c)** The decomposition of $KClO_3$ proceeds spontaneously when it is heated. Do you think that the reverse reaction, the formation of $KClO_3$ from KCl and $O_2$, is likely to be feasible under ordinary conditions? Explain your answer.

**5.47** Consider the combustion of liquid methanol, $CH_3OH(l)$:

$$CH_3OH(l) + \tfrac{3}{2}\,O_2(g) \longrightarrow CO_2(g) + 2\,H_2O(l)$$
$$\Delta H = -726.5\ \text{kJ}$$

**(a)** What is the enthalpy change for the reverse reaction? **(b)** Balance the forward reaction with whole-number coefficients. What is $\Delta H$ for the reaction represented by this equation? **(c)** Which is more likely to be thermodynamically favored, the forward reaction or the reverse reaction? **(d)** If the reaction were written to produce $H_2O(g)$ instead of $H_2O(l)$, would you expect the magnitude of $\Delta H$ to increase, decrease, or stay the same? Explain.

**5.48** Consider the decomposition of liquid benzene, $C_6H_6(l)$, to gaseous acetylene, $C_2H_2(g)$:

$$C_6H_6(l) \longrightarrow 3\,C_2H_2(g) \qquad \Delta H = +630\ \text{kJ}$$

**(a)** What is the enthalpy change for the reverse reaction? **(b)** What is $\Delta H$ for the formation of 1 mol of acetylene? **(c)** Which is more likely to be thermodynamically favored, the forward reaction or the reverse reaction? **(d)** If $C_6H_6(g)$ were consumed instead of $C_6H_6(l)$, would you expect the magnitude of $\Delta H$ to increase, decrease, or stay the same? Explain.

# CALORIMETRY (section 5.5)

**5.49** (a) What are the units of molar heat capacity? (b) What are the units of specific heat? (c) If you know the specific heat of copper, what additional information do you need to calculate the heat capacity of a particular piece of copper pipe?

**5.50** Two solid objects, A and B, are placed in boiling water and allowed to come to temperature there. Each is then lifted out and placed in separate beakers containing 1000 g water at 10.0 °C. Object A increases the water temperature by 3.50 °C; B increases the water temperature by 2.60 °C. (a) Which object has the larger heat capacity? (b) What can you say about the specific heats of A and B?

**5.51** (a) What is the specific heat of liquid water? (b) What is the molar heat capacity of liquid water? (c) What is the heat capacity of 185 g of liquid water? (d) How many kJ of heat are needed to raise the temperature of 10.00 kg of liquid water from 24.6 °C to 46.2 °C?

**5.52** (a) Which substance in Table 5.2 requires the smallest amount of energy to increase the temperature of 50.0 g of that substance by 10 K? (b) Calculate the energy needed for this temperature change.

**5.53** The specific heat of *octane*, $C_8H_{18}(l)$, is 2.22 J/g-K. (a) How many J of heat are needed to raise the temperature of 80.0 g of octane from 10.0 °C to 25.0 °C? (b) Which will require more heat, increasing the temperature of 1 mol of $C_8H_{18}(l)$ by a certain amount or increasing the temperature of 1 mol of $H_2O(l)$ by the same amount?

**5.54** Consider the data about gold metal in Exercise 5.28(b). (a) Based on the data, calculate the specific heat of Au(s). (b) Suppose that the same amount of heat is added to two 10.0-g blocks of metal, both initially at the same temperature. One block is gold metal and one is iron metal. Which block will have the greater rise in temperature after the addition of the heat? (c) What is the molar heat capacity of Au(s)?

**5.55** When a 6.50-g sample of solid sodium hydroxide dissolves in 100.0 g of water in a coffee-cup calorimeter (Figure 5.18), the temperature rises from 21.6 °C to 37.8 °C. Calculate $\Delta H$ (in kJ/mol NaOH) for the solution process

$$NaOH(s) \longrightarrow Na^+(aq) + OH^-(aq)$$

Assume that the specific heat of the solution is the same as that of pure water.

**5.56** (a) When a 4.25-g sample of solid ammonium nitrate dissolves in 60.0 g of water in a coffee-cup calorimeter (Figure 5.18), the temperature drops from 22.0 °C to 16.9 °C. Calculate $\Delta H$ (in kJ/mol $NH_4NO_3$) for the solution process

$$NH_4NO_3(s) \longrightarrow NH_4^+(aq) + NO_3^-(aq)$$

Assume that the specific heat of the solution is the same as that of pure water. (b) Is this process endothermic or exothermic?

**5.57** A 2.200-g sample of quinone ($C_6H_4O_2$) is burned in a bomb calorimeter whose total heat capacity is 7.854 kJ/°C. The temperature of the calorimeter increases from 23.44 °C to 30.57 °C. What is the heat of combustion per gram of quinone? Per mole of quinone?

**5.58** A 1.800-g sample of phenol ($C_6H_5OH$) was burned in a bomb calorimeter whose total heat capacity is 11.66 kJ/°C. The temperature of the calorimeter plus contents increased from 21.36 °C to 26.37 °C. (a) Write a balanced chemical equation for the bomb calorimeter reaction. (b) What is the heat of combustion per gram of phenol? Per mole of phenol?

**5.59** Under constant-volume conditions, the heat of combustion of glucose ($C_6H_{12}O_6$) is 15.57 kJ/g. A 3.500-g sample of glucose is burned in a bomb calorimeter. The temperature of the calorimeter increased from 20.94 °C to 24.72 °C. (a) What is the total heat capacity of the calorimeter? (b) If the size of the glucose sample had been exactly twice as large, what would the temperature change of the calorimeter have been?

**5.60** Under constant-volume conditions, the heat of combustion of benzoic acid ($C_6H_5COOH$) is 26.38 kJ/g. A 2.760-g sample of benzoic acid is burned in a bomb calorimeter. The temperature of the calorimeter increases from 21.60 °C to 29.93 °C. (a) What is the total heat capacity of the calorimeter? (b) A 1.440-g sample of a new organic substance is combusted in the same calorimeter. The temperature of the calorimeter increases from 22.14 °C to 27.09 °C. What is the heat of combustion per gram of the new substance? (c) Suppose that in changing samples, a portion of the water in the calorimeter were lost. In what way, if any, would this change the heat capacity of the calorimeter?

# HESS'S LAW (section 5.6)

**5.61** What is the connection between Hess's law and the fact that $H$ is a state function?

**5.62** Consider the following hypothetical reactions:

$$A \longrightarrow B \qquad \Delta H = +30 \text{ kJ}$$
$$B \longrightarrow C \qquad \Delta H = +60 \text{ kJ}$$

(a) Use Hess's law to calculate the enthalpy change for the reaction $A \longrightarrow C$. (b) Construct an enthalpy diagram for substances A, B, and C, and show how Hess's law applies.

**5.63** Calculate the enthalpy change for the reaction

$$P_4O_6(s) + 2 O_2(g) \longrightarrow P_4O_{10}(s)$$

given the following enthalpies of reaction:

$$P_4(s) + 3 O_2(g) \longrightarrow P_4O_6(s) \qquad \Delta H = -1640.1 \text{ kJ}$$
$$P_4(s) + 5 O_2(g) \longrightarrow P_4O_{10}(s) \qquad \Delta H = -2940.1 \text{ kJ}$$

**5.64** From the enthalpies of reaction

$$2 C(s) + O_2(g) \longrightarrow 2 CO(g) \qquad \Delta H = -221.0 \text{ kJ}$$
$$2 C(s) + O_2(g) + 4 H_2(g) \longrightarrow 2 CH_3OH(g) \qquad \Delta H = -402.4 \text{ kJ}$$

calculate $\Delta H$ for the reaction

$$CO(g) + 2 H_2(g) \longrightarrow CH_3OH(g)$$

**5.65** From the enthalpies of reaction

$$H_2(g) + F_2(g) \longrightarrow 2 HF(g) \qquad \Delta H = -537 \text{ kJ}$$
$$C(s) + 2 F_2(g) \longrightarrow CF_4(g) \qquad \Delta H = -680 \text{ kJ}$$
$$2 C(s) + 2 H_2(g) \longrightarrow C_2H_4(g) \qquad \Delta H = +52.3 \text{ kJ}$$

calculate $\Delta H$ for the reaction of ethylene with $F_2$:

$$C_2H_4(g) + 6 F_2(g) \longrightarrow 2 CF_4(g) + 4 HF(g)$$

**5.66** Given the data

$$N_2(g) + O_2(g) \longrightarrow 2\,NO(g) \qquad \Delta H = +180.7 \text{ kJ}$$
$$2\,NO(g) + O_2(g) \longrightarrow 2\,NO_2(g) \qquad \Delta H = -113.1 \text{ kJ}$$
$$2\,N_2O(g) \longrightarrow 2\,N_2(g) + O_2(g) \qquad \Delta H = -163.2 \text{ kJ}$$

use Hess's law to calculate $\Delta H$ for the reaction

$$N_2O(g) + NO_2(g) \longrightarrow 3\,NO(g)$$

# ENTHALPIES OF FORMATION (section 5.7)

**5.67** (a) What is meant by the term *standard conditions* with reference to enthalpy changes? (b) What is meant by the term *enthalpy of formation*? (c) What is meant by the term *standard enthalpy of formation*?

**5.68** (a) Why are tables of standard enthalpies of formation so useful? (b) What is the value of the standard enthalpy of formation of an element in its most stable form? (c) Write the chemical equation for the reaction whose enthalpy change is the standard enthalpy of formation of sucrose (table sugar), $C_{12}H_{22}O_{11}(s)$, $\Delta H_f^o[C_{12}H_{22}O_{11}]$.

**5.69** For each of the following compounds, write a balanced thermochemical equation depicting the formation of one mole of the compound from its elements in their standard states and use Appendix C to obtain the value of $\Delta H_f^o$: (a) $NO_2(g)$, (b) $SO_3(g)$, (c) $NaBr(s)$, (d) $Pb(NO_3)_2(s)$.

**5.70** Write balanced equations that describe the formation of the following compounds from elements in their standard states, and use Appendix C to obtain the values of their standard enthalpies of formation: (a) $H_2O_2(g)$, (b) $CaCO_3(s)$, (c) $POCl_3(l)$, (d) $C_2H_5OH(l)$.

**5.71** The following is known as the thermite reaction [Figure 5.8(b)]:

$$2\,Al(s) + Fe_2O_3(s) \longrightarrow Al_2O_3(s) + 2\,Fe(s)$$

This highly exothermic reaction is used for welding massive units, such as propellers for large ships. Using standard enthalpies of formation in Appendix C, calculate $\Delta H^o$ for this reaction.

**5.72** Many portable gas heaters and grills use propane, $C_3H_8(g)$, as a fuel. Using standard enthalpies of formation, calculate the quantity of heat produced when 10.0 g of propane is completely combusted in air under standard conditions.

**5.73** Using values from Appendix C, calculate the standard enthalpy change for each of the following reactions:

(a) $2\,SO_2(g) + O_2(g) \longrightarrow 2\,SO_3(g)$
(b) $Mg(OH)_2(s) \longrightarrow MgO(s) + H_2O(l)$
(c) $N_2O_4(g) + 4\,H_2(g) \longrightarrow N_2(g) + 4\,H_2O(g)$
(d) $SiCl_4(l) + 2\,H_2O(l) \longrightarrow SiO_2(s) + 4\,HCl(g)$

**5.74** Using values from Appendix C, calculate the value of $\Delta H^o$ for each of the following reactions:

(a) $CaO(s) + 2\,HCl(g) \longrightarrow CaCl_2(s) + H_2O(g)$
(b) $4\,FeO(s) + O_2(g) \longrightarrow 2\,Fe_2O_3(s)$
(c) $2\,CuO(s) + NO(g) \longrightarrow Cu_2O(s) + NO_2(g)$
(d) $4\,NH_3(g) + O_2(g) \longrightarrow 2\,N_2H_4(g) + 2\,H_2O(l)$

**5.75** Complete combustion of 1 mol of acetone ($C_3H_6O$) liberates 1790 kJ:

$$C_3H_6O(l) + 4\,O_2(g) \longrightarrow 3\,CO_2(g) + 3\,H_2O(l)$$
$$\Delta H^o = -1790 \text{ kJ}$$

Using this information together with data from Appendix C, calculate the enthalpy of formation of acetone.

**5.76** Calcium carbide ($CaC_2$) reacts with water to form acetylene ($C_2H_2$) and $Ca(OH)_2$. From the following enthalpy of reaction data and data in Appendix C, calculate $\Delta H_f^o$ for $CaC_2(s)$:

$$CaC_2(s) + 2\,H_2O(l) \longrightarrow Ca(OH)_2(s) + C_2H_2(g)$$
$$\Delta H^o = -127.2 \text{ kJ}$$

**5.77** Gasoline is composed primarily of hydrocarbons, including many with eight carbon atoms, called *octanes*. One of the cleanest-burning octanes is a compound called 2,3,4-trimethylpentane, which has the following structural formula:

$$\begin{array}{ccc} CH_3 & CH_3 & CH_3 \\ | & | & | \\ H_3C-CH-CH-CH-CH_3 \end{array}$$

The complete combustion of one mole of this compound to $CO_2(g)$ and $H_2O(g)$ leads to $\Delta H^o = -5064.9$ kJ/mol. (a) Write a balanced equation for the combustion of 1 mol of $C_8H_{18}(l)$. (b) Write a balanced equation for the formation of $C_8H_{18}(l)$ from its elements. (c) By using the information in this problem and data in Table 5.3, calculate $\Delta H_f^o$ for 2,3,4-trimethylpentane.

**5.78** Diethyl ether, $C_4H_{10}O(l)$, a flammable compound that has long been used as a surgical anesthetic, has the structure

$$CH_3-CH_2-O-CH_2-CH_3$$

The complete combustion of 1 mol of $C_4H_{10}O(l)$ to $CO_2(g)$ and $H_2O(l)$ yields $\Delta H^o = -2723.7$ kJ. (a) Write a balanced equation for the combustion of 1 mol of $C_4H_{10}O(l)$. (b) Write a balanced equation for the formation of $C_4H_{10}O(l)$ from its elements. (c) By using the information in this problem and data in Table 5.3, calculate $\Delta H_f^o$ for diethyl ether.

**5.79** Ethanol ($C_2H_5OH$) is currently blended with gasoline as an automobile fuel. (a) Write a balanced equation for the combustion of liquid ethanol in air. (b) Calculate the standard enthalpy change for the reaction, assuming $H_2O(g)$ as a product. (c) Calculate the heat produced per liter of ethanol by combustion of ethanol under constant pressure. Ethanol has a density of 0.789 g/mL. (d) Calculate the mass of $CO_2$ produced per kJ of heat emitted.

**5.80** Methanol ($CH_3OH$) is used as a fuel in race cars. (a) Write a balanced equation for the combustion of liquid methanol in air. (b) Calculate the standard enthalpy change for the reaction, assuming $H_2O(g)$ as a product. (c) Calculate the heat produced by combustion per liter of methanol. Methanol has a density of 0.791 g/mL. (d) Calculate the mass of $CO_2$ produced per kJ of heat emitted.

# FOODS AND FUELS (section 5.8)

**5.81** (a) What is meant by the term *fuel value*? (b) Which is a greater source of energy as food, 5 g of fat or 9 g of carbohydrate? (c) The metabolism of glucose produces $CO_2(g)$ and $H_2O(l)$. How does the human body expel these reaction products?

**5.82** (a) Why are fats well suited for energy storage in the human body? (b) A particular chip snack food is composed of 12% protein, 14% fat, and the rest carbohydrate. What percentage of the calorie content of this food is fat? (c) How many grams of protein provide the same fuel value as 25 g of fat?

**5.83** (a) A serving of a particular ready-to-serve chicken noodle soup contains 2.5 g fat, 14 g carbohydrate, and 7 g protein. Estimate the number of Calories in a serving. (b) According to its nutrition label, the same soup also contains 690 mg of sodium. Do you think the sodium contributes to the caloric content of the soup?

**5.84** A pound of plain M&M® candies contains 96 g fat, 320 g carbohydrate, and 21 g protein. What is the fuel value in kJ in a 42-g (about 1.5 oz) serving? How many Calories does it provide?

**5.85** The heat of combustion of fructose, $C_6H_{12}O_6$, is −2812 kJ/mol. If a fresh golden delicious apple weighing 4.23 oz (120 g) contains 16.0 g of fructose, what caloric content does the fructose contribute to the apple?

**5.86** The heat of combustion of ethanol, $C_2H_5OH(l)$, is −1367 kJ/mol. A batch of Sauvignon Blanc wine contains 10.6% ethanol by mass. Assuming the density of the wine to be 1.0 g/mL, what is the caloric content due to the alcohol (ethanol) in a 6-oz glass of wine (177 mL)?

**5.87** The standard enthalpies of formation of gaseous propyne $(C_3H_4)$, propylene $(C_3H_6)$, and propane $(C_3H_8)$ are +185.4, +20.4, and −103.8 kJ/mol, respectively. (a) Calculate the heat evolved per mole on combustion of each substance to yield $CO_2(g)$ and $H_2O(g)$. (b) Calculate the heat evolved on combustion of 1 kg of each substance. (c) Which is the most efficient fuel in terms of heat evolved per unit mass?

**5.88** It is interesting to compare the "fuel value" of a hydrocarbon in a world where fluorine rather than oxygen is the combustion agent. The enthalpy of formation of $CF_4(g)$ is −679.9 kJ/mol. Which of the following two reactions is the more exothermic?

$$CH_4(g) + 2\,O_2(g) \longrightarrow CO_2(g) + 2\,H_2O(g)$$
$$CH_4(g) + 4\,F_2(g) \longrightarrow CF_4(g) + 4\,HF(g)$$

**[5.89]** At the end of 2009, global population was about 6.8 billion people. What mass of glucose in kg would be needed to provide 1500 Cal/person/day of nourishment to the global population for one year? Assume that glucose is metabolized entirely to $CO_2(g)$ and $H_2O(l)$ according to the following thermochemical equation:

$$C_6H_{12}O_6(s) + 6\,O_2(g) \longrightarrow 6\,CO_2(g) + 6H_2O(l)$$
$$\Delta H° = -2803 \text{ kJ}$$

**[5.90]** The automobile fuel called E85 consists of 85% ethanol and 15% gasoline. E85 can be used in so-called "flex-fuel" vehicles (FFVs), which can use gasoline, ethanol, or a mix as fuels. Assume that gasoline consists of a mixture of octanes (different isomers of $C_8H_{18}$), that the average heat of combustion of $C_8H_{18}(l)$ is 5400 kJ/mol, and that gasoline has an average density of 0.70 g/mL. The density of ethanol is 0.79 g/mL. (a) By using the information given as well as data in Appendix C, compare the energy produced by combustion of 1.0 L of gasoline and of 1.0 L of ethanol. (b) Assume that the density and heat of combustion of E85 can be obtained by using 85% of the values for ethanol and 15% of the values for gasoline. How much energy could be released by the combustion of 1.0 L of E85? (c) How many gallons of E85 would be needed to provide the same energy as 10 gal of gasoline? (d) If gasoline costs $3.10 per gallon in the United States, what is the break-even price per gallon of E85 if the same amount of energy is to be delivered?

# ADDITIONAL EXERCISES

**5.91** At 20 °C (approximately room temperature) the average velocity of $N_2$ molecules in air is 1050 mph. (a) What is the average speed in m/s? (b) What is the kinetic energy (in J) of an $N_2$ molecule moving at this speed? (c) What is the total kinetic energy of 1 mol of $N_2$ molecules moving at this speed?

**5.92** Suppose an Olympic diver who weighs 52.0 kg executes a straight dive from a 10-m platform. At the apex of the dive, the diver is 10.8 m above the surface of the water. (a) What is the potential energy of the diver at the apex of the dive, relative to the surface of the water? (b) Assuming that all the potential energy of the diver is converted into kinetic energy at the surface of the water, at what speed in m/s will the diver enter the water? (c) Does the diver do work on entering the water? Explain.

**5.93** The air bags that provide protection in autos in the event of an accident expand because of a rapid chemical reaction. From the viewpoint of the chemical reactants as the system, what do you expect for the signs of $q$ and $w$ in this process?

**[5.94]** An aluminum can of a soft drink is placed in a freezer. Later, you find that the can is split open and its contents frozen.

Work was done on the can in splitting it open. Where did the energy for this work come from?

**[5.95]** Consider a system consisting of the following apparatus, in which gas is confined in one flask and there is a vacuum in the other flask. The flasks are separated by a valve that, when opened, connects the two flasks. Assume that the flasks are perfectly insulated and will not allow the flow of heat into or out of the flasks to the surroundings. (a) When the valve is opened, gas flows from the filled flask to the evacuated one. Does that surprise you? (b) Is work performed during the expansion of the gas? Why or why not? (c) Can you determine the value of $\Delta E$ for the process? Does the answer surprise you? (We will talk about this system more in Chapter 19.)

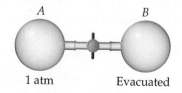

1 atm                    Evacuated

[5.96] A sample of gas is contained in a cylinder-and-piston arrangement. It undergoes the change in state shown in the drawing. **(a)** Assume first that the cylinder and piston are perfect thermal insulators that do not allow heat to be transferred. What is the value of $q$ for the state change? What is the sign of $w$ for the state change? What can be said about $\Delta E$ for the state change? **(b)** Now assume that the cylinder and piston are made up of a thermal conductor such as a metal. During the state change, the cylinder gets warmer to the touch. What is the sign of $q$ for the state change in this case? Describe the difference in the state of the system at the end of the process in the two cases. What can you say about the relative values of $\Delta E$?

[5.97] Limestone stalactites and stalagmites are formed in caves by the following reaction:

$$Ca^{2+}(aq) + 2\ HCO_3^-(aq) \longrightarrow CaCO_3(s) + CO_2(g) + H_2O(l)$$

If 1 mol of $CaCO_3$ forms at 298 K under 1 atm pressure, the reaction performs 2.47 kJ of $P$-$V$ work, pushing back the atmosphere as the gaseous $CO_2$ forms. At the same time, 38.95 kJ of heat is absorbed from the environment. What are the values of $\Delta H$ and of $\Delta E$ for this reaction?

[5.98] Consider the systems shown in Figure 5.10. In one case the battery becomes completely discharged by running the current through a heater and in the other case by running a fan. Both processes occur at constant pressure. In both cases the change in state of the system is the same: The battery goes from being fully charged to being fully discharged. Yet in one case the heat evolved is large, and in the other it is small. Is the enthalpy change the same in the two cases? If not, how can enthalpy be considered a state function? If it is, what can you say about the relationship between enthalpy change and $q$ in this case, as compared with others that we have considered?

5.99 A house is designed to have passive solar energy features. Brickwork incorporated into the interior of the house acts as a heat absorber. Each brick weighs approximately 1.8 kg. The specific heat of the brick is 0.85 J/g-K. How many bricks must be incorporated into the interior of the house to provide the same total heat capacity as $1.7 \times 10^3$ gal of water?

[5.100] A coffee-cup calorimeter of the type shown in Figure 5.18 contains 150.0 g of water at 25.1 °C. A 121.0-g block of copper metal is heated to 100.4 °C by putting it in a beaker of boiling water. The specific heat of Cu(s) is 0.385 J/g-K. The Cu is added to the calorimeter, and after a time the contents of the cup reach a constant temperature of 30.1 °C. **(a)** Determine the amount of heat, in J, lost by the copper block. **(b)** Determine the amount of heat gained by the water. The specific heat of water is 4.18 J/g-K. **(c)** The difference between your answers for (a) and (b) is due to heat loss through the

Styrofoam® cups and the heat necessary to raise the temperature of the inner wall of the apparatus. The heat capacity of the calorimeter is the amount of heat necessary to raise the temperature of the apparatus (the cups and the stopper) by 1 K. Calculate the heat capacity of the calorimeter in J/K. **(d)** What would be the final temperature of the system if all the heat lost by the copper block were absorbed by the water in the calorimeter?

[5.101] **(a)** When a 0.235-g sample of benzoic acid is combusted in a bomb calorimeter (Figure 5.19), the temperature rises 1.642 °C. When a 0.265-g sample of caffeine, $C_8H_{10}O_2N_4$, is burned, the temperature rises 1.525 °C. Using the value 26.38 kJ/g for the heat of combustion of benzoic acid, calculate the heat of combustion per mole of caffeine at constant volume. **(b)** Assuming that there is an uncertainty of 0.002 °C in each temperature reading and that the masses of samples are measured to 0.001 g, what is the estimated uncertainty in the value calculated for the heat of combustion per mole of caffeine?

5.102 Meals-ready-to-eat (MREs) are military meals that can be heated on a flameless heater. The heat is produced by the following reaction: $Mg(s) + 2\ H_2O(l) \longrightarrow Mg(OH)_2(s) + H_2(g)$. **(a)** Calculate the standard enthalpy change for this reaction. **(b)** Calculate the number of grams of Mg needed for this reaction to release enough energy to increase the temperature of 75 mL of water from 21 °C to 79 °C.

5.103 Burning methane in oxygen can produce three different carbon-containing products: soot (very fine particles of graphite), CO(g), and $CO_2(g)$. **(a)** Write three balanced equations for the reaction of methane gas with oxygen to produce these three products. In each case assume that $H_2O(l)$ is the only other product. **(b)** Determine the standard enthalpies for the reactions in part (a). **(c)** Why, when the oxygen supply is adequate, is $CO_2(g)$ the predominant carbon-containing product of the combustion of methane?

5.104 **(a)** Calculate the standard enthalpy of formation of gaseous diborane ($B_2H_6$) using the following thermochemical information:

$$4\ B(s) + 3\ O_2(g) \longrightarrow 2\ B_2O_3(s) \qquad \Delta H° = -2509.1\ \text{kJ}$$
$$2\ H_2(g) + O_2(g) \longrightarrow 2\ H_2O(l) \qquad \Delta H° = -571.7\ \text{kJ}$$
$$B_2H_6(g) + 3\ O_2(g) \longrightarrow B_2O_3(s) + 3\ H_2O(l) \quad \Delta H° = -2147.5\ \text{kJ}$$

**(b)** Pentaborane ($B_5H_9$) is another boron hydride. What experiment or experiments would you need to perform to yield the data necessary to calculate the heat of formation of $B_5H_9(l)$? Explain by writing out and summing any applicable chemical reactions.

5.105 From the following data for three prospective fuels, calculate which could provide the most energy per unit volume:

| Fuel | Density at 20 °C (g/cm³) | Molar Enthalpy of Combustion (kJ/mol) |
|---|---|---|
| Nitroethane, $C_2H_5NO_2(l)$ | 1.052 | -1368 |
| Ethanol, $C_2H_5OH(l)$ | 0.789 | -1367 |
| Methylhydrazine, $CH_6N_2(l)$ | 0.874 | -1307 |

5.106 The hydrocarbons acetylene ($C_2H_2$) and benzene ($C_6H_6$) have the same empirical formula. Benzene is an "aromatic" hydrocarbon, one that is unusually stable because of its structure. **(a)** By using the data in Appendix C, determine the standard enthalpy change for the reaction $3\ C_2H_2(g) \longrightarrow C_6H_6(l)$.

**(b)** Which has greater enthalpy, 3 mol of acetylene gas or 1 mol of liquid benzene? **(c)** Determine the fuel value in kJ/g for acetylene and benzene.

[5.107] Ammonia ($NH_3$) boils at $-33$ °C; at this temperature it has a density of 0.81 g/cm³. The enthalpy of formation of $NH_3(g)$ is $-46.2$ kJ/mol, and the enthalpy of vaporization of $NH_3(l)$ is 23.2 kJ/mol. Calculate the enthalpy change when 1 L of liquid $NH_3$ is burned in air to give $N_2(g)$ and $H_2O(g)$. How does this compare with $\Delta H$ for the complete combustion of 1 L of liquid methanol, $CH_3OH(l)$? For $CH_3OH(l)$, the density at 25 °C is 0.792 g/cm³, and $\Delta H_f^\circ = -239$ kJ/mol.

[5.108] Three common hydrocarbons that contain four carbons are listed here, along with their standard enthalpies of formation:

| Hydrocarbon | Formula | $\Delta H_f^\circ$ (kJ/mol) |
|---|---|---|
| 1,3-Butadiene | $C_4H_6(g)$ | 111.9 |
| 1-Butene | $C_4H_8(g)$ | 1.2 |
| n-Butane | $C_4H_{10}(g)$ | $-124.7$ |

**(a)** For each of these substances, calculate the molar enthalpy of combustion to $CO_2(g)$ and $H_2O(l)$. **(b)** Calculate the fuel value in kJ/g for each of these compounds. **(c)** For each hydrocarbon, determine the percentage of hydrogen by mass. **(d)** By comparing your answers for parts (b) and (c), propose a relationship between hydrogen content and fuel value in hydrocarbons.

5.109 A 200-lb man decides to add to his exercise routine by walking up three flights of stairs (45 ft) 20 times per day. He figures that the work required to increase his potential energy in this way will permit him to eat an extra order of French fries, at 245 Cal, without adding to his weight. Is he correct in this assumption?

5.110 The Sun supplies about 1.0 kilowatt of energy for each square meter of surface area (1.0 kW/m², where a watt = 1 J/s). Plants produce the equivalent of about 0.20 g of sucrose ($C_{12}H_{22}O_{11}$) per hour per square meter. Assuming that the sucrose is produced as follows, calculate the percentage of sunlight used to produce sucrose.

$$12\ CO_2(g) + 11\ H_2O(l) \longrightarrow C_{12}H_{22}O_{11} + 12\ O_2(g)$$
$$\Delta H = 5645\ kJ$$

[5.111] It is estimated that the net amount of carbon dioxide fixed by photosynthesis on the landmass of Earth is $5.5 \times 10^{16}$ g/yr of $CO_2$. Assume that all this carbon is converted into glucose. **(a)** Calculate the energy stored by photosynthesis on land per year in kJ. **(b)** Calculate the average rate of conversion of solar energy into plant energy in MW (1W = 1 J/s). A large nuclear power plant produces about $10^3$ MW. The energy of how many such nuclear power plants is equivalent to the solar energy conversion?

# INTEGRATIVE EXERCISES

5.112 Consider the combustion of a single molecule of $CH_4(g)$ forming $H_2O(l)$ as a product. **(a)** How much energy, in J, is produced during this reaction? **(b)** A typical X-ray light source has an energy of 8 keV. How does the energy of combustion compare to the energy of the X-ray?

5.113 Consider the following unbalanced oxidation-reduction reactions in aqueous solution:

$$Ag^+(aq) + Li(s) \longrightarrow Ag(s) + Li^+(aq)$$
$$Fe(s) + Na^+(aq) \longrightarrow Fe^{2+}(aq) + Na(s)$$
$$K(s) + H_2O(l) \longrightarrow KOH(aq) + H_2(g)$$

**(a)** Balance each of the reactions. **(b)** By using data in Appendix C, calculate $\Delta H°$ for each of the reactions. **(c)** Based on the values you obtain for $\Delta H°$, which of the reactions would you expect to be thermodynamically favored? **(d)** Use the activity series to predict which of these reactions should occur. ∞∞ (Section 4.4) Are these results in accord with your conclusion in part (c) of this problem?

[5.114] Consider the following acid-neutralization reactions involving the strong base NaOH($aq$):

$$HNO_3(aq) + NaOH(aq) \longrightarrow NaNO_3(aq) + H_2O(l)$$
$$HCl(aq) + NaOH(aq) \longrightarrow NaCl(aq) + H_2O(l)$$
$$NH_4^+(aq) + NaOH(aq) \longrightarrow NH_3(aq) + Na^+(aq) + H_2O(l)$$

**(a)** By using data in Appendix C, calculate $\Delta H°$ for each of the reactions. **(b)** As we saw in Section 4.3, nitric acid and hydrochloric acid are strong acids. Write net ionic equations for the neutralization of these acids. **(c)** Compare the values of $\Delta H°$ for the first two reactions. What can you conclude? **(d)** In the third equation $NH_4^+(aq)$ is acting as an acid. Based on the value of $\Delta H°$ for this reaction, do you think it is a strong or a weak acid? Explain.

5.115 Consider two solutions, the first being 50.0 mL of 1.00 M $CuSO_4$ and the second 50.0 mL of 2.00 M KOH. When the two solutions are mixed in a constant-pressure calorimeter, a precipitate forms and the temperature of the mixture rises from 21.5 °C to 27.7 °C. **(a)** Before mixing, how many grams of Cu are present in the solution of $CuSO_4$? **(b)** Predict the identity of the precipitate in the reaction. **(c)** Write complete and net ionic equations for the reaction that occurs when the two solutions are mixed. **(d)** From the calorimetric data, calculate $\Delta H$ for the reaction that occurs on mixing. Assume that the calorimeter absorbs only a negligible quantity of heat, that the total volume of the solution is 100.0 mL, and that the specific heat and density of the solution after mixing are the same as that of pure water.

5.116 The precipitation reaction between $AgNO_3(aq)$ and $NaCl(aq)$ proceeds as follows:

$$AgNO_3(aq) + NaCl(aq) \longrightarrow NaNO_3(aq) + AgCl(s)$$

**(a)** By using Appendix C, calculate $\Delta H°$ for the net ionic equation of this reaction. **(b)** What would you expect for the value of $\Delta H°$ of the overall molecular equation compared to that for the net ionic equation? Explain. **(c)** Use the results from (a) and (b) along with data in Appendix C to determine the value of $\Delta H_f^\circ$ for $AgNO_3(aq)$.

**[5.117]** A sample of a hydrocarbon is combusted completely in $O_2(g)$ to produce 21.83 g $CO_2(g)$, 4.47 g $H_2O(g)$, and 311 kJ of heat. **(a)** What is the mass of the hydrocarbon sample that was combusted? **(b)** What is the empirical formula of the hydrocarbon? **(c)** Calculate the value of $\Delta H_f^\circ$ per empirical-formula unit of the hydrocarbon. **(d)** Do you think that the hydrocarbon is one of those listed in Appendix C? Explain your answer.

**5.118** The methane molecule, $CH_4$, has the geometry shown in Figure 2.19. Imagine a hypothetical process in which the methane molecule is "expanded," by simultaneously extending all four C—H bonds to infinity. We then have the process

$$CH_4(g) \longrightarrow C(g) + 4\,H(g)$$

**(a)** Compare this process with the reverse of the reaction that represents the standard enthalpy of formation of $CH_4(g)$ . **(b)** Calculate the enthalpy change in each case. Which is the more endothermic process? What accounts for the difference in $\Delta H^\circ$ values? **(c)** Suppose that 3.45 g $CH_4(g)$ reacts with 1.22 g $F_2(g)$, forming $CF_4(g)$ and $HF(g)$ as sole products. What is the limiting reagent in this reaction? If the reaction occurs at constant pressure, what amount of heat is evolved?

**5.119** World energy supplies are often measured in the unit of quadrillion British thermal units ($10^{12}$ Btu), generally called a "quad." In 2015, world energy consumption is projected to be $5.81 \times 10^{17}$ kJ. **(a)** With reference to Exercise 5.17, how many quads of energy does this quantity represent? **(b)** Current annual energy consumption in the United States is 99.5 quads. Assume that all this energy is to be generated by burning $CH_4(g)$ in the form of natural gas. If the combustion of the $CH_4(g)$ were complete and 100% efficient, how many moles of $CH_4(g)$ would need to be combusted in order to provide the U.S. energy demand? **(c)** How many kilograms of $CO_2(g)$ would be generated in the combustion in part (b)? **(d)** Compare your answer to part (c) with information given in Exercise 5.111. Do you think that photosynthesis is an adequate means to maintain a stable level of $CO_2$ in the atmosphere?

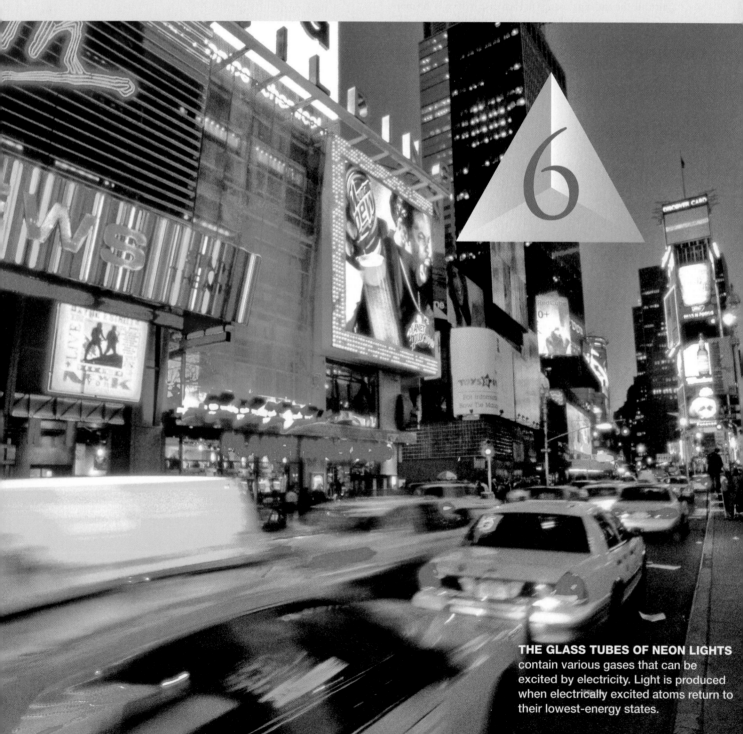

**THE GLASS TUBES OF NEON LIGHTS** contain various gases that can be excited by electricity. Light is produced when electrically excited atoms return to their lowest-energy states.

orbitals. The orbitals can be described in a shorthand notation using *quantum numbers*.

## 6.6 REPRESENTATIONS OF ORBITALS
We consider the three-dimensional shapes of orbitals and how they can be represented by graphs of electron density.

## 6.7 MANY-ELECTRON ATOMS
We recognize that the energy levels for an atom with one electron are altered when the atom contains multiple electrons. Each electron has a quantum-mechanical property called *spin*. The *Pauli exclusion principle* states that no two electrons in an atom can have the same four quantum numbers (three for the orbital and one for the spin). Therefore, an orbital can hold a maximum of two electrons.

## 6.8 ELECTRON CONFIGURATIONS
We learn that knowing orbital energies as well as some fundamental characteristics of electrons described by *Hund's rule* allows us to determine how electrons are distributed in an atom (*electron configurations*).

## 6.9 ELECTRON CONFIGURATIONS AND THE PERIODIC TABLE
We observe that the electron configuration of an atom is related to the location of the element in the periodic table.

# ELECTRONIC STRUCTURE OF ATOMS

WHAT HAPPENS WHEN SOMEONE switches on a neon light? Electrons in the neon atoms are excited to a higher energy by electricity. An electron can remain in a higher-energy state for only a very short time, and it emits light when it returns to a lower energy. The resulting glow is explained by one of the most revolutionary discoveries of the twentieth century—the *quantum theory,* which explains much of the behavior of electrons in atoms.

In this chapter we explore the quantum theory and its importance in chemistry. We begin by looking at the nature of light and how our description of light was changed by the quantum theory. We will explore some of the tools used in *quantum mechanics,* the "new" physics that had to be developed to describe atoms correctly. We will then use the quantum theory to describe the arrangements of electrons in atoms— what we call the **electronic structure** of atoms. The electronic structure of an atom refers to the number of electrons in the atom as well as their distribution around the nucleus and their energies. We will see that the quantum description of the electronic structure of atoms helps us to understand the arrangement of the elements in the periodic table—why, for example, helium and neon are both unreactive gases, whereas sodium and potassium are both soft, reactive metals.

▲ FIGURE 6.1 **Water waves.** The movement of a boat through the water forms waves that move away from the boat.

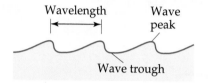

▲ FIGURE 6.2 **Water waves.** The *wavelength* is the distance between two adjacent peaks or two adjacent troughs.

GO FIGURE

If wave (a) has a wavelength of 1.0 m and a frequency of $3.0 \times 10^8$ cycles/s, what are the wavelength and frequency of wave (b)?

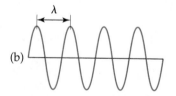

▲ FIGURE 6.3 **Electromagnetic waves.** Like water waves, electromagnetic radiation can be characterized by a wavelength. Notice that the shorter the wavelength, $\lambda$, the higher the frequency, $\nu$. The wavelength in (b) is half as long as that in (a), and the frequency of the wave in (b) is therefore twice as great as the frequency in (a).

# 6.1 | THE WAVE NATURE OF LIGHT

Much of our present understanding of the electronic structure of atoms has come from analysis of the light either emitted or absorbed by substances. To understand electronic structure, therefore, we must first learn about light. The light we see with our eyes, *visible light,* is one type of **electromagnetic radiation**. Because electromagnetic radiation carries energy through space, it is also known as *radiant energy.*

There are many types of electromagnetic radiation in addition to visible light. These different types—radio waves that carry music to our radios, infrared radiation (heat) from a glowing fireplace, X-rays—may seem very different from one another, but they all share certain fundamental characteristics.

All types of electromagnetic radiation move through a vacuum at $3.00 \times 10^8$ m/s, the *speed of light.* All have wavelike characteristics similar to those of waves that move through water. Water waves are the result of energy imparted to the water, perhaps by the dropping of a stone or the movement of a boat on the water surface (◄ **FIGURE 6.1**). This energy is expressed as the up-and-down movements of the water.

A cross section of a water wave (◄ **FIGURE 6.2**) shows that it is *periodic,* which means that the pattern of peaks and troughs repeats itself at regular intervals. The distance between two adjacent peaks (or between two adjacent troughs) is called the **wavelength**. The number of complete wavelengths, or *cycles,* that pass a given point each second is the **frequency** of the wave.

Just as with water waves, we can assign a frequency and wavelength to electromagnetic waves, as illustrated in ◄ **FIGURE 6.3**. These and all other wave characteristics of electromagnetic radiation are due to the periodic oscillations in the intensities of the electric and magnetic fields associated with the radiation.

The speed of water waves can vary depending on how they are created—for example, the waves produced by a speedboat travel faster than those produced by a rowboat. In contrast, all electromagnetic radiation moves at the same speed, $3.00 \times 10^8$ m/s, the speed of light. As a result, the wavelength and frequency of electromagnetic radiation are always related in a straightforward way. If the wavelength is long, fewer cycles of the wave pass a given point per second, and so the frequency is low. Conversely, for a wave to have a high frequency, it must have a short wavelength. This inverse relationship between the frequency and wavelength of electromagnetic radiation is expressed by the equation

$$c = \lambda\nu \qquad\qquad [6.1]$$

where $c$ is the speed of light, $\lambda$ (lambda) is wavelength, and $\nu$ (nu) is frequency.

Why do different types of electromagnetic radiation have different properties? Their differences are due to their different wavelengths. ► FIGURE 6.4 shows the various types of electromagnetic radiation arranged in order of increasing wavelength, a display called the *electromagnetic spectrum.* Notice that the wavelengths span an enormous range. The wavelengths of gamma rays are comparable to the diameters of atomic nuclei, whereas the wavelengths of radio waves can be longer than a football field. Notice also that visible light, which corresponds to wavelengths of about 400 to 750 nm ($4 \times 10^{-7}$ m to $7 \times 10^{-7}$ m), is an extremely small portion of the electromagnetic spectrum. The unit of length chosen to express wavelength depends on the type of radiation, as shown in ▼ TABLE 6.1.

| TABLE 6.1 • Common Wavelength Units for Electromagnetic Radiation | | | |
|---|---|---|---|
| **Unit** | **Symbol** | **Length (m)** | **Type of Radiation** |
| Angstrom | Å | $10^{-10}$ | X-ray |
| Nanometer | nm | $10^{-9}$ | Ultraviolet, visible |
| Micrometer | $\mu$m | $10^{-6}$ | Infrared |
| Millimeter | mm | $10^{-3}$ | Microwave |
| Centimeter | cm | $10^{-2}$ | Microwave |
| Meter | m | 1 | Television, radio |
| Kilometer | km | 1000 | Radio |

## GO FIGURE

**How do the wavelength and frequency of an X-ray compare with those of the red light from a neon sign?**

◀ **FIGURE 6.4 The electromagnetic spectrum.** Wavelengths in the spectrum range from very short gamma rays to very long radio waves.

Frequency is expressed in cycles per second, a unit also called a *hertz* (Hz). Because it is understood that cycles are involved, the units of frequency are normally given simply as "per second," which is denoted by $s^{-1}$ or /s. For example, a frequency of 820 kilohertz (kHz), a typical frequency for an AM radio station, could be written as 820 kHz, 820,000 Hz, 820,000 $s^{-1}$, or 820,000/s.

---

**SAMPLE EXERCISE 6.1** **Concepts of Wavelength and Frequency**

Two electromagnetic waves are represented in the margin. **(a)** Which wave has the higher frequency? **(b)** If one wave represents visible light and the other represents infrared radiation, which wave is which?

### SOLUTION

**(a)** The lower wave has a longer wavelength (greater distance between peaks). The longer the wavelength, the lower the frequency ($\nu = c/\lambda$). Thus, the lower wave has the lower frequency, and the upper wave has the higher frequency.

**(b)** The electromagnetic spectrum (Figure 6.4) indicates that infrared radiation has a longer wavelength than visible light. Thus, the lower wave would be the infrared radiation.

### PRACTICE EXERCISE

If one of the waves in the margin represents blue light and the other red light, which is which?

**Answer:** The expanded visible-light portion of Figure 6.4 tells you that red light has a longer wavelength than blue light. The lower wave has the longer wavelength (lower frequency) and would be the red light.

---

## A CLOSER LOOK

### THE SPEED OF LIGHT

How do we know that light has a finite speed and does not move infinitely fast?

During the late 1600s, the Danish astronomer Ole Rømer (1644–1710) measured the orbits of several of Jupiter's moons. These moons move much faster than our own—they have orbits of 1–7 days and are eclipsed by Jupiter's shadow at every revolution. Over many months, Rømer measured discrepancies of up to 10 minutes in the times of these orbits. He reasoned that the discrepancies occurred because Jupiter was farther from Earth at different times of the year. Thus, light from the Sun, which reflected off Jupiter and ultimately to his telescope, had farther to travel at different times of the year, implying that light travels at a finite speed. Rømer's data led to the first estimate of the speed of light, $3.5 \times 10^8$ m/s.

Since Rømer's time, increasingly sophisticated techniques have been used to measure the speed of light. For example, in 1927, A. A. Michelson (1852–1931) set up a rotating mirror at the top of Mount Wilson in California. The mirror bounced light to the top of Mount San Antonio, 22 miles away, where another mirror bounced the light back to Mount Wilson. Michelson was able to change the speed of the rotating mirror and measure small displacements in the position of the reflected spot. The value for the speed of light (in air) based on this experiment was $2.9980 \pm 0.0002 \times 10^8$ m/s. The main source of error was the distance between the mirrors, which was measured within a fifth of an inch in 22 miles.

By 1975, the measured value was even more precise, $2.99792458 \pm 0.00000004 \times 10^8$ m/s (in vacuum), the error being mostly due to the uncertainty in the length of the meter. In 1983, the meter was redefined based on the distance that light travels in vacuum in one second. As a result, the value for the speed of light became a fixed, exact quantity, $c = 2.99792458 \times 10^8$ m/s.

**SAMPLE EXERCISE 6.2** | Calculating Frequency from Wavelength

The yellow light given off by a sodium vapor lamp used for public lighting has a wavelength of 589 nm. What is the frequency of this radiation?

**SOLUTION**

**Analyze** We are given the wavelength, $\lambda$, of the radiation and asked to calculate its frequency, $\nu$.

**Plan** The relationship between the wavelength and the frequency is given by Equation 6.1. We can solve for $\nu$ and use the values of $\lambda$ and $c$ to obtain a numerical answer. (The speed of light, $c$, is a fundamental constant whose value is $3.00 \times 10^8$ m/s.)

**Solve** Solving Equation 6.1 for frequency gives $\nu = c/\lambda$. When we insert the values for $c$ and $\lambda$, we note that the units of length in these two quantities are different. We can convert the wavelength from nanometers to meters, so the units cancel:

$$\nu = \frac{c}{\lambda} = \left( \frac{3.00 \times 10^8 \text{ m/s}}{589 \text{ nm}} \right)\left( \frac{1 \text{ nm}}{10^{-9} \text{ m}} \right) = 5.09 \times 10^{14} \text{ s}^{-1}$$

**Check** The high frequency is reasonable because of the short wavelength. The units are proper because frequency has units of "per second," or $s^{-1}$.

**PRACTICE EXERCISE**

(a) A laser used in eye surgery to fuse detached retinas produces radiation with a wavelength of 640.0 nm. Calculate the frequency of this radiation. (b) An FM radio station broadcasts electromagnetic radiation at a frequency of 103.4 MHz (megahertz; 1 MHz $= 10^6$ $s^{-1}$). Calculate the wavelength of this radiation. The speed of light is $2.998 \times 10^8$ m/s to four significant digits.

**Answers:** (a) $4.688 \times 10^{14}$ $s^{-1}$, (b) 2.899 m

⚠ GIVE IT SOME THOUGHT

Our bodies are penetrated by X-rays but not by visible light. Is this because X-rays travel faster than visible light?

---

◀ GO FIGURE

**Which area in the photograph corresponds to the highest temperature?**

▲ **FIGURE 6.5 Color and temperature.** The color and intensity of the light emitted by a hot object, such as this pour of molten steel, depend on the temperature of the object.

# 6.2 | QUANTIZED ENERGY AND PHOTONS

Although the wave model of light explains many aspects of its behavior, this model cannot explain several phenomena. Three of these are particularly pertinent to our understanding of how electromagnetic radiation and atoms interact: (1) the emission of light from hot objects (referred to as *blackbody radiation* because the objects studied appear black before heating), (2) the emission of electrons from metal surfaces on which light shines (the *photoelectric effect*), and (3) the emission of light from electronically excited gas atoms (*emission spectra*). We examine the first two phenomena here and the third in Section 6.3.

## Hot Objects and the Quantization of Energy

When solids are heated, they emit radiation, as seen in the red glow of an electric stove burner or the bright white light of a tungsten lightbulb. The wavelength distribution of the radiation depends on temperature; a red-hot object, for instance, is cooler than a yellowish or white-hot one (◀ **FIGURE 6.5**). During the late 1800s, a number of physicists studied this phenomenon, trying to understand the relationship between the temperature and the intensity and wavelength of the emitted radiation. The prevailing laws of physics could not account for the observations.

In 1900 a German physicist named Max Planck (1858–1947) solved the problem by assuming that energy can be either released or absorbed by atoms only in discrete "chunks" of some minimum size. Planck gave the name **quantum** (meaning "fixed amount") to the smallest quantity of energy that can be emitted or absorbed as electromagnetic radiation. He proposed that the energy, $E$, of a single quantum equals a constant times the frequency of the radiation:

$$E = h\nu \qquad \text{[6.2]}$$

Potential energy of person walking up steps increases in stepwise, quantized manner

Potential energy of person walking up ramp increases in uniform, continuous manner

◀ **FIGURE 6.6    Quantized versus continuous change in energy.**

The constant $h$ is called **Planck's constant** and has a value of $6.626 \times 10^{-34}$ joule-second (J-s).

According to Planck's theory, matter can emit and absorb energy only in whole-number multiples of $h\nu$, such as $h\nu$, $2h\nu$, $3h\nu$, and so forth. If the quantity of energy emitted by an atom is $3h\nu$, for example, we say that three quanta of energy have been emitted (*quanta* being the plural of *quantum*). Because the energy can be released only in specific amounts, we say that the allowed energies are *quantized*—their values are restricted to certain quantities. Planck's revolutionary proposal that energy is quantized was proved correct, and he was awarded the 1918 Nobel Prize in Physics for his work on the quantum theory.

If the notion of quantized energies seems strange, it might be helpful to draw an analogy by comparing a ramp and a staircase (▲ **FIGURE 6.6**). As you walk up a ramp, your potential energy increases in a uniform, continuous manner. When you climb a staircase, you can step only *on* individual stairs, not *between* them, so that your potential energy is restricted to certain values and is therefore quantized.

If Planck's quantum theory is correct, why are its effects not obvious in our daily lives? Why do energy changes seem continuous rather than quantized, or "jagged"? Notice that Planck's constant is an extremely small number. Thus, a quantum of energy, $h\nu$, is an extremely small amount. Planck's rules regarding the gain or loss of energy are always the same, whether we are concerned with objects on the scale of our ordinary experience or with microscopic objects. With everyday objects, however, the gain or loss of a single quantum of energy is so small that it goes completely unnoticed. In contrast, when dealing with matter at the atomic level, the impact of quantized energies is far more significant.

 **GIVE IT SOME THOUGHT**

Calculate the energy (to one significant figure) of one quantum of electromagnetic radiation whose frequency is $5 \times 10^{-3}$ s$^{-1}$. Can this radiation produce a burst of energy $E = 5 \times 10^{-36}$ J? Why or why not?

## The Photoelectric Effect and Photons

A few years after Planck presented his quantum theory, scientists began to see its applicability to many experimental observations. In 1905, Albert Einstein (1879–1955) used Planck's theory to explain the **photoelectric effect** (▶ **FIGURE 6.7**). Light shining on a clean metal surface causes the surface to emit electrons. A minimum frequency of light, different for different metals, is required for the emission of electrons. For example, light with a frequency of $4.60 \times 10^{14}$ s$^{-1}$ or greater causes cesium metal to emit electrons, but light of lower frequency has no effect.

To explain the photoelectric effect, Einstein assumed that the radiant energy striking the metal surface behaves like a stream of tiny energy packets. Each packet, which is like a "particle" of energy, is called a **photon**. Extending Planck's quantum theory,

**GO FIGURE**

Why is it necessary to carry out this experiment in an evacuated chamber?

▲ **FIGURE 6.7    The photoelectric effect.**

Einstein deduced that each photon must have an energy equal to Planck's constant times the frequency of the light:

$$\text{Energy of photon} = E = h\nu \qquad [6.3]$$

Thus, radiant energy itself is quantized.

Under the right conditions, photons striking a metal surface can transfer their energy to electrons in the metal. A certain amount of energy—called the *work function*—is required for the electrons to overcome the attractive forces holding them in the metal. If the photons striking the metal have less energy than the work function, the electrons do not acquire sufficient energy to escape from the metal, even if the light beam is intense. If the photons have energy greater than the work function of the particular metal, however, electrons are emitted. The intensity (brightness) of the light is related to the number of photons striking the surface per unit time but not to the energy of each photon. Einstein won the Nobel Prize in Physics in 1921 for his explanation of the photoelectric effect.

To better understand what a photon is, imagine you have a light source that produces radiation of a single wavelength. Further suppose that you could switch the light on and off faster and faster to provide ever-smaller bursts of energy. Einstein's photon theory tells us that you would eventually come to the smallest energy burst, given by $E = h\nu$. This smallest burst consists of a single photon of light.

---

**SAMPLE EXERCISE 6.3** | **Energy of a Photon**

Calculate the energy of one photon of yellow light that has a wavelength of 589 nm.

**SOLUTION**

**Analyze** Our task is to calculate the energy, $E$, of a photon, given $\lambda = 589$ nm.

**Plan** We can use Equation 6.1 to convert the wavelength to frequency: $\qquad \nu = c/\lambda$

We can then use Equation 6.3 to calculate energy: $\qquad E = h\nu$

**Solve** The frequency, $\nu$, is calculated from the given wavelength, as shown in Sample Exercise 6.2:

$$\nu = c/\lambda = 5.09 \times 10^{14}\ \text{s}^{-1}$$

The value of Planck's constant, $h$, is given both in the text and in the table of physical constants on the inside back cover of the text, and so we can easily calculate $E$:

$$E = (6.626 \times 10^{-34}\ \text{J-s})(5.09 \times 10^{14}\ \text{s}^{-1}) = 3.37 \times 10^{-19}\ \text{J}$$

**Comment** If one photon of radiant energy supplies $3.37 \times 10^{-19}$ J, then one mole of these photons will supply

$$(6.02 \times 10^{23}\ \text{photons/mol})(3.37 \times 10^{-19}\ \text{J/photon})$$
$$= 2.03 \times 10^{5}\ \text{J/mol}$$

**PRACTICE EXERCISE**

(a) A laser emits light that has a frequency of $4.69 \times 10^{14}\ \text{s}^{-1}$. What is the energy of one photon of this radiation? (b) If the laser emits a pulse containing $5.0 \times 10^{17}$ photons of this radiation, what is the total energy of that pulse? (c) If the laser emits $1.3 \times 10^{-2}$ J of energy during a pulse, how many photons are emitted?

**Answers:** (a) $3.11 \times 10^{-19}$ J, (b) 0.16 J, (c) $4.2 \times 10^{16}$ photons

---

The idea that the energy of light depends on its frequency helps us understand the diverse effects of different kinds of electromagnetic radiation. For example, because of the high frequency (short wavelength) of X-rays (Figure 6.4), X-ray photons cause tissue damage and even cancer. Thus, signs are normally posted around X-ray equipment warning us of high-energy radiation.

Although Einstein's theory of light as a stream of photons rather than a wave explains the photoelectric effect and a great many other observations, it also poses a dilemma. Is light a wave, or is it particle-like? The only way to resolve this dilemma is to adopt what might seem to be a bizarre position: We must consider that light possesses both wave-like and particle-like characteristics and, depending on the situation, will behave more like waves or more like particles. We will soon see that this dual nature of light is also a characteristic trait of matter.

> ◢ **GIVE IT SOME THOUGHT**
> Which has more energy, a photon of infrared light or a photon of ultraviolet light?

# 6.3 | LINE SPECTRA AND THE BOHR MODEL

The work of Planck and Einstein paved the way for understanding how electrons are arranged in atoms. In 1913, the Danish physicist Niels Bohr (▶ FIGURE 6.8) offered a theoretical explanation of *line spectra*, another phenomenon that had puzzled scientists during the nineteenth century.

## Line Spectra

A particular source of radiant energy may emit a single wavelength, as in the light from a laser. Radiation composed of a single wavelength is *monochromatic*. However, most common radiation sources, including lightbulbs and stars, produce radiation containing many different wavelengths and is *polychromatic*. A **spectrum** is produced when radiation from such sources is separated into its component wavelengths, as shown in ▶ FIGURE 6.9. The resulting spectrum consists of a continuous range of colors—violet merges into indigo, indigo into blue, and so forth, with no blank spots. This rainbow of colors, containing light of all wavelengths, is called a **continuous spectrum**. The most familiar example of a continuous spectrum is the rainbow produced when raindrops or mist acts as a prism for sunlight.

Not all radiation sources produce a continuous spectrum. When a high voltage is applied to tubes that contain different gases under reduced pressure, the gases emit different colors of light (▶ FIGURE 6.10). The light emitted by neon gas is the familiar red-orange glow of many "neon" lights, whereas sodium vapor emits the yellow light characteristic of some modern streetlights. When light coming from such tubes is passed through a prism, only a few wavelengths are present in the resultant spectra (▼ FIGURE 6.11). Each colored line in such spectra represents light of one wavelength. A spectrum containing radiation of only specific wavelengths is called a **line spectrum**.

When scientists first detected the line spectrum of hydrogen in the mid-1800s, they were fascinated by its simplicity. At that time, only four lines at wavelengths of 410 nm (violet), 434 nm (blue), 486 nm (blue-green), and 656 nm (red) were observed (Figure 6.11). In 1885, a Swiss schoolteacher named Johann Balmer showed that the wavelengths of these four lines fit an intriguingly simple formula that relates the wavelengths to integers. Later, additional lines were found in the ultraviolet and infrared regions of hydrogen's line spectrum. Soon Balmer's equation was extended to a more general one, called the *Rydberg equation,* which allows us to calculate the wavelengths of all the spectral lines of hydrogen:

$$\frac{1}{\lambda} = (R_H)\left(\frac{1}{n_1^2} - \frac{1}{n_2^2}\right) \qquad [6.4]$$

In this formula $\lambda$ is the wavelength of a spectral line, $R_H$ is the *Rydberg constant* $(1.096776 \times 10^7 \text{ m}^{-1})$, and $n_1$ and $n_2$ are positive integers, with $n_2$ being larger

▲ FIGURE 6.8 **Quantum giants.** Niels Bohr (right) with Albert Einstein. Bohr (1885–1962) made major contributions to the quantum theory and was awarded the Nobel Prize in Physics in 1922.

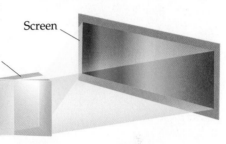

▲ FIGURE 6.9 **Creating a spectrum.** A continuous visible spectrum is produced when a narrow beam of white light is passed through a prism. The white light could be sunlight or light from an incandescent lamp.

Hydrogen (H)          Neon (Ne)

▲ FIGURE 6.10 **Atomic emission of hydrogen and neon.** Different gases emit light of different characteristic colors when an electric current is passed through them.

H

400    450    500    550    600    650    700 nm

Ne

400    450    500    550    600    650    700 nm

▲ FIGURE 6.11 **Line spectra of hydrogen and neon.**

than $n_1$. How could the remarkable simplicity of this equation be explained? It took nearly 30 more years to answer this question.

## Bohr's Model

To explain the line spectrum of hydrogen, Bohr assumed that electrons in hydrogen atoms move in circular orbits around the nucleus, but this assumption posed a problem. According to classical physics, a charged particle (such as an electron) moving in a circular path should continuously lose energy. As an electron loses energy, therefore, it should spiral into the positively charged nucleus. This behavior, however, does not happen—hydrogen atoms are stable. So how can we explain this apparent violation of the laws of physics? Bohr approached this problem in much the same way that Planck had approached the problem of the nature of the radiation emitted by hot objects: He assumed that the prevailing laws of physics were inadequate to describe all aspects of atoms. Furthermore, he adopted Planck's idea that energies are quantized.

Bohr based his model on three postulates:

1. Only orbits of certain radii, corresponding to certain specific energies, are permitted for the electron in a hydrogen atom.
2. An electron in a permitted orbit is in an "allowed" energy state. An electron in an allowed energy state does not radiate energy and, therefore, does not spiral into the nucleus.
3. Energy is emitted or absorbed by the electron only as the electron changes from one allowed energy state to another. This energy is emitted or absorbed as a photon that has energy $E = h\nu$.

### GIVE IT SOME THOUGHT

Before reading further about Bohr's model, speculate as to how it explains the fact that hydrogen gas emits a line spectrum (Figure 6.11) rather than a continuous spectrum.

## The Energy States of the Hydrogen Atom

Starting with his three postulates and using classical equations for motion and for interacting electrical charges, Bohr calculated the energies corresponding to the allowed orbits for the electron in the hydrogen atom. Ultimately, the calculated energies fit the formula

$$E = (-hcR_H)\left(\frac{1}{n^2}\right) = (-2.18 \times 10^{-18}\ \text{J})\left(\frac{1}{n^2}\right) \quad [6.5]$$

where $h$, $c$, and $R_H$ are Planck's constant, the speed of light, and the Rydberg constant, respectively. The integer $n$, which can have whole-number values of $1, 2, 3, \ldots\infty$, is called the *principal quantum number*. Each orbit corresponds to a different value of $n$, and the radius of the orbit gets larger as $n$ increases. Thus, the first allowed orbit (the one closest to the nucleus) has $n = 1$, the next allowed orbit (the one second closest to the nucleus) has $n = 2$, and so forth. The electron in the hydrogen atom can be in any allowed orbit, and Equation 6.5 tells us the energy the electron has in each allowed orbit.

Note that the energies of the electron given by Equation 6.5 are negative for all values of $n$. The lower (more negative) the energy is, the more stable the atom is. The energy is lowest (most negative) for $n = 1$. As $n$ gets larger, the energy becomes less negative and therefore increases. We can liken the situation to a ladder in which the rungs are numbered from the bottom. The higher one climbs (the greater the value of $n$), the higher the energy. The lowest-energy state ($n = 1$, analogous to the bottom rung) is called the **ground state** of the atom. When the electron is in a higher-energy state ($n = 2$ or higher), the atom is said to be in an **excited state**. ◀ FIGURE 6.12 shows the energy of the electron in a hydrogen atom for several values of $n$.

### GO FIGURE

If the transition of an electron from the $n = 3$ state to the $n = 2$ state results in emission of visible light, is the transition from the $n = 2$ state to the $n = 1$ state more likely to result in the emission of infrared or ultraviolet radiation?

▲ FIGURE 6.12 **Energy states in the hydrogen atom.** Only states for $n = 1$ through $n = 4$ and $n = \infty$ are shown. Energy is released or absorbed when an electron moves from one energy state to another.

What happens to the orbit radius and the energy as $n$ becomes infinitely large? The radius increases as $n^2$, so when $n = \infty$ the electron is completely separated from the nucleus, and the energy of the electron is zero:

$$E = (-2.18 \times 10^{-18}\,\text{J})\left(\frac{1}{\infty^2}\right) = 0$$

The state in which the electron is removed from the nucleus is called the reference, or zero-energy, state of the hydrogen atom.

In his third postulate, Bohr assumed that the electron can "jump" from one allowed orbit to another by either absorbing or emitting photons whose radiant energy corresponds exactly to the energy difference between the two orbits. The electron must absorb energy in order to move to a higher-energy state (higher value of $n$). Conversely, radiant energy is emitted when the electron jumps to a lower-energy state (lower value of $n$).

If the electron jumps from an initial state of energy $E_i$ to a final state of energy $E_f$, the change in energy is

$$\Delta E = E_f - E_i = E_{\text{photon}} = h\nu \qquad [6.6]$$

Bohr's model of the hydrogen atom states, therefore, that only the specific frequencies of light that satisfy Equation 6.6 can be absorbed or emitted by the atom.

Substituting the energy expression in Equation 6.5 into Equation 6.6 and recalling that $\nu = c/\lambda$, we have

$$\Delta E = h\nu = \frac{hc}{\lambda} = (-2.18 \times 10^{-18}\,\text{J})\left(\frac{1}{n_f^2} - \frac{1}{n_i^2}\right) \qquad [6.7]$$

where $n_i$ and $n_f$ are the principal quantum numbers of the initial and final states of the atom, respectively. If $n_f$ is smaller than $n_i$, the electron moves closer to the nucleus and $\Delta E$ is a negative number, indicating that the atom releases energy. For example, if the electron moves from $n_i = 3$ to $n_f = 1$, we have

$$\Delta E = (-2.18 \times 10^{-18}\,\text{J})\left(\frac{1}{1^2} - \frac{1}{3^2}\right) = (-2.18 \times 10^{-18}\,\text{J})\left(\frac{8}{9}\right) = -1.94 \times 10^{-18}\,\text{J}$$

Knowing the energy of the emitted photon, we can calculate either its frequency or its wavelength. For the wavelength, we have

$$\lambda = \frac{c}{\nu} = \frac{hc}{\Delta E} = \frac{(6.626 \times 10^{-34}\,\text{J-s})(3.00 \times 10^8\,\text{m/s})}{1.94 \times 10^{-18}\,\text{J}} = 1.02 \times 10^{-7}\,\text{m}$$

We have not included the negative sign of the energy in this calculation because wavelength and frequency are always reported as positive quantities. The direction of energy flow is indicated by saying that a photon of wavelength $1.02 \times 10^{-7}$ m has been *emitted*.

If we solve Equation 6.7 for $1/\lambda$ and replace $(-2.18 \times 10^{-18}\,\text{J})$ by its equivalent, $hcR_H$ from Equation 6.5, we find that Equation 6.7 derived from Bohr's theory corresponds to the Rydberg equation, Equation 6.4, which was obtained using experimental data:

$$\frac{1}{\lambda} = \frac{-hcR_H}{hc}\left(\frac{1}{n_f^2} - \frac{1}{n_i^2}\right) = R_H\left(\frac{1}{n_i^2} - \frac{1}{n_f^2}\right)$$

Thus, the existence of discrete spectral lines can be attributed to the quantized jumps of electrons between energy levels.

## ▲ GIVE IT SOME THOUGHT

As the electron in a hydrogen atom jumps from the $n = 3$ orbit to the $n = 7$ orbit, does it absorb energy or emit energy?

**SAMPLE EXERCISE 6.4** | Electronic Transitions in the Hydrogen Atom

Using Figure 6.12, predict which of these electronic transitions produces the spectral line having the longest wavelength: $n = 2$ to $n = 1$, $n = 3$ to $n = 2$, or $n = 4$ to $n = 3$.

**SOLUTION**

The wavelength increases as frequency decreases ($\lambda = c/\nu$). Hence, the longest wavelength will be associated with the lowest frequency. According to Planck's equation, $E = h\nu$, the lowest frequency is associated with the lowest energy. In Figure 6.12 the energy levels (horizontal lines) that are closest together represents the smallest energy change. Thus, the $n = 4$ to $n = 3$ transition produces the longest wavelength (lowest frequency) line.

**PRACTICE EXERCISE**

Indicate whether each of the following electronic transitions emits energy or requires the absorption of energy: (a) $n = 3$ to $n = 1$; (b) $n = 2$ to $n = 4$.

*Answers:* (a) emits energy, (b) requires absorption of energy

## Limitations of the Bohr Model

Although the Bohr model explains the line spectrum of the hydrogen atom, it cannot explain the spectra of other atoms, except in a crude way. Bohr also avoided the problem of why the negatively charged electron would not just fall into the positively charged nucleus by simply assuming it would not happen. Furthermore, there is a problem with describing an electron merely as a small particle circling the nucleus. As we will see in Section 6.4, the electron exhibits wavelike properties, a fact that any acceptable model of electronic structure must accommodate. As it turns out, the Bohr model was only an important step along the way toward the development of a more comprehensive model. What is most significant about Bohr's model is that it introduces two important ideas that are also incorporated into our current model:

1. *Electrons exist only in certain discrete energy levels, which are described by quantum numbers.*

2. *Energy is involved in the transition of an electron from one level to another.*

We will now start to develop the successor to the Bohr model, which requires that we take a closer look at the behavior of matter.

## 6.4 | THE WAVE BEHAVIOR OF MATTER

In the years following the development of Bohr's model for the hydrogen atom, the dual nature of radiant energy became a familiar concept. Depending on the experimental circumstances, radiation appears to have either a wave-like or a particle-like (photon) character. Louis de Broglie (1892–1987), who was working on his Ph.D. thesis in physics at the Sorbonne in Paris, boldly extended this idea. If radiant energy could, under appropriate conditions, behave as though it were a stream of particles (photons), could matter, under appropriate conditions, possibly show the properties of a wave?

De Broglie suggested that an electron moving about the nucleus of an atom behaves like a wave and therefore has a wavelength. He proposed that the wavelength of the electron, or of any other particle, depends on its mass, $m$, and on its velocity, $v$:

$$\lambda = \frac{h}{mv} \qquad [6.8]$$

(where $h$ is Planck's constant). The quantity $mv$ for any object is called its **momentum**. De Broglie used the term **matter waves** to describe the wave characteristics of material particles.

Because de Broglie's hypothesis is applicable to all matter, any object of mass $m$ and velocity $v$ would give rise to a characteristic matter wave. However, Equation 6.8 indicates that the wavelength associated with an object of ordinary size, such as a golf ball, is so tiny as to be completely unobservable. This is not so for an electron because its mass is so small, as we see in Sample Exercise 6.5.

**SAMPLE EXERCISE 6.5**   **Matter Waves**

What is the wavelength of an electron moving with a speed of $5.97 \times 10^6$ m/s? The mass of the electron is $9.11 \times 10^{-31}$ kg.

**SOLUTION**

**Analyze** We are given the mass, $m$, and velocity, $v$, of the electron, and we must calculate its de Broglie wavelength, $\lambda$.

**Plan** The wavelength of a moving particle is given by Equation 6.8, so $\lambda$ is calculated by inserting the known quantities $h$, $m$, and $v$. In doing so, however, we must pay attention to units.

**Solve** Using the value of Planck's constant,   $h = 6.626 \times 10^{-34}$ J-s

we have the following:

$$\lambda = \frac{h}{mv}$$

$$= \frac{(6.626 \times 10^{-34} \text{ J-s})}{(9.11 \times 10^{-31} \text{ kg})(5.97 \times 10^6 \text{ m/s})}\left(\frac{1 \text{ kg-m}^2/\text{s}^2}{1 \text{ J}}\right)$$

$$= 1.22 \times 10^{-10} \text{ m} = 0.122 \text{ nm} = 1.22 \text{ Å}$$

**Comment** By comparing this value with the wavelengths of electromagnetic radiation shown in Figure 6.4, we see that the wavelength of this electron is about the same as that of X-rays.

**PRACTICE EXERCISE**

Calculate the velocity of a neutron whose de Broglie wavelength is 500 pm. The mass of a neutron is given in the table inside the back cover of the text.

**Answer:** $7.92 \times 10^2$ m/s

A few years after de Broglie published his theory, the wave properties of the electron were demonstrated experimentally. When X-rays pass through a crystal, an interference pattern results that is characteristic of the wavelike properties of electromagnetic radiation. This phenomenon is called X-ray *diffraction*. As electrons pass through a crystal, they are similarly diffracted. Thus, a stream of moving electrons exhibits the same kinds of wave behavior as X-rays and all other types of electromagnetic radiation.

The technique of electron diffraction has been highly developed. In the electron microscope, for instance, the wave characteristics of electrons are used to obtain images at the atomic scale. This microscope is an important tool for studying surface phenomena at very high magnifications (▶ **FIGURE 6.13**). Electron microscopes can magnify objects by 3,000,000 times (×), far more than can be done with visible light (1000×), because the wavelength of the electrons is so much smaller than the wavelengths of visible light.

▲ **FIGURE 6.13   Electrons as waves.** The white dots in this transmission electron micrograph indicate the tops of columns of atoms.

⚠ **GIVE IT SOME THOUGHT**

A baseball pitcher throws a fastball that moves at 95 miles per hour. Does that moving baseball generate matter waves? If so, can we observe them?

## The Uncertainty Principle

The discovery of the wave properties of matter raised some new and interesting questions. Consider, for example, a ball rolling down a ramp. Using the equations of classical physics, we can calculate, with great accuracy, the ball's position, direction of motion, and speed at any instant. Can we do the same for an electron, which exhibits wave properties? A wave extends in space and its location is not precisely defined. We might therefore anticipate that it is impossible to determine exactly where an electron is located at a specific instant.

The German physicist Werner Heisenberg (▶ **FIGURE 6.14**) proposed that the dual nature of matter places a fundamental limitation on how precisely we can know both the location and

◀ **FIGURE 6.14   Werner Heisenberg (1901–1976).** During his postdoctoral assistantship with Niels Bohr, Heisenberg formulated his famous uncertainty principle. At 32 he was one of the youngest scientists to receive a Nobel Prize.

the momentum of an object at a given instant. The limitation becomes important only when we deal with matter at the subatomic level (that is, with masses as small as that of an electron). Heisenberg's principle is called the **uncertainty principle**. When applied to the electrons in an atom, this principle states that it is impossible for us to know simultaneously both the exact momentum of the electron and its exact location in space.

Heisenberg mathematically related the uncertainty in position, $\Delta x$, and the uncertainty in momentum, $\Delta(mv)$, to a quantity involving Planck's constant:

$$\Delta x \cdot \Delta(mv) \geq \frac{h}{4\pi} \qquad [6.9]$$

A brief calculation illustrates the dramatic implications of the uncertainty principle. The electron has a mass of $9.11 \times 10^{-31}$ kg and moves at an average speed of about $5 \times 10^6$ m/s in a hydrogen atom. Let's assume that we know the speed to an uncertainty of 1% [that is, an uncertainty of $(0.01)(5 \times 10^6 \text{ m/s}) = 5 \times 10^4$ m/s] and that this is the only important source of uncertainty in the momentum, so that $\Delta(mv) = m\,\Delta v$. We can use Equation 6.9 to calculate the uncertainty in the position of the electron:

$$\Delta x \geq \frac{h}{4\pi m \Delta v} = \left( \frac{6.626 \times 10^{-34} \text{ J-s}}{4\pi(9.11 \times 10^{-31} \text{ kg})(5 \times 10^4 \text{ m/s})} \right) = 1 \times 10^{-9} \text{ m}$$

Because the diameter of a hydrogen atom is about $1 \times 10^{-10}$ m, the uncertainty in the position of the electron in the atom is an order of magnitude greater than the size of the atom. Thus, we have essentially no idea where the electron is located in the atom. On the other hand, if we were to repeat the calculation with an object of ordinary mass, such as a tennis ball, the uncertainty would be so small that it would be inconsequential. In that case, $m$ is large and $\Delta x$ is out of the realm of measurement and therefore of no practical consequence.

De Broglie's hypothesis and Heisenberg's uncertainty principle set the stage for a new and more broadly applicable theory of atomic structure. In this approach, any attempt to define precisely the instantaneous location and momentum of the electron is abandoned. The wave nature of the electron is recognized, and its behavior is described in terms appropriate to waves. The result is a model that precisely describes the energy of the electron while describing its location not precisely but rather in terms of probabilities.

## A CLOSER LOOK

### MEASUREMENT AND THE UNCERTAINTY PRINCIPLE

Whenever any measurement is made, some uncertainty exists. Our experience with objects of ordinary dimensions, such as balls or trains or laboratory equipment, indicates that using more precise instruments can decrease the uncertainty of a measurement. In fact, we might expect that the uncertainty in a measurement can be made indefinitely small. However, the uncertainty principle states that there is an actual limit to the accuracy of measurements. This limit is not a restriction on how well instruments can be made; rather, it is inherent in nature. This limit has no practical consequences when dealing with ordinary-sized objects, but its implications are enormous when dealing with subatomic particles, such as electrons.

To measure an object, we must disturb it, at least a little, with our measuring device. Imagine using a flashlight to locate a large rubber ball in a dark room. You see the ball when the light from the flashlight bounces off the ball and strikes your eyes. When a beam of photons strikes an object of this size, it does not alter its position or momentum to any practical extent. Imagine, however, that you wish to locate an electron by similarly bouncing light off it into some detector. Objects can be located to an accuracy no greater than the wavelength of the radiation used. Thus, if we want an accurate position measurement for an electron, we must use a short wavelength. This means that photons of high energy must be employed. The more energy the photons have, the more momentum they impart to the electron when they strike it, which changes the electron's motion in an unpredictable way. The attempt to measure accurately the electron's position introduces considerable uncertainty in its momentum; the act of measuring the electron's position at one moment makes our knowledge of its future position inaccurate.

Suppose, then, that we use photons of longer wavelength. Because these photons have lower energy, the momentum of the electron is not so appreciably changed during measurement, but its position will be correspondingly less accurately known. This is the essence of the uncertainty principle: *There is an uncertainty in simultaneously knowing either the position or the momentum of the electron that cannot be reduced beyond a certain minimum level.* The more accurately one is known, the less accurately the other is known. Although we can never know the exact position and momentum of the electron, we can talk about the probability of its being at certain locations in space. In Section 6.5 we introduce a model of the atom that provides the probability of finding electrons of specific energies at certain positions in atoms.

*RELATED EXERCISES:* 6.47 and 6.48

▲ GIVE IT SOME THOUGHT

What is the principal reason we must consider the uncertainty principle when discussing electrons and other subatomic particles but not when discussing our macroscopic world?

# 6.5 | QUANTUM MECHANICS AND ATOMIC ORBITALS

In 1926 the Austrian physicist Erwin Schrödinger (1887–1961) proposed an equation, now known as Schrödinger's wave equation, that incorporates both the wave-like behavior of the electron and its particle-like behavior. His work opened a new approach to dealing with subatomic particles, an approach known as *quantum mechanics* or *wave mechanics*. The application of Schrödinger's equation requires advanced calculus, and so we will not be concerned with its details. We will, however, qualitatively consider the results Schrödinger obtained because they give us a powerful new way to view electronic structure. Let's begin by examining the electronic structure of the simplest atom, hydrogen.

Schrödinger treated the electron in a hydrogen atom like the wave on a plucked guitar string (▼ FIGURE 6.15). Because such waves do not travel in space, they are called *standing waves*. Just as the plucked guitar string produces a standing wave that has a fundamental frequency and higher overtones (harmonics), the electron exhibits a lowest-energy standing wave and higher-energy ones. Furthermore, just as the overtones of the guitar string have *nodes,* points where the amplitude of the wave is zero, so do the waves characteristic of the electron.

Solving Schrödinger's equation for the hydrogen atom leads to a series of mathematical functions called **wave functions** that describe the electron in an atom. These wave functions are usually represented by the symbol $\psi$ (lowercase Greek letter *psi*). Although the wave function has no direct physical meaning, the square of the wave function, $\psi^2$, provides information about the electron's location when it is in an allowed energy state.

For the hydrogen atom, the allowed energies are the same as those predicted by the Bohr model. However, the Bohr model assumes that the electron is in a circular orbit of some particular radius about the nucleus. In the quantum mechanical model, the electron's location cannot be described so simply.

According to the uncertainty principle, if we know the momentum of the electron with high accuracy, our simultaneous knowledge of its location is very uncertain. Thus, we cannot hope to specify the exact location of an individual electron around the

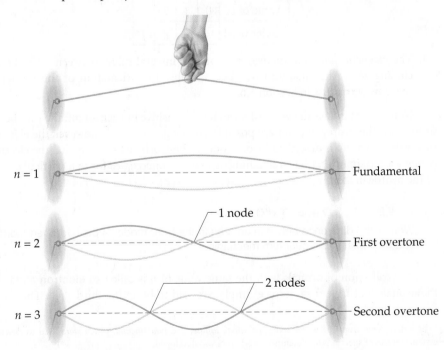

$n = 1$        Fundamental

1 node

$n = 2$        First overtone

2 nodes

$n = 3$        Second overtone

◀ **FIGURE 6.15  Standing waves in a vibrating string.**

**Where in the figure is the region of highest electron density?**

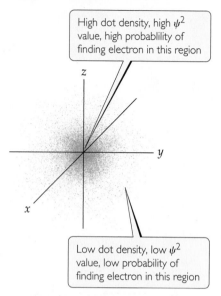

High dot density, high $\psi^2$ value, high probability of finding electron in this region

Low dot density, low $\psi^2$ value, low probability of finding electron in this region

▲ **FIGURE 6.16 Electron-density distribution.** This rendering represents the probability, $\psi^2$, of finding the electron in a hydrogen atom in its ground state. The origin of the coordinate system is at the nucleus.

nucleus. Rather, we must be content with a kind of statistical knowledge. We therefore speak of the *probability* that the electron will be in a certain region of space at a given instant. As it turns out, the square of the wave function, $\psi^2$, at a given point in space represents the probability that the electron will be found at that location. For this reason, $\psi^2$ is called either the **probability density** or the **electron density**.

One way of representing the probability of finding the electron in various regions of an atom is shown in ◀ **FIGURE 6.16**, where the density of the dots represents the probability of finding the electron. The regions with a high density of dots correspond to relatively large values for $\psi^2$ and are therefore regions where there is a high probability of finding the electron. Based on this representation, we often describe atoms as consisting of a nucleus surrounded by an electron cloud.

## Orbitals and Quantum Numbers

The solution to Schrödinger's equation for the hydrogen atom yields a set of wave functions called **orbitals**. Each orbital has a characteristic shape and energy. For example, the lowest-energy orbital in the hydrogen atom has the spherical shape illustrated in Figure 6.16 and an energy of $-2.18 \times 10^{-18}$ J. Note that an *orbital* (quantum mechanical model, which describes electrons in terms of probabilities, visualized as "electron clouds") is not the same as an *orbit* (Bohr model, which visualizes the electron moving in a physical orbit, like a planet around a star). The quantum mechanical model does not refer to orbits because the motion of the electron in an atom cannot be precisely determined (Heisenberg uncertainty principle).

The Bohr model introduced a single quantum number, $n$, to describe an orbit. The quantum mechanical model uses three quantum numbers, $n$, $l$, and $m_l$, which result naturally from the mathematics used, to describe an orbital.

1. The *principal quantum number, n,* can have positive integral values 1, 2, 3, . . . . As $n$ increases, the orbital becomes larger, and the electron spends more time farther from the nucleus. An increase in $n$ also means that the electron has a higher energy and is therefore less tightly bound to the nucleus. For the hydrogen atom, $E_n = -(2.18 \times 10^{-18} \text{ J})(1/n^2)$, as in the Bohr model.

2. The second quantum number—the *angular momentum quantum number, l*—can have integral values from 0 to $(n - 1)$ for each value of $n$. This quantum number defines the shape of the orbital. The value of $l$ for a particular orbital is generally designated by the letters $s$, $p$, $d$, and $f$,* corresponding to $l$ values of 0, 1, 2, and 3:

| Value of $l$ | 0 | 1 | 2 | 3 |
|---|---|---|---|---|
| Letter used | $s$ | $p$ | $d$ | $f$ |

3. The *magnetic quantum number, $m_l$,* can have integral values between $-l$ and $l$, including zero. This quantum number describes the orientation of the orbital in space, as we discuss in Section 6.6.

Notice that because the value of $n$ can be any positive integer, an infinite number of orbitals for the hydrogen atom are possible. At any given instant, however, the electron in a hydrogen atom is described by only one of these orbitals—we say that the electron *occupies* a certain orbital. The remaining orbitals are *unoccupied* for that particular state of the hydrogen atom.

◢ GIVE IT SOME THOUGHT

What is the difference between an *orbit* in the Bohr model of the hydrogen atom and an *orbital* in the quantum mechanical model?

The collection of orbitals with the same value of $n$ is called an **electron shell**. All the orbitals that have $n = 3$, for example, are said to be in the third shell. The set of

---

*The letters come from the words *sharp, principal, diffuse,* and *fundamental,* which were used to describe certain features of spectra before quantum mechanics was developed.

**TABLE 6.2** • Relationship among Values of *n*, *l*, and *m*<sub>*l*</sub> through *n* = 4

| *n* | Possible Values of *l* | Subshell Designation | Possible Values of $m_l$ | Number of Orbitals in Subshell | Total Number of Orbitals in Shell |
|---|---|---|---|---|---|
| 1 | 0 | 1*s* | 0 | 1 | 1 |
| 2 | 0 | 2*s* | 0 | 1 | |
| | 1 | 2*p* | 1, 0, −1 | 3 | 4 |
| 3 | 0 | 3*s* | 0 | 1 | |
| | 1 | 3*p* | 1, 0, −1 | 3 | |
| | 2 | 3*d* | 2, 1, 0, −1, −2 | 5 | 9 |
| 4 | 0 | 4*s* | 0 | 1 | |
| | 1 | 4*p* | 1, 0, −1 | 3 | |
| | 2 | 4*d* | 2, 1, 0, −1, −2 | 5 | |
| | 3 | 4*f* | 3, 2, 1, 0, −1, −2, −3 | 7 | 16 |

orbitals that have the same *n* and *l* values is called a **subshell**. Each subshell is designated by a number (the value of *n*) and a letter (*s*, *p*, *d*, or *f*, corresponding to the value of *l* ). For example, the orbitals that have *n* = 3 and *l* = 2 are called 3*d* orbitals and are in the 3*d* subshell.

▲ TABLE 6.2 summarizes the possible values of *l* and $m_l$ for values of *n* through *n* = 4. The restrictions on possible values give rise to the following very important observations:

1. The shell with principal quantum number *n* consists of exactly *n* subshells. Each subshell corresponds to a different allowed value of *l* from 0 to (*n* − 1). Thus, the first shell (*n* = 1) consists of only one subshell, the 1*s* (*l* = 0); the second shell (*n* = 2) consists of two subshells, the 2*s* (*l* = 0) and 2*p* (*l* = 1); the third shell consists of three subshells, 3*s*, 3*p*, and 3*d*, and so forth.

2. Each subshell consists of a specific number of orbitals. Each orbital corresponds to a different allowed value of $m_l$. For a given value of *l*, there are (2*l* + 1) allowed values of $m_l$, ranging from −*l* to +*l*. Thus, each *s* (*l* = 0) subshell consists of one orbital; each *p* (*l* = 1) subshell consists of three orbitals; each *d* (*l* = 2) subshell consists of five orbitals, and so forth.

3. The total number of orbitals in a shell is $n^2$, where *n* is the principal quantum number of the shell. The resulting number of orbitals for the shells—1, 4, 9, 16—are related to a pattern seen in the periodic table: We see that the number of elements in the rows of the periodic table—2, 8, 18, and 32—equals twice these numbers. We will discuss this relationship further in Section 6.9.

▶ FIGURE 6.17 shows the relative energies of the hydrogen atom orbitals through *n* = 3. Each box represents an orbital, and orbitals of the same subshell, such as the three 2*p* orbitals, are grouped together. When the electron occupies the lowest-energy orbital (1*s* ), the hydrogen atom is said to be in its *ground state*. When the electron occupies any other orbital, the atom is in an *excited state*. (The electron can be excited to a higher-energy orbital by absorption of a photon of appropriate energy.) At ordinary temperatures, essentially all hydrogen atoms are in the ground state.

▲ **GIVE IT SOME THOUGHT**

Notice in Figure 6.17 that the energy difference between the *n* = 1 and *n* = 2 levels is much greater than the energy difference between the *n* = 2 and *n* = 3 levels. How does Equation 6.5 explain this trend?

▲ **GO FIGURE**

**If the fourth shell (the *n* = 4 energy level) were shown, how many subshells would it contain? How would they be labeled?**

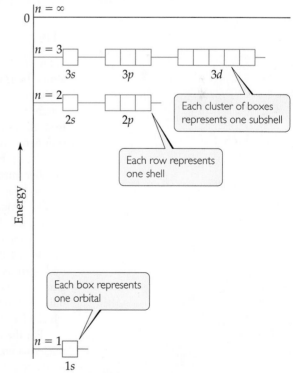

*n* = 1 shell has one orbital
*n* = 2 shell has two subshells composed of four orbitals
*n* = 3 shell has three subshells composed of nine orbitals

▲ **FIGURE 6.17 Energy levels in the hydrogen atom.**

**SAMPLE EXERCISE 6.6** | **Subshells of the Hydrogen Atom**

(a) Without referring to Table 6.2, predict the number of subshells in the fourth shell, that is, for $n = 4$. (b) Give the label for each of these subshells. (c) How many orbitals are in each of these subshells?

**Analyze and Plan** We are given the value of the principal quantum number, $n$. We need to determine the allowed values of $l$ and $m_l$ for this given value of $n$ and then count the number of orbitals in each subshell.

**SOLUTION**

There are four subshells in the fourth shell, corresponding to the four possible values of $l$ (0, 1, 2, and 3).

These subshells are labeled $4s$, $4p$, $4d$, and $4f$. The number given in the designation of a subshell is the principal quantum number, $n$; the letter designates the value of the angular momentum quantum number, $l$: for $l = 0$, $s$; for $l = 1$, $p$; for $l = 2$, $d$; for $l = 3$, $f$.

There is one $4s$ orbital (when $l = 0$, there is only one possible value of $m_l$: 0). There are three $4p$ orbitals (when $l = 1$, there are three possible values of $m_l$: 1, 0, $-1$). There are five $4d$ orbitals (when $l = 2$, there are five allowed values of $m_l$: 2, 1, 0, $-1$, $-2$). There are seven $4f$ orbitals (when $l = 3$, there are seven permitted values of $m_l$: 3, 2, 1, 0, $-1$, $-2$, $-3$).

**PRACTICE EXERCISE**

(a) What is the designation for the subshell with $n = 5$ and $l = 1$? (b) How many orbitals are in this subshell? (c) Indicate the values of $m_l$ for each of these orbitals.

*Answers:* (a) $5p$; (b) 3; (c) 1, 0, $-1$

# 6.6 | REPRESENTATIONS OF ORBITALS

So far we have emphasized orbital energies, but the wave function also provides information about an electron's probable location in space. Let's examine the ways in which we can picture orbitals because their shapes help us visualize how the electron density is distributed around the nucleus.

## The s Orbitals

We have already seen one representation of the lowest-energy orbital of the hydrogen atom, the $1s$ (Figure 6.16). The first thing we notice about the electron density for the $1s$ orbital is that it is *spherically symmetric*—in other words, the electron density at a given distance from the nucleus is the same regardless of the direction in which we proceed from the nucleus. All of the other $s$ orbitals ($2s$, $3s$, $4s$, and so forth) are also spherically symmetric and centered on the nucleus.

Recall that the $l$ quantum number for the $s$ orbitals is 0; therefore, the $m_l$ quantum number must be 0. Thus, for each value of $n$, there is only one $s$ orbital.

So how do $s$ orbitals differ as the value of $n$ changes? One way to address this question is to look at the **radial probability function**, also called the *radial probability density*, which is defined as the probability that we will find the electron at a specific distance from the nucleus.

▶ **FIGURE 6.18** shows the radial probability density for the $1s$, $2s$, and $3s$ orbitals of hydrogen as a function of $r$, the distance from the nucleus. Three features of these graphs are noteworthy: the number of peaks, the number of points at which the probability function goes to zero (called **nodes**), and how spread out the distribution is, which gives a sense of the size of the orbital.

For the $1s$ orbital, we see that the probability rises rapidly as we move away from the nucleus, maximizing at about 0.5 Å. Thus, when the electron occupies the $1s$ orbital, it is *most likely* to be found this distance from the nucleus.* Notice also that in the $1s$ orbital the probability of finding the electron at a distance greater than about 3 Å from the nucleus is essentially zero.

---

*In the quantum mechanical model, the most probable distance at which to find the electron in the $1s$ orbital is actually 0.529 Å, the same as the radius of the orbit predicted by Bohr for $n = 1$. The distance 0.529 Å is often called the Bohr radius.

## GO FIGURE

**How many maxima would you expect to find in the radial probability function for the 4s orbital of the hydrogen atom? How many nodes would you expect in this function?**

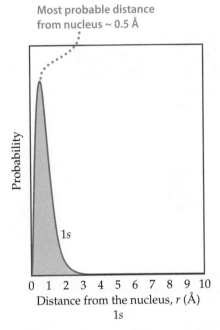

Most probable distance from nucleus ~ 0.5 Å

Probability

1s

0 1 2 3 4 5 6 7 8 9 10
Distance from the nucleus, $r$ (Å)
1s

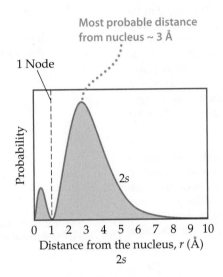

Most probable distance from nucleus ~ 3 Å

1 Node

Probability

2s

0 1 2 3 4 5 6 7 8 9 10
Distance from the nucleus, $r$ (Å)
2s

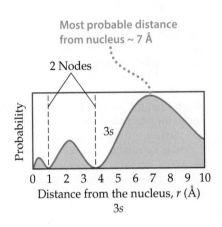

Most probable distance from nucleus ~ 7 Å

2 Nodes

Probability

3s

0 1 2 3 4 5 6 7 8 9 10
Distance from the nucleus, $r$ (Å)
3s

▲ **FIGURE 6.18   Radial probability distributions for the 1s, 2s, and 3s orbitals of hydrogen.** These graphs of the radial probability function plot probability of finding the electron as a function of distance from the nucleus. As $n$ increases, the most likely distance at which to find the electron (the highest peak) moves farther from the nucleus.

Comparing the radial probability distributions for the 1s, 2s, and 3s orbitals reveals three trends:

1. *The number of peaks increases with increasing* n, *with the outermost peak being larger than inner ones.*

2. *The number of nodes increases with increasing* n.

3. *The electron density becomes more spread out with increasing* n.

One widely used method of representing orbital *shape* is to draw a boundary surface that encloses some substantial portion, say 90%, of the electron density for the orbital. This type of drawing is called a *contour representation*, and the contour representations for the s orbitals are spheres (▼ **FIGURE 6.19**). All the orbitals have the same shape, but they differ in size, becoming larger as $n$ increases, reflecting the fact that the electron density becomes more spread out as $n$ increases. Although the details of how

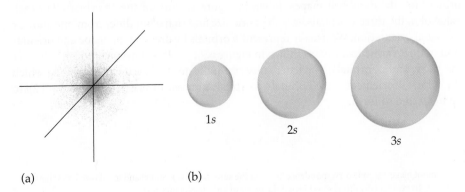

1s

2s

3s

(a)                    (b)

◀ **FIGURE 6.19   Comparison of the 1s, 2s, and 3s orbitals.** (a) Electron-density distribution of a 1s orbital. (b) Contour representations of the 1s, 2s, and 3s orbitals. Each sphere is centered on the atom's nucleus and encloses the volume in which there is a 90% probability of finding the electron.

# A CLOSER LOOK

## PROBABILITY DENSITY AND RADIAL PROBABILITY FUNCTIONS

According to quantum mechanics, we must describe the position of the electron in the hydrogen atom in terms of probabilities. The information about the probability is contained in the wave functions, $\psi$, obtained from Schrödinger's equation. The square of the wave function, $\psi^2$, called either the probability density or the electron density, as noted earlier, gives the probability that the electron is at any *point* in space. Because s orbitals are spherically symmetric, the value of $\psi$ for an s electron depends only on its distance from the nucleus, $r$. Thus, the probability density can be written as $[\psi(r)]^2$, where $\psi(r)$ is the value of $\psi$ at $r$. This function $[\psi(r)]^2$ gives the probability density for any point located a distance $r$ from the nucleus.

The radial probability function, which we used in Figure 6.18, differs from the probability density. The radial probability function equals the *total* probability of finding the electron at all the points at any distance $r$ from the nucleus. In other words, to calculate this function, we need to "add up" the probability densities $[\psi(r)]^2$ over all points located a distance $r$ from the nucleus. ▶ FIGURE 6.20 compares the probability density at a point ($[\psi(r)]^2$) with the radial probability function.

Let's examine the difference between probability density and radial probability function more closely. ▶ FIGURE 6.21 shows plots of $[\psi(r)]^2$ as a function of $r$ for the 1s, 2s, and 3s orbitals of the

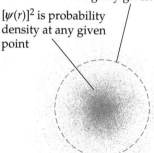

$4\pi r^2[\psi(r)]^2$ is radial probability function = sum of all $[\psi(r)]^2$ having any given value of $r$

$[\psi(r)]^2$ is probability density at any given point

▲ FIGURE 6.20 Comparing probability density $[\psi(r)]^2$ and radial probability function $4\pi r^2[\psi(r)]^2$.

electron density varies within a given contour representation are lost in these representations, this is not a serious disadvantage. For qualitative discussions, the most important features of orbitals are shape and relative size, which are adequately displayed by contour representations.

## The p Orbitals

The distribution of electron density for a 2p orbital is shown in ▶ FIGURE 6.22(a). The electron density is not distributed spherically as in an s orbital. Instead, the density is concentrated in two regions on either side of the nucleus, separated by a node at the nucleus. We say that this dumbbell-shaped orbital has two *lobes*. Recall that we are making no statement of how the electron is moving within the orbital. Figure 6.22(a) portrays only the *averaged* distribution of the electron density in a 2p orbital.

Beginning with the $n = 2$ shell, each shell has three p orbitals. Recall that the $l$ quantum number for p orbitals is 1. Therefore, the magnetic quantum number $m_l$ can have three possible values: $-1$, 0, and $+1$. Thus, there are three 2p orbitals, three 3p orbitals, and so forth, corresponding to the three possible values of $m_l$. Each set of p orbitals has the dumbbell shapes shown in Figure 6.22(a) for the 2p orbitals. For each value of $n$, the three p orbitals have the same size and shape but differ from one another in spatial orientation. We usually represent p orbitals by drawing the shape and orientation of their wave functions, as shown in Figure 6.22(b). It is convenient to label these as the $p_x$, $p_y$, and $p_z$ orbitals. The letter subscript indicates the Cartesian axis along which the orbital is oriented.* Like s orbitals, p orbitals increase in size as we move from 2p to 3p to 4p, and so forth.

*We cannot make a simple correspondence between the subscripts ($x$, $y$, and $z$) and the allowed $m_l$ values (1, 0, and $-1$). To explain why this is so is beyond the scope of an introductory text.

hydrogen atom. You will notice that these plots look distinctly different from the radial probability functions shown in Figure 6.18.

As shown in Figure 6.20, the collection of points a distance $r$ from the nucleus is the surface of a sphere of radius $r$. The probability density at each point on that spherical surface is $[\psi(r)]^2$. To add up all the individual probability densities requires calculus and so is beyond the scope of this text. However, the result of that calculation tells us that the radial probability function is the probability density, $[\psi(r)]^2$, multiplied by the surface area of the sphere, $4\pi r^2$:

$$\text{Radial probability function} = 4\pi r^2 [\psi(r)]^2$$

Thus, the plots of radial probability function in Figure 6.18 are equal to the plots of $[\psi(r)]^2$ in Figure 6.21 multiplied by $4\pi r^2$. The fact that $4\pi r^2$ increases rapidly as we move away from the nucleus makes the two sets of plots look very different from each other. For example, the plot of $[\psi(r)]^2$ for the 3s orbital in Figure 6.21 shows that the function generally gets smaller the farther we go from the nucleus. But when we multiply by $4\pi r^2$, we see peaks that get larger and larger as we move away from the nucleus (Figure 6.18).

The radial probability functions in Figure 6.18 provide us with the more useful information because they tell us the probability of finding the electron at *all* points a distance $r$ from the nucleus, not just one particular point.

*RELATED EXERCISES:* 6.50, 6.59, 6.60, and 6.91

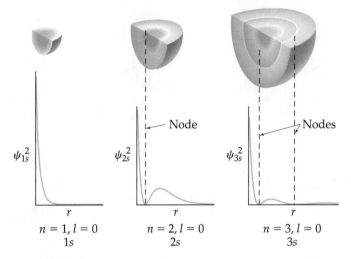

▲ **FIGURE 6.21   Probability density $[\psi(r)]^2$ in the 1s, 2s, and 3s orbitals of hydrogen.**

---

**GO FIGURE**

**(a) Note on the left that the color is deep pink in the interior of each lobe but fades to pale pink at the edges. What does this change in color represent? (b) What label is applied to the 2p orbital aligned along the x axis?**

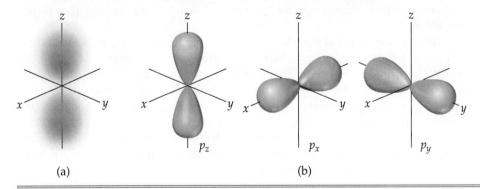

(a)

(b)

◄ **FIGURE 6.22   The p orbitals.**
(a) Electron-density distribution of a 2p orbital.
(b) Contour representations of the three p orbitals. The subscript on the orbital label indicates the axis along which the orbital lies.

## The d and f Orbitals

When $n$ is 3 or greater, we encounter the $d$ orbitals (for which $l = 2$). There are five 3d orbitals, five 4d orbitals, and so forth because in each shell there are five possible values for the $m_l$ quantum number: $-2, -1, 0, 1,$ and 2. The different $d$ orbitals in a given shell have different shapes and orientations in space, as shown in ▶ **FIGURE 6.23**. Four of the $d$-orbital contour representations have a "four-leaf clover" shape, and each lies primarily in a plane. The $d_{xy}, d_{xz},$ and $d_{yz}$ lie in the $xy, xz,$ and $yz$ planes, respectively, with the lobes oriented *between* the axes. The lobes of the $d_{x^2-y^2}$ orbital also lie in the $xy$ plane, but the lobes lie *along* the $x$ and $y$ axes. The $d_{z^2}$ orbital looks very different from the other four: It has two lobes along the $z$ axis and a "doughnut" in the $xy$ plane. Even though the $d_{z^2}$ orbital looks different from the other $d$ orbitals, it has the same energy as the other four

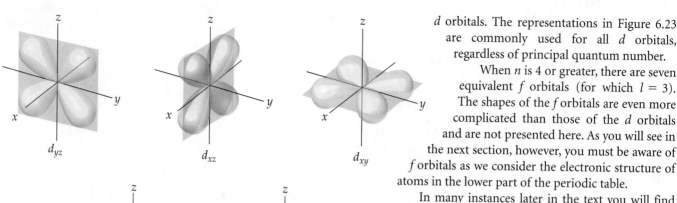

**▲ FIGURE 6.23** Contour representations of the five *d* orbitals.

*d* orbitals. The representations in Figure 6.23 are commonly used for all *d* orbitals, regardless of principal quantum number.

When *n* is 4 or greater, there are seven equivalent *f* orbitals (for which *l* = 3). The shapes of the *f* orbitals are even more complicated than those of the *d* orbitals and are not presented here. As you will see in the next section, however, you must be aware of *f* orbitals as we consider the electronic structure of atoms in the lower part of the periodic table.

In many instances later in the text you will find that knowing the number and shapes of atomic orbitals will help you understand chemistry at the molecular level. You will therefore find it useful to memorize the shapes of the *s*, *p*, and *d* orbitals shown in Figures 6.19, 6.22, and 6.23.

# 6.7 | MANY-ELECTRON ATOMS

One of our goals in this chapter has been to determine the electronic structures of atoms. So far, we have seen that quantum mechanics leads to an elegant description of the hydrogen atom. This atom, however, has only one electron. How does our description change when we consider an atom with two or more electrons (a *many-electron atom*)? To describe such an atom, we must consider the nature of orbitals and their relative energies as well as how the electrons populate the available orbitals.

## Orbitals and Their Energies

We can describe the electronic structure of a many-electron atom in terms of orbitals like those of the hydrogen atom. Thus, we continue to designate orbitals as 1s, $2p_x$, and so forth. Further, these orbitals have the same general shapes as the corresponding hydrogen orbitals.

Although the shapes of the orbitals of a many-electron atom are the same as those for hydrogen, the presence of more than one electron greatly changes the energies of the orbitals. In hydrogen the energy of an orbital depends only on its principal quantum number, *n* (Figure 6.17). For instance, the 3s, 3p, and 3d subshells all have the same energy. In a many-electron atom, however, the electron–electron repulsions cause the various subshells in a given shell to be at different energies, as shown in ◀ **FIGURE 6.24**.

To explain this fact, we must consider the forces between the electrons and how these forces are affected by the shapes of the orbitals. We will, however, forgo this analysis until Chapter 7.

The important idea is this: *In a many-electron atom, for a given value of n, the energy of an orbital increases with increasing value of l.* For example, notice in Figure 6.24 that the *n* = 3 orbitals increase in energy in the order 3s < 3p < 3d. Notice also that all orbitals of a given subshell (such as the five 3d orbitals) have the same energy as one another. Orbitals with the same energy are said to be **degenerate**.

Figure 6.24 is a *qualitative* energy-level diagram; the exact energies of the orbitals and their spacings differ from one atom to another.

**GO FIGURE**

Not all of the orbitals in the *n* = 4 shell are shown in this figure. Which subshells are missing?

Orbitals in a subshell are degenerate (have same energy)

Energies of subshells follow order
ns < np < nd < nf

**▲ FIGURE 6.24** General energy ordering of orbitals for a many-electron atom.

**GIVE IT SOME THOUGHT**

a. How may orbitals have the principal quantum number *n* = 3?
b. In a many-electron atom, what are the relative energies of these orbitals?

# Electron Spin and the Pauli Exclusion Principle

We have now seen that we can use hydrogen-like orbitals to describe many-electron atoms. What, however, determines which orbitals the electrons occupy? That is, how do the electrons of a many-electron atom populate the available orbitals? To answer this question, we must consider an additional property of the electron.

When scientists studied the line spectra of many-electron atoms in great detail, they noticed a very puzzling feature: Lines that were originally thought to be single were actually closely spaced pairs. This meant, in essence, that there were twice as many energy levels as there were "supposed" to be. In 1925 the Dutch physicists George Uhlenbeck and Samuel Goudsmit proposed a solution to this dilemma. They postulated that electrons have an intrinsic property, called **electron spin**, that causes each electron to behave as if it were a tiny sphere spinning on its own axis.

By now it probably does not surprise you to learn that electron spin is quantized. This observation led to the assignment of a new quantum number for the electron, in addition to $n$, $l$, and $m_l$, which we have already discussed. This new quantum number, the **spin magnetic quantum number**, is denoted $m_s$ (the subscript $s$ stands for *spin*). Two possible values are allowed for $m_s$, $+\frac{1}{2}$ or $-\frac{1}{2}$, which was first interpreted as indicating the two opposite directions in which the electron can spin. A spinning charge produces a magnetic field. The two opposite directions of spin therefore produce oppositely directed magnetic fields (▶ **FIGURE 6.25**).* These two opposite magnetic fields lead to the splitting of spectral lines into closely spaced pairs.

Electron spin is crucial for understanding the electronic structures of atoms. In 1925 the Austrian-born physicist Wolfgang Pauli (1900–1958) discovered the principle that governs the arrangements of electrons in many-electron atoms. The **Pauli exclusion principle** states that *no two electrons in an atom can have the same set of four quantum numbers* n, l, m$_l$, *and* m$_s$. For a given orbital, the values of $n$, $l$, and $m_l$ are fixed. Thus, if we

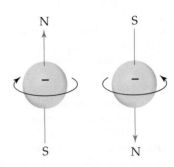

▲ **FIGURE 6.25 Electron spin.** The electron behaves as if it were spinning about an axis, thereby generating a magnetic field whose direction depends on the direction of spin. The two directions for the magnetic field correspond to the two possible values for the spin quantum number, $m_s$.

## A CLOSER LOOK

### EXPERIMENTAL EVIDENCE FOR ELECTRON SPIN

Even before electron spin had been proposed, there was experimental evidence that electrons had an additional property that needed explanation. In 1921, Otto Stern and Walter Gerlach succeeded in separating a beam of electrically neutral atoms into two groups by passing them through a nonhomogeneous magnetic field (▶ **FIGURE 6.26**).

Let's assume they used a beam of hydrogen atoms (in actuality, they used silver atoms, which contain just one unpaired electron). We would normally expect electrically neutral atoms to be unaffected by a magnetic field. However, the magnetic field arising from the electron's spin interacts with the magnet's field, deflecting the atom from its straight-line path. As shown in Figure 6.26, the magnetic field splits the beam in two, suggesting that there are two (and only two) equivalent values for the electron's magnetic field. The Stern–Gerlach experiment could be readily interpreted once it was realized that there are exactly two values for the spin of the electron. These values produce equal magnetic fields that are opposite in direction.

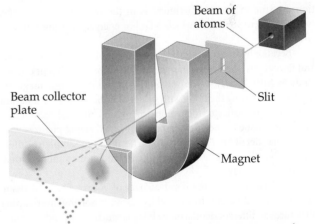

Atoms having unpaired electron with spin quantum number $m_s = +1/2$ deflect in one direction; those having unpaired electron with $m_s = -1/2$ deflect in opposite direction

▲ **FIGURE 6.26 The Stern–Gerlach experiment.**

---

*As we discussed earlier, the electron has both particle-like and wave-like properties. Thus, the picture of an electron as a spinning charged sphere is, strictly speaking, just a useful pictorial representation that helps us understand the two directions of magnetic field that an electron can possess.

# CHEMISTRY AND LIFE

## NUCLEAR SPIN AND MAGNETIC RESONANCE IMAGING

A major challenge facing medical diagnosis is seeing inside the human body. Until recently, this was accomplished primarily by using X-rays to image human bones, muscles, and organs. However, there are several drawbacks to using X-rays for medical imaging. First, X-rays do not give well-resolved images of overlapping physiological structures. Moreover, because damaged or diseased tissue often yields the same image as healthy tissue, X-rays frequently fail to detect illness or injuries. Finally, X-rays are high-energy radiation that can cause physiological harm, even in low doses.

During the 1980s, a technique called *magnetic resonance imaging* (MRI) moved to the forefront of medical imaging technology. The foundation of MRI is a phenomenon called nuclear magnetic resonance (NMR), which was discovered in the mid-1940s. Today NMR has become one of the most important spectroscopic methods used in chemistry. It is based on the observation that, like electrons, the nuclei of many elements possess an intrinsic spin. Like electron spin, nuclear spin is quantized. For example, the nucleus of $^1$H has two possible magnetic nuclear spin quantum numbers, $+\frac{1}{2}$ and $-\frac{1}{2}$. The hydrogen nucleus is the most common one studied by NMR.

A spinning hydrogen nucleus acts like a tiny magnet. In the absence of external effects, the two spin states have the same energy. However, when the nuclei are placed in an external magnetic field, they can align either parallel or opposed (antiparallel) to the field, depending on their spin. The parallel alignment is lower in energy than the antiparallel one by a certain amount, $\Delta E$ (▶ FIGURE 6.27). If the nuclei are irradiated with photons having energy equal to $\Delta E$, the spin of the nuclei can be "flipped," that is, excited from the parallel to the antiparallel alignment. Detection of the flipping of nuclei between the two spin states leads to an NMR spectrum. The radiation used in an NMR experiment is in the radiofrequency range, typically 100 to 900 MHz, which is far less energetic per photon than X-rays.

Because hydrogen is a major constituent of aqueous body fluids and fatty tissue, the hydrogen nucleus is the most convenient one for study by MRI. In MRI a person's body is placed in a strong magnetic field. By irradiating the body with pulses of radiofrequency radiation and using sophisticated detection techniques, medical technicians can image tissue at specific depths in the body, giving pictures with spectacular detail (▶ FIGURE 6.28). The ability to sample at different depths allows the technicians to construct a three-dimensional picture of the body.

MRI has none of the disadvantages of X-rays. Diseased tissue appears very different from healthy tissue, resolving overlapping structures at different depths in the body is much easier, and the radio frequency radiation is not harmful to humans in the doses used. The technique has had such a profound influence on the modern practice of medicine that Paul Lauterbur, a chemist, and Peter Mansfield, a physicist, were awarded the 2003 Nobel Prize in Physiology or

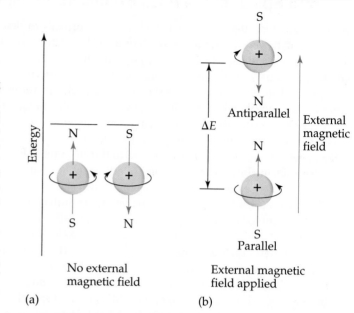

(a)  (b)

▲ FIGURE 6.27 **Nuclear spin.** Like electron spin, nuclear spin generates a small magnetic field and has two allowed values. (a) In the absence of an external magnetic field, the two spin states have the same energy. (b) When an external magnetic field is applied, the spin state in which the spin direction is parallel to the direction of the external field is lower in energy than the spin state in which the spin direction is antiparallel to the field direction. The energy difference, $\Delta E$, is in the radio frequency portion of the electromagnetic spectrum.

▲ FIGURE 6.28 **MRI image.** This image of a human head, obtained using magnetic resonance imaging, shows a normal brain, airways, and facial tissues.

Medicine for their discoveries concerning MRI. The major drawback of this technique is expense: The current cost of a new MRI instrument for clinical applications is over $1.5 million.

*RELATED EXERCISE:* 6.93

want to put more than one electron in an orbital *and* satisfy the Pauli exclusion principle, our only choice is to assign different $m_s$ values to the electrons. Because there are only two such values, we conclude that *an orbital can hold a maximum of two electrons and they must have opposite spins.* This restriction allows us to index the electrons in an atom, giving their quantum numbers and thereby defining the region in space where each electron is most likely to be found. It also provides the key to understanding the structure of the periodic table of the elements.

# 6.8 | ELECTRON CONFIGURATIONS

Armed with knowledge of the relative energies of orbitals and the Pauli exclusion principle, we are in a position to consider the arrangements of electrons in atoms. The way electrons are distributed among the various orbitals of an atom is called the **electron configuration** of the atom.

The most stable electron configuration—the ground state—is that in which the electrons are in the lowest possible energy states. If there were no restrictions on the possible values for the quantum numbers of the electrons, all the electrons would crowd into the 1s orbital because it is the lowest in energy (Figure 6.24). The Pauli exclusion principle tells us, however, that there can be at most two electrons in any single orbital. Thus, *the orbitals are filled in order of increasing energy, with no more than two electrons per orbital.* For example, consider the lithium atom, which has three electrons. (Recall that the number of electrons in a neutral atom equals its atomic number.) The 1s orbital can accommodate two of the electrons. The third one goes into the next lowest energy orbital, the 2s.

We can represent any electron configuration by writing the symbol for the occupied subshell and adding a superscript to indicate the number of electrons in that subshell. For example, for lithium we write $1s^2 2s^1$ (read "1s two, 2s one"). We can also show the arrangement of the electrons as

Li $\boxed{\uparrow\downarrow}$ $\boxed{\uparrow}$

1s    2s

In this representation, which we call an *orbital diagram*, each orbital is denoted by a box and each electron by a half arrow. A half arrow pointing up ( $\uparrow$ ) represents an electron with a positive spin magnetic quantum number ($m_s = +\frac{1}{2}$) and a half arrow pointing down ( $\downarrow$ ) represents an electron with a negative spin magnetic quantum number ($m_s = -\frac{1}{2}$). This pictorial representation of electron spin, which corresponds to the directions of the magnetic fields in Figure 6.25, is quite convenient.

Electrons having opposite spins are said to be *paired* when they are in the same orbital ($\uparrow\downarrow$). An *unpaired electron* is one not accompanied by a partner of opposite spin. In the lithium atom the two electrons in the 1s orbital are paired and the electron in the 2s orbital is unpaired.

## Hund's Rule

Consider now how the electron configurations of the elements change as we move from element to element across the periodic table. Hydrogen has one electron, which occupies the 1s orbital in its ground state:

H $\boxed{\uparrow}$ : $1s^1$

1s

The choice of a spin-up electron here is arbitrary; we could equally well show the ground state with one spin-down electron. It is customary, however, to show unpaired electrons with their spins up.

**TABLE 6.3** • **Electron Configurations of Several Lighter Elements**

| Element | Total Electrons | Orbital Diagram | | | | Electron Configuration |
|---------|-----------------|-----------------|---|---|---|------------------------|
| | | 1s | 2s | 2p | 3s | |
| Li | 3 | ↑↓ | ↑ | | | | $1s^2 2s^1$ |
| Be | 4 | ↑↓ | ↑↓ | | | | $1s^2 2s^2$ |
| B | 5 | ↑↓ | ↑↓ | ↑ | | | $1s^2 2s^2 2p^1$ |
| C | 6 | ↑↓ | ↑↓ | ↑ ↑ | | | $1s^2 2s^2 2p^2$ |
| N | 7 | ↑↓ | ↑↓ | ↑ ↑ ↑ | | $1s^2 2s^2 2p^3$ |
| Ne | 10 | ↑↓ | ↑↓ | ↑↓ ↑↓ ↑↓ | | $1s^2 2s^2 2p^6$ |
| Na | 11 | ↑↓ | ↑↓ | ↑↓ ↑↓ ↑↓ | ↑ | $1s^2 2s^2 2p^6 3s^1$ |

The next element, helium, has two electrons. Because two electrons with opposite spins can occupy the same orbital, both of helium's electrons are in the 1s orbital:

$$\text{He} \quad \boxed{↑↓} \; : 1s^2$$
$$\text{\small 1s}$$

The two electrons present in helium complete the filling of the first shell. This arrangement represents a very stable configuration, as is evidenced by the chemical inertness of helium.

The electron configurations of lithium and several elements that follow it in the periodic table are shown in ▲ **TABLE 6.3**. For the third electron of lithium, the change in principal quantum number from $n = 1$ for the first two electrons to $n = 2$ for the third electron represents a large jump in energy and a corresponding jump in the average distance of the electron from the nucleus. In other words, it represents the start of a new shell occupied with electrons. As you can see by examining the periodic table, lithium starts a new row of the table. It is the first member of the alkali metals (group 1A).

The element that follows lithium is beryllium; its electron configuration is $1s^2 2s^2$ (Table 6.3). Boron, atomic number 5, has the electron configuration $1s^2 2s^2 2p^1$. The fifth electron must be placed in a 2p orbital because the 2s orbital is filled. Because all the three 2p orbitals are of equal energy, it does not matter which 2p orbital we place this fifth electron in.

With the next element, carbon, we encounter a new situation. We know that the sixth electron must go into a 2p orbital. However, does this new electron go into the 2p orbital that already has one electron or into one of the other two 2p orbitals? This question is answered by **Hund's rule**, which states that *for degenerate orbitals, the lowest energy is attained when the number of electrons having the same spin is maximized.* This means that electrons occupy orbitals singly to the maximum extent possible and that these single electrons in a given subshell all have the same spin magnetic quantum number. Electrons arranged in this way are said to have *parallel spins.* For a carbon atom to achieve its lowest energy, therefore, the two 2p electrons must have the same spin. For this to happen, the electrons must be in different 2p orbitals, as shown in Table 6.3. Thus, a carbon atom in its ground state has two unpaired electrons.

Similarly, for nitrogen in its ground state, Hund's rule requires that the three 2p electrons singly occupy each of the three 2p orbitals. This is the only way that all three electrons can have the same spin. For oxygen and fluorine, we place four and five electrons, respectively, in the $2p$ orbitals. To achieve this, we pair up electrons in the $2p$ orbitals, as we will see in Sample Exercise 6.7.

Hund's rule is based in part on the fact that electrons repel one another. By occupying different orbitals, the electrons remain as far as possible from one another, thus minimizing electron–electron repulsions.

---

**SAMPLE EXERCISE 6.7**   **Orbital Diagrams and Electron Configurations**

Draw the orbital diagram for the electron configuration of oxygen, atomic number 8. How many unpaired electrons does an oxygen atom possess?

**SOLUTION**

**Analyze and Plan**   Because oxygen has an atomic number of 8, each oxygen atom has 8 electrons. Figure 6.24 shows the ordering of orbitals. The electrons (represented as arrows) are placed in the orbitals (represented as boxes) beginning with the lowest-energy orbital, the $1s$. Each orbital can hold a maximum of two electrons (the Pauli exclusion principle). Because the $2p$ orbitals are degenerate, we place one electron in each of these orbitals (spin-up) before pairing any electrons (Hund's rule).

**Solve**   Two electrons each go into the $1s$ and $2s$ orbitals with their spins paired. This leaves four electrons for the three degenerate $2p$ orbitals. Following Hund's rule, we put one electron into each $2p$ orbital until all three orbitals have one electron each. The fourth electron is then paired up with one of the three electrons already in a $2p$ orbital, so that the orbital diagram is

$$\boxed{\uparrow\downarrow} \quad \boxed{\uparrow\downarrow} \quad \boxed{\uparrow\downarrow\,|\,\uparrow\,|\,\uparrow}$$

$$\;\;1s \qquad 2s \qquad\quad 2p$$

The corresponding electron configuration is written $1s^2 2s^2 2p^4$. The atom has two unpaired electrons.

**PRACTICE EXERCISE**

**(a)** Write the electron configuration for phosphorus, element 15. **(b)** How many unpaired electrons does a phosphorus atom possess?

**Answers:** **(a)** $1s^2 2s^2 2p^6 3s^2 3p^3$, **(b)** three

---

# Condensed Electron Configurations

The filling of the $2p$ subshell is complete at neon (Table 6.3), which has a stable configuration with eight electrons (an *octet*) in the outermost occupied shell. The next element, sodium, atomic number 11, marks the beginning of a new row of the periodic table. Sodium has a single $3s$ electron beyond the stable configuration of neon. We can therefore abbreviate the electron configuration of sodium as

$$\text{Na:} \quad [\text{Ne}]3s^1$$

The symbol [Ne] represents the electron configuration of the ten electrons of neon, $1s^2 2s^2 2p^6$. Writing the electron configuration as $[\text{Ne}]3s^1$ focuses attention on the outermost electron of the atom, which is the one largely responsible for how sodium behaves chemically.

We can generalize what we have just done for the electron configuration of sodium. In writing the *condensed electron configuration* of an element, the electron configuration of the nearest noble-gas element of lower atomic number is represented by its chemical symbol in brackets. For lithium, for example, we write

$$\text{Li:} \quad [\text{He}]2s^1$$

We refer to the electrons represented by the bracketed symbol as the *noble-gas core* of the atom. More usually, these inner-shell electrons are referred to as the **core electrons**. The electrons given after the noble-gas core are called the *outer-shell electrons*. The outer-shell electrons include the electrons involved in chemical bonding, which are called the **valence electrons**. For the elements with atomic number of 30 or less, all of the outer-shell electrons are valence electrons. By comparing the condensed electron configurations of lithium and sodium, we can appreciate why these two elements are so

1A

| 3 |
|---|
| **Li** |
| [He]2$s^1$ |

| 11 |
|---|
| **Na** |
| [Ne]3$s^1$ |

| 19 |
|---|
| **K** |
| [Ar]4$s^1$ |

| 37 |
|---|
| **Rb** |
| [Kr]5$s^1$ |

| 55 |
|---|
| **Cs** |
| [Xe]6$s^1$ |

| 87 |
|---|
| **Fr** |
| [Rn]7$s^1$ |

Alkali
metals

▲ **FIGURE 6.29** **The outer-shell electron configurations of the alkali metals (group 1A in the periodic table).**

similar chemically. They have the same type of electron configuration in the outermost occupied shell. Indeed, all the members of the alkali metal group (1A) have a single *s* valence electron beyond a noble-gas configuration (◄ **FIGURE 6.29**).

## Transition Metals

The noble-gas element argon ($1s^2 2s^2 2p^6 3s^2 3p^6$) marks the end of the row started by sodium. The element following argon in the periodic table is potassium (K), atomic number 19. In all its chemical properties, potassium is clearly a member of the alkali metal group. The experimental facts about the properties of potassium leave no doubt that the outermost electron of this element occupies an *s* orbital. But this means that the electron with the highest energy has *not* gone into a 3*d* orbital, which we might expect it to do. Because the 4*s* orbital is lower in energy than the 3*d* orbital (Figure 6.24), the condensed electron configuration of potassium is

$$K: \quad [Ar]4s^1$$

Following the complete filling of the 4*s* orbital (this occurs in the calcium atom), the next set of orbitals to be filled is the 3*d*. (You will find it helpful as we go along to refer often to the periodic table on the front inside cover.) Beginning with scandium and extending through zinc, electrons are added to the five 3*d* orbitals until they are completely filled. Thus, the fourth row of the periodic table is ten elements wider than the two previous rows. These ten elements are known as either **transition elements** or **transition metals**. Note the position of these elements in the periodic table.

In writing the electron configurations of the transition elements, we fill orbitals in accordance with Hund's rule—we add them to the 3*d* orbitals singly until all five orbitals have one electron each and then place additional electrons in the 3*d* orbitals with spin pairing until the shell is completely filled. The condensed electron configurations and the corresponding orbital diagram representations of two transition elements are as follows:

Once all the 3*d* orbitals have been filled with two electrons each, the 4*p* orbitals begin to be occupied until the completed octet of outer electrons ($4s^2 4p^6$) is reached with krypton (Kr), atomic number 36, another of the noble gases. Rubidium (Rb) marks the beginning of the fifth row. Refer again to the periodic table on the front inside cover. Notice that this row is in every respect like the preceding one, except that the value for *n* is greater by 1.

 **GIVE IT SOME THOUGHT**

Based on the structure of the periodic table, which becomes occupied first, the 6*s* orbital or the 5*d* orbitals?

## The Lanthanides and Actinides

The sixth row of the periodic table begins with one electron in the 6*s* orbital of cesium (Cs) and two electrons in the 6*s* orbital of barium (Ba). Notice, however, that the periodic table then has a break, with elements 57–70 placed below the main portion of the table. This break point is where we begin to encounter a new set of orbitals, the 4*f*.

There are seven degenerate 4*f* orbitals, corresponding to the seven allowed values of $m_l$, ranging from 3 to −3. Thus, it takes 14 electrons to fill the 4*f* orbitals completely. The 14 elements corresponding to the filling of the 4*f* orbitals are known as either the **lanthanide elements** or the **rare earth elements**. These elements are set below the other elements to avoid making the periodic table unduly wide. The properties of the lanthanide elements are all quite similar, and these elements occur together in nature. For many years it was virtually impossible to separate them from one another.

Because the energies of the 4f and 5d orbitals are very close to each other, the electron configurations of some of the lanthanides involve 5d electrons. For example, the elements lanthanum (La), cerium (Ce), and praseodymium (Pr) have the following electron configurations:

$$[Xe]6s^25d^1 \quad [Xe]6s^25d^14f^1 \quad [Xe]6s^24f^3$$

Lanthanum        Cerium        Praseodymium

Because La has a single 5d electron, it is sometimes placed below yttrium (Y) as the first member of the third series of transition elements; Ce is then placed as the first member of the lanthanides. Based on their chemistry, however, La can be considered the first element in the lanthanide series. Arranged this way, there are fewer apparent exceptions to the regular filling of the 4f orbitals among the subsequent members of the series.

After the lanthanide series, the third transition element series is completed by the filling of the 5d orbitals, followed by the filling of the 6p orbitals. This brings us to radon (Rn), heaviest of the known noble-gas elements.

The final row of the periodic table begins by filling the 7s orbitals. The **actinide elements**, of which uranium (U, element 92) and plutonium (Pu, element 94) are the best known, are then built up by completing the 5f orbitals. The actinide elements are radioactive, and most of them are not found in nature.

# 6.9 | ELECTRON CONFIGURATIONS AND THE PERIODIC TABLE

We just saw that the electron configurations of the elements correspond to their locations in the periodic table. Thus, elements in the same column of the table have related outer-shell (valence) electron configurations. As ▶ TABLE 6.4 shows, for example, all 2A elements have an $ns^2$ outer configuration, and all 3A elements have an $ns^2np^1$ outer configuration, with the value of $n$ increasing as we move down each column.

As shown in ▼ FIGURE 6.30, the periodic table can be divided into four blocks based on the filling order of orbitals. On the left are *two* blue columns of elements. These elements, known as the alkali metals (group 1A) and alkaline earth metals (group 2A), are those in which the valence s orbitals are being filled. These two columns make up the s block of the periodic table.

On the right is a block of *six* pink columns that comprises the p block, where the valence p orbitals are being filled. The s block and the p block elements together are the **representative elements**, sometimes called the **main-group elements**.

The orange block in Figure 6.30 has *ten* columns containing the transition metals. These are the elements in which the valence d orbitals are being filled and make up the d block.

**TABLE 6.4**
**Electron Configurations of Group 2A and 3A Elements**

**Group 2A**

| | |
|---|---|
| Be | $[He]2s^2$ |
| Mg | $[Ne]3s^2$ |
| Ca | $[Ar]4s^2$ |
| Sr | $[Kr]5s^2$ |
| Ba | $[Xe]6s^2$ |
| Ra | $[Rn]7s^2$ |

**Group 3A**

| | |
|---|---|
| B | $[He]2s^22p^1$ |
| Al | $[Ne]3s^23p^1$ |
| Ga | $[Ar]3d^{10}4s^24p^1$ |
| In | $[Kr]4d^{10}5s^25p^1$ |
| Tl | $[Xe]4f^{14}5d^{10}6s^26p^1$ |

▲ **FIGURE 6.30** **Regions of the periodic table.** The order in which electrons are added to orbitals is read left to right beginning in the top left corner.

The elements in the two tan rows containing *14* columns are the ones in which the valence *f* orbitals are being filled and make up the *f* block. Consequently, these elements are often referred to as the **f-block metals**. In most tables, the *f* block is positioned below the periodic table to save space:

The number of columns in each block corresponds to the maximum number of electrons that can occupy each kind of subshell. Recall that 2, 6, 10, and 14 are the numbers of electrons that can fill the *s, p, d,* and *f* subshells, respectively. Thus, the *s* block has 2 columns, the *p* block has 6, the *d* block has 10, and the *f* block has 14. Recall also that l*s* is the first *s* subshell, 2*p* is the first *p* subshell, 3*d* is the first *d* subshell, and 4*f* is the first *f* subshell, as Figure 6.30 shows. Using these facts, you can write the electron configuration of an element based merely on its position in the periodic table.

Let's use the periodic table to write the electron configuration of selenium (Se, element 34). We first locate Se in the table and then move backward from it through the table, from element 34 to 33 to 32 and so forth, until we come to the noble gas that precedes Se. In this case, the noble gas is argon, Ar, element 18. Thus, the noble-gas core for Se is [Ar]. Our next step is to write symbols for the outer electrons. We do this by moving across period 4 from K, the element following Ar, to Se:

Because K is in the fourth period and the *s* block, we begin with the 4*s* electrons, meaning our first two outer electrons are written $4s^2$. We then move into the *d* block, which begins with the 3*d* electrons. (The principal quantum number in the *d* block is always one less than that of the preceding elements in the *s* block, as seen in Figure 6.30.) Traversing the *d* block adds ten electrons, $3d^{10}$. Finally we move into the *p* block, whose principal quantum number is always the same as that of the *s* block. Counting the squares as we move across the *p* block to Se tells us that we need four electrons, $4p^4$. The electron configuration for Se is therefore $[Ar]4s^2 3d^{10}4p^4$. This configuration can also be written with the subshells arranged in order of increasing principal quantum number: $[Ar]3d^{10}4s^2 4p^3$.

As a check, we add the number of electrons in the [Ar] core, 18, to the number of electrons we added to the 4*s*, 3*d*, and 4*p* subshells. This sum should equal the atomic number of Se, 34: $18 + 2 + 10 + 4 = 34$.

**SAMPLE EXERCISE 6.8**    **Electron Configurations for a Group**

What is the characteristic valence electron configuration of the group 7A elements, the halogens?

**SOLUTION**

**Analyze and Plan**  We first locate the halogens in the periodic table, write the electron configurations for the first two elements, and then determine the general similarity between the configurations.

**Solve**  The first member of the halogen group is fluorine (F, element 9). Moving backward from F, we find that the noble-gas core is [He]. Moving from He to the element of next higher atomic number brings us to Li, element 3. Because Li is in the second period of the $s$ block, we add electrons to the $2s$ subshell. Moving across this block gives $2s^2$. Continuing to move to the right, we enter the $p$ block. Counting the squares to F gives $2p^5$. Thus, the condensed electron configuration for fluorine is

$$\text{F:}\quad [\text{He}]2s^2 2p^5$$

The electron configuration for chlorine, the second halogen, is

$$\text{Cl:}\quad [\text{Ne}]3s^2 3p^5$$

From these two examples, we see that the characteristic valence electron configuration of a halogen is $ns^2 np^5$, where $n$ ranges from 2 in the case of fluorine to 6 in the case of astatine.

**PRACTICE EXERCISE**

Which family of elements is characterized by an $ns^2 np^2$ electron configuration in the outermost occupied shell?

***Answer:*** group 4A

---

**SAMPLE EXERCISE 6.9**    **Electron Configurations from the Periodic Table**

**(a)** Based on its position in the periodic table, write the condensed electron configuration for bismuth, element 83. **(b)** How many unpaired electrons does a bismuth atom have?

**SOLUTION**

**(a)** Our first step is to write the noble-gas core. We do this by locating bismuth, element 83, in the periodic table. We then move backward to the nearest noble gas, which is Xe, element 54. Thus, the noble-gas core is [Xe].

Next, we trace the path in order of increasing atomic numbers from Xe to Bi. Moving from Xe to Cs, element 55, we find ourselves in period 6 of the $s$ block. Knowing the block and the period identifies the subshell in which we begin placing outer electrons, $6s$. As we move through the $s$ block, we add two electrons: $6s^2$.

As we move beyond the $s$ block, from element 56 to element 57, the curved arrow below the periodic table reminds us that we are entering the $f$ block. The first row of the $f$ block corresponds to the $4f$ subshell. As we move across this block, we add 14 electrons: $4f^{14}$.

With element 71, we move into the third row of the $d$ block. Because the first row of the $d$ block is $3d$, the second row is $4d$ and the third row is $5d$. Thus, as we move through the ten elements of the $d$ block, from element 71 to element 80, we fill the $5d$ subshell with ten electrons: $5d^{10}$.

Moving from element 80 to element 81 puts us into the $p$ block in the $6p$ subshell. (Remember that the principal quantum number in the $p$ block is the same as in the $s$ block.) Moving across to Bi requires 3 electrons: $6p^3$. The path we have taken is

Putting the parts together, we obtain the condensed electron configuration: $[Xe]6s^24f^{14}5d^{10}6p^3$. This configuration can also be written with the subshells arranged in order of increasing principal quantum number: $[Xe]4f^{14}5d^{10}6s^26p^3$.

Finally, we check our result to see if the number of electrons equals the atomic number of Bi, 83: Because Xe has 54 electrons (its atomic number), we have $54 + 2 + 14 + 10 + 3 = 83$. (If we had 14 electrons too few, we would realize that we have missed the $f$ block.)

**(b)** We see from the condensed electron configuration that the only partially occupied subshell is $6p$. The orbital diagram representation for this subshell is

| ↑ | ↑ | ↑ |
|---|---|---|

In accordance with Hund's rule, the three $6p$ electrons occupy the three $6p$ orbitals singly, with their spins parallel. Thus, there are three unpaired electrons in the bismuth atom.

**PRACTICE EXERCISE**

Use the periodic table to write the condensed electron configuration for **(a)** Co (element 27), **(b)** Te (element 52).

***Answers:*** **(a)** $[Ar]4s^23d^7$ or $[Ar]3d^74s^2$, **(b)** $[Kr]5s^24d^{10}5p^4$ or $[Kr]4d^{10}5s^25p^4$

▼ **FIGURE 6.31** gives, for all the elements, the ground-state electron configurations for the valence electrons. You can use this figure to check your answers as you practice writing electron configurations. We have written these configurations with orbitals

▲ **FIGURE 6.31** **Valence electron configurations of the elements.**

listed in order of increasing principal quantum number. As we saw in Sample Exercise 6.9, the orbitals can also be listed in order of filling, as they would be read off the periodic table.

Figure 6.31 allow us to reexamine the concept of *valence electrons*. Notice, for example, that as we proceed from Cl ($[Ne]3s^2 3p^5$) to Br ($[Ar]3d^{10}4s^2 4p^5$) we add a complete subshell of $3d$ electrons to the electrons beyond the [Ar] core. Although the $3d$ electrons are outer-shell electrons, they are not involved in chemical bonding and are therefore not considered valence electrons. Thus, we consider only the $4s$ and $4p$ electrons of Br to be valence electrons. Similarly, if we compare the electron configurations of Ag (element 47) and Au (element 79), we see that Au has a completely full $4f^{14}$ subshell beyond its noble-gas core, but those $4f$ electrons are not involved in bonding. In general, *for representative elements we do not consider the electrons in completely filled d or f subshells to be valence electrons,* and *for transition elements we do not consider the electrons in a completely filled f subshell to be valence electrons.*

## Anomalous Electron Configurations

The electron configurations of certain elements appear to violate the rules we have just discussed. For example, Figure 6.31 shows that the electron configuration of chromium (element 24) is $[Ar]3d^5 4s^1$ rather than the $[Ar]3d^4 4s^2$ configuration we might expect. Similarly, the configuration of copper (element 29) is $[Ar]3d^{10}4s^1$ instead of $[Ar]3d^9 4s^2$.

This anomalous behavior is largely a consequence of the closeness of the $3d$ and $4s$ orbital energies. It frequently occurs when there are enough electrons to form precisely half-filled sets of degenerate orbitals (as in chromium) or a completely filled $d$ subshell (as in copper). There are a few similar cases among the heavier transition metals (those with partially filled $4d$ or $5d$ orbitals) and among the $f$-block metals. Although these minor departures from the expected are interesting, they are not of great chemical significance.

 **GIVE IT SOME THOUGHT**

The elements Ni, Pd, and Pt are all in the same group. By examining the electron configurations for these elements in Figure 6.31, what can you conclude about the relative energies of the $nd$ and $(n + 1)s$ orbitals for this group?

| SAMPLE INTEGRATIVE EXERCISE | Putting Concepts Together |

Boron, atomic number 5, occurs naturally as two isotopes, $^{10}B$ and $^{11}B$, with natural abundances of 19.9% and 80.1%, respectively. **(a)** In what ways do the two isotopes differ from each other? Does the electronic configuration of $^{10}B$ differ from that of $^{11}B$? **(b)** Draw the orbital diagram for an atom of $^{11}B$. Which electrons are the valence electrons? **(c)** Indicate three major ways in which the $1s$ electrons in boron differ from its $2s$ electrons. **(d)** Elemental boron reacts with fluorine to form $BF_3$, a gas. Write a balanced chemical equation for the reaction of solid boron with fluorine gas. **(e)** $\Delta H_f^\circ$ for $BF_3(g)$ is $-1135.6$ kJ/mol. Calculate the standard enthalpy change in the reaction of boron with fluorine. **(f)** When $BCl_3$, also a gas at room temperature, comes into contact with water, the two react to form hydrochloric acid and boric acid, $H_3BO_3$, a very weak acid in water. Write a balanced net ionic equation for this reaction.

**SOLUTION**

**(a)** The two isotopes of boron differ in the number of neutrons in the nucleus. ∞∞ (Sections 2.3 and 2.4) Each of the isotopes contains five protons, but $^{10}B$ contains five neutrons, whereas $^{11}B$ contains six neutrons. The two isotopes of boron have identical electron configurations, $1s^2 2s^2 2p^1$, because each has five electrons.

**(b)** The complete orbital diagram is

The valence electrons are the ones in the outermost occupied shell, the $2s^2$ and $2p^1$ electrons. The $1s^2$ electrons constitute the core electrons, which we represent as [He] when we write the condensed electron configuration, $[He]2s^2 2p^1$.

**(c)** The 1s and 2s orbitals are both spherical, but they differ in three important respects: First, the 1s orbital is lower in energy than the 2s orbital. Second, the average distance of the 2s electrons from the nucleus is greater than that of the 1s electrons, so the 1s orbital is smaller than the 2s. Third, the 2s orbital has one node, whereas the 1s orbital has no nodes (Figure 6.18).

**(d)** The balanced chemical equation is

$$2 B(s) + 3 F_2(g) \longrightarrow 2 BF_3(g)$$

**(e)** $\Delta H° = 2(-1135.6) - [0 + 0] = -2271.2$ kJ. The reaction is strongly exothermic.

**(f)** $BCl_3(g) + 3 H_2O(l) \longrightarrow H_3BO_3(aq) + 3 H^+(aq) + 3 Cl^-(aq)$. Note that because $H_3BO_3$ is a very weak acid, its chemical formula is written in molecular form, as discussed in Section 4.3.

# CHAPTER SUMMARY AND KEY TERMS

**INTRODUCTION AND SECTION 6.1** The **electronic structure** of an atom describes the energies and arrangement of electrons around the atom. Much of what is known about the electronic structure of atoms was obtained by observing the interaction of light with matter. Visible light and other forms of **electromagnetic radiation** (also known as radiant energy) move through a vacuum at the speed of light, $c = 3.00 \times 10^8$ m/s. Electromagnetic radiation has both electric and magnetic components that vary periodically in wavelike fashion. The wave characteristics of radiant energy allow it to be described in terms of **wavelength**, $\lambda$, and **frequency**, $\nu$, which are interrelated: $c = \lambda\nu$.

**SECTION 6.2** Planck proposed that the minimum amount of radiant energy that an object can gain or lose is related to the frequency of the radiation: $E = h\nu$. This smallest quantity is called a **quantum** of energy. The constant $h$ is called **Planck's constant**: $h = 6.626 \times 10^{-34}$ J-s. In the quantum theory, energy is quantized, meaning that it can have only certain allowed values. Einstein used the quantum theory to explain the **photoelectric effect**, the emission of electrons from metal surfaces when exposed to light. He proposed that light behaves as if it consists of quantized energy packets called **photons**. Each photon carries energy, $E = h\nu$.

**SECTION 6.3** Dispersion of radiation into its component wavelengths produces a **spectrum**. If the spectrum contains all wavelengths, it is called a **continuous spectrum**; if it contains only certain specific wavelengths, the spectrum is called a **line spectrum**. The radiation emitted by excited hydrogen atoms forms a line spectrum.

Bohr proposed a model of the hydrogen atom that explains its line spectrum. In this model the energy of the electron in the hydrogen atom depends on the value of a quantum number, $n$. The value of $n$ must be a positive integer $(1, 2, 3, \ldots)$, and each value of $n$ corresponds to a different specific energy, $E_n$. The energy of the atom increases as $n$ increases. The lowest energy is achieved for $n = 1$; this is called the **ground state** of the hydrogen atom. Other values of $n$ correspond to **excited states**. Light is emitted when the electron drops from a higher-energy state to a lower-energy state; light is absorbed to excite the electron from a lower energy state to a higher one. The frequency of light emitted or absorbed is such that $h\nu$ equals the difference in energy between two allowed states.

**SECTION 6.4** De Broglie proposed that matter, such as electrons, should exhibit wavelike properties. This hypothesis of **matter waves** was proved experimentally by observing the diffraction of electrons. An object has a characteristic wavelength that depends on its **momentum**, $mv$: $\lambda = h/mv$. Discovery of the wave properties of the electron led to Heisenberg's **uncertainty principle**, which states that there is an inherent limit to the accuracy with which the position and momentum of a particle can be measured simultaneously.

**SECTION 6.5** In the quantum mechanical model of the hydrogen atom, the behavior of the electron is described by mathematical functions called **wave functions**, denoted with the Greek letter $\psi$. Each allowed wave function has a precisely known energy, but the location of the electron cannot be determined exactly; rather, the probability of it being at a particular point in space is given by the **probability density**, $\psi^2$. The **electron density** distribution is a map of the probability of finding the electron at all points in space.

The allowed wave functions of the hydrogen atom are called **orbitals**. An orbital is described by a combination of an integer and a letter, corresponding to values of three quantum numbers. The *principal quantum number*, $n$, is indicated by the integers 1, 2, 3, . . . . This quantum number relates most directly to the size and energy of the orbital. The *angular momentum quantum number, l*, is indicated by the letters $s$, $p$, $d$, $f$, and so on, corresponding to the values of 0, 1, 2, 3, . . . . The $l$ quantum number defines the shape of the orbital. For a given value of $n$, $l$ can have integer values ranging from 0 to $(n - 1)$. The *magnetic quantum number, $m_l$*, relates to the orientation of the orbital in space. For a given value of $l$, $m_l$ can have integral values ranging from $-l$ to $l$, including 0. Subscripts can be used to label the orientations of the orbitals. For example, the three $3p$ orbitals are designated $3p_x$, $3p_y$, and $3p_z$, with the subscripts indicating the axis along which the orbital is oriented.

An **electron shell** is the set of all orbitals with the same value of $n$, such as $3s$, $3p$, and $3d$. In the hydrogen atom all the orbitals in an electron shell have the same energy. A **subshell** is the set of one or more orbitals with the same $n$ and $l$ values; for example, $3s$, $3p$, and $3d$ are each subshells of the $n = 3$ shell. There is one orbital in an $s$ subshell, three in a $p$ subshell, five in a $d$ subshell, and seven in an $f$ subshell.

**SECTION 6.6** Contour representations are useful for visualizing the shapes of the orbitals. Represented this way, $s$ orbitals appear as spheres that increase in size as $n$ increases. The **radial probability function** tells us the probability that the electron will be found at a certain distance from the nucleus. The wave function for each $p$ orbital has two lobes on opposite sides of the nucleus. They are oriented along the $x$, $y$, and $z$ axes. Four of the $d$ orbitals appear as shapes with four lobes around the nucleus; the fifth one, the $d_{z^2}$ orbital, is represented as two lobes along the $z$ axis and a "doughnut" in the $xy$ plane. Regions in which the wave function is zero are called **nodes**. There is zero probability that the electron will be found at a node.

**SECTION 6.7** In many-electron atoms, different subshells of the same electron shell have different energies. For a given value of $n$, the energy of the subshells increases as the value of $l$ increases: $ns<np<nd<nf$. Orbitals within the same subshell are **degenerate**, meaning they have the same energy.

Electrons have an intrinsic property called **electron spin**, which is quantized. The **spin magnetic quantum number**, $m_s$, can have two possible values, $+\frac{1}{2}$ and $-\frac{1}{2}$, which can be envisioned as the two directions of an electron spinning about an axis. The **Pauli exclusion principle** states that no two electrons in an atom can have the same values for $n$, $l$, $m_l$, and $m_s$. This principle places a limit of two on the number of electrons that can occupy any one atomic orbital. These two electrons differ in their value of $m_s$.

**SECTIONS 6.8 AND 6.9** The **electron configuration** of an atom describes how the electrons are distributed among the orbitals of the atom. The ground-state electron configurations are generally obtained by placing the electrons in the atomic orbitals of lowest possible energy with the restriction that each orbital can hold no more than two electrons. When electrons occupy a subshell with more than one degenerate orbital, such as the $2p$ subshell, **Hund's rule** states that the lowest energy is attained by maximizing the number of electrons with the same electron spin. For example, in the ground-state electron configuration of carbon, the two $2p$ electrons have the same spin and must occupy two different $2p$ orbitals.

Elements in any given group in the periodic table have the same type of electron arrangements in their outermost shells. For example, the electron configurations of the halogens fluorine and chlorine are $[\text{He}]2s^22p^5$ and $[\text{Ne}]3s^23p^5$, respectively. The outer-shell electrons are those that lie outside the orbitals occupied in the next lowest noble-gas element. The outer-shell electrons that are involved in chemical bonding are the **valence electrons** of an atom; for the elements with atomic number 30 or less, all the outer-shell electrons are valence electrons. The electrons that are not valence electrons are called **core electrons**.

The periodic table is partitioned into different types of elements, based on their electron configurations. Those elements in which the outermost subshell is an $s$ or $p$ subshell are called the **representative** (or **main-group**) **elements**. The alkali metals (group 1A), halogens (group 7A), and noble gases (group 8A) are representative elements. Those elements in which a $d$ subshell is being filled are called the **transition elements** (or **transition metals**). The elements in which the $4f$ subshell is being filled are called the **lanthanide** (or **rare earth**) **elements**. The **actinide elements** are those in which the $5f$ subshell is being filled. The lanthanide and actinide elements are collectively referred to as the **f-block metals**. These elements are shown as two rows of 14 elements below the main part of the periodic table. The structure of the periodic table, summarized in Figure 6.30, allows us to write the electron configuration of an element from its position in the periodic table.

# KEY SKILLS

- Calculate the wavelength of electromagnetic radiation given its frequency or its frequency given its wavelength. (Section 6.1)

- Order the common kinds of radiation in the electromagnetic spectrum according to their wavelengths or energy. (Section 6.1)

- Explain what photons are and be able to calculate their energies given either their frequency or wavelength. (Section 6.2)

- Explain how line spectra relate to the idea of quantized energy states of electrons in atoms. (Section 6.3)

- Calculate the wavelength of a moving object. (Section 6.4)

- Explain how the uncertainty principle limits how precisely we can specify the position and the momentum of subatomic particles such as electrons. (Section 6.4)

- Relate the quantum numbers to the number and type of orbitals and recognize the different orbital shapes. (Section 6.5)

- Interpret radial probability function graphs for the orbitals. (Section 6.6)

- Draw an energy-level diagram for the orbitals in a many-electron atom and describe how electrons populate the orbitals in the ground state of an atom, using the Pauli exclusion principle and Hund's rule. (Section 6.8)

- Use the periodic table to write condensed electron configurations and determine the number of unpaired electrons in an atom. (Section 6.9)

# KEY EQUATIONS

- $c = \lambda\nu$  [6.1]  light as a wave: $c$ = speed of light ($3.00 \times 10^8$ m/s), $\lambda$ = wavelength in meters, $\nu$ = frequency in s$^{-1}$

- $E = h\nu$  [6.2]  light as a particle (photon): $E$ = energy of photon in joules, $h$ = Planck's constant ($6.626 \times 10^{-34}$ J-s), $\nu$ = frequency in s$^{-1}$ (same frequency as previous formula)

- $\lambda = h/mv$  [6.8]  matter as a wave: $\lambda$ = wavelength, $h$ = Planck's constant, $m$ = mass of object in kg, $v$ = speed of object in m/s

- $\Delta x \cdot \Delta(mv) \geq \dfrac{h}{4\pi}$  [6.9]  Heisenberg's uncertainty principle. The uncertainty in position ($\Delta x$) and momentum [$\Delta(mv)$] of an object cannot be zero; the smallest value of their product is $h/4\pi$

# EXERCISES

## VISUALIZING CONCEPTS

**6.1** Consider the water wave shown here. **(a)** How could you measure the speed of this wave? **(b)** How would you determine the wavelength of the wave? **(c)** Given the speed and wavelength of the wave, how could you determine the frequency of the wave? **(d)** Suggest an independent experiment to determine the frequency of the wave. [Section 6.1]

**6.2** A popular kitchen appliance produces electromagnetic radiation with a frequency of 2450 MHz. With reference to Figure 6.4, answer the following: **(a)** Estimate the wavelength of this radiation. **(b)** Would the radiation produced by the appliance be visible to the human eye? **(c)** If the radiation is not visible, do photons of this radiation have more or less energy than photons of visible light? **(d)** Propose the identity of the kitchen appliance. [Section 6.1]

**6.3** The following diagrams represent two electromagnetic waves. Which wave corresponds to the higher-energy radiation? Explain. [Section 6.2]

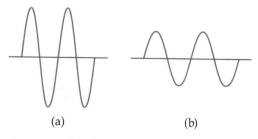

(a)                              (b)

**6.4** As shown in the accompanying photograph, an electric stove burner on its highest setting exhibits an orange glow. **(a)** When the burner setting is changed to low, the burner continues to produce heat but the orange glow disappears. How can this observation be explained with reference to one of the fundamental observations that led to the notion of quanta? **(b)** Suppose that the energy provided to the burner could be increased beyond the highest setting of the stove. What would we expect to observe with regard to visible light emitted by the burner? [Section 6.2]

**6.5** The familiar phenomenon of a rainbow results from the diffraction of sunlight through raindrops. **(a)** Does the wavelength of light increase or decrease as we proceed outward from the innermost band of the rainbow? **(b)** Does the frequency of light increase or decrease as we proceed outward? **(c)** Suppose that instead of sunlight, the visible light from a hydrogen discharge tube (Figure 6.10) was used as the light source. What do you think the resulting "hydrogen discharge rainbow" would look like? [Section 6.3]

**6.6** A certain quantum mechanical system has the energy levels shown in the diagram below. The energy levels are indexed by a single quantum number $n$ that is an integer. **(a)** As drawn, which quantum numbers are involved in the transition that requires the most energy? **(b)** Which quantum numbers are involved in the transition that requires the least energy? **(c)** Based on the drawing, put the following in order of increasing wavelength of the light absorbed or emitted during the transition: (*i*) $n = 1$ to $n = 2$; (*ii*) $n = 3$ to $n = 2$; (*iii*) $n = 2$ to $n = 4$; (*iv*) $n = 3$ to $n = 1$. [Section 6.3]

**6.7** Consider a fictitious one-dimensional system with one electron. The wave function for the electron, drawn at the top of the next page, is $\psi(x) = \sin x$ from $x = 0$ to $x = 2\pi$. **(a)** Sketch the probability density, $\psi^2(x)$, from $x = 0$ to $x = 2\pi$. **(b)** At what value or values of $x$ will there be the greatest probability of finding the electron? **(c)** What is the probability that the electron will be found at $x = \pi$? What is such a point in a wave function called? [Section 6.5]

**6.8** The contour representation of one of the orbitals for the $n = 3$ shell of a hydrogen atom is shown below. **(a)** What is the quantum number $l$ for this orbital? **(b)** How do we label this orbital? **(c)** How would you modify this sketch to show the analogous orbital for the $n = 4$ shell? [Section 6.6]

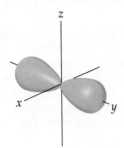

**6.9** The drawing below shows part of the orbital diagram for an element. **(a)** As drawn, the drawing is *incorrect*. Why? **(b)** How would you correct the drawing without changing the number of electrons? **(c)** To which group in the periodic table does the element belong? [Section 6.8]

**6.10** State where in the periodic table these elements appear:
**(a)** elements with the valence-shell electron configuration $ns^2np^5$
**(b)** elements that have three unpaired $p$ electrons
**(c)** an element whose valence electrons are $4s^24p^1$
**(d)** the $d$-block elements

# THE WAVE NATURE OF LIGHT (section 6.1)

**6.11** What are the basic SI units for **(a)** the wavelength of light, **(b)** the frequency of light, **(c)** the speed of light?

**6.12** **(a)** What is the relationship between the wavelength and the frequency of radiant energy? **(b)** Ozone in the upper atmosphere absorbs energy in the 210–230-nm range of the spectrum. In what region of the electromagnetic spectrum does this radiation occur?

**6.13** Label each of the following statements as true or false. For those that are false, correct the statement. **(a)** Visible light is a form of electromagnetic radiation. **(b)** Ultraviolet light has longer wavelengths than visible light. **(c)** X-rays travel faster than microwaves. **(d)** Electromagnetic radiation and sound waves travel at the same speed.

**6.14** Determine which of the following statements are false and correct them. **(a)** The frequency of radiation increases as the wavelength increases. **(b)** Electromagnetic radiation travels through a vacuum at a constant speed, regardless of wavelength. **(c)** Infrared light has higher frequencies than visible light. **(d)** The glow from a fireplace, the energy within a microwave oven, and a foghorn blast are all forms of electromagnetic radiation.

**6.15** Arrange the following kinds of electromagnetic radiation in order of increasing wavelength: infrared, green light, red light, radio waves, X-rays, ultraviolet light.

**6.16** List the following types of electromagnetic radiation in order of increasing wavelength: **(a)** the gamma rays produced by a radioactive nuclide used in medical imaging; **(b)** radiation from an FM radio station at 93.1 MHz on the dial; **(c)** a radio signal from an AM radio station at 680 kHz on the dial; **(d)** the yellow light from sodium vapor streetlights; **(e)** the red light of a light-emitting diode, such as in a calculator display.

**6.17** **(a)** What is the frequency of radiation that has a wavelength of 10 $\mu$m, about the size of a bacterium? **(b)** What is the wavelength of radiation that has a frequency of $5.50 \times 10^{14}$ s$^{-1}$? **(c)** Would the radiations in part (a) or part (b) be visible to the human eye? **(d)** What distance does electromagnetic radiation travel in 50.0 $\mu$s?

**6.18** **(a)** What is the frequency of radiation whose wavelength is $5.0 \times 10^{-5}$ m? **(b)** What is the wavelength of radiation that has a frequency of $2.5 \times 10^8$ s$^{-1}$? **(c)** Would the radiations in part (a) or part (b) be detected by an X-ray detector? **(d)** What distance does electromagnetic radiation travel in 10.5 fs?

**6.19** An argon ion laser emits light at 532 nm. What is the frequency of this radiation? Using Figure 6.4, predict the color associated with this wavelength.

**6.20** It is possible to convert radiant energy into electrical energy using photovoltaic cells. Assuming equal efficiency of conversion, would infrared or ultraviolet radiation yield more electrical energy on a per-photon basis?

# QUANTIZED ENERGY AND PHOTONS (section 6.2)

**6.21** If human height were quantized in one-foot increments, what would happen to the height of a child as she grows up?

**6.22** Einstein's 1905 paper on the photoelectric effect was the first important application of Planck's quantum hypothesis. Describe Planck's original hypothesis, and explain how Einstein made use of it in his theory of the photoelectric effect.

**6.23** (a) Calculate the energy of a photon of electromagnetic radiation whose frequency is $6.75 \times 10^{12}$ s$^{-1}$. (b) Calculate the energy of a photon of radiation whose wavelength is 322 nm. (c) What wavelength of radiation has photons of energy $2.87 \times 10^{-18}$ J?

**6.24** (a) A red laser pointer emits light with a wavelength of 650 nm. What is the frequency of this light? (b) What is the energy of one of these photons? (c) The laser pointer emits light because electrons in the material are excited (by a battery) from their ground state to an upper excited state. When the electrons return to the ground state, they lose the excess energy in the form of 650 nm photons. What is the energy gap between the ground state and excited state in the laser material?

**6.25** (a) Calculate and compare the energy of a photon of wavelength 3.3 $\mu$m with that of wavelength 0.154 nm. (b) Use Figure 6.4 to identify the region of the electromagnetic spectrum to which each belongs.

**6.26** An AM radio station broadcasts at 1010 kHz, and its FM partner broadcasts at 98.3 MHz. Calculate and compare the energy of the photons emitted by these two radio stations.

**6.27** One type of sunburn occurs on exposure to UV light of wavelength in the vicinity of 325 nm. (a) What is the energy of a photon of this wavelength? (b) What is the energy of a mole of these photons? (c) How many photons are in a 1.00 mJ burst of this radiation? (d) These UV photons can break chemical bonds in your skin to cause sunburn—a form of radiation damage. If the 325-nm radiation provides exactly the energy to break an average chemical bond in the skin, estimate the average energy of these bonds in kJ/mol.

**6.28** The energy from radiation can be used to cause the rupture of chemical bonds. A minimum energy of 941 kJ/mol is required to break the nitrogen–nitrogen bond in $N_2$. What is the longest wavelength of radiation that possesses the necessary energy to break the bond? What type of electromagnetic radiation is this?

**6.29** A diode laser emits at a wavelength of 987 nm. (a) In what portion of the electromagnetic spectrum is this radiation found? (b) All of its output energy is absorbed in a detector that measures a total energy of 0.52 J over a period of 32 s. How many photons per second are being emitted by the laser?

**6.30** A stellar object is emitting radiation at 3.55 mm. (a) What type of electromagnetic spectrum is this radiation? (b) If a detector is capturing $3.2 \times 10^8$ photons per second at this wavelength, what is the total energy of the photons detected in one hour?

**6.31** Molybdenum metal must absorb radiation with a minimum frequency of $1.09 \times 10^{15}$ s$^{-1}$ before it can eject an electron from its surface via the photoelectric effect. (a) What is the minimum energy needed to eject an electron? (b) What wavelength of radiation will provide a photon of this energy? (c) If molybdenum is irradiated with light of wavelength of 120 nm, what is the maximum possible kinetic energy of the emitted electrons?

**6.32** Sodium metal requires a photon with a minimum energy of $4.41 \times 10^{-19}$ J to emit electrons. (a) What is the minimum frequency of light necessary to emit electrons from sodium via the photoelectric effect? (b) What is the wavelength of this light? (c) If sodium is irradiated with light of 405 nm, what is the maximum possible kinetic energy of the emitted electrons? (d) What is the maximum number of electrons that can be freed by a burst of light whose total energy is 1.00 $\mu$J ?

# BOHR'S MODEL; MATTER WAVES (sections 6.3 and 6.4)

**6.33** Explain how the existence of line spectra is consistent with Bohr's theory of quantized energies for the electron in the hydrogen atom.

**6.34** (a) In terms of the Bohr theory of the hydrogen atom, what process is occurring when excited hydrogen atoms emit radiant energy of certain wavelengths and only those wavelengths? (b) Does a hydrogen atom "expand" or "contract" as it moves from its ground state to an excited state?

**6.35** Is energy emitted or absorbed when the following electronic transitions occur in hydrogen: (a) from $n = 4$ to $n = 2$, (b) from an orbit of radius 2.12 Å to one of radius 8.46 Å, (c) an electron adds to the $H^+$ ion and ends up in the $n = 3$ shell?

**6.36** Indicate whether energy is emitted or absorbed when the following electronic transitions occur in hydrogen: (a) from $n = 2$ to $n = 6$, (b) from an orbit of radius 4.76 Å to one of radius 0.529 Å, (c) from the $n = 6$ to the $n = 9$ state.

**6.37** (a) Using Equation 6.5, calculate the energy of an electron in the hydrogen atom when $n = 2$ and when $n = 6$. Calculate the wavelength of the radiation released when an electron moves from $n = 6$ to $n = 2$. (b) Is this line in the visible region of the electromagnetic spectrum? If so, what color is it?

**6.38** (a) Calculate the energies of an electron in the hydrogen atom for $n = 1$ and for $n = \infty$. How much energy does it require to move the electron out of the atom completely (from $n = 1$ to $n = \infty$), according to Bohr? Put your answer in kJ/mol. (b) The energy for the process $H + energy \rightarrow H^+ + e^-$ is called the ionization energy of hydrogen. The experimentally determined value for the ionization energy of hydrogen is 1310 kJ/mol. How does this compare to your calculation?

**6.39** The visible emission lines observed by Balmer all involved $n_f = 2$. (a) Explain why only the lines with $n_f = 2$ were observed in the visible region of the electromagnetic spectrum. (b) Calculate the wavelengths of the first three lines in the Balmer series—those for which $n_i = 3$, 4, and 5—and identify these lines in the emission spectrum shown in Figure 6.11.

**6.40** The Lyman series of emission lines of the hydrogen atom are those for which $n_f = 1$. (a) Determine the region of the electromagnetic spectrum in which the lines of the Lyman series are observed. (b) Calculate the wavelengths of the first three lines in the Lyman series—those for which $n_i = 2$, 3, and 4.

**6.41** One of the emission lines of the hydrogen atom has a wavelength of 93.8 nm. (a) In what region of the electromagnetic spectrum is this emission found? (b) Determine the initial and final values of $n$ associated with this emission.

**6.42** The hydrogen atom can absorb light of wavelength 2626 nm. **(a)** In what region of the electromagnetic spectrum is this absorption found? **(b)** Determine the initial and final values of $n$ associated with this absorption.

**6.43** Use the de Broglie relationship to determine the wavelengths of the following objects: **(a)** an 85-kg person skiing at 50 km/hr, **(b)** a 10.0-g bullet fired at 250 m/s, **(c)** a lithium atom moving at $2.5 \times 10^5$ m/s, **(d)** an ozone ($O_3$) molecule in the upper atmosphere moving at 550 m/s.

**6.44** Among the elementary subatomic particles of physics is the muon, which decays within a few nanoseconds after formation. The muon has a rest mass 206.8 times that of an electron. Calculate the de Broglie wavelength associated with a muon traveling at a velocity of $8.85 \times 10^5$ cm/s.

**6.45** Neutron diffraction is an important technique for determining the structures of molecules. Calculate the velocity of a neutron needed to achieve a wavelength of 0.955 Å. (Refer to the inside cover for the mass of the neutron).

**6.46** The electron microscope has been widely used to obtain highly magnified images of biological and other types of materials. When an electron is accelerated through a particular potential field, it attains a speed of $8.95 \times 10^6$ m/s. What is the characteristic wavelength of this electron? Is the wavelength comparable to the size of atoms?

**6.47** Using Heisenberg's uncertainty principle, calculate the uncertainty in the position of **(a)** a 1.50-mg mosquito moving at a speed of 1.40 m/s if the speed is known to within ±0.01 m/s; **(b)** a proton moving at a speed of $(5.00 \pm 0.01) \times 10^4$ m/s. (The mass of a proton is given in the table of fundamental constants in the inside cover of the text.)

**6.48** Calculate the uncertainty in the position of **(a)** an electron moving at a speed of $(3.00 \pm 0.01) \times 10^5$ m/s, **(b)** a neutron moving at this same speed. (The masses of an electron and a neutron are given in the table of fundamental constants in the inside cover of the text.) **(c)** What are the implications of these calculations to our model of the atom?

# QUANTUM MECHANICS AND ATOMIC ORBITALS (sections 6.5 and 6.6)

**6.49** **(a)** Why does the Bohr model of the hydrogen atom violate the uncertainty principle? **(b)** In what way is the description of the electron using a wave function consistent with de Broglie's hypothesis? **(c)** What is meant by the term *probability density*? Given the wave function, how do we find the probability density at a certain point in space?

**6.50** **(a)** According to the Bohr model, an electron in the ground state of a hydrogen atom orbits the nucleus at a specific radius of 0.53 Å. In the quantum mechanical description of the hydrogen atom, the most probable distance of the electron from the nucleus is 0.53 Å. Why are these two statements different? **(b)** Why is the use of Schrödinger's wave equation to describe the location of a particle very different from the description obtained from classical physics? **(c)** In the quantum mechanical description of an electron, what is the physical significance of the square of the wave function, $\psi^2$?

**6.51** **(a)** For $n = 4$, what are the possible values of $l$? **(b)** For $l = 2$, what are the possible values of $m_l$? **(c)** If $m_l$ is 2, what are the possible values for $l$?

**6.52** How many possible values for $l$ and $m_l$ are there when **(a)** $n = 3$; **(b)** $n = 5$?

**6.53** Give the numerical values of $n$ and $l$ corresponding to each of the following orbital designations: **(a)** 3p, **(b)** 2s, **(c)** 4f, **(d)** 5d.

**6.54** Give the values for $n$, $l$, and $m_l$ for **(a)** each orbital in the 2p subshell, **(b)** each orbital in the 5d subshell.

**6.55** Which of the following represent impossible combinations of $n$ and $l$: **(a)** 1p, **(b)** 4s, **(c)** 5f, **(d)** 2d?

**6.56** For the table that follows, write which orbital goes with the quantum numbers. Don't worry about $x$, $y$, $z$ subscripts. If the quantum numbers are not allowed, write "not allowed."

| $n$ | $l$ | $m_l$ | Orbital |
|---|---|---|---|
| 2 | 1 | −1 | 2p (example) |
| 1 | 0 | 0 | |
| 3 | −3 | 2 | |
| 3 | 2 | −2 | |
| 2 | 0 | −1 | |
| 0 | 0 | 0 | |
| 4 | 2 | 1 | |
| 5 | 3 | 0 | |

**6.57** Sketch the shape and orientation of the following types of orbitals: **(a)** $s$, **(b)** $p_z$, **(c)** $d_{xy}$.

**6.58** Sketch the shape and orientation of the following types of orbitals: **(a)** $p_x$, **(b)** $d_{z^2}$, **(c)** $d_{x^2-y^2}$.

**6.59** **(a)** What are the similarities and differences between the 1s and 2s orbitals of the hydrogen atom? **(b)** In what sense does a 2p orbital have directional character? Compare the "directional" characteristics of the $p_x$ and $d_{x^2-y^2}$ orbitals. (That is, in what direction or region of space is the electron density concentrated?) **(c)** What can you say about the average distance from the nucleus of an electron in a 2s orbital as compared with a 3s orbital? **(d)** For the hydrogen atom, list the following orbitals in order of increasing energy (that is, most stable ones first): 4f, 6s, 3d, 1s, 2p.

**6.60** **(a)** With reference to Figure 6.18, what is the relationship between the number of nodes in an $s$ orbital and the value of the principal quantum number? **(b)** Identify the number of nodes; that is, identify places where the electron density is zero, in the $2p_x$ orbital; in the 3s orbital. **(c)** What information is obtained from the radial probability functions in Figure 6.18? **(d)** For the hydrogen atom, list the following orbitals in order of increasing energy: 3s, 2s, 2p, 5s, 4d.

# MANY-ELECTRON ATOMS AND ELECTRON CONFIGURATIONS (sections 6.7–6.9)

**6.61** For a given value of the principal quantum number, $n$, how do the energies of the $s$, $p$, $d$, and $f$ subshells vary for **(a)** hydrogen, **(b)** a many-electron atom?

**6.62** **(a)** The average distance from the nucleus of a 3s electron in a chlorine atom is smaller than that for a 3p electron. In light of this fact, which orbital is higher in energy? **(b)** Would you expect it to require more or less energy to remove a 3s electron from the chlorine atom, as compared with a 2p electron? Explain.

**6.63** **(a)** What experimental evidence is there for the electron having a "spin"? **(b)** Draw an energy-level diagram that shows the relative energetic positions of a 1s orbital and a 2s orbital. Put two electrons in the 1s orbital. (c) Draw an arrow showing the excitation of an electron from the 1s to the 2s orbital.

**6.64** (a) State the Pauli exclusion principle in your own words. (b) The Pauli exclusion principle is, in an important sense, the key to understanding the periodic table. Explain.

**6.65** What is the maximum number of electrons that can occupy each of the following subshells: (a) 3p, (b) 5d, (c) 2s, (d) 4f?

**6.66** What is the maximum number of electrons in an atom that can have the following quantum numbers: (a) $n = 2$, $m_s = -\frac{1}{2}$, (b) $n = 5$, $l = 3$; (c) $n = 4$, $l = 3$, $m_l = -3$; (d) $n = 4$, $l = 0$, $m_l = 0$?

**6.67** (a) What are "valence electrons"? (b) What are "core electrons"? (c) What does each box in an orbital diagram represent? (d) What quantity is represented by the half arrows in an orbital diagram?

**6.68** For each element, indicate the number of valence electrons, core electrons, and unpaired electrons in the ground state: (a) carbon, (b) phosphorus, (c) neon.

**6.69** Write the condensed electron configurations for the following atoms, using the appropriate noble-gas core abbreviations: (a) Cs, (b) Ni, (c) Se, (d) Cd, (e) U, (f) Pb.

**6.70** Write the condensed electron configurations for the following atoms and indicate how many unpaired electrons each has: (a) Mg, (b) Ge, (c) Br, (d) V, (e) Y, (f) Lu.

**6.71** Identify the specific element that corresponds to each of the following electron configurations and indicate the number of unpaired electrons for each: (a) $1s^2 2s^2$, (b) $1s^2 2s^2 2p^4$, (c) $[Ar]4s^1 3d^5$, (d) $[Kr]5s^2 4d^{10} 5p^4$.

**6.72** Identify the group of elements that corresponds to each of the following generalized electron configurations and indicate the number of unpaired electrons for each:
(a) [noble gas] $ns^2 np^5$
(b) [noble gas] $ns^2 (n-1)d^2$
(c) [noble gas] $ns^2 (n-1)d^{10} np^1$
(d) [noble gas] $ns^2 (n-2)f^6$

**6.73** What is wrong with the following electron configurations for atoms in their ground states? (a) $1s^2 2s^2 3s^1$, (b) $[Ne]2s^2 2p^3$, (c) $[Ne]3s^2 3d^5$.

**6.74** The following electron configurations represent excited states. Identify the element, and write its ground-state condensed electron configuration. (a) $1s^2 2s^2 3p^2 4p^1$, (b) $[Ar]3d^{10} 4s^1 4p^4 5s^1$, (c) $[Kr]4d^6 5s^2 5p^1$.

# ADDITIONAL EXERCISES

**6.75** Consider the two waves shown here, which we will consider to represent two electromagnetic radiations:
(a) What is the wavelength of wave A? Of wave B?
(b) What is the frequency of wave A? Of wave B?
(c) Identify the regions of the electromagnetic spectrum to which waves A and B belong.

**6.76** If you put 120 volts of electricity through a pickle, the pickle will smoke and start glowing orange-yellow. The light is emitted because sodium ions in the pickle become excited; their return to the ground state results in light emission. (a) The wavelength of this emitted light is 589 nm. Calculate its frequency. (b) What is the energy of 0.10 mole of these photons? (c) Calculate the energy gap between the excited and ground states for the sodium ion. (d) If you soaked the pickle for a long time in a different salt solution, such as strontium chloride, would you still observe 589-nm light emission? Why or why not?

**6.77** Certain elements emit light of a specific wavelength when they are burned. Historically, chemists used such emission wavelengths to determine whether specific elements were present in a sample. Characteristic wavelengths for some of the elements are given in the following table:

| Ag | 328.1 nm | Fe | 372.0 nm |
|----|----------|----|----------|
| Au | 267.6 nm | K  | 404.7 nm |
| Ba | 455.4 nm | Mg | 285.2 nm |
| Ca | 422.7 nm | Na | 589.6 nm |
| Cu | 324.8 nm | Ni | 341.5 nm |

(a) Determine which elements emit radiation in the visible part of the spectrum. (b) Which element emits photons of highest energy? Of lowest energy? (c) When burned, a sample of an unknown substance is found to emit light of frequency $6.59 \times 10^{14}$ s$^{-1}$. Which of these elements is probably in the sample?

**6.78** In June 2004, the Cassini–Huygens spacecraft began orbiting Saturn and transmitting images to Earth. The closest distance between Saturn and Earth is 746 million miles. What is the minimum amount of time it takes for the transmitted signals to travel from the spacecraft to Earth?

**6.79** The rays of the Sun that cause tanning and burning are in the ultraviolet portion of the electromagnetic spectrum. These rays are categorized by wavelength. So-called UV-A radiation has wavelengths in the range of 320–380 nm, whereas UV-B radiation has wavelengths in the range of 290–320 nm. (a) Calculate the frequency of light that has a wavelength of 320 nm. (b) Calculate the energy of a mole of 320-nm photons. (c) Which are more energetic, photons of UV-A radiation or photons of UV-B radiation? (d) The UV-B radiation from the Sun is considered a greater cause of sunburn in humans than is UV-A radiation. Is this observation consistent with your answer to part (c)?

**6.80** The watt is the derived SI unit of power, the measure of energy per unit time: $1$ W $= 1$ J-s. A semiconductor laser in a CD player has an output wavelength of 780 nm and a power level of 0.10 mW. How many photons strike the CD surface during the playing of a CD 69 minutes in length?

**6.81** Carotenoids are yellow, orange, and red pigments synthesized by plants. The observed color of an object is not the color of light it absorbs but rather the complementary color, as described by a color wheel such as the one shown here. On this wheel, complementary colors are across from each other. (a) Based on this wheel, what color is absorbed most strongly if a plant is orange? (b) If a particular carotenoid absorbs photons at 455 nm, what is the energy of the photon?

**6.82** A photocell is a device used to measure the intensity of light. In a certain experiment, when light of wavelength 630 nm is directed onto the photocell, electrons are emitted at the rate of $2.6 \times 10^{-12}$ C/s (coulombs per second). Assume that each photon that impinges on the photocell emits one electron. How many photons per second are striking the photocell? How much energy per second is the photocell absorbing?

**6.83** In an experiment to study the photoelectric effect, a scientist measures the kinetic energy of ejected electrons as a function of the frequency of radiation hitting a metal surface. She obtains the following plot. The point labeled "$\nu_0$" corresponds to light with a wavelength of 680 nm. (a) What is the value of $\nu_0$ in $s^{-1}$? (b) What is the value of the work function of the metal in units of kJ/mol of ejected electrons? (c) What happens when the metal is irradiated with light of frequency less than $\nu_0$? (d) Note that when the frequency of the light is greater than $\nu_0$, the plot shows a straight line with a nonzero slope. Why is this the case? (e) Can you determine the slope of the line segment discussed in part (d)? Explain.

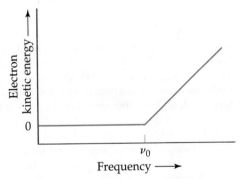

**6.84** The human retina has three types of receptor cones, each sensitive to a different range of wavelengths of visible light, as shown in this figure (the colors are merely to differentiate the three curves from one another; they do not indicate the actual colors represented by each curve):

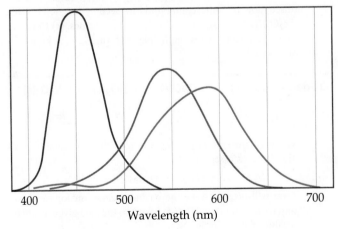

(a) Estimate the energies of photons with wavelengths at the maximum for each type of cone. (b) The color of the sky is due to scattering of solar light by the molecules of the atmosphere. Lord Rayleigh was one of the first to study scattering of this kind. He showed that the amount of scattering for very small particles such as molecules is inversely proportional to the fourth power of the wavelength. Estimate the ratio of the scattering efficiency of light at the wavelength of the maximum for the "blue" cones, as compared with that for the "green" cones. (c) Explain why the sky appears blue even though all wavelengths of solar light are scattered by the atmosphere.

**6.85** The series of emission lines of the hydrogen atom for which $n_f = 3$ is called the *Paschen series*. (a) Determine the region of the electromagnetic spectrum in which the lines of the Paschen series are observed. (b) Calculate the wavelengths of the first three lines in the Paschen series—those for which $n_i = 4$, 5, and 6.

**6.86** When the spectrum of light from the Sun is examined in high resolution in an experiment similar to that illustrated in Figure 6.9, dark lines are evident. These are called Fraunhofer lines, after the scientist who studied them extensively in the early nineteenth century. Altogether, about 25,000 lines have been identified in the solar spectrum between 2950 Å and 10,000 Å. The Fraunhofer lines are attributed to absorption of certain wavelengths of the Sun's "white" light by gaseous elements in the Sun's atmosphere. (a) Describe the process that causes absorption of specific wavelengths of light from the solar spectrum. (b) To determine which Fraunhofer lines belonged to a given element, say neon, what experiments could a scientist conduct here on Earth?

**[6.87]** Bohr's model can be used for hydrogen-like ions—ions that have only one electron, such as $He^+$ and $Li^{2+}$. (a) Why is the Bohr model applicable to $He^+$ ions but not to neutral He atoms? (b) The ground-state energies of H, $He^+$, and $Li^{2+}$ are tabulated as follows:

| Atom or ion | H | He⁺ | Li²⁺ |
|---|---|---|---|
| Ground-state energy | $-2.18 \times 10^{-18}$ J | $-8.72 \times 10^{-18}$ J | $-1.96 \times 10^{-17}$ J |

By examining these numbers, propose a relationship between the ground-state energy of hydrogen-like systems and the nuclear charge, $Z$. (c) Use the relationship you derive in part (b) to predict the ground-state energy of the $C^{5+}$ ion.

**[6.88]** An electron is accelerated through an electric potential to a kinetic energy of 18.6 keV. What is its characteristic wavelength? [*Hint:* Recall that the kinetic energy of a moving object is $E = \frac{1}{2} m v^2$, where $m$ is the mass of the object and $v$ is the speed of the object.]

**6.89** In the television series *Star Trek*, the transporter beam is a device used to "beam down" people from the *Starship Enterprise* to another location, such as the surface of a planet. The writers of the show put a "Heisenberg compensator" into the transporter beam mechanism. Explain why such a compensator (which is entirely fictional) would be necessary to get around Heisenberg's uncertainty principle.

**6.90** Which of the quantum numbers governs (a) the shape of an orbital, (b) the energy of an orbital, (c) the spin properties of the electron, (d) the spatial orientation of the orbital?

**[6.91]** Consider the discussion of radial probability functions in "A Closer Look" in Section 6.6. (a) What is the difference between the probability density as a function of $r$ and the radial probability function as a function of $r$? (b) What is the significance of the term $4\pi r^2$ in the radial probability functions for the $s$ orbitals? (c) Based on Figures 6.18 and 6.21, make sketches of what you think the probability density as a function of $r$ and the radial probability function would look like for the $4s$ orbital of the hydrogen atom.

[6.92] For orbitals that are symmetric but not spherical, the contour representations (as in Figures 6.22 and 6.23) suggest where nodal planes exist (that is, where the electron density is zero). For example, the $p_x$ orbital has a node wherever $x = 0$. This equation is satisfied by all points on the $yz$ plane, so this plane is called a nodal plane of the $p_x$ orbital. (a) Determine the nodal plane of the $p_z$ orbital. (b) What are the two nodal planes of the $d_{xy}$ orbital? (c) What are the two nodal planes of the $d_{x^2-y^2}$ orbital?

[6.93] The "Chemistry and Life" box in Section 6.7 described the techniques called NMR and MRI. (a) Instruments for obtaining MRI data are typically labeled with a frequency, such as 600 MHz. Why do you suppose this label is relevant to the experiment? (b) What is the value of $\Delta E$ in Figure 6.27 that would correspond to the absorption of a photon of radiation with frequency 450 MHz? (c) In general, the stronger the magnetic field, the greater the information obtained from an NMR or MRI experiment. Why do you suppose this is the case?

6.94 Suppose that the spin quantum number, $m_s$, could have *three* allowed values instead of two. How would this affect the number of elements in the first four rows of the periodic table?

6.95 Using the periodic table as a guide, write the condensed electron configuration and determine the number of unpaired electrons for the ground state of (a) Si, (b) Zn, (c) Zr, (d) Sn, (e) Ba, (f) Tl.

6.96 Scientists have speculated that element 126 might have a moderate stability, allowing it to be synthesized and characterized. Predict what the condensed electron configuration of this element might be.

# INTEGRATIVE EXERCISES

6.97 Microwave ovens use microwave radiation to heat food. The energy of the microwaves is absorbed by water molecules in food and then transferred to other components of the food. (a) Suppose that the microwave radiation has a wavelength of 11.2 cm. How many photons are required to heat 200 mL of coffee from 23 °C to 60 °C? (b) Suppose the microwave's power is 900 W (1 Watt = 1 joule-second). How long would you have to heat the coffee in part (a)?

6.98 The stratospheric ozone ($O_3$) layer helps to protect us from harmful ultraviolet radiation. It does so by absorbing ultraviolet light and falling apart into an $O_2$ molecule and an oxygen atom, a process known as photodissociation.

$$O_3(g) \longrightarrow O_2(g) + O(g)$$

Use the data in Appendix C to calculate the enthalpy change for this reaction. What is the maximum wavelength a photon can have if it is to possess sufficient energy to cause this dissociation? In what portion of the spectrum does this wavelength occur?

6.99 The discovery of hafnium, element number 72, provided a controversial episode in chemistry. G. Urbain, a French chemist, claimed in 1911 to have isolated an element number 72 from a sample of rare earth (elements 58–71) compounds. However, Niels Bohr believed that hafnium was more likely to be found along with zirconium than with the rare earths. D. Coster and G. von Hevesy, working in Bohr's laboratory in Copenhagen, showed in 1922 that element 72 was present in a sample of Norwegian zircon, an ore of zirconium. (The name hafnium comes from the Latin name for Copenhagen, *Hafnia*). (a) How would you use electron configuration arguments to justify Bohr's prediction? (b) Zirconium, hafnium's neighbor in group 4B, can be produced as a metal by reduction of solid $ZrCl_4$ with molten sodium metal. Write a balanced chemical equation for the reaction. Is this an oxidation-reduction reaction? If yes, what is reduced and what is oxidized? (c) Solid zirconium dioxide, $ZrO_2$, is reacted with chlorine gas in the presence of carbon. The products of the reaction are $ZrCl_4$ and two gases, $CO_2$ and CO in the ratio 1:2. Write a balanced chemical equation for the reaction. Starting with a 55.4-g sample of $ZrO_2$, calculate the mass of $ZrCl_4$ formed, assuming that $ZrO_2$ is the limiting reagent and assuming 100% yield. (d) Using their electron configurations, account for the fact that Zr and Hf form chlorides $MCl_4$ and oxides $MO_2$.

6.100 (a) Account for formation of the following series of oxides in terms of the electron configurations of the elements and the discussion of ionic compounds in Section 2.7: $K_2O$, CaO, $Sc_2O_3$, $TiO_2$, $V_2O_5$, $CrO_3$. (b) Name these oxides. (c) Consider the metal oxides whose enthalpies of formation (in kJ mol$^{-1}$) are listed here.

| Oxide | $K_2O(s)$ | $CaO(s)$ | $TiO_2(s)$ | $V_2O_5(s)$ |
|---|---|---|---|---|
| $\Delta H_f^\circ$ | $-363.2$ | $-635.1$ | $-938.7$ | $-1550.6$ |

Calculate the enthalpy changes in the following general reaction for each case:

$$M_nO_m(s) + H_2(g) \longrightarrow nM(s) + mH_2O(g)$$

(You will need to write the balanced equation for each case and then compute $\Delta H^\circ$.) (d) Based on the data given, estimate a value of $\Delta H_f^\circ$ for $Sc_2O_3(s)$.

**6.101** The first 25 years of the twentieth century were momentous for the rapid pace of change in scientists' understanding of the nature of matter. **(a)** How did Rutherford's experiments on the scattering of $\alpha$ particles by a gold foil set the stage for Bohr's theory of the hydrogen atom? **(b)** In what ways is de Broglie's hypothesis, as it applies to electrons, consistent with J. J. Thomson's conclusion that the electron has mass? In what sense is it consistent with proposals preceding Thomson's work that the cathode rays are a wave phenomenon?

**[6.102]** The two most common isotopes of uranium are $^{235}$U and $^{238}$U. **(a)** Compare the number of protons, the number of electrons, and the number of neutrons in atoms of these two isotopes. **(b)** Using the periodic table in the front inside cover, write the electron configuration for a U atom. **(c)** Compare your answer to part (b) to the electron configuration given in Figure 6.31. How can you explain any differences between these two electron configurations? **(d)** $^{238}$U undergoes radioactive decay to $^{234}$Th. How many protons, electrons, and neutrons are gained or lost by the $^{238}$U atom during this process? **(e)** Examine the electron configuration for Th in Figure 6.31. Are you surprised by what you find? Explain.

**6.103** Imagine sunlight falling on three square areas. One is an inert black material. The second is a photovoltaic cell surface, which converts radiant energy into electricity. The third is an area on a green tree leaf. Draw diagrams that show the energy conversions in each case, using Figure 5.9 as a model. How are these three examples related to the idea of sustainable energy sources?

# WHAT'S AHEAD

### 7.1 DEVELOPMENT OF THE PERIODIC TABLE
We begin our discussion with a brief history of the periodic table.

### 7.2 EFFECTIVE NUCLEAR CHARGE
We next explore the many properties of atoms that depend on the net attraction of the outer electrons to the nucleus and on the average distance of those electrons from the nucleus. The net positive charge of the nucleus experienced by the outer electrons is called the *effective nuclear charge*.

### 7.3 SIZES OF ATOMS AND IONS
We explore the relative sizes of atoms and ions, both of which follow trends that are related to their placement in the periodic table.

### 7.4 IONIZATION ENERGY
We next encounter the *ionization energy* required to remove one or more electrons from an atom. The periodic trends in ionization energy depend on variations in effective nuclear charge and atomic radii.

Light-emitting diodes, LEDs.

# PERIODIC PROPERTIES OF THE ELEMENTS

**THE BRILLIANT COLORS OF** light-emitting diodes (LEDs) arise from the composition of the materials from which they are made. The LEDs shown here are compounds of gallium and aluminum mixed with nitrogen, phosphorus, and arsenic. GaN, GaP, and GaAs can make solid solutions with each other and with AlN, AlP, and AlAs; the composition of each solid solution dictates the wavelength of light emitted by a given LED. Because these elements are in groups 3A and 5A, we say that LEDs are composed of "3-5" materials.

As we saw in Chapter 6, the periodic nature of the periodic table arises from repeating patterns in the electron configurations of the elements. Elements in the same column contain the same number of electrons in their **valence orbitals**, which are the occupied orbitals that hold the electrons involved in bonding. For example, O ($[He]2s^2 2p^4$) and S ($[Ne]3s^2 3p^4$) are both in group 6A. The similarity of the electron distribution in their valence $s$ and $p$ orbitals leads to similarities in the properties of these two elements. When we compare elemental O and elemental S, however, it is apparent that they exhibit differences as well, not the least of which is that at room temperature oxygen is a colorless gas but sulfur is a yellow solid. One major difference between O and S atoms is that the outermost electrons of O are in the second shell, whereas those of S are in the third shell. Thus, electron configurations can be used to explain differences as well as similarities in the properties of elements.

In this chapter we explore how some of the important properties of elements change as we move across a row or down a column of the periodic table. In many cases the trends in a row or column allow us to predict the physical and chemical properties of the elements.

# 7.1 | DEVELOPMENT OF THE PERIODIC TABLE

The discovery of chemical elements has been ongoing since ancient times (▼ FIGURE 7.1). Certain elements, such as gold (Au), appear in nature in elemental form and were thus discovered thousands of years ago. In contrast, some elements, such as technetium (Tc), are radioactive and intrinsically unstable. We know about them only because of technology developed during the twentieth century.

The majority of elements readily form compounds and, consequently, are not found in nature in their elemental form. For centuries, therefore, scientists were unaware of their existence. During the early nineteenth century, advances in chemistry made it easier to isolate elements from their compounds. As a result, the number of known elements more than doubled from 31 in 1800 to 63 by 1865.

As the number of known elements increased, scientists began classifying them. In 1869, Dmitri Mendeleev in Russia and Lothar Meyer in Germany published nearly identical classification schemes. Both scientists noted that similar chemical and physical properties recur periodically when the elements are arranged in order of increasing atomic weight. Scientists at that time had no knowledge of atomic numbers. Atomic weights, however, generally increase with increasing atomic number, so both Mendeleev and Meyer fortuitously arranged the elements in proper sequence. Although Mendeleev and Meyer came to essentially the same conclusion about the periodicity of elemental properties, Mendeleev is given credit for advancing his ideas more vigorously and stimulating new work. His insistence that elements with similar characteristics be listed in the same column forced him to leave blank spaces in his table. For example, both gallium (Ga) and germanium (Ge) were unknown to Mendeleev. He boldly predicted their

GO FIGURE

**Which row of the periodic table contains the most recently discovered elements? Can you suggest a reason?**

▶ FIGURE 7.1 Discovering the elements.

**TABLE 7.1** • **Comparison of the Properties of Eka-Silicon Predicted by Mendeleev with the Observed Properties of Germanium**

| Property | Mendeleev's Predictions for Eka-Silicon (made in 1871) | Observed Properties of Germanium (discovered in 1886) |
|---|---|---|
| Atomic weight | 72 | 72.59 |
| Density (g/cm³) | 5.5 | 5.35 |
| Specific heat (J/g-K) | 0.305 | 0.309 |
| Melting point (°C) | High | 947 |
| Color | Dark gray | Grayish white |
| Formula of oxide | $XO_2$ | $GeO_2$ |
| Density of oxide (g/cm³) | 4.7 | 4.70 |
| Formula of chloride | $XCl_4$ | $GeCl_4$ |
| Boiling point of chloride (°C) | A little under 100 | 84 |

existence and properties, referring to them as *eka-aluminum* ("under" aluminum) and *eka-silicon* ("under" silicon), respectively, after the elements under which they appeared in his table. When these elements were discovered, their properties closely matched those predicted by Mendeleev, as shown in ▲ **TABLE 7.1**.

In 1913, two years after Rutherford proposed the nuclear model of the atom ∞ (Section 2.2), English physicist Henry Moseley (1887–1915) developed the concept of atomic numbers. Bombarding different elements with high-energy electrons, Moseley found that each element produced X-rays of a unique frequency and that the frequency generally increased as the atomic mass increased. He arranged the X-ray frequencies in order by assigning a unique whole number, called an *atomic number*, to each element. Moseley correctly identified the atomic number as the number of protons in the nucleus of the atom. ∞ (Section 2.3)

The concept of atomic number clarified some problems in the periodic table of Moseley's day, which was based on atomic weights. For example, the atomic weight of Ar (atomic number 18) is greater than that of K (atomic number 19), yet the chemical and physical properties of Ar are much more like those of Ne and Kr than like those of Na and Rb. However, when the elements are arranged in order of increasing atomic number, rather than increasing atomic weight, Ar and K appear in their correct places in the table. Moseley's studies also made it possible to identify "holes" in the periodic table, which led to the discovery of previously unknown elements.

 **GIVE IT SOME THOUGHT**

Arranging the elements by atomic weight leads to an order slightly different from that in a modern periodic table, where the arrangement is by atomic number. Why does this happen? Looking at the periodic table on the inside front cover, can you find an example other than Ar and K where the order of the elements would be different if the elements were arranged in order of increasing atomic weight?

# 7.2 | EFFECTIVE NUCLEAR CHARGE

Many properties of atoms depend on electron configuration and on how strongly the outer electrons in the atoms are attracted to the nucleus. Coulomb's law tells us that the strength of the interaction between two electrical charges depends on the magnitudes of the charges and on the distance between them. ∞ (Section 2.3) Thus, the attractive force between an electron and the nucleus depends on the magnitude of the nuclear charge and on the average distance between the nucleus and the electron. The force increases as the nuclear charge increases and decreases as the electron moves farther from the nucleus.

Sodium nucleus
contains 11 protons (11⁺)

$e^-$

Valence electron (3s)

10⁻

Each of the 11 electrons is
attracted to positively
charged nucleus

Sodium atoms contains 10 core
electrons (10⁻) that screen the 3s
valence electron

▲ **FIGURE 7.2 Effective nuclear charge.** The effective nuclear charge experienced by the valence electron in a sodium atom depends mostly on the 11+ charge of the nucleus and the 10− charge of the core electrons.

**GO FIGURE**

**Which orbital has more electron density near the nucleus, 2s or 2p?**

No peak here tells you
2p electron stays far
from the nucleus

This peak tells you the
2s electron spends some
time close to nucleus

▲ **FIGURE 7.3 2s and 2p radial probability functions.**

In a many-electron atom, each electron is simultaneously attracted to the nucleus and repelled by the other electrons. In general, there are so many electron–electron repulsions that we cannot analyze the situation exactly. We can, however, estimate the attractive force between any one electron and the nucleus by considering how the electron interacts with the *average* environment created by the nucleus and the other electrons in the atom. We treat each electron as though it were moving in the net electric field created by the nucleus and the electron density of the other electrons. We view this net electric field as if it results from a single positive charge located at the nucleus, called the **effective nuclear charge**, $Z_{eff}$. The effective nuclear charge acting on an electron in an atom is smaller than the *actual* nuclear charge ($Z_{eff} < Z$) because the effective nuclear charge includes the effect of the other electrons in the atom.

In any many-electron atom, the inner electrons partially *screen* outer electrons from the attraction of the nucleus, and the relationship between $Z_{eff}$ and the number of protons in the nucleus $Z$ is

$$Z_{eff} = Z - S \qquad [7.1]$$

where $S$ is a positive number called the *screening constant*. It represents the portion of the nuclear charge that is screened from a valence electron by the other electrons in the atom. Because core electrons are most effective at screening a valence electron from the nucleus, *the value of S is usually close to the number of core electrons in an atom.* (Electrons in the same valence shell do not screen one another very effectively, but they do affect the value of $S$ slightly; see "A Closer Look: Effective Nuclear Charge.")

Let's look at the Na atom to see what to expect for the magnitude of $Z_{eff}$. Sodium has the electron configuration [Ne]$3s^1$. The nuclear charge is $Z = 11+$, and there are 10 core electrons ($1s^2 2s^2 2p^6$). We therefore expect $S$ to equal 10 and the 3s electron to experience an effective nuclear charge of $Z_{eff} = 11 - 10 = 1+$ (◀ **FIGURE 7.2**). The situation is more complicated, however, because the 3s electron has a small probability of being closer to the nucleus, in the region occupied by the core electrons. ∞ (Section 6.6) Thus, there is a probability that this electron experiences a greater attraction than our simple $S = 10$ model suggests. This greater attraction turns out to increase the value of $Z_{eff}$ for the 3s electron in Na from our expected $Z_{eff} = 1+$ to $Z_{eff} = 2.5+$. In other words, the fact that the 3s electron spends some small amount of time close to the nucleus changes the value of $S$ in Equation 7.1 from 10 to 8.5.

The notion of effective nuclear charge also explains an important effect we noted in Section 6.7: For a many-electron atom, the energies of orbitals with the same $n$ value increase with increasing $l$ value. For example, in the carbon atom, electron configuration $1s^2 2s^2 2p^2$, the energy of the 2p orbital ($l = 1$) is higher than that of the 2s orbital ($l = 0$) even though both orbitals are in the $n = 2$ shell (Figure 6.24). This difference in energies is due to the radial probability functions for the orbitals (◀ **FIGURE 7.3**). The greater attraction between the 2s electron and the nucleus leads to a lower energy for the 2s orbital than for the 2p orbital. The same reasoning explains the general trend in orbital energies ($ns < np < nd$) in many-electron atoms.

Finally, let's examine trends in valence-electron $Z_{eff}$ values. *The effective nuclear charge increases from left to right across any period of the periodic table.* Although the number of core electrons stays the same across the period, the number of protons increases. The valence electrons added to counterbalance the increasing nuclear charge screen one another ineffectively. Thus, $Z_{eff}$ increases steadily. For example, the core electrons of lithium ($1s^2 2s^1$) screen the $2s$ valence electron from the 3+ nucleus fairly efficiently. Consequently, the valence electron experiences an effective nuclear charge of roughly $3 - 2 = 1+$. For beryllium ($1s^2 2s^2$) the effective nuclear charge experienced by each valence electron is larger because here the $1s$ electrons screen a 4+ nucleus, and each $2s$ electron only partially screens the other. Consequently, the effective nuclear charge experienced by each $2s$ electron is about $4 - 2 = 2+$.

# A CLOSER LOOK

## EFFECTIVE NUCLEAR CHARGE

To get a sense of how effective nuclear charge varies as both nuclear charge and number of electrons increase, consider ▼ **FIGURE 7.4**. Although the details of how the $Z_{eff}$ values in the graph were calculated are beyond the scope of our discussion, the trends are instructive.

The effective nuclear charge felt by the outermost electrons is smaller than that felt by inner electrons because of screening by the inner electrons. In addition, the effective nuclear charge felt by the outermost electrons does not increase as steeply with increasing atomic number because the valence electrons make a small but non-negligible contribution to the screening constant $S$. The most striking feature associated with the $Z_{eff}$ value for the outermost electrons is the sharp drop between the last period 2 element (Ne) and the first period 3 element (Na). This drop reflects the fact that the core electrons are much more effective than the valence electrons at screening the nuclear charge.

Because $Z_{eff}$ can be used to understand many physically measurable quantities, it is desirable to have a simple method for estimating it. The value of $Z$ in Equation 7.1 is known exactly, so the challenge boils down to estimating the value of $S$. In the text, we estimated $S$ by assuming that each core electron contributes 1.00 to $S$ and the outer electrons contribute nothing. A more accurate approach was developed by John Slater, however, and we can use his approach if we limit ourselves to elements that do not have electrons in $d$ or $f$ subshells.

Electrons for which the principal quantum number $n$ is larger than the value of $n$ for the electron of interest contribute 0 to the value of $S$. Electrons with the same value of $n$ as the electron of interest contribute 0.35 to the value of $S$. Electrons for which $n$ is 1 less than $n$ for the electron of interest contribute 0.85, while those with even smaller values of $n$ contribute 1.00. For example, consider fluorine, which has the ground-state electron configuration $1s^2 2s^2 2p^5$. For a valence electron in fluorine, Slater's rules tell us that $S = (0.35 \times 6) + (0.85 \times 2) = 3.8$. (Slater's rules ignore the contribution of an electron to itself in screening; therefore, we consider only six $n = 2$ electrons, not all seven). Thus, $Z_{eff} = Z - S = 9 - 3.8 = 5.2+$.

Values of $Z_{eff}$ estimated using the simple method outlined in the text, as well as those estimated with Slater's rules, are plotted in Figure 7.4. While neither of these methods exactly replicate the values of $Z_{eff}$ obtained from more sophisticated calculations, both methods effectively capture the periodic variation in $Z_{eff}$. While Slater's approach is more accurate, the method outlined in the text does a reasonably good job of estimating $Z_{eff}$ despite its simplicity. For our purposes, therefore, we can assume that the screening constant $S$ in Equation 7.1 is roughly equal to the number of core electrons.

▲ **FIGURE 7.4** **Variations in effective nuclear charge for period 2 and period 3 elements.** Moving from one element to the next in the periodic table, the increase in $Z_{eff}$ felt by the innermost (1s) electrons (red circles) closely tracks the increase in nuclear charge Z (black line) because these electrons are not screened. The results of several methods to calculate $Z_{eff}$ for valence electrons are shown in other colors.

*RELATED EXERCISES:* 7.11, 7.12, 7.13, 7.14, 7.34, 7.35, 7.84, 7.85

*Going down a column, the effective nuclear charge experienced by valence electrons changes far less than it does across a period.* For example, we would expect the effective nuclear charge experienced by the valence electrons in lithium and sodium to be about the same, roughly $3 - 2 = 1+$ for lithium and $11 - 10 = 1+$ for sodium. In fact, however, effective nuclear charge increases slightly as we go down a column because the more diffuse core electron cloud is less able to screen the valence electrons from the nuclear charge. In the case of the alkali metals, $Z_{eff}$ increases from $1.3+$ for lithium, to $2.5+$ for sodium, to $3.5+$ for potassium.

 **GIVE IT SOME THOUGHT**

Which would you expect to experience a greater effective nuclear charge, a $2p$ electron of a Ne atom or a $3s$ electron of a Na atom?

# 7.3 | SIZES OF ATOMS AND IONS

We often think of atoms as hard, spherical objects. According to the quantum mechanical model, however, atoms do not have sharply defined boundaries at which the electron distribution becomes zero. ∞ (Section 6.5) Nevertheless, we can define atomic size in several ways, based on the distances between atoms in various situations.

Imagine a collection of argon atoms in the gas phase. When two of these atoms collide with each other, they ricochet apart like colliding billiard balls. This ricocheting happens because the electron clouds of the colliding atoms cannot penetrate each other to any significant extent. The shortest distance separating the two nuclei during such collisions is twice the radii of the atoms. We call this radius the *nonbonding atomic radius* or the *van der Waals* radius (◀ FIGURE 7.5).

In molecules, an attractive interaction exists between any two adjacent atoms in the molecule, leading to a chemical bond between the atoms. We discuss bonding in Chapter 8. For now, we only need to realize that this attractive interaction brings the two atoms closer together than they would be in a nonbonding collision where the atoms ricochet apart. We can define an atomic radius based on the distance separating the nuclei when two atoms are bonded to each other, shown as distance $d$ in Figure 7.5. The **bonding atomic radius** for any atom in a molecule is equal to half of the nucleus-to-nucleus distance $d$. Note from Figure 7.5 that the bonding atomic radius (also known as the *covalent radius*) is shorter than the nonbonding atomic radius. Unless otherwise noted, we mean the bonding atomic radius when we speak of the "size" of an atom.

Scientists have developed a variety of techniques for measuring the distances separating nuclei in molecules. From observations of these distances in many molecules, each element can be assigned a bonding atomic radius. For example, in the $I_2$ molecule, the distance separating the nuclei is observed to be 2.66 Å, which means the bonding atomic radius of an iodine atom is $(2.66 Å)/2 = 1.33$ Å.* Similarly, the distance separating adjacent carbon nuclei in diamond (a three-dimensional solid network of carbon atoms) is 1.54 Å; thus, the bonding atomic radius of carbon is 0.77 Å. The bonding atomic radii of other elements can be similarly defined (▶ FIGURE 7.6). (For helium and neon, the bonding atomic radii must be estimated because there are no known compounds of these elements.)

Knowing atomic radii allows us to estimate bond lengths in molecules. For example, the Cl—Cl bond length in $Cl_2$ is 1.99 Å, so a bonding atomic radius of 0.99 Å is assigned to Cl. In $CCl_4$ the measured length of the C—Cl bond is 1.77 Å, very close to the sum $(0.77 + 0.99 Å)$ of the bonding atomic radii of C and Cl.

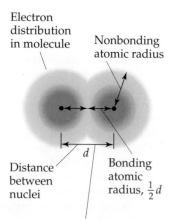

Electron distribution in molecule

Nonbonding atomic radius

Distance between nuclei

$d$

Bonding atomic radius, $\frac{1}{2}d$

**Nuclei cannot get any closer to each other because of electron–electron repulsion**

▲ **FIGURE 7.5** Distinction between nonbonding and bonding atomic radii within a molecule.

---

*Remember: The angstrom (1 Å $= 10^{-10}$ m) is a convenient metric unit for atomic measurements of length. It is not an SI unit. The most commonly used SI unit for atomic measurements is the picometer (1 pm $= 10^{-12}$ m; 1 Å = 100 pm).

## GO FIGURE

**Which part of the periodic table (top/bottom, left/right) has the elements with the largest atoms?**

◄ **FIGURE 7.6   Trends in bonding atomic radii for periods 1 through 5.**

---

**SAMPLE EXERCISE 7.1   Bond Lengths in a Molecule**

Natural gas used in home heating and cooking is odorless. Because natural gas leaks pose the danger of explosion or suffocation, various smelly substances are added to the gas to allow detection of a leak. One such substance is methyl mercaptan, $CH_3SH$. Use Figure 7.6 to predict the lengths of the C—S, C—H, and S—H bonds in this molecule.

### SOLUTION

**Analyze and Plan** We are given three bonds and told to use Figure 7.6 for bonding atomic radii. We will assume that each bond length is the sum of the bonding atomic radii of the two atoms involved.

**Solve**

C—S bond length = bonding atomic radius of C + bonding atomic radius of S

$$= 0.77\,Å + 1.02\,Å = 1.79\,Å$$

C—H bond length = $0.77\,Å + 0.37\,Å = 1.14\,Å$

S—H bond length = $1.02\,Å + 0.37\,Å = 1.39\,Å$

**Check** The experimentally determined bond lengths are C—S = 1.82 Å, C—H = 1.10 Å, and S—H = 1.33 Å. (In general, the lengths of bonds involving hydrogen show larger deviations from the values predicted from bonding atomic radii than do bonds involving larger atoms.)

**Comment** Notice that our estimated bond lengths are close but not exact matches to the measured bond lengths. Bonding atomic radii must be used with some caution in estimating bond lengths.

### PRACTICE EXERCISE

Using Figure 7.6, predict which is longer, the P—Br bond in $PBr_3$ or the As—Cl bond in $AsCl_3$.

***Answer:*** P—Br

Methyl mercaptan

---

## Periodic Trends in Atomic Radii

Figure 7.6 shows two interesting trends:

1.  Within each group, bonding atomic radius tends to increase from top to bottom. This trend results primarily from the increase in the principal quantum number ($n$) of the outer electrons. As we go down a column, the outer electrons have a greater probability of being farther from the nucleus, causing the atomic radius to increase.

2. Within each period, bonding atomic radius tends to decrease from left to right. The major factor influencing this trend is the increase in effective nuclear charge $Z_{eff}$ across a period. The increasing effective nuclear charge steadily draws the valence electrons closer to the nucleus, causing the bonding atomic radius to decrease.

 GIVE IT SOME THOUGHT

In Section 7.2 we said that $Z_{eff}$ generally increases when you move down a column of the periodic table, whereas in Chapter 6 we saw that the "size" of an orbital increases as the principal quantum number $n$ increases. With respect to atomic radii, do these trends work together or against each other? Which effect is larger?

---

**SAMPLE EXERCISE 7.2**    **Atomic Radii**

Referring to a periodic table, arrange (as much as possible) the atoms $_{15}P$, $_{16}S$, $_{33}As$, and $_{34}Se$ in order of increasing size. (Atomic numbers are given to help you locate the atoms quickly in the table.)

**SOLUTION**

**Analyze and Plan** We are given the chemical symbols for four elements and told to use their relative positions in the periodic table to predict the relative size of their atomic radii. We can use the two periodic trends just described to help with this problem.

**Solve** P and S are in the same period, with S to the right of P. Therefore, we expect the radius of S to be smaller than that of P because radii decrease as we move across a period. Likewise, the radius of Se is expected to be smaller than that of As. As is directly below P, and Se is directly below S. We expect, therefore, the radius of P to be smaller than that of As and the radius of S to be smaller than that of Se. Thus, so far we can say S < P, P < As, S < Se, Se < As. We can therefore conclude that S has the smallest radius and As has the largest radius and so can write S < ? < ? < As.

Our two periodic trends for atomic size do not supply enough information to allow us to determine whether P or Se (represented by the two question marks) has the larger radius, however. Going from P to Se in the periodic table, we move down (radius tends to increase) and to the right (radius tends to decrease). In Figure 7.6 we see that the radius of Se is greater than that of P. If you examine the figure carefully, you will discover that for the s- and p-block elements the increase in radius moving down a column tends to be the greater effect. There are exceptions, however.

**Check** From Figure 7.6, we have S$(1.02\text{Å})$ < P$(1.06\text{Å})$ < Se$(1.16\text{Å})$ < As$(1.19\text{Å})$.

**Comment** Note that the trends we have just discussed are for the s- and p-block elements. Figure 7.6 shows that the transition elements do not show a regular decrease moving across a period.

**PRACTICE EXERCISE**

Arrange $_{11}Na$, $_4Be$, and $_{12}Mg$ in order of increasing atomic radius.
**Answer:** Be < Mg < Na

---

## Periodic Trends in Ionic Radii

Just as bonding atomic radii can be determined from interatomic distances in molecules, ionic radii can be determined from interatomic distances in ionic compounds. Like the size of an atom, the size of an ion depends on its nuclear charge, the number of electrons it possesses, and the orbitals in which the valence electrons reside. When a cation is formed from a neutral atom, electrons are removed from the occupied atomic orbitals that are the most spatially extended from the nucleus. Also, the number of electron–electron repulsions is reduced. Therefore, *cations are smaller than their parent atoms* (▶ **FIGURE 7.7**). The opposite is true of anions. When electrons are added to an atom to form an anion, the increased electron–electron repulsions cause the electrons to spread out more in space. Thus, *anions are larger than their parent atoms.*

## GO FIGURE

How do cations of the same charge change in radius as you move down a column in the periodic table?

| Group 1A | Group 2A | Group 3A | Group 6A | Group 7A |
|---|---|---|---|---|
| $Li^+$ 0.90 | $Be^{2+}$ 0.59 | $B^{3+}$ 0.41 | $O^{2-}$ 1.26 | $F^-$ 1.19 |
| Li 1.34 | Be 0.90 | B 0.82 | O 0.73 | F 0.71 |
| $Na^+$ 1.16 | $Mg^{2+}$ 0.86 | $Al^{3+}$ 0.68 | $S^{2-}$ 1.70 | $Cl^-$ 1.67 |
| Na 1.54 | Mg 1.30 | Al 1.18 | S 1.02 | Cl 0.99 |
| $K^+$ 1.52 | $Ca^{2+}$ 1.14 | $Ga^{3+}$ 0.76 | $Se^{2-}$ 1.84 | $Br^-$ 1.82 |
| K 1.96 | Ca 1.24 | Ga 1.26 | Se 1.16 | Br 1.14 |
| $Rb^+$ 1.66 | $Sr^{2+}$ 1.32 | $In^{3+}$ 0.94 | $Te^{2-}$ 2.07 | $I^-$ 2.06 |
| Rb 2.11 | Sr 1.92 | In 1.44 | Te 1.35 | I 1.33 |

= cation      = anion      = neutral atom

▲ **FIGURE 7.7  Cation and anion size.** Radii, in angstroms, of atoms and their ions for five groups of representative elements.

For ions carrying the same charge, ionic radius increases as we move down a column in the periodic table (Figure 7.7). In other words, as the principal quantum number of the outermost occupied orbital of an ion increases, the radius of the ion increases.

---

**SAMPLE EXERCISE 7.3**  **Atomic and Ionic Radii**

Arrange $Mg^{2+}$, $Ca^{2+}$, and Ca in order of decreasing radius.

**SOLUTION**

Cations are smaller than their parent atoms, and so $Ca^{2+} <$ Ca. Because Ca is below Mg in group 2A, $Ca^{2+}$ is larger than $Mg^{2+}$. Consequently, Ca $>$ $Ca^{2+}$ $>$ $Mg^{2+}$.

**PRACTICE EXERCISE**

Which of the following atoms and ions is largest: $S^{2-}$, S, $O^{2-}$?

**Answer:** $S^{2-}$

An **isoelectronic series** is a group of ions all containing the same number of electrons. For example, each ion in the isoelectronic series $O^{2-}$, $F^-$, $Na^+$, $Mg^{2+}$, $Al^{3+}$ has 10 electrons. In any isoelectronic series we can list the members in order of increasing atomic number; therefore, nuclear charge increases as we move through the series. Because the number of electrons remains constant, ionic radius decreases with increasing nuclear charge as the electrons are more strongly attracted to the nucleus:

$$\text{—Increasing nuclear charge} \longrightarrow$$

| $O^{2-}$ | $F^-$ | $Na^+$ | $Mg^{2+}$ | $Al^{3+}$ |
|---|---|---|---|---|
| 1.26 Å | 1.19 Å | 1.16 Å | 0.86 Å | 0.68 Å |

$$\text{—Decreasing ionic radius} \longrightarrow$$

Notice the positions and atomic numbers of these elements in the periodic table. The nonmetal anions precede the noble gas Ne in the table. The metal cations follow Ne. Oxygen, the largest ion in this isoelectronic series, has the lowest atomic number, 8. Aluminum, the smallest of these ions, has the highest atomic number, 13.

# CHEMISTRY PUT TO WORK

## Ion Movement Powers Electronics

Ionic size plays a major role in determining the properties of devices that rely on movement of ions. "Lithium ion" batteries are everywhere—cell phones, iPods, laptop computers—and so let's see how a lithium ion battery works.

A fully charged battery spontaneously produces an electric current and, therefore, power when its positive and negative electrodes are connected in an electrical circuit. The positive electrode is called the anode, and the negative electrode is called the cathode. The materials used for the electrodes in lithium ion batteries are under intense development. Currently the anode material is graphite, a form of carbon, and the cathode is most frequently $LiCoO_2$, lithium cobalt oxide (▶ FIGURE 7.8). Between anode and cathode is a *separator,* a solid material that allows lithium ions, but not electrons, to pass through.

When the battery is being charged by an external source, lithium ions migrate from the cathode to the anode where they insert between the layers of carbon atoms. Lithium ions are smaller and lighter than most other elements, which means that many can fit between the layers. When the battery discharges and its electrodes are properly connected, it is energetically favorable for the lithium ions to move from anode to cathode. In order to maintain charge balance, electrons simultaneously migrate from anode to cathode through an external circuit, thereby producing electricity.

At the cathode, lithium ions then insert in the oxide material. Again, the small size of lithium ions is an advantage. For every lithium ion that inserts into the lithium cobalt oxide cathode, a $Co^{4+}$ ion is reduced to a $Co^{3+}$ by an electron that has traveled through the external circuit.

The ion migration and the changes in structure that result when lithium ions enter and leave the electrode materials are complicated.

Teams all over the world are trying to discover new cathode and anode materials that will easily accept and release lithium ions without falling apart over many repeated cycles. New separator materials that allow for faster lithium ion passage are also under development. Some research groups are looking at using sodium ions instead of lithium ions because sodium is far more abundant on Earth than lithium; new materials that allow sodium ion insertion and release are therefore under development. In the next decade we expect great advances in battery technology based on chemistry.

*RELATED EXERCISE: 7.91*

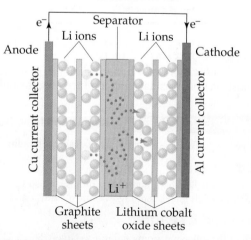

▲ FIGURE 7.8 **Schematic of a lithium ion battery.**

**SAMPLE EXERCISE 7.4**    **Ionic Radii in an Isoelectronic Series**

Arrange the ions $K^+$, $Cl^-$, $Ca^{2+}$, and $S^{2-}$ in order of decreasing size.

**SOLUTION**

This is an isoelectronic series, with all ions having 18 electrons. In such a series, size decreases as nuclear charge (atomic number) increases. The atomic numbers of the ions are S 16, Cl 17, K 19, Ca 20. Thus, the ions decrease in size in the order $S^{2-} > Cl^- > K^+ > Ca^{2+}$.

**PRACTICE EXERCISE**

In the isoelectronic series $Rb^+$, $Sr^{2+}$, $Y^{3+}$, which ion is largest?

**Answer:** $Rb^+$

# 7.4 | IONIZATION ENERGY

The ease with which electrons can be removed from an atom or ion has a major impact on chemical behavior. The **ionization energy** of an atom or ion is the minimum energy required to remove an electron from the ground state of the isolated gaseous atom or ion. The *first ionization energy,* $I_1$, is the energy needed to remove the first electron from a neutral atom. For example, the first ionization energy for the sodium atom is the energy required for the process

$$Na(g) \longrightarrow Na^+(g) + e^- \qquad [7.2]$$

The *second ionization energy,* $I_2$, is the energy needed to remove the second electron, and so forth, for successive removals of additional electrons. Thus, $I_2$ for the sodium atom is the energy associated with the process

$$Na^+(g) \longrightarrow Na^{2+}(g) + e^- \qquad [7.3]$$

The greater the ionization energy, the more difficult it is to remove an electron.

## Variations in Successive Ionization Energies

Notice in ▼ **TABLE 7.2** that ionization energies for a given element increase as successive electrons are removed: $I_1 < I_2 < I_3$, and so forth. This trend exists because with each successive removal, an electron is being pulled away from an increasingly more positive ion, requiring increasingly more energy.

 **GIVE IT SOME THOUGHT**

Light can be used to ionize atoms and ions. Which of the two processes shown in Equations 7.2 and 7.3 requires shorter-wavelength radiation?

A second important feature shown in Table 7.2 is the sharp increase in ionization energy that occurs when an inner-shell electron is removed. For example, consider silicon, $1s^2 2s^2 2p^6 3s^2 3p^2$. The ionization energies increase steadily from 786 kJ/mol to

**TABLE 7.2 •    Successive Values of Ionization Energies, *I*, for the Elements Sodium through Argon (kJ/mol)**

| Element | $I_1$ | $I_2$ | $I_3$ | $I_4$ | $I_5$ | $I_6$ | $I_7$ |
|---------|-------|-------|-------|-------|-------|-------|-------|
| Na | 496 | 4562 | | | (inner-shell electrons) | | |
| Mg | 738 | 1451 | 7733 | | | | |
| Al | 578 | 1817 | 2745 | 11,577 | | | |
| Si | 786 | 1577 | 3232 | 4356 | 16,091 | | |
| P | 1012 | 1907 | 2914 | 4964 | 6274 | 21,267 | |
| S | 1000 | 2252 | 3357 | 4556 | 7004 | 8496 | 27,107 |
| Cl | 1251 | 2298 | 3822 | 5159 | 6542 | 9362 | 11,018 |
| Ar | 1521 | 2666 | 3931 | 5771 | 7238 | 8781 | 11,995 |

4356 kJ/mol for the four electrons in the $3s$ and $3p$ subshells. Removal of the fifth electron, which comes from the $2p$ subshell, requires a great deal more energy: 16,091 kJ/mol. The large increase occurs because the $2p$ electron is much more likely to be found close to the nucleus than are the four $n = 3$ electrons and, therefore, the $2p$ electron experiences a much greater effective nuclear charge than do the $3s$ and $3p$ electrons.

 GIVE IT SOME THOUGHT

Which would you expect to be greater, $I_1$ for a boron atom or $I_2$ for a carbon atom?

Every element exhibits a large increase in ionization energy when one of its inner electrons is removed. This observation supports the idea that only the outermost electrons are involved in the sharing and transfer of electrons that give rise to chemical bonding and reactions. The inner electrons are too tightly bound to the nucleus to be lost from the atom or even shared with another atom.

---

**SAMPLE EXERCISE 7.5** | **Trends in Ionization Energy**

Three elements are indicated in the periodic table in the margin. Which one has the largest second ionization energy?

**SOLUTION**

**Analyze and Plan** The locations of the elements in the periodic table allow us to predict the electron configurations. The greatest ionization energies involve removal of core electrons. Thus, we should look first for an element with only one electron in the outermost occupied shell.

**Solve** The red box represents Na, which has one valence electron. The second ionization energy of this element is associated, therefore, with the removal of a core electron. The other elements indicated, S (green) and Ca (blue), have two or more valence electrons. Thus, Na should have the largest second ionization energy.

**Check** A chemistry handbook gives these $I_2$ values: Ca 1145 kJ/mol, S 2252 kJ/mol, Na 4562 kJ/mol.

**PRACTICE EXERCISE**

Which has the greater third ionization energy, Ca or S?
*Answer:* Ca

---

## Periodic Trends in First Ionization Energies

▶ **FIGURE 7.9** shows, for the first 54 elements, the trends we observe in first ionization energy as we move from one element to another in the periodic table. The important trends are as follows:

1. $I_1$ generally increases as we move across a period. The alkali metals show the lowest ionization energy in each period, and the noble gases show the highest. There are slight irregularities in this trend that we will discuss shortly.

2. $I_1$ generally decreases as we move down any column in the periodic table. For example, the ionization energies of the noble gases follow the order He > Ne > Ar > Kr > Xe.

3. The $s$- and $p$-block elements show a larger range of $I_1$ values than do the transition-metal elements. Generally, the ionization energies of the transition metals increase slowly from left to right in a period. The $f$-block metals (not shown in Figure 7.9) also show only a small variation in the values of $I_1$.

In general, smaller atoms have higher ionization energies. The same factors that influence atomic size also influence ionization energies. The energy needed to remove an electron from the outermost occupied shell depends on both the effective nuclear charge and the average distance of the electron from the nucleus. Either increasing the effective nuclear charge or decreasing the distance from the nucleus increases the attraction

## GO FIGURE

**Which has a larger first ionization energy, Ar or As? Why?**

▲ **FIGURE 7.9   Trends in first ionization energies of the elements.**

between the electron and the nucleus. As this attraction increases, it becomes more difficult to remove the electron and, thus, the ionization energy increases. As we move across a period, there is both an increase in effective nuclear charge and a decrease in atomic radius, causing the ionization energy to increase. As we move down a column, the atomic radius increases while the effective nuclear charge increases rather gradually. Thus, the attraction between the nucleus and the electron decreases, causing the ionization energy to decrease.

The irregularities in a given period are subtle but still readily explained. For example, the decrease in ionization energy from beryllium ($[He]2s^2$) to boron ($[He]2s^2 2p^1$), shown in Figure 7.9, occurs because the third valence electron of B must occupy the $2p$ subshell, which is empty for Be. Recall that the $2p$ subshell is at a higher energy than the $2s$ subshell (Figure 6.24). The decrease in ionization energy when moving from nitrogen ($[He]2s^2 2p^3$) to oxygen ($[He]2s^2 2p^4$) is because of the repulsion of paired electrons in the $p^4$ configuration (▶ **FIGURE 7.10**). Remember that according to Hund's rule, each electron in the $p^3$ configuration resides in a different $p$ orbital, which minimizes the electron–electron repulsion among the three $2p$ electrons. ⌁⌁(Section 6.8)

## GO FIGURE

**Explain why it is easier to remove a 2p electron from an oxygen atom than from a nitrogen atom.**

$2p$ | ↑↓ | ↑ | ↑ |
Oxygen

$2p$ | ↑ | ↑ | ↑ |
Nitrogen

▲ **FIGURE 7.10   2p orbital filling in nitrogen and oxygen.**

### SAMPLE EXERCISE 7.6   Periodic Trends in Ionization Energy

Referring to a periodic table, arrange the atoms Ne, Na, P, Ar, K in order of increasing first ionization energy.

### SOLUTION

**Analyze and Plan** We are given the chemical symbols for five elements. To rank them according to increasing first ionization energy, we need to locate each element in the periodic table. We can then use their relative positions and the trends in first ionization energies to predict their order.

**Solve** Ionization energy increases as we move left to right across a period and decreases as we move down a group. Because Na, P, and Ar are in the same period, we expect $I_1$ to vary in the order Na < P < Ar. Because Ne is above Ar in group 8A, we expect Ar < Ne. Similarly, K is directly below Na in group 1A, and so we expect K < Na.

From these observations, we conclude that the ionization energies follow the order

$$K < Na < P < Ar < Ne$$

**Check** The values shown in Figure 7.9 confirm this prediction.

**PRACTICE EXERCISE**

Which has the lowest first ionization energy, B, Al, C, or Si? Which has the highest?

**Answer:** Al lowest, C highest

## Electron Configurations of Ions

When electrons are removed from an atom to form a cation, they are always removed first from the occupied orbitals having the largest principal quantum number, $n$. For example, when one electron is removed from a lithium atom ($1s^2 2s^1$), it is the $2s^1$ electron:

$$\text{Li} \, (1s^2 2s^1) \Rightarrow \text{Li}^+ \, (1s^2) + e^-$$

Likewise, when two electrons are removed from Fe ($[\text{Ar}]3d^6 4s^2$), the $4s^2$ electrons are the ones removed:

$$\text{Fe} \, ([\text{Ar}]3d^6 4s^2) \Rightarrow \text{Fe}^{2+} \, ([\text{Ar}]3d^6) + 2e^-$$

If an additional electron is removed, forming $\text{Fe}^{3+}$, it comes from a $3d$ orbital because all the orbitals with $n = 4$ are empty:

$$\text{Fe}^{2+} \, ([\text{Ar}]3d^6) \Rightarrow \text{Fe}^{3+} \, ([\text{Ar}]3d^5) + e^-$$

It may seem odd that $4s$ electrons are removed before $3d$ electrons in forming transition-metal cations. After all, in writing electron configurations, we added the $4s$ electrons before the $3d$ ones. In writing electron configurations for atoms, however, we are going through an imaginary process in which we move through the periodic table from one element to another. In doing so, we are adding both an electron to an orbital and a proton to the nucleus to change the identity of the element. In ionization, we do not reverse this process because no protons are being removed.

If there is more than one occupied subshell for a given value of $n$, the electrons are first removed from the orbital with the highest value of $l$. For example, a tin atom loses its $5p$ electrons before it loses its $5s$ electrons:

$$\text{Sn} \, ([\text{Kr}]4d^{10}5s^2 5p^2) \Rightarrow \text{Sn}^{2+} \, ([\text{Kr}]4d^{10}5s^2) + 2e^- \Rightarrow \text{Sn}^{4+} \, ([\text{Kr}]4d^{10}) + 4e^-$$

Electrons added to an atom to form an anion are added to the empty or partially filled orbital having the lowest value of $n$. For example, an electron added to a fluorine atom to form the $\text{F}^-$ ion goes into the one remaining vacancy in the $2p$ subshell:

$$\text{F} \, (1s^2 2s^2 2p^5) + e^- \Rightarrow \text{F}^- \, (1s^2 2s^2 2p^6)$$

 **GIVE IT SOME THOUGHT**

Do $\text{Cr}^{3+}$ and $\text{V}^{2+}$ have the same or different electron configurations?

**SAMPLE EXERCISE 7.7** | Electron Configurations of Ions

Write the electron configuration for (a) $\text{Ca}^{2+}$, (b) $\text{Co}^{3+}$, and (c) $\text{S}^{2-}$.

**SOLUTION**

**Analyze and Plan** We are asked to write electron configurations for three ions. To do so, we first write the electron configuration of each parent atom, then remove or add electrons to form the ions. Electrons are first removed from the orbitals having the highest value of $n$. They are added to the empty or partially filled orbitals having the lowest value of $n$.

**Solve**

**(a)** Calcium (atomic number 20) has the electron configuration $[Ar]4s^2$. To form a 2+ ion, the two outer electrons must be removed, giving an ion that is isoelectronic with Ar:

$$Ca^{2+}: [Ar]$$

**(b)** Cobalt (atomic number 27) has the electron configuration $[Ar]3d^74s^2$. To form a 3+ ion, three electrons must be removed. As discussed in the text, the $4s$ electrons are removed before the $3d$ electrons. Consequently, the electron configuration for $Co^{3+}$ is

$$Co^{3+}: [Ar]3d^6$$

**(c)** Sulfur (atomic number 16) has the electron configuration $[Ne]3s^23p^4$. To form a 2− ion, two electrons must be added. There is room for two additional electrons in the $3p$ orbitals. Thus, the $S^{2-}$ electron configuration is

$$S^{2-}: [Ne]3s^2\,3p^6 = [Ar]$$

**Comment**  Remember that many of the common ions of the $s$- and $p$-block elements, such as $Ca^{2+}$ and $S^{2-}$, have the same number of electrons as the closest noble gas.  ⚭⚭⚭ (Section 2.7)

**PRACTICE EXERCISE**

Write the electron configuration for **(a)** $Ga^{3+}$, **(b)** $Cr^{3+}$, and **(c)** $Br^-$.

**Answers:**  **(a)** $[Ar]3d^{10}$, **(b)** $[Ar]3d^3$, **(c)** $[Ar]3d^{10}4s^24p^6 = [Kr]$

# 7.5 | ELECTRON AFFINITIES

The first ionization energy of an atom is a measure of the energy change associated with removing an electron from the atom to form a cation. For example, the first ionization energy of $Cl(g)$, 1251 kJ/mol, is the energy change associated with the process

$$\textit{Ionization energy: } Cl(g) \longrightarrow Cl^+(g) + e^- \qquad \Delta E = 1251 \text{ kJ/mol} \qquad [7.4]$$
$$\quad [Ne]3s^23p^5 \quad\quad [Ne]3s^23p^4$$

The positive ionization energy means that energy must be put into the atom to remove the electron.

Most atoms can also gain electrons to form anions. The energy change that occurs when an electron is added to a gaseous atom is called the **electron affinity** because it measures the attraction, or *affinity*, of the atom for the added electron. For most atoms, energy is released when an electron is added. For example, the addition of an electron to a chlorine atom is accompanied by an energy change of −349 kJ/mol, the negative sign indicating that energy is released during the process. We therefore say that the electron affinity of Cl is −349 kJ/mol.*

$$\textit{Electron affinity: } Cl(g) + e^- \longrightarrow Cl^-(g) \qquad \Delta E = -349 \text{ kJ/mol} \qquad [7.5]$$
$$\quad [Ne]3s^23p^5 \quad\quad [Ne]3s^23p^6$$

It is important to understand the difference between ionization energy and electron affinity: Ionization energy measures the ease with which an atom *loses* an electron, whereas electron affinity measures the ease with which an atom *gains* an electron.

The greater the attraction between an atom and an added electron, the more negative the atom's electron affinity. For some elements, such as the noble gases, the electron affinity has a positive value, meaning that the anion is higher in energy than are the separated atom and electron:

$$Ar(g) + e^- \longrightarrow Ar^-(g) \qquad \Delta E > 0 \qquad [7.6]$$
$$[Ne]3s^23p^6 \quad\quad [Ne]3s^23p^64s^1$$

---

*Two sign conventions are used for electron affinity. In most introductory texts, including this one, the thermodynamic sign convention is used: A negative sign indicates that addition of an electron is an exothermic process, as in the electron affinity for chlorine, −349 kJ/mol. Historically, however, electron affinity has been defined as the energy released when an electron is added to a gaseous atom or ion. Because 349 kJ/mol is released when an electron is added to $Cl(g)$, the electron affinity by this convention would be +349 kJ/mol.

**GO FIGURE**

**Which of the groups shown here has the most negative electron affinities? Why does this make sense?**

| 1A | | | | | | | 8A |
|---|---|---|---|---|---|---|---|
| **H** −73 | 2A | 3A 4A 5A 6A 7A | | | | | **He** >0 |
| **Li** −60 | **Be** >0 | **B** −27 | **C** −122 | **N** >0 | **O** −141 | **F** −328 | **Ne** >0 |
| **Na** −53 | **Mg** >0 | **Al** −43 | **Si** −134 | **P** −72 | **S** −200 | **Cl** −349 | **Ar** >0 |
| **K** −48 | **Ca** −2 | **Ga** −30 | **Ge** −119 | **As** −78 | **Se** −195 | **Br** −325 | **Kr** >0 |
| **Rb** −47 | **Sr** −5 | **In** −30 | **Sn** −107 | **Sb** −103 | **Te** −190 | **I** −295 | **Xe** >0 |

▲ **FIGURE 7.11 Electron affinity in kJ/mol for selected s- and p-block elements.**

The fact that the electron affinity is positive means that an electron will not attach itself to an Ar atom; the Ar⁻ ion is unstable and does not form.

◄ **FIGURE 7.11** shows the electron affinities for the s- and p-block elements of the first five periods. Notice that the trends are not as evident as they are for ionization energy. The halogens, which are one electron shy of a filled p subshell, have the most-negative electron affinities. By gaining an electron, a halogen atom forms a stable anion that has a noble-gas configuration (Equation 7.5). The addition of an electron to a noble gas, however, requires that the electron reside in a higher-energy subshell that is empty in the atom (Equation 7.6). Because occupying a higher-energy subshell is energetically unfavorable, the electron affinity is highly positive. The electron affinities of Be and Mg are positive for the same reason; the added electron would reside in a previously empty p subshell that is higher in energy.

The electron affinities of the group 5A elements are also interesting. Because these elements have half-filled p subshells, the added electron must be put in an orbital that is already occupied, resulting in larger electron–electron repulsions. Consequently, these elements have electron affinities that are either positive (N) or less negative than the electron affinities of their neighbors to the left (P, As, Sb). Recall that in Section 7.4 we saw a discontinuity in the trends for first ionization energy for the same reason.

Electron affinities do not change greatly as we move down a group (Figure 7.11). For F, for instance, the added electron goes into a 2p orbital, for Cl a 3p orbital, for Br a 4p orbital, and so forth. As we proceed from F to I, therefore, the average distance between the added electron and the nucleus steadily increases, causing the electron–nucleus attraction to decrease. However, the orbital that holds the outermost electron is increasingly spread out, so that as we proceed from F to I, the electron–electron repulsions are also reduced. As a result, the reduction in the electron–nucleus attraction is counterbalanced by the reduction in electron–electron repulsions.

 **GIVE IT SOME THOUGHT**

What is the relationship between the value for the first ionization energy of a Cl⁻(g) ion and the electron affinity of Cl(g)?

## 7.6 | METALS, NONMETALS, AND METALLOIDS

Atomic radii, ionization energies, and electron affinities are properties of individual atoms. With the exception of the noble gases, however, none of the elements exist in nature as individual atoms. To get a broader understanding of the properties of elements, we must also examine periodic trends in properties that involve large collections of atoms.

The elements can be broadly grouped as metals, nonmetals, and metalloids (► **FIGURE 7.12**). ∞ (Section 2.5) Some of the distinguishing properties of metals and nonmetals are summarized in ▼ **TABLE 7.3**.

In the following sections, we explore some common patterns of reactivity across the periodic table. We will examine reactivity for nonmetals and metals in more depth in later chapters.

**TABLE 7.3 • Characteristic Properties of Metals and Nonmetals**

| Metals | Nonmetals |
|---|---|
| Have a shiny luster; various colors, although most are silvery | Do not have a luster; various colors |
| Solids are malleable and ductile | Solids are usually brittle; some are hard, some are soft |
| Good conductors of heat and electricity | Poor conductors of heat and electricity |
| Most metal oxides are ionic solids that are basic | Most nonmetal oxides are molecular substances that form acidic solutions |
| Tend to form cations in aqueous solution | Tend to form anions or oxyanions in aqueous solution |

## GO FIGURE

Notice that germanium, Ge, is a metalloid but tin, Sn, is a metal. What changes in atomic properties do you think are important in explaining this difference?

Increasing metallic character →

Increasing metallic character ↓

**▲ FIGURE 7.12 Metals, metalloids, and nonmetals.**

The more an element exhibits the physical and chemical properties of metals, the greater its **metallic character**. As indicated in Figure 7.12, metallic character generally increases as we proceed down a group of the periodic table and decreases as we proceed right across a period. Let's now examine the close relationships that exist between electron configurations and the properties of metals, nonmetals, and metalloids.

## Metals

Most metallic elements exhibit the shiny luster we associate with metals (▶ **FIGURE 7.13**). Metals conduct heat and electricity. In general they are malleable (can be pounded into thin sheets) and ductile (can be drawn into wires). All are solids at room temperature except mercury (melting point = −39 °C), which is a liquid at room temperature. Two metals melt at slightly above room temperature, cesium at 28.4 °C and gallium at 29.8 °C. At the other extreme, many metals melt at very high temperatures. For example, chromium melts at 1900 °C.

*Metals tend to have low ionization energies* (Figure 7.9) *and therefore tend to form cations relatively easily.* As a result, metals are oxidized (lose electrons) when they undergo chemical reactions. Among the fundamental atomic properties (radius, electron configuration, electron affinity, and so forth), first ionization energy is the best indicator of whether an element behaves as a metal or a nonmetal.

▶ **FIGURE 7.14** shows the oxidation states of representative ions of metals and nonmetals. As noted in Section 2.7, the charge on any alkali metal ion in a compound is always 1+, and that on any alkaline earth metal is always 2+. For atoms belonging to either of these groups, the outer $s$ electrons are easily lost, yielding a noble-gas electron configuration. For metals belonging to groups with partially occupied $p$ orbitals (groups 3A–7A), cations are formed either by losing only the outer $p$ electrons (such as $Sn^{2+}$) or the outer $s$ and $p$ electrons (such as $Sn^{4+}$). The charge on transition-metal ions does not follow an obvious pattern. One characteristic of the transition metals is their ability to form more than one cation. For example, iron is 2+ in some compounds and 3+ in others.

**▲ FIGURE 7.13 Metals are shiny and malleable.**

## GIVE IT SOME THOUGHT

Describe a general relationship between trends in metallic character and trends in ionization energy.

**GO FIGURE**

The red stepped line divides metals from nonmetals. How are common oxidation states divided by this line?

| 1A | | | | | | | | | | | | | 3A | 4A | 5A | 6A | 7A | 8A |
|----|----|----|----|----|----|----|----|----|----|----|----|----|----|----|----|----|----|----|
| $H^+$ | | | | | | | | | | | | | | | | | $H^-$ | N |
| $Li^+$ | 2A | | | | Transition metals | | | | | | | | | | $N^{3-}$ | $O^{2-}$ | $F^-$ | O |
| $Na^+$ | $Mg^{2+}$ | | | | | | | | | | | | $Al^{3+}$ | | $P^{3-}$ | $S^{2-}$ | $Cl^-$ | B L E |
| $K^+$ | $Ca^{2+}$ | $Sc^{3+}$ | $Ti^{4+}$ | $V^{5+}$ $V^{4+}$ | $Cr^{3+}$ | $Mn^{2+}$ $Mn^{4+}$ | $Fe^{2+}$ $Fe^{3+}$ | $Co^{2+}$ $Co^{3+}$ | $Ni^{2+}$ | $Cu^+$ $Cu^{2+}$ | $Zn^{2+}$ | | | | | $Se^{2-}$ | $Br^-$ | G A S E S |
| $Rb^+$ | $Sr^{2+}$ | | | | | | | | $Pd^{2+}$ | $Ag^+$ | $Cd^{2+}$ | | $Sn^{2+}$ $Sn^{4+}$ | $Sb^{3+}$ $Sb^{5+}$ | $Te^{2-}$ | | $I^-$ | |
| $Cs^+$ | $Ba^{2+}$ | | | | | | | | $Pt^{2+}$ | $Au^+$ $Au^{3+}$ | $Hg_2^{2+}$ $Hg^{2+}$ | | $Pb^{2+}$ $Pb^{4+}$ | $Bi^{3+}$ $Bi^{5+}$ | | | | |

▲ **FIGURE 7.14** **Representative oxidation states of the elements.** Note that hydrogen has both positive and negative oxidation numbers, +1 and −1.

*Compounds made up of a metal and a nonmetal tend to be ionic substances.* For example, most metal oxides and halides are ionic solids. To illustrate, the reaction between nickel metal and oxygen produces nickel oxide, an ionic solid containing $Ni^{2+}$ and $O^{2-}$ ions:

$$2\,Ni(s) + O_2(g) \longrightarrow 2\,NiO(s) \tag{7.7}$$

The oxides are particularly important because of the great abundance of oxygen in our environment.

*Most metal oxides are basic.* Those that dissolve in water react to form metal hydroxides, as in the following examples:

$$\text{Metal oxide} + \text{water} \longrightarrow \text{metal hydroxide}$$

$$Na_2O(s) + H_2O(l) \longrightarrow 2\,NaOH(aq) \tag{7.8}$$

$$CaO(s) + H_2O(l) \longrightarrow Ca(OH)_2(aq) \tag{7.9}$$

The basicity of metal oxides is due to the oxide ion, which reacts with water:

$$O^{2-}(aq) + H_2O(l) \longrightarrow 2\,OH^-(aq) \tag{7.10}$$

Even metal oxides that are insoluble in water demonstrate their basicity by reacting with acids to form a salt plus water, as illustrated in ▼ **FIGURE 7.15**:

$$\text{Metal oxide} + \text{acid} \longrightarrow \text{salt} + \text{water}$$

$$NiO(s) + 2\,HNO_3(aq) \longrightarrow Ni(NO_3)_2(aq) + H_2O(l) \tag{7.11}$$

▶ **FIGURE 7.15** **Metal oxides react with acids.** NiO does not dissolve in water but does react with nitric acid ($HNO_3$) to give a green solution of $Ni(NO_3)_2$.

Nickle oxide (NiO), nitric acid ($HNO_3$), and water

Insoluble NiO

NiO is insoluble in water but reacts with $HNO_3$ to give a green solution of the salt $Ni(NO_3)_2$

**SAMPLE EXERCISE 7.8** | **Metal Oxides**

(a) Would you expect scandium oxide to be a solid, liquid, or gas at room temperature?
(b) Write the balanced chemical equation for the reaction of scandium oxide with nitric acid.

**SOLUTION**

**Analyze and Plan** We are asked about one physical property of scandium oxide—its state at room temperature—and one chemical property—how it reacts with nitric acid.

**Solve**

(a) Because scandium oxide is the oxide of a metal, we expect it to be an ionic solid. Indeed it is, with the very high melting point of 2485 °C.

(b) In compounds, scandium has a 3+ charge, $Sc^{3+}$, and the oxide ion is $O^{2-}$. Consequently, the formula of scandium oxide is $Sc_2O_3$. Metal oxides tend to be basic and, therefore, to react with acids to form a salt plus water. In this case the salt is scandium nitrate, $Sc(NO_3)_3$:

$$Sc_2O_3(s) + 6\,HNO_3(aq) \longrightarrow 2\,Sc(NO_3)_3(aq) + 3\,H_2O(l)$$

**PRACTICE EXERCISE**

Write the balanced chemical equation for the reaction between copper(II) oxide and sulfuric acid.

*Answer:* $CuO(s) + H_2SO_4(aq) \longrightarrow CuSO_4(aq) + H_2O(l)$

# Nonmetals

Nonmetals can be solid, liquid, or gas. They are not lustrous and generally are poor conductors of heat and electricity. Their melting points are generally lower than those of metals (although diamond, a form of carbon, is an exception and melts at 3570 °C). Under ordinary conditions, seven nonmetals exist as diatomic molecules. Five of these are gases ($H_2$, $N_2$, $O_2$, $F_2$, and $Cl_2$), one is a liquid ($Br_2$), and one is a volatile solid ($I_2$). Excluding the noble gases, the remaining nonmetals are solids that can be either hard, such as diamond, or soft, such as sulfur (▶ **FIGURE 7.16**).

*Because of their relatively large, negative electron affinities, nonmetals tend to gain electrons when they react with metals.* For example, the reaction of aluminum with bromine produces the ionic compound aluminum bromide:

$$2\,Al(s) + 3\,Br_2(l) \longrightarrow 2\,AlBr_3(s) \qquad [7.12]$$

A nonmetal typically will gain enough electrons to fill its outermost occupied *p* subshell, giving a noble-gas electron configuration. For example, the bromine atom gains one electron to fill its 4*p* subshell:

$$Br\ ([Ar]4s^23d^{10}4p^5) + e^- \Rightarrow Br^-\ ([Ar]4s^23d^{10}4p^6)$$

*Compounds composed entirely of nonmetals are typically molecular substances* that tend to be gases, liquids, or low-melting solids at room temperature. Examples include the common hydrocarbons we use for fuel (methane, $CH_4$; propane, $C_3H_8$; octane, $C_8H_{18}$) and the gases HCl, $NH_3$, and $H_2S$. Many drugs are molecules composed of C, H, N, O, and other nonmetals. For example, the molecular formula for the drug Celebrex is $C_{17}H_{14}F_3N_3O_2S$. *Most nonmetal oxides are acidic*, which means that those that dissolve in water form acids:

$$\text{Nonmetal oxide} + \text{water} \longrightarrow \text{acid}$$
$$CO_2(g) + H_2O(l) \longrightarrow H_2CO_3(aq) \qquad [7.13]$$
$$P_4O_{10}(s) + 6\,H_2O(l) \longrightarrow 4\,H_3PO_4(aq) \qquad [7.14]$$

The reaction of carbon dioxide with water (▶ **FIGURE 7.17**) accounts for the acidity of carbonated water and, to some extent, rainwater. Because sulfur is present in oil and coal, combustion of these common fuels produces sulfur dioxide and sulfur trioxide. These

▲ **FIGURE 7.16** **Sulfur, known to the medieval world as "brimstone," is a nonmetal.**

▲ **FIGURE 7.17** **The reaction of $CO_2$ with water containing a bromthymol blue indicator.** Initially, the blue color tells us the water is slightly basic. When a piece of solid carbon dioxide ("dry ice") is added, the color changes to yellow, indicating an acidic solution. The mist is water droplets condensed from the air by the cold $CO_2$ gas.

substances dissolve in water to produce *acid rain*, a major pollutant in many parts of the world. Like acids, most nonmetal oxides dissolve in basic solutions to form a salt plus water:

$$Nonmetal\ oxide + base \longrightarrow salt + water$$

$$CO_2(g) + 2\,NaOH(aq) \longrightarrow Na_2CO_3(aq) + H_2O(l) \qquad [7.15]$$

### ▲ GIVE IT SOME THOUGHT

A compound $ACl_3$ (A is an element) has a melting point of $-112\ °C$. Would you expect the compound to be molecular or ionic? If you were told that A is either scandium or phosphorus, which do you think is the more likely choice?

---

**SAMPLE EXERCISE 7.9** | **Nonmetal Oxides**

Write the balanced chemical equation for the reaction of solid selenium dioxide, $SeO_2(s)$, with **(a)** water, **(b)** aqueous sodium hydroxide.

**SOLUTION**

**Analyze and Plan** We note that selenium is a nonmetal. We therefore need to write chemical equations for the reaction of a nonmetal oxide with water and with a base, NaOH. Nonmetal oxides are acidic, reacting with water to form an acid and with bases to form a salt and water.

**Solve**

**(a)** The reaction between selenium dioxide and water is like that between carbon dioxide and water (Equation 7.13):

$$SeO_2(s) + H_2O(l) \longrightarrow H_2SeO_3(aq)$$

(It does not matter that $SeO_2$ is a solid and $CO_2$ is a gas under ambient conditions; the point is that both are water-soluble nonmetal oxides.)

**(b)** The reaction with sodium hydroxide is like the reaction in Equation 7.15:

$$SeO_2(s) + 2\,NaOH(aq) \longrightarrow Na_2SeO_3(aq) + H_2O(l)$$

**PRACTICE EXERCISE**

Write the balanced chemical equation for the reaction of solid tetraphosphorus hexoxide with water.

***Answer:*** $P_4O_6(s) + 6\,H_2O(l) \longrightarrow 4\,H_3PO_3(aq)$

---

## Metalloids

Metalloids have properties intermediate between those of metals and those of nonmetals. They may have some characteristic metallic properties but lack others. For example, the metalloid silicon *looks* like a metal (◄ **FIGURE 7.18**), but it is brittle rather than malleable and does not conduct heat or electricity nearly as well as metals do. Compounds of metalloids can have characteristics of the compounds of metals or nonmetals.

Several metalloids, most notably silicon, are electrical semiconductors and are the principal elements used in integrated circuits and computer chips. One of the reasons metalloids can be used for integrated circuits is that their electrical conductivity is intermediate between that of metals and that of nonmetals. Very pure silicon is an electrical insulator, but its conductivity can be dramatically increased with the addition of specific impurities called *dopants*. This modification provides a mechanism for controlling the electrical conductivity by controlling the chemical composition. We will return to this point in Chapter 12.

▲ **FIGURE 7.18 Elemental silicon.** Although it looks metallic, silicon, a metalloid, is brittle and a poor thermal and electrical conductor.

# 7.7 | TRENDS FOR GROUP 1A AND GROUP 2A METALS

As we have seen, elements in a given group possess general similarities. However, trends also exist within each group. In this section we use the periodic table and our knowledge of electron configurations to examine the chemistry of the **alkali metals** and **alkaline earth metals**.

**TABLE 7.4 • Some Properties of the Alkali Metals**

| Element | Electron Configuration | Melting Point (°C) | Density (g/cm³) | Atomic Radius (Å) | $I_1$ (kJ/mol) |
|---|---|---|---|---|---|
| Lithium | $[He]2s^1$ | 181 | 0.53 | 1.34 | 520 |
| Sodium | $[Ne]3s^1$ | 98 | 0.97 | 1.54 | 496 |
| Potassium | $[Ar]4s^1$ | 63 | 0.86 | 1.96 | 419 |
| Rubidium | $[Kr]5s^1$ | 39 | 1.53 | 2.11 | 403 |
| Cesium | $[Xe]6s^1$ | 28 | 1.88 | 2.25 | 376 |

## Group 1A: The Alkali Metals

The alkali metals are soft metallic solids (▶ FIGURE 7.19). All have characteristic metallic properties, such as a silvery, metallic luster and high thermal and electrical conductivity. The name *alkali* comes from an Arabic word meaning "ashes." Many compounds of sodium and potassium, two alkali metals, were isolated from wood ashes by early chemists.

As ▲ TABLE 7.4 shows, the alkali metals have low densities and melting points, and these properties vary in a fairly regular way with increasing atomic number. We see the usual trends as we move down the group, such as increasing atomic radius and decreasing first ionization energy. The alkali metal of any given period has the lowest $I_1$ value in the period (Figure 7.9), which reflects the relative ease with which its outer *s* electron can be removed. As a result, the alkali metals are all very reactive, readily losing one electron to form ions carrying a 1+ charge. ∞ (Section 2.7)

The alkali metals exist in nature only as compounds. Sodium and potassium are relatively abundant in Earth's crust, in seawater, and in biological systems, usually as the cations of ionic compounds. All alkali metals combine directly with most nonmetals. For example, they react with hydrogen to form hydrides and with sulfur to form sulfides:

$$2 M(s) + H_2(g) \longrightarrow 2 MH(s) \qquad [7.16]$$

$$2 M(s) + S(s) \longrightarrow M_2S(s) \qquad [7.17]$$

where M represents any alkali metal. In hydrides of the alkali metals (LiH, NaH, and so forth), hydrogen is present as $H^-$, the **hydride ion**. A hydrogen atom that has *gained* an electron, this ion is distinct from the hydrogen ion, $H^+$, formed when a hydrogen atom *loses* its electron.

The alkali metals react vigorously with water, producing hydrogen gas and a solution of an alkali metal hydroxide:

$$2 M(s) + 2 H_2O(l) \longrightarrow 2 MOH(aq) + H_2(g) \qquad [7.18]$$

These reactions are very exothermic. In many cases enough heat is generated to ignite the $H_2$, producing a fire or sometimes even an explosion (▼ FIGURE 7.20). The reaction is most violent for the heavier alkali metals, in keeping with their lower ionization energies.

▲ FIGURE 7.19 **Sodium, like the other alkali metals, is soft enough to be cut with a knife.**

Li            Na            K

◀ FIGURE 7.20 **The alkali metals react vigorously with water.**

Li   Na   K

▲ **FIGURE 7.21**   Placed in a flame, ions of each alkali metal emit light of a characteristic wavelength.

The reactions between the alkali metals and oxygen are complex. Metal oxides, which contain the $O^{2-}$ ion, are usually formed:

$$4\,Li(s) + O_2(g) \longrightarrow 2\,Li_2O(s)$$
$$\text{lithium oxide}$$

[7.19]

When dissolved in water, $Li_2O$ and other soluble metal oxides form hydroxide ions from the reaction of $O^{2-}$ ions with $H_2O$ (Equation 7.10). In contrast, the other alkali metals react with oxygen to form metal *peroxides*, which contain the $O_2^{2-}$ ion:

$$2\,Na(s) + O_2(g) \longrightarrow Na_2O_2(s)$$
$$\text{sodium peroxide}$$

[7.20]

Potassium, rubidium, and cesium also form compounds that contain the $O_2^-$ ion, which we call the *superoxide ion*. For example, potassium forms potassium superoxide, $KO_2$:

$$K(s) + O_2(g) \longrightarrow KO_2(s)$$
$$\text{potassium superoxide}$$

[7.21]

Be aware that the reactions in Equations 7.20 and 7.21 are somewhat surprising; in most cases, the reaction of oxygen with a metal forms the metal oxide.

As is evident from Equations 7.18 through 7.21, the alkali metals are extremely reactive toward water and oxygen. Because of this, the metals are usually stored submerged in a liquid hydrocarbon, such as mineral oil or kerosene.

Although alkali metal ions are colorless, each emits a characteristic color when placed in a flame (▲ **FIGURE 7.21**). The ions are reduced to gaseous metal atoms in the flame. The high temperature excites the valence electron from the ground state to a higher-energy orbital, causing the atom to be in an excited state. The atom then emits energy in the form of visible light as the electron falls back into the lower-energy orbital and the atom returns to its ground state. The light emitted is at a specific wavelength for each element, just as we saw earlier for line spectra of hydrogen and sodium ∞ (Section 6.3). The characteristic yellow emission of sodium at 589 nm is the basis for sodium vapor lamps (◀ **FIGURE 7.22**).

**GO FIGURE**

If we had potassium vapor lamps, what color would they be?

▲ **FIGURE 7.22**   The characteristic yellow light in a sodium lamp is the result of electrons in the high-energy $3p$ orbital falling back to the lower-energy $3s$ orbital. The energy gap corresponds to the energy of yellow light.

▲ **GIVE IT SOME THOUGHT**

Cesium tends to be the most reactive of the stable alkali metals (francium, Fr, is radioactive and has not been extensively studied). What *atomic* property of Cs is most responsible for its high reactivity?

**SAMPLE EXERCISE 7.10** | Reactions of an Alkali Metal

Write a balanced equation for the reaction of cesium metal with (**a**) $Cl_2(g)$, (**b**) $H_2O(l)$, (**c**) $H_2(g)$.

**SOLUTION**

**Analyze and Plan** Because cesium is an alkali metal, we expect its chemistry to be dominated by oxidation of the metal to $Cs^+$ ions. Further, we recognize that Cs is far down the periodic table, which means it is among the most active of all metals and probably reacts with all three substances.

**Solve** The reaction between Cs and $Cl_2$ is a simple combination reaction between a metal and a nonmetal, forming the ionic compound CsCl:

$$2\,Cs(s) + Cl_2(g) \longrightarrow 2\,CsCl(s)$$

From Equations 7.18 and 7.16, we predict the reactions of cesium with water and hydrogen to proceed as follows:

$$2\,Cs(s) + 2\,H_2O(l) \longrightarrow 2\,CsOH(aq) + H_2(g)$$
$$2\,Cs(s) + H_2(g) \longrightarrow 2\,CsH(s)$$

All three reactions are redox reactions where cesium forms a $Cs^+$ ion. The $Cl^-$, $OH^-$, and $H^-$ are all 1– ions, which means the products have 1:1 stoichiometry with $Cs^+$.

**PRACTICE EXERCISE**

Write a balanced equation for the reaction between potassium metal and elemental sulfur.

**Answer:** $2\,K(s) + S(s) \longrightarrow K_2S(s)$

# CHEMISTRY AND LIFE

## THE IMPROBABLE DEVELOPMENT OF LITHIUM DRUGS

Alkali metal ions tend to play an unexciting role in most chemical reactions. As noted in Section 4.2, all salts of the alkali metal ions are soluble in water, and the ions are spectators in most aqueous reactions (except for those involving the alkali metals in their elemental form, such as in Equations 7.16 through 7.21). However, these ions play an important role in human physiology. Sodium and potassium ions, for example, are major components of blood plasma and intracellular fluid, respectively, with average concentrations of 0.1 $M$. These electrolytes serve as vital charge carriers in normal cellular function. In contrast, the lithium ion has no known function in normal human physiology. Since the discovery of lithium in 1817, however, people have believed that salts of the element possessed almost mystical healing powers. There were even claims that lithium ions were an ingredient in ancient "fountain of youth" formulas. In 1927, C. L. Grigg began marketing a soft drink that contained lithium. The original unwieldy name of the beverage was "Bib-Label Lithiated Lemon-Lime Soda," which was soon changed to the simpler and more familiar name 7UP® (▶ **FIGURE 7.23**).

Because of concerns of the Food and Drug Administration, lithium was removed from 7UP® during the early 1950s. At nearly the same time, psychiatrists discovered that the lithium ion has a remarkable therapeutic effect on the mental disorder called *bipolar affective disorder*, or *manic-depressive illness*. Over 1 million Americans suffer from this psychosis, undergoing severe mood swings from deep depression to a manic euphoria. The lithium ion smoothes these mood swings, allowing the bipolar patient to function more effectively in daily life.

The antipsychotic action of $Li^+$ was discovered by accident in the 1940s by Australian psychiatrist John Cade as he was researching the use of uric acid—a component of urine—to treat manic-depressive illness. He administered the acid to manic laboratory animals in the form of its most soluble salt, lithium urate, and found that many of the manic symptoms seemed to disappear. Later studies showed that uric acid has no role in the therapeutic effects observed; rather, the $Li^+$ ions were responsible. Because lithium overdose can cause severe side effects in humans, including kidney failure and death, lithium salts were not approved as antipsychotic drugs for humans until 1970. Today $Li^+$ is usually administered orally in the form of $Li_2CO_3$, which is the active ingredient in prescription drugs such as Eskalith®. Lithium drugs are effective for about 70% of bipolar patients who take it.

In this age of sophisticated drug design and biotechnology, the simple lithium ion is still the most effective treatment of this destructive psychological disorder. Remarkably, in spite of intensive research, scientists still do not fully understand the biochemical action of lithium that leads to its therapeutic effects. Because of its similarity to $Na^+$, $Li^+$ is incorporated into blood plasma, where it can affect the behavior of nerve and muscle cells. Because $Li^+$ has a smaller radius than $Na^+$ (Figure 7.7), the way $Li^+$ interacts with molecules in human cells is different from the way $Na^+$ interacts with the molecules. Other studies indicate that $Li^+$ alters the function of certain neurotransmitters, which might lead to its effectiveness as an antipsychotic drug.

▲ **FIGURE 7.23 Lithium no more.** The soft drink 7UP® originally contained a lithium salt that was claimed to give the beverage healthful benefits, including "an abundance of energy, enthusiasm, a clear complexion, lustrous hair, and shining eyes!" The lithium was removed from the beverage in the early 1950s, about the time that the antipsychotic action of $Li^+$ was discovered.

**TABLE 7.5 • Some Properties of the Alkaline Earth Metals**

| Element | Electron Configuration | Melting Point (°C) | Density (g/cm³) | Atomic Radius (Å) | $I_1$ (kJ/mol) |
|---------|------------------------|--------------------|-----------------|--------------------|--------------------|
| Beryllium | $[He]2s^2$ | 1287 | 1.85 | 0.90 | 899 |
| Magnesium | $[Ne]3s^2$ | 650 | 1.74 | 1.30 | 738 |
| Calcium | $[Ar]4s^2$ | 842 | 1.55 | 1.74 | 590 |
| Strontium | $[Kr]5s^2$ | 777 | 2.63 | 1.92 | 549 |
| Barium | $[Xe]6s^2$ | 727 | 3.51 | 1.98 | 503 |

▲ FIGURE 7.24  **Elemental calcium reacts with water.**

## Group 2A: The Alkaline Earth Metals

Like the alkali metals, the alkaline earth metals are all solids at room temperature and have typical metallic properties (▲ TABLE 7.5). Compared with the alkali metals, the alkaline earth metals are harder and more dense and melt at higher temperatures.

The first ionization energies of the alkaline earth metals are low but not as low as those of the alkali metals. Consequently, the alkaline earth metals are less reactive than their alkali metal neighbors. As noted in Section 7.4, the ease with which the elements lose electrons decreases as we move across a period and increases as we move down a group. Thus, beryllium and magnesium, the lightest alkaline earth metals, are the least reactive.

The trend of increasing reactivity within the group is shown by the way the alkaline earth metals behave in the presence of water. Beryllium does not react with either water or steam, even when heated red-hot. Magnesium reacts slowly with liquid water and more readily with steam:

$$Mg(s) + H_2O(g) \longrightarrow MgO(s) + H_2(g) \qquad [7.22]$$

Calcium and the elements below it react readily with water at room temperature (although more slowly than the alkali metals adjacent to them in the periodic table). The reaction between calcium and water (◄ FIGURE 7.24), for example, is

$$Ca(s) + 2H_2O(l) \longrightarrow Ca(OH)_2(aq) + H_2(g) \qquad [7.23]$$

Equations 7.22 and 7.23 illustrate the dominant pattern in the reactivity of the alkaline earth elements: They tend to lose their two outer $s$ electrons and form 2+ ions. For example, magnesium reacts with chlorine at room temperature to form $MgCl_2$ and burns with dazzling brilliance in air to give MgO:

$$Mg(s) + Cl_2(g) \longrightarrow MgCl_2(s) \qquad [7.24]$$
$$2Mg(s) + O_2(g) \longrightarrow 2MgO(s) \qquad [7.25]$$

In the presence of $O_2$, magnesium metal is protected by a thin coating of water-insoluble MgO. Thus, even though Mg is high in the activity series ◯◯◯ (Section 4.4), it can be incorporated into lightweight structural alloys used in, for example, automobile wheels. The heavier alkaline earth metals (Ca, Sr, and Ba) are even more reactive toward nonmetals than is magnesium.

The heavier alkaline earth ions give off characteristic colors when heated in a hot flame. Strontium salts produce the brilliant red color in fireworks, and barium salts produce the green color.

Like their neighbors sodium and potassium, magnesium and calcium are relatively abundant on Earth and in seawater and are essential for living organisms as cations in ionic compounds. Calcium is particularly important for growth and maintenance of bones and teeth.

▲ **GIVE IT SOME THOUGHT**

Calcium carbonate, $CaCO_3$, is often used as a dietary calcium supplement for bone health. Although $CaCO_3(s)$ is insoluble in water (Table 4.1), it can be taken orally to allow for the delivery of $Ca^{2+}(aq)$ ions to the musculoskeletal system. Why is this the case? [Hint: Recall the reactions of metal carbonates discussed in Section 4.3.]

# 7.8 | TRENDS FOR SELECTED NONMETALS

## Hydrogen

Because hydrogen has the electron configuration $1s^1$, its usual position in the periodic table is above the alkali metals. However, hydrogen does not truly belong to any particular group. Unlike the alkali metals, it is a nonmetal that occurs as a colorless diatomic gas, $H_2(g)$, under most conditions.

Owing to the complete absence of nuclear screening of its sole electron, the ionization energy of hydrogen, 1312 kJ/mol, is more than double that of any of the alkali metals. In fact, hydrogen's ionization energy is comparable to the $I_1$ values of other nonmetals, such as oxygen and chlorine. As a result, hydrogen does not lose its valence electron as easily as do the alkali metals. Instead, hydrogen shares its electron with nonmetals and thereby forms molecular compounds. Reactions between hydrogen and another nonmetal can be quite exothermic, as evidenced by the combustion reaction between hydrogen and oxygen to form water:

$$2\,H_2(g) + O_2(g) \longrightarrow 2\,H_2O(l) \qquad \Delta H° = -571.7\,\text{kJ} \qquad [7.26]$$

We saw in Equation 7.16 that hydrogen reacts with active metals to form solid metal hydrides that contain the hydride ion, $H^-$. The fact that hydrogen can gain an electron further illustrates that it is not truly an alkali metal. In fact, in terms of chemical reactivity, hydrogen has more in common with the halogens than with the alkali metals.

In addition to its ability to form covalent bonds and metal hydrides, probably the most important characteristic of hydrogen is its ability to lose its electron to form a cation. Indeed, the aqueous chemistry of hydrogen is dominated by the $H^+(aq)$ ion. (Section 4.1)

## Group 6A: The Oxygen Group

As we proceed down group 6A, there is a change from nonmetallic to metallic character (Figure 7.12). Oxygen, sulfur, and selenium are typical nonmetals. Tellurium is a metalloid, and polonium, which is radioactive and quite rare, is a metal. Oxygen is a colorless gas at room temperature; all of the other members of group 6A are solids. Some of the physical properties of the group 6A elements are given in ▼ TABLE 7.6.

As we saw in Section 2.6, oxygen is encountered in two molecular forms, $O_2$ and $O_3$. Because $O_2$ is the more common form, people generally mean it when they say "oxygen," although the name *dioxygen* is more descriptive. The $O_3$ form is **ozone**. The two forms of oxygen are examples of *allotropes,* defined as different forms of the same element in the same state. (In this case both forms are gases.) About 21% of dry air consists of $O_2$ molecules. Ozone is present in very small amounts in the upper atmosphere and in polluted air. It is also formed from $O_2$ in electrical discharges, such as in lightning storms:

$$3\,O_2(g) \longrightarrow 2\,O_3(g) \qquad \Delta H° = 284.6\,\text{kJ} \qquad [7.27]$$

This reaction is strongly endothermic, telling us that $O_3$ is less stable than $O_2$.

Although both $O_2$ and $O_3$ are colorless and therefore do not absorb visible light, $O_3$ absorbs certain wavelengths of ultraviolet light that $O_2$ does not. Because of this difference, the presence of ozone in the upper atmosphere is beneficial, filtering out harmful

**TABLE 7.6 • Some Properties of the Group 6A Elements**

| Element | Electron Configuration | Melting Point (°C) | Density | Atomic Radius (Å) | $I_1$ (kJ/mol) |
|---|---|---|---|---|---|
| Oxygen | $[He]2s^22p^4$ | −218 | 1.43 g/L | 0.73 | 1314 |
| Sulfur | $[Ne]3s^23p^4$ | 115 | 1.96 g/cm$^3$ | 1.02 | 1000 |
| Selenium | $[Ar]3d^{10}4s^24p^4$ | 221 | 4.82 g/cm$^3$ | 1.16 | 941 |
| Tellurium | $[Kr]4d^{10}5s^25p^4$ | 450 | 6.24 g/cm$^3$ | 1.35 | 869 |
| Polonium | $[Xe]4f^{14}5d^{10}6s^26p^4$ | 254 | 9.20 g/cm$^3$ | — | 812 |

UV light. Ozone and oxygen also have different chemical properties. Ozone, which has a pungent odor, is a powerful oxidizing agent. Because of this property, ozone is sometimes added to water to kill bacteria or used in low levels to help to purify air. However, the reactivity of ozone also makes its presence in polluted air near Earth's surface detrimental to human health.

Oxygen has a great tendency to attract electrons from other elements (to *oxidize* them). Oxygen in combination with a metal is almost always present as the oxide ion, $O^{2-}$. This ion has a noble-gas configuration and is particularly stable. As shown in Equation 7.26, the formation of nonmetal oxides is also often very exothermic and thus energetically favorable.

In our discussion of the alkali metals, we noted two less common oxygen anions—the peroxide ($O_2^{2-}$) ion and the superoxide ($O_2^-$) ion. Compounds of these ions often react to produce an oxide and $O_2$:

$$2\,H_2O_2(aq) \longrightarrow 2\,H_2O(l) + O_2(g) \qquad \Delta H° = -196.1 \text{ kJ} \qquad [7.28]$$

For this reason, bottles of aqueous hydrogen peroxide are topped with caps that are able to release the $O_2(g)$ produced before the pressure inside becomes too great (◄ FIGURE 7.25).

▲ **FIGURE 7.25 Hydrogen peroxide solution in bottle with venting cap.**

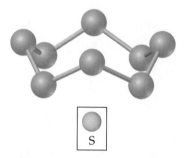

▲ **FIGURE 7.26 Elemental sulfur exists as the $S_8$ molecule.** At room temperature, this is the most common allotropic form of sulfur.

### GIVE IT SOME THOUGHT

Hydrogen peroxide is light sensitive and so is stored in brown bottles because its O—O bond is relatively weak. If we assume that the brown bottle absorbs all visible wavelengths of light ∞∞(Section 6.1), how might you estimate the energy of the O—O bond in hydrogen peroxide?

After oxygen, the most important member of group 6A is sulfur. This element exists in several allotropic forms, the most common and stable of which is the yellow solid having the molecular formula $S_8$. This molecule consists of an eight-membered ring of sulfur atoms (◄ FIGURE 7.26). Even though solid sulfur consists of $S_8$ rings, we usually write it simply as $S(s)$ in chemical equations to simplify the stoichiometric coefficients.

Like oxygen, sulfur has a tendency to gain electrons from other elements to form sulfides, which contain the $S^{2-}$ ion. In fact, most sulfur in nature is present as metal sulfides. Sulfur is below oxygen in the periodic table, and the tendency of sulfur to form sulfide anions is not as great as that of oxygen to form oxide ions. As a result, the chemistry of sulfur is more complex than that of oxygen. In fact, sulfur and its compounds (including those in coal and petroleum) can be burned in oxygen. The main product is sulfur dioxide, a major air pollutant:

$$S(s) + O_2(g) \longrightarrow SO_2(g) \qquad [7.29]$$

Below sulfur in group 6A is selenium, Se. This relatively rare element is essential for life in trace quantities, although it is toxic at high doses. There are many allotropes of Se, including several eight-membered ring structures that resemble the $S_8$ ring.

The next element in the group is tellurium, Te. Its elemental structure is even more complex than that of Se, consisting of long, twisted chains of Te—Te bonds. Both Se and Te favor the −2 oxidation state, as do O and S.

From O to S to Se to Te, the elements form larger and larger molecules and become increasingly metallic. The thermal stability of group 6A compounds with hydrogen decreases down the column: $H_2O > H_2S > H_2Se > H_2Te$, with $H_2O$, water, being the most stable of the series.

## Group 7A: The Halogens

Some of the properties of the group 7A elements, the **halogens**, are given in ▶ TABLE 7.7. Astatine, which is both extremely rare and radioactive, is omitted because many of its properties are not yet known.

Unlike the group 6A elements, all the halogens are typical nonmetals. Their melting and boiling points increase with increasing atomic number. Fluorine and chlorine are gases at room temperature, bromine is a liquid, and iodine is a solid. Each element consists of diatomic molecules: $F_2$, $Cl_2$, $Br_2$, and $I_2$ (▶ FIGURE 7.27).

◀ **FIGURE 7.27**  **The elemental halogens exist as diatomic molecules.**

Br$_2$

Cl$_2$

I$_2$

**TABLE 7.7 • Some Properties of the Halogens**

| Element | Electron Configuration | Melting Point (°C) | Density | Atomic Radius (Å) | $I_1$ (kJ/mol) |
|---------|----------------------|-------------------|---------|------------------|---------------|
| Fluorine | [He]$2s^2 2p^5$ | −220 | 1.69 g/L | 0.71 | 1681 |
| Chlorine | [Ne]$3s^2 3p^5$ | −102 | 3.12 g/L | 0.99 | 1251 |
| Bromine | [Ar]$3d^{10} 4s^2 4p^5$ | −7.3 | 3.12 g/cm$^3$ | 1.14 | 1140 |
| Iodine | [Kr]$4d^{10} 5s^2 5p^5$ | 114 | 4.94 g/cm$^3$ | 1.33 | 1008 |

◢ **GIVE IT SOME THOUGHT**

The halogens do not exist as X$_8$ molecules like sulfur and selenium do. Can you speculate why?

The halogens have highly negative electron affinities (Figure 7.11). Thus, it is not surprising that the chemistry of the halogens is dominated by their tendency to gain electrons from other elements to form halide ions, X$^-$. (In many equations X is used to indicate any one of the halogen elements.) Fluorine and chlorine are more reactive than bromine and iodine. In fact, fluorine removes electrons from almost any substance with which it comes into contact, including water, and usually does so very exothermically, as in the following examples:

$$2\,\text{H}_2\text{O}(l) + 2\,\text{F}_2(g) \longrightarrow 4\,\text{HF}(aq) + \text{O}_2(g) \qquad \Delta H = -758.9\;\text{kJ} \qquad [7.30]$$

$$\text{SiO}_2(s) + 2\,\text{F}_2(g) \longrightarrow \text{SiF}_4(g) + \text{O}_2(g) \qquad \Delta H = -704.0\;\text{kJ} \qquad [7.31]$$

As a result, fluorine gas is difficult and dangerous to use in the laboratory, requiring specialized equipment.

Chlorine is the most industrially useful of the halogens. In 2008, total production was 21 billion pounds, making it one of the top ten most produced chemicals in the United States ∞ (Section 1.1). Unlike fluorine, chlorine reacts slowly with water to form relatively stable aqueous solutions of HCl and HOCl (hypochlorous acid):

$$\text{Cl}_2(g) + \text{H}_2\text{O}(l) \longrightarrow \text{HCl}(aq) + \text{HOCl}(aq) \qquad [7.32]$$

Chlorine is often added to drinking water and swimming pools, where the HOCl($aq$) that is generated serves as a disinfectant.

The halogens react directly with most metals to form ionic halides. The halogens also react with hydrogen to form gaseous hydrogen halide compounds:

$$H_2(g) + X_2 \longrightarrow 2\,HX(g) \qquad\qquad [7.33]$$

These compounds are all very soluble in water and dissolve to form the hydrohalic acids. As we discussed in Section 4.3, $HCl(aq)$, $HBr(aq)$, and $HI(aq)$ are strong acids, whereas $HF(aq)$ is a weak acid.

 GIVE IT SOME THOUGHT

Can you use data in Table 7.7 to provide estimates for the atomic radius and first ionization energy of an astatine atom?

## Group 8A: The Noble Gases

The group 8A elements, known as the **noble gases**, are all nonmetals that are gases at room temperature. They are all *monatomic* (that is, they consist of single atoms rather than molecules). Some physical properties of the noble-gas elements are listed in ▼ TABLE 7.8. The high radioactivity of radon (Rn, atomic number 86) has limited the study of its reaction chemistry and some of its properties.

The noble gases have completely filled *s* and *p* subshells. All elements of group 8A have large first ionization energies, and we see the expected decrease as we move down the column. Because the noble gases possess such stable electron configurations, they are exceptionally unreactive. In fact, until the early 1960s the elements were called the *inert gases* because they were thought to be incapable of forming chemical compounds. In 1962, Neil Bartlett at the University of British Columbia reasoned that the ionization energy of Xe might be low enough to allow it to form compounds. In order for this to happen, Xe would have to react with a substance with an extremely high ability to remove electrons from other substances, such as fluorine. Bartlett synthesized the first noble-gas compound by combining Xe with the fluorine-containing compound $PtF_6$. Xenon also reacts directly with $F_2(g)$ to form the molecular compounds $XeF_2$, $XeF_4$, and $XeF_6$. Krypton has a higher $I_1$ value than xenon and is therefore less reactive. In fact, only a single stable compound of krypton is known, $KrF_2$. In 2000, Finnish scientists reported the first neutral molecule that contains argon, the HArF molecule, which is stable only at low temperatures.

**TABLE 7.8 • Some Properties of the Noble Gases**

| Element | Electron Configuration | Boiling Point (K) | Density (g/L) | Atomic Radius* (Å) | $I_1$ (kJ/mol) |
|---------|------------------------|-------------------|---------------|--------------------|-----------------|
| Helium | $1s^2$ | 4.2 | 0.18 | 0.32 | 2372 |
| Neon | $[He]2s^22p^6$ | 27.1 | 0.90 | 0.69 | 2081 |
| Argon | $[Ne]3s^23p^6$ | 87.3 | 1.78 | 0.97 | 1521 |
| Krypton | $[Ar]3d^{10}4s^24p^6$ | 120 | 3.75 | 1.10 | 1351 |
| Xenon | $[Kr]4d^{10}5s^25p^6$ | 165 | 5.90 | 1.30 | 1170 |
| Radon | $[Xe]4f^{14}5d^{10}6s^26p^6$ | 211 | 9.73 | 1.45 | 1037 |

*Only the heaviest of the noble-gas elements form chemical compounds. Thus, the atomic radii for the lighter noble-gas elements are estimated values.

**SAMPLE INTEGRATIVE EXERCISE** **Putting Concepts Together**

The element bismuth (Bi, atomic number 83) is the heaviest member of group 5A. A salt of the element, bismuth subsalicylate, is the active ingredient in Pepto-Bismol®, an over-the-counter medication for gastric distress.

**(a)** The bonding atomic radii of thallium (Tl) and lead (Pb) are 1.48 Å and 1.47 Å, respectively. Using these values and those in Figure 7.6, predict the bonding atomic radius of the element bismuth (Bi). Explain your answer.

**(b)** What accounts for the general increase in atomic radius going down the group 5A elements?

(c) Another major use of bismuth has been as an ingredient in low-melting metal alloys, such as those used in fire sprinkler systems and in typesetting. The element itself is a brittle white crystalline solid. How do these characteristics fit with the fact that bismuth is in the same periodic group with such nonmetallic elements as nitrogen and phosphorus?

(d) $Bi_2O_3$ is a basic oxide. Write a balanced chemical equation for its reaction with dilute nitric acid. If 6.77 g of $Bi_2O_3$ is dissolved in dilute acidic solution to make 0.500 L of solution, what is the molarity of the solution of $Bi^{3+}$ ion?

(e) $^{209}Bi$ is the heaviest stable isotope of any element. How many protons and neutrons are present in this nucleus?

(f) The density of Bi at 25 °C is 9.808 $g/cm^3$. How many Bi atoms are present in a cube of the element that is 5.00 cm on each edge? How many moles of the element are present?

## SOLUTION

(a) Note that there is a gradual decrease in radius of the elements in groups 3A–5A as we proceed across the fifth period, that is, in the series In–Sn–Sb. Therefore, it is reasonable to expect a decrease of about 0.02 Å as we move from Pb to Bi, leading to an estimate of 1.45 Å. The tabulated value is 1.46 Å.

(b) The general increase in radius with increasing atomic number in the group 5A elements occurs because additional shells of electrons are being added, with corresponding increases in nuclear charge. The core electrons in each case largely screen the outermost electrons from the nucleus, so the effective nuclear charge does not vary greatly as we go to higher atomic numbers. However, the principal quantum number, $n$, of the outermost electrons steadily increases, with a corresponding increase in orbital radius.

(c) The contrast between the properties of bismuth and those of nitrogen and phosphorus illustrates the general rule that there is a trend toward increased metallic character as we move down in a given group. Bismuth, in fact, is a metal. The increased metallic character occurs because the outermost electrons are more readily lost in bonding, a trend that is consistent with its lower ionization energy.

(d) Following the procedures described in Section 4.2 for writing molecular and net ionic equations, we have the following:

> Molecular equation: $Bi_2O_3(s) + 6\,HNO_3(aq) \longrightarrow 2\,Bi(NO_3)_3(aq) + 3\,H_2O(l)$
>
> Net ionic equation: $Bi_2O_3(s) + 6\,H^+(aq) \longrightarrow 2\,Bi^{3+}(aq) + 3\,H_2O(l)$

In the net ionic equation, nitric acid is a strong acid and $Bi(NO_3)_3$ is a soluble salt, so we need show only the reaction of the solid with the hydrogen ion forming the $Bi^{3+}(aq)$ ion and water. To calculate the concentration of the solution, we proceed as follows (Section 4.5):

$$\frac{6.77\ g\ Bi_2O_3}{0.500\ L\ soln} \times \frac{1\ mol\ Bi_2O_3}{466.0\ g\ Bi_2O_3} \times \frac{2\ mol\ Bi^{3+}}{1\ mol\ Bi_2O_3} = \frac{0.0581\ mol\ Bi^{3+}}{L\ soln} = 0.0581\ M$$

(e) We can proceed as in Section 2.3. Bismuth is element 83; there are therefore 83 protons in the nucleus. Because the atomic mass number is 209, there are $209 - 83 = 126$ neutrons in the nucleus.

(f) We proceed as in Sections 1.4 and 3.4: The volume of the cube is $(5.00)^3\ cm^3 = 125\ cm^3$. Then we have

$$125\ cm^3\ Bi \times \frac{9.808\ g\ Bi}{1\ cm^3} \times \frac{1\ mol\ Bi}{209.0\ g\ Bi} = 5.87\ mol\ Bi$$

$$5.87\ mol\ Bi \times \frac{6.022 \times 10^{23}\ atom\ Bi}{1\ mol\ Bi} = 3.53 \times 10^{24}\ atoms\ Bi$$

# CHAPTER SUMMARY AND KEY TERMS

**INTRODUCTION AND SECTION 7.1** The periodic table was first developed by Mendeleev and Meyer on the basis of the similarity in chemical and physical properties exhibited by certain elements. Moseley established that each element has a unique atomic number, which added more order to the periodic table. We now recognize that elements in the same column of the periodic table have the same number of electrons in their **valence orbitals**. This similarity in valence electronic structure leads to the similarities among elements in the same group. The differences among elements in the same group arise because their valence orbitals are in different shells.

**SECTION 7.2** Many properties of atoms are due to the average distance of the outer electrons from the nucleus and to the **effective nuclear charge** experienced by these electrons. The core electrons are very effective in screening the outer electrons from the full charge of the nucleus, whereas electrons in the same shell do not screen each other effectively. As a result, the effective nuclear charge experienced by valence electrons increases as we move left to right across a period.

**SECTION 7.3** The size of an atom can be gauged by its **bonding atomic radius**, based on measurements of the distances separating atoms in their chemical compounds. In general, atomic radii increase as we go down a column in the periodic table and decrease as we proceed left to right across a row.

Cations are smaller than their parent atoms; anions are larger than their parent atoms. For ions of the same charge, size increases going down a column of the periodic table. An **isoelectronic series** is a series of ions that has the same number of electrons. For such a series, size decreases with increasing nuclear charge as the electrons are attracted more strongly to the nucleus.

**SECTION 7.4** The first **ionization energy** of an atom is the minimum energy needed to remove an electron from the atom in the gas phase, forming a cation. The second ionization energy is the energy needed to remove a second electron, and so forth. Ionization energies show a sharp increase after all the valence electrons have been removed because of the much higher effective nuclear charge experienced by the core electrons. The first ionization energies of the elements show periodic trends that are opposite those seen for atomic radii, with smaller atoms having higher first ionization energies. Thus, first ionization energies decrease as we go down a column and increase as we proceed left to right across a row.

We can write electron configurations for ions by first writing the electron configuration of the neutral atom and then removing or adding the appropriate number of electrons. Electrons are removed first from the orbitals with the largest value of $n$. If there are two valence orbitals with the same value of $n$ (such as $4s$ and $4p$), then the electrons are lost first from the orbital with a higher value of $l$ (in this case, $4p$). Electrons are added to orbitals in the reverse order.

**SECTION 7.5** The **electron affinity** of an element is the energy change upon adding an electron to an atom in the gas phase, forming an anion. A negative electron affinity means that the anion is stable; a positive electron affinity means that the anion is not stable relative to the separated atom and electron, in which case its exact value cannot be measured. In general, electron affinities become more negative as we proceed from left to right across the periodic table. The halogens have the most-negative electron affinities. The electron affinities of the noble gases are positive because the added electron would have to occupy a new, higher-energy subshell.

**SECTION 7.6** The elements can be categorized as metals, nonmetals, and metalloids. Most elements are metals; they occupy the left side and the middle of the periodic table. Nonmetals appear in the upper-right section of the table. Metalloids occupy a narrow band between the metals and nonmetals. The tendency of an element to exhibit the properties of metals, called the **metallic character**, increases as we proceed down a column and decreases as we proceed from left to right across a row.

Metals have a characteristic luster, and they are good conductors of heat and electricity. When metals react with nonmetals, the metal atoms are oxidized to cations and ionic substances are generally formed. Most metal oxides are basic; they react with acids to form salts and water.

Nonmetals lack metallic luster and are generally poor conductors of heat and electricity. Several are gases at room temperature. Compounds composed entirely of nonmetals are generally molecular. Nonmetals usually form anions in their reactions with metals. Nonmetal oxides are acidic; they react with bases to form salts and water. Metalloids have properties that are intermediate between those of metals and nonmetals.

**SECTION 7.7** The periodic properties of the elements can help us understand the properties of groups of the representative elements. The **alkali metals** (group 1A) are soft metals with low densities and low melting points. They have the lowest ionization energies of the elements. As a result, they are very reactive toward nonmetals, easily losing their outer $s$ electron to form 1+ ions. The **alkaline earth metals** (group 2A) are harder and more dense and have higher melting points than the alkali metals. They are also very reactive toward nonmetals, although not as reactive as the alkali metals. The alkaline earth metals readily lose their two outer $s$ electrons to form 2+ ions. Both alkali and alkaline earth metals react with hydrogen to form ionic substances that contain the **hydride ion**, $H^-$.

**SECTION 7.8** Hydrogen is a nonmetal with properties that are distinct from any of the groups of the periodic table. It forms molecular compounds with other nonmetals, such as oxygen and the halogens.

Oxygen and sulfur are the most important elements in group 6A. Oxygen is usually found as a diatomic molecule, $O_2$. **Ozone**, $O_3$, is an important allotrope of oxygen. Oxygen has a strong tendency to gain electrons from other elements, thus oxidizing them. In combination with metals, oxygen is usually found as the oxide ion, $O^{2-}$, although salts of the peroxide ion, $O_2^{2-}$, and superoxide ion, $O_2^-$, are sometimes formed. Elemental sulfur is most commonly found as $S_8$ molecules. In combination with metals, it is most often found as the sulfide ion, $S^{2-}$.

The **halogens** (group 7A) are nonmetals that exist as diatomic molecules. The halogens have the most negative electron affinities of the elements. Thus, their chemistry is dominated by a tendency to form 1− ions, especially in reactions with metals.

The **noble gases** (group 8A) are nonmetals that exist as monatomic gases. They are very unreactive because they have completely filled $s$ and $p$ subshells. Only the heaviest noble gases are known to form compounds, and they do so only with very active nonmetals, such as fluorine.

# KEY SKILLS

- Understand the meaning of effective nuclear charge, $Z_{eff}$, and how $Z_{eff}$ depends on nuclear charge and electron configuration. (Section 7.2)

- Use the periodic table to predict the trends in atomic radii, ionic radii, ionization energy, and electron affinity. (Sections 7.2, 7.3, 7.4, and 7.5)

- Explain how the radius of an atom changes upon losing electrons to form a cation or gaining electrons to form an anion. (Section 7.3)

- Be able to write the electron configurations of ions. (Section 7.3)

- Explain how the ionization energy changes as we remove successive electrons. Recognize the jump in ionization energy that occurs when the ionization corresponds to removing a core electron. (Section 7.4)

- Understand how irregularities in the periodic trends for electron affinity can be related to electron configuration. (Section 7.5)

- Recognize the differences in chemical and physical properties of metals and nonmetals, including the basicity of metal oxides and the acidity of nonmetal oxides. (Section 7.6)

- Understand how the atomic properties, such as ionization energy and electron configuration, are related to the chemical reactivity and physical properties of the alkali and alkaline earth metals (groups 1A and 2A). (Section 7.7)

- Be able to write balanced equations for the reactions of the group 1A and 2A metals with water, oxygen, hydrogen, and the halogens. (Sections 7.7 and 7.8)

- Understand and recognize the unique characteristics of hydrogen. (Section 7.7)

- Understand how the atomic properties (such as ionization energy, electron configuration, and electron affinity) of group 6A, 7A, and 8A elements are related to their chemical reactivity and physical properties. (Section 7.8)

## KEY EQUATIONS

- $Z_{eff} = Z - S$  [7.1]  Estimating effective nuclear charge

# EXERCISES

## VISUALIZING CONCEPTS

**7.1** We can draw an analogy between the attraction of an electron to a nucleus and seeing a lightbulb—in essence, the more nuclear charge the electron "sees," the greater the attraction. **(a)** Within this analogy, discuss how the screening by core electrons is analogous to putting a frosted-glass lampshade between the lightbulb and your eyes, as shown in the illustration. **(b)** Explain how we could mimic moving to the right in a row of the periodic table by changing the wattage of the lightbulb. **(c)** How would you change the wattage of the bulb and/or the frosted glass to mimic the effect of moving down a column of the periodic table? [Section 7.2]

Lightbulb     Frosted
              glass

Observer

**7.2** If you look up the radius of the sulfur atom in this book, you will find just one number: 1.02 Å. However, if you look deeper into the chemical literature, you can find another number for the radius of a sulfur atom: the nonbonding radius of 1.80 Å. This is a very large difference! Explain. [Section 7.3]

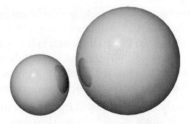

**7.3** Consider the $A_2X_4$ molecule depicted here, where A and X are elements. The A—A bond length in this molecule is $d_1$, and the four A—X bond lengths are each $d_2$. **(a)** In terms of $d_1$ and $d_2$, how could you define the bonding atomic radii of atoms A and X? **(b)** In terms of $d_1$ and $d_2$, what would you predict for the X—X bond length of an $X_2$ molecule? [Section 7.3]

**7.4** Make a simple sketch of the shape of the main part of the periodic table, as shown. **(a)** Ignoring H and He, write a single straight arrow from the element with the smallest bonding atomic radius to the element with the largest. **(b)** Ignoring H and He, write a single straight arrow from the element with the smallest first ionization energy to the element with the largest. **(c)** What significant observation can you make from the arrows you drew in parts (a) and (b)? [Sections 7.3 and 7.4]

**7.5** In the chemical process called *electron transfer*, an electron is transferred from one atom or molecule to another. (We will talk about electron transfer extensively in Chapter 20.) A simple electron transfer reaction is

$$A(g) + A(g) \longrightarrow A^+(g) + A^-(g)$$

In terms of the ionization energy and electron affinity of atom A, what is the energy change for this reaction? For a representative nonmetal such as chlorine, is this process exothermic? For a representative metal such as sodium, is this process exothermic? [Sections 7.4 and 7.5]

**7.6** An element X reacts with $F_2(g)$ to form the molecular product shown here. (a) Write a balanced equation for this reaction (do not worry about the phases for X and the product). (b) Do you think that X is a metal or nonmetal? Explain. [Section 7.6]

# PERIODIC TABLE; EFFECTIVE NUCLEAR CHARGE (sections 7.1 and 7.2)

**7.7** Explain the structure of the periodic table—two columns on the left, a block of ten for the transition metals, a block of six on the right, and a pair of 14-member rows below, with reference to the orbitals we discussed in Chapter 6.

**7.8** The prefix *eka-* comes from the Sanskrit word for "one." Mendeleev used this prefix to indicate that the unknown element was one place away from the known element that followed the prefix. For example, *eka-silicon*, which we now call germanium, is one element below silicon. Mendeleev also predicted the existence of *eka-manganese*, which was not experimentally confirmed until 1937 because this element is radioactive and does not occur in nature. Based on the periodic table shown in Figure 7.1, what do we now call the element Mendeleev called *eka-manganese*?

**7.9** You might have expected that the elements would have been discovered in order of their relative abundance in the Earth's crust (Figure 1.6), but this is not the case. Suggest a general reason.

**7.10** (a) Moseley's experiments on X-rays emitted from atoms led to the concept of atomic numbers. Where exactly do these X-rays come from? Draw an energy-level diagram to explain. (b) Why are chemical and physical properties of the elements more closely related to atomic number than they are to atomic weight?

**7.11** (a) What is meant by the term *effective nuclear charge*? (b) How does the effective nuclear charge experienced by the valence electrons of an atom vary going from left to right across a period of the periodic table?

**7.12** (a) How is the concept of effective nuclear charge used to simplify the numerous electron–electron repulsions in a many-electron atom? (b) Which experiences a greater effective nuclear charge in a Be atom, the $1s$ electrons or the $2s$ electrons? Explain.

**7.13** Detailed calculations show that the value of $Z_{\text{eff}}$ for the outermost electrons in Na and K atoms is 2.51+ and 3.49+, respectively. (a) What value do you estimate for $Z_{\text{eff}}$ experienced by the outermost electron in both Na and K by assuming core electrons contribute 1.00 and valence electrons contribute 0.00 to the screening constant? (b) What values do you estimate for $Z_{\text{eff}}$ using Slater's rules? (c) Which approach gives a more accurate estimate of $Z_{\text{eff}}$? (d) Does either method of approximation account for the gradual increase in $Z_{\text{eff}}$ that occurs upon moving down a group? (e) Predict $Z_{\text{eff}}$ for the outermost electrons in the Rb atom based on the calculations for Na and K.

**7.14** Detailed calculations show that the value of $Z_{\text{eff}}$ for the outermost electrons in Si and Cl atoms is 4.29+ and 6.12+, respectively. (a) What value do you estimate for $Z_{\text{eff}}$ experienced by the outermost electron in both Si and Cl by assuming core electrons contribute 1.00 and valence electrons contribute 0.00 to the screening constant? (b) What values do you estimate for $Z_{\text{eff}}$ using Slater's rules? (c) Which approach gives a more accurate estimate of $Z_{\text{eff}}$? (d) Which method of approximation more accurately accounts for the steady increase in $Z_{\text{eff}}$ that occurs upon moving left to right across a period? (e) Predict $Z_{\text{eff}}$ for a valence electron in P, phosphorus, based on the calculations for Si and Cl.

**7.15** Which will experience the greater effective nuclear charge, the electrons in the $n = 3$ shell in Ar or the $n = 3$ shell in Kr? Which will be closer to the nucleus? Explain.

**7.16** Arrange the following atoms in order of increasing effective nuclear charge experienced by the electrons in the $n = 3$ electron shell: K, Mg, P, Rh, and Ti. Explain the basis for your order.

# ATOMIC AND IONIC RADII (section 7.3)

**7.17** (a) Because an exact outer boundary cannot be measured or even calculated for an atom, how are atomic radii determined? (b) What is the difference between a bonding radius and a nonbonding radius? (c) For a given element, which one is larger? (d) If a free atom reacts to become part of a molecule, would you say that the atom gets smaller or larger?

**7.18** (a) Why does the quantum mechanical description of many-electron atoms make it difficult to define a precise atomic radius? (b) When nonbonded atoms come up against one another, what determines how closely the nuclear centers can approach?

**7.19** Tungsten has the highest melting point of any metal in the periodic table: 3422 °C. The distance between W atoms in tungsten metal is 2.74 Å. (a) What is the atomic radius of a tungsten atom in this environment? (This radius is called the *metallic radius*.) (b) If you put tungsten metal under high pressure, predict what would happen to the distance between W atoms.

**7.20** Based on the radii presented in Figure 7.6, predict the distance between Si atoms in solid silicon. How does this compare to the distance between the C atoms in diamond, which has the same structure as solid silicon?

**7.21** Estimate the As—I bond length from the data in Figure 7.6, and compare your value to the experimental As—I bond length in arsenic triiodide, $AsI_3$, 2.55 Å.

**7.22** The experimental Bi—I bond length in bismuth triiodide, $BiI_3$, is 2.81 Å. Based on this value and data in Figure 7.6, predict the atomic radius of Bi.

**7.23** How do the sizes of atoms change as we move **(a)** from left to right across a row in the periodic table, **(b)** from top to bottom in a group in the periodic table? **(c)** Arrange the following atoms in order of increasing atomic radius: O, Si, I, Ge.

**7.24** **(a)** Among the nonmetallic elements, the change in atomic radius in moving one place left or right in a row is smaller than the change in moving one row up or down. Explain these observations. **(b)** Arrange the following atoms in order of increasing atomic radius: Si, Al, Ge, Ga.

**7.25** Using only the periodic table, arrange each set of atoms in order from largest to smallest: **(a)** K, Li, Cs; **(b)** Pb, Sn, Si; **(c)** F, O, N.

**7.26** Using only the periodic table, arrange each set of atoms in order of increasing radius: **(a)** Ba, Ca, Na; **(b)** Sn, Sb, As; **(c)** Al, Be, Si.

**7.27** True or False: **(a)** Cations are larger than their corresponding neutral atoms. **(b)** $Li^+$ is smaller than Li. **(c)** $Cl^-$ is bigger than $I^-$.

**7.28** Explain the following variations in atomic or ionic radii:
**(a)** $I^- > I > I^+$, **(b)** $Ca^{2+} > Mg^{2+} > Be^{2+}$,
**(c)** $Fe > Fe^{2+} > Fe^{3+}$.

**7.29** In the reaction

Reactants                    Products

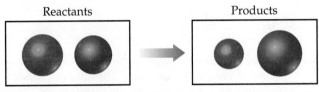

which sphere represents a metal and which represents a nonmetal? Explain your answer.

**7.30** Which of these spheres represents F, which represents Br, and which represents $Br^-$?

**7.31** **(a)** What is an isoelectronic series? **(b)** Which neutral atom is isoelectronic with each of the following ions: $Ga^{3+}$, $Zr^{4+}$, $Mn^{7+}$, $I^-$, $Pb^{2+}$?

**7.32** Identify at least two ions that have the following ground-state electron configurations: **(a)** [Ar]; **(b)** $[Ar]3d^5$; **(c)** $[Kr]5s^24d^{10}$.

**7.33** Some ions do not have a corresponding neutral atom that has the same electron configuration. For each of the following ions, identify the neutral atom that has the same number of electrons and determine if this atom has the same electron configuration. If such an atom does not exist, explain why. **(a)** $Cl^-$, **(b)** $Sc^{3+}$, **(c)** $Fe^{2+}$, **(d)** $Zn^{2+}$, **(e)** $Sn^{4+}$.

**7.34** Consider the isoelectronic ions $F^-$ and $Na^+$. **(a)** Which ion is smaller? **(b)** Using Equation 7.1 and assuming that core electrons contribute 1.00 and valence electrons contribute 0.00 to the screening constant, $S$, calculate $Z_{eff}$ for the $2p$ electrons in both ions. **(c)** Repeat this calculation using Slater's rules to estimate the screening constant, $S$. **(d)** For isoelectronic ions, how are effective nuclear charge and ionic radius related?

**7.35** Consider the isoelectronic ions $Cl^-$ and $K^+$. **(a)** Which ion is smaller? **(b)** Using Equation 7.1 and assuming that core electrons contribute 1.00 and valence electrons contribute nothing to the screening constant, $S$, calculate $Z_{eff}$ for these two ions. **(c)** Repeat this calculation using Slater's rules to estimate the screening constant, $S$. **(d)** For isoelectronic ions, how are effective nuclear charge and ionic radius related?

**7.36** Consider S, Cl, and K and their most common ions. **(a)** List the atoms in order of increasing size. **(b)** List the ions in order of increasing size. **(c)** Explain any differences in the orders of the atomic and ionic sizes.

**7.37** For each of the following sets of atoms and ions, arrange the members in order of increasing size: **(a)** $Se^{2-}$, $Te^{2-}$, Se; **(b)** $Co^{3+}$, $Fe^{2+}$, $Fe^{3+}$; **(c)** Ca, $Ti^{4+}$, $Sc^{3+}$; **(d)** $Be^{2+}$, $Na^+$, Ne.

**7.38** In the ionic compounds LiF, NaCl, KBr, and RbI, the measured cation–anion distances are 2.01 Å (Li–F), 2.82 Å (Na–Cl), 3.30 Å (K–Br), and 3.67 Å (Rb–I), respectively. **(a)** Predict the cation–anion distance using the values of ionic radii given in Figure 7.7. **(b)** Calculate the difference between the experimentally measured ion–ion distances and the ones predicted from Figure 7.7. Assuming we have an accuracy of 0.04 Å in the measurement, would you say that the two sets of ion–ion distances are the same or not? **(c)** What estimates of the cation–anion distance would you obtain for these four compounds using *bonding atomic radii*? Are these estimates as accurate as the estimates using ionic radii?

# IONIZATION ENERGIES; ELECTRON AFFINITIES (sections 7.4 and 7.5)

**7.39** Write equations that show the processes that describe the first, second, and third ionization energies of an aluminum atom. Which process would require the least amount of energy?

**7.40** Write equations that show the process for **(a)** the first two ionization energies of lead and **(b)** the fourth ionization energy of zirconium.

**7.41** Identify each statement as true or false. If it is false, rewrite it so that it is true: **(a)** Ionization energies are always negative quantitites. **(b)** Oxygen has a larger first ionization energy

than fluorine. **(c)** The second ionization energy of an atom is always greater than its first ionization energy.

**7.42** **(a)** Why does Li have a larger first ionization energy than Na? **(b)** The difference between the third and fourth ionization energies of scandium is much larger than the difference between the third and fourth ionization energies of titanium. Why? **(c)** Why does Li have a much larger second ionization energy than Be?

**7.43** **(a)** What is the general relationship between the size of an atom and its first ionization energy? **(b)** Which element in the periodic table has the largest ionization energy? Which has the smallest?

**7.44** (a) What is the trend in first ionization energies as one proceeds down the group 7A elements? Explain how this trend relates to the variation in atomic radii. (b) What is the trend in first ionization energies as one moves across the fourth period from K to Kr? How does this trend compare with the trend in atomic radii?

**7.45** Based on their positions in the periodic table, predict which atom of the following pairs will have the smaller first ionization energy: (a) Cl, Ar; (b) Be, Ca; (c) K, Co; (d) S, Ge; (e) Sn, Te.

**7.46** For each of the following pairs, indicate which element has the smaller first ionization energy: (a) Ti, Ba; (b) Ag, Cu; (c) Ge, Cl; (d) Pb, Sb. (In each case use electron configuration and effective nuclear charge to explain your answer.)

**7.47** Write the electron configurations for the following ions: (a) $Fe^{2+}$, (b) $Hg^{2+}$, (c) $Mn^{2+}$, (d) $Pt^{2+}$, (e) $P^{3-}$.

**7.48** Write electron configurations for the following ions, and determine which have noble-gas configurations: (a) $Cr^{3+}$, (b) $N^{3-}$, (c) $Sc^{3+}$, (d) $Cu^{2+}$, (e) $Tl^+$, (f) $Au^+$.

**7.49** Find three examples of ions in the periodic table that have an electron configuration of $nd^8$ ($n = 3, 4, 5...$).

**7.50** Find three atoms in the periodic table whose ions have an electron configuration of $nd^6$ ($n = 3, 4, 5...$).

**7.51** The first ionization energy and electron affinity of Ar are both positive values. (a) What is the significance of the positive value in each case? (b) What are the units of electron affinity?

**7.52** If the electron affinity for an element is a negative number, does it mean that the anion of the element is more stable than the neutral atom? Explain.

**7.53** Although the electron affinity of bromine is a negative quantity, it is positive for Kr. Use the electron configurations of the two elements to explain the difference.

**7.54** What is the relationship between the ionization energy of an anion with a 1− charge such as $F^-$ and the electron affinity of the neutral atom, F?

**7.55** Consider the first ionization energy of neon and the electron affinity of fluorine. (a) Write equations, including electron configurations, for each process. (b) These two quantities will have opposite signs. Which will be positive, and which will be negative? (c) Would you expect the **magnitudes** of these two quantities to be equal? If not, which one would you expect to be larger? Explain your answer.

**7.56** Write an equation for the process that corresponds to the electron affinity of the $Mg^+$ ion. Also write the electron configurations of the species involved. What is the magnitude of the energy change in the process? [*Hint:* The answer is in Table 7.2.]

## PROPERTIES OF METALS AND NONMETALS (section 7.6)

**7.57** How are metallic character and first ionization energy related?

**[7.58]** It is possible to define *metallic character* as we do in this book and base it on the reactivity of the element and the ease with which it loses electrons. Alternatively, one could measure how well electricity is conducted by each of the elements to determine how "metallic" the elements are. On the basis of conductivity, there is not much of a trend in the periodic table: Silver is the most conductive metal, and manganese the least. Look up the first ionization energies of silver and manganese; which of these two elements would you call more metallic based on the way we define it in this book?

**7.59** Discussing this chapter, a classmate says, "An element that commonly forms a cation is a metal." Do you agree or disagree? Explain your answer.

**7.60** Discussing this chapter, a classmate says, "Since elements that form cations are metals and elements that form anions are nonmetals, elements that do not form ions are metalloids." Do you agree or disagree? Explain your answer.

**7.61** Predict whether each of the following oxides is ionic or molecular: $SnO_2$, $Al_2O_3$, $CO_2$, $Li_2O$, $Fe_2O_3$, $H_2O$. Explain the reasons for your choices.

**7.62** Some metal oxides, such as $Sc_2O_3$, do not react with pure water, but they do react when the solution becomes either acidic or basic. Do you expect $Sc_2O_3$ to react when the solution becomes acidic or when it becomes basic? Write a balanced chemical equation to support your answer.

**7.63** (a) What is meant by the terms *acidic oxide* and *basic oxide*? (b) How can we predict whether an oxide will be acidic or basic based on its composition?

**7.64** Arrange the following oxides in order of increasing acidity: $CO_2$, CaO, $Al_2O_3$, $SO_3$, $SiO_2$, and $P_2O_5$.

**7.65** Chlorine reacts with oxygen to form $Cl_2O_7$. (a) What is the name of this product (see Table 2.6)? (b) Write a balanced equation for the formation of $Cl_2O_7(l)$ from the elements. (c) Under usual conditions, $Cl_2O_7$ is a colorless liquid with a boiling point of 81 °C. Is this boiling point expected or surprising? (d) Would you expect $Cl_2O_7$ to be more reactive toward $H^+(aq)$ or $OH^-(aq)$? Explain. (e) If the oxygen in $Cl_2O_7$ is considered to have the −2 oxidation state, what is the oxidation state of the Cl? What is the electron configuration of Cl in this oxidation state?

**[7.66]** An element X reacts with oxygen to form $XO_2$ and with chlorine to form $XCl_4$. $XO_2$ is a white solid that melts at high temperatures (above 1000 °C). Under usual conditions, $XCl_4$ is a colorless liquid with a boiling point of 58 °C. (a) $XCl_4$ reacts with water to form $XO_2$ and another product. What is the likely identity of the other product? (b) Do you think that element X is a metal, nonmetal, or metalloid? Explain. (c) By using a sourcebook such as the *CRC Handbook of Chemistry and Physics,* try to determine the identity of element X.

**7.67** Write balanced equations for the following reactions: (a) barium oxide with water, (b) iron(II) oxide with perchloric acid, (c) sulfur trioxide with water, (d) carbon dioxide with aqueous sodium hydroxide.

**7.68** Write balanced equations for the following reactions: (a) potassium oxide with water, (b) diphosphorus trioxide with water, (c) chromium(III) oxide with dilute hydrochloric acid, (d) selenium dioxide with aqueous potassium hydroxide.

# GROUP TRENDS IN METALS AND NONMETALS (sections 7.7 and 7.8)

**7.69** Does the reactivity of a metal correlate with its first ionization energy? Explain.

**7.70** Silver and rubidium both form +1 ions, but silver is far less reactive. Suggest an explanation, taking into account the ground-state electron configurations of these elements and atomic radii.

**7.71** (a) Why is calcium generally more reactive than magnesium? (b) Why is calcium generally less reactive than potassium?

**7.72** (a) One of the alkali metals reacts with oxygen to form a solid white substance. When this substance is dissolved in water, the solution gives a positive test for hydrogen peroxide, $H_2O_2$. When the solution is tested in a burner flame, a lilac-purple flame is produced. What is the likely identity of the metal? (b) Write a balanced chemical equation for reaction of the white substance with water.

**7.73** Write a balanced equation for the reaction that occurs in each of the following cases: (a) Potassium metal burns in an atmosphere of chlorine gas. (b) Strontium oxide is added to water. (c) A fresh surface of lithium metal is exposed to oxygen gas. (d) Sodium metal is reacted with molten sulfur.

**7.74** Write a balanced equation for the reaction that occurs in each of the following cases: (a) Cesium is added to water. (b) Strontium is added to water. (c) Sodium reacts with oxygen. (d) Calcium reacts with iodine.

**7.75** (a) As described in Section 7.7, the alkali metals react with hydrogen to form hydrides and react with halogens—for example, fluorine—to form halides. Compare the roles of hydrogen and the halogen in these reactions. How are the forms of hydrogen and halogen in the products alike? (b) Write balanced equations for the reaction of fluorine with calcium and for the reaction of hydrogen with calcium. What are the similarities among the products of these reactions?

**7.76** The interior of the planets Jupiter and Saturn are believed to contain *metallic hydrogen*: hydrogen that is put under such tremendous pressure that it no longer exists as $H_2$ molecules, but instead exists as an extended metallic solid. Predict what properties metallic hydrogen might have compared to "normal" hydrogen in terms of first ionization energy, atomic size, and reactivity.

**7.77** Compare the elements bromine and chlorine with respect to the following properties: (a) electron configuration, (b) most common ionic charge, (c) first ionization energy, (d) reactivity toward water, (e) electron affinity, (f) atomic radius. Account for the differences between the two elements.

**7.78** Little is known about the properties of astatine, At, because of its rarity and high radioactivity. Nevertheless, it is possible for us to make many predictions about its properties. (a) Do you expect the element to be a gas, liquid, or solid at room temperature? Explain. (b) Would you expect At to be a metal, nonmetal, or metalloid? Explain. (c) What is the chemical formula of the compound it forms with Na?

**7.79** Until the early 1960s the group 8A elements were called the inert gases; before that they were called the rare gases. The term *rare gases* was dropped after it was discovered that argon accounts for roughly 1% of Earth's atmosphere. (a) Why was the term *inert gases* dropped? (b) What discovery triggered this change in name? (c) What name is applied to the group now?

**7.80** (a) Why does xenon react with fluorine, whereas neon does not? (b) Using reference sources such as the *CRC Handbook of Chemistry and Physics* or online sources, look up the bond lengths of Xe—F bonds in several molecules. How do these numbers compare to the radii of the elements?

**7.81** Write a balanced equation for the reaction that occurs in each of the following cases: (a) Ozone decomposes to dioxygen. (b) Xenon reacts with fluorine. (Write three different equations.) (c) Sulfur reacts with hydrogen gas. (d) Fluorine reacts with water.

**7.82** Write a balanced equation for the reaction that occurs in each of the following cases: (a) Chlorine reacts with water. (b) Barium metal is heated in an atmosphere of hydrogen gas. (c) Lithium reacts with sulfur. (d) Fluorine reacts with magnesium metal.

# ADDITIONAL EXERCISES

**7.83** Consider the stable elements through lead ($Z = 82$). In how many instances are the atomic weights of the elements in the reverse order relative to the atomic numbers of the elements? What is the explanation for these cases?

**[7.84]** We saw in Chapter 6 that the probability of finding an electron in three-dimensional space depends on what orbital it is in. Look back at Figures 6.19 and 6.22, which show the radial probability distribution functions for the s orbitals and contour plots of the 2p orbitals, respectively. (a) Which orbitals, 2s or 2p, have more electron density at the nucleus? (b) How would you modify Slater's rules to adjust for the difference in electronic penetration of the nucleus for the 2s and 2p orbitals?

**7.85** (a) If the core electrons were totally effective at screening the valence electrons and the valence electrons provided no screening for each other, what would be the effective nuclear charge acting on the 3s and 3p valence electrons in P? (b) Repeat these calculations using Slater's rules. (c) Detailed calculations indicate that the effective nuclear charge is 5.6+ for the 3s electrons and 4.9+ for the 3p electrons. Why are the values for the 3s and 3p electrons different? (d) If you remove a single electron from a P atom, which orbital will it come from? Explain.

**7.86** The size of an atomic nucleus is on the order of $10^{-15}$ m. If two protons were able to make a bond, what would you predict the bond length to be?

**7.87** As we move across a period of the periodic table, why do the sizes of the transition elements change more gradually than those of the representative elements?

**7.88** In the series of group 5A hydrides, of general formula $MH_3$, the measured bond distances are P—H, 1.419 Å; As—H, 1.519 Å; Sb—H, 1.707 Å. **(a)** Compare these values with those estimated by use of the atomic radii in Figure 7.6. **(b)** Explain the steady increase in M—H bond distance in this series in terms of the electronic configurations of the M atoms.

**7.89** Elements in group 7A in the periodic table are the halogens; elements in group 6A are called the chalcogens. **(a)** What is the most common oxidation state of the chalcogens compared to the halogens? Can you suggest an explanation for the difference? **(b)** For each of the following periodic properties, state whether the halogens or the chalcogens have larger values: atomic radii; ionic radii of the most common oxidation state; first ionization energy; second ionization energy.

**7.90** Note from the following table that the increase in atomic radius in moving from Zr to Hf is smaller than in moving from Y to La. Suggest an explanation for this effect.

**Atomic Radii (Å)**

| Sc | 1.44 | Ti | 1.36 |
| Y | 1.62 | Zr | 1.48 |
| La | 1.69 | Hf | 1.50 |

**[7.91] (a)** Which ion is smaller, $Co^{3+}$ or $Co^{4+}$? **(b)** In a lithium ion battery that is discharging to power a device, for every $Li^+$ that inserts into the lithium cobalt oxide electrode, a $Co^{4+}$ ion must be reduced to a $Co^{3+}$ ion in order to balance charge. Using the *CRC Handbook of Chemistry and Physics* or other standard reference, find the ionic radii of $Li^+$, $Co^{3+}$, and $Co^{4+}$. Order these ions from smallest to largest. **(c)** Will the lithium cobalt electrode expand or contract as lithium ions are inserted? **(d)** Lithium is not nearly as abundant as sodium. If sodium ion batteries were developed that function as lithium ion ones, do you think "sodium cobalt oxide" would still work as the electrode material? Explain. **(e)** If you don't think cobalt would work as the redox-active partner ion in the sodium version of the electrode, suggest an alternative metal ion and explain your reasoning.

**[7.92]** The ionic substance strontium oxide, SrO, forms from the reaction of strontium metal with molecular oxygen. The arrangement of the ions in solid SrO is analogous to that in solid NaCl (Figure 2.21):

**(a)** Write a balanced equation for the formation of SrO(*s*) from its elements. **(b)** Based on the ionic radii in Figure 7.7, predict the length of the side of the cube in the figure (the distance from the center of an atom at one corner to the center of an atom at a neighboring corner). **(c)** The density of SrO is 5.10 g/cm³. Given your answer to part (b), how many formula units of SrO are contained in the cube shown here?

**7.93** Explain the variation in ionization energies of carbon, as displayed in this graph:

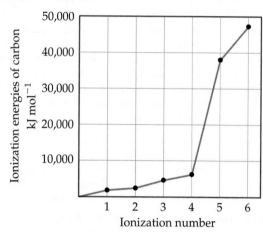

**7.94** Group 4A elements have much more negative electron affinities than their neighbors in groups 3A and 5A (see Figure 7.11). Suggest an explanation.

**7.95 (a)** Use orbital diagrams to illustrate what happens when an oxygen atom gains two electrons. **(b)** Why does $O^{3-}$ not exist?

**[7.96]** Use electron configurations to explain the following observations: **(a)** The first ionization energy of phosphorus is greater than that of sulfur. **(b)** The electron affinity of nitrogen is lower (less negative) than those of both carbon and oxygen. **(c)** The second ionization energy of oxygen is greater than the first ionization energy of fluorine. **(d)** The third ionization energy of manganese is greater than those of both chromium and iron.

**7.97** The electron affinities, in kJ/mol, for the group 1B and group 2B metals are

| Cu −119 | Zn > 0 |
| Ag −126 | Cd > 0 |
| Au −223 | Hg > 0 |

**(a)** Why are the electron affinities of the group 2B elements greater than zero? **(b)** Why do the electron affinities of the group 1B elements become more negative as we move down the group? [*Hint:* Examine the trends in the electron affinity of other groups as we proceed down the periodic table.]

**7.98** Hydrogen is an unusual element because it behaves in some ways like the alkali metal elements and in other ways like nonmetals. Its properties can be explained in part by its electron configuration and by the values for its ionization energy and electron affinity. **(a)** Explain why the electron affinity of hydrogen is much closer to the values for the alkali elements than for the halogens. **(b)** Is the following statement true? "Hydrogen has the smallest bonding atomic radius of any element that forms chemical compounds." If not, correct it. If it is, explain in terms of electron configurations. (c) Explain why the ionization energy of hydrogen is closer to the values for the halogens than for the alkali metals. (d) The hydride ion is $H^-$. Write out the process corresponding to the first ionization energy of hydride. (e) How does the process you wrote in part (d) compare to the process for the electron affinity of elemental hydrogen?

[7.99] The first ionization energy of the oxygen molecule is the energy required for the following process:

$$O_2(g) \longrightarrow O_2^+(g) + e^-$$

The energy needed for this process is 1175 kJ/mol, very similar to the first ionization energy of Xe. Would you expect $O_2$ to react with $F_2$? If so, suggest a product or products of this reaction.

7.100 The elements of group 4A—carbon, silicon, germanium, tin, and lead—go from nonmetal through metalloid to metal as we go down the column. (a) Predict the order of melting temperature from highest to lowest in this group and justify your logic. (b) Using the *CRC Handbok of Chemistry and Physics* or other resource, look up the melting points of these elements. How accurate was your prediction?

7.101 Zinc in its 2+ oxidation state is an essential metal ion for life. $Zn^{2+}$ is found bound to many proteins that are involved in biological processes, but unfortunately $Zn^{2+}$ is hard to detect by common chemical methods. Therefore, scientists who are interested in studying $Zn^{2+}$-containing proteins will frequently substitute $Cd^{2+}$ for $Zn^{2+}$, since $Cd^{2+}$ is easier to detect. (a) On the basis of the properties of the elements and ions discussed in this chapter and their positions in the periodic table, describe the pros and cons of using $Cd^{2+}$ as a $Zn^{2+}$ substitute. (b) Proteins that speed up (catalyze) chemical reactions are called *enzymes*. Many enzymes are required for proper metabolic reactions in the body. One problem with using $Cd^{2+}$ to replace $Zn^{2+}$ in enzymes is that $Cd^{2+}$ substitution can decrease or even eliminate enzymatic activity. Can you suggest a different metal ion that might replace $Zn^{2+}$ in enzymes instead of $Cd^{2+}$? Justify your answer.

# INTEGRATIVE EXERCISES

[7.105] Moseley established the concept of atomic number by studying X-rays emitted by the elements. The X-rays emitted by some of the elements have the following wavelengths:

| Element | Wavelength (Å) |
|---------|----------------|
| Ne | 14.610 |
| Ca | 3.358 |
| Zn | 1.435 |
| Zr | 0.786 |
| Sn | 0.491 |

(a) Calculate the frequency, $\nu$, of the X-rays emitted by each of the elements, in Hz. (b) Using the appropriate graphing program on your computer, plot the square root of $\nu$ versus the atomic number of the element. What do you observe about the plot? (c) Explain how the plot in part (b) allowed Moseley to predict the existence of undiscovered elements. (d) Use the result from part (b) to predict the X-ray wavelength emitted by iron. (e) A particular element emits X-rays with a wavelength of 0.980 Å. What element do you think it is?

[7.102] A historian discovers a nineteenth-century notebook in which some observations, dated 1822, were recorded on a substance thought to be a new element. Here are some of the data recorded in the notebook: "Ductile, silver-white, metallic looking. Softer than lead. Unaffected by water. Stable in air. Melting point: 153 °C. Density: 7.3 g/cm³. Electrical conductivity: 20% that of copper. Hardness: About 1% as hard as iron. When 4.20 g of the unknown is heated in an excess of oxygen, 5.08 g of a white solid is formed. The solid could be sublimed by heating to over 800 °C." (a) Using information in the text and the *CRC Handbook of Chemistry and Physics,* and making allowances for possible variations in numbers from current values, identify the element reported. (b) Write a balanced chemical equation for the reaction with oxygen. (c) Judging from Figure 7.1, might this nineteenth-century investigator have been the first to discover a new element?

7.103 In April 2010, a research team reported that they had made Element 117. The report has yet to be confirmed. Write out Element 117's ground-state electron configuration, and estimate values for its first ionization energy, electron affinity, atomic size, and common oxidation state based on its position in the periodic table.

7.104 We will see in Chapter 12 that semiconductors are materials that conduct electricity better than nonmetals but not as well as metals. The only two elements in the periodic table that are technologically useful semiconductors are silicon and germanium. Integrated circuits in computer chips today are based on silicon. Compound semiconductors are also used in the electronics industry. Examples are gallium arsenide, GaAs; gallium phosphide, GaP; cadmium sulfide, CdS; cadium selenide, CdSe. (a) What is the relationship between the compound semiconductors' compositions and the positions of their elements on the periodic table relative to Si and Ge? (b) Workers in the semiconductor industry refer to "II-VI" and "III-V" materials, using Roman numerals; can you identify which compound semiconductors are II-VI and which are III-V? (c) Suggest other compositions of compound semiconductors based on the positions of their elements in the periodic table.

[7.106] (a) Write the electron configuration for Li, and estimate the effective nuclear charge experienced by the valence electron. (b) The energy of an electron in a one-electron atom or ion equals $(-2.18 \times 10^{-18} \text{ J})\left(\dfrac{Z^2}{n^2}\right)$ where $Z$ is the nuclear charge and $n$ is the principal quantum number of the electron. Estimate the first ionization energy of Li. (c) Compare the result of your calculation with the value reported in Table 7.4 and explain the difference. (d) What value of the effective nuclear charge gives the proper value for the ionization energy? Does this agree with your explanation in (c)?

[7.107] One way to measure ionization energies is ultraviolet photoelectron spectroscopy (UPS, or just PES), a technique based on the photoelectric effect. ⚬⚬ (Section 6.2) In PES, monochromatic light is directed onto a sample, causing electrons to be emitted. The kinetic energy of the emitted electrons is measured. The difference between the energy of the photons and the kinetic energy of the electrons corresponds to the energy needed to remove the electrons (that is, the ionization energy). Suppose that a PES experiment is performed in which mercury vapor is irradiated with ultraviolet light of wavelength 58.4 nm. (a) What is the energy of a photon of this light in eV? **(b)** Write an equation that shows the process corresponding to the first ionization energy of Hg. **(c)** The kinetic energy of the emitted electrons is measured to be 10.75 eV. What is the first ionization energy of Hg in kJ/mol? **(d)** Using Figure 7.9, determine which of the halogen elements has a first ionization energy closest to that of mercury.

**7.108** Mercury in the environment can exist in oxidation states 0, +1, and +2. One major question in environmental chemistry research is how to best measure the oxidation state of mercury in natural systems; this is made more complicated by the fact that mercury can be reduced or oxidized on surfaces differently than it would be if it were free in solution. XPS, X-ray photoelectron spectroscopy, is a technique related to PES (see Exercise 7.107), but instead of using ultraviolet light to eject valence electrons, X-rays are used to eject core electrons. The energies of the core electrons are different for different oxidation states of the element. In one set of experiments, researchers examined mercury contamination of minerals in water. They measured the XPS signals that corresponded to electrons ejected from mercury's 4f orbitals at 105 eV, from an X-ray source that provided 1253.6 eV of energy. The oxygen on the mineral surface gave emitted electron energies at 531 eV, corresponding to the 1s orbital of oxygen. Overall the researchers concluded that oxidation states were +2 for Hg and −2 for O. **(a)** Calculate the wavelength of the X-rays used in this experiment. **(b)** Compare the energies of the 4f electrons in mercury and the 1s electrons in oxygen from these data to the first ionization energies of mercury and oxygen from the data in this chapter. **(c)** Write out the ground-state electron configurations for $Hg^{2+}$ and $O^{2-}$; which electrons are the valence electrons in each case? **(d)** Use Slater's rules to estimate $Z_{eff}$ for the 4f and valence electrons of $Hg^{2+}$ and $O^{2-}$; assume for this purpose that all the inner electrons with $(n-3)$ or less screen a full +1.

**7.109** Consider the gas-phase transfer of an electron from a sodium atom to a chlorine atom:

$$Na(g) + Cl(g) \longrightarrow Na^+(g) + Cl^-(g)$$

**(a)** Write this reaction as the sum of two reactions, one that relates to an ionization energy and one that relates to an electron affinity. **(b)** Use the result from part (a), data in this chapter, and Hess's law to calculate the enthalpy of the preceding reaction. Is the reaction exothermic or endothermic? **(c)** The reaction between sodium metal and chlorine gas is highly exothermic and produces NaCl(s), whose structure was discussed in Section 2.7. Comment on this observation relative to the calculated enthalpy for the aforementioned gas-phase reaction.

**[7.110]** When magnesium metal is burned in air (Figure 3.6), two products are produced. One is magnesium oxide, MgO. The other is the product of the reaction of Mg with molecular nitrogen, magnesium nitride. When water is added to magnesium nitride, it reacts to form magnesium oxide and ammonia gas. **(a)** Based on the charge of the nitride ion (Table 2.5), predict the formula of magnesium nitride. **(b)** Write a balanced equation for the reaction of magnesium nitride with water. What is the driving force for this reaction? **(c)** In an experiment a piece of magnesium ribbon is burned in air in a crucible. The mass of the mixture of MgO and magnesium nitride after burning is 0.470 g. Water is added to the crucible, further reaction occurs, and the crucible is heated to dryness until the final product is 0.486 g of MgO. What was the mass percentage of magnesium nitride in the mixture obtained after the initial burning? **(d)** Magnesium nitride can also be formed by reaction of the metal with ammonia at high temperature. Write a balanced equation for this reaction. If a 6.3-g Mg ribbon reacts with 2.57 g $NH_3(g)$ and the reaction goes to completion, which component is the limiting reactant? What mass of $H_2(g)$ is formed in the reaction? **(e)** The standard enthalpy of formation of solid magnesium nitride is $-461.08$ kJ/mol. Calculate the standard enthalpy change for the reaction between magnesium metal and ammonia gas.

**7.111 (a)** The measured Bi — Br bond length in bismuth tribromide, $BiBr_3$, is 2.63 Å. Based on this value and the data in Figure 7.7, predict the atomic radius of Bi. **(b)** Bismuth tribromide is soluble in acidic solution. It is formed by treating solid bismuth(III) oxide with aqueous hydrobromic acid. Write a balanced chemical equation for this reaction. **(c)** While bismuth(III) oxide is soluble in acidic solutions, it is insoluble in basic solutions such as NaOH($aq$). Based on these properties, is bismuth characterized as a metallic, metalloid, or nonmetallic element? **(d)** Treating bismuth with fluorine gas forms $BiF_5$. Use the electron configuration of Bi to explain the formation of a compound with this formulation. **(e)** While it is possible to form $BiF_5$ in the manner just described, pentahalides of bismuth are not known for the other halogens. Explain why the pentahalide might form with fluorine but not with the other halogens. How does the behavior of bismuth relate to the fact that xenon reacts with fluorine to form compounds but not with the other halogens?

**7.112** Potassium superoxide, $KO_2$, is often used in oxygen masks (such as those used by firefighters) because $KO_2$ reacts with $CO_2$ to release molecular oxygen. Experiments indicate that 2 mol of $KO_2(s)$ react with each mole of $CO_2(g)$. **(a)** The products of the reaction are $K_2CO_3(s)$ and $O_2(g)$. Write a balanced equation for the reaction between $KO_2(s)$ and $CO_2(g)$. **(b)** Indicate the oxidation number for each atom involved in the reaction in part (a). What elements are being oxidized and reduced? **(c)** What mass of $KO_2(s)$ is needed to consume 18.0 g $CO_2(g)$? What mass of $O_2(g)$ is produced during this reaction?

# WHAT'S AHEAD

### 8.1 LEWIS SYMBOLS AND THE OCTET RULE
We begin with descriptions of the three main types of chemical bonds: *ionic, covalent,* and *metallic*. In evaluating bonding, *Lewis symbols* provide a useful shorthand for keeping track of valence electrons.

### 8.2 IONIC BONDING
We observe that in ionic substances the atoms are held together by the electrostatic attractions between ions of opposite charge. We discuss the energetics of forming ionic substances and describe the *lattice energy* of these substances.

### 8.3 COVALENT BONDING
We examine the bonding in molecular substances in which atoms bond by sharing one or more electron pairs. In general, the electrons are shared in such a way that each atom attains an *octet* of electrons.

### 8.4 BOND POLARITY AND ELECTRONEGATIVITY
We define *electronegativity* as the ability of an atom in a compound to attract electrons to itself. In general, electron pairs are shared unequally between atoms with different electro-negativities, leading to *polar covalent bonds*.

**CHEMICAL BONDING AS ART.** The *Atomium* is a 110-m-high steel sculpture commissioned for the 1958 World's Fair in Brussels. The nine spheres represent atoms, and the connecting rods evoke the chemical bonds holding them together. One sphere sits in the center of a cube formed by the other eight, a common arrangement of the atoms in metallic elements, such as iron.

# BASIC CONCEPTS OF CHEMICAL BONDING

WHENEVER TWO ATOMS OR IONS are strongly held together, we say there is a **chemical bond** between them. There are three general types of chemical bonds: *ionic, covalent, and metallic* (▶ **FIGURE 8.1**). We can get a glimpse of these three types of bonds by thinking about the simple act of using a stainless-steel spoon to add table salt to a glass of water. Table salt is sodium chloride, $NaCl$, which consists of sodium ions, $Na^+$, and chloride ions, $Cl^-$. The structure is held together by **ionic bonds**, which are due to the attractions between oppositely charged ions. The water consists mainly of $H_2O$ molecules. The hydrogen and oxygen atoms are bonded to one another through **covalent bonds**, in which molecules are formed by the sharing of electrons between atoms. The spoon consists mainly of iron metal, in which Fe atoms are connected to one another via **metallic bonds**, which are formed by electrons that are relatively free to move through the metal. These different substances—$NaCl$, $H_2O$, and Fe metal—behave as they do because of the ways in which their constituent atoms are connected to one another.

What determines the type of bonding in any substance? How do the characteristics of these bonds give rise to different physical and chemical properties? The keys to answering the first question are found in the electronic structure of the atoms involved, discussed in Chapters 6 and 7. In this chapter and the next, we examine the relationship between the electronic structure of atoms and the ionic and covalent chemical bonds they form. We will discuss metallic bonding in greater detail in Chapter 12.

**Metallic**
Electrons delocalized

**Ionic**
Electrostatic attraction

**Covalent**
Electrons shared

▲ **FIGURE 8.1 Ionic, covalent, and metallic bonds.** Different types of interactions between atoms lead to different types of chemical bonds.

# 8.1 | LEWIS SYMBOLS AND THE OCTET RULE

The electrons involved in chemical bonding are the *valence electrons*, which, for most atoms, are those in the outermost occupied shell. ∞ (Section 6.8) The American chemist G. N. Lewis (1875–1946) suggested a simple way of showing the valence electrons in an atom and tracking them during bond formation, using what are now known as either *Lewis electron-dot symbols* or simply Lewis symbols.

The **Lewis symbol** for an element consists of the element's chemical symbol plus a dot for each valence electron. Sulfur, for example, has the electron configuration $[Ne]3s^2 3p^4$ and therefore six valence electrons. Its Lewis symbol is

$$\cdot \ddot{\underset{\cdot \cdot}{S}} \cdot$$

The dots are placed on the four sides of the symbol—top, bottom, left, and right—and each side can accommodate up to two electrons. All four sides are equivalent, which means that the choice of on which sides to place two electrons rather than one electron is arbitrary. In general, we spread out the dots as much as possible. In the Lewis symbol for S, for instance, we prefer the dot arrangement shown rather the arrangement having two electrons on three of the sides and none on the fourth.

The electron configurations and Lewis symbols for the main-group elements of periods 2 and 3 are shown in ▼ **TABLE 8.1**. Notice that the number of valence electrons in any representative element is the same as the element's group number. For example, the Lewis symbols for oxygen and sulfur, members of group 6A, both show six dots.

▲ **GIVE IT SOME THOUGHT**

Are all these Lewis symbols for Cl correct?

$$:\ddot{\underset{\cdot}{C}l}\cdot \qquad :\ddot{C}l: \qquad :\ddot{\underset{\cdot}{C}l}\cdot$$

## The Octet Rule

Atoms often gain, lose, or share electrons to achieve the same number of electrons as the noble gas closest to them in the periodic table. The noble gases have very stable electron arrangements, as evidenced by their high ionization energies, low affinity for additional electrons, and general lack of chemical reactivity. ∞ (Section 7.8) Because all the noble gases except He have eight valence electrons, many atoms undergoing reactions end up with eight valence electrons. This observation has led to a guideline known as the **octet rule**: *Atoms tend to gain, lose, or share electrons until they are surrounded by eight valence electrons.*

An octet of electrons consists of full $s$ and $p$ subshells in an atom. In a Lewis symbol, an octet is shown as four pairs of valence electrons arranged around the element symbol, as in the Lewis symbols for Ne and Ar in Table 8.1. There are exceptions to the octet rule, but it provides a useful framework for introducing many important concepts of bonding.

**TABLE 8.1 • Lewis Symbols**

| Group | Element | Electron Configuration | Lewis Symbol | Element | Electron Configuration | Lewis Symbol |
|---|---|---|---|---|---|---|
| 1A | Li | $[He]2s^1$ | Li· | Na | $[Ne]3s^1$ | Na· |
| 2A | Be | $[He]2s^2$ | ·Be· | Mg | $[Ne]3s^2$ | ·Mg· |
| 3A | B | $[He]2s^2 2p^1$ | ·$\dot{B}$· | Al | $[Ne]3s^2 3p^1$ | ·$\dot{Al}$· |
| 4A | C | $[He]2s^2 2p^2$ | ·$\dot{\underset{\cdot}{C}}$· | Si | $[Ne]3s^2 3p^2$ | ·$\dot{\underset{\cdot}{Si}}$· |
| 5A | N | $[He]2s^2 2p^3$ | ·$\ddot{\underset{\cdot}{N}}$· | P | $[Ne]3s^2 3p^3$ | ·$\ddot{\underset{\cdot}{P}}$· |
| 6A | O | $[He]2s^2 2p^4$ | :$\ddot{\underset{\cdot\cdot}{O}}$· | S | $[Ne]3s^2 3p^4$ | :$\ddot{\underset{\cdot\cdot}{S}}$· |
| 7A | F | $[He]2s^2 2p^5$ | ·$\ddot{\underset{\cdot\cdot}{F}}$: | Cl | $[Ne]3s^2 3p^5$ | ·$\ddot{\underset{\cdot\cdot}{Cl}}$: |
| 8A | Ne | $[He]2s^2 2p^6$ | :$\ddot{\underset{\cdot\cdot}{Ne}}$: | Ar | $[Ne]3s^2 3p^6$ | :$\ddot{\underset{\cdot\cdot}{Ar}}$: |

Do you expect a similar reaction between potassium metal and elemental bromine?

Electrons transfer
from Na(s) to $Cl_2(g)$,
forming $Na^+$ and $Cl^-$

NaCl(s) forms

Highly exothermic reaction
forming sodium chloride, an ionic
compound composed of sodium
ions, $Na^+$, and chloride ions, $Cl^-$

▲ **FIGURE 8.2   Reaction of sodium metal with chlorine gas to form the ionic compound sodium chloride.**

# 8.2 | IONIC BONDING

Ionic substances generally result from the interaction of metals on the left side of the periodic table with nonmetals on the right side (excluding the noble gases, group 8A). For example, when sodium metal, Na(s), is brought into contact with chlorine gas, $Cl_2(g)$, a violent reaction ensues (▲ **FIGURE 8.2**). The product of this very exothermic reaction is sodium chloride, NaCl(s):

$$Na(s) + \tfrac{1}{2} Cl_2(g) \longrightarrow NaCl(s) \qquad \Delta H_f^\circ = -410.9 \text{ kJ} \qquad [8.1]$$

Sodium chloride is composed of $Na^+$ and $Cl^-$ ions arranged in a three-dimensional array (▶ **FIGURE 8.3**).

The formation of $Na^+$ from Na and $Cl^-$ from $Cl_2$ indicates that an electron has been lost by a sodium atom and gained by a chlorine atom—we can envision an *electron transfer* from the Na atom to the Cl atom. Two of the atomic properties discussed in Chapter 7 give us an indication of how readily electron transfer occurs: ionization energy, which indicates how easily an electron can be removed from an atom, and electron affinity, which measures how much an atom wants to gain an electron. ∞ (Sections 7.4 and 7.5) Electron transfer to form oppositely charged ions occurs when one atom readily gives up an electron (low ionization energy) and another atom readily gains an electron (high electron affinity). Thus, NaCl is a typical ionic compound because it consists of a metal of low ionization energy and a nonmetal of high electron affinity. Using Lewis electron-dot symbols (and showing a chlorine atom rather than the $Cl_2$ molecule), we can represent this reaction as

$$Na\cdot + \cdot \ddot{\underset{..}{Cl}}: \longrightarrow Na^+ + [:\ddot{\underset{..}{Cl}}:]^- \qquad [8.2]$$

The arrow indicates the transfer of an electron from the Na atom to the Cl atom. Each ion has an octet of electrons, the $Na^+$ octet being the $2s^2 2p^6$ electrons that lie below the single 3s valence electron of the Na atom. We have put a bracket around the chloride ion to emphasize that all eight electrons are located on it.

If no color key were provided, is there a way for you to guess whether the green spheres represent $Na^+$ or $Cl^-$? If so, what information would you use?

 = $Na^+$     = $Cl^-$

Each $Na^+$ ion surrounded by six $Cl^-$ ions

Each $Cl^-$ ion surrounded by six $Na^+$ ions

▲ **FIGURE 8.3   The crystal structure of sodium chloride.**

**GIVE IT SOME THOUGHT**

Describe the electron transfers that occur in the formation of calcium fluoride from elemental calcium and elemental fluorine.

Ionic substances possess several characteristic properties. They are usually brittle substances with high melting points. They are usually crystalline. Furthermore, ionic crystals often can be cleaved; that is, they break apart along smooth, flat surfaces. These characteristics result from electrostatic forces that maintain the ions in a rigid, well-defined, three-dimensional arrangement such as that shown in Figure 8.3.

## Energetics of Ionic Bond Formation

The formation of sodium chloride from sodium and chlorine is *very* exothermic, as indicated by the large negative enthalpy of formation value given in Equation 8.1, $\Delta H_f^\circ = -410.9$ kJ. Appendix C shows that the heat of formation of other ionic substances is also quite negative. What factors make the formation of ionic compounds so exothermic?

In Equation 8.2 we represented the formation of NaCl as the transfer of an electron from Na to Cl. Recall from Section 7.4 that the loss of electrons from an atom is always an endothermic process. Removing an electron from Na(*g*) to form Na$^+$(*g*), for instance, requires 496 kJ/mol. Recall from Section 7.5 that when a nonmetal gains an electron, the process is generally exothermic, as seen from the negative electron affinities of the elements. Adding an electron to Cl(*g*), for example, releases 349 kJ/mol. From the magnitudes of these energies, we can see that the transfer of an electron from a Na atom to a Cl atom would not be exothermic—the overall process would be an endothermic process that requires $496 - 349 = 147$ kJ/mol. This endothermic process corresponds to the formation of sodium and chloride ions that are infinitely far apart—in other words, the positive energy change assumes that the ions do not interact with each other, which is quite different from the situation in ionic solids.

 **GIVE IT SOME THOUGHT**

Consider the trends in ionization energies of the alkali metals and electron affinities of the halogens shown in Figures 7.9 and 7.11. For which pair is electron transfer from the alkali metal atom to the halogen atom most likely to be an exothermic process?

The principal reason ionic compounds are stable is the attraction between ions of opposite charge. This attraction draws the ions together, releasing energy and causing the ions to form a solid array, or lattice, such as that shown in Figure 8.3. A measure of how much stabilization results from arranging oppositely charged ions in an ionic solid is given by the **lattice energy**, which is *the energy required to completely separate one mole of a solid ionic compound into its gaseous ions.*

To envision this process for NaCl, imagine that the structure in Figure 8.3 expands from within, so that the distances between the ions increase until the ions are very far apart. This process requires 788 kJ/mol, which is the value of the lattice energy:

$$\text{NaCl}(s) \longrightarrow \text{Na}^+(g) + \text{Cl}^-(g) \qquad \Delta H_{\text{lattice}} = +788 \text{ kJ/mol} \qquad [8.3]$$

Notice that this process is highly endothermic. The reverse process—the coming together of Na$^+$(*g*) and Cl$^-$(*g*) to form NaCl(*s*)—is therefore highly exothermic ($\Delta H = -788$ kJ/mol).

▶ **TABLE 8.2** lists the lattice energies for a number of ionic compounds. The large positive values indicate that the ions are strongly attracted to one another in ionic solids. The energy released by the attraction between ions of unlike charge more than makes up for the endothermic nature of ionization energies, making the formation of ionic compounds an exothermic process. The strong attractions also cause most ionic materials to be hard and brittle with high melting points—for example, NaCl melts at 801 °C.

**TABLE 8.2 • Lattice Energies for Some Ionic Compounds**

| Compound | Lattice Energy (kJ/mol) | Compound | Lattice Energy (kJ/mol) |
|---|---|---|---|
| LiF | 1030 | $MgCl_2$ | 2326 |
| LiCl | 834 | $SrCl_2$ | 2127 |
| LiI | 730 | | |
| NaF | 910 | MgO | 3795 |
| NaCl | 788 | CaO | 3414 |
| NaBr | 732 | SrO | 3217 |
| NaI | 682 | | |
| KF | 808 | ScN | 7547 |
| KCl | 701 | | |
| KBr | 671 | | |
| CsCl | 657 | | |
| CsI | 600 | | |

The magnitude of the lattice energy of an ionic solid depends on the charges of the ions, their sizes, and their arrangement in the solid. We saw in Section 5.1 that the potential energy of two interacting charged particles is given by

$$E_{el} = \frac{\kappa Q_1 Q_2}{d} \qquad [8.4]$$

In this equation $Q_1$ and $Q_2$ are the charges on the particles, $d$ is the distance between their centers, and $\kappa$ is a constant, $8.99 \times 10^9$ J-m/C$^2$. Equation 8.4 indicates that the attractive interaction between two oppositely charged ions increases as the magnitudes of their charges increase and as the distance between their centers decreases. Thus, *for a given arrangement of ions, the lattice energy increases as the charges on the ions increase and as their radii decrease.* The magnitude of lattice energies depends predominantly on the ionic charges because ionic radii vary over only a limited range.

---

**SAMPLE EXERCISE 8.1**  **Magnitudes of Lattice Energies**

Without consulting Table 8.2, arrange the ionic compounds NaF, CsI, and CaO in order of increasing lattice energy.

**SOLUTION**

**Analyze** From the formulas for three ionic compounds, we must determine their relative lattice energies.

**Plan** We need to determine the charges and relative sizes of the ions in the compounds. We then use Equation 8.4 qualitatively to determine the relative energies, knowing that (a) the larger the ionic charges, the greater the energy and (b) the farther apart the ions are, the lower the energy.

**Solve** NaF consists of $Na^+$ and $F^-$ ions, CsI of $Cs^+$ and $I^-$ ions, and CaO of $Ca^{2+}$ and $O^{2-}$ ions. Because the product $Q_1Q_2$ appears in the numerator of Equation 8.4, the lattice energy increases dramatically when the charges increase. Thus, we expect the lattice energy of CaO, which has 2+ and 2− ions, to be the greatest of the three.

The ionic charges are the same in NaF and CsI. As a result, the difference in their lattice energies depends on the difference in the distance between ions in the lattice. Because ionic size increases as we go down a group in the periodic table ∞ (Section 7.3), we know that $Cs^+$ is larger than $Na^+$ and $I^-$ is larger than $F^-$. Therefore, the distance between $Na^+$ and $F^-$ ions in NaF is less than the distance between the $Cs^+$ and $I^-$ ions in CsI. As a result, the lattice energy of NaF should be greater than that of CsI. In order of increasing energy, therefore, we have CsI < NaF < CaO.

**Check** Table 8.2 confirms our predicted order is correct.

**PRACTICE EXERCISE**

Which substance do you expect to have the greatest lattice energy, $MgF_2$, $CaF_2$, or $ZrO_2$?

*Answer:* $ZrO_2$

**Using this figure, can you place an upper and lower limit on the lattice energy of KF?**

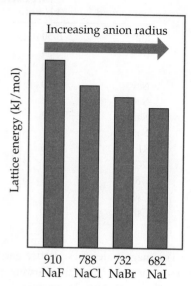

▶ **FIGURE 8.4 Periodic trends in lattice energy as a function of cation or anion radius.**

Because lattice energy decreases as distance between ions increases, lattice energies follow trends that parallel those in ionic radius shown in Figure 7.6. In particular, because ionic radius increases as we go down a group of the periodic table, we find that, for a given type of ionic compound, lattice energy decreases as we go down a group. ▲ FIGURE 8.4 illustrates this trend for the alkali chlorides MCl (M = Li, Na, K, Rb, Cs) and the sodium halides NaX (X = F, Cl, Br, I).

## Electron Configurations of Ions of the s- and p-Block Elements

The energetics of ionic bond formation helps explain why many ions tend to have noble-gas electron configurations. For example, sodium readily loses one electron to form $Na^+$, which has the same electron configuration as Ne:

$$Na \qquad 1s^2 2s^2 2p^6 3s^1 = [Ne]3s^1$$

$$Na^+ \qquad 1s^2 2s^2 2p^6 \quad = [Ne]$$

Even though lattice energy increases with increasing ionic charge, we never find ionic compounds that contain $Na^{2+}$ ions. The second electron removed would have to come from an inner shell of the sodium atom, and removing electrons from an inner shell requires a very large amount of energy. ∞ (Section 7.4) The increase in lattice energy is not enough to compensate for the energy needed to remove an inner-shell electron. Thus, sodium and the other group 1A metals are found in ionic substances only as 1+ ions.

Similarly, adding electrons to nonmetals is either exothermic or only slightly endothermic as long as the electrons are added to the valence shell. Thus, a Cl atom easily adds an electron to form $Cl^-$, which has the same electron configuration as Ar:

$$Cl \qquad 1s^2 2s^2 2p^6 3s^2 3p^5 = [Ne]3s^2 3p^5$$

$$Cl^- \qquad 1s^2 2s^2 2p^6 3s^2 3p^6 = [Ne]3s^2 3p^6 = [Ar]$$

To form a $Cl^{2-}$ ion, the second electron would have to be added to the next higher shell of the Cl atom, an addition that is energetically very unfavorable. Therefore, we never observe $Cl^{2-}$ ions in ionic compounds. We thus expect ionic compounds of the representative metals from groups 1A, 2A, and 3A to contain 1+, 2+, and 3+ cations, respectively, and usually expect ionic compounds of the representative nonmetals of groups 5A, 6A, and 7A to contain 3−, 2−, and 1− anions, respectively.

# A CLOSER LOOK

## CALCULATION OF LATTICE ENERGIES: THE BORN–HABER CYCLE

Lattice energies cannot be determined directly by experiment. They can, however, be calculated by envisioning the formation of an ionic compound as occurring in a series of well-defined steps. We can then use Hess's law ∞ (Section 5.6) to combine the steps in a way that gives the lattice energy for the compound. By so doing, we construct a **Born–Haber cycle**, a thermochemical cycle named after the German scientists Max Born (1882–1970) and Fritz Haber (1868–1934), who introduced it to analyze the factors contributing to the stability of ionic compounds.

In the Born–Haber cycle for NaCl, we consider the formation of NaCl(s) from Na(s) and $Cl_2(g)$ by two routes, as shown in ▶ FIGURE 8.5. The enthalpy change for the direct route (red arrow) is the heat of formation of NaCl(s):

$$Na(s) + \tfrac{1}{2} Cl_2(g) \longrightarrow NaCl(s) \quad \Delta H_f^\circ[NaCl(s)] = -411 \text{ kJ} \quad [8.5]$$

The indirect route has five steps (green arrows in Figure 8.5). First, we generate Na(g) atoms by vaporizing Na(s). Then we form Cl(g) atoms by breaking the bonds in $Cl_2$ molecules. The enthalpy changes are (Appendix C):

$$Na(s) \longrightarrow Na(g) \quad \Delta H_f^\circ[Na(g)] = 108 \text{ kJ} \quad [8.6]$$

$$\tfrac{1}{2} Cl_2(g) \longrightarrow Cl(g) \quad \Delta H_f^\circ[Cl(g)] = 122 \text{ kJ} \quad [8.7]$$

Note that both processes are endothermic.

In the next two steps we remove the electron from Na(g) to form $Na^+(g)$ and then add the electron to Cl(g) to form $Cl^-(g)$. The enthalpy changes for these processes equal the first ionization energy of Na, $I_1(Na)$, and the electron affinity of Cl, denoted $E(Cl)$, respectively: ∞ (Sections 7.4, 7.5)

$$Na(g) \longrightarrow Na^+(g) + e^- \quad \Delta H = I_1(Na) = 496 \text{ kJ} \quad [8.8]$$

$$Cl(g) + e^- \longrightarrow Cl^-(g) \quad \Delta H = E(Cl) = -349 \text{ kJ} \quad [8.9]$$

Finally, we combine the $Na^+(g)$ and $Cl^-(g)$ to form NaCl(s). Because forming solid NaCl is the reverse of breaking the solid into its gaseous ions, the enthalpy change for solid formation is the negative of the lattice energy, the quantity we want to determine:

$$Na^+(g) + Cl^-(g) \longrightarrow NaCl(s) \quad \Delta H = -\Delta H_{lattice} = ? \quad [8.10]$$

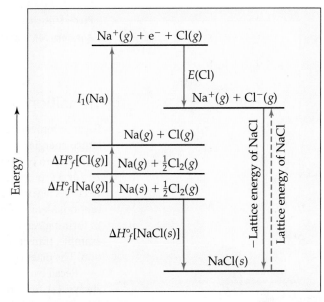

▲ **FIGURE 8.5  Born–Haber cycle for formation of NaCl.** This Hess's law representation shows the energetic relationships in the formation of the ionic solid from its elements.

The result of the five-step pathway is formation of NaCl(s) from Na(s) and $\tfrac{1}{2} Cl_2(g)$. Thus, from Hess's law we know that the sum of the enthalpy changes for the five steps equals the enthalpy change for the direct reaction (Equation 8.5):

$$\Delta H_f^\circ[NaCl(s)] = \Delta H_f^\circ[Na(g)] + \Delta H_f^\circ[Cl(g)]$$
$$+ I_1(Na) + E(Cl) - \Delta H_{lattice}$$

$$-411 \text{ kJ} = 108 \text{ kJ} + 122 \text{ kJ} + 496 \text{ kJ} - 349 \text{ kJ} - \Delta H_{lattice}$$

Solving for $\Delta H_{lattice}$:

$$\Delta H_{lattice} = 108 \text{ kJ} + 122 \text{ kJ} + 496 \text{ kJ} - 349 \text{ kJ} + 411 \text{ kJ}$$
$$= 788 \text{ kJ}$$

Thus, the lattice energy of NaCl is 788 kJ/mol.

*RELATED EXERCISES:* 8.28, 8.29, 8.30, 8.83, 8.102, 8.103

---

**SAMPLE EXERCISE 8.2**  **Charges on Ions**

Predict the ion generally formed by (**a**) Sr, (**b**) S, (**c**) Al.

### SOLUTION

**Analyze**  We must decide how many electrons are most likely to be gained or lost by atoms of Sr, S, and Al.

**Plan**  In each case we can use the element's position in the periodic table to predict whether the element forms a cation or an anion. We can then use its electron configuration to determine the most likely ion formed.

**Solve**  (**a**) Strontium is a metal in group 2A and therefore forms a cation. Its electron configuration is $[Kr]5s^2$, and so we expect that the two valence electrons can be lost easily to give an $Sr^{2+}$ ion. (**b**) Sulfur is a nonmetal in group 6A and will thus tend to be found as an anion. Its electron configuration ($[Ne]3s^23p^4$) is two electrons short of a noble-gas configuration. Thus, we expect that sulfur will form $S^{2-}$ ions. (**c**) Aluminum is a metal in group 3A. We therefore expect it to form $Al^{3+}$ ions.

**Check** The ionic charges we predict here are confirmed in Tables 2.4 and 2.5.

**PRACTICE EXERCISE**
Predict the charges on the ions formed when magnesium reacts with nitrogen.
**Answer:** $Mg^{2+}$ and $N^{3-}$

## Transition-Metal Ions

Because ionization energies increase rapidly for each successive electron removed, the lattice energies of ionic compounds are generally large enough to compensate for the loss of up to only three electrons from atoms. Thus, we find cations with charges of 1+, 2+, or 3+ in ionic compounds. Most transition metals, however, have more than three electrons beyond a noble-gas core. Silver, for example, has a $[Kr]4d^{10}5s^1$ electron configuration. Metals of group 1B (Cu, Ag, Au) often occur as 1+ ions (as in CuBr and AgCl). In forming $Ag^+$, the $5s$ electron is lost, leaving a completely filled $4d$ subshell. As in this example, transition metals generally do not form ions that have a noble-gas configuration. The octet rule, although useful, is clearly limited in scope.

Recall from Section 7.4 that when a positive ion forms from an atom, electrons are always lost first from the subshell having the largest value of $n$. Thus, *in forming ions, transition metals lose the valence-shell s electrons first, then as many d electrons as required to reach the charge of the ion.* For instance, in forming $Fe^{2+}$ from Fe, which has the electron configuration $[Ar]3d^64s^2$, the two $4s$ electrons are lost, leading to an $[Ar]3d^6$ configuration. Removal of an additional electron gives $Fe^{3+}$, whose electron configuration is $[Ar]3d^5$.

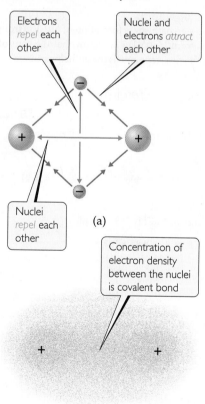

**GO FIGURE**

What would happen to the magnitudes of the attractions and repulsions represented in (a) if the nuclei were farther apart?

Electrons *repel* each other

Nuclei and electrons *attract* each other

Nuclei *repel* each other

(a)

Concentration of electron density between the nuclei is covalent bond

(b)

▲ **FIGURE 8.6  The covalent bond in H₂.** (a) The attractions and repulsions among electrons and nuclei in the hydrogen molecule. (b) Electron distribution in the $H_2$ molecule.

**GIVE IT SOME THOUGHT**

Which element forms a 3+ ion that has the electron configuration $[Kr]4d^6$?

# 8.3 | COVALENT BONDING

The vast majority of chemical substances do not have the characteristics of ionic materials. Most of the substances with which we come into daily contact—such as water—tend to be gases, liquids, or solids with low melting points. Many, such as gasoline, vaporize readily. Many are pliable in their solid forms—for example, plastic bags and paraffin.

For the very large class of substances that do not behave like ionic substances, we need a different model for the bonding between atoms. G. N. Lewis reasoned that atoms might acquire a noble-gas electron configuration by sharing electrons with other atoms. A chemical bond formed by sharing a pair of electrons is a *covalent bond.*

The hydrogen molecule, $H_2$, provides the simplest example of a covalent bond. When two hydrogen atoms are close to each other, the two positively charged nuclei repel each other, the two negatively charged electrons repel each other, and the nuclei and electrons attract each other, as shown in ◀ FIGURE 8.6(a). Because the molecule is stable, we know that the attractive forces must overcome the repulsive ones. Let's take a closer look at the attractive forces that hold this molecule together.

By using quantum mechanical methods analogous to those used for atoms in Section 6.5, we can calculate the distribution of electron density in molecules. Such a calculation for $H_2$ shows that the attractions between the nuclei and the electrons cause electron density to concentrate between the nuclei, as shown in Figure 8.6(b). As a result, the overall electrostatic interactions are attractive. Thus, the atoms in $H_2$ are held together principally because the two positive nuclei are attracted to the concentration of negative charge between them. In essence, the shared pair of electrons in any covalent bond acts as a kind of "glue" to bind atoms together.

⚠ **GIVE IT SOME THOUGHT**

Ionizing an $H_2$ molecule to $H_2^+$ changes the strength of the bond. Based on the description of covalent bonding given previously, do you expect the H—H bond in $H_2^+$ to be weaker or stronger than the H—H bond in $H_2$?

## Lewis Structures

The formation of covalent bonds can be represented with Lewis symbols. The formation of the $H_2$ molecule from two H atoms, for example, can be represented as

$$H \cdot \; + \; \cdot H \longrightarrow \; \boxed{H : H}$$

In forming the covalent bond, each hydrogen atom acquires a second electron, achieving the stable, two-electron, noble-gas electron configuration of helium.

Formation of a covalent bond between two Cl atoms to give a $Cl_2$ molecule can be represented in a similar way:

$$:\!\ddot{Cl}\cdot \; + \; \cdot\ddot{Cl}\!: \longrightarrow \; \boxed{:\!\ddot{Cl}\!:\!\ddot{Cl}\!:}$$

By sharing the bonding electron pair, each chlorine atom has eight electrons (an octet) in its valence shell, thus achieving the noble-gas electron configuration of argon.

The structures shown here for $H_2$ and $Cl_2$ are called either **Lewis structures** or *Lewis electron-dot structures.* In writing Lewis structures, we usually show each shared electron pair as a line and any unshared electron pairs as dots. Written this way, the Lewis structures for $H_2$ and $Cl_2$ are

$$H{-}H \qquad\qquad :\!\ddot{Cl}{-}\ddot{Cl}\!:$$

For nonmetals, the number of valence electrons in a neutral atom is the same as the group number. Therefore, one might predict that 7A elements, such as F, would form one covalent bond to achieve an octet; 6A elements, such as O, would form two covalent bonds; 5A elements, such as N, would form three; and 4A elements, such as C, would form four. These predictions are borne out in many compounds, as in, for example, the compounds with hydrogen of the nonmetals of the second row of the periodic table:

$$H{-}\ddot{\underset{\phantom{H}}{F}}\!: \qquad H{-}\underset{\underset{H}{|}}{\overset{\cdot\cdot}{O}} \qquad H{-}\underset{\underset{H}{|}}{\overset{\cdot\cdot}{N}}{-}H \qquad H{-}\underset{\underset{H}{|}}{\overset{\overset{\displaystyle H}{|}}{C}}{-}H$$

---

**SAMPLE EXERCISE 8.3** | **Lewis Structure of a Compound**

Given the Lewis symbols for nitrogen and fluorine in Table 8.1, predict the formula of the stable binary compound (a compound composed of two elements) formed when nitrogen reacts with fluorine and draw its Lewis structure.

**SOLUTION**

**Analyze** The Lewis symbols for nitrogen and fluorine reveal that nitrogen has five valence electrons and fluorine has seven.

**Plan** We need to find a combination of the two elements that results in an octet of electrons around each atom. Nitrogen requires three additional electrons to complete its octet, and fluorine requires one. Sharing a pair of electrons between one N atom and one F atom will result in an octet of electrons for fluorine but not for nitrogen. We therefore need to figure out a way to get two more electrons for the N atom.

**Solve** Nitrogen must share a pair of electrons with three fluorine atoms to complete its octet. Thus, the binary compound these two elements form must be $NF_3$:

$$\cdot\dot{N}\cdot \; + \; 3\; \cdot\ddot{F}\!: \longrightarrow \; :\!\ddot{F}\!:\!\ddot{N}\!:\!\ddot{F}\!: \longrightarrow \; :\!\ddot{F}{-}\underset{\underset{:\ddot{F}:}{|}}{\ddot{N}}{-}\ddot{F}\!:$$
$$\phantom{xxxxxxxxxxxxxxxx}\overset{\cdot\cdot}{\underset{\cdot\cdot}{:}F\!:}$$

**Check** The Lewis structure in the center shows that each atom is surrounded by an octet of electrons. Once you are accustomed to thinking of each line in a Lewis structure as representing *two* electrons, you can just as easily use the structure on the right to check for octets.

**PRACTICE EXERCISE**

Compare the Lewis symbol for neon with the Lewis structure for methane, $CH_4$. In what important way are the electron arrangements about neon and carbon alike? In what important way are they different?

**Answer:** Both atoms have an octet of electrons. However, the electrons about neon are unshared electron pairs, whereas those about carbon are shared with four hydrogen atoms.

## Multiple Bonds

A shared electron pair constitutes a single covalent bond, generally referred to simply as a **single bond**. In many molecules, atoms attain complete octets by sharing more than one pair of electrons. When two electron pairs are shared, two lines are drawn in the Lewis structure, representing a **double bond**. In carbon dioxide, for example, bonding occurs between carbon, with four valence electrons, and oxygen, with six:

$$:\ddot{O}: + \cdot\dot{C}\cdot + :\ddot{O}: \longrightarrow \ddot{O}::C::\ddot{O} \quad (\text{or } \ddot{O}=C=\ddot{O})$$

As the diagram shows, each oxygen atom acquires an octet by sharing two electron pairs with carbon. Carbon acquires an octet by sharing two electron pairs with each of the two oxygen atoms; each double bond involves four electrons.

A **triple bond** corresponds to the sharing of three pairs of electrons, such as in the $N_2$ molecule:

$$:\dot{N}\cdot + \cdot\dot{N}: \longrightarrow :N:::N: \quad (\text{or } :N\equiv N:)$$

Because each nitrogen atom has five valence electrons, three electron pairs must be shared to achieve the octet configuration.

The properties of $N_2$ are in complete accord with its Lewis structure. Nitrogen is a diatomic gas with exceptionally low reactivity that results from the very stable nitrogen–nitrogen bond. The nitrogen atoms are separated by only 1.10 Å. The short separation distance between the two N atoms is a result of the triple bond between the atoms. From studies of the structures of many different substances in which nitrogen atoms share one or two electron pairs, we have learned that the average distance between bonded nitrogen atoms varies with the number of shared electron pairs:

| N—N | N=N | N≡N |
|:---:|:---:|:---:|
| 1.47 Å | 1.24 Å | 1.10 Å |

As a general rule, the length of the bond between two atoms decreases as the number of shared electron pairs increases.

**△ GIVE IT SOME THOUGHT**

The C—O bond length in carbon monoxide, CO, is 1.13 Å, whereas the C—O bond length in $CO_2$ is 1.24 Å. Without drawing a Lewis structure, do you think that CO contains a single, double, or triple bond?

# 8.4 | BOND POLARITY AND ELECTRONEGATIVITY

When two identical atoms bond, as in $Cl_2$ or $H_2$, the electron pairs must be shared equally. When two atoms from opposites sides of the periodic table bond, such as NaCl, there is relatively little sharing of electrons, which means that NaCl is best described as composed of $Na^+$ and $Cl^-$ ions. The 3s electron of the Na atom is, in effect, transferred completely to chlorine. The bonds that are found in most substances fall somewhere between these extremes.

**Bond polarity** is a measure of how equally or unequally the electrons in any covalent bond are shared. A **nonpolar covalent bond** is one in which the electrons are shared equally, as in $Cl_2$ and $N_2$. In a **polar covalent bond**, one of the atoms exerts a greater attraction for the bonding electrons than the other. If the difference in relative ability to attract electrons is large enough, an ionic bond is formed.

## Electronegativity

We use a quantity called electronegativity to estimate whether a given bond is nonpolar covalent, polar covalent, or ionic. **Electronegativity** is defined as the ability of an atom *in a molecule* to attract electrons to itself. The greater an atom's electronegativity, the greater its ability to attract electrons to itself. The electronegativity of an atom in a molecule is related to the atom's ionization energy and electron affinity, which are properties of isolated atoms. An atom with a very negative electron affinity and a high ionization energy both attracts electrons from other atoms and resists having its electrons attracted away; it is highly electronegative.

Electronegativity values can be based on a variety of properties, not just ionization energy and electron affinity. The American chemist Linus Pauling (1901–1994) developed the first and most widely used electronegativity scale, which is based on thermochemical data. As ▼ **FIGURE 8.7** shows, there is generally an increase in electronegativity from left to right across a period—that is, from the most metallic to the most nonmetallic elements. With some exceptions (especially in the transition metals), electronegativity decreases with increasing atomic number in a group. This is what we expect because we know that ionization energies decrease with increasing atomic number in a group and electron affinities do not change very much.

You do not need to memorize electronegativity values. Instead, you should know the periodic trends so that you can predict which of two elements is more electronegative.

### ▲ GIVE IT SOME THOUGHT

How does the *electronegativity* of an element differ from its *electron affinity*?

### ▲ GO FIGURE

For the group 6A elements, what is the trend in electronegativity with increasing atomic number?

◄ **FIGURE 8.7   Electronegativity values based on Pauling's thermochemical data.**

## Electronegativity and Bond Polarity

We can use the difference in electronegativity between two atoms to gauge the polarity of the bond the atoms form. Consider these three fluorine-containing compounds:

|  | F$_2$ | HF | LiF |
|---|---|---|---|
| Electronegativity difference | $4.0 - 4.0 = 0$ | $4.0 - 2.1 = 1.9$ | $4.0 - 1.0 = 3.0$ |
| Type of bond | Nonpolar covalent | Polar covalent | Ionic |

In F$_2$ the electrons are shared equally between the fluorine atoms and, thus, the covalent bond is *nonpolar*. A nonpolar covalent bond results when the electronegativities of the bonded atoms are equal.

In HF the fluorine atom has a greater electronegativity than the hydrogen atom, with the result that the electrons are shared unequally—the bond is *polar*. In general, a polar covalent bond results when the atoms differ in electronegativity. In HF the more electronegative fluorine atom attracts electron density away from the less electronegative hydrogen atom, leaving a partial positive charge on the hydrogen atom and a partial negative charge on the fluorine atom. We can represent this charge distribution as

$$\overset{\delta+}{H} - \overset{\delta-}{F}$$

The $\delta+$ and $\delta-$ (read "delta plus" and "delta minus") symbolize the partial positive and negative charges, respectively.

In LiF the electronegativity difference is very large, meaning that the electron density is shifted far toward F. The resultant bond is therefore most accurately described as *ionic*.

The shift of electron density toward the more electronegative atom in a bond can be seen in the results of calculations of electron density distributions. For the three species in our example, the calculated electron density distributions are shown in ▼ **FIGURE 8.8.** You can see that in F$_2$ the distribution is symmetrical, in HF the electron density is clearly shifted toward fluorine, and in LiF the shift is even greater. These examples illustrate, therefore, that *the greater the difference in electronegativity between two atoms, the more polar their bond.*

F$_2$        HF        LiF

▲ **FIGURE 8.8  Electron density distribution.** This computer-generated rendering shows the calculated electron-density distribution on the surface of the F$_2$, HF, and LiF molecules.

### GIVE IT SOME THOUGHT

Based on differences in electronegativity, how would you characterize the bonding in sulfur dioxide, SO$_2$? Do you expect the bonds between S and O to be nonpolar, polar covalent, or ionic?

### SAMPLE EXERCISE 8.4 | Bond Polarity

In each case, which bond is more polar: **(a)** B—Cl or C—Cl, **(b)** P—F or P—Cl? Indicate in each case which atom has the partial negative charge.

### SOLUTION

**Analyze** We are asked to determine relative bond polarities, given nothing but the atoms involved in the bonds.

**Plan**  Because we are not asked for quantitative answers, we can use the periodic table and our knowledge of electronegativity trends to answer the question.

**Solve**
**(a)**  The chlorine atom is common to both bonds. Therefore, the analysis reduces to a comparison of the electronegativities of B and C. Because boron is to the left of carbon in the periodic table, we predict that boron has the lower electronegativity. Chlorine, being on the right side of the table, has a higher electronegativity. The more polar bond will be the one between the atoms having the lowest electronegativity (boron) and the highest electronegativity (chlorine). Consequently, the B—Cl bond is more polar; the chlorine atom carries the partial negative charge because it has a higher electronegativity.

**(b)**  In this example phosphorus is common to both bonds, and the analysis reduces to a comparison of the electronegativities of F and Cl. Because fluorine is above chlorine in the periodic table, it should be more electronegative and will form the more polar bond with P. The higher electronegativity of fluorine means that it will carry the partial negative charge.

**Check**
**(a)**  Using Figure 8.7: The difference in the electronegativities of chlorine and boron is $3.0 - 2.0 = 1.0$; the difference between chlorine and carbon is $3.0 - 2.5 = 0.5$. Hence, the B—Cl bond is more polar, as we had predicted.

**(b)**  Using Figure 8.7: The difference in the electronegativities of chlorine and phosphorus is $3.0 - 2.1 = 0.9$; the difference between fluorine and phosphorus is $4.0 - 2.1 = 1.9$. Hence, the P—F bond is more polar, as we had predicted.

**PRACTICE EXERCISE**
Which of the following bonds is most polar: S—Cl, S—Br, Se—Cl, or Se—Br ?
*Answer:*  Se—Cl

# Dipole Moments

The difference in electronegativity between H and F leads to a polar covalent bond in the HF molecule. As a consequence, there is a concentration of negative charge on the more electronegative F atom, leaving the less electronegative H atom at the positive end of the molecule. A molecule such as HF, in which the centers of positive and negative charge do not coincide, is a **polar molecule**. Thus, we describe both bonds and entire molecules as being polar and nonpolar.

We can indicate the polarity of the HF molecule in two ways:

$$\overset{\delta+\quad\delta-}{\text{H}-\text{F}}\quad or\quad \overset{\longmapsto}{\text{H}-\text{F}}$$

In the notation on the right, the arrow denotes the shift in electron density toward the fluorine atom. The crossed end of the arrow can be thought of as a plus sign designating the positive end of the molecule.

Polarity helps determine many properties we observe at the macroscopic level in the laboratory and in everyday life. Polar molecules align themselves with respect to one another, with the negative end of one molecule and the positive end of another attracting each other. Polar molecules are likewise attracted to ions. The negative end of a polar molecule is attracted to a positive ion, and the positive end is attracted to a negative ion. These interactions account for many properties of liquids, solids, and solutions, as you will see in Chapters 11, 12, and 13.

How can we quantify the polarity of a molecule? Whenever two electrical charges of equal magnitude but opposite sign are separated by a distance, a **dipole** is established. The quantitative measure of the magnitude of a dipole is called its **dipole moment**, denoted $\mu$. If two equal and opposite charges $Q+$ and $Q-$ are separated by a distance $r$, as in ▶ FIGURE 8.9, the magnitude of the dipole moment is the product of $Q$ and $r$:

$$\mu = Qr \qquad\qquad [8.11]$$

◢ GO FIGURE

**If the charged particles are moved closer together, does $\mu$ increase, decrease, or stay the same?**

Dipole moment $\mu = Qr$

▲ **FIGURE 8.9  Dipole and dipole moment.**  When charges of equal magnitude and opposite sign $Q+$ and $Q-$ are separated by a distance $r$, a dipole is produced.

This expression tells us that dipole moment increases as the magnitude of $Q$ increases and as $r$ increases. For a nonpolar molecule, such as $F_2$, the dipole moment is zero because there is no charge separation.

 **GIVE IT SOME THOUGHT**

Chlorine monofluoride, ClF, and iodine monofluoride, IF, are *interhalogen* compounds—compounds that contain bonds between different halogen elements. Which of these molecules has the larger dipole moment?

Dipole moments are usually reported in *debyes* (D), a unit that equals $3.34 \times 10^{-30}$ coulomb-meters (C-m). For molecules, we usually measure charge in units of the electronic charge $e$, $1.60 \times 10^{-19}$ C, and distance in angstroms. This means we need to convert units whenever we want to report a dipole moment in debyes. Suppose that two charges $1+$ and $1-$ (in units of $e$) are separated by $1.00$ Å. The dipole moment produced is

$$\mu = Qr = (1.60 \times 10^{-19} \text{C})(1.00 \text{ Å})\left(\frac{10^{-10} \text{m}}{1 \text{ Å}}\right)\left(\frac{1 \text{ D}}{3.34 \times 10^{-30} \text{C-m}}\right) = 4.79 \text{ D}$$

Measurement of the dipole moments can provide us with valuable information about the charge distributions in molecules, as illustrated in Sample Exercise 8.5.

---

**SAMPLE EXERCISE 8.5** | **Dipole Moments of Diatomic Molecules**

The bond length in the HCl molecule is $1.27$ Å. **(a)** Calculate the dipole moment, in debyes, that results if the charges on the H and Cl atoms were $1+$ and $1-$, respectively. **(b)** The experimentally measured dipole moment of HCl($g$) is $1.08$ D. What magnitude of charge, in units of $e$, on the H and Cl atoms leads to this dipole moment?

**SOLUTION**

**Analyze and Plan** We are asked in (a) to calculate the dipole moment of HCl that would result if there were a full charge transferred from H to Cl. We can use Equation 8.11 to obtain this result. In (b), we are given the actual dipole moment for the molecule and will use that value to calculate the actual partial charges on the H and Cl atoms.

**Solve:**

**(a)** The charge on each atom is the electronic charge, $e = 1.60 \times 10^{-19}$ C. The separation is $1.27$ Å. The dipole moment is therefore

$$\mu = Qr = (1.60 \times 10^{-19} \text{C})(1.27 \text{ Å})\left(\frac{10^{-10} \text{ m}}{1 \text{ Å}}\right)\left(\frac{1 \text{ D}}{3.34 \times 10^{-30} \text{C-m}}\right) = 6.08 \text{ D}$$

**(b)** We know the value of $\mu$, $1.08$ D, and the value of $r$, $1.27$ Å. We want to calculate the value of $Q$:

$$Q = \frac{\mu}{r} = \frac{(1.08 \text{ D})\left(\dfrac{3.34 \times 10^{-30} \text{C-m}}{1 \text{ D}}\right)}{(1.27 \text{ Å})\left(\dfrac{10^{-10} \text{ m}}{1 \text{ Å}}\right)} = 2.84 \times 10^{-20} \text{C}$$

We can readily convert this charge to units of $e$:

$$\text{Charge in } e = (2.84 \times 10^{-20} \text{ C})\left(\frac{1 \ e}{1.60 \times 10^{-19} \text{C}}\right) = 0.178e$$

Thus, the experimental dipole moment indicates that the charge separation in the HCl molecule is

$$\overset{0.178+}{\text{H}} — \overset{0.178-}{\text{Cl}}$$

Because the experimental dipole moment is less than that calculated in part (a), the charges on the atoms are much less than a full electronic charge. We could have anticipated this because the H—Cl bond is polar covalent rather than ionic.

---

**PRACTICE EXERCISE**

The dipole moment of chlorine monofluoride, ClF($g$), is $0.88$ D. The bond length of the molecule is $1.63$ Å. **(a)** Which atom is expected to have the partial negative charge? **(b)** What is the charge on that atom in units of $e$?

*Answers:* **(a)** F, **(b)** $0.11-$

**TABLE 8.3 ● Bond Lengths, Electronegativity Differences, and Dipole Moments of the Hydrogen Halides**

| Compound | Bond Length (Å) | Electronegativity Difference | Dipole Moment (D) |
|----------|-----------------|------------------------------|-------------------|
| HF | 0.92 | 1.9 | 1.82 |
| HCl | 1.27 | 0.9 | 1.08 |
| HBr | 1.41 | 0.7 | 0.82 |
| HI | 1.61 | 0.4 | 0.44 |

▲ **TABLE 8.3** presents the bond lengths and dipole moments of the hydrogen halides. Notice that as we proceed from HF to HI, the electronegativity difference decreases and the bond length increases. The first effect decreases the amount of charge separated and causes the dipole moment to decrease from HF to HI, even though the bond length is increasing. Calculations identical to those used in Sample Exercise 8.5 show that the charges on the atoms decrease from 0.41+ and 0.41− in HF to 0.057+ and 0.057− in HI. We can visualize the varying degree of electronic charge shift in these substances from computer-generated renderings based on calculations of electron distribution, as shown in ▼ **FIGURE 8.10**. For these molecules, the change in the electronegativity difference has a greater effect on the dipole moment than does the change in bond length.

**GIVE IT SOME THOUGHT**

The bond between carbon and hydrogen is one of the most important types of bonds in chemistry. The length of a H—C bond is approximately 1.1 Å. Based on this distance and differences in electronegativity, do you expect the dipole moment of an individual H—C bond to be larger or smaller than that of the H—I bond?

Before leaving this section, let's return to the LiF molecule in Figure 8.8. Under standard conditions, LiF exists as an ionic solid with an arrangement of atoms analogous to the sodium chloride structure shown in Figure 8.3. However, it is possible to generate LiF *molecules* by vaporizing the ionic solid at high temperature. The molecules have a dipole moment of 6.28 D and a bond distance of 1.53 Å. From these values we can calculate the charge on lithium and fluorine to be 0.857+ and 0.857−, respectively. This bond is extremely polar, and the presence of such large charges strongly favors the formation of an extended ionic lattice in which each lithium ion is surrounded by fluoride ions and vice versa.

**GO FIGURE**

How do you interpret the fact that there is no red in the HBr and HI representations?

HF       HCl       HBr       HI

▲ **FIGURE 8.10  Charge separation in the hydrogen halides.** In HF, the strongly electronegative F pulls much of the electron density away from H. In HI, the I, being much less electronegative than F, does not attract the shared electrons as strongly and, consequently, there is far less polarization of the bond.

## Differentiating Ionic and Covalent Bonding

To understand the interactions responsible for chemical bonding, it is advantageous to treat ionic and covalent bonding separately. That is the approach taken in this chapter, as well as in most other undergraduate-level chemistry texts. In reality, however, there is a continuum between the extremes of ionic and covalent bonding. This lack of a well-defined separation between the two types of bonding may seem unsettling or confusing at first.

The simple models of ionic and covalent bonding presented in this chapter go a long way toward understanding and predicting the structures and properties of chemical compounds. When covalent bonding is dominant, more often than not we expect compounds to exist as molecules,* having all the properties we associate with molecular substances, such as relatively low melting and boiling points and nonelectrolyte behavior when dissolved in water. When ionic bonding is dominant, we expect the compounds to be brittle, high-melting solids with extended lattice structures and exhibiting strong electrolyte behavior when dissolved in water.

There are, of course, exceptions to these general characterizations, some of which we examine later in the book. Nonetheless, the ability to quickly categorize the predominant bonding interactions in a substance as covalent or ionic imparts considerable insight into the properties of that substance. The question then becomes the best way to recognize which type of bonding dominates.

The simplest approach is to assume that the interaction between a metal and a nonmetal is ionic and that between two nonmetals is covalent. While this classification scheme is reasonably predictive, there are far too many exceptions to use it blindly. For example, tin is a metal and chlorine is a nonmetal, but $SnCl_4$ is a molecular substance that exists as a colorless liquid at room temperature. It freezes at $-33\,°C$ and boils at $114\,°C$. Clearly this substance does not have the characteristics of an ionic substance. A more sophisticated approach is to use the difference in electronegativity as the main criterion for determining whether ionic or covalent bonding will be dominant. This approach correctly predicts the bonding in $SnCl_4$ to be polar covalent based on an electronegativity difference of 1.2 and at the same time correctly predicts the bonding in NaCl to be predominantly ionic based on an electronegativity difference of 2.1.

Evaluating bonding based on electronegativity difference is a useful system, but it has one shortcoming. The electronegativity values given in Figure 8.7 do not take into account changes in bonding that accompany changes in the oxidation state of the metal. For example, Figure 8.7 gives the electronegativity difference between manganese and oxygen as $3.5 - 1.5 = 2.0$, which falls in the range where the bonding is normally considered ionic (the electronegativity difference for NaCl is $3.0 - 0.9 = 2.1$). Therefore, it is not surprising to learn that manganese(II) oxide, MnO, is a green solid that melts at $1842\,°C$ and has the same crystal structure as NaCl.

However, the bonding between manganese and oxygen is not always ionic. Manganese(VII) oxide, $Mn_2O_7$, is a green liquid that freezes at $5.9\,°C$, which indicates that covalent rather than ionic bonding dominates. The change in the oxidation state of manganese is responsible for the change in bonding. In general, as the oxidation state of a metal increases, so does the degree of covalent bonding. When the oxidation state of the metal is highly positive (roughly speaking, $+4$ or larger), we should expect significant covalency in the bonds it forms with nonmetals. Thus, with metals in high oxidation states we find molecular substances, such as $Mn_2O_7$, or polyatomic ions, such as $MnO_4^-$ and $CrO_4^{2-}$, rather than ionic compounds.

### ▲ GIVE IT SOME THOUGHT

You have a yellow solid that melts at 41 °C and boils at 131 °C and a green solid that melts at 2320 °C. If you are told that one of them is $Cr_2O_3$ and the other is $OsO_4$, which one do you expect to be the yellow solid?

---

*There are some exceptions to this statement, such as network solids, including diamond, silicon, and germanium, where an extended structure is formed even though the bonding is clearly covalent. These examples are discussed in Section 12.7.

# 8.5 | DRAWING LEWIS STRUCTURES

Lewis structures can help us understand the bonding in many compounds and are frequently used when discussing the properties of molecules. For this reason, drawing Lewis structures is an important skill that you should practice. To do so, you should use the following procedure.

1. **Sum the valence electrons from all atoms.** (Use the periodic table to help you determine the number of valence electrons in each atom.) For an anion, add one electron to the total for each negative charge. For a cation, subtract one electron from the total for each positive charge. Do not worry about keeping track of which electrons come from which atoms. Only the total number is important.

2. **Write the symbols for the atoms, show which atoms are attached to which, and connect them with a single bond** (*a dash, representing* two *electrons*). Chemical formulas are often written in the order in which the atoms are connected in the molecule or ion. The formula HCN, for example, tells you that the carbon atom is bonded to the H and to the N. In many polyatomic molecules and ions, the central atom is usually written first, as in $CO_3^{2-}$ and $SF_4$. Remember that the central atom is generally less electronegative than the atoms surrounding it. In other cases, you may need more information before you can draw the Lewis structure.

3. **Complete the octets around all the atoms bonded to the central atom.** Remember, however, that a hydrogen atom has only a single pair of electrons around it.

4. **Place any leftover electrons on the central atom,** even if doing so results in more than an octet of electrons around the atom.

5. **If there are not enough electrons to give the central atom an octet, try multiple bonds.** Use one or more of the unshared pairs of electrons on the atoms bonded to the central atom to form double or triple bonds.

---

**SAMPLE EXERCISE 8.6** | **Drawing a Lewis Structure**

Draw the Lewis structure for phosphorus trichloride, $PCl_3$.

### SOLUTION

**Analyze and Plan** We are asked to draw a Lewis structure from a molecular formula. Our plan is to follow the five-step procedure just described.

**Solve**

First, we sum the valence electrons. Phosphorus (group 5A) has five valence electrons, and each chlorine (group 7A) has seven. The total number of valence electrons is therefore

$$5 + (3 \times 7) = 26$$

Second, we arrange the atoms to show which atom is connected to which, and we draw a single bond between them. There are various ways the atoms might be arranged. In binary compounds, however, the first element in the chemical formula is generally surrounded by the remaining atoms. Thus, we begin with a skeleton structure that shows a single bond between the P atom and each Cl atom:

$$\text{Cl—P—Cl} \atop | \atop \text{Cl}$$

(It is not crucial that the Cl atoms be left of, right of, and below the P atom—any structure that shows each of the three Cl atoms bonded to P will work.)

Third, we complete the octets on the atoms bonded to the central atom. Placing octets around each Cl atom accounts for 24 electrons (remember, each line in our structure represents *two* electrons):

$$:\!\ddot{\text{Cl}}\!-\!\text{P}\!-\!\ddot{\text{Cl}}\!: \atop | \atop :\!\ddot{\text{Cl}}\!:$$

Fourth, recalling that our total number of electrons is 26, we place the remaining two electrons on the central atom, completing the octet around it:

$$:\!\ddot{\text{Cl}}\!-\!\ddot{\text{P}}\!-\!\ddot{\text{Cl}}\!: \atop | \atop :\!\ddot{\text{Cl}}\!:$$

This structure gives each atom an octet, so we stop at this point. (In checking for octets, remember to count both electrons in a single bond twice, once for each atom in the bond.)

**PRACTICE EXERCISE**

(a) How many valence electrons should appear in the Lewis structure for $CH_2Cl_2$?
(b) Draw the Lewis structure.

*Answers:* (a) 20, (b)

$$\ddot{\underset{..}{Cl}}\!\!-\!\!\underset{\overset{\displaystyle H}{|}}{\overset{\overset{\displaystyle H}{|}}{C}}\!\!-\!\!\ddot{\underset{..}{Cl}}\!:$$

---

**SAMPLE EXERCISE 8.7** | **Lewis Structure with a Multiple Bond**

Draw the Lewis structure for HCN.

**SOLUTION**

Hydrogen has one valence electron, carbon (group 4A) has four, and nitrogen (group 5A) has five. The total number of valence electrons is, therefore, $1 + 4 + 5 = 10$. In principle, there are different ways in which we might choose to arrange the atoms. Because hydrogen can accommodate only one electron pair, it always has only one single bond associated with it. Therefore, C—H—N is an impossible arrangement. The remaining two possibilities are H—C—N and H—N—C. The first is the arrangement found experimentally. You might have guessed this because (a) the formula is written with the atoms in this order and (b) carbon is less electronegative than nitrogen. Thus, we begin with the skeleton structure

$$H\!-\!C\!-\!N$$

The two bonds account for four electrons. The H atom can have only two electrons associated with it, and so we will not add any more electrons to it. If we place the remaining six electrons around N to give it an octet, we do not achieve an octet on C:

$$H\!-\!C\!-\!\ddot{\underset{..}{N}}:$$

We therefore try a double bond between C and N, using one of the unshared pairs we placed on N. Again we end up with fewer than eight electrons on C, and so we next try a triple bond. This structure gives an octet around both C and N:

$$H\!-\!C\!\overset{\curvearrowleft}{\underset{..}{N}}: \longrightarrow H\!-\!C\!\equiv\!N:$$

The octet rule is satisfied for the C and N atoms, and the H atom has two electrons around it. This is a correct Lewis structure.

**PRACTICE EXERCISE**

Draw the Lewis structure for (a) $NO^+$ ion, (b) $C_2H_4$.

*Answers:* (a) $[:N\!\equiv\!O:]^+$, (b)

$$\underset{\displaystyle H}{\overset{\displaystyle H}{\diagdown}}C\!=\!C\underset{\displaystyle H}{\overset{\displaystyle H}{\diagup}}$$

---

**SAMPLE EXERCISE 8.8** | **Lewis Structure for a Polyatomic Ion**

Draw the Lewis structure for the $BrO_3^-$ ion.

**SOLUTION**

Bromine (group 7A) has seven valence electrons, and oxygen (group 6A) has six. We must add one more electron to our sum to account for the $1-$ charge of the ion. The total number of valence electrons is, therefore, $7 + (3 \times 6) + 1 = 26$. For oxyanions—$BrO_3^-$, $SO_4^{2-}$, $NO_3^-$, $CO_3^{2-}$, and so forth—the oxygen atoms surround the central nonmetal atom. After following this format and then putting in the single bonds and distributing the unshared electron pairs, we have

$$\left[:\ddot{\underset{..}{O}}\!-\!\underset{\underset{\displaystyle :\ddot{\underset{..}{O}}:}{|}}{\ddot{Br}}\!-\!\ddot{\underset{..}{O}}:\right]^-$$

Notice that the Lewis structure for an ion is written in brackets and the charge is shown outside the brackets at the upper right.

## PRACTICE EXERCISE

Draw the Lewis structure for **(a)** $ClO_2^-$, **(b)** $PO_4^{3-}$.

*Answers:* **(a)** $\left[ \ddot{\underset{..}{O}} - \ddot{\underset{..}{Cl}} - \ddot{\underset{..}{O}} \colon \right]^-$  **(b)** $\left[ \begin{array}{c} \ddot{O} \colon \\ | \\ \colon \ddot{O} - P - \ddot{O} \colon \\ | \\ \colon \ddot{O} \colon \end{array} \right]^{3-}$

# Formal Charge and Alternative Lewis Structures

When we draw a Lewis structure, we are describing how the electrons are distributed in a molecule or polyatomic ion. In some instances we can draw more than one Lewis structure and have all of them obey the octet rule. All these structures can be thought of as contributing to the *actual* arrangement of the electrons in the molecule, but not all of them will contribute to the same extent. How do we decide which of several Lewis structures is the most important? One approach is to do some "bookkeeping" of the valence electrons to determine the *formal charge* of each atom in each Lewis structure. The **formal charge** of any atom in a molecule is the charge the atom would have if all the atoms in the molecule had the same electronegativity (that is, if each bonding electron pair in the molecule were shared equally between its two atoms).

To calculate the formal charge on any atom in a Lewis structure, we assign electrons to the atom as follows:

1. *All* unshared (nonbonding) electrons are assigned to the atom on which they are found.

2. For any bond—single, double, or triple—*half* of the bonding electrons are assigned to each atom in the bond.

The formal charge of each atom is calculated *by subtracting the number of electrons assigned to the atom from the number of valence electrons in the neutral atom.*

Let's practice by calculating the formal charges in the cyanide ion, $CN^-$, which has the Lewis structure

$$[\colon C \equiv N \colon]^-$$

For the C atom, there are two nonbonding electrons and three electrons from the six in the triple bond ($\frac{1}{2} \times 6 = 3$) for a total of five. The number of valence electrons on a neutral C atom is four. Thus, the formal charge on C is $4 - 5 = -1$. For N, there are two nonbonding electrons and three electrons from the triple bond. Because the number of valence electrons on a neutral N atom is five, its formal charge is $5 - 5 = 0$:

$$[\overset{-1}{\colon C} \equiv \overset{0}{N} \colon]^-$$

Notice that the sum of the formal charges equals the overall charge on the ion, $1-$. The formal charges on a neutral molecule must add to zero, whereas those on an ion add to give the charge on the ion.

If we can draw several Lewis structures for a molecule, the concept of formal charge can help us decide which is the most important, which we shall call the *dominant* Lewis structure. One Lewis structure for $CO_2$, for instance, has two double bonds, as we saw on page 298. However, we can also satisfy the octet rule by drawing a Lewis structure having one single bond and one triple bond. Calculating formal charges in these structures, we have

$$\ddot{O} = C = \ddot{O} \qquad \colon \ddot{O} - C \equiv O \colon$$

|  | | | | | | |
|---|---|---|---|---|---|---|
| Valence electrons: | 6 | 4 | 6 | 6 | 4 | 6 |
| −(Electrons assigned to atom): | 6 | 4 | 6 | 7 | 4 | 5 |
| Formal charge: | 0 | 0 | 0 | −1 | 0 | +1 |

Note that in both cases the formal charges add up to zero, as they must because $CO_2$ is a neutral molecule. So, which is the more correct structure? As a general rule, when more than one Lewis structure is possible, we will use the following guidelines to choose the dominant one:

1. The dominant Lewis structure is generally the one in which the atoms bear formal charges closest to zero.

2. A Lewis structure in which any negative charges reside on the more electronegative atoms is generally more dominant than one that has negative charges on the less electronegative atoms.

Thus, the first Lewis structure of $CO_2$ is the dominant one because the atoms carry no formal charges and so satisfy the first guideline. The other Lewis structure shown (and the similar one that has a triple bond to the left O and a single bond to the right O) do contribute to the actual structure but to a much smaller extent.

Although the concept of formal charge helps us to arrange alternative Lewis structures in order of importance, it is important that you remember that *formal charges do not represent real charges on atoms*. These charges are just a bookkeeping convention. The actual charge distributions in molecules and ions are determined not by formal charges but by a number of other factors, including electronegativity differences between atoms.

 **GIVE IT SOME THOUGHT**

Suppose a Lewis structure for a neutral fluorine-containing molecule results in a formal charge on the fluorine atom of +1. What conclusion would you draw?

---

**SAMPLE EXERCISE 8.9** | **Lewis Structures and Formal Charges**

Three possible Lewis structures for the thiocyanate ion, $NCS^-$, are

$$[:\ddot{N}-C\equiv S:]^- \qquad [\ddot{N}=C=\ddot{S}]^- \qquad [:N\equiv C-\ddot{S}:]^-$$

(a) Determine the formal charges in each structure. (b) Based on the formal charges, which Lewis structure is the dominant one?

**SOLUTION**

(a) Neutral N, C, and S atoms have five, four, and six valence electrons, respectively. We can determine the formal charges in the three structures by using the rules we just discussed:

$$\overset{-2\quad0\quad+1}{[:\ddot{N}-C\equiv S:]^-} \qquad \overset{-1\quad0\quad0}{[\ddot{N}=C=\ddot{S}]^-} \qquad \overset{0\quad0\quad-1}{[:N\equiv C-\ddot{S}:]^-}$$

As they must, the formal charges in all three structures sum to $1-$, the overall charge of the ion.
(b) The dominant Lewis structure generally produces formal charges of the smallest magnitude (guideline 1). That rules out the left structure as the dominant one. Further, as discussed in Section 8.4, N is more electronegative than C or S. Therefore, we expect any negative formal charge to reside on the N atom (guideline 2). For these two reasons, the middle Lewis structure is the dominant one for $NCS^-$.

**PRACTICE EXERCISE**

The cyanate ion, $NCO^-$, has three possible Lewis structures. (a) Draw these three structures and assign formal charges in each. (b) Which Lewis structure is dominant?

$$\overset{-2\quad0\quad+1}{[:\ddot{N}-C\equiv O:]^-} \qquad \overset{-1\quad0\quad0}{[\ddot{N}=C=\ddot{O}]^-} \qquad \overset{0\quad0\quad-1}{[:N\equiv C-\ddot{O}:]^-}$$

**Answers:** (a)

(i)            (ii)            (iii)

(b) Structure (iii), which places a negative charge on oxygen, the most electronegative element in the ion, is the dominant Lewis structure.

# A CLOSER LOOK

## OXIDATION NUMBERS, FORMAL CHARGES, AND ACTUAL PARTIAL CHARGES

In Chapter 4 we introduced the rules for assigning *oxidation numbers* to atoms. The concept of electronegativity is the basis of these numbers. An atom's oxidation number is the charge the atom would have if its bonds were completely ionic. That is, in determining oxidation number, all shared electrons are counted with the more electronegative atom. For example, consider the Lewis structure of HCl in ▼ FIGURE 8.11(a). To assign oxidation numbers, both electrons in the covalent bond between the atoms are assigned to the more electronegative Cl atom. This procedure gives Cl eight valence electrons, one more than in the neutral atom. Thus, its oxidation number is −1. Hydrogen has no valence electrons when they are counted this way, giving it an oxidation number of +1.

To assign formal charges in this molecule, we ignore electronegativity and assign the electrons in bonds equally to the two bonded atoms. In the case of HCl, we divide the bonding pair of electrons equally between H and Cl, as in Figure 8.11(b). In this case Cl has seven assigned electrons, the same as that of the neutral Cl atom, and H has one assigned electron. Thus, the formal charges of both Cl and H in this compound are 0.

Neither oxidation number nor formal charge gives an accurate depiction of the actual charges on atoms because oxidation numbers overstate the role of electronegativity and formal charges ignore it.

It seems reasonable that electrons in covalent bonds should be apportioned according to the relative electronegativities of the bonded atoms. From Figure 8.7 we see that Cl has an electronegativity of 3.0, while that of H is 2.1. The more electronegative Cl atom might therefore be expected to have roughly $3.0/(3.0 + 2.1) = 0.59$ of the electrical charge in the bonding pair, whereas the H atom has $2.1/(3.0 + 2.1) = 0.41$ of the charge. Because the bond consists of two electrons, the Cl atom's share is $0.59 \times 2e = 1.18e$, or $0.18e$ more than the neutral Cl atom. This gives rise to a partial negative charge of 0.18− on Cl and a partial positive charge of 0.18+ on H. (Notice again that we place the plus and minus signs *before* the magnitude in writing oxidation numbers and formal charges but *after* the magnitude in writing actual charges.)

The dipole moment of HCl gives an experimental measure of the partial charge on each atom. In Sample Exercise 8.5 we saw that the dipole moment of HCl indicates a partial charge of 0.178+ on H and 0.178− on Cl, in remarkably good agreement with our simple approximation based on electronegativities. Although our approximation method provides "ballpark" numbers for the magnitude of charge on atoms, the relationship between electronegativities and charge separation is generally more complicated. As we have already seen, computer programs employing quantum mechanical principles have been developed to obtain more accurate estimates of the partial charges on atoms, even in complex molecules. A computer-graphical representation of the charge distribution in HCl is shown in Figure 8.11(c).

*RELATED EXERCISES* 8.8, 8.49, 8.50, 8.51, 8.52, 8.86, 8.87, 8.90, and 8.91

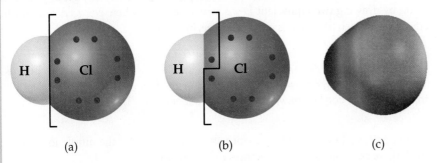

(a)          (b)          (c)

◄ **FIGURE 8.11 Oxidation number, formal charge, and electron density distribution for the HCl molecule.**

# 8.6 | RESONANCE STRUCTURES

We sometimes encounter molecules and ions in which the experimentally determined arrangement of atoms is not adequately described by a single dominant Lewis structure. Consider ozone, $O_3$, which is a bent molecule with two equal O—O bond lengths (► FIGURE 8.12). Because each oxygen atom contributes 6 valence electrons, the ozone molecule has 18 valence electrons. This means the Lewis structure must have one O—O single bond and one O=O double bond to attain an octet about each atom:

However, this single structure cannot by itself be dominant because it requires that one O—O bond be different from the other, contrary to the observed structure—we would expect the O=O double bond to be shorter than the O—O single bond. ∞ (Section 8.3) In drawing the Lewis structure, however, we could just as easily have put the O=O bond on the left:

GO FIGURE

**What feature of this structure suggests that the two outer O atoms are in some way equivalent to each other?**

1.278 Å   1.278 Å

117°

▲ **FIGURE 8.12 Molecular structure of ozone.**

Is the electron density consistent with equal weights for the two resonance structures for $O_3$? Explain.

Primary color    Primary color

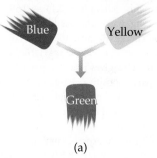

(a)

Resonance structure    Resonance structure

Ozone molecule

(b)

▲ FIGURE 8.13 **Resonance.** Describing a molecule as a blend of different resonance structures is similar to describing a paint color as a blend of primary colors. (a) Green paint is a blend of blue and yellow. We cannot describe green as a single primary color. (b) The ozone molecule is a blend of two resonance structures. We cannot describe the ozone molecule in terms of a single Lewis structure.

There is no reason for one of these Lewis structures to be dominant because they are equally valid representations of the molecule. The placement of the atoms in these two alternative but completely equivalent Lewis structures is the same, but the placement of the electrons is different. Lewis structures of this sort are called **resonance structures.** To describe the structure of ozone properly, we write both resonance structures and use a double-headed arrow to indicate that the real molecule is described by an average of the two:

To understand why certain molecules require more than one resonance structure, we can draw an analogy to mixing paint (◄ FIGURE 8.13). Blue and yellow are both primary colors of paint pigment. An equal blend of blue and yellow pigments produces green pigment. We cannot describe green paint in terms of a single primary color, yet it still has its own identity. Green paint does not oscillate between its two primary colors: It is not blue part of the time and yellow the rest of the time. Similarly, molecules such as ozone cannot be described as oscillating between the two individual Lewis structures shown previously—there are two equivalent dominant Lewis structures that contribute equally to the actual structure of the molecule.

The actual arrangement of the electrons in molecules such as $O_3$ must be considered as a blend of two (or more) Lewis structures. By analogy to the green paint, the molecule has its own identity separate from the individual resonance structures. For example, the ozone molecule always has two equivalent O—O bonds whose lengths are intermediate between the lengths of an oxygen–oxygen single bond and an oxygen–oxygen double bond. Another way of looking at it is to say that the rules for drawing Lewis structures do not allow us to have a single dominant structure for the ozone molecule. For example, there are no rules for drawing half-bonds. We can get around this limitation by drawing two equivalent Lewis structures that, when averaged, amount to something very much like what is observed experimentally.

△ **GIVE IT SOME THOUGHT**

The O—O bonds in ozone are often described as "one-and-a-half" bonds. Is this description consistent with the idea of resonance?

As an additional example of resonance structures, consider the nitrate ion, $NO_3^-$, for which three equivalent Lewis structures can be drawn:

Notice that the arrangement of atoms is the same in each structure—only the placement of electrons differs. In writing resonance structures, the same atoms must be bonded to each other in all structures, so that the only differences are in the arrangements of electrons. All three $NO_3^-$ Lewis structures are equally dominant and taken together adequately describe the ion, in which all three N—O bond lengths are the same.

△ **GIVE IT SOME THOUGHT**

In the same sense that we describe the O—O bonds in $O_3$ as "one-and-a-half" bonds, how would you describe the N—O bonds in $NO_3^-$?

In some instances, all the possible Lewis structures for a species may not be equivalent to one another. Instead, one or more may be dominant. We will encounter examples of this as we proceed.

**SAMPLE EXERCISE 8.10**   **Resonance Structures**

Which is predicted to have the shorter sulfur–oxygen bonds, $SO_3$ or $SO_3^{2-}$?

**SOLUTION**

The sulfur atom has six valence electrons, as does oxygen. Thus, $SO_3$ contains 24 valence electrons. In writing the Lewis structure, we see that three equivalent resonance structures can be drawn:

As with $NO_3^-$, the actual structure of $SO_3$ is an equal blend of all three. Thus, each S—O bond length should be about one-third of the way between the length of a single bond and the length of a double bond. That is, they should be shorter than single bonds but not as short as double bonds.

The $SO_3^{2-}$ ion has 26 electrons, which leads to a dominant Lewis structure in which all the S—O bonds are single:

Our analysis of the Lewis structures leads us to conclude that $SO_3$ should have the shorter S—O bonds and $SO_3^{2-}$ the longer ones. This conclusion is correct: The experimentally measured S—O bond lengths are 1.42 Å in $SO_3$ and 1.51 Å in $SO_3^{2-}$.

**PRACTICE EXERCISE**

Draw two equivalent resonance structures for the formate ion, $HCO_2^-$.

*Answer:*

# Resonance in Benzene

Resonance is an important concept in describing the bonding in organic molecules, particularly *aromatic* organic molecules, a category that includes the hydrocarbon *benzene*, $C_6H_6$. The six C atoms are bonded in a hexagonal ring, and one H atom is bonded to each C atom. We can write two equivalent dominant Lewis structures for benzene, each of which satisfies the octet rule. These two structures are in resonance:

Note that the double bonds are in different places in the two structures. Each of these resonance structures shows three carbon–carbon single bonds and three carbon–carbon double bonds. However, experimental data show that all six C—C bonds are of equal length, 1.40 Å, intermediate between the typical bond lengths for a C—C single bond (1.54 Å) and a C=C double bond (1.34 Å). Each of the C—C bonds in benzene can be thought of as a blend of a single bond and a double bond (▶ **FIGURE 8.14**).

Benzene is commonly represented by omitting the hydrogen atoms and showing only the carbon–carbon framework with the vertices unlabeled. In this convention, the resonance in the molecule is represented either by two structures separated by a double-headed arrow or by a shorthand notation in which we draw a hexagon with a circle inside:

or

The shorthand notation reminds us that benzene is a blend of two resonance structures— it emphasizes that the C=C double bonds cannot be assigned to specific edges of the hexagon. Chemists use both representations of benzene interchangeably.

▲ GO FIGURE

**What is the significance of the dashed bonds in this ball-and-stick model?**

▲ FIGURE 8.14   **Benzene, an "aromatic" organic compound.** The benzene molecule is a regular hexagon of carbon atoms with a hydrogen atom bonded to each one. The dashed lines represent the blending of two equivalent resonance structures, leading to C—C bonds that are intermediate between single and double bonds.

The bonding arrangement in benzene confers special stability to the molecule. As a result, millions of organic compounds contain the six-membered ring characteristic of benzene. Many of these compounds are important in biochemistry, in pharmaceuticals, and in the production of modern materials.

### GIVE IT SOME THOUGHT

Each Lewis structure of benzene has three C=C double bonds. Another hydrocarbon containing three C=C double bonds is *hexatriene*, $C_6H_8$. A Lewis structure of hexatriene is

H   H   H   H   H   H
|    |    |    |    |    |
C=C—C=C—C=C
|                  |
H                 H

Do you expect hexatriene to have multiple resonance structures? If not, why is this molecule different from benzene with respect to resonance?

---

# 8.7 | EXCEPTIONS TO THE OCTET RULE

The octet rule is so simple and useful in introducing the basic concepts of bonding that you might assume it is always obeyed. In Section 8.2, however, we noted its limitation in dealing with ionic compounds of the transition metals. The rule also fails in many situations involving covalent bonding. These exceptions to the octet rule are of three main types:

1. Molecules and polyatomic ions containing an odd number of electrons

2. Molecules and polyatomic ions in which an atom has fewer than an octet of valence electrons

3. Molecules and polyatomic ions in which an atom has more than an octet of valence electrons

## Odd Number of Electrons

In the vast majority of molecules and polyatomic ions, the total number of valence electrons is even, and complete pairing of electrons occurs. However, in a few molecules and polyatomic ions, such as $ClO_2$, NO, $NO_2$, and $O_2^-$, the number of valence electrons is odd. Complete pairing of these electrons is impossible, and an octet around each atom cannot be achieved. For example, NO contains $5 + 6 = 11$ valence electrons. The two most important Lewis structures for this molecule are

$\ddot{\text{N}}=\ddot{\text{O}}$    and    $\dot{\ddot{\text{N}}}=\ddot{\text{O}}$

### GIVE IT SOME THOUGHT

Which of the Lewis structures for NO is dominant based on analysis of the formal charges?

## Less than an Octet of Valence Electrons

A second type of exception occurs when there are fewer than eight valence electrons around an atom in a molecule or polyatomic ion. This situation is also relatively rare (with the exception of hydrogen and helium as we have already discussed), most often encountered in compounds of boron and beryllium. As an example, let's consider boron trifluoride, $BF_3$. If we follow the first four steps of our procedure for drawing Lewis structures, we obtain the structure which has only six electrons around the boron atom. The formal charge is zero on both B and F, and we could complete the octet around boron by forming a double bond (step 5). In so doing, we see that there are three equivalent resonance structures (the formal charges are shown in red):

Each of these structures forces a fluorine atom to share additional electrons with the boron atom, which is inconsistent with the high electronegativity of fluorine. In fact, the formal charges tell us that this is an unfavorable situation. In each structure, the F atom involved in the B=F double bond has a formal charge of +1, while the less electronegative B atom has a formal charge of −1. Thus, the resonance structures containing a B=F double bond are less important than the one in which there are fewer than an octet of valence electrons around boron:

|   Dominant   |   Less important   |

We usually represent $BF_3$ solely by the dominant resonance structure, in which there are only six valence electrons around boron. The chemical behavior of $BF_3$ is consistent with this representation. In particular, $BF_3$ reacts energetically with molecules having an unshared pair of electrons that can be used to form a bond with boron, as, for example, in the reaction

In the stable compound $NH_3BF_3$, boron has an octet of valence electrons.

## More than an Octet of Valence Electrons

The third and largest class of exceptions consists of molecules or polyatomic ions in which there are more than eight electrons in the valence shell of an atom. When we draw the Lewis structure for $PF_5$, for example, we are forced to place ten electrons around the central phosphorus atom:

Molecules and ions with more than an octet of electrons around the central atom are often called *hypervalent*. Other examples of hypervalent species are $SF_4$, $AsF_6^-$, and $ICl_4^-$. The corresponding molecules with a second-period atom as the central atom, such as $NCl_5$ and $OF_4$, do *not* exist.

Hypervalent molecules are formed only for central atoms from period 3 and below in the periodic table. The principal reason for their formation is the relatively larger size of the central atom. For example, a P atom is large enough that five F (or even five Cl) atoms can be bonded to it without being too crowded. By contrast, an N atom is too small to accommodate five atoms bonded to it. Because size is a factor, hypervalent molecules occur most often when the central atom is bonded to the smallest and most electronegative atoms—F, Cl, and O.

The notion of a valence shell containing more than an octet of electrons is also consistent with the presence of unfilled $nd$ orbitals in atoms from period 3 and below. By comparison, elements of the second period have only the $2s$ and $2p$ valence orbitals available for bonding. Detailed analyses of the bonding in molecules such as $PF_5$ and $SF_6$ suggest that the presence of unfilled $3d$ orbitals in P and S has a relatively minor impact on the formation of hypervalent molecules, and the general current belief is that the increased size of third-period atoms is the more important factor.

---

**SAMPLE EXERCISE 8.11**    **Lewis Structure for an Ion with More than an Octet of Electrons**

Draw the Lewis structure for $ICl_4^-$.

**SOLUTION**

Iodine (group 7A) has seven valence electrons. Each chlorine atom (group 7A) also has seven. An extra electron is added to account for the 1− charge of the ion. Therefore, the total number of valence electrons is

$$7 + (4 \times 7) + 1 = 36$$

The I atom is the central atom in the ion. Putting eight electrons around each Cl atom (including a pair of electrons between I and each Cl to represent the single bond between these atoms) requires $8 \times 4 = 32$ electrons.

We are thus left with $36 - 32 = 4$ electrons to be placed on the larger iodine:

Iodine has 12 valence electrons around it, four more than needed for an octet.

**PRACTICE EXERCISE**

**(a)** Which of the following atoms is never found with more than an octet of valence electrons around it: S, C, P, Br? **(b)** Draw the Lewis structure for $XeF_2$.

**Answers:** (a) C, (b)

---

Finally, there are Lewis structures where you might have to choose between satisfying the octet rule and obtaining the most favorable formal charges by using more than an octet of electrons. For example, consider these Lewis structures for the phosphate ion, $PO_4^{3-}$:

The formal charges on the atoms are shown in red. In the left structure, the P atom obeys the octet rule. In the right structure, however, the P atom has five electron pairs, leading to smaller formal charges on the atoms. (You should be able to see that there are three additional resonance structures for the Lewis structure on the right.)

Chemists are still debating which of these two structures is dominant for $PO_4^{3-}$. Recent theoretical calculations based on quantum mechanics suggest to some researchers that the left structure is the dominant one. Other researchers claim that the bond lengths in the ion are more consistent with the right structure being dominant. This disagreement is a convenient reminder that, in general, multiple Lewis structures can contribute to the actual electron distribution in an atom or molecule.

# 8.8 | STRENGTHS OF COVALENT BONDS

The stability of a molecule is related to the strengths of its covalent bonds. The strength of a covalent bond between two atoms is determined by the energy required to break the bond. It is easiest to relate bond strength to the enthalpy change in reactions in which bonds are broken. ∞ (Section 5.4) The **bond enthalpy** is the enthalpy change, $\Delta H$, for the breaking of a particular bond in one mole of a gaseous substance. For example, the bond enthalpy for the bond in $Cl_2$ is the enthalpy change when 1 mol of $Cl_2(g)$ dissociates into chlorine atoms:

$$:\ddot{C}l\!-\!\ddot{C}l\!:(g) \longrightarrow 2 :\ddot{C}l\cdot(g)$$

We use the letter $D$ followed by the bond in question to represent bond enthalpies. Thus, for example, $D(Cl\!-\!Cl)$ is the bond enthalpy for the $Cl_2$ bond, and $D(H\!-\!Br)$ is the bond enthalpy for the HBr bond.

It is relatively simple to assign bond enthalpies to the bond in a diatomic molecule because in these cases the bond enthalpy is just the energy required to break the molecule into its atoms. However, many important bonds, such as the $C\!-\!H$ bond, exist only in polyatomic molecules. For these bonds, we usually use *average* bond enthalpies. For example, the enthalpy change for the following process in which a methane molecule is decomposed into its five atoms (a process called *atomization*) can be used to define an average bond enthalpy for the $C\!-\!H$ bond, $D(C\!-\!H)$:

$$
\begin{array}{c}
\text{H} \\
| \\
\text{H}\!-\!\overset{\textstyle |}{\underset{\textstyle |}{\text{C}}}\!-\!\text{H}(g) \longrightarrow \cdot\dot{\text{C}}\cdot(g) + 4\,\text{H}\cdot(g) \qquad \Delta H = 1660 \text{ kJ}\\
\text{H}
\end{array}
$$

Because there are four equivalent $C\!-\!H$ bonds in methane, the enthalpy of atomization is equal to the sum of the bond enthalpies of the four $C\!-\!H$ bonds. Therefore, the average $C\!-\!H$ bond enthalpy for $CH_4$ is $D(C\!-\!H) = (1660/4) \text{ kJ/mol} = 415 \text{ kJ/mol}$.

The bond enthalpy for a given pair of atoms, say $C\!-\!H$, depends on the rest of the molecule containing the atom pair. However, the variation from one molecule to another is generally small, which supports the idea that bonding electron pairs are localized between atoms. If we consider $C\!-\!H$ bond enthalpies in many different compounds, we find that the average bond enthalpy is 413 kJ/mol, close to the 415 kJ/mol we just calculated from $CH_4$.

 **GIVE IT SOME THOUGHT**

How can you use the enthalpy of atomization of the hydrocarbon ethane, $C_2H_6(g)$, along with the value $D(C\!-\!H) = 413$ kJ/mol to estimate the value for $D(C\!-\!C)$ ?

▶ TABLE 8.4 lists average bond enthalpies for a number of atom pairs. *The bond enthalpy is always a positive quantity*; energy is always required to break chemical bonds. Conversely, energy is *always* released when a bond forms between two gaseous atoms or molecular fragments. The greater the bond enthalpy, the stronger the bond. Further, a molecule with strong chemical bonds generally has less tendency to undergo chemical change than does one with weak bonds. For example, $N_2$, which has a very strong $N\!\equiv\!N$ triple bond, is very unreactive, whereas hydrazine, $N_2H_4$, which has an $N\!-\!N$ single bond, is highly reactive.

**GIVE IT SOME THOUGHT**

Based on bond enthalpies, which do you expect to be more reactive, oxygen, $O_2$, or hydrogen peroxide, $H_2O_2$?

**TABLE 8.4 • Average Bond Enthalpies (kJ/mol)**

**Single Bonds**

| | | | | | | | |
|---|---|---|---|---|---|---|---|
| C—H | 413 | N—H | 391 | O—H | 463 | F—F | 155 |
| C—C | 348 | N—N | 163 | O—O | 146 | | |
| C—N | 293 | N—O | 201 | O—F | 190 | Cl—F | 253 |
| C—O | 358 | N—F | 272 | O—Cl | 203 | Cl—Cl | 242 |
| C—F | 485 | N—Cl | 200 | O—I | 234 | | |
| C—Cl | 328 | N—Br | 243 | | | Br—F | 237 |
| C—Br | 276 | | | S—H | 339 | Br—Cl | 218 |
| C—I | 240 | H—H | 436 | S—F | 327 | Br—Br | 193 |
| C—S | 259 | H—F | 567 | S—Cl | 253 | | |
| | | H—Cl | 431 | S—Br | 218 | I—Cl | 208 |
| Si—H | 323 | H—Br | 366 | S—S | 266 | I—Br | 175 |
| Si—Si | 226 | H—I | 299 | | | I—I | 151 |
| Si—C | 301 | | | | | | |
| Si—O | 368 | | | | | | |
| Si—Cl | 464 | | | | | | |

**Multiple Bonds**

| | | | | | |
|---|---|---|---|---|---|
| C=C | 614 | N=N | 418 | $O_2$ | 495 |
| C≡C | 839 | N≡N | 941 | | |
| C=N | 615 | N=O | 607 | S=O | 523 |
| C≡N | 891 | | | S=S | 418 |
| C=O | 799 | | | | |
| C≡O | 1072 | | | | |

## Bond Enthalpies and the Enthalpies of Reactions

We can use average bond enthalpies to estimate the enthalpies of reactions in which bonds are broken and new bonds are formed. This procedure allows us to estimate quickly whether a given reaction will be endothermic ($\Delta H > 0$) or exothermic ($\Delta H < 0$) even if we do not know $\Delta H_f^\circ$ for all the species involved.

Our strategy for estimating reaction enthalpies is a straightforward application of Hess's law. ∞ (Section 5.6) We use the fact that breaking bonds is always endothermic and forming bonds is always exothermic. We therefore imagine that the reaction occurs in two steps:

1. We supply enough energy to break those bonds in the reactants that are not present in the products. The enthalpy of the system is increased by the sum of the bond enthalpies of the bonds that are broken.

2. We form the bonds in the products that were not present in the reactants. This step releases energy and therefore lowers the enthalpy of the system by the sum of the bond enthalpies of the bonds that are formed.

The enthalpy of the reaction, $\Delta H_{rxn}$, is estimated as the sum of the bond enthalpies of the bonds broken minus the sum of the bond enthalpies of the bonds formed:

$$\Delta H_{rxn} = \Sigma(\text{bond enthalpies of bonds broken}) -$$
$$\Sigma(\text{bond enthalpies of bonds formed}) \quad [8.12]$$

Consider, for example, the gas-phase reaction between methane, $CH_4$, and chlorine to produce methyl chloride, $CH_3Cl$, and hydrogen chloride, HCl:

$$H—CH_3(g) + Cl—Cl(g) \longrightarrow Cl—CH_3(g) + H—Cl(g) \quad \Delta H_{rxn} = ? \quad [8.13]$$

**GO FIGURE:**

**Is this reaction exothermic or endothermic?**

◄ **FIGURE 8.15   Using bond enthalpies to calculate $\Delta H_{rxn}$.** Average bond enthalpies are used to estimate $\Delta H_{rxn}$ for the reaction in Equation 8.13.

Our two-step procedure is outlined in ▲ **FIGURE 8.15.** We note that the following bonds are broken and made:

*Bonds broken:* 1 mol C—H, 1 mol Cl—Cl

*Bonds made:* 1 mol C—Cl, 1 mol H—Cl

We first supply enough energy to break the C—H and Cl—Cl bonds, which raises the enthalpy of the system (indicated as $\Delta H_1 > 0$ in Figure 8.15). We then form the C—Cl and H—Cl bonds, which release energy and lower the enthalpy of the system ($\Delta H_2 < 0$). We then use Equation 8.12 and data from Table 8.4 to estimate the enthalpy of the reaction:

$$\Delta H_{rxn} = [D(C\!-\!H) + D(Cl\!-\!Cl)] - [D(Cl\!-\!Cl) + D(H\!-\!Cl)]$$
$$= (413\ kJ + 242\ kJ) - (328\ kJ + 431\ kJ) = -104\ kJ$$

The reaction is exothermic because the bonds in the products (especially the H—Cl bond) are stronger than the bonds in the reactants (especially the Cl—Cl bond).

We usually use bond enthalpies to estimate $\Delta H_{rxn}$ only if we do not have the needed $\Delta H_f^\circ$ values readily available. For the preceding reaction, we cannot calculate $\Delta H_{rxn}$ from $\Delta H_f^\circ$ values and Hess's law because $\Delta H_f^\circ$ for $CH_3Cl(g)$ is not given in Appendix C. If we obtain the value of $\Delta H_f^\circ$ for $CH_3Cl(g)$ from another source and use Equation 5.31,

$$\Delta H_{rxn}^\circ = \Sigma n \Delta H_f^\circ(\text{products}) - \Sigma m \Delta H_f^\circ(\text{reactants})$$

we find that $\Delta H_{rxn} = -99.8\ kJ$ for the reaction in Equation 8.13. Thus, the use of average bond enthalpies provides a reasonably accurate estimate of the actual reaction enthalpy change.

It is important to remember that bond enthalpies are derived for *gaseous* molecules and that they are often *averaged* values. Nonetheless, average bond enthalpies are useful for estimating reaction enthalpies quickly, especially for gas-phase reactions.

**TABLE 8.5 • Average Bond Lengths for Some Single, Double, and Triple Bonds**

| Bond | Bond Length (Å) | Bond | Bond Length (Å) |
|------|-----------------|------|-----------------|
| C—C | 1.54 | N—N | 1.47 |
| C=C | 1.34 | N=N | 1.24 |
| C≡C | 1.20 | N≡N | 1.10 |
| C—N | 1.43 | N—O | 1.36 |
| C=N | 1.38 | N=O | 1.22 |
| C≡N | 1.16 | | |
| | | O—O | 1.48 |
| C—O | 1.43 | O=O | 1.21 |
| C=O | 1.23 | | |
| C≡O | 1.13 | | |

---

**SAMPLE EXERCISE 8.12** | **Using Average Bond Enthalpies**

Using data from Table 8.4, estimate $\Delta H$ for the reaction

$$2 \; \text{H}-\overset{\overset{\displaystyle \text{H}}{|}}{\underset{\underset{\displaystyle \text{H}}{|}}{\text{C}}}-\overset{\overset{\displaystyle \text{H}}{|}}{\underset{\underset{\displaystyle \text{H}}{|}}{\text{C}}}-\text{H}(g) \;+\; 7 \; \text{O}_2(g) \longrightarrow 4 \; \text{O}{=}\text{C}{=}\text{O}(g) \;+\; 6 \; \text{H}-\text{O}-\text{H}(g)$$

**SOLUTION**

**Analyze** We are asked to estimate the enthalpy change for a chemical reaction by using average bond enthalpies for the bonds broken and formed.

**Plan** In the reactants, we must break twelve C—H bonds and two C—C bonds in the two molecules of $\text{C}_2\text{H}_6$ and seven $\text{O}_2$ bonds in the seven $\text{O}_2$ molecules. In the products, we form eight C=O bonds (two in each $\text{CO}_2$) and twelve O—H bonds (two in each $\text{H}_2\text{O}$).

**Solve** Using Equation 8.12 and data from Table 8.4, we have

$$\Delta H = [12D(\text{C}{-}\text{H}) + 2D(\text{C}{-}\text{C}) + 7D(\text{O}_2)] - [8D(\text{C}{=}\text{O}) + 12D(\text{O}{-}\text{H})]$$

$$= [12(413 \text{ kJ}) + 2(348 \text{ kJ}) + 7(495 \text{ kJ})] - [8(799 \text{ kJ}) + 12(463 \text{ kJ})]$$

$$= 9117 \text{ kJ} - 11948 \text{ kJ}$$

$$= -2831 \text{ kJ}$$

**Check** This estimate can be compared with the value of −2856 kJ calculated from more accurate thermochemical data; the agreement is good.

**PRACTICE EXERCISE**

Using Table 8.4, estimate $\Delta H$ for the reaction

$$\text{H}-\overset{\overset{\displaystyle \text{H}}{|}}{\text{N}}-\overset{\overset{\displaystyle \text{H}}{|}}{\text{N}}-\text{H}(g) \longrightarrow \text{N}{\equiv}\text{N}(g) \;+\; 2 \; \text{H}-\text{H}(g)$$

*Answer:* −86 kJ

---

## Bond Enthalpy and Bond Length

Just as we can define an average bond enthalpy, we can also define an average bond length for a number of common bonds (▲ **TABLE 8.5**). Of particular interest is the relationship, in any atom pair, among bond enthalpy, bond length, and number of bonds between the atoms. For example, we can use data in Tables 8.4 and 8.5 to compare the bond lengths and bond enthalpies of carbon–carbon single, double, and triple bonds:

| C—C | C=C | C≡C |
|-----|-----|-----|
| 1.54 Å | 1.34 Å | 1.20 Å |
| 348 kJ/mol | 614 kJ/mol | 839 kJ/mol |

# CHEMISTRY PUT TO WORK

## Explosives and Alfred Nobel

Enormous amounts of energy can be stored in chemical bonds. Perhaps the most graphic illustration of this fact is seen in certain molecular substances used as explosives. Our discussion of bond enthalpies allows us to examine more closely some of the properties of such explosive substances.

A useful explosive substance must (1) decompose very exothermically, (2) have gaseous products so that a tremendous gas pressure accompanies the decomposition, (3) decompose very rapidly, and (4) be stable enough so that it can be detonated predictably. The combination of the first three effects leads to the violent evolution of heat and gases.

To give the most exothermic reaction, an explosive should have weak chemical bonds and should decompose into molecules that have very strong bonds. Table 8.4 tells us that $N\equiv N$, $C\equiv O$, and $C=O$ bonds are among the strongest. Not surprisingly, explosives are usually designed to produce the gaseous products $N_2(g)$, $CO(g)$, and $CO_2(g)$. Water vapor is nearly always produced as well.

Many common explosives are organic molecules that contain nitro ($NO_2$) or nitrate ($NO_3$) groups attached to a carbon skeleton. The Lewis structures of two of the most familiar explosives, nitroglycerin and trinitrotoluene (TNT), are shown here (resonance structures are not shown for clarity). TNT contains the six-membered ring characteristic of benzene.

Nitroglycerin

Trinitrotoluene (TNT)

Nitroglycerin is a pale yellow, oily liquid. It is highly *shock-sensitive*: Merely shaking the liquid can cause its explosive decomposition into nitrogen, carbon dioxide, water, and oxygen gases:

$$4\ C_3H_5N_3O_9(l) \longrightarrow 6\ N_2(g) + 12\ CO_2(g) + 10\ H_2O(g) + O_2(g)$$

The large bond enthalpies of $N_2$ (941 kJ/mol), $CO_2$ ($2 \times 799$ kJ/mol), and $H_2O$ ($2 \times 463$ kJ/mol) make this reaction enormously exothermic. Nitroglycerin is an exceptionally unstable explosive because it is in nearly perfect *explosive balance*: With the exception of a small amount of $O_2(g)$ produced, the only products are $N_2$, $CO_2$, and $H_2O$. Note also that, unlike combustion reactions ∞ (Section 3.2), explosions are entirely self-contained. No other reagent, such as $O_2(g)$, is needed for the explosive decomposition.

Because nitroglycerin is so unstable, it is difficult to use as a controllable explosive. The Swedish inventor Alfred Nobel (▼ FIGURE 8.16) found that mixing nitroglycerin with an absorbent solid material such as diatomaceous earth or cellulose gives a solid explosive (*dynamite*) that is much safer than liquid nitroglycerin.

*RELATED EXERCISES:* 8.98 and 8.99

▲ FIGURE 8.16  **Alfred Nobel (1833–1896), Swedish inventor of dynamite.** By many accounts Nobel's discovery that nitroglycerin could be made more stable by absorbing it onto cellulose was an accident. This discovery made Nobel a wealthy man. He was also a complex and lonely man, however, who never married, was frequently ill, and suffered from chronic depression. He had invented the most powerful military explosive to date, but he strongly supported international peace movements. His will stated that his fortune be used to establish prizes awarding those who "have conferred the greatest benefit on mankind," including the promotion of peace and "fraternity between nations." The Nobel Prize is probably the most coveted award that a scientist, writer, or peace advocate can receive.

As the number of bonds between the carbon atoms increases, the bond length decreases and the bond enthalpy increases. That is, the carbon atoms are held more closely and more tightly together. In general, *as the number of bonds between two atoms increases, the bond grows shorter and stronger.* This trend is illustrated in ▶ FIGURE 8.17 for N—N single, double, and triple bonds.

⚠ GO FIGURE

The line segments in the graph both have negative slopes. Why does this make sense?

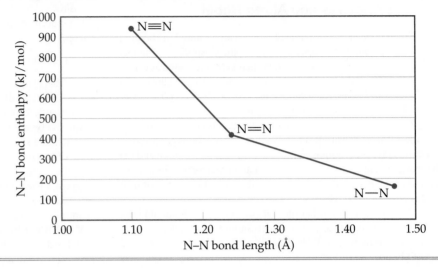

▶ **FIGURE 8.17** **Bond strength versus bond length for N–N bonds.**

---

**SAMPLE INTEGRATIVE EXERCISE** **Putting Concepts Together**

Phosgene, a substance used in poisonous gas warfare during World War I, is so named because it was first prepared by the action of sunlight on a mixture of carbon monoxide and chlorine gases. Its name comes from the Greek words *phos* (light) and *genes* (born of). Phosgene has the following elemental composition:12.14% C, 16.17% O, and 71.69% Cl by mass. Its molar mass is 98.9 g/mol. **(a)** Determine the molecular formula of this compound. **(b)** Draw three Lewis structures for the molecule that satisfy the octet rule for each atom. (The Cl and O atoms bond to C.) **(c)** Using formal charges, determine which Lewis structure is the dominant one. **(d)** Using average bond enthalpies, estimate $\Delta H$ for the formation of gaseous phosgene from $CO(g)$ and $Cl_2(g)$.

**SOLUTION**

**(a)** The empirical formula of phosgene can be determined from its elemental composition. ∞ (Section 3.5) Assuming 100 g of the compound and calculating the number of moles of C, O, and Cl in this sample, we have

$$(12.14 \text{ g C})\left(\frac{1 \text{ mol C}}{12.01 \text{ g C}}\right) = 1.011 \text{ mol C}$$

$$(16.17 \text{ g O})\left(\frac{1 \text{ mol O}}{16.00 \text{ g O}}\right) = 1.011 \text{ mol O}$$

$$(71.69 \text{ g Cl})\left(\frac{1 \text{ mol Cl}}{35.45 \text{ g Cl}}\right) = 2.022 \text{ mol Cl}$$

The ratio of the number of moles of each element, obtained by dividing each number of moles by the smallest quantity, indicates that there is one C and one O for each two Cl in the empirical formula, $COCl_2$.

The molar mass of the empirical formula is $12.01 + 16.00 + 2(35.45) = 98.91$ g/mol, the same as the molar mass of the molecule. Thus, $COCl_2$ is the molecular formula.

**(b)** Carbon has four valence electrons, oxygen has six, and chlorine has seven, giving $4 + 6 + 2(7) = 24$ electrons for the Lewis structures. Drawing a Lewis structure with all single bonds does not give the central carbon atom an octet. Using multiple bonds, three structures satisfy the octet rule:

**(c)** Calculating the formal charges on each atom gives

$$
\overset{0}{:\!\ddot{O}\!:} \qquad \overset{-1}{:\!\ddot{O}\!:} \qquad \overset{-1}{:\!\ddot{O}\!:}
$$

$$
\overset{0}{:\!\ddot{C}l} \!-\! \overset{\parallel}{C} \!-\! \overset{0}{\ddot{C}l\!:} \quad\longleftrightarrow\quad \overset{+1}{:\!\ddot{C}l} \!=\! \overset{0}{C} \!-\! \overset{0}{\ddot{C}l\!:} \quad\longleftrightarrow\quad \overset{0}{:\!\ddot{C}l} \!-\! \overset{0}{C} \!=\! \overset{+1}{\ddot{C}l\!:}
$$

The first structure is expected to be the dominant one because it has the lowest formal charges on each atom. Indeed, the molecule is usually represented by this single Lewis structure.

**(d)** Writing the chemical equation in terms of the Lewis structures of the molecules, we have

$$
:C\equiv O: \quad + \quad :\ddot{C}l\!-\!\ddot{C}l: \quad\longrightarrow\quad :\ddot{C}l\!-\!\overset{\overset{\textstyle :O:}{\parallel}}{C}\!-\!\ddot{C}l:
$$

Thus, the reaction involves breaking a $C\equiv O$ bond and a $Cl\!-\!Cl$ bond and forming a $C\!=\!O$ bond and two $C\!-\!Cl$ bonds. Using bond enthalpies from Table 8.4, we have

$$
\Delta H = D(C\equiv O) + D(Cl\!-\!Cl) - [D(C\!=\!O) + 2D(C\!-\!Cl)]
$$

$$
= 1072 \text{ kJ} + 242 \text{ kJ} - [799 \text{ kJ} + 2(328 \text{ kJ})] = -141 \text{ kJ}
$$

Notice that the reaction is exothermic. Nevertheless, energy is needed from sunlight or another source for the reaction to begin, as is the case for the combustion of $H_2(g)$ and $O_2(g)$ to form $H_2O(g)$ (Figure 5.14).

# CHAPTER SUMMARY AND KEY TERMS

**INTRODUCTION AND SECTION 8.1** In this chapter we have focused on the interactions that lead to the formation of **chemical bonds**. We classify these bonds into three broad groups: **ionic bonds**, which result from the electrostatic forces that exist between ions of opposite charge; **covalent bonds**, which result from the sharing of electrons by two atoms; and **metallic bonds**, which result from a delocalized sharing of electrons in metals. The formation of bonds involves interactions of the outermost electrons of atoms, their valence electrons. The valence electrons of an atom can be represented by electron-dot symbols, called **Lewis symbols**. The tendencies of atoms to gain, lose, or share their valence electrons often follow the **octet rule**, which can be viewed as an attempt by atoms to achieve a noble-gas electron configuration.

**SECTION 8.2** Ionic bonding results from the transfer of electrons from one atom to another, leading to the formation of a three-dimensional lattice of charged particles. The stabilities of ionic substances result from the strong electrostatic attractions between an ion and the surrounding ions of opposite charge. The magnitude of these interactions is measured by the **lattice energy**, which is the energy needed to separate an ionic lattice into gaseous ions. Lattice energy increases with increasing charge on the ions and with decreasing distance between the ions. The **Born–Haber cycle** is a useful thermochemical cycle in which we use Hess's law to calculate the lattice energy as the sum of several steps in the formation of an ionic compound.

**SECTION 8.3** A covalent bond results from the sharing of electrons. We can represent the electron distribution in molecules by means of **Lewis structures**, which indicate how many valence electrons are involved in forming bonds and how many remain as unshared electron pairs. The octet rule helps determine how many bonds will be formed between two atoms. The sharing of one pair of electrons produces a **single bond**; the sharing of two or three pairs of electrons between two atoms produces **double** or **triple bonds**, respectively. Double and triple

bonds are examples of multiple bonding between atoms. The bond length decreases as the number of bonds between the atoms increases.

**SECTION 8.4** In covalent bonds, the electrons may not necessarily be shared equally between two atoms. **Bond polarity** helps describe unequal sharing of electrons in a bond. In a **nonpolar covalent bond** the electrons in the bond are shared equally by the two atoms; in a **polar covalent bond** one of the atoms exerts a greater attraction for the electrons than the other.

**Electronegativity** is a numerical measure of the ability of an atom to compete with other atoms for the electrons shared between them. Fluorine is the most electronegative element, meaning it has the greatest ability to attract electrons from other atoms. Electronegativity values range from 0.7 for Cs to 4.0 for F. Electronegativity generally increases from left to right in a row of the periodic table and decreases going down a column. The difference in the electronegativities of bonded atoms can be used to determine the polarity of a bond. The greater the electronegativity difference, the more polar the bond.

A **polar molecule** is one whose centers of positive and negative charge do not coincide. Thus, a polar molecule has a positive side and a negative side. This separation of charge produces a **dipole**, the magnitude of which is given by the **dipole moment**, which is measured in debyes (D). Dipole moments increase with increasing amount of charge separated and increasing distance of separation. Any diatomic molecule $X\!-\!Y$ in which X and Y have different electronegativities is a polar molecule.

Most bonding interactions lie between the extremes of covalent and ionic bonding. While it is generally true that the bonding between a metal and a nonmetal is predominantly ionic, exceptions to this guideline are not uncommon when the difference in electronegativity of the atoms is relatively small or when the oxidation state of the metal becomes large.

**SECTIONS 8.5 AND 8.6** If we know which atoms are connected to one another, we can draw Lewis structures for molecules and ions by a simple procedure. Once we do so, we can determine the **formal charge** of each atom in a Lewis structure, which is the charge that the atom would have if all atoms had the same electronegativity. In general, the dominant Lewis structure will have low formal charges with any negative formal charges residing on more electronegative atoms.

Sometimes a single dominant Lewis structure is inadequate to represent a particular molecule (or ion). In such situations, we describe the molecule by using two or more **resonance structures** for the molecule. The molecule is envisioned as a blend of these multiple resonance structures. Resonance structures are important in describing the bonding in molecules such as ozone, $O_3$, and the organic molecule benzene, $C_6H_6$.

**SECTION 8.7**    The octet rule is not obeyed in all cases. Exceptions occur when (a) a molecule has an odd number of electrons, (b) it is not possible to complete an octet around an atom without forcing an unfavorable distribution of electrons, or (c) a large atom is surrounded by a sufficiently large number of small electronegative atoms that it has more than an octet of electrons around it. Lewis structures with more than an octet of electrons are observed for atoms in the third row and beyond in the periodic table.

**SECTION 8.8**    The strength of a covalent bond is measured by its **bond enthalpy**, which is the molar enthalpy change upon breaking a particular bond. Average bond enthalpies can be determined for a wide variety of covalent bonds. The strengths of covalent bonds increase with the number of electron pairs shared between two atoms. We can use bond enthalpies to estimate the enthalpy change during chemical reactions in which bonds are broken and new bonds formed. The average bond length between two atoms decreases as the number of bonds between the atoms increases, consistent with the bond being stronger as the number of bonds increases.

## KEY SKILLS

- Write Lewis symbols for atoms and ions. (Section 8.1)
- Understand lattice energy and be able to arrange compounds in order of increasing lattice energy based on the charges and sizes of the ions involved. (Section 8.2)
- Use atomic electron configurations and the octet rule to write Lewis structures for molecules to determine their electron distribution. (Section 8.3)
- Use electronegativity differences to identify nonpolar covalent, polar covalent, and ionic bonds. (Section 8.4)
- Calculate charge separation in diatomic molecules based on the experimentally measured dipole moment and bond distance. (Section 8.4)
- Calculate formal charges from Lewis structures and use those formal charges to identify the dominant Lewis structure for a molecule or ion. (Section 8.5)
- Recognize molecules where resonance structures are needed to describe the bonding. (Section 8.6)
- Recognize exceptions to the octet rule and draw accurate Lewis structures even when the octet rule is not obeyed. (Section 8.7)
- Understand the relationship between bond type (single, double, and triple), bond strength (or enthalpy), and bond length. (Section 8.8)
- Use bond enthalpies to estimate enthalpy changes for reactions involving gas-phase reactants and products. (Section 8.8)

## KEY EQUATIONS

- $E_{el} = \dfrac{\kappa Q_1 Q_2}{d}$    [8.4]    The potential energy of two interacting charges

- $\mu = Qr$    [8.11]    The dipole moment of two charges of equal magnitude but opposite sign, separated by a distance $r$

- $\Delta H_{rxn} = \Sigma(\text{bond enthalpies of bonds broken}) - \Sigma(\text{bond enthalpies of bonds formed})$    [8.12]    The enthalpy change as a function of bond enthalpies for reactions involving gas-phase molecules

# EXERCISES

## VISUALIZING CONCEPTS

8.1    For each of these Lewis symbols, indicate the group in the periodic table in which the element X belongs: [Section 8.1]

(a)  $\cdot\dot{X}\cdot$        (b)  $\cdot X\cdot$        (c)  $:\dot{X}\cdot$

8.2    Illustrated are four ions—A, B, X, and Y— showing their relative ionic radii. The ions shown in red carry positive charges: a

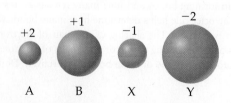

2+ charge for A and a 1+ charge for B. Ions shown in blue carry negative charges: a 1− charge for X and a 2− charge for Y. **(a)** Which combinations of these ions produce ionic compounds where there is a 1:1 ratio of cations and anions? **(b)** Among the combinations in part (a), which leads to the ionic compound having the largest lattice energy? **(c)** Which combination of ions leads to the ionic compound having the smallest lattice energy? [Section 8.2]

**8.3** A portion of a two-dimensional "slab" of NaCl(*s*) is shown here (see Figure 8.3) in which the ions are numbered. **(a)** Of the following types of interactions (identified by color), which are attractive and which are repulsive: "purple-purple," "purple-green," "green-green"? Explain. **(b)** Consider the "green-green" interactions between ions 1 and 3, ions 1 and 5, and ions 3 and 5. Which one or more of these three will result in the interaction of largest magnitude? Which one or more will result in the interaction of the smallest magnitude? **(c)** Consider the "green-green" interactions between ions 1 and 5 and the "green-purple" interactions between ions 1 and 2. Which of these will have the greater magnitude? **(d)** Does your answer to part (c) help explain why NaCl is a stable ionic solid? [Section 8.2]

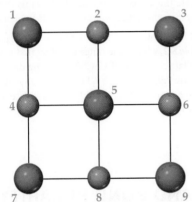

**8.4** The orbital diagram that follows shows the valence electrons for a 2+ ion of an element. **(a)** What is the element? **(b)** What is the electron configuration of an atom of this element? [Section 8.2]

4*d*

**8.5** In the Lewis structure shown here, A, D, E, Q, X, and Z represent elements in the first two rows of the periodic table (H—Ne). Identify all six elements so that the formal charges of all atoms are zero. [Section 8.3]

$$:\ddot{E}: \quad X$$
$$:\ddot{A}—\ddot{D}—\ddot{Q}—Z$$

**8.6** Incomplete Lewis structures for the nitrous acid molecule, $HNO_2$, and the nitrite ion, $NO_2^-$, are shown below. **(a)** Complete each Lewis structure by adding electron pairs as needed. **(b)** Is the formal charge on N the same or different in these two species? **(c)** Would either $HNO_2$ or $NO_2^-$ be expected to exhibit resonance? **(d)** Would you expect the N=O bond in $HNO_2$ to be longer, shorter, or the same length as the N—O bonds in $NO_2^-$? Explain. [Sections 8.5 and 8.6]

$$H—O—N=O \qquad O—N=O$$

**8.7** The partial Lewis structure that follows is for a hydrocarbon molecule. In the full Lewis structure, each carbon atom satisfies the octet rule, and there are no unshared electron pairs in the molecule. The carbon–carbon bonds are labeled 1, 2, and 3. **(a)** Determine where the hydrogen atoms are in the molecule. **(b)** Rank the carbon–carbon bonds in order of increasing bond length. **(c)** Rank the carbon–carbon bonds in order of increasing bond enthalpy. [Sections 8.3 and 8.8]

$$C \overset{1}{=} C \overset{2}{-} C \overset{3}{\equiv} C$$

**8.8** Consider the Lewis structure for the polyatomic oxyanion shown here, where X is an element from the third period (Na—Ar). By changing the overall charge, *n*, from 1− to 2− to 3− we get three different polyatomic ions. For each of these ions **(a)** identify the central atom, X; **(b)** determine the formal charge of the central atom, X; **(c)** draw a Lewis structure that makes the formal charge on the central atom equal to zero. [Sections 8.5, 8.6, and 8.7]

$$\left[ \begin{array}{c} :\ddot{O}: \\ | \\ :\ddot{O}—X—\ddot{O}: \\ | \\ :\ddot{O}: \end{array} \right]^{n-}$$

# LEWIS SYMBOLS (section 8.1)

**8.9** **(a)** What are valence electrons? **(b)** How many valence electrons does a nitrogen atom possess? **(c)** An atom has the electron configuration $1s^2 2s^2 2p^6 3s^2 3p^2$. How many valence electrons does the atom have?

**8.10** **(a)** What is the octet rule? **(b)** How many electrons must a sulfur atom gain to achieve an octet in its valence shell? **(c)** If an atom has the electron configuration $1s^2 2s^2 2p^3$, how many electrons must it gain to achieve an octet?

**8.11** Write the electron configuration for silicon. Identify the valence electrons in this configuration and the nonvalence electrons. From the standpoint of chemical reactivity, what is the important difference between them?

**8.12** **(a)** Write the electron configuration for the element titanium, Ti. How many valence electrons does this atom possess? **(b)** Hafnium, Hf, is also found in group 4B. Write the electron configuration for Hf. **(c)** Ti and Hf behave as though they possess the same number of valence electrons. Which of the subshells in the electron configuration of Hf behave as valence orbitals? Which behave as core orbitals?

**8.13** Write the Lewis symbol for atoms of each of the following elements: **(a)** Al, **(b)** Br, **(c)** Ar, **(d)** Sr.

**8.14** What is the Lewis symbol for each of the following atoms or ions: **(a)** K, **(b)** As, **(c)** $Sn^{2+}$, **(d)** $N^{3-}$?

# IONIC BONDING (section 8.2)

**8.15** Using Lewis symbols, diagram the reaction between magnesium and oxygen atoms to give the ionic substance MgO.

**8.16** Use Lewis symbols to represent the reaction that occurs between Ca and F atoms.

**8.17** Predict the chemical formula of the ionic compound formed between the following pairs of elements: (a) Al and F, (b) K and S, (c) Y and O, (d) Mg and N.

**8.18** Which ionic compound is expected to form from combining the following pairs of elements: (a) barium and fluorine, (b) cesium and chlorine, (c) lithium and nitrogen, (d) aluminum and oxygen?

**8.19** Write the electron configuration for each of the following ions, and determine which ones possess noble-gas configurations: (a) $Sr^{2+}$, (b) $Ti^{2+}$, (c) $Se^{2-}$, (d) $Ni^{2+}$, (e) $Br^-$, (f) $Mn^{3+}$.

**8.20** Write electron configurations for the following ions, and determine which have noble-gas configurations: (a) $Cd^{2+}$, (b) $P^{3-}$, (c) $Zr^{4+}$, (d) $Ru^{3+}$, (e) $As^{3-}$, (f) $Ag^+$.

**8.21** (a) Define the term *lattice energy*. (b) Which factors govern the magnitude of the lattice energy of an ionic compound?

**8.22** NaCl and KF have the same crystal structure. The only difference between the two is the distance that separates cations and anions. (a) The lattice energies of NaCl and KF are given in Table 8.2. Based on the lattice energies, would you expect the Na—Cl or the K—F distance to be longer? (b) Use the ionic radii given in Figure 7.7 to estimate the Na—Cl and K—F distances. Does this estimate agree with the prediction you made based on the lattice energies?

**8.23** The ionic substances KF, CaO, and ScN are isoelectronic (they have the same number of electrons). Examine the lattice energies for these substances in Table 8.2, and account for the trends you observe.

**8.24** (a) Does the lattice energy of an ionic solid increase or decrease (i) as the charges of the ions increase, (ii) as the sizes of the ions increase? (b) Arrange the following substances not listed in Table 8.2 according to their expected lattice energies, listing them from lowest lattice energy to the highest: MgS, KI, GaN, LiBr.

**8.25** The lattice energies of KBr and CsCl are nearly equal (Table 8.2). What can you conclude from this observation?

**8.26** Explain the following trends in lattice energy: (a) NaCl > RbBr > CsBr; (b) BaO > KF; (c) SrO > $SrCl_2$.

**8.27** Energy is required to remove two electrons from Ca to form $Ca^{2+}$ and is required to add two electrons to O to form $O^{2-}$. Why, then, is CaO stable relative to the free elements?

**8.28** List the individual steps used in constructing a Born–Haber cycle for the formation of $BaI_2$ from the elements. Which of the steps would you expect to be exothermic?

**8.29** Use data from Appendix C, Figure 7.9, and Figure 7.11 to calculate the lattice energy of RbCl. Is this value greater than or less than the lattice energy of NaCl? Explain.

**8.30** (a) Based on the lattice energies of $MgCl_2$ and $SrCl_2$ given in Table 8.2, what is the range of values that you would expect for the lattice energy of $CaCl_2$? (b) Using data from Appendix C, Figure 7.9, and Figure 7.11 and the value of the second ionization energy for Ca, 1145 kJ/mol, calculate the lattice energy of $CaCl_2$.

# COVALENT BONDING, ELECTRONEGATIVITY, AND BOND POLARITY (sections 8.3 and 8.4)

**8.31** (a) What is meant by the term *covalent bond*? (b) Give three examples of covalent bonding. (c) A substance XY, formed from two different elements, boils at $-33\,°C$. Is XY likely to be a covalent or an ionic substance? Explain.

**8.32** Which of these elements are unlikely to form covalent bonds: S, H, K, Ar, Si? Explain your choices.

**8.33** Using Lewis symbols and Lewis structures, diagram the formation of $SiCl_4$ from Si and Cl atoms.

**8.34** Use Lewis symbols and Lewis structures to diagram the formation of $PF_3$ from P and F atoms.

**8.35** (a) Construct a Lewis structure for $O_2$ in which each atom achieves an octet of electrons. (b) Explain why it is necessary to form a double bond in the Lewis structure. (c) The bond in $O_2$ is shorter than the O—O bond in compounds that contain an O—O single bond. Explain this observation.

**8.36** (a) Construct a Lewis structure for hydrogen peroxide, $H_2O_2$, in which each atom achieves an octet of electrons. (b) Do you expect the O—O bond in $H_2O_2$ to be longer or shorter than the O—O bond in $O_2$?

**8.37** (a) What is meant by the term *electronegativity*? (b) On the Pauling scale what is the range of electronegativity values for the elements? (c) Which element has the greatest electronegativity? (d) Which element has the smallest electronegativity?

**8.38** (a) What is the trend in electronegativity going from left to right in a row of the periodic table? (b) How do electronegativity values generally vary going down a column in the periodic table? (c) How do periodic trends in electronegativity relate to those for ionization energy and electron affinity?

**8.39** Using only the periodic table as your guide, select the most electronegative atom in each of the following sets: (a) Na, Mg, K, Ca; (b) P, S, As, Se; (c) Be, B, C, Si; (d) Zn, Ge, Ga, As.

**8.40** By referring only to the periodic table, select (a) the most electronegative element in group 6A; (b) the least electronegative element in the group Al, Si, P; (c) the most electronegative element in the group Ga, P, Cl, Na; (d) the element in the group K, C, Zn, F that is most likely to form an ionic compound with Ba.

**8.41** Which of the following bonds are polar: (a) B—F, (b) Cl—Cl, (c) Se—O, (d) H—I ? Which is the more electronegative atom in each polar bond?

**8.42** Arrange the bonds in each of the following sets in order of increasing polarity: (a) C—F, O—F, Be—F; (b) O—Cl, S—Br, C—P; (c) C—S, B—F, N—O.

**8.43** (a) From the data in Table 8.3, calculate the effective charges on the H and Br atoms of the HBr molecule in units of the electronic charge, *e*. (b) Compare your answers to part

(a) with those in Sample Exercise 8.5 for the HCl molecule. Can you explain why the values are different?

**8.44** The iodine monobromide molecule, IBr, has a bond length of 2.49 Å and a dipole moment of 1.21 D. (a) Which atom of the molecule is expected to have a negative charge? Explain. (b) Calculate the effective charges on the I and Br atoms in IBr, in units of the electronic charge, $e$.

**8.45** In the following pairs of binary compounds determine which one is a molecular substance and which one is an ionic substance. Use the appropriate naming convention (for ionic or molecular substances) to assign a name to each compound: (a) $SiF_4$ and $LaF_3$, (b) $FeCl_2$ and $ReCl_6$, (c) $PbCl_4$ and $RbCl$.

**8.46** In the following pairs of binary compounds determine which one is a molecular substance and which one is an ionic substance. Use the appropriate naming convention (for ionic or molecular substances) to assign a name to each compound: (a) $TiCl_4$ and $CaF_2$, (b) $ClF_3$ and $VF_3$, (c) $SbCl_5$ and $AlF_3$.

# LEWIS STRUCTURES; RESONANCE STRUCTURES (sections 8.5 and 8.6)

**8.47** Draw Lewis structures for the following: (a) $SiH_4$, (b) CO, (c) $SF_2$, (d) $H_2SO_4$ (H is bonded to O), (e) $ClO_2^-$, (f) $NH_2OH$.

**8.48** Write Lewis structures for the following: (a) $H_2CO$ (both H atoms are bonded to C), (b) $H_2O_2$, (c) $C_2F_6$ (contains a C—C bond), (d) $AsO_3^{3-}$, (e) $H_2SO_3$ (H is bonded to O), (f) $C_2H_2$.

**8.49** (a) When talking about atoms in a Lewis structure, what is meant by the term *formal charge*? (b) Does the formal charge of an atom represent the actual charge on that atom? Explain. (c) How does the formal charge of an atom in a Lewis structure differ from the oxidation number of the atom?

**8.50** (a) Write a Lewis structure for the phosphorus trifluoride molecule, $PF_3$. Is the octet rule satisfied for all the atoms in your structure? (b) Determine the oxidation numbers of the P and F atoms. (c) Determine the formal charges of the P and F atoms. (d) Is the oxidation number for the P atom the same as its formal charge? Explain.

**8.51** Write Lewis structures that obey the octet rule for each of the following, and assign oxidation numbers and formal charges to each atom: (a) OCS, (b) $SOCl_2$ (S is bonded to the two Cl atoms and to the O), (c) $BrO_3^-$, (d) $HClO_2$ (H is bonded to O).

**8.52** For each of the following molecules or ions of sulfur and oxygen, write a single Lewis structure that obeys the octet rule, and calculate the oxidation numbers and formal charges on all the atoms: (a) $SO_2$, (b) $SO_3$, (c) $SO_3^{2-}$. (d) Arrange these molecules/ions in order of increasing S—O bond distance.

**8.53** (a) Write one or more appropriate Lewis structures for the nitrite ion, $NO_2^-$. (b) With what allotrope of oxygen is it isoelectronic? (c) What would you predict for the lengths of the bonds in $NO_2^-$ relative to N—O single bonds and double bonds?

**8.54** Consider the formate ion, $HCO_2^-$, which is the anion formed when formic acid loses an $H^+$ ion. The H and the two O atoms are bonded to the central C atom. (a) Write one or more appropriate Lewis structures for this ion. (b) Are resonance structures needed to describe the structure? (c) What would you predict for the C—O bond lengths in the formate ion relative to those in $CO_2$?

**8.55** Predict the ordering of the C—O bond lengths in CO, $CO_2$, and $CO_3^{2-}$.

**8.56** Based on Lewis structures, predict the ordering of N—O bond lengths in $NO^+$, $NO_2^-$, and $NO_3^-$.

**8.57** (a) Use the concept of resonance to explain why all six C—C bonds in benzene are equal in length. (b) Are the C—C bond lengths in benzene shorter than C—C single bonds? Are they shorter than C=C double bonds?

**8.58** Mothballs are composed of naphthalene, $C_{10}H_8$, a molecule of which consists of two six-membered rings of carbon fused along an edge, as shown in this incomplete Lewis structure:

(a) Write two complete Lewis structures for naphthalene. (b) The observed C—C bond lengths in the molecule are intermediate between C—C single and C=C double bonds. Explain. (c) Represent the resonance in naphthalene in a way analogous to that used to represent it in benzene.

# EXCEPTIONS TO THE OCTET RULE (section 8.7)

**8.59** (a) State the octet rule. (b) Does the octet rule apply to ionic as well as to covalent compounds? Explain using examples as appropriate.

**8.60** Considering the nonmetals, what is the relationship between the group number for an element (carbon, for example, belongs to group 4A; see the periodic table on the inside front cover) and the number of single covalent bonds that element needs to form to conform to the octet rule?

**8.61** The chlorine oxides, in which a chlorine atom is bonded to one or more oxygen atoms, are important molecules in the chemistry of the atmosphere. Will any of the chlorine oxides obey the octet rule? Why or why not?

**8.62** For elements in the third row of the periodic table and beyond, the octet rule is often not obeyed. What factors are usually cited to explain this fact?

**8.63** Draw the Lewis structures for each of the following ions or molecules. Identify those that do not obey the octet rule, and explain why they do not: (a) $SO_3^{2-}$, (b) $AlH_3$, (c) $N_3^-$, (d) $CH_2Cl_2$, (e) $SbF_5$.

**8.64** Draw the Lewis structures for each of the following molecules or ions. Which do not obey the octet rule? (a) NO, (b) $BF_3$, (c) $ICl_2^-$, (d) $OPBr_3$ (the P is the central atom), (e) $XeF_4$.

**8.65** In the vapor phase, $BeCl_2$ exists as a discrete molecule. (a) Draw the Lewis structure of this molecule, using only single bonds. Does this Lewis structure satisfy the octet rule? **(b)** What other resonance structures are possible that satisfy the octet rule? **(c)** On the basis of the formal charges, which Lewis structure is expected to be dominant for $BeCl_2$?

**8.66** **(a)** Describe the molecule xenon trioxide, $XeO_3$, using four possible Lewis structures, one each with zero, one, two, or three Xe—O double bonds. **(b)** Do any of these resonance structures satisfy the octet rule for every atom in the molecule? **(c)** Do any of the four Lewis structures have multiple resonance structures? If so, how many resonance structures do you find? **(d)** Which of the Lewis structures in (a) yields the most favorable formal charges for the molecule?

**8.67** Consider the following statement: "For some molecules and ions, a Lewis structure that satisfies the octet rule does not lead to the lowest formal charges, and a Lewis structure that leads to the lowest formal charges does not satisfy the octet rule." Illustrate this statement using the hydrogen sulfite ion, $HSO_3^-$, as an example (the H atom is bonded to one of the O atoms).

**8.68** Some chemists believe that satisfaction of the octet rule should be the top criterion for choosing the dominant Lewis structure of a molecule or ion. Other chemists believe that achieving the best formal charges should be the top criterion. Consider the dihydrogen phosphate ion, $H_2PO_4^-$, in which the H atoms are bonded to O atoms. **(a)** What would be the predicted dominant Lewis structure if satisfying the octet rule is the top criterion? **(b)** What would it be if achieving the best formal charges is the top criterion? **(c)** Is there another Lewis structure you can draw that satisfies neither of these criteria?

# BOND ENTHALPIES (section 8.8)

**8.69** Using Table 8.4, estimate $\Delta H$ for each of the following gas-phase reactions:

**(a)**

**(b)**

**(c)**   $2\ Cl—N—Cl \longrightarrow N{\equiv}N + 3\ Cl—Cl$
          |
          Cl

**8.70** Using Table 8.4, estimate $\Delta H$ for the following gas-phase reactions:

**(a)**

**(b)**

**(c)**   $H—N—N—H + Cl—Cl \longrightarrow 2\ H—N—Cl$

**8.71** Using Table 8.4, estimate $\Delta H$ for each of the following reactions:
**(a)** $2\ CH_4(g) + O_2(g) \longrightarrow 2\ CH_3OH(g)$
**(b)** $H_2(g) + Br_2(g) \longrightarrow 2\ HBr(g)$
**(c)** $2\ H_2O_2(g) \longrightarrow 2\ H_2O(g) + O_2(g)$

**8.72** Use Table 8.4 to estimate the enthalpy change for each of the following reactions:
**(a)** $H_2C{=}O(g) + HCl(g) \longrightarrow H_3C—O—Cl(g)$
**(b)** $H_2O_2(g) + 2\ CO(g) \longrightarrow H_2(g) + 2\ CO_2(g)$
**(c)** $3\ H_2C{=}CH_2(g) \longrightarrow C_6H_{12}(g)$ (the six carbon atoms form a six-membered ring with two H atoms on each C atom)

**8.73** Ammonia is produced directly from nitrogen and hydrogen by using the Haber process. The chemical reaction is

$$N_2(g) + 3\ H_2(g) \longrightarrow 2\ NH_3(g)$$

**(a)** Use Table 8.4 to estimate the enthalpy change for the reaction. Is it exothermic or endothermic? **(b)** Compare the enthalpy change you calculate in (a) to the true enthalpy change as obtained using $\Delta H_f^\circ$ values.

**8.74** **(a)** Use bond enthalpies to estimate the enthalpy change for the reaction of hydrogen with ethylene:

$$H_2(g) + C_2H_4(g) \longrightarrow C_2H_6(g)$$

**(b)** Calculate the standard enthalpy change for this reaction, using heats of formation. Why does this value differ from that calculated in (a)?

**8.75** Given the following bond-dissociation energies, calculate the average bond enthalpy for the Ti—Cl bond.

|  | $\Delta H$(kJ/mol) |
|---|---|
| $TiCl_4(g) \longrightarrow TiCl_3(g) + Cl(g)$ | 335 |
| $TiCl_3(g) \longrightarrow TiCl_2(g) + Cl(g)$ | 423 |
| $TiCl_2(g) \longrightarrow TiCl(g) + Cl(g)$ | 444 |
| $TiCl(g) \longrightarrow Ti(g) + Cl(g)$ | 519 |

**[8.76]** **(a)** Using average bond enthalpies, predict which of the following reactions will be most exothermic:
(i) $C(g) + 2\ F_2(g) \longrightarrow CF_4(g)$
(ii) $CO(g) + 3\ F_2 \longrightarrow CF_4(g) + OF_2(g)$
(iii) $CO_2(g) + 4\ F_2 \longrightarrow CF_4(g) + 2\ OF_2(g)$
**(b)** Explain the trend, if any, that exists between reaction exothermicity and the extent to which the carbon atom is bonded to oxygen.

# ADDITIONAL EXERCISES

**8.77** How many elements in the periodic table are represented by a Lewis symbol with a single dot? Are all these elements in the same group? Explain.

**[8.78]** From Equation 8.4 and the ionic radii given in Figure 7.7, calculate the potential energy of the following pairs of ions. Assume that the ions are separated by a distance equal to the sum of their ionic radii: (a) $Na^+$, $Br^-$; (b) $Rb^+$, $Br^-$; (c) $Sr^{2+}$, $S^{2-}$.

**8.79** (a) Explain the following trend in lattice energy: $BeH_2$, 3205 kJ/mol; $MgH_2$, 2791 kJ/mol; $CaH_2$, 2410 kJ/mol; $SrH_2$, 2250 kJ/mol; $BaH_2$, 2121 kJ/mol. (b) The lattice energy of $ZnH_2$ is 2870 kJ/mol. Based on the data given in part (a), the radius of the $Zn^{2+}$ ion is expected to be closest to that of which group 2A element?

**8.80** Based on data in Table 8.2, estimate (within 30 kJ/mol) the lattice energy for (a) LiBr, (b) CsBr, (c) $CaCl_2$.

**8.81** An ionic substance of formula MX has a lattice energy of $6 \times 10^3$ kJ/mol. Is the charge on the ion M likely to be 1+, 2+ or 3+? Explain your reasoning.

**[8.82]** From the ionic radii given in Figure 7.7, calculate the potential energy of a $Ca^{2+}$ and $O^{2-}$ ion pair that is just touching (the magnitude of the electronic charge is given on the back inside cover). Calculate the energy of a mole of such pairs. How does this value compare with the lattice energy of CaO (Table 8.2)? Explain the difference.

**8.83** Construct a Born–Haber cycle for the formation of the hypothetical compound $NaCl_2$, where the sodium ion has a 2+ charge (the second ionization energy for sodium is given in Table 7.2). (a) How large would the lattice energy need to be for the formation of $NaCl_2$ to be exothermic? (b) If we were to estimate the lattice energy of $NaCl_2$ to be roughly equal to that of $MgCl_2$ (2326 kJ/mol from Table 8.2), what value would you obtain for the standard enthalpy of formation, $\Delta H_f^\circ$, of $NaCl_2$?

**8.84** (a) How does a polar molecule differ from a nonpolar one? (b) Atoms X and Y have different electronegativities. Will the diatomic molecule X—Y necessarily be polar? Explain. (c) What factors affect the size of the dipole moment of a diatomic molecule?

**8.85** For the following collection of nonmetallic elements, O, P, Te, I, B, (a) which two would form the most polar single bond? (b) Which two would form the longest single bond? (c) Which two would be likely to form a compound of formula $XY_2$? (d) Which combinations of elements would likely yield a compound of empirical formula $X_2Y_3$? In each case explain your answer.

**8.86** The substance chlorine monoxide, ClO(g), is important in atmospheric processes that lead to depletion of the ozone layer. The ClO molecule has a dipole moment of 1.24 D and the Cl—O bond length is 1.60 Å. (a) Determine the magnitude of the charges on the Cl and O atoms in units of the electronic charge, $e$. (b) Based on the electronegativities of the elements, which atom would you expect to have a negative charge in the ClO molecule? (c) By using formal charges as a guide, propose the dominant Lewis structure for the molecule. Are the formal charges consistent with your answers to parts (a) and (b)? Can you reconcile any differences you find?

**[8.87]** Using the electronegativities of Br and Cl, estimate the partial charges on the atoms in the Br—Cl molecule. Using these partial charges and the atomic radii given in Figure 7.7, estimate the dipole moment of the molecule. The measured dipole moment is 0.57 D.

**8.88** A major challenge in implementing the "hydrogen economy" is finding a safe, lightweight, and compact way of storing hydrogen for use as a fuel. The hydrides of light metals are attractive for hydrogen storage because they can store a high weight percentage of hydrogen in a small volume. For example, $NaAlH_4$ can release 5.6% of its mass as $H_2$ upon decomposing to NaH(s), Al(s), and $H_2(g)$. $NaAlH_4$ possesses both covalent bonds, which hold polyatomic anions together, and ionic bonds. (a) Write a balanced equation for the decomposition of $NaAlH_4$. (b) Which element in $NaAlH_4$ is the most electronegative? Which one is the least electronegative? (c) Based on electronegativity differences, what do you think is the identity of the polyatomic anion? Draw a Lewis structure for this ion.

**8.89** Although $I_3^-$ is known, $F_3^-$ is not. Using Lewis structures, explain why $F_3^-$ does not form.

**8.90** Calculate the formal charge on the indicated atom in each of the following molecules or ions: (a) the central oxygen atom in $O_3$, (b) phosphorus in $PF_6^-$, (c) nitrogen in $NO_2$, (d) iodine in $ICl_3$, (e) chlorine in $HClO_4$ (hydrogen is bonded to O).

**8.91** (a) Determine the formal charge on the chlorine atom in the hypochlorite ion, $ClO^-$, and the perchlorate ion, $ClO_4^-$, using resonance structures where the Cl atom has an octet. (b) What are the oxidation numbers of chlorine in $ClO^-$ and in $ClO_4^-$? (c) Is it uncommon for the formal charge and the oxidation state to be different? Explain. (d) Perchlorate is a much stronger oxidizing agent than hypochlorite. Would you expect there to be any relationship between the oxidizing power of the oxyanion and either the oxidation state or the formal charge of chlorine?

**8.92** The following three Lewis structures can be drawn for $N_2O$:

$$:N\equiv N-\ddot{\ddot{O}}: \longleftrightarrow :\ddot{N}-N\equiv O: \longleftrightarrow :\ddot{N}=N=\ddot{O}:$$

(a) Using formal charges, which of these three resonance forms is likely to be the most important? (b) The N—N bond length in $N_2O$ is 1.12 Å, slightly longer than a typical $N\equiv N$ bond; and the N—O bond length is 1.19 Å, slightly shorter than a typical $N=O$ bond. (See Table 8.5.) Rationalize these observations in terms of the resonance structures shown previously and your conclusion for part (a).

**[8.93]** (a) Triazine, $C_3H_3N_3$, is like benzene except that in triazine every other C—H group is replaced by a nitrogen atom. Draw the Lewis structure(s) for the triazine molecule. (b) Estimate the carbon–nitrogen bond distances in the ring.

**[8.94]** Ortho-dichlorobenzene, $C_6H_4Cl_2$, is obtained when two of the adjacent hydrogen atoms in benzene are replaced with Cl atoms. A skeleton of the molecule is shown here. (a) Complete a Lewis structure for the molecule using bonds and electron pairs as needed. (b) Are there any resonance structures for the molecule? If so, sketch them. (c) Are the resonance structures in (a) and (b) equivalent to one another as they are in benzene? If not, explain what makes them different.

**8.95** Consider the hypothetical molecule B—A=B. How could you use an experimentally determined structure of the molecule to decide whether resonance is important in it?

**8.96** An important reaction for the conversion of natural gas to other useful hydrocarbons is the conversion of methane to ethane.

$$2 \, CH_4(g) \longrightarrow C_2H_6(g) + H_2(g)$$

In practice, this reaction is carried out in the presence of oxygen, which converts the hydrogen produced to water.

$$2 \, CH_4(g) + \tfrac{1}{2} O_2(g) \longrightarrow C_2H_6(g) + H_2O(g)$$

Use Table 8.4 to estimate $\Delta H$ for these two reactions. Why is the conversion of methane to ethane more favorable when oxygen is used?

**8.97** Two compounds are isomers if they have the same chemical formula but a different arrangement of atoms. Use Table 8.4 to estimate $\Delta H$ for each of the following gas-phase isomerization reactions, and indicate which isomer has the lower enthalpy:

**(a)**

Ethanol          Dimethyl ether

**(b)**

Ethylene oxide     Acetaldehyde

**(c)**

Cyclopentene          Pentadiene

**(d)**

Methyl isocyanide      Acetonitrile

**[8.98]** With reference to the "Chemistry Put to Work" box on explosives, (a) use bond enthalpies to estimate the enthalpy change for the explosion of 1.00 g of nitroglycerin. (b) Write a balanced equation for the decomposition of TNT. Assume that, upon explosion, TNT decomposes into $N_2(g)$, $CO_2(g)$, $H_2O(g)$, and $C(s)$.

**[8.99]** The "plastic" explosive C-4, often used in action movies, contains the molecule *cyclotrimethylenetrinitramine*, which is often called RDX (for Royal Demolition eXplosive):

Cyclotrimethylenetrinitramine (RDX)

(a) Complete the Lewis structure for the molecule by adding unshared electron pairs where they are needed. (b) Does the Lewis structure you drew in part (a) have any resonance structures? If so, how many? (c) The molecule causes an explosion by decomposing into $CO(g)$, $N_2(g)$, and $H_2O(g)$. Write a balanced equation for the decomposition reaction. (d) With reference to Table 8.4, which is the weakest type of bond in the molecule? (e) Use average bond enthalpies to estimate the enthalpy change when 5.0 g of RDX decomposes.

**8.100** The bond lengths of carbon–carbon, carbon–nitrogen, carbon–oxygen, and nitrogen–nitrogen single, double, and triple bonds are listed in Table 8.5. Plot bond enthalpy (Table 8.4) versus bond length for these bonds (as in Figure 8.17). What do you conclude about the relationship between bond length and bond enthalpy? What do you conclude about the relative strengths of C—C, C—N, C—O, and N—N bonds?

# INTEGRATIVE EXERCISES

**8.101** The $Ti^{2+}$ ion is isoelectronic with the Ca atom. (a) Are there any differences in the electron configurations of $Ti^{2+}$ and Ca? (b) With reference to Figure 6.24, comment on the changes in the ordering of the $4s$ and $3d$ subshells in Ca and $Ti^{2+}$. (c) Will Ca and $Ti^{2+}$ have the same number of unpaired electrons? Explain.

**[8.102]** (a) Write the chemical equations that are used in calculating the lattice energy of $SrCl_2(s)$ via a Born–Haber cycle. (b) The second ionization energy of $Sr(g)$ is 1064 kJ/mol. Use this fact along with data in Appendix C, Figure 7.9, Figure 7.11, and Table 8.2 to calculate $\Delta H_f^\circ$ for $SrCl_2(s)$.

**[8.103]** The electron affinity of oxygen is $-141$ kJ/mol, corresponding to the reaction

$$O(g) + e^- \longrightarrow O^-(g)$$

The lattice energy of $K_2O(s)$ is 2238 kJ/mol. Use these data along with data in Appendix C and Figure 7.9 to calculate the "second electron affinity" of oxygen, corresponding to the reaction

$$O^-(g) + e^- \longrightarrow O^{2-}(g)$$

**8.104** You and a partner are asked to complete a lab entitled "Oxides of Ruthenium" that is scheduled to extend over two lab periods. The first lab, which is to be completed by your partner, is devoted to carrying out compositional analysis. In the second lab, you are to determine melting points. Upon going to lab you find two unlabeled vials, one containing a soft yellow substance and the other a black powder. You also find the following notes in your partner's notebook—*Compound 1*: 76.0% Ru and 24.0% O (by mass), *Compound 2*: 61.2% Ru and

38.8% O (by mass). **(a)** What is the empirical formula for Compound 1? **(b)** What is the empirical formula for Compound 2? **(c)** Upon determining the melting points of these two compounds, you find that the yellow compound melts at 25 °C, while the black powder does not melt up to the maximum temperature of your apparatus, 1200 °C. What is the identity of the yellow compound? What is the identity of the black compound? Be sure to use the appropriate naming convention depending on whether the compound is better described as a molecular or ionic compound.

[8.105] One scale for electronegativity is based on the concept that the electronegativity of any atom is proportional to the ionization energy of the atom minus its electron affinity: electronegativity = $k(IE - EA)$, where $k$ is a proportionality constant. **(a)** How does this definition explain why the electronegativity of F is greater than that of Cl even though Cl has the greater electron affinity? **(b)** Why are both ionization energy and electron affinity relevant to the notion of electronegativity? **(c)** By using data in Chapter 7, determine the value of $k$ that would lead to an electronegativity of 4.0 for F under this definition. **(d)** Use your result from part (c) to determine the electronegativities of Cl and O using this scale. Do these values follow the trend shown in Figure 8.7?

**8.106** The compound chloral hydrate, known in detective stories as knockout drops, is composed of 14.52% C, 1.83% H, 64.30% Cl, and 19.35% O by mass and has a molar mass of 165.4 g/mol. **(a)** What is the empirical formula of this substance? **(b)** What is the molecular formula of this substance? **(c)** Draw the Lewis structure of the molecule, assuming that the Cl atoms bond to a single C atom and that there are a C—C bond and two C—O bonds in the compound.

**8.107** Barium azide is 62.04% Ba and 37.96% N. Each azide ion has a net charge of 1–. **(a)** Determine the chemical formula of the azide ion. **(b)** Write three resonance structures for the azide ion. **(c)** Which structure is most important? **(d)** Predict the bond lengths in the ion.

**8.108** Acetylene ($C_2H_2$) and nitrogen ($N_2$) both contain a triple bond, but they differ greatly in their chemical properties. **(a)** Write the Lewis structures for the two substances. **(b)** By referring to Appendix C, look up the enthalpies of formation of acetylene and nitrogen and compare their reactivities. **(c)** Write balanced chemical equations for the complete oxidation of $N_2$ to form $N_2O_5(g)$ and of acetylene to form $CO_2(g)$ and $H_2O(g)$. **(d)** Calculate the enthalpy of oxidation per mole of $N_2$ and $C_2H_2$ (the enthalpy of formation of $N_2O_5(g)$ is 11.30 kJ/mol). How do these comparative values relate to your response to part (b)? Both $N_2$ and $C_2H_2$ possess triple bonds with quite high bond enthalpies (Table 8.4). What aspect of chemical bonding in these molecules or in the oxidation products seems to account for the difference in chemical reactivities?

[8.109] Under special conditions, sulfur reacts with anhydrous liquid ammonia to form a binary compound of sulfur and nitrogen.

The compound is found to consist of 69.6% S and 30.4% N. Measurements of its molecular mass yield a value of 184.3 g $mol^{-1}$. The compound occasionally detonates on being struck or when heated rapidly. The sulfur and nitrogen atoms of the molecule are joined in a ring. All the bonds in the ring are of the same length. **(a)** Calculate the empirical and molecular formulas for the substance. **(b)** Write Lewis structures for the molecule, based on the information you are given. (*Hint:* You should find a relatively small number of dominant Lewis structures.) **(c)** Predict the bond distances between the atoms in the ring. (*Note:* The S—S distance in the $S_8$ ring is 2.05 Å.) **(d)** The enthalpy of formation of the compound is estimated to be 480 kJ $mol^{-1}$. $\Delta H_f^\circ$ of S(g) is 222.8 kJ $mol^{-1}$. Estimate the average bond enthalpy in the compound.

[8.110] A common form of elemental phosphorus is the tetrahedral $P_4$ molecule, where all four phosphorus atoms are equivalent:

$P_4$

At room temperature phosphorus is a solid. **(a)** Do you think there are any unshared pairs of electrons in the $P_4$ molecule? **(b)** How many P—P bonds are there in the molecule? **(c)** Can you draw a Lewis structure for a linear $P_4$ molecule that satisfies the octet rule? **(d)** Using formal charges, what can you say about the stability of the linear molecule versus that of the tetrahedral molecule?

[8.111] Consider benzene ($C_6H_6$) in the gas phase. **(a)** Write the reaction for breaking all the bonds in $C_6H_6(g)$, and use data in Appendix C to determine the enthalpy change for this reaction. **(b)** Write a reaction that corresponds to breaking all the carbon–carbon bonds in $C_6H_6(g)$. **(c)** By combining your answers to parts (a) and (b) and using the average bond enthalpy for C—H from Table 8.4, calculate the average bond enthalpy for the carbon–carbon bonds in $C_6H_6(g)$. **(d)** Comment on your answer from part (c) as compared to the values for C—C single bonds and C=C double bonds in Table 8.4.

**8.112** Average bond enthalpies are generally defined for gas-phase molecules. Many substances are liquids in their standard state. ∞ (Section 5.7) By using appropriate thermochemical data from Appendix C, calculate average bond enthalpies in the liquid state for the following bonds, and compare these values to the gas-phase values given in Table 8.4: **(a)** Br—Br, from $Br_2(l)$; **(b)** C—Cl, from $CCl_4(l)$; **(c)** O—O, from $H_2O_2(l)$ (assume that the O—H bond enthalpy is the same as in the gas phase). **(d)** What can you conclude about the process of breaking bonds in the liquid as compared to the gas phase? Explain the difference in the $\Delta H$ values between the two phases.

# WHAT'S AHEAD

### 9.1 MOLECULAR SHAPES
We begin by discussing *molecular shapes* and examining some shapes commonly encountered in molecules.

### 9.2 THE VSEPR MODEL
We consider how molecular geometries can be predicted using the *valence-shell electron-pair repulsion,* or *VSEPR,* model, which is based on Lewis structures and the repulsions between regions of high electron density.

### 9.3 MOLECULAR SHAPE AND MOLECULAR POLARITY
Once we know the geometry of a molecule and the types of bonds it contains, we can determine whether the molecule is *polar* or *nonpolar.*

### 9.4 COVALENT BONDING AND ORBITAL OVERLAP
We recognize that electrons are shared between atoms in a covalent bond. In *valence-bond theory,* the bonding electrons are visualized as originating in atomic orbitals on two atoms. A covalent bond is formed when these orbitals overlap.

**9**

**THE DRUG SHOWN HERE IS DIAZEPAM,** better known as Valium. It is commonly prescribed for a wide range of disorders, including *anxiety, insomnia, seizures, muscle spasms, restless legs syndrome,* and *obsessive-compulsive disorder.* Valium was invented by Leo Sternbach at Hoffmann-LaRoche Pharmaceuticals and first licensed for use in 1960. It was the top-selling pharmaceutical in the United States from 1969 to 1982, with peak sales in 1978 of 2.3 billion tablets! It continues to be an important medication and is on the World Health Organization's Essential Drugs list.

# MOLECULAR GEOMETRY AND BONDING THEORIES

**WE SAW IN CHAPTER 8 THAT LEWIS STRUCTURES** help us understand the compositions of molecules and their covalent bonds. However, Lewis structures do not show one of the most important aspects of molecules—their overall shapes. The shape and size of molecules—sometimes referred to as molecular *architecture*—are defined by the angles and distances between the nuclei of the component atoms.

The shape and size of a molecule of a substance, together with the strength and polarity of its bonds, largely determine the properties of that substance. Some of the most dramatic examples of the important roles of molecular architecture are seen in biochemical reactions. For example, the chapter-opening photograph shows a molecular model of diazepam, better known as Valium. In the body, this relatively simple molecule enters into an extraordinary array of biochemical interactions. Valium works by binding to certain important sites in the central nervous system. Its effectiveness is highly dependent on the shape and size of the molecule as well on the charge distributions within it. Even a small modification to molecular shape or size alters the drug's effectiveness.

One of our goals in this chapter is to develop a sense of the shapes of molecules and how those shapes are governed in large measure by the kinds of bonds that exist between the atoms making up the molecules.

Our first goal is to learn the relationship between two-dimensional Lewis structures and three-dimensional molecular shapes. Armed with this knowledge, we can examine the nature of covalent bonds. The lines used to depict bonds in Lewis structures provide important clues about the orbitals that molecules use in bonding. By examining these orbitals, we can gain a greater understanding of the behavior of molecules. Mastering the material in this chapter will help you in later discussions of the physical and chemical properties of substances.

# 9.1 | MOLECULAR SHAPES

In Chapter 8 we used Lewis structures to account for the formulas of covalent compounds. ∞ (Section 8.5) Lewis structures, however, do not indicate the shapes of molecules; they simply show the number and types of bonds. For example, the Lewis structure of $CCl_4$ tells us only that four Cl atoms are bonded to a central C atom:

$$:\overset{..}{\underset{..}{C}}l:$$
$$:\overset{..}{\underset{..}{C}}l - C - \overset{..}{\underset{..}{C}}l:$$
$$:\overset{..}{\underset{..}{C}}l:$$

The Lewis structure is drawn with the atoms all in the same plane. As shown in ▼ **FIGURE 9.1**, however, the actual arrangement is the Cl atoms at the corners of a *tetrahedron*, a geometric object with four corners and four faces, each an equilateral triangle.

The shape of a molecule is determined by its **bond angles**, the angles made by the lines joining the nuclei of the atoms in the molecule. The bond angles of a molecule, together with the bond lengths ∞ (Section 8.8), define the shape and size of the molecule. In Figure 9.1, you should be able to see that there are six Cl—C—Cl bond angles in $CCl_4$ and that they all have the same value of 109.5°, the angle size characteristic of a tetrahedron. In addition, all four C—Cl bonds are the same length (1.78 Å). Thus, the shape and size of $CCl_4$ are completely described by stating that the molecule is tetrahedral with C—Cl bonds of length 1.78 Å.

We begin our discussion of molecular shapes with molecules (and ions) that, like $CCl_4$, have a single central atom bonded to two or more atoms of the same type. Such molecules have the general formula $AB_n$ in which the central atom A is bonded to $n$

 GO FIGURE

**In the space-filling model, what determines the relative sizes of the spheres?**

Four equivalent faces

All C—Cl bond lengths 1.78 Å

$CCl_4$

$CCl_4$

All Cl—C—Cl angles 109.5°

Tetrahedron

Ball and stick model

Space-filling model

▲ **FIGURE 9.1** Tetrahedral shape of $CCl_4$.

**▲ FIGURE 9.2 Shapes of AB₂ and AB₃ molecules.**

B atoms. Both $CO_2$ and $H_2O$ are $AB_2$ molecules, for example, whereas $SO_3$ and $NH_3$ are $AB_3$ molecules, and so on.

The number of shapes possible for $AB_n$ molecules depends on the value of $n$. Those commonly found for $AB_2$ and $AB_3$ molecules are shown in ▲ **FIGURE 9.2.** An $AB_2$ molecule must be either linear (bond angle $= 180°$) or bent (bond angle $\neq 180°$). For $AB_3$ molecules, the two most common shapes place the B atoms at the corners of an equilateral triangle. If the A atom lies in the same plane as the B atoms, the shape is *trigonal planar*. If the A atom lies above the plane of the B atoms, the shape is *trigonal pyramidal* (a pyramid with an equilateral triangle as its base). Some $AB_3$ molecules, such as $ClF_3$, are *T-shaped*, the relatively unusual shape shown in Figure 9.2. The atoms lie in one plane, but the angles between them vary as shown.

Compare Figures 9.1 and 9.2 to notice the difference between $NF_3$ and $CCl_4$. The $CCl_4$ molecule is tetrahedral because the four atoms bonded to the carbon are disposed at the four apexes of a tetrahedron around the central atom. The $NF_3$ molecule is pyramidal because the three atoms bonded to nitrogen lie at the base of a trigonal pyramid.

The shapes that maximize the separation of outer atoms are shown in ▼ **FIGURE 9.3.** In addition to the shapes we have already seen, this figure shows those encountered when there are five or six atoms surrounding a central atom. The trigonal bipyramid can be thought of as two face-to-face trigonal pyramids; the octahedron is like two face-to-face square pyramids.

⚠ **GO FIGURE**

**Which of these molecular shapes do you expect for the $SF_6$ molecule?**

**◄ FIGURE 9.3 Shapes allowing maximum distances between atoms in $AB_n$ molecules.**

Removal of one corner atom

Removal of a second corner atom

Tetrahedral → Trigonal pyramidal → Bent

▶ **FIGURE 9.4** **Derivatives of the tetrahedral molecular shape.**

Some molecules have shapes other than those shown in Figure 9.3, but we can usually derive the shape of those molecules from Figure 9.3. Neither trigonal pyramidal nor bent is shown in Figure 9.3, for instance, but ▲ **FIGURE 9.4** shows how we can arrive at these shapes by removing atoms from the tetrahedral shape.

Why do so many $AB_n$ molecules have shapes related to those shown in Figure 9.3, and can we predict these shapes? When A is a representative element (one from the $s$ block or $p$ block of the periodic table), we can answer these questions by using the **valence-shell electron-pair repulsion (VSEPR) model**. Although the name is rather imposing, the model is quite simple. It has useful predictive capabilities, as we will see in Section 9.2.

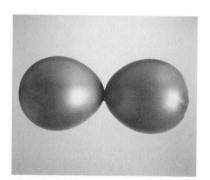

Two balloons linear orientation

⚠️ **GIVE IT SOME THOUGHT**

In addition to tetrahedral, another common shape for $AB_4$ molecules is *square planar.* All five atoms lie in the same plane, with the B atoms at the corners of a square and the A atom at the center of the square. Which shape in Figure 9.3 could lead to a square-planar shape upon removal of one or more atoms?

# 9.2 | THE VSEPR MODEL

Imagine tying two identical balloons together at their ends. As shown in ◀ **FIGURE 9.5**, the two balloons naturally orient themselves to point away from each other; that is, they try to "get out of each other's way" as much as possible. If we add a third balloon, the balloons orient themselves toward the vertices of an equilateral triangle, and if we add a fourth balloon, they adopt a tetrahedral shape. We see that an optimum geometry exists for each number of balloons.

Three balloons trigonal-planar orientation

In some ways, the electrons in molecules behave like these balloons. We have seen that a single covalent bond is formed between two atoms when a pair of electrons occupies the space between the atoms. ⬭ (Section 8.3) A **bonding pair** of electrons thus defines a region in which the electrons are most likely to be found. We will refer to such a region as an **electron domain**. Likewise, a **nonbonding pair** (or **lone pair**) of electrons defines an electron domain that is located principally on one atom. For example, the Lewis structure of $NH_3$ has four electron domains around the central nitrogen atom (three bonding pairs, represented as usual by short lines, and one nonbonding pair, represented by dots):

$$H—\overset{..}{N}—H$$
$$|$$
$$H$$

Four balloons tetrahedral orientation

Each multiple bond in a molecule also constitutes a single electron domain. Thus, the resonance structure for $O_3$ has three electron domains around the central oxygen atom (a single bond, a double bond, and a nonbonding pair of electrons):

$$:\overset{..}{O}—\overset{..}{O}=\overset{..}{O}$$

In general, *each nonbonding pair, single bond, or multiple bond produces a single electron domain around the central atom in a molecule.*

▲ **FIGURE 9.5** **A balloon analogy for electron domains.**

## GIVE IT SOME THOUGHT

Suppose a particular $AB_3$ molecule has the resonance structure

$$:\!\overset{\displaystyle :B:}{\underset{\displaystyle \ }{\underset{\displaystyle B}{\overset{\displaystyle \|}{\phantom{|}}}}}$$

:B:
‖
:B̈—Ä—B̈:

Does this structure follow the octet rule? How many electron domains are there around the A atom?

The VSEPR model is based on the idea that electron domains are negatively charged and therefore repel one another. Like the balloons in Figure 9.5, electron domains try to stay out of one another's way. *The best arrangement of a given number of electron domains is the one that minimizes the repulsions among them.* In fact, the analogy between electron domains and balloons is so close that the same preferred geometries are found in both cases. Like the balloons in Figure 9.5, two electron domains orient *linearly,* three domains orient in a *trigonal-planar* fashion, and four orient *tetrahedrally.* These arrangements, together with those for five- and six-electron domains, are summarized in ▼ TABLE 9.1. If you compare the geometries in Table 9.1 with those in Figure 9.3,

**TABLE 9.1 • Electron-Domain Geometries as a Function of Number of Electron Domains**

| Number of Electron Domains | Arrangement of Electron Domains | Electron-Domain Geometry | Predicted Bond Angles |
|---|---|---|---|
| 2 | 180° | Linear | 180° |
| 3 | 120° | Trigonal planar | 120° |
| 4 | 109.5° | Tetrahedral | 109.5° |
| 5 | 90° 120° | Trigonal bipyramidal | 120° 90° |
| 6 | 90° 90° | Octahedral | 90° |

you will see that they are the same. *The shapes of different AB$_n$ molecules or ions depend on the number of electron domains surrounding the central atom.*

The arrangement of electron domains about the central atom of an AB$_n$ molecule or ion is called its **electron-domain geometry**. In contrast, the **molecular geometry** is the arrangement of *only the atoms* in a molecule or ion—any nonbonding pairs in the molecule are *not* part of the description of the molecular geometry.

In determining the shape of any molecule, we first use the VSEPR model to predict the electron-domain geometry. From knowing how many of the domains are due to nonbonding pairs, we can then predict the molecular geometry. When all the electron domains in a molecule arise from bonds, the molecular geometry is identical to the electron-domain geometry. When, however, one or more domains involve nonbonding pairs of electrons, we must remember to ignore those domains when talking about molecular shape.

We can generalize the steps we follow in using the VSEPR model to predict the shapes of molecules or ions:

1. Draw the *Lewis structure* of the molecule or ion, and count the number of electron domains around the central atom. Each nonbonding electron pair, each single bond, each double bond, and each triple bond counts as one electron domain.

2. Determine the *electron-domain geometry* by arranging the electron domains about the central atom so that the repulsions among them are minimized, as shown in Table 9.1.

3. Use the arrangement of the bonded atoms to determine the *molecular geometry*.

▼ **FIGURE 9.6** shows how these steps are applied to predict the geometry of the NH$_3$ molecule. The three bonds and one nonbonding pair in the Lewis structure tell us we have four electron domains. We know from Table 9.1 that the repulsions among four electron domains are minimized when the domains point toward the vertices of a tetrahedron, so the electron-domain geometry of NH$_3$ is tetrahedral. We know from the Lewis structure that one electron domain holds a nonbonding pair of electrons, which occupies one of the four vertices of the tetrahedron. The bonding arrangement is therefore three atoms bonded to a central atom, with the central atom not in the same plane as the three others. This is just the situation we find in the middle molecule of Figure 9.4. Hence, the molecular geometry of NH$_3$ is trigonal pyramidal. Notice that the tetrahedral arrangement of the four electron domains leads us to predict the trigonal-pyramidal molecular geometry.

Because the trigonal-pyramidal molecular geometry is based on a tetrahedral electron-domain geometry, the *ideal bond angles* are 109.5°. As we will soon see, bond angles deviate from ideal values when the surrounding atoms and electron domains are not identical.

**△ GIVE IT SOME THOUGHT**

From the standpoint of the VSEPR model, what do nonbonding electron pairs, single bonds, and multiple bonds have in common?

NH$_3$

1. Draw Lewis structure

2. Determine electron-domain geometry by counting *all* electron domains, then use Table 9.1 to determine appropriate electron domain geomtry.

3. Determine molecular geometry by counting *only bonding* electron domains to see arrangement of bonded atoms (trigonal pyramidal)

▶ **FIGURE 9.6** Determining the molecular geometry of NH$_3$.

As one more example, let's determine the shape of the $CO_2$ molecule. Its Lewis structure reveals two electron domains (each one a double bond) around the central carbon:

$$\ddot{O}=C=\ddot{O}$$

Two electron domains orient in a linear electron-domain geometry (Table 9.1). Because neither domain is a nonbonding pair of electrons, the molecular geometry is also linear, and the $O-C-O$ bond angle is 180°.

▼ TABLE 9.2 summarizes the possible molecular geometries when an $AB_n$ molecule has four or fewer electron domains about A. These geometries are important because they include all the shapes usually seen in molecules or ions that obey the octet rule.

**TABLE 9.2 • Electron-Domain and Molecular Geometries for Two, Three, and Four Electron Domains around a Central Atom**

| Number of Electron Domains | Electron-Domain Geometry | Bonding Domains | Nonbonding Domains | Molecular Geometry | Example |
|---|---|---|---|---|---|
| 2 | Linear | 2 | 0 | Linear | $\ddot{O}=C=\ddot{O}$ |
| 3 | Trigonal planar | 3 | 0 | Trigonal planar | $BF_3$ structure |
|  |  | 2 | 1 | Bent | $[NO_2]^-$ structure |
| 4 | Tetrahedral | 4 | 0 | Tetrahedral | $CH_4$ structure |
|  |  | 3 | 1 | Trigonal pyramidal | $NH_3$ structure |
|  |  | 2 | 2 | Bent | $H_2O$ structure |

**SAMPLE EXERCISE 9.1** | **Using the VSEPR Model**

Use the VSEPR model to predict the molecular geometry of (**a**) $O_3$, (**b**) $SnCl_3^-$.

**SOLUTION**

**Analyze** We are given the molecular formulas of a molecule and a polyatomic ion, both conforming to the general formula $AB_n$ and both having a central atom from the $p$ block of the periodic table.

**Plan** To predict the molecular geometries, we draw their Lewis structures and count electron domains around the central atom to get the electron-domain geometry. We then obtain the molecular geometry from the arrangement of the domains that are due to bonds.

**Solve**

(**a**) We can draw two resonance structures for $O_3$:

$$:\ddot{O}-\ddot{O}=\ddot{O}: \longleftrightarrow \ddot{O}=\ddot{O}-\ddot{O}:$$

Because of resonance, the bonds between the central O atom and the outer O atoms are of equal length. In both resonance structures the central O atom is bonded to the two outer O atoms and has one nonbonding pair. Thus, there are three electron domains about the central O atoms. (Remember that a double bond counts as a single electron domain.) The arrangement of three electron domains is trigonal planar (Table 9.1). Two of the domains are from bonds, and one is due to a nonbonding pair. So, the molecule has a bent shape with an ideal bond angle of 120° (Table 9.2).

**Comment** As this example illustrates, when a molecule exhibits resonance, any one of the resonance structures can be used to predict the molecular geometry.

(**b**) The Lewis structure for $SnCl_3^-$ is

$$\left[:\ddot{Cl}-\ddot{Sn}-\ddot{Cl}:\right]^-$$
$$:\ddot{Cl}:$$

The central Sn atom is bonded to the three Cl atoms and has one nonbonding pair; thus, we have four electron domains, meaning tetrahedral electron-domain geometry (Table 9.1) with one vertex occupied by a nonbonding pair of electrons. Tetrahedral electron-domain geometry with three bonding and one nonbonding domains means the molecular geometry is trigonal pyramidal (Table 9.2).

**PRACTICE EXERCISE**

Predict the electron-domain and molecular geometries for (**a**) $SeCl_2$, (**b**) $CO_3^{2-}$.

**Answers:** (**a**) tetrahedral, bent; (**b**) trigonal planar, trigonal planar

## Effect of Nonbonding Electrons and Multiple Bonds on Bond Angles

We can refine the VSEPR model to explain slight distortions from the ideal geometries summarized in Table 9.2. For example, consider methane ($CH_4$), ammonia ($NH_3$), and water ($H_2O$). All three have a tetrahedral electron-domain geometry, but their bond angles differ slightly:

Notice that the bond angles decrease as the number of nonbonding electron pairs increases. A bonding pair of electrons is attracted by both nuclei of the bonded atoms, but a nonbonding pair is attracted primarily by only one nucleus. Because a nonbonding pair experiences less nuclear attraction, its electron domain is spread out more in space than is the electron domain for a bonding pair (▶ FIGURE 9.7). Nonbonding electron pairs therefore take up more space than bonding pairs. As a result, *electron domains for nonbonding electron pairs exert greater repulsive forces on adjacent electron domains and tend to compress bond angles.*

Because multiple bonds contain a higher electronic-charge density than single bonds, multiple bonds also represent enlarged electron domains. Consider the Lewis structure of phosgene:

$$:\overset{..}{\underset{..}{C}l} \\ \qquad \diagdown \\ \qquad \quad C = \overset{..}{O} \\ \qquad \diagup \\ :\overset{..}{\underset{..}{C}l}$$

Because three electron domains surround the central atom, we might expect a trigonal-planar geometry with 120° bond angles. The double bond, however, seems to act much like a nonbonding pair of electrons, reducing the Cl—C—Cl bond angle to 111.4°:

$$\text{Cl} \underset{\diagup}{\overset{\diagdown}{\underset{111.4°}{C}}} \overset{\leftarrow 124.3°}{=\!=\!= O} \\ \text{Cl} \quad \overset{\leftarrow 124.3°}{}$$

In general, *electron domains for multiple bonds exert a greater repulsive force on adjacent electron domains than do electron domains for single bonds.*

**GO FIGURE**

**Why is the volume occupied by the nonbonding electron pair domain larger than the volume occupied by the bonding domain?**

Bonding electron pair

Nuclei

Nonbonding pair

Nucleus

▲ **FIGURE 9.7** **Relative volumes occupied by bonding and nonbonding electron domains.**

 GIVE IT SOME THOUGHT

One resonance structure of the nitrate ion is

$$\left[ \begin{array}{c} :O: \\ \| \\ \overset{..}{\underset{..}{O}} \diagup N \diagdown \overset{..}{\underset{..}{O}} \end{array} \right]^{-}$$

The bond angles in this ion are 120°. Is this observation consistent with the preceding discussion of the effect of multiple bonds on bond angles?

## Molecules with Expanded Valence Shells

Atoms from period 3 and beyond may be surrounded by more than four electron pairs. ∞ (Section 8.7) Molecules with five or six electron domains around the central atom have molecular geometries based on either a *trigonal-bipyramidal* (five domains) or *octahedral* (six domains) electron-domain geometry (▶ TABLE 9.3).

The most stable electron-domain geometry for five electron domains is the trigonal bipyramid (two trigonal pyramids sharing a base). Unlike the other arrangements we have seen, the electron domains in a trigonal bipyramid can point toward two geometrically distinct types of positions. Two domains point toward *axial positions* and three point toward *equatorial positions* (▶ FIGURE 9.8). Each axial domain makes a 90° angle with any equatorial domain. Each equatorial domain makes a 120° angle with either of the other two equatorial domains and a 90° angle with either axial domain.

Suppose a molecule has five electron domains, and there are one or more nonbonding pairs. Will the domains from the nonbonding pairs occupy axial or equatorial positions? To answer this question, we must determine which location minimizes repulsion between domains. Repulsion between two domains is much greater when they are situated 90° from each other than when they are at 120°. An equatorial domain is 90° from only two other domains (the axial domains), but an axial domain is 90° from *three* other domains (the equatorial domains). Hence, an equatorial domain experiences less repulsion than an axial domain. Because the domains from nonbonding pairs exert larger repulsions than those from bonding pairs, nonbonding domains always occupy the equatorial positions in a trigonal bipyramid.

 GIVE IT SOME THOUGHT

It might seem that a square-planar geometry of four electron domains around a central atom would be more favorable than a tetrahedron. Can you rationalize why the tetrahedron is preferred, based on angles between electron domains?

**GO FIGURE**

**What is the bond angle formed by an axial atom, the central atom, and any equatorial atom?**

Axial position

Three equatorial positions form an equilateral triangle

Axial position

▲ **FIGURE 9.8** **In a trigonal-bipyramidal geometry, there are two types of positions for the outer atoms.**

**TABLE 9.3 • Electron-Domain and Molecular Geometries for Five and Six Electron Domains around a Central Atom**

| Number of Electron Domains | Electron-Domain Geometry | Bonding Domains | Nonbonding Domains | Molecular Geometry | Example |
|---|---|---|---|---|---|
| 5 | Trigonal bipyramidal | 5 | 0 | Trigonal bipyramidal | $PCl_5$ |
| | | 4 | 1 | Seesaw | $SF_4$ |
| | | 3 | 2 | T-shaped | $ClF_3$ |
| | | 2 | 3 | Linear | $XeF_2$ |
| 6 | Octahedral | 6 | 0 | Octahedral | $SF_6$ |
| | | 5 | 1 | Square pyramidal | $BrF_5$ |
| | | 4 | 2 | Square planar | $XeF_4$ |

The most stable electron-domain geometry for six electron domains is the *octahedron*. An octahedron is a polyhedron with six vertices and eight faces, each an equilateral triangle. An atom with six electron domains around it can be visualized as being at the center of the octahedron with the electron domains pointing toward the six vertices, as shown in Table 9.3. All the bond angles are 90°, and all six vertices are equivalent. Therefore, if an atom has five bonding electron domains and one nonbonding domain, we can put the nonbonding domain at any of the six vertices of the octahedron. The result is always a *square-pyramidal* molecular geometry. When there are two nonbonding electron domains, however, their repulsions are minimized by pointing them toward opposite sides of the octahedron, producing a *square-planar* molecular geometry, as shown in Table 9.3.

---

**SAMPLE EXERCISE 9.2**  **Molecular Geometries of Molecules with Expanded Valence Shells**

Use the VSEPR model to predict the molecular geometry of (**a**) $SF_4$, (**b**) $IF_5$.

**SOLUTION**

**Analyze**  The molecules are of the $AB_n$ type with a central *p*-block atom.

**Plan**  We first draw Lewis structures and then use the VSEPR model to determine the electron-domain geometry and molecular geometry.

**Solve**
(**a**) The Lewis structure for $SF_4$ is

The sulfur has five electron domains around it: four from the S—F bonds and one from the nonbonding pair. Each domain points toward a vertex of a trigonal bipyramid. The domain from the nonbonding pair will point toward an equatorial position. The four bonds point toward the remaining four positions, resulting in a molecular geometry that is described as seesaw-shaped:

**Comment**  The experimentally observed structure is shown on the right. We can infer that the nonbonding electron domain occupies an equatorial position, as predicted. The axial and equatorial S—F bonds are slightly bent away from the nonbonding domain, suggesting that the bonding domains are "pushed" by the nonbonding domain, which exerts a greater repulsion (Figure 9.7).

(**b**) The Lewis structure of $IF_5$ is

The iodine has six electron domains around it, one of which is nonbonding. The electron-domain geometry is therefore octahedral, with one position occupied by the nonbonding pair, and the molecular geometry is *square pyramidal* (Table 9.3):

**Comment**  Because the nonbonding domain is larger than the bonding domains, we predict that the four F atoms in the base of the pyramid will be tipped up slightly toward the top F atom. Experimentally, we find that the angle between the base atoms and top F atom is 82°, smaller than the ideal 90° angle of an octahedron.

**PRACTICE EXERCISE**

Predict the electron-domain and molecular geometries of (**a**) $BrF_3$, (**b**) $ICl_4^-$.
***Answers:*** (**a**) trigonal bipyramidal, T-shaped; (**b**) octahedral, square planar

⚠ **GO FIGURE**

**Although the electron-domain geometry around the right O is tetrahedral, the C—O—H bond is slightly less than 109.5°. Explain.**

Electron-domain geometry tetrahedral, molecular geometry tetrahedral

Electron-domain geometry trigonal planar, molecular geometry trigonal planar

Electron-domain geometry tetrahedral, molecular geometry bent

▲ **FIGURE 9.9** Acetic acid, $CH_3COOH$.

## Shapes of Larger Molecules

Although the molecules and ions we have considered contain only a single central atom, the VSEPR model can be extended to more complex molecules. For the acetic acid molecule, for example,

we can use the VSEPR model to predict the geometry about each atom:

| | $\begin{array}{c} H \\ | \\ H—C— \\ | \\ H \end{array}$ | $\begin{array}{c} :O: \\ || \\ —C— \end{array}$ | $\begin{array}{c} .. \\ —O—H \\ .. \end{array}$ |
|---|---|---|---|
| Number of electron domains | 4 | 3 | 4 |
| Electron-domain geometry | Tetrahedral | Trigonal planar | Tetrahedral |
| Predicted bond angles | 109.5° | 120° | 109.5° |

The left C has four electron domains (all bonding), and so the electron-domain and molecular geometries around that atom are both tetrahedral. The central C has three electron domains (counting the double bond as one domain), making both the electron-domain and the molecular geometries trigonal planar. The O on the right has four electron domains (two bonding, two nonbonding), so its electron-domain geometry is tetrahedral and its molecular geometry is bent. The bond angles about the central C atom and the O atom are expected to deviate slightly from the ideal values of 120° and 109.5° because of the spatial demands of multiple bonds and nonbonding electron pairs.

The structure of the acetic acid molecule is shown in ◄ **FIGURE 9.9.**

---

**SAMPLE EXERCISE 9.3** | **Predicting Bond Angles**

Eyedrops for dry eyes usually contain a water-soluble polymer called *poly(vinyl alcohol)*, which is based on the unstable organic molecule *vinyl alcohol*:

Predict the approximate values for the H—O—C and O—C—C bond angles in vinyl alcohol.

### SOLUTION

**Analyze** We are given a Lewis structure and asked to determine two bond angles.

**Plan** To predict a bond angle, we determine the number of electron domains surrounding the middle atom in the bond. The ideal angle corresponds to the electron-domain geometry around the atom. The angle will be compressed somewhat by nonbonding electrons or multiple bonds.

**Solve** In H—O—C, the O atom has four electron domains (two bonding, two nonbonding). The electron-domain geometry around O is therefore tetrahedral, which gives an ideal angle of 109.5°. The H—O—C angle is compressed somewhat by the nonbonding pairs, so we expect this angle to be slightly less than 109.5°.

To predict the O—C—C bond angle, we examine the middle atom in the angle. In the molecule, there are three atoms bonded to this C atom and no nonbonding pairs, and so it has three electron domains about it. The predicted electron-domain geometry is trigonal planar, resulting in an ideal bond angle of 120°. Because of the larger size of the C=C domain, the bond angle should be slightly greater than 120°.

**PRACTICE EXERCISE**

Predict the H—C—H and C—C—C bond angles in *propyne*:

$$H-\underset{\underset{H}{|}}{\overset{\overset{H}{|}}{C}}-C\equiv C-H$$

**Answers:** 109.5°, 180°

# 9.3 | MOLECULAR SHAPE AND MOLECULAR POLARITY

Recall that bond polarity is a measure of how equally the electrons in a bond are shared between the two atoms of the bond. As the difference in electronegativity between the two atoms increases, so does the bond polarity. ∞ (Section 8.4) We saw that the dipole moment of a diatomic molecule is a measure of the amount of charge separation in the molecule.

For a molecule consisting of more than two atoms, *the dipole moment depends on both the polarities of the individual bonds and the geometry of the molecule.* For each bond in the molecule, we consider the **bond dipole**, which is the dipole moment due only to the two atoms in that bond. Consider the linear $CO_2$ molecule, for example. As shown in ▶ **FIGURE 9.10**, each C=O bond is polar, and because the C=O bonds are identical, the bond dipoles are equal in magnitude. A plot of the molecule's electron density clearly shows that the individual bonds are polar, but what can we say about the *overall* dipole moment of the molecule?

Bond dipoles and dipole moments are vector quantities; that is, they have both a magnitude and a direction. The dipole moment of a polyatomic molecule is the vector sum of its bond dipoles. Both the magnitudes *and* the directions of the bond dipoles must be considered when summing vectors. The two bond dipoles in $CO_2$, although equal in magnitude, are opposite in direction. Adding them is the same as adding two numbers that are equal in magnitude but opposite in sign, such as $100 + (-100)$. The bond dipoles, like the numbers, "cancel" each other. Therefore, the dipole moment of $CO_2$ is zero, even though the individual bonds are polar. The geometry of the molecule dictates that the overall dipole moment be zero, making $CO_2$ a *nonpolar* molecule.

Now consider $H_2O$, a bent molecule with two polar bonds (▶ **FIGURE 9.11**). Again, the two bonds are identical, and the bond dipoles are equal in magnitude. Because the molecule is bent, however, the bond dipoles do not directly oppose each other and therefore do not cancel. Hence, the $H_2O$ molecule has an overall nonzero dipole moment ($\mu = 1.85$ D) and is therefore a *polar* molecule. The oxygen atom carries a partial negative charge, and the hydrogen atoms each have a partial positive charge, as shown in the electron-density model.

### GIVE IT SOME THOUGHT

The molecule O=C=S is linear and has a Lewis structure analogous to that of $CO_2$. Would you expect this molecule to have a dipole moment?

▶ **FIGURE 9.12** shows some polar and nonpolar molecules, all with polar bonds. The molecules in which the central atom is symmetrically surrounded by identical atoms ($BF_3$ and $CCl_4$) are nonpolar. For $AB_n$ molecules in which all the B atoms are the same, certain symmetrical shapes—linear ($AB_2$), trigonal planar ($AB_3$), tetrahedral and square planar ($AB_4$), trigonal bipyramidal ($AB_5$), and octahedral ($AB_6$)—must lead to nonpolar molecules even though the individual bonds might be polar.

**GO FIGURE**

Explain how the directions of the red bond dipole arrows relate to the electron density picture.

Equal and oppositely directed bond dipoles

**▲ FIGURE 9.10 $CO_2$, a nonpolar molecule.** The numbers are electronegativity values for these two atoms.

Bond dipoles

Overall dipole moment

**▲ FIGURE 9.11 $H_2O$, a polar molecule.** The numbers are electronegativity values.

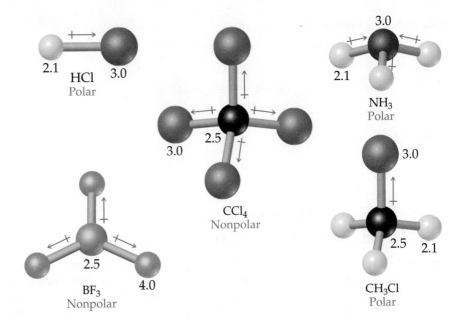

▶ **FIGURE 9.12 Polar and nonpolar molecules containing polar bonds.** The numbers are electronegativity values.

---

### SAMPLE EXERCISE 9.4 | Polarity of Molecules

Predict whether these molecules are polar or nonpolar: (a) BrCl, (b) SO$_2$, (c) SF$_6$.

#### SOLUTION

**Analyze** We are given three molecular formulas and asked to predict whether the molecules are polar.

**Plan** A molecule containing only two atoms is polar if the atoms differ in electronegativity. The polarity of a molecule containing three or more atoms depends on both the molecular geometry and the individual bond polarities. Thus, we must draw a Lewis structure for each molecule containing three or more atoms and determine its molecular geometry. We then use electronegativity values to determine the direction of the bond dipoles. Finally, we see whether the bond dipoles cancel to give a nonpolar molecule or reinforce each other to give a polar one.

**Solve**
(a) Chlorine is more electronegative than bromine. All diatomic molecules with polar bonds are polar molecules. Consequently, BrCl is polar, with chlorine carrying the partial negative charge:

$$\overset{\longmapsto}{\text{Br}-\text{Cl}}$$

The measured dipole moment of BrCl is $\mu = 0.57$ D.

(b) Because oxygen is more electronegative than sulfur, SO$_2$ has polar bonds. Three resonance forms can be written:

$$:\ddot{\text{O}}-\ddot{\text{S}}=\ddot{\text{O}}: \longleftrightarrow :\ddot{\text{O}}=\ddot{\text{S}}-\ddot{\text{O}}: \longleftrightarrow :\ddot{\text{O}}=\ddot{\text{S}}=\ddot{\text{O}}:$$

For each of these, the VSEPR model predicts a bent molecular geometry. Because the molecule is bent, the bond dipoles do not cancel, and the molecule is polar:

The measured dipole moment of SO$_2$ is $\mu = 1.63$ D.

(c) Fluorine is more electronegative than sulfur, so the bond dipoles point toward fluorine. For clarity, only one S—F dipole is shown. The six S—F bonds are arranged octahedrally around the central sulfur:

Because the octahedral molecular geometry is symmetrical, the bond dipoles cancel, and the molecule is nonpolar, meaning that $\mu = 0$.

**PRACTICE EXERCISE**
Determine whether the following molecules are polar or nonpolar: (**a**) $NF_3$, (**b**) $BCl_3$.
**Answers:** (**a**) polar because polar bonds are arranged in a trigonal-pyramidal geometry, (**b**) nonpolar because polar bonds are arranged in a trigonal-planar geometry

# 9.4 | COVALENT BONDING AND ORBITAL OVERLAP

The VSEPR model provides a simple means for predicting molecular geometries but does not explain why bonds exist between atoms. In developing theories of covalent bonding, chemists have approached the problem from another direction, using quantum mechanics. How can we use atomic orbitals to explain bonding and to account for molecular geometries? The marriage of Lewis's notion of electron-pair bonds and the idea of atomic orbitals leads to a model of chemical bonding, called **valence-bond theory**, in which bonding electron pairs are concentrated in the regions between atoms and nonbonding electron pairs lie in directed regions of space. By extending this approach to include the ways in which atomic orbitals can mix with one another, we obtain an explanatory picture that corresponds to the VSEPR model.

In Lewis theory, covalent bonding occurs when atoms share electrons because the sharing concentrates electron density between the nuclei. In valence-bond theory, we visualize the buildup of electron density between two nuclei as occurring when a valence atomic orbital of one atom shares space, or *overlaps*, with a valence atomic orbital of another atom. The overlap of orbitals allows two electrons of opposite spin to share the space between the nuclei, forming a covalent bond.

The coming together of two H atoms to form $H_2$ is depicted in ▶ **FIGURE 9.13**. Each atom has a single electron in a $1s$ orbital. As the orbitals overlap, electron density is concentrated between the nuclei. Because the electrons in the overlap region are simultaneously attracted to both nuclei, they hold the atoms together, forming a covalent bond.

The idea of orbital overlap producing a covalent bond applies equally well to other molecules. In HCl, for example, chlorine has the electron configuration $[Ne]3s^2 3p^5$. All the valence orbitals of chlorine are full except one $3p$ orbital, which contains a single electron. This $3p$ electron pairs with the single $1s$ electron of H to form a covalent bond (Figure 9.13). Because the other two chlorine $3p$ orbitals are already filled with a pair of electrons, they do not participate in the bonding to hydrogen. Likewise, we can explain the covalent bond in $Cl_2$ in terms of the overlap of the singly occupied $3p$ orbital of one Cl atom with the singly occupied $3p$ orbital of another.

There is always an optimum distance between the two nuclei in any covalent bond. ▶ **FIGURE 9.14** shows how the potential energy of a system consisting of two H atoms changes as the atoms come together to form an $H_2$ molecule. When the atoms are infinitely far apart, they do not "feel" each other and so the energy approaches zero. As the distance between the atoms decreases, the overlap between their $1s$ orbitals increases. Because of the resultant increase in electron density between the nuclei, the potential energy of the system decreases. That is, the strength of the bond increases, as shown by the decrease in the potential energy of the two-atom system. However, Figure 9.14 also shows that as the atoms come closer together than 0.74 Å, the energy increases sharply. This increase, which becomes significant at short internuclear distances, is due mainly to the electrostatic repulsion between the nuclei. The internuclear distance, or bond length, is the distance that corresponds to the minimum of the potential-energy curve. The potential energy at this minimum corresponds to the bond strength. Thus, the observed bond length is the distance at which the attractive forces between unlike charges (electrons and nuclei) are balanced by the repulsive forces between like charges (electron–electron and nucleus–nucleus).

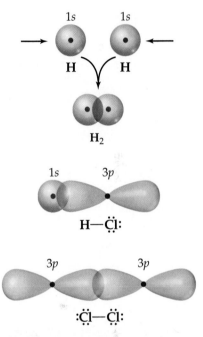

▲ **FIGURE 9.13  Covalent bonds in $H_2$, HCl, and $Cl_2$ result from overlap of atomic orbitals.**

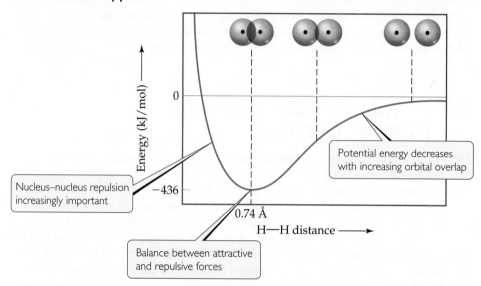

**On the left part of the curve the potential energy rises above zero. What causes this to happen?**

▲ **FIGURE 9.14** **Formation of the H₂ molecule as atomic orbitals overlap.**

# 9.5 | HYBRID ORBITALS

The VSEPR model, simple as it is, does a surprisingly good job at predicting molecular shape, despite the fact that it has no obvious relationship to the filling and shapes of atomic orbitals. For example, based on the shapes and orientations of the $2s$ and $2p$ orbitals on a carbon atom, it is not obvious why a $CH_4$ molecule should have a tetrahedral geometry. How can we reconcile the notion that covalent bonds are formed from overlap of atomic orbitals with the molecular geometries that come from the VSEPR model?

To begin with, we recall that atomic orbitals are mathematical functions that come from the quantum mechanical model for atomic structure. ∞ (Section 6.5) To explain molecular geometries, we can assume that the atomic orbitals on an atom (usually the central atom) mix to form new orbitals called **hybrid orbitals**. The shape of any hybrid orbital is different from the shapes of the original atomic orbitals. The process of mixing atomic orbitals is a mathematical operation called **hybridization**. The total number of atomic orbitals on an atom remains constant, so the number of hybrid orbitals on an atom equals the number of atomic orbitals that are mixed.

As we examine the common types of hybridization, notice the connection between the type of hybridization and certain of the molecular geometries predicted by the VSEPR model: linear, bent, trigonal planar, and tetrahedral.

## *sp* Hybrid Orbitals

To illustrate the process of hybridization, consider the $BeF_2$ molecule, which has the Lewis structure

$$:\ddot{F}—Be—\ddot{F}:$$

The VSEPR model correctly predicts that $BeF_2$ is linear with two identical Be—F bonds. How can we use valence-bond theory to describe the bonding? The electron configuration of F $(1s^2 2s^2 2p^5)$ indicates an unpaired electron in a $2p$ orbital. This electron can be paired with an unpaired Be electron to form a polar covalent bond. Which orbitals on the Be atom, however, overlap with those on the F atoms to form the Be—F bonds?

The orbital diagram for a ground-state Be atom is

Because it has no unpaired electrons, the Be atom in its ground state cannot bond with the fluorine atoms. The Be atom could form two bonds, however, by "promoting" one of the 2s electrons to a 2p orbital:

The Be atom now has two unpaired electrons and can therefore form two polar covalent bonds with F atoms. The two bonds would not be identical, however, because a Be 2s orbital would be used to form one of the bonds and a 2p orbital would be used to form the other. Therefore, although the promotion of an electron allows two Be — F bonds to form, we still have not explained the structure of BeF₂.

We can solve this dilemma by "mixing" the 2s orbital with one 2p orbital to generate two new orbitals, as shown in ▼ **FIGURE 9.15**. Like p orbitals, each new orbital has two lobes. Unlike p orbitals, however, one lobe is much larger than the other. The two new orbitals are identical in shape, but their large lobes point in opposite directions. These two new orbitals, which we color-code purple in Figure 9.15, are hybrid orbitals. Because we have hybridized one s and one p orbital, we call each hybrid an sp hybrid orbital. *According to the valence-bond model, a linear arrangement of electron domains implies sp hybridization.*

One s atomic orbital    One p atomic orbital      Two sp hybrid orbitals    sp hybrid orbitals shown together (large lobes only)

▲ FIGURE 9.15  **Formation of *sp* hybrid orbitals.**

For the Be atom of BeF₂, we write the orbital diagram for the formation of two sp hybrid orbitals as

The electrons in the sp hybrid orbitals can form bonds with the two fluorine atoms (▼ **FIGURE 9.16**). Because the sp hybrid orbitals are equivalent but point in opposite

GO FIGURE

**Why is it reasonable to take account of only the large lobes of the Be hybrid orbitals in considering the bonding to F?**

Large lobes from two Be *sp* hybrid orbitals

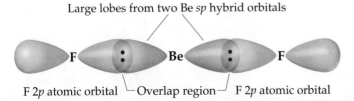

F 2p atomic orbital   Overlap region   F 2p atomic orbital

◄ FIGURE 9.16  **Formation of two equivalent Be — F bonds in BeF₂.**

directions, $BeF_2$ has two identical bonds and a linear geometry. The remaining two $2p$ atomic orbitals of Be remain unhybridized and are vacant. Remember also that each fluorine atom has two other valence $p$ atomic orbitals, each containing one nonbonding electron pair. Those atomic orbitals are omitted from Figure 9.16 to keep the illustration simpler.

  **GIVE IT SOME THOUGHT**

What is the orientation of the two unhybridized $p$ orbitals on Be with respect to the two Be—F bonds?

## $sp^2$ and $sp^3$ Hybrid Orbitals

Whenever we mix a certain number of atomic orbitals, we get the same number of hybrid orbitals. Each hybrid orbital is equivalent to the others but points in a different direction. Thus, mixing one $2s$ and one $2p$ atomic orbital yields two equivalent $sp$ hybrid orbitals that point in opposite directions (Figure 9.15). Other combinations of atomic orbitals can be hybridized to obtain different geometries. In $BF_3$, for example, mixing the $2s$ and two of the $2p$ atomic orbitals yields three equivalent $sp^2$ (pronounced "s-p-two") hybrid orbitals (▼ **FIGURE 9.17**).

The three $sp^2$ hybrid orbitals lie in the same plane, 120° apart from one another. They are used to make three equivalent bonds with the three fluorine atoms, leading to the trigonal-planar molecular geometry of $BF_3$. Notice that an unfilled $2p$ atomic orbital remains unhybridized. This unhybridized orbital will be important when we discuss double bonds in Section 9.6.

  **GIVE IT SOME THOUGHT**

In an $sp^2$ hybridized atom, what is the orientation of the unhybridized $p$ atomic orbital relative to the three $sp^2$ hybrid orbitals?

An $s$ atomic orbital can also mix with all three $p$ atomic orbitals in the same subshell. For example, the carbon atom in $CH_4$ forms four equivalent bonds with the four

 **GO FIGURE.**

**How many atomic orbitals contribute to form the three $sp^2$ hybrid orbitals?**

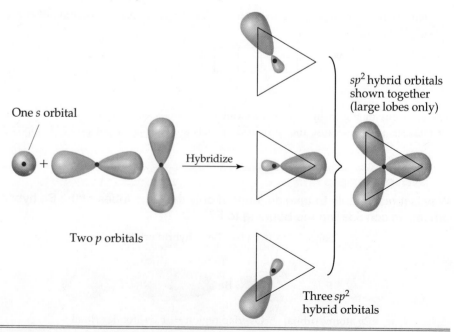

One $s$ orbital

Two $p$ orbitals

Hybridize

$sp^2$ hybrid orbitals shown together (large lobes only)

Three $sp^2$ hybrid orbitals

▶ **FIGURE 9.17  Formation of $sp^2$ hybrid orbitals.**

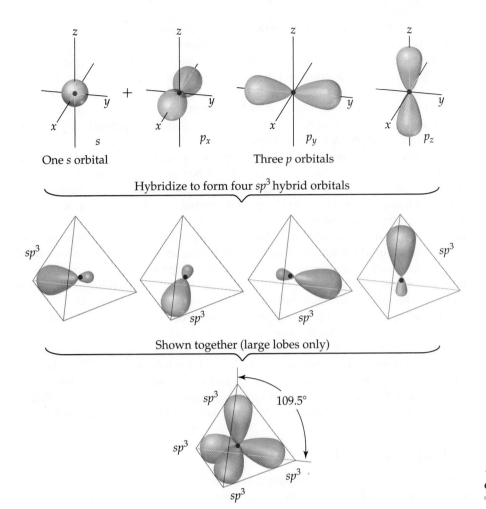

◀ **FIGURE 9.18** **Formation of *sp*³ hybrid orbitals.**

hydrogen atoms. We envision this process as resulting from the mixing of the 2*s* and all three 2*p* atomic orbitals of carbon to create four equivalent *sp*³ (pronounced "*s-p-three*") hybrid orbitals. Each *sp*³ hybrid orbital has a large lobe that points toward one vertex of a tetrahedron (▲ **FIGURE 9.18**). These hybrid orbitals can be used to form two-electron bonds by overlap with the atomic orbitals of another atom, such as H. Using valence-bond theory, we can describe the bonding in $CH_4$ as the overlap of four equivalent *sp*³ hybrid orbitals on C with the 1*s* orbitals of the four H atoms to form four equivalent bonds.

The idea of hybridization is also used to describe the bonding in molecules containing nonbonding pairs of electrons. In $H_2O$, for example, the electron-domain geometry around the central O atom is approximately tetrahedral (▶ **FIGURE 9.19**). Thus, the four electron pairs can be envisioned as occupying *sp*³ hybrid orbitals. Two of the hybrid orbitals contain nonbonding pairs of electrons, and the other two form bonds with the hydrogen atoms.

So far our discussion of hybridization has extended only to period 2 elements, specifically carbon, nitrogen, and oxygen. The elements of period 3 and beyond introduce a new consideration because in many of their compounds these elements have more than an octet of electrons in the valence shell, as we saw in Section 9.2. How do we analyze the bonding in compounds such as $PCl_5$, $SF_6$, or $BrF_5$? The use of only *s* and *p* orbitals on the central atom limits us to four hybrid orbitals, yet in these compounds the central atom is involved in bonding to five or six other atoms.

For such elements, the number of hybrid orbitals formed could be increased by including valence-shell *d* orbitals. For example, to explain the bonding in $SF_6$ we could include two sulfur 3*d* orbitals

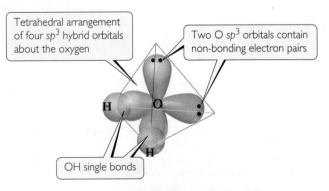

Tetrahedral arrangement of four *sp*³ hybrid orbitals about the oxygen

Two O *sp*³ orbitals contain non-bonding electron pairs

OH single bonds

▲ **FIGURE 9.19** **Hybrid orbital description of $H_2O$.**

in addition to the *3s* and three *3p* orbitals. These six atomic orbitals could make six hybrid orbitals, but there is more involved in hybridization than simply finding a set of orbitals that point in the right directions; we must also consider orbital energies. The sulfur *3d* orbitals lie substantially higher in energy than the *3s* and *3p* orbitals. The amount of energy needed to form the six hybrid orbitals is greater than the amount returned by forming bonds with the six fluorine atoms. Theoretical calculations seem to show that the sulfur *3d* orbitals do not participate to a significant degree in the bonding between sulfur and the six fluorine atoms.

The valence-bond model we have developed for period 2 elements works well for compounds of period 3 elements so long as we have no more than an octet of electrons in the valence-shell orbitals. Thus, for example, it is appropriate to discuss the bonding in $PF_3$ or $H_2Se$ in terms of hybrid *s* and *p* orbitals on the central atom. However, the model turns out not to be appropriate when there is more than an octet of electrons about the central atom. How then do we account for the bonding in $SF_6$ and other compounds of the main group elements in which the central atom has more than an octet of valence electrons? To address that question from the viewpoint of bonding theory requires a treatment beyond the scope of a general chemistry text. Fortunately, the VSEPR model, although it does not explain the bonding in such molecules, can accurately predict their geometries.

This discussion points up the important fact that models in science are not reality but rather are our attempts to describe aspects of reality that we have been able to measure, such as bond distances, bond energies, molecular geometries, and so on. A model may work well up to a certain point but not beyond it, as with the idea of hybrid orbitals. The hybrid orbital model for period 2 elements has proven very useful and is an essential part of any modern discussion of bonding and molecular geometry in organic chemistry. When it comes to substances such as $SF_6$, however, we encounter the limitations of the model.

## Hybrid Orbital Summary

Overall, hybrid orbitals provide a convenient model for using valence-bond theory to describe covalent bonds in molecules in which the molecular geometry conforms to the electron-domain geometry predicted by the VSEPR model. The picture of hybrid orbitals has limited predictive value. When we know the electron-domain geometry, however, we can employ hybridization to describe the atomic orbitals used by the central atom in bonding.

The following steps allow us to describe the hybrid orbitals used by an atom in bonding:

1. Draw the *Lewis structure* for the molecule or ion.

2. Use the VSEPR model to determine the electron-domain geometry around the central atom.

3. Specify the *hybrid orbitals* needed to accommodate the electron pairs based on their geometric arrangement (▶ TABLE 9.4).

These steps are illustrated in ▼ FIGURE 9.20, which shows how the hybridization at N in $NH_3$ is determined.

▶ FIGURE 9.20 **Hybrid orbital description of bonding in NH₃.** Note the comparison with Figure 9.6. Here we focus on the hybrid orbitals used to make bonds and hold nonbonding electron pairs.

1. Draw Lewis structure

2. Determine electron-domain geometry about central atom from VSEPR model and Table 9.1

3. Using Table 9.4, select $sp^3$ hybrid orbital set

**TABLE 9.4** • **Geometric Arrangements Characteristic of Hybrid Orbital Sets**

| Atomic Orbital Set | Hybrid Orbital Set | Geometry | Examples |
|---|---|---|---|
| $s,p$ | Two $sp$ | Linear — 180° | $BeF_2$, $HgCl_2$ |
| $s,p,p$ | Three $sp^2$ | Trigonal planar — 120° | $BF_3$, $SO_3$ |
| $s,p,p,p$ | Four $sp^3$ | Tetrahedral — 109.5° | $CH_4$, $NH_3$, $H_2O$, $NH_4^+$ |

---

**SAMPLE EXERCISE 9.5**   **Hybridization**

Indicate the orbital hybridization around the central atom in $NH_2^-$.

**SOLUTION**

**Analyze**  We are given the chemical formula for a polyatomic anion and asked to describe the type of hybrid orbitals surrounding the central atom.

**Plan**  To determine the central atom hybrid orbitals, we must know the electron-domain geometry around the atom. Thus, we draw the Lewis structure to determine the number of electron domains around the central atom. The hybridization conforms to the number and geometry of electron domains around the central atom as predicted by the VSEPR model.

**Solve**  The Lewis structure is

$$\left[ H \!:\! \ddot{N} \!:\! H \right]^-$$

Because there are four electron domains around N, the electron-domain geometry is tetrahedral. The hybridization that gives a tetrahedral electron-domain geometry is $sp^3$ (Table 9.4). Two of the $sp^3$ hybrid orbitals contain nonbonding pairs of electrons, and the other two are used to make bonds with the hydrogen atoms.

**PRACTICE EXERCISE**

Predict the electron-domain geometry and hybridization of the central atom in $SO_3^{2-}$.

**Answer:**  tetrahedral, $sp^3$

---

# 9.6 | MULTIPLE BONDS

In the covalent bonds we have considered thus far, the electron density is concentrated along the line connecting the nuclei (the *internuclear axis*). In other words, the line joining the two nuclei passes through the middle of the overlap region. These bonds are called **sigma ($\sigma$) bonds**. The overlap of two $s$ orbitals in $H_2$, the overlap of an $s$ and a $p$

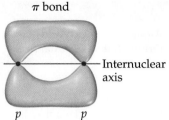

σ bond

π bond

Internuclear axis

Internuclear axis

*p* *p*

*p* *p*

► **FIGURE 9.21 Comparison of σ and π bonds.** Note that the two regions of overlap in the π bond, above and below the internuclear axis, constitute a *single* π bond.

orbital in HCl, the overlap of two *p* orbitals in Cl₂ (all shown in Figure 9.13), and the overlap of a *p* orbital and an *sp* hybrid orbital in BeF₂ (Figure 9.16) are all σ bonds.

To describe multiple bonding, we must consider a second kind of bond, this one the result of overlap between two *p* orbitals oriented perpendicularly to the internuclear axis (▲ **FIGURE 9.21**). This sideways overlap of *p* orbitals produces a **pi (π) bond**. A π bond is one in which the overlap regions lie above and below the internuclear axis. Unlike in a σ bond, in a π bond the electron density is not concentrated on the internuclear axis. Although it is not evident in Figure 9.21, the sideways orientation of *p* orbitals in a π bond makes for weaker overlap. As a result, π bonds are generally weaker than σ bonds.

In almost all cases, single bonds are σ bonds. A double bond consists of one σ bond and one π bond, and a triple bond consists of one σ bond and two π bonds:

H—H

One σ bond

One σ bond plus one π bond

:N≡N:

One σ bond plus two π bonds

▲ **FIGURE 9.22 Trigonal-planar molecular geometry of ethylene.** The double bond is made up of one C—C σ bond and one C—C π bond.

To see how these ideas are used, consider ethylene (C₂H₄), which has a C=C double bond. As illustrated by the ball-and-stick model of ◄ **FIGURE 9.22**, the three bond angles about each carbon are all approximately 120°, suggesting that each carbon atom uses *sp*² hybrid orbitals (Figure 9.17) to form σ bonds with the other carbon and with two hydrogens. Because carbon has four valence electrons, after *sp*² hybridization one electron in each carbon remains in the unhybridized 2*p* orbital, which is directed perpendicular to the plane that contains the three *sp*² hybrid orbitals.

Each *sp*² hybrid orbital on a carbon atom contains one electron. ► **FIGURE 9.23** shows how the C—H σ bonds are formed by overlap of *sp*² hybrid orbitals on C with the 1*s* orbitals on each H atom. We use eight electrons to form these four C—H bonds. The C—C σ bond is formed by the overlap of two *sp*² hybrid orbitals, one on each carbon atom, and requires two more electrons. Thus, ten of the 12 valence electrons in the C₂H₄ molecule are used to form five σ bonds.

The remaining two valence electrons reside in the unhybridized 2*p* orbitals, one electron on each carbon. These two orbitals can overlap sideways with each other, as shown in Figure 9.23. The resultant electron density is concentrated above and below the C—C bond axis, which means this is a π bond (Figure 9.21). Thus, the C=C double bond in ethylene consists of one σ bond and one π bond. You should note one point about the carbon *p* orbitals that form the π bond. It appears from Figure 9.21 that the *p* orbitals on the two carbons don't overlap sufficiently to form a π bond. The problem is that we can't show the true extent of overlap in the drawing without obscuring other aspects of the figure. Although π bonding of the *p* orbitals does occur, as pointed out earlier, π bonds are generally weaker than σ bonds.

Although we cannot experimentally observe a π bond directly (all we can observe are the positions of the atoms), the structure of ethylene provides strong support for its presence. First, the C—C bond length in ethylene (1.34 Å) is much shorter than in compounds with C—C single bonds (1.54 Å), consistent with the presence of a stronger C=C double bond. Second, all six atoms in C₂H₄ lie in the same plane. The 2*p* orbitals that make up the π bond can achieve a good overlap only when the two CH₂

⚠ **GO FIGURE**

Why is it important that the *sp²* hybrid orbitals of the two carbon atoms lie in the same plane?

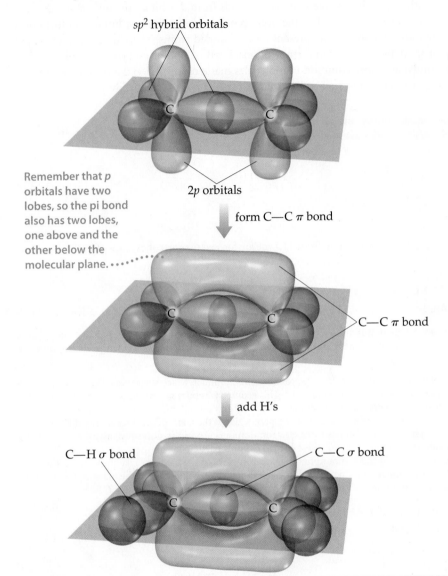

Remember that *p* orbitals have two lobes, so the pi bond also has two lobes, one above and the other below the molecular plane. ⋯⋯

◀ **FIGURE 9.23**   **The orbital structure of ethylene.**

fragments lie in the same plane. If the $\pi$ bond were absent, there would be no reason for the two $CH_2$ fragments to lie in the same plane. Because $\pi$ bonds require that portions of a molecule be planar, they can introduce rigidity into molecules.

⚠ **GIVE IT SOME THOUGHT**

The molecule called *diazine* has the formula $N_2H_2$ and the Lewis structure

$$\text{H}-\ddot{\text{N}}=\ddot{\text{N}}-\text{H}$$

Do you expect diazine to be a linear molecule (all four atoms on the same line)? If not, do you expect the molecule to be planar (all four atoms in the same plane)?

Triple bonds can also be explained using hybrid orbitals. Acetylene ($C_2H_2$), for example, is a linear molecule containing a triple bond: $H-C\equiv C-H$. The linear geometry suggests that each carbon atom uses *sp* hybrid orbitals to form $\sigma$ bonds with the other

▲ GO FIGURE

Based on the models of bonding in ethylene and acetylene, which molecule should have the higher carbon–carbon bond energy?

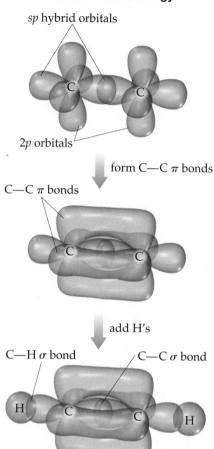

*sp* hybrid orbitals

2*p* orbitals

form C—C π bonds

C—C π bonds

add H's

C—H σ bond          C—C σ bond

H                         H

▲ **FIGURE 9.24** Formation of two π bonds in acetylene, C$_2$H$_2$.

carbon and one hydrogen. Each carbon atom thus has two unhybridized 2*p* orbitals at right angles to each other and to the axis of the *sp* hybrid set (◄ FIGURE 9.24). These *p* orbitals overlap to form a pair of π bonds. Thus, the triple bond in acetylene consists of one σ bond and two π bonds.

Although it is possible to make π bonds from *d* orbitals, the only π bonds we will consider are those formed by the overlap of *p* orbitals. These π bonds can form only if unhybridized *p* orbitals are present on the bonded atoms. Therefore, only atoms having *sp* or *sp*$^2$ hybridization can form π bonds. Further, double and triple bonds (and hence π bonds) are more common in molecules made up of period 2 atoms, especially C, N, and O. Larger atoms, such as S, P, and Si, form π bonds less readily.

---

**SAMPLE EXERCISE 9.6**   **Describing σ and π Bonds in a Molecule**

Formaldehyde has the Lewis structure

$$\begin{array}{c} H \\ \backslash \\ C=\ddot{O}: \\ / \\ H \end{array}$$

Describe how the bonds in formaldehyde are formed in terms of overlaps of hybrid and unhybridized orbitals.

**SOLUTION**

**Analyze**  We are asked to describe the bonding in formaldehyde in terms of hybrid orbitals.

**Plan**  Single bonds are σ bonds, and double bonds consist of one σ bond and one π bond. The ways in which these bonds form can be deduced from the molecular geometry, which we predict using the VSEPR model.

**Solve**  The C atom has three electron domains around it, which suggests a trigonal-planar geometry with bond angles of about 120°. This geometry implies *sp*$^2$ hybrid orbitals on C (Table 9.4). These hybrids are used to make the two C—H and one C—O σ bonds to C. There remains an unhybridized 2*p* orbital on carbon, perpendicular to the plane of the three *sp*$^2$ hybrids.

The O atom also has three electron domains around it, and so we assume it has *sp*$^2$ hybridization as well. One of these hybrid orbitals participates in the C—O σ bond, while the other two hold the two nonbonding electron pairs of the O atom. Like the C atom, therefore, the O atom has an unhybridized 2*p* orbital that is perpendicular to the plane of the molecule. These two orbitals overlap to form a C—O π bond (▼ FIGURE 9.25).

**PRACTICE EXERCISE**

**(a)** Predict the bond angles around each carbon atom in acetonitrile:

$$\begin{array}{c} H \\ | \\ H-C-C\equiv N: \\ | \\ H \end{array}$$

**(b)** Describe the hybridization at each carbon atom, and **(c)** determine the number of σ and π bonds in the molecule.

***Answers:***  **(a)** approximately 109° around the left C and 180° around the right C; **(b)** *sp*$^3$, *sp*; **(c)** five σ bonds and two π bonds

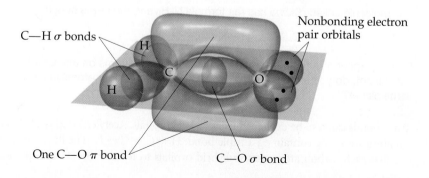

C—H σ bonds

Nonbonding electron pair orbitals

H

H

One C—O π bond          C—O σ bond

▶ **FIGURE 9.25**  Formation of σ and π bonds in formaldehyde, H$_2$CO.

# Resonance Structures, Delocalization, and $\pi$ Bonding

In the molecules we have discussed thus far in this section, the bonding electrons are *localized*. By this we mean that the $\sigma$ and $\pi$ electrons are associated totally with the two atoms that form the bond. In many molecules, however, we cannot adequately describe the bonding as being entirely localized. This situation arises particularly in molecules that have two or more resonance structures involving $\pi$ bonds.

One molecule that cannot be described with localized $\pi$ bonds is benzene ($C_6H_6$), which has two resonance structures: ∞ (Section 8.6)

To describe the bonding in benzene using hybrid orbitals, we first choose a hybridization scheme consistent with the geometry of the molecule. Because each carbon is surrounded by three atoms at 120° angles, the appropriate hybrid set is $sp^2$. Six localized C—C $\sigma$ bonds and six localized C—H $\sigma$ bonds are formed from the $sp^2$ hybrid orbitals, as shown in ▼ FIGURE 9.26(a). This leaves on each carbon a $2p$ orbital oriented perpendicular to the plane of the molecule. The situation is very much like that in ethylene except we now have six carbon $2p$ orbitals arranged in a ring [Figure 9.26(b)]. Each unhybridized $2p$ orbital is occupied by one electron, leaving six electrons to be accounted for by $\pi$ bonding.

▲ GO FIGURE

**What are the two kinds of $\sigma$ bonds found in benzene?**

(a) $\sigma$ bonds

(b) $2p$ atomic orbitals

◀ **FIGURE 9.26   $\sigma$ and $\pi$ bond networks in benzene, $C_6H_6$.** (a) The $\sigma$ bond framework. (b) The $\pi$ bonds are formed from overlap of the unhybridized $2p$ orbitals on the six carbon atoms.

We could envision using the unhybridized $2p$ orbitals to form three localized $\pi$ bonds. As shown in ▼ FIGURE 9.27, there are two equivalent ways to make these localized bonds, each corresponding to one resonance structure. However, a representation that reflects *both* resonance structures has the six $\pi$ electrons "smeared out" among all six carbon atoms, as shown on the right in Figure 9.27. Notice how this combined representation corresponds to the circle-in-a-hexagon drawing we often use to represent benzene. This model leads us to predict that all the carbon–carbon bond lengths will be identical, with a bond length between that of a C—C single bond (1.54 Å) and that of a C=C double bond (1.34 Å). This prediction is consistent with the observed carbon–carbon bond length in benzene (1.40 Å).

Localized $\pi$ bond                                    Delocalized $\pi$ bond

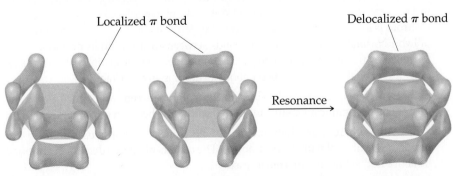

Resonance

◀ **FIGURE 9.27   Delocalized $\pi$ bonds in benzene.**

Because we cannot describe the $\pi$ bonds in benzene as individual bonds between neighboring atoms, we say that the $\pi$ bonds are **delocalized** among the six carbon atoms. Delocalization of the electrons in its $\pi$ bonds gives benzene a special stability. Delocalization of $\pi$ bonds is also responsible for the color of many organic molecules. A final important point to remember about delocalized $\pi$ bonds is the constraint they place on the geometry of a molecule. For optimal overlap of the unhybridized $p$ orbitals, all the atoms involved in a delocalized $\pi$ bonding network should lie in the same plane. This restriction imparts a certain rigidity to the molecule that is absent in molecules containing only $\sigma$ bonds (see the "Chemistry and Life" box on vision).

If you take a course in organic chemistry, you will see many examples of how electron delocalization influences the properties of organic molecules.

---

**SAMPLE EXERCISE 9.7** Delocalized Bonding

Describe the bonding in the nitrate ion, $NO_3^-$. Does this ion have delocalized $\pi$ bonds?

**SOLUTION**

**Analyze** Given the chemical formula for a polyatomic anion, we are asked to describe the bonding and determine whether the ion has delocalized $\pi$ bonds.

**Plan** Our first step is to draw Lewis structures. Multiple resonance structures involving the placement of the double bonds in different locations suggest that the $\pi$ component of the double bonds is delocalized.

**Solve** In Section 8.6 we saw that $NO_3^-$ has three resonance structures:

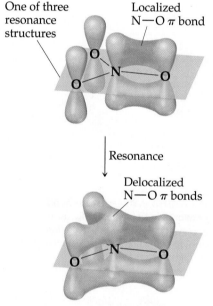

In each structure, the electron-domain geometry at nitrogen is trigonal planar, which implies $sp^2$ hybridization of the N atom. The $sp^2$ hybrid orbitals are used to construct the three N—O $\sigma$ bonds present in each resonance structure.

The unhybridized $2p$ orbital on the N atom can be used to make $\pi$ bonds. For any one of the three resonance structures shown, we might imagine a single localized N—O $\pi$ bond formed by the overlap of the unhybridized $2p$ orbital on N and a $2p$ orbital on one of the O atoms, as shown in ◀ **FIGURE 9.28**. Because each resonance structure contributes equally to the observed structure of $NO_3^-$, however, we represent the $\pi$ bonding as delocalized over the three N—O bonds, as shown in the figure.

**PRACTICE EXERCISE**

Which of these species have delocalized bonding: $SO_3$, $SO_3^{2-}$, $H_2CO$, $O_3$, $NH_4^+$?

**Answer:** $SO_3$ and $O_3$, as indicated by the presence of two or more resonance structures involving $\pi$ bonding for each of these molecules

---

One of three resonance structures

Localized N—O $\pi$ bond

Resonance

Delocalized N—O $\pi$ bonds

▲ **FIGURE 9.28 Localized and delocalized $\pi$ bonds in $NO_3^-$.**

---

## General Conclusions

On the basis of the examples we have seen, we can draw a few helpful conclusions for using hybrid orbitals to describe molecular structures:

1. Every pair of bonded atoms shares one or more pairs of electrons. The lines we draw in Lewis structures represent two electrons each. In every bond at least one pair of electrons is localized in the space between the atoms in a $\sigma$ bond. The appropriate set of hybrid orbitals used to form the $\sigma$ bonds between an atom and its neighbors is determined by the observed geometry of the molecule. The correlation between the set of hybrid orbitals and the geometry about an atom is given in Table 9.4.

2. The electrons in $\sigma$ bonds are localized in the region between two bonded atoms and do not make a significant contribution to the bonding between any other two atoms.

3. When atoms share more than one pair of electrons, one pair is used to form a $\sigma$ bond; the additional pairs form $\pi$ bonds. The centers of charge density in a $\pi$ bond lie above and below the internuclear axis.

4. Molecules with two or more resonance structures can have $\pi$ bonds that extend over more than two bonded atoms. Electrons in $\pi$ bonds that extend over more than two atoms are said to be "delocalized."

# CHEMISTRY AND LIFE

## THE CHEMISTRY OF VISION

Vision begins when light is focused by the lens of the eye onto the retina, the layer of cells lining the interior of the eyeball. The retina contains *photoreceptor* cells called rods and cones (▼ FIGURE 9.29). The rods are sensitive to dim light and are used in night vision. The cones are sensitive to colors. The tops of the rods and cones contain a molecule called *rhodopsin*, which consists of a protein, *opsin*, bonded to a reddish purple pigment called *retinal*. Structural changes around a double bond in the retinal portion of the molecule trigger a series of chemical reactions that result in vision.

We know that a double bond between two atoms is stronger than a single bond between the same atom, but our recent discussions allow us to appreciate another aspect of double bonds: the rigidity they introduce into molecules.

Imagine rotating one —CH₂ group in ethylene relative to the other —CH₂ group, as in ▶ FIGURE 9.30. This rotation destroys the overlap of $p$ orbitals, breaking the $\pi$ bond, a process that requires

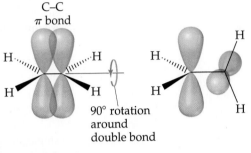

▲ **FIGURE 9.30   Rotation about the carbon–carbon double bond in ethylene breaks the $\pi$ bond.**

considerable energy. Thus, the presence of a double bond restricts bond rotation in a molecule. In contrast, molecules can rotate almost freely around the bond axis in single ($\sigma$) bonds because this motion has no effect on the orbital overlap for a $\sigma$ bond. This rotation allows molecules with single bonds to twist and fold almost as if their atoms were attached by hinges.

Our vision depends on the rigidity of double bonds in retinal. In its normal form, retinal is held rigid by its double bonds. Light entering the eye is absorbed by rhodopsin, and the energy is used to break the $\pi$-bond portion of the double bond shown in red in ▼ FIGURE 9.31. The molecule then rotates around this bond, changing its geometry. The retinal then separates from the opsin, triggering the reactions that produce a nerve impulse that the brain interprets as the sensation of vision. It takes as few as five closely spaced molecules reacting in this fashion to produce the sensation of vision. Thus, only five photons of light are necessary to stimulate the eye.

The retinal slowly reverts to its original form and reattaches to the opsin. The slowness of this process helps explain why intense bright light causes temporary blindness. The light causes all the retinal to separate from opsin, leaving no molecules to absorb light.

*RELATED EXERCISES:* 9.108 and 9.112

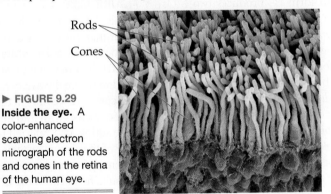

Rods
Cones

▶ **FIGURE 9.29**
**Inside the eye.** A color-enhanced scanning electron micrograph of the rods and cones in the retina of the human eye.

180° rotation about this bond when light absorbed

Retinal

▲ **FIGURE 9.31   The rhodopsin molecule, the chemical basis of vision.** When rhodopsin absorbs visible light, the $\pi$ component of the double bond shown in red breaks, allowing rotation that produces a change in molecular geometry before the $\pi$ bond re-forms.

⚠ GIVE IT SOME THOUGHT

When two atoms are bonded by a triple bond, what is the hybridization of the orbitals that make up the $\sigma$-bond component of the bond?

# 9.7 | MOLECULAR ORBITALS

Valence-bond theory and hybrid orbitals allow us to move in a straightforward way from Lewis structures to rationalizing the observed geometries of molecules in terms of atomic orbitals. The valence-bond model, however, does not explain all aspects of bonding. It is not successful, for example, in describing the excited states of molecules, which we must understand to explain how molecules absorb light, giving them color.

Some aspects of bonding are better explained by a more sophisticated model called **molecular orbital theory**. In Chapter 6 we saw that electrons in atoms can be described by wave functions, which we call atomic orbitals. In a similar way, molecular orbital theory describes the electrons in molecules by using specific wave functions called **molecular orbitals (MO)**.

Molecular orbitals have many of the same characteristics as atomic orbitals. For example, an MO can hold a maximum of two electrons (with opposite spins), it has a definite energy, and we can visualize its electron-density distribution by using a contour representation, as we did with atomic orbitals. Unlike atomic orbitals, however, MOs are associated with an entire molecule, not with a single atom.

## The Hydrogen Molecule

We begin our study of MO theory with the hydrogen molecule, $H_2$. *Whenever two atomic orbitals overlap, two molecular orbitals form.* Thus, the overlap of the $1s$ orbitals of two hydrogen atoms to form $H_2$ produces two MOs (▼ FIGURE 9.32). One MO is formed by adding the wave functions for the two $1s$ orbitals. We refer to this as *constructive combination*. The energy of the resulting MO is lower than the energy of the two atomic orbitals from which it was made. It is called the **bonding molecular orbital**.

The other MO is formed by combining the two atomic orbitals in a way that causes the electron density to be more or less canceled in the central region where the two overlap. We refer to this as *destructive combination*. The process is discussed more fully in the "Closer Look" box later in the chapter; we don't need to concern ourselves with it to understand molecular orbital bond formation. The energy of the resulting MO, referred to as the **antibonding molecular orbital**, is higher than the energy of the atomic orbitals.

As illustrated in Figure 9.32, in the bonding MO electron density is concentrated in the region between the two nuclei. This sausage-shaped MO results from summing the

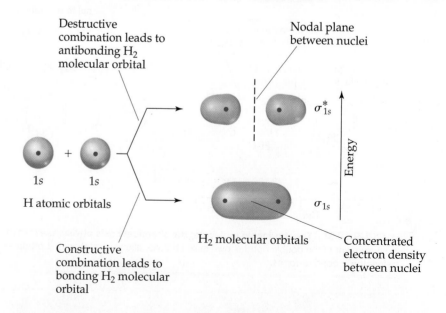

▶ FIGURE 9.32 **The two molecular orbitals of $H_2$, one a bonding MO and one an antibonding MO.**

Destructive combination leads to antibonding $H_2$ molecular orbital

Nodal plane between nuclei

$1s$        $1s$

H atomic orbitals

$\sigma_{1s}^{*}$

Energy

Constructive combination leads to bonding $H_2$ molecular orbital

$H_2$ molecular orbitals

$\sigma_{1s}$

Concentrated electron density between nuclei

two atomic orbitals so that the atomic orbital wave functions combine in the region between the two nuclei. Because an electron in this MO is attracted to both nuclei, the electron is more stable (it has lower energy) than it is in the $1s$ atomic orbital of an isolated hydrogen atom. Further, because this bonding MO concentrates electron density between the nuclei, it holds the atoms together in a covalent bond.

By contrast, the antibonding MO has very little electron density between the nuclei. Instead of combining in the region between the nuclei, the atomic orbital wave functions cancel each other in this region, leaving the greatest electron density on opposite sides of the two nuclei. Thus, this MO excludes electrons from the very region in which a bond must be formed. Antibonding orbitals invariably have a nodal plane in the region between the nuclei, where the electron density is zero. (The nodal plane is shown as a dashed line in Figure 9.32 and subsequent figures.) An electron in an antibonding MO is repelled from the bonding region and is therefore less stable (it has higher energy) than it is in the $1s$ atomic orbital of a hydrogen atom.

Notice from Figure 9.32 that the electron density in both the bonding MO and the antibonding MO of $H_2$ is centered about the internuclear axis. MOs of this type are called **sigma ($\sigma$) molecular orbitals** (by analogy to $\sigma$ bonds). The bonding sigma MO of $H_2$ is labeled $\sigma_{1s}$; the subscript indicates that the MO is formed from two $1s$ orbitals. The antibonding sigma MO of $H_2$ is labeled $\sigma_{1s}^*$ (read "sigma-star-one-$s$"); the asterisk denotes that the MO is antibonding.

The relative energies of two $1s$ atomic orbitals and the molecular orbitals formed from them are represented by an **energy-level diagram** (also called a **molecular orbital diagram**). Such diagrams show the interacting atomic orbitals on the left and right and the MOs in the middle, as shown in ▼ **FIGURE 9.33**. Like atomic orbitals, each MO can accommodate two electrons with their spins paired (Pauli exclusion principle). ∞ (Section 6.7)

As the MO diagram for $H_2$ in Figure 9.33 shows, each H atom brings one electron to the molecule, so there are two electrons in $H_2$. These two electrons occupy the lower-energy bonding ($\sigma_{1s}$) MO, and their spins are paired. Electrons occupying a bonding molecular orbital are called *bonding electrons*. Because the $\sigma_{1s}$ MO is lower in energy than the $1s$ atomic orbitals, the $H_2$ molecule is more stable than the two separate H atoms.

By analogy with atomic electron configurations, the electron configurations for molecules can be written with superscripts to indicate electron occupancy. The electron configuration for $H_2$, then, is $\sigma_{1s}^2$.

---

△ **GO FIGURE**

By referring to Figure 9.32, determine which molecular orbital in He$_2$ has a node between the nuclei.

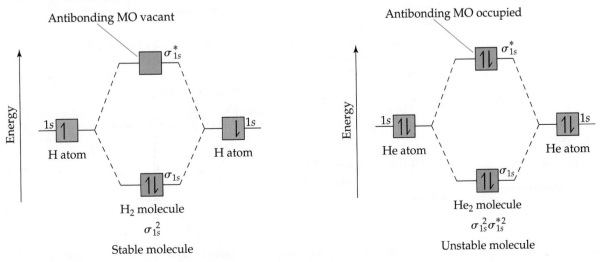

▲ **FIGURE 9.33**   Energy-level diagrams and electron configurations for H$_2$ and He$_2$.

Figure 9.33 also shows the energy-level diagram for the hypothetical $He_2$ molecule, which requires four electrons to fill its molecular orbitals. Because only two electrons can go in the $\sigma_{1s}$ MO, the other two electrons must go in the $\sigma_{1s}^*$ MO. The electron configuration of $He_2$ is thus $\sigma_{1s}^2 \sigma_{1s}^{*2}$. The energy decrease realized in going from He atomic orbitals to the He bonding MO is offset by the energy increase realized in going from the atomic orbitals to the He antibonding MO.† Hence, $He_2$ is an unstable molecule. Molecular orbital theory correctly predicts that hydrogen forms diatomic molecules but helium does not.

## Bond Order

In molecular orbital theory, the stability of a covalent bond is related to its **bond order**, defined as half the difference between the number of bonding electrons and the number of antibonding electrons:

$$\text{Bond order} = \tfrac{1}{2}(\text{no. of bonding electrons} - \text{no. of antibonding electrons}) \quad [9.1]$$

We take half the difference because we are used to thinking of bonds as pairs of electrons. *A bond order of 1 represents a single bond, a bond order of 2 represents a double bond, and a bond order of 3 represents a triple bond.* Because MO theory also treats molecules containing an odd number of electrons, bond orders of 1/2, 3/2, or 5/2 are possible.

Because, as Figure 9.33 shows, $H_2$ has two bonding electrons and zero antibonding electrons, it has a bond order of 1. Because $He_2$ has two bonding electrons and two antibonding electrons, it has a bond order of 0. A bond order of 0 means that no bond exists.

 **GIVE IT SOME THOUGHT**

Suppose one electron in $H_2$ is excited from the $\sigma_{1s}$ MO to the $\sigma_{1s}^*$ MO. Would you expect the H atoms to remain bonded to each other, or would the molecule fall apart?

---

**SAMPLE EXERCISE 9.8**    **Bond Order**

What is the bond order of the $He_2^+$ ion? Would you expect this ion to be stable relative to the separated He atom and $He^+$ ion?

**SOLUTION**

**Analyze** We will determine the bond order for the $He_2^+$ ion and use it to predict whether the ion is stable.

**Plan** To determine the bond order, we must determine the number of electrons in the molecule and how these electrons populate the available MOs. The valence electrons of He are in the $1s$ orbital, and the $1s$ orbitals combine to give an MO diagram like that for $H_2$ or $He_2$ (Figure 9.33). If the bond order is greater than 0, we expect a bond to exist, and the ion is stable.

**Solve** The energy-level diagram for the $He_2^+$ ion is shown in ◀ **FIGURE 9.34**. This ion has three electrons. Two are placed in the bonding orbital and the third in the antibonding orbital. Thus, the bond order is

$$\text{Bond order} = \tfrac{1}{2}(2 - 1) = \tfrac{1}{2}$$

Because the bond order is greater than 0, we predict the $He_2^+$ ion to be stable relative to the separated He and $He^+$. Formation of $He_2^+$ in the gas phase has been demonstrated in laboratory experiments.

**PRACTICE EXERCISE**

Determine the bond order of the $H_2^-$ ion.
**Answer:** $\tfrac{1}{2}$

 **GO FIGURE**

**Which electrons in this diagram contribute to the stability of the $He_2^+$ ion?**

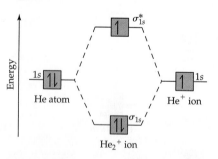

▲ **FIGURE 9.34    Energy-level diagram for the $He_2^+$ ion.**

---

†Antibonding MOs are slightly more energetically unfavorable than bonding MOs are energetically favorable. Thus, whenever there is an equal number of electrons in bonding and antibonding orbitals, the energy of the molecule is slightly higher than that for the separated atoms. As a result, no bond is formed.

# 9.8 | PERIOD 2 DIATOMIC MOLECULES

In considering the MO description of diatomic molecules other than $H_2$, we will initially restrict our discussion to *homonuclear* diatomic molecules (those composed of two identical atoms) of period 2 elements.

Period 2 atoms have valence $2s$ and $2p$ orbitals, and we need to consider how they interact to form MOs. The following rules summarize some of the guiding principles for the formation of MOs and for how they are populated by electrons:

1. The number of MOs formed equals the number of atomic orbitals combined.

2. Atomic orbitals combine most effectively with other atomic orbitals of similar energy.

3. The effectiveness with which two atomic orbitals combine is proportional to their overlap. That is, as the overlap increases, the energy of the bonding MO is lowered and the energy of the antibonding MO is raised.

4. Each MO can accommodate, at most, two electrons, with their spins paired (Pauli exclusion principle). ∞ (Section 6.7)

5. When MOs of the same energy are populated, one electron enters each orbital (with the same spin) before spin pairing occurs (Hund's rule). ∞ (Section 6.8)

## Molecular Orbitals for Li₂ and Be₂

Lithium has the electron configuration $1s^2 2s^1$. When lithium metal is heated above its boiling point (1342 °C), $Li_2$ molecules are found in the vapor phase. The Lewis structure for $Li_2$ indicates a Li—Li single bond. We will now use MOs to describe the bonding in $Li_2$.

▶ FIGURE 9.35 shows that the Li $1s$ and $2s$ atomic orbitals have substantially different energy levels. From this, we can assume that the $1s$ orbital on one Li atom interacts only with the $1s$ orbital on the other atom (rule 2), just as Figure 9.35 indicates. Likewise, the $2s$ orbitals interact only with each other. Notice that combining four atomic orbitals produces four MOs (rule 1).

The Li $1s$ orbitals combine to form $\sigma_{1s}$ and $\sigma_{1s}^*$ bonding and antibonding MOs, as they did for $H_2$. The $2s$ orbitals interact with one another in exactly the same way, producing bonding ($\sigma_{2s}$) and antibonding ($\sigma_{2s}^*$) MOs. In general, the separation between bonding and antibonding MOs depends on the extent to which the constituent atomic orbitals overlap. Because the Li $2s$ orbitals extend farther from the nucleus than the $1s$ orbitals do, the $2s$ orbitals overlap more effectively. As a result, the energy difference between the $\sigma_{2s}$ and $\sigma_{2s}^*$ orbitals is greater than the energy difference between the $\sigma_{1s}$ and $\sigma_{1s}^*$ orbitals. The $1s$ orbitals of Li are so much lower in energy than the $2s$ orbitals, however, that the energy of the $\sigma_{1s}^*$ antibonding MO is much lower than the energy of $\sigma_{2s}$ bonding MO.

Each Li atom has three electrons, so six electrons must be placed in $Li_2$ MOs. As shown in Figure 9.35, these electrons occupy the $\sigma_{1s}$, $\sigma_{1s}^*$, and $\sigma_{2s}$ MOs, each with two electrons. There are four electrons in bonding orbitals and two in antibonding orbitals, so the bond order is $\frac{1}{2}(4 - 2) = 1$. The molecule has a single bond, in agreement with its Lewis structure.

Because both the $\sigma_{1s}$ and $\sigma_{1s}^*$ MOs of $Li_2$ are completely filled, the $1s$ orbitals contribute almost nothing to the bonding. The single bond in $Li_2$ is due essentially to the interaction of the valence $2s$ orbitals on the Li atoms. This example illustrates the general rule that *core electrons usually do not contribute significantly to bonding in molecules.* The rule is equivalent to using only the valence electrons when drawing Lewis structures. Thus, we need not consider further the $1s$ orbitals while discussing the other period 2 diatomic molecules.

The MO description of $Be_2$ follows readily from the energy-level diagram for $Li_2$. Each Be atom has four electrons ($1s^2 2s^2$), so we must place eight electrons in molecular orbitals. Thus, we completely fill the

GO FIGURE

Why do the 1s orbitals of the Li atoms not contribute to the bonding in Li₂?

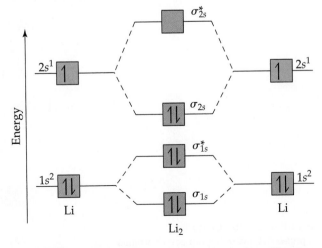

▲ FIGURE 9.35   Energy-level diagram for the Li₂ molecule.

$\sigma_{1s}$, $\sigma_{1s}^{*}$, $\sigma_{2s}$, and $\sigma_{2s}^{*}$ MOs. With equal numbers of bonding and antibonding electrons, the bond order is zero; thus, $Be_2$ does not exist.

### GIVE IT SOME THOUGHT

Would you expect $Be_2^+$ to be a stable ion?

## Molecular Orbitals from 2p Atomic Orbitals

Before we can consider the remaining period 2 diatomic molecules, we must look at the MOs that result from combining $2p$ atomic orbitals. The interactions between $p$ orbitals are shown in ▼ **FIGURE 9.36**, where we have arbitrarily chosen the internuclear axis to be the $z$-axis. The $2p_z$ orbitals face each other head to head. Just as with $s$ orbitals, we can combine $2p_z$ orbitals in two ways. One combination concentrates electron density between the nuclei and is, therefore, a bonding molecular orbital. The other combination excludes electron density from the bonding region and so is an antibonding molecular orbital. In both MOs the electron density lies along the internuclear axis, so they are $\sigma$ molecular orbitals: $\sigma_{2p}$ and $\sigma_{2p}^{*}$.

The other $2p$ orbitals overlap sideways and thus concentrate electron density above and below the internuclear axis. MOs of this type are called **pi ($\pi$) molecular orbitals** by

### GO FIGURE

**In what types of MOs do we find nodal planes?**

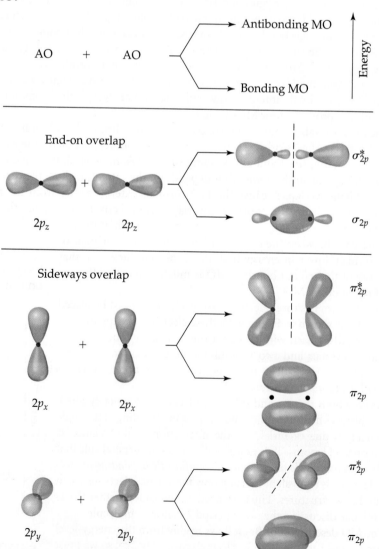

▶ **FIGURE 9.36 Contour representations of the molecular orbitals formed by 2p orbitals.**

# A CLOSER LOOK

## PHASES IN ATOMIC AND MOLECULAR ORBITALS

Our discussion of atomic orbitals in Chapter 6 and molecular orbitals in this chapter highlights some of the most important applications of quantum mechanics in chemistry. In the quantum mechanical treatment of electrons in atoms and molecules, we are mainly interested in determining two characteristics of the electrons—their energies and their distribution in space. Recall that solving Schrödinger's wave equation yields the electron's energy, $E$, and wave function, $\psi$, but that $\psi$ does not have a direct physical meaning. ⚭ (Section 6.5) The contour representations of atomic and molecular orbitals we have presented thus far are based on $\psi^2$ (the *probability density*), which gives the probability of finding the electron at a given point in space.

Because probability densities are squares of functions, their values must be nonnegative (zero or positive) at all points in space. However, the functions themselves can have negative values. Consider, for example, the sine function plotted in ▶ **FIGURE 9.37**. In the top graph, the sine function is negative for $x$ between 0 and $-\pi$ and positive for $x$ between 0 and $+\pi$. We say that the *phase* of the sine function is negative between 0 and $-\pi$ and positive between 0 and $+\pi$. If we square the sine function (bottom graph), we get two peaks that are symmetrical about the origin. Both peaks are positive because squaring a negative number produces a positive number. In other words, *we lose the phase information of the function upon squaring it.*

Like the sine function, the more complicated wave functions for atomic orbitals can also have phases. Consider, for example, the representations of the 1s orbital in ▼ **FIGURE 9.38**. Note that here we

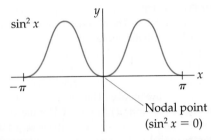

▲ **FIGURE 9.37** **Graphs for a sine function and the same function squared.**

plot this orbital a bit differently from what is shown in Section 6.6. The origin is the point where the nucleus resides, and the wave function for

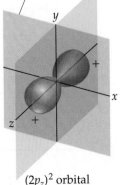

▲ **FIGURE 9.38**  **Phases in wave functions of *s* and *p* atomic orbitals.**

the 1s orbital extends from the origin out into space. The plot shows the value of $\psi$ for a slice taken along the $z$-axis. Below the plot is a contour representation of the 1s orbital. Notice that the value of the 1s wave function is always a positive number. Thus, it has only one phase. Notice also that the wave function approaches zero only at a long distance from the nucleus. It therefore has no nodes, as we saw in Figure 6.21.

In the Figure 9.38 graph for the $2p_z$ orbital, the wave function changes sign when it passes through $z = 0$. Notice that the two halves of the wave have the same shape except that one has positive values and the other negative values. Analogously to the sine function, the wave function changes phase when it passes through the origin. Mathematically the $2p_z$ wave function is equal to zero whenever $z = 0$. This corresponds to any point on the $xy$ plane, so we say that the $xy$ plane is a *nodal plane* of the $2p_z$ orbital. The wave function for a $p$ orbital is much like a sine function because it has two equal parts that have opposite phases. Figure 9.38 gives a typical representation used by chemists of the wave function for a $p_z$ orbital.* The plus and minus signs indicate the phases of the orbital. As with the sine function, the origin is a node.

The third graph in Figure 9.38 shows that when we square the wave function of the $2p_z$ orbital, we get two peaks that are symmetrical about the origin. Both peaks are positive because squaring a negative number produces a positive number. Thus, *we lose the phase information of the function upon squaring it* just as we did for the sine function. When we square the wave function for the $p_z$ orbital, we get the probability density for the orbital, which is given as a contour representation in Figure 9.38. This is what we saw in the earlier presentation of $p$ orbitals. ∞ (Section 6.6) For this squared wave function, both lobes have the same phase and therefore the same sign. We use this representation throughout most of this book because it has a simple physical interpretation: The square of the wave function at any point in space represents the electron density at that point.

The lobes of the wave functions for the $d$ orbitals also have different phases. For example, the wave function for a $d_{xy}$ orbital has four lobes, with the phase of each lobe opposite the phase of its nearest neighbors (▶ **FIGURE 9.39**). The wave functions for the other $d$ orbitals likewise have lobes in which the phase in one lobe is opposite that in an adjacent lobe.

Why do we need to consider the complexity introduced by considering the phase of the wave function? While it is true that the phase is not necessary to visualize the shape of an atomic orbital in an isolated atom, it does become important when we consider overlap of orbitals in molecular orbital theory. Let's use the sine function as an example again. If you add two sine functions having the same phase, they add *constructively*, resulting in increased amplitude:

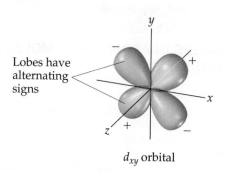

Lobes have alternating signs

$d_{xy}$ orbital

▲ **FIGURE 9.39** **Phases in *d* orbitals.**

but if you add two sine functions having opposite phases, they add *destructively* and cancel each other.

The idea of constructive and destructive interactions of wave functions is key to understanding the origin of bonding and antibonding molecular orbitals. For example, the wave function of the $\sigma_{1s}$ MO of $H_2$ is generated by adding the wave function for the 1s orbital on one atom to the wave function for the 1s orbital on the other atom, with both orbitals having the same phase. The atomic wave functions overlap *constructively* in this case to increase the electron density between the two atoms (▼ **FIGURE 9.40**). The wave function of the $\sigma_{1s}^*$ MO of $H_2$ is generated by subtracting the wave function for a 1s orbital on one atom from the wave function for a 1s orbital on the other atom. The result is that the atomic orbital wave functions overlap *destructively* to create a region of zero electron density between the two atoms—a node. Notice the similarity between this figure and Figure 9.32. In Figure 9.40 we use plus and minus signs to denote positive and negative phases in the H atomic orbitals. However, chemists may alternatively draw contour representations in different colors to denote the two phases.

When we square the wave function of the $\sigma_{1s}^*$ MO, we get the electron density representation which we saw earlier, in Figure 9.32. Notice once again that we lose the phase information when we look at the electron density.

*RELATED EXERCISES: 9.103, 9.115, 9.117*

Destructive addition

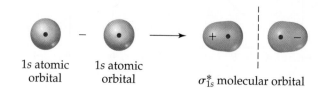

1s atomic orbital    1s atomic orbital    $\sigma_{1s}^*$ molecular orbital

Contructive addition

1s atomic orbital    1s atomic orbital    $\sigma_{1s}$ molecular orbital

▲ **FIGURE 9.40** **Molecular orbitals from atomic orbital wave functions.**

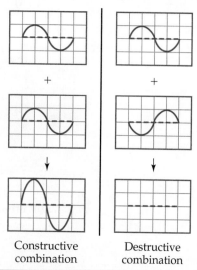

Constructive combination    Destructive combination

*The mathematical development of this three-dimensional function (and its square) is beyond the scope of this book and, as is typically done by chemists, we have used lobes that are the same shape as in Figure 6.22.

analogy to $\pi$ bonds. We get one $\pi$ bonding MO by combining the $2p_x$ atomic orbitals and another from the $2p_y$ atomic orbitals. These two $\pi_{2p}$ molecular orbitals have the same energy; in other words, they are degenerate. Likewise, we get two degenerate $\pi_{2p}^*$ antibonding MOs that are perpendicular to each other like the $2p$ orbitals from which they were made. These $\pi_{2p}^*$ orbitals have four lobes, pointing away from the two nuclei, as shown in Figure 9.36. The $2p_z$ orbitals on two atoms point directly at each other. Hence, the overlap of two $2p_z$ orbitals is greater than that of two $2p_x$ or $2p_y$ orbitals. From rule 3 we therefore expect the $\sigma_{2p}$ MO to be lower in energy (more stable) than the $\pi_{2p}$ MOs. Similarly, the $\sigma_{2p}^*$ MO should be higher in energy (less stable) than the $\pi_{2p}^*$ MOs.

## Electron Configurations for $B_2$ through $Ne_2$

We can combine our analyses of MOs formed from *s* orbitals (Figure 9.32) and from *p* orbitals (Figure 9.36) to construct an energy-level diagram (▼ FIGURE 9.41) for homonuclear diatomic molecules of the elements boron through neon, all of which have valence $2s$ and $2p$ atomic orbitals. The following features of the diagram are notable:

1. The $2s$ atomic orbitals are substantially lower in energy than the $2p$ atomic orbitals. ∞ (Section 6.7) Consequently, both MOs formed from the $2s$ orbitals are lower in energy than the lowest-energy MO derived from the $2p$ atomic orbitals.

2. The overlap of the two $2p_z$ orbitals is greater than that of the two $2p_x$ or $2p_y$ orbitals. As a result, the bonding $\sigma_{2p}$ MO is lower in energy than the $\pi_{2p}$ MOs, and the antibonding $\sigma_{2p}^*$ MO is higher in energy than the $\pi_{2p}^*$ MOs.

3. Both the $\pi_{2p}$ and $\pi_{2p}^*$ MOs are *doubly degenerate*; that is, there are two degenerate MOs of each type.

Before we can add electrons to Figure 9.41, we must consider one more effect. We have constructed the diagram assuming no interaction between the $2s$ orbital on one atom and the $2p$ orbitals on the other. In fact, such interactions can and do take place. ▶ FIGURE 9.42 shows the overlap of a $2s$ orbital on one of the atoms with a $2p$ orbital on the other. These interactions increase the energy difference between the $\sigma_{2s}$ and $\sigma_{2p}$ MOs, with the $\sigma_{2s}$ energy decreasing and the $\sigma_{2p}$ energy increasing (Figure 9.42). These $2s$–$2p$ interactions can be strong enough that the energetic ordering of the MOs can be altered: For $B_2$, $C_2$, and $N_2$, the $\sigma_{2p}$ MO is above the $\pi_{2p}$ MOs in energy. For $O_2$, $F_2$, and $Ne_2$, the $\sigma_{2p}$ MO is below the $\pi_{2p}$ MOs .

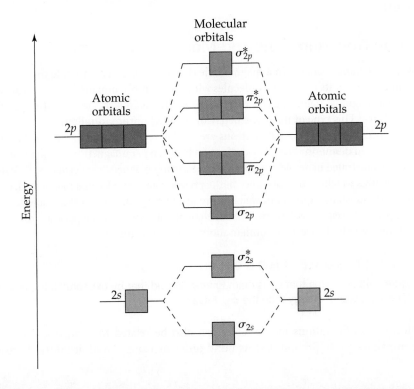

◀ **FIGURE 9.41 Energy-level diagram for MOs of period 2 homonuclear diatomic molecules.** The diagram assumes no interaction between the $2s$ atomic orbital on one atom and the $2p$ atomic orbitals on the other atom, and experiment shows that it fits only for $O_2$, $F_2$, and $Ne_2$.

▲ GO FIGURE

Which molecular orbitals have switched relative energy in the group on the right as compared with the group on the left?

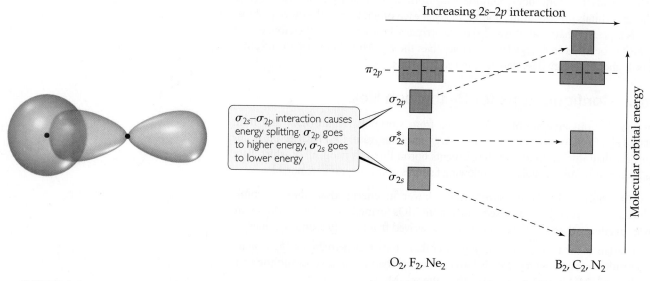

▲ **FIGURE 9.42** **The effect of interactions between 2s and 2p atomic orbitals.**

Given the energy ordering of the molecular orbitals, it is a simple matter to determine the electron configurations for the diatomic molecules $B_2$ through $Ne_2$. For example, a boron atom has three valence electrons. (Remember that we are ignoring the $1s$ electrons.) Thus, for $B_2$ we must place six electrons in MOs. Four of them fill the $\sigma_{2s}$ and $\sigma_{2s}^*$ MOs, leading to no net bonding. The fifth electron goes in one $\pi_{2p}$ MO, and the sixth goes in the other $\pi_{2p}$ MO, with the two electrons having the same spin. Therefore, $B_2$ has a bond order of 1.

Each time we move one element to the right in period 2, two more electrons must be placed in the diagram of Figure 9.41. For example, on moving to $C_2$, we have two more electrons than in $B_2$, and these electrons are placed in the $\pi_{2p}$ MOs, completely filling them. The electron configurations and bond orders for $B_2$ through $Ne_2$ are given in ▶ **FIGURE 9.43**.

## Electron Configurations and Molecular Properties

The way a substance behaves in a magnetic field can in some cases provide insight into the arrangements of its electrons. Molecules with one or more unpaired electrons are attracted to a magnetic field. The more unpaired electrons in a species, the stronger the attractive force. This type of magnetic behavior is called **paramagnetism**.

Substances with no unpaired electrons are weakly repelled by a magnetic field. This property is called **diamagnetism**. The distinction between paramagnetism and diamagnetism is nicely illustrated in an older method for measuring magnetic properties (▶ **FIGURE 9.44**). It involves weighing the substance in the presence and absence of a magnetic field. A paramagnetic substance appears to weigh more in the magnetic field; a diamagnetic substance appears to weigh less. The magnetic behaviors observed for the period 2 diatomic molecules agree with the electron configurations shown in Figure 9.43.

▲ GIVE IT SOME THOUGHT

Figure 9.43 indicates that $C_2$ is diamagnetic. Would that be expected if the $\sigma_{2p}$ MO were lower in energy than the $\pi_{2p}$ MOs?

Electron configurations in molecules can also be related to bond distances and bond enthalpies. ⬭ (Section 8.8) As bond order increases, bond distances decrease

## GO FIGURE

What difference in electron configuration accounts for most of the difference between the bond enthalpy of $N_2$ and that of $F_2$?

| | Large 2s–2p interaction | | | Small 2s–2p interaction | | |
|---|---|---|---|---|---|---|
| | $B_2$ | $C_2$ | $N_2$ | $O_2$ | $F_2$ | $Ne_2$ |
| $\sigma_{2p}^*$ | ☐ | ☐ | ☐ | ☐ | ☐ | ↑↓ |
| $\pi_{2p}^*$ | ☐ ☐ | ☐ ☐ | ☐ ☐ | ↑ ↑ | ↑↓ ↑↓ | ↑↓ ↑↓ |
| $\sigma_{2p}$ | | | ↑↓ | ↑↓ ↑↓ | ↑↓ ↑↓ | ↑↓ ↑↓ |
| $\pi_{2p}$ | ↑ ↑ | ↑↓ ↑↓ | ↑↓ ↑↓ | ↑↓ | ↑↓ | ↑↓ |
| $\sigma_{2s}^*$ | ↑↓ | ↑↓ | ↑↓ | ↑↓ | ↑↓ | ↑↓ |
| $\sigma_{2s}$ | ↑↓ | ↑↓ | ↑↓ | ↑↓ | ↑↓ | ↑↓ |
| Bond order | 1 | 2 | 3 | 2 | 1 | 0 |
| Bond enthalpy (kJ/mol) | 290 | 620 | 941 | 495 | 155 | — |
| Bond length (Å) | 1.59 | 1.31 | 1.10 | 1.21 | 1.43 | — |
| Magnetic behavior | Paramagnetic | Diamagnetic | Diamagnetic | Paramagnetic | Diamagnetic | — |

▲ **FIGURE 9.43**  Molecular orbital electron configurations and some experimental data for period 2 diatomic molecules.

Weigh sample in absence of a magnetic field

Sample

A diamagnetic sample appears to weigh less in magnetic field (weak effect)

A paramagnetic sample appears to weigh more in magnetic field

◄ **FIGURE 9.44**  Determining the magnetic properties of a sample.

and bond enthalpies increase. $N_2$, for example, whose bond order is 3, has a short bond distance and a large bond enthalpy. The $N_2$ molecule does not react readily with other substances to form nitrogen compounds. The relatively high bond order of the molecule helps explain its exceptional stability. We should also note, however, that molecules with the same bond orders do *not* have the same bond distances and bond enthalpies. Bond order is only one factor influencing these properties. Other factors include nuclear charge and extent of orbital overlap.

Bonding in $O_2$ provides an interesting test case for molecular orbital theory. The Lewis structure for this molecule shows a double bond and complete pairing of electrons:

$$\ddot{O}=\ddot{O}$$

The short O—O bond distance (1.21 Å) and relatively high bond enthalpy (495 kJ/mol) are in agreement with the presence of a double bond. However, Figure 9.43 tells us that

▲ **GO FIGURE**

What would you expect to see if liquid nitrogen were poured between the poles of the magnet?

Because $O_2$ molecules are paramagnetic ...

... they are attracted into the magnetic field.

▲ **FIGURE 9.45** **Paramagnetism of $O_2$.**

the molecule contains two unpaired electrons, a detail not discernible in the Lewis structure. Unpaired electrons mean paramagnetism, and the paramagnetism of $O_2$ is demonstrated in ▲ **FIGURE 9.45**. The Lewis structure fails to account for this paramagnetism, but molecular orbital theory correctly predicts two unpaired electrons in the $\pi_{2p}^{*}$ orbital. The MO description also correctly indicates a bond order of 2.

Going from $O_2$ to $F_2$, we add two electrons, completely filling the $\pi_{2p}^{*}$ MOs. Thus, $F_2$ is expected to be diamagnetic and have an F—F single bond, in accord with its Lewis structure. Finally, the addition of two more electrons to make $Ne_2$ fills all the bonding and antibonding MOs. Therefore, the bond order of $Ne_2$ is zero, and the molecule is not expected to exist.

---

**SAMPLE EXERCISE 9.9** | **Molecular Orbitals of a Period 2 Diatomic Ion**

For the $O_2^{+}$ ion, predict (**a**) number of unpaired electrons, (**b**) bond order, (**c**) bond enthalpy and bond length.

**SOLUTION**

**Analyze** Our task is to predict several properties of the cation $O_2^{+}$.

**Plan** We will use the MO description of $O_2^{+}$ to determine the desired properties. We must first determine the number of electrons in $O_2^{+}$ and then draw its MO energy diagram. The unpaired electrons are those without a partner of opposite spin. The bond order is one-half the difference between the number of bonding and antibonding electrons. After calculating the bond order, we can use Figure 9.43 to estimate the bond enthalpy and bond length.

**Solve**

(**a**) The $O_2^{+}$ ion has 11 valence electrons, one fewer than $O_2$. The electron removed from $O_2$ to form $O_2^{+}$ is one of the two unpaired $\pi_{2p}^{*}$ electrons (see Figure 9.43). Therefore, $O_2^{+}$ has one unpaired electron.

**(b)** The molecule has eight bonding electrons (the same as $O_2$) and three antibonding electrons (one fewer than $O_2$). Thus, its bond order is

$$\tfrac{1}{2}(8 - 3) = 2\tfrac{1}{2}$$

**(c)** The bond order of $O_2{}^+$ is between that for $O_2$ (bond order 2) and $N_2$ (bond order 3). Thus, the bond enthalpy and bond length should be about midway between those for $O_2$ and $N_2$, approximately 700 kJ/mol and 1.15 Å. (The experimentally measured values are 625 kJ/mol and 1.123 Å.)

**PRACTICE EXERCISE**
Predict the magnetic properties and bond orders of **(a)** the peroxide ion, $O_2{}^{2-}$; **(b)** the acetylide ion, $C_2{}^{2-}$.
**Answers:** **(a)** diamagnetic, 1; **(b)** diamagnetic, 3

## Heteronuclear Diatomic Molecules

The principles we have used in developing an MO description of homonuclear diatomic molecules can be extended to *heteronuclear* diatomic molecules—those in which the two atoms in the molecule are not the same—and we conclude this section with a fascinating heteronuclear diatomic molecule—nitric oxide, NO.

The NO molecule controls several important human physiological functions. Our bodies use it, for example, to relax muscles, kill foreign cells, and reinforce memory. The 1998 Nobel Prize in Physiology or Medicine was awarded to three scientists for their research that uncovered the importance of NO as a "signaling" molecule in the cardiovascular system. NO also functions as a neurotransmitter and is implicated in many other biological pathways. That NO plays such an important role in human metabolism was unsuspected before 1987 because NO has an odd number of electrons and is highly reactive. The molecule has 11 valence electrons, and two possible Lewis structures can be drawn. The Lewis structure with the lower formal charges places the odd electron on the N atom:

$$\overset{0}{\ddot{\text{N}}}=\overset{0}{\ddot{\text{O}}} \longleftrightarrow \overset{-1}{\ddot{\text{N}}}=\overset{+1}{\ddot{\text{O}}}$$

Both structures indicate the presence of a double bond, but when compared with the molecules in Figure 9.43, the experimental bond length of NO (1.15 Å) suggests a bond order greater than 2. How do we treat NO using the MO model?

If the atoms in a heteronuclear diatomic molecule do not differ too greatly in electronegativities, their MOs resemble those in homonuclear diatomics, with one important modification: The energy of the atomic orbitals of the more electronegative atom is lower than that of the atomic orbitals of the less electronegative element. In ▶ **FIGURE 9.46**, you see that the 2s and 2p atomic orbitals of oxygen are slightly lower than those of nitrogen because oxygen is more electronegative than nitrogen. The MO energy-level diagram for NO is much like that of a homonuclear diatomic molecule—because the 2s and 2p orbitals on the two atoms interact, the same types of MOs are produced.

There is one other important difference in the MOs of heteronuclear molecules. The MOs are still a mix of atomic orbitals from both atoms, but in general *an MO in a heteronuclear diatomic molecule has a greater contribution from the atomic orbital to which it is closer in energy.* In the case of NO, for example, the $\sigma_{2s}$ bonding MO is closer in energy to the O 2s atomic orbital than to the N 2s atomic orbital. As a result, the $\sigma_{2s}$ MO has a slightly greater contribution from O than from N—the orbital is no longer an equal mixture of the two atoms, as was the case for the homonuclear diatomic molecules. Similarly, the $\sigma_{2s}^*$ antibonding MO is weighted more heavily toward the N atom because that MO is closest in energy to the N 2s atomic orbital.

▲ **GO FIGURE**

**How many valence-shell electrons are there in NO?**

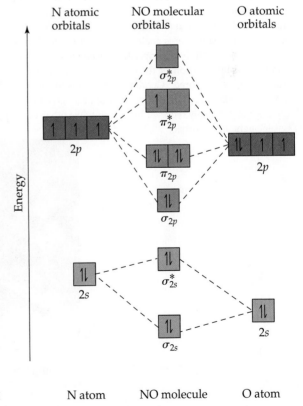

▲ **FIGURE 9.46**  The energy-level diagram for atomic and molecular orbitals in NO.

# CHEMISTRY PUT TO WORK

## Orbitals and Energy

Asked to identify the major technological challenge for the twenty-first century, you might say "energy," reasoning that development of sustainable energy sources is crucial to meet the needs of future generations of people on our planet. Currently, the majority of the world, in one way or another, relies on exothermic combustion reactions of oil, coal, or natural gas to provide heat and power. These are all *fossil fuels*—carbon-containing compounds that are the long-term decomposition products of ancient plants and animals.

Fossil fuels are not renewable in the several-hundred-year timeframe in which we need them, but every day our planet receives plenty of energy from the Sun to easily power the world for millions of years. Whereas combustion of fossil fuels releases $CO_2$ into the atmosphere, solar energy represents a renewable energy source that is potentially less harmful to the environment. One way to utilize solar energy is to convert it into electrical energy via photovoltaic solar cells. The problem with this alternative is that the current efficiency of solar-cell devices is low; only about 10–15% of sunlight is converted into useful energy. Furthermore, the cost of manufacturing solar cells is relatively high.

How does solar energy conversion work? Fundamentally, we need to be able to use photons from the Sun to excite electrons in molecules and materials to different energy levels. The brilliant colors around you—those of your clothes, the photographs in this book, the foods you eat—are due to the selective absorption of light by chemicals. Light excites electrons in molecules. In a molecular orbital picture, we can envision light exciting an electron from a filled molecular orbital to an empty one at higher energy. Because the MOs have definite energies, only light of the proper wavelengths can excite electrons. The situation is analogous to that of atomic line spectra. ∞ (Section 6.3) If the appropriate wavelength for exciting electrons is in the visible portion of the electromagnetic spectrum, the substance appears colored: Certain wavelengths of white light are absorbed; others are not. A green leaf appears green because green light is most strongly reflected by the leaf while other wavelengths of visible light are absorbed.

In discussing light absorption by molecules, we can focus on two MOs. The *highest occupied molecular orbital* (HOMO) is the MO of highest energy that has electrons in it. The *lowest unoccupied molecular orbital* (LUMO) is the MO of lowest energy that does not have electrons in it. In $N_2$, for example, the HOMO is the $\sigma_{2p}$ MO and the LUMO is the $\pi_{2p}^{*}$ MO (Figure 9.43).

The energy difference between the HOMO and the LUMO—known as the HOMO–LUMO gap—is related to the minimum energy needed to excite an electron in the molecule. Colorless or white substances usually have such a large HOMO–LUMO gap that visible light is not energetic enough to excite an electron to the higher level. The minimum energy needed to excite an electron from the HOMO to the LUMO in $N_2$ corresponds to light with a wavelength of less than 200 nm, which is far into the ultraviolet part of the spectrum. ∞ (Figure 6.4) As a result, $N_2$ cannot absorb visible light and is therefore colorless.

The magnitude of the energy gap between filled and empty electronic states is critical for solar energy conversion. Ideally, we want a substance that absorbs as many solar photons as possible and then converts the energy of those photons into a useful form of energy. Titanium dioxide is a readily available material that can be reasonably efficient at converting light directly into electricity. However, $TiO_2$ is white and absorbs only a small amount of the Sun's radiant energy. Scientists are working to make solar cells in which $TiO_2$ is mixed with highly colored molecules, whose HOMO–LUMO gaps correspond to visible and near-infrared light. That way, the molecules can absorb more of the solar spectrum. The molecule's HOMO must also be higher in energy than the $TiO_2$'s HOMO so that the excited electrons can flow from the molecules into the $TiO_2$, thereby generating electricity when the device is illuminated with light and connected to an external circuit.

▼ FIGURE 9.47 shows a solar cell made from ruthenium-containing molecules, which appear red, mixed with $TiO_2$ in a paste that is sandwiched between two glass plates. Incoming light excites electrons on the ruthenium-containing molecules from occupied MOs to empty MOs. The electrons are then transferred into the $TiO_2$ and move through the external circuit, generating enough current to run the small fan.

*RELATED EXERCISES: 9.105, 9.116*

TiO$_2$ matrix

Incoming light source

Light excites electrons in a ruthenium complex.

Excited electrons flow in external circuit, powering fan

▲ FIGURE 9.47 **Light into electricity.**

We complete the MO diagram for NO by filling the MOs in Figure 9.46 with the 11 valence electrons. Eight bonding and three antibonding electrons give a bond order of $\frac{1}{2}(8 - 3) = 2\frac{1}{2}$, which agrees better with experiment than the Lewis structures do. The unpaired electron resides in one of the $\pi_{2p}^*$ MOs, which are more heavily weighted toward the N atom. (We could have placed this electron in either the left or right $\pi_{2p}^*$ MO.) Thus, the Lewis structure that places the unpaired electron on nitrogen (the one preferred on the basis of formal charge) is the more accurate description of the true electron distribution in the molecule.

---

**SAMPLE INTEGRATIVE EXERCISE**   **Putting Concepts Together**

Elemental sulfur is a yellow solid that consists of $S_8$ molecules. The structure of the $S_8$ molecule is a puckered, eight-membered ring (see Figure 7.26). Heating elemental sulfur to high temperatures produces gaseous $S_2$ molecules:

$$S_8(s) \longrightarrow 4\, S_2(g)$$

**(a)** The electron configuration of which period 2 element is most similar to that of sulfur? **(b)** Use the VSEPR model to predict the S—S—S bond angles in $S_8$ and the hybridization at S in $S_8$. **(c)** Use MO theory to predict the sulfur–sulfur bond order in $S_2$. Do you expect this molecule to be diamagnetic or paramagnetic? **(d)** Use average bond enthalpies (Table 8.4) to estimate the enthalpy change for this reaction. Is the reaction exothermic or endothermic?

**SOLUTION**

**(a)** Sulfur is a group 6A element with an $[Ne]3s^2 3p^4$ electron configuration. It is expected to be most similar electronically to oxygen (electron configuration, $[He]2s^2 2p^4$), which is immediately above it in the periodic table.

**(b)** The Lewis structure of $S_8$ is

There is a single bond between each pair of S atoms and two nonbonding electron pairs on each S atom. Thus, we see four electron domains around each S atom and expect a tetrahedral electron-domain geometry corresponding to $sp^3$ hybridization. Because of the nonbonding pairs, we expect the S—S—S angles to be somewhat less than 109.5°, the tetrahedral angle. Experimentally, the S—S—S angle in $S_8$ is 108°, in good agreement with this prediction. Interestingly, if $S_8$ were a planar ring, it would have S—S—S angles of 135°. Instead, the $S_8$ ring puckers to accommodate the smaller angles dictated by $sp^3$ hybridization.

**(c)** The MOs of $S_2$ are analogous to those of $O_2$, although the MOs for $S_2$ are constructed from the 3s and 3p atomic orbitals of sulfur. Further, $S_2$ has the same number of valence electrons as $O_2$. Thus, by analogy with $O_2$, we expect $S_2$ to have a bond order of 2 (a double bond) and to be paramagnetic with two unpaired electrons in the $\pi_{3p}^*$ molecular orbitals of $S_2$.

**(d)** We are considering the reaction in which an $S_8$ molecule falls apart into four $S_2$ molecules. From parts (b) and (c), we see that $S_8$ has S—S single bonds and $S_2$ has S=S double bonds. During the reaction, therefore, we are breaking eight S—S single bonds and forming four S=S double bonds. We can estimate the enthalpy of the reaction by using Equation 8.12 and the average bond enthalpies in Table 8.4:

$$\Delta H_{rxn} = 8\, D(S\!-\!S) - 4\, D(S\!=\!S) = 8(266 \text{ kJ}) - 4(418 \text{ kJ}) = +456 \text{ kJ}$$

Recall that $D(X\!-\!Y)$ represents the X—Y bond enthalpy. Because $\Delta H_{rxn} > 0$, the reaction is endothermic. ⚭ (Section 5.4) The very positive value of $\Delta H_{rxn}$ suggests that high temperatures are required to cause the reaction to occur.

# CHAPTER SUMMARY AND KEY TERMS

**INTRODUCTION AND SECTION 9.1** The three-dimensional shapes and sizes of molecules are determined by their **bond angles** and bond lengths. Molecules with a central atom A surrounded by $n$ atoms B, denoted $AB_n$, adopt a number of different geometric shapes, depending on the value of $n$ and on the particular atoms involved. In the overwhelming majority of cases, these geometries are related to five basic shapes (linear, trigonal pyramidal, tetrahedral, trigonal bipyramidal, and octahedral).

**SECTION 9.2** The **valence-shell electron-pair repulsion (VSEPR) model** rationalizes molecular geometries based on the repulsions between **electron domains**, which are regions about a central atom in which electrons are likely to be found. **Bonding pairs** of electrons, which are those involved in making bonds, and **nonbonding pairs** of electrons, also called **lone pairs**, both create electron domains around an atom. According to the VSEPR model, electron domains orient themselves to minimize electrostatic repulsions; that is, they remain as far apart as possible. Electron domains from nonbonding pairs exert slightly greater repulsions than those from bonding pairs, which leads to certain preferred positions for nonbonding pairs and to the departure of bond angles from idealized values. Electron domains from multiple bonds exert slightly greater repulsions than those from single bonds. The arrangement of electron domains around a central atom is called the **electron-domain geometry**; the arrangement of atoms is called the **molecular geometry**.

**SECTION 9.3** The dipole moment of a polyatomic molecule depends on the vector sum of the dipole moments associated with the individual bonds, called the **bond dipoles**. Certain molecular shapes, such as linear $AB_2$ and trigonal planar $AB_3$, assure that the bond dipoles cancel, producing a nonpolar molecule, which is one whose dipole moment is zero. In other shapes, such as bent $AB_2$ and trigonal pyramidal $AB_3$, the bond dipoles do not cancel and the molecule will be polar (that is, it will have a nonzero dipole moment).

**SECTION 9.4** **Valence-bond theory** is an extension of Lewis's notion of electron-pair bonds. In valence-bond theory, covalent bonds are formed when atomic orbitals on neighboring atoms overlap one another. The overlap region is one of low energy, or greater stability, for the two electrons because of their simultaneous attraction to two nuclei. The greater the overlap between two orbitals, the stronger will be the bond that is formed.

**SECTION 9.5** To extend the ideas of valence-bond theory to polyatomic molecules, we must envision mixing $s$, $p$, and sometimes $d$ orbitals to form **hybrid orbitals**. The process of **hybridization** leads to hybrid atomic orbitals that have a large lobe directed to overlap with orbitals on another atom to make a bond. Hybrid orbitals can also accommodate nonbonding pairs. A particular mode of hybridization can be associated with each of three common electron-domain geometries (linear = $sp$; trigonal planar = $sp^2$; tetrahedral = $sp^3$).

**SECTION 9.6** Covalent bonds in which the electron density lies along the line connecting the atoms (the internuclear axis) are called **sigma ($\sigma$) bonds**. Bonds can also be formed from the sideways overlap of $p$ orbitals. Such a bond is called a **pi ($\pi$) bond**. A double bond, such as that in $C_2H_4$, consists of one $\sigma$ bond and one $\pi$ bond; a triple bond, such as that in $C_2H_2$, consists of one $\sigma$ and two $\pi$ bonds. The formation of a $\pi$ bond requires that molecules adopt a specific orientation; the two $CH_2$ groups in $C_2H_4$, for example, must lie in the same plane. As a result, the presence of $\pi$ bonds introduces rigidity into molecules. In molecules that have multiple bonds and more than one resonance structure, such as $C_6H_6$, the $\pi$ bonds are **delocalized**; that is, the $\pi$ bonds are spread among several atoms.

**SECTION 9.7** **Molecular orbital theory** is another model used to describe the bonding in molecules. In this model the electrons exist in allowed energy states called **molecular orbitals (MOs)**. An MO can extend over all the atoms of a molecule. Like an atomic orbital, a molecular orbital has a definite energy and can hold two electrons of opposite spin. We can think of molecular orbitals as built up by combining atomic orbitals on different atomic centers. In the simplest case, the combination of two atomic orbitals leads to the formation of two MOs, one at lower energy and one at higher energy relative to the energy of the atomic orbitals. The lower-energy MO concentrates charge density in the region between the nuclei and is called a **bonding molecular orbital**. The higher-energy MO excludes electrons from the region between the nuclei and is called an **antibonding molecular orbital**. Occupation of bonding MOs favors bond formation, whereas occupation of antibonding MOs is unfavorable. The bonding and antibonding MOs formed by the combination of $s$ orbitals are **sigma ($\sigma$) molecular orbitals**; they lie on the internuclear axis.

The combination of atomic orbitals and the relative energies of the molecular orbitals are shown by an **energy-level** (or **molecular orbital**) **diagram**. When the appropriate number of electrons are put into the MOs, we can calculate the **bond order** of a bond, which is half the difference between the number of electrons in bonding MOs and the number of electrons in antibonding MOs. A bond order of 1 corresponds to a single bond, and so forth. Bond orders can be fractional numbers.

**SECTION 9.8** Electrons in core orbitals do not contribute to the bonding between atoms, so a molecular orbital description usually needs to consider only electrons in the outermost electron subshells. In order to describe the MOs of period 2 homonuclear diatomic molecules, we need to consider the MOs that can form by the combination of $p$ orbitals. The $p$ orbitals that point directly at one another can form $\sigma$ bonding and $\sigma^*$ antibonding MOs. The $p$ orbitals that are oriented perpendicular to the internuclear axis combine to form **pi ($\pi$) molecular orbitals**. In diatomic molecules the $\pi$ molecular orbitals occur as a pair of degenerate (same energy) bonding MOs and a pair of degenerate antibonding MOs. The $\sigma_{2p}$ bonding MO is expected to be lower in energy than the $\pi_{2p}$ bonding MOs because of larger orbital overlap of the $p$ orbitals directed along the internuclear axis. However, this ordering is reversed in $B_2$, $C_2$, and $N_2$ because of interaction between the $2s$ and $2p$ atomic orbitals of different atoms.

The molecular orbital description of period 2 diatomic molecules leads to bond orders in accord with the Lewis structures of these molecules. Further, the model predicts correctly that $O_2$ should exhibit **paramagnetism**, which leads to attraction of a molecule into a magnetic field due to the influence of unpaired electrons. Molecules in which all the electrons are paired exhibit **diamagnetism**, which leads to weak repulsion from a magnetic field.

## KEY SKILLS

- Be able to describe the three-dimensional shapes of molecules using the VSEPR model. (Section 9.2)
- Determine whether a molecule is polar or nonpolar based on its geometry and the individual bond dipole moments. (Section 9.3)
- Be able to explain the role of orbital overlap in the formation of covalent bonds. (Section 9.4)
- Be able to specify the hybridization state of atoms in molecules based on observed molecular structures. (Section 9.5)
- Be able to sketch how orbitals overlap to form sigma ($\sigma$) and pi ($\pi$) bonds. (Section 9.6)
- Be able to explain the existence of delocalized $\pi$ bonds in molecules such as benzene. (Section 9.6)
- Be able to explain the concept of bonding and antibonding orbitals. (Section 9.7)
- Be able to draw molecular orbital energy-level diagrams and place electrons into them to obtain the bond orders and electron configurations of diatomic molecules using molecular orbital theory. (Sections 9.7 and 9.8)
- Understand the relationships among bond order, bond strength (bond enthalpy), and bond length. (Section 9.8)

## KEY EQUATION

- Bond order = $\frac{1}{2}$ (no. of bonding electrons $-$ no. of antibonding electrons)     [9.1]

# EXERCISES

## VISUALIZING CONCEPTS

9.1 A certain AB$_4$ molecule has a "seesaw" shape:

From which of the fundamental geometries shown in Figure 9.3 could you remove one or more atoms to create a molecule having this seesaw shape? [Section 9.1]

9.2 **(a)** If these three balloons are all the same size, what angle is formed between the red one and the green one? **(b)** If additional air is added to the blue balloon so that it gets larger, what happens to the angle between the red and green balloons? **(c)** What aspect of the VSEPR model is illustrated by part (b)? [Section 9.2]

9.3 For each molecule (a)-(f), indicate how many different electron-domain geometries are consistent with the molecular geometry shown. [Section 9.2]

(a)                    (b)

(c)                    (d)

(e)                    (f)

9.4 The molecule shown here is *difluoromethane* ($CH_2F_2$), which is used as a refrigerant called R-32. **(a)** Based on the structure, how many electron domains surround the C atom in this molecule? **(b)** Would the molecule have a nonzero dipole moment? **(c)** If the molecule is polar, in what direction will the overall dipole moment vector point in the molecule? [Sections 9.2 and 9.3]

**9.5** The following plot shows the potential energy of two Cl atoms as a function of the distance between them. (a) To what does an energy of zero correspond in this diagram? (b) According to the valence-bond model, why does the energy decrease as the Cl atoms move from a large separation to a smaller one? (c) What is the significance of the Cl—Cl distance at the minimum point in the plot? (d) Why does the energy rise at Cl—Cl distances less than that at the minimum point in the plot? (e) How can you estimate the bond strength of the Cl—Cl bond from the plot? [Section 9.4]

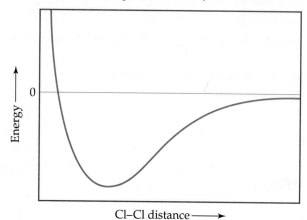

**9.6** In the series $SiF_4$, $PF_3$, and $SF_2$, estimate the F—X—F bond angle in each case and explain your rationale. [Section 9.2]

**9.7** The orbital diagram that follows presents the final step in the formation of hybrid orbitals by a silicon atom. What type of hybrid orbital is produced in this hybridization? [Section 9.5]

**9.8** In the hydrocarbon

$$H-\overset{\overset{\displaystyle H}{|}}{C}=\overset{\overset{\displaystyle H}{|}}{C}-\overset{\overset{\displaystyle H}{|}}{\underset{\underset{\displaystyle H}{|}}{C}}-C\equiv C-\overset{\overset{\displaystyle H}{|}}{\underset{\underset{\displaystyle H}{|}}{C}}-H$$

(a) What is the hybridization at each carbon atom in the molecule? (b) How many $\sigma$ bonds are there in the molecule? (c) How many $\pi$ bonds? (d) Identify all the 120° bond angles in the molecule. [Section 9.6]

**9.9** For each of these contour representations of molecular orbitals, identify (a) the atomic orbitals (*s* or *p*) used to construct the MO (b) the type of MO ($\sigma$ or $\pi$), (c) whether the MO is bonding or antibonding, and (d) the locations of nodal planes. [Sections 9.7 and 9.8]

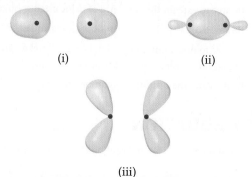

**9.10** The diagram that follows shows the highest-energy occupied MOs of a neutral molecule CX, where element X is in the same row of the periodic table as C. (a) Based on the number of electrons, can you determine the identity of X? (b) Would the molecule be diamagnetic or paramagnetic? (c) Consider the $\pi_{2p}$ MOs of the molecule. Would you expect them to have a greater atomic orbital contribution from C, have a greater atomic orbital contribution from X, or be an equal mixture of atomic orbitals from the two atoms? [Section 9.8]

$\sigma_{2p}$ $\boxed{\uparrow}$

$\pi_{2p}$ $\boxed{\uparrow\downarrow \,|\, \uparrow\downarrow}$

# MOLECULAR SHAPES; THE VSEPR MODEL (sections 9.1 and 9.2)

**9.11** An $AB_2$ molecule is described as linear, and the A—B bond length is known. (a) Does this information completely describe the geometry of the molecule? (b) Can you tell how many nonbonding pairs of electrons are around the A atom from this information?

**9.12** (a) Methane ($CH_4$) and the perchlorate ion ($ClO_4^-$) are both described as tetrahedral. What does this indicate about their bond angles? (b) The $NH_3$ molecule is trigonal pyramidal, while $BF_3$ is trigonal planar. Which of these molecules is flat?

**9.13** How does a trigonal pyramid differ from a tetrahedron so far as molecular geometry is concerned?

**9.14** Describe the bond angles to be found in each of the following molecular structures: (a) planar trigonal, (b) tetrahedral, (c) octahedral, (d) linear.

**9.15** (a) What is meant by the term *electron domain*? (b) Explain in what way electron domains behave like the balloons in Figure 9.5. Why do they do so?

**9.16** What property of the electron causes electron domains to have an effect on molecular shapes?

**9.17** (a) How does one determine the number of electron domains in a molecule or ion? (b) What is the difference between a *bonding electron domain* and a *nonbonding electron domain*?

**9.18** Would you expect the nonbonding electron-pair domain in $NH_3$ to be greater or less in size than for the corresponding one in $PH_3$? Explain.

**9.19** In which of these molecules or ions does the presence of nonbonding electron pairs produce an effect on molecular shape, assuming they are all in the gaseous state? (a) $SiH_4$, (b) $PF_3$, (c) HBr, (d) HCN, (e) $SO_2$.

**9.20** In which of the following molecules can you confidently predict the bond angles about the central atom, and for which would you be a bit uncertain? Explain in each case. (a) $H_2S$, (b) $BCl_3$, (c) $CH_3I$, (d) $CBr_4$, (e) $TeBr_4$.

**9.21** How many nonbonding electron pairs are there in each of the following molecules: **(a)** $(CH_3)_2S$, **(b)** HCN, **(c)** $H_2C_2$, **(d)** $CH_3F$?

**9.22** Describe the characteristic electron-domain geometry of each of the following numbers of electron domains about a central atom: **(a)** 3, **(b)** 4, **(c)** 5, **(d)** 6.

**9.23** What is the difference between the electron-domain geometry and the molecular geometry of a molecule? Use the water molecule as an example in your discussion. Why do we need to make this distinction?

**9.24** An $AB_3$ molecule is described as having a trigonal-bipyramidal electron-domain geometry. How many nonbonding domains are on atom A? Explain.

**9.25** Give the electron-domain and molecular geometries of a molecule that has the following electron domains on its central atom: **(a)** four bonding domains and no nonbonding domains, **(b)** three bonding domains and two nonbonding domains, **(c)** five bonding domains and one nonbonding domain, **(d)** four bonding domains and two nonbonding domains.

**9.26** What are the electron-domain and molecular geometries of a molecule that has the following electron domains on its central atom? **(a)** three bonding domains and no nonbonding domains, **(b)** three bonding domains and one nonbonding domain, **(c)** two bonding domains and two nonbonding domains.

**9.27** Give the electron-domain and molecular geometries for the following molecules and ions: **(a)** HCN, **(b)** $SO_3{}^{2-}$, **(c)** $SF_4$, **(d)** $PF_6{}^-$, **(e)** $NH_3Cl^+$, **(f)** $N_3{}^-$.

**9.28** Draw the Lewis structure for each of the following molecules or ions, and predict their electron-domain and molecular geometries: **(a)** $AsF_3$, **(b)** $CH_3{}^+$, **(c)** $BrF_3$, **(d)** $ClO_3{}^-$, **(e)** $XeF_2$, **(f)** $BrO_2{}^-$.

**9.29** The figure that follows shows ball-and-stick drawings of three possible shapes of an $AF_3$ molecule. **(a)** For each shape, give the electron-domain geometry on which the molecular geometry is based. **(b)** For each shape, how many nonbonding electron domains are there on atom A? **(c)** Which of the following elements will lead to an $AF_3$ molecule with the shape in (ii): Li, B, N, Al, P, Cl? **(d)** Name an element A that is expected to lead to the $AF_3$ structure shown in (iii). Explain your reasoning.

(i)                    (ii)                    (iii)

**9.30** The figure that follows contains ball-and-stick drawings of three possible shapes of an $AF_4$ molecule. **(a)** For each shape, give the electron-domain geometry on which the molecular geometry is based. **(b)** For each shape, how many nonbonding electron domains are there on atom A? **(c)** Which of the following elements will lead to an $AF_4$ molecule with the shape in (iii): Be, C, S, Se, Si, Xe? **(d)** Name an element A that is expected to lead to the $AF_4$ structure shown in (i).

(i)                    (ii)                    (iii)

**9.31** Give the approximate values for the indicated bond angles in the following molecules:

**(a)**   H—Ö—Cl—Ö:
                  |
                 :Ö:

**(b)**   H—C—Ö—H
          (with H atoms above and below C)

**(c)**   H—C≡C—H

**(d)**   H—C—Ö—C—H
          (with O double bond and H atoms)

**9.32** Give approximate values for the indicated bond angles in the following molecules:

**(a)**   H—Ö—N=Ö

**(b)**   H—C—C=Ö
          (with H atoms on C)

**(c)**   H—N—Ö—H
          (with H atoms)

**(d)**   H—C—C≡N:
          (with H atoms)

**9.33** In which of the following $AF_n$ molecules or ions is there more than one F—A—F bond angle: $SiF_4$, $PF_5$, $SF_4$, $AsF_3$?

**9.34** The three species $NH_2{}^-$, $NH_3$, and $NH_4{}^+$ have H—N—H bond angles of 105°, 107°, and 109°, respectively. Explain this variation in bond angles.

**9.35** **(a)** Explain why $BrF_4{}^-$ is square planar, whereas $BF_4{}^-$ is tetrahedral. **(b)** How would you expect the H—X—H bond angle to vary in the series $H_2O$, $H_2S$, $H_2Se$? Explain. (*Hint:* The size of an electron pair domain depends in part on the electronegativity of the central atom.)

**9.36** **(a)** Explain why the following ions have different bond angles: $ClO_2{}^-$ and $NO_2{}^-$. Predict the bond angle in each case. **(b)** Explain why the $XeF_2$ molecule is linear.

# SHAPES AND POLARITY OF POLYATOMIC MOLECULES (section 9.3)

**9.37** What is the distinction between a bond dipole and a molecular dipole moment?

**9.38** Consider a molecule with formula $AX_3$. Supposing the A—X bond is polar, how would you expect the dipole moment of the $AX_3$ molecule to change as the X—A—X bond angle increases from $100°$ to $120°$?

**9.39** (a) Does $SCl_2$ have a dipole moment? If so, in which direction does the net dipole point? (b) Does $BeCl_2$ have a dipole moment? If so, in which direction does the net dipole point?

**9.40** (a) The $PH_3$ molecule is polar. Does this offer experimental proof that the molecule cannot be planar? Explain. (b) It turns out that ozone, $O_3$, has a small dipole moment. How is this possible, given that all the atoms are the same?

**9.41** (a) Consider the $AF_3$ molecules in Exercise 9.29. Which of these will have a nonzero dipole moment? Explain. (b) Which of the $AF_4$ molecules in Exercise 9.30 will have a zero dipole moment?

**9.42** (a) What conditions must be met if a molecule with polar bonds is nonpolar? (b) What geometries will signify nonpolar molecules for $AB_2$, $AB_3$, and $AB_4$ geometries?

**9.43** Predict whether each of the following molecules is polar or nonpolar: (a) IF, (b) $CS_2$, (c) $SO_3$, (d) $PCl_3$, (e) $SF_6$, (f) $IF_5$.

**9.44** Predict whether each of the following molecules is polar or nonpolar: (a) $CCl_4$, (b) $NH_3$, (c) $SF_4$, (d) $XeF_4$, (e) $CH_3Br$, (f) $GaH_3$.

**9.45** Dichloroethylene ($C_2H_2Cl_2$) has three forms (isomers), each of which is a different substance. (a) Draw Lewis structures of the three isomers, all of which have a carbon–carbon double bond. (b) Which of these isomers has a zero dipole moment? (c) How many isomeric forms can chloroethylene, $C_2H_3Cl$, have? Would they be expected to have dipole moments?

**9.46** Dichlorobenzene, $C_6H_4Cl_2$, exists in three forms (isomers) called *ortho*, *meta*, and *para*:

*ortho*          *meta*          *para*

Which of these has a nonzero dipole moment? Explain.

# ORBITAL OVERLAP; HYBRID ORBITALS (sections 9.4 and 9.5)

**9.47** (a) What is meant by the term *orbital overlap*? (b) Describe what a chemical bond is in terms of electron density between two atoms.

**9.48** Draw sketches illustrating the overlap between the following orbitals on two atoms: (a) the $2s$ orbital on each atom, (b) the $2p_z$ orbital on each atom (assume both atoms are on the z-axis), (c) the $2s$ orbital on one atom and the $2p_z$ orbital on the other atom.

**9.49** Consider the bonding in an $MgH_2$ molecule. (a) Draw a Lewis structure for the molecule, and predict its molecular geometry. (b) What hybridization scheme is used in $MgH_2$? (c) Sketch one of the two-electron bonds between an Mg hybrid orbital and an H $1s$ atomic orbital.

**9.50** How would you expect the extent of overlap of the bonding atomic orbitals to vary in the series IF, ICl, IBr, and $I_2$? Explain your answer.

**9.51** Fill in the blank spaces in the following chart. If the molecule column is blank, find an example that fulfills the conditions of the rest of the row.

| Molecule | Electron-Domain Geometry | Hybridization of Central Atom | Dipole Moment? Yes or No |
|---|---|---|---|
| $CO_2$ | | | |
| | | $sp^3$ | Yes |
| | | $sp^3$ | No |
| | Trigonal planar | | No |
| $SF_4$ | | | |
| | Octahedral | | No |
| | | $sp^2$ | Yes |
| | Trigonal bipyramidal | | No |
| $XeF_2$ | | | |

**9.52** Why are there no $sp^4$ or $sp^5$ hybrid orbitals?

**9.53** (a) Starting with the orbital diagram of a boron atom, describe the steps needed to construct hybrid orbitals appropriate to describe the bonding in $BF_3$. (b) What is the name given to the hybrid orbitals constructed in (a)? (c) Sketch the large lobes of the hybrid orbitals constructed in part (a). (d) Are any valence atomic orbitals of B left unhybridized? If so, how are they oriented relative to the hybrid orbitals?

**9.54** (a) Starting with the orbital diagram of a sulfur atom, describe the steps needed to construct hybrid orbitals appropriate to describe the bonding in $SF_2$. (b) What is the name given to the hybrid orbitals constructed in (a)? (c) Sketch the large lobes of these hybrid orbitals. (d) Would the hybridization scheme in part (a) be appropriate for $SF_4$? Explain.

**9.55** Indicate the hybridization of the central atom in (a) $BCl_3$, (b) $AlCl_4^-$, (c) $CS_2$, (d) $GeH_4$.

**9.56** What is the hybridization of the central atom in (a) $SiCl_4$, (b) HCN, (c) $SO_3$, (d) $TeCl_2$.

**9.57** Shown here are three pairs of hybrid orbitals, with each set at a characteristic angle. For each pair, determine the type of hybridization, if any, that could lead to hybrid orbitals at the specified angle.

**9.58** (a) Which geometry and central atom hybridization would you expect in the series $BH_4^-$, $CH_4$, $NH_4^+$? (b) What would you expect for the magnitude and direction of the bond dipoles in this series? (c) Write the formulas for the analogous species of the elements of period 3; would you expect them to have the same hybridization at the central atom?

# MULTIPLE BONDS (section 9.6)

**9.59** (a) Draw a picture showing how two *p* orbitals on two different atoms can be combined to make a sigma bond. (b) Sketch a $\pi$ bond that is constructed from *p* orbitals. (c) Which is generally stronger, a $\sigma$ bond or a $\pi$ bond? Explain. (d) Can two *s* orbitals combine to form a $\pi$ bond? Explain.

**9.60** (a) If the valence atomic orbitals of an atom are *sp* hybridized, how many unhybridized *p* orbitals remain in the valence shell? How many $\pi$ bonds can the atom form? (b) Imagine that you could hold two atoms that are bonded together, twist them, and not change the bond length. Would it be easier to twist (rotate) around a single $\sigma$ bond or around a double ($\sigma$ plus $\pi$) bond, or would they be the same? Explain.

**9.61** (a) Draw Lewis structures for ethane ($C_2H_6$), ethylene ($C_2H_4$), and acetylene ($C_2H_2$). (b) What is the hybridization of the carbon atoms in each molecule? (c) Predict which molecules, if any, are planar. (d) How many $\sigma$ and $\pi$ bonds are there in each molecule? (e) Suppose that silicon could form molecules that are precisely the analogs of ethane, ethylene, and acetylene. How would you describe the bonding about Si in terms of hybrid orbitals? Silicon does not readily form some of the analogous compounds containing $\pi$ bonds. Why might this be the case?

**9.62** The nitrogen atoms in $N_2$ participate in multiple bonding, whereas those in hydrazine, $N_2H_4$, do not. (a) Draw Lewis structures for both molecules. (b) What is the hybridization of the nitrogen atoms in each molecule? (c) Which molecule has the stronger N—N bond?

**9.63** Propylene, $C_3H_6$, is a gas that is used to form the important polymer called polypropylene. Its Lewis structure is

$$\text{H—C=C—C—H}$$

(a) What is the total number of valence electrons in the propylene molecule? (b) How many valence electrons are used to make $\sigma$ bonds in the molecule? (c) How many valence electrons are used to make $\pi$ bonds in the molecule? (d) How many valence electrons remain in nonbonding pairs in the molecule? (e) What is the hybridization at each carbon atom in the molecule?

**9.64** Ethyl acetate, $C_4H_8O_2$, is a fragrant substance used both as a solvent and as an aroma enhancer. Its Lewis structure is

$$\text{H—C—C—O—C—C—H}$$

(a) What is the hybridization at each of the carbon atoms of the molecule? (b) What is the total number of valence electrons in ethyl acetate? (c) How many of the valence electrons are used to make $\sigma$ bonds in the molecule? (d) How many

valence electrons are used to make $\pi$ bonds? (e) How many valence electrons remain in nonbonding pairs in the molecule?

**9.65** Consider the Lewis structure for glycine, the simplest amino acid:

$$\text{H—N—C—C—O—H}$$

(a) What are the approximate bond angles about each of the two carbon atoms, and what are the hybridizations of the orbitals on each of them? (b) What are the hybridizations of the orbitals on the two oxygens and the nitrogen atom, and what are the approximate bond angles at the nitrogen? (c) What is the total number of $\sigma$ bonds in the entire molecule, and what is the total number of $\pi$ bonds?

**9.66** Acetylsalicylic acid, better known as aspirin, has the Lewis structure

(a) What are the approximate values of the bond angles labeled 1, 2, and 3? (b) What hybrid orbitals are used about the central atom of each of these angles? (c) How many $\sigma$ bonds are in the molecule?

**9.67** (a) What is the difference between a localized $\pi$ bond and a delocalized one? (b) How can you determine whether a molecule or ion will exhibit delocalized $\pi$ bonding? (c) Is the $\pi$ bond in $NO_2^-$ localized or delocalized?

**9.68** (a) Write a single Lewis structure for $SO_3$, and determine the hybridization at the S atom. (b) Are there other equivalent Lewis structures for the molecule? (c) Would you expect $SO_3$ to exhibit delocalized $\pi$ bonding? Explain.

**9.69** Predict the molecular geometry of each of the following molecules:

(a) $\text{H—C}\equiv\text{C—C}\equiv\text{C—C}\equiv\text{N}$

(b) $\text{H—O—C—C—O—H}$

(c) $\text{H—N}=\text{N—H}$

**9.70** What hybridization do you expect for the atom indicated in red in each of the following species?
(a) $CH_3CO_2^-$; (b) $PH_4^+$; (c) $AlF_3$; (d) $H_2C{=}CH{-}CH_2^+$

# MOLECULAR ORBITALS AND SECOND-ROW DIATOMIC MOLECULES (sections 9.7 and 9.8)

**9.71** (a) What is the difference between hybrid orbitals and molecular orbitals? (b) How many electrons can be placed into each MO of a molecule? (c) Can antibonding molecular orbitals have electrons in them?

**9.72** (a) If you combine two atomic orbitals on two different atoms to make a new orbital, is this a hybrid orbital or a molecular orbital? (b) If you combine two atomic orbitals on *one* atom to make a new orbital, is this a hybrid orbital or a molecular orbital? (c) Does the Pauli exclusion principle (Section 6.7) apply to MOs? Explain.

**9.73** Consider the $H_2^+$ ion. (a) Sketch the molecular orbitals of the ion and draw its energy-level diagram. (b) How many electrons are there in the $H_2^+$ ion? (c) Draw the electron configuration of the ion in terms of its MOs. (d) What is the bond order in $H_2^+$? (e) Suppose that the ion is excited by light so that an electron moves from a lower-energy to a higher-energy MO. Would you expect the excited-state $H_2^+$ ion to be stable or to fall apart? Explain.

**9.74** (a) Sketch the molecular orbitals of the $H_2^-$ ion and draw its energy-level diagram. (b) Write the electron configuration of the ion in terms of its MOs. (c) Calculate the bond order in $H_2^-$. (d) Suppose that the ion is excited by light, so that an electron moves from a lower-energy to a higher-energy molecular orbital. Would you expect the excited-state $H_2^-$ ion to be stable? Explain.

**9.75** Draw a picture that shows all three $2p$ orbitals on one atom and all three $2p$ orbitals on another atom. (a) Imagine the atoms coming close together to bond. How many $\sigma$ bonds can the two sets of $2p$ orbitals make with each other? (b) How many $\pi$ bonds can the two sets of $2p$ orbitals make with each other? (c) How many antibonding orbitals, and of what type, can be made from the two sets of $2p$ orbitals?

**9.76** (a) What is the probability of finding an electron on the internuclear axis if the electron occupies a $\pi$ molecular orbital? (b) For a homonuclear diatomic molecule, what similarities and differences are there between the $\pi_{2p}$ MO made from the $2p_x$ atomic orbitals and the $\pi_{2p}$ MO made from the $2p_y$ atomic orbitals? (c) How do the $\pi_{2p}^*$ MOs formed from the $2p_x$ and $2p_y$ atomic orbitals differ from the $\pi_{2p}$ MOs in terms of energies and electron distributions?

**9.77** (a) What are the relationships among bond order, bond length, and bond energy? (b) According to molecular orbital theory, would either $Be_2$ or $Be_2^+$ be expected to exist? Explain.

**9.78** Explain the following: (a) The *peroxide* ion, $O_2^{2-}$, has a longer bond length than the *superoxide* ion, $O_2^-$. (b) The magnetic properties of $B_2$ are consistent with the $\pi_{2p}$ MOs being lower in energy than the $\sigma_{2p}$ MO. (c) The $O_2^{2+}$ ion has a stronger O—O bond than $O_2$ itself.

**9.79** (a) What does the term *diamagnetism* mean? (b) How does a diamagnetic substance respond to a magnetic field? (c) Which of the following ions would you expect to be diamagnetic: $N_2^{2-}$, $O_2^{2-}$, $Be_2^{2+}$, $C_2^-$?

**9.80** (a) What does the term *paramagnetism* mean? (b) How can one determine experimentally whether a substance is paramagnetic? (c) Which of the following ions would you expect to be paramagnetic: $O_2^+$, $N_2^{2-}$, $Li_2^+$, $O_2^{2-}$? For those ions that are paramagnetic, determine the number of unpaired electrons.

**9.81** Using Figures 9.35 and 9.43 as guides, draw the molecular orbital electron configuration for (a) $B_2^+$, (b) $Li_2^+$, (c) $N_2^+$, (d) $Ne_2^{2+}$. In each case indicate whether the addition of an electron to the ion would increase or decrease the bond order of the species.

**9.82** If we assume that the energy-level diagrams for homonuclear diatomic molecules shown in Figure 9.43 can be applied to heteronuclear diatomic molecules and ions, predict the bond order and magnetic behavior of (a) $CO^+$, (b) $NO^-$, (c) $OF^+$, (d) $NeF^+$.

**9.83** Determine the electron configurations for $CN^+$, $CN$, and $CN^-$. (a) Which species has the strongest C—N bond? (b) Which species, if any, has unpaired electrons?

**9.84** (a) The nitric oxide molecule, NO, readily loses one electron to form the $NO^+$ ion. Why is this consistent with the electronic structure of NO? (b) Predict the order of the N—O bond strengths in NO, $NO^+$, and $NO^-$, and describe the magnetic properties of each. (c) With what neutral homonuclear diatomic molecules are the $NO^+$ and $NO^-$ ions isoelectronic (same number of electrons)?

**[9.85]** Consider the molecular orbitals of the $P_2$ molecule. Assume that the MOs of diatomics from the third row of the periodic table are analogous to those from the second row. (a) Which valence atomic orbitals of P are used to construct the MOs of $P_2$? (b) The figure that follows shows a sketch of one of the MOs for $P_2$. What is the label for this MO? (c) For the $P_2$ molecule, how many electrons occupy the MO in the figure? (d) Is $P_2$ expected to be diamagnetic or paramagnetic? Explain.

**[9.86]** The iodine bromide molecule, IBr, is an *interhalogen compound*. Assume that the molecular orbitals of IBr are analogous to the homonuclear diatomic molecule $F_2$. (a) Which valence atomic orbitals of I and of Br are used to construct the MOs of IBr? (b) What is the bond order of the IBr molecule? (c) One of the valence MOs of IBr is sketched here. Why are the atomic orbital contributions to this MO different in size? (d) What is the label for the MO? (e) For the IBr molecule, how many electrons occupy the MO?

## ADDITIONAL EXERCISES

**9.87** (a) What is the physical basis for the VSEPR model? (b) When applying the VSEPR model, we count a double or triple bond as a single electron domain. Why is this justified?

**9.88** What is the fundamental basis on which we assign electrons to electron domains in pairs and with their spins paired?

**9.89** The molecules $SiF_4$, $SF_4$, and $XeF_4$ have molecular formulas of the type $AF_4$, but the molecules have different molecular geometries. Predict the shape of each molecule, and explain why the shapes differ.

**9.90** Consider the molecule $PF_4Cl$. (a) Draw a Lewis structure for the molecule, and predict its electron-domain geometry. (b)

Which would you expect to take up more space, a P—F bond or a P—Cl bond? Explain. (c) Predict the molecular geometry of $PF_4Cl$. How did your answer for part (b) influence your answer here in part (c)? (d) Would you expect the molecule to distort from its ideal electron-domain geometry? If so, how would it distort?

**[9.91]** The vertices of a tetrahedron correspond to four alternating corners of a cube. By using analytical geometry, demonstrate that the angle made by connecting two of the vertices to a point at the center of the cube is 109.5°, the characteristic angle for tetrahedral molecules.

**9.92** From their Lewis structures, determine the number of $\sigma$ and $\pi$ bonds in each of the following molecules or ions: **(a)** $CO_2$; **(b)** cyanogen, $(CN)_2$; **(c)** formaldehyde, $H_2CO$; **(d)** formic acid, HCOOH, which has one H and two O atoms attached to C.

**9.93** The lactic acid molecule, $CH_3CH(OH)COOH$, gives sour milk its unpleasant, sour taste. **(a)** Draw the Lewis structure for the molecule, assuming that carbon always forms four bonds in its stable compounds. **(b)** How many $\pi$ and how many $\sigma$ bonds are in the molecule? **(c)** Which CO bond is shortest in the molecule? **(d)** What is the hybridization of atomic orbitals around the carbon atom associated with that short bond? **(e)** What are the approximate bond angles around each carbon atom in the molecule?

**9.94** The $PF_3$ molecule has a dipole moment of 1.03 D, but $BF_3$ has a dipole moment of zero. How can you explain the difference?

**9.95** An $AB_5$ molecule adopts the geometry shown here. **(a)** What is the name of this geometry? **(b)** Do you think there are any non-bonding electron pairs on atom A? Why or why not? **(c)** Suppose the atoms B are halogen atoms. Can you determine uniquely to which group in the periodic table atom A belongs?

**9.96** There are two compounds of the formula $Pt(NH_3)_2Cl_2$:

$$\begin{array}{ccc} & NH_3 & & & Cl \\ & | & & & | \\ Cl-&Pt&-Cl & Cl-&Pt&-NH_3 \\ & | & & & | \\ & NH_3 & & & NH_3 \end{array}$$

The compound on the right, *cisplatin,* is used in cancer therapy. The compound on the left, *transplatin,* is ineffective for cancer therapy. Both compounds have a square-planar geometry. **(a)** Which compound has a nonzero dipole moment? **(b)** The reason cisplatin is a good anticancer drug is that it binds tightly to DNA. Cancer cells are rapidly dividing, producing a lot of DNA. Consequently, cisplatin kills cancer cells at a faster rate than normal cells. However, since normal cells also are making DNA, cisplatin also attacks healthy cells, which leads to unpleasant side effects. The way both molecules bind to DNA involves the $Cl^-$ ions leaving the Pt ion, to be replaced by two nitrogens in DNA. Draw a picture in which a long vertical line represents a piece of DNA. Draw the $Pt(NH_3)_2$ fragments of cisplatin and transplatin with the proper shape. Also draw them attaching to your DNA line. Can you explain from your drawing why the shape of the cisplatin causes it to bind to DNA more effectively than transplatin?

**[9.97]** The O—H bond lengths in the water molecule ($H_2O$) are 0.96 Å, and the H—O—H angle is 104.5°. The dipole moment of the water molecule is 1.85 D. **(a)** In what directions do the bond dipoles of the O—H bonds point? In what direction does the dipole moment vector of the water molecule point? **(b)** Calculate the magnitude of the bond dipole of the O—H bonds. (*Note:* You will need to use vector addition to do this.) **(c)** Compare your answer from part (b) to the dipole moments of the hydrogen halides (Table 8.3). Is your answer in accord with the relative electronegativity of oxygen?

**[9.98]** The reaction of three molecules of fluorine gas with a Xe atom produces the substance xenon hexafluoride, $XeF_6$:

$$Xe(g) + 3\,F_2(g) \longrightarrow XeF_6(s)$$

**(a)** Draw a Lewis structure for $XeF_6$. **(b)** If you try to use the VSEPR model to predict the molecular geometry of $XeF_6$, you run into a problem. What is it? **(c)** What could you do to resolve the difficulty in part (b)? **(d)** The molecule $IF_7$ has a pentagonal-bipyramidal structure (five equatorial fluorine atoms at the vertices of a regular pentagon and two axial fluorine atoms). Based on the structure of $IF_7$, suggest a structure for $XeF_6$.

**[9.99]** The Lewis structure for allene is

$$\begin{array}{cccc} H & & & H \\ \diagdown & & & \diagup \\ & C=C=C & \\ \diagup & & & \diagdown \\ H & & & H \end{array}$$

Make a sketch of the structure of this molecule that is analogous to Figure 9.25. In addition, answer the following three questions: **(a)** Is the molecule planar? **(b)** Does it have a nonzero dipole moment? **(c)** Would the bonding in allene be described as delocalized? Explain.

**[9.100]** The azide ion, $N_3^-$, is linear with two N—N bonds of equal length, 1.16 Å. **(a)** Draw a Lewis structure for the azide ion. **(b)** With reference to Table 8.5, is the observed N—N bond length consistent with your Lewis structure? **(c)** What hybridization scheme would you expect at each of the nitrogen atoms in $N_3^-$? **(d)** Show which hybridized and unhybridized orbitals are involved in the formation of $\sigma$ and $\pi$ bonds in $N_3^-$. **(e)** It is often observed that $\sigma$ bonds that involve an $sp$ hybrid orbital are shorter than those that involve only $sp^2$ or $sp^3$ hybrid orbitals. Can you propose a reason for this? Is this observation applicable to the observed bond lengths in $N_3^-$?

**[9.101]** In ozone, $O_3$, the two oxygen atoms on the ends of the molecule are equivalent to one another. **(a)** What is the best choice of hybridization scheme for the atoms of ozone? **(b)** For one of the resonance forms of ozone, which of the orbitals are used to make bonds and which are used to hold nonbonding pairs of electrons? **(c)** Which of the orbitals can be used to delocalize the $\pi$ electrons? **(d)** How many electrons are delocalized in the $\pi$ system of ozone?

**9.102** Butadiene, $C_4H_6$, is a planar molecule that has the following carbon–carbon bond lengths:

$$H_2C \underset{1.34\,\text{Å}}{=\!\!=\!\!=} CH \underset{1.48\,\text{Å}}{-\!\!\!-\!\!\!-} CH \underset{1.34\,\text{Å}}{=\!\!=\!\!=} CH_2$$

**(a)** Predict the bond angles around each of the carbon atoms and sketch the molecule.

**(b)** Compare the bond lengths to the average bond lengths listed in Table 8.5. Can you explain any differences?

**[9.103]** The following sketches show the atomic orbital wave functions (with phases) used to construct some of the MOs of a homonuclear diatomic molecule. For each sketch, determine the type of MO that will result from mixing the atomic orbital wave functions as drawn. Use the same labels for the MOs as in the "Closer Look" box on phases.

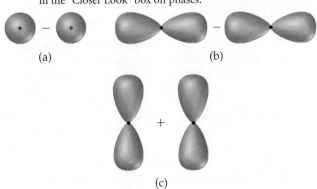

(a)  (b)

(c)

**9.104** Write the electron configuration for the first excited state for $N_2$ —that is, the state with the highest-energy electron moved to the next available energy level. (a) Is the nitrogen in its first excited state diamagnetic or paramagnetic? (b) Is the N—N bond strength in the first excited state stronger or weaker compared to that in the ground state? Explain.

**9.105** *Azo dyes* are organic dyes that are used for many applications, such as the coloring of fabrics. Many azo dyes are derivatives of the organic substance *azobenzene*, $C_{12}H_{10}N_2$. A closely related substance is *hydrazobenzene*, $C_{12}H_{12}N_2$. The Lewis structures of these two substances are

Azobenzene                    Hydrazobenzene

(Recall the shorthand notation used for benzene.) (a) What is the hybridization at the N atom in each of the substances? (b) How many unhybridized atomic orbitals are there on the N and the C atoms in each of the substances? (c) Predict the N—N—C angles in each of the substances. (d) Azobenzene is said to have greater delocalization of its $\pi$ electrons than hydrazobenzene. Discuss this statement in light of your answers to (a) and (b). (e) All the atoms of azobenzene lie in one plane, whereas those of hydrazobenzene do not. Is this observation consistent with the statement in part (d)? (f) Azobenzene is an intense red-orange color, whereas hydrazobenzene is nearly colorless. Which molecule would be a better one to use in a solar energy conversion device? (See the "Chemistry Put to Work" box for more information about solar cells.)

**[9.106]** (a) Using only the valence atomic orbitals of a hydrogen atom and a fluorine atom, and following the model of Figure 9.46, how many MOs would you expect for the HF molecule? (b) How many of the MOs from part (a) would be occupied by electrons? (c) It turns out that the difference in energies between the valence atomic orbitals of H and F are sufficiently different that we can neglect the interaction of the 1s orbital of

hydrogen with the 2s orbital of fluorine. The 1s orbital of hydrogen will mix only with one 2p orbital of fluorine. Draw pictures showing the proper orientation of all three 2p orbitals on F interacting with a 1s orbital on H. Which of the 2p orbitals can actually make a bond with a 1s orbital, assuming that the atoms lie on the z-axis? (d) In the most accepted picture of HF, all the other atomic orbitals on fluorine move over at the same energy into the molecular orbital energy-level diagram for HF. These are called "nonbonding orbitals." Sketch the energy-level diagram for HF using this information and calculate the bond order. (Nonbonding electrons do not contribute to bond order.) (e) Look at the Lewis structure for HF. Where are the nonbonding electrons?

**[9.107]** Carbon monoxide, CO, is isoelectronic to $N_2$. (a) Draw a Lewis structure for CO that satisfies the octet rule. (b) Assume that the diagram in Figure 9.46 can be used to describe the MOs of CO. What is the predicted bond order for CO? Is this answer in accord with the Lewis structure you drew in part (a)? (c) Experimentally, it is found that the highest-energy electrons in CO reside in a $\sigma$-type MO. Is that observation consistent with Figure 9.46? If not, what modification needs to be made to the diagram? How does this modification relate to Figure 9.43? (d) Would you expect the $\pi_{2p}$ MOs of CO to have equal atomic orbital contributions from the C and O atoms? If not, which atom would have the greater contribution?

**9.108** The energy-level diagram in Figure 9.36 shows that the sideways overlap of a pair of p orbitals produces two molecular orbitals, one bonding and one antibonding. In ethylene there is a pair of electrons in the bonding $\pi$ orbital between the two carbons. Absorption of a photon of the appropriate wavelength can result in promotion of one of the bonding electrons from the $\pi_{2p}$ to the $\pi^*_{2p}$ molecular orbital. (a) What would you expect this electronic transition to do to the carbon–carbon bond order in ethylene? (b) How does this relate to the fact that absorption of a photon of appropriate wavelength can cause ready rotation about the carbon–carbon bond, as described in the "Chemistry and Life" box and shown in Figure 9.30?

# INTEGRATIVE EXERCISES

**9.109** A compound composed of 2.1% H, 29.8% N, and 68.1% O has a molar mass of approximately 50 g/mol. (a) What is the molecular formula of the compound? (b) What is its Lewis structure if H is bonded to O? (c) What is the geometry of the molecule? (d) What is the hybridization of the orbitals around the N atom? (e) How many $\sigma$ and how many $\pi$ bonds are there in the molecule?

**9.110** Sulfur tetrafluoride ($SF_4$) reacts slowly with $O_2$ to form sulfur tetrafluoride monoxide ($OSF_4$) according to the following unbalanced reaction:

$$SF_4(g) + O_2(g) \longrightarrow OSF_4(g)$$

The O atom and the four F atoms in $OSF_4$ are bonded to a central S atom. (a) Balance the equation. (b) Write a Lewis structure of $OSF_4$ in which the formal charges of all atoms are zero. (c) Use average bond enthalpies (Table 8.4) to estimate the enthalpy of the reaction. Is it endothermic or exothermic? (d) Determine the electron-domain geometry of $OSF_4$, and write two possible molecular geometries for the molecule based on this electron-domain geometry. (e) Which of the molecular geometries in part (d) is more likely to be observed for the molecule? Explain.

**[9.111]** The phosphorus trihalides ($PX_3$) show the following variation in the bond angle X—P—X: $PF_3$, 96.3°; $PCl_3$, 100.3°; $PBr_3$, 101.0°; $PI_3$, 102.0°. The trend is generally attributed to the change in the electronegativity of the halogen. (a) Assuming that all electron domains are the same size, what value of the X—P—X angle is predicted by the VSEPR model? (b) What is the general trend in the X—P—X angle as the halide electronegativity increases? (c) Using the VSEPR model, explain the observed trend in X—P—X angle as the electronegativity of X changes. (d) Based on your answer to part (c), predict the structure of $PBrCl_4$.

**[9.112]** The molecule 2-butene, $C_4H_8$, can undergo a geometric change called *cis-trans isomerization*:

*cis*-2-butene                    *trans*-2-butene

As discussed in the "Chemistry and Life" box on the chemistry of vision, such transformations can be induced by light and are the key to human vision. **(a)** What is the hybridization at the two central carbon atoms of 2-butene? **(b)** The isomerization occurs by rotation about the central C—C bond. With reference to Figure 9.30, explain why the $\pi$ bond between the two central carbon atoms is destroyed halfway through the rotation from *cis-* to *trans-*2-butene. **(c)** Based on average bond enthalpies (Table 8.4), how much energy per molecule must be supplied to break the C—C $\pi$ bond? **(d)** What is the longest wavelength of light that will provide photons of sufficient energy to break the C—C $\pi$ bond and cause the isomerization? **(e)** Is the wavelength in your answer to part (d) in the visible portion of the electromagnetic spectrum? Comment on the importance of this result for human vision.

**9.113** **(a)** Compare the bond enthalpies (Table 8.4) of the carbon–carbon single, double, and triple bonds to deduce an average $\pi$-bond contribution to the enthalpy. What fraction of a single bond does this quantity represent? **(b)** Make a similar comparison of nitrogen–nitrogen bonds. What do you observe? **(c)** Write Lewis structures of $N_2H_4$, $N_2H_2$, and $N_2$, and determine the hybridization around nitrogen in each case. **(d)** Propose a reason for the large difference in your observations of parts (a) and (b).

**9.114** Use average bond enthalpies (Table 8.4) to estimate $\Delta H$ for the atomization of benzene, $C_6H_6$:

$$C_6H_6(g) \longrightarrow 6\ C(g) + 6\ H(g)$$

Compare the value to that obtained by using $\Delta H_f^\circ$ data given in Appendix C and Hess's law. To what do you attribute the large discrepancy in the two values?

**[9.115]** Many compounds of the transition-metal elements contain direct bonds between metal atoms. We will assume that the *z*-axis is defined as the metal–metal bond axis. **(a)** Which of the 3*d* orbitals (Figure 6.23) can be used to make a $\sigma$ bond between metal atoms? **(b)** Sketch the $\sigma_{3d}$ bonding and $\sigma_{3d}^*$ antibonding MOs. **(c)** With reference to the "Closer Look" box on the phases of orbitals, explain why a node is generated in the $\sigma_{3d}^*$ MO. **(d)** Sketch the energy-level diagram for the $Sc_2$ molecule, assuming that only the 3*d* orbital from part (a) is important. **(e)** What is the bond order in $Sc_2$?

**[9.116]** The organic molecules shown here are derivatives of benzene in which six-membered rings are "fused" at the edges of the hexagons.

Naphthalene      Anthracene

Tetracene

**(a)** Determine the empirical formula of benzene and of these three compounds. **(b)** Suppose you are given a sample of one of the compounds. Could combustion analysis be used to determine unambiguously which of the three it is? **(c)** Naphthalene, the active ingredient in mothballs, is a white solid. Write a balanced equation for the combustion of naphthalene to $CO_2(g)$ and $H_2O(g)$. **(d)** Using the Lewis structure for naphthalene and the average bond enthalpies in Table 8.4, estimate the heat of combustion of naphthalene in kJ/mol. **(e)** Would you expect naphthalene, anthracene, and tetracene to have multiple resonance structures? If so, draw the additional resonance structures for naphthalene. **(f)** Benzene, naphthalene, and anthracene are colorless, but tetracene is orange. What does this imply about the relative HOMO–LUMO energy gaps in these molecules? See the "Chemistry Put to Work" box on orbitals and energy.

**[9.117]** Antibonding molecular orbitals can be used to make bonds to other atoms in a molecule. For example, metal atoms can use appropriate *d* orbitals to overlap with the $\pi_{2p}^*$ orbitals of the carbon monoxide molecule. This is called *d–$\pi$ backbonding*. **(a)** Draw a coordinate axis system in which the *y*-axis is vertical in the plane of the paper and the *x*-axis horizontal. Write "M" at the origin to denote a metal atom. **(b)** Now, on the *x*-axis to the right of M, draw the Lewis structure of a CO molecule, with the carbon nearest the M. The CO bond axis should be on the *x*-axis. **(c)** Draw the CO $\pi_{2p}^*$ orbital, with phases (see the "Closer Look" box on phases) in the plane of the paper. Two lobes should be pointing toward M. **(d)** Now draw the $d_{xy}$ orbital of M, with phases. Can you see how they will overlap with the $\pi_{2p}^*$ orbital of CO? **(e)** What kind of bond is being made with the orbitals between M and C, $\sigma$ or $\pi$? **(f)** Predict what will happen to the strength of the CO bond in a metal–CO complex compared to CO alone.

**9.118** Methyl isocyanate, $CH_3NCO$, was made infamous in 1984 when an accidental leakage of this compound from a storage tank in Bhopal, India, resulted in the deaths of about 3,800 people and severe and lasting injury to many thousands more. **(a)** Draw a Lewis structure for methyl isocyanate. **(b)** Draw a ball-and-stick model of the structure, including estimates of all the bond angles in the compound. **(c)** Predict all the bond distances in the molecule. **(d)** Do you predict that the molecule will have a dipole moment? Explain.

# WHAT'S AHEAD

**10.1** CHARACTERISTICS OF GASES
We begin by comparing the distinguishing characteristics of gases with those of liquids and solids.

**10.2** PRESSURE
We then study gas *pressure,* how it is measured, and the units used to express it, as well as consider Earth's atmosphere and the pressure it exerts.

**10.3** THE GAS LAWS
We next see that the state of a gas can be expressed in terms of its volume, pressure, temperature, and quantity and examine several *gas laws,* which are empirical relationships among these four variables.

**10.4** THE IDEAL-GAS EQUATION
We find that the gas laws yield the *ideal-gas equation, PV = nRT*. Although this equation is not obeyed exactly by any real gas, most gases come very close to obeying it at ordinary temperatures and pressures.

**10.5** FURTHER APPLICATIONS OF THE IDEAL-GAS EQUATION
We use the ideal-gas equation in many calculations, such as the calculation of the density or molar mass of a gas.

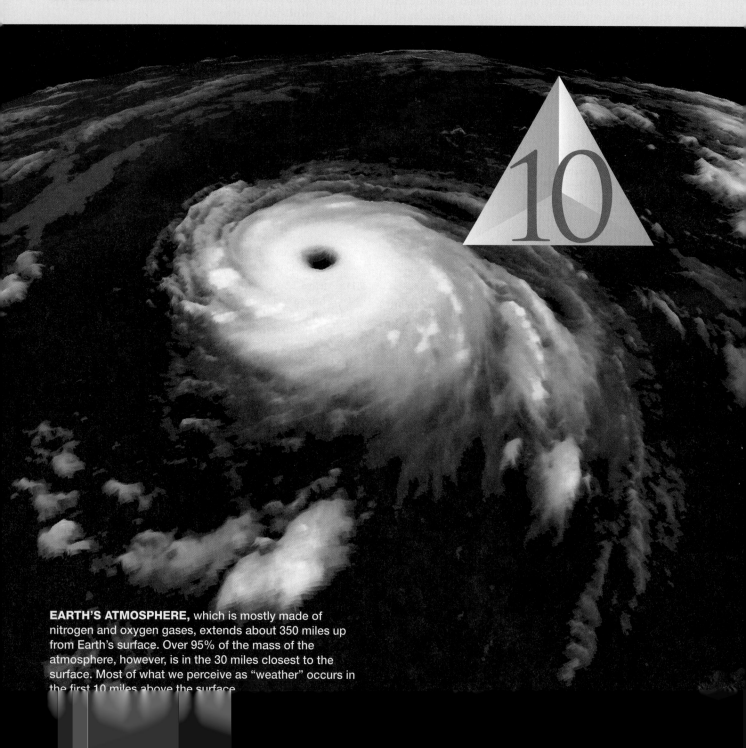

**EARTH'S ATMOSPHERE,** which is mostly made of nitrogen and oxygen gases, extends about 350 miles up from Earth's surface. Over 95% of the mass of the atmosphere, however, is in the 30 miles closest to the surface. Most of what we perceive as "weather" occurs in the first 10 miles above the surface.

## 10.6 GAS MIXTURES AND PARTIAL PRESSURES
We recognize that in a mixture of gases, each gas exerts a pressure that is part of the total pressure. This *partial pressure* is the pressure the gas would exert if it were by itself.

## 10.7 THE KINETIC-MOLECULAR THEORY OF GASES
We see that this theory helps us understand gas behavior on the molecular level. According to the theory, the atoms or molecules that make up a gas move with an average kinetic energy that is proportional to the gas temperature.

## 10.8 MOLECULAR EFFUSION AND DIFFUSION
We observe that the kinetic-molecular theory helps us account for such gas properties as *effusion,* movement through tiny openings, and *diffusion,* movement through another substance.

## 10.9 REAL GASES: DEVIATIONS FROM IDEAL BEHAVIOR
We learn that real gases deviate from ideal behavior because the gas molecules have finite volume and because attractive forces exist between molecules. The *van der Waals equation* gives an accurate account of real gas behavior at high pressures and low temperatures.

# GASES

**IN THE PAST SEVERAL CHAPTERS** we learned about the electronic structure of atoms and about how atoms combine to form molecules and ionic substances. In everyday life, however, we do not have any direct experience with atoms. Instead, we encounter matter as gases, liquids, or solids made up of

enormous numbers of atoms or molecules. Large collections of gas atoms and gas molecules in the atmosphere, for example, are responsible for weather—the gentle breezes and the gales, the humidity and the rain. Hurricanes, such as the one shown in the chapter-opening photo, are large storms (up to 500 miles in diameter) that form over the ocean and are characterized by a low-pressure center (the "eye"), heavy rains, and violent winds, with wind speeds up to 200 miles per hour. Hurricane formation is still not completely understood, but in general the atoms and molecules of the atmosphere are driven by a combination of low pressures, warm temperatures at the sea surface that rapidly cool with height, and high humidity to produce the storms.

We now know that the properties of gases (as well as those of liquids and solids) are readily understood in terms of the behavior of their component atoms, ions, and molecules; in this chapter we examine the physical properties of gases and explain these properties in terms of the behavior of gas molecules.

# 10.1 | CHARACTERISTICS OF GASES

In many ways gases are the most easily understood form of matter. Even though different gaseous substances may have very different *chemical* properties, they behave quite similarly as far as their *physical* properties are concerned. For example, we live in an atmosphere composed of the mixture of gases we refer to as air, a mixture of primarily $N_2$ (78%) and $O_2$ (21%), with small amounts of several other gases, including Ar (0.9%). Although $N_2$ and $O_2$ have very different chemical properties—$O_2$ supports human life but $N_2$ does not, to name just one difference—these two components of air behave physically as one gaseous material because their physical properties are essentially identical. Of the few elements that exist as gases at ordinary temperatures and pressures, He, Ne, Ar, Kr, and Xe are monatomic and $H_2$, $N_2$, $O_2$, $F_2$, and $Cl_2$ are diatomic. Many molecular compounds are gases, and ▼ TABLE 10.1 lists a few of them. Notice that all of these gases are composed entirely of nonmetallic elements. Furthermore, all have simple molecular formulas and, therefore, low molar masses.

Substances that are liquids or solids under ordinary conditions can also exist in the gaseous state, where they are often referred to as **vapors**. The substance $H_2O$, for example, can exist as liquid water, solid ice, or water vapor.

Gases differ significantly from solids and liquids in several respects. For example, a gas expands spontaneously to fill its container. Consequently, the volume of a gas equals the volume of its container. Gases also are highly compressible: When pressure is applied to a gas, its volume readily decreases. Solids and liquids, on the other hand, do not expand to fill their containers and are not readily compressible.

Two or more gases form a homogeneous mixture regardless of the identities or relative proportions of the gases; the atmosphere serves as an excellent example. Two or more liquids or two or more solids may or may not form homogeneous mixtures, depending on their chemical nature. For example, when water and gasoline are mixed, the two liquids remain as separate layers. In contrast, the water vapor and gasoline vapors above the liquids form a homogeneous gas mixture.

The characteristic properties of gases—expanding to fill a container, being highly compressible, forming homogeneous mixtures—arise because the molecules are relatively far apart. In any given volume of air, for example, the molecules take up only about 0.1% of the total volume with the rest being empty space. Thus, each molecule behaves largely as though the others were not present. As a result, different gases behave similarly even though they are made up of different molecules.

 **GIVE IT SOME THOUGHT**

Do the compounds in Table 10.1 have small (less than 100 g/mol) or large molecular weights?

**TABLE 10.1 • Some Common Compounds That Are Gases at Room Temperature**

| Formula | Name | Characteristics |
|---------|------|-----------------|
| HCN | Hydrogen cyanide | Very toxic, slight odor of bitter almonds |
| $H_2S$ | Hydrogen sulfide | Very toxic, odor of rotten eggs |
| CO | Carbon monoxide | Toxic, colorless, odorless |
| $CO_2$ | Carbon dioxide | Colorless, odorless |
| $CH_4$ | Methane | Colorless, odorless, flammable |
| $C_2H_4$ | Ethene (Ethylene) | Colorless, ripens fruit |
| $C_3H_8$ | Propane | Colorless, odorless, bottled gas |
| $N_2O$ | Nitrous oxide | Colorless, sweet odor, laughing gas |
| $NO_2$ | Nitrogen dioxide | Toxic, red-brown, irritating odor |
| $NH_3$ | Ammonia | Colorless, pungent odor |
| $SO_2$ | Sulfur dioxide | Colorless, irritating odor |

# 10.2 | PRESSURE

In everyday terms, **pressure** conveys the idea of force, a push that tends to move something in a given direction. Pressure, $P$, is defined in science as the force, $F$, that acts on a given area, $A$.

$$P = \frac{F}{A} \qquad\qquad [10.1]$$

Gases exert a pressure on any surface with which they are in contact. The gas in an inflated balloon, for example, exerts a pressure on the inside surface of the balloon.

## Atmospheric Pressure and the Barometer

People, coconuts, and nitrogen molecules all experience an attractive gravitational force that pulls them toward the center of Earth. When a coconut comes loose from a tree, for example, this force causes the coconut to be accelerated toward Earth, its speed increasing as its potential energy is converted into kinetic energy. ∞ (Section 5.1) The gas atoms and molecules of the atmosphere also experience a gravitational acceleration. Because these particles have such tiny masses, however, their thermal energies of motion (their kinetic energies) override the gravitational forces, so the particles that make up the atmosphere don't pile up at Earth's surface. Nevertheless, the gravitational force does operate, and it causes the atmosphere as a whole to press down on Earth's surface, creating atmospheric pressure, defined as the force exerted by the atmosphere on a given surface area.

You can demonstrate the existence of atmospheric pressure with an empty plastic water bottle. If you suck on the mouth of the empty bottle, chances are you can cause the bottle to partially cave in. When you break the partial vacuum you have created, the bottle pops out to its original shape. The bottle caves in because, once you've sucked out some of the air molecules, air molecules in the atmosphere exert a force on the outside of the bottle that is greater than the force exerted by the lesser number of air molecules inside the bottle. We calculate the magnitude of this atmospheric pressure as follows: The force, $F$, exerted by any object is the product of its mass, $m$, and its acceleration, $a$: $F = ma$. The acceleration given by Earth's gravitational force to any object located near Earth's surface is 9.8 m/s². Now imagine a column of air 1 m² in cross section extending through the entire atmosphere (▶ **FIGURE 10.1**). That column has a mass of roughly 10,000 kg. The downward gravitational force exerted on this column is

$$F = (10{,}000 \text{ kg})(9.8 \text{ m/s}^2) = 1 \times 10^5 \text{ kg-m/s}^2 = 1 \times 10^5 \text{ N}$$

where N is the abbreviation for *newton*, the SI unit for force: $1 \text{ N} = 1 \text{ kg-m/s}^2$. The pressure exerted by the column is this force divided by the cross-sectional area, $A$, over which the force is applied. Because our air column has a cross-sectional area of 1 m², we have for the magnitude of atmospheric pressure at sea level

$$P = \frac{F}{A} = \frac{1 \times 10^5 \text{ N}}{1 \text{ m}^2} = 1 \times 10^5 \text{ N/m}^2 = 1 \times 10^5 \text{ Pa} = 1 \times 10^2 \text{ kPa}$$

The SI unit of pressure is the **pascal** (Pa), named for Blaise Pascal (1623–1662), a French scientist who studied pressure: $1 \text{ Pa} = 1 \text{ N/m}^2$. A related pressure unit is the **bar**: $1 \text{ bar} = 10^5 \text{ Pa} = 10^5 \text{ N/m}^2$. Thus, the atmospheric pressure at sea level we just calculated, 100 kPa, can be reported as 1 bar. (The actual atmospheric pressure at any location depends on weather conditions and altitude.) Another pressure unit is pounds per square inch (psi, lbs/in.²). At sea level, atmospheric pressure is 14.7 psi.

⚠ GIVE IT SOME THOUGHT

Assume the top of your head has a surface area of 10 in. × 10 in. How many pounds of air are you carrying on your head if you are at sea level?

In the seventeenth century many scientists and philosophers believed that the atmosphere had no weight. Evangelista Torricelli (1608–1647), a student of Galileo's,

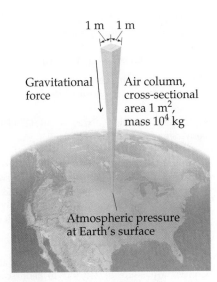

1 m   1 m

Gravitational force

Air column, cross-sectional area 1 m², mass 10⁴ kg

Atmospheric pressure at Earth's surface

▲ **FIGURE 10.1  Calculating atmospheric pressure.**

What happens to *h,* the height of the mercury column, if the atmospheric pressure increases?

Pressure exerted by Hg column on Hg surface

Vacuum

Hg

Pressure exerted by atmosphere on Hg surface

*h*

▲ **FIGURE 10.2** **A mercury barometer.**

proved this untrue. He invented the *barometer* (◄ **FIGURE 10.2**), which is made from a glass tube more than 760 mm long that is closed at one end, completely filled with mercury, and inverted into a dish of mercury. (Care must be taken so that no air gets into the tube.) When the tube is inverted into the dish, some of the mercury flows out of the tube, but a column of mercury remains in the tube. Torricelli argued that the mercury surface in the dish experiences the full force of Earth's atmosphere, which pushes the mercury up the tube until the pressure exerted by the mercury column downward, due to gravity, equals the atmospheric pressure at the base of the tube. Therefore the height, *h,* of the mercury column is a measure of atmospheric pressure and changes as atmospheric pressure changes.

Although Torricelli's explanation met with fierce opposition, it also had supporters. Blaise Pascal, for example, had one of Torricelli's barometers carried to the top of a mountain and compared its reading there with the reading on a duplicate barometer at the base of the mountain. As the barometer was carried up, the height of the mercury column diminished, as expected, because the amount of atmosphere pressing down on the mercury in the dish decreased as the instrument was carried higher. These and other experiments eventually prevailed, and the idea that the atmosphere has weight became accepted.

**Standard atmospheric pressure**, which corresponds to the typical pressure at sea level, is the pressure sufficient to support a column of mercury 760 mm high. In SI units this pressure is $1.01325 \times 10^5$ Pa. Standard atmospheric pressure defines some common non–SI units used to express gas pressure, such as the **atmosphere** (atm) and the *millimeter of mercury* (mm Hg). The latter unit is also called the **torr**, after Torricelli: 1 torr = 1 mm Hg. Thus, we have

1 atm = 760. mm Hg = 760. torr = $1.01325 \times 10^5$ Pa = 101.325 kPa = 1.01325 bar

We will usually express gas pressure in atmospheres, pascals, kilopascals, or torr, so you should be comfortable converting pressures from one unit to another.

---

**SAMPLE EXERCISE 10.1** **Converting Pressure Units**

**(a)** Convert 0.357 atm to torr. **(b)** Convert $6.6 \times 10^{-2}$ torr to atmospheres. **(c)** Convert 147.2 kPa to torr.

**SOLUTION**

**Analyze** In each case we are given the pressure in one unit and asked to convert it to another unit. Our task, therefore, is to choose the appropriate conversion factors.

**Plan** We can use dimensional analysis to perform the desired conversions.

**Solve**

**(a)** To convert atmospheres to torr, we use the relationship 760 torr = 1 atm:

$$(0.357 \text{ atm})\left(\frac{760 \text{ torr}}{1 \text{ atm}}\right) = 271 \text{ torr}$$

Note that the units cancel in the required manner.

**(b)** We use the same relationship as in part (a). To get the appropriate units to cancel, we must use the conversion factor as follows:

$$(6.6 \times 10^{-2} \text{ torr})\left(\frac{1 \text{ atm}}{760 \text{ torr}}\right) = 8.7 \times 10^{-5} \text{ atm}$$

**(c)** The relationship 760 torr = 101.325 kPa allows us to write an appropriate conversion factor for this problem:

$$(147.2 \text{ kPa})\left(\frac{760 \text{ torr}}{101.325 \text{ kPa}}\right) = 1104 \text{ torr}$$

**Check** In each case, compare the magnitude of the answer with the starting value. The torr is a much smaller unit than the atmosphere (since there are 760 torr in 1 atm), so we expect the *numerical* answer to be larger than the starting quantity in (a) and smaller in (b). In (c) notice that there are nearly 8 torr per kPa, so the numerical answer in torr should be about eight times larger than its value in kPa, consistent with our calculation.

**PRACTICE EXERCISE**

**(a)** In countries that use the metric system, atmospheric pressure in weather reports is given in kilopascals. Convert a pressure of 745 torr to kilopascals. **(b)** The pressure at the center of Hurricane Katrina was 902 mbar (millibars). There are 1000 mbar in 1 bar; convert this pressure to atmospheres.

*Answers:* **(a)** 99.3 kPa, **(b)** 0.890 atm

We use various devices to measure the pressures of enclosed gases. Tire gauges, for example, measure the pressure of air in automobile and bicycle tires. In laboratories we sometimes use a *manometer*, which operates on a principle similar to that of a barometer, as shown in Sample Exercise 10.2.

---

**SAMPLE EXERCISE 10.2**  **Using a Manometer to Measure Gas Pressure**

On a certain day a laboratory barometer indicates that the atmospheric pressure is 764.7 torr. A sample of gas is placed in a flask attached to an open-end mercury manometer (▶ **FIGURE 10.3**), and a meter stick is used to measure the height of the mercury in the two arms of the U tube. The height of the mercury in the open-end arm is 136.4 mm, and the height in the arm in contact with the gas in the flask is 103.8 mm. What is the pressure of the gas in the flask (**a**) in atmospheres, (**b**) in kilopascals?

$$P_{gas} = P_{atm} + P_h$$

▲ **FIGURE 10.3**  **A mercury manometer.**

**SOLUTION**

**Analyze**  We are given the atmospheric pressure (764.7 torr) and the mercury heights in the two arms of the manometer and asked to determine the gas pressure in the flask. Recall that millimeters of mercury is a pressure unit. We know that the gas pressure from the flask must be greater than atmospheric pressure because the mercury level in the arm on the flask side (103.8 mm) is lower than the level in the arm open to the atmosphere (136.4 mm). Therefore, the gas from the flask is pushing mercury from the arm in contact with the flask into the arm open to the atmosphere.

**Plan**  We will use the difference in height between the two arms ($h$ in Figure 10.3) to obtain the amount by which the pressure of the gas exceeds atmospheric pressure. Because an open-end mercury manometer is used, the height difference directly measures the pressure difference in mm Hg or torr between the gas and the atmosphere.

**Solve**

(**a**) The pressure of the gas equals the atmospheric pressure plus $h$:

$$P_{gas} = P_{atm} + h$$
$$= 764.7 \text{ torr} + (136.4 \text{ torr} - 103.8 \text{ torr})$$
$$= 797.3 \text{ torr}$$

We convert the pressure of the gas to atmospheres:

$$P_{gas} = (797.3 \text{ torr})\left(\frac{1 \text{ atm}}{760 \text{ torr}}\right) = 1.049 \text{ atm}$$

(**b**) To calculate the pressure in kPa, we employ the conversion factor between atmospheres and kPa:

$$1.049 \text{ atm}\left(\frac{101.3 \text{ kPa}}{1 \text{ atm}}\right) = 106.3 \text{ kPa}$$

**Check**  The calculated pressure is a bit more than 1 atm, which is about 101 kPa. This makes sense because we anticipated that the pressure in the flask would be greater than the atmospheric pressure (764.7 torr = 1.01 atm) acting on the manometer.

**PRACTICE EXERCISE**

Convert a pressure of 0.975 atm into Pa and kPa.
**Answers:** $9.88 \times 10^4$ Pa and 98.8 kPa

---

# 10.3 | THE GAS LAWS

Four variables are needed to define the physical condition, or *state*, of a gas: temperature, pressure, volume, and amount of gas, usually expressed as number of moles. The equations that express the relationships among these four variables are known as the *gas laws*. Because volume is easily measured, the first gas laws to be studied expressed the effect of one of the variables on volume, with the remaining two variables held constant.

# CHEMISTRY AND LIFE

## BLOOD PRESSURE

When your blood pressure is measured, two values are reported, such as 120/80 (120 over 80). The first measurement is *systolic pressure,* the maximum pressure when the heart is pumping. The second is *diastolic pressure,* the pressure when the heart is in the resting part of its pumping cycle. The units associated with these pressure measurements are torr.

Blood pressure is measured using a pressure gauge attached to a closed, air-filled cuff applied like a tourniquet to the arm (▶ **FIGURE 10.4**). The pressure gauge may be a mercury manometer or related device. A small pump is used to increase the pressure in the cuff until it is above the systolic pressure and therefore prevents blood from flowing. The pressure inside the cuff is slowly reduced until blood just begins to pulse through the artery, and the person measuring the pressure hears, through a stethoscope, a characteristic sound. At this point the pressure in the cuff equals the pressure that the blood exerts inside the artery. Reading the gauge gives the systolic pressure. The pressure in the cuff is then reduced further until the blood flows freely, indicated by another characteristic sound. The pressure at this point is the diastolic pressure.

*Hypertension* is abnormally high blood pressure. The usual criterion is a blood pressure greater than 140/90, although recent studies suggest that health risks increase for systolic readings above 120. Hypertension significantly increases the workload on the heart and places a stress on the walls of the blood vessels throughout the body. These effects increase the risk of aneurysms, heart attacks, and strokes.

▲ **FIGURE 10.4   Measuring blood pressure.**

## The Pressure–Volume Relationship: Boyle's Law

An inflated weather balloon released at Earth's surface expands as it rises (◀ **FIGURE 10.5**) because the pressure of the atmosphere decreases with increasing elevation. Thus, for our first pressure–volume relationship we can use our experience with balloons to say that gas volume increases as the pressure exerted on the gas decreases.

British chemist Robert Boyle (1627–1691) first investigated the relationship between the pressure of a gas and its volume, using a J-shaped tube like that shown in ▼ **FIGURE 10.6**. In the tube on the left, a quantity of gas is trapped above a column of mercury. Boyle then changed the pressure on the gas by adding mercury to the tube. He found that the volume of the gas decreased as the pressure increased. For example, doubling the pressure caused the gas volume to decrease to half its original value.

**GO FIGURE**

Does atmospheric pressure increase or decrease as altitude increases? (Neglect changes in temperature.)

Atmosphere

Balloon rises up through atmosphere

▲ **FIGURE 10.5   As a balloon rises in the atmosphere, its volume increases.**

**GO FIGURE**

What is the total pressure on the gas after the 760 mm Hg has been added?

Atmospheric pressure = 760 torr

Gas volume = 60 mL

760 mmHg added

Atmospheric pressure = 760 torr

Gas volume = 30 mL

760 mm

▲ **FIGURE 10.6   Boyle's experiment relating pressure and volume for a gas.**

What would a plot of *P* versus 1/*V* look like for a fixed quantity of gas at a fixed temperature?

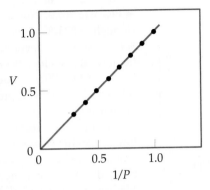

▲ **FIGURE 10.7** **Boyle's Law.** For a fixed quantity of gas at constant temperature, the volume of the gas is inversely proportional to its pressure.

**Boyle's law**, which summarizes these observations, states that *the volume of a fixed quantity of gas maintained at constant temperature is inversely proportional to the pressure*. When two measurements are inversely proportional, one gets smaller as the other gets larger. Boyle's law can be expressed mathematically as

$$V = \text{constant} \times \frac{1}{P} \quad \text{or} \quad PV = \text{constant} \qquad [10.2]$$

The value of the constant depends on temperature and on the amount of gas in the sample.

The graph of *V* versus *P* in ▲ **FIGURE 10.7** shows the curve obtained for a given quantity of gas at a fixed temperature. A linear relationship is obtained when *V* is plotted versus 1/*P* as shown on the right in Figure 10.7.

Boyle's law occupies a special place in the history of science because Boyle was the first to carry out experiments in which one variable was systematically changed to determine the effect on another variable. The data from the experiments were then employed to establish an empirical relationship—a "law."

We apply Boyle's law every time we breathe. The rib cage, which can expand and contract, and the diaphragm, a muscle beneath the lungs, govern the volume of the lungs. Inhalation occurs when the rib cage expands and the diaphragm moves downward. Both actions increase the volume of the lungs, thus decreasing the gas pressure inside the lungs. Atmospheric pressure then forces air into the lungs until the pressure in the lungs equals atmospheric pressure. Exhalation reverses the process—the rib cage contracts and the diaphragm moves up, decreasing the volume of the lungs. Air is forced out of the lungs by the resulting increase in pressure.

GIVE IT SOME THOUGHT

What happens to the pressure of a gas if you double its volume while its temperature is held constant?

## The Temperature–Volume Relationship: Charles's Law

As ▶ **FIGURE 10.8** illustrates, the volume of an inflated balloon increases when the temperature of the gas inside the balloon increases and decreases when the temperature of the gas decreases.

▲ **FIGURE 10.8** **The effect of temperature on volume.**

▲ **FIGURE 10.9 Charles's Law.** For a fixed quantity of gas at constant pressure, the volume of the gas is proportional to its temperature.

The relationship between gas volume and temperature—volume increases as temperature increases and decreases as temperature decreases—was discovered in 1787 by French scientist Jacques Charles (1746–1823). Some typical volume–temperature data are shown in ◀ **FIGURE 10.9.** Notice that the extrapolated (dashed) line passes through −273 °C. Note also that the gas is predicted to have zero volume at this temperature. This condition is never realized, however, because all gases liquefy or solidify before reaching this temperature.

In 1848 William Thomson (1824–1907), a British physicist whose title was Lord Kelvin, proposed an absolute-temperature scale, now known as the Kelvin scale. On this scale 0 K, called *absolute zero*, equals −273.15 °C. ∞ (Section 1.4) In terms of the Kelvin scale, **Charles's law** states: *The volume of a fixed amount of gas maintained at constant pressure is directly proportional to its absolute temperature.* Thus, doubling the absolute temperature causes the gas volume to double. Mathematically, Charles's law takes the form

$$V = \text{constant} \times T \quad \text{or} \quad \frac{V}{T} = \text{constant} \qquad [10.3]$$

with the value of the constant depending on the pressure and on the amount of gas.

▲ **GIVE IT SOME THOUGHT**

Does the volume of a fixed quantity of gas decrease to half its original value when the temperature is lowered from 100 °C to 50 °C ?

## The Quantity–Volume Relationship: Avogadro's Law

The relationship between the quantity of a gas and its volume follows from the work of Joseph Louis Gay-Lussac (1778–1823) and Amedeo Avogadro (1776–1856).

Gay-Lussac was one of those extraordinary figures in the history of science who could truly be called an adventurer. In 1804 he ascended to 23,000 ft in a hot-air balloon—an exploit that held the altitude record for several decades. To better control the balloon, Gay-Lussac studied the properties of gases. In 1808 he observed the *law of combining volumes*: At a given pressure and temperature, the volumes of gases that react with one another are in the ratios of small whole numbers. For example, two volumes of hydrogen gas react with one volume of oxygen gas to form two volumes of water vapor. ∞ (Section 3.1)

Three years later Amedeo Avogadro interpreted Gay-Lussac's observation by proposing what is now known as **Avogadro's hypothesis**: *Equal volumes of gases at the same temperature and pressure contain equal numbers of molecules.* For example, 22.4 L of any gas at 0 °C and 1 atm contain $6.02 \times 10^{23}$ gas molecules (that is, 1 mol), as depicted in ▼ **FIGURE 10.10.**

▲ **GO FIGURE**

How many moles of gas are in each vessel?

▶ **FIGURE 10.10 Avogadro's hypothesis.** At the same volume, pressure, and temperature, samples of different gases have the same number of molecules but different masses.

|  | He | N₂ | CH₄ |
|---|---|---|---|
| Volume | 22.4 L | 22.4 L | 22.4 L |
| Pressure | 1 atm | 1 atm | 1 atm |
| Temperature | 0 °C | 0 °C | 0 °C |
| Mass of gas | 4.00 g | 28.0 g | 16.0 g |
| Number of gas molecules | $6.02 \times 10^{23}$ | $6.02 \times 10^{23}$ | $6.02 \times 10^{23}$ |

**Avogadro's law** follows from Avogadro's hypothesis: *The volume of a gas maintained at constant temperature and pressure is directly proportional to the number of moles of the gas.* That is,

$$V = \text{constant} \times n \qquad \qquad [10.4]$$

where $n$ is number of moles. Thus, for instance, doubling the number of moles of gas causes the volume to double if $T$ and $P$ remain constant.

---

**SAMPLE EXERCISE 10.3** | **Evaluating the Effects of Changes in *P*, *V*, *n*, and *T* on a Gas**

Suppose we have a gas confined to a cylinder with a movable piston. ∞∞ (Sections 5.2, 5.3) Consider the following changes (assuming no leaks): **(a)** Heat the gas from 298 K to 360 K at constant pressure. **(b)** Reduce the volume from 1 L to 0.5 L at constant temperature. **(c)** Inject additional gas, keeping temperature and volume constant. Indicate how each change affects the average distance between molecules, the pressure of the gas, and the number of moles of gas in the cylinder.

**SOLUTION**

**Analyze** We need to think how each change affects (1) the distance between molecules, (2) the pressure of the gas, and (3) the number of moles of gas in the cylinder.

**Plan** We will use the gas laws and the general properties of gases to analyze each situation.

**Solve**

**(a)** Heating the gas while maintaining constant pressure will cause the piston to move and the volume to increase (Charles's law). Thus, the distance between molecules will increase. At constant pressure, obviously, the pressure will not change. The total number of moles of gas remains the same.

**(b)** Compressing the gas into a smaller volume does not change the total number of gas molecules; thus, the total number of moles remains the same. The average distance between molecules, however, must decrease because of the smaller volume. The reduction in volume causes the pressure to increase (Boyle's law).

**(c)** Injecting more gas into the cylinder while keeping the volume and temperature constant results in more molecules and, thus, an increase in the number of moles of gas in the cylinder. The average distance between molecules must decrease because their number per unit volume increases. Avogadro's law tells us that the volume of the cylinder should have increased when we added more gas, but here the volume is fixed. Boyle's law comes to our aid: If the volume is low, then pressure is high. Therefore, we expect that the pressure will increase in the cylinder if we inject more gas, keeping volume and temperature constant.

**PRACTICE EXERCISE**

Recall that density is mass per volume. ∞∞ (Section 1.4) What happens to the density of a gas as **(a)** the gas is heated in a constant-volume container; **(b)** the gas is compressed at constant temperature; **(c)** additional gas is added to a constant-volume container?

***Answers:*** **(a)** no change, **(b)** increases, **(c)** increases

---

# 10.4 | THE IDEAL-GAS EQUATION

All three laws we just examined were obtained by holding two of the four variables $P$, $V$, $T$, and $n$ constant and seeing how the remaining two variables affect each other. We can express each law as a proportionality relationship. Using the symbol $\propto$ for "is proportional to," we have

$$\text{Boyle's law:} \qquad V \propto \frac{1}{P} \quad (\text{constant } n, T)$$

$$\text{Charles's law:} \qquad V \propto T \quad (\text{constant } n, P)$$

$$\text{Avogadro's law:} \qquad V \propto n \quad (\text{constant } P, T)$$

We can combine these relationships into a general gas law:

$$V \propto \frac{nT}{P}$$

and if we call the proportionality constant $R$, we obtain an equality:

$$V = R\left(\frac{nT}{P}\right)$$

which we can rearrange to

$$PV = nRT \qquad\qquad [10.5]$$

which is the **ideal-gas equation** (also called the **ideal-gas law**). An **ideal gas** is a hypothetical gas whose pressure, volume, and temperature relationships are described completely by the ideal-gas equation.

In deriving the ideal-gas equation, we assume (a) that the molecules of an ideal gas do not interact with one another and (b) that the combined volume of the molecules is much smaller than the volume the gas occupies; for this reason, we consider the molecules as taking up no space in the container. In many cases, the small error introduced by these assumptions is acceptable. If more accurate calculations are needed, we can correct for the assumptions if we know something about the attraction molecules have for one another and if we know the diameter of the molecules.

The term $R$ in the ideal-gas equation is the **gas constant**. The value and units of $R$ depend on the units of $P$, $V$, $n$, and $T$. The value for $T$ in the ideal-gas equation must *always* be the absolute temperature (in kelvins instead of degrees Celsius). The quantity of gas, $n$, is normally expressed in moles. The units chosen for pressure and volume are most often atmospheres and liters, respectively. However, other units can be used. In most countries other than the United States, the pascal is most commonly used for pressure. ◄ TABLE 10.2 shows the numerical value for $R$ in various units. In working with the ideal-gas equation, you must choose the form of $R$ in which the units agree with the units of $P$, $V$, $n$, and $T$ given in the problem. In this chapter we will most often use $R = 0.08206$ L-atm/mol-K because pressure is most often given in atmospheres.

Suppose we have 1.000 mol of an ideal gas at 1.000 atm and 0.00 °C (273.15 K). According to the ideal-gas equation, the volume of the gas is

$$V = \frac{nRT}{P} = \frac{(1.000\ \text{mol})(0.08206\ \text{L-atm/mol-K})(273.15\ \text{K})}{1.000\ \text{atm}} = 22.41\ \text{L}$$

The conditions 0 °C and 1 atm are referred to as **standard temperature and pressure (STP)**. The volume occupied by 1 mol of ideal gas at STP, 22.41 L, is known as the *molar volume* of an ideal gas at STP.

### ▲ GIVE IT SOME THOUGHT

How many molecules are in 22.41 L of an ideal gas at STP?

The ideal-gas equation accounts adequately for the properties of most gases under a variety of circumstances. The equation is not exactly correct, however, for any real gas. Thus, the measured volume for given values of $P$, $n$, and $T$ might differ from the volume calculated from $PV = nRT$ (▼ FIGURE 10.11). Although real gases do not always

**TABLE 10.2 • Numerical Values of the Gas Constant $R$ in Various Units**

| Units | Numerical Value |
|---|---|
| L-atm/mol-K | 0.08206 |
| J/mol-K* | 8.314 |
| cal/mol-K | 1.987 |
| m³-Pa/mol-K* | 8.314 |
| L-torr/mol-K | 62.36 |

*SI unit

### ▲ GO FIGURE

Suggest an explanation for the "ideal" nature of helium compared to the other gases.

▶ FIGURE 10.11 **Comparison of molar volumes at STP.**

behave ideally, their behavior differs so little from ideal behavior that we can ignore any deviations for all but the most accurate work.

## SAMPLE EXERCISE 10.4 | Using the Ideal-Gas Equation

Calcium carbonate, $CaCO_3(s)$, the principal compound in lime-stone, decomposes upon heating to $CaO(s)$ and $CO_2(g)$. A sample of $CaCO_3$ is decomposed, and the carbon dioxide is collected in a 250-mL flask. After decomposition is complete, the gas has a pressure of 1.3 atm at a temperature of 31 °C. How many moles of $CO_2$ gas were generated?

### SOLUTION

**Analyze** We are given the volume (250 mL), pressure (1.3 atm), and temperature (31 °C) of a sample of $CO_2$ gas and asked to calculate the number of moles of $CO_2$ in the sample.

**Plan** Because we are given $V$, $P$, and $T$, we can solve the ideal-gas equation for the unknown quantity, $n$.

**Solve** In analyzing and solving gas law problems, it is helpful to tabulate the information given in the problems and then to convert the values to units that are consistent with those for $R$ (0.08206 L-atm/mol-K). In this case the given values are

$$V = 250 \text{ mL} = 0.250 \text{ L}$$
$$P = 1.3 \text{ atm}$$
$$T = 31 \text{ °C} = (31 + 273) \text{ K} = 304 \text{ K}$$

Remember: *Absolute temperature must always be used when the ideal-gas equation is solved.*

We now rearrange the ideal-gas equation (Equation 10.5) to solve for $n$

$$n = \frac{PV}{RT}$$

$$n = \frac{(1.3 \text{ atm})(0.250 \text{ L})}{(0.08206 \text{ L-atm/mol-K})(304 \text{ K})} = 0.013 \text{ mol } CO_2$$

**Check** Appropriate units cancel, thus ensuring that we have properly rearranged the ideal-gas equation and have converted to the correct units.

### PRACTICE EXERCISE

Tennis balls are usually filled with either air or $N_2$ gas to a pressure above atmospheric pressure to increase their bounce. If a tennis ball has a volume of $144 \text{ cm}^3$ and contains 0.33 g of $N_2$ gas, what is the pressure inside the ball at 24 °C ?

*Answer:* 2.0 atm

# STRATEGIES IN CHEMISTRY

## CALCULATIONS INVOLVING MANY VARIABLES

In this chapter we encounter a variety of problems based on the ideal-gas equation, which contains four variables—$P$, $V$, $n$, and $T$—and one constant, $R$. Depending on the type of problem, we might need to solve for any of the four variables.

To extract the necessary information from problems involving more than one variable, we suggest the following steps:

1. **Tabulate information.** Read the problems carefully to determine which variable is the unknown and which variables have numeric values given. Every time you encounter a numerical value, jot it down. In many cases constructing a table of the given information will be useful.

2. **Convert to consistent units.** Make certain that quantities are converted to the proper units. In using the ideal-gas equation, for example, we usually use the value of $R$ that has units of L-atm/mol-K. If you are given a pressure in torr, you will need to convert it to atmospheres before using this value of $R$ in your calculations.

3. **If a single equation relates the variables, solve the equation for the unknown.** For the ideal-gas equation, these algebraic rearrangements will all be used at one time or another:

$$P = \frac{nRT}{V}, \quad V = \frac{nRT}{P}, \quad n = \frac{PV}{RT}, \quad T = \frac{PV}{nR}$$

4. **Use dimensional analysis.** Carry the units through your calculation. Using dimensional analysis enables you to check that you have solved an equation correctly. If the units in the equation cancel to give the units of the desired variable, you have probably used the equation correctly.

Sometimes you will not be given explicit values for several variables, making it look like a problem cannot be solved. In these cases, however, you will be given information that can be used to determine the needed variables. For example, suppose you are using the ideal-gas equation to calculate a pressure in a problem that gives a value for $T$ but not for $n$ or $V$. However, the problem states that "the sample contains 0.15 mol of gas per liter." We can turn this statement into the expression

$$\frac{n}{V} = 0.15 \text{ mol/L}$$

Solving the ideal-gas equation for pressure yields

$$P = \frac{nRT}{V} = \left(\frac{n}{V}\right)RT$$

Thus, we can solve the equation even though we are not given values for $n$ and $V$.

As we have continuously stressed, the most important thing you can do to become proficient at solving chemistry problems is to do the practice exercises and end-of-chapter exercises. By using systematic procedures, such as those described here, you should be able to minimize difficulties in solving problems involving many variables.

## Relating the Ideal-Gas Equation and the Gas Laws

The gas laws we discussed in Section 10.3 are special cases of the ideal-gas equation. For example, when $n$ and $T$ are held constant, the product $nRT$ contains three constants and so must itself be a constant:

$$PV = nRT = \text{constant} \quad \text{or} \quad PV = \text{constant} \qquad [10.6]$$

Thus, we have Boyle's law. We see that if $n$ and $T$ are constant, the values of $P$ and $V$ can change, but the product $PV$ must remain constant.

We can use Boyle's law to determine how the volume of a gas changes when its pressure changes. For example, if a cylinder fitted with a movable piston holds 50.0 L of $O_2$ gas at 18.5 atm and 21 °C, what volume will the gas occupy if the temperature is maintained at 21 °C while the pressure is reduced to 1.00 atm? Because the product $PV$ is a constant when a gas is held at constant $n$ and $T$, we know that

$$P_1V_1 = P_2V_2 \qquad [10.7]$$

where $P_1$ and $V_1$ are initial values and $P_2$ and $V_2$ are final values. Dividing both sides of this equation by $P_2$ gives the final volume, $V_2$:

$$V_2 = V_1 \times \frac{P_1}{P_2} = (50.0 \text{ L})\left(\frac{18.5 \text{ atm}}{1.00 \text{ atm}}\right) = 925 \text{ L}$$

The answer is reasonable because a gas expands as its pressure decreases.

In a similar way, we can start with the ideal-gas equation and derive relationships between any other two variables, $V$ and $T$ (Charles's law), $n$ and $V$ (Avogadro's law), or $P$ and $T$.

---

**SAMPLE EXERCISE 10.5** | **Calculating the Effect of Temperature Changes on Pressure**

The gas pressure in an aerosol can is 1.5 atm at 25 °C. Assuming that the gas obeys the ideal-gas equation, what is the pressure when the can is heated to 450 °C?

**SOLUTION**

**Analyze** We are given the initial pressure (1.5 atm) and temperature (25 °C) of the gas and asked for the pressure at a higher temperature (450 °C).

**Plan** The volume and number of moles of gas do not change, so we must use a relationship connecting pressure and temperature. Converting temperature to the Kelvin scale and tabulating the given information, we have

| | $P$ | $T$ |
|---|---|---|
| **INITIAL** | 1.5 atm | 298 K |
| **FINAL** | $P_2$ | 723 K |

**Solve** To determine how $P$ and $T$ are related, we start with the ideal-gas equation and isolate the quantities that do not change ($n$, $V$, and $R$) on one side and the variables ($P$ and $T$) on the other side.

$$\frac{P}{T} = \frac{nR}{V} = \text{constant}$$

Because the quotient $P/T$ is a constant, we can write

$$\frac{P_1}{T_1} = \frac{P_2}{T_2}$$

(where the subscripts 1 and 2 represent the initial and final states, respectively). Rearranging to solve for $P_2$ and substituting the given data give

$$P_2 = (1.5 \text{ atm})\left(\frac{723 \text{ K}}{298 \text{ K}}\right) = 3.6 \text{ atm}$$

**Check** This answer is intuitively reasonable—increasing the temperature of a gas increases its pressure.

**Comment** It is evident from this example why aerosol cans carry a warning not to incinerate.

**PRACTICE EXERCISE**

The pressure in a natural-gas tank is maintained at 2.20 atm. On a day when the temperature is −15 °C, the volume of gas in the tank is $3.25 \times 10^3$ m$^3$. What is the volume of the same quantity of gas on a day when the temperature is 31 °C?

**Answer:** $3.83 \times 10^3$ m$^3$

We are often faced with the situation in which $P$, $V$, and $T$ all change for a fixed number of moles of gas. Because $n$ is constant in this situation, the ideal-gas equation gives

$$\frac{PV}{T} = nR = \text{constant}$$

If we represent the initial and final conditions by subscripts 1 and 2, respectively, we can write

$$\frac{P_1 V_1}{T_1} = \frac{P_2 V_2}{T_2} \qquad\qquad [10.8]$$

This equation is often called the *combined gas law*.

---

| SAMPLE EXERCISE 10.6 | Calculating the Effect of Changing *P* and *T* on Gas Volume |

An inflated balloon has a volume of 6.0 L at sea level (1.0 atm) and is allowed to ascend until the pressure is 0.45 atm. During ascent, the temperature of the gas falls from 22 °C to −21 °C. Calculate the volume of the balloon at its final altitude.

**SOLUTION**

**Analyze** We need to determine a new volume for a gas sample when both pressure and temperature change.

**Plan** Let's again proceed by converting temperatures to kelvins and tabulating our information.

|         | P        | V      | T     |
|---------|----------|--------|-------|
| **INITIAL** | 1.0 atm  | 6.0 L  | 295 K |
| **FINAL**   | 0.45 atm | $V_2$  | 252 K |

Because $n$ is constant, we can use Equation 10.8.

**Solve** Rearranging Equation 10.8 to solve for $V_2$ gives

$$V_2 = V_1 \times \frac{P_1}{P_2} \times \frac{T_2}{T_1} = (6.0\ \text{L}) \left( \frac{1.0\ \text{atm}}{0.45\ \text{atm}} \right) \left( \frac{252\ \text{K}}{295\ \text{K}} \right) = 11\ \text{L}$$

**Check** The result appears reasonable. Notice that the calculation involves multiplying the initial volume by a ratio of pressures and a ratio of temperatures. Intuitively, we expect decreasing pressure to cause the volume to increase. Similarly, decreasing temperature should cause the volume to decrease. Because the pressure difference is more dramatic than the temperature difference, we expect the effect of the pressure change to predominate in determining the final volume, as it does.

**PRACTICE EXERCISE**

A 0.50-mol sample of oxygen gas is confined at 0 °C and 1.0 atm in a cylinder with a movable piston. The piston compresses the gas so that the final volume is half the initial volume and the final pressure is 2.2 atm. What is the final temperature of the gas in degrees Celsius?
**Answer:** 27 °C

---

# 10.5 | FURTHER APPLICATIONS OF THE IDEAL-GAS EQUATION

In this section, we use the ideal-gas equation first to define the relationship between the density of a gas and its molar mass, and then to calculate the volumes of gases formed or consumed in chemical reactions.

## Gas Densities and Molar Mass

Recall that density has units of mass per unit volume ($d = m/V$). ∞ (Section 1.4) We can arrange the ideal-gas equation to obtain the similar units of moles per unit volume:

$$\frac{n}{V} = \frac{P}{RT}$$

If we multiply both sides of this equation by the molar mass, $\mathcal{M}$, which is the number of grams in 1 mol of a substance, we obtain

$$\frac{n\mathcal{M}}{V} = \frac{P\mathcal{M}}{RT} \qquad [10.9]$$

The term on the left equals the density in grams per liter:

$$\frac{\text{moles}}{\text{liter}} \times \frac{\text{grams}}{\text{mole}} = \frac{\text{grams}}{\text{liter}}$$

Thus, the density of the gas is also given by the expression on the right in Equation 10.9:

$$d = \frac{n\mathcal{M}}{V} = \frac{P\mathcal{M}}{RT} \qquad [10.10]$$

This equation tells us that the density of a gas depends on its pressure, molar mass, and temperature. The higher the molar mass and pressure, the denser the gas. The higher the temperature, the less dense the gas. Although gases form homogeneous mixtures, a less dense gas will lie above a denser gas in the absence of mixing. For example, $CO_2$ has a higher molar mass than $N_2$ or $O_2$ and is therefore denser than air. For this reason, $CO_2$ released from a $CO_2$ fire extinguisher blankets a fire, preventing $O_2$ from reaching the combustible material. "Dry ice," which is solid $CO_2$, converts directly to $CO_2$ gas at room temperature, and the resulting "fog" (which is actually condensed water droplets cooled by the $CO_2$) flows downhill in air (◀ FIGURE 10.12).

When we have equal molar masses of two gases at the same pressure but different temperatures, the hotter gas is less dense than the cooler one, so the hotter gas rises. The difference between the densities of hot and cold air is responsible for the lift of hot-air balloons. It is also responsible for many phenomena in weather, such as the formation of large thunderhead clouds during thunderstorms.

▲ **FIGURE 10.12 Carbon dioxide gas flows downhill because it is denser than air.** The $CO_2$ "fog" is not the gas made visible but rather is made up of drops of water that have condensed from water vapor in the air.

### GIVE IT SOME THOUGHT

Is water vapor more or less dense than $N_2$ under the same conditions of temperature and pressure?

---

**SAMPLE EXERCISE 10.7** Calculating Gas Density

What is the density of carbon tetrachloride vapor at 714 torr and 125 °C ?

**SOLUTION**

**Analyze** We are asked to calculate the density of a gas given its name, its pressure, and its temperature. From the name we can write the chemical formula of the substance and determine its molar mass.

**Plan** We can use Equation 10.10 to calculate the density. Before we can do that, however, we must convert the given quantities to the appropriate units, degrees Celsius to kelvins and pressure to atmospheres. We must also calculate the molar mass of $CCl_4$.

**Solve** The absolute temperature is $125 + 273 = 398$ K. The pressure is (714 torr) (1 atm/760 torr) = 0.939 atm. The molar mass of $CCl_4$ is $12.01 + (4)(35.45) = 153.8$ g/mol. Therefore,

$$d = \frac{(0.939 \text{ atm})(153.8 \text{ g/mol})}{(0.08206 \text{ L-atm/mol-K})(398 \text{ K})} = 4.42 \text{ g/L}$$

**Check** If we divide molar mass (g/mol) by density (g/L), we end up with L/mol. The numerical value is roughly 154/4.4 = 35. That is in the right ballpark for the molar volume of a gas heated to 125 °C at near atmospheric pressure, so our answer is reasonable.

**PRACTICE EXERCISE**

The mean molar mass of the atmosphere at the surface of Titan, Saturn's largest moon, is 28.6 g/mol. The surface temperature is 95 K, and the pressure is 1.6 atm. Assuming ideal behavior, calculate the density of Titan's atmosphere.

*Answer:* 5.9 g/L

Equation 10.10 can be rearranged to solve for the molar mass of a gas:

$$\mathcal{M} = \frac{dRT}{P} \qquad\qquad [10.11]$$

Thus, we can use the experimentally measured density of a gas to determine the molar mass of the gas molecules, as shown in Sample Exercise 10.8.

**SAMPLE EXERCISE 10.8** | Calculating the Molar Mass of a Gas

A large evacuated flask initially has a mass of 134.567 g. When the flask is filled with a gas of unknown molar mass to a pressure of 735 torr at 31 °C, its mass is 137.456 g. When the flask is evacuated again and then filled with water at 31 °C, its mass is 1067.9 g. (The density of water at this temperature is 0.997 g/mL.) Assuming the ideal-gas equation applies, calculate the molar mass of the gas.

**SOLUTION**

**Analyze** We are given the temperature (31 °C) and pressure (735 torr) for a gas, together with information to determine its volume and mass, and we are asked to calculate its molar mass.

**Plan** We need to use the mass information given to calculate the volume of the container and the mass of the gas in it. From this we calculate the gas density and then apply Equation 10.11 to calculate the molar mass of the gas.

**Solve** The gas mass is the difference between the mass of the flask filled with gas and the mass of the evacuated flask:

137.456 g − 134.567 g = 2.889 g

The gas volume equals the volume of water the flask can hold, calculated from the mass and density of the water. The mass of the water is the difference between the masses of the full and evacuated flask:

1067.9 g − 134.567 g = 933.3 g

Rearranging the equation for density ($d = m/V$), we have

$$V = \frac{m}{d} = \frac{(933.3 \text{ g})}{(0.997 \text{ g/mL})} = 936 \text{ mL} = 0.936 \text{ L}$$

Knowing the mass of the gas (2.889 g) and its volume (0.936 L), we can calculate the density of the gas:

2.889 g/0.936 L = 3.09 g/L

After converting pressure to atmospheres and temperature to kelvins, we can use Equation 10.11 to calculate the molar mass:

$$\mathcal{M} = \frac{dRT}{P}$$
$$= \frac{(3.09 \text{ g/L})(0.08206 \text{ L-atm/mol-K})(304 \text{ K})}{(0.09671) \text{ atm}}$$
$$= 79.7 \text{ g/mol}$$

**Check** The units work out appropriately, and the value of molar mass obtained is reasonable for a substance that is gaseous near room temperature.

**PRACTICE EXERCISE**

Calculate the average molar mass of dry air if it has a density of 1.17 g/L at 21 °C and 740.0 torr.

*Answer:* 29.0 g/mol

## Volumes of Gases in Chemical Reactions

We are often concerned with knowing the identity and/or quantity of a gas involved in a chemical reaction. Thus, it is useful to be able to calculate the volumes of gases consumed or produced in reactions. Such calculations are based on the mole concept and balanced chemical equations. ∞ (Section 3.6) The coefficients in a balanced chemical equation tell us the relative amounts (in moles) of reactants and products in a reaction. The ideal-gas equation relates the number of moles of a gas to *P, V,* and *T.*

# CHEMISTRY PUT TO WORK

### Gas Pipelines

Throughout the developed world, mostly invisible underground pipelines move massive quantities of liquids and gases over hundreds of miles. Essentially all substances that are gases at STP are transported commercially by pipeline, but the largest volume transported by far is natural gas (▼ **FIGURE 10.13**). This methane-rich gas from oil and gas wells is processed to remove particulates, water, and various gaseous impurities such as hydrogen sulfide and carbon dioxide. The gas is then compressed to pressures ranging from 3.5 MPa (35 atm) to 10 MPa (100 atm), depending on the age and diameter of the pipe. Large compressor stations along the pipeline, spaced at 50- to 100-mile intervals, maintain pressure.

Recall from Figure 5.25 that natural gas is a major source of energy for the United States. To meet this demand, methane must be transported from source wells throughout the United States and Canada to all parts of the nation. The total length of pipeline for natural-gas transport in the United States is about $6 \times 10^5$ km and growing. The United States is divided into seven regions. The total deliverability of natural gas to the seven regions exceeds $2.7 \times 10^{12}$ L (measured at STP), almost 100 billion cubic feet per day! The total pipeline volume is not large enough for the enormous quantities of natural gas placed into and taken out of the system on a continuing basis. For this reason, underground storage facilities, such as salt caverns and other natural formations, are employed to hold large quantities of gas.

*RELATED EXERCISE:* 10.126

◀ **FIGURE 10.13 Natural gas pipeline network in the United States.** The thickest arrow represents flow of 15,000 million cubic feet of gas per day; the thinnest arrow represents flow of 1000 million cubic feet per day.

---

**SAMPLE EXERCISE 10.9** | **Relating a Gas Volume to the Amount of Another Substance in a Reaction**

Automobile air bags are inflated by nitrogen gas generated by the rapid decomposition of sodium azide, $NaN_3$:

$$2\,NaN_3(s) \longrightarrow 2\,Na(s) + 3\,N_2(g)$$

If an air bag has a volume of 36 L and is to be filled with nitrogen gas at 1.15 atm and 26.0 °C, how many grams of $NaN_3$ must be decomposed?

#### SOLUTION

**Analyze** This is a multistep problem. We are given the volume, pressure, and temperature of the $N_2$ gas and the chemical equation for the reaction by which the $N_2$ is generated. We must use this information to calculate the number of grams of $NaN_3$ needed to obtain the necessary $N_2$.

**Plan** We need to use the gas data (*P*, *V*, and *T*) and the ideal-gas equation to calculate the number of moles of $N_2$ gas that should be formed for the air bag to operate correctly. We can then use the balanced equation to determine the number of moles of $NaN_3$ needed. Finally, we can convert moles of $NaN_3$ to grams.

**Solve** The number of moles of $N_2$ is determined using the ideal-gas equation:

$$n = \frac{PV}{RT} = \frac{(1.15 \text{ atm})(36 \text{ L})}{(0.08206 \text{ L-atm/mol-K})(299 \text{ K})} = 1.69 \text{ mol } N_2$$

We use the coefficients in the balanced equation to calculate the number of moles of $NaN_3$:

$$(1.69 \text{ mol } N_2)\left(\frac{2 \text{ mol } NaN_3}{3 \text{ mol } N_2}\right) = 1.12 \text{ mol } NaN_3$$

Finally, using the molar mass of $NaN_3$, we convert moles of $NaN_3$ to grams:

$$(1.12 \text{ mol } NaN_3)\left(\frac{65.0 \text{ g } NaN_3}{1 \text{ mol } NaN_3}\right) = 73 \text{ g } NaN_3$$

**Check** The units cancel properly at each step in the calculation, leaving us with the correct units in the answer, g $NaN_3$.

**PRACTICE EXERCISE**

In the first step in the industrial process for making nitric acid, ammonia reacts with oxygen in the presence of a suitable catalyst to form nitric oxide and water vapor:

$$4 \text{ NH}_3(g) + 5 \text{ O}_2(g) \longrightarrow 4 \text{ NO}(g) + 6 \text{ H}_2\text{O}(g)$$

How many liters of $NH_3(g)$ at 850 °C and 5.00 atm are required to react with 1.00 mol of $O_2(g)$ in this reaction?

*Answer:* 14.8 L

# 10.6 | GAS MIXTURES AND PARTIAL PRESSURES

Thus far we have considered mainly pure gases—those that consist of only one substance in the gaseous state. How do we deal with mixtures of two or more different gases? While studying the properties of air, John Dalton ∞ (Section 2.1) made an important observation: *The total pressure of a mixture of gases equals the sum of the pressures that each would exert if it were present alone.* The pressure exerted by a particular component of a mixture of gases is called the **partial pressure** of that component. Dalton's observation is known as **Dalton's law of partial pressures.**

⚠ **GIVE IT SOME THOUGHT**

How is the pressure exerted by $N_2$ gas affected when some $O_2$ is introduced into a container if the temperature and volume remain constant?

If we let $P_t$ be the total pressure of a mixture of gases and $P_1$, $P_2$, $P_3$, and so forth be the partial pressures of the individual gases, we can write Dalton's law of partial pressures as

$$P_t = P_1 + P_2 + P_3 + \cdots \qquad [10.12]$$

This equation implies that each gas behaves independently of the others, as we can see by the following analysis. Let $n_1$, $n_2$, $n_3$, and so forth be the number of moles of each of the gases in the mixture and $n_t$ be the total number of moles of gas. If each gas obeys the ideal-gas equation, we can write

$$P_1 = n_1\left(\frac{RT}{V}\right); \quad P_2 = n_2\left(\frac{RT}{V}\right); \quad P_3 = n_3\left(\frac{RT}{V}\right); \quad \text{and so forth}$$

All the gases are at the same temperature and occupy the same volume. Therefore, by substituting into Equation 10.12, we obtain

$$P_t = (n_1 + n_2 + n_3 + \cdots)\left(\frac{RT}{V}\right) = n_t\left(\frac{RT}{V}\right) \qquad [10.13]$$

That is, at constant temperature and constant volume the total pressure of a gas sample is determined by the total number of moles of gas present, whether that total represents just one gas or a mixture of gases.

---

**SAMPLE EXERCISE 10.10** | Applying Dalton's Law of Partial Pressures

A mixture of 6.00 g $O_2(g)$ and 9.00 g $CH_4(g)$ is placed in a 15.0-L vessel at 0 °C. What is the partial pressure of each gas, and what is the total pressure in the vessel?

**SOLUTION**

**Analyze** We need to calculate the pressure for two gases in the same volume and at the same temperature.

**Plan** Because each gas behaves independently, we can use the ideal-gas equation to calculate the pressure each would exert if the other were not present. The total pressure is the sum of these two partial pressures.

**Solve** We first convert the mass of each gas to moles:

$$n_{O_2} = (6.00 \text{ g } O_2)\left(\frac{1 \text{ mol } O_2}{32.0 \text{ g } O_2}\right) = 0.188 \text{ mol } O_2$$

$$n_{CH_4} = (9.00 \text{ g } CH_4)\left(\frac{1 \text{ mol } CH_4}{16.0 \text{ g } CH_4}\right) = 0.563 \text{ mol } CH_4$$

We use the ideal-gas equation to calculate the partial pressure of each gas:

$$P_{O_2} = \frac{n_{O_2}RT}{V} = \frac{(0.188 \text{ mol})(0.08206 \text{ L-atm/mol-K})(273 K)}{15.0 L} = 0.281 \text{ atm}$$

$$P_{CH_4} = \frac{n_{CH_2}RT}{V} = \frac{(0.563 \text{ mol})(0.08206 \text{ L-atm/mol-K})(273 K)}{15.0 L} = 0.841 \text{ atm}$$

According to Dalton's law of partial pressures (Equation 10.12), the total pressure in the vessel is the sum of the partial pressures: $P_t = P_{O_2} + P_{CH_4} = 0.281 \text{ atm} + 0.841 \text{ atm} = 1.122 \text{ atm}$

**Check** A pressure of roughly 1 atm seems right for a mixture of about 0.2 mol $O_2$ and a bit more than 0.5 mol $CH_4$, together in a 15-L volume, because 1 mol of an ideal gas at 1 atm pressure and 0 °C occupies about 22 L.

**PRACTICE EXERCISE**

What is the total pressure exerted by a mixture of 2.00 g of $H_2(g)$ and 8.00 g of $N_2(g)$ at 273 K in a 10.0-L vessel?

*Answer:* 2.86 atm

---

## Partial Pressures and Mole Fractions

Because each gas in a mixture behaves independently, we can relate the amount of a given gas in a mixture to its partial pressure. For an ideal gas, we can write

$$\frac{P_1}{P_t} = \frac{n_1 RT/V}{n_t RT/V} = \frac{n_1}{n_t} \qquad [10.14]$$

The ratio $n_1/n_t$ is called the *mole fraction of gas 1*, which we denote $X_1$. The **mole fraction**, $X$, is a dimensionless number that expresses the ratio of the number of moles of one component in a mixture to the total number of moles in the mixture. Thus, for gas 1 we have

$$X_1 = \frac{\text{moles of compound 1}}{\text{total moles}} = \frac{n_1}{n_t} \qquad [10.15]$$

We can combine Equations 10.14 and 10.15 to give

$$P_1 = \left(\frac{n_1}{n_t}\right)P_t = X_1 P_t \qquad [10.16]$$

The mole fraction of $N_2$ in air is 0.78—that is, 78% of the molecules in air are $N_2$ (◄ **FIGURE 10.14**). This means that if the barometric pressure is 760 torr, the partial pressure of $N_2$ is

$$P_{N_2} = (0.78)(760 \text{ torr}) = 590 \text{ torr}$$

This result makes intuitive sense: Because $N_2$ makes up 78% of the mixture, it contributes 78% of the total pressure.

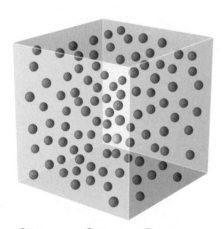

● Nitrogen ● Oxygen ◐ Other gases

▲ **FIGURE 10.14** Air is approximately 78% nitrogen, 21% oxygen, plus a mixture of many other gases.

---

**SAMPLE EXERCISE 10.11** | Relating Mole Fractions and Partial Pressures

A study of the effects of certain gases on plant growth requires a synthetic atmosphere composed of 1.5 mol percent $CO_2$, 18.0 mol percent $O_2$, and 80.5 mol percent Ar. (a) Calculate the partial pressure of $O_2$ in the mixture if the total pressure of the atmosphere is to be 745 torr. (b) If this atmosphere is to be held in a 121-L space at 295 K, how many moles of $O_2$ are needed?

## SOLUTION

**Analyze** For (a) we need to calculate the partial pressure of $O_2$ given its mole percent and the total pressure of the mixture. For (b) we need to calculate the number of moles of $O_2$ in the mixture given its volume (121 L), temperature (745 torr), and partial pressure from part (a).

**Plan** We calculate the partial pressures using Equation 10.16, and then use $P_{O_2}$, $V$, and $T$ in the ideal-gas equation to calculate the number of moles of $O_2$.

**Solve**

(a) The mole percent is the mole fraction times 100. Therefore, the mole fraction of $O_2$ is 0.180. Equation 10.16 gives

$$P_{O_2} = (0.180)(745 \text{ torr}) = 134 \text{ torr}$$

(b) Tabulating the given variables and converting to appropriate units, we have

$$P_{O_2} = (134 \text{ torr})\left(\frac{1 \text{ atm}}{760 \text{ torr}}\right) = 0.176 \text{ atm}$$

$$V = 121 \text{ L}$$

$$n_{O_2} = ?$$

$$R = 0.08206 \frac{\text{L-atm}}{\text{mol-K}}$$

$$T = 295 \text{ K}$$

Solving the ideal-gas equation for $n_{O_2}$, we have

$$n_{O_2} = P_{O_2}\left(\frac{V}{RT}\right)$$

$$= (0.176 \text{ atm})\frac{121 \text{ L}}{(0.08206 \text{ L-atm/mol-K})(295 \text{ K})} = 0.879 \text{ mol}$$

**Check** The units check out, and the answer seems to be the right order of magnitude.

### PRACTICE EXERCISE

From data gathered by *Voyager 1*, scientists have estimated the composition of the atmosphere of Titan, Saturn's largest moon. The pressure on the surface of Titan is 1220 torr. The atmosphere consists of 82 mol percent $N_2$, 12 mol percent Ar, and 6.0 mol percent $CH_4$. Calculate the partial pressure of each gas.

**Answer:** $1.0 \times 10^3$ torr $N_2$, $1.5 \times 10^2$ torr Ar, and 73 torr $CH_4$

## Collecting Gases over Water

An experiment often run in general chemistry laboratories involves determining the number of moles of gas generated in a reaction. Sometimes the gas is collected over water. For example, solid potassium chlorate, $KClO_3$, can be decomposed by heating it in the arrangement shown in ▼ **FIGURE 10.15**. The balanced equation for the reaction is

$$2 \text{ KClO}_3(s) \longrightarrow 2 \text{ KCl}(s) + 3 \text{ O}_2(g) \qquad [10.17]$$

The oxygen gas is collected in a bottle that is initially filled with water and inverted in a water pan.

Once the reaction is complete, the volume of gas collected is measured by raising or lowering the bottle as necessary until the water levels inside and outside the bottle are the same. When this condition is met, the pressure inside the bottle is equal to atmospheric

1 $O_2(g)$ released from heated $KClO_3(s)$

2 $O_2(g)$ bubbled through water into collection bottle

Gas collection

3 Bottle raised or lowered until water level in bottle equals water level in dish; at this point, $P_{total}$ inside bottle = $P_{atm}$

Gas volume measurement

$P_{total}$    $P_{atm}$

◀ **FIGURE 10.15   Collecting a water-insoluble gas over water.**

pressure. The total pressure inside is the sum of the pressure of gas collected and the pressure of water vapor in equilibrium with liquid water:

$$P_{total} = P_{gas} + P_{H_2O} \tag{10.18}$$

Values for $P_{H_2O}$ at various temperatures are listed in Appendix B.

---

**SAMPLE EXERCISE 10.12** | **Calculating the Amount of Gas Collected over Water**

When a sample of $KClO_3$ is partially decomposed in the setup shown in Figure 10.15, the volume of gas collected is 0.250 L at 26 °C and 765 torr total pressure. **(a)** How many moles of $O_2$ are collected? **(b)** How many grams of $KClO_3$ were decomposed?

**SOLUTION**

**(a) Analyze** We need to calculate the number of moles of $O_2$ gas in a container that also contains water vapor.

**Plan** We are given values for $V$ and $T$. To use the ideal-gas equation to calculate the unknown, $n_{O_2}$, we must know the partial pressure of $O_2$ in the system. We can calculate this partial pressure from the total pressure (765 torr) and the vapor pressure of water.

**Solve** The partial pressure of the $O_2$ gas is the difference between the total pressure and the pressure of the water vapor at 26 °C, 25 torr (Appendix B):

$$P_{O_2} = 765 \text{ torr} - 25 \text{ torr} = 740 \text{ torr}$$

We use the ideal-gas equation to calculate the number of moles of $O_2$:

$$n_{O_2} = \frac{P_{O_2}V}{RT} = \frac{(740 \text{ torr})(1 \text{ atm}/760 \text{ torr})(0.250 \text{ L})}{(0.08206 \text{ L-atm/mol-K})(299 \text{ K})} = 9.92 \times 10^{-3} \text{ mol } O_2$$

**(b) Analyze** We need to calculate the number of moles of reactant $KClO_3$ decomposed.

**Plan** We can use the number of moles of $O_2$ formed and the balanced chemical equation to determine the number of moles of $KClO_3$ decomposed, which we can then convert to grams of $KClO_3$.

**Solve** From Equation 10.17, we have 2 mol $KCl_3 \mathrel{\hat{=}} 3$ mol $O_2$. The molar mass of $KClO_3$ is 122.6 g/mol. Thus, we can convert the number of moles of $O_2$ from part (a) to moles of $KClO_3$ and then to grams of $KClO_3$:

$$(9.92 \times 10^{-3} \text{ mol } O_2)\left(\frac{2 \text{ mol } KClO_3}{3 \text{ mol } O_2}\right)\left(\frac{122.6 \text{ g } KClO_3}{1 \text{ mol } KClO_3}\right) = 0.811 \text{ g } KClO_3$$

**Check** The units cancel appropriately in the calculations. The numbers of moles of $O_2$ and $KClO_3$ seem reasonable, given the small volume of gas collected.

**PRACTICE EXERCISE**

Ammonium nitrite, $NH_4NO_2$, decomposes on heating to form $N_2$ gas:

$$NH_4NO_2(s) \longrightarrow N_2(g) + 2 H_2O(l)$$

When a sample of $NH_4NO_2$ is decomposed in the apparatus of Figure 10.15, 511 mL of $N_2$ gas is collected over water at 26 °C and 745 torr total pressure. How many grams of $NH_4NO_2$ were decomposed?

**Answer:** 1.26 g

---

# 10.7 | THE KINETIC-MOLECULAR THEORY OF GASES

The ideal-gas equation describes *how* gases behave but not *why* they behave as they do. Why does a gas expand when heated at constant pressure? Or why does its pressure increase when the gas is compressed at constant temperature? To understand the physical properties of gases, we need a model that helps us picture what happens to gas particles when conditions such as pressure or temperature change. Such a model, known as the **kinetic-molecular theory of gases**, was developed over a period of about 100 years, culminating in 1857 when Rudolf Clausius (1822–1888) published a complete and satisfactory form of the theory.

The kinetic-molecular theory (the theory of moving molecules) is summarized by the following statements:

1. Gases consist of large numbers of molecules that are in continuous, random motion. (The word *molecule* is used here to designate the smallest particle of any gas even though some gases, such as the noble gases, consist of individual atoms. All we learn about gas behavior from the kinetic-molecular theory applies equally to atomic gases.)

2. The combined volume of all the molecules of the gas is negligible relative to the total volume in which the gas is contained.

3. Attractive and repulsive forces between gas molecules are negligible.

4. Energy can be transferred between molecules during collisions but, as long as temperature remains constant, the *average* kinetic energy of the molecules does not change with time.

5. The average kinetic energy of the molecules is proportional to the absolute temperature. At any given temperature the molecules of all gases have the same average kinetic energy.

The kinetic-molecular theory explains both pressure and temperature at the molecular level. The pressure of a gas is caused by collisions of the molecules with the walls of the container (▶ **FIGURE 10.16**). The magnitude of the pressure is determined by how often and how forcefully the molecules strike the walls.

The absolute temperature of a gas is a measure of the *average* kinetic energy of its molecules. If two gases are at the same temperature, their molecules have the same average kinetic energy (statement 5 of the kinetic-molecular theory). If the absolute temperature of a gas is doubled, the average kinetic energy of its molecules doubles. Thus, molecular motion increases with increasing temperature.

Pressure inside container comes from collisions of gas molecules with container walls

▲ **FIGURE 10.16 The molecular origin of gas pressure.**

## Distributions of Molecular Speed

Although collectively the molecules in a sample of gas have an *average* kinetic energy and hence an average speed, the individual molecules are moving at different speeds. Each molecule collides frequently with other molecules. Momentum is conserved in each collision, but one of the colliding molecules might be deflected off at high speed while the other is nearly stopped. The result is that, at any instant, the molecules in the sample have a wide range of speeds. In ▼ **FIGURE 10.17**(a), which shows the distribution of molecular speeds for nitrogen gas at 0 °C and 100 °C, we see that a larger fraction of the 100 °C molecules moves at the higher speeds. This means that the 100 °C sample has the higher average kinetic energy.

▲ **GO FIGURE**

**Estimate the fraction of molecules at 100 °C with speeds less than 300 m/s.**

At 0 °C, fewer than half the molecules move at speeds greater than 500 m/s.

At 100 °C, more than half the molecules move at speeds greater than 500 m/s.

— 0 °C
— 100 °C

Fraction of molecules

$5 \times 10^2$    $10 \times 10^2$

Molecular speed (m/s)

(a)

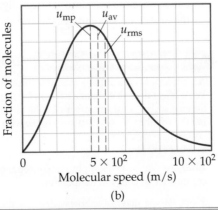

Fraction of molecules

$u_{mp}$    $u_{av}$    $u_{rms}$

$5 \times 10^2$    $10 \times 10^2$

Molecular speed (m/s)

(b)

◀ **FIGURE 10.17 Distribution of molecular speeds for nitrogen gas.** (a) The effect of temperature on molecular speed. The relative area under the curve for a range of speeds gives the relative fraction of molecules that have those speed. (b) Position of most probable ($u_{mp}$), average ($u_{av}$), and root-mean-square ($u_{rms}$) speeds of gas molecules. The data shown here are for nitrogen gas at 0 °C.

In any graph of the distribution of molecular speeds in a gas sample, the peak of the curve represents the most probable speed, $u_{mp}$, which is the speed of the largest number of molecules [Figure 10.17(b)]. The most probable speeds in Figure 10.17(a), for instance, are $4 \times 10^2$ m/s for the 0 °C sample and $5 \times 10^2$ m/s for the 100 °C sample. Figure 10.17(b) also shows the **root-mean-square (rms) speed**, $u_{rms}$, of the molecules. This is the speed of a molecule possessing a kinetic energy identical to the average kinetic energy of the sample. The rms speed is not quite the same as the average (mean) speed, $u_{av}$. The difference between the two is small, however. In Figure 10.17(b), for example, the root-mean-square speed is almost $5 \times 10^2$ m/s and the average speed is about $4.5 \times 10^2$ m/s.

If you calculate the rms speeds as we will in Section 10.8, you will find that the rms speed is almost $6 \times 10^2$ m/s for the 100 °C sample but slightly less than $5 \times 10^2$ m/s for the 0 °C sample. Notice that the distribution curve broadens as we go to a higher temperature, which tells us that the range of molecular speeds increases with temperature.

The rms speed is important because the average kinetic energy of the gas molecules in a sample is equal to $\frac{1}{2} m(u_{rms})^2$.  (Section 5.1) Because mass does not change with temperature, the increase in the average kinetic energy $\frac{1}{2} m(u_{rms})^2$ as the temperature increases implies that the rms speed of the molecules (as well as their average speed) increases as temperature increases.

⚠ **GIVE IT SOME THOUGHT**

Consider three gases all at 298 K: HCl, $H_2$, and $O_2$. List the gases in order of increasing average speed.

## Application of Kinetic-Molecular Theory to the Gas Laws

The empirical observations of gas properties as expressed by the various gas laws are readily understood in terms of the kinetic-molecular theory. The following examples illustrate this point:

1. **An increase in volume at constant temperature causes pressure to decrease.** A constant temperature means that the average kinetic energy of the gas molecules remains unchanged. This means that the rms speed of the molecules remains unchanged. When the volume is increased, the molecules must move a longer distance between collisions. Consequently, there are fewer collisions per unit time with the container walls, which means the pressure decreases. Thus, kinetic-molecular theory explains Boyle's law.

2. **A temperature increase at constant volume causes pressure to increase.** An increase in temperature means an increase in the average kinetic energy of the molecules and in $u_{rms}$. Because there is no change in volume, the temperature increase causes more collisions with the walls per unit time because the molecules are all moving faster. Furthermore, the momentum in each collision increases (the molecules strike the walls more forcefully). A greater number of more forceful collisions means the pressure increases, and the theory explains this increase.

---

**SAMPLE EXERCISE 10.13** | **Applying the Kinetic-Molecular Theory**

A sample of $O_2$ gas initially at STP is compressed to a smaller volume at constant temperature. What effect does this change have on **(a)** the average kinetic energy of the molecules, **(b)** their average speed, **(c)** the number of collisions they make with the container walls per unit time, **(d)** the number of collisions they make with a unit area of container wall per unit time?

**SOLUTION**

**Analyze** We need to apply the concepts of the kinetic-molecular theory of gases to a gas compressed at constant temperature.

**Plan** We will determine how each of the quantities in (a)–(d) is affected by the change in volume at constant temperature.

# A CLOSER LOOK

## THE IDEAL-GAS EQUATION

The ideal-gas equation can be derived from the five statements given in the text for the kinetic-molecular theory. Rather than perform the derivation, however, let's consider in qualitative terms how the ideal-gas equation might follow from these statements. The total force of the molecular collisions on the walls and hence the pressure (force per unit area, Section 10.2) produced by these collisions depend both on how strongly the molecules strike the walls (impulse imparted per collision) and on the rate at which the collisions occur:

$$P \propto \text{impulse imparted per collision} \times \text{collision rate}$$

For a molecule traveling at the rms speed, the impulse imparted by a collision with a wall depends on the momentum of the molecule; that is, it depends on the product of the molecule's mass and speed: $mu_{rms}$. The collision rate is proportional to the number of molecules per unit volume, $n/V$, and to their speed, which is $u_{rms}$ because we are talking about only molecules traveling at this speed. If there are more molecules in a container, there will be more frequent collisions with the walls. As the molecular speed increases or the container volume decreases, the time required for molecules to travel from one wall to another is reduced, and the molecules collide more frequently with the walls. Thus, we have

$$P \propto mu_{rms} \times \frac{n}{V} \times u_{rms} \propto \frac{nm(u_{rms})^2}{V} \qquad [10.19]$$

Because the average kinetic energy, $\frac{1}{2}m(u_{rms})^2$, is proportional to temperature, we have $m(u_{rms})^2 \propto T$. Making this substitution in Equation 10.19 gives

$$P \propto \frac{nm(u_{rms})^2}{V} \propto \frac{nT}{V} \qquad [10.20]$$

If we put in a proportionality constant, calling it $R$, the gas constant, you can see that we obtain the ideal-gas equation:

$$P = \frac{nRT}{V} \qquad [10.21]$$

Swiss mathematician Daniel Bernoulli (1700–1782) conceived of a model for gases that was, for all practical purposes, the same as the model described by the kinetic-molecular theory of gases. From this model, Bernoulli derived Boyle's law and the ideal-gas equation. His was one of the first examples in science of developing a mathematical model from a set of assumptions, or hypothetical statements. However, Bernoulli's work on this subject was completely ignored, only to be rediscovered a hundred years later by Clausius and others. It was ignored because it conflicted with popular beliefs and was in conflict with Isaac Newton's incorrect model for gases. Those idols of the times had to fall before the way was clear for the kinetic-molecular theory. As this story illustrates, science is not a straight road running from here to the "truth." The road is built by humans, so it zigs and zags.

*RELATED EXERCISES:* 10.77, 10.78, 10.79, and 10.80

**Solve** (a) Because the average kinetic energy of the $O_2$ molecules is determined only by temperature, this energy is unchanged by the compression. (b) Because the average kinetic energy of the molecules does not change, their average speed remains constant. (c) The number of collisions with the walls per unit time increases because the molecules are moving in a smaller volume but with the same average speed as before. Under these conditions they must encounter a wall more frequently. (d) The number of collisions with a unit area of wall per unit time increases because the total number of collisions with the walls per unit time increases and the area of the walls decreases.

**Check** In a conceptual exercise of this kind, there is no numerical answer to check. All we can check in such cases is our reasoning in the course of solving the problem.

## PRACTICE EXERCISE

How is the rms speed of $N_2$ molecules in a gas sample changed by (a) an increase in temperature, (b) an increase in volume, (c) mixing with a sample of Ar at the same temperature?

*Answers:* (a) increases, (b) no effect, (c) no effect

# 10.8 | MOLECULAR EFFUSION AND DIFFUSION

According to the kinetic-molecular theory of gases, the average kinetic energy of *any* collection of gas molecules, $\frac{1}{2}m(u_{rms})^2$, has a specific value at a given temperature. Thus, for two gases at the same temperature a gas composed of low-mass particles, such as He, has the same average kinetic energy as one composed of more massive particles, such as Xe. The mass of the particles in the He sample is smaller than that in the Xe sample. Consequently, the He particles must have a higher rms speed than the Xe particles. The equation that expresses this fact quantitatively is

$$u_{rms} = \sqrt{\frac{3RT}{\mathcal{M}}} \qquad [10.22]$$

where $\mathcal{M}$ is the molar mass of the particles, which can be derived from the kinetic-molecular theory. Because $\mathcal{M}$ appears in the denominator, the less massive the gas particles, the higher their rms speed.

**GO FIGURE**

How does root-mean-square speed vary with molar mass?

▶ **FIGURE 10.18 The effect of molar mass on molecular speed at 25 °C.**

▲ **FIGURE 10.18** shows the distribution of molecular speeds for several gases at 25 °C. Notice how the distributions are shifted toward higher speeds for gases of lower molar masses.

---

**SAMPLE EXERCISE 10.14** | **Calculating a Root-Mean-Square Speed**

Calculate the rms speed of the molecules in a sample of $N_2$ gas at 25 °C.

**SOLUTION**

**Analyze** We are given the identity of a gas and the temperature, the two quantities we need to calculate the rms speed.

**Plan** We calculate the rms speed using Equation 10.22.

**Solve** We must convert each quantity in our equation to SI units. We will also use $R$ in units of J/mol-K (Table 10.2) to make the units cancel correctly.

$$T = 25 + 273 = 298 \text{ K}$$

$$\mathcal{M} = 28.0 \text{ g/mol} = 28.0 \times 10^{-3} \text{ kg/mol}$$

$$R = 8.314 \text{ J/mol-K} = 8.314 \text{ kg-m}^2/\text{s}^2\text{-mol-K} \quad (\text{Since } 1 \text{ J} = 1 \text{ kg-m}^2/\text{s}^2)$$

$$u_{rms} = \sqrt{\frac{3(8.314 \text{ kg-m}^2/\text{s}^2\text{-mol-K})(298 \text{ K})}{28.0 \times 10^{-3} \text{ kg/mol}}} = 5.15 \times 10^2 \text{ m/s}$$

**Comment** This corresponds to a speed of 1150 mi/hr. Because the average molecular weight of air molecules is slightly greater than that of $N_2$, the rms speed of air molecules is a little lower than that for $N_2$.

**PRACTICE EXERCISE**

What is the rms speed of an atom in a sample of He gas at 25 °C ?

**Answer:** $1.36 \times 10^3$ m/s

---

The most probable speed of a gas molecule can also be derived:

Gas molecules in top half effuse through pinhole only when they happen to hit pinhole

▲ **FIGURE 10.19 Effusion.**

$$u_{mp} = \sqrt{\frac{2RT}{\mathcal{M}}} \qquad [10.23]$$

▲ **GIVE IT SOME THOUGHT**

What is the ratio of $u_{rms}$ to $u_{mp}$ for a certain gas at a given temperature?

The dependence of molecular speed on mass has two interesting consequences. The first is **effusion**, which is the escape of gas molecules through a tiny hole (◀ **FIGURE 10.19**). The second is **diffusion**, which is the spread of one substance throughout a space or throughout a second substance. For example, the molecules of a perfume diffuse throughout a room.

# Graham's Law of Effusion

In 1846 Thomas Graham (1805–1869) discovered that the effusion rate of a gas is inversely proportional to the square root of its molar mass. Assume we have two gases at the same temperature and pressure in two containers with identical pinholes. If the rates of effusion of the two gases are $r_1$ and $r_2$ and their molar masses are $\mathcal{M}_1$ and $\mathcal{M}_2$, **Graham's law** states that

$$\frac{r_1}{r_2} = \sqrt{\frac{\mathcal{M}_2}{\mathcal{M}_1}} \qquad\qquad [10.24]$$

a relationship that indicates that the lighter gas has the higher effusion rate.

The only way for a molecule to escape from its container is for it to "hit" the hole in the partitioning wall of Figure 10.19. The faster the molecules are moving, the greater is the likelihood that a molecule will hit the hole and effuse. This implies that the rate of effusion is directly proportional to the rms speed of the molecules. Because $R$ and $T$ are constant, we have, from Equation 10.22

$$\frac{r_1}{r_2} = \frac{u_{rms1}}{u_{rms2}} = \sqrt{\frac{3RT/\mathcal{M}_1}{3RT/\mathcal{M}_2}} = \sqrt{\frac{\mathcal{M}_2}{\mathcal{M}_1}} \qquad\qquad [10.25]$$

As expected from Graham's law, helium escapes from containers through tiny pinhole leaks more rapidly than other gases of higher molecular weight (▼ **FIGURE 10.20**).

 GO FIGURE

**Because pressure and temperature are constant in this figure but volume changes, which other quantity in the ideal-gas equation must also change?**

Both gases effuse through pores in balloon, but lighter helium gas effuses faster than heavier argon gas

◀ FIGURE 10.20    An illustration of Graham's law of effusion.

---

**SAMPLE EXERCISE 10.15**    **Applying Graham's Law**

An unknown gas composed of homonuclear diatomic molecules effuses at a rate that is 0.355 times the rate at which $O_2$ gas effuses at the same temperature. Calculate the molar mass of the unknown and identify it.

**SOLUTION**

**Analyze** We are given the rate of effusion of an unknown gas relative to that of $O_2$ and asked to find the molar mass and identity of the unknown. Thus, we need to connect relative rates of effusion to relative molar masses.

**Plan** We use Equation 10.24, to determine the molar mass of the unknown gas. If we let $r_x$ and $\mathcal{M}_x$ represent the rate of effusion and molar mass of the gas, we can write

$$\frac{r_x}{r_{O_2}} = \sqrt{\frac{\mathcal{M}_{O_2}}{\mathcal{M}_x}}$$

**Solve** From the information given,

$$r_x = 0.355 \times r_{O_2}$$

Thus,

$$\frac{r_x}{r_{O_2}} = 0.355 = \sqrt{\frac{32.0 \text{ g/mol}}{\mathcal{M}_x}}$$

$$\frac{32.0 \text{ g/mol}}{\mathcal{M}_x} = (0.355)^2 = 0.126$$

$$\mathcal{M}_x = \frac{32.0 \text{ g/mol}}{0.126} = 254 \text{ g/mol}$$

Because we are told that the unknown gas is composed of homonuclear diatomic molecules, it must be an element. The molar mass must represent twice the atomic weight of the atoms in the unknown gas. We conclude that the unknown gas is $I_2$.

**PRACTICE EXERCISE**

Calculate the ratio of the effusion rates of $N_2$ gas and $O_2$ gas.

*Answer:* $r_{N_2}/r_{O_2} = 1.07$

## Diffusion and Mean Free Path

Although diffusion, like effusion, is faster for lower-mass molecules than for higher-mass ones, molecular collisions make diffusion more complicated than effusion.

Graham's law, Equation 10.24, approximates the ratio of the diffusion rates of two gases under identical conditions. We can see from the horizontal axis in Figure 10.18 that the speeds of molecules are quite high. For example, the rms speed of molecules of $N_2$ gas at room temperature is 515 m/s. In spite of this high speed, if someone opens a vial of perfume at one end of a room, some time elapses—perhaps a few minutes—before the scent is detected at the other end of the room. This tells us that the diffusion rate of gases throughout a volume of space is much slower than molecular speeds.* This difference is due to molecular collisions, which occur frequently for a gas at atmospheric pressure—about $10^{10}$ times per second for each molecule. Collisions occur because real gas molecules have finite volumes.

## CHEMISTRY PUT TO WORK

### Gas Separations

The fact that lighter molecules move at higher average speeds than more massive ones has many interesting applications. For example, developing the atomic bomb during World War II required scientists to separate the relatively low-abundance uranium isotope $^{235}U$ (0.7%) from the much more abundant $^{238}U$ (99.3%). This separation was accomplished by converting the uranium into a volatile compound, $UF_6$, that was then allowed to pass through a porous barrier. (Because of the pore diameters, this process is not simple effusion. Nevertheless, the way in which rate of passing through the pores depends on molar mass is essentially the same as in effusion.) The slight difference in molar mass between $^{235}UF_6$ and $^{238}UF_6$ caused the molecules to move at slightly different rates:

$$\frac{r_{235}}{r_{238}} = \sqrt{\frac{352.04}{349.03}} = 1.0043$$

Thus, the gas initially appearing on the opposite side of the barrier was very slightly enriched in $^{235}U$. The process was repeated thousands of times, leading to a nearly complete separation of the two isotopes.

Separation of uranium isotopes by effusion has been largely replaced by a technique that uses centrifuges. In this procedure, cylindrical rotors containing $UF_6$ vapor spin at high speed inside an evacuated casing. Molecules of $^{238}UF_6$ move closer to the spinning walls, whereas molecules of $^{235}UF_6$ remain in the middle of the cylinders. A stream of gas moves the $^{235}UF_6$ from the center of one centrifuge into another. Plants that use centrifuges consume less energy than those that use effusion and can be constructed in a more compact, modular fashion. Such plants are frequently in the news today as countries such as Iran and North Korea enrich uranium in the $^{235}U$ isotope for both nuclear power and nuclear weaponry.

*RELATED EXERCISES:* 10.89 and 10.90

---

*The rate at which the perfume moves across the room also depends on how well stirred the air is from temperature gradients and the movement of people. Nevertheless, even with the aid of these factors, it still takes much longer for the molecules to traverse the room than one would expect from their rms speed.

Because of molecular collisions, the direction of motion of a gas molecule is constantly changing. Therefore, the diffusion of a molecule from one point to another consists of many short, straight-line segments as collisions buffet it around in random directions (▶ FIGURE 10.21).

The average distance traveled by a molecule between collisions, called the molecule's **mean free path**, varies with pressure as the following analogy illustrates. Imagine walking through a shopping mall. When the mall is crowded (high pressure), the average distance you can walk before bumping into someone is short (short mean free path). When the mall is empty (low pressure), you can walk a long way (long mean free path) before bumping into someone. The mean free path for air molecules at sea level is about 60 nm. At about 100 km in altitude, where the air density is much lower, the mean free path is about 10 cm, over 1 million times longer than at Earth's surface.

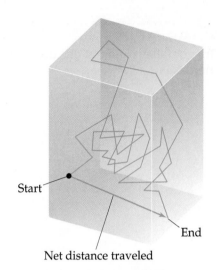

▲ **FIGURE 10.21   Diffusion of a gas molecule.** For clarity, no other gas molecules in the container are shown.

⚠ GIVE IT SOME THOUGHT

Will these changes increase, decrease, or have no effect on the mean free path of the molecules in a gas sample?
a. increasing pressure.
b. increasing temperature.

# 10.9 | REAL GASES: DEVIATIONS FROM IDEAL BEHAVIOR

The extent to which a real gas departs from ideal behavior can be seen by rearranging the ideal-gas equation to solve for $n$:

$$\frac{PV}{RT} = n \qquad [10.26]$$

This form of the equation tells us that for 1 mol of ideal gas, the quantity $PV/RT$ equals 1 at all pressures. In ▼ FIGURE 10.22 $PV/RT$ is plotted as a function of $P$ for 1 mol of several real gases. At high pressures (generally above 10 atm) the deviation from ideal behavior ($PV/RT = 1$) is large and different for each gas. *Real gases, in other words, do not behave ideally at high pressure.* At lower pressures (usually below 10 atm), however, the deviation from ideal behavior is small, and we can use the ideal-gas equation without generating serious error.

⚠ GO FIGURE

**Does molar mass correlate with nonideal-gas behavior below 200 atm?**

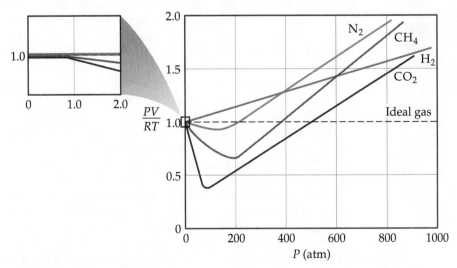

▲ **FIGURE 10.22   The effect of pressure on the behavior of several real gases.** Data for 1 mol of gas in all cases. Data for $N_2$, $CH_4$, and $H_2$ are at 300 K; for $CO_2$ data are at 313 K because under high pressure $CO_2$ liquefies at 300 K.

## GO FIGURE

True or false: Nitrogen gas behaves more like an ideal gas as the temperature increases.

▶ **FIGURE 10.23 The effect of temperature and pressure on the behavior of nitrogen gas.**

Deviation from ideal behavior also depends on temperature. As temperature increases, the behavior of a real gas more nearly approaches that of the ideal gas (▲ **FIGURE 10.23**). In general, *the deviation from ideal behavior increases as temperature decreases,* becoming significant near the temperature at which the gas liquefies.

 **GIVE IT SOME THOUGHT**

Under which conditions do you expect helium gas to deviate most from ideal behavior?
a. 100 K and 1 atm,
b. 100 K and 5 atm, or
c. 300 K and 2 atm.

The basic assumptions of the kinetic-molecular theory of gases give us insight into why real gases deviate from ideal behavior. The molecules of an ideal gas are assumed to occupy no space and have no attraction for one another. *Real molecules, however, do have finite volumes and do attract one another.* As ◀ **FIGURE 10.24** shows, the unoccupied space in which real molecules can move is less than the container volume. At low pressures the combined volume of the gas molecules is negligible relative to the container volume. Thus, the unoccupied volume available to the molecules is essentially the container volume. At high pressures, the combined volume of the gas molecules is *not* negligible relative to the container volume. Now the unoccupied volume available to the molecules is less than the container volume. At high pressures, therefore, gas volumes tend to be slightly greater than those predicted by the ideal-gas equation.

Another reason for nonideal behavior at high pressures is that the attractive forces between molecules come into play at the short intermolecular distances found when molecules are crowded together at high pressures. Because of these attractive forces, the impact of a given molecule with the container wall is lessened. If we could stop the motion in a gas, as illustrated in ▶ **FIGURE 10.25**, we would see that a molecule about to collide with the wall experiences the attractive forces of nearby molecules. These attractions lessen the force with which the molecule hits the wall. As a result, the gas pressure is less than that of an ideal gas. This effect decreases $PV/RT$ to below its ideal value, as seen at the lower pressures in Figures 10.22 and 10.23. When the pressure is sufficiently high, however, the volume effects dominate and $PV/RT$ increases to above the ideal value.

Low pressure          High pressure

▲ **FIGURE 10.24 Gases behave more ideally at low pressure than at high pressure.** The combined volume of the molecules can be neglected at low pressure but not at high pressure.

GO FIGURE

How would you expect the pressure of a gas to change if suddenly the intermolecular forces were repulsive rather than attractive?

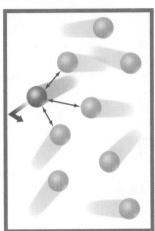

Ideal gas                                    Real gas

▲ **FIGURE 10.25**  **In any real gas, attractive intermolecular forces reduce pressure to values lower than in an ideal gas.**

Temperature determines how effective attractive forces between gas molecules are in causing deviations from ideal behavior at lower pressures. Figure 10.23 shows that, at pressures below about 400 atm, cooling increases the extent to which a gas deviates from ideal behavior. As the gas cools, the average kinetic energy of the molecules decreases. This drop in kinetic energy means the molecules do not have the energy needed to overcome intermolecular attraction, and the molecules will be more likely to stick to each other than bounce off each other.

As the temperature of a gas increases—as, say, from 200 K to 1000 K in Figure 10.23—the negative deviation of $PV/RT$ from the ideal value of 1 disappears. As noted earlier, the deviations seen at high temperatures stem mainly from the effect of the finite volumes of the molecules.

 GIVE IT SOME THOUGHT

List two reasons why gases deviate from ideal behavior.

## The van der Waals Equation

Engineers and scientists who work with gases at high pressures often cannot use the ideal-gas equation because departures from ideal behavior are too large. One useful equation developed to predict the behavior of real gases was proposed by the Dutch scientist Johannes van der Waals (1837–1923).

Van der Waals recognized that the ideal-gas equation could be corrected to account for the effects of intermolecular attractive forces and for molecular volumes. He introduced two constants for these corrections: $a$, a measure of how strongly the gas molecules attract one another, and $b$, a measure of the finite volume occupied by the molecules. His description of gas behavior is known as the **van der Waals equation:**

$$\left(P + \frac{n^2a}{V^2}\right)(V - nb) = nRT \qquad [10.27]$$

The term $n^2a/V^2$ accounts for the attractive forces. The equation adjusts the pressure upward by adding $n^2a/V^2$ because attractive forces between molecules tend to reduce the pressure (Figure 10.25). The added term has the form $n^2a/V^2$ because the attractive force between pairs of molecules increases as the square of the number of molecules per unit volume, $(n/V)^2$.

| TABLE 10.3 • Van der Waals Constants for Gas Molecules | | |
|---|---|---|
| Substance | $a(L^2\text{-atm/mol}^2)$ | $b$ (L/mol) |
| He | 0.0341 | 0.02370 |
| Ne | 0.211 | 0.0171 |
| Ar | 1.34 | 0.0322 |
| Kr | 2.32 | 0.0398 |
| Xe | 4.19 | 0.0510 |
| $H_2$ | 0.244 | 0.0266 |
| $N_2$ | 1.39 | 0.0391 |
| $O_2$ | 1.36 | 0.0318 |
| $Cl_2$ | 6.49 | 0.0562 |
| $H_2O$ | 5.46 | 0.0305 |
| $CH_4$ | 2.25 | 0.0428 |
| $CO_2$ | 3.59 | 0.0427 |
| $CCl_4$ | 20.4 | 0.1383 |

The term $nb$ accounts for the small but finite volume occupied by the gas molecules (Figure 10.24). The van der Waals equation subtracts $nb$ to adjust the volume downward to give the volume that would be available to the molecules in the ideal case. The constants $a$ and $b$, called *van der Waals constants*, are experimentally determined, positive quantities that differ from one gas to another. Notice in ▲ TABLE 10.3 that $a$ and $b$ generally increase with increasing molecular mass. Larger, more massive molecules have larger volumes and tend to have greater intermolecular attractive forces.

---

**SAMPLE EXERCISE 10.16** | **Using the van der Waals Equation**

If 1.000 mol of an ideal gas were confined to 22.41 L at 0.0 °C, it would exert a pressure of 1.000 atm. Use the van der Waals equation and Table 10.3 to estimate the pressure exerted by 1.000 mol of $Cl_2(g)$ in 22.41 L at 0.0 °C.

**SOLUTION**

**Analyze** We need to determine a pressure. Because we will use the van der Waals equation, we must identify the appropriate values for the constants that appear there.

**Plan** Solving Equation 10.27 for $P$, we have

$$P = \frac{nRT}{V - nb} - \frac{n^2a}{V^2}$$

**Solve** Substituting $n = 1.000$ mol, $R = 0.08206$ L-atm/mol-K, $T = 273.2$ K, $V = 22.41$ L, $a = 6.49$ $L^2$-atm/mol$^2$, and $b = 0.0562$ L/mol:

$$P = \frac{(1.000\text{ mol})(0.08206\text{ L-atm/mol-K})(273.2\text{ K})}{22.41\text{ L} - (1.000\text{ mol})(0.0562\text{ L/mol})} - \frac{(1.000\text{ mol})^2(6.49\text{ L}^2\text{-atm/mol}^2)}{(22.14\text{ L})^2}$$

$$= 1.003\text{ atm} - 0.013\text{ atm} = 0.990\text{ atm}$$

**Check** We expect a pressure not far from 1.000 atm, which would be the value for an ideal gas, so our answer seems very reasonable.

**Comment** Notice that the term 1.003 atm is the pressure corrected for molecular volume. This value is higher than the ideal value, 1.000 atm, because the volume in which the molecules are free to move is smaller than the container volume, 22.41 L. Thus, the molecules collide more frequently with the container walls. The term 0.013 atm corrects for intermolecular forces. The intermolecular attractions between molecules reduce the pressure to 0.990 atm. We conclude, therefore, that the intermolecular attractions are the main cause of the slight deviation of $Cl_2(g)$ from ideal behavior under the stated experimental conditions.

**PRACTICE EXERCISE**

A sample of 1.000 mol of $CO_2(g)$ is confined to a 3.000-L container at 0.000 °C. Calculate the pressure of the gas using (a) the ideal-gas equation and (b) the van der Waals equation.

*Answers:* (a) 7.47 atm, (b) 7.18 atm

**SAMPLE INTEGRATIVE EXERCISE** | Putting Concepts Together

Cyanogen, a highly toxic gas, is 46.2% C and 53.8% N by mass. At 25 °C and 751 torr, 1.05 g of cyanogen occupies 0.500 L. **(a)** What is the molecular formula of cyanogen? Predict **(b)** its molecular structure and **(c)** its polarity.

**SOLUTION**

**Analyze** We need to determine the molecular formula of a gas from elemental analysis data and data on its properties. Then we need to predict the structure of the molecule and from that, its polarity.

**(a) Plan** We can use the percentage composition of the compound to calculate its empirical formula. ∞∞ (Section 3.5) Then we can determine the molecular formula by comparing the mass of the empirical formula with the molar mass. ∞∞ (Section 3.5)

**Solve** To determine the empirical formula, we assume we have a 100-g sample and calculate the number of moles of each element in the sample:

$$\text{Moles C} = (46.2 \text{ g C})\left(\frac{1 \text{ mol C}}{12.01 \text{ g C}}\right) = 3.85 \text{ mol C}$$

$$\text{Moles N} = (53.8 \text{ g N})\left(\frac{1 \text{ mol N}}{14.01 \text{ g N}}\right) = 3.84 \text{ mol N}$$

Because the ratio of the moles of the two elements is essentially 1:1, the empirical formula is CN. To determine the molar mass, we use Equation 10.11.

$$\mathcal{M} = \frac{dRT}{P} = \frac{(1.05 \text{ g/0.500 L})(0.08206 \text{ L-atm/mol-K})(298 \text{ K})}{(751/760)\text{atm}} = 52.0 \text{ g/mol}$$

The molar mass associated with the empirical formula CN is 12.0 + 14.0 = 26.0 g/mol. Dividing the molar mass by that of its empirical formula gives (52.0 g/mol)/(26.0 g/mol) = 2.00. Thus, the molecule has twice as many atoms of each element as the empirical formula, giving the molecular formula $C_2N_2$.

**(b) Plan** To determine the molecular structure, we must determine the Lewis structure. ∞∞ (Section 8.5) We can then use the VSEPR model to predict the structure. ∞∞ (Section 9.2)

**Solve** The molecule has 2(4) + 2(5) = 18 valence-shell electrons. By trial and error, we seek a Lewis structure with 18 valence electrons in which each atom has an octet and the formal charges are as low as possible. The structure

$$:\text{N}\equiv\text{C}-\text{C}\equiv\text{N}:$$

meets these criteria. (This structure has zero formal charge on each atom.)

The Lewis structure shows that each atom has two electron domains. (Each nitrogen has a nonbonding pair of electrons and a triple bond, whereas each carbon has a triple bond and a single bond.) Thus, the electron-domain geometry around each atom is linear, causing the overall molecule to be linear.

**(c) Plan** To determine the polarity of the molecule, we must examine the polarity of the individual bonds and the overall geometry of the molecule.

**Solve** Because the molecule is linear, we expect the two dipoles created by the polarity in the carbon–nitrogen bond to cancel each other, leaving the molecule with no dipole moment.

# CHAPTER SUMMARY AND KEY TERMS

**SECTION 10.1** Substances that are gases at room temperature tend to be molecular substances with low molar masses. Air, a mixture composed mainly of $N_2$ and $O_2$, is the most common gas we encounter. Some liquids and solids can also exist in the gaseous state, where they are known as **vapors**. Gases are compressible; they mix in all proportions because their component molecules are far apart from each other.

**SECTION 10.2** To describe the state or condition of a gas, we must specify four variables: pressure (*P*), volume (*V*), temperature (*T*), and quantity (*n*). Volume is usually measured in liters, temperature in kelvins, and quantity of gas in moles. **Pressure** is the force per unit

area. It is expressed in SI units as **pascals**, Pa (1 Pa = 1 N/m²). A related unit, the **bar**, equals $10^5$ Pa. In chemistry, **standard atmospheric pressure** is used to define the **atmosphere** (atm) and the **torr** (also called the millimeter of mercury). One atmosphere of pressure equals 101.325 kPa, or 760 torr. A barometer is often used to measure the atmospheric pressure. A manometer can be used to measure the pressure of enclosed gases.

**SECTIONS 10.3 AND 10.4** Studies have revealed several simple gas laws: For a constant quantity of gas at constant temperature, the volume of the gas is inversely proportional to the pressure (**Boyle's law**).

For a fixed quantity of gas at constant pressure, the volume is directly proportional to its absolute temperature (**Charles's law**). Equal volumes of gases at the same temperature and pressure contain equal numbers of molecules (**Avogadro's hypothesis**). For a gas at constant temperature and pressure, the volume of the gas is directly proportional to the number of moles of gas (**Avogadro's law**). Each of these gas laws is a special case of the ideal-gas equation.

The **ideal-gas equation**, $PV = nRT$, is the equation of state for an **ideal gas**. The term $R$ in this equation is the **gas constant**. We can use the ideal-gas equation to calculate variations in one variable when one or more of the others are changed. Most gases at pressures less than 10 atm and temperatures near 273 K and above obey the ideal-gas equation reasonably well. The conditions of 273 K (0 °C) and 1 atm are known as the **standard temperature and pressure (STP)**. In all applications of the ideal-gas equation we must remember to convert temperatures to the absolute-temperature scale (the Kelvin scale).

**SECTIONS 10.5 AND 10.6**　Using the ideal-gas equation, we can relate the density of a gas to its molar mass: $\mathcal{M} = dRT/P$. We can also use the ideal-gas equation to solve problems involving gases as reactants or products in chemical reactions.

In gas mixtures the total pressure is the sum of the **partial pressures** that each gas would exert if it were present alone under the same conditions (**Dalton's law of partial pressures**). The partial pressure of a component of a mixture is equal to its mole fraction times the total pressure: $P_1 = X_1 P_t$. The **mole fraction** is the ratio of the moles of one component of a mixture to the total moles of all components. In calculating the quantity of a gas collected over water, correction must be made for the partial pressure of water vapor in the gas mixture.

**SECTION 10.7**　The **kinetic-molecular theory of gases** accounts for the properties of an ideal gas in terms of a set of statements about the nature of gases. Briefly, these statements are as follows: Molecules are in continuous chaotic motion. The volume of gas molecules is negligible compared to the volume of their container. The gas molecules neither attract nor repel each other. The average kinetic energy of the gas molecules is proportional to the absolute temperature and does not change if the temperature remains constant.

The individual molecules of a gas do not all have the same kinetic energy at a given instant. Their speeds are distributed over a wide range; the distribution varies with the molar mass of the gas and with temperature. The **root-mean-square (rms) speed**, $u_{rms}$, varies in proportion to the square root of the absolute temperature and inversely with the square root of the molar mass: $u_{rms} = \sqrt{3RT/\mathcal{M}}$. The most probable speed of a gas molecule is given by $u_{mp} = \sqrt{2RT/\mathcal{M}}$.

**SECTION 10.8**　It follows from kinetic-molecular theory that the rate at which a gas undergoes **effusion** (escapes through a tiny hole) is inversely proportional to the square root of its molar mass (**Graham's law**). The **diffusion** of one gas through the space occupied by a second gas is another phenomenon related to the speeds at which molecules move. Because molecules undergo frequent collisions with one another, the **mean free path**—the mean distance traveled between collisions—is short. Collisions between molecules limit the rate at which a gas molecule can diffuse.

**SECTION 10.9**　Departures from ideal behavior increase in magnitude as pressure increases and as temperature decreases. The extent of nonideality of a real gas can be seen by examining the quantity $PV = RT$ for one mole of the gas as a function of pressure; for an ideal gas, this quantity is exactly 1 at all pressures. Real gases depart from ideal behavior because the molecules possess finite volume and because the molecules experience attractive forces for one another. The **van der Waals equation** is an equation of state for gases that modifies the ideal-gas equation to account for intrinsic molecular volume and intermolecular forces.

# KEY SKILLS

- Convert between pressure units with an emphasis on torr and atmospheres. (Section 10.2)

- Calculate $P$, $V$, $n$, or $T$ using the ideal-gas equation. (Section 10.4)

- Understand how the gas laws relate to the ideal-gas equation and apply the gas laws in calculations. (Sections 10.3 and 10.4)

- Calculate the density or molecular weight of a gas. (Section 10.5)

- Calculate the volume of gas consumed or formed in a chemical reaction. (Section 10.5)

- Calculate the total pressure of a gas mixture given its partial pressures or given information for calculating partial pressures. (Section 10.6)

- Describe the kinetic-molecular theory of gases and how it explains the pressure and temperature of a gas, the gas laws, and the rates of effusion and diffusion. (Sections 10.7 and 10.8)

- Explain why intermolecular attractions and molecular volumes cause real gases to deviate from ideal behavior at high pressure or low temperature. (Section 10.9)

# KEY EQUATIONS

- $PV = nRT$　　　　　　[10.5]　　　　Ideal-gas equation

- $\dfrac{P_1 V_1}{T_1} = \dfrac{P_2 V_2}{T_2}$　　[10.8]　　　　The combined gas law, showing how $P$, $V$, and $T$ are related for a constant $n$

- $d = \dfrac{P\mathcal{M}}{RT}$　　　　　[10.10]　　　Calculating the density or molar mass of a gas

- $P_t = P_1 + P_2 + P_3 + \dots$　　[10.12]　　　Relating the total pressure of a gas mixture to the partial pressures of its components (Dalton's law of partial pressures)

- $P_1 = \left(\dfrac{n_1}{n_t}\right) P_t = X_1 P_t$      [10.16]      Relating partial pressure to mole fraction

- $u_{rms} = \sqrt{\dfrac{3RT}{\mathcal{M}}}$      [10.22]      Definition of the root-mean-square (rms) speed of gas molecules

- $\dfrac{r_1}{r_2} = \sqrt{\dfrac{\mathcal{M}_2}{\mathcal{M}_1}}$      [10.24]      Relating the relative rates of effusion of two gases to their molar masses

# EXERCISES

## VISUALIZING CONCEPTS

**10.1** Mars has an average atmospheric pressure of 0.007 atm. Would it be easier or harder to drink from a straw on Mars than on Earth? Explain. [Section 10.2]

**10.2** You have a sample of gas in a container with a movable piston, such as the one in the drawing. **(a)** Redraw the container to show what it might look like if the temperature of the gas is increased from 300 K to 500 K while the pressure is kept constant. **(b)** Redraw the container to show what it might look like if the external pressure on the piston is increased from 1.0 atm to 2.0 atm while the temperature is kept constant. **(c)** Redraw the container to show what it might look like if the temperature of the gas decreases from 300 K to 200 K while the pressure is kept constant (assume the gas does not liquefy). [Section 10.3]

**10.3** Consider the sample of gas depicted here. What would the drawing look like if the volume and temperature remained constant while you removed enough of the gas to decrease the pressure by a factor of 2? [Section 10.3]

**10.4** Imagine that the reaction $2\,CO(g) + O_2(g) \longrightarrow 2\,CO_2(g)$ occurs in a container that has a piston that moves to maintain a constant pressure when the reaction occurs at constant temperature. **(a)** What happens to the volume of the container as a result of the reaction? Explain. **(b)** If the piston is not allowed to move, what happens to the pressure as a result of the reaction? [Sections 10.3 and 10.5]

**10.5** Suppose you have a fixed amount of an ideal gas at a constant volume. If the pressure of the gas is doubled while the volume is held constant, what happens to its temperature? [Section 10.4]

**10.6** The apparatus shown here has two gas-filled containers and one empty container, all attached to a hollow horizontal tube. When the valves are opened and the gases are allowed to mix at constant temperature, what is the distribution of atoms in each container? Assume that the containers are of equal volume and ignore the volume of the connecting tube. Which gas has the greater partial pressure after the valves are opened? [Section 10.6]

**10.7** The accompanying drawing represents a mixture of three different gases. **(a)** Rank the three components in order of increasing partial pressure. **(b)** If the total pressure of the mixture is 1.40 atm, calculate the partial pressure of each gas. [Section 10.6]

**10.8** On a single plot, qualitatively sketch the distribution of molecular speeds for **(a)** Kr(g) at −50 °C, **(b)** Kr(g) at 0 °C, **(c)** Ar(g) at 0 °C. [Section 10.7]

**10.9** Consider the following graph. **(a)** If curves A and B refer to two different gases, He and $O_2$, at the same temperature, which is which? Explain. **(b)** If A and B refer to the same gas at two different temperatures, which represents the higher temperature? **(c)** Redraw the graph and put in vertical lines that indicate the approximate positions of the most probable speeds and root-mean-square speeds for each curve. [Section 10.7]

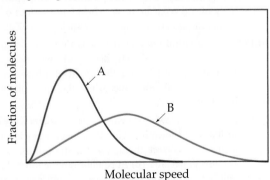

**10.10** Consider the following samples of gases:

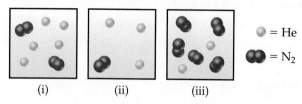

(i)       (ii)       (iii)

If the three samples are all at the same temperature, rank them with respect to **(a)** total pressure, **(b)** partial pressure of helium, **(c)** density, **(d)** average kinetic energy of particles. [Section 10.6 and 10.7]

**10.11** A thin glass tube 1 m long is filled with Ar gas at 1 atm, and the ends are stoppered with cotton plugs:

HCl gas is introduced at one end of the tube, and simultaneously $NH_3$ gas is introduced at the other end. When the two gases diffuse through the cotton plugs down the tube and meet, a white ring appears due to the formation of $NH_4Cl(s)$. At which location—a, b, or c—do you expect the ring to form? Explain your choice. [Section 10.8]

**10.12** Which substances in Table 10.3 would you expect to deviate most from ideal-gas behavior at low temperature and high pressure? Which would deviate least? Explain. [Section 10.9]

# GAS CHARACTERISTICS; PRESSURE (sections 10.1 and 10.2)

**10.13** How does a gas compare with a liquid for each of the following properties: **(a)** density, **(b)** compressibility, **(c)** ability to mix with other substances of the same phase to form homogeneous mixtures, **(d)** ability to conform to the shape of its container?

**10.14** **(a)** A liquid and a gas are moved to larger containers. How does their behavior differ once they are in the larger containers? Explain the difference in molecular terms. **(b)** Although liquid water and carbon tetrachloride, $CCl_4(l)$, do not mix, their vapors form a homogeneous mixture. Explain. **(c)** Gas densities are generally reported in grams per liter, whereas liquid densities are reported in grams per milliliter. Explain the molecular basis for this difference.

**10.15** Suppose that a woman weighing 130 lb and wearing high-heeled shoes momentarily places all her weight on the heel of one foot. If the area of the heel is $0.50$ in.$^2$, calculate the pressure exerted on the underlying surface in **(a)** kilopascals, **(b)** atmospheres, and **(c)** pounds per square inch.

**10.16** A set of bookshelves rests on a hard floor surface on four legs, each having a cross-sectional dimension of $3.0 \times 4.1$ cm in contact with the floor. The total mass of the shelves plus the books stacked on them is 262 kg. Calculate the pressure in pascals exerted by the shelf footings on the surface.

**10.17** **(a)** How high in meters must a column of water be to exert a pressure equal to that of a 760-mm column of mercury? The density of water is $1.0$ g/mL, whereas that of mercury is $13.6$ g/mL. **(b)** What is the pressure, in atmospheres, on the body of a diver if he is 39 ft below the surface of the water when atmospheric pressure at the surface is 0.97 atm?

**10.18** The compound 1-iodododecane is a nonvolatile liquid with a density of $1.20$ g/mL. The density of mercury is $13.6$ g/mL. What do you predict for the height of a barometer column based on 1-iodododecane, when the atmospheric pressure is 749 torr?

**10.19** Each of the following statements concerns a mercury barometer such as that shown in Figure 10.2. Identify any incorrect statements and correct them. **(a)** The tube must be $1$ cm$^2$ in cross-sectional area. **(b)** At equilibrium the force of gravity per unit area acting on the mercury column equals the force of gravity per unit area acting on the atmosphere. **(c)** The column of mercury is held up by the vacuum at the top of the column. **(d)** If you took the mercury barometer with you on a trip from the beach to high mountains, the height of the mercury column would increase with elevation.

**10.20** Suppose you make a mercury barometer using a glass tube about 50 cm in length, closed at one end. What would you expect to see if the tube is filled with mercury and inverted in a mercury dish, as in Figure 10.2? Explain.

**10.21** The typical atmospheric pressure on top of Mt. Everest (29,028 ft) is about 265 torr. Convert this pressure to **(a)** atm, **(b)** mm Hg, **(c)** pascals, **(d)** bars, **(e)** psi.

**10.22** Perform the following conversions: **(a)** 0.912 atm to torr, **(b)** 0.685 bar to kilopascals, **(c)** 655 mm Hg to atmospheres, **(d)** $1.323 \times 10^5$ Pa to atmospheres, **(e)** 2.50 atm to psi.

**10.23** In the United States, barometric pressures are generally reported in inches of mercury (in. Hg). On a beautiful summer day in Chicago the barometric pressure is 30.45 in. Hg. **(a)** Convert this pressure to torr. **(b)** Convert this pressure to atm. **(c)** A meteorologist explains the nice weather by referring to a "high-pressure area." In light of your answer to parts (a) and (b), explain why this term makes sense.

**10.24** Hurricane Wilma of 2005 is the most intense hurricane on record in the Atlantic basin, with a low-pressure reading of 882 mbar (millibars). Convert this reading into **(a)** atmospheres, **(b)** torr, and **(c)** inches of Hg.

**10.25** If the atmospheric pressure is 0.995 atm, what is the pressure of the enclosed gas in each of the three cases depicted in the drawing? Assume that the gray liquid is mercury.

Open end       Open end       Closed end

$h = 52$ cm    $h = 67$ cm    $h = 10.3$ cm

(i)       (ii)       (iii)

**10.26** An open-end manometer containing mercury is connected to a container of gas, as depicted in Sample Exercise 10.2. What is the pressure of the enclosed gas in torr in each of the following situations? (a) The mercury in the arm attached to the gas is 15.4 mm higher than in the one open to the atmosphere; atmospheric pressure is 0.985 atm. (b) The mercury in the arm attached to the gas is 12.3 mm lower than in the one open to the atmosphere; atmospheric pressure is 0.99 atm.

# THE GAS LAWS (section 10.3)

**10.27** You have a gas confined to a cylinder with a movable piston. What would happen to the gas pressure inside the cylinder if you do the following? (a) Decrease the volume to one-fourth the original volume while holding the temperature constant. (b) Reduce the temperature (in kelvins) to half its original value while holding the volume constant. (c) Reduce the amount of gas to one-fourth while keeping the volume and temperature constant.

**10.28** A fixed quantity of gas at 21 °C exhibits a pressure of 752 torr and occupies a volume of 5.12 L. (a) Calculate the volume the gas will occupy if the pressure is increased to 1.88 atm while the temperature is held constant. (b) Calculate the volume the gas will occupy if the temperature is increased to 175 °C while the pressure is held constant.

**10.29** (a) How is the law of combining volumes explained by Avogadro's hypothesis? (b) Consider a 1.0-L flask containing neon gas and a 1.5-L flask containing xenon gas. Both gases are at the same pressure and temperature. According to Avogadro's law, what can be said about the ratio of the number of atoms in the two flasks? (c) Will 1 mol of an ideal gas always occupy the same volume at a given temperature and pressure? Explain.

**10.30** Nitrogen and hydrogen gases react to form ammonia gas as follows:

$$N_2(g) + 3 H_2(g) \longrightarrow 2 NH_3(g)$$

At a certain temperature and pressure, 1.2 L of $N_2$ reacts with 3.6 L of $H_2$. If all the $N_2$ and $H_2$ are consumed, what volume of $NH_3$, at the same temperature and pressure, will be produced?

# THE IDEAL-GAS EQUATION (section 10.4)

**10.31** (a) What is an ideal gas? (b) Show how Boyle's law, Charles's law, and Avogadro's law can be combined to give the ideal-gas equation. (c) Write the ideal-gas equation, and give the units used for each term when $R = 0.08206$ L-atm/mol-K. (d) If you measure pressure in bars instead of atmospheres, calculate the corresponding value of $R$ in L-bar/mol-K.

**10.32** (a) What conditions are represented by the abbreviation STP? (b) What is the molar volume of an ideal gas at STP? (c) Room temperature is often assumed to be 25 °C. Calculate the molar volume of an ideal gas at 25 °C and 1 atm pressure.

**10.33** Suppose you are given two 1-L flasks and told that one contains a gas of molar mass 30, the other a gas of molar mass 60, both at the same temperature. The pressure in flask A is X atm, and the mass of gas in the flask is 1.2 g. The pressure in flask B is 0.5X atm, and the mass of gas in that flask is 1.2 g. Which flask contains the gas of molar mass 30, and which contains the gas of molar mass 60?

**10.34** Suppose you are given two flasks at the same temperature, one of volume 2 L and the other of volume 3 L. The 2-L flask contains 4.8 g of gas, and the gas pressure is X atm. The 3-L flask contains 0.36 g of gas, and the gas pressure is 0.1X. Do the two gases have the same molar mass? If not, which contains the gas of higher molar mass?

**10.35** Complete the following table for an ideal gas:

| P | V | n | T |
|---|---|---|---|
| 2.00 atm | 1.00 L | 0.500 mol | ? K |
| 0.300 atm | 0.250 L | ? mol | 27 °C |
| 650 torr | ? L | 0.333 mol | 350 K |
| ? atm | 585 mL | 0.250 mol | 295 K |

**10.36** Calculate each of the following quantities for an ideal gas: (a) the volume of the gas, in liters, if 1.50 mol has a pressure of 1.25 atm at a temperature of −6 °C; (b) the absolute tempera-ture of the gas at which $3.33 \times 10^{-3}$ mol occupies 478 mL at 750 torr; (c) the pressure, in atmospheres, if 0.00245 mol occupies 413 mL at 138 °C; (d) the quantity of gas, in moles, if 126.5 L at 54 °C has a pressure of 11.25 kPa.

**10.37** The Goodyear blimps, which frequently fly over sporting events, hold approximately 175,000 ft³ of helium. If the gas is at 23 °C and 1.0 atm, what mass of helium is in a blimp?

**10.38** A neon sign is made of glass tubing whose inside diameter is 2.5 cm and whose length is 5.5 m. If the sign contains neon at a pressure of 1.78 torr at 35 °C, how many grams of neon are in the sign? (The volume of a cylinder is $\pi r^2 h$.)

**10.39** (a) Calculate the number of molecules in a deep breath of air whose volume is 2.25 L at body temperature, 37 °C, and a pressure of 735 torr. (b) The adult blue whale has a lung capacity of $5.0 \times 10^3$ L. Calculate the mass of air (assume an average molar mass 28.98 g/mol) contained in an adult blue whale's lungs at 0.0 °C and 1.00 atm, assuming the air behaves ideally.

**10.40** (a) If the pressure exerted by ozone, $O_3$, in the stratosphere is $3.0 \times 10^{-3}$ atm and the temperature is 250 K, how many ozone molecules are in a liter? (b) Carbon dioxide makes up approximately 0.04% of Earth's atmosphere. If you collect a 2.0-L sample from the atmosphere at sea level (1.00 atm) on a warm day (27 °C), how many $CO_2$ molecules are in your sample?

**10.41** A scuba diver's tank contains 0.29 kg of $O_2$ compressed into a volume of 2.3 L. (a) Calculate the gas pressure inside the tank at 9 °C. (b) What volume would this oxygen occupy at 26 °C and 0.95 atm?

**10.42** An aerosol spray can with a volume of 250 mL contains 2.30 g of propane gas ($C_3H_8$) as a propellant. (a) If the can is at 23 °C, what is the pressure in the can? (b) What volume would the propane occupy at STP? (c) The can's label says that exposure to temperatures above 130 °F may cause the can to burst. What is the pressure in the can at this temperature?

**10.43** Chlorine is widely used to purify municipal water supplies and to treat swimming pool waters. Suppose that the volume of a particular sample of $Cl_2$ gas is 8.70 L at 895 torr and 24 °C. **(a)** How many grams of $Cl_2$ are in the sample? **(b)** What volume will the $Cl_2$ occupy at STP? **(c)** At what temperature will the volume be 15.00 L if the pressure is $8.76 \times 10^2$ torr? **(d)** At what pressure will the volume equal 5.00 L if the temperature is 58 °C ?

**10.44** Many gases are shipped in high-pressure containers. Consider a steel tank whose volume is 55.0 gallons that contains $O_2$ gas at a pressure of 16,500 kPa at 23 °C. **(a)** What mass of $O_2$ does the tank contain? **(b)** What volume would the gas occupy at STP? **(c)** At what temperature would the pressure in the tank equal 150.0 atm? **(d)** What would be the pressure of the gas, in kPa, if it were transferred to a container at 24 °C whose volume is 55.0 L?

**10.45** In an experiment reported in the scientific literature, male cockroaches were made to run at different speeds on a miniature treadmill while their oxygen consumption was measured. In one hour the average cockroach running at 0.08 km/hr consumed 0.8 mL of $O_2$ at 1 atm pressure and 24 °C per gram of insect mass. **(a)** How many moles of $O_2$ would be consumed in 1 hr by a 5.2-g cockroach moving at this speed? **(b)** This same cockroach is caught by a child and placed in a 1-qt fruit jar with a tight lid. Assuming the same level of continuous activity as in the research, will the cockroach consume more than 20% of the available $O_2$ in a 48-hr period? (Air is 21 mol percent $O_2$.)

**10.46** The physical fitness of athletes is measured by "$V_{O_2}$ max," which is the maximum volume of oxygen consumed by an individual during incremental exercise (for example, on a treadmill). An average male has a $V_{O_2}$ max of 45 mL $O_2$/kg body mass/min, but a world-class male athlete can have a $V_{O_2}$ max reading of 88.0 mL $O_2$/kg body mass/min. **(a)** Calculate the volume of oxygen, in mL, consumed in 1 hr by an average man who weighs 185 lbs and has a $V_{O_2}$ max reading of 47.5 mL $O_2$/kg body mass/min. **(b)** If this man lost 20 lb, exercised, and increased his $V_{O_2}$ max to 65.0 mL $O_2$/kg body mass/min, how many mL of oxygen would he consume in 1 hr?

**10.47** Mercury is a liquid at room temperature and pressure, but its vapor is present in the atmosphere from natural sources, such as volcanoes, and from human ("anthropogenic") activities such as coal burning and gold mining. Elemental Hg becomes extremely toxic when oxidized to Hg(I) or Hg(II) compounds. **(a)** The Environmental Protection Agency has estimated that 119 tons of mercury are currently emitted to Earth's atmosphere annually due to human activities; this has decreased significantly from the mid-1970s before pollution controls were in place. What volume would the 119 tons of mercury occupy if it were a pure vapor at 1.00 atm and 298 K? **(b)** Geological records suggest that before the Industrial Revolution began in 1750, the baseline level of atmospheric Hg was 35 ppb (parts per billion, by volume, or 35 L Hg for every $10^9$ L of air); current estimates are 245 ppb. For an estimated atmospheric volume of $51 \times 10^{12}$ $m^3$, calculate the number of moles Hg estimated to be in the atmosphere today.

**10.48** After the large eruption of Mount St. Helens in 1980, gas samples from the volcano were taken by sampling the downwind gas plume. The unfiltered gas samples were passed over a gold-coated wire coil to absorb mercury (Hg) present in the gas. The mercury was recovered from the coil by heating it and then analyzed. In one particular set of experiments scientists found a mercury vapor level of 1800 ng of Hg per cubic meter in the plume at a gas temperature of 10 °C. Calculate **(a)** the partial pressure of Hg vapor in the plume, **(b)** the number of Hg atoms per cubic meter in the gas, **(c)** the total mass of Hg emitted per day by the volcano if the daily plume volume was 1600 $km^3$.

# FURTHER APPLICATIONS OF THE IDEAL-GAS EQUATION (section 10.5)

**10.49** Which gas is most dense at 1.00 atm and 298 K: $CO_2$, $N_2O$, or $Cl_2$? Explain.

**10.50** Rank the following gases from least dense to most dense at 1.00 atm and 298 K: $SO_2$, HBr, $CO_2$. Explain.

**10.51** Which of the following statements best explains why a closed balloon filled with helium gas rises in air?
**(a)** Helium is a monatomic gas, whereas nearly all the molecules that make up air, such as nitrogen and oxygen, are diatomic.
**(b)** The average speed of helium atoms is higher than the average speed of air molecules, and the higher speed of collisions with the balloon walls propels the balloon upward.
**(c)** Because the helium atoms are of lower mass than the average air molecule, the helium gas is less dense than air. The mass of the balloon is thus less than the mass of the air displaced by its volume.
**(d)** Because helium has a lower molar mass than the average air molecule, the helium atoms are in faster motion. This means that the temperature of the helium is higher than the air temperature. Hot gases tend to rise.

**10.52** Which of the following statements best explains why nitrogen gas at STP is less dense than Xe gas at STP?
**(a)** Because Xe is a noble gas, there is less tendency for the Xe atoms to repel one another, so they pack more densely in the gas state.

**(b)** Xe atoms have a higher mass than $N_2$ molecules. Because both gases at STP have the same number of molecules per unit volume, the Xe gas must be denser.
**(c)** The Xe atoms are larger than $N_2$ molecules and thus take up a larger fraction of the space occupied by the gas.
**(d)** Because the Xe atoms are much more massive than the $N_2$ molecules, they move more slowly and thus exert less upward force on the gas container and make the gas appear denser.

**10.53** **(a)** Calculate the density of $NO_2$ gas at 0.970 atm and 35 °C. **(b)** Calculate the molar mass of a gas if 2.50 g occupies 0.875 L at 685 torr and 35 °C.

**10.54** **(a)** Calculate the density of sulfur hexafluoride gas at 707 torr and 21 °C. **(b)** Calculate the molar mass of a vapor that has a density of 7.135 g/L at 12 °C and 743 torr.

**10.55** In the Dumas-bulb technique for determining the molar mass of an unknown liquid, you vaporize the sample of a liquid that boils below 100 °C in a boiling-water bath and determine the mass of vapor required to fill the bulb (see drawing, next page). From the following data, calculate the molar mass of the unknown liquid: mass of unknown vapor, 1.012 g; volume of bulb, 354 $cm^3$; pressure, 742 torr; temperature, 99 °C.

Dumas bulb filled with vaporized unknown substance

Boiling water

**10.56** The molar mass of a volatile substance was determined by the Dumas-bulb method described in Exercise 10.55. The unknown vapor had a mass of 0.846 g; the volume of the bulb was 354 cm³, pressure 752 torr, and temperature 100 °C. Calculate the molar mass of the unknown vapor.

**10.57** Magnesium can be used as a "getter" in evacuated enclosures to react with the last traces of oxygen. (The magnesium is usually heated by passing an electric current through a wire or ribbon of the metal.) If an enclosure of 0.452 L has a partial pressure of $O_2$ of $3.5 \times 10^{-6}$ torr at 27 °C, what mass of magnesium will react according to the following equation?

$$2\,Mg(s) + O_2(g) \longrightarrow 2\,MgO(s)$$

**10.58** Calcium hydride, $CaH_2$, reacts with water to form hydrogen gas:

$$CaH_2(s) + 2\,H_2O(l) \longrightarrow Ca(OH)_2(aq) + 2\,H_2(g)$$

This reaction is sometimes used to inflate life rafts, weather balloons, and the like, when a simple, compact means of generating $H_2$ is desired. How many grams of $CaH_2$ are needed to generate 145 L of $H_2$ gas if the pressure of $H_2$ is 825 torr at 21 °C?

**10.59** The metabolic oxidation of glucose, $C_6H_{12}O_6$, in our bodies produces $CO_2$, which is expelled from our lungs as a gas:

$$C_6H_{12}O_6(aq) + 6\,O_2(g) \longrightarrow 6\,CO_2(g) + 6\,H_2O(l)$$

(a) Calculate the volume of dry $CO_2$ produced at body temperature (37 °C) and 0.970 atm when 24.5 g of glucose is consumed in this reaction. (b) Calculate the volume of oxygen you would need, at 1.00 atm and 298 K, to completely oxidize 50.0 g of glucose.

**10.60** Both Jacques Charles and Joseph Louis Guy-Lussac were avid balloonists. In his original flight in 1783, Jacques Charles used a balloon that contained approximately 31,150 L of $H_2$. He generated the $H_2$ using the reaction between iron and hydrochloric acid:

$$Fe(s) + 2\,HCl(aq) \longrightarrow FeCl_2(aq) + H_2(g)$$

How many kilograms of iron were needed to produce this volume of $H_2$ if the temperature was 22 °C?

**10.61** Hydrogen gas is produced when zinc reacts with sulfuric acid:

$$Zn(s) + H_2SO_4(aq) \longrightarrow ZnSO_4(aq) + H_2(g)$$

If 159 mL of wet $H_2$ is collected over water at 24 °C and a barometric pressure of 738 torr, how many grams of Zn have been consumed? (The vapor pressure of water is tabulated in Appendix B.)

**10.62** Acetylene gas, $C_2H_2(g)$, can be prepared by the reaction of calcium carbide with water:

$$CaC_2(s) + 2\,H_2O(l) \longrightarrow Ca(OH)_2(s) + C_2H_2(g)$$

Calculate the volume of $C_2H_2$ that is collected over water at 23 °C by reaction of 1.524 g of $CaC_2$ if the total pressure of the gas is 753 torr. (The vapor pressure of water is tabulated in Appendix B.)

# PARTIAL PRESSURES (section 10.6)

**10.63** Consider the apparatus shown in the following drawing. (a) When the valve between the two containers is opened and the gases allowed to mix, how does the volume occupied by the $N_2$ gas change? What is the partial pressure of $N_2$ after mixing? (b) How does the volume of the $O_2$ gas change when the gases mix? What is the partial pressure of $O_2$ in the mixture? (c) What is the total pressure in the container after the gases mix?

| | |
|---|---|
| 2.0 L | 3.0 L |
| 1.0 atm | 2.0 atm |
| 25 °C | 25 °C |

**10.64** Consider a mixture of two gases, A and B, confined in a closed vessel. A quantity of a third gas, C, is added to the same vessel at the same temperature. How does the addition of gas C affect the following: (a) the partial pressure of gas A, (b) the total pressure in the vessel, (c) the mole fraction of gas B?

**10.65** A mixture containing 0.765 mol He(g), 0.330 mol Ne(g), and 0.110 mol Ar(g) is confined in a 10.00-L vessel at 25 °C. (a) Calculate the partial pressure of each of the gases in the mixture. (b) Calculate the total pressure of the mixture.

**10.66** A deep-sea diver uses a gas cylinder with a volume of 10.0 L and a content of 51.2 g of $O_2$ and 32.6 g of He. Calculate the partial pressure of each gas and the total pressure if the temperature of the gas is 19 °C.

**10.67** The atmospheric concentration of $CO_2$ gas is presently 390 ppm (parts per million, by volume; that is, 390 L of every $10^6$ L of the atmosphere are $CO_2$). What is the mole fraction of $CO_2$ in the atmosphere?

**10.68** A plasma-screen TV contains thousands of tiny cells filled with a mixture of Xe, Ne, and He gases that emits light of specific wavelengths when a voltage is applied. A particular plasma cell, 0.900 mm × 0.300 mm × 10.0 mm, contains 4% Xe in a 1:1 Ne:He mixture at a total pressure of 500 torr. Calculate the number of Xe, Ne, and He atoms in the cell and state the assumptions you need to make in your calculation.

**10.69** A piece of dry ice (solid carbon dioxide) with a mass of 5.50 g is placed in a 10.0-L vessel that already contains air at 705 torr and 24 °C. After the carbon dioxide has totally vaporized, what is the partial pressure of carbon dioxide and the total pressure in the container at 24 °C?

**10.70** A sample of 5.00 mL of diethylether ($C_2H_5OC_2H_5$, density = 0.7134 g/mL) is introduced into a 6.00-L vessel that already contains a mixture of $N_2$ and $O_2$, whose partial pressures are $P_{N_2} = 0.751$ atm and $P_{O_2} = 0.208$ atm. The temperature is held at 35.0 °C, and the diethylether totally evaporates. (a) Calculate the partial pressure of the diethylether. (b) Calculate the total pressure in the container.

**10.71** A mixture of gases contains 0.75 mol $N_2$, 0.30 mol $O_2$, and 0.15 mol $CO_2$. If the total pressure of the mixture is 2.15 atm, what is the partial pressure of each component?

**10.72** A mixture of gases contains 10.25 g of $N_2$, 1.83 g of $H_2$, and 7.95 g of $NH_3$. If the total pressure of the mixture is 1.85 atm, what is the partial pressure of each component?

**10.73** At an underwater depth of 250 ft, the pressure is 8.38 atm. What should the mole percent of oxygen be in the diving gas for the partial pressure of oxygen in the mixture to be 0.21 atm, the same as in air at 1 atm?

**10.74** (a) What are the mole fractions of each component in a mixture of 15.08 g of $O_2$, 8.17 g of $N_2$, and 2.64 g of $H_2$? (b) What is the partial pressure in atm of each component of this mixture if it is held in a 15.50-L vessel at 15 °C?

**10.75** A quantity of $N_2$ gas originally held at 5.25 atm pressure in a 1.00-L container at 26 °C is transferred to a 12.5-L container at 20 °C. A quantity of $O_2$ gas originally at 5.25 atm and 26 °C in a 5.00-L container is transferred to this same container. What is the total pressure in the new container?

**10.76** A sample of 3.00 g of $SO_2(g)$ originally in a 5.00-L vessel at 21 °C is transferred to a 10.0-L vessel at 26 °C. A sample of 2.35 g $N_2(g)$ originally in a 2.50-L vessel at 20 °C is transferred to this same 10.0-L vessel. (a) What is the partial pressure of $SO_2(g)$ in the larger container? (b) What is the partial pressure of $N_2(g)$ in this vessel? (c) What is the total pressure in the vessel?

# KINETIC-MOLECULAR THEORY OF GASES; EFFUSION AND DIFFUSION (sections 10.7 and 10.8)

**10.77** What change or changes in the state of a gas bring about each of the following effects? (a) The number of impacts per unit time on a given container wall increases. (b) The average energy of impact of molecules with the wall of the container decreases. (c) The average distance between gas molecules increases. (d) The average speed of molecules in the gas mixture is increased.

**10.78** Indicate which of the following statements regarding the kinetic-molecular theory of gases are correct. For those that are false, formulate a correct version of the statement. (a) The average kinetic energy of a collection of gas molecules at a given temperature is proportional to $m^{1/2}$. (b) The gas molecules are assumed to exert no forces on each other. (c) All the molecules of a gas at a given temperature have the same kinetic energy. (d) The volume of the gas molecules is negligible in comparison to the total volume in which the gas is contained. (e) All gas molecules move with the same speed if they are at the same temperature.

**10.79** What property or properties of gases can you point to that support the assumption that most of the volume in a gas is empty space?

**10.80** Newton had an incorrect theory of gases in which he assumed that all gas molecules repel one another and the walls of their container. Thus, the molecules of a gas are statically and uniformly distributed, trying to get as far apart as possible from one another and the vessel walls. This repulsion gives rise to pressure. Explain why Charles's law argues for the kinetic-molecular theory and against Newton's model.

**10.81** Explain the difference between average speed and root-mean-square speed. Which is larger for a given gas sample at a fixed temperature?

**[10.82]** You have an evacuated container of fixed volume and known mass and introduce a known mass of a gas sample. Measuring the pressure at constant temperature over time, you are surprised to see it slowly dropping. You measure the mass of the gas-filled container and find that the mass is what it should be—gas plus container—and the mass does not change over time, so you do not have a leak. Suggest an explanation for your observations.

**10.83** The temperature of a 5.00-L container of $N_2$ gas is increased from 20 °C to 250 °C. If the volume is held constant, predict qualitatively how this change affects the following: (a) the average kinetic energy of the molecules; (b) the root-mean-square speed of the molecules; (c) the strength of the impact of an average molecule with the container walls; (d) the total number of collisions of molecules with walls per second.

**10.84** Suppose you have two 1-L flasks, one containing $N_2$ at STP, the other containing $CH_4$ at STP. How do these systems compare with respect to (a) number of molecules, (b) density, (c) average kinetic energy of the molecules, (d) rate of effusion through a pinhole leak?

**10.85** (a) Place the following gases in order of increasing average molecular speed at 25 °C: Ne, HBr, $SO_2$, $NF_3$, CO. (b) Calculate the rms speed of $NF_3$ molecules at 25 °C. (c) Calculate the most probable speed of an ozone molecule in the stratosphere, where the temperature is 270 K.

**10.86** (a) Place the following gases in order of increasing average molecular speed at 300 K: CO, $SF_6$, $H_2S$, $Cl_2$, HBr. (b) Calculate and compare the rms speeds of CO and $Cl_2$ molecules at 300 K. (c) Calculate and compare the most probable speeds of CO and $Cl_2$ molecules at 300 K.

**10.87** Explain the difference between effusion and diffusion.

**[10.88]** At constant pressure, the mean free path ($\lambda$) of a gas molecule is directly proportional to temperature. At constant temperature, $\lambda$ is inversely proportional to pressure. If you compare two different gas molecules at the same temperature and pressure, $\lambda$ is inversely proportional to the square of the diameter of the gas molecules. Put these facts together to create a formula for the mean free path of a gas molecule with a proportionality constant (call it $R_{mfp}$, like the ideal-gas constant) and define units for $R_{mfp}$.

**10.89** Hydrogen has two naturally occurring isotopes, $^1H$ and $^2H$. Chlorine also has two naturally occurring isotopes, $^{35}Cl$ and $^{37}Cl$. Thus, hydrogen chloride gas consists of four distinct types of molecules: $^1H^{35}Cl$, $^1H^{37}Cl$, $^2H^{35}Cl$, and $^2H^{37}Cl$. Place these four molecules in order of increasing rate of effusion.

**10.90** As discussed in the "Chemistry Put to Work" box in Section 10.8, enriched uranium can be produced by gaseous diffusion of $UF_6$. Suppose a process were developed to allow diffusion of gaseous uranium atoms, U(g). Calculate the ratio of diffusion rates for $^{235}U$ and $^{238}U$, and compare it to the ratio for $UF_6$ given in the essay.

**10.91** Arsenic(III) sulfide sublimes readily, even below its melting point of 320 °C. The molecules of the vapor phase are found to effuse through a tiny hole at 0.28 times the rate of effusion of Ar atoms under the same conditions of temperature and pressure. What is the molecular formula of arsenic(III) sulfide in the gas phase?

**10.92** A gas of unknown molecular mass was allowed to effuse through a small opening under constant-pressure conditions. It required 105 s for 1.0 L of the gas to effuse. Under identical experimental conditions it required 31 s for 1.0 L of $O_2$ gas to effuse. Calculate the molar mass of the unknown gas. (Remember that the faster the rate of effusion, the shorter the time required for effusion of 1.0 L; that is, rate and time are inversely proportional.)

# NONIDEAL-GAS BEHAVIOR (section 10.9)

**10.93** (a) List two experimental conditions under which gases deviate from ideal behavior. (b) List two reasons why the gases deviate from ideal behavior. (c) Explain how the function $PV/RT$ can be used to show how gases behave nonideally.

**10.94** The planet Jupiter has a surface temperature of 140 K and a mass 318 times that of Earth. Mercury (the planet) has a surface temperature between 600 K and 700 K and a mass 0.05 times that of Earth. On which planet is the atmosphere more likely to obey the ideal-gas law? Explain.

**10.95** Based on their respective van der Waals constants (Table 10.3), is Ar or $CO_2$ expected to behave more nearly like an ideal gas at high pressures? Explain.

**10.96** Briefly explain the significance of the constants $a$ and $b$ in the van der Waals equation.

**10.97** In Sample Exercise 10.16, we found that one mole of $Cl_2$ confined to 22.41 L at 0 °C deviated slightly from ideal behavior. Calculate the pressure exerted by 1.00 mol $Cl_2$ confined to a smaller volume, 5.00 L, at 25 °C. (a) First use the ideal-gas equation and (b) then use the van der Waals equation for your calculation. (Values for the van der Waals constants are given in Table 10.3.) (c) Why is the difference between the result for an ideal gas and that calculated using the van der Waals equation greater when the gas is confined to 5.00 L compared to 22.4 L?

**10.98** Calculate the pressure that $CCl_4$ will exert at 40 °C if 1.00 mol occupies 33.3 L, assuming that (a) $CCl_4$ obeys the ideal-gas equation; (b) $CCl_4$ obeys the van der Waals equation. (Values for the van der Waals constants are given in Table 10.3.) (c) Which would you expect to deviate more from ideal behavior under these conditions, $Cl_2$ or $CCl_4$? Explain.

**[10.99]** Table 10.3 shows that the van der Waals $b$ parameter has units of L/mol. This implies that we can calculate the size of atoms or molecules from $b$. Using the value of $b$ for Xe, calculate the radius of a Xe atom and compare it to the value found in Figure 7.6, 1.30 Å. Recall that the volume of a sphere is $(4/3)\pi r^3$.

**[10.100]** Table 10.3 shows that the van der Waals $b$ parameter has units of L/mol. This means that we can calculate the sizes of atoms or molecules from the $b$ parameter. Refer back to the discussion in Section 7.3. Is the van der Waals radius we calculate from the $b$ parameter of Table 10.3 more closely associated with the bonding or nonbonding atomic radius discussed there? Explain.

# ADDITIONAL EXERCISES

**10.101** A gas bubble with a volume of 1.0 mm$^3$ originates at the bottom of a lake where the pressure is 3.0 atm. Calculate its volume when the bubble reaches the surface of the lake where the pressure is 730 torr, assuming that the temperature doesn't change.

**10.102** A 15.0-L tank is filled with helium gas at a pressure of $1.00 \times 10^2$ atm. How many balloons (each 2.00 L) can be inflated to a pressure of 1.00 atm, assuming that the temperature remains constant and that the tank cannot be emptied below 1.00 atm?

**10.103** To minimize the rate of evaporation of the tungsten filament, $1.4 \times 10^{-5}$ mol of argon is placed in a 600-cm$^3$ lightbulb. What is the pressure of argon in the lightbulb at 23 °C?

**10.104** Carbon dioxide, which is recognized as the major contributor to global warming as a "greenhouse gas," is formed when fossil fuels are combusted, as in electrical power plants fueled by coal, oil, or natural gas. One potential way to reduce the amount of $CO_2$ added to the atmosphere is to store it as a compressed gas in underground formations. Consider a 1000-megawatt coal-fired power plant that produces about $6 \times 10^6$ tons of $CO_2$ per year. (a) Assuming ideal-gas behavior, 1.00 atm, and 27 °C, calculate the volume of $CO_2$ produced by this power plant. (b) If the $CO_2$ is stored underground as a liquid at 10 °C and 120 atm and a density of 1.2 g/cm$^3$, what volume does it possess? (c) If it is stored underground as a gas at 36 °C and 90 atm, what volume does it occupy?

**10.105** Propane, $C_3H_8$, liquefies under modest pressure, allowing a large amount to be stored in a container. (a) Calculate the number of moles of propane gas in a 110-L container at 3.00 atm and 27 °C. (b) Calculate the number of moles of liquid propane that can be stored in the same volume if the density of the liquid is 0.590 g/mL. (c) Calculate the ratio of the number of moles of liquid to moles of gas. Discuss this ratio in light of the kinetic-molecular theory of gases.

**[10.106]** Nickel carbonyl, $Ni(CO)_4$, is one of the most toxic substances known. The present maximum allowable concentration in laboratory air during an 8-hr workday is 1 ppb (parts per billion) by volume, which means that there is one mole of $Ni(CO)_4$ for every $10^9$ moles of gas. Assume 24 °C and 1.00 atm pressure. What mass of $Ni(CO)_4$ is allowable in a laboratory room that is 12 ft × 20 ft × 9 ft?

**10.107** When a large evacuated flask is filled with argon gas, its mass increases by 3.224 g. When the same flask is again evacuated and then filled with a gas of unknown molar mass, the mass increase is 8.102 g. (a) Based on the molar mass of argon, estimate the molar mass of the unknown gas. (b) What assumptions did you make in arriving at your answer?

**10.108** Consider the arrangement of bulbs shown in the drawing. Each of the bulbs contains a gas at the pressure shown. What is the pressure of the system when all the stopcocks are opened, assuming that the temperature remains constant? (We can neglect the volume of the capillary tubing connecting the bulbs.)

| 1.0 L | 1.0 L | 0.5 L |
| 265 torr | 800 torr | 532 torr |

**10.109** Assume that a single cylinder of an automobile engine has a volume of $524 \text{ cm}^3$. **(a)** If the cylinder is full of air at 74 °C and 0.980 atm, how many moles of $O_2$ are present? (The mole fraction of $O_2$ in dry air is 0.2095.) **(b)** How many grams of $C_8H_{18}$ could be combusted by this quantity of $O_2$, assuming complete combustion with formation of $CO_2$ and $H_2O$?

**10.110** Assume that an exhaled breath of air consists of 74.8% $N_2$, 15.3% $O_2$, 3.7% $CO_2$, and 6.2% water vapor. **(a)** If the total pressure of the gases is 0.985 atm, calculate the partial pressure of each component of the mixture. **(b)** If the volume of the exhaled gas is 455 mL and its temperature is 37 °C, calculate the number of moles of $CO_2$ exhaled. **(c)** How many grams of glucose ($C_6H_{12}O_6$) would need to be metabolized to produce this quantity of $CO_2$? (The chemical reaction is the same as that for combustion of $C_6H_{12}O_6$. See Section 3.2 and Problem 10.59.)

**10.111** A 1.42-g sample of helium and an unknown mass of $O_2$ are mixed in a flask at room temperature. The partial pressure of the helium is 42.5 torr, and that of the oxygen is 158 torr. What is the mass of the oxygen?

**10.112** A gaseous mixture of $O_2$ and Kr has a density of 1.104 g/L at 355 torr and 400 K. What is the mole percent $O_2$ in the mixture?

**10.113** The density of a gas of unknown molar mass was measured as a function of pressure at 0 °C, as in the table that follows. **(a)** Determine a precise molar mass for the gas. [*Hint*: Graph $d/P$ versus $P$.] **(b)** Why is $d/P$ not a constant as a function of pressure?

| Pressure (atm) | 1.00 | 0.666 | 0.500 | 0.333 | 0.250 |
|---|---|---|---|---|---|
| Density (g/L) | 2.3074 | 1.5263 | 1.1401 | 0.7571 | 0.5660 |

**10.114** A glass vessel fitted with a stopcock valve has a mass of 337.428 g when evacuated. When filled with Ar, it has a mass of 339.854 g. When evacuated and refilled with a mixture of Ne and Ar, under the same conditions of temperature and pressure, it has a mass of 339.076 g. What is the mole percent of Ne in the gas mixture?

**10.115** You have a sample of gas at −33 °C. You wish to increase the rms speed by a factor of 2. To what temperature should the gas be heated?

**10.116** Consider the following gases, all at STP: Ne, $SF_6$, $N_2$, $CH_4$. **(a)** Which gas is most likely to depart from the assumption of the kinetic-molecular theory that says there are no attractive or repulsive forces between molecules? **(b)** Which one is closest to an ideal gas in its behavior? **(c)** Which one has the highest root-mean-square molecular speed at a given temperature? **(d)** Which one has the highest total molecular volume relative to the space occupied by the gas? **(e)** Which has the highest average kinetic-molecular energy? **(f)** Which one would effuse more rapidly than $N_2$? **(g)** Which one would have the largest van der Waals $b$ parameter?

**10.117** Does the effect of intermolecular attraction on the properties of a gas become more significant or less significant if **(a)** the gas is compressed to a smaller volume at constant temperature; **(b)** the temperature of the gas is increased at constant volume?

**10.118** Which of the noble gases other than radon would you expect to depart most readily from ideal behavior? Use the density data in Table 7.8 to show evidence in support of your answer.

**10.119** It turns out that the van der Waals constant $b$ equals four times the total volume actually occupied by the molecules of a mole of gas. Using this figure, calculate the fraction of the volume in a container actually occupied by Ar atoms **(a)** at STP, **(b)** at 200 atm pressure and 0 °C. (Assume for simplicity that the ideal-gas equation still holds.)

**[10.120]** Large amounts of nitrogen gas are used in the manufacture of ammonia, principally for use in fertilizers. Suppose 120.00 kg of $N_2(g)$ is stored in a 1100.0-L metal cylinder at 280 °C. **(a)** Calculate the pressure of the gas, assuming ideal-gas behavior. **(b)** By using data in Table 10.3, calculate the pressure of the gas according to the van der Waals equation. **(c)** Under the conditions of this problem, which correction dominates, the one for finite volume of gas molecules or the one for attractive interactions?

# INTEGRATIVE EXERCISES

**10.121** Cyclopropane, a gas used with oxygen as a general anesthetic, is composed of 85.7% C and 14.3% H by mass. **(a)** If 1.56 g of cyclopropane has a volume of 1.00 L at 0.984 atm and 50.0 °C, what is the molecular formula of cyclopropane? **(b)** Judging from its molecular formula, would you expect cyclopropane to deviate more or less than Ar from ideal-gas behavior at moderately high pressures and room temperature? Explain. **(c)** Would cyclopropane effuse through a pinhole faster or more slowly than methane, $CH_4$?

**[10.122]** Consider the combustion reaction between 25.0 mL of liquid methanol (density = 0.850 g/mL) and 12.5 L of oxygen gas measured at STP. The products of the reaction are $CO_2(g)$ and $H_2O(g)$. Calculate the volume of liquid $H_2O$ formed if the reaction goes to completion and you condense the water vapor.

**10.123** An herbicide is found to contain only C, H, N, and Cl. The complete combustion of a 100.0-mg sample of the herbicide in excess oxygen produces 83.16 mL of $CO_2$ and 73.30 mL of $H_2O$ vapor at STP. A separate analysis shows that the sample also contains 16.44 mg of Cl. **(a)** Determine the percent composition of the substance. **(b)** Calculate its empirical formula. **(c)** What other information would you need to know about this compound to calculate its true molecular formula?

**10.124** A 4.00-g sample of a mixture of CaO and BaO is placed in a 1.00-L vessel containing $CO_2$ gas at a pressure of 730 torr and a temperature of 25 °C. The $CO_2$ reacts with the CaO and BaO, forming $CaCO_3$ and $BaCO_3$. When the reaction is complete, the pressure of the remaining $CO_2$ is 150 torr. **(a)** Calculate the number of moles of $CO_2$ that have reacted. **(b)** Calculate the mass percentage of CaO in the mixture.

**[10.125]** Ammonia and hydrogen chloride react to form solid ammonium chloride:

$$NH_3(g) + HCl(g) \longrightarrow NH_4Cl(s)$$

Two 2.00-L flasks at 25 °C are connected by a valve, as shown in the drawing on the next page. One flask contains 5.00 g $NH_3(g)$, and the other contains 5.00 g $HCl(g)$. When the valve is opened, the gases react until one is completely consumed. **(a)** Which gas will remain in the system after the reaction is complete? **(b)** What will be the final pressure of the system after the reaction is complete? (Neglect the volume of the ammonium chloride formed.) **(c)** What mass of ammonium chloride will be formed?

NH₃(g)    HCl(g)
5.00 g    5.00 g
2.00 L    2.00 L
25 °C     25 °C

**10.126** The "Chemistry Put to Work" box on pipelines in Section 10.5 mentions that the total deliverability of natural gas (methane, $CH_4$) to the various regions of the United States is on the order of $2.7 \times 10^{12}$ L per day, measured at STP. Calculate the total enthalpy change for combustion of this quantity of methane. (*Note*: Less than this amount of methane is actually combusted daily. Some of the delivered gas is passed through to other regions.)

**10.127** Chlorine dioxide gas ($ClO_2$) is used as a commercial bleaching agent. It bleaches materials by oxidizing them. In the course of these reactions, the $ClO_2$ is itself reduced. **(a)** What is the Lewis structure for $ClO_2$? **(b)** Why do you think that $ClO_2$ is reduced so readily? **(c)** When a $ClO_2$ molecule gains an electron, the chlorite ion, $ClO_2^-$, forms. Draw the Lewis structure for $ClO_2^-$. **(d)** Predict the O—Cl—O bond angle in the $ClO_2^-$ ion. **(e)** One method of preparing $ClO_2$ is by the reaction of chlorine and sodium chlorite:

$$Cl_2(g) + 2\ NaClO_2(s) \longrightarrow 2\ ClO_2(g) + 2\ NaCl(s)$$

If you allow 15.0 g of $NaClO_2$ to react with 2.00 L of chlorine gas at a pressure of 1.50 atm at 21 °C, how many grams of $ClO_2$ can be prepared?

**10.128** Natural gas is very abundant in many Middle Eastern oil fields. However, the costs of shipping the gas to markets in other parts of the world are high because it is necessary to liquefy the gas, which is mainly methane and has a boiling point at atmospheric pressure of −164 °C. One possible strategy is to oxidize the methane to methanol, $CH_3OH$, which has a boiling point of 65 °C and can therefore be shipped more readily. Suppose that $10.7 \times 10^9$ ft³ of methane at atmospheric pressure and 25 °C is oxidized to methanol. **(a)** What volume of methanol is formed if the density of $CH_3OH$ is 0.791 g/mL ? **(b)** Write balanced chemical equations for the oxidations of methane and methanol to $CO_2(g)$ and $H_2O(l)$. Calculate the total enthalpy change for complete combustion of the $10.7 \times 10^9$ ft³ of methane just described and for complete combustion of the equivalent amount of methanol, as calculated in part (a). **(c)** Methane, when liquefied, has a density of 0.466 g/mL; the density of methanol at 25 °C is 0.791 g/mL. Compare the enthalpy change upon combustion of a unit volume of liquid methane and liquid methanol. From the standpoint of energy production, which substance has the higher enthalpy of combustion per unit volume?

**[10.129]** Gaseous iodine pentafluoride, $IF_5$, can be prepared by the reaction of solid iodine and gaseous fluorine:

$$I_2(s) + 5\ F_2(g) \longrightarrow 2\ IF_5(g)$$

A 5.00-L flask containing 10.0 g $I_2$ is charged with 10.0 g $F_2$, and the reaction proceeds until one of the reagents is completely consumed. After the reaction is complete, the temperature in the flask is 125 °C. **(a)** What is the partial pressure of $IF_5$ in the flask? **(b)** What is the mole fraction of $IF_5$ in the flask **(c)** Draw the Lewis structure of $IF_5$. **(d)** What is the total mass of reactants and products in the flask?

**[10.130]** A 6.53-g sample of a mixture of magnesium carbonate and calcium carbonate is treated with excess hydrochloric acid. The resulting reaction produces 1.72 L of carbon dioxide gas at 28 °C and 743 torr pressure. **(a)** Write balanced chemical equations for the reactions that occur between hydrochloric acid and each component of the mixture. **(b)** Calculate the total number of moles of carbon dioxide that forms from these reactions. **(c)** Assuming that the reactions are complete, calculate the percentage by mass of magnesium carbonate in the mixture.

# WHAT'S AHEAD

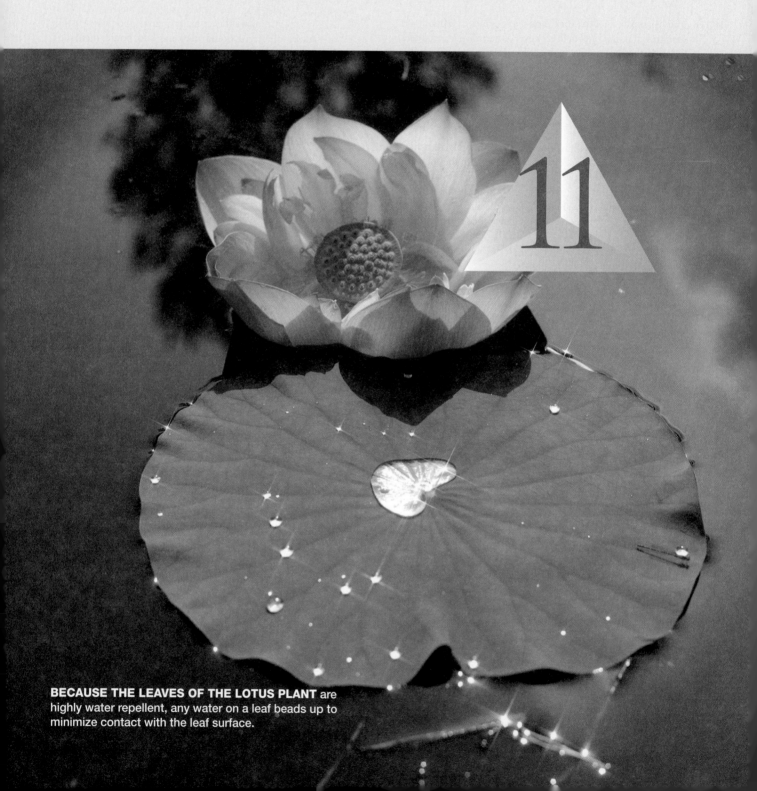

**BECAUSE THE LEAVES OF THE LOTUS PLANT** are highly water repellent, any water on a leaf beads up to minimize contact with the leaf surface.

# LIQUIDS AND INTERMOLEC-ULAR FORCES

**THE LOTUS PLANT GROWS** in aquatic environments. In order to thrive in such an environment the surface of a lotus leaf is highly water repellent. Scientists call surfaces with this property "superhydrophobic." The superhydrophobic character of the lotus leaf not only allows it to float on water but also causes

any water that falls on the leaf to bead up and roll off. The water drops collect dirt as they roll off, keeping the leaf clean, even in the muddy ponds and lakes where lotus plants tend to grow. Because of its self-cleaning properties, the lotus plant is considered a symbol of purity in many Eastern cultures.

What forces cause the lotus leaf to repel water so efficiently? Although this plant's self-cleaning nature has been known for millennia, the effect was not fully understood until the 1970s when scanning electron microscopy images revealed a rough, one might say mountainous, leaf surface (▶ **FIGURE 11.1**). The rough surface helps minimize contact between water and leaf.

Another important factor contributing to the plant's self-cleaning nature is the contrast between the molecular composition of the leaf and that of the water. The leaf is coated by hydrocarbon molecules that are held together by forces that are different

20 μm

▲ **FIGURE 11.1  A microscopic view of a water droplet on the surface of a lotus leaf.**

from those that hold the water molecules together. As a result the water molecules preferentially surround themselves with other water molecules, thereby minimizing their contact with the surface.

The lotus effect has inspired scientists to design superhydrophobic surfaces for applications such as self-cleaning windows and water-repellent clothing. To understand the lotus effect and other phenomena involving liquids and solids, we must understand **intermolecular forces**, the forces that exist *between* molecules. Only by understanding the nature and strength of these forces can we understand how the composition and structure of a substance are related to its physical properties in the liquid or solid state.

# 11.1 | A MOLECULAR COMPARISON OF GASES, LIQUIDS, AND SOLIDS

As we learned in Chapter 10, the molecules in a gas are widely separated and in a state of constant, chaotic motion. One of the key tenets of kinetic-molecular theory is the assumption that we can neglect the interactions between molecules.  ∞ (Section 10.7) The properties of liquids and solids are quite different from gases largely because the intermolecular forces in liquids and solids are much stronger. A comparison of the properties of gases, liquids, and solids is given in ▼ TABLE 11.1.

In liquids the intermolecular attractive forces are strong enough to hold particles close together. Thus, liquids are much denser and far less compressible than gases. Unlike gases, liquids have a definite volume, independent of the size and shape of their container. The attractive forces in liquids are not strong enough, however, to keep the particles from moving past one another. Thus, any liquid can be poured, and assumes the shape of the container it occupies.

In solids the intermolecular attractive forces are strong enough to hold particles close together and to lock them virtually in place. Solids, like liquids, are not very compressible because the particles have little free space between them. Because the particles in a solid or liquid are fairly close together compared with those of a gas, we often refer to solids and liquids as *condensed phases*. We will study solids in Chapter 12. For now it is sufficient to know that the particles of a solid are not free to undergo long-range movement, which makes solids rigid.*

| TABLE 11.1 • Some Characteristic Properties of the States of Matter | |
| --- | --- |
| Gas | Assumes both volume and shape of its container |
| | Expands to fill its container |
| | Is compressible |
| | Flows readily |
| | Diffusion within a gas occurs rapidly |
| Liquid | Assumes shape of portion of container it occupies |
| | Does not expand to fill its container |
| | Is virtually incompressible |
| | Flows readily |
| | Diffusion within a liquid occurs slowly |
| Solid | Retains own shape and volume |
| | Does not expand to fill its container |
| | Is virtually incompressible |
| | Does not flow |
| | Diffusion within a solid occurs extremely slowly |

*The atoms in a solid are able to vibrate in place. As the temperature of a solid increases, the vibrational motion increases.

GO FIGURE

**For a given substance, do you expect the density of the substance in its liquid state to be closer to the density in the gaseous state or in the solid state?**

Strength of intermolecular attractions increasing

| Gas | Liquid | Crystalline solid |

Chlorine, $Cl_2$
Particles far apart;
possess complete
freedom of motion

Bromine, $Br_2$
Particles are closely packed but
randomly oriented; retain freedom
of motion; rapidly change neighbors

Iodine, $I_2$
Particles are closely packed in
an ordered array; positions
are essentially fixed

▲ **FIGURE 11.2   Gases, liquids, and solids.** Chlorine, bromine, and iodine are all made up of diatomic molecules as a result of covalent bonding. However, due to differences in the strength of the intermolecular forces, they exist in three different states at room temperature and standard pressure: $Cl_2$ gaseous, $Br_2$ liquid, $I_2$ solid.

▲ FIGURE 11.2 compares the three states of matter. *The state of a substance depends largely on the balance between the kinetic energies of the particles (atoms, molecules or ions) and the interparticle energies of attraction.* The kinetic energies, which depend on temperature, tend to keep the particles apart and moving. The interparticle attractions tend to draw the particles together. Substances that are gases at room temperature have much weaker interparticle attractions than those that are liquids; substances that are liquids have weaker interparticle attractions than those that are solids. The different states of matter adopted by the halogens at room temperature—iodine is solid, bromine is a liquid, and chlorine is a gas—is a direct consequence of a decrease in the strength of the intermolecular forces as we move from $I_2$ to $Br_2$ to $Cl_2$.

We can change a substance from one state to another by heating or cooling, which changes the average kinetic energy of the particles. NaCl, for example, a solid at room temperature, melts at 1074 K and boils at 1686 K under 1 atm pressure, and $Cl_2$, a gas at room temperature, liquefies at 239 K and solidifies at 172 K under 1 atm pressure. As the temperature of a gas decreases, the average kinetic energy of its particles decreases, allowing the attractions between the particles to first draw the particles close together, forming a liquid, and then to virtually lock them in place, forming a solid. Increasing the pressure on a gas can also drive transformations from gas to liquid to solid because the increased pressure brings the molecules closer together, thus making intermolecular forces more effective. For example, propane ($C_3H_8$) is a gas at room temperature and 1 atm pressure, whereas liquefied propane (LP) is a liquid at room temperature because it is stored under much higher pressure.

## 11.2 | INTERMOLECULAR FORCES

Strong intramolecular attraction (covalent bond)

Weak intermolecular attraction

▲ FIGURE 11.3  **Intermolecular and intramolecular forces.**

The strengths of intermolecular forces in different substances vary over a wide range but are generally much weaker than intramolecular forces—ionic, metallic or covalent bonds (◄ FIGURE 11.3). Less energy, therefore, is required to vaporize a liquid or melt a solid than to break covalent bonds. For example, only 16 kJ/mol is required to overcome the intermolecular attractions in liquid HCl in order to vaporize it. In contrast, the energy required to break the covalent bond in HCl is 431 kJ/mol. Thus, when a molecular substance such as HCl changes from solid to liquid to gas, the molecules remain intact.

Many properties of liquids, including *boiling points,* reflect the strength of the intermolecular forces. A liquid boils when bubbles of its vapor form within the liquid. The molecules of the liquid must overcome their attractive forces in order to separate and form a vapor. The stronger the attractive forces, the higher the temperature at which the liquid boils. Similarly, the *melting points* of solids increase as the strengths of the intermolecular forces increase. As shown in ▼ TABLE 11.2, the melting and boiling points of substances in which the particles are held together by chemical bonds tend to be much higher than those of substances in which the particles are held together by intermolecular forces.

Three types of intermolecular attractions exist between electrically neutral molecules: dispersion forces, dipole–dipole attractions, and hydrogen bonding. The first two are collectively called *van der Waals forces* after Johannes van der Waals, who developed the equation for predicting the deviation of gases from ideal behavior. ∞ (Section 10.9) Another kind of attractive force, the ion–dipole force, is important in solutions.

All intermolecular interactions are electrostatic, involving attractions between positive and negative species, much like ionic bonds. ∞ (Section 8.2) Why then are intermolecular forces so much weaker than ionic bonds? Recall from Equation 8.4 that electrostatic interactions get stronger as the magnitude of the charges increases and weaker as the distance between charges increases. The charges responsible for intermolecular forces are generally much smaller than the charges in ionic compounds. For example, from its dipole moment it is possible to estimate charges of +0.178 and −0.178 for the hydrogen and chlorine ends of the HCl molecule (see Sample Exercise 8.5). Furthermore, the distances between molecules are often larger than the distances between atoms held together by chemical bonds.

| **TABLE 11.2 • Melting and Boiling Points of Representative Substances** | | | |
|---|---|---|---|
| **Force Holding Particles Together** | **Substance** | **Melting Point (K)** | **Boiling Point (K)** |
| *Chemical bonds* | | | |
| Covalent bonds | Diamond (C) | 3800 | 4300 |
| Metallic bonds | Beryllium (Be) | 1560 | 2742 |
| Ionic bonds | Lithium fluoride (LiF) | 1118 | 1949 |
| *Intermolecular forces* | | | |
| Dispersion force | Nitrogen ($N_2$) | 63 | 77 |
| Dipole–dipole force | Hydrogen chloride (HCl) | 158 | 188 |
| Hydrogen bonding force | Hydrogen fluoride (HF) | 190 | 293 |

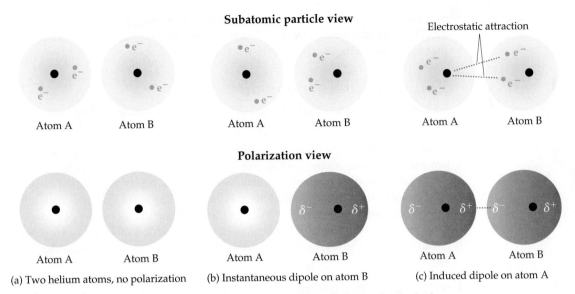

**FIGURE 11.4  Dispersion forces.** "Snapshots" of the charge distribution for a pair of helium atoms at three instants.

## Dispersion Forces

You might think there would be no electrostatic interactions between electrically neutral, nonpolar atoms and/or molecules. Yet some kind of attractive interactions must exist because nonpolar gases like helium, argon, and nitrogen can be liquefied. Fritz London, a German-American physicist, first proposed the origin of this attraction in 1930. London recognized that the motion of electrons in an atom or molecule can create an *instantaneous,* or momentary, dipole moment.

In a collection of helium atoms, for example, the *average* distribution of the electrons about each nucleus is spherically symmetrical, as shown in ▲ **FIGURE 11.4**(a). The atoms are nonpolar and so possess no permanent dipole moment. The *instantaneous* distribution of the electrons, however, can be different from the average distribution. If we could freeze the motion of the electrons at any given instant, both electrons could be on one side of the nucleus. At just that instant, the atom has an instantaneous dipole moment as shown in Figure 11.4(b). The motions of electrons in one atom influence the motions of electrons in its neighbors. The instantaneous dipole on one atom can induce an instantaneous dipole on an adjacent atom, causing the atoms to be attracted to each other as shown in Figure 11.4(c). This attractive interaction is called the **dispersion force** (or the *London dispersion force* in some texts). It is significant only when molecules are very close together.

The strength of the dispersion force depends on the ease with which the charge distribution in a molecule can be distorted to induce an instantaneous dipole. The ease with which the charge distribution is distorted is called the molecule's **polarizability**. We can think of the polarizability of a molecule as a measure of the "squashiness" of its electron cloud: The greater the polarizability, the more easily the electron cloud can be distorted to give an instantaneous dipole. Therefore, more polarizable molecules have larger dispersion forces.

In general, polarizability increases as the number of electrons in an atom or molecule increases. The strength of dispersion forces therefore tends to increase with increasing atomic or molecular size. Because molecular size and mass generally parallel each other, *dispersion forces tend to increase in strength with increasing molecular weight.* We can see this in the boiling points of the halogens and noble gases (▶ **FIGURE 11.5**), where dispersion forces are the only intermolecular forces at

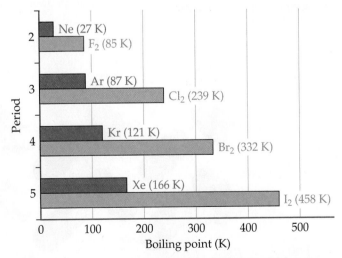

▲ **FIGURE 11.5  Boiling points of the halogens and noble gases.** This plot shows how the boiling points increase as the molecular weight increases due to stronger dispersion forces.

Linear molecule, larger surface area enhances intermolecular contact and increases dispersion force ·····

*n*-Pentane (C₅H₁₂)
bp = 309.4 K

Spherical molecule, smaller surface area diminishes intermolecular contact and decreases dispersion force ·····

Neopentane (C₅H₁₂)
bp = 282.7 K

▲ **FIGURE 11.6 Molecular shape affects intermolecular attraction.** Molecules of *n*-pentane make more contact with each other than do neopentane molecules. Thus, *n*-pentane has stronger intermolecular attractive forces and a higher boiling point.

work. In both families the molecular weight increases on moving down the periodic table. The higher molecular weights translate into stronger dispersion forces, which in turn lead to higher boiling points.

 **GIVE IT SOME THOUGHT**

List the substances CCl₄, CBr₄, and CH₄ in order of increasing boiling point.

Molecular shape also influences the magnitudes of dispersion forces. For example, *n*-pentane* and neopentane (◄ **FIGURE 11.6**) have the same molecular formula (C₅H₁₂), yet the boiling point of *n*-pentane is about 27 K higher than that of neopentane. The difference can be traced to the different shapes of the two molecules. Intermolecular attraction is greater for *n*-pentane because the molecules can come in contact over the entire length of the long, somewhat cylindrical molecules. Less contact is possible between the more compact and nearly spherical neopentane molecules.

## Dipole–Dipole Forces

The presence of a permanent dipole moment in polar molecules gives rise to **dipole–dipole forces**. These forces originate from electrostatic attractions between the partially positive end of one molecule and partially negative end of a neighboring molecule. Repulsions can also occur when the positive (or negative) ends of two molecules are in close proximity. Dipole–dipole forces are effective only when molecules are very close together.

To see the effect of dipole–dipole forces, we compare the boiling points of two compounds of similar molecular weight: acetonitrile (CH₃CN, MW 41 amu, bp 355 K) and propane (CH₃CH₂CH₃, MW 44 amu, bp 231 K). Acetonitrile is a polar molecule, with a dipole moment of 3.9 D, so dipole–dipole forces are present. However, propane is essentially nonpolar, which means that dipole–dipole forces are absent. Because acetonitrile and propane have similar molecular weights, dispersion forces are similar for these two molecules. Therefore, the higher boiling point of acetonitrile can be attributed to dipole–dipole forces.

To better understand these forces, consider how CH₃CN molecules pack together in the solid and liquid states. In the solid [▼ **FIGURE 11.7**(a)], the molecules are arranged with the negatively charged nitrogen end of each molecule close to the positively charged —CH₃ ends of its neighbors. In the liquid [Figure 11.7(b)], the molecules are free to move with respect to one another, and their arrangement becomes more disordered. This means that, at any given instant, both attractive and repulsive dipole–dipole interactions are pres-

Attractive dipole–dipole force (red)    Repulsive dipole–dipole force (blue)

(a) Solid CH₃CN    (b) Liquid CH₃CN

▲ **FIGURE 11.7 Dipole–dipole interactions.** The dipole–dipole interactions in (a) crystalline CH₃CN and (b) liquid CH₃CN.

*The *n* in *n*-pentane is an abbreviation for the word *normal*. A normal hydrocarbon is one in which the carbon atoms are arranged in a straight chain. ∞∞ (Section 2.9)

| Propane | Dimethyl ether | Acetaldehyde | Acetonitrile |
|---|---|---|---|
| $CH_3CH_2CH_3$ | $CH_3OCH_3$ | $CH_3CHO$ | $CH_3CN$ |
| MW = 44 amu | MW = 46 amu | MW = 44 amu | MW = 41 amu |
| $\mu$ = 0.1 D | $\mu$ = 1.3 D | $\mu$ = 2.7 D | $\mu$ = 3.9 D |
| bp = 231 K | bp = 248 K | bp = 294 K | bp = 355 K |

Increasing polarity
Increasing strength of dipole–dipole forces

◀ **FIGURE 11.8** **Molecular weights, dipole moments, and boiling points of several simple organic substances.**

ent. However, not only are there more attractive interactions than repulsive ones, but also molecules that are attracting each other spend more time near each other than do molecules that are repelling each other. The overall effect is a net attraction strong enough to keep the molecules in liquid $CH_3CN$ from moving apart to form a gas.

*For molecules of approximately equal mass and size, the strength of intermolecular attractions increases with increasing polarity,* a trend we see in ▲ **FIGURE 11.8**. Notice how the boiling point increases as the dipole moment increases.

## Hydrogen Bonding

▼ **FIGURE 11.9** shows the boiling points of the binary compounds that form between hydrogen and the elements in groups 4A through 7A. The boiling points of the compounds containing group 4A elements ($CH_4$ through $SnH_4$, all nonpolar) increase systematically moving down the group. This is the expected trend because polarizability and, hence, dispersion forces generally increase as molecular weight increases. The three heavier members of groups 5A, 6A, and 7A follow the same trend, but $NH_3$, $H_2O$, and HF have boiling points that

**GO FIGURE**

Why is the boiling point of $SnH_4$ higher than that of $CH_4$?

◀ **FIGURE 11.9** **Boiling points of the covalent hydrides of the elements in groups 4A–7A as a function of molecular weight.**

△ GO FIGURE

**To form a hydrogen bond what must the non-hydrogen atom (N, O, or F) involved in the bond possess?**

Covalent bond,        Hydrogen bond,
*intra*molecular        *inter*molecular

H—Ö:·····H—Ö:
    |             |
    H          H

H—F̈:·····H—F̈:

    H         H
    |         |
H—N:·····H—N:
    |         |
    H         H

    H
    |
H—N:·····H—Ö:
    |         |
    H         H

              H
              |
H—Ö:·····H—N:
    |         |
    H         H

▲ **FIGURE 11.10   Hydrogen bonding.**

are much higher than expected. In fact, these three compounds also have many other characteristics that distinguish them from other substances of similar molecular weight and polarity. For example, water has a high melting point, a high specific heat, and a high heat of vaporization. Each of these properties indicates that the intermolecular forces are abnormally strong.

The strong intermolecular attractions in HF, $H_2O$, and $NH_3$ result from hydrogen bonding. **Hydrogen bonding** *is a special type of intermolecular attraction between the hydrogen atom in a polar bond (particularly H—F, H—O, and H—N) and nonbonding electron pair on a nearby small electronegative ion or atom usually F, O, or N (in another molecule).* For example, a hydrogen bond exists between the H atom in an HF molecule and the F atom of an adjacent HF molecule, as shown in ◄ **FIGURE 11.10** along with several additional examples.

Hydrogen bonds can be considered a type of dipole–dipole attraction. Because N, O, and F are so electronegative, a bond between hydrogen and any of these elements is quite polar, with hydrogen at the positive end (remember the + on the right-hand side of the dipole symbol represents the positive end of the dipole):

$$\overset{\longleftarrow\ +}{N—H}\qquad \overset{\longleftarrow\ +}{O—H}\qquad \overset{\longleftarrow\ +}{F—H}$$

The hydrogen atom has no inner electrons. Thus, the positive side of the dipole has the concentrated charge of the nearly bare hydrogen nucleus. This positive charge is attracted to the negative charge of an electronegative atom in a nearby molecule. Because the electron-poor hydrogen is so small, it can approach an electronegative atom very closely and, thus, interact strongly with it.

| SAMPLE EXERCISE 11.1 | Identifying Substances That Can Form Hydrogen Bonds |
| --- | --- |

In which of these substances is hydrogen bonding likely to play an important role in determining physical properties: methane ($CH_4$), hydrazine ($H_2NNH_2$), methyl fluoride ($CH_3F$), hydrogen sulfide ($H_2S$)?

**SOLUTION**

**Analyze** We are given the chemical formulas of four compounds and asked to predict whether they can participate in hydrogen bonding. All the compounds contain H, but hydrogen bonding usually occurs only when the hydrogen is covalently bonded to N, O, or F.

**Plan** We analyze each formula to see if it contains N, O, or F directly bonded to H. There also needs to be a nonbonding pair of electrons on an electronegative atom (usually N, O, or F) in a nearby molecule, which can be revealed by drawing the Lewis structure for the molecule.

**Solve** The foregoing criteria eliminate $CH_4$ and $H_2S$, which do not contain H bonded to N, O, or F. They also eliminate $CH_3F$, whose Lewis structure shows a central C atom surrounded by three H atoms and an F atom. (Carbon always forms four bonds, whereas hydrogen and fluorine form one each.) Because the molecule contains a C—F bond and not a H—F bond, it does not form hydrogen bonds. In $H_2NNH_2$, however, we find N—H bonds, and the Lewis structure shows a nonbonding pair of electrons on each N atom, telling us hydrogen bonds can exist between the molecules:

    H H        H H
    |  |        |  |
:N—N:·····H—N—N:
    |  |       ··  |
    H H            H

**Check** Although we can generally identify substances that participate in hydrogen bonding based on their containing N, O, or F covalently bonded to H, drawing the Lewis structure for the interaction provides a way to check the prediction.

**PRACTICE EXERCISE**

In which of these substances is significant hydrogen bonding possible: methylene chloride ($CH_2Cl_2$), phosphine ($PH_3$), hydrogen peroxide (HOOH), acetone ($CH_3COCH_3$)?
*Answer:* HOOH

The energies of hydrogen bonds vary from about 5 kJ/mol to 25 kJ/mol, although there are isolated examples of hydrogen bond energies close to 100 kJ/mol. Thus, hydrogen bonds are typically much weaker than covalent bonds, which have bond enthalpies of 150–1100 kJ/mol (see Table 8.4). Nevertheless, because hydrogen bonds are generally stronger than dipole–dipole or dispersion forces, they play important roles in many chemical systems, including those of biological significance. For example, hydrogen bonds help stabilize the structures of proteins and are also responsible for the way that DNA is able to carry genetic information.

One remarkable consequence of hydrogen bonding is seen in the densities of ice and liquid water. In most substances the molecules in the solid are more densely packed than in the liquid, making the solid phase denser than the liquid phase. By contrast, the density of ice at 0 °C (0.917 g/mL) is less than that of liquid water at 0 °C (1.00 g/mL), so ice floats on liquid water.

The lower density of ice can be understood in terms of hydrogen bonding. In ice, the $H_2O$ molecules assume the ordered, open arrangement shown in ▼ **FIGURE 11.11.** This arrangement optimizes hydrogen bonding between molecules, with each $H_2O$ molecule forming hydrogen bonds to four neighboring $H_2O$ molecules. These hydrogen bonds, however, create the cavities seen in the middle image of Figure 11.11. When ice melts,

**△ GO FIGURE**

What is the approximate H—O····H bond angle in ice, where H—O is the covalent bond and O····H is the hydrogen bond?

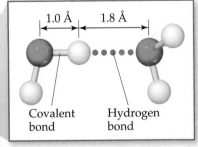

◀ **FIGURE 11.11   Hydrogen bonding in ice.** The empty channels in the structure of ice make water less dense as a solid than as a liquid.

▲ **FIGURE 11.12** **Expansion of water upon freezing.**

the motions of the molecules cause the structure to collapse. The hydrogen bonding in the liquid is more random than in the solid but is strong enough to hold the molecules close together. Consequently, liquid water has a denser structure than ice, meaning that a given mass of water occupies a smaller volume than the same mass of ice.

The expansion of water upon freezing (◄ FIGURE 11.12) is responsible for many phenomena we take for granted. It causes icebergs to float and water pipes to burst in cold weather. The lower density of ice compared to liquid water also profoundly affects life on Earth. Because ice floats, it covers the top of the water when a lake freezes, thereby insulating the water. If ice were denser than water, ice forming at the top of a lake would sink to the bottom, and the lake could freeze solid. Most aquatic life could not survive under these conditions.

## Ion–Dipole Forces

An **ion–dipole force** exists between an ion and a polar molecule (▼ FIGURE 11.13). Cations are attracted to the negative end of a dipole, and anions are attracted to the positive end. The magnitude of the attraction increases as either the ionic charge or the magnitude of the dipole moment increases. Ion–dipole forces are especially important for solutions of ionic substances in polar liquids, such as a solution of NaCl in water. ∞ (Section 4.1)

▲ **GIVE IT SOME THOUGHT**

In which mixture do you expect to find ion–dipole forces: $CH_3OH$ in water or $Ca(NO_3)_2$ in water?

## Comparing Intermolecular Forces

We can identify the intermolecular forces operative in a substance by considering its composition and structure. *Dispersion forces are found in all substances.* The strength of these attractive forces increases with increasing molecular weight and depends on molecular shapes. With polar molecules dipole–dipole forces are also operative, but these forces often make a smaller contribution to the total intermolecular attraction than dispersion forces. For example, in liquid HCl dispersion forces are estimated to account for more than 80% of the total attraction between molecules, while dipole–dipole attractions account for the rest. Hydrogen bonds, when present, make an important contribution to the total intermolecular interaction. In general, the energies associated with dispersion and dipole–dipole forces are 2–10 kJ/mol, while the energies of hydrogen bonds are 5–25 kJ/mol. Ion–dipole attractions have energies of approximately 15 kJ/mol. All these interactions are considerably weaker than covalent and ionic bonds, which have energies that are hundreds of kilojoules per mole.

▶ **FIGURE 11.13** **Ion–dipole forces.**

Positive ends of polar molecules are oriented toward negatively charged anion

Negative ends of polar molecules are oriented toward positively charged cation

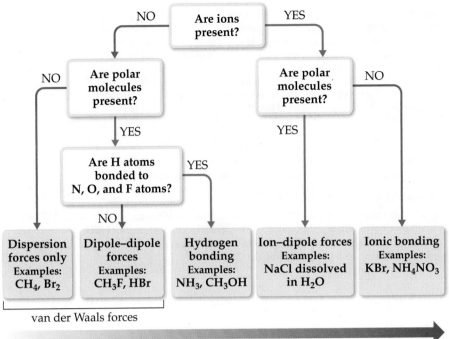

Dispersion forces only
Examples:
$CH_4$, $Br_2$

Dipole–dipole forces
Examples:
$CH_3F$, HBr

Hydrogen bonding
Examples:
$NH_3$, $CH_3OH$

Ion–dipole forces
Examples:
NaCl dissolved in $H_2O$

Ionic bonding
Examples:
KBr, $NH_4NO_3$

van der Waals forces

Increasing interaction strength

◀ **FIGURE 11.14 Flowchart for determining intermolecular forces.** Multiple types of intermolecular forces can be at work in a given substance or mixture. In particular, dispersion forces occur in all substances.

When comparing the relative strengths of intermolecular attractions, consider these generalizations:

1. When the molecules of two substances have comparable molecular weights and shapes, dispersion forces are approximately equal in the two substances. Differences in the magnitudes of the intermolecular forces are due to differences in the strengths of dipole–dipole attractions. The intermolecular forces get stronger as molecule polarity increases, with those molecules capable of hydrogen bonding having the strongest interactions.

2. When the molecules of two substances differ widely in molecular weights, dispersion forces tend to determine which substance has the stronger intermolecular attractions. Intermolecular attractive forces are generally higher in the substance with higher molecular weight.

▲ **FIGURE 11.14** presents a systematic way of identifying the intermolecular forces in a particular system.

It is important to realize that the effects of all these attractions are additive. For example, acetic acid, $CH_3COOH$, and 1-propanol, $CH_3CH_2CH_2OH$, have the same molecular weight, 60 amu, and both are capable of forming hydrogen bonds. However, a pair of acetic acid molecules can form two hydrogen bonds, whereas a pair of 1-propanol molecules can form only one (▶ **FIGURE 11.15**). Hence, the boiling point of acetic acid is higher. These effects can be important, especially for very large polar molecules such as proteins, which have multiple dipoles over their surfaces. These molecules can be held together in solution to a surprisingly high degree due to the presence of multiple dipole–dipole attractions.

Each molecule can form two hydrogen bonds with a neighbor

Acetic acid, $CH_3COOH$
MW = 60 amu
bp = 391 K

Each molecule can form one hydrogen bond with a neighbor

1-Propanol, $CH_3CH_2CH_2OH$
MW = 60 amu
bp = 370 K

▲ **FIGURE 11.15 Hydrogen bonding in acetic acid and 1-propanol.** The greater the number of hydrogen bonds possible, the more tightly the molecules are held together and, therefore, the higher the boiling point.

---

**SAMPLE EXERCISE 11.2** | **Predicting Types and Relative Strengths of Intermolecular Attractions**

List the substances $BaCl_2$, $H_2$, CO, HF, and Ne in order of increasing boiling point.

### SOLUTION

**Analyze** We need to assess the intermolecular forces in these substances and use that information to determine the relative boiling points.

**Plan** The boiling point depends in part on the attractive forces in each substance. We need to order these according to the relative strengths of the different kinds of intermolecular attractions.

**Solve** The attractive forces are stronger for ionic substances than for molecular ones, so $BaCl_2$ should have the highest boiling point. The intermolecular forces of the remaining substances depend on molecular weight, polarity, and hydrogen bonding. The molecular weights are $H_2$ (2), CO (28), HF (20), and Ne (20). The boiling point of $H_2$ should be the lowest because it is nonpolar and has the lowest molecular weight. The molecular weights of CO, HF, and Ne are similar. Because HF can hydrogen bond, however, it should have the highest boiling point of the three. Next is CO, which is slightly polar and has the highest molecular weight. Finally, Ne, which is nonpolar, should have the lowest boiling point of these three. The predicted order of boiling points is, therefore,

$$H_2 < Ne < CO < HF < BaCl_2$$

**Check** The boiling points reported in the literature are $H_2$ (20 K), Ne (27 K), CO (83 K), HF (293 K), and $BaCl_2$ (1813 K)—in agreement with our predictions.

**PRACTICE EXERCISE**

(a) Identify the intermolecular attractions present in the following substances, and (b) select the substance with the highest boiling point: $CH_3CH_3$, $CH_3OH$, and $CH_3CH_2OH$.
**Answers:** (a) $CH_3CH_3$ has only dispersion forces, whereas the other two substances have both dispersion forces and hydrogen bonds, (b) $CH_3CH_2OH$

# CHEMISTRY PUT TO WORK

## Ionic Liquids

The strong electrostatic attractions between cations and anions are responsible for the fact that most ionic compounds are solids at room temperature, with high melting and boiling points. However, the melting point of an ionic compound can be low if the ionic charges are not too high and the cation–anion distance is sufficiently large. For example, the melting point of $NH_4NO_3$, where both cation and anion are larger polyatomic ions, is 170 °C. If the ammonium cation is replaced by the even larger ethylammonium cation, $CH_3CH_2NH_3^+$, the melting point drops to 12 °C, making ethylammonium nitrate a liquid at room temperature! Ethylammonium nitrate is an example of an *ionic liquid*: a salt that is a liquid at room temperature.

Not only is $CH_3CH_2NH_3^+$ larger than $NH_4^+$ but also it is less symmetric. In general, the larger and more irregularly shaped the ions in an ionic substance, the better the chances of forming an ionic liquid. Although many cations form ionic liquids, one of the most popular is the 1-butyl-3-methylimidazolium cation (bmim$^+$, ▼ FIGURE 11.16 and ▶ TABLE 11.3), which has two arms of different lengths coming off a five-atom central ring. This feature gives bmim$^+$ an irregular shape, which makes it difficult for the molecules to pack together in a solid.

**TABLE 11.3 • Melting Point and Decomposition Temperature of Four 1-Butyl-3-methylimidazolium (bmim$^+$) Salts**

| Cation | Anion | Melting Point (°C) | Decomposition Temperature (°C) |
|--------|-------|--------------------|---------------------------------|
| bmim$^+$ | $Cl^-$ | 41 | 254 |
| bmim$^+$ | $I^-$ | −72 | 265 |
| bmim$^+$ | $PF_6^-$ | 10 | 349 |
| bmim$^+$ | $BF_4^-$ | −81 | 403 |

Common anions found in ionic liquids include the $PF_6^-$, $BF_4^-$, and halide ions.

Ionic liquids have properties that are attractive for some applications. Unlike most molecular liquids, they tend to have a very low vapor pressure. Because they are nonvolatile (that is, they don't evaporate), they tend to be nonflammable and remain in the liquid state at temperatures up to 673 K. Most molecular substances are liquids only at much lower temperatures, for example, 373 K or less in many cases (see Table 11.2). Because they are good solvents for a wide range of inorganic, organic, and polymeric substances, ionic liquids can be used for a variety of reactions and separations. These properties make them attractive replacements for volatile organic solvents in many industrial processes. Relative to traditional organic solvents, ionic liquids offer the promise of reduced volumes, safer handling, and easier reuse. For these reasons and others, there is considerable excitement about the promise of ionic liquids for reducing the environmental impact of industrial chemical processes.

▲ **FIGURE 11.16 Representative ions found in ionic liquids.**

*RELATED EXERCISES: 11.31, 11.32, 11.81*

# 11.3 | SELECT PROPERTIES OF LIQUIDS

The intermolecular attractions we have just discussed can help us understand many familiar properties of liquids. In this section we examine two: viscosity and surface tension.

## Viscosity

Some liquids, such as molasses and motor oil, flow very slowly; others, such as water and gasoline, flow easily. The resistance of a liquid to flow is called **viscosity**. The greater a liquid's viscosity, the more slowly it flows. Viscosity can be measured by timing how long it takes a certain amount of the liquid to flow through a thin vertical tube (▶ FIGURE 11.17). Viscosity can also be determined by measuring the rate at which steel balls fall through the liquid. The balls fall more slowly as the viscosity increases.

Viscosity is related to the ease with which the molecules of the liquid can move relative to one another. It depends on the attractive forces between molecules and on whether the shapes of the molecules are such that they tend to become entangled (for example, long molecules can become tangled like spaghetti). For a series of related compounds, viscosity increases with molecular weight, as illustrated in ▼ TABLE 11.4. The SI units for viscosity are kg/m-s. For any given substance, viscosity decreases with increasing temperature. Octane, for example, has a viscosity of $7.06 \times 10^{-4}$ kg/m-s at 0 °C and $4.33 \times 10^{-4}$ kg/m-s at 40 °C. At higher temperatures the greater average kinetic energy of the molecules overcomes the attractive forces between molecules.

SAE 40      SAE 10
higher number    lower number
higher viscosity    lower viscosity
slower pouring    faster pouring

▲ FIGURE 11.17 **Comparing viscosities.** The Society of Automotive Engineers (SAE) has established a numeric scale to indicate motor-oil viscosity.

## Surface Tension

The surface of water behaves almost as if it had an elastic skin, as evidenced by the ability of certain insects to "walk" on water. This behavior is due to an imbalance of intermolecular forces at the surface of the liquid. As shown in ▶ FIGURE 11.18, molecules in the interior are attracted equally in all directions, but those at the surface experience a net inward force. This net force tends to pull surface molecules toward the interior, thereby reducing the surface area and making the molecules at the surface pack closely together.

Because spheres have the smallest surface area for their volume, water droplets assume an almost spherical shape. This explains the tendency of water to "bead up" when it contacts a surface made of nonpolar molecules, like a lotus leaf or a newly waxed car.

A measure of the net inward force that must be overcome to expand the surface area of a liquid is given by its surface tension. **Surface tension** is the energy required to increase the surface area of a liquid by a unit amount. For example, the surface tension of water at 20 °C is $7.29 \times 10^{-2}$ J/m², which means that an energy of $7.29 \times 10^{-2}$ J must be supplied to increase the surface area of a given amount of water by 1 m². Water has a high surface tension because of its strong hydrogen bonds. The surface tension of mercury is even higher ($4.6 \times 10^{-1}$ J/m²) because of even stronger metallic bonds between the atoms of mercury.

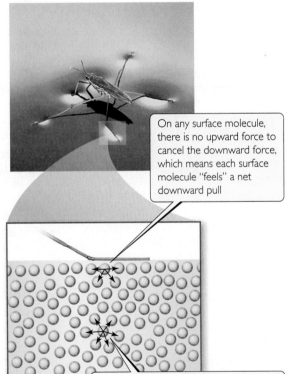

On any surface molecule, there is no upward force to cancel the downward force, which means each surface molecule "feels" a net downward pull

On any interior molecule, each force is balanced by a force pulling in the opposite direction, which means that interior molecules "feel" no net pull in any direction

▲ FIGURE 11.18 **Molecular-level view of surface tension.** A water strider does not sink because of the high surface tension of water.

| TABLE 11.4 • Viscosities of a Series of Hydrocarbons at 20 °C | | |
|---|---|---|
| **Substance** | **Formula** | **Viscosity (kg/m-s)** |
| Hexane | $CH_3CH_2CH_2CH_2CH_2CH_3$ | $3.26 \times 10^{-4}$ |
| Heptane | $CH_3CH_2CH_2CH_2CH_2CH_2CH_3$ | $4.09 \times 10^{-4}$ |
| Octane | $CH_3CH_2CH_2CH_2CH_2CH_2CH_2CH_3$ | $5.42 \times 10^{-4}$ |
| Nonane | $CH_3CH_2CH_2CH_2CH_2CH_2CH_2CH_2CH_3$ | $7.11 \times 10^{-4}$ |
| Decane | $CH_3CH_2CH_2CH_2CH_2CH_2CH_2CH_2CH_2CH_3$ | $1.42 \times 10^{-3}$ |

If the inside surface of each tube were coated with wax, would the general shape of the water meniscus change? Would the general shape of the mercury meniscus change?

Water

Mercury

$H_2O$–glass adhesive forces

Hg–glass adhesive forces

$H_2O$–$H_2O$ cohesive forces

Hg–Hg cohesive forces

Because adhesive > cohesive, $H_2O$ molecules touching glass adhere to the wall more than to each other, forming concave surface

Because cohesive > adhesive, Hg molecules touching glass adhere to the wall less than to each other, forming convex surface

▶ **FIGURE 11.19** **Meniscus shapes for water and mercury in glass tubes.**

▲ GIVE IT SOME THOUGHT

How do viscosity and surface tension change
a. as temperature increases,
b. as intermolecular forces of attraction become stronger?

Intermolecular forces that bind similar molecules to one another, such as the hydrogen bonding in water, are called *cohesive forces*. Intermolecular forces that bind a substance to a surface are called *adhesive forces*. Water placed in a glass tube adheres to the glass because the adhesive forces between the water and glass are greater than the cohesive forces between water molecules. The curved surface, or *meniscus*, of the water is therefore U-shaped (▲ **FIGURE 11.19**). For mercury, however, the situation is different. Mercury atoms can form bonds with one another but not with the glass. As a result the cohesive forces are much greater than the adhesive forces and the meniscus is shaped like an inverted U.

When a small-diameter glass tube, or capillary, is placed in water, water rises in the tube. The rise of liquids up very narrow tubes is called **capillary action**. The adhesive forces between the liquid and the walls of the tube tend to increase the surface area of the liquid. The surface tension of the liquid tends to reduce the area, thereby pulling the liquid up the tube. The liquid climbs until the force of gravity on the liquid balances the adhesive and cohesive forces. Capillary action helps water and dissolved nutrients move upward through plants.

# 11.4 | PHASE CHANGES

Liquid water left uncovered in a glass eventually evaporates. An ice cube left in a warm room quickly melts. Solid $CO_2$ (sold as a product called dry ice) *sublimes* at room temperature; that is, it changes directly from solid to gas. In general, each state of matter—solid, liquid, gas—can transform into either of the other two states. ▶ FIGURE 11.20 shows the names associated with these transformations, which are called either **phase changes** or *changes of state*.

## Energy Changes Accompanying Phase Changes

Every phase change is accompanied by a change in the energy of the system. In a solid, for example, the particles—either molecules, ions, or atoms—are in more or less fixed positions with respect to one another and closely arranged to minimize the energy of the system. As the temperature of the solid increases, the particles vibrate about their equilibrium positions with increasingly energetic motion. When the solid melts, the particles are freed to move relative to one another, which ordinarily means the average distance between particles increases.

Melting is called (somewhat confusingly) *fusion*. The increased freedom of motion of the particles comes at a price, measured by the **heat of fusion** or *enthalpy of fusion*, $\Delta H_{fus}$. The heat of fusion of ice, for example, is 6.01 kJ/mol.

As the temperature of the liquid increases, the particles move about with increasing energy. One measure of this increasing energy is that the concentration of gas-phase particles above the liquid surface increases with temperature. These gas-phase particles exert a pressure called *vapor pressure*. We explore vapor pressure in Section 11.5. For now we just need to understand that vapor pressure increases with increasing temperature until it equals the external pressure above the liquid, typically atmospheric pressure. At this point the liquid boils—the particles move into the gaseous state where they are widely separated. The energy required to cause this transition is called either the **heat of vaporization** or the *enthalpy of vaporization*, $\Delta H_{vap}$. For water, the heat of vaporization is 40.7 kJ/mol.

▼ FIGURE 11.21 shows $\Delta H_{fus}$ and $\Delta H_{vap}$ values for four substances. The values of $\Delta H_{vap}$ tend to be larger than the values of $\Delta H_{fus}$ because in the transition from liquid to gas, particles must essentially sever all their interparticle attractive interactions, whereas in the transition from solid to liquid, many of these attractive interactions remain operative.

The particles of a solid can move directly into the gaseous state. The enthalpy change required for this transition is called the **heat of sublimation**, denoted $\Delta H_{sub}$. As illustrated in Figure 11.21, $\Delta H_{sub}$ is the sum of $\Delta H_{fus}$ and $\Delta H_{vap}$. Thus, $\Delta H_{sub}$ for water is approximately 47 kJ/mol.

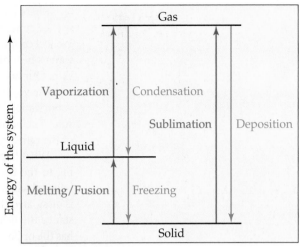

—— Endothermic process (energy added to substance)
—— Exothermic process (energy released from substance)

▲ **FIGURE 11.20** **Phase changes and the names associated with them.**

---

◢ GO FIGURE

**Is it possible to calculate the heat of sublimation for a substance given its heats of vaporization and fusion? If so, what is the relationship?**

◀ **FIGURE 11.21** **Heats of fusion, vaporization, and sublimation.**

Phase changes show up in important ways in our everyday experiences. When we use ice cubes to cool a drink, for instance, the heat of fusion of the ice cools the liquid. We feel cool when we step out of a swimming pool or a warm shower because the liquid water's heat of vaporization is drawn from our bodies as the water evaporates from our skin. Our bodies use this mechanism to regulate body temperature, especially when we exercise vigorously in warm weather. A refrigerator also relies on the cooling effects of vaporization. Its mechanism contains an enclosed gas that can be liquefied under pressure. The liquid absorbs heat as it subsequently evaporates, thereby cooling the interior of the refrigerator.

What happens to the heat absorbed when the liquid refrigerant vaporizes? According to the first law of thermodynamics ∞ (Section 5.2), this absorbed heat must be released when the gas condenses to liquid. As this phase change occurs, the heat released is dissipated through cooling coils in the back of the refrigerator. Just as for a given substance the heat of condensation is equal in magnitude to the heat of vaporization and has the opposite sign, so also the *heat of deposition* for a given substance is exothermic to the same degree that the heat of sublimation is endothermic; the *heat of freezing* is exothermic to the same degree that the heat of fusion is endothermic (see Figure 11.20).

### ▲ GIVE IT SOME THOUGHT

What is the name of the phase change that occurs when ice left at room temperature changes to liquid water? Is this change exothermic or endothermic?

## Heating Curves

When we heat an ice cube initially at −25 °C and 1 atm pressure, the temperature of the ice increases. As long as the temperature is below 0 °C, the ice cube remains in the solid state. When the temperature reaches 0 °C, the ice begins to melt. Because melting is an endothermic process, the heat we add at 0 °C is used to convert ice to liquid water, and *the temperature remains constant until all the ice has melted*. Once all the ice has melted, adding more heat causes the temperature of the liquid water to increase.

A graph of temperature versus amount of heat added is called a *heating curve.* ◀ FIGURE 11.22 shows the heating curve for transforming ice, $H_2O(s)$, initially at −25 °C to steam, $H_2O(g)$, at 125 °C. Heating the $H_2O(s)$ from −25 °C to 0 °C is represented by the line segment $AB$, and converting the $H_2O(s)$ at 0 °C to $H_2O(\ell)$ at 0 °C is the horizontal segment $BC$. Additional heat increases the temperature of the $H_2O(\ell)$ until the temperature reaches 100 °C (segment $CD$). The heat is then used to convert $H_2O(\ell)$ to $H_2O(g)$ at a constant temperature of 100 °C (segment $DE$). Once all the $H_2O(\ell)$ has been converted to $H_2O(g)$, the $H_2O(g)$ is heated to its final temperature of 125 °C (segment $EF$).

We can calculate the enthalpy change of the system for each segment of the heating curve. In segments $AB$, $CD$, and $EF$ we are heating a single phase from one temperature to another. As we saw in Section 5.5, the amount of heat needed to raise the temperature of a substance is given by the product of the specific heat, mass, and temperature change (Equation 5.22). The greater the specific heat of a substance, the more heat we must add to accomplish a certain temperature increase. Because the specific heat of water is greater than that of ice, the slope of segment $CD$ is less than that of segment $AB$. This lesser slope means the amount of heat we must add to a given mass of liquid water to achieve a 1 °C temperature change is greater than the amount we must add to achieve a 1 °C temperature change in the same mass of ice.

In segments $BC$ and $DE$ we are converting one phase to another at a constant temperature. The temperature remains constant during these phase changes because the added energy is used to overcome the attractive forces between molecules rather than to increase their average kinetic energy. For segment $BC$, the enthalpy change can be calculated by using $\Delta H_{fus}$, and for segment $DE$ we can use $\Delta H_{vap}$.

**Vaporization, temperature does not change until all $H_2O(l)$ becomes $H_2O(g)$** ⋯

Steam

Liquid water

⋯**Melting, temperature does not change until all $H_2O(s)$ becomes $H_2O(l)$**

Ice

Heat added

▲ **FIGURE 11.22  Heating curve for water.** Changes that occur when 1.00 mol of $H_2O$ is heated from $H_2O(s)$ at −25 °C to $H_2O(g)$ at 125 °C at a constant pressure of 1 atm. Heat is added over the entire temperature range, but the temperature of the system increases only when the $H_2O$ is either all solid or all liquid or all gas (blue lines). Even though heat is being added continuously, the system temperature does not change during the two phase changes (red lines).

**SAMPLE EXERCISE 11.3**  **Calculating $\Delta H$ for Temperature and Phase Changes**

Calculate the enthalpy change upon converting 1.00 mol of ice at $-25\,°C$ to steam at $125\,°C$ under a constant pressure of 1 atm. The specific heats of ice, liquid water, and steam are 2.03 J/g-K, 4.18 J/g-K, and 1.84 J/g-K, respectively. For $H_2O$, $\Delta H_{fus} = 6.01$ kJ/mol and $\Delta H_{vap} = 40.67$ kJ/mol.

**SOLUTION**

**Analyze** Our goal is to calculate the total heat required to convert 1 mol of ice at $-25\,°C$ to steam at $125\,°C$.

**Plan** We can calculate the enthalpy change for each segment and then sum them to get the total enthalpy change (Hess's law, Section 5.6).

**Solve:** For segment $AB$ in Figure 11.22, we are adding enough heat to ice to increase its temperature by $25\,°C$. A temperature change of $25\,°C$ is the same as a temperature change of 25 K, so we can use the specific heat of ice to calculate the enthalpy change during this process:

$AB$: $\Delta H = (1.00\text{ mol})(18.0\text{ g/mol})(2.03\text{ J/g-K})(25\text{ K}) = 914\text{ J} = 0.91\text{ kJ}$

For segment $BC$ in Figure 11.22, in which we convert ice to water at $0\,°C$, we can use the molar enthalpy of fusion directly:

$BC$: $\Delta H = (1.00\text{ mol})(6.01\text{ kJ/mol}) = 6.01\text{ kJ}$

The enthalpy changes for segments $CD$, $DE$, and $EF$ can be calculated in similar fashion:

$CD$: $\Delta H = (1.00\text{ mol})(18.0\text{ g/mol})(4.18\text{ J/g-K})(100\text{ K}) = 7520\text{ J} = 7.52\text{ kJ}$
$DE$: $\Delta H = (1.00\text{ mol})(40.67\text{ kJ/mol}) = 40.7\text{ kJ}$
$EF$: $\Delta H = (1.00\text{ mol})(18.0\text{ g/mol})(1.84\text{ J/g-K})(25\text{ K}) = 830\text{ J} = 0.83\text{ kJ}$

The total enthalpy change is the sum of the changes of the individual steps:

$\Delta H = 0.91\text{ kJ} + 6.01\text{ kJ} + 7.52\text{ kJ} + 40.7\text{ kJ} + 0.83\text{ kJ} = 56.0\text{ kJ}$

**Check** The components of the total energy change are reasonable relative to the horizontal lengths (heat added) of the segments in Figure 11.22. Notice that the largest component is the heat of vaporization.

**PRACTICE EXERCISE**

What is the enthalpy change during the process in which 100.0 g of water at $50.0\,°C$ is cooled to ice at $-30.0\,°C$? (Use the specific heats and enthalpies for phase changes given in Sample Exercise 11.3.)
**Answer:** $-20.9\text{ kJ} - 33.4\text{ kJ} - 6.09\text{ kJ} = -60.4\text{ kJ}$

If we start with 1 mole of steam at $125\,°C$ and cool it, we move right to left across Figure 11.22. We first lower the temperature of the $H_2O(g)$ ($F \longrightarrow E$), then condense it ($E \longrightarrow D$) to $H_2O(\ell)$, and so forth.

Sometimes as we remove heat from a liquid, we can temporarily cool it below its freezing point without forming a solid. This phenomenon, called *supercooling*, occurs when the heat is removed so rapidly that the molecules have no time to assume the ordered structure of a solid. A supercooled liquid is unstable; particles of dust entering the solution or gentle stirring is often sufficient to cause the substance to solidify quickly.

## Critical Temperature and Pressure

A gas normally liquefies at some point when pressure is applied. Suppose we have a cylinder fitted with a piston, and the cylinder contains water vapor at $100\,°C$. If we increase the pressure on the water vapor, liquid water will form when the pressure is 760 torr. However, if the temperature is $110\,°C$, the liquid phase does not form until the pressure is 1075 torr. At $374\,°C$ the liquid phase forms only at $1.655 \times 10^5$ torr (217.7 atm). Above this temperature no amount of pressure causes a distinct liquid phase to form. Instead, as pressure increases, the gas becomes steadily more compressed. The highest temperature at which a distinct liquid phase can form is called the **critical temperature**. The **critical pressure** is the pressure required to bring about liquefaction at this critical temperature.

**TABLE 11.5 • Critical Temperatures and Pressures of Selected Substances**

| Substance | Critical Temperature (K) | Critical Pressure (atm) |
|---|---|---|
| Nitrogen, $N_2$ | 126.1 | 33.5 |
| Argon, Ar | 150.9 | 48.0 |
| Oxygen, $O_2$ | 154.4 | 49.7 |
| Methane, $CH_4$ | 190.0 | 45.4 |
| Carbon dioxide, $CO_2$ | 304.3 | 73.0 |
| Phosphine, $PH_3$ | 324.4 | 64.5 |
| Propane, $CH_3CH_2CH_3$ | 370.0 | 42.0 |
| Hydrogen sulfide, $H_2S$ | 373.5 | 88.9 |
| Ammonia, $NH_3$ | 405.6 | 111.5 |
| Water, $H_2O$ | 647.6 | 217.7 |

The critical temperature is the highest temperature at which a liquid can exist. Above the critical temperature, the kinetic energies of the molecules are greater than the attractive forces that lead to the liquid state regardless of how much the substance is compressed to bring the molecules closer together. The greater the intermolecular forces, the higher the critical temperature of a substance.

Several critical temperatures and pressures are listed in ▲ TABLE 11.5. Notice that nonpolar, low-molecular-weight substances, which have weak intermolecular attractions, have lower critical temperatures and pressures than substances that are polar or of higher molecular weight. Notice also that water and ammonia have exceptionally high critical temperatures and pressures as a consequence of strong intermolecular hydrogen-bonding forces.

Because they provide information about the conditions under which gases liquefy, critical temperatures and pressures are often of considerable importance to engineers and other people working with gases. Sometimes we want to liquefy a gas; other times we want to avoid liquefying it. It is useless to try to liquefy a gas by applying pressure if the gas is above its critical temperature. For example, $O_2$ has a critical temperature of 154.4 K. It must be cooled below this temperature before it can be liquefied by pressure. In contrast, ammonia has a critical temperature of 405.6 K. Thus, it can be liquefied at room temperature (approximately 295 K) by applying sufficient pressure.

When the temperature exceeds the critical temperature and the pressure exceeds the critical pressure, the liquid and gas phases are indistinguishable from each other, and the substance is in a state called a **supercritical fluid**. Like liquids, supercritical fluids can behave as solvents dissolving a wide range of substances. Using *supercritical fluid extraction,* the components of mixtures can be separated from one another. Supercritical fluid extraction has been successfully used to separate complex mixtures in the chemical, food, pharmaceutical, and energy industries. Supercritical $CO_2$ is a popular choice because it is relatively inexpensive and there are no problems associated with disposing of solvent, nor are there toxic residues resulting from the process.

# 11.5 | VAPOR PRESSURE

Molecules can escape from the surface of a liquid into the gas phase by evaporation. Suppose we place a quantity of ethanol ($CH_3CH_2OH$) in an evacuated, closed container, as in ▶ FIGURE 11.23. The ethanol quickly begins to evaporate. As a result, the pressure exerted by the vapor in the space above the liquid increases. After a short time the pressure of the vapor attains a constant value, which we call the **vapor pressure**.

At any instant, some of the ethanol molecules at the liquid surface possess sufficient kinetic energy to overcome the attractive forces of their neighbors and, therefore, escape into the gas phase. At any particular temperature, the movement of molecules from liquid phase to gas phase goes on continuously. As the number of gas-phase molecules

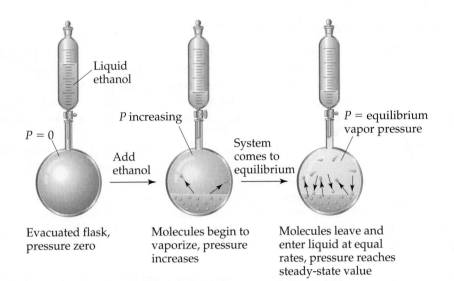

Liquid ethanol

$P = 0$

Evacuated flask, pressure zero

Add ethanol

$P$ increasing

System comes to equilibrium

Molecules begin to vaporize, pressure increases

$P =$ equilibrium vapor pressure

Molecules leave and enter liquid at equal rates, pressure reaches steady-state value

◀ **FIGURE 11.23  Equilibrium vapor pressure over a liquid.**

increases, however, the probability increases that a molecule in the gas phase will strike the liquid surface and be recaptured by the liquid, as shown in the flask on the right in Figure 11.23. Eventually, the rate at which molecules return to the liquid equals the rate at which they escape. The number of molecules in the gas phase then reaches a steady value, and the pressure exerted by the vapor becomes constant.

The condition in which two opposing processes occur simultaneously at equal rates is called **dynamic equilibrium** (or simply *equilibrium*). A liquid and its vapor are in dynamic equilibrium when evaporation and condensation occur at equal rates. It may appear that nothing is occurring at equilibrium because there is no net change in the system. In fact, though, a great deal is happening as molecules continuously pass from liquid state to gas state and from gas state to liquid state. *The vapor pressure of a liquid is the pressure exerted by its vapor when the liquid and vapor are in dynamic equilibrium.*

## Volatility, Vapor Pressure, and Temperature

When vaporization occurs in an open container, as when water evaporates from a bowl, the vapor spreads away from the liquid. Little, if any, is recaptured at the surface of the liquid. Equilibrium never occurs, and the vapor continues to form until the liquid evaporates to dryness. Substances with high vapor pressure (such as gasoline) evaporate more quickly than substances with low vapor pressure (such as motor oil). Liquids that evaporate readily are said to be **volatile**.

Hot water evaporates more quickly than cold water because vapor pressure increases with increasing temperature. To see why this statement is true, we begin with the fact that the molecules of a liquid move at various speeds. ▶ **FIGURE 11.24** shows the distribution of kinetic energies of the molecules at the surface of a liquid at two temperatures. (The curves are like those shown for gases in Section 10.7.) As the temperature is increased, the molecules move more energetically and more of them can break free from their neighbors and enter the gas phase, increasing the vapor pressure.

▶ **FIGURE 11.25** depicts the variation in vapor pressure with temperature for four common substances that differ greatly in volatility. Note that the vapor pressure in all cases increases nonlinearly with increasing temperature. The weaker the intermolecular forces in the liquid, the more easily molecules can escape and, therefore, the higher the vapor pressure at a given temperature.

▲ **GO FIGURE**

As the temperature increases, does the rate of molecules escaping into the gas phase increase or decrease?

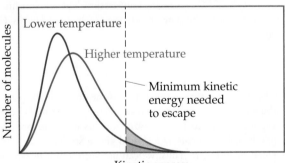

Lower temperature

Higher temperature

Minimum kinetic energy needed to escape

Number of molecules

Kinetic energy

Blue area = number of molecules having enough energy to evaporate at lower temperature

Red + blue areas = number of molecules having enough energy to evaporate at higher temperature

▲ **FIGURE 11.24  The effect of temperature on the distribution of kinetic energies in a liquid.**

▲ **GIVE IT SOME THOUGHT**

Which compound do you think is more volatile at 25 °C: $CCl_4$ or $CBr_4$?

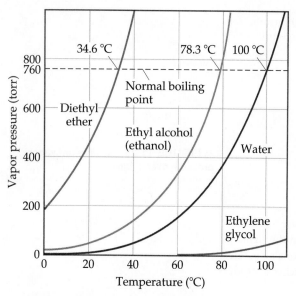

**GO FIGURE**

**What is the vapor pressure of ethylene glycol at its normal boiling point?**

▲ FIGURE 11.25 **Vapor pressure for four liquids as a function of temperature.**

## Vapor Pressure and Boiling Point

A liquid boils when its vapor pressure equals the external pressure acting on the liquid surface. At this point, bubbles of vapor form within the liquid. The temperature at which a given liquid boils increases with increasing external pressure. The boiling point of a liquid at 1 atm (760 torr) pressure is called its **normal boiling point**. From Figure 11.25 we see that the normal boiling point of water is 100 °C.

The time required to cook food in boiling water depends on the water temperature. In an open container, that temperature is 100 °C, but it is possible to boil at higher temperatures. Pressure cookers work by allowing steam to escape only when it exceeds a predetermined pressure; the pressure above the water can therefore increase above atmospheric pressure. The higher pressure causes the water to boil at a higher temperature, thereby allowing the food to get hotter and to cook more rapidly.

The effect of pressure on boiling point also explains why it takes longer to cook food at high elevations than it does at sea level. The atmospheric pressure is lower at higher altitudes, so water boils at a temperature lower than 100 °C, and foods generally take longer to cook.

## A CLOSER LOOK

### THE CLAUSIUS–CLAPEYRON EQUATION

You might have noticed that the plots in Figure 11.25 have a distinct shape: For each substance, the vapor pressure curves sharply upward with increasing temperature. The relationship between vapor pressure and temperature is given by the *Clausius–Clapeyron equation*:

$$\ln P = \frac{-\Delta H_{vap}}{RT} + C \qquad [11.1]$$

where $P$ is the vapor pressure, $T$ is the absolute temperature, $R$ is the gas constant (8.314 J/mol-K), $\Delta H_{vap}$ is the molar enthalpy of vaporization, and $C$ is a constant. This equation predicts that a graph of $\ln P$ versus $1/T$ should give a straight line with a slope equal to $\Delta H_{vap}/R$. Thus, we can use such a plot to determine the enthalpy of vaporization of a substance by using the relationship

$$\Delta H_{vap} = -\text{slope} \times R$$

As an example of how we use the Clausius–Clapeyron equation, the vapor-pressure data for ethanol shown in Figure 11.25 are graphed as $\ln P$ versus $1/T$ in ▶ **FIGURE 11.26**. The data lie on a straight line with a negative slope. We can use the slope to determine $\Delta H_{vap}$ for ethanol, 38.56 kJ/mol. We can also extrapolate the line to obtain the vapor pressure of ethanol at temperatures above and below the temperature range for which we have data.

*RELATED EXERCISES:* 11.83, 11.84, 11.85

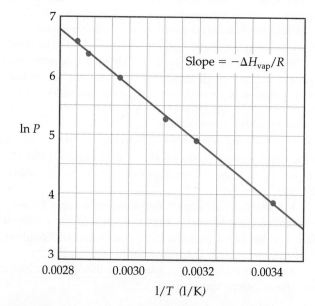

▲ FIGURE 11.26 **The natural logarithm of vapor pressure versus 1/T for ethanol.**

---

| SAMPLE EXERCISE 11.4 | Relating Boiling Point to Vapor Pressure |

Use Figure 11.25 to estimate the boiling point of diethyl ether under an external pressure of 0.80 atm.

### SOLUTION

**Analyze** We are asked to read a graph of vapor pressure versus temperature to determine the boiling point of a substance at a particular pressure. The boiling point is the temperature at which the vapor pressure is equal to the external pressure.

**Plan** We need to convert 0.80 atm to torr because that is the pressure scale on the graph. We estimate the location of that pressure on the graph, move horizontally to the vapor pressure curve, and then drop vertically from the curve to estimate the temperature.

**Solve** The pressure equals (0.80 atm)(760 torr/atm) = 610 torr. From Figure 11.25 we see that the boiling point at this pressure is about 27 °C, which is close to room temperature.

**Comment** We can make a flask of diethyl ether boil at room temperature by using a vacuum pump to lower the pressure above the liquid to about 0.8 atm.

### PRACTICE EXERCISE

At what external pressure will ethanol have a boiling point of 60 °C?

*Answer:* about 340 torr (0.45 atm)

---

## 11.6 | PHASE DIAGRAMS

The equilibrium between a liquid and its vapor is not the only dynamic equilibrium that can exist between states of matter. Under appropriate conditions, a solid can be in equilibrium with its liquid or even with its vapor. A **phase diagram** is a graphic way to summarize the conditions under which equilibria exist between the different states of matter. Such a diagram also allows us to predict which phase of a substance is present at any given temperature and pressure.

The phase diagram for any substance that can exist in all three phases of matter is shown in ▼ FIGURE 11.27. The diagram contains three important curves, each of which represents the temperature and pressure at which the various phases can coexist

---

△ GO FIGURE

**If the pressure exerted on a liquid is increased, while the temperature is held constant, what type of phase transition will eventually occur?**

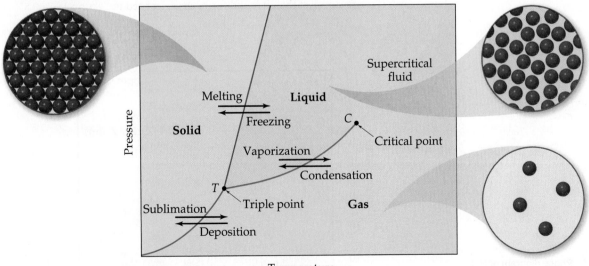

▲ FIGURE 11.27   **Generic phase diagram for a pure substance.** The green line is the sublimation curve, the blue line is the melting curve, and the red line is the vapor pressure curve.

at equilibrium. The only substance present in the system is the one whose phase diagram is under consideration. The pressure shown in the diagram is either the pressure applied to the system or the pressure generated by the substance. The curves may be described as follows:

1. The red curve is the *vapor-pressure curve* of the liquid, representing equilibrium between the liquid and gas phases. The point on this curve where the vapor pressure is 1 atm is the normal boiling point of the substance. The vapor-pressure curve ends at the *critical point* (*C*), which corresponds to the critical temperature and critical pressure of the substance. Beyond the critical point, the liquid and gas phases are indistinguishable from each other, and the substance is a *supercritical fluid*.

2. The green curve, the *sublimation curve*, separates the solid phase from the gas phase and represents the change in the vapor pressure of the solid as it sublimes at different temperatures.

3. The blue curve, the *melting curve*, separates the solid phase from the liquid phase and represents the change in melting point of the solid with increasing pressure. This curve usually slopes slightly to the right as pressure increases because for most substances the solid form is denser than the liquid form. An increase in pressure usually favors the more compact solid phase; thus, higher temperatures are required to melt the solid at higher pressures. The melting point at 1 atm is the **normal melting point.**

Point *T*, where the three curves intersect, is the **triple point,** and here all three phases are in equilibrium. Any other point on any of the three curves represents equilibrium between two phases. Any point on the diagram that does not fall on one of the curves corresponds to conditions under which only one phase is present. The gas phase, for example, is stable at low pressures and high temperatures, whereas the solid phase is stable at low temperatures and high pressures. Liquids are stable in the region between the other two.

## The Phase Diagrams of $H_2O$ and $CO_2$

▼ **FIGURE 11.28** shows the phase diagram of $H_2O$. Because of the large range of pressures covered in the diagram, a logarithmic scale is used to represent pressure. The melting curve (blue line) of $H_2O$ is atypical, slanting slightly to the left with increasing pressure, indicating that for water the melting point *decreases* with increasing pressure. This unusual behavior occurs because water is among the very few substances whose liquid form is more compact than its solid form, as we learned in Section 11.2.

► **FIGURE 11.28 Phase diagram of $H_2O$.**
Note that a linear scale is used to represent temperature and a logarithmic scale to represent pressure.

If the pressure is held constant at 1 atm, it is possible to move from the solid to liquid to gaseous regions of the phase diagram by changing the temperature, as we expect from our everyday encounters with water. The triple point of H₂O falls at a relatively low pressure, 0.00603 atm. Below this pressure, liquid water is not stable and ice sublimes to water vapor on heating. This property of water is used to "freeze-dry" foods and beverages. The food or beverage is frozen to a temperature below 0 °C. Next it is placed in a low-pressure chamber (below 0.00603 atm) and then warmed so that the water sublimes, leaving behind dehydrated food or beverage.

The phase diagram for CO₂ is shown in ▼ **FIGURE 11.29**. The melting curve (blue line) behaves typically, slanting to the right with increasing pressure, telling us that the melting point of CO₂ increases with increasing pressure. Because the pressure at the triple point is relatively high, 5.11 atm, CO₂ does not exist as a liquid at 1 atm, which means that solid CO₂ does not melt when heated, but instead sublimes. Thus, CO₂ does not have a normal melting point; instead, it has a normal sublimation point, −78.5 °C. Because CO₂ sublimes rather than melts as it absorbs energy at ordinary pressures, this makes solid CO₂ (dry ice) a convenient coolant.

---

### SAMPLE EXERCISE 11.5  Interpreting a Phase Diagram

Use the phase diagram for methane, CH₄, shown in ▼ **FIGURE 11.30** to answer the following questions. **(a)** What are the approximate temperature and pressure of the critical point? **(b)** What are the approximate temperature and pressure of the triple point? **(c)** Is methane a solid, liquid, or gas at 1 atm and 0 °C? **(d)** If solid methane at 1 atm is heated while the pressure is held constant, will it melt or sublime? **(e)** If methane at 1 atm and 0 °C is compressed until a phase change occurs, in which state is the methane when the compression is complete?

#### SOLUTION

**Analyze** We are asked to identify key features of the phase diagram and to use it to deduce what phase changes occur when specific pressure and temperature changes take place.

**Plan** We must identify the triple and critical points on the diagram and also identify which phase exists at specific temperatures and pressures.

#### Solve
**(a)** The critical point is the point where the liquid, gaseous, and supercritical fluid phases coexist. It is marked point 3 in the phase diagram and located at approximately −80 °C and 50 atm.

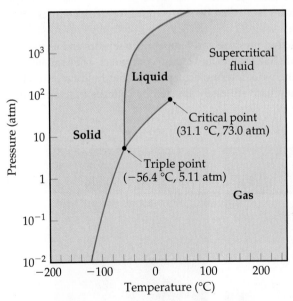

▲ **FIGURE 11.29  Phase diagram of CO₂.** Note that a linear scale is used to represent temperature and a logarithmic scale to represent pressure.

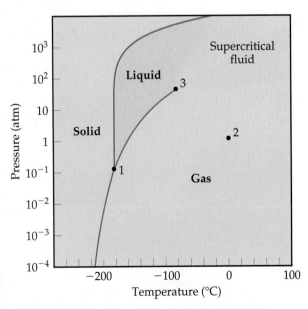

▲ **FIGURE 11.30  Phase diagram of CH₄.** Note that a linear scale is used to represent temperature and a logarithmic scale to represent pressure.

**(b)** The triple point is the point where the solid, liquid, and gaseous phases coexist. It is marked point 1 in the phase diagram and located at approximately −180 °C and 0.1 atm.

**(c)** The intersection of 0 °C and 1 atm is marked point 2 in the phase diagram. It is well within the gaseous region of the phase diagram.

**(d)** If we start in the solid region at $P = 1$ atm and move horizontally (this means we hold the pressure constant), we cross first into the liquid region, at $T \approx -180$ °C, and then into the gaseous region, at $T \approx -160$ °C. Therefore, solid methane melts when the pressure is 1 atm. (In order for methane to sublime, the pressure must be below the triple point pressure.)

**(e)** Moving vertically up from point 2, which is 1 atm and 0 °C, the first phase change we come to is from gas to supercritical fluid. This phase change happens when we exceed the critical pressure (~50 atm).

**Check** The pressure and temperature at the critical point are higher than those at the triple point, which is expected. Methane is the principal component of natural gas. So it seems reasonable that it exists as a gas at 1 atm and 0 °C.

**PRACTICE EXERCISE**

Use the phase diagram of methane to answer the following questions. **(a)** What is the normal boiling point of methane? **(b)** Over what pressure range does solid methane sublime? **(c)** Liquid methane does not exist above what temperature?

***Answers:*** **(a)** −162 °C; **(b)** It sublimes whenever the pressure is less than 0.1 atm; **(c)** The highest temperature at which a liquid can exist is defined by the critical temperature. So we do not expect to find liquid methane when the temperature is higher than −80 °C.

# 11.7 | LIQUID CRYSTALS

In 1888 Frederick Reinitzer, an Austrian botanist, discovered that the organic compound cholesteryl benzoate has an interesting and unusual property, shown in ▼ **FIGURE 11.31**. Solid cholesteryl benzoate melts at 145 °C, forming a viscous milky liquid; then at 179 °C the milky liquid becomes clear and remains that way at temperatures above 179 °C. When cooled, the clear liquid turns viscous and milky at 179 °C, and the milky liquid solidifies at 145 °C. Reinitzer's work represents the first systematic report of what we call a **liquid crystal**, the term we use today for the viscous, milky state.

Instead of passing directly from the solid phase to the liquid phase when heated, some substances, such as cholesteryl benzoate, pass through an intermediate liquid crystalline phase that has some of the structure of solids and some of the freedom of motion of liquids. Because of the partial ordering, liquid crystals may be viscous and possess properties intermediate between those of solids and those of liquids. The region in which they exhibit these properties is marked by sharp transition temperatures, as in Reinitzer's sample.

Today liquid crystals are used as pressure and temperature sensors and as the display element in such devices as digital watches and laptop computers. They can be used for these applications because the weak intermolecular forces that hold the molecules together in the liquid crystalline phase are easily affected by changes in temperature, pressure, and electric fields.

145 °C < T < 179 °C
Liquid crystalline phase

T > 179 °C
Liquid phase

▶ **FIGURE 11.31 Cholesteryl benzoate in its liquid and liquid crystalline states.**

**Liquid phase**

Molecules arranged randomly

**Nematic liquid crystalline phase**

Long axes of molecules aligned, but ends are not aligned

**Smectic A liquid crystalline phase**

Molecules aligned in layers, long axes of molecules perpendicular to layer planes

**Smectic C liquid crystalline phase**

Molecules aligned in layers, long axes of molecules inclined with respect to layer planes

◀ **FIGURE 11.32 Molecular order in nematic and smectic liquid crystals.** In the liquid phase of any substance, the molecules are arranged randomly, whereas in the liquid crystalline phases the molecules are arranged in a partially ordered way.

## Types of Liquid Crystals

Substances that form liquid crystals are often composed of rod-shaped molecules that are somewhat rigid in the middle. In the liquid phase, these molecules are oriented randomly. In the liquid crystalline phase, by contrast, the molecules are arranged in specific patterns as illustrated in ▲ FIGURE 11.32. Depending on the nature of the ordering, liquid crystals are classified as nematic, smectic A, smectic C, or cholesteric.

In a **nematic liquid crystal**, the molecules are aligned so that their long axes tend to point in the same direction but the ends are not aligned with one another. In **smectic A** and **smectic C liquid crystals**, the molecules maintain the long-axis alignment seen in nematic crystals, but in addition they pack into layers.

Two molecules that exhibit liquid crystalline phases are shown in ▼ FIGURE 11.33. The lengths of these molecules are much greater than their widths. The double bonds, including those in the benzene rings, add rigidity to the molecules, and the rings, because they are flat, help the molecules stack with one another. The polar $CH_3O$ and COOH groups give rise to dipole–dipole interactions and promote alignment of the molecules. Thus, the molecules order themselves quite naturally along their long axes. They can, however, rotate around their axes and slide parallel to one another. In smectic liquid crystals, the intermolecular forces (dispersion forces, dipole–dipole attractions, and hydrogen bonding) limit the ability of the molecules to slide past one another.

▲ **FIGURE 11.33 Molecular structure and liquid crystal temperature range for two typical liquid crystalline materials.**

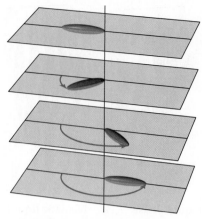

In a cholesteric liquid crystal the molecules pack into layers; the long axis of each molecule is oriented parallel to its neighbors within the same layer

The direction along which the molecules point rotates from one layer to the next, resulting in a spiraling pattern resembling the threads of a screw

▲ FIGURE 11.34 **Molecular order in a cholesteric liquid crystal.**

In a **cholesteric liquid crystal**, the molecules are arranged in layers, with their long axes parallel to the other molecules within the same layer.* Upon moving from one layer to the next, the orientation of the molecules rotates, resulting in the spiral pattern shown in ▲ **FIGURE 11.34**. These liquid crystals are so named because many derivatives of cholesterol adopt this structure.

The molecular arrangement in cholesteric liquid crystals produces unusual coloring patterns with visible light. Changes in temperature and pressure change the order and, hence, the color. Cholesteric liquid crystals are used to monitor temperature changes in situations where conventional methods are not feasible. For example, they can detect hot spots in microelectronic circuits, which may signal the presence of flaws. They can also be fashioned into thermometers for measuring the skin temperature of infants. Because cholesteric liquid crystal displays can be built that draw very little power, they are also being investigated for use in electronic paper (◀ **FIGURE 11.35**).

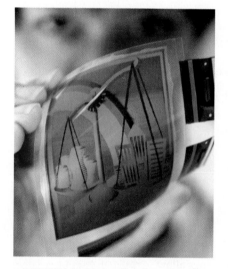

▲ FIGURE 11.35 **Electronic paper (e-paper) based on cholesteric liquid crystal technology.**

---

**SAMPLE EXERCISE 11.6** **Properties of Liquid Crystals**

Which of these substances is most likely to exhibit liquid crystalline behavior?

$$CH_3-CH_2-\underset{\underset{CH_3}{|}}{\overset{\overset{CH_3}{|}}{C}}-CH_2-CH_3$$

(i)

$$CH_3CH_2-\bigcirc-N{=}N-\bigcirc-\overset{\overset{O}{\|}}{C}-OCH_3$$

(ii)

$$\bigcirc-CH_2-\overset{\overset{O}{\|}}{C}-O^-Na^+$$

(iii)

---

*Cholesteric liquid crystals are sometimes called chiral nematic phases because the molecules within each plane adopt an arrangement similar to a nematic liquid crystal.

## SOLUTION

**Analyze** We have three molecules with different structures, and we are asked to determine which one is most likely to be a liquid crystalline substance.

**Plan** We need to identify all structural features that might induce liquid crystalline behavior.

**Solve** Molecule (i) is not likely to be liquid crystalline because the absence of double and/or triple bonds make this molecule flexible rather than rigid. Molecule (iii) is ionic and the generally high melting points of ionic materials make it unlikely that this substance is liquid crystalline. Molecule (ii) possesses the characteristic long axis and the kinds of structural features often seen in liquid crystals: The molecule has a rodlike shape, the double bonds and benzene rings provide rigidity, and the polar $COOCH_3$ group creates a dipole moment.

### PRACTICE EXERCISE

Suggest a reason why decane

$$CH_3CH_2CH_2CH_2CH_2CH_2CH_2CH_2CH_2CH_3$$

does not exhibit liquid crystalline behavior.

***Answer:*** Because rotation can occur about carbon–carbon single bonds, molecules whose backbone consists predominantly of C—C single bonds are too flexible; the molecules tend to coil in random ways and, thus, are not rodlike.

## CHEMISTRY PUT TO WORK

### Liquid Crystal Displays

Liquid crystals displays (LCDs) are widely used in electronic devices such as watches, calculators, and computer screens. These applications are possible because an applied electrical field changes the orientation of liquid crystal molecules and thus affects the optical properties of the device.

LCDs come in a variety of designs, but the structure illustrated in ▼ **FIGURE 11.36** is typical. A thin layer (5–20 $\mu$m) of liquid crystalline material is placed between electrically conducting, transparent glass electrodes. Ordinary light passes through a vertical polarizer that permits light in only the vertical plane to pass. Using a special process during fabrication, the liquid crystal molecules are oriented so that the molecules at the front electrode are oriented vertically and those at the back electrode horizontally. The orientation of the molecules in between the two electrodes varies systematically from vertical to horizontal, as shown in Figure 11.36(a). The plane of polarization of the light is turned by 90° as it passes through the liquid crystal layer and is thus in the correct orientation to pass through the

horizontal polarizer. In a watch display, a mirror reflects the light back, and the light retraces its path, allowing the device to look bright. When a voltage is applied to the plates, the liquid crystalline molecules align with the voltage, as shown in Figure 11.36(b). The light rays thus are not properly oriented to pass through the horizontal polarizer, and the device appears dark. Displays of this kind are called "twisted nematic." As the name implies, materials that order as nematic liquid crystals are used for this application.

Liquid crystal displays for computer and televisions employ a light source in place of the reflector, but the principle is the same. The screen is divided into a large number of tiny cells, with the voltages at points on the screen surface controlled by transistors made from thin films of amorphous silicon. Red-green-blue color filters are employed to provide full color. The entire display is refreshed at a frequency of about 60 Hz, so the display can change rapidly with respect to the response time of the human eye. Displays of this kind are remarkable technical achievements based on a combination of basic scientific discovery and creative engineering.

*RELATED EXERCISES:* 11.68, 11.86

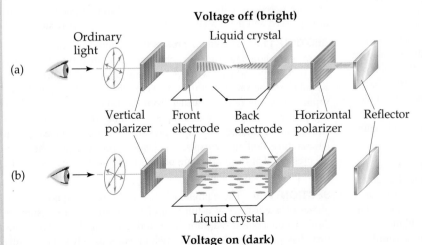

**Voltage off (bright)**

**Voltage on (dark)**

◀ **FIGURE 11.36    Schematic illustration of the operation of a twisted nematic liquid crystal display (LCD).** (a) When the voltage is off, the molecules in the liquid crystal are aligned so that they rotate the polarization of the light by 90°. This alignment allows light to pass through both the vertical and horizontal polarizers before being reflected and retracing its path to give a bright display. (b) When a voltage is applied to the electrodes, the liquid crystal molecules align parallel to the light path. In this state the light retains the vertical polarization and cannot pass through the horizontal polarizer. The area covered by the front electrode therefore appears dark.

**SAMPLE INTEGRATIVE EXERCISE** Putting Concepts Together

The substance $CS_2$ has a melting point of $-110.8$ °C and a boiling point of 46.3 °C. Its density at 20 °C is 1.26 g/cm$^3$. It is highly flammable. **(a)** What is the name of this compound? **(b)** List the intermolecular forces that $CS_2$ molecules exert on one other. **(c)** Write a balanced equation for the combustion of this compound in air. (You will have to decide on the most likely oxidation products.) **(d)** The critical temperature and pressure for $CS_2$ are 552 K and 78 atm, respectively. Compare these values with those for $CO_2$ (Table 11.5) and discuss the possible origins of the differences. **(e)** Would you expect the density of $CS_2$ at 40 °C to be greater or less than at 20 °C? What accounts for the difference?

**SOLUTION**

**(a)** The compound is named carbon disulfide, in analogy with the naming of other binary molecular compounds such as carbon dioxide. ⇔ (Section 2.8)

**(b)** Only dispersion forces affect $CS_2$; it does not have a dipole moment, based upon its molecular shape, and obviously cannot undergo hydrogen bonding.

**(c)** The most likely products of the combustion will be $CO_2$ and $SO_2$. ⇔ (Section 3.2) Under some conditions $SO_3$ might be formed, but this would be the less likely outcome. Thus, we have the following equation for combustion:

$$CS_2(l) + 3\,O_2(g) \longrightarrow CO_2(g) + 2\,SO_2(g)$$

**(d)** The critical temperature and pressure of $CS_2$ (552 K and 78 atm) are both higher than those given for $CO_2$ in Table 11.5 (304 K and 73 atm). The difference in critical temperatures is especially notable. The higher values for $CS_2$ arise from the greater dispersion attractions between the $CS_2$ molecules compared with $CO_2$. These greater attractions are due to the larger size of the sulfur compared to oxygen and, therefore, its greater polarizability.

**(e)** The density would be lower at the higher temperature. Density decreases with increasing temperature because the molecules possess higher kinetic energies. Their more energetic movements result in larger average distances between molecules, which translate into lower densities.

# CHAPTER SUMMARY AND KEY TERMS

**INTRODUCTION AND SECTION 11.1** Substances that are gases or liquids at room temperature are usually composed of molecules. In gases the intermolecular attractive forces are negligible compared to the kinetic energies of the molecules; thus, the molecules are widely separated and undergo constant, chaotic motion. In liquids the **intermolecular forces** are strong enough to keep the molecules in close proximity; nevertheless, the molecules are free to move with respect to one another. In solids the intermolecular attractive forces are strong enough to restrain molecular motion and to force the particles to occupy specific locations in a three-dimensional arrangement.

**SECTION 11.2** Three types of intermolecular forces exist between neutral molecules: **dispersion forces, dipole–dipole forces,** and **hydrogen bonding.** Dispersion forces operate between all molecules (and atoms, for atomic substances such as He, Ne, Ar, and so forth). As molecular weight increases, the **polarizability** of a molecule increases, which results in stronger dispersion forces. Molecular shape is also an important factor. Dipole–dipole forces increase in strength as the polarity of the molecule increases. Hydrogen bonding occurs in compounds containing O—H, N—H, and F—H bonds. Hydrogen bonds are generally stronger than dipole–dipole or dispersion forces. **Ion–dipole forces** are important in solutions in which ionic compounds are dissolved in polar solvents.

**SECTION 11.3** The stronger the intermolecular forces, the greater is the **viscosity,** or resistance to flow, of a liquid. The surface tension of a liquid also increases as intermolecular forces increase in strength. **Surface tension** is a measure of the tendency of a liquid to maintain a minimum surface area. The adhesion of a liquid to the walls of a narrow tube and the cohesion of the liquid account for

**capillary action** and the formation of a meniscus at the surface of a liquid.

**SECTION 11.4** A substance may exist in more than one state of matter, or phase. **Phase changes** are transformations from one phase to another. Changes of a solid to liquid (melting), solid to gas (sublimation), and liquid to gas (vaporization) are all endothermic processes. Thus, the **heat of fusion** (melting), the **heat of sublimation,** and the **heat of vaporization** are all positive quantities. The reverse processes (freezing, deposition, and condensation) are exothermic. A gas cannot be liquefied by application of pressure if the temperature is above its **critical temperature.** The pressure required to liquefy a gas at its critical temperature is called the **critical pressure.** When the temperature exceeds the critical temperature and the pressure exceeds the critical pressure, the liquid and gas phases cannot be distinguished and the substance is in a state called a **supercritical fluid.**

**SECTION 11.5** The **vapor pressure** of a liquid indicates the tendency of the liquid to evaporate. The vapor pressure is the partial pressure of the vapor when it is in **dynamic equilibrium** with the liquid. At equilibrium the rate of transfer of molecules from the liquid to the vapor equals the rate of transfer from the vapor to the liquid. The higher the vapor pressure of a liquid, the more readily it evaporates and the more **volatile** it is. Vapor pressure increases nonlinearly with temperature. Boiling occurs when the vapor pressure equals the external pressure. The **normal boiling point** is the temperature at which the vapor pressure equals 1 atm.

**SECTION 11.6** The equilibria between the solid, liquid, and gas phases of a substance as a function of temperature and pressure are displayed on a **phase diagram.** A line indicates equilibria between any two phases. The line through the melting point usually slopes slightly to the right as pressure increases, because the solid is usually more dense than the liquid. The melting point at 1 atm is the **normal melting point**. The point on the diagram at which all three phases co-exist in equilibrium is called the **triple point**.

**SECTION 11.7** A **liquid crystal** is a substance that exhibits one or more ordered phases at a temperature above the melting point of the solid. In a **nematic liquid crystal** the molecules are aligned along a common direction, but the ends of the molecules are not lined up. In a smectic liquid crystal the ends of the molecules are lined up so that the molecules form layers. In **smectic A liquid crystals** the long axes of the molecules line up perpendicular to the layers. In **smectic C liquid crystals** the long axes of molecules are inclined with respect to the layers. A **cholesteric liquid crystal** is composed of molecules that align parallel to each other within a layer, as they do in nematic liquid crystalline phases, but the direction along which the long axes of the molecules align rotates from one layer to the next to form a helical structure. Substances that form liquid crystals are generally composed of molecules with fairly rigid, elongated shapes, as well as polar groups to help align molecules through dipole-dipole interactions.

# KEY SKILLS

- Identify the intermolecular attractive interactions (dispersion, dipole–dipole, hydrogen bonding, ion–dipole) that exist between molecules or ions based on their composition and molecular structure and be able to compare the relative strengths of these intermolecular forces. (Section 11.2)
- Explain the concept of polarizability and how it relates to dispersion forces. (Section 11.2)
- Explain the concepts of viscosity and surface tension in liquids. (Section 11.3)
- Know the names of the various changes of state for a pure substance. (Section 11.4)
- Interpret heating curves and be able to calculate quantities related to temperature and enthalpies of phase changes. (Section 11.4)
- Define critical pressure, critical temperature, vapor pressure, normal boiling point, normal melting point, critical point, and triple point. (Sections 11.5 and 11.6)
- Be able to interpret and sketch phase diagrams. Explain how water's phase diagram differs from most other substances, and why. (Section 11.6)
- Understand how the molecular arrangements characteristic of nematic, smectic, and cholesteric liquid crystals differ from ordinary liquids and from each other. Be able to recognize the features of molecules that favor formation of liquid crystalline phases. (Section 11.7)

# EXERCISES

## VISUALIZING CONCEPTS

11.1 Does the diagram

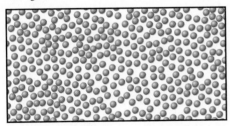

best describe a crystalline solid, a liquid, or a gas? Explain. [Section 11.1]

**11.2** **(a)** Which kind of intermolecular attractive force is shown in each case here?

**(b)** Predict which of the four interactions is the weakest. [Section 11.2]

**11.3** Do you expect the viscosity of glycerol, $C_3H_5(OH)_3$, to be larger or smaller than that of 1-propanol, $C_3H_7OH$? Explain. [Section 11.3]

(a) Glycerol       (b) 1-Propanol

**11.4** If 42.0 kJ of heat is added to a 32.0-g sample of liquid methane under 1 atm of pressure at a temperature of −170 °C, what are the final state and temperature of the methane once the system equilibrates? Assume no heat is lost to the surroundings. The normal boiling point of methane is −161.5 °C. The specific heats of liquid and gaseous methane are 3.48 and 2.22 J/g-K, respectively. [Section 11.4]

$P = 1.00$ atm

42.0 kJ

32.0 g $CH_4$
$\Delta H_{vap} = 8.20$ kJ/mol
$T = -170$ °C

**11.5** Using this graph of $CS_2$ data,

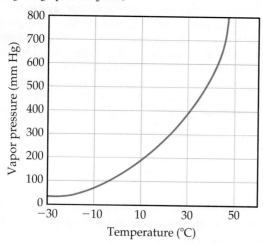

determine **(a)** the approximate vapor pressure of $CS_2$ at 30 °C, **(b)** the temperature at which the vapor pressure equals 300 torr, **(c)** the normal boiling point of $CS_2$. [Section 11.5]

**11.6** The molecules

|                        |                           |
|:----------------------:|:-------------------------:|
| **(a)** Propanol       | **(b)** Ethyl methyl ether |
| 97.2 °C                | 10.8 °C                   |

have the same molecular formula ($C_3H_8O$) but different normal boiling points, as shown. Rationalize the difference in boiling points. [Sections 11.2 and 11.5]

**11.7** The phase diagram of a hypothetical substance is

**(a)** Estimate the normal boiling point and freezing point of the substance.

**(b)** What is the physical state of the substance under the following conditions: (i) $T = 150$ K, $P = 0.2$ atm, (ii) $T = 100$ K, $P = 0.8$ atm, (iii) $T = 300$ K, $P = 1.0$ atm?

**(c)** What is the triple point of the substance? [Section 11.6]

**11.8** At three different temperatures, $T_1$, $T_2$, and $T_3$, the molecules in a liquid crystal align in these ways:

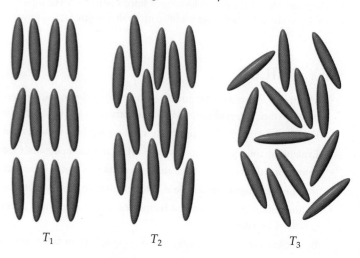

|        |        |        |
|:------:|:------:|:------:|
| $T_1$  | $T_2$  | $T_3$  |

**(a)** At which temperature or temperatures is the substance in a liquid crystalline state? At those temperatures, which type of liquid crystalline phase is depicted?

**(b)** Which is the highest of the three temperatures?

# MOLECULAR COMPARISONS OF GASES, LIQUIDS, AND SOLIDS (section 11.1)

**11.9** List the three states of matter in order of **(a)** increasing molecular disorder and **(b)** increasing intermolecular attractions. **(c)** Which state of matter is most easily compressed?

**11.10** **(a)** How does the average kinetic energy of molecules compare with the average energy of attraction between molecules in solids, liquids, and gases? **(b)** Why does increasing the temperature cause a solid substance to change in succession from a solid to a liquid to a gas? **(c)** What happens to a gas if you put it under extremely high pressure?

**11.11** Arrange substances $CCl_4$, Si, and Ar in order of increasing boiling point.

**11.12** Arrange substances Ga, Ne, and $Br_2$ in order of increasing boiling point.

**11.13** At standard temperature and pressure the molar volume of $Cl_2$ and $NH_3$ gases are 22.06 L and 22.40 L, respectively. **(a)** Given the different molecular weights, dipole moments, and molecular shapes, why are their molar volumes nearly the same? **(b)** On cooling to 160 K, both substances form crystalline solids. Do you expect the molar volumes to decrease or increase on cooling to 160 K? (c) The densities of crystalline $Cl_2$ and $NH_3$ at 160 K are 2.02 $g/cm^3$ and 0.84 $g/cm^3$, respectively. Calculate their molar volumes. (d) Are the molar volumes in the solid state as similar as they are in the gaseous state? Explain. (e) Would you expect the molar volumes in the liquid state to be closer to those in the solid or gaseous state?

**11.14** Benzoic acid, $C_6H_5COOH$, melts at 122 °C. The density in the liquid state at 130 °C is 1.08 $g/cm^3$. The density of solid benzoic acid at 15 °C is 1.266 $g/cm^3$. (a) In which of these two states is the average distance between molecules greater? (b) Explain the difference in densities at the two temperatures in terms of the relative kinetic energies of the molecules.

# INTERMOLECULAR FORCES (section 11.2)

**11.15** Which type of intermolecular attractive force operates between (a) all molecules, (b) polar molecules, (c) the hydrogen atom of a polar bond and a nearby small electronegative atom?

**11.16** Based on what you have learned about intermolecular forces, would you say that matter is fundamentally attracted or repulsed by other matter?

**11.17** Describe the intermolecular forces that must be overcome to convert these substances from a liquid to a gas: (a) $SO_2$, (b) $CH_3COOH$, (c) $H_2S$.

**11.18** Which type of intermolecular force accounts for each of these differences: (a) $CH_3OH$ boils at 65 °C; $CH_3SH$ boils at 6 °C. (b) Xe is liquid at atmospheric pressure and 120 K, whereas Ar is a gas under the same conditions. (c) Kr, atomic weight 84, boils at 120.9 K, whereas $Cl_2$, molecular weight about 71, boils at 238 K. (d) Acetone boils at 56 °C, whereas 2-methylpropane boils at −12 °C.

$$CH_3-\overset{\overset{\displaystyle O}{\|}}{C}-CH_3 \qquad CH_3-\overset{\overset{\displaystyle CH_3}{|}}{CH}-CH_3$$

Acetone          2-Methylpropane

**11.19** (a) What is meant by the term *polarizability*? (b) Which of the following atoms would you expect to be most polarizable: N, P, As, Sb? Explain. (c) Put the following molecules in order of increasing polarizability: $GeCl_4$, $CH_4$, $SiCl_4$, $SiH_4$, and $GeBr_4$. (d) Predict the order of boiling points of the substances in part (c).

**11.20** True or false:

(a) For molecules with similar molecular weights, the dispersion forces become stronger as the molecules become more polarizable.

(b) For the noble gases the dispersion forces decrease while the boiling points increase as you go down the column in the periodic table.

(c) In terms of the total attractive forces for a given substance dipole–dipole interactions, when present, are always larger than dispersion forces.

(d) All other factors being the same, dispersion forces between linear molecules are greater than dispersion forces between molecules whose shapes are nearly spherical.

**11.21** Which member in each pair has the larger dispersion forces: (a) $H_2O$ or $H_2S$, (b) $CO_2$ or CO, (c) $SiH_4$ or $GeH_4$?

**11.22** Which member in each pair has the stronger intermolecular dispersion forces: (a) $Br_2$ or $O_2$, (b) $CH_3CH_2CH_2CH_2SH$ or $CH_3CH_2CH_2CH_2CH_2SH$, (c) $CH_3CH_2CH_2Cl$ or $(CH_3)_2CHCl$?

**11.23** Butane and 2-methylpropane, whose space-filling models are shown at the top of the next column, are both nonpolar and have the same molecular formula, $C_4H_{10}$, yet butane has the higher boiling point (−0.5 °C compared to −11.7 °C). Explain.

(a) Butane          (b) 2-Methylpropane

**11.24** Propyl alcohol ($CH_3CH_2CH_2OH$) and isopropyl alcohol [$(CH_3)_2CHOH$], whose space-filling models are shown, have boiling points of 97.2 °C and 82.5 °C, respectively. Explain why the boiling point of propyl alcohol is higher, even though both have the molecular formula $C_3H_8O$.

(a) Propyl alcohol          (b) Isopropyl alcohol

**11.25** (a) What atoms must a molecule contain to participate in hydrogen bonding with other molecules of the same kind? (b) Which of the following molecules can form hydrogen bonds with other molecules of the same kind: $CH_3F$, $CH_3NH_2$, $CH_3OH$, $CH_3Br$?

**11.26** Rationalize the difference in boiling points in each pair: (a) HF (20 °C) and HCl (−85 °C), (b) $CHCl_3$ (61 °C) and $CHBr_3$ (150 °C), (c) $Br_2$ (59 °C) and ICl (97 °C).

**11.27** Ethylene glycol ($HOCH_2CH_2OH$), the major substance in antifreeze, has a normal boiling point of 198 °C. By comparison, ethyl alcohol ($CH_3CH_2OH$) boils at 78 °C at atmospheric pressure. Ethylene glycol dimethyl ether ($CH_3OCH_2CH_2OCH_3$) has a normal boiling point of 83 °C, and ethyl methyl ether ($CH_3CH_2OCH_3$) has a normal boiling point of 11 °C. (a) Explain why replacement of a hydrogen on the oxygen by a $CH_3$ group generally results in a lower boiling point. (b) What are the major factors responsible for the difference in boiling points of the two ethers?

**11.28** Identify the type or types of intermolecular forces present in each substance and then select the substance in each pair that has the higher boiling point: (a) propane $C_3H_8$ or *n*-butane $C_4H_{10}$, (b) diethyl ether $CH_3CH_2OCH_2CH_3$ or 1-butanol $CH_3CH_2CH_2CH_2OH$, (c) sulfur dioxide $SO_2$ or sulfur trioxide $SO_3$, (d) phosgene $Cl_2CO$ or formaldehyde $H_2CO$.

**11.29** Look up and compare the normal boiling points and normal melting points of $H_2O$ and $H_2S$. (a) Based on these physical properties, which substance has stronger intermolecular forces? What kind of intermolecular forces exist for each molecule? **(b)** Predict whether solid $H_2S$ is more or less dense than liquid $H_2S$. How does this compare to $H_2O$? Explain. **(c)** Water has an unusually high specific heat. Is this related to its intermolecular forces? Explain.

**11.30** The following quote about ammonia ($NH_3$) is from a textbook of inorganic chemistry: "It is estimated that 26% of the hydrogen bonding in $NH_3$ breaks down on melting, 7% on warming from the melting to the boiling point, and the final 67% on transfer to the gas phase at the boiling point." From the standpoint of the kinetic energy of the molecules, explain **(a)** why there is a decrease of hydrogen-bonding energy on melting and **(b)** why most of the loss in hydrogen bonding occurs in the transition from the liquid to the vapor state.

**11.31** A number of salts containing the tetrahedral polyatomic anion, $BF_4^-$, are ionic liquids, whereas salts containing the somewhat larger tetrahedral ion $SO_4^{2-}$ do not form ionic liquids. Explain this observation.

**11.32** The generic structural formula for a 1-alkyl-3-methylimidazolium cation is

where R is a —$CH_2(CH_2)_nCH_3$ alkyl group. The melting points of the salts that form between the 1-alkyl-3-methylimidazolium cation and the $PF_6^-$ anion are as follows: R = $CH_2CH_3$ (m.p. = 60 °C), R = $CH_2CH_2CH_3$ (m.p. = 40 °C), R = $CH_2CH_2CH_2CH_3$ (m.p. = 10 °C) and R = $CH_2CH_2CH_2CH_2CH_3$ (m.p. = −61 °C ). Why does the melting point decrease as the length of alkyl group increases?

## SELECT PROPERTIES OF LIQUIDS (section 11.3)

**11.33** **(a)** Explain why surface tension and viscosity decrease with increasing temperature. **(b)** Why do substances with high surface tensions also tend to have high viscosities?

**11.34** **(a)** Distinguish between adhesive forces and cohesive forces. **(b)** What adhesive and cohesive forces are involved when a paper towel absorbs water? **(c)** Explain the cause for the U-shaped meniscus formed when water is in a glass tube.

**11.35** Explain the following observations: **(a)** The surface tension of $CHBr_3$ is greater than that of $CHCl_3$. **(b)** As temperature increases, oil flows faster through a narrow tube. **(c)** Raindrops that collect on a waxed automobile hood take on a nearly spherical shape. **(d)** Oil droplets that collect on a waxed automobile hood take on a flat shape.

**11.36** Hydrazine ($H_2NNH_2$), hydrogen peroxide (HOOH), and water ($H_2O$) all have exceptionally high surface tensions compared with other substances of comparable molecular weights. **(a)** Draw the Lewis structures for these three compounds. **(b)** What structural property do these substances have in common, and how might that account for the high surface tensions?

**11.37** The boiling points, surface tensions, and viscosities of water and several alchohols are as follows:

| | Boiling Point (°C) | Surface Tension (J/m²) | Viscosity (kg/m-s) |
|---|---|---|---|
| Water, $H_2O$ | 100 | $7.3 \times 10^{-2}$ | $0.9 \times 10^{-3}$ |
| Ethanol, $CH_3CH_2OH$ | 78 | $2.3 \times 10^{-2}$ | $1.1 \times 10^{-3}$ |
| Propanol, $CH_3CH_2CH_2OH$ | 97 | $2.4 \times 10^{-2}$ | $2.2 \times 10^{-3}$ |
| n-Butanol, $CH_3CH_2CH_2CH_2OH$ | 117 | $2.6 \times 10^{-2}$ | $2.6 \times 10^{-3}$ |
| Ethylene glycol, $HOCH_2CH_2OH$ | 197 | $4.8 \times 10^{-2}$ | $26 \times 10^{-3}$ |

**(a)** For ethanol, propanol, and n-butanol the boiling points, surface tensions, and viscosities all increase. What is the reason for this increase? **(b)** How do you explain the fact that propanol and ethylene glycol have similar molecular weights (60 versus 62 amu), yet the viscosity of ethylene glycol is more than 10 times larger than propanol? **(c)** How do you explain the fact that water has the highest surface tension but the lowest viscosity?

**11.38** **(a)** Would you expect the viscosity of n-pentane, $CH_3CH_2CH_2CH_2CH_3$, to be larger or smaller than the viscosity of n-hexane ($3.26 \times 10^{-4}$ kg/m-s from Table 11.4)? **(b)** If you compared their viscosities at 270 K, would you expect the viscosity of neopentane, $(CH_3)_4C$, to be smaller or larger than n-pentane? (See Figure 11.6 to see the shapes of these molecules.)

## PHASE CHANGES (section 11.4)

**11.39** Name the phase transition in each of the following situations and indicate whether it is exothermic or endothermic: **(a)** When ice is heated, it turns to water. **(b)** Wet clothes dry on a warm summer day. **(c)** Frost appears on a window on a cold winter day. **(d)** Droplets of water appear on a cold glass of beer.

**11.40** Name the phase transition in each of the following situations and indicate whether it is exothermic or endothermic: **(a)** Bromine vapor turns to bromine liquid as it is cooled. **(b)** Crystals of iodine disappear from an evaporating dish as they stand in a fume hood. **(c)** Rubbing alcohol in an open container slowly disappears. **(d)** Molten lava from a volcano turns into solid rock.

**11.41** Explain why any substance's heat of fusion is generally lower than its heat of vaporization.

**11.42** Ethyl chloride ($C_2H_5Cl$) boils at 12 °C. When liquid $C_2H_5Cl$ under pressure is sprayed on a room-temperature (25 °C) surface in air, the surface is cooled considerably. (a) What does this observation tell us about the specific heat of $C_2H_5Cl(g)$ as compared with $C_2H_5Cl(l)$? (b) Assume that the heat lost by the surface is gained by ethyl chloride. What enthalpies must you consider if you were to calculate the final temperature of the surface?

**11.43** For many years drinking water has been cooled in hot climates by evaporating it from the surfaces of canvas bags or porous clay pots. How many grams of water can be cooled from 35 °C to 20 °C by the evaporation of 60 g of water? (The heat of vaporization of water in this temperature range is 2.4 kJ/g. The specific heat of water is 4.18 J/g-K.)

**11.44** Compounds like $CCl_2F_2$ are known as chlorofluorocarbons, or CFCs. These compounds were once widely used as refrigerants but are now being replaced by compounds that are believed to be less harmful to the environment. The heat of vaporization of $CCl_2F_2$ is 289 J/g. What mass of this substance must evaporate to freeze 200 g of water initially at 15 °C? (The heat of fusion of water is 334 J/g; the specific heat of water is 4.18 J/g-K.)

**11.45** Ethanol ($C_2H_5OH$) melts at −114 °C and boils at 78 °C. The enthalpy of fusion of ethanol is 5.02 kJ/mol, and its enthalpy of vaporization is 38.56 kJ/mol. The specific heats of solid and liquid ethanol are 0.97 J/g-K and 2.3 J/g-K, respectively. (a) How much heat is required to convert 42.0 g of ethanol at 35 °C to the vapor phase at 78 °C? (b) How much heat is required to convert the same amount of ethanol at −155 °C to the vapor phase at 78 °C?

**11.46** The fluorocarbon compound $C_2Cl_3F_3$ has a normal boiling point of 47.6 °C. The specific heats of $C_2Cl_3F_3(l)$ and $C_2Cl_3F_3(g)$ are 0.91 J/g-K and 0.67 J/g-K, respectively. The heat of vaporization for the compound is 27.49 kJ/mol. Calculate the heat required to convert 35.0 g of $C_2Cl_3F_3$ from a liquid at 10.00 °C to a gas at 105.00 °C.

**11.47** (a) What is the significance of the critical pressure of a substance? (b) What happens to the critical temperature of a series of compounds as the force of attraction between molecules increases? (c) Which of the substances listed in Table 11.5 can be liquefied at the temperature of liquid nitrogen (−196 °C)?

**11.48** The critical temperatures (K) and pressures (atm) of a series of halogenated methanes are as follows:

| Compound | $CCl_3F$ | $CCl_2F_2$ | $CClF_3$ | $CF_4$ |
|---|---|---|---|---|
| Critical temperature | 471 | 385 | 302 | 227 |
| Critical pressure | 43.5 | 40.6 | 38.2 | 37.0 |

(a) List the intermolecular forces that occur for each compound. (b) Predict the order of increasing intermolecular attraction, from least to most, for this series of compounds. (c) Predict the critical temperature and pressure for $CCl_4$ based on the trends in this table. Look up the experimentally determined critical temperatures and pressures for $CCl_4$, using a source such as the *CRC Handbook of Chemistry and Physics*, and suggest a reason for any discrepancies.

# VAPOR PRESSURE (section 11.5)

**11.49** Explain how each of the following affects the vapor pressure of a liquid: (a) volume of the liquid, (b) surface area, (c) intermolecular attractive forces, (d) temperature, (e) density of the liquid.

**11.50** Acetone, $H_3CCOCH_3$, has a boiling point of 56 °C. Based on the data given in Figure 11.25, would you expect acetone to have a higher or lower vapor pressure than ethanol at 25 °C?

**11.51** (a) Place the following substances in order of increasing volatility: $CH_4$, $CBr_4$, $CH_2Cl_2$, $CH_3Cl$, $CHBr_3$, and $CH_2Br_2$. Explain. (b) How do the boiling points vary through this series?

**11.52** True or false:
(a) $CBr_4$ is more volatile than $CCl_4$.
(b) $CBr_4$ has a higher boiling point than $CCl_4$.
(c) $CBr_4$ has weaker intermolecular forces than $CCl_4$.
(d) $CBr_4$ has a higher vapor pressure at the same temperature than $CCl_4$.

**11.53** (a) Two pans of water are on different burners of a stove. One pan of water is boiling vigorously, while the other is boiling gently. What can be said about the temperature of the water in the two pans? (b) A large container of water and a small one are at the same temperature. What can be said about the relative vapor pressures of the water in the two containers?

**11.54** Explain the following observations: (a) Water evaporates more quickly on a hot, dry day than on a hot, humid day. (b) It takes longer to cook an egg in boiling water at high altitudes than it does at lower altitudes.

**11.55** Using the vapor-pressure curves in Figure 11.25, (a) estimate the boiling point of ethanol at an external pressure of 200 torr; (b) estimate the external pressure at which ethanol will boil at 60 °C; (c) estimate the boiling point of diethyl ether at 400 torr; (d) estimate the external pressure at which diethyl ether will boil at 40 °C.

**11.56** Appendix B lists the vapor pressure of water at various external pressures.
(a) Plot the data in Appendix B, vapor pressure (torr) versus temperature (°C). From your plot, estimate the vapor pressure of water at body temperature, 37 °C.
(b) Explain the significance of the data point at 760.0 torr, 100 °C.
(c) A city at an altitude of 5000 ft above sea level has a barometric pressure of 633 torr. To what temperature would you have to heat water to boil it in this city?
(d) A city at an altitude of 500 ft below sea level would have a barometric pressure of 774 torr. To what temperature would you have to heat water to boil it in this city?
(e) For the two cities in parts (c) and (d), compare the average kinetic energies of the water molecules at their boiling points. Are the kinetic energies the same or different? Explain.

# PHASE DIAGRAMS (section 11.6)

**11.57** (a) What is the significance of the critical point in a phase diagram? (b) Why does the line that separates the gas and liquid phases end at the critical point?

**11.58** (a) What is the significance of the triple point in a phase diagram? (b) Could you measure the triple point of water by measuring the temperature in a vessel in which water vapor, liquid water, and ice are in equilibrium under one atmosphere of air? Explain.

**11.59** Referring to Figure 11.28, describe all the phase changes that would occur in each of the following cases: (a) Water vapor originally at 0.005 atm and −0.5 °C is slowly compressed at constant temperature until the final pressure is 20 atm. (b) Water originally at 100.0 °C and 0.50 atm is cooled at constant pressure until the temperature is −10 °C.

**11.60** Referring to Figure 11.29, describe the phase changes (and the temperatures at which they occur) when $CO_2$ is heated from −80 °C to −20 °C at (a) a constant pressure of 3 atm, (b) a constant pressure of 6 atm.

**11.61** The phase diagram for neon is

Use the phase diagram to answer the following questions. (a) What is the approximate value of the normal melting point?

(b) Over what pressure range will solid neon sublime? (c) At room temperature ($T = 25$ °C) can neon be liquefied by compressing it?

**11.62** Use the phase diagram of neon to answer the following questions. (a) What is the approximate value of the normal boiling point? (b) What can you say about the strength of the intermolecular forces in neon and argon based on the critical points of Ne and Ar? (See Table 11.5.)

**11.63** The fact that water on Earth can readily be found in all three states (solid, liquid, and gas) is in part a consequence of the fact that the triple point of water ($T = 0.01$ °C, $P = 0.006$ atm) falls within a range of temperatures and pressures found on Earth. Saturn's largest moon Titan has a considerable amount of methane in its atmosphere. The conditions on the surface of Titan are estimated to be $P = 1.6$ atm and $T = -178$ °C. As seen from the phase diagram of methane (Figure 11.30), these conditions are not far from the triple point of methane, raising the tantalizing possibility that solid, liquid, and gaseous methane can be found on Titan. (a) What state would you expect to find methane in on the surface of Titan? (b) On moving upward through the atmosphere the pressure will decrease. If we assume that the temperature does not change, what phase change would you expect to see as we move away from the surface?

**11.64** At 25 °C gallium is a solid with a density of 5.91 g/cm³. Its melting point, 29.8 °C, is low enough that you can melt it by holding it in your hand. The density of liquid gallium just above the melting point is 6.1 g/cm³. Based on this information, what unusual feature would you expect to find in the phase diagram of gallium?

# LIQUID CRYSTALS (section 11.7)

**11.65** In terms of the arrangement and freedom of motion of the molecules, how are the nematic liquid crystalline phase and an ordinary liquid phase similar? How are they different?

**11.66** What observations made by Reinitzer on cholesteryl benzoate suggested that this substance possesses a liquid crystalline phase?

**11.67** The molecules shown in Figure 11.33 possess polar groups (that is, groupings of atoms that give rise to sizable dipole moments within the molecules). How might the presence of polar groups enhance the tendency toward liquid crystal formation?

**11.68** One of the more effective liquid crystalline substances employed in LCDs is the molecule

$$CH_3(CH_2)_2CH=CH-CH\begin{matrix}CH_2-CH_2\\ \\CH_2-CH_2\end{matrix}CH-CH\begin{matrix}CH_2-CH_2\\ \\CH_2-CH_2\end{matrix}CH-C\equiv N$$

(a) How many double bonds are there in this molecule? (b) Describe the features of the molecule that make it prone to show liquid crystalline behavior.

**11.69** For a given substance, the liquid crystalline phase tends to be more viscous than the liquid phase. Why?

**11.70** Describe how a cholesteric liquid crystal phase differs from a nematic phase.

**11.71** It often happens that a substance possessing a smectic liquid crystalline phase just above the melting point passes into a nematic liquid crystalline phase at a higher temperature. Account for this type of behavior.

**11.72** The smectic liquid crystalline phase can be said to be more highly ordered than the nematic phase. In what sense is this true?

# ADDITIONAL EXERCISES

**11.73** As the intermolecular attractive forces between molecules increase in magnitude, do you expect each of the following to increase or decrease in magnitude? (a) vapor pressure, (b) heat of vaporization, (c) boiling point, (d) freezing point, (e) viscosity, (f) surface tension, (g) critical temperature.

**11.74** Suppose you have two colorless molecular liquids, one boiling at $-84\,°C$, the other at $34\,°C$, and both at atmospheric pressure. Which of the following statements is correct? For each statement that is not correct, modify the statement so that it is correct. (a) The higher-boiling liquid has greater total intermolecular forces than the lower-boiling liquid. (b) The lower-boiling liquid must consist of nonpolar molecules. (c) The lower-boiling liquid has a lower molecular weight than the higher-boiling liquid. (d) The two liquids have identical vapor pressures at their normal boiling points. (e) At $-84\,°C$ both liquids have vapor pressures of 760 mm Hg.

**11.75** Two isomers of the planar compound 1,2-dichloroethylene are shown here.

cis isomer          trans isomer

(a) Which of the two isomers will have the stronger dipole–dipole forces? (b) One isomer has a boiling point of $60.3\,°C$ and the other $47.5\,°C$. Which isomer has which boiling point?

**11.76** In dichloromethane, $CH_2Cl_2$ ($\mu = 1.60$ D), the dispersion force contribution to the intermolecular attractive forces is about five times larger than the dipole–dipole contribution. Compared to $CH_2Cl_2$, would you expect the relative importance of the dipole–dipole contribution to increase or decrease (a) in dibromomethane ($\mu = 1.43$ D), (b) in difluoromethane ($\mu = 1.93$ D)? Explain.

**11.77** When an atom or group of atoms is substituted for an H atom in benzene ($C_6H_6$), the boiling point changes. Explain the order of the following boiling points: $C_6H_6$ ($80\,°C$), $C_6H_5Cl$ ($132\,°C$), $C_6H_5Br$ ($156\,°C$), $C_6H_5OH$ ($182\,°C$).

**11.78** The DNA double helix (Figure 24.30) at the atomic level looks like a twisted ladder, where the "rungs" of the ladder consist of molecules that are hydrogen-bonded together. Sugar and phosphate groups make up the sides of the ladder. Shown are the structures of the adenine-thymine (AT) "base pair" and the guanine-cytosine (GC) base pair:

Thymine          Adenine

Cytosine          Guanine

You can see that AT base pairs are held together by two hydrogen bonds, and the GC base pairs are held together by three hydrogen bonds. Which base pair is more stable to heating? Why?

**11.79** Ethylene glycol ($HOCH_2CH_2OH$) is the major component of antifreeze. It is a slightly viscous liquid, not very volatile at room temperature, with a boiling point of $198\,°C$. Pentane ($C_5H_{12}$), which has about the same molecular weight, is a nonviscous liquid that is highly volatile at room temperature and whose boiling point is $36.1\,°C$. Explain the differences in the physical properties of the two substances.

**11.80** Use the normal boiling points

propane, $C_3H_8$, $-42.1\,°C$
butane, $C_4H_{10}$, $-0.5\,°C$
pentane, $C_5H_{12}$, $36.1\,°C$
hexane, $C_6H_{14}$, $68.7\,°C$
heptane, $C_7H_{16}$, $98.4\,°C$

to estimate the normal boiling point of octane, $C_8H_{18}$. Explain the trend in the boiling points.

**11.81** One of the attractive features of ionic liquids is their low vapor pressure, which in turn tends to make them nonflammable. Why do you think ionic liquids have lower vapor pressures than most room-temperature molecular liquids?

**11.82** (a) When you exercise vigorously, you sweat. How does this help your body cool? (b) A flask of water is connected to a vacuum pump. A few moments after the pump is turned on, the water begins to boil. After a few minutes, the water begins to freeze. Explain why these processes occur.

**[11.83]** The following table gives the vapor pressure of hexafluorobenzene ($C_6F_6$) as a function of temperature:

| Temperature (K) | Vapor Pressure (torr) |
| --- | --- |
| 280.0 | 32.42 |
| 300.0 | 92.47 |
| 320.0 | 225.1 |
| 330.0 | 334.4 |
| 340.0 | 482.9 |

(a) By plotting these data in a suitable fashion, determine whether the Clausius–Clapeyron equation (Equation 11.1) is obeyed. If it is obeyed, use your plot to determine $\Delta H_{vap}$ for $C_6F_6$. (b) Use these data to determine the boiling point of the compound.

**[11.84]** Suppose the vapor pressure of a substance is measured at two different temperatures. (a) By using the Clausius–Clapeyron equation (Equation 11.1) derive the following relationship between the vapor pressures, $P_1$ and $P_2$, and the absolute temperatures at which they were measured, $T_1$ and $T_2$:

$$\ln \frac{P_1}{P_2} = -\frac{\Delta H_{vap}}{R}\left(\frac{1}{T_1} - \frac{1}{T_2}\right)$$

(b) Gasoline is a mixture of hydrocarbons, a major component of which is octane, $CH_3CH_2CH_2CH_2CH_2CH_2CH_2CH_3$. Octane has a vapor pressure of 13.95 torr at $25\,°C$ and a vapor pressure of 144.78 torr at $75\,°C$. Use these data and the equation in part (a) to calculate the heat of vaporization of octane. (c) By using the equation in part (a) and the data given in part (b), calculate the normal boiling point of octane. Compare your answer to the one you obtained from Exercise 11.80. (d) Calculate the vapor pressure of octane at $-30\,°C$.

[11.85] The following data present the temperatures at which certain vapor pressures are achieved for dichloromethane ($CH_2Cl_2$) and methyl iodide ($CH_3I$):

| Vapor Pressure (torr): | 10.0 | 40.0 | 100.0 | 400.0 |
|---|---|---|---|---|
| T for $CH_2Cl_2$ (°C): | −43.3 | −22.3 | −6.3 | 24.1 |
| T for $CH_3I$ (°C): | −45.8 | −24.2 | −7.0 | 25.3 |

(a) Which of the two substances is expected to have the greater dipole–dipole forces? Which is expected to have the greater dispersion forces? Based on your answers, explain why it is difficult to predict which compound would be more volatile. (b) Which compound would you expect to have the higher boiling point? Check your answer in a reference book such as the *CRC Handbook of Chemistry and Physics*. (c) The order of volatility of these two substances changes as the temperature is increased. What quantity must be different for the two substances in order for this phenomenon to occur? (d) Substantiate your answer for part (c) by drawing an appropriate graph.

11.86 A watch with a liquid crystal display (LCD) does not function properly when it is exposed to low temperatures during a trip to Antarctica. Explain why the LCD might not function well at low temperature.

[11.87] A particular liquid crystalline substance has the phase diagram shown in the figure. By analogy with the phase diagram for a non–liquid crystalline substance, identify the phase present in each area.

## INTEGRATIVE EXERCISES

11.88 (a) At the molecular level, what factor is responsible for the steady increase in viscosity with increasing molecular weight in the hydrocarbon series shown in Table 11.4? (b) Although the viscosity varies over a factor of more than two in the series from hexane to nonane, the surface tension at 25 °C increases by only about 20% in the same series. How do you account for this? (c) *n*-Octyl alcohol, $CH_3(CH_2)_7OH$, has a viscosity of $1.01 \times 10^{-2}$ kg/m-s, much higher than nonane, which has about the same molecular weight. What accounts for this difference? How does your answer relate to the difference in normal boiling points for these two substances?

11.89 Acetone, $(CH_3)_2CO$, is widely used as an industrial solvent. (a) Draw the Lewis structure for the acetone molecule and predict the geometry around each carbon atom. (b) Is the acetone molecule polar or nonpolar? (c) What kinds of intermolecular attractive forces exist between acetone molecules? (d) 1-Propanol, $CH_3CH_2CH_2OH$, has a molecular weight that is very similar to that of acetone, yet acetone boils at 56.5 °C and 1-propanol boils at 97.2 °C. Explain the difference.

11.90 The table shown here lists the molar heats of vaporization for several organic compounds. Use specific examples from this list to illustrate how the heat of vaporization varies with (a) molar mass, (b) molecular shape, (c) molecular polarity, (d) hydrogen-bonding interactions. Explain these comparisons in terms of the nature of the intermolecular forces at work. (You may find it helpful to draw out the structural formula for each compound.)

| Compound | Heat of Vaporization (kJ/mol) |
|---|---|
| $CH_3CH_2CH_3$ | 19.0 |
| $CH_3CH_2CH_2CH_2CH_3$ | 27.6 |
| $CH_3CHBrCH_3$ | 31.8 |
| $CH_3COCH_3$ | 32.0 |
| $CH_3CH_2CH_2Br$ | 33.6 |
| $CH_3CH_2CH_2OH$ | 47.3 |

**11.91** Liquid butane, $C_4H_{10}$, is stored in cylinders to be used as a fuel. The normal boiling point of butane is listed as $-0.5\,°C$. **(a)** Suppose the tank is standing in the sun and reaches a temperature of 35 °C. Would you expect the pressure in the tank to be greater or less than atmospheric pressure? How does the pressure within the tank depend on how much liquid butane is in it? **(b)** Suppose the valve to the tank is opened and a few liters of butane are allowed to escape rapidly. What do you expect would happen to the temperature of the remaining liquid butane in the tank? Explain. **(c)** How much heat must be added to vaporize 250 g of butane if its heat of vaporization is 21.3 kJ/mol ? What volume does this much butane occupy at 755 torr and 35 °C?

**[11.92]** Using information in Appendices B and C, calculate the minimum number of grams of propane, $C_3H_8(g)$, that must be combusted to provide the energy necessary to convert 5.50 kg of ice at $-20\,°C$ to liquid water at 75 °C.

**11.93** The vapor pressure of a volatile liquid can be determined by slowly bubbling a known volume of gas through it at a known temperature and pressure. In an experiment, 5.00 L of $N_2$ gas is passed through 7.2146 g of liquid benzene, $C_6H_6$, at 26.0 °C. The liquid remaining after the experiment weighs 5.1493 g. Assuming that the gas becomes saturated with benzene vapor and that the total gas volume and temperature remain constant, what is the vapor pressure of the benzene in torr?

**11.94** The relative humidity of air equals the ratio of the partial pressure of water in the air to the equilibrium vapor pressure of water at the same temperature times 100%. If the relative humidity of the air is 58% and its temperature is 68 °F, how many molecules of water are present in a room measuring 12 ft $\times$ 10 ft $\times$ 8 ft?

## 12.1 CLASSIFICATIONS OF SOLIDS

We see that solids can be classified according to the types of bonding interactions that hold the atoms together. This classification helps us make general predictions about the properties of solids.

## 12.2 STRUCTURES OF SOLIDS

We learn that in *crystalline solids* the atoms are arranged in an orderly, repeating pattern but in *amorphous solids* this order is missing. We learn about *lattices* and *unit cells*, which define the repeating patterns that characterize crystalline solids.

## 12.3 METALLIC SOLIDS

We examine the properties and structures of metals. We learn that many metals have structures in which the atoms pack together as closely as possible. We examine various types of *alloys*, materials that contain more than one element and display the characteristic properties of a metal.

## 12.4 METALLIC BONDING

We take a closer look at metallic bonding and how it is responsible for the properties of metals, in terms of two models— the *electron-sea model* and the molecular-orbital model. We learn how overlap of atomic orbitals gives rise to *bands* in metals.

**THE HARD DRIVE OF A COMPUTER** is made from an extremely smooth glass disc coated with a thin layer of a magnetic alloy of cobalt. To store and retrieve information, the read/write head must glide over the disc at a height of ~1 μm (less than 1/200 the width of a human hair) while the disk moves at speeds in excess of 7000 rpm. Devices such as this would not be possible without advanced

## 12.5 IONIC SOLIDS

We examine the structures and properties of solids held together by the mutual attractions between cations and anions. We learn how the structures of *ionic solids* depend on the relative sizes of the ions and their stoichiometry.

## 12.6 MOLECULAR SOLIDS

We take a brief look at the solids that form when molecules are held together by weak intermolecular forces.

## 12.7 COVALENT-NETWORK SOLIDS

We learn about solids in which the atoms are held together by extended networks of covalent bonds. We learn how the electronic structure and properties of semiconductors differ from those of metals.

## 12.8 POLYMERIC SOLIDS

We investigate *polymers*—long chainlike molecules in which the motif of a small molecule is repeated many times over. We see how both molecular shape and interactions between polymer chains affect the physical properties of polymers.

## 12.9 NANOMATERIALS

We learn how the physical and chemical properties of materials change when their crystals become very small. These effects begin to occur when materials have sizes on the order of 1–100 nm. We explore lower-dimensional forms of carbon—fullerenes, carbon nanotubes, and graphene.

# SOLIDS AND MODERN MATERIALS

**MODERN DEVICES LIKE COMPUTERS** and cell phones are built from solids with very specific physical properties. For example, the integrated circuit that is at the heart of many electronic devices is built from semiconductors like silicon, metals like copper, and insulators like hafnium oxide. Hard drives, which store information in computers and other devices, consist of a thin layer of a magnetic alloy deposited on glass substrate.

Scientists and engineers turn almost exclusively to solids for materials used in many other technologies: alloys for magnets and airplane turbines, semiconductors for solar cells and light-emitting diodes, polymers for packaging and biomedical applications. Chemists have contributed to the discovery and development of new materials either by inventing new substances or by developing the means for processing natural materials to form substances that have specific electrical, magnetic, optical, or mechanical properties. In this chapter, we explore the structures and properties of solids. As we do so, we will examine some of the solid materials used in modern technology.

# 12.1 | CLASSIFICATIONS OF SOLIDS

Solids can be as hard as diamond or as soft as wax. Some readily conduct electricity, whereas others do not. The shapes of some solids can easily be manipulated, while others are brittle and resistant to any change in shape. The physical properties as well as the structures of solids are dictated by the types of bonds that hold the atoms in place. We can classify solids according to those forces (▼ FIGURE 12.1).

**Metallic solids** are held together by a delocalized "sea" of collectively shared valence electrons. This form of bonding allows metals to conduct electricity. It is also responsible for the fact that most metals are relatively strong without being brittle. **Ionic solids** are held together by the mutual attraction between cations and anions. Differences between ionic and metallic bonding make the electrical and mechanical properties of ionic solids very different from those of metals. **Covalent-network solids** are held together by an extended network of covalent bonds. This type of bonding can result in materials that are extremely hard, like diamond, and it is also responsible for the unique properties of semiconductors. **Molecular solids** are held together by the intermolecular forces we studied in Chapter 11: dispersion forces, dipole–dipole interactions, and hydrogen bonds. Because these forces are relatively weak, molecular solids tend to be soft and have low melting points.

We will also consider two classes of solids that do not fall neatly into the preceding categories: polymers and nanomaterials. **Polymers** contain long chains of atoms, where the atoms within a given chain are connected by covalent bonds and adjacent chains held to one another largely by weaker intermolecular forces. Polymers are normally stronger and have higher melting points than molecular solids, and they are more flexible than metallic, ionic, or covalent-network solids. **Nanomaterials** are solids in which the dimensions of individual crystals have been reduced to the order of 1–100 nm. As we will see, the properties of conventional materials change when their crystals become this small.

**Metallic solids**

Extended networks of atoms held together by metallic bonding (Cu, Fe)

**Ionic solids**

Extended networks of ions held together by ion–ion interactions (NaCl, MgO)

**Covalent-network solids**

Extended networks of atoms held together by covalent bonds (C, Si)

**Molecular solids**

Discrete molecules held together by intermolecular forces (HBr, $H_2O$)

▲ **FIGURE 12.1** **Classifications of solids according to predominant bonding type.**

# 12.2 | STRUCTURES OF SOLIDS

## Crystalline and Amorphous Solids

Solids contain large numbers of atoms. For example, a 1-mm$^3$ cube of NaCl contains over $2 \times 10^{19}$ atoms. How can we hope to describe such a large collection of atoms? Fortunately, the structures of many solids have patterns that repeat over and over in three dimensions. We can visualize the solid as being formed by stacking a large number of small, identical structural units, much like a wall can be built by stacking identical bricks.

Solids in which atoms are arranged in an orderly repeating pattern are called **crystalline solids**. These solids usually have flat surfaces, or *faces*, that make definite angles with one another. The orderly arrangements of atoms that produce these faces also cause the solids to have highly regular shapes (▶ FIGURE 12.2). Examples of crystalline solids include sodium chloride, quartz, and diamond.

**Amorphous solids** (from the Greek words for "without form") lack the order found in crystalline solids. At the atomic level the structures of amorphous solids are similar to the structures of liquids, but the molecules, atoms, and/or ions lack the freedom of motion they have in liquids. Amorphous solids do not have the well-defined faces and shapes of a crystal. Familiar amorphous solids are rubber, glass, and obsidian (volcanic glass).

## Unit Cells and Crystal Lattices

In a crystalline solid there is a relatively small repeating unit, called a **unit cell**, that is made up of a unique arrangement of atoms and embodies the structure of the solid. The structure of the crystal can be built by stacking this unit over and over in all three dimensions. Thus, the structure of a crystalline solid is defined by (a) the size and shape of the unit cell and (b) the locations of atoms within the unit cell.

The geometrical pattern of points on which the unit cells are arranged is called a **crystal lattice**. The crystal lattice is, in effect, an abstract (that is, not real) scaffolding for the crystal structure. We can imagine forming the entire crystal structure by first building the scaffolding and then filling in each unit cell with the same atom or group of atoms.

Before describing the structures of solids, we need to understand the properties of crystal lattices. It's useful to begin with two-dimensional lattices because they are simpler to visualize than three-dimensional ones. ▶ FIGURE 12.3 shows a two-dimensional array of **lattice points**. Each lattice point has an identical environment. The positions of the lattice points are defined by the **lattice vectors** $a$ and $b$. Beginning from any lattice point it is possible to move to any other lattice point by adding together whole-number multiples of the two lattice vectors.*

The parallelogram formed by the lattice vectors, the shaded region in Figure 12.3, defines the unit cell. In two dimensions the unit cells must *tile*, or fit together in space, in such a way that they completely cover the area of the lattice with no gaps. In three dimensions the unit cells must stack together to fill all space.

In a two-dimensional lattice, the unit cells can take only one of the four shapes shown in ▶ FIGURE 12.4. The most general type of lattice is the *oblique lattice*. In this lattice, the lattice vectors are of different lengths and the angle $\gamma$ between them is of arbitrary size, which makes the unit cell an arbitrarily shaped parallelogram. A *square lattice* results when the lattice vectors are equal in length and perpendicular to each other. If the two vectors are perpendicular to each other but of different lengths, a *rectangular lattice* is formed. The fourth type of two-dimensional lattice, where $a$ and $b$ are the same length and $\gamma$ is 120°, is a *hexagonal lattice*.† The lattices in Figure 12.4

Iron pyrite ($FeS_2$), a crystalline solid

Obsidian (typically $KAlSi_3O_8$), an amorphous solid

▲ **FIGURE 12.2 Examples of crystalline and amorphous solids.** The atoms in crystalline solids repeat in an orderly, periodic fashion that leads to well-defined faces at the macroscopic level. This order is lacking in amorphous solids like obsidian (volcanic glass).

▲ **FIGURE 12.3 A crystalline lattice in two dimensions.** An infinite array of lattice points is generated by adding together the lattice vectors $a$ and $b$. The unit cell is a parallelogram defined by the lattice vectors.

---

*A vector is a quantity involving both a direction and a magnitude. The magnitudes of the vectors in Figure 12.3 are indicated by their lengths, and their directions are indicated by the arrowheads.
†You may wonder why the hexagonal unit cell is not shaped like a hexagon. Remember that the unit cell is by definition a *parallelogram* whose size and shape are defined by the lattice vectors $a$ and $b$.

▲ FIGURE 12.4 **The four two-dimensional lattices.** The unit cell for each lattice is shaded.

Oblique lattice ($a \neq b$, $\gamma$ = arbitrary)

Square lattice ($a = b$, $\gamma = 90°$)

Rectangular lattice ($a \neq b$, $\gamma = 90°$)

Hexagonal lattice ($a = b$, $\gamma = 120°$)

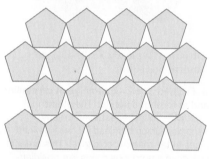

▲ FIGURE 12.5 **Not all shapes tile space.** Tiling means covering a surface entirely, which is impossible for some geometric shapes, as shown here for pentagons.

represent tiling of four basic shapes: squares, rectangles, hexagons, and arbitrary parallelograms. Other polygons, such as pentagons, cannot cover space without leaving gaps, as ◄ **FIGURE 12.5** shows.

To understand real crystals, we must move from two dimensions to three. In three dimensions, a lattice is defined by three lattice vectors $a$, $b$, and $c$ (▼ **FIGURE 12.6**). These lattice vectors define a unit cell that is a parallelepiped (a six-sided figure whose faces are all parallelograms) and is described by the lengths $a$, $b$, $c$ of the cell edges and the angles $\alpha$, $\beta$, $\gamma$ between these edges. There are seven possible shapes for a three-dimensional unit cell, as shown in Figure 12.6.

⚠ **GIVE IT SOME THOUGHT**

Imagine you generate a three-dimensional lattice by taking $a$ and $b$ vectors that form a two-dimensional square lattice. Then add a third vector, $c$, that is of different length and perpendicular to the first two. Which of the seven three-dimensional lattices results?

**Cubic**
$a = b = c$
$\alpha = \beta = \gamma = 90°$

**Tetragonal**
$a = b \neq c$
$\alpha = \beta = \gamma = 90°$

**Orthorhombic**
$a \neq b \neq c$
$\alpha = \beta = \gamma = 90°$

**Rhombohedral**
$a = b = c$
$\alpha = \beta = \gamma \neq 90°$

**Hexagonal**
$a \neq b \neq c$
$\alpha = \beta = 90°, \gamma = 120°$

**Monoclinic**
$a \neq b \neq c$
$\alpha = \gamma = 90°, \beta \neq 90°$

**Triclinic**
$a \neq b \neq c$
$\alpha \neq \beta \neq \gamma$

▲ FIGURE 12.6 **The seven three-dimensional primitive lattices.**

If we place a lattice point at each corner of a unit cell, we get a **primitive lattice**. All seven lattices in Figure 12.6 are primitive lattices. It is also possible to generate what are called *centered lattices* by placing additional lattice points in specific locations in the unit cell. This is illustrated for a cubic lattice in ▶ FIGURE 12.7. A **body-centered cubic lattice** has one lattice point at the center of the unit cell in addition to the lattice points at the eight corners. A **face-centered cubic lattice** has one lattice point at the center of each of the six faces of the unit cell in addition to the lattice points at the eight corners. Centered lattices exist for other types of unit cells as well. Examples include body-centered tetragonal and face-centered orthorhombic. Counting all seven primitive lattices as well as the various types of centered lattices, there are a total of 14 three-dimensional lattices. For the crystals discussed in this chapter we need only consider the lattices shown in Figures 12.6 and 12.7.

## Filling the Unit Cell

The lattice by itself does not define a crystal structure. To generate a crystal structure, we need to associate an atom or group of atoms with each lattice point. In the simplest case, the crystal structure consists of identical atoms, and each atom lies directly on a lattice point. When this happens, the crystal structure and the lattice points have identical patterns. Many metallic elements adopt such structures, as we will see in Section 12.3. Keep in mind that *only elements* can form structures of this type. For compounds, even if we were to put an atom on every lattice point, the points would not be identical because the atoms are not all of the same.

In most crystals the atoms are not exactly coincident with the lattice points. Instead, a group of atoms, called a **motif**, is associated with each lattice point. The unit cell contains a specific motif of atoms, and the crystal structure is built up by repeating the unit cell over and over. This process is illustrated in ▼ FIGURE 12.8 for a two-dimensional crystal based on a hexagonal unit cell and a two-carbon-atom motif. The resulting infinite two-dimensional honeycomb structure is a two-dimensional crystal called graphene. Each carbon atom is covalently bonded to three neighboring carbon atoms in what amounts to an infinite sheet of interconnected hexagonal rings.

The crystal structure of graphene illustrates two important characteristics of crystals. First, we see that no atoms lie on the lattice points. While most of the structures we discuss in this chapter do have atoms on the lattice points, there are many examples, like graphene, where this is not the case. Thus, to build up a structure you must know the location and orientation of the atoms in the motif with respect to the lattice points. Second, we see that bonds can be formed between atoms in neighboring unit cells. This happens in many crystals, particularly metallic, ionic, and network-covalent solids.

Lattice points only at corners

**Primitive cubic lattice**

Lattice points at corners plus one lattice point in center of unit cell

**Body-centered cubic lattice**

Lattice points at corners plus one lattice point at the center of each face

**Face-centered cubic lattice**

▲ FIGURE 12.7 **The three types of cubic lattices.**

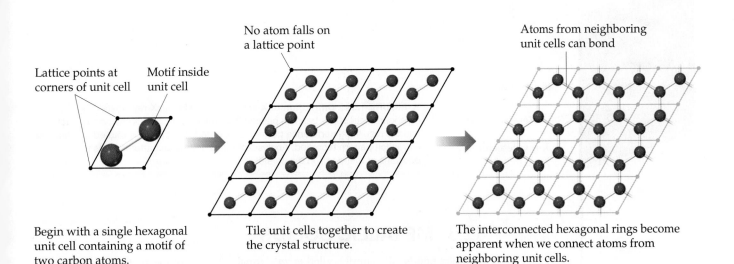

Lattice points at corners of unit cell    Motif inside unit cell

No atom falls on a lattice point

Atoms from neighboring unit cells can bond

Begin with a single hexagonal unit cell containing a motif of two carbon atoms.

Tile unit cells together to create the crystal structure.

The interconnected hexagonal rings become apparent when we connect atoms from neighboring unit cells.

▲ FIGURE 12.8 **Two-dimensional structure of graphene built up from a single unit cell.**

# A CLOSER LOOK

## X-RAY DIFFRACTION

When light waves pass through a narrow slit, they are scattered in such a way that the wave seems to spread out. This physical phenomenon is called *diffraction*. When light passes through many evenly spaced narrow slits (a *diffraction grating*), the scattered waves interact to form a series of bright and dark bands, known as a diffraction pattern. The bright bands correspond to constructive overlapping of the light waves, and the dark bands correspond to destructive overlapping of the light waves (Section 9.8, "A Closer Look: Phases in Atomic and Molecular Orbitals"). The most effective diffraction of light occurs when the wavelength of the light and the width of the slits are similar in magnitude.

The spacing of the layers of atoms in solid crystals is usually about 2–20 Å. The wavelengths of X-rays are also in this range. Thus, a crystal can serve as an effective diffraction grating for X-rays. X-ray diffraction results from the scattering of X-rays by a regular arrangement of atoms, molecules, or ions. Much of what we know about crystal structures has been obtained by looking at the diffraction patterns that result when X-rays pass through a crystal, a technique known as *X-ray crystallography*. As shown in ▼ FIGURE 12.9 a monochromatic beam of X-rays is passed through a crystal. The diffraction pattern that results is recorded. For many years the diffracted

X-rays were detected by photographic film. Today, crystallographers use an *array detector*, a device analogous to that used in digital cameras, to capture and measure the intensities of the diffracted rays.

The pattern of spots on the detector in Figure 12.9 depends on the particular arrangement of atoms in the crystal. The spacing and symmetry of the bright spots, where constructive interference occurs, provide information about the size and shape of the unit cell. The intensities of the spots provide information that can be used to determine the locations of the atoms within the unit cell. When combined, these two pieces of information give the atomic structure that defines the crystal.

X-ray crystallography is used extensively to determine the structures of molecules in crystals. The instruments used to measure X-ray diffraction, known as *X-ray diffractometers*, are now computer controlled, making the collection of diffraction data highly automated. The diffraction pattern of a crystal can be determined very accurately and quickly (sometimes in a matter of hours), even though thousands of diffraction spots are measured. Computer programs are then used to analyze the diffraction data and determine the arrangement and structure of the molecules in the crystal. X-ray diffraction is an important technique in industries ranging from steel and cement manufacture to pharmaceuticals.

*RELATED EXERCISES: 12.105, 12.106, 12.107*

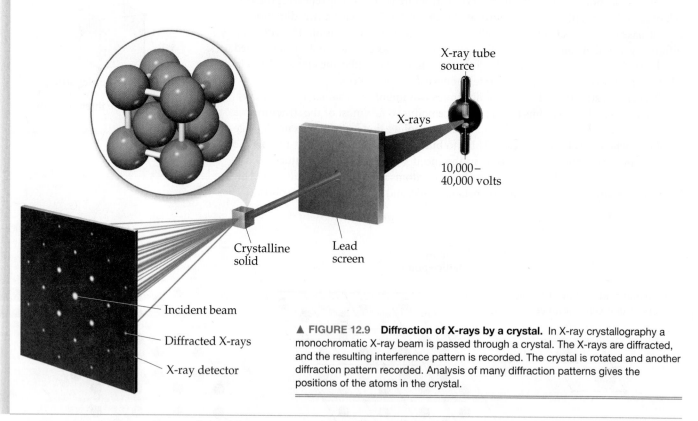

▲ **FIGURE 12.9 Diffraction of X-rays by a crystal.** In X-ray crystallography a monochromatic X-ray beam is passed through a crystal. The X-rays are diffracted, and the resulting interference pattern is recorded. The crystal is rotated and another diffraction pattern recorded. Analysis of many diffraction patterns gives the positions of the atoms in the crystal.

# 12.3 | METALLIC SOLIDS

**Metallic solids**, also simply called *metals*, consist entirely of metal atoms. The bonding in metals is too strong to be due to dispersion forces, and yet there are not enough valence electrons to form covalent bonds between atoms. The bonding, called *metallic*

*bonding*, results from the fact that the valence electrons are *delocalized* throughout the entire solid. That is, the valence electrons are not associated with specific atoms or bonds but are spread throughout the solid. In fact, we can visualize a metal as an array of positive ions immersed in a "sea" of delocalized valence electrons.

You have probably held a length of copper wire or an iron bolt. Perhaps you have even seen the surface of a freshly cut piece of sodium metal. These substances, although distinct from one another, share certain similarities that enable us to classify them as metallic. A clean metal surface has a characteristic luster. In addition, metals that we can handle with bare hands have a characteristic cold feeling related to their high thermal conductivity. Metals also have high electrical conductivity, which means that electrically charged particles flow easily through them. The thermal conductivity of a metal usually parallels its electrical conductivity. Silver and copper, for example, which possess the highest electrical conductivities among the elements, also possess the highest thermal conductivities.

Most metals are *malleable*, which means that they can be hammered into thin sheets, and *ductile*, which means that they can be drawn into wires (▶ **FIGURE 12.10**). These properties indicate that the atoms are capable of slipping past one another. Ionic and covalent-network solids do not exhibit such behavior. They are typically brittle and fracture easily. Consider, for example, the difference between dropping a ceramic plate and an aluminum cooking pan onto a concrete floor.

▲ **FIGURE 12.10  Malleability and ductility.** Gold leaf demonstrates the characteristic malleability of metals, and copper wire demonstrates their ductility.

## The Structures of Metallic Solids

The crystal structures of many metals are simple enough that we can generate the structure by placing a single atom on each lattice point. The structures corresponding to the three cubic lattices are shown in ▼ **FIGURE 12.11**. Metals with a primitive cubic structure are rare, one of the few examples being the radioactive element polonium. Body-centered cubic metals include iron, chromium, sodium, and tungsten. Examples of face-centered cubic metals include aluminum, lead, copper, silver, and gold.

Notice in the bottom row of Figure 12.11 that the atoms on the corners and faces of a unit cell do not lie wholly within the unit cell. These corner and face atoms are shared by neighboring unit cells. Because a cube has eight corners, each primitive cubic unit

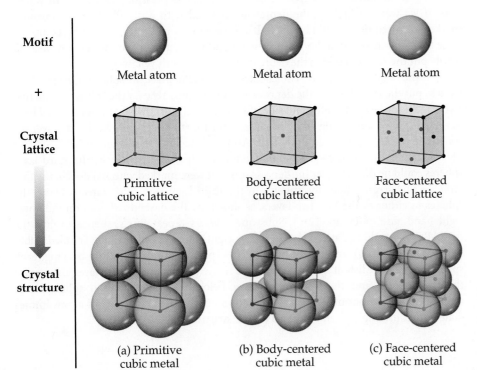

**Motif**

Metal atom   Metal atom   Metal atom

**+**

**Crystal lattice**

Primitive cubic lattice   Body-centered cubic lattice   Face-centered cubic lattice

**Crystal structure**

(a) Primitive cubic metal   (b) Body-centered cubic metal   (c) Face-centered cubic metal

◀ **FIGURE 12.11  The structures of (a) primitive cubic, (b) body-centered cubic, and (c) face-centered cubic metals.** Each structure can be generated by the combination of a single-atom motif and the appropriate lattice.

$\frac{1}{8}$ atom at
8 corners

(a) Primitive cubic metal
1 atom per unit cell

$\frac{1}{8}$ atom at
8 corners

1 atom
at center

(b) Body-centered cubic metal
2 atoms per unit cell

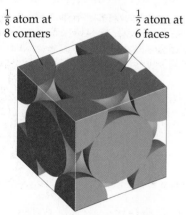

$\frac{1}{8}$ atom at
8 corners

$\frac{1}{2}$ atom at
6 faces

(c) Face-centered cubic metal
4 atoms per unit cell

▲ **FIGURE 12.12 A space-filling view of unit cells for metals with a cubic structure.** Only the portion of each atom that falls within the unit cell is shown.

cell contains $(1/8) \times 8 = 1$ atom, as shown in ◄ **FIGURE 12.12**(a). Similarly, each body-centered cubic unit cell [Figure 12.12(b)] contains two atoms, $(1/8) \times 8 = 1$ from the corners and 1 at the center of the unit cell. Atoms that lie on the face of a unit cell, as they do in a face-centered cubic metal, are shared by two unit cells so that only one-half of the atom belongs to each unit cell. Therefore, a face-centered cubic unit cell [Figure 12.12(c)] contains four atoms, $(1/8) \times 8 = 1$ atom from the corners and $(1/2) \times 6 = 3$ atoms from the faces.

▼ **TABLE 12.1** summarizes how the fractional part of each atom that resides within a unit cell depends on the atom's location in the cell.

**TABLE 12.1 • Fraction of Any Atom as a Function of Location Within the Unit Cell[*]**

| Atom Location | Number of Unit Cells Sharing Atom | Fraction of Atom Within Unit Cell |
|---|---|---|
| Corner | 8 | 1/8 or 12.5% |
| Edge | 4 | 1/4 or 25% |
| Face | 2 | 1/2 or 50% |
| Anywhere else | 1 | 1 or 100% |

[*]It is only the position of the center of the atom that matters. Atoms that reside near the boundary of the unit cell but not on a corner, edge, or face are counted as residing 100% within the unit cell.

## Close Packing

The shortage of valence electrons and the fact that they are collectively shared make it favorable for the atoms in a metal to pack together closely. Because atoms are spherical objects, we can understand the structures of metals by considering how spheres pack. The most efficient way to pack one layer of equal-sized spheres is to surround each sphere by six neighbors, as shown at the top of ► **FIGURE 12.13**. To form a three-dimensional structure, we need to stack additional layers on top of this base layer. To maximize packing efficiency the second layer of spheres must sit in the depressions formed by the spheres in the first layer. If we start by placing an atom in the depression marked b1, the remaining spheres will fill all of the depressions marked with yellow dots. If we were to first fill the depression marked with a c1, all of the depressions marked with red dots would be filled. It's important to realize that the spheres are too large to simultaneously fill both sets of depressions. For the sake of discussion we arbitrarily put the second layer in the depressions marked with yellow dots.

For the third layer, we have two choices for where to place the spheres. One possibility is to put the third layer in the depressions that lie directly over the spheres in the first layer. This is done on the left-hand side of Figure 12.13, as shown by the dashed red lines in the side view. Continuing with this pattern, the fourth layer would lie directly over the spheres in the second layer, leading to the ABAB … stacking shown on the left. This type of stacking is called **hexagonal close packing** (hcp). Alternatively, the third-layer spheres could lie directly over the depressions that were marked with red dots in the first layer. In this arrangement the spheres in the third layer do not sit directly above the spheres in either of the first two layers, as shown by the dashed red lines on the lower right hand side of Figure 12.13. Subsequent layers repeat this sequence to give the ABCABC … stacking pattern shown on the right. This type of stacking is called **cubic close packing** (ccp). In both hexagonal close packing and cubic close packing, each sphere has 12 equidistant nearest neighbors: six neighbors in the same layer, three from the layer above, and three from the layer below. We say that each sphere has a **coordination number** of 12. The coordination number is the number of atoms immediately surrounding a given atom in a crystal structure.

△ **GO FIGURE**

**What type of two-dimensional lattice describes the structure of a single layer of close-packed atoms?**

**Hexagonal close packing (hcp)**     **Cubic close packing (ccp)**

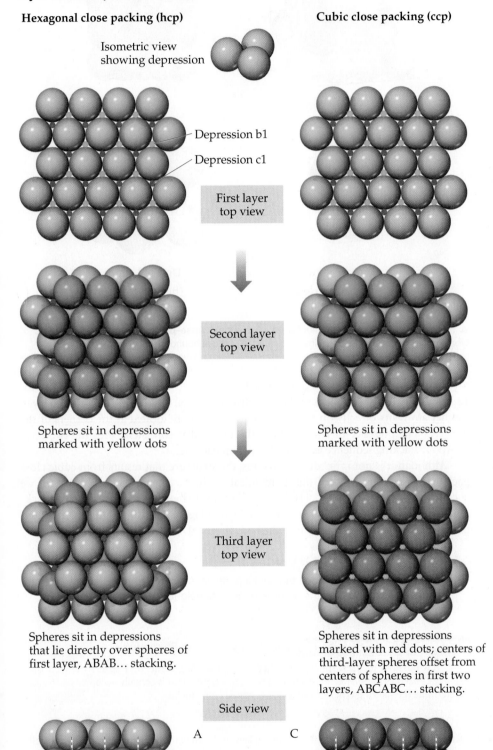

Isometric view
showing depression

— Depression b1

— Depression c1

First layer
top view

Second layer
top view

Spheres sit in depressions     Spheres sit in depressions
marked with yellow dots     marked with yellow dots

Third layer
top view

Spheres sit in depressions     Spheres sit in depressions
that lie directly over spheres of     marked with red dots; centers of
first layer, ABAB… stacking.     third-layer spheres offset from
     centers of spheres in first two
     layers, ABCABC… stacking.

Side view

A     C
B     B
A     A

◀ **FIGURE 12.13   Close packing of
equal-sized spheres.** Hexagonal (left) close
packing and cubic (right) close packing are
equally efficient ways of packing spheres.

Side view

Side view

Unit cell view

(a) Hexagonal close-
packed metal

Unit cell view

(b) Cubic close-
packed metal

▲ **FIGURE 12.14** **The unit cells for (a) a hexagonal close-packed metal and (b) a cubic close-packed metal.** The solid lines indicate the unit cell boundaries.

The extended structure of a hexagonal close-packed metal is shown in ▲ **FIGURE 12.14**(a). There are two atoms in the primitive hexagonal unit cell, one from each layer. Neither atom sits directly on the lattice points, which are located at the corners of the unit cell. The presence of two atoms in the unit cell is consistent with the two-layer ABAB … stacking sequence associated with hcp packing.

Although it is not immediately obvious, the structure that results from cubic close packing possesses a unit cell that is identical to the face-centered cubic unit cell we encountered earlier [Figure 12.11(c)]. The relationship between the ABC … layer stacking and the face-centered cubic unit cell is shown in Figure 12.14(b). In this figure we see that the layers stack perpendicular to the body diagonal of the cubic unit cell.

 GIVE IT SOME THOUGHT

For metallic structures, does the packing efficiency (see Sample Exercise 12.1) increase or decrease as the number of nearest neighbors (the coordination number) decreases?

**SAMPLE EXERCISE 12.1** **Calculating Packing Efficiency**

It is not possible to pack spheres together without leaving some void spaces between the spheres. *Packing efficiency* is the fraction of space in a crystal that is actually occupied by atoms. Determine the packing efficiency of a face-centered cubic metal.

**SOLUTION**

**Analyze** We must determine the volume taken up by the atoms that reside in the unit cell and divide this number by the volume of the unit cell.

**Plan** We can calculate the volume taken up by atoms by multiplying the number of atoms per unit cell by the volume of a sphere, $4\pi r^3/3$. To determine the volume of the unit cell, we must first identify the direction along which the atoms touch each other. We can then use geometry to express the length of the cubic unit cell edge, $a$, in terms of the radius of the atoms. Once we know the edge length, the cell volume is simply $a^3$.

**Solve** As shown in Figure 12.12, a face-centered cubic metal has four atoms per unit cell. Therefore, the volume occupied by the atoms is

$$\text{Occupied volume} = 4 \times \left(\frac{4\pi r^3}{3}\right) = \frac{16\pi r^3}{3}$$

For a face-centered cubic metal the atoms touch along the diagonal of a face of the unit cell:

Therefore, a diagonal across a face of the unit cell is equal to 4 times the atomic radius, $r$. Using simple trigonometry, and the identity $\cos(45°) = \sqrt{2}/2$, we can show that

$$a = 4r\cos(45°) = 4r\left(\sqrt{2}/2\right) = (2\sqrt{2})r$$

Finally, we calculate the packing efficiency by dividing the volume occupied by atoms by the volume of the cubic unit cell, $a^3$:

$$\text{Packing efficiency} = \frac{\text{volume of atoms}}{\text{volume of unit cell}} = \frac{\left(\frac{16}{3}\right)\pi r^3}{(2\sqrt{2})^3 r^3} = 0.74 \text{ or } 74\%$$

**PRACTICE EXERCISE**
Determine the packing efficiency by calculating the fraction of space occupied by atoms in a body-centered cubic metal.
**Answer:** 0.68 or 68%

# Alloys

An **alloy** is a material that contains more than one element and has the characteristic properties of a metal. The alloying of metals is of great importance because it is one of the primary ways of modifying the properties of pure metallic elements. Nearly all the common uses of iron, for example, involve alloy compositions. Bronze is formed by alloying copper and tin, while brass is an alloy of copper and zinc. Pure gold is too soft to be used in jewelry, but alloys of gold are much harder (see "Chemistry Put to Work Box: Alloys of Gold"). Other common alloys are described in ▼ TABLE 12.2.

**TABLE 12.2 • Some Common Alloys**

| Name | Primary Element | Typical Composition (by Mass) | Properties | Uses |
|------|------|------|------|------|
| Wood's metal | Bismuth | 50% Bi, 25% Pb, 12.5% Sn, 12.5% Cd | Low melting point (70 °C) | Fuse plugs, automatic sprinklers |
| Yellow brass | Copper | 67% Cu, 33% Zn | Ductile, takes polish | Hardware items |
| Bronze | Copper | 88% Cu, 12% Sn | Tough and chemically stable in dry air | Important alloy for early civilizations |
| Stainless steel | Iron | 80.6% Fe, 0.4% C, 18% Cr, 1% Ni | Resists corrosion | Tableware, surgical instruments |
| Plumber's solder | Lead | 67% Pb, 33% Sn | Low melting point (275 °C) | Soldering joints |
| Sterling silver | Silver | 92.5% Ag, 7.5% Cu | Bright surface | Tableware |
| Dental amalgam | Silver | 70% Ag, 18% Sn, 10% Cu, 2% Hg | Easily worked | Dental fillings |

△ **GO FIGURE**

**What determines which species in a solid solution is the solute and which is the solvent?**

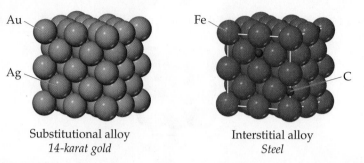

Substitutional alloy
*14-karat gold*

Interstitial alloy
*Steel*

▲ **FIGURE 12.15** **The distribution of solute and solvent atoms in a substitutional alloy and an interstitial alloy.** Both types of alloys are solid solutions and, therefore, homogeneous mixtures.

Alloys can be divided into four categories: substitutional alloys, interstitial alloys, heterogeneous alloys, and intermetallic compounds. Substitutional and interstitial alloys are both homogeneous mixtures in which components are dispersed randomly and uniformly (▲ **FIGURE 12.15**). ∞ (Section 1.2) Solids that form homogeneous mixtures are called solid solutions. When atoms of the solute in a solid solution occupy positions normally occupied by a solvent atom, we have a **substitutional alloy**. When the solute atoms occupy interstitial positions in the "holes" between solvent atoms, we have an **interstitial alloy** (Figure 12.15).

Substitutional alloys are formed when the two metallic components have similar atomic radii and chemical-bonding characteristics. For example, silver and gold form such an alloy over the entire range of possible compositions. When two metals differ in radii by more than about 15%, solubility is generally more limited.

For an interstitial alloy to form, the solute atoms must have a much smaller bonding atomic radius than the solvent atoms. Typically, the interstitial element is a nonmetal that makes covalent bonds to the neighboring metal atoms. The presence of the extra bonds provided by the interstitial component causes the metal lattice to become harder, stronger, and less ductile. For example, steel, which is much harder and stronger than pure iron, is an alloy of iron that contains up to 3% carbon. *Mild steels* contain less than 0.2% carbon; they are malleable and ductile and are used to make cables, nails, and chains. *Medium steels* contain 0.2–0.6% carbon; they are tougher than mild steels and are used to make girders and rails. *High-carbon steel*, used in cutlery, tools, and springs, contains 0.6–1.5% carbon. In all three types, other elements may be added to form *alloy steels*. Vanadium and chromium may be added to impart strength, for instance, and to increase resistance to fatigue and corrosion.

△ **GIVE IT SOME THOUGHT**

Would you expect the alloy $PdB_{0.15}$ to be a substitutional alloy or an interstitial alloy?

One of the most important iron alloys is stainless steel, which contains about 0.4% carbon, 18% chromium, and 1% nickel. The chromium is obtained by carbon reduction of chromite ($FeCr_2O_4$) in an electric furnace. The product of the reduction is *ferrochrome* ($FeCr_2$), which is added in the appropriate amount to molten iron to achieve the desired steel composition. The ratio of elements present in the steel may vary over a wide range, imparting a variety of specific physical and chemical properties to the materials.

Fe metal

Fe₃C

10 μm

◀ **FIGURE 12.16  Microscopic view of the structure of the heterogeneous alloy pearlite.** The dark regions are body-centered cubic iron metal, and the lighter regions are cementite, Fe₃C.

In a **heterogeneous alloy** the components are not dispersed uniformly. For example, the heterogeneous alloy pearlite contains two phases (▲ **FIGURE 12.16**). One phase is essentially pure body-centered cubic iron, and the other is the compound Fe₃C, known as cementite. In general, the properties of heterogeneous alloys depend on both the composition and the manner in which the solid is formed from the molten mixture. The properties of a heterogeneous alloy formed by rapid cooling of a molten mixture, for example, are distinctly different from the properties of an alloy formed by slow cooling of the same mixture.

**Intermetallic compounds** are compounds rather than mixtures. Because they are compounds, they have definite properties and their composition cannot be varied. Unlike the atoms in substitutional and interstitial alloys, the different types of atoms in an intermetallic compound are ordered rather than randomly distributed. The ordering of atoms in an intermetallic compound generally leads to better structural stability and higher melting points than what is observed in the constituent metals. These features can be attractive for high-temperature applications. On the negative side, intermetallic compounds are often more brittle than substitutional alloys.

Intermetallic compounds play many important roles in modern society. The intermetallic compound Ni₃Al is a major component of jet aircraft engines because of its strength at high temperature and its low density. Razor blades are often coated with Cr₃Pt, which adds hardness, allowing the blade to stay sharp longer. Both compounds have the structure shown on the left hand side of ▼ **FIGURE 12.17**. The compound Nb₃Sn, also shown in Figure 12.17, is a superconductor, a substance that, when cooled below a critical temperature, conducts electricity with no resistance. In the case of Nb₃Sn superconductivity is observed only when the temperature falls below 18 K. Superconductors are used in the magnets in MRI scanners widely employed for medical imaging. The need to keep the magnets cooled to such a low temperature is part of the reason why MRI devices are expensive to operate. The hexagonal intermetallic compound SmCo₅, shown on the right hand side of Figure 12.17, is used to make the permanent magnets found in lightweight headsets and high-fidelity speakers. A related compound with the same structure, LaNi₅, is used as the anode in nickel-metal hydride batteries.

**GO FIGURE**

In the unit cell drawing on the right, why do we see eight Sm atoms and nine Co atoms if the empirical formula is SmCo₅?

Ni    Al

Nb    Sn

Sm    Co

Ni₃Al

Nb₃Sn

SmCo₅

▲ **FIGURE 12.17  Three examples of intermetallic compounds.**

# CHEMISTRY PUT TO WORK

## Alloys of Gold

Gold has long been a metal of choice for decorative objects, jewelry, and coins. The popularity of gold is driven by its unusual color (for a metal), its resistance to many chemical reactions, and the fact that it can easily be worked. However, pure gold is too soft for many applications, including jewelry. To increase its strength and hardness, as well as to modify its color, gold is often alloyed with other metals. In the jewelry trade pure gold is termed 24 karat. The karat number decreases as the mass percent of gold decreases. The most common alloys used in jewelry are 14 karat, which is $(14/24) \times 100 = 58\%$ gold, and 18 karat, which is $(18/24) \times 100 = 75\%$ gold. As an example of how alloying changes a metal's properties, an alloy that is 75% Au, 12.5% Ag, and 12.5% Cu (marked with the blue dot in Figure 12.18) has a tensile strength that is more than 10 times higher than that of pure gold and is more than 7 times harder than pure gold.

The color of gold varies depending on the metals it is alloyed with. Gold is typically alloyed with silver and/or copper. All three elements crystallize with a face-centered cubic structure. The fact that all three elements have similar radii (Au and Ag are nearly the same size, Cu is roughly 11% smaller) and crystallize with the same type of structure make it possible to form substitutional alloys with nearly any composition. The variations in color of these alloys as a function of composition are shown in ▶ FIGURE 12.18. Gold alloyed with equal parts silver and copper takes on the golden yellow color we associate with gold jewelry. Red or rose gold is a copper-rich alloy (▶ FIGURE 12.19). Silver-rich alloys take on a greenish hue, eventually giving way to silvery-white colors as silver becomes the majority constituent.

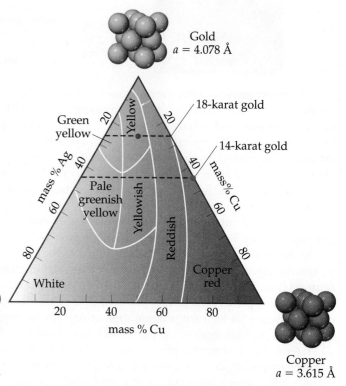

▲ FIGURE 12.18 **Colors of Au-Ag-Cu alloys as a function of composition.**

# 12.4 | METALLIC BONDING

Consider the structures of elements of the third period (Na–Ar). Argon with eight valence electrons has a complete octet; as a result it does not form any bonds. Chlorine, sulfur, and phosphorus form molecules ($Cl_2$, $S_8$, and $P_4$) in which the atoms make one, two, and three bonds, respectively (▶ FIGURE 12.20). Silicon forms an extended network solid in which each atom is bonded to four equidistant neighbors. Each of these elements forms $8-N$ bonds, where $N$ is the number of valence electrons. This behavior can easily be understood through application of the octet rule.

If the $8-N$ trend continued as we move left across the periodic table, we would expect aluminum (three valence electrons) to form five bonds. Like many other metals, however, aluminum adopts a close-packed structure with 12 near neighbors. Magnesium and sodium also adopt metallic structures. What is responsible for this abrupt change in the preferred bonding mechanism? The answer is that, as noted earlier, metals do not have enough valence-shell electrons to satisfy their bonding requirements by forming localized electron-pair bonds. In response to this deficiency, the valence electrons are collectively shared. A structure in which the atoms are close-packed facilitates this delocalized sharing of electrons.

## GO FIGURE

**In which of these alloys are the gold atoms and the other atoms (Cu or Al) arranged randomly?**

14-karat red gold, a substitutional alloy
marked with a red dot in Figure 12.18

Purple gold, the intermetallic compound $AuAl_2$

Gold can also be alloyed with many other metals. White gold is generally obtained by alloying either nickel or palladium with gold. Although Ni-Au alloys are cheaper, they are generally considered inferior because they are harder to work and because many people suffer an allergic reaction to nickel. All of these alloys are substitutional alloys, but gold also forms some interesting intermetallic compounds. Reacting gold and aluminum in a 1:2 mole ratio produces the intermetallic compound $AuAl_2$, which is known as purple gold for its unusual color. If the aluminum is replaced with indium to form $AuIn_2$ the color changes to blue. Because they are intermetallic compounds, purple and blue gold are brittle, which makes it very difficult to form them into rings and other jewelry pieces. They can be used as gemstones or inlays, however, as in the ring shown in Figure 12.19.

*RELATED EXERCISES:* 12.41, 12.42, 12.110

▲ **FIGURE 12.19    Red and purple gold at the macroscopic and microscopic levels.**

## GO FIGURE

**How many nonbonding electron pairs are there per atom in chlorine, sulfur, phosphorus, and silicon?**

| Group 3A | Group 4A | Group 5A | Group 6A | Group 7A |
|---|---|---|---|---|

| **Al** | **Si** | **$P_4$** | **$S_8$** | **$Cl_2$** |
|---|---|---|---|---|
| 12 nearest neighbors | 4 valence electrons<br>$8 - 4 = 4$ bonds<br>per atom | 5 valence electrons<br>$8 - 5 = 3$ bonds<br>per atom | 6 valence electrons<br>$8 - 6 = 2$ bonds<br>per atom | 7 valence electrons<br>$8 - 7 = 1$ bond<br>per atom |

Metallic bonding                    Covalent bonding

▲ **FIGURE 12.20    Bonding in period 3 elements.**

Metal ion (nucleus
+ core electrons)

Sea of mobile
valence electrons

▲ **FIGURE 12.21 Electron-sea model of metallic bonding.** The valence electrons delocalize to form a sea of mobile electrons that surrounds and binds together an extended array of metal ions.

## Electron-Sea Model

A simple model that accounts for some of the most important characteristics of metals is the **electron-sea model**, which pictures the metal as an array of metal cations in a "sea" of valence electrons (◄ **FIGURE 12.21**). The electrons are confined to the metal by electrostatic attractions to the cations, and they are uniformly distributed throughout the structure. The electrons are mobile, however, and no individual electron is confined to any particular metal ion. When a voltage is applied to a metal wire, the electrons, being negatively charged, flow through the metal toward the positively charged end of the wire.

The high thermal conductivity of metals is also accounted for by the presence of mobile electrons. The movement of electrons in response to temperature gradients permits ready transfer of kinetic energy throughout the solid.

The ability of metals to deform (their malleability and ductility) can be explained by the fact that metal atoms form bonds to many neighbors. Changes in the positions of the atoms brought about in reshaping the metal are partly accommodated by a redistribution of electrons.

## Molecular-Orbital Model

Although the electron-sea model works surprisingly well given its simplicity, it does not adequately explain many properties of metals. According to the model, for example, the strength of bonding between metal atoms should steadily increase as the number of valence electrons increases, resulting in a corresponding increase in the melting points. However, elements near the middle of the transition metal series, rather than those at the end, have the highest melting points in their respective periods (▼ **FIGURE 12.22**). This trend implies that the strength of metallic bonding first increases with increasing number of electrons and then decreases. Similar trends are seen in other physical properties of the metals, such as the boiling point, heat of fusion, and hardness.

To obtain a more accurate picture of the bonding in metals, we must turn to molecular-orbital theory. In Sections 9.7 and 9.8 we learned how molecular orbitals are created from the overlap of atomic orbitals. Let's briefly review some of the rules of molecular-orbital theory:

▲ **GO FIGURE**

**Which element in each period has the highest melting point? In each case, is the element you named at the beginning, middle, or end of its period?**

▲ **FIGURE 12.22 The melting points of metals from periods 4, 5, and 6.**

**How does the energy spacing between molecular orbitals change as the number of atoms in the chain increases?**

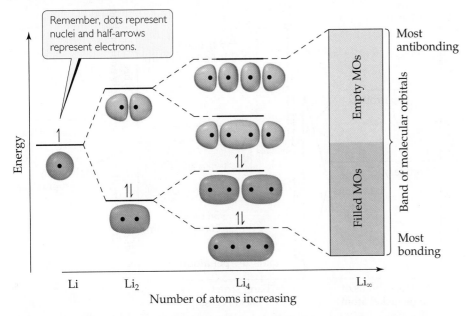

▲ **FIGURE 12.23   Discrete energy levels in individual molecules become continuous energy bands in a solid.** Occupied orbitals are shaded blue, and empty orbitals red.

1. Atomic orbitals combine to make molecular orbitals that can extend over the entire molecule.

2. A molecular orbital can contain zero, one, or two electrons.

3. The number of molecular orbitals in a molecule equals the number of atomic orbitals that combine to form molecular orbitals.

The electronic structures of crystalline solids and small molecules have similarities as well as differences. To illustrate, consider how the molecular-orbital diagram for a chain of lithium atoms changes as we increase the length of the chain (▲ **FIGURE 12.23**). Each lithium atom contains a half-filled $2s$ orbital in its valence shell. The molecular-orbital diagram for $Li_2$ is analogous to that of an $H_2$ molecule: one filled bonding molecular orbital and one empty antibonding molecular orbital with a nodal plane between the atoms. ∞ (Section 9.7) For $Li_4$, there are four molecular orbitals, ranging from the lowest-energy orbital, where the orbital interactions are completely bonding (0 nodal planes), to the highest-energy orbital, where all interactions are antibonding (3 nodal planes).

As the length of the chain increases, the number of molecular orbitals increases. Regardless of chain length, the lowest-energy orbitals are always the most bonding and the highest-energy orbitals always the most antibonding. Furthermore, because each lithium atom has only one valence shell atomic orbital, the number of molecular orbitals is equal to the number of lithium atoms in the chain. Because each lithium atom has one valence electron, half of the molecular orbitals are fully occupied and the other half are empty, regardless of chain length.*

If the chain becomes very long, there are so many molecular orbitals that the energy separation between them becomes vanishingly small. As the chain length goes to infinity, the allowed energy states become a continuous **band**. For a crystal large enough to see with the eye (or even an optical microscope), the number of atoms is extremely large. Consequently, the electronic structure of the crystal is like that of the infinite chain, consisting of bands, as shown on the right-hand side of Figure 12.23.

*This is strictly true only for chains with an even number of atoms.

**GO FIGURE**

If the metal were potassium rather than nickel, which bands—4s, 4p, and/or 3d—would be partially occupied?

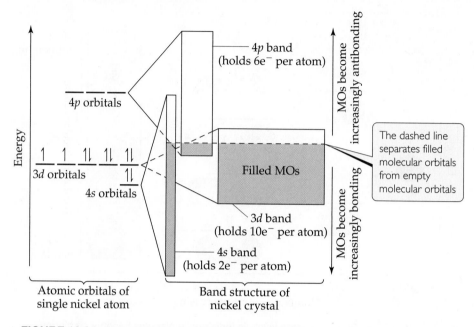

▲ **FIGURE 12.24** **The electronic band structure of nickel.**

The electronic structures of most metals are more complicated than shown in Figure 12.23 because we have to consider more than one type of atomic orbital on each atom. Because each type of orbital can give rise to its own band, the electronic structure of a solid usually consists of a series of bands. The electronic structure of a bulk solid is referred to as a **band structure**.

The band structure for a typical metal is shown schematically in ▲ **FIGURE 12.24.** The electron filling depicted corresponds to nickel metal, but the basic features of other metals are similar. The electron configuration of a nickel atom is $[Ar]3d^8 4s^2$, as shown on the left side of the figure. The energy bands that form from each of these orbitals are shown on the right side. The 4s, 4p, and 3d orbitals are treated independently, each giving rise to a band of molecular orbitals. In practice, these overlapping bands are not completely independent of each other, but for our purposes this simplification is reasonable.

The 4s, 4p, and 3d bands differ from one another in the energy range they span (represented by the heights of the rectangles on the right side of Figure 12.24) and in the number of electrons they can hold (represented by the area of the rectangles). The 4s, 4p, and 3d bands can hold 2, 6, and 10 electrons per atom, respectively, two per orbital, as dictated by the Pauli exclusion principle. ∞ (Section 6.7) The energy range spanned by the 3d band is smaller than the range spanned by the 4s and 4p bands because the 3d orbitals are smaller and, therefore, overlap with orbitals on neighboring atoms less effectively. This reduces the strength of the bonding interactions, which dominate the bottom of the band, as well as the antibonding interactions, which dominate the top of the band. As a result, the 3d band spans a narrower range of energy than the 4s and 4p bands.

Many properties of metals can be understood from Figure 12.24. We can think of the energy band as a partially filled container for electrons. The incomplete filling of the energy band gives rise to characteristic metallic properties. The electrons in orbitals near the top of the occupied levels require very little energy input to be "promoted" to higher-energy orbitals that are unoccupied. Under the influence of any source of excitation, such as an applied electrical potential or an input of thermal energy, electrons move into previously vacant levels and are thus freed to move through the lattice, giving rise to electrical and thermal conductivity.

Without the overlap of energy bands, the periodic properties of metals could not be explained. In the absence of the *d*- and *p*-bands, we would expect the *s*-band to be half-filled for the alkali metals (group 1A) and completely filled for the alkaline-earth metals (group 2A). If that were true, metals like magnesium, calcium, and strontium would not be good electrical and thermal conductors, in disagreement with experimental observations.

While the conductivity of metals can be qualitatively understood using either the electron-sea model or the molecular-orbital model, many physical properties of transition metals, such as the melting points plotted in Figure 12.22, can be explained only with the latter model. The molecular-orbital model predicts that bonding first becomes stronger as the number of valence electrons increases and the bonding orbitals are populated. Upon moving past the middle elements of the transition metal series, the bonds grow weaker as we fill the antibonding orbitals. Strong bonds between atoms lead to metals with higher melting and boiling points, higher heats of fusion, higher hardness, and so forth.

## GIVE IT SOME THOUGHT

Which element, W or Au, has the greater number of electrons in antibonding orbitals? Which one would you expect to have the higher melting point?

# 12.5 | IONIC SOLIDS

**Ionic solids** are held together by the electrostatic attraction between cations and anions—ionic bonds. ∞ (Section 8.2) The high melting and boiling points of ionic compounds are a testament to the strength of the ionic bonds. The strength of an ionic bond depends on the charges and sizes of the ions. As discussed in Chapters 8 and 11, the attractions between cations and anions increase as the charges of the ions go up. Thus NaCl, where the ions have charges of 1+ and 1−, melts at 801 °C, whereas MgO, where the ions have charges of 2+ and 2−, melts at 2852 °C. The interactions between cations and anions also increase as the ions get smaller, as we see from the melting points of the alkali metal halides in ▼ TABLE 12.3. These trends mirror the trends in lattice energy discussed in Section 8.2.

Although ionic and metallic solids both have high melting and boiling points, the differences between ionic and metallic bonding are responsible for important differences in their properties. Because the valence electrons in ionic compounds are confined to the anions, rather than being delocalized, ionic compounds are typically electrical insulators. They tend to be brittle, a property explained by repulsive interactions between ions of like charge. When a stress is applied to an ionic solid, as in ▶ FIGURE 12.25, the planes of atoms, which before the stress were arranged with cations next to anions, shift so that the alignment becomes cation–cation, anion–anion. The resulting repulsive interaction causes the planes to split away from each other. Brittleness is not necessarily a negative quality, of course, as evidenced by the beauty of a cut gemstone. The multiple facets that are the basis of this beauty are possible because crystals cleave along well-defined directions with respect to the crystalline lattice.

## GO FIGURE

Why don't metals cleave in the way depicted here for ionic substances?

**1** A shear stress is applied to an ionic crystal

Cation
Anion

**2** Planes of atoms slide in response to stress

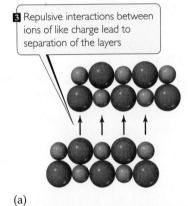

**3** Repulsive interactions between ions of like charge lead to separation of the layers

(a)

(b)

▲ **FIGURE 12.25 Brittleness and faceting in ionic crystals.** (a) When a shear stress is applied to an ionic solid, the crystal separates along a plane of atoms as shown here. (b) This property of ionic crystals is used to facet gemstones, such as rubies.

**TABLE 12.3 • Properties of the Alkali Metal Halides**

| Compound | Cation–Anion Distance (Å) | Lattice Energy (kJ/mol) | Melting Point (°C) |
|---|---|---|---|
| LiF | 2.01 | 1030 | 845 |
| NaCl | 2.83 | 788 | 801 |
| KBr | 3.30 | 671 | 734 |
| RbI | 3.67 | 632 | 674 |

## Structures of Ionic Solids

Like metallic solids, ionic solids tend to adopt structures with symmetric, close-packed arrangements of atoms. However, important differences arise because we now have to pack together spheres that have different radii and opposite charges. Because cations are often considerably smaller than anions ∞ (Section 7.3) the coordination numbers in ionic compounds are smaller than those in close-packed metals. Even if the anions and cations were the same size, the close-packed arrangements seen in metals cannot be replicated without letting ions of like charge come in contact with each other. The repulsions between ions of the same type make such arrangements unfavorable. The most favorable structures are those where the cation–anion distances are as close as permitted by ionic radii but the anion–anion and cation–cation distances are maximized.

### GIVE IT SOME THOUGHT

Is it possible for all atoms in an ionic compound to lie on the lattice points as they do in the metallic structures shown in Figure 12.11?

Three common ionic structure types are shown in ▼ FIGURE 12.26. The cesium chloride (CsCl) structure is based on a primitive cubic lattice. Anions sit on the lattice points at the corners of the unit cell, and a cation sits at the center of each cell. (Remember, there is no lattice point inside a primitive unit cell.) With this arrangement, both cations and anions are surrounded by a cube of eight ions of the opposite type.

The sodium chloride (NaCl) and zinc blende (ZnS) structures are based on a face-centered cubic lattice. In both structures the anions sit on the lattice points that lie on the corners and faces of the unit cell, but the two-atom motif is slightly different for the two structures. In NaCl the $Na^+$ ions are displaced from the $Cl^-$ ions along the edge of the unit cell, whereas in ZnS the $Zn^{2+}$ ions are displaced from the $S^{2-}$ ions along the

### GO FIGURE

Do the anions touch each other in any of these three structures? If not, which ions do touch each other?

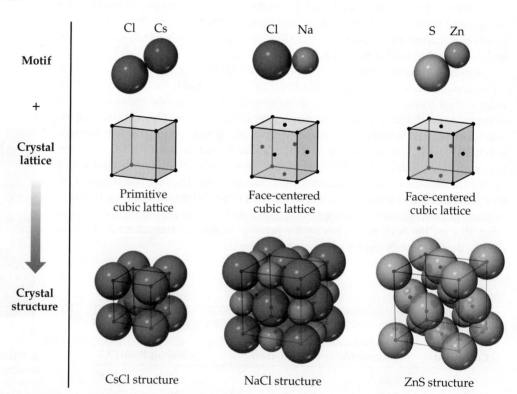

▲ FIGURE 12.26  **The structures of CsCl, NaCl, and ZnS.** Each structure type can be generated by the combination of a two-atom motif and the appropriate lattice.

Decreasing $r_+/r_-$

| | CsCl | NaCl | ZnS |
|---|---|---|---|
| Cation radius, $r_+$ (Å) | 1.81 | 1.16 | 0.88 |
| Anion radius, $r_-$ (Å) | 1.67 | 1.67 | 1.70 |
| $r_+/r_-$ | 1.08 | 0.69 | 0.52 |
| Cation coord. number | 8 | 6 | 4 |
| Anion coord. number | 8 | 6 | 4 |

◀ **FIGURE 12.27  Coordination environments in CsCl, NaCl, and ZnS.** The sizes of the ions have been reduced to show the coordination environments clearly.

body diagonal of the unit cell. This difference leads to different coordination numbers. In sodium chloride, each cation and each anion are surrounded by six ions of the opposite type, leading to an octahedral coordination environment. In zinc blende, each cation and each anion are surrounded by four ions of the opposite type, leading to a tetrahedral coordination geometry. The cation coordination environments can be seen in ▲ **FIGURE 12.27**.

For a given ionic compound, we might ask which type of structure is most favorable. There are a number of factors that come into play, but two of the most important are the relative sizes of the ions and the stoichiometry. Consider first ion size. Notice in Figure 12.27 that the coordination number changes from 8 to 6 to 4 on moving from CsCl to NaCl to ZnS. This trend is driven in part by the fact that for these three compounds the ionic radius of the cation gets smaller while the ionic radius of the anion changes very little. When the cation and anion are similar in size, a large coordination number is favored and the CsCl structure is often realized. As the relative size of the cation gets smaller, eventually it is no longer possible to maintain the cation–anion contacts and simultaneously keep the anions from touching each other. When this occurs, the coordination number drops from 8 to 6, and the sodium chloride structure becomes more favorable. As the cation size decreases further, eventually the coordination number must be reduced again, this time from 6 to 4, and the zinc blende structure becomes favored. *Remember that, in ionic crystals, ions of opposite charge touch each other but ions of the same charge should not touch.*

The relative number of cations and anions also helps determine the most stable structure type. All the structures in Figure 12.27 have equal numbers of cations and anions. These structure types can be realized only for ionic compounds in which the number of cations and anions are equal. When this is not the case, other crystal structures must result. As an example, consider NaF, $MgF_2$, and $ScF_3$ (▶ **FIGURE 12.28**). Sodium fluoride has the sodium chloride structure with a coordination number of 6 for both cation and anion. Magnesium fluoride has a tetragonal crystal structure called the *rutile structure*. The cation coordination number is still 6, but the fluoride coordination number is now only 3. In the scandium fluoride structure, the cation coordination number is still 6 but the fluoride coordination number has dropped to 2. As the cation/anion ratio goes down, there are fewer cations to surround each anion, and so the anion coordination number must decrease. We can state this quantitatively with the relationship

$$\frac{\text{Number of cations per formula unit}}{\text{Number of anions per formula unit}} = \frac{\text{anion coordination number}}{\text{cation coordination number}} \qquad [12.1]$$

GO FIGURE

How many cations are there per unit cell for each of these structures? How
many anions per unit cell?

Increasing anion-to-cation ratio

| | **NaF** | **MgF$_2$** | **ScF$_3$** |
|---|---|---|---|
| Cation coordination number | 6 | 6 | 6 |
| Cation coordination geometry | Octahedral | Octahedral | Octahedral |
| Anion coordination number | 6 | 3 | 2 |
| Anion coordination geometry | Octahedral | Trigonal planar | Linear |

► FIGURE 12.28  **Coordination numbers
depend on stoichiometry.** The sizes of the
ions have been reduced to show the
coordination environments clearly.

▲ GIVE IT SOME THOUGHT

In the crystal structure of potassium oxide, the oxide ions are coordinated by
eight potassium ions. What is the coordination number of potassium?

| SAMPLE EXERCISE 12.2 | **Calculating the Empirical Formula and Density
of an Ionic Solid** |
|---|---|

The unit cell of a binary compound of copper and oxygen is shown here. Given this image and
the ionic radii $r_{Cu^+} = 0.74$ Å and $r_{O^{2-}} = 1.26$ Å, (**a**) determine the empirical formula of this
compound, (**b**) determine the coordination numbers of copper and oxygen, (**c**) estimate the
length of the edge of the cubic unit cell, and (**d**) estimate the density of the compound.

**SOLUTION**

**Analyze and Plan**  There are four parts to this problem.

(**a**) To determine the empirical formula we need to determine how many of each type of ion
there are per unit cell.

(**b**) If we can visually determine the coordination number of one of the ions, we can use Equation 12.1 to determine the coordination number of the other ion.

(**c**) To estimate the length of the unit cell edge we must first determine the direction along
which the ions touch. We can then use ionic radii and trigonometry to estimate the size of the
unit cell.

(**d**) Because density is an intensive property, the density of the unit cell is the same as the density of a bulk crystal. To calculate the density we must divide the mass of the atoms per unit cell
by the volume of the unit cell.

**Solve**

(a) There are four copper ions and one oxygen ion located completely inside the unit cell. In addition there are eight oxygen ions on the corners of the unit cell. Therefore, the number of oxygen ions per unit cell is $1 + 8(1/8) = 2$. Given the fact that there are four copper ions and two oxygen ions per unit cell the empirical formula is $Cu_2O$. This is copper(I) oxide.

(b) It is easier to see the coordination environments of atoms within the unit cell because we do not have to visualize the atoms in neighboring unit cells. In this example we see that the oxygen ion at the center of the unit cell is tetrahedrally coordinated by four copper ions. The copper ions appear to have two oxygen neighbors, but we can double check this conclusion using Equation 12.1:

$$\text{Cation coordination number} = \text{anion coordination number}\left(\frac{\text{\# of anions per formula unit}}{\text{\# of cations per formula unit}}\right)$$

$$\text{Copper coordination number} = 4\left(\frac{1}{2}\right) = 2$$

This result matches our expectations from inspection of the picture.

(c) In this structure the ions touch along the body diagonal of the unit cell. This is shown more clearly in the following figure, where the atoms in the front half of the unit cell have been removed for clarity:

$$y = \sqrt{a^2 + x^2}$$
$$y = \sqrt{a^2 + \left(\sqrt{2}a\right)^2} = \sqrt{3}a$$

Body diagonal, $y$

Cell edge, $a$

Face diagonal, $x$

$$x = \sqrt{a^2 + a^2} = \sqrt{2}a$$

Starting in the lower right-hand corner of the unit cell, the distance from the center of the oxygen ion at the corner of the unit cell to the center of the oxygen at the body center of the unit cell is $r(O^{2-}) + 2r(Cu^+) + r(O^{2-}) = 2r(O^{2-}) + 2r(Cu^+)$. Twice this distance is equal to the body diagonal, $y$.

$$y = 2[2r(Cu^+) + 2r(O^{2-})] = 4[r(Cu^+) + r(O^{2-})] = 4[0.74\text{ Å} + 1.26\text{ Å}] = 8.00\text{ Å}$$

Using trigonometry and the Pythagorean theorem, it can be shown that the body diagonal of a cube is $\sqrt{3}$ times longer than the edge of the cube, $a$. We can use this relationship to determine the edge length of the unit cell:

$$a = y/(\sqrt{3}) = (8.00\text{ Å})/(\sqrt{3}) = 4.62\text{ Å}$$

(d) Because we now know the number of atoms per unit cell and the size of the unit cell, we are in a position to calculate the density from the atomic weights of copper (65.55 amu) and oxygen (16.00 amu) and the appropriate conversions:

$$\rho = \frac{\text{mass}}{\text{volume}} = \frac{[4(65.55\text{ amu}) + 2(16.00\text{ amu})]\left(1\text{ g}/6.022\times10^{23}\text{ amu}\right)}{\left[(4.62\text{ Å})\left(1\text{ cm}/1\times10^8\text{ Å}\right)\right]^3}$$

$$\rho = 4.95\text{ g/cm}^3$$

**Check** Copper is often found in the +1 oxidation state, so $Cu_2O$ is a realistic empirical formula. The densities of most solids fall between the density of lithium ($0.5\text{ g/cm}^3$) and that of iridium ($22.6\text{ g/cm}^3$), so this value is reasonable.

**PRACTICE EXERCISE**

Estimate the length of the cubic unit cell edge and the density of CsCl (Figure 12.26) from the ionic radii of cesium, 1.81 Å, and chloride, 1.67 Å.

**Answer:** $a = 4.02\text{ Å}$ and $\rho = 4.31\text{ g/cm}^3$

# 12.6 | MOLECULAR SOLIDS

**Molecular solids** consist of atoms or molecules held together by dipole–dipole forces, dispersion forces, and/or hydrogen bonds. Because these intermolecular forces are weak, molecular solids are soft and have relatively low melting points (usually below 200 °C). Most substances that are gases or liquids at room temperature form molecular solids at low temperature. Examples include Ar, $H_2O$, and $CO_2$.

The properties of molecular solids depend in large part on the strengths of the forces between molecules. Consider, for example, the properties of sucrose (table sugar, $C_{12}H_{22}O_{11}$). Each sucrose molecule has eight –OH groups, which allows for the formation of multiple hydrogen bonds. Consequently, sucrose exists as a crystalline solid at room temperature, and its melting point, 184 °C, is relatively high for a molecular solid.

Molecular shape is also important because it dictates how efficiently molecules pack together in three dimensions. Benzene ($C_6H_6$), for example, is a highly symmetrical planar molecule. ∞ (Section 8.6) It has a higher melting point than toluene, a compound in which one of the hydrogen atoms of benzene has been replaced by a $CH_3$ group (◄ **FIGURE 12.29**). The lower symmetry of toluene molecules prevents them from packing as efficiently as benzene molecules. As a result, the intermolecular forces that depend on close contact are not as effective and the melting point is lower. In contrast, the boiling point of toluene is higher than that of benzene, indicating that the intermolecular attractive forces are larger in liquid toluene than in liquid benzene. The melting and boiling points of phenol, another substituted benzene shown in Figure 12.29, are higher than those of benzene because the OH group of phenol can form hydrogen bonds.

**GO FIGURE**

In which substance, benzene or toluene, are the intermolecular forces stronger? In which substance do the molecules pack more efficiently?

| | Benzene | Toluene | Phenol |
|---|---|---|---|
| Melting point (°C) | 5 | −95 | 43 |
| Boiling point (°C) | 80 | 111 | 182 |

▲ **FIGURE 12.29** Melting and boiling points for benzene, toluene, and phenol.

# 12.7 | COVALENT-NETWORK SOLIDS

**Covalent-network solids** consist of atoms held together in large networks by covalent bonds. Because covalent bonds are much stronger than intermolecular forces, these solids are much harder and have higher melting points than molecular solids. Diamond and graphite, two allotropes of carbon, are two of the most familiar covalent-network solids. Other examples are silicon, germanium, quartz ($SiO_2$), silicon carbide (SiC), and boron nitride (BN).

In diamond, each carbon atom is bonded tetrahedrally to four other carbon atoms (▼ **FIGURE 12.30**). The structure of diamond can be derived from the zinc blende structure (Figure 12.27) if carbon atoms replace both the zinc and sulfide ions. The carbon atoms are $sp^3$-hybridized and held together by strong carbon–carbon single covalent bonds. The strength and directionality of these bonds make diamond the hardest known material. For this reason, industrial-grade diamonds are employed in saw blades

▶ **FIGURE 12.30** **The structures of (a) diamond and (b) graphite.** The blue color in (b) is added to emphasize the planarity of the carbon layers.

(a) Diamond

(b) Graphite

used for the most demanding cutting jobs. The stiff, interconnected bond network is also responsible for the fact that diamond is one of the best-known thermal conductors. Not surprisingly, diamond has a high melting point, 3550 °C.

In graphite (Figure 12.30b), the carbon atoms form covalently bonded layers that are held together by intermolecular forces. The layers in graphite are the same as the graphene sheet shown in Figure 12.8. Graphite has a hexagonal unit cell containing two layers offset so that the carbon atoms in a given layer sit over the middle of the hexagons of the layer below. Each carbon is covalently bonded to three other carbons in the same layer to form interconnected hexagonal rings. The distance between adjacent carbon atoms in the plane, 1.42 Å, is very close to the C—C distance in benzene, 1.395 Å. In fact, the bonding resembles that of benzene, with delocalized $\pi$ bonds extending over the layers. ∞ (Section 9.6) Electrons move freely through the delocalized orbitals, making graphite a good electrical conductor along the layers. (In fact, graphite is used as a conducting electrode in batteries.) These $sp^2$-hybridized sheets of carbon atoms are separated by 3.35 Å from one another, and the sheets are held together only by dispersion forces. Thus, the layers readily slide past one another when rubbed, giving graphite a greasy feel. This tendency is enhanced when impurity atoms are trapped between the layers, as is typically the case in commercial forms of the material.

Graphite is used as a lubricant and as the "lead" in pencils. The enormous differences in physical properties of graphite and diamond—both of which are pure carbon—arise from differences in their three-dimensional structure and bonding.

## Semiconductors

Silicon and germanium lie immediately below carbon in the periodic table. Like carbon, each of these elements has four valence electrons, just the right number to satisfy the octet rule by forming single covalent bonds with four neighbors. Hence, silicon and germanium, as well as the gray form of tin, crystallize with the same infinite network of covalent bonds as diamond.

When atomic $s$ and $p$ orbitals overlap, they form bonding molecular orbitals and antibonding molecular orbitals. Each pair of $s$ orbitals overlaps to give one bonding and one antibonding molecular orbital, whereas the $p$ orbitals overlap to give three bonding and three antibonding molecular orbitals. The extended network of bonds leads to the formation of the same type of bands we saw in discussing the electronic structures of metals in Section 12.4. The band that forms from bonding molecular orbitals is called the **valence band**, and the band that forms from antibonding orbitals is called the **conduction band** (▼ **FIGURE 12.31**). In a semiconductor, the valence band is filled with electrons and the conduction band is empty. These two bands are separated by an energy band gap, $E_g$.

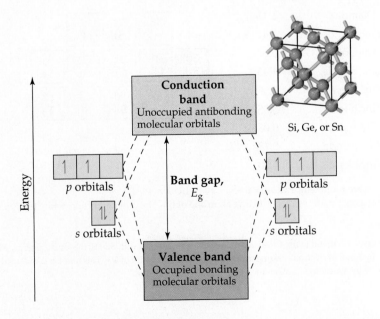

▲ **FIGURE 12.31  The electronic band structure of semiconductors that have the diamond crystal structure.**

Semiconductors can be divided into two classes, **elemental semiconductors**, which contain only one type of atom, and **compound semiconductors**, which contain two or more elements. The elemental semiconductors all come from group 4A. As we move down the periodic table, bond distances increase, which decreases orbital overlap. This decrease in overlap reduces the difference between the bonding molecular orbitals of the valence band and the antibonding molecular orbitals of the conduction band. As a result, the **band gap** decreases on going from diamond (5.5 eV) to silicon (1.11 eV) to germanium (0.67 eV) to gray tin (0.08 eV). Moving one element down to lead, the band gap collapses altogether. As a result, lead has the structure and properties of a metal.

Note that in discussing semiconductors, the electron volt, eV, is the preferred energy unit: $1 \text{ eV} = 1.602 \times 10^{-19} \text{ J.}$ *

Compound semiconductors maintain the same *average* valence electron count as elemental semiconductors—four per atom. For example, when gallium (group 3A) and arsenic (group 5A) combine to form gallium arsenide, GaAs, each Ga atom contributes three electrons and each As atom contributes five, which averages out to four per atom—the same number as in silicon or germanium. Hence, GaAs is a semiconductor. Other examples are InP, where indium contributes three valence electrons and phosphorus contributes five, and CdTe, where cadmium provides two valence electrons and tellurium contributes six. In both cases, the average is again four valence electrons per atom. GaAs, InP, and CdTe all crystallize with a zinc blende structure.

There is a tendency for the band gap of a compound semiconductor to increase as the difference in group numbers increases. For example, the band gap in a Ge semiconductor (made up of only group 4A atoms) is 0.67 eV, but the gap in a GaAs semiconductor (made up of 3A atoms and 5A atoms) is 1.43 eV. If we increase the difference in group number to four, as in ZnSe (groups 2B and 6A), the band gap increases to 2.70 eV. Increasing the horizontal separation of the elements even more leads to a band gap of 3.05 eV in CuBr. This progression is a result of the transition from pure covalent bonding in elemental semiconductors to polar covalent bonding in compound semiconductors. As the difference in electronegativity of the elements increases, the bonding becomes more polar and the band gap increases.

Electrical engineers manipulate both the orbital overlap and the bond polarity to control the band gaps of compound semiconductors for use in a wide range of electrical and optical devices. The band gaps of several elemental and compound semiconductors are given in ▼ **TABLE 12.4.**

**TABLE 12.4 • Band Gaps of Select Elemental and Compound Semiconductors**

| Material | Structure Type | Band Gap Energy, eV[†] |
|---|---|---|
| Si | Diamond | 1.11 |
| AlP | Zinc blende | 2.43 |
| Ge | Diamond | 0.67 |
| GaAs | Zinc blende | 1.43 |
| ZnSe | Zinc blende | 2.58 |
| CuBr | Zinc blende | 3.05 |
| Sn[‡] | Diamond | 0.08 |
| InSb | Zinc blende | 0.18 |
| CdTe | Zinc blende | 1.50 |

|  | 13 Al | 14 Si | 15 P |  |
|---|---|---|---|---|
| 30 Zn | 31 Ga | 32 Ge | 33 As | 34 Se |
| 48 Cd | 49 In | 50 Sn | 51 Sb | 52 Te |

[†] Band gap energies are room temperature values, $1 \text{ eV} = 1.602 \times 10^{-19} \text{ J.}$
[‡] These data are for gray tin, the semiconducting allotrope of tin. The other allotrope, white tin, is a metal.

*In some cases it is useful to use the *molar equivalent* of an electron volt, that is, the kinetic energy that would be gained by 1 mol of electrons passing through a potential difference of 1 V. This number is obtained by multiplying 1 eV by Avogadro's number and is equal to 96.48534 kJ/mol.

**SAMPLE EXERCISE 12.3** | Qualitative Comparison of Semiconductor Band Gaps

Will GaP have a larger or smaller band gap than ZnS? Will it have a larger or smaller band gap than GaN?

**SOLUTION**

**Analyze** The size of the band gap depends on the vertical and horizontal positions of the elements in the periodic table. The band gap will increase when either of the following conditions is met: (1) The elements are located higher up in the periodic table, where enhanced orbital overlap leads to a larger splitting between bonding and antibonding orbitals, or (2) the horizontal separation between the elements increases, which leads to an increase in the electronegativity difference and bond polarity.

**Plan** We must look at the periodic table and compare the relative positions of the elements in each case.

**Solve** Gallium is in the fourth period and group 3A. Phosphorus is in the third period and group 5A. Zinc and sulfur are in the same periods as gallium and phosphorus, respectively. However, zinc, in group 2B, is one element to the left of gallium; sulfur in group 6A is one element to the right of phosphorus. Thus, we would expect the electronegativity difference to be larger for ZnS, which should result in ZnS having a larger band gap than GaP.

For both GaP and GaN the more electropositive element is gallium. So we need only compare the positions of the more electronegative elements, P and N. Nitrogen is located above phosphorus in group 5A. Therefore, based on increased orbital overlap, we would expect GaN to have a larger band gap than GaP.

**Check** External references show that the band gap of GaP is 2.26 eV, ZnS is 3.6 eV, and GaN is 3.4 eV.

**PRACTICE EXERCISE**

Will ZnSe have a larger or smaller band gap than ZnS?

***Answer:*** Because zinc is common to both compounds and selenium is below sulfur in the periodic table, the band gap of ZnSe will be smaller than ZnS.

## Semiconductor Doping

The electrical conductivity of a semiconductor is influenced by the presence of small numbers of impurity atoms. The process of adding controlled amounts of impurity atoms to a material is known as **doping**. Consider what happens when a few phosphorus atoms (known as dopants) replace silicon atoms in a silicon crystal. In pure Si all of the valence-band molecular orbitals are filled and all of the conduction-band molecular orbitals are empty, as ▼ **FIGURE 12.32**(a) shows. Because phosphorus has five valence electrons but

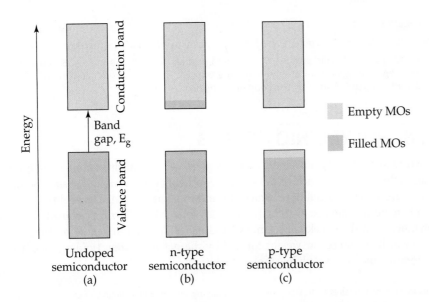

◀ **FIGURE 12.32**  The addition of small amounts of impurities (doping) to a semiconductor changes the electronic properties of the material.

silicon has only four, the "extra" electrons that come with the dopant phosphorus atoms are forced to occupy the conduction band [Figure 12.32(b)]. The doped material is called an *n-type* semiconductor, *n* signifying that the number of *negatively* charged electrons in the conduction band has increased. These extra electrons can move very easily in the conduction band. Thus, just a few parts per million (ppm) of phosphorus in silicon can increase silicon's intrinsic conductivity by a factor of a million!

The dramatic change in conductivity in response to the addition of a trace amount of a dopant means that extreme care must be taken to control the impurities in semiconductors. It also provides an opportunity for controlling the electrical conductivity through precise control of the type and concentration of dopants.

It is also possible to dope semiconductors with atoms that have fewer valence electrons than the host material. Consider what happens when a few aluminum atoms replace silicon atoms in a silicon crystal. Aluminum has only three valence electrons compared to silicon's four. Thus, there are electron vacancies, known as **holes**, in the valence band when silicon is doped with aluminum [Figure 12.32(c)]. Since the negatively charged electron is not there, the hole can be thought of as having a positive charge. Any adjacent electron that jumps into the hole leaves behind a new hole. Thus, the positive hole moves about in the lattice like a particle.* A material like this is called a *p-type* semiconductor, *p* signifying that the number of *positive* holes in the material has increased.

As with n-type conductivity, p-type dopant levels of only parts per million can lead to a millionfold increase in conductivity—but in this case, the holes in the valence band are doing the conduction [Figure 12.32(c)].

The junction of an n-type semiconductor with a p-type semiconductor forms the basis for diodes, transistors, solar cells, and other devices.

---

**SAMPLE EXERCISE 12.4**  **Identifying Types of Semiconductors**

Which of the following elements, if doped into silicon, would yield an n-type semiconductor: Ga, As, or C?

**SOLUTION**

**Analyze**  An n-type semiconductor means that the dopant atoms must have more valence electrons than the host material. Silicon is the host material in this case.

**Plan**  We must look at the periodic table and determine the number of valence electrons associated with Si, Ga, As, and C. The elements with more valence electrons than silicon are the ones that will produce an n-type material upon doping.

**Solve**  Si is in column 4A, and so has four valence electrons. Ga is in column 3A, and so has three valence electrons. As is in column 5A, and so has five valence electrons; C is in column 4A, and so has four valence electrons. Therefore, As, if doped into silicon, would yield an n-type semiconductor.

**PRACTICE EXERCISE**

Suggest an element that could be used to dope silicon to yield a p-type material.

***Answer:***  Because Si is in group 4A, we need to pick an element in group 3A. Boron and aluminum are both good choices—both are in group 3A. In the semiconductor industry boron and aluminum are commonly used dopants for silicon.

---

# 12.8 | POLYMERIC SOLIDS

In nature we find many substances of very high molecular weight, running into millions of amu, that make up much of the structure of living organisms and tissues. Some examples are starch and cellulose, which abound in plants, as well as proteins, which are found in both plants and animals. In 1827 Jons Jakob Berzelius coined the word **polymer** (from the Greek *polys*, "many," and *meros*, "parts") to denote molecular substances of high molecular weight formed by the *polymerization* (joining together) of **monomers**, molecules with low molecular weight.

---

*This movement is analogous to watching people changing seats in a classroom; you can watch the people (electrons) move about the seats (atoms), or you can watch the empty seats (holes) "move."

# CHEMISTRY PUT TO WORK

## Solid-State Lighting

Artificial lighting is so widespread we take it for granted. As described in Chapter 1, major savings in energy would be realized if incandescent lights can be replaced by light-emitting diodes (LEDs) (Section 1.4, "Chemistry Put to Work"). Because LEDs are made from semiconductors, this is an appropriate place to take a closer look at the operation of an LED.

The heart of an LED is a p–n diode, which is formed by bringing an n-type semiconductor in contact with a p-type semiconductor. In the junction where they meet there are very few electrons or holes to carry the charge and the conductivity decreases. When an appropriate voltage is applied, it drives electrons from the conduction band of the n-doped side into the junction, where they meet holes that are pushed in from the valence band of the p-doped side. The electrons fall into the empty holes, and their energy is converted into light whose photons have energy equal to the band gap (▼ **FIGURE 12.33**). In this way electrical energy is converted into optical energy.

Because the wavelength of light that is emitted depends on the band gap of the semiconductor, the color of light produced by the LED can be controlled by appropriate choice of semiconductor. Most red LEDs are made of a mixture of GaP and GaAs. The band gap of GaP is 2.26 eV ($3.62 \times 10^{-19}$ J), which corresponds to a green photon with a wavelength of 549 nm, while GaAs has a band gap of 1.43 eV ($2.29 \times 10^{-19}$ J), which corresponds to an infrared photon with a wavelength of 867 nm. ∞ (Section 6.1 and 6.2) By forming solid solutions of these two compounds, with stoichiometries of $GaP_{1-x}As_x$, the band gap can be adjusted to any intermediate value. Thus, $GaP_{1-x}As_x$ is the solid solution of choice for red, orange, and yellow LEDs. Green LEDs are made from mixtures of GaP and AlP ($E_g = 2.43$ eV, $\lambda = 510$ nm).

Red LEDs have been in the market for decades, but to make white light an efficient blue LED was needed. The first prototype bright blue LED was demonstrated in Japan in 1993. In 2006, only 13 years later, over \$4 billion worth of blue LEDs were sold worldwide. The blue LEDs are based on combinations of GaN ($E_g = 3.4$ eV, $\lambda = 365$ nm) and InN ($E_g = 2.4$ eV, $\lambda = 517$ nm). With the availability of blue LEDs there are various strategies for making white LEDs. In some cases, light is combined from blue, green, and red LEDs. More commonly a blue LED is coated with a phosphor, a material that converts some of the blue light into yellow light. In either case the combined colors appear white to the eye. Some examples of different color LEDs are shown in ▼ **FIGURE 12.34**.

*RELATED EXERCISES:* 12.71, 12.72, 12.73, 12.74

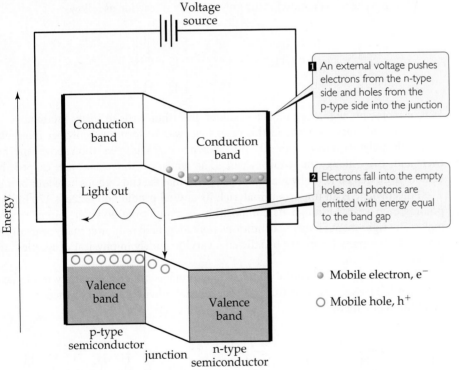

**1** An external voltage pushes electrons from the n-type side and holes from the p-type side into the junction

**2** Electrons fall into the empty holes and photons are emitted with energy equal to the band gap

● Mobile electron, $e^-$

○ Mobile hole, $h^+$

▲ **FIGURE 12.33** **Light-emitting diodes.** The heart of a light-emitting diode is a p–n junction in which an applied voltage drives electrons and holes to combine and give off light.

▲ **FIGURE 12.34** **Different colors of light-emitting diodes.**

Historically natural polymers, such as wool, leather, silk, and natural rubber, were processed into usable materials. During the past 70 years or so, chemists have learned to form synthetic polymers by polymerizing monomers through controlled chemical reactions. A great many of these synthetic polymers have a backbone of carbon–carbon bonds because carbon atoms have an exceptional ability to form strong stable bonds with one another.

**Plastics** are materials that can be formed into various shapes, usually by the application of heat and pressure. **Thermoplastic** materials can be reshaped. For example, plastic milk containers are made from the polymer *polyethylene*. These containers can be melted down and the polymer recycled for some other use. In contrast, a **thermosetting plastic** is shaped through irreversible chemical processes and, therefore, cannot be reshaped readily. An **elastomer** is a material that exhibits rubbery or elastic behavior. When subjected to stretching or bending, an elastomer regains its original shape upon removal of the distorting force, if it has not been distorted beyond some elastic limit. Rubber is the most familiar example of an elastomer.

Some polymers, such as nylon and polyesters, both of which are thermosetting plastics, can be formed into fibers that, like hair, are very long relative to their cross-sectional area. These fibers can be woven into fabrics and cords and fashioned into clothing, tire cord, and other useful objects.

## Making Polymers

The simplest example of a polymerization reaction is the formation of polyethylene from ethylene molecules (▼ FIGURE 12.35). In this reaction, the double bond in each ethylene molecule "opens up," and two of the electrons originally in this bond are used to form new C—C single bonds with two other ethylene molecules. This type of polymerization, in which monomers are coupled through their multiple bonds, is called **addition polymerization**.

We can write the equation for the polymerization reaction as follows:

$$n\ CH_2{=}CH_2 \longrightarrow \left[ \begin{array}{cc} H & H \\ | & | \\ C & -C \\ | & | \\ H & H \end{array} \right]_n$$

Here $n$ represents the large number—ranging from hundreds to many thousands—of monomer molecules (ethylene in this case) that react to form one polymer molecule. Within the polymer, a repeat unit (the unit shown in brackets in equation above) appears over and over along the entire chain. The ends of the chain are capped by carbon–hydrogen bonds or by some other bond, so that the end carbons have four bonds.

Polyethylene is an important material; its annual production exceeds 170 billion pounds each year. Although its composition is simple, the polymer is not easy to make. The right manufacturing conditions were identified only after many years of research. Today many forms of polyethylene, varying widely in physical properties, are known.

Polymers of other chemical compositions provide still greater variety in physical and chemical properties. ▶ TABLE 12.5 lists several other common polymers obtained by addition polymerization.

▲ FIGURE 12.35 The polymerization of ethylene monomers to make the polymer polyethylene.

**TABLE 12.5 • Polymers of Commercial Importance**

| Polymer | Structure | Uses |
|---|---|---|
| **Addition Polymers** | | |
| Polyethylene | $-(CH_2-CH_2)_n$ | Films, packaging, bottles |
| Polypropylene | $\begin{bmatrix} CH_2-CH \\ \quad\quad CH_3 \end{bmatrix}_n$ | Kitchenware, fibers, appliances |
| Polystyrene | $\begin{bmatrix} CH_2-CH \\ \quad\quad C_6H_5 \end{bmatrix}_n$ | Packaging, disposable food containers, insulation |
| Polyvinyl chloride (PVC) | $\begin{bmatrix} CH_2-CH \\ \quad\quad Cl \end{bmatrix}_n$ | Pipe fittings, clear film for meat packaging |
| **Condensation Polymers** | | |
| Polyurethane | $\begin{bmatrix} C-NH-R-NH-C-O-R'-O \\ \parallel \quad\quad\quad\quad\quad \parallel \\ O \quad\quad\quad\quad\quad\quad\quad O \end{bmatrix}_n$ $R, R' = -CH_2-CH_2-$ (for example) | "Foam" furniture stuffing, spray-on insulation, automotive parts, footwear, water-protective coatings |
| Polyethylene terephthalate (a polyester) | $\begin{bmatrix} O-CH_2-CH_2-O-C-\bigcirc-C \\ \quad\quad\quad\quad\quad\quad\quad \parallel \quad\quad\quad \parallel \\ \quad\quad\quad\quad\quad\quad\quad O \quad\quad\quad O \end{bmatrix}_n$ | Tire cord, magnetic tape, apparel, soft-drink bottles |
| Nylon 6,6 | $\begin{bmatrix} NH-(CH_2)_6-NH-C-(CH_2)_4-C \\ \quad\quad\quad\quad\quad\quad\quad\quad \parallel \quad\quad\quad\quad \parallel \\ \quad\quad\quad\quad\quad\quad\quad\quad O \quad\quad\quad\quad O \end{bmatrix}_n$ | Home furnishings, apparel, carpet, fishing line, toothbrush bristles |
| Polycarbonate | $\begin{bmatrix} \quad\quad\quad\quad CH_3 \quad\quad\quad\quad O \\ O-\bigcirc-C-\bigcirc-O-C \\ \quad\quad\quad\quad CH_3 \end{bmatrix}_n$ | Shatterproof eyeglass lenses, CDs, DVDs, bulletproof windows, greenhouses |

A second general reaction used to synthesize commercially important polymers is **condensation polymerization**. In a condensation reaction two molecules are joined to form a larger molecule by elimination of a small molecule, such as $H_2O$. For example, an amine (a compound containing $-NH_2$) reacts with a carboxylic acid (a compound containing $-COOH$) to form a bond between N and C plus an $H_2O$ molecule (▼ **FIGURE 12.37**).

▲ **FIGURE 12.37 A condensation polymerization.**

# CHEMISTRY PUT TO WORK

### Recycling Plastics

If you look at the bottom of a plastic container, you are likely to see a recycle symbol containing a number, as shown in ▶ FIGURE 12.36. The number and the letter abbreviation below it indicate the kind of polymer from which the container is made, as summarized in ▼ TABLE 12.6. (The chemical structures of these polymers are shown in Table 12.5.) These symbols make it possible to sort containers by composition. In general, the lower the number, the greater the ease with which the material can be recycled.

**TABLE 12.6 • Categories Used for Recycling Polymeric Materials in the United States**

| Number | Abbreviation | Polymer |
|--------|--------------|---------|
| 1 | PET or PETE | Polyethylene terephthalate |
| 2 | HDPE | High-density polyethylene |
| 3 | V or PVC | Polyvinyl chloride (PVC) |
| 4 | LDPE | Low-density polyethylene |
| 5 | PP | Polypropylene |
| 6 | PS | Polystyrene |

▲ FIGURE 12.36 **Recycling symbols.** Most plastic containers manufactured today carry a recycling symbol indicating the type of polymer used to make the container and the polymer's suitability for recycling.

▶ FIGURE 12.38
**The formation of the copolymer nylon 6,6.**

$$n\ \text{H—N}(\text{CH}_2)_6\text{N—H} + n\ \text{HOC}(\text{CH}_2)_4\text{COH} \longrightarrow [\text{N(CH}_2)_6\text{N—C(CH}_2)_4\text{C}]_n + 2n\ \text{H}_2\text{O}$$

Diamine      Adipic acid      Nylon 6,6

Polymers formed from two different monomers are called **copolymers**. In the formation of many nylons, a *diamine*, a compound with an —NH$_2$ group at each end, is reacted with a *diacid*, a compound with a —COOH group at each end. For example, the copolymer nylon 6,6 is formed when a diamine that has six carbon atoms and an amino group on each end is reacted with adipic acid, which also has six carbon atoms (▲ FIGURE 12.38). A condensation reaction occurs on each end of the diamine and the acid. The components of H$_2$O are split out, and N—C bonds are formed between molecules.

Table 12.5 lists nylon 6,6 and some other common polymers obtained by condensation polymerization. Notice that these polymers have backbones containing N or O atoms as well as C atoms.

### GIVE IT SOME THOUGHT

Is this molecule a better starting material for an addition polymer or a condensation polymer?

$$\text{H}_2\text{N}—\bigcirc—\overset{\displaystyle O}{\overset{\|}{\text{C}}}—\text{O}—\text{H}$$

## Structure and Physical Properties of Polymers

The simple structural formulas given for polyethylene and other polymers are deceptive. Because four bonds surround each carbon atom in polyethylene, the atoms are arranged in a tetrahedral fashion, so that the chain is not straight as we have depicted it. Furthermore, the atoms are relatively free to rotate around the C—C single bonds. Rather than being straight and rigid, therefore, the chains are flexible, folding readily (▶ FIGURE 12.39). The flexibility in the molecular chains causes any material made of this polymer to be very flexible.

Both synthetic and natural polymers commonly consist of a collection of *macromolecules* (large molecules) of different molecular weights. Depending on the conditions of formation, the molecular weights may be distributed over a wide range or may be closely clustered around an average value. In part because of this distribution in molecular weights, polymers are largely amorphous (noncrystalline) materials. Rather than exhibiting a well-defined crystalline phase with a sharp melting point, polymers soften over a range of temperatures. They may, however, possess short-range order in some regions of the solid, with chains lined up in regular arrays as shown in ▶ FIGURE 12.40. The extent of such ordering is indicated by the degree of **crystallinity** of the polymer. Mechanical stretching or pulling to align the chains as the molten polymer is drawn through small holes can frequently enhance the crystallinity of a polymer. Intermolecular forces between the polymer chains hold the chains together in the ordered crystalline regions, making the polymer denser, harder, less soluble, and more resistant to heat. ▼ TABLE 12.7 shows how the properties of polyethylene change as the degree of crystallinity increases.

The linear structure of polyethylene is conducive to intermolecular interactions that lead to crystallinity. However, the degree of crystallinity in polyethylene strongly depends on the average molecular weight. Polymerization results in a mixture of macromolecules with varying values of $n$ and, hence, varying molecular weights. Low-density polyethylene (LDPE), used in forming films and sheets, has an average molecular weight in the range of $10^4$ amu and has substantial chain branching. That is, there are side chains off the main chain of the polymer. These side chains inhibit the formation of crystalline regions, reducing the density of the material. High-density polyethylene (HDPE), used to form bottles, drums, and pipes, has an average molecular weight in the range of $10^6$ amu. This form has fewer side chains and thus a higher degree of crystallinity.

▲ FIGURE 12.39 **A segment of a polyethylene chain.** This segment consists of 28 carbon atoms. In commercial polyethylenes, the chain lengths range from about $10^3$ to $10^5$ $CH_2$ units.

### GIVE IT SOME THOUGHT

In copolymers made of ethylene and vinyl acetate monomers, melting point and degree of crystallinity decrease as the percentage of vinyl acetate increases. Suggest an explanation.

$$CH_2{=}CH$$
$$\underset{\underset{O}{\overset{\|}{}}}{OCCH_3}$$

$$\underset{H}{\overset{H}{}}C{=}C\underset{H}{\overset{H}{}}$$

Ethylene          Vinyl acetate

Polymers can be made stiffer by introducing chemical bonds between chains. Forming bonds between chains is called **cross-linking** (▶ FIGURE 12.41). The greater the number of cross-links, the more rigid the polymer. Whereas thermoplastic materials consist of independent polymer chains, thermosetting ones become cross-linked when heated; the cross-links allow them to hold their shapes.

▲ FIGURE 12.40 **Interactions between polymer chains.** In the circled regions, the forces that operate between adjacent segments of the chains lead to ordering analogous to the ordering in crystals, though less regular.

| TABLE 12.7 • Properties of Polyethylene as a Function of Crystallinity | | | | | |
|---|---|---|---|---|---|
| | **Crystallinity** | | | | |
| | **55%** | **62%** | **70%** | **77%** | **85%** |
| Melting point (°C) | 109 | 116 | 125 | 130 | 133 |
| Density (g/cm³) | 0.92 | 0.93 | 0.94 | 0.95 | 0.96 |
| Stiffness* | 25 | 47 | 75 | 120 | 165 |
| Yield stress* | 1700 | 2500 | 3300 | 4200 | 5100 |

▲ FIGURE 12.41 **Cross-linking of polymer chains.** The cross-linking groups (red) constrain the relative motions of the polymer chains, making the material harder and less flexible than when the cross-links are not present.

*These test results show that the mechanical strength of the polymer increases with increased crystallinity. The physical units for the stiffness test are psi × 10⁻³ (psi = pounds per square inch); those for the yield stress test are psi. Discussion of the exact meaning and significance of these tests is beyond the scope of this text.

► **FIGURE 12.42 Vulcanization of natural rubber.** (a) Formation of polymeric natural rubber from the monomer isoprene. (b) Adding sulfur to rubber creates sulfur-atom links between chains. These links form as the carbon-carbon double bonds in the natural rubber polymer open up.

An important example of cross-linking is the **vulcanization** of natural rubber, a process discovered by Charles Goodyear in 1839. Natural rubber is formed from a liquid resin derived from the inner bark of the *Hevea brasiliensis* tree. Chemically, it is a polymer of isoprene, $C_5H_8$ (▲ **FIGURE 12.42**). Because rotation about the carbon–carbon double bond does not readily occur, the orientation of the groups bound to the carbons is rigid. In natural rubber, the chain extensions are on the same side of the double bond, as shown in Figure 12.42(a).

Natural rubber is not a useful polymer because it is too soft and too chemically reactive. Goodyear accidentally discovered that adding sulfur and then heating the mixture makes the rubber harder and reduces its susceptibility to oxidation or other chemical attack. The sulfur changes rubber into a thermosetting polymer by cross-linking the polymer chains through reactions at some of the double bonds, as shown schematically in Figure 12.42(b). Cross-linking of about 5% of the double bonds creates a flexible, resilient rubber. When the rubber is stretched, the cross-links help prevent the chains from slipping, so that the rubber retains its elasticity. Because heating was an important step in his process, Goodyear named it after Vulcan, the Roman god of fire.

# 12.9 | NANOMATERIALS

The prefix *nano* means $10^{-9}$. ∞ (Section 1.4) When people speak of "nanotechnology," they usually mean making devices that are on the 1–100-nm scale. It turns out that the properties of semiconductors and metals change in this size range. **Nanomaterials**—materials that have dimensions on the 1–100-nm scale—are under intense investigation in research laboratories around the world, and chemistry plays a central role in this investigation.

Smallest particles,
largest band gap

Largest particles,
smallest band gap

◀ FIGURE 12.43  **Cd₃P₂ powders with different particle sizes.** The arrows indicate decreasing particle size and a corresponding increase in the band gap energy.

## Semiconductors on the Nanoscale

Figure 12.23 shows that, in small molecules, electrons occupy discrete molecular orbitals whereas in macroscale solids the electrons occupy delocalized bands. At what point does a molecule get so large that it starts behaving as though it has delocalized bands rather than localized molecular orbitals? For semiconductors, both theory and experiment tell us that the answer is roughly at 1 to 10 nm (about 10–100 atoms across). The exact number depends on the specific semiconductor material. The equations of quantum mechanics that were used for electrons in atoms can be applied to electrons (and holes) in semiconductors to estimate the size where materials undergo a crossover from molecular orbitals to bands. Because these effects become important at 1 to 10 nm, semiconductor particles with diameters in this size range are called *quantum dots*.

One of the most spectacular effects of reducing the size of a semiconductor crystal is that the band gap changes substantially with size in the 1–10-nm range. As the particle gets smaller, the band gap gets larger, an effect observable by the naked eye, as shown in ▲ FIGURE 12.43. On the macro level, the semiconductor cadmium phosphide looks black because its band gap is small ($E_g = 0.5$ eV), and it absorbs all wavelengths of visible light. As the crystals are made smaller, the material progressively changes color until it looks white! It looks white because now no visible light is absorbed. The band gap is so large that only high-energy ultraviolet light can excite electrons into the conduction band ($E_g > 3.0$ eV).

Making quantum dots is most easily accomplished using chemical reactions in solution. For example, to make CdS, you can mix $Cd(NO_3)_2$ and $Na_2S$ in water. If you do not do anything else, you will precipitate large crystals of CdS. However, if you first add a negatively charged polymer to the water (such as polyphosphate, $—(OPO_2)_n—$), the $Cd^{2+}$ associates with the polymer, like tiny "meatballs" in the polymer "spaghetti." When sulfide is added, CdS particles grow, but the polymer keeps them from forming large crystals. A great deal of fine-tuning of reaction conditions is necessary to produce nanocrystals that are of uniform size and shape.

As we learned in Section 12.7 some semiconductor devices can emit light when a voltage is applied. Another way to make semiconductors emit light is to illuminate them with light whose photons have energies larger than the energy of the band gap of the semiconductor. This process is called *photoluminescence*. A valence-band electron absorbs a photon and is promoted to the conduction band. If the excited electron then falls back down into the hole it left in the valence band, it emits a photon having energy equal to the band gap energy. In the case of quantum dots, the band gap is tunable with the crystal size, and thus all the colors of the rainbow can be obtained from just one material, as shown for CdSe in ▶ FIGURE 12.44.

### GO FIGURE

**As the size of the quantum dots decreases, does the wavelength of the emitted light increase or decrease?**

Size of CdSe quantum dots

2 nm —————————————————→ 7 nm

2.7 eV —————————————————→ 2.0 eV

Band gap energy, $E_g$

▲ FIGURE 12.44  **Photoluminescence.** When illuminated with ultraviolet light, these solutions, each containing nanoparticles of the semiconductor CdSe, emit light that corresponds to their respective band gap energies. The light emitted depends on the size of the CdSe nanoparticles.

▲ **GIVE IT SOME THOUGHT**

Large crystals of ZnS can show photoluminescence, emitting ultraviolet photons with energies equal to the band gap energy and a wavelength of 340 nm. Is it possible to shift the luminescence so that the emitted photons are in the visible region of the spectrum by making appropriately sized nanocrystals?

Quantum dots are being explored for applications ranging from electronics to lasers to medical imaging because they are very bright, very stable, and small enough to be taken up by living cells even after being coated with a biocompatible surface layer.

Semiconductors do not have to be shrunk to the nanoscale in all three dimensions in order to show new properties. They can be laid down in relatively large two-dimensional areas on a substrate but be only a few nanometers thick to make *quantum wells. Quantum wires,* in which the semiconductor wire diameter is only a few nanometers but its length is very long, have also been made by various chemical routes. In both quantum wells and quantum wires, measurements along the nanoscale dimension(s) show quantum behavior, but in the long dimension, the properties seem to be just like those of the bulk material.

## Metals on the Nanoscale

Metals also have unusual properties on the 1–100-nm-length scale. Fundamentally, this is because the mean free path ∞ (Section 10.8) of an electron in a metal at room temperature is typically about 1–100 nm. So when the particle size of a metal is 100 nm or less, one might expect unusual effects.

Although it was not fully understood, people have known for hundreds of years that metals are different when they are very finely divided. Dating back to the middle ages, the makers of stained-glass windows knew that gold dispersed in molten glass made the glass a beautiful deep red (◀ FIGURE 12.45). Much later, in 1857, Michael Faraday reported that dispersions of small gold particles could be made stable and were deeply colored—some of the original colloidal solutions that he made are still in the Royal Institution of Great Britain's Faraday Museum in London (◀ FIGURE 12.46).

Other physical and chemical properties of metallic nanoparticles are also different from the properties of the bulk materials. Gold particles less than 20 nm in diameter melt at a far lower temperature than bulk gold, for instance, and when the particles are between 2 and 3 nm in diameter, gold is no longer a "noble," unreactive metal; in this size range it becomes chemically reactive.

At nanoscale dimensions, silver has properties analogous to those of gold in its beautiful colors, although it is more reactive than gold. Currently, there is great interest in research laboratories around the world in taking advantage of the unusual optical properties of metal nanoparticles for applications in biomedical imaging and chemical detection.

▲ **FIGURE 12.45 Stained glass window from the Chartres Cathedral in France.** Gold nanoparticles are responsible for the red color in this window, which dates from the 12th century.

▲ **FIGURE 12.46 The solutions of colloidal gold nanoparticles made by Michael Faraday in the 1850s.** These are on display in the Faraday Museum, London.

## Fullerenes, Carbon Nanotubes, and Graphene

We have seen that elemental carbon is quite versatile. In its $sp^3$-hybridized solid-state form, it is diamond; in its $sp^2$-hybridized solid-state form, it is graphite. Over the past three decades, scientists have discovered that $sp^2$-hybridized carbon can also form discrete molecules, one-dimensional tubes, and two-dimensional sheets. Each of these forms of carbon shows very interesting properties.

Until the mid-1980s, pure solid carbon was thought to exist in only two forms: the covalent-network solids diamond and graphite. In 1985, however, a group of researchers led by Richard Smalley and Robert Curl of Rice University in Houston and Harry Kroto of the University of Sussex, England, vaporized a sample of graphite with an intense pulse of laser light and used a stream of helium gas to carry the vaporized carbon into a mass spectrometer (Section 2.4, "A Closer Look: The Mass Spectrometer"). The mass spectrum showed peaks corresponding to clusters of carbon atoms, with a particularly strong peak corresponding to molecules composed of 60 carbon atoms, $C_{60}$.

Because $C_{60}$ clusters were so preferentially formed, the group proposed a radically different form of carbon, namely, nearly spherical $C_{60}$ *molecules*. They proposed that the carbon atoms of $C_{60}$ form a "ball" with 32 faces, 12 of them pentagons and 20 hexagons (▶ FIGURE 12.47), exactly like a soccer ball. The shape of this molecule is reminiscent of the geodesic dome invented by the U.S. engineer and philosopher R. Buckminster Fuller, so $C_{60}$ was whimsically named "buckminsterfullerene," or "buckyball" for short. Since the discovery of $C_{60}$, other related molecules of carbon atoms have been discovered. These molecules are now known as fullerenes.

Appreciable amounts of buckyball can be prepared by electrically evaporating graphite in an atmosphere of helium gas. About 14% of the resulting soot consists of $C_{60}$ and a related molecule, $C_{70}$, which has a more elongated structure. The carbon-rich gases from which $C_{60}$ and $C_{70}$ condense also contain other fullerenes, mostly containing more carbon atoms, such as $C_{76}$ and $C_{84}$. The smallest possible fullerene, $C_{20}$, was first detected in 2000. This small, ball-shaped molecule is much more reactive than the larger fullerenes. Because fullerenes are composed of individual molecules, they dissolve in various organic solvents, whereas diamond and graphite do not. This solubility permits fullerenes to be separated from the other components of soot and even from one another. It also allows the study of their reactions in solution.

Soon after the discovery of $C_{60}$, chemists discovered carbon nanotubes (▼ FIGURE 12.48). You can think of these as sheets of graphite rolled up and capped at one or both ends by half of a $C_{60}$ molecule. Carbon nanotubes are made in a manner similar to that used to make $C_{60}$. They can be made in either *multiwall* or *single-walled* forms. Multiwall carbon nanotubes consist of tubes within tubes, nested together, whereas single-walled carbon nanotubes consist of single tubes. Single-walled carbon nanotubes can be 1000 nm long or even longer but are only about 1 nm in diameter. Depending on the diameter of the graphite sheet and how it is rolled up, carbon nanotubes can behave as either semiconductors or metals.

The fact that carbon nanotubes can be made either semiconducting or metallic without any doping is unique among solid-state materials, and a great deal of work is going on to make carbon-based electronic devices. Carbon nanotubes are also being explored for their mechanical properties. The carbon–carbon bonded framework of the nanotubes means that the imperfections that might appear in a metal nanowire of similar dimensions are nearly absent. Experiments on individual carbon nanotubes suggest that they are stronger than steel, if steel were the dimensions of a carbon nanotube. Carbon nanotubes have been spun into fibers with polymers, adding great strength and toughness to the composite material.

The two-dimensional form of carbon, graphene, is the most recent low-dimensional form of carbon to be experimentally isolated and studied. Although its properties had been the subject of theoretical predictions for over 60 years, it was not until 2004 that

**GO FIGURE**

**How many bonds does each carbon atom in $C_{60}$ make? Based on this observation would you expect the bonding in $C_{60}$ to be more like that in diamond or that in graphite?**

▲ **FIGURE 12.47 Buckminsterfullerene, $C_{60}$.** The molecule has a highly symmetric structure in which the 60 carbon atoms sit at the vertices of a truncated icosahedron. The bottom view shows only the bonds between carbon atoms.

◀ **FIGURE 12.48 Atomic models of carbon nanotubes.** Left: "Armchair" nanotube, which shows metallic behavior. Right: "Zigzag" nanotube, which can be either semiconducting or metallic, depending on tube diameter.

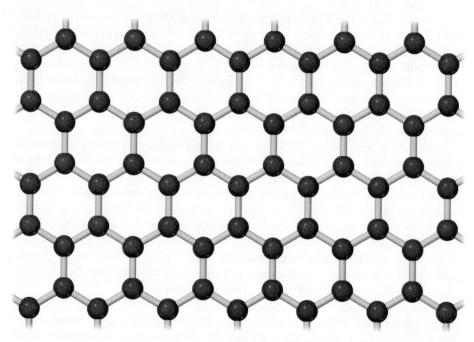

► **FIGURE 12.49  A portion of a two-dimensional graphene sheet.**

researchers at the University of Manchester in England isolated and identified individual sheets of carbon atoms with the honeycomb structure shown in ▲ **FIGURE 12.49**. Amazingly, the technique they used to isolate single-layer graphene was to successively peel away thin layers of graphite using an adhesive tape. Individual layers of graphene were then transferred to a silicon wafer having a precisely defined overcoat of $SiO_2$. When a single layer of graphene is left on the wafer, an interference-like contrast pattern results that can be seen with an optical microscope. If not for this simple yet effective way to scan for individual graphene crystals, they would probably still remain undiscovered. Subsequently, it has been shown that graphene can be deposited on clean surfaces of other types of crystals. The scientists who led the effort at the University of Manchester, Andre Geim and Konstantin Novoselov, were awarded the 2010 Nobel prize in physics for their work.

The properties of graphene are remarkable. It is very strong and has a record thermal conductivity, topping carbon nanotubes in both categories. Graphene is a semimetal, which means its electronic structure is like that of a semiconductor in which the energy gap is exactly zero. The combination of graphene's two-dimensional character and the fact that it is a semimetal allows the electrons to travel very long distances, up to 0.3 µm, without scattering from another electron, atom, or impurity. Graphene can sustain electrical current densities six orders of magnitude higher than those sustainable in copper. Scientists are currently exploring ways to incorporate graphene in various technologies.

**SAMPLE INTEGRATIVE EXERCISE**   Putting Concepts Together

A *conducting polymer* is a polymer that can conduct electricity. Some polymers can be made semiconducting; others can be nearly metallic. Polyacetylene is an example of a polymer that is a semiconductor. It can also be doped to increase its conductivity.

Polyacetylene is made from acetylene in a reaction that looks simple but is actually tricky to do:

$$H-C\equiv C-H \qquad \left[ CH=CH \right]_n$$

Acetylene                    Polyacetylene

**(a)** What is the hybridization of the carbon atoms, and the geometry around those atoms, in acetylene and in polyacetylene?

(**b**) Write a balanced equation to make polyacetylene from acetylene.

(**c**) Acetylene is a gas at room temperature and pressure (298 K, 1.00 atm). How many grams of polyacetylene can you make from a 5.00-L vessel of acetylene gas at room temperature and room pressure? Assume acetylene behaves ideally, and that the polymerization reaction occurs with 100% yield.

(**d**) Using the average bond enthalpies in Table 8.4, predict whether the formation of polyacetylene from acetylene is endothermic or exothermic.

## SOLUTION

**Analyze** For part (a), we need to recall what we have learned about $sp$, $sp^2$, and $sp^3$ hybridization and geometry. ∞ (Section 9.5) For part (b), we need to write a balanced equation. For part (c), we need to use the ideal-gas equation. ∞ (Section 10.4) For part (d), we need to recall the definitions of endothermic and exothermic and how bond enthalpies can be used to predict overall reaction enthalpies. ∞ (Section 8.8)

**Plan** For part (a), we should draw out the chemical structures of the reactant and product. For part (b), we need to make sure the equation is properly balanced. For part (c), we need to convert from liters of gas to moles of gas, using the ideal-gas equation ($PV = nRT$); then we need to convert from moles of acetylene gas to moles of polyacetylene using the answer from part (b); then we can convert to grams of polyacetylene. For part (d), we need to recall that $\Delta H_{rxn} = \Sigma$(bond enthalpies of bonds broken) $-$ $\Sigma$(bond enthalpies of bonds formed).

## Solve

(**a**) Carbon always forms four bonds. Thus, each C atom must have a single bond to H and a triple bond to the other C atom in acetylene. As a result, each C atom has two electron domains and must be $sp$ hybridized. This $sp$ hybridization also means that the H—C—C angles in acetylene are 180° and the molecule is linear.

We can write out the partial structure of polyacetylene as follows:

Each carbon is identical but now has three bonding electron domains that surround it. Therefore, the hybridization of each carbon atom is $sp^2$, and each carbon has local trigonal planar geometry with 120° angles.

(**b**) We can write:

$$n\ C_2H_2(g) \longrightarrow -[CH{=}CH]_n-$$

Note that all atoms originally present in acetylene end up in the polyacetylene product.

(**c**) We can use the ideal-gas equation as follows:

$$PV = nRT$$
$$(1.00\ \text{atm})(5.00\ \text{L}) = n(0.08206\ \text{L-atm/K-mol})(298\ \text{K})$$
$$n = 0.204\ \text{mol}$$

Acetylene has a molar mass of 26.0 g/mol; therefore, the mass of 0.204 mol is

$$(0.204\ \text{mol})(26.0\ \text{g/mol}) = 5.32\ \text{g acetylene}$$

Note that from the answer to part (b), all the atoms in acetylene go into polyacetylene. Due to conservation of mass, then, the mass of polyacetylene produced must also be 5.32 g, if we assume 100% yield.

(**d**) Let's consider the case for $n = 1$. We note that the reactant side of the equation in part (b) has one C≡C triple bond and two C—H single bonds. The product side of the equation in part (b) has one C=C double bond, one C—C single bond (to link to the adjacent monomer), and two C—H single bonds. Therefore, we are breaking one C≡C triple bond and are forming one C=C double bond and one C—C single bond. Accordingly, the enthalpy change for polyacetylene formation is:

$$\Delta H_{rxn} = (\text{C}{\equiv}\text{C triple bond enthalpy}) - (\text{C}{=}\text{C double bond enthalpy})$$
$$- (\text{C—C single bond enthalpy})$$
$$\Delta H_{rxn} = (839\ \text{kJ/mol}) - (614\ \text{kJ/mol}) - (348\ \text{kJ/mol})$$
$$= -123\ \text{kJ/mol}$$

Because $\Delta H$ is a negative number, the reaction releases heat and is exothermic.

# CHAPTER SUMMARY AND KEY TERMS

**INTRODUCTION AND SECTION 12.1** The structures and properties of solids can be classified according to the forces that hold the atoms together. **Metallic solids** are held together by a delocalized sea of collectively shared valence electrons. **Ionic solids** are held together by the mutual attraction between cations and anions. **Covalent-network solids** are held together by an extended network of covalent bonds. **Molecular solids** are held together by weak intermolecular forces. **Polymers** contain very long chains of atoms held together by covalent bonds. These chains are usually held to one another by weaker intermolecular forces. **Nanomaterials** are solids where the dimensions of individual crystals have been reduced to the order of 1–100 nm.

**SECTION 12.2** In **crystalline solids**, particles are arranged in a regularly repeating pattern. In **amorphous solids**, however, particles show no long-range order. In a crystalline solid the smallest repeating unit is called a **unit cell**. All unit cells in a crystal contain an identical arrangement of atoms. The geometrical pattern of points on which the unit cells are arranged is called a **crystal lattice**. To generate a crystal structure a **motif**, which is an atom or group of atoms, is associated with each and every **lattice point**.

In two dimensions the unit cell is a parallelogram whose size and shape are defined by two **lattice vectors** (a and b). There are four **primitive lattices**, lattices where the lattice points are located only at the corners of the unit cell: square, hexagonal, rectangular, and oblique. In three dimensions the unit cell is a parallelepiped whose size and shape are defined by three lattice vectors (a, b and c), and there are seven primitive lattices: cubic, tetragonal, hexagonal, rhombohedral, orthorhombic, monoclinic, and triclinic. Placing an additional lattice point at the center of a cubic unit cell leads to a **body-centered cubic lattice**, while placing an additional point at the center of each face of the unit cell leads to a **face-centered cubic lattice**.

**SECTION 12.3** **Metallic solids** are typically good conductors of electricity and heat, *malleable*, which means that they can be hammered into thin sheets, and *ductile*, which means that they can be drawn into wires. Metals tend to form structures where the atoms are closely packed. Two related forms of close packing, **cubic close packing** and **hexagonal close packing**, are possible. In both, each atom has a **coordination number** of 12.

**Alloys** are materials that possess characteristic metallic properties and are composed of more than one element. The elements in an alloy can be distributed either homogeneously or heterogeneously. Alloys which contain homogeneous mixtures of elements can either be substitutional or interstitial alloys. In a **substitutional alloy** the atoms of the minority element(s) occupy positions normally occupied by atoms of the majority element. In an **interstitial alloy** atoms of the minority element(s), often smaller nonmetallic atoms, occupy interstitial positions that lie in the "holes" between atoms of the majority element. In a **heterogeneous alloy** the elements are not distributed uniformly; instead, two or more distinct phases with characteristic compositions are present. **Intermetallic compounds** are alloys that have a fixed composition and definite properties.

**SECTION 12.4** The properties of metals can be accounted for in a qualitative way by the **electron-sea model**, in which the electrons are visualized as being free to move throughout the metal. In the molecular-

orbital model the valence atomic orbitals of the metal atoms interact to form energy **bands** that are incompletely filled by valence electrons. Consequently, the electronic structure of a bulk solid is referred to as a **band structure**. The orbitals that constitute the energy band are delocalized over the atoms of the metal, and their energies are closely spaced. In a metal the valence shell s, p, and d orbitals form bands and these bands overlap resulting in one or more partially filled bands. Because the energy differences between orbitals *within a band* are extremely small, promoting electrons to higher-energy orbitals requires very little energy. This gives rise to high electrical and thermal conductivity, as well as other characteristic metallic properties.

**SECTION 12.5** **Ionic solids** consist of cations and anions held together by electrostatic attractions. Because these interactions are quite strong, ionic compounds tend to have high melting points. The attractions become stronger as the charges of the ions increase and/or the sizes of the ions decrease. The presence of both attractive (cation–anion) and repulsive (cation–cation and anion–anion) interactions helps to explain why ionic compounds are brittle. Like metals the structures of ionic compounds tend to be symmetric, but to avoid direct contact between ions of like charge the coordination numbers (typically 4 to 8) are necessarily smaller than those seen in close-packed metals. The exact structure depends on the relative sizes of the ions and the cation-to-anion ratio in the empirical formula.

**SECTION 12.6** **Molecular solids** consist of atoms or molecules held together by intermolecular forces. Because these forces are relatively weak, molecular solids tend to be soft and possess low melting points. The melting point depends on the strength of the intermolecular forces, as well as the efficiency with which the molecules can pack together.

**SECTION 12.7** **Covalent-network solids** consist of atoms held together in large networks by covalent bonds. These solids are much harder and have higher melting points than molecular solids. Important examples include diamond, where the carbons are tetrahedrally coordinated to each other, and graphite where the carbon atoms form hexagonal layers through $sp^2$ bonds.

**Elemental semiconductors**, like Si and Ge, as well as **compound semiconductors**, like GaAs, InP, and CdTe, are important examples of covalent-network solids. In a semiconductor the filled bonding molecular orbitals make up the **valence band**, while the empty antibonding molecular orbitals make up the **conduction band**. The valence and conduction bands are separated by an energy that is referred to as the **band gap**. The size of the band gap increases as the bond distance decreases, and as the difference in electronegativity between the two elements increases.

**Doping** semiconductors changes their ability to conduct electricity by orders of magnitude. An n-type semiconductor is one that is doped so that there are excess electrons in the conduction band; a p-type semiconductor is one that is doped so that there are missing electrons, which are called **holes**, in the valence band.

**SECTION 12.8** **Polymers** are molecules of high molecular weight formed by joining together large numbers of small molecules called **monomers**. **Plastics** are materials that can be formed into various shapes, usually by the application of heat and pressure. **Thermoplastic** polymers can be reshaped, typically through heating, in contrast to **thermosetting plastics**, which are formed into objects through an irreversible chemical process and cannot readily be reshaped. An **elastomer** is a material that exhibits elastic behavior; that is, it returns to its original shape following stretching or bending.

In an **addition polymerization** reaction, the molecules form new linkages by opening existing $\pi$ bonds. Polyethylene forms, for example, when the carbon–carbon double bonds of ethylene open up. In a **condensation polymerization** reaction, the monomers are joined by splitting out a small molecule from between them. The various kinds of nylon are formed, for example, by removing a water molecule from between an amine and a carboxylic acid. A polymer formed from two different monomers is called a **copolymer**.

Polymers are largely amorphous, but some materials possess a degree of **crystallinity**. For a given chemical composition, the crystallinity depends on the molecular weight and the degree of branching along the main polymer chain. Polymer properties are also strongly affected by **cross-linking**, in which short chains of atoms connect the long polymer chains. Rubber is cross-linked by short chains of sulfur atoms in a process called **vulcanization**.

**SECTION 12.9** When one or more dimensions of a material become sufficiently small, generally smaller than 100 nm, the properties of the material change. Materials with dimensions on this length scale are called **nanomaterials**. Quantum dots are semiconductor particles with diameters of 1–10 nm. In this size range the material's band gap energy becomes size-dependent. Metal nanoparticles have different chemical and physical properties in the 1–100-nm size range. Gold, for example, is more reactive and no longer has a golden color. Nanoscience has produced a number of previously unknown forms of $sp^2$-hybridized carbon. Fullerenes, like $C_{60}$, are large molecules containing only carbon atoms. Carbon nanotubes are sheets of graphite rolled up. They can behave as either semiconductors or metals depending on how the sheet was rolled. Graphene, which is an isolated layer from graphite, is a two-dimensional form of carbon. Applications of these nanomaterials are being developed now for imaging, electronics, and medicine.

# KEY SKILLS

- Classify solids based on their bonding/intermolecular forces and understand how difference in bonding relates to physical properties. [Section 12.1]

- Know the difference between crystalline and amorphous solids. Understand the relationships between lattice vectors and unit cell. [Section 12.2]

- Understand why there are a limited number of lattices. Be able to recognize the four two-dimensional and the seven three-dimensional primitive lattices. Know the locations of lattice points for body-centered and face-centered lattices. [Section 12.2]

- Calculate the empirical formula and density of ionic and metallic solids from a picture of the unit cell. Be able to estimate the length of a cubic unit cell from the radii of the atoms/ions present. [Sections 12.3 and 12.5]

- Explain how homogeneous and heterogeneous alloys differ. Describe the differences between substitutional alloys, interstitial alloys, and intermetallic compounds. [Section 12.3]

- Use the molecular-orbital model to qualitatively predict the trends in melting point, boiling point, and hardness of metals. [Section 12.4]

- Predict the structures of ionic solids from their ionic radii and empirical formula. [Section 12.5]

- Be able to use the periodic table to qualitatively compare the band gap energies of semiconductors. [Section 12.7]

- Understand how n-type and p-type doping can be used to control the conductivity of semiconductors. [Section 12.7]

- Understand how polymers are formed from monomers and recognize the features of a molecule that allow it to react to form a polymer. Understand the differences between addition polymerization and condensation polymerization. [Section 12.8]

- Understand how the interactions between polymer chains impact the physical properties of polymers. [Section 12.8]

- Understand how the properties of bulk semiconductors and metals change as the size of the crystals decreases into the nanometer-length scale. [Section 12.9]

- Be familiar with the structures and unique properties of fullerenes, carbon nanotubes, and graphene. [Section 12.9]

# KEY EQUATION

- $$\frac{\text{Number of cations per formula unit}}{\text{Number of anions per formula unit}} = \frac{\text{anion coordination number}}{\text{cation coordination number}}$$  [12.1]  Relationship between cation and anion coordination numbers and the empirical formula of an ionic compound

# EXERCISES

## VISUALIZING CONCEPTS

**12.1** For each of the two-dimensional structures shown here (**a**) draw the unit cell, (**b**) determine the type of two-dimensional lattice (from Figure 12.4), and (**c**) determine how many of each type of circle (white or black) there are per unit cell. [Section 12.2]

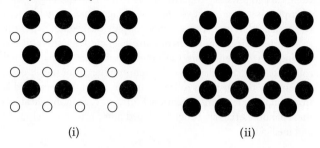

(i)                              (ii)

**12.2** (**a**) What kind of packing arrangement is seen in the accompanying photo? (**b**) What is the coordination number of each cannonball in the interior of the stack? [Section 12.3]

**12.3** Rhenium oxide crystallizes with a structure that has a primitive cubic lattice, as shown here. In the image on the left, the sizes of the ions have been reduced to show the entire unit cell. (**a**) How many atoms of each type are there per unit cell? (**b**) Use the ionic radii of rhenium (0.70 Å) and oxygen (1.26 Å) to estimate the length of the edge of the unit cell. (**c**) Use your answers to parts (**a**) and (**b**) to estimate the density of this compound. [Section 12.5].

● Re ● O

**12.4** The electronic structure of a doped semiconductor is shown here. (**a**) Which band, A or B, is the valence band? (**b**) Which band is the conduction band? (**c**) Which band consists of bonding molecular orbitals? (**d**) Is this an example of an n-type or p-type doped semiconductor? (**e**) If the semiconductor is germanium, which of the following elements could be the dopant: Ga, Si, or P? [Section 12.7]

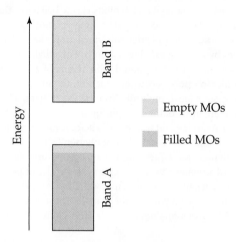

Empty MOs

Filled MOs

**12.5** Shown here are cartoons of two different polymers. Based on these cartoons, which polymer would you expect to be denser? Which one would have the higher melting point? [Section 12.8]

(a)                              (b)

**12.6** The accompanying image shows photoluminescence from four different samples of CdTe nanocrystals, each embedded in a polymer matrix. The photoluminescence occurs because the samples are being irradiated by a UV light source. The nanocrystals in each vial have different average sizes. The sizes are 4.0, 3.5, 3.2, and 2.8 nm. (**a**) Which vial contains the 4.0-nm nanocrystals? (**b**) Which vial contains the 2.8-nm nanocrystals? (**c**) Crystals of CdTe that have sizes that are larger than approximately 100 nm have a band gap of 1.5 eV. What would be the wavelength and frequency of light emitted from these crystals? What type of light is this? [Sections 12.7 and 12.9]

# CLASSIFICATIONS OF SOLIDS (section 12.1)

**12.7** Covalent bonding occurs in both molecular and covalent-network solids. Why do these two kinds of solids differ so greatly in their hardness and melting points?

**12.8** Silicon is the fundamental component of integrated circuits. Si has the same structure as diamond. Is Si a molecular, metallic, ionic, or covalent-network solid?

**12.9** What kinds of attractive forces exist between particles in **(a)** molecular crystals, **(b)** covalent-network crystals, **(c)** ionic crystals, **(d)** metallic crystals?

**12.10** Which type (or types) of crystalline solid is characterized by each of the following: **(a)** high mobility of electrons throughout the solid; **(b)** softness, relatively low melting point; **(c)** high melting point and poor electrical conductivity; **(d)** network of covalent bonds?

**12.11** Indicate the type of crystal (molecular, metallic, ionic, or covalent-network) each of the following would form upon solidification: **(a)** $CaCO_3$, **(b)** Pt, **(c)** $ZrO_2$ (melting point, 2677 °C), **(d)** table sugar ($C_{12}H_{22}O_{11}$), **(e)** benzene ($C_6H_6$), **(f)** $I_2$.

**12.12** Indicate the type of crystal (molecular, metallic, ionic, or covalent-network) each of the following would form upon solidification: **(a)** InAs, **(b)** MgO, **(c)** HgS, **(d)** In, **(e)** HBr.

**12.13** A white substance melts with some decomposition at 730 °C. As a solid, it does not conduct electricity, but it dissolves in water to form a conducting solution. Which type of solid (molecular, metallic, covalent-network, or ionic) might the substance be?

**12.14** You are given a white substance that sublimes at 3000 °C; the solid is a nonconductor of electricity and is insoluble in water. Which type of solid (molecular, metallic, covalent-network, or ionic) might this substance be?

# STRUCTURES OF SOLIDS (section 12.2)

**12.15** **(a)** Draw a picture that represents a crystalline solid at the atomic level. **(b)** Now draw a picture that represents an amorphous solid at the atomic level.

**12.16** Amorphous silica, $SiO_2$, has a density of about 2.2 g/cm³, whereas the density of crystalline quartz is 2.65 g/cm³. Account for this difference in densities.

**12.17** Two patterns of packing different types of spheres are shown here. For each structure **(a)** draw the two-dimensional unit cell, **(b)** determine the angle between the lattice vectors, $\gamma$, and whether the lattice vectors are the same length or of different lengths, **(c)** determine the type of two-dimensional lattice (from Figure 12.4).

(i)                                    (ii)

**12.18** Two patterns of packing different types of spheres are shown here. For each structure **(a)** draw the two-dimensional unit cell, **(b)** determine the angle between the lattice vectors, $\gamma$, and whether the lattice vectors are the same length or of different lengths, **(c)** determine the type of two-dimensional lattice (from Figure 12.4).

(i)                                    (ii)

**12.19** Of the seven three-dimensional primitive lattices, **(a)** which one has a unit cell where the $a$ and $b$ lattice vectors form a rectangular base, while the $c$ lattice vector is perpendicular to the other two and of a different length? **(b)** What is the lattice if the $a$ and $b$ lattice vectors form a square base and the $c$ lattice vector is perpendicular to the other two and of a different length?

**12.20** Of the seven three-dimensional primitive lattices, **(a)** which one has a unit cell where the $a$ and $b$ lattice vectors form a base that is an arbitrary parallelogram (like the unit cell of a two-dimensional oblique lattice), while the $c$ lattice vector is perpendicular to the other two? **(b)** What is the lattice if the $a$ and $b$ lattice vectors form a base that corresponds to the two-dimensional hexagonal unit cell and the $c$ lattice vector is perpendicular to the other two?

**12.21** Of the seven three-dimensional primitive lattices, which ones have a unit cell where no two lattice vectors are perpendicular to each other?

**12.22** Of the seven three-dimensional primitive lattices, which ones have a unit cell where all three lattice vectors are of the same length?

**12.23** What is the minimum number of atoms that could be contained in the unit cell of an element with a body-centered cubic lattice?

**12.24** What is the minimum number of atoms that could be contained in the unit cell of an element with a face-centered cubic lattice?

**12.25** The unit cell of nickel arsenide is shown here. **(a)** What type of lattice does this crystal possess? **(b)** What is the empirical formula?

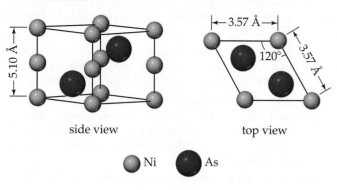

side view          top view

Ni          As

**12.26** The unit cell of a compound containing strontium, iron, and oxygen is shown here. **(a)** What type of lattice does this crystal possess (all three lattice vectors are mutually perpendicular)? **(b)** What is the empirical formula?

O          Sr          Fe

## METALLIC SOLIDS (section 12.3)

**12.27** The densities of the elements K, Ca, Sc, and Ti are 0.86, 1.5, 3.2, and 4.5 g/cm$^3$, respectively. What factors are likely to be of major importance in determining this variation? Which factor do you think will be the most important?

**12.28** Which of the following substances would you expect to possess metallic properties: **(a)** $TiCl_4$, **(b)** NiCo alloy, **(c)** W, **(d)** Ge, **(e)** ScN?

**12.29** Consider the unit cells shown here for three different structures that are commonly observed for metallic elements. **(a)** Which structure(s) corresponds to the densest packing of atoms? **(b)** Which structure(s) corresponds to the least dense packing of atoms?

Structure type A     Structure type B     Structure type C

**12.30** Sodium metal (atomic weight 22.99 g/cm$^3$) adopts a body-centered cubic structure with a density of 0.97 g/cm$^3$. **(a)** Use this information and Avogadro's number ($N_A = 6.022 \times 10^{23}$) to estimate the atomic radius of sodium. **(b)** If it didn't react so vigorously, sodium could float on water. Use the answer from part (a) to estimate the density of Na if its structure were that of a cubic close-packed metal. Would it still float on water?

**12.31** Iridium crystallizes in a face-centered cubic unit cell that has an edge length of 3.833 Å. **(a)** Calculate the atomic radius of an iridium atom. **(b)** Calculate the density of iridium metal.

**12.32** Calcium crystallizes with a body-centered cubic structure. **(a)** How many Ca atoms are contained in each unit cell? **(b)** How many nearest neighbors does each Ca atom possess? **(c)** Estimate the length of the unit cell edge, $a$, from the atomic radius of calcium (1.97 Å). **(d)** Estimate the density of Ca metal.

**12.33** Aluminum metal crystallizes in a cubic close-packed structure [face-centered cubic cell, Figure 12.14(a)]. **(a)** How many aluminum atoms are in a unit cell? **(b)** What is the coordination number of each aluminum atom? **(c)** Estimate the length of the unit cell edge, $a$, from the atomic radius of aluminum (1.43 Å). **(d)** Calculate the density of aluminum metal.

**12.34** An element crystallizes in a body-centered cubic lattice. The edge of the unit cell is 2.86 Å, and the density of the crystal is 7.92 g/cm$^3$. Calculate the atomic weight of the element.

**12.35** Define the term *alloy*. Distinguish among solid solution alloys, heterogeneous alloys, and intermetallic compounds.

**12.36** Distinguish between substitutional and interstitial alloys. What conditions favor formation of substitutional alloys?

**12.37** For each of the following alloy compositions indicate whether you would expect it to be a substitutional alloy, an interstitial alloy, or an intermetallic compound: **(a)** $Fe_{0.97}Si_{0.03}$, **(b)** $Fe_{0.60}Ni_{0.40}$, **(c)** $SmCo_5$.

**12.38** For each of the following alloy compositions indicate whether you would expect it to be a substitutional alloy, an interstitial alloy, or an intermetallic compound: **(a)** $Cu_{0.66}Zn_{0.34}$, **(b)** $Ag_3Sn$, **(c)** $Ti_{0.99}O_{0.01}$.

**12.39** Classify each of the following statements as true or false:
**(a)** Substitutional alloys tend to be more ductile than interstitial alloys.
**(b)** Interstitial alloys tend to form between elements with similar ionic radii.
**(c)** Nonmetallic elements are never found in alloys.

**12.40** Classify each of the following statements as true or false:
**(a)** Intermetallic compounds have a fixed composition.
**(b)** Copper is the majority component in both brass and bronze.
**(c)** In stainless steel the chromium atoms occupy interstitial positions.

**12.41** Which element or elements are alloyed with gold to make the following types of "colored gold" used in the jewelry industry? For each type indicate what type of alloy is formed: **(a)** white gold, **(b)** rose gold, **(c)** blue gold, **(d)** green gold.

**12.42** What is the chemical composition of purple gold? Is the composition variable? Why don't jewelers use purple gold to make rings or necklaces?

# METALLIC BONDING (section 12.4)

**12.43** Explain how the electron-sea model accounts for the high electrical and thermal conductivity of metals.

**12.44** (a) Compare the electronic structures of atomic chromium and atomic selenium. In what respects are they similar, and in what respects do they differ? (b) Chromium is a metal, and selenium is a nonmetal. What factors are important in determining this difference in properties?

**12.45** The molecular-orbital diagrams for two- and four-atom linear chains of lithium atoms are shown in Figure 12.23. Construct a molecular-orbital diagram for a chain containing six lithium atoms and use it to answer the following questions. (a) How many molecular orbitals are there in the diagram? (b) How many nodes are in the lowest-energy molecular orbital? (c) How many nodes are in the highest-energy molecular orbital? (d) How many nodes are in the highest-energy occupied molecular orbital (HOMO)? (e) How many nodes are in the lowest-energy unoccupied molecular orbital (LUMO)?

**12.46** Repeat Exercise 12.45 for a linear chain of eight lithium atoms.

**12.47** Which would you expect to be the more ductile element, (a) Ag or Mo, (b) Zn or Si? In each case explain your reasoning.

**12.48** How do you account for the observation that the alkali metals, like sodium and potassium, are soft enough to be cut with a knife?

**12.49** Explain this trend in melting points: Y 1522 °C, Zr 1852 °C, Nb 2468 °C, Mo 2617 °C.

**12.50** For each of the following groups which metal would you expect to have the highest melting point; (a) gold (Au), rhenium (Re), or cesium (Cs); (b) rubidium (Rb), molybdenum (Mo), or indium (In); (c) ruthenium (Ru), strontium (Sr), or cadmium (Cd)?

# IONIC AND MOLECULAR SOLIDS (section 12.5 and 12.6)

**12.51** Tausonite, a mineral composed of Sr, O, and Ti, has the cubic unit cell shown in the drawing. (a) What is the empirical formula of this mineral? (b) It is easy to see that Ti is coordinated by six oxygen atoms because the Ti atom is located at the center of the unit cell. To see the full coordination environment of the other ions, we have to consider neighboring unit cells. How many oxygens are coordinated to strontium?

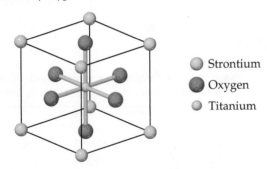

- Strontium
- Oxygen
- Titanium

**12.52** Rutile is a mineral composed of Ti and O. Its unit cell, shown in the drawing, contains Ti atoms at each corner and a Ti atom at the center of the cell. Four O atoms are on the opposite faces of the cell, and two are entirely within the cell. (a) What is the chemical formula of this mineral? (b) What is the coordination number of each atom?

- Oxygen
- Titanium

**12.53** NaF has the same structure as NaCl. (a) Use ionic radii from Chapter 7 to estimate the length of the unit cell edge for NaF. (b) Use the unit cell size calculated in part (a) to estimate the density of NaF.

**12.54** Clausthalite is a mineral composed of lead selenide (PbSe). The mineral adopts a NaCl-type structure. The density of PbSe at 25 °C is 8.27 g/cm$^3$. Calculate the length of an edge of the PbSe unit cell.

**12.55** A particular form of cinnabar (HgS) adopts the zinc blende structure, Figure 12.26. The length of the unit cell edge is 5.852 Å. (a) Calculate the density of HgS in this form. (b) The mineral tiemmanite (HgSe) also forms a solid phase with the zinc blende structure. The length of the unit cell edge in this mineral is 6.085 Å. What accounts for the larger unit cell length in tiemmanite? (c) Which of the two substances has the higher density? How do you account for the difference in densities?

**12.56** At room temperature and pressure RbI crystallizes with the NaCl-type structure. (a) Use ionic radii to predict the length of the cubic unit cell edge. (b) Use this value to estimate the density. (c) At high pressure the structure transforms to one with a CsCl-type structure. (c) Use ionic radii to predict the length of the cubic unit cell edge for the high-pressure form of RbI. (d) Use this value to estimate the density. How does this density compare with the density you calculated in part (b)?

**12.57** CuI, CsI, and NaI each adopt a different type of structure. The three different structures are those shown in Figure 12.26. (a) Use ionic radii, Cs$^+$($r = 1.81$ Å), Na$^+$($r = 1.16$ Å), Cu$^+$($r = 0.74$ Å), and I$^-$($r = 2.06$ Å), to predict which compound will crystallize with which structure. (b) What is the coordination number of iodide in each of these structures?

**12.58** The rutile and fluorite structures, shown here (anions are colored green), are two of the most common structure types for ionic compounds where the cation to anion ratio is 1:2. **(a)** For $CaF_2$ and $ZnF_2$ use ionic radii, $Ca^{2+}(r = 1.14 Å)$, $Zn^{2+}(r = 0.88 Å)$, $F^-(r = 1.19 Å)$, to predict which compound is more likely to crystallize with the fluorite structure and which with the rutile structure. **(b)** What are the coordination numbers of the cations and anions in each of these structures?

Rutile

Fluorite

**12.59** The coordination number for $Mg^{2+}$ ion is usually six. Assuming this assumption holds, determine the anion coordination number in the following compounds: **(a)** MgS, **(b)** $MgF_2$, **(c)** MgO.

**12.60** The coordination number for the $Al^{3+}$ ion is typically between four and six. Use the anion coordination number to determine the $Al^{3+}$ coordination number in the following compounds: **(a)** $AlF_3$ where the fluoride ions are two coordinate, **(b)** $Al_2O_3$ where the oxygen ions are six coordinate, **(c)** AlN where the nitride ions are four coordinate.

**12.61** Classify each of the following statements as true or false:

**(a)** Although both molecular solids and covalent-network solids have covalent bonds, the melting points of molecular solids are much lower because their covalent bonds are much weaker.

**(b)** Other factors being equal, highly symmetric molecules tend to form solids with higher melting points than asymmetrically shaped molecules.

**12.62** Classify each of the following statements as true or false:

**(a)** For molecular solids the melting point generally increases as the strengths of the covalent bonds increase.

**(b)** For molecular solids the melting point generally increases as the strengths of the intermolecular forces increase.

# COVALENT-NETWORK SOLIDS (section 12.7)

**12.63** Both covalent-network solids and ionic solids can have melting points well in excess of room temperature, and both can be poor conductors of electricity in their pure form. However, in other ways their properties are quite different.
  **(a)** Which type of solid is more likely to dissolve in water?
  **(b)** Which type of solid can become an electrical conductor via chemical substitution?

**12.64** Which of the following properties are typical characteristics of a covalent-network solid, a metallic solid, or both: **(a)** ductility, **(b)** hardness, **(c)** high melting point?

**12.65** For each of the following pairs of semiconductors, which one will have the larger band gap: **(a)** CdS or CdTe, **(b)** GaN or InP, **(c)** GaAs or InAs?

**12.66** For each of the following pairs of semiconductors, which one will have the larger band gap: **(a)** InP or InAs, **(b)** Ge or AlP, **(c)** AgI or CdTe?

**12.67** If you want to dope GaAs to make an n-type semiconductor with an element to replace Ga, which element(s) would you pick?

**12.68** If you want to dope GaAs to make a p-type semiconductor with an element to replace As, which element(s) would you pick?

**12.69** Silicon has a band gap of 1.1 eV at room temperature. **(a)** What wavelength of light would a photon of this energy correspond to? **(b)** Draw a vertical line at this wavelength in the figure shown, which shows the light output of the sun as a function of wavelength. Does silicon absorb all, none, or a portion of the visible light that comes from the sun?

**12.70** Cadmium telluride is an important material for solar cells. **(a)** What is the band gap of CdTe? **(b)** What wavelength of light would a photon of this energy correspond to? **(c)** Draw a vertical line at this wavelength in the figure shown with Exercise 12.69, which shows the light output of the sun as a function of wavelength. **(d)** With respect to silicon, does CdTe absorb a larger or smaller portion of the solar spectrum?

**12.71** The semiconductor GaP has a band gap of 2.2 eV. Green LEDs are made from pure GaP. What wavelength of light would be emitted from an LED made from GaP?

**12.72** The first LEDs were made from GaAs, which has a band gap of 1.43 eV. What wavelength of light would be emitted from an LED made from GaAs? What region of the electromagnetic spectrum does this light correspond to: UV, visible, or IR?

**12.73** GaAs and GaP ($E_g = 2.26$ eV) make solid solutions that have the same crystal structure as the parent materials, with As and P randomly distributed throughout the crystal. $GaP_xAs_{1-x}$ exists for any value of $x$. If we assume that the band gap varies linearly with composition between $x = 0$ and $x = 1$, estimate the band gap for $GaP_{0.5}As_{0.5}$. What wavelength of light does this correspond to?

**12.74** Red light-emitting diodes are made from GaAs and GaP solid solutions, $GaP_xAs_{1-x}$ (see Exercise 12.73). The original red LEDs emitted light with a wavelength of 660 nm. If we assume that the band gap varies linearly with composition between $x = 0$ and $x = 1$, estimate the composition (the value of $x$) that is used in these LEDs.

# POLYMERIC SOLIDS (section 12.8)

**12.75** What is a monomer? Give three examples of monomers taken from the examples given in this chapter.

**12.76** The molecular formula of *n*-decane is $CH_3(CH_2)_8CH_3$. Decane is not considered a polymer, whereas polyethylene is. What is the distinction?

**12.77** An ester is a compound formed by a condensation reaction between a carboxylic acid and an alcohol. Read the discussion of esters in Section 24.4 and then give an example of a reaction forming an ester. How might this kind of reaction be extended to form a polymer (a polyester)?

**12.78** Write a chemical equation for formation of a polymer via a condensation reaction from the monomers succinic acid ($HOOCCH_2CH_2COOH$) and ethylenediamine ($H_2NCH_2CH_2NH_2$).

**12.79** Draw the structure of the monomer(s) employed to form each of the following polymers shown in Table 12.5: (a) polyvinyl chloride, (b) nylon 6,6, (c) polyethylene terephthalate.

**12.80** Write the chemical equation that represents the formation of (a) polychloroprene from chloroprene (polychloroprene is used in highway-pavement seals, expansion joints, conveyor belts, and wire and cable jackets);

$$CH_2{=}CH{-}\underset{\underset{Cl}{|}}{C}{=}CH_2$$

Chloroprene

(b) polyacrylonitrile from acrylonitrile (polyacrylonitrile is used in home furnishings, craft yarns, clothing, and many other items).

$$CH_2{=}\underset{\underset{CN}{|}}{CH}$$

Acrylonitrile

**12.81** The nylon Nomex®, a condensation polymer, has the following structure:

Draw the structures of the two monomers that yield Nomex®.

**12.82** Proteins are polymers formed by condensation reactions of amino acids, which have the general structure

In this structure, R represents $-H$, $-CH_3$, or another group of atoms. Draw the general structure for a polyamino acid polymer formed by condensation polymerization of the molecule shown here.

**12.83** What molecular features make a polymer flexible? Explain how cross-linking affects the chemical and physical properties of the polymer.

**12.84** What molecular structural features cause high-density polyethylene to be denser than low-density polyethylene?

**12.85** Are high molecular weights and a high degree of crystallinity always desirable properties of a polymer? Explain.

**12.86** Briefly describe each of the following: (a) elastomer, (b) thermoplastic, (c) thermosetting plastic.

# NANOMATERIALS (section 12.9)

**12.87** Explain why "bands" may not be the most accurate description of bonding in a solid when the solid has nanoscale dimensions.

**12.88** CdS has a band gap of 2.4 eV. If large crystals of CdS are illuminated with ultraviolet light, they emit light equal to the band gap energy. (a) What color is the emitted light? (b) Would appropriately sized CdS quantum dots be able to emit blue light? (c) What about red light?

**12.89** True or false:
(a) The band gap of a semiconductor decreases as the particle size decreases in the 1–10-nm range.
(b) The light that is emitted from a semiconductor, upon external stimulation, becomes longer in wavelength as the particle size of the semiconductor decreases.

**12.90** True or false:
If you want a semiconductor that emits blue light, you could either use a material that has a band gap corresponding to the energy of a blue photon or you could use a material that has a smaller band gap but make an appropriately sized nanoparticle of the same material.

**12.91** Gold adopts a face-centered cubic structure with a unit cell edge of 4.08 Å (Figure 12.11). How many gold atoms are there in a sphere that is 20 nm in diameter? Recall that the volume of a sphere is $\frac{4}{3}\pi r^3$.

**12.92** Cadmium telluride, CdTe, takes the zinc blende structure (Figure 12.26) with a unit cell edge length of 6.49 Å. There are four cadmium atoms and four tellurium atoms per unit cell. How many of each type of atom are there in a cubic crystal with an edge length of 5.00 nm?

# ADDITIONAL EXERCISES

[12.93] A face-centered tetragonal lattice is not one of the 14 three-dimensional lattices. Show that a face-centered tetragonal unit cell can be redefined as a body-centered tetragonal lattice with a smaller unit cell.

12.94 Pure iron crystallizes with a body-centered cubic structure, but small amounts of impurities can stabilize a face-centered cubic structure. Which form of iron has a higher density?

[12.95] Introduction of carbon into a metallic lattice generally results in a harder, less ductile substance with lower electrical and thermal conductivities. Explain why this might be so.

12.96 As mentioned in Section 12.3, Ni$_3$Al is used in the turbines of aircraft engines because of its strength and low density. Nickel metal has a cubic close-packed structure with a face-centered cubic unit cell, while Ni$_3$Al has the ordered cubic structure shown in Figure 12.17. The length of the cubic unit cell edge is 3.53 Å for nickel and 3.56 Å for Ni$_3$Al. Use these data to calculate and compare the densities of these two materials.

12.97 For each of the intermetallic compounds shown in Figure 12.17 determine the number of each type of atom in the unit cell. Do your answers correspond to ratios expected from the empirical formulas: Ni$_3$Al, Nb$_3$Sn, and SmCo$_5$?

12.98 What type of lattice—primitive cubic, body-centered cubic, or face-centered cubic—does each of the following structure types possess: (a) CsCl, (b) Au, (c) NaCl, (d) Po, (e) ZnS?

12.99 Tin exists in two allotropic forms: Gray tin has a diamond structure, and white tin has a close-packed structure. One of these allotropic forms is a semiconductor with a small band gap while the other is a metal. Which one is which? Which form would you expect to have the longer Sn—Sn bond distance?

[12.100] The electrical conductivity of titanium is approximately 2500 times greater than that of silicon. Titanium has a hexagonal close-packed structure, and silicon has the diamond structure. Explain how the structures relate to the relative electrical conductivities of the elements.

12.101 Silicon carbide, SiC, has the three-dimensional structure shown in the figure.

(a) Name another compound that has the same structure. (b) Would you expect the bonding in SiC to be predominantly ionic, metallic, or covalent? (c) How do the bonding and structure of SiC lead to its high thermal stability (to 2700 °C) and exceptional hardness?

[12.102] Unlike metals, semiconductors increase their conductivity as you heat them (up to a point). Suggest an explanation.

12.103 Teflon® is a polymer formed by the polymerization of F$_2$C=CF$_2$. Draw the structure of a section of this polymer. What type of polymerization reaction is required to form it?

12.104 Hydrogen bonding between polyamide chains plays an important role in determining the properties of a nylon such as nylon 6,6 (Table 12.5). Draw the structural formulas for two adjacent chains of nylon 6,6 and show where hydrogen-bonding interactions could occur between them.

12.105 Explain why X-rays can be used to measure atomic distances in crystals but visible light cannot be used for this purpose.

12.106 In their study of X-ray diffraction, William and Lawrence Bragg determined that the relationship among the wavelength of the radiation ($\lambda$), the angle at which the radiation is diffracted ($\theta$), and the distance between planes of atoms in the crystal that cause the diffraction ($d$) is given by $n\lambda = 2d \sin \theta$. X-rays from a copper X-ray tube that have a wavelength of 1.54 Å are diffracted at an angle of 14.22 degrees by crystalline silicon. Using the Bragg equation, calculate the distance between the planes of atoms responsible for diffraction in this crystal, assuming $n = 1$ (first-order diffraction).

12.107 Germanium has the same structure as silicon, but the unit cell size is different because Ge and Si atoms are not the same size. If you were to repeat the experiment described in the previous problem but replace the Si crystal with a Ge crystal, would you expect the X-rays to be diffracted at a larger or smaller angle, $\theta$?

[12.108] (a) The density of diamond [Figure 12.30(a)] is 3.5 g/cm$^3$ and that of graphite [Figure 12.30(b)] is 2.3 g/cm$^3$. Based on the structure of buckminsterfullerene (Figure 12.47), what would you expect its density to be relative to these other forms of carbon? (b) X-ray diffraction studies of buckminsterfullerene show that it has a face-centered cubic lattice of C$_{60}$ molecules. The length of an edge of the unit cell is 14.2 Å. Calculate the density of buckminsterfullerene.

12.109 The valence band of a semiconductor is made up of bonding molecular orbitals and the conduction band of antibonding molecular orbitals. (a) Given this fact would you expect n-type doping to strengthen or weaken the bonds in a semiconductor? (b) Would you expect p-type doping to strengthen or weaken the bonds in a semiconductor?

# INTEGRATIVE EXERCISES

**12.110** The karat scale used to describe gold alloys is based on mass percentages. **(a)** If an alloy is formed that is 50 mol% silver and 50 mol% gold, what is the karat number of the alloy? Use Figure 12.18 to estimate the color of this alloy. **(b)** If an alloy is formed that is 50 mol% copper and 50 mol% gold, what is the karat number of the alloy? What is the color of this alloy?

**12.111** Spinel is a mineral that contains 37.9% Al, 17.1% Mg, and 45.0% O, by mass, and has a density of 3.57 g/cm$^3$. The unit cell is cubic with an edge length of 8.09 Å. How many atoms of each type are in the unit cell?

**12.112** **(a)** What are the C—C—C bond angles in diamond? **(b)** What are they in graphite?

**[12.113]** Employing the bond enthalpy values listed in Table 8.4, estimate the molar enthalpy change occurring upon **(a)** polymerization of ethylene, **(b)** formation of nylon 6,6, **(c)** formation of polyethylene terephthalate (PET).

**[12.114]** Although polyethylene can twist and turn in random ways, the most stable form is a linear one with the carbon backbone oriented as shown in the following figure:

The solid wedges in the figure indicate bonds from carbon that come out of the plane of the page; the dashed wedges indicate bonds that lie behind the plane of the page.

**(a)** What is the hybridization of orbitals at each carbon atom? What angles do you expect between the bonds?

**(b)** Now imagine that the polymer is polypropylene rather than polyethylene. Draw structures for polypropylene in which (i) the CH$_3$ groups all lie on the same side of the plane of the paper (this form is called isotactic polypropylene); (ii) the CH$_3$ groups lie on alternating sides of the plane (syndiotactic polypropylene); or (iii) the CH$_3$ groups are randomly distributed on either side (atactic polypropylene). Which of these forms would you expect to have the highest crystallinity and melting point, and which the lowest? Explain in terms of intermolecular interactions and molecular shapes.

**(c)** Polypropylene fibers have been employed in athletic wear. The product is said to be superior to cotton or polyester clothing in wicking moisture away from the body through the fabric to the outside. Explain the difference between polypropylene and polyester or cotton (which has many —OH groups along the molecular chain) in terms of intermolecular interactions with water.

**12.115** **(a)** In polyvinyl chloride shown in Table 12.5, which bonds have the lowest average bond enthalpy? **(b)** When subjected to high pressure and heated polyvinyl chloride converts to diamond. During this transformation which bonds are most likely to break first? **(c)** Employing the values of average bond enthalpy in Table 8.4, estimate the overall enthalpy change for converting PVC to diamond.

**[12.116]** Silicon has the diamond structure (Figure 12.30(a)) with unit cell edge length of 5.43 Å and eight atoms per unit cell. **(a)** How many silicon atoms are there in 1 cm$^3$ of material? **(b)** Suppose you dope that 1-cm$^3$ sample of silicon with 1 ppm of phosphorus that will increase the conductivity by a factor of a million. How many milligrams of phosphorus are required?

**12.117** KCl has the same structure as NaCl. The length of the unit cell is 6.28 Å. The density of KCl is 1.984 g/cm$^3$, and its formula mass is 74.55 amu. Using this information, calculate Avogadro's number.

**12.118** Look up the diameter of a silicon atom, in Å. The channel length in a Pentium 4 processor chip is 65 nm long. How many silicon atoms does this correspond to?

# WHAT'S AHEAD

## 13.1 THE SOLUTION PROCESS

We begin by considering what happens at the molecular level when a substance dissolves, paying particular attention to the role of *intermolecular forces*. Two important aspects of the solution process are the natural tendency of particles to mix and changes in *energy*.

## 13.2 SATURATED SOLUTIONS AND SOLUBILITY

We learn that when a *saturated solution* is in contact with undissolved solute, the dissolved and undissolved solutes are in *equilibrium*. The amount of solute in a saturated solution defines the *solubility* of the solute, the extent to which a particular solute dissolves in a particular solvent.

## 13.3 FACTORS AFFECTING SOLUBILITY

We next consider the major factors affecting solubility. The nature of the solute and solvent determines the kinds of intermolecular forces among solute and solvent particles and strongly influences solubility. Temperature also affects solubility: Most solids are more soluble in water at higher temperatures, whereas gases are less soluble in water at higher temperatures. The solubility of gases increases with increasing pressure.

**A TROPICAL BEACH.** Ocean water is a complex aqueous solution of many dissolved substances with sodium chloride having the highest concentration. *Dana Edmunds/ PacificStock.com*

**13.4 EXPRESSING SOLUTION CONCENTRATION**
We examine several common ways of expressing concentration, including *mole fraction*, *molarity*, and *molality*.

**13.5 COLLIGATIVE PROPERTIES**
We observe that some physical properties of solutions depend only on concentration and not on the identity of the solute. These *colligative properties* include the extent to which the solute lowers the vapor pressure, increases the boiling point, and decreases the

freezing point of the solvent. The *osmotic pressure* of a solution is also a colligative property.

**13.6 COLLOIDS**
We close the chapter by investigating *colloids*, mixtures that are not true solutions but consist of a solute-like phase (the dispersed phase) and a solvent-like phase (the dispersion medium). The dispersed phase consists of particles larger than typical molecular sizes.

# PROPERTIES OF SOLUTIONS

IN CHAPTERS 10, 11, AND 12, we explored the properties of gases, liquids, and solids. Most of the discussion focused on pure substances. However, the matter that we encounter in our daily lives, such as air, seawater, and sand, is usually composed of mixtures. In this chapter we examine homogeneous mixtures.

As we noted in earlier chapters, homogeneous mixtures are called *solutions*. ∞ (Sections 1.2 and 4.1)

When we think of solutions, we usually think of liquids, such as a solution of a salt in water, like the seawater shown in this chapter's opening photograph. Solutions, however, can also be solids or gases. For example, sterling silver is a homogeneous mixture of about 7% copper in silver and so is a solid solution. The air we breathe is a homogeneous mixture of several gases, making air a gaseous solution. Because liquid solutions are the most common, however, we focus our attention on them in this chapter.

Each substance in a solution is called a *component* of the solution. As we saw in Chapter 4, the *solvent* is normally the component present in the greatest amount, and all the other components are called *solutes*. In this chapter we compare the physical properties of solutions with the properties of the components in their pure form. We will be particularly concerned with *aqueous solutions*, which contain water as the solvent and either a gas, liquid, or solid as a solute.

# 13.1 | THE SOLUTION PROCESS

A solution is formed when one substance disperses uniformly throughout another. The ability of substances to form solutions depends on two factors: (1) the natural tendency of substances to mix and spread into larger volumes when not restrained in some way and (2) the types of intermolecular interactions involved in the solution process.

## The Natural Tendency toward Mixing

Suppose we have $O_2(g)$ and $Ar(g)$ separated by a barrier, as in ▼ **FIGURE 13.1**. If the barrier is removed, the gases mix to form a solution. The molecules experience very little in the way of intermolecular interactions and behave like ideal gas particles. As a result, their molecular motion causes them to spread through the larger volume, and a gaseous solution is formed.

The mixing of gases is a *spontaneous* process, meaning it occurs of its own accord without any input of energy from outside the system. The extent of spreading of the molecules and their associated kinetic energies is related to a thermodynamic quantity called *entropy*. We will examine spontaneous processes and entropy in Chapter 19. For our discussion of solutions, it is sufficient to merely recognize that the mixing that occurs when solutions form is associated with an entropy increase. Furthermore, it is the balance of the tendencies of systems to increase their entropy and decrease their energy (or enthalpy) that determines whether a process is spontaneous. Thus, the *formation of solutions is favored by the increase in entropy that accompanies mixing.*

When molecules of different types are brought together, mixing occurs spontaneously unless the molecules are restrained either by sufficiently strong intermolecular forces or by physical barriers. Thus, gases spontaneously mix unless restrained by their containers because with gases intermolecular forces are too weak to restrain the molecules. However, when the solvent or solute is a solid or liquid, intermolecular forces become important in determining whether or not a solution forms. For example, although ionic bonds hold sodium and chloride ions together in solid sodium chloride (Section 8.2), the solid dissolves in water because of the compensating strength of the attractive forces between the ions and water molecules. Sodium chloride does not dissolve in gasoline, however, because the intermolecular forces between the ions and the gasoline molecules are too weak.

⚠ **GIVE IT SOME THOUGHT**
Which two thermodynamic quantities determine whether or not a process is spontaneous?

## The Effect of Intermolecular Forces on Solution Formation

Any of the various intermolecular forces discussed in Chapter 11 can operate between solute and solvent particles in a solution. These forces are summarized in ▶ **FIGURE 13.2**. Dispersion forces, for example, dominate when one nonpolar substance, such as $C_7H_{16}$, dissolves in another, such as $C_5H_{12}$, and ion–dipole forces dominate in solutions of ionic substances in water.

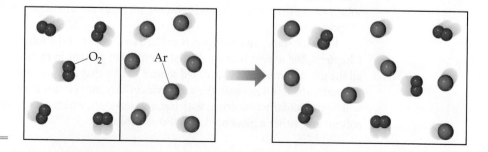

▶ **FIGURE 13.1** **Spontaneous mixing of two gases to form a homogeneous mixture (solution).**

GO FIGURE

**Why does the oxygen atom in H₂O point toward Na⁺ in the ion–dipole interaction?**

Dispersion    Dipole–dipole    Hydrogen bond    Ion–dipole

Heptane     Pentane
(C₇H₁₆)     (C₅H₁₂)

Acetone     Chloroform     Ethanol     Water
(C₃H₆O)     (CHCl₃)       (C₂H₅OH)    (H₂O)

▲ **FIGURE 13.2**  Intermolecular interactions involved in solutions.

Three kinds of intermolecular interactions are involved in solution formation:

1. *Solute–solute* interactions between solute particles must be overcome in order to disperse the solute particles through the solvent.

2. *Solvent–solvent* interactions between solvent particles must be overcome to make room for the solute particles in the solvent.

3. *Solvent–solute* interactions between solvent and solute particles occur as the particles mix.

The extent to which one substance is able to dissolve in another depends on the relative magnitudes of these three types of interactions. Solutions form when the magnitudes of the solvent–solute interactions are either comparable to or greater than the solute–solute and solvent–solvent interactions. For example, heptane ($C_7H_{16}$) and pentane ($C_5H_{12}$) dissolve in each other in all proportions. For this discussion, let's arbitrarily call heptane the solvent and pentane the solute. Both substances are nonpolar, and the magnitudes of the solvent–solute interactions (attractive dispersion forces) are comparable to the solute–solute and the solvent–solvent interactions. Thus, no forces impede mixing, and the tendency to mix (increase entropy) causes the solution to form spontaneously.

Solid NaCl dissolves readily in water because the attractive solvent–solute interactions between the polar $H_2O$ molecules and the ions are strong enough to overcome the attractive solute–solute interactions between ions in the NaCl($s$) and the attractive solvent–solvent interactions between $H_2O$ molecules. When NaCl is added to water (▶ **FIGURE 13.3**), the water molecules orient themselves on the surface of the NaCl crystals with the positive end of the water dipole oriented toward Cl⁻ ions and the negative end oriented toward Na⁺ ions. These ion–dipole attractions are strong enough to pull the surface ions away from the solid, thus overcoming the solute–solute interactions. In order for the solid to dissolve, some solvent–solvent interactions must also be overcome to create room for the ions to "fit" among all the water molecules.

Once separated from the solid, the Na⁺ and Cl⁻ ions are surrounded by water molecules. Interactions such as this between solute and solvent molecules are known as **solvation**. When the solvent is water, the interactions are referred to as **hydration**.

GIVE IT SOME THOUGHT

Why doesn't NaCl dissolve in nonpolar solvents such as hexane, C₆H₁₄?

## Energetics of Solution Formation

Solution processes are typically accompanied by changes in enthalpy. For example, when NaCl dissolves in water, the process is slightly endothermic, $\Delta H_{soln} = 3.9 \text{ kJ/mol}$. We can use Hess's law to analyze how the solute–solute, solvent–solvent, and solute–solute interactions influence the enthalpy of solution. ∞ (Section 5.6)

△ GO FIGURE

How does the orientation of $H_2O$ molecules around $Na^+$ differ from that around $Cl^-$?

Solvent–solute interactions between water molecules and NaCl allow solid to dissolve

Crystal of NaCl in water

Ions hydrated in solution

Hydrated $Cl^-$ ion     Hydrated $Na^+$ ion

▲ **FIGURE 13.3  Dissolution of an ionic solid in water.**

We can consider the solution process as having three components, each with an associated enthalpy change: Solute particles separate from one another ($\Delta H_{solute}$), solvent particles separate from one another ($\Delta H_{solvent}$), and solute and solvent particles mix ($\Delta H_{mix}$). The overall enthalpy change, $\Delta H_{soln}$, is

$$\Delta H_{soln} = \Delta H_{solute} + \Delta H_{solvent} + \Delta H_{mix} \qquad [13.1]$$

Separation of the solute particles from one another always requires an input of energy to overcome their attractive interactions. The process is therefore endothermic ($\Delta H_{solute} > 0$). Likewise, separation of solvent molecules to accommodate the solute also always requires energy ($\Delta H_{solvent} > 0$). The third component, which arises from the attractive interactions between solute particles and solvent particles, is always exothermic ($\Delta H_{mix} < 0$).

As shown in ▶ **FIGURE 13.4**, the three enthalpy terms in Equation 13.1 can be added together to give either a negative or a positive sum. Thus, the formation of a solution can be either exothermic or endothermic. For example, when magnesium sulfate ($MgSO_4$) is added to water, the solution process is exothermic: $\Delta H_{soln} = -91.2$ kJ/mol. In contrast, the dissolution of ammonium nitrate ($NH_4NO_3$) is endothermic: $\Delta H_{soln} = 26.4$ kJ/mol. These particular salts are the main components in the instant heat packs and ice packs used to treat athletic injuries (▶ **FIGURE 13.5**). The packs consist of a pouch of water and the solid salt sealed off from the water—$MgSO_4(s)$ for hot packs and $NH_4NO_3(s)$ for cold packs. When the pack is squeezed, the seal separating the solid from the water is broken and a solution forms, either increasing or decreasing the temperature.

The enthalpy change for a process can provide insight into the extent to which the process occurs. ∞ (Section 5.4) Exothermic processes tend to proceed spontaneously. On the other hand, if $\Delta H_{soln}$ is too endothermic, the solute might not dissolve to any

How does the magnitude of $\Delta H_{mix}$ compare with the magnitude of $\Delta H_{solute} + \Delta H_{solute}$ for exothermic solution processes?

Exothermic solution process

Endothermic solution process

▲ **FIGURE 13.4 Enthalpy changes accompanying the solution process.**

▲ **FIGURE 13.5 Ammonium nitrate instant ice pack.**

significant extent in the chosen solvent. Thus, for solutions to form, the solvent–solute interaction must be strong enough to make $\Delta H_{mix}$ comparable in magnitude to $\Delta H_{solute} + \Delta H_{solvent}$. This fact further explains why ionic solutes do not dissolve in nonpolar solvents. The nonpolar solvent molecules experience only weak attractive interactions with the ions, and these interactions do not compensate for the energies required to separate the ions from one another.

By similar reasoning, a polar liquid solute, such as water, does not dissolve in a nonpolar liquid solvent, such as octane ($C_8H_{18}$). The water molecules experience strong hydrogen-bonding interactions with one another. ∞ (Section 11.2) These attractive forces must be overcome in order to disperse the water molecules throughout the octane solvent. The energy required to separate the $H_2O$ molecules from one another is not recovered in the form of attractive interactions between the $H_2O$ and $C_8H_{18}$ molecules.

 GIVE IT SOME THOUGHT

Label the following processes as exothermic or endothermic:
a. breaking solvent–solvent interactions to form separated particles;
b. forming solvent–solute interactions from separated particles.

## Solution Formation and Chemical Reactions

In discussing solutions, we must be careful to distinguish the physical process of solution formation from chemical reactions that lead to a solution. For example, nickel metal dissolves on contact with hydrochloric acid solution because the following reaction occurs:

$$Ni(s) + 2\,HCl(aq) \longrightarrow NiCl_2(aq) + H_2(g) \qquad [13.2]$$

In this instance the resultant solution is not that of the Ni metal but rather its salt $NiCl_2$. If the solution is evaporated to dryness, $NiCl_2 \cdot 6\,H_2O(s)$ is recovered (▶ **FIGURE 13.6**). When $NaCl(s)$ is dissolved in water, on the other hand, no chemical reaction occurs. If the solution is evaporated to dryness, NaCl is recovered. Our focus throughout this chapter is on solutions from which the solute can be recovered unchanged from the solution.

Nickel metal and hydrochloric acid

Nickel reacts with hydrochloric acid, forming $NiCl_2(aq)$ and $H_2(g)$. The solution is of $NiCl_2$, not Ni metal

$NiCl_2 \cdot 6H_2O(s)$ remains when solvent evaporated

▲ FIGURE 13.6 **The reaction between nickel metal and hydrochloric acid is *not* a simple dissolution.**

## A CLOSER LOOK

### HYDRATES

Frequently, hydrated ions remain in crystalline salts that are obtained by evaporation of water from aqueous solutions. Common examples include $FeCl_3 \cdot 6H_2O$ [iron(III) chloride hexahydrate] and $CuSO_4 \cdot 5H_2O$ [copper(II) sulfate pentahydrate]. The $FeCl_3 \cdot 6H_2O$ consists of $Fe(H_2O)_6^{3+}$ and $Cl^-$ ions; the $CuSO_4 \cdot 5H_2O$ consists of $Cu(H_2O)_4^{2+}$ and $SO_4(H_2O)^{2-}$ ions. Water molecules can also occur in positions in the crystal lattice that are not specifically associated with either a cation or an anion. $BaCl_2 \cdot 2H_2O$ (barium chloride dihydrate) is an example. Compounds such as $FeCl_3 \cdot 6H_2O$, $CuSO_4 \cdot 5H_2O$, and $BaCl_2 \cdot 2H_2O$, which contain a salt and water combined in definite proportions, are known as *hydrates*. The water associated with them is called *water of hydration*. ▶ FIGURE 13.7 shows a hydrate and the corresponding anhydrous (water-free) substance.

*RELATED EXERCISE: 13.4*

$CuSO_4 \cdot 5H_2O$        $CuSO_4$

▲ FIGURE 13.7 **A hydrate and its anhydrous salt.** The anhydrous salt is the white substance, which turns blue upon addition of water.

## 13.2 | SATURATED SOLUTIONS AND SOLUBILITY

As a solid solute begins to dissolve in a solvent, the concentration of solute particles in solution increases, increasing the chances that some solute particles will collide with the surface of the solid and reattach. This process, which is the opposite of the solution process, is called **crystallization**. Thus, two opposing processes occur in a solution in contact with undissolved solute. This situation is represented in a chemical equation by two half arrows:

$$\text{Solute + solvent} \underset{\text{crystallize}}{\overset{\text{dissolve}}{\rightleftharpoons}} \text{solution} \qquad [13.3]$$

GO FIGURE

**What two processes are represented in this figure, and what are their relative rates at equilibrium?**

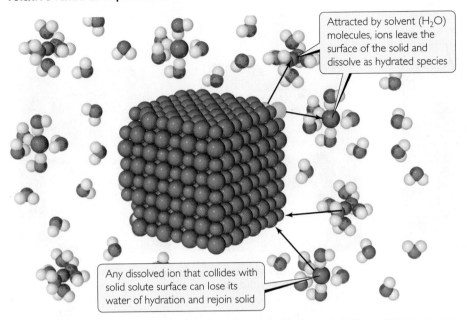

Attracted by solvent ($H_2O$) molecules, ions leave the surface of the solid and dissolve as hydrated species

Any dissolved ion that collides with solid solute surface can lose its water of hydration and rejoin solid

▲ **FIGURE 13.8  Dynamic equilibrium in a saturated solution with excess ionic solute.**

When the rates of these opposing processes become equal, a *dynamic equilibrium* is established and there is no further increase in the amount of solute in solution. (▲ **FIGURE 13.8**)

A solution that is in equilibrium with undissolved solute is **saturated**. Additional solute will not dissolve if added to a saturated solution. The amount of solute needed to form a saturated solution in a given quantity of solvent is known as the **solubility** of that solute. That is, *the solubility of a given solute in a given solvent is the maximum amount of the solute that can dissolve in a given amount of the solvent at a specified temperature, given that excess solute is present.* For example, the solubility of NaCl in water at 0 °C is 35.7 g per 100 mL of water. This is the maximum amount of NaCl that can be dissolved in water to give a stable equilibrium solution at that temperature.

If we dissolve less solute than the amount needed to form a saturated solution, the solution is **unsaturated**. Thus, a solution containing 10.0 g of NaCl per 100 mL of water at 0 °C is unsaturated because it has the capacity to dissolve more solute.

Under suitable conditions it is possible to form solutions that contain a greater amount of solute than needed to form a saturated solution. Such solutions are **supersaturated**. For example, when a saturated solution of sodium acetate is made at a high temperature and then slowly cooled, all of the solute may remain dissolved even though its solubility decreases as the temperature decreases. Because the solute in a supersaturated solution is present in a concentration higher than the equilibrium concentration, supersaturated solutions are unstable. For crystallization to occur, however, the solute particles must arrange themselves properly to form crystals. The addition of a small crystal of the solute (a seed crystal) provides a template for crystallization of the excess solute, leading to a saturated solution in contact with excess solid (▶ **FIGURE 13.9**).

GIVE IT SOME THOUGHT

What happens if solute is added to a saturated solution?

◢ GO FIGURE

**What is the evidence that the solution in the left photograph is supersaturated?**

Amount of sodium acetate dissolved is greater than its solubility at this temperature

Seed crystal of sodium acetate added to supersaturated solution

Excess sodium acetate crystallizes from solution

Solution arrives at saturation

▲ **FIGURE 13.9** **Precipitation from a supersaturated sodium acetate solution.** The solution on the left was formed by dissolving about 170 g of the salt in 100 mL of water at 100 °C and then slowly cooling it to 20 °C. Because the solubility of sodium acetate in water at 20 °C is 46 g per 100 mL of water, the solution is supersaturated. Addition of a sodium acetate crystal causes the excess solute to crystallize from solution.

# 13.3 | FACTORS AFFECTING SOLUBILITY

The extent to which one substance dissolves in another depends on the nature of both substances. ∞ (Section 13.1) It also depends on temperature and, at least for gases, on pressure.

## Solute–Solvent Interactions

The natural tendency of substances to mix and the various interactions among solute and solvent particles are all involved in determining solubilities. Nevertheless, insight into variations in solubility can often be gained by simply focusing on the interaction between the solute and solvent. The data in ◀ **TABLE 13.1** show, for example, that the solubilities of various simple gases in water increase with increasing molecular mass or increasing polarity. The attractive forces between the gas molecules and solvent molecules are mainly dispersion forces, which increase with increasing size and molecular mass. ∞ (Section 11.2) Thus, the data indicate that the solubilities of gases in water increase as the attraction between solute (gas) and solvent (water) increases. In general, when other factors are comparable, *the stronger the attractions between solute and solvent molecules, the greater the solubility of the solute in that solvent.*

Because of favorable dipole–dipole attractions between solvent molecules and solute molecules, *polar liquids tend to dissolve in polar solvents.* Water is both polar and able to form hydrogen bonds. ∞ (Section 11.2) Thus, polar molecules, especially those that can form hydrogen bonds with water molecules, tend to be soluble in water. For example, acetone, a polar molecule with the structural formula shown in the margin, mixes in all proportions with water. Acetone has a strongly polar C=O bond and pairs of nonbonding electrons on the O atom that can form hydrogen bonds with water.

**TABLE 13.1** • **Solubilities of Gases in Water at 20 °C, with 1 atm Gas Pressure**

| Gas | Solubility ($M$) |
|-----|------------------|
| $N_2$ | $0.69 \times 10^{-3}$ |
| CO | $1.04 \times 10^{-3}$ |
| $O_2$ | $1.38 \times 10^{-3}$ |
| Ar | $1.50 \times 10^{-3}$ |
| Kr | $2.79 \times 10^{-3}$ |

$$\overset{:\ddot{O}:}{\underset{}{\overset{\|}{CH_3CCH_3}}}$$

Acetone

Pairs of liquids that mix in all proportions, such as acetone and water, are **miscible**, whereas those that do not dissolve in one another are **immiscible**. Gasoline, which is a mixture of hydrocarbons, is immiscible with water. Hydrocarbons are nonpolar substances because of several factors: The C—C bonds are nonpolar, the C—H bonds are nearly nonpolar, and the molecules are symmetrical enough to cancel much of the weak C—H bond dipoles. The attraction between the polar water molecules and the nonpolar hydrocarbon molecules is not sufficiently strong to allow the formation of a solution. *Nonpolar liquids tend to be insoluble in polar liquids,* as ▶ **FIGURE 13.10** shows for hexane ($C_6H_{14}$) and water.

Many organic compounds have polar groups attached to a nonpolar framework of carbon and hydrogen atoms. For example, the series of organic compounds in ▼ **TABLE 13.2** all contain the polar OH group. Organic compounds with this molecular feature are called *alcohols.* The O—H bond is able to form hydrogen bonds. For example, ethanol ($CH_3CH_2OH$) molecules can form hydrogen bonds with water molecules as well as with each other (▼ **FIGURE 13.11**). As a result, the solute–solute, solvent–solvent, and solute–solvent forces are not greatly different in a mixture of $CH_3CH_2OH$ and $H_2O$. No major change occurs in the environments of the molecules as they are mixed. Therefore, the increased entropy when the components mix plays a significant role in solution formation, and ethanol is completely miscible with water.

▲ **FIGURE 13.10** **Hexane is immiscible with water.** Hexane is the top layer because it is less dense than water.

Hydrogen bond between two ethanol molecules

Hydrogen bond between ethanol molecule and water molecule

▲ **FIGURE 13.11** **Hydrogen bonding involving OH groups.**

Notice in Table 13.2 that the number of carbon atoms in an alcohol affects its solubility in water. As this number increases, the polar OH group becomes an ever smaller part of the molecule, and the molecule behaves more like a hydrocarbon. The solubility of the alcohol in water decreases correspondingly. On the other hand, the solubility of alcohols in a nonpolar solvent like hexane ($C_6H_{14}$) increases as the nonpolar hydrocarbon chain lengthens.

One way to enhance the solubility of a substance in water is to increase the number of polar groups the substance contains. For example, increasing the number of OH groups in a solute increases the extent of hydrogen bonding between that solute and water, thereby increasing solubility. Glucose ($C_6H_{12}O_6$, ▶ **FIGURE 13.12**) has five OH groups on a six-carbon framework, which makes the molecule very soluble in water (83 g dissolves in 100 mL of water at 17.5 °C).

Cyclohexane, $C_6H_{12}$, which has no polar OH groups, is essentially insoluble in water

OH groups enhance the aqueous solubility because of their ability to hydrogen bond with $H_2O$.

Hydrogen-bonding sites

Glucose, $C_6H_{12}O_6$, has five OH groups and is highly soluble in water

▲ **FIGURE 13.12** **Structure and solubility.**

**TABLE 13.2 • Solubilities of Some Alcohols in Water and in Hexane***

| Alcohol | Solubility in $H_2O$ | Solubility in $C_6H_{14}$ |
|---|---|---|
| $CH_3OH$ (methanol) | ∞ | 0.12 |
| $CH_3CH_2OH$ (ethanol) | ∞ | ∞ |
| $CH_3CH_2CH_2OH$ (propanol) | ∞ | ∞ |
| $CH_3CH_2CH_2CH_2OH$ (butanol) | 0.11 | ∞ |
| $CH_3CH_2CH_2CH_2CH_2OH$ (pentanol) | 0.030 | ∞ |
| $CH_3CH_2CH_2CH_2CH_2CH_2OH$ (hexanol) | 0.0058 | ∞ |

*Expressed in mol alcohol/100 g solvent at 20 °C. The infinity symbol (∞) indicates that the alcohol is completely miscible with the solvent.

# CHEMISTRY AND LIFE

## FAT-SOLUBLE AND WATER-SOLUBLE VITAMINS

Vitamins have unique chemical structures that affect their solubilities in different parts of the human body. Vitamin C and the B vitamins are soluble in water, for example, whereas vitamins A, D, E, and K are soluble in nonpolar solvents and in fatty tissue (which is nonpolar). Because of their water solubility, vitamins B and C are not stored to any appreciable extent in the body, and so foods containing these vitamins should be included in the daily diet. In contrast, the fat-soluble vitamins are stored in sufficient quantities to keep vitamin-

deficiency diseases from appearing even after a person has subsisted for a long period on a vitamin-deficient diet.

That some vitamins are soluble in water and others are not can be explained in terms of their structures. Notice in ▼ FIGURE 13.13 that vitamin A (retinol) is an alcohol with a very long carbon chain. Because the OH group is such a small part of the molecule, the molecule resembles the long-chain alcohols listed in Table 13.2. This vitamin is nearly nonpolar. In contrast, the vitamin C molecule is smaller and has several OH groups that can form hydrogen bonds with water. In this regard, it is somewhat like glucose.

*RELATED EXERCISES: 13.7, 13.48*

▲ FIGURE 13.13 **Vitamins A and C.**

Over the years, examination of different solvent–solute combinations has led to an important generalization: *Substances with similar intermolecular attractive forces tend to be soluble in one another.* This generalization is often simply stated as "*like dissolves like.*" Nonpolar substances are more likely to be soluble in nonpolar solvents; ionic and polar solutes are more likely to be soluble in polar solvents. Network solids such as diamond and quartz are not soluble in either polar or nonpolar solvents because of the strong bonding forces within the solid.

## ▲ GIVE IT SOME THOUGHT

Suppose the hydrogens on the OH groups in glucose (Figure 13.12) were replaced with methyl groups, $CH_3$. Would you expect the water solubility of the resulting molecule to be higher than, lower than, or about the same as the solubility of glucose?

## SAMPLE EXERCISE 13.1 Predicting Solubility Patterns

Predict whether each of the following substances is more likely to dissolve in the nonpolar solvent carbon tetrachloride ($CCl_4$) or in water: $C_7H_{16}$, $Na_2SO_4$, HCl, and $I_2$.

## SOLUTION

**Analyze** We are given two solvents, one that is nonpolar ($CCl_4$) and the other that is polar ($H_2O$), and asked to determine which will be the better solvent for each solute listed.

**Plan** By examining the formulas of the solutes, we can predict whether they are ionic or molecular. For those that are molecular, we can predict whether they are polar or nonpolar. We can then apply the idea that the nonpolar solvent will be better for the nonpolar solutes, whereas the polar solvent will be better for the ionic and polar solutes.

**Solve** $C_7H_{16}$ is a hydrocarbon, so it is molecular and nonpolar. $Na_2SO_4$, a compound containing a metal and nonmetals, is ionic. HCl, a diatomic molecule containing two nonmetals that differ in electronegativity, is polar. $I_2$, a diatomic molecule with atoms of equal electronegativity, is nonpolar. We would therefore predict that $C_7H_{16}$ and $I_2$ (the nonpolar solutes) would be more soluble in the nonpolar $CCl_4$ than in polar $H_2O$, whereas water would be the better solvent for $Na_2SO_4$ and HCl (the ionic and polar covalent solutes).

## PRACTICE EXERCISE

Arrange the following substances in order of increasing solubility in water:

**Answer:** $C_5H_{12} < C_5H_{11}Cl < C_5H_{11}OH < C_5H_{10}(OH)_2$ (in order of increasing polarity and hydrogen-bonding ability)

## Pressure Effects

The solubilities of solids and liquids are not appreciably affected by pressure, whereas *the solubility of a gas in any solvent is increased as the partial pressure of the gas above the solvent increases.* We can understand the effect of pressure on gas solubility by considering ▼ **FIGURE 13.14**, which shows carbon dioxide gas distributed between the gas and

⯅ GO FIGURE

**If the partial pressure of a gas over a solution is doubled, how has the concentration of gas in the solution changed after equilibrium is restored?**

Equilibrium                Pressure is increased.      Equilibrium restored
                           More $CO_2$ dissolves

▲ **FIGURE 13.14  Effect of pressure on gas solubility.**

How do the slopes of the lines vary with the molecular weight of the gas? Explain the trend.

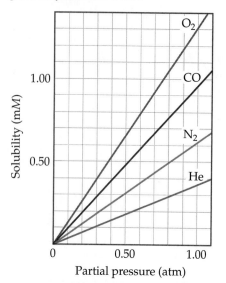

▲ **FIGURE 13.15** **The solubility of a gas in water is directly proportional to the partial pressure of the gas.** The solubilities are in millimoles per liter of solution.

▲ **FIGURE 13.16** **Gas solubility decreases as pressure decreases.** $CO_2$ bubbles out of solution when a carbonated beverage is opened because the $CO_2$ partial pressure above the solution is reduced.

solution phases. When equilibrium is established, the rate at which gas molecules enter the solution equals the rate at which solute molecules escape from the solution to enter the gas phase. The equal number of up and down arrows in the left container in Figure 13.14 represent these opposing processes.

Now suppose we exert greater pressure on the piston and compress the gas above the solution, as shown in the middle container in Figure 13.14. If we reduce the gas volume to half its original value, the pressure of the gas increases to about twice its original value. As a result of this pressure increase, the rate at which gas molecules strike the liquid surface and enter the solution phase increases. Thus, the solubility of the gas in the solution increases until equilibrium is again established; that is, solubility increases until the rate at which gas molecules enter the solution equals the rate at which they escape from the solution. Thus, *the solubility of a gas in a liquid solvent increases in direct proportion to the partial pressure of the gas above the solution* (◀ **FIGURE 13.15**).

The relationship between pressure and gas solubility is expressed by **Henry's law**:

$$S_g = kP_g \qquad [13.4]$$

Here, $S_g$ is the solubility of the gas in the solvent (usually expressed as molarity), $P_g$ is the partial pressure of the gas over the solution, and $k$ is a proportionality constant known as the *Henry's law constant*. The value of this constant depends on the solute, solvent, and temperature. As an example, the solubility of $N_2$ gas in water at 25 °C and 0.78 atm pressure is $4.75 \times 10^{-4}$ $M$. The Henry's law constant for $N_2$ in 25 °C water is thus $(4.75 \times 10^{-4}$ mol/L$)/0.78$ atm $= 6.1 \times 10^{-4}$ mol/L-atm. If the partial pressure of $N_2$ is doubled, Henry's law predicts that the solubility in water at 25 °C also doubles to $9.50 \times 10^{-4}$ $M$.

Bottlers use the effect of pressure on solubility in producing carbonated beverages, which are bottled under a carbon dioxide pressure greater than 1 atm. When the bottles are opened to the air, the partial pressure of $CO_2$ above the solution decreases. Hence, the solubility of $CO_2$ decreases, and $CO_2(g)$ escapes from the solution as bubbles (◀ **FIGURE 13.16**).

**SAMPLE EXERCISE 13.2** **A Henry's Law Calculation**

Calculate the concentration of $CO_2$ in a soft drink that is bottled with a partial pressure of $CO_2$ of 4.0 atm over the liquid at 25 °C. The Henry's law constant for $CO_2$ in water at this temperature is $3.4 \times 10^{-2}$ mol/L-atm.

**SOLUTION**

**Analyze** We are given the partial pressure of $CO_2$, $P_{CO_2}$, and the Henry's law constant, $k$, and asked to calculate the concentration of $CO_2$ in the solution.

**Plan** With the information given, we can use Henry's law, Equation 13.4, to calculate the solubility, $S_{CO_2}$.

**Solve** $S_{CO_2} = kP_{CO_2} = (3.4 \times 10^{-2}$ mol/L-atm$)(4.0$ atm$) = 0.14$ mol/L $= 0.14$ $M$

**Check** The units are correct for solubility, and the answer has two significant figures consistent with both the partial pressure of $CO_2$ and the value of Henry's constant.

**PRACTICE EXERCISE**

Calculate the concentration of $CO_2$ in a soft drink after the bottle is opened and equilibrates at 25 °C under a $CO_2$ partial pressure of $3.0 \times 10^{-4}$ atm.
*Answer:* $1.0 \times 10^{-5}$ $M$

## CHEMISTRY AND LIFE

### BLOOD GASES AND DEEP-SEA DIVING

Because gas solubility increases with increasing pressure, divers who breathe compressed air (▶ **FIGURE 13.17**) must be concerned about the solubility of gases in their blood. Although the gases are not very soluble at sea level, their solubilities can be appreciable at deep levels where their partial pressures are greater. Thus, divers must ascend slowly to prevent dissolved gases from being released rapidly from solution and forming bubbles in the blood and other fluids in the body. These bubbles affect nerve impulses and cause decompression sickness, or "the bends," which is a painful and potentially fatal condition. Nitrogen is the main problem because it has the highest partial pressure in air and because it can be removed from the body only through the respiratory system. Oxygen, in contrast, is consumed in metabolism.

Deep-sea divers sometimes substitute helium for nitrogen in the air they breathe because helium has a much lower solubility in biological fluids than $N_2$. For example, divers working at a depth of 100 ft experience a pressure of about 4 atm. At this pressure a mixture of 95% helium and 5% oxygen gives an oxygen partial pressure of about 0.2

▲ **FIGURE 13.17  Gas solubility increases as pressure increases.** Divers who use compressed gases must be concerned about the solubility of the gases in their blood.

atm, which is the partial pressure of oxygen in normal air at 1 atm. If the oxygen partial pressure becomes too great, the urge to breathe is reduced, $CO_2$ is not removed from the body, and $CO_2$ poisoning occurs. At excessive concentrations in the body, carbon dioxide acts as a neurotoxin, interfering with nerve conduction and transmission.

*RELATED EXERCISES: 13.59, 13.60, 13.107*

## Temperature Effects

*The solubility of most solid solutes in water increases as the solution temperature increases,* as ▼ **FIGURE 13.18** shows. There are exceptions to this rule, however, as seen for $Ce_2(SO_4)_3$, whose solubility curve slopes downward with increasing temperature.

In contrast to solid solutes, *the solubility of gases in water decreases with increasing temperature* (▼ **FIGURE 13.19**). If a glass of cold tap water is warmed, you can see bubbles on the inside of the glass because some of the dissolved air comes out of solution.

### GO FIGURE

How does the solubility of KCl at 80 °C compare with that of NaCl at the same temperature?

▲ **FIGURE 13.18  Solubilities of some ionic compounds in water as a function of temperature.**

### GO FIGURE

Where would you expect $N_2$ to fit on this graph?

▲ **FIGURE 13.19  Solubilities of four gases in water as a function of temperature.** The solubilities are in millimoles per liter of solution, for a constant total pressure of 1 atm in the gas phase.

Similarly, as carbonated beverages are allowed to warm, the solubility of $CO_2$ decreases, and $CO_2(g)$ escapes from the solution.

The decreased solubility of $O_2$ in water as temperature increases is one of the effects of *thermal pollution* of lakes and streams. The effect is particularly serious in deep lakes because warm water is less dense than cold water. Warm water therefore tends to remain on top of cold water, at the surface. This situation impedes the dissolving of oxygen in the deeper layers, thus stifling the respiration of all aquatic life needing oxygen. Fish may suffocate and die under these conditions.

 **GIVE IT SOME THOUGHT**

Why do bubbles form on the inside wall of a cooking pot when water is heated on the stove, even though the water temperature is well below the boiling point of water?

# 13.4 | EXPRESSING SOLUTION CONCENTRATION

The concentration of a solution can be expressed either qualitatively or quantitatively. The terms *dilute* and *concentrated* are used to describe a solution qualitatively. A solution with a relatively small concentration of solute is said to be dilute; one with a large concentration is said to be concentrated. Chemists use various ways to express concentration quantitatively, and we examine several of these next.

## Mass Percentage, ppm, and ppb

One of the simplest quantitative expressions of concentration is the **mass percentage** of a component in a solution, given by

$$\text{Mass \% of component} = \frac{\text{mass of component in soln}}{\text{total mass of soln}} \times 100 \qquad [13.5]$$

Because *percent* means "per hundred," a solution of hydrochloric acid that is 36% HCl by mass contains 36 g of HCl for each 100 g of solution.

We often express the concentration of very dilute solutions in **parts per million (ppm)** or **parts per billion (ppb)**. These quantities are similar to mass percentage but use $10^6$ (a million) or $10^9$ (a billion), respectively, in place of 100 as a multiplier for the ratio of the mass of solute to the mass of solution. Thus, parts per million is defined as

$$\text{ppm of component} = \frac{\text{mass of component in soln}}{\text{total mass of soln}} \times 10^6 \qquad [13.6]$$

A solution whose solute concentration is 1 ppm contains 1 g of solute for each million ($10^6$) grams of solution or, equivalently, 1 mg of solute per kilogram of solution. Because the density of water is 1 g/mL, 1 kg of a dilute aqueous solution has a volume very close to 1 L. Thus, 1 ppm also corresponds to 1 mg of solute per liter of aqueous solution.

The acceptable maximum concentrations of toxic or carcinogenic substances in the environment are often expressed in ppm or ppb. For example, the maximum allowable concentration of arsenic in drinking water in the United States is 0.010 ppm; that is, 0.010 mg of arsenic per liter of water. This concentration corresponds to 10 ppb.

 **GIVE IT SOME THOUGHT**

A solution of $SO_2$ in water contains 0.00023 g of $SO_2$ per liter of solution. What is the concentration of $SO_2$ in ppm? In ppb?

**SAMPLE EXERCISE 13.3** **Calculation of Mass-Related Concentrations**

**(a)** A solution is made by dissolving 13.5 g of glucose ($C_6H_{12}O_6$) in 0.100 kg of water. What is the mass percentage of solute in this solution? **(b)** A 2.5-g sample of groundwater was found to contain 5.4 $\mu$g of $Zn^{2+}$. What is the concentration of $Zn^{2+}$ in parts per million?

## SOLUTION

**(a) Analyze** We are given the number of grams of solute (13.5 g) and the number of grams of solvent (0.100 kg = 100 g). From this we must calculate the mass percentage of solute.

**Plan** We can calculate the mass percentage by using Equation 13.5. The mass of the solution is the sum of the mass of solute (glucose) and the mass of solvent (water).

**Solve** Mass % of glucose $= \dfrac{\text{mass glucose}}{\text{mass soln}} \times 100 = \dfrac{13.5\,\text{g}}{13.5\,\text{g} + 100\,\text{g}} \times 100 = 11.9\%$

**Comment** The mass percentage of water in this solution is $(100-11.9)\% = 88.1\%$.

**(b) Analyze** In this case we are given the number of micrograms of solute. Because $1\,\mu\text{g}$ is $1 \times 10^{-6}\,\text{g}$, $5.4\,\mu\text{g} = 5.4 \times 10^{-6}\,\text{g}$.

**Plan** We calculate the parts per million using Equation 13.6.

**Solve** ppm $= \dfrac{\text{mass of solute}}{\text{mass of soln}} \times 10^6 = \dfrac{5.4 \times 10^{-6}\,\text{g}}{2.5\,\text{g}} \times 10^6 = 2.2\,\text{ppm}$

### PRACTICE EXERCISE

**(a)** Calculate the mass percentage of NaCl in a solution containing 1.50 g of NaCl in 50.0 g of water. **(b)** A commercial bleaching solution contains 3.62 mass % sodium hypochlorite, NaOCl. What is the mass of NaOCl in a bottle containing 2.50 kg of bleaching solution?

**Answers:** **(a)** 2.91%, **(b)** 90.5 g of NaOCl

## Mole Fraction, Molarity, and Molality

Concentration expressions are often based on the number of moles of one or more components of the solution. Recall from Section 10.6 that the *mole fraction* of a component of a solution is given by

$$\text{Mole fraction of component} = \frac{\text{moles of component}}{\text{total moles of all components}} \qquad [13.7]$$

The symbol $X$ is commonly used for mole fraction, with a subscript to indicate the component of interest. For example, the mole fraction of HCl in a hydrochloric acid solution is represented as $X_{\text{HCl}}$. Thus, if a solution contains 1.00 mol of HCl (36.5 g) and 8.00 mol of water (144 g), the mole fraction of HCl is $X_{\text{HCl}} = (1.00\,\text{mol})/(1.00\,\text{mol} + 8.00\,\text{mol}) = 0.111$. Mole fractions have no units because the units in the numerator and the denominator cancel. The sum of the mole fractions of all components of a solution must equal 1. Thus, in the aqueous HCl solution, $X_{\text{H}_2\text{O}} = 1.000 - 0.111 = 0.889$. Mole fractions are very useful when dealing with gases, as we saw in Section 10.6, but have limited use when dealing with liquid solutions.

Recall from Section 4.5 that the *molarity* ($M$) of a solute in a solution is defined as

$$\text{Molarity} = \frac{\text{moles of solute}}{\text{liters of soln}} \qquad [13.8]$$

For example, if you dissolve 0.500 mol of $Na_2CO_3$ in enough water to form 0.250 L of solution, the molarity of $Na_2CO_3$ in the solution is $(0.500\,\text{mol})/(0.250\,\text{L}) = 2.00\,M$. Molarity is especially useful for relating the volume of a solution to the quantity of solute contained in that volume, as we saw in our discussions of titrations. ∞ (Section 4.6)

The **molality** of a solution, denoted $m$, is a concentration unit that is also based on moles of solute. Molality equals the number of moles of solute per kilogram of solvent:

$$\text{Molality} = \frac{\text{moles of solute}}{\text{kilograms of solvent}} \qquad [13.9]$$

Thus, if you form a solution by mixing 0.200 mol of NaOH (8.00 g) and 0.500 kg of water (500 g), the concentration of the solution is $(0.200\,\text{mol})/(0.500\,\text{kg}) = 0.400\,m$ (that is, 0.400 molal) in NaOH.

The definitions of molarity and molality are similar enough that they can be easily confused. Molarity depends on the *volume* of *solution*, whereas molality depends on the *mass* of *solvent*. When water is the solvent, the molality and molarity of dilute solutions are numerically about the same because 1 kg of solvent is nearly the same as 1 kg of solution, and 1 kg of the solution has a volume of about 1 L.

The molality of a given solution does not vary with temperature because masses do not vary with temperature. The molarity of the solution does change with temperature, however, because the volume of the solution expands or contracts with temperature. Thus, molality is often the concentration unit of choice when a solution is to be used over a range of temperatures.

## ⚠ GIVE IT SOME THOUGHT

If an aqueous solution is very dilute, will its molality be greater than its molarity, nearly the same as its molarity, or smaller than its molarity?

---

**SAMPLE EXERCISE 13.4** | **Calculation of Molality**

A solution is made by dissolving 4.35 g glucose ($C_6H_{12}O_6$) in 25.0 mL of water at 25 °C. Calculate the molality of glucose in the solution. Water has a density of 1.00 g/mL.

### SOLUTION

**Analyze** We are asked to calculate a molality. To do this, we must determine the number of moles of solute (glucose) and the number of kilograms of solvent (water).

**Plan** We use the molar mass of $C_6H_{12}O_6$ to convert grams to moles. We use the density of water to convert milliliters to kilograms. The molality equals the number of moles of solute divided by the number of kilograms of solvent (Equation 13.9).

**Solve** Use the molar mass of glucose, 180.2 g/mol, to convert grams to moles:

$$\text{Mol } C_6H_{12}O_6 = (4.35 \text{ g } C_6H_{12}O_6)\left(\frac{1 \text{ mol } C_6H_{12}O_6}{180.2 \text{ g } C_6H_{12}O_6}\right) = 0.0241 \text{ mol } C_6H_{12}O_6$$

Because water has a density of 1.00 g/mL, the mass of the solvent is

$$(25.0 \text{ mL})(1.00 \text{ g/mL}) = 25.0 \text{ g} = 0.0250 \text{ kg}$$

Finally, use Equation 13.9 to obtain the molality:

$$\text{Molality of } C_6H_{12}O_6 = \frac{0.0241 \text{ mol } C_6H_{12}O_6}{0.0250 \text{ kg } H_2O} = 0.964 \, m$$

### PRACTICE EXERCISE

What is the molality of a solution made by dissolving 36.5 g of naphthalene ($C_{10}H_8$) in 425 g of toluene ($C_7H_8$)?
**Answer:** 0.670 $m$

---

## Converting Concentration Units

Sometimes the concentration of a given solution needs to be known in several concentration units. It is possible to interconvert concentration units as shown in Sample Exercise 13.5.

---

**SAMPLE EXERCISE 13.5** | **Calculation of Mole Fraction and Molality**

An aqueous solution of hydrochloric acid contains 36% HCl by mass. (a) Calculate the mole fraction of HCl in the solution. (b) Calculate the molality of HCl in the solution.

### SOLUTION

**Analyze** We are asked to calculate the concentration of the solute, HCl, in two related concentration units, given only the percentage by mass of the solute in the solution.

**Plan** In converting concentration units based on the mass or moles of solute and solvent (mass percentage, mole fraction, and molality), it is useful to assume a certain total mass of solution. Let's assume that there is exactly 100 g of solution. Because the solution is 36% HCl, it contains 36 g of HCl and $(100 - 36) \text{ g} = 64 \text{ g of } H_2O$. We must convert grams of solute (HCl) to moles to calculate either mole fraction or molality. We must convert grams of solvent ($H_2O$) to moles to calculate mole fractions and to kilograms to calculate molality.

**Solve** (a) To calculate the mole fraction of HCl, we convert the masses of HCl and $H_2O$ to moles and then use Equation 13.7:

$$\text{Moles HCl} = (36 \text{ g HCl})\left(\frac{1 \text{ mol HCl}}{36.5 \text{ g HCl}}\right) = 0.99 \text{ mol HCl}$$

$$\text{Moles H}_2\text{O} = (64 \text{ g H}_2\text{O})\left(\frac{1 \text{ mol H}_2\text{O}}{18 \text{ g H}_2\text{O}}\right) = 3.6 \text{ mol H}_2\text{O}$$

$$X_{HCl} = \frac{\text{moles HCl}}{\text{moles H}_2\text{O} + \text{moles HCl}} = \frac{0.99}{3.6 + 0.99} = \frac{0.99}{4.6} = 0.22$$

(b) To calculate the molality of HCl in the solution, we use Equation 13.9. We calculated the number of moles of HCl in part (a), and the mass of solvent is 64 g = 0.064 kg:

$$\text{Molality of HCl} = \frac{0.99 \text{ mol HCl}}{0.064 \text{ kg H}_2\text{O}} = 15 \ m$$

### PRACTICE EXERCISE

A commercial bleach solution contains 3.62 mass % NaOCl in water. Calculate (a) the mole fraction and (b) the molality of NaOCl in the solution.

**Answers:** (a) $9.00 \times 10^{-3}$, (b) $0.505 \ m$

To interconvert molality and molarity, we need to know the density of the solution. ▼ FIGURE 13.20 outlines the calculation of the molarity and molality of a solution from the mass of solute and the mass of solvent. The mass of the solution is the sum of masses of the solvent and solute. The volume of the solution can be calculated from its mass and density.

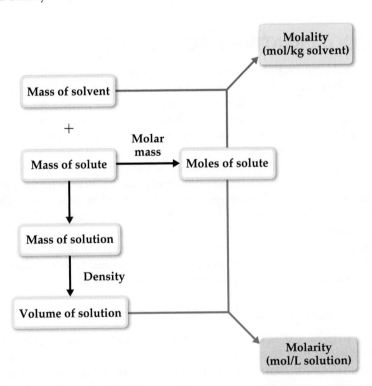

◄ FIGURE 13.20 **Calculating molality and molarity from solute mass, solvent mass, and solution density.**

### SAMPLE EXERCISE 13.6 Calculation of Molarity Using the Density of the Solution

A solution with a density of 0.876 g/mL contains 5.0 g of toluene ($C_7H_8$) and 225 g of benzene. Calculate the molarity of the solution.

#### SOLUTION

**Analyze** Our goal is to calculate the molarity of a solution, given the masses of solute (5.0 g) and solvent (225 g) and the density of the solution (0.876 g/mL).

**Plan** The molarity of a solution is the number of moles of solute divided by the number of liters of solution (Equation 13.8). The number of moles of solute ($C_7H_8$) is calculated from the number of grams of solute and its molar mass. The volume of the solution is obtained from the mass of the solution (mass of solute + mass of solvent = 5.0 g + 225 g = 230 g) and its density.

**Solve**  The number of moles of solute is

$$\text{Moles C}_7\text{H}_8 = (5.0 \text{ g C}_7\text{H}_8)\left(\frac{1 \text{ mol C}_7\text{H}_8}{92 \text{ g C}_7\text{H}_8}\right) = 0.054 \text{ mol}$$

The density of the solution is used to convert the mass of the solution to its volume:

$$\text{Milliliters soln} = (230 \text{ g})\left(\frac{1 \text{ mL}}{0.876 \text{ g}}\right) = 263 \text{ mL}$$

Molarity is moles of solute per liter of solution:

$$\text{Molarity} = \left(\frac{\text{moles C}_7\text{H}_8}{\text{liter soln}}\right) = \left(\frac{0.054 \text{ mol C}_7\text{H}_8}{263 \text{ mL soln}}\right)\left(\frac{1000 \text{ mL soln}}{1 \text{ L soln}}\right) = 0.21 \ M$$

**Check**  The magnitude of our answer is reasonable. Rounding moles to 0.05 and liters to 0.25 gives a molarity of $(0.05 \text{ mol})/(0.25 \text{ L}) = 0.2 \ M$

The units for our answer (mol/L) are correct, and the answer, 0.21, has two significant figures, corresponding to the number of significant figures in the mass of solute (2).

**Comment**  Because the mass of the solvent (0.225 kg) and the volume of the solution (0.263) are similar in magnitude, the molarity and molality are also similar in magnitude:  $(0.054 \text{ mol C}_7\text{H}_8)/(0.225 \text{ kg solvent}) = 0.24 \ m$

**PRACTICE EXERCISE**

A solution containing equal masses of glycerol ($C_3H_8O_3$) and water has a density of 1.10 g/mL. Calculate **(a)** the molality of glycerol, **(b)** the mole fraction of glycerol, **(c)** the molarity of glycerol in the solution.
**Answers:** **(a)** 10.9 $m$, **(b)** $X_{C_3H_8O_3} = 0.163$, **(c)** 5.97 $M$

## 13.5 | COLLIGATIVE PROPERTIES

Some physical properties of solutions differ in important ways from those of the pure solvent. For example, pure water freezes at 0 °C, but aqueous solutions freeze at lower temperatures. We utilize this behavior when we add ethylene glycol antifreeze to a car's radiator to lower the freezing point of the solution. The added solute also raises the boiling point of the solution above that of pure water, making it possible to operate the engine at a higher temperature.

Lowering of the freezing point and raising of the boiling point are physical properties of solutions that depend on the *quantity* (concentration) but not the *kind* or *identity* of the solute particles. Such properties are called **colligative properties**. (*Colligative* means "depending on the collection"; colligative properties depend on the collective effect of the number of solute particles.)

In addition to freezing-point lowering and boiling-point raising, vapor-pressure lowering and osmotic pressure are also colligative properties. As we examine each one, notice how solute concentration quantitatively affects the property.

### Vapor-Pressure Lowering

A liquid in a closed container establishes equilibrium with its vapor. ∞ (Section 11.5) The *vapor pressure* is the pressure exerted by the vapor when it is at equilibrium with the liquid (that is, when the rate of vaporization equals the rate of condensation). A substance that has no measurable vapor pressure is *nonvolatile*, whereas one that exhibits a vapor pressure is *volatile*.

A solution consisting of a volatile liquid solvent and a nonvolatile solute forms spontaneously because of the increase in entropy that accompanies their mixing. In effect, the solvent molecules are stabilized in their liquid state by this process and thus have a lower tendency to escape into the vapor state. Therefore, when a nonvolatile solute is present, the vapor pressure of the solvent is lower than the vapor pressure of the pure solvent, as illustrated in ▶ **FIGURE 13.21**.

The vapor pressure of a volatile solvent above a solution containing a nonvolatile solute is proportional to the solvent's concentration in the solution. This relationship is expressed quantitatively by **Raoult's law**, which states that the partial pressure exerted

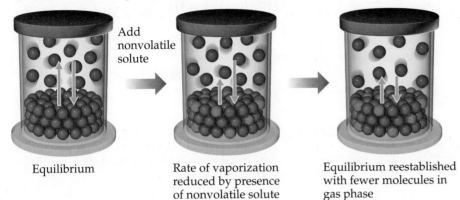

● Volatile solvent particles

● Nonvolatile solute particles

Equilibrium

Add nonvolatile solute

Rate of vaporization reduced by presence of nonvolatile solute

Equilibrium reestablished with fewer molecules in gas phase

◄ **FIGURE 13.21   Vapor-pressure lowering.** The presence of nonvolatile solute particles in a liquid solvent results in a reduction of the vapor pressure above the liquid.

by solvent vapor above the solution, $P_{solution}$, equals the product of the mole fraction of the solvent, $X_{solvent}$, times the vapor pressure of the pure solvent, $P°_{solvent}$:

$$P_{solution} = X_{solvent}P°_{solvent} \qquad [13.10]$$

For example, the vapor pressure of pure water at 20 °C is $P°_{H_2O} = 17.5$ torr. Imagine holding the temperature constant while adding glucose ($C_6H_{12}O_6$) to the water so that the mole fractions in the resulting solution are $X_{H_2O} = 0.800$ and $X_{C_6H_{12}O_6} = 0.200$. According to Equation 13.10, the vapor pressure of the water above this solution is 80.0% of that of pure water:

$$P_{solution} = (0.800)(17.5 \text{ torr}) = 14.0 \text{ torr}$$

The presence of the nonvolatile solute lowers the vapor pressure of the volatile solvent by 17.5 torr − 14.0 torr = 3.5 torr.

The vapor-pressure lowering, $\Delta P$, is directly proportional to the mole fraction of the solute, $X_{solute}$:

$$\Delta P = X_{solute}P°_{solvent} \qquad [13.11]$$

Thus, for the example of the solution of glucose in water, we have

$$\Delta P = X_{C_6H_{12}O_6}\, P°_{H_2O} = (0.200)(17.5 \text{ torr}) = 3.50 \text{ torr}$$

The vapor-pressure lowering caused by adding a nonvolatile solute depends on the total concentration of solute particles, regardless of whether they are molecules or ions. Remember that vapor-pressure lowering is a colligative property, so its value for any solution depends on the concentration of solute particles and not on their kind or on their identity.

▲ **GIVE IT SOME THOUGHT**

Adding 1 mol of NaCl to 1 kg of water lowers the vapor pressure of water more than adding 1 mol of $C_6H_{12}O_6$. Explain.

**SAMPLE EXERCISE 13.7**   **Calculation of Vapor Pressure of a Solution**

Glycerin ($C_3H_8O_3$) is a nonvolatile nonelectrolyte with a density of 1.26 g/mL at 25 °C. Calculate the vapor pressure at 25 °C of a solution made by adding 50.0 mL of glycerin to 500.0 mL of water. The vapor pressure of pure water at 25 °C is 23.8 torr (Appendix B), and its density is 1.00 g/mL.

**SOLUTION**

**Analyze**   Our goal is to calculate the vapor pressure of a solution, given the volumes of solute and solvent and the density of the solute.

**Plan**   We can use Raoult's law (Equation 13.10) to calculate the vapor pressure of a solution. The mole fraction of the solvent in the solution, $X_{solvent}$, is the ratio of the number of moles of solvent ($H_2O$) to total moles of solution (moles $C_3H_8O_3$ + moles $H_2O$).

**Solve** To calculate the mole fraction of water in the solution, we must determine the number of moles of $C_3H_8O_3$ and $H_2O$:

$$\text{Moles } C_3H_8O_3 = (50.0 \text{ mL } C_3H_8O_3)\left(\frac{1.26 \text{ g } C_3H_8O_3}{1 \text{ mL } C_3H_8O_3}\right)\left(\frac{1 \text{ mol } C_3H_8O_3}{92.1 \text{ g } C_3H_8O_3}\right) = 0.684 \text{ mol}$$

$$\text{Moles } H_2O = (500.0 \text{ mL } H_2O)\left(\frac{1.00 \text{ g } H_2O}{1 \text{ mL } H_2O}\right)\left(\frac{1 \text{ mol } H_2O}{18.0 \text{ g } H_2O}\right) = 27.8 \text{ mol}$$

$$X_{H_2O} = \frac{\text{mol } H_2O}{\text{mol } H_2O + \text{mol } C_3H_8O_3} = \frac{27.8}{27.8 + 0.684} = 0.976$$

We now use Raoult's law to calculate the vapor pressure of water for the solution:

$$P_{H_2O} = X_{H_2O} P_{H_2O}^\circ = (0.976)(23.8 \text{ torr}) = 23.2 \text{ torr}$$

**Comment** The vapor pressure of the solution has been lowered by 23.8 torr − 23.2 torr = 0.6 torr relative to that of pure water. The vapor-pressure lowering can be calculated directly using Equation 13.11 together with the mole fraction of the solute, $C_3H_8O_3$:

$\Delta P = X_{C_3H_8O_3} P_{H_2O}^\circ = (0.024)(23.8 \text{ torr}) = 0.57 \text{ torr}$. Notice that the use of Equation 13.11 gives one more significant figure than the number obtained by subtracting the vapor pressure of the solution from that of the pure solvent.

**PRACTICE EXERCISE**

The vapor pressure of pure water at 110 °C is 1070 torr. A solution of ethylene glycol and water has a vapor pressure of 1.00 atm at 110 °C. Assuming that Raoult's law is obeyed, what is the mole fraction of ethylene glycol in the solution?

*Answer:* 0.290

---

# A CLOSER LOOK

## IDEAL SOLUTIONS WITH TWO OR MORE VOLATILE COMPONENTS

Solutions sometimes have two or more volatile components. Gasoline, for example, is a solution of several volatile liquids. To gain some understanding of such mixtures, consider an ideal solution of two volatile liquids, A and B. (For our purposes here, it does not matter which we call the solute and which the solvent.) The partial pressures above the solution are given by Raoult's law:

$$P_A = X_A P_A^\circ \text{ and } P_B = X_B P_B^\circ$$

and the total vapor pressure above the solution is

$$P_{total} = P_A + P_B = X_A P_A^\circ + X_B P_B^\circ$$

Consider a mixture of 1.0 mol of benzene ($C_6H_6$) and 2.0 mol of toluene ($C_7H_8$) ($X_{ben} = 0.33$, $X_{tol} = 0.67$). At 20 °C the vapor pressures of the pure substances are $P_{ben}^\circ = 75$ torr and $P_{tol}^\circ = 22$ torr. Thus, the partial pressures above the solution are

$$P_{ben} = (0.33)(75 \text{ torr}) = 25 \text{ torr}$$
$$P_{tol} = (0.67)(22 \text{ torr}) = 15 \text{ torr}$$

and the total vapor pressure above the liquid is

$$P_{total} = P_{ben} + P_{tol} = 25 \text{ torr} + 15 \text{ torr} = 40 \text{ torr}$$

Note that the vapor is richer in benzene, the more volatile component.

The mole fraction of benzene in the vapor is given by the ratio of its vapor pressure to the total pressure (Equations 10.14 and 10.15):

$$X_{ben} \text{ in vapor} = \frac{P_{ben}}{P_{tol}} = \frac{25 \text{ torr}}{40 \text{ torr}} = 0.63$$

Although benzene constitutes only 33% of the molecules in the solution, it makes up 63% of the molecules in the vapor.

When an ideal liquid solution containing two volatile components is in equilibrium with its vapor, the more volatile component will be relatively richer in the vapor. This fact forms the basis of *distillation*, a technique used to separate (or partially separate) mixtures containing volatile components. Distillation is the procedure by which a moonshiner obtains whiskey using a still and by which petrochemical plants achieve the separation of crude petroleum into gasoline, diesel fuel, lubricating oil, and so forth (◀ FIGURE 13.22). Distillation is also used routinely on a small scale in the laboratory.

*RELATED EXERCISES:* 13.67, 13.68

◀ FIGURE 13.22 **The volatile components of organic mixtures can be separated on an industrial scale.**

An ideal gas is defined as one that obeys the ideal-gas equation ⟳ (Section 10.4), and an **ideal solution** is defined as one that obeys Raoult's law. Whereas ideality for a gas arises from a complete lack of intermolecular interaction, ideality for a solution implies total uniformity of interaction. The molecules in an ideal solution all influence one another in the same way—in other words, solute–solute, solvent–solvent, and solute–solvent interactions are indistinguishable from one another. Real solutions best approximate ideal behavior when the solute concentration is low and solute and solvent have similar molecular sizes and take part in similar types of intermolecular attractions.

Many solutions do not obey Raoult's law exactly and so are not ideal. If, for instance, the solvent–solute interactions in a solution are weaker than either the solvent–solvent or solute–solute interactions, the vapor pressure tends to be greater than predicted by Raoult's law (that is, the vapor-pressure lowering is less than what Raoult's law predicts). When the solute–solvent interactions in a solution are exceptionally strong, as might be the case when hydrogen bonding exists, the vapor pressure is lower than Raoult's law predicts (the vapor-pressure lowering is *greater* than what the law predicts). Although you should be aware that these departures from ideality occur, we will ignore them for the remainder of this chapter.

## Boiling-Point Elevation

In Sections 11.5 and 11.6 we examined the vapor pressures of pure substances and how to use them to construct phase diagrams. How does the phase diagram of a solution and, hence, its boiling and freezing points differ from that of the pure solvent? The addition of a nonvolatile solute lowers the vapor pressure of the solution. Thus, in ▼ FIGURE 13.23 the vapor-pressure curve of the solution is shifted downward relative to the vapor-pressure curve of the pure solvent.

Recall from Section 11.5 that the normal boiling point of a liquid is the temperature at which its vapor pressure equals 1 atm. Because the solution has a lower vapor pressure than the pure solvent, a higher temperature is required for the solution to achieve a vapor pressure of 1 atm. As a result, *the boiling point of the solution is higher than that of the pure solvent.* This effect is seen in Figure 13.23. We find the normal boiling points of the pure solvent from the graph by locating the point where the horizontal line at 1 atm intersects the black vapor-pressure curve and then tracing this point down to the temperature axis. For the solution, the horizontal line at 1 atm intersects the blue vapor-pressure curve at a higher temperature, indicating that the solution has a higher boiling point than the pure solvent.

The increase in boiling point relative to that of the pure solvent, $\Delta T_b$, is a positive quantity obtained by subtracting the boiling point of the pure solvent from the boiling point of the solution. The value of $\Delta T_b$ is directly proportional to the solution molality:

$$\Delta T_b = K_b m \qquad [13.12]$$

The magnitude of $K_b$, which is called the **molal boiling-point-elevation constant**, depends only on the solvent. Some typical values for several common solvents are given in

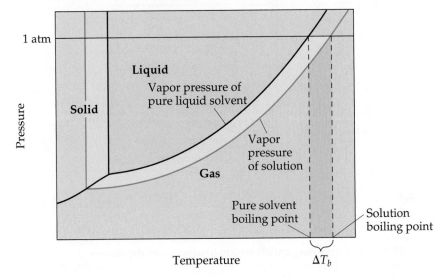

1 atm

Liquid

Solid

Vapor pressure of pure liquid solvent

Vapor pressure of solution

Gas

Pressure

Pure solvent boiling point

Solution boiling point

Temperature

$\Delta T_b$

◀ **FIGURE 13.23**  Phase diagram illustrating boiling-point elevation.

| | TABLE 13.3 • Molal Boiling-Point-Elevation and Freezing-Point-Depression Constants | | | | |
|---|---|---|---|---|---|

| Solvent | Normal Boiling Point (°C) | $K_b$ (°C/$m$) | Normal Freezing Point (°C) | $K_f$ (°C/$m$) |
|---|---|---|---|---|
| Water, $H_2O$ | 100.0 | 0.51 | 0.0 | 1.86 |
| Benzene, $C_6H_6$ | 80.1 | 2.53 | 5.5 | 5.12 |
| Ethanol, $C_2H_5OH$ | 78.4 | 1.22 | −114.6 | 1.99 |
| Carbon tetrachloride, $CCl_4$ | 76.8 | 5.02 | −22.3 | 29.8 |
| Chloroform, $CHCl_3$ | 61.2 | 3.63 | −63.5 | 4.68 |

▲ **TABLE 13.3.** For water, the table shows $K_b = 0.51$ °C/$m$, which means that the boiling point of any aqueous solution that is 1 $m$ in nonvolatile solute particles is 0.51 °C higher than the boiling point of pure water. Because solutions generally do not behave ideally, the constants listed in Table 13.3 serve well only for solutions that are not too concentrated.

It is important to remember that boiling-point elevation is proportional to the *total* concentration of solute particles, regardless of whether the particles are molecules or ions. When NaCl dissolves in water, 2 mol of solute particles (1 mol of $Na^+$ and 1 mol of $Cl^-$) are formed for each mole of NaCl that dissolves. Therefore, a 1 $m$ aqueous solution of NaCl is 1 $m$ in $Na^+$ and 1 $m$ in $Cl^-$, making it 2 $m$ in total solute particles. As a result, the boiling-point elevation of a 1 $m$ aqueous solution of NaCl is approximately $(2\ m)(0.51$ °C/$m) = 1$ °C, twice as large as the boiling-point elevation of a 1 $m$ solution of a nonelectrolyte such as sucrose. Thus, to properly predict the effect of a particular solute on boiling-point elevation (or any other colligative property), it is important to know whether the solute is an electrolyte or a nonelectrolyte. ∞ (Sections 4.1 and 4.3)

 **GIVE IT SOME THOUGHT**

A solute dissolved in water causes the boiling point to increase by 0.51 °C. Does this necessarily mean that the concentration of the solute is 1.0 $m$?

## Freezing-Point Depression

The vapor-pressure curves for the liquid and solid phases meet at the triple point. ∞ (Section 11.6) In ▼ **FIGURE 13.24** we see that the triple-point temperature of the solution is lower than the triple-point temperature of pure liquid because the solution has a lower vapor pressure than the pure liquid.

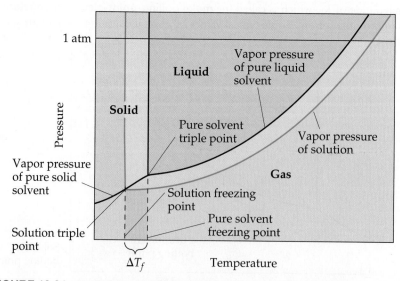

▲ **FIGURE 13.24** **Phase diagram illustrating freezing-point depression.**

The freezing point of a solution is the temperature at which the first crystals of pure solvent form in equilibrium with the solution. Recall from Section 11.6 that the line representing the solid–liquid equilibrium rises nearly vertically from the triple point. Because the triple-point temperature of the solution is lower than that of the pure liquid, *the freezing point of the solution is lower than that of the pure liquid*. The decrease in freezing point, $\Delta T_f$, is a positive quantity obtained by subtracting the freezing point of the solution from the freezing point of the pure solvent.

Like the boiling-point elevation, $\Delta T_f$ is directly proportional to solute molality:

$$\Delta T_f = K_f m \qquad\qquad [13.13]$$

The values of $K_f$, the **molal freezing-point-depression constant**, for several common solvents are given in Table 13.3. For water, $K_f$ is 1.86 °C/$m$. Therefore, any aqueous solution that is 1 $m$ in nonvolatile solute particles (such as 1 $m$ $C_6H_{12}O_6$ or 0.5 $m$ NaCl) freezes at the temperature that is 1.86 °C lower than the freezing point of pure water.

The freezing-point depression caused by solutes explains the use of antifreeze in cars and the use of calcium chloride ($CaCl_2$) to melt ice on roads during winter.

---

| SAMPLE EXERCISE 13.8 | Calculation of Boiling-Point Elevation and Freezing-Point Depression |
|---|---|

Automotive antifreeze consists of ethylene glycol, $CH_2(OH)CH_2(OH)$, a nonvolatile nonelectrolyte. Calculate the boiling point and freezing point of a 25.0 mass % solution of ethylene glycol in water.

### SOLUTION

**Analyze**  We are given that a solution contains 25.0 mass % of a nonvolatile, nonelectrolyte solute and asked to calculate the boiling and freezing points of the solution. To do this, we need to calculate the boiling-point elevation and freezing-point depression.

**Plan**  To calculate the boiling-point elevation and the freezing-point depression using Equations 13.12 and 13.13, we must express the concentration of the solution as molality. Let's assume for convenience that we have 1000 g of solution. Because the solution is 25.0 mass % ethylene glycol, the masses of ethylene glycol and water in the solution are 250 and 750 g, respectively. Using these quantities, we can calculate the molality of the solution, which we use with the molal boiling-point-elevation and freezing-point-depression constants (Table 13.3) to calculate $\Delta T_b$ and $\Delta T_f$. We add $\Delta T_b$ to the boiling point and subtract $\Delta T_f$ from the freezing point of the solvent to obtain the boiling point and freezing point of the solution.

**Solve**  The molality of the solution is calculated as follows:

$$\text{Molality} = \frac{\text{moles } C_2H_6O_2}{\text{kilograms } H_2O} = \left(\frac{250 \text{ g } C_2H_6O_2}{750 \text{ g } H_2O}\right)\left(\frac{1 \text{ mol } C_2H_6O_2}{62.1 \text{ g } C_2H_6O_2}\right)\left(\frac{1000 \text{ g } H_2O}{1 \text{ kg } H_2O}\right)$$

$$= 5.37 \ m$$

We can now use Equations 13.12 and 13.13 to calculate the changes in the boiling and freezing points:

$$\Delta T_b = K_b m = (0.51 \text{ °C}/m)(5.37 \ m) = 2.7 \text{ °C}$$
$$\Delta T_f = K_f m = (1.86 \text{ °C}/m)(5.37 \ m) = 10.0 \text{ °C}$$

Hence, the boiling and freezing points of the solution are

$$\text{Boiling point} = (\text{normal bp of solvent}) + \Delta T_b$$
$$= 100.0 \text{ °C} + 2.7 \text{ °C} = 102.7 \text{ °C}$$

$$\text{Freezing point} = (\text{normal fp of solvent}) - \Delta T_f$$
$$= 0.0 \text{ °C} - 10.0 \text{ °C} = -10.0 \text{ °C}$$

**Comment**  Notice that the solution is a liquid over a larger temperature range than the pure solvent.

### PRACTICE EXERCISE

Calculate the freezing point of a solution containing 0.600 kg of $CHCl_3$ and 42.0 g of eucalyptol ($C_{10}H_{18}O$), a fragrant substance found in the leaves of eucalyptus trees. (See Table 13.3.)
***Answer:***  −65.6 °C

**SAMPLE EXERCISE 13.9** | Freezing-Point Depression in Aqueous Solutions

List the following aqueous solutions in order of their expected freezing point: 0.050 $m$ $CaCl_2$, 0.15 $m$ NaCl, 0.10 $m$ HCl, 0.050 $m$ $CH_3COOH$, 0.10 $m$ $C_{12}H_{22}O_{11}$.

**SOLUTION**

**Analyze** We must order five aqueous solutions according to expected freezing points, based on molalities and the solute formulas.

**Plan** The lowest freezing point will correspond to the solution with the greatest concentration of solute particles. To determine the total concentration of solute particles in each case, we must determine whether the substance is a nonelectrolyte or an electrolyte and consider the number of ions formed when an electrolyte ionizes.

**Solve** $CaCl_2$, NaCl, and HCl are strong electrolytes, $CH_3COOH$ (acetic acid) is a weak electrolyte, and $C_{12}H_{22}O_{11}$ is a nonelectrolyte. The molality of each solution in total particles is as follows:

$$0.050\ m\ CaCl_2 \Rightarrow 0.050\ m\ \text{in}\ Ca^{2+}\ \text{and}\ 0.10\ m\ \text{in}\ Cl^- \Rightarrow 0.15\ m\ \text{in particles}$$

$$0.15\ m\ NaCl \Rightarrow 0.15\ m\ \text{in}\ Na^+\ \text{and}\ 0.15\ m\ \text{in}\ Cl^- \Rightarrow 0.30\ m\ \text{in particles}$$

$$0.10\ m\ HCl \Rightarrow 0.10\ m\ \text{in}\ H^+\ \text{and}\ 0.10\ m\ \text{in}\ Cl^- \Rightarrow 0.20\ m\ \text{in particles}$$

$$0.050\ m\ CH_3COOH \Rightarrow \text{weak electrolyte} \Rightarrow \text{between}\ 0.050\ m\ \text{and}\ 0.10\ m\ \text{in particles}$$

$$0.10\ m\ C_{12}H_{22}O_{11} \Rightarrow \text{nonelectrolyte} \Rightarrow 0.10\ m\ \text{in particles}$$

Because the freezing points depend on the total molality of particles in solution, the expected ordering is 0.15 $m$ NaCl (lowest freezing point), 0.10 $m$ HCl, 0.050 $m$ $CaCl_2$, 0.10 $m$ $C_{12}H_{22}O_{11}$, and 0.050 $m$ $CH_3COOH$ (highest freezing point).

**PRACTICE EXERCISE**

Which of the following solutes will produce the largest increase in boiling point upon addition to 1 kg of water: 1 mol of $Co(NO_3)_2$, 2 mol of KCl, 3 mol of ethylene glycol ($C_2H_6O_2$)?

**Answer:** 2 mol of KCl because it contains the highest concentration of particles, 2 $m$ $K^+$ and 2 $m$ $Cl^-$, giving 4 $m$ in all

## Osmosis

Certain materials, including many membranes in biological systems and synthetic substances such as cellophane, are *semipermeable*. When in contact with a solution, these materials allow only small molecules—water molecules, for instance—to pass through their network of tiny pores.

Consider a situation in which only solvent molecules are able to pass through a semipermeable membrane placed between two solutions of different concentrations. The rate at which the solvent passes from the less concentrated solution (lower solute concentration but higher solvent concentration) to the more concentrated solution (higher solute concentration but lower solvent concentration) is greater than the rate in the opposite direction. Thus, there is a net movement of solvent molecules from the solution with a lower solute concentration into the one with a higher solute concentration. In this process, called **osmosis**, *the net movement of solvent is always toward the solution with the higher solute concentration*, as if the solutions were driven to attain equal concentrations.

▶ FIGURE 13.25 shows the osmosis that occurs between an aqueous solution and pure water. The U-tube contains water on the left and an aqueous solution on the right. There is a net movement of water through the membrane from left to right, As a result, the liquid levels in the two arms become unequal. Eventually, the pressure difference resulting from the unequal liquid heights becomes so large that the net flow of water ceases. The pressure required to stop osmosis from a pure solvent to a solution is the **osmotic pressure** of the solution. If an external pressure equal to the osmotic pressure is applied to the solution, the liquid levels in the two arms can be equalized, as shown in the right panel of Figure 13.25.

**GO FIGURE**

**If the pure water in the left arm of the U-tube is replaced by a solution more concentrated than the one in the right arm, what will happen?**

**Initially**

Pure solvent

Solution

Solvent particle (H₂O)

Solute particle

Semipermeable membrane

Net movement of H₂O is from pure water side to solution side

**At equilibrium**

Flow of H₂O same in both directions. No net movement of H₂O

Pressure applied to equalize fluid levels in both arms equals osmotic pressure, $\Pi$

Flow of H₂O same in both direction. No net movement of H₂O

▲ **FIGURE 13.25   Osmosis.**

The osmotic pressure obeys a law similar in form to the ideal-gas law, $\Pi V = nRT$, where $\Pi$ is the osmotic pressure, $V$ is the volume of the solution, $n$ is the number of moles of solute, $R$ is the ideal-gas constant, and $T$ is the Kelvin temperature. From this equation, we can write

$$\Pi = \left(\frac{n}{V}\right)RT = MRT \qquad\qquad [13.14]$$

where $M$ is the molarity of the solution. Because the osmotic pressure for any solution depends on the solution concentration, osmotic pressure is a colligative property.

If two solutions of identical osmotic pressure are separated by a semipermeable membrane, no osmosis will occur. The two solutions are *isotonic* with respect to each other. If one solution is of lower osmotic pressure, it is *hypotonic* with respect to the more concentrated solution. The more concentrated solution is *hypertonic* with respect to the dilute solution.

 **GIVE IT SOME THOUGHT**

Of two KBr solutions, one 0.50 *m* and the other 0.20 *m,* which is hypotonic with respect to the other?

Osmosis plays an important role in living systems. The membranes of red blood cells, for example, are semipermeable. Placing a red blood cell in a solution that is *hyper*tonic relative to the intracellular solution (the solution inside the cells) causes water to move out of the cell (▶ **FIGURE 13.26**). This causes the cell to shrivel, a process called *crenation.* Placing the cell in a solution that is *hypo*tonic relative to the intracellular fluid causes water to move into the cell. This may cause the cell to rupture, a process called *hemolysis.* People who need body fluids or nutrients replaced but cannot be fed orally are given solutions by intravenous (IV) infusion, which feeds nutrients directly into the veins. To prevent crenation or hemolysis of red blood cells, the IV solutions must be isotonic with the intracellular fluids of the blood cells.

## GO FIGURE

If the fluid surrounding a patient's red blood cells is depleted in electrolytes, is crenation or hemolysis more likely to occur?

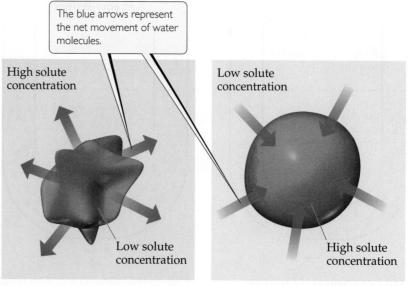

The blue arrows represent the net movement of water molecules.

High solute concentration

Low solute concentration

Low solute concentration

High solute concentration

▶ **FIGURE 13.26 Osmosis through red blood cell wall.**

Crenation of red blood cell placed in hypertonic environment

Hemolysis of red blood cell placed in hypotonic environment

---

**SAMPLE EXERCISE 13.10** | Calculation Involving Osmotic Pressure

The average osmotic pressure of blood is 7.7 atm at 25 °C. What molarity of glucose ($C_6H_{12}O_6$) will be isotonic with blood?

### SOLUTION

**Analyze** We are asked to calculate the concentration of glucose in water that would be isotonic with blood, given that the osmotic pressure of blood at 25 °C is 7.7 atm.

**Plan** Because we are given the osmotic pressure and temperature, we can solve for the concentration, using Equation 13.14.

**Solve**

$$\Pi = MRT$$

$$M = \frac{\Pi}{RT} = \frac{7.7 \text{ atm}}{\left(0.0821 \dfrac{\text{L-atm}}{\text{mol-K}}\right)(298 \text{ K})} = 0.31 \ M$$

**Comment** In clinical situations the concentrations of solutions are generally expressed as mass percentages. The mass percentage of a 0.31 $M$ solution of glucose is 5.3%. The concentration of NaCl that is isotonic with blood is 0.16 $M$, because NaCl ionizes to form two particles, $Na^+$ and $Cl^-$ (a 0.155 $M$ solution of NaCl is 0.310 $M$ in particles). A 0.16 $M$ solution of NaCl is 0.9 mass % in NaCl. This kind of solution is known as a physiological saline solution.

### PRACTICE EXERCISE

What is the osmotic pressure at 20 °C of a 0.0020 $M$ sucrose ($C_{12}H_{22}O_{11}$) solution?

**Answer:** 0.048 atm, or 37 torr

---

There are many interesting biological examples of osmosis. A cucumber placed in concentrated brine loses water via osmosis and shrivels into a pickle. People who eat a lot of salty food retain water in tissue cells and intercellular space because of osmosis. The resultant swelling or puffiness is called *edema*. Water moves from soil into plant roots partly because of osmosis. Bacteria on salted meat or candied fruit lose water through osmosis, shrivel, and die—thus preserving the food.

Movement of a substance from an area where its concentration is high to an area where it is low is spontaneous. Biological cells transport water and other select materials through their membranes, permitting nutrients to enter and waste materials to exit. In some cases substances must be moved across the cell membrane from an area of low concentration to one of high concentration. This movement—called *active transport*—is not spontaneous, so cells must expend energy to do it.

### ⚠ GIVE IT SOME THOUGHT

Is the osmotic pressure of a 0.10 *M* solution of NaCl greater than, less than, or equal to that of a 0.10 *M* solution of KBr?

## Determination of Molar Mass

The colligative properties of solutions provide a useful means of determining molar mass. Any of the four colligative properties can be used, as shown in Sample Exercises 13.11 and 13.12.

---

### SAMPLE EXERCISE 13.11 | Molar Mass from Freezing-Point Depression

A solution of an unknown nonvolatile nonelectrolyte was prepared by dissolving 0.250 g of the substance in 40.0 g of $CCl_4$. The boiling point of the resultant solution was 0.357 °C higher than that of the pure solvent. Calculate the molar mass of the solute.

#### SOLUTION

**Analyze** Our goal is to calculate the molar mass of a solute based on knowledge of the boiling-point elevation of its solution in $CCl_4$, $\Delta T_b = 0.357$ °C, and the masses of solute and solvent. Table 13.3 gives $K_b$ for the solvent ($CCl_4$), $K_b = 5.02$ °C/$m$.

**Plan** We can use Equation 13.12, $\Delta T_b = K_b m$, to calculate the molality of the solution. Then we can use molality and the quantity of solvent (40.0 g $CCl_4$) to calculate the number of moles of solute. Finally, the molar mass of the solute equals the number of grams per mole, so we divide the number of grams of solute (0.250 g) by the number of moles we have just calculated.

---

**Solve** From Equation 13.12 we have

$$\text{Molality} = \frac{\Delta T_b}{K_b} = \frac{0.357 \text{ °C}}{5.02 \text{ °C}/m} = 0.0711 \ m$$

Thus, the solution contains 0.0711 mol of solute per kilogram of solvent. The solution was prepared using 40.0 g = 0.0400 kg of solvent ($CCl_4$). The number of moles of solute in the solution is therefore

$$(0.0400 \text{ kg } CCl_4)\left(0.0711 \ \frac{\text{mol solute}}{\text{kg } CCl_4}\right) = 2.84 \times 10^{-3} \text{ mol solute}$$

The molar mass of the solute is the number of grams per mole of the substance:

$$\text{Molar mass} = \frac{0.250 \text{ g}}{2.84 \times 10^{-3} \text{ mol}} = 88.0 \text{ g/mol}$$

#### PRACTICE EXERCISE

Camphor ($C_{10}H_{16}O$) melts at 179.8 °C, and it has a particularly large freezing-point-depression constant, $K_f = 40.0$ °C/$m$. When 0.186 g of an organic substance of unknown molar mass is dissolved in 22.01 g of liquid camphor, the freezing point of the mixture is found to be 176.7 °C. What is the molar mass of the solute?

***Answer:*** 110 g/mol

---

### SAMPLE EXERCISE 13.12 | Molar Mass from Osmotic Pressure

The osmotic pressure of an aqueous solution of a certain protein was measured to determine the protein's molar mass. The solution contained 3.50 mg of protein dissolved in sufficient water to form 5.00 mL of solution. The osmotic pressure of the solution at 25 °C was found to be 1.54 torr. Treating the protein as a nonelectrolyte, calculate its molar mass.

#### SOLUTION

**Analyze** Our goal is to calculate the molar mass of a high-molecular-mass protein, based on its osmotic pressure and a knowledge of the mass of protein and solution volume.

**Plan** The temperature ($T = 25$ °C) and osmotic pressure ($\Pi = 1.54$ torr) are given, and we know the value of $R$ so we can use Equation 13.14 to calculate the molarity of the solution, $M$. In doing so, we must convert temperature from °C to K and the osmotic pressure from torr to atm. We then use the molarity and the volume of the solution (5.00 mL) to determine the number of moles of solute. Finally, we obtain the molar mass by dividing the mass of the solute (3.50 mg) by the number of moles of solute.

**Solve** Solving Equation 13.14 for molarity gives

$$\text{Molarity} = \frac{\Pi}{RT} = \frac{(1.54 \text{ torr})\left(\dfrac{1 \text{ atm}}{760 \text{ torr}}\right)}{\left(0.0821\dfrac{\text{L-atm}}{\text{mol-K}}\right)(298 \text{ K})} = 8.28 \times 10^{-5} \frac{\text{mol}}{\text{L}}$$

Because the volume of the solution is 5.00 mL = $5.00 \times 10^{-3}$ L, the number of moles of protein must be

$$\text{Moles} = (8.28 \times 10^{-5} \text{ mol/L})(5.00 \times 10^{-3} \text{ L}) = 4.14 \times 10^{-7} \text{ mol}$$

The molar mass is the number of grams per mole of the substance. The sample has a mass of 3.50 mg = $3.50 \times 10^{-3}$ g. The molar mass is the number of grams divided by the number of moles:

$$\text{Molar mass} = \frac{\text{grams}}{\text{moles}} = \frac{3.50 \times 10^{-3} \text{ g}}{4.14 \times 10^{-7} \text{ mol}} = 8.45 \times 10^{3} \text{ g/mol}$$

**Comment** Because small pressures can be measured easily and accurately, osmotic pressure measurements provide a useful way to determine the molar masses of large molecules.

**PRACTICE EXERCISE**

A sample of 2.05 g of polystyrene of uniform polymer chain length was dissolved in enough toluene to form 0.100 L of solution. The osmotic pressure of this solution was found to be 1.21 kPa at 25 °C. Calculate the molar mass of the polystyrene.

**Answer:** $4.20 \times 10^{4}$ g/mol

---

# A CLOSER LOOK

## COLLIGATIVE PROPERTIES OF ELECTROLYTE SOLUTIONS

The colligative properties of solutions depend on the *total* concentration of solute particles, regardless of whether the particles are ions or molecules. Thus, we expect a 0.100 *m* solution of NaCl to have a freezing-point depression of $(0.200 \text{ } m)(1.86 \text{ °C}/m) = 0.372 \text{ °C}$ because it is 0.100 *m* in $Na^+(aq)$ and 0.100 *m* in $Cl^-(aq)$. The measured freezing-point depression is only 0.348 °C, however, and the situation is similar for other strong electrolytes. A 0.100 *m* solution of KCl, for example, freezes at −0.344 °C.

The difference between expected and observed colligative properties for strong electrolytes is due to electrostatic attractions between ions. As the ions move about in solution, ions of opposite charge collide and "stick together" for brief moments. While they are together, they behave as a single particle called an *ion pair* (▶ FIGURE 13.27). The number of independent particles is thereby reduced, causing a reduction in the freezing-point depression (as well as in boiling-point elevation, vapor-pressure reduction, and osmotic pressure).

One measure of the extent to which electrolytes dissociate is the *van't Hoff factor*, *i*. This factor is the ratio of the actual value of a colligative property to the value calculated when the substance is assumed to be a nonelectrolyte. Using the freezing-point depression, for example, we have

$$i = \frac{\Delta T_f(\text{measured})}{\Delta T_f(\text{calculated for nonelectrolyte})} \quad [13.15]$$

The limiting value of *i* can be determined for a salt from the number of ions per formula unit. For NaCl, for example, the limiting van't Hoff factor is 2 because NaCl consists of one $Na^+$ and one $Cl^-$ per formula unit; for $K_2SO_4$ it is 3 because $K_2SO_4$ consists of two $K^+$ and one $SO_4^{2-}$ per formula unit. In the absence of any information about the actual value of *i* for a solution, we will use the limiting value in calculations.

▲ FIGURE 13.27 **Ion pairing and colligative properties.** A solution of NaCl contains not only separated $Na^+(aq)$ and $Cl^-(aq)$ ions but ion pairs as well.

Two trends are evident in ▶ **TABLE 13.4**, which gives measured van't Hoff factors for several substances at different dilutions. First, dilution affects the value of $i$ for electrolytes; the more dilute the solution, the more closely $i$ approaches the limiting value. Thus, we conclude that the extent of ion pairing in electrolyte solutions decreases upon dilution. Second, the lower the charges on the ions, the less $i$ departs from the limiting value because the extent of ion pairing decreases as the ionic charges decrease. Both trends are consistent with simple electrostatics: The force of interaction between charged particles decreases as their separation increases and as their charges decrease.

*RELATED EXERCISES:* 13.83, 13.84, 13.103, 13.105

**TABLE 13.4 • van't Hoff Factors for Several Substances at 25 °C**

| Compound | Concentration | | | Limiting Value |
|---|---|---|---|---|
| | 0.100 $m$ | 0.0100 $m$ | 0.00100 $m$ | |
| Sucrose | 1.00 | 1.00 | 1.00 | 1.00 |
| NaCl | 1.87 | 1.94 | 1.97 | 2.00 |
| $K_2SO_4$ | 2.32 | 2.70 | 2.84 | 3.00 |
| $MgSO_4$ | 1.21 | 1.53 | 1.82 | 2.00 |

# 13.6 | COLLOIDS

Finely divided clay particles dispersed in water eventually settle out because of gravity. This happens because clay molecules, which consist of thousands or even millions of atoms, are much larger than most molecules. In contrast, the dispersed particles in a solution (ions in a salt solution, say, or glucose molecules in a sugar solution) are smaller. Between these extremes lie dispersed particles that are larger than typical molecules but not so large that the components of the mixture separate under the influence of gravity. These intermediate types of dispersions are called either **colloidal dispersions** or simply **colloids**. Colloids form the dividing line between solutions and heterogeneous mixtures. Like solutions, colloids can be gases, liquids, or solids. Examples of each are listed in ▼ **TABLE 13.5**.

Particle size can be used to classify a mixture as colloid or solution. Colloid particles range in diameter from 5 to 1000 nm; solute particles are smaller than 5 nm in diameter. A colloid particle may even consist of a single giant molecule. The hemoglobin molecule, for example, which carries oxygen in your blood, has molecular dimensions of 6.5 × 5.5 × 5.0 nm and a molar mass of 64,500 g/mol.

Although colloid particles may be so small that the dispersion appears uniform even under a microscope, they are large enough to scatter light. Consequently, most colloids appear cloudy or opaque unless they are very dilute. (Homogenized milk is a colloid.) Furthermore, because they scatter light, a light beam can be seen as it passes through a colloidal dispersion (▶ **FIGURE 13.28**). This scattering of light by colloidal particles, known as the **Tyndall effect**, makes it possible to see the light beam of an automobile on a dusty dirt road or the sunlight coming through a forest canopy

**TABLE 13.5 • Types of Colloids**

| Phase of Colloid | Dispersing (solvent-like) Substance | Dispersed (solute-like) Substance | Colloid Type | Example |
|---|---|---|---|---|
| Gas | Gas | Gas | — | None (all are solutions) |
| Gas | Gas | Liquid | Aerosol | Fog |
| Gas | Gas | Solid | Aerosol | Smoke |
| Liquid | Liquid | Gas | Foam | Whipped cream |
| Liquid | Liquid | Liquid | Emulsion | Milk |
| Liquid | Liquid | Solid | Sol | Paint |
| Solid | Solid | Gas | Solid foam | Marshmallow |
| Solid | Solid | Liquid | Solid emulsion | Butter |
| Solid | Solid | Solid | Solid sol | Ruby glass |

▶ **FIGURE 13.28 Tyndall effect in the laboratory.** The glass on the right contains a colloidal dispersion; that on the left contains a solution.

▶ **FIGURE 13.28 Tyndall effect in the laboratory.** The glass on the right contains a colloidal dispersion; that on the left contains a solution.

(▼ **FIGURE 13.29**). Not all wavelengths are scattered to the same extent. Colors at the violet end of the visible spectrum are scattered more than those at the red end. As a result, brilliant red sunsets are seen when the sun is near the horizon and the air contains dust, smoke, or other particles of colloidal size.

## Hydrophilic and Hydrophobic Colloids

The most important colloids are those in which the dispersing medium is water. These colloids may be **hydrophilic** (water loving) or **hydrophobic** (water fearing). Hydrophilic colloids are most like the solutions that we have previously examined. In the human body the extremely large molecules that make up such important substances as enzymes and antibodies are kept in suspension by interaction with surrounding water molecules. A hydrophilic molecule folds in such a way that its hydrophobic groups are away from the water molecules, on the "inside" of the folded molecule, while its hydrophilic, polar groups are on the surface, interacting with the water molecules. The hydrophilic groups generally contain oxygen or nitrogen and often carry a charge (▶ **FIGURE 13.30**).

Hydrophobic colloids can be dispersed in water only if they are stabilized in some way. Otherwise, their natural lack of affinity for water causes them to separate from the water. One method of stabilization involves adsorbing ions on the surface of the hydrophobic particles (▶ **FIGURE 13.31**). (*Adsorption* means to adhere to a surface. It differs from *absorption*, which means to pass into the interior, as when a sponge absorbs water.) The adsorbed ions can interact with water, thereby stabilizing the colloid. At the same time, the repulsion between adsorbed ions on neighboring colloid particles keeps the particles from sticking together rather than dispersing in the water.

▶ **FIGURE 13.29 Tyndall effect in nature.**

GO FIGURE

**What is the chemical composition of the groups that carry a negative charge?**

Hydrophilic polar and charged groups on molecule surface help molecule remain dispersed in water and other polar solvents

▲ **FIGURE 13.30  Hydrophilic colloidal particle.** Examples of the hydrophilic groups that help to keep a giant molecule (macromolecule) suspended in water.

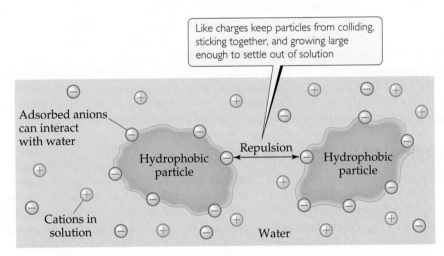

Like charges keep particles from colliding, sticking together, and growing large enough to settle out of solution

Adsorbed anions can interact with water

Repulsion

Hydrophobic particle

Hydrophobic particle

Cations in solution

Water

▲ **FIGURE 13.31  Hydrophobic colloids stabilized by adsorbed anions.**

Hydrophobic colloids can also be stabilized by hydrophilic groups on their surfaces. Oil drops are hydrophobic, for example, so they do not remain suspended in water. Instead, they aggregate, forming an oil slick on the water surface. Sodium stearate (▶ **FIGURE 13.32**), or any similar substance having one end that is hydrophilic (either polar or charged) and one end that is hydrophobic (nonpolar), will stabilize a suspension of oil in water. Stabilization results from the interaction of the hydrophobic ends of the stearate ions with the oil drops and the hydrophilic ends with the water.

GIVE IT SOME THOUGHT

Why don't oil drops stabilized by sodium stearate coagulate to form larger oil drops?

⬛ **GO FIGURE**

**Which kind of intermolecular force attracts the stearate ion to the oil drop?**

▲ **FIGURE 13.32** **Stabilization of an emulsion of oil in water by stearate ions.**

Colloid stabilization has an interesting application in the human digestive system. When fats in our diet reach the small intestine, a hormone causes the gallbladder to excrete a fluid called bile. Among the components of bile are compounds that have chemical structures similar to sodium stearate; that is, they have a hydrophilic (polar) end and a hydrophobic (nonpolar) end. These compounds emulsify the fats in the intestine and thus permit digestion and absorption of fat-soluble vitamins through the intestinal wall. The term *emulsify* means "to form an emulsion," a suspension of one liquid in another, with milk being one example (Table 13.5). A substance that aids in the formation of an emulsion is called an emulsifying agent. If you read the labels on foods and other materials, you will find that a variety of chemicals are used as emulsifying agents. These chemicals typically have a hydrophilic end and a hydrophobic end.

## Removal of Colloidal Particles

Colloidal particles frequently must be removed from a dispersing medium, as in the removal of smoke from smokestacks or butterfat from milk. Because colloidal particles are too small to be separated by simple filtration, they must be enlarged in a process called *coagulation*. The coagulated particles can then be separated by filtration or merely allowed to settle out of the dispersing medium.

Heating a colloidal dispersion or adding an electrolyte may bring about coagulation. Heating increases the particle motion and so the number of collisions. The particles get larger as they stick together after colliding. Addition of an electrolyte neutralizes the surface charges of the particles, thereby removing the electrostatic repulsions that prevent them from coming together. Wherever a river empties into the ocean, for example, the clay suspended in the river is deposited as a delta as it mixes with the electrolytes in the salt water.

A semipermeable membrane can be used to separate ions from colloidal particles because the ions can pass through the membrane but the colloidal particles cannot. This type of separation is known as *dialysis* and is used to purify blood in artificial kidney machines. Our kidneys normally remove waste products from blood. In a kidney machine, blood is circulated through a dialyzing tube immersed in a washing solution. The solution contains the same concentrations and kinds of ions as blood but no waste products. Dissolved wastes therefore dialyze out of the blood, but the large colloidal particles such as proteins do not.

# CHEMISTRY AND LIFE

## SICKLE-CELL ANEMIA

Our blood contains the complex protein *hemoglobin,* which carries oxygen from the lungs to other parts of the body. In the genetic disease known as *sickle-cell anemia,* hemoglobin molecules are abnormal and have a lower solubility, especially in their unoxygenated form. Consequently, as much as 85% of the hemoglobin in red blood cells crystallizes out of solution.

The cause of the insolubility is a structural change in one part of an amino acid. Normal hemoglobin molecules contain an amino acid that has a —$CH_2CH_2COOH$ chain:

$$-CH_2-CH_2-\overset{\overset{\displaystyle O}{\|}}{C}-OH$$

Normal                Normal

The polarity of the —COOH group contributes to the solubility of the hemoglobin molecule in water. In the hemoglobin molecules of sickle-cell anemia patients, the —$CH_2CH_2COOH$ chain is absent and in its place we find only the nonpolar (hydrophobic) —$CH(CH_3)_2$ group:

$$-CH-CH_3 \\ \ \ \ | \\ \ \ \ CH_3$$

Abnormal              Abnormal

This change leads to the aggregation of the defective form of hemoglobin into particles too large to remain suspended in biological fluids. It also causes the cells to distort into the sickle shape shown in ▼ **FIGURE 13.33.** The sickled cells tend to clog capillaries, causing severe pain, weakness, and the gradual deterioration of vital organs. The disease is hereditary, and if both parents carry the defective genes, it is likely that their children will possess only abnormal hemoglobin.

▲ **FIGURE 13.33  Normal and sickled red blood cells.** Normal red blood cells are about $1 \times 10^{-3}$ mm in diameter.

---

**SAMPLE INTEGRATIVE EXERCISE**   **Putting Concepts Together**

A 0.100-L solution is made by dissolving 0.441 g of $CaCl_2(s)$ in water. **(a)** Calculate the osmotic pressure of this solution at 27 °C, assuming that it is completely dissociated into its component ions. **(b)** The measured osmotic pressure of this solution is 2.56 atm at 27 °C. Explain why it is less than the value calculated in (a), and calculate the van't Hoff factor, *i*, for the solute in this solution. (See the "A Closer Look" box on Colligative Properties of Electrolyte Solutions in Section 13.5.) **(c)** The enthalpy of solution for $CaCl_2$ is $\Delta H = -81.3$ kJ/mol. If the final temperature of the solution is 27 °C, what was its initial temperature? (Assume that the density of the solution is 1.00 g/mL, that its specific heat is 4.18 J/g-K, and that the solution loses no heat to its surroundings.)

### SOLUTION

**(a)** The osmotic pressure is given by Equation 13.14, $\Pi = MRT$. We know the temperature, $T = 27\ °C = 300$ K, and the gas constant, $R = 0.0821$ L-atm/mol-K. We can calculate the molarity of the solution from the mass of $CaCl_2$ and the volume of the solution:

$$\text{Molarity} = \left(\frac{0.441 \text{ g } CaCl_2}{0.100 \text{ L}}\right)\left(\frac{1 \text{ mol } CaCl_2}{110 \text{ g } CaCl_2}\right) = 0.0397 \text{ mol } CaCl_2/\text{L}$$

Soluble ionic compounds are strong electrolytes. ⚬⚬⚬ (Sections 4.1 and 4.3) Thus, $CaCl_2$ consists of metal cations ($Ca^{2+}$) and nonmetal anions ($Cl^-$). When completely dissociated, each $CaCl_2$ unit forms three ions (one $Ca^{2+}$ and two $Cl^-$). Hence, the total concentration of ions in the solution is (3)(0.0397 *M*) = 0.119 *M*, and the calculated osmotic pressure is

$$\Pi = MRT = (0.119 \text{ mol/L})(0.0821 \text{ L-atm/mol-K})(300 \text{ K}) = 2.93 \text{ atm}$$

**(b)** The actual values of colligative properties of electrolytes are less than those calculated because the electrostatic interactions between ions limit their independent movements. In this case the van't Hoff factor, which measures the extent to which electrolytes actually dissociate into ions, is given by

$$i = \frac{\Pi(\text{measured})}{\Pi(\text{calculated for nonelectrolyte})}$$

$$= \frac{2.56 \text{ atm}}{(0.0397 \text{ mol/L})(0.0821 \text{ L-atm/mol-K})(300 \text{ K})} = 2.62$$

Thus, the solution behaves as if the $CaCl_2$ has dissociated into 2.62 particles instead of the ideal 3.

**(c)** If the solution is 0.0397 $M$ in $CaCl_2$ and has a total volume of 0.100 L, the number of moles of solute is $(0.100 \text{ L})(0.0397 \text{ mol/L}) = 0.00397$ mol. Hence, the quantity of heat generated in forming the solution is $(0.00397 \text{ mol})(-81.3 \text{ kJ/mol}) = -0.323$ kJ. The solution absorbs this heat, causing its temperature to increase. The relationship between temperature change and heat is given by Equation 5.22:

$$q = (\text{specific heat})(\text{grams})(\Delta T)$$

The heat absorbed by the solution is $q = +0.323 \text{ kJ} = 323 \text{ J}$. The mass of the 0.100 L of solution is $(100 \text{ mL})(1.00 \text{ g/mL}) = 100 \text{ g}$ (to three significant figures). Thus, the temperature change is

$$\Delta T = \frac{q}{(\text{specific heat of solution})(\text{grams of solution})}$$

$$= \frac{323 \text{ J}}{(4.18 \text{ J/g-K})(100 \text{ g})} = 0.773 \text{ K}$$

A kelvin has the same size as a degree Celsius. ∞ (Section 1.4) Because the solution temperature increases by 0.773 °C, the initial temperature was 27.0 °C − 0.773 °C = 26.2 °C.

# CHAPTER SUMMARY AND KEY TERMS

**SECTION 13.1** Solutions form when one substance disperses uniformly throughout another. The attractive interaction of solvent molecules with solute is called **solvation**. When the solvent is water, the interaction is called **hydration**. The dissolution of ionic substances in water is promoted by hydration of the separated ions by the polar water molecules. The overall enthalpy change upon solution formation may be either positive or negative. Solution formation is favored both by a positive entropy change, corresponding to an increased dispersal of the components of the solution, and by a negative enthalpy change, indicating an exothermic process.

**SECTION 13.2** The equilibrium between a saturated solution and undissolved solute is dynamic; the process of solution and the reverse process, **crystallization**, occur simultaneously. In a solution in equilibrium with undissolved solute, the two processes occur at equal rates, giving a **saturated** solution. If there is less solute present than is needed to saturate the solution, the solution is **unsaturated**. When solute concentration is greater than the equilibrium concentration value, the solution is **supersaturated**. This is an unstable condition, and separation of some solute from the solution will occur if the process is initiated with a solute seed crystal. The amount of solute needed to form a saturated solution at any particular temperature is the **solubility** of that solute at that temperature.

**SECTION 13.3** The solubility of one substance in another depends on the tendency of systems to become more random, by becoming more dispersed in space, and on the relative intermolecular solute–solute and solvent–solvent energies compared with solute–solute interactions. Polar and ionic solutes tend to dissolve in polar solvents, and nonpolar solutes tend to dissolve in nonpolar solvents ("like dissolves like"). Liquids that mix in all proportions are **miscible**; those

that do not dissolve significantly in one another are **immiscible**. Hydrogen-bonding interactions between solute and solvent often play an important role in determining solubility; for example, ethanol and water, whose molecules form hydrogen bonds with each other, are miscible. The solubilities of gases in a liquid are generally proportional to the pressure of the gas over the solution, as expressed by **Henry's law**: $S_g = kP_g$. The solubilities of most solid solutes in water increase as the temperature of the solution increases. In contrast, the solubilities of gases in water generally decrease with increasing temperature.

**SECTION 13.4** Concentrations of solutions can be expressed quantitatively by several different measures, including **mass percentage** [(mass solute/mass solution) $\times 10^2$], **parts per million (ppm)**, **parts per billion (ppb)**, and mole fraction. Molarity, $M$, is defined as moles of solute per liter of solution; **molality**, $m$, is defined as moles of solute per kg of solvent. Molarity can be converted to these other concentration units if the density of the solution is known.

**SECTION 13.5** A physical property of a solution that depends on the concentration of solute particles present, regardless of the nature of the solute, is a **colligative property**. Colligative properties include vapor-pressure lowering, freezing-point lowering, boiling-point elevation, and osmotic pressure. **Raoult's law** expresses the lowering of vapor pressure. An **ideal solution** obeys Raoult's law. Differences in solvent–solute as compared with solvent–solvent and solute–solute intermolecular forces cause many solutions to depart from ideal behavior.

A solution containing a nonvolatile solute possesses a higher boiling point than the pure solvent. The **molal boiling-point-elevation constant**, $K_b$, represents the increase in boiling point for a 1 $m$ solution of solute particles as compared with the pure solvent. Similarly, the

**molal freezing-point-depression constant**, $K_f$, measures the lowering of the freezing point of a solution for a 1 $m$ solution of solute particles. The temperature changes are given by the equations $\Delta T_b = K_b m$ and $\Delta T_f = K_f m$. When NaCl dissolves in water, two moles of solute particles are formed for each mole of dissolved salt. The boiling point or freezing point is thus elevated or depressed, respectively, approximately twice as much as that of a nonelectrolyte solution of the same concentration. Similar considerations apply to other strong electrolytes.

**Osmosis** is the movement of solvent molecules through a semipermeable membrane from a less concentrated to a more concentrated solution. This net movement of solvent generates an **osmotic pressure**, $\Pi$, which can be measured in units of gas pressure, such as atm. The osmotic pressure of a solution is proportional to the solution molarity: $\Pi = MRT$. Osmosis is a very important process in living systems, in which cell walls act as semipermeable membranes, permitting the passage of water but restricting the passage of ionic and macromolecular components.

**SECTION 13.6** Particles that are large on the molecular scale but still small enough to remain suspended indefinitely in a solvent system form **colloids**, or **colloidal dispersions**. Colloids, which are intermediate between solutions and heterogeneous mixtures, have many practical applications. One useful physical property of colloids, the scattering of visible light, is referred to as the **Tyndall effect**. Aqueous colloids are classified as **hydrophilic** or **hydrophobic**. Hydrophilic colloids are common in living organisms, in which large molecular aggregates (enzymes, antibodies) remain suspended because they have many polar, or charged, atomic groups on their surfaces that interact with water. Hydrophobic colloids, such as small droplets of oil, may remain in suspension through adsorption of charged particles on their surfaces.

# KEY SKILLS

- Describe how enthalpy and entropy changes affect solution formation. (Section 13.1)
- Describe the relationship between intermolecular forces and solubility, including use of the "like dissolves like" rule. (Sections 13.1 and 13.3)
- Describe the role of equilibrium in the solution process and its relationship to the solubility of a solute. (Section 13.2)
- Describe the effect of temperature on the solubility of solids and gases. (Section 13.3)
- Describe the relationship between the partial pressure of a gas and its solubility. (Section 13.3)
- Calculate the concentration of a solution in terms of molarity, molality, mole fraction, percent composition, and parts per million and be able to interconvert between them. (Section 13.4)
- Describe what a colligative property is and explain the difference between the effects of nonelectrolytes and electrolytes on colligative properties. (Section 13.5)
- Calculate the vapor pressure of a solvent over a solution. (Section 13.5)
- Calculate the boiling-point elevation and freezing-point depression of a solution. (Section 13.5)
- Calculate the osmotic pressure of a solution. (Section 13.5)
- Explain the difference between a solution and a colloid. (Section 13.6)

# KEY EQUATIONS

- $S_g = kP_g$ [13.4] Henry's law, relating gas solubility to partial pressure

- Mass % of component $= \dfrac{\text{mass of component in soln}}{\text{total mass of soln}} \times 100$ [13.5] Defining concentration in terms of mass percent

- ppm of component $= \dfrac{\text{mass of component in soln}}{\text{total mass of soln}} \times 10^6$ [13.6] Defining concentration in terms of parts per million (ppm)

- Mole fraction of component $= \dfrac{\text{moles of component}}{\text{total moles of all components}}$ [13.7] Defining concentration in terms of mole fraction

- Molarity $= \dfrac{\text{moles of solute}}{\text{liters of soln}}$ [13.8] Defining concentration in terms of molarity

- Molality $= \dfrac{\text{moles of solute}}{\text{kilograms of solvent}}$ [13.9] Defining concentration in terms of molality

- $P_{\text{solution}} = X_{\text{solvent}} P^\circ_{\text{solvent}}$ [13.10] Raoult's law, calculating vapor pressure of solvent above a solution

- $\Delta T_b = K_b m$ [13.12] Calculating the boiling-point elevation of a solution

- $\Delta T_f = K_f m$ [13.13] Calculating the freezing-point depression of a solution

- $\Pi = \left(\dfrac{n}{V}\right) RT = MRT$ [13.14] Calculating the osmotic pressure of a solution

# EXERCISES

## VISUALIZING CONCEPTS

**13.1** Rank the contents of the following containers in order of increasing entropy: [Section 13.1]

(a)  (b)  (c)

**13.2** This figure shows the interaction of a cation with surrounding water molecules.

Would you expect the energy of ion–solvent interaction to be greater for Na⁺ or Li⁺? Explain. [Section 13.1]

**13.3** How does the lattice energy of an ionic solid affect its solubility in water? [Section 13.1]

**13.4** A quantity of the blue solid on the left in Figure 13.7 is placed in an oven and heated for a time. It slowly turns from blue to the white of the solid on the right. What has occurred? [Section 13.1]

**13.5** Which of the following is the best representation of a saturated solution? Explain your reasoning. [Section 13.2]

(a)  (b)  (c)

**13.6** The solubility of Xe in water at 1 atm pressure and 20 °C is approximately $5 \times 10^{-3}$ M. Compare this with the solubilities of Ar and Kr in water (Table 13.1) and explain what properties of the rare gas atoms account for the variation in solubility. [Section 13.3]

**13.7** The structures of vitamins E and $B_6$ are shown below. Predict which is largely water soluble and which is largely fat soluble. Explain. [Section 13.3]

Vitamin $B_6$          Vitamin E

**13.8** If you wanted to prepare a solution of CO in water at 25 °C in which the CO concentration was 2.5 mM, what pressure of CO would you need to use? (See Figure 13.19.) [Section 13.3]

**13.9** The figure shows two identical volumetric flasks containing the same solution at two temperatures.

**(a)** Does the molarity of the solution change with the change in temperature? Explain.

**(b)** Does the molality of the solution change with the change in temperature? Explain. [Section 13.4]

25 °C          55 °C

**13.10** The following diagram shows the vapor-pressure curves of a volatile solvent and a solution of that solvent containing a nonvolatile solute. **(a)** Which line represents the solution? **(b)** What are the normal boiling points of the solvent and the solution? [Section 13.5]

**13.11** Suppose you had a balloon made of some highly flexible semipermeable membrane. The balloon is filled completely with a 0.2 $M$ solution of some solute and is submerged in a 0.1 $M$ solution of the same solute:

0.1 $M$

0.2 $M$

Initially, the volume of solution in the balloon is 0.25 L. Assuming the volume outside the semipermeable membrane is large, as the illustration shows, what would you expect for the solution volume inside the balloon once the system has come to equilibrium through osmosis? [Section 13.5]

**13.12** The molecule *n*-octylglucoside, shown here, is widely used in biochemical research as a nonionic detergent for "solubilizing" large hydrophobic protein molecules. What characteristics of this molecule are important for its use in this way? [Section 13.6]

# THE SOLUTION PROCESS (section 13.1)

**13.13** In general, the attractive intermolecular forces between solvent and solute particles must be comparable or greater than solute–solute interactions for significant solubility to occur. Explain this statement in terms of the overall energetics of solution formation.

**13.14** **(a)** Considering the energetics of solute–solute, solvent–solvent, and solute–solvent interactions, explain why NaCl dissolves in water but not in benzene ($C_6H_6$). **(b)** What factors cause a cation to be strongly hydrated?

**13.15** Indicate the type of solute–solvent interaction (Section 11.2) that should be most important in each of the following solutions: **(a)** $CCl_4$ in benzene ($C_6H_6$), **(b)** methanol ($CH_3OH$) in water, **(c)** KBr in water, **(d)** HCl in acetonitrile ($CH_3CN$).

**13.16** Indicate the principal type of solute–solvent interaction in each of the following solutions and rank the solutions from weakest to strongest solute–solvent interaction: **(a)** KCl in water, **(b)** $CH_2Cl_2$ in benzene ($C_6H_6$), **(c)** methanol ($CH_3OH$) in water.

**13.17** An ionic compound has a very negative $\Delta H_{soln}$ in water. Would you expect it to be very soluble or nearly insoluble in water? Explain in terms of the enthalpy and entropy changes that accompany the process.

**13.18** When ammonium chloride dissolves in water, the solution becomes colder. **(a)** Is the solution process exothermic or endothermic? **(b)** Why does the solution form?

**13.19** **(a)** In Equation 13.1 which of the enthalpy terms for dissolving an ionic solid would correspond to the lattice energy? **(b)** Which energy term in this equation is always exothermic?

**13.20** The schematic diagram of the solution process as the net sum of three steps in Figure 13.4 does not show the relative magnitudes of the three components because these will vary from case to case. For the dissolution of LiCl in water, $\Delta H_{soln} = -37$ KJ/mol. Which of the three enthalpy changes would you expect to be much more negative than the other two? Explain.

**13.21** When two nonpolar organic liquids such as hexane ($C_6H_{14}$) and heptane ($C_7H_{16}$) are mixed, the enthalpy change that occurs is generally quite small. **(a)** Use the enthalpy diagram in Figure 13.4 to explain why. **(b)** Given that $\Delta H_{soln} \approx 0$, explain why hexane and heptane spontaneously form a solution.

**13.22** The enthalpy of solution of KBr in water is about +198 kJ/mol. Nevertheless, the solubility of KBr in water is relatively high. Why does the solution process occur even though it is endothermic?

# SATURATED SOLUTIONS; FACTORS AFFECTING SOLUBILITY (sections 13.2 and 13.3)

**13.23** The solubility of $Cr(NO_3)_3 \cdot 9 H_2O$ in water is 208 g per 100 g of water at 15 °C. A solution of $Cr(NO_3)_3 \cdot 9 H_2O$ in water at 35 °C is formed by dissolving 324 g in 100 g water. When this solution is slowly cooled to 15 °C, no precipitate forms. **(a)** What term describes this solution? **(b)** What action might you take to initiate crystallization? Use molecular-level processes to explain how your suggested procedure works.

**13.24** The solubility of $MnSO_4 \cdot H_2O$ in water at 20 °C is 70 g per 100 mL of water. **(a)** Is a 1.22 $M$ solution of $MnSO_4 \cdot H_2O$ in water at 20 °C saturated, supersaturated, or unsaturated? **(b)** Given a solution of $MnSO_4 \cdot H_2O$ of unknown concentration, what experiment could you perform to determine whether the new solution is saturated, supersaturated, or unsaturated?

**13.25** By referring to Figure 13.18, determine whether the addition of 40.0 g of each of the following ionic solids to 100 g of water at 40 °C will lead to a saturated solution: **(a)** $NaNO_3$, **(b)** $KCl$, **(c)** $K_2Cr_2O_7$, **(d)** $Pb(NO_3)_2$.

**13.26** By referring to Figure 13.18, determine the mass of each of the following salts required to form a saturated solution in 250 g of water at 30 °C: **(a)** $KClO_3$, **(b)** $Pb(NO_3)_2$, **(c)** $Ce_2(SO_4)_3$.

**13.27** Water and glycerol, $CH_2(OH)CH(OH)CH_2OH$, are miscible in all proportions. What does this mean? How do the OH groups of the alcohol molecule contribute to this miscibility?

**13.28** Oil and water are immiscible. What does this mean? Explain in terms of the structural features of their respective molecules and the forces between them.

**13.29** Common laboratory solvents include acetone ($CH_3COCH_3$), methanol ($CH_3OH$), toluene ($C_6H_5CH_3$), and water. Which of these is the best solvent for nonpolar solutes? Explain.

**13.30** Would you expect alanine (an amino acid) to be more soluble in water or in hexane? Explain.

Alanine

**13.31** **(a)** Would you expect stearic acid, $CH_3(CH_2)_{16}COOH$, to be more soluble in water or in carbon tetrachloride? Explain.

**(b)** Which would you expect to be more soluble in water, cyclohexane or dioxane? Explain.

Dioxane          Cyclohexane

**13.32** Ibuprofen, widely used as a pain reliever, has a limited solubility in water, less than 1 mg/mL. Which feature of the molecule contributes to its low solubility in water, and which feature contributes to its solubility?

Ibuprophen

**13.33** Which of the following in each pair is likely to be more soluble in hexane, $C_6H_{14}$: **(a)** $CCl_4$ or $CaCl_2$; **(b)** benzene ($C_6H_6$) or glycerol, $CH_2(OH)CH(OH)CH_2OH$; **(c)** octanoic acid, $CH_3CH_2CH_2CH_2CH_2CH_2CH_2COOH$, or acetic acid, $CH_3COOH$? Explain your answer in each case.

**13.34** Which of the following in each pair is likely to be more soluble in water: **(a)** cyclohexane ($C_6H_{12}$) or glucose ($C_6H_{12}O_6$) (Figure 13.12); **(b)** propionic acid ($CH_3CH_2COOH$) or sodium propionate ($CH_3CH_2COONa$); **(c)** HCl or ethyl chloride ($CH_3CH_2Cl$)? Explain in each case.

**13.35** **(a)** Explain why carbonated beverages must be stored in sealed containers. **(b)** Once the beverage has been opened, why does it maintain more carbonation when refrigerated than at room temperature?

**13.36** Explain why pressure substantially affects the solubility of $O_2$ in water but has little effect on the solubility of NaCl in water.

**13.37** The Henry's law constant for helium gas in water at 30 °C is $3.7 \times 10^{-4}$ $M$/atm and the constant for $N_2$ at 30 °C is $6.0 \times 10^{-4}$ $M$/atm. If the two gases are each present at 1.5 atm pressure, calculate the solubility of each gas.

**13.38** The partial pressure of $O_2$ in air at sea level is 0.21 atm. Using the data in Table 13.1, together with Henry's law, calculate the molar concentration of $O_2$ in the surface water of a mountain lake saturated with air at 20 °C and an atmospheric pressure of 650 torr.

# CONCENTRATIONS OF SOLUTIONS (section 13.4)

**13.39** (a) Calculate the mass percentage of $Na_2SO_4$ in a solution containing 10.6 g $Na_2SO_4$ in 483 g water. (b) An ore contains 2.86 g of silver per ton of ore. What is the concentration of silver in ppm?

**13.40** (a) What is the mass percentage of iodine ($I_2$) in a solution containing 0.035 mol $I_2$ in 125 g of $CCl_4$? (b) Seawater contains 0.0079 g $Sr^{2+}$ per kilogram of water. What is the concentration of $Sr^{2+}$ measured in ppm?

**13.41** A solution is made containing 14.6 g of $CH_3OH$ in 184 g $H_2O$. Calculate (a) the mole fraction of $CH_3OH$, (b) the mass percent of $CH_3OH$, (c) the molality of $CH_3OH$.

**13.42** A solution is made containing 20.8 g phenol ($C_6H_5OH$) in 425 g ethanol ($C_2H_5OH$). Calculate (a) the mole fraction of phenol, (b) the mass percent of phenol, (c) the molality of phenol.

**13.43** Calculate the molarity of the following aqueous solutions: (a) 0.540 g $Mg(NO_3)_2$ in 250.0 mL of solution, (b) 22.4 g $LiClO_4 \cdot 3 H_2O$ in 125 mL of solution, (c) 25.0 mL of 3.50 $M$ $HNO_3$ diluted to 0.250 L.

**13.44** What is the molarity of each of the following solutions: (a) 15.0 g $Al_2(SO_4)_3$ in 0.250 mL solution, (b) 5.25 g $Mn(NO_3)_2 \cdot 2 H_2O$ in 175 mL of solution, (c) 35.0 mL of 9.00 $M$ $H_2SO_4$ diluted to 0.500 L?

**13.45** Calculate the molality of each of the following solutions: (a) 8.66 g benzene ($C_6H_6$) dissolved in 23.6 g carbon tetrachloride ($CCl_4$), (b) 4.80 g NaCl dissolved in 0.350 L of water.

**13.46** (a) What is the molality of a solution formed by dissolving 1.12 mol of KCl in 16.0 mol of water? (b) How many grams of sulfur ($S_8$) must be dissolved in 100.0 g naphthalene ($C_{10}H_8$) to make a 0.12 $m$ solution?

**13.47** A sulfuric acid solution containing 571.6 g of $H_2SO_4$ per liter of solution has a density of 1.329 $g/cm^3$. Calculate (a) the mass percentage, (b) the mole fraction, (c) the molality, (d) the molarity of $H_2SO_4$ in this solution.

**13.48** Ascorbic acid (vitamin C, $C_6H_8O_6$) is a water-soluble vitamin. A solution containing 80.5 g of ascorbic acid dissolved in 210 g of water has a density of 1.22 g/mL at 55 °C. Calculate (a) the mass percentage, (b) the mole fraction, (c) the molality, (d) the molarity of ascorbic acid in this solution.

**13.49** The density of acetonitrile ($CH_3CN$) is 0.786 g/mL and the density of methanol ($CH_3OH$) is 0.791 g/mL. A solution is made by dissolving 22.5 mL $CH_3OH$ in 98.7 mL $CH_3CN$. (a) What is the mole fraction of methanol in the solution? (b) What is the molality of the solution? (c) Assuming that the volumes are additive, what is the molarity of $CH_3OH$ in the solution?

**13.50** The density of toluene ($C_7H_8$) is 0.867 g/mL, and the density of thiophene ($C_4H_4S$) is 1.065 g/mL. A solution is made by dissolving 8.10 g of thiophene in 250.0 mL of toluene. (a) Calculate the mole fraction of thiophene in the solution. (b) Calculate the molality of thiophene in the solution. (c) Assuming that the volumes of the solute and solvent are additive, what is the molarity of thiophene in the solution?

**13.51** Calculate the number of moles of solute present in each of the following aqueous solutions: (a) 600 mL of 0.250 $M$ $SrBr_2$, (b) 86.4 g of 0.180 $m$ KCl, (c) 124.0 g of a solution that is 6.45% glucose ($C_6H_{12}O_6$) by mass.

**13.52** Calculate the number of moles of solute present in each of the following solutions: (a) 255 mL of 1.50 $M$ $HNO_3(aq)$, (b) 50.0 mg of an aqueous solution that is 1.50 $m$ NaCl, (c) 75.0 g of an aqueous solution that is 1.50% sucrose ($C_{12}H_{22}O_{11}$) by mass.

**13.53** Describe how you would prepare each of the following aqueous solutions, starting with solid KBr: (a) 0.75 L of $1.5 \times 10^{-2}$ $M$ KBr, (b) 125 g of 0.180 $m$ KBr, (c) 1.85 L of a solution that is 12.0% KBr by mass (the density of the solution is 1.10 g/mL), (d) a 0.150 $M$ solution of KBr that contains just enough KBr to precipitate 16.0 g of AgBr from a solution containing 0.480 mol of $AgNO_3$.

**13.54** Describe how you would prepare each of the following aqueous solutions: (a) 1.50 L of 0.110 $M$ $(NH_4)_2SO_4$ solution, starting with solid $(NH_4)_2SO_4$; (b) 225 g of a solution that is 0.65 $m$ in $Na_2CO_3$, starting with the solid solute; (c) 1.20 L of a solution that is 15.0% $Pb(NO_3)_2$ by mass (the density of the solution is 1.16 g/mL), starting with solid solute; (d) a 0.50 $M$ solution of HCl that would just neutralize 5.5 g of $Ba(OH)_2$ starting with 6.0 $M$ HCl.

**13.55** Commercial aqueous nitric acid has a density of 1.42 g/mL and is 16 $M$. Calculate the percent $HNO_3$ by mass in the solution.

**13.56** Commercial concentrated aqueous ammonia is 28% $NH_3$ by mass and has a density of 0.90 g/mL. What is the molarity of this solution?

**13.57** Brass is a substitutional alloy consisting of a solution of copper and zinc. A particular sample of red brass consisting of 80.0% Cu and 20.0% Zn by mass has a density of 8750 $kg/m^3$. (a) What is the molality of Zn in the solid solution? (b) What is the molarity of Zn in the solution?

**13.58** Caffeine ($C_8H_{10}N_4O_2$) is a stimulant found in coffee and tea. If a solution of caffeine in chloroform ($CHCl_3$) as a solvent has a concentration of 0.0500 $m$, calculate (a) the percent caffeine by mass, (b) the mole fraction of caffeine.

Caffeine

**13.59** During a typical breathing cycle, the $CO_2$ concentration in the expired air rises to a peak of 4.6% by volume. Calculate the partial pressure of the $CO_2$ at this point, assuming 1 atm pressure. What is the molarity of the $CO_2$ in air at this point, assuming a body temperature of 37 °C?

**13.60** Breathing air that contains 4.0% by volume $CO_2$ over time causes rapid breathing, throbbing headache, and nausea, among other symptoms. What is the concentration of $CO_2$ in such air in terms of (a) mol percentage, (b) molarity, assuming 1 atm pressure and a body temperature of 37 °C?

# COLLIGATIVE PROPERTIES (section 13.5)

**13.61** List four properties of a solution that depend on the total concentration but not the type of particle or particles present as solute. Write the mathematical expression that describes how each of these properties depends on concentration.

**13.62** How does increasing the concentration of a nonvolatile solute in water affect the following properties: **(a)** vapor pressure, **(b)** freezing point, **(c)** boiling point; **(d)** osmotic pressure?

**13.63** Consider two solutions, one formed by adding 10 g of glucose ($C_6H_{12}O_6$) to 1 L of water and the other formed by adding 10 g of sucrose ($C_{12}H_{22}O_{11}$) to 1 L of water. Are the vapor pressures over the two solutions the same? Why or why not?

**13.64** **(a)** What is an *ideal solution*? **(b)** The vapor pressure of pure water at 60 °C is 149 torr. The vapor pressure of water over a solution at 60 °C containing equal numbers of moles of water and ethylene glycol (a nonvolatile solute) is 67 torr. Is the solution ideal according to Raoult's law? Explain.

**13.65** **(a)** Calculate the vapor pressure of water above a solution prepared by adding 22.5 g of lactose ($C_{12}H_{22}O_{11}$) to 200.0 g of water at 338 K. (Vapor-pressure data for water are given in Appendix B.) **(b)** Calculate the mass of propylene glycol ($C_3H_8O_2$) that must be added to 0.340 kg of water to reduce the vapor pressure by 2.88 torr at 40 °C.

**13.66** **(a)** Calculate the vapor pressure of water above a solution prepared by dissolving 28.5 g of glycerin ($C_3H_8O_3$) in 125 g of water at 343 K. (The vapor pressure of water is given in Appendix B.) **(b)** Calculate the mass of ethylene glycol ($C_2H_6O_2$) that must be added to 1.00 kg of ethanol ($C_2H_5OH$) to reduce its vapor pressure by 10.0 torr at 35 °C. The vapor pressure of pure ethanol at 35 °C is $1.00 \times 10^2$ torr.

**[13.67]** At 63.5 °C the vapor pressure of $H_2O$ is 175 torr, and that of ethanol ($C_2H_5OH$) is 400 torr. A solution is made by mixing equal masses of $H_2O$ and $C_2H_5OH$. **(a)** What is the mole fraction of ethanol in the solution? **(b)** Assuming ideal-solution behavior, what is the vapor pressure of the solution at 63.5 °C? **(c)** What is the mole fraction of ethanol in the vapor above the solution?

**[13.68]** At 20 °C the vapor pressure of benzene ($C_6H_6$) is 75 torr, and that of toluene ($C_7H_8$) is 22 torr. Assume that benzene and toluene form an ideal solution. **(a)** What is the composition in mole fractions of a solution that has a vapor pressure of 35 torr at 20 °C ? **(b)** What is the mole fraction of benzene in the vapor above the solution described in part (a)?

**13.69** **(a)** Why does a 0.10 *m* aqueous solution of NaCl have a higher boiling point than a 0.10 *m* aqueous solution of $C_6H_{12}O_6$? **(b)** Calculate the boiling point of each solution. **(c)** The experimental boiling point of the NaCl solution is lower than that calculated, assuming that NaCl is completely dissociated in solution. Why is this the case?

**13.70** Arrange the following aqueous solutions, each 10% by mass in solute, in order of increasing boiling point: glucose ($C_6H_{12}O_6$), sucrose ($C_{12}H_{22}O_{11}$), sodium nitrate (NaNO₃).

**13.71** List the following aqueous solutions in order of increasing boiling point: 0.120 *m* glucose, 0.050 *m* LiBr, 0.050 *m* Zn(NO₃)₂.

**13.72** List the following aqueous solutions in order of decreasing freezing point: 0.040 *m* glycerin ($C_3H_8O_3$), 0.020 *m* KBr, 0.030 *m* phenol ($C_6H_5OH$).

**13.73** Using data from Table 13.3, calculate the freezing and boiling points of each of the following solutions: **(a)** 0.22 *m* glycerol ($C_3H_8O_3$) in ethanol, **(b)** 0.240 mol of naphthalene ($C_{10}H_8$) in 2.45 mol of chloroform, **(c)** 1.50 g NaCl in 0.250 kg of water, **(d)** 2.04 g KBr and 4.82 g glucose ($C_6H_{12}O_6$) in 188 g of water.

**13.74** Using data from Table 13.3, calculate the freezing and boiling points of each of the following solutions: **(a)** 0.25 *m* glucose in ethanol; **(b)** 20.0 g of decane, $C_{10}H_{22}$, in 50.0 g CHCl₃; **(c)** 3.50 g NaOH in 175 g of water, **(d)** 0.45 mol ethylene glycol and 0.15 mol KBr in 150 g $H_2O$.

**13.75** How many grams of ethylene glycol ($C_2H_6O_2$) must be added to 1.00 kg of water to produce a solution that freezes at −5.00 °C?

**13.76** What is the freezing point of an aqueous solution that boils at 105.0 °C?

**13.77** What is the osmotic pressure formed by dissolving 44.2 mg of aspirin ($C_9H_8O_4$) in 0.358 L of water at 25 °C?

**13.78** Seawater contains 3.4 g of salts for every liter of solution. Assuming that the solute consists entirely of NaCl (over 90% is), calculate the osmotic pressure of seawater at 20 °C.

**13.79** Adrenaline is the hormone that triggers the release of extra glucose molecules in times of stress or emergency. A solution of 0.64 g of adrenaline in 36.0 g of CCl₄ elevates the boiling point by 0.49 °C. Is the molar mass of adrenaline calculated from the boiling-point elevation in agreement with the following structural formula?

Adrenaline

**13.80** Lauryl alcohol is obtained from coconut oil and is used to make detergents. A solution of 5.00 g of lauryl alcohol in 0.100 kg of benzene freezes at 4.1 °C. What is the approximate molar mass of lauryl alcohol?

**13.81** Lysozyme is an enzyme that breaks bacterial cell walls. A solution containing 0.150 g of this enzyme in 210 mL of solution has an osmotic pressure of 0.953 torr at 25 °C. What is the molar mass of lysozyme?

**13.82** A dilute aqueous solution of an organic compound soluble in water is formed by dissolving 2.35 g of the compound in water to form 0.250 L of solution. The resulting solution has an osmotic pressure of 0.605 atm at 25 °C. Assuming that the organic compound is a nonelectrolyte, what is its molar mass?

**[13.83]** The osmotic pressure of a 0.010 *M* aqueous solution of CaCl₂ is found to be 0.674 atm at 25 °C. **(a)** Calculate the van't Hoff factor, *i*, for the solution. **(b)** How would you expect the value of *i* to change as the solution becomes more concentrated? Explain.

**[13.84]** Based on the data given in Table 13.4, which solution would give the larger freezing-point lowering, a 0.030 *m* solution of NaCl or a 0.020 *m* solution of K₂SO₄? How do you explain the departure from ideal behavior and the differences observed between the two salts?

# COLLOIDS (section 13.6)

**13.85** **(a)** Why is there no colloid in which both the dispersed substance and the dispersing substance are gases? **(b)** Michael Faraday first prepared ruby-red colloids of gold particles in water that were stable indefinitely. To the unaided eye these brightly colored colloids are not distinguishable from solutions. How could you determine whether a given colored preparation is a solution or colloid?

**13.86** **(a)** Many proteins that remain homogeneously distributed in water have molecular masses in the range of 30,000 amu and larger. In what sense is it appropriate to consider such suspensions to be colloids rather than solutions? Explain. **(b)** What general name is given to a colloidal dispersion of one liquid in another? What is an emulsifying agent?

**13.87** Indicate whether each of the following is a hydrophilic or a hydrophobic colloid: **(a)** butterfat in homogenized milk,

**(b)** hemoglobin in blood, **(c)** vegetable oil in a salad dressing, **(d)** colloidal gold particles in water.

**13.88** Explain how each of the following factors helps determine the stability or instability of a colloidal dispersion: **(a)** particulate mass, **(b)** hydrophobic character, **(c)** charges on colloidal particles.

**13.89** Colloidal dispersions of proteins, such as a gelatin, can often be caused to separate into two layers by addition of a solution of an electrolyte. Given that protein molecules may carry electrical charges on their outer surface as illustrated in Figure 13.30, what do you believe happens when the electrolyte solution is added?

**13.90** Explain how **(a)** a soap such as sodium stearate stabilizes a colloidal dispersion of oil droplets in water; **(b)** milk curdles upon addition of an acid.

# ADDITIONAL EXERCISES

**13.91** Butylated hydroxytoluene (BHT) has the following molecular structure:

BHT

It is widely used as a preservative in a variety of foods, including dried cereals. Based on its structure, would you expect BHT to be more soluble in water or in hexane ($C_6H_{14}$)? Explain.

**13.92** A saturated solution of sucrose ($C_{12}H_{22}O_{11}$) is made by dissolving excess table sugar in a flask of water. There are 50 g of undissolved sucrose crystals at the bottom of the flask in contact with the saturated solution. The flask is stoppered and set aside. A year later a single large crystal of mass 50 g is at the bottom of the flask. Explain how this experiment provides evidence for a dynamic equilibrium between the saturated solution and the undissolved solute.

**13.93** Most fish need at least 4 ppm dissolved $O_2$ for survival. **(a)** What is this concentration in mol/L? **(b)** What partial pressure of $O_2$ above the water is needed to obtain this concentration at 10 °C? (The Henry's law constant for $O_2$ at this temperature is $1.71 \times 10^{-3}$ mol/L-atm.)

**13.94** The presence of the radioactive gas radon (Rn) in well water obtained from aquifers that lie in rock deposits presents a possible health hazard in parts of the United States. **(a)** Assuming that the solubility of radon in water with 1 atm pressure of the gas over the water at 30 °C is $7.27 \times 10^{-3}$ $M$, what is the Henry's law constant for radon in water at this temperature? **(b)** A sample consisting of various gases contains $3.5 \times 10^{-6}$ mole fraction of radon. This gas at a total pressure of 32 atm is shaken with water at 30 °C. Calculate the molar concentration of radon in the water.

**13.95** Glucose makes up about 0.10% by mass of human blood. Calculate the concentration in **(a)** ppm, **(b)** molality. What further information would you need to determine the molarity of the solution?

**13.96** The concentration of gold in seawater has been reported to be between 5 ppt (parts per trillion) and 50 ppt. Assuming that seawater contains 13 ppt of gold, calculate the number of grams of gold contained in $1.0 \times 10^3$ gal of seawater.

**13.97** The maximum allowable concentration of lead in drinking water is 9.0 ppb. **(a)** Calculate the molarity of lead in a 9.0-ppb solution. What assumption did you have to make in your calculation? **(b)** How many grams of lead are in a swimming pool containing 9.0 ppb lead in 60 $m^3$ of water?

**13.98** Acetonitrile ($CH_3CN$) is a polar organic solvent that dissolves a wide range of solutes, including many salts. The density of a 1.80 $M$ LiBr solution in acetonitrile is 0.826 g/cm$^3$. Calculate the concentration of the solution in **(a)** molality, **(b)** mole fraction of LiBr, **(c)** mass percentage of $CH_3CN$.

**13.99** A "canned heat" product used to warm chafing dishes consists of a homogeneous mixture of ethanol ($C_2H_5OH$) and paraffin that has an average formula of $C_{24}H_{50}$. What mass of $C_2H_5OH$ should be added to 620 kg of the paraffin in formulating the mixture if the vapor pressure of ethanol at 35 °C over the mixture is to be 8 torr? The vapor pressure of pure ethanol at 35 °C is 100 torr.

**13.100** A solution contains 0.115 mol $H_2O$ and an unknown number of moles of sodium chloride. The vapor pressure of the solution at 30 °C is 25.7 torr. The vapor pressure of pure water at this temperature is 31.8 torr. Calculate the number of moles of sodium chloride in the solution. (*Hint:* Remember that sodium chloride is a strong electrolyte.)

**[13.101]** Two beakers are placed in a sealed box at 25 °C. One beaker contains 30.0 mL of a 0.050 $M$ aqueous solution of a nonvolatile nonelectrolyte. The other beaker contains 30.0 mL of a 0.035 $M$ aqueous solution of NaCl. The water vapor from the two solutions reaches equilibrium. **(a)** In which beaker does the solution level rise, and in which one does it fall? **(b)** What are the volumes in the two beakers when equilibrium is attained, assuming ideal behavior?

**13.102** A car owner who knows no chemistry has to put antifreeze in his car's radiator. The instructions recommend a mixture of 30% ethylene glycol and 70% water. Thinking he will improve his protection he uses pure ethylene glycol. He is saddened to find that the solution does not provide as much protection as he hoped. Why not?

**13.103** Calculate the freezing point of a 0.100 $m$ aqueous solution of $K_2SO_4$, (a) ignoring interionic attractions, and (b) taking interionic attractions into consideration by using the van't Hoff factor (Table 13.4).

**13.104** Carbon disulfide ($CS_2$) boils at 46.30 °C and has a density of 1.261 g/mL. (a) When 0.250 mol of a nondissociating solute is dissolved in 400.0 mL of $CS_2$, the solution boils at 47.46 °C. What is the molal boiling-point-elevation constant for $CS_2$? (b) When 5.39 g of a nondissociating unknown is dissolved in 50.0 mL of $CS_2$, the solution boils at 47.08 °C. What is the molecular weight of the unknown?

**[13.105]** A lithium salt used in lubricating grease has the formula $LiC_nH_{2n+1}O_2$. The salt is soluble in water to the extent of 0.036 g per 100 g of water at 25 °C. The osmotic pressure of this solution is found to be 57.1 torr. Assuming that molality and molarity in such a dilute solution are the same and that the lithium salt is completely dissociated in the solution, determine an appropriate value of $n$ in the formula for the salt.

## INTEGRATIVE EXERCISES

**13.106** Fluorocarbons (compounds that contain both carbon and fluorine) were, until recently, used as refrigerants. The compounds listed in the following table are all gases at 25 °C, and their solubilities in water at 25 °C and 1 atm fluorocarbon pressure are given as mass percentages. (a) For each fluorocarbon, calculate the molality of a saturated solution. (b) Explain why the molarity of each of the solutions should be very close numerically to the molality. (c) Based on their molecular structures, account for the differences in solubility of the four fluorocarbons. (d) Calculate the Henry's law constant at 25 °C for $CHClF_2$, and compare its magnitude to that for $N_2(6.8 \times 10^{-4}$ mol/L-atm). Can you account for the difference in magnitude?

| Fluorocarbon | Solubility (mass %) |
| --- | --- |
| $CF_4$ | 0.0015 |
| $CClF_3$ | 0.009 |
| $CCl_2F_2$ | 0.028 |
| $CHClF_2$ | 0.30 |

**[13.107]** At ordinary body temperature (37 °C) the solubility of $N_2$ in water in contact with air at ordinary atmospheric pressure (1.0 atm) is 0.015 g/L. Air is approximately 78 mol % $N_2$. Calculate the number of moles of $N_2$ dissolved per liter of blood, which is essentially an aqueous solution. At a depth of 100 ft in water, the pressure is 4.0 atm. What is the solubility of $N_2$ from air in blood at this pressure? If a scuba diver suddenly surfaces from this depth, how many milliliters of $N_2$ gas, in the form of tiny bubbles, are released into the bloodstream from each liter of blood?

**[13.108]** Consider the following values for enthalpy of vaporization (kJ/mol) of several organic substances:

$$\overset{\overset{\textstyle O}{\|}}{CH_3C}-H \quad 30.4$$

Acetaldehyde

$$H_2C \overset{O}{\diagdown\!\diagup} CH_2 \quad 28.5$$

Ethylene oxide

$$\overset{\overset{\textstyle O}{\|}}{CH_3CCH_3} \quad 32.0$$

Acetone

$$H_2C \overset{CH_2}{\diagup\;\diagdown} CH_2 \quad 24.7$$

Cyclopropane

(a) Use variations in the intermolecular forces operating in these organic substances to account for their variations in heats of vaporization. (b) How would you expect the solubilities of these substances to vary in hexane as solvent? In ethanol? Use intermolecular forces, including hydrogen-bonding interactions where applicable, to explain your responses.

**[13.109]** A textbook on chemical thermodynamics states, "The heat of solution represents the difference between the lattice energy of the crystalline solid and the solvation energy of the gaseous ions." (a) Draw a simple energy diagram to illustrate this statement. (b) A salt such as NaBr is insoluble in most polar nonaqueous solvents such as acetonitrile ($CH_3CN$) or nitromethane ($CH_3NO_2$), but salts of large cations, such as tetramethylammonium bromide [$(CH_3)_4NBr$], are generally more soluble. Use the thermochemical cycle you drew in part (a) and the factors that determine the lattice energy (Section 8.2) to explain this fact.

**13.110** (a) A sample of hydrogen gas is generated in a closed container by reacting 2.050 g of zinc metal with 15.0 mL of 1.00 $M$ sulfuric acid. Write the balanced equation for the reaction, and calculate the number of moles of hydrogen formed, assuming that the reaction is complete. (b) The volume over the solution is 122 mL. Calculate the partial pressure of the hydrogen gas in this volume at 25 °C, ignoring any solubility of the gas in the solution. (c) The Henry's law constant for hydrogen in water at 25 °C is $7.8 \times 10^{-4}$ mol/L-atm. Estimate the number of moles of hydrogen gas that remain dissolved in the solution. What fraction of the gas molecules in the system is dissolved in the solution? Was it reasonable to ignore any dissolved hydrogen in part (b)?

[13.111] The following table presents the solubilities of several gases in water at 25 °C under a total pressure of gas and water vapor of 1 atm. **(a)** What volume of $CH_4(g)$ under standard conditions of temperature and pressure is contained in 4.0 L of a saturated solution at 25 °C ? **(b)** Explain the variation in solubility among the hydrocarbons listed (the first three compounds), based on their molecular structures and intermolecular forces. **(c)** Compare the solubilities of $O_2$, $N_2$, and NO, and account for the variations based on molecular structures and intermolecular forces. **(d)** Account for the much larger values observed for $H_2S$ and $SO_2$ as compared with the other gases listed. **(e)** Find several pairs of substances with the same or nearly the same molecular masses (for example, $C_2H_4$ and $N_2$), and use intermolecular interactions to explain the differences in their solubilities.

| Gas | Solubility (m$M$) |
| --- | --- |
| $CH_4$ (methane) | 1.3 |
| $C_2H_6$ (ethane) | 1.8 |
| $C_2H_4$ (ethylene) | 4.7 |
| $N_2$ | 0.6 |
| $O_2$ | 1.2 |
| NO | 1.9 |
| $H_2S$ | 99 |
| $SO_2$ | 1476 |

13.112 A small cube of lithium (density = 0.535 g/cm$^3$) measuring 1.0 mm on each edge is added to 0.500 L of water. The following reaction occurs:

$$2\ Li(s) + 2\ H_2O(l) \rightarrow 2\ LiOH(aq) + H_2(g)$$

What is the freezing point of the resultant solution?

[13.113] At 35 °C the vapor pressure of acetone, $(CH_3)_2CO$, is 360 torr, and that of chloroform, $CHCl_3$, is 300 torr. Acetone and chloroform can form very weak hydrogen bonds between one another as follows:

A solution composed of an equal number of moles of acetone and chloroform has a vapor pressure of 250 torr at 35 °C. **(a)** What would be the vapor pressure of the solution if it exhibited ideal behavior? **(b)** Use the existence of hydrogen bonds between acetone and chloroform molecules to explain the deviation from ideal behavior. **(c)** Based on the behavior of the solution, predict whether the mixing of acetone and chloroform is an exothermic ($\Delta H_{soln} < 0$) or endothermic ($\Delta H_{soln} > 0$) process.

# WHAT'S AHEAD

**14.1** FACTORS THAT AFFECT REACTION RATES
We explore four variables that affect reaction rates: concentration, physical states of reactants, temperature, and presence of catalysts. These factors can be understood in terms of the collisions among reactant molecules that lead to reaction.

**14.2** REACTION RATES
We consider how to express *reaction rates* and how reactant disappearance rates and product appearance rates are related to the reaction stoichiometry.

**14.3** CONCENTRATION AND RATE LAWS
We then show that the effect of concentration on rate is expressed quantitatively by *rate laws* and show how rate laws and *rate constants* are determined experimentally.

**14.4** THE CHANGE OF CONCENTRATION WITH TIME
We learn that rate equations can be written to express how concentrations change with time and look at several examples of rate equations: *zero-order, first-order,* and *second-order* reactions.

**THE BELOUSOV-ZHABOTINSKY REACTION** is one of the most famous reactions in the chemical world. The swirls of colors correspond to products forming at different places and times in the unstirred petri dish.

# CHEMICAL KINETICS

**CHEMICAL REACTIONS CONVERT SUBSTANCES** that have well-defined properties into other substances that have different properties. The chapter-opening photograph, for instance, shows that we can watch complex reactions as they happen in time by observing the different colors of reactants and products.

In this particular case, multiple redox reactions are occurring, with the products of one reaction becoming the reactants in other reactions.

So far, we have been concerned with the beginning and end of chemical reactions: We start with certain reactants and see what products they yield. This view is useful but does not tell us what happens in the middle, that is, which chemical bonds are broken, which are formed, and in what order these events occur. The speed at which a chemical reaction occurs is called the **reaction rate**. To investigate how reactions happen, we must examine the reaction rates and the factors that influence them. Experimental information on the rate of a given reaction provides important evidence that helps us formulate a *reaction mechanism,* which is a step-by-step, molecular-level view of the pathway from reactants to products.

Some chemical reactions are complete within a fraction of a second, such as explosions, whereas others can take thousands or even millions of years, such as the formation of minerals in Earth's crust (▶ **FIGURE 14.1**).

$10^{-15}$ s

1 s

$10^9$ s
(30 years)

$10^{15}$ s
(30 million years)

Time scale

▲ FIGURE 14.1 **Reaction rates span an enormous range of time scales.** The absorption of light by an atom or molecule is complete within one femtosecond; explosions occur within seconds; corrosion can occur over years; and the weathering of rocks can occur over millions of years.

Steel wool heated in air (about 20% $O_2$) glows red-hot but oxidizes to $Fe_2O_3$ slowly

Red-hot steel wool in 100% $O_2$ burns vigorously, forming $Fe_2O_3$ quickly

▲ FIGURE 14.2 **Effect of concentration on reaction rate.** The difference in behavior is due to the different concentrations of $O_2$ in the two environments.

The area of chemistry concerned with the speeds, or rates, of reactions is **chemical kinetics**. Chemical kinetics relates to how quickly a medicine works in the body, to whether the processes that form and deplete ozone in the atmosphere are in balance, and to such industrial challenges as the development of new *catalysts*, materials that speed up reactions.

Our goal in this chapter is to understand how to determine reaction rates and to consider the factors that control these rates. What factors determine how rapidly food spoils, for instance, or how does one design a fast-setting material for dental fillings? What determines the rate at which steel rusts, or how can we remove hazardous pollutants in automobile exhaust before the exhaust leaves the tailpipe? Although we will not address these specific questions, we will see that the rates of all chemical reactions are subject to the same principles.

# 14.1 | FACTORS THAT AFFECT REACTION RATES

Four factors allow us to change the rate at which any particular reaction occurs:

1. **Physical state of the reactants.** Reactants must come together to react. The more readily reactant molecules collide with one another, the more rapidly they react. Most of the reactions we consider are homogeneous, involving either all gases or all liquids. When reactants are in different phases, however, we have heterogeneous conditions, and the reaction is limited by the area of contact of the reactants. Thus, heterogeneous reactions that involve solids tend to proceed faster if the surface area of the solid is increased. For example, a medicine in the form of a fine powder dissolves in the stomach and enters the blood more quickly than the same medicine in the form of a tablet.

2. **Reactant concentrations.** Most chemical reactions proceed faster if the concentration of one or more reactants is increased. For example, steel wool burns only slowly in air, which contains 20% $O_2$, but bursts into flame in pure oxygen (◄ FIGURE 14.2). As reactant concentration increases, the frequency with which the reactant molecules collide increases, leading to increased rates.

3. **Reaction temperature.** Reaction rates generally increase as temperature is increased. The bacterial reactions that spoil milk, for instance, proceed more rapidly at room temperature than at the lower temperature of a refrigerator. Increasing temperature increases the kinetic energies of molecules. ∞ (Section 10.7) As molecules move more rapidly, they collide more frequently and with higher energy, leading to increased reaction rates.

4. **The presence of a catalyst.** *Catalysts* are agents that increase reaction rates without themselves being used up. They affect the kinds of collisions (and therefore alter the mechanism) that lead to reaction. Catalysts play many crucial roles in living organisms, including ourselves.

On a molecular level, reaction rates depend on the frequency of collisions between molecules. The greater the frequency of collisions, the higher the reaction rate. For a collision to lead to a reaction, however, it must occur with sufficient energy to break bonds and with suitable orientation for new bonds to form in the proper locations. We will consider these factors as we proceed through this chapter.

 GIVE IT SOME THOUGHT

In a reaction involving reactants in the gas state, how does increasing the partial pressures of the gases affect the reaction rate?

## 14.2 | REACTION RATES

The *speed* of an event is defined as the *change* that occurs in a given *time* interval, which means that whenever we talk about speed, we necessarily bring in the notion of time. For example, the speed of a car is expressed as the change in the car's position over a certain time interval. The units of this speed are usually miles per hour—that is, the quantity that is changing (position measured in miles) divided by a time interval (measured in hours).

Similarly, the speed of a chemical reaction—its reaction rate—is the change in the concentration of reactants or products per unit of time. The units for reaction rate are usually molarity per second ($M/s$)—that is, the change in concentration measured in molarity divided by a time interval measured in seconds.

Let's consider the hypothetical reaction A $\longrightarrow$ B, depicted in ▼ FIGURE 14.3. Each red sphere represents 0.01 mol of A, each blue sphere represents 0.01 mol of B, and the container has a volume of 1.00 L. At the beginning of the reaction, there is 1.00 mol A, so the concentration is 1.00 mol/L = 1.00 $M$. After 20 s the concentration of A has fallen to 0.54 $M$ and the concentration of B has risen to 0.46 $M$. The sum of the concentrations is still 1.00 $M$ because 1 mol of B is produced for each mole of A that reacts. After 40 s the concentration of A is 0.30 $M$ and that of B is 0.70 $M$.

▲ GO FIGURE

If A converts completely to B, what type of molecules will the container hold?

|           |           |           |
|-----------|-----------|-----------|
| 1.00 mol A | 0.54 mol A | 0.30 mol A |
| 0 mol B   | 0.46 mol B | 0.70 mol B |

▲ FIGURE 14.3  **Progress of a hypothetical reaction A $\longrightarrow$ B.**

The rate of this reaction can be expressed either as the rate of disappearance of reactant A or as the rate of appearance of product B. The *average* rate of appearance of B over a particular time interval is given by the change in concentration of B divided by the change in time:

$$\text{Average rate of appearance of B} = \frac{\text{change in concentration of B}}{\text{change in time}}$$

$$= \frac{[B] \text{ at } t_2 - [B] \text{ at } t_1}{t_2 - t_1} = \frac{\Delta[B]}{\Delta t} \quad [14.1]$$

We use brackets around a chemical formula, as in [B], to indicate molarity. The Greek letter delta, $\Delta$, is read "change in" and is always equal to a final value minus an initial value. ∞ (Section 5.2) The average rate of appearance of B over the 20-s interval from the beginning of the reaction ($t_1 = 0$ s to $t_2 = 20$ s) is

$$\text{Average rate} = \frac{0.46 \, M - 0.00 \, M}{20 \, s - 0 \, s} = 2.3 \times 10^{-2} \, M/s$$

We could equally well express the reaction rate in term of the reactant, A. In this case we would be describing the rate of disappearance of A, which we express as

$$\text{Average rate of disappearance of A} = -\frac{\text{change in concentration of A}}{\text{change in time}}$$

$$= -\frac{\Delta[A]}{\Delta t} \quad [14.2]$$

Notice the minus sign in this equation, which we use to indicate that the concentration of A decreases. By convention, *rates are always expressed as positive quantities.* Because [A] decreases, $\Delta[A]$ is a negative number. The minus sign we put in the equation converts the negative $\Delta[A]$ to a positive rate of disappearance.

Because one molecule of A is consumed for every molecule of B that forms, the average rate of disappearance of A equals the average rate of appearance of B:

$$\text{Average rate} = -\frac{\Delta[A]}{\Delta t} = -\frac{0.54 \, M - 1.00 \, M}{20 \, s - 0 \, s} = 2.3 \times 10^{-2} \, M/s$$

---

**SAMPLE EXERCISE 14.1** | **Calculating an Average Rate of Reaction**

From the data in Figure 14.3, calculate the average rate at which A disappears over the time interval from 20 s to 40 s.

**SOLUTION**

**Analyze** We are given the concentration of A at 20 s (0.54 $M$) and at 40 s (0.30 $M$) and asked to calculate the average rate of reaction over this time interval.

**Plan** The average rate is given by the change in concentration, $\Delta[A]$, divided by the change in time, $\Delta t$. Because A is a reactant, a minus sign is used in the calculation to make the rate a positive quantity.

**Solve** Average rate $= -\dfrac{\Delta[A]}{\Delta t} = -\dfrac{0.30 \, M - 0.54 \, M}{40 \, s - 20 \, s} = 1.2 \times 10^{-2} \, M/s$

**PRACTICE EXERCISE**

Use the data in Figure 14.3 to calculate the average rate of appearance of B over the time interval from 0 s to 40 s.

*Answer:* $1.8 \times 10^{-2} \, M/s$

## TABLE 14.1 • Rate Data for Reaction of C₄H₉Cl with Water

| Time, $t$(s) | [C₄H₉Cl]($M$) | Average Rate ($M$/s) |
|---|---|---|
| 0.0 | 0.1000 | $1.9 \times 10^{-4}$ |
| 50.0 | 0.0905 | $1.7 \times 10^{-4}$ |
| 100.0 | 0.0820 | $1.6 \times 10^{-4}$ |
| 150.0 | 0.0741 | $1.4 \times 10^{-4}$ |
| 200.0 | 0.0671 | $1.22 \times 10^{-4}$ |
| 300.0 | 0.0549 | $1.01 \times 10^{-4}$ |
| 400.0 | 0.0448 | $0.80 \times 10^{-4}$ |
| 500.0 | 0.0368 | $0.560 \times 10^{-4}$ |
| 800.0 | 0.0200 | |
| 10,000 | 0 | |

## Change of Rate with Time

Now let's consider the reaction between butyl chloride ($C_4H_9Cl$) and water to form butyl alcohol ($C_4H_9OH$) and hydrochloric acid:

$$C_4H_9Cl(aq) + H_2O(l) \longrightarrow C_4H_9OH(aq) + HCl(aq) \qquad [14.3]$$

Suppose we prepare a 0.1000-$M$ aqueous solution of $C_4H_9Cl$ and then measure the concentration of $C_4H_9Cl$ at various times after time zero (which is the instant at which the reactants are mixed, thereby initiating the reaction). We can use the resulting data, shown in the first two columns of ▲ TABLE 14.1, to calculate the average rate of disappearance of $C_4H_9Cl$ over various time intervals; these rates are given in the third column. Notice that the average rate decreases over each 50-s interval for the first several measurements and continues to decrease over even larger intervals through the remaining measurements. *It is typical for rates to decrease as a reaction proceeds because the concentration of reactants decreases.* The change in rate as the reaction proceeds is also seen in a graph of [$C_4H_9Cl$] versus time (▶ FIGURE 14.4). Notice how the steepness of the curve decreases with time, indicating a decreasing reaction rate.

## Instantaneous Rate

Graphs showing how the concentration of a reactant or product changes with time, such as Figure 14.4, allow us to evaluate the **instantaneous rate** of a reaction, which is the rate at a particular instant during the reaction. The instantaneous rate is determined from the slope of the curve at a particular point in time. We have drawn two tangent lines in Figure 14.4, a dashed line running through the point at $t = 0$ s and a solid line running through the point at $t = 600$ s. The slopes of these tangent lines give the instantaneous rates at these two time points.* To determine the instantaneous rate at 600 s, we construct horizontal and vertical lines to form the blue right triangle in Figure 14.4. The slope of the tangent line is the ratio of the height of the vertical side to the length of the horizontal side:

$$\text{Instantaneous rate} = -\frac{\Delta[C_4H_9Cl]}{\Delta t} = -\frac{(0.017 - 0.042)\,M}{(800 - 400)\text{s}}$$
$$= 6.3 \times 10^{-5}\,M/s$$

▲ **GO FIGURE**

How does the instantaneous rate of reaction change as the reaction proceeds?

$$C_4H_9Cl(aq) + H_2O(l) \longrightarrow C_4H_9OH(aq) + HCl(aq)$$

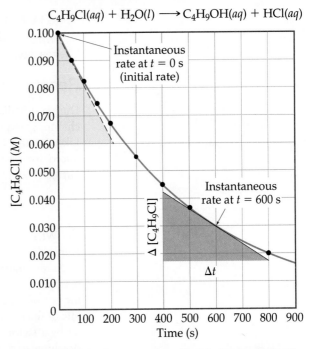

▲ **FIGURE 14.4   Concentration of butyl chloride (C₄H₉Cl) as a function of time.**

---

*You may wish to review graphical determination of slopes in Appendix A. If you are familiar with calculus, you may recognize that the average rate approaches the instantaneous rate as the time interval approaches zero. This limit, in the notation of calculus, is represented as $-d[C_4H_9Cl]/dt$.

In discussions that follow, the term *rate* means instantaneous rate unless indicated otherwise. The instantaneous rate at $t = 0$ is called the *initial rate* of the reaction. To understand the difference between average and instantaneous rates, imagine you have just driven 98 mi in 2.0 hr. Your average speed for the trip is 49 mi/hr, but your instantaneous speed at any moment during the trip is the speedometer reading at that moment.

---

**SAMPLE EXERCISE 14.2**    Calculating an Instantaneous Rate of Reaction

Using Figure 14.4, calculate the instantaneous rate of disappearance of $C_4H_9Cl$ at $t = 0$ s (the initial rate).

**SOLUTION**

**Analyze** We are asked to determine an instantaneous rate from a graph of reactant concentration versus time.

**Plan** To obtain the instantaneous rate at $t = 0$ s, we must determine the slope of the curve at $t = 0$. The tangent is drawn on the graph as the hypotenuse of the tan triangle. The slope of this straight line equals the change in the vertical axis divided by the corresponding change in the horizontal axis (that is, change in molarity over change in time).

**Solve** The tangent line falls from $[C_4H_9Cl] = 0.100\ M$ to $0.060\ M$ in the time change from 0 s to 210 s. Thus, the initial rate is

$$\text{Rate} = -\frac{\Delta[C_4H_9Cl]}{\Delta t} = -\frac{(0.060 - 0.100)\ M}{(210 - 0)\ s} = 1.9 \times 10^{-4}\ M/s$$

**PRACTICE EXERCISE**

Using Figure 14.4, determine the instantaneous rate of disappearance of $C_4H_9Cl$ at $t = 300$ s.
**Answer:** $1.1 \times 10^{-4}\ M/s$

---

 **GIVE IT SOME THOUGHT**

What is the difference between average rate and instantaneous rate? In a given reaction, can these two rates ever have the same numeric value?

## Reaction Rates and Stoichiometry

During our discussion of the hypothetical reaction $A \longrightarrow B$, we saw that the stoichiometry requires that the rate of disappearance of A equal the rate of appearance of B. Likewise, the stoichiometry of Equation 14.3 indicates that 1 mol of $C_4H_9OH$ is produced for each mole of $C_4H_9Cl$ consumed. Therefore, the rate of appearance of $C_4H_9OH$ equals the rate of disappearance of $C_4H_9Cl$:

$$\text{Rate} = -\frac{\Delta[C_4H_9Cl]}{\Delta t} = \frac{\Delta[C_4H_9OH]}{\Delta t}$$

What happens when the stoichiometric relationships are not one-to-one? For example, consider the reaction $2\ HI(g) \rightarrow H_2(g) + I_2(g)$. We can measure either the rate of disappearance of HI or the rate of appearance of either $H_2$ or $I_2$. Because 2 mol of HI disappear for each mole of $H_2$ or $I_2$ that forms, the rate of disappearance of HI is twice the rate of appearance of either $H_2$ or $I_2$. How do we decide which number to use for the rate of the reaction? Depending on whether we monitor HI, $I_2$, or $H_2$, the rates can differ by a factor of two. To fix this problem, we need to take into account the reaction stoichiometry. To arrive at a number for the reaction rate that does not depend on which component we measured, we must divide the rate of disappearance of HI by 2 (its coefficient in the balanced chemical equation):

$$\text{Rate} = -\frac{1}{2}\frac{\Delta[HI]}{\Delta t} = \frac{\Delta[H_2]}{\Delta t} = \frac{\Delta[I_2]}{\Delta t}$$

In general, for the reaction

$$a\,A + b\,B \longrightarrow c\,C + d\,D$$

the rate is given by

$$\text{Rate} = -\frac{1}{a}\frac{\Delta[A]}{\Delta t} = -\frac{1}{b}\frac{\Delta[B]}{\Delta t} = \frac{1}{c}\frac{\Delta[C]}{\Delta t} = \frac{1}{d}\frac{\Delta[D]}{\Delta t} \qquad [14.4]$$

When we speak of the rate of a reaction without specifying a particular reactant or product, we mean the rate in this sense.*

---

**SAMPLE EXERCISE 14.3** | **Relating Rates at Which Products Appear and Reactants Disappear**

**(a)** How is the rate at which ozone disappears related to the rate at which oxygen appears in the reaction $2 O_3(g) \longrightarrow 3 O_2(g)$? **(b)** If the rate at which $O_2$ appears, $\Delta[O_2]/\Delta t$, is $6.0 \times 10^{-5}$ M/s at a particular instant, at what rate is $O_3$ disappearing at this same time, $-\Delta[O_3]/\Delta t$?

**SOLUTION**

**Analyze** We are given a balanced chemical equation and asked to relate the rate of appearance of the product to the rate of disappearance of the reactant.

**Plan** We can use the coefficients in the chemical equation as shown in Equation 14.4 to express the relative rates of reactions.

**Solve**
**(a)** Using the coefficients in the balanced equation and the relationship given by Equation 14.4, we have:

$$\text{Rate} = -\frac{1}{2}\frac{\Delta[O_3]}{\Delta t} = \frac{1}{3}\frac{\Delta[O_2]}{\Delta t}$$

**(b)** Solving the equation from part (a) for the rate at which $O_3$ disappears, $-\Delta[O_3]/\Delta t$, we have:

$$-\frac{\Delta[O_3]}{\Delta t} = \frac{2}{3}\frac{\Delta[O_2]}{\Delta t} = \frac{2}{3}(6.0 \times 10^{-5} \text{ M/s}) = 4.0 \times 10^{-5} \text{ M/s}$$

**Check** We can apply a stoichiometric factor to convert the $O_2$ formation rate to the $O_3$ disappearance rate:

$$-\frac{\Delta[O_3]}{\Delta t} = \left(6.0 \times 10^{-5} \frac{\text{mol } O_2/L}{s}\right)\left(\frac{2 \text{ mol } O_3}{3 \text{ mol } O_2}\right) = 4.0 \times 10^{-5} \frac{\text{mol } O_3/L}{s}$$
$$= 4.0 \times 10^{-5} \text{ M/s}$$

**PRACTICE EXERCISE**

If the rate of decomposition of $N_2O_5$ in the reaction $2 N_2O_5(g) \longrightarrow 4 NO_2(g) + O_2(g)$ at a particular instant is $4.2 \times 10^{-7}$ M/s, what is the rate of appearance of **(a)** $NO_2$ and **(b)** $O_2$ at that instant?
***Answers:*** **(a)** $8.4 \times 10^{-7}$ M/s, **(b)** $2.1 \times 10^{-7}$ M/s

---

# 14.3 | CONCENTRATION AND RATE LAWS

One way of studying the effect of concentration on reaction rate is to determine the way in which the initial rate of a reaction depends on the initial concentrations. For example, we might study the rate of the reaction

$$NH_4^+(aq) + NO_2^-(aq) \longrightarrow N_2(g) + 2 H_2O(l)$$

by measuring the concentration of $NH_4^+$ or $NO_2^-$ as a function of time or by measuring the volume of $N_2$ collected as a function of time. Because the stoichiometric coefficients on $NH_4^+$, $NO_2^-$, and $N_2$ are the same, all of these rates are the same.

▼ **TABLE 14.2** shows that changing the initial concentration of either reactant changes the initial reaction rate. If we double $[NH_4^+]$ while holding $[NO_2^-]$ constant,

**TABLE 14.2 • Rate Data for the Reaction of Ammonium and Nitrite Ions in Water at 25 °C**

| Experiment Number | Initial $NH_4^+$ Concentration (M) | Initial $NO_2^-$ Concentration (M) | Observed Initial Rate (M/s) |
|---|---|---|---|
| 1 | 0.0100 | 0.200 | $5.4 \times 10^{-7}$ |
| 2 | 0.0200 | 0.200 | $10.8 \times 10^{-7}$ |
| 3 | 0.0400 | 0.200 | $21.5 \times 10^{-7}$ |
| 4 | 0.200 | 0.0202 | $10.8 \times 10^{-7}$ |
| 5 | 0.200 | 0.0404 | $21.6 \times 10^{-7}$ |
| 6 | 0.200 | 0.0808 | $43.3 \times 10^{-7}$ |

---

*Equation 14.4 does not hold true if substances other than C and D are formed in significant amounts. For example, sometimes intermediate substances build in concentration before forming the final products. In that case, the relationship between the rate of disappearance of reactants and the rate of appearance of products is not given by Equation 14.4. All reactions whose rates we consider in this chapter obey Equation 14.4.

the rate doubles (compare experiments 1 and 2). If we increase $[NH_4^+]$ by a factor of 4 but leave $[NO_2^-]$ unchanged (experiments 1 and 3), the rate changes by a factor of 4, and so forth. These results indicate that the initial reaction rate is proportional to $[NH_4^+]$. When $[NO_2^-]$ is similarly varied while $[NH_4^+]$ is held constant, the rate is affected in the same manner. Thus, the rate is also directly proportional to the concentration of $NO_2^-$.

# A CLOSER LOOK

## USING SPECTROSCOPIC METHODS TO MEASURE REACTION RATES

A variety of techniques can be used to monitor reactant and product concentration during a reaction, including spectroscopic methods, which rely on the ability of substances to absorb (or emit) light. Spectroscopic kinetic studies are often performed with the reaction mixture in the sample compartment of a *spectrometer*, an instrument that measures the amount of light transmitted or absorbed by a sample at different wavelengths. For kinetic studies, the spectrometer is set to measure the light absorbed at a wavelength characteristic of one of the reactants or products. In the decomposition of $HI(g)$ into $H_2(g)$ and $I_2(g)$, for example, both HI and $H_2$ are colorless, whereas $I_2$ is violet. During the reaction, the violet color of the reaction mixture gets deeper as $I_2$ forms. Thus, visible light of appropriate wavelength can be used to monitor the reaction (▶ FIGURE 14.5).

▼ FIGURE 14.6 shows the components of a spectrometer. The spectrometer measures the amount of light absorbed by the sample by comparing the intensity of the light emitted from the light source with the intensity of the light transmitted through the sample, for various wavelengths. As the concentration of $I_2$ increases and its color becomes more intense, the amount of light absorbed by the reaction mixture increases, as Figure 14.5 shows, causing less light to reach the detector.

*Beer's law* relates the amount of light absorbed to the concentration of the absorbing substance:

$$A = \epsilon bc \qquad [14.5]$$

In this equation, $A$ is the measured absorbance, $\epsilon$ is the extinction coefficient (a characteristic of the substance being monitored at a given wavelength of light), $b$ is the path length through which the

▲ FIGURE 14.5 Visible spectra of $I_2$ at different concentrations.

light passes, and $c$ is the molar concentration of the absorbing substance. Thus, the concentration is directly proportional to absorbance. Many chemical and pharmaceutical companies routinely use Beer's law to calculate the concentration of purified solutions of the compounds that they make.

*RELATED EXERCISES:* 14.107, 14.108

▲ FIGURE 14.6 Components of a spectrometer.

We express the way in which the rate depends on the reactant concentrations by the equation

$$\text{Rate} = k[\text{NH}_4^+][\text{NO}_2^-] \qquad [14.6]$$

An equation such as Equation 14.6, which shows how the rate depends on reactant concentrations, is called a **rate law**. For the general reaction

$$a\,\text{A} + b\,\text{B} \longrightarrow c\,\text{C} + d\,\text{D}$$

the rate law generally has the form

$$\text{Rate} = k[\text{A}]^m[\text{B}]^n \qquad [14.7]$$

The constant $k$ is called the **rate constant**. The magnitude of $k$ changes with temperature and therefore determines how temperature affects rate, as we will see in Section 14.5. The exponents $m$ and $n$ are typically small whole numbers. As we will learn shortly, if we know $m$ and $n$ for a reaction, we can gain great insight into the individual steps that occur during the reaction.

 **GIVE IT SOME THOUGHT**

How do reaction rate, rate constant, and rate law differ?

Once we know the rate law for a reaction and the reaction rate for a set of reactant concentrations, we can calculate the value of $k$. For example, using the values for experiment 1 in Table 14.2, we can substitute into Equation 14.6:

$$5.4 \times 10^{-7}\,M/s = k(0.0100\,M)(0.200\,M)$$

$$k = \frac{5.4 \times 10^{-7}\,M/s}{(0.0100\,M)(0.200\,M)} = 2.7 \times 10^{-4}\,M^{-1}s^{-1}$$

You may wish to verify that this same value of $k$ is obtained using any of the other experimental results in Table 14.2.

Once we have both the rate law and the $k$ value for a reaction, we can calculate the reaction rate for any set of concentrations. For example, using Equation 14.7 with $k = 2.7 \times 10^{-4}\,M^{-1}s^{-1}$, $m = 1$, and $n = 1$, we can calculate the rate for $[\text{NH}_4^+] = 0.100\,M$ and $[\text{NO}_2^-] = 0.100\,M$:

$$\text{Rate} = (2.7 \times 10^{-4}\,M^{-1}\,s^{-1})(0.100\,M)\,(0.100\,M) = 2.7 \times 10^{-6}\,M/s$$

**GIVE IT SOME THOUGHT**

Does the rate constant have the same units as the rate? Explain your answer.

## Reaction Orders: The Exponents in the Rate Law

The rate law for most reactions has the form

$$\text{Rate} = k[\text{reactant 1}]^m[\text{reactant 2}]^n \ldots \qquad [14.8]$$

The exponents $m$ and $n$ are called **reaction orders**. For example, consider again the rate law for the reaction of $\text{NH}_4^+$ with $\text{NO}_2^-$:

$$\text{Rate} = k[\text{NH}_4^+][\text{NO}_2^-]$$

Because the exponent of $[\text{NH}_4^+]$ is 1, the rate is *first order* in $\text{NH}_4^+$. The rate is also first order in $\text{NO}_2^-$. (The exponent 1 is not shown in rate laws.) The **overall reaction order** is the sum of the orders with respect to each reactant represented in the rate law. Thus, for the $\text{NH}_4^+ - \text{NO}_2^-$ reaction, the rate law has an overall reaction order of $1 + 1 = 2$, and the reaction is *second order overall*.

The exponents in a rate law indicate how the rate is affected by each reactant concentration. Because the rate at which $\text{NH}_4^+$ reacts with $\text{NO}_2^-$ depends on $[\text{NH}_4^+]$ raised to the first power, the rate doubles when $[\text{NH}_4^+]$ doubles, triples when $[\text{NH}_4^+]$ triples, and so forth. Doubling or tripling $[\text{NO}_2^-]$ likewise doubles or triples the rate. If a rate law is second order with respect to a reactant, $[A]^2$, then doubling the concentration of that substance causes the reaction rate to quadruple because $[2]^2 = 4$, whereas tripling the concentration causes the rate to increase ninefold: $[3]^2 = 9$.

The following are some additional examples of experimentally determined rate laws:

$$2\,N_2O_5(g) \longrightarrow 4\,NO_2(g) + O_2(g) \quad \text{Rate} = k[N_2O_5] \quad\quad [14.9]$$

$$CHCl_3(g) + Cl_2(g) \longrightarrow CCl_4(g) + HCl(g) \quad \text{Rate} = k[CHCl_3][Cl_2]^{1/2} \quad [14.10]$$

$$H_2(g) + I_2(g) \longrightarrow 2\,HI(g) \quad\quad\quad\quad \text{Rate} = k[H_2][I_2] \quad\quad [14.11]$$

Although the exponents in a rate law are sometimes the same as the coefficients in the balanced equation, this is not necessarily the case, as Equations 14.9 and 14.10 show. For any reaction, *the rate law must be determined experimentally*. In most rate laws, reaction orders are 0, 1, or 2. However, we also occasionally encounter rate laws in which the reaction order is fractional (such as Equation 14.10) or even negative.

 GIVE IT SOME THOUGHT

The experimentally determined rate law for the reaction $2\,NO(g) + 2\,H_2(g) \longrightarrow N_2(g) + 2\,H_2O(g)$ is rate $= k[NO]^2[H_2]$.
a. What are the reaction orders in this rate law?
b. Does doubling the concentration of NO have the same effect on rate as doubling the concentration of $H_2$?

---

**SAMPLE EXERCISE 14.4** | **Relating a Rate Law to the Effect of Concentration on Rate**

Consider a reaction $A + B \longrightarrow C$ for which rate $= k[A][B]^2$. Each of the following boxes represents a reaction mixture in which A is shown as red spheres and B as purple ones. Rank these mixtures in order of increasing rate of reaction.

(1)                (2)                (3)

**SOLUTION**

**Analyze** We are given three boxes containing different numbers of spheres representing mixtures containing different reactant concentrations. We are asked to use the given rate law and the compositions of the boxes to rank the mixtures in order of increasing reaction rates.

**Plan** Because all three boxes have the same volume, we can put the number of spheres of each kind into the rate law and calculate the rate for each box.

**Solve**

Box 1 contains 5 red spheres and 5 purple spheres, giving the following rate:

$$\text{Box 1: Rate} = k(5)(5)^2 = 125k$$

Box 2 contains 7 red spheres and 3 purple spheres:

$$\text{Box 2: Rate} = k(7)(3)^2 = 63k$$

Box 3 contains 3 red spheres and 7 purple spheres:

$$\text{Box 3: Rate} = k(3)(7)^2 = 147k$$

The slowest rate is $63k$ (box 2), and the highest is $147k$ (box 3). Thus, the rates vary in the order $2 < 1 < 3$.

**Check** Each box contains 10 spheres. The rate law indicates that in this case [B] has a greater influence on rate than [A] because B has a higher reaction order. Hence, the mixture with the highest concentration of B (most purple spheres) should react fastest. This analysis confirms the order 2 < 1 < 3.

**PRACTICE EXERCISE**
Assuming that rate = $k$[A][B], rank the mixtures represented in this Sample Exercise in order of increasing rate.
*Answer:* 2 = 3 < 1

## Magnitudes and Units of Rate Constants

If chemists want to compare reactions to evaluate which ones are relatively fast and which ones are relatively slow, the quantity of interest is the rate constant. A good general rule is that a large value of $k$ ($\sim 10^9$ or higher) means a fast reaction and a small value of $k$ (10 or lower) means a slow reaction.

 **GIVE IT SOME THOUGHT**
What does it mean if $k$ is 0?

The units of the rate constant depend on the overall reaction order of the rate law. In a reaction that is second order overall, for example, the units of the rate constant must satisfy the equation:

$$\text{Units of rate} = (\text{units of rate constant})(\text{units of concentration})^2$$

Hence, in our usual units of molarity for concentration and seconds for time, we have

$$\text{Units of rate constant} = \frac{\text{units of rate}}{(\text{units of concentration})^2} = \frac{M/s}{M^2} = M^{-1}\,s^{-1}$$

---

**SAMPLE EXERCISE 14.5**  **Determining Reaction Orders and Units for Rate Constants**

**(a)** What are the overall reaction orders for the reactions described in Equations 14.9 and 14.10? **(b)** What are the units of the rate constant for the rate law in Equation 14.9?

**SOLUTION**

**Analyze** We are given two rate laws and asked to express **(a)** the overall reaction order for each and **(b)** the units for the rate constant for the first reaction.

**Plan** The overall reaction order is the sum of the exponents in the rate law. The units for the rate constant, $k$, are found by using the normal units for rate ($M/s$) and concentration ($M$) in the rate law and applying algebra to solve for $k$.

**Solve**
**(a)** The rate of the reaction in Equation 14.9 is first order in $N_2O_5$ and first order overall. The reaction in Equation 14.10 is first order in $CHCl_3$ and one-half order in $Cl_2$. The overall reaction order is three halves.

**(b)** For the rate law for Equation 14.9, we have

$$\text{Units of rate} = (\text{units of rate constant})(\text{units of concentration})$$

so

$$\text{Units of rate constant} = \frac{\text{units of rate}}{\text{units of concentration}} = \frac{M/s}{M} = s^{-1}$$

Notice that the units of the rate constant change as the overall order of the reaction changes.

**PRACTICE EXERCISE**
**(a)** What is the reaction order of the reactant $H_2$ in Equation 14.11? **(b)** What are the units of the rate constant for Equation 14.11?
*Answers:* **(a)** 1, **(b)** $M^{-1}\,s^{-1}$

## Using Initial Rates to Determine Rate Laws

We have seen that the rate law for most reactions has the general form

$$\text{Rate} = k[\text{reactant 1}]^m[\text{reactant 2}]^n \ldots$$

Thus, the task of determining the rate law becomes one of determining the reaction orders, $m$ and $n$. In most reactions the reaction orders are 0, 1, or 2. If a reaction is zero order in a particular reactant, changing the concentration of that reactant has no effect on rate (as long as some of the reactant is present) because any concentration raised to the zero power equals 1. On the other hand, when a reaction is first order in a reactant, changes in the concentration of that reactant produce proportional changes in the rate. Thus, doubling the concentration will double the rate, and so forth. Finally, when the rate law is second order in a particular reactant, doubling its concentration increases the rate by a factor of $2^2 = 4$, tripling its concentration causes the rate to increase by a factor of $3^2 = 9$, and so forth.

In working with rate laws, it is important to realize that the *rate* of a reaction depends on concentration but the *rate constant* does not. As we will see later in this chapter, the rate constant (and hence the reaction rate) are affected by temperature and by the presence of a catalyst.

---

**SAMPLE EXERCISE 14.6** | **Determining a Rate Law from Initial Rate Data**

The initial rate of a reaction $A + B \longrightarrow C$ was measured for several different starting concentrations of A and B, and the results are as follows:

| Experiment Number | [A] (M) | [B] (M) | Initial Rate (M/s) |
|---|---|---|---|
| 1 | 0.100 | 0.100 | $4.0 \times 10^{-5}$ |
| 2 | 0.100 | 0.200 | $4.0 \times 10^{-5}$ |
| 3 | 0.200 | 0.100 | $16.0 \times 10^{-5}$ |

Using these data, determine (a) the rate law for the reaction, (b) the rate constant, (c) the rate of the reaction when [A] = 0.050 $M$ and [B] = 0.100 $M$.

### SOLUTION

**Analyze** We are given a table of data that relates concentrations of reactants with initial rates of reaction and asked to determine (a) the rate law, (b) the rate constant, and (c) the rate of reaction for a set of concentrations not listed in the table.

**Plan**
(a) We assume that the rate law has the following form: Rate = $k[A]^m[B]^n$. So we must use the given data to deduce the reaction orders $m$ and $n$ by determining how changes in the concentration change the rate. (b) Once we know $m$ and $n$, we can use the rate law and one of the sets of data to determine the rate constant $k$. (c) Now that we know both the rate constant and the reaction orders, we can use the rate law with the given concentrations to calculate rate.

**Solve**
(a) If we compare experiments 1 and 2, we see that [A] is held constant and [B] is doubled. Thus, this pair of experiments shows how [B] affects the rate, allowing us to deduce the order of the rate law with respect to B. Because the rate remains the same when [B] is doubled, the concentration of B has no effect on the reaction rate. The rate law is therefore zero order in B (that is, $n = 0$).

In experiments 1 and 3, [B] is held constant, so these data show how [A] affects rate. Holding [B] constant while doubling [A] increases the rate fourfold. This result indicates that rate is proportional to $[A]^2$ (that is, the reaction is second order in A). Hence, the rate law is

$$\text{Rate} = k[A]^2[B]^0 = k[A]^2$$

(b) Using the rate law and the data from experiment 1, we have

$$k = \frac{\text{rate}}{[A]^2} = \frac{4.0 \times 10^{-5}\, M/s}{(0.100\, M)^2} = 4.0 \times 10^{-3}\, M^{-1}\, s^{-1}$$

(c) Using the rate law from part (a) and the rate constant from part (b), we have

$$\text{Rate} = k[A]^2 = (4.0 \times 10^{-3}\, M^{-1}\, s^{-1})(0.050\, M)^2 = 1.0 \times 10^{-5}\, M/s$$

Because [B] is not part of the rate law, it is irrelevant to the rate if there is at least some B present to react with A.

**Check**  A good way to check our rate law is to use the concentrations in experiment 2 or 3 and see if we can correctly calculate the rate. Using data from experiment 3, we have

$$\text{Rate} = k[A]^2 = (4.0 \times 10^{-3}\, M^{-1}\, s^{-1})(0.200\, M)^2 = 1.6 \times 10^{-4}\, M/s$$

Thus, the rate law correctly reproduces the data, giving both the correct number and the correct units for the rate.

**PRACTICE EXERCISE**

The following data were measured for the reaction of nitric oxide with hydrogen:

$$2\, NO(g) + 2\, H_2(g) \longrightarrow N_2(g) + 2\, H_2O(g)$$

| Experiment Number | [NO] (*M*) | [H₂] (*M*) | Initial Rate (*M*/s) |
|---|---|---|---|
| 1 | 0.10 | 0.10 | $1.23 \times 10^{-3}$ |
| 2 | 0.10 | 0.20 | $2.46 \times 10^{-3}$ |
| 3 | 0.20 | 0.10 | $4.92 \times 10^{-3}$ |

**(a)** Determine the rate law for this reaction. **(b)** Calculate the rate constant. **(c)** Calculate the rate when [NO] = 0.050 *M* and [H₂] = 0.150 *M*.

***Answers:*** **(a)** rate = $k[NO]^2[H_2]$, **(b)** $k = 1.2\, M^{-2}\, s^{-1}$ **(c)** rate = $4.5 \times 10^{-4}\, M/s$

## 14.4 | THE CHANGE OF CONCENTRATION WITH TIME

The rate laws we have examined so far enable us to calculate the rate of a reaction from the rate constant and reactant concentrations. These rate laws can also be converted into equations that show the relationship between concentrations of reactants or products and time. The mathematics required to accomplish this conversion involves calculus. We do not expect you to be able to perform the calculus operations, but you should be able to use the resulting equations. We will apply this conversion to three of the simplest rate laws: those that are first order overall, those that are second order overall, and those that are zero order overall.

### First-Order Reactions

A **first-order reaction** is one whose rate depends on the concentration of a single reactant raised to the first power. For a reaction of the type A → products, the rate law may be first order:

$$\text{Rate} = -\frac{\Delta[A]}{\Delta t} = k[A]$$

This form of a rate law, which expresses how rate depends on concentration, is called the *differential rate law*. Using an operation from calculus called integration, this relationship can be transformed into an equation that relates the initial concentration of A, $[A]_0$, to its concentration at any other time $t$, $[A]_t$:

$$\ln[A]_t - \ln[A]_0 = -kt \qquad \text{or} \qquad \ln\frac{[A]_t}{[A]_0} = -kt \qquad [14.12]$$

This form of the rate law is called the *integrated rate law*. The function "ln" in Equation 14.12 is the natural logarithm (Appendix A.2). Equation 14.12 can also be rearranged to

$$\ln[A]_t = -kt + \ln[A]_0 \qquad [14.13]$$

Equations 14.12 and 14.13 can be used with any concentration units as long as the units are the same for both $[A]_t$ and $[A]_0$.

For a first-order reaction, Equation 14.12 or 14.13 can be used in several ways. Given any three of the following quantities, we can solve for the fourth: $k$, $t$, $[A]_0$, and $[A]_t$. Thus, you can use these equations to determine (1) the concentration of a reactant remaining at any time after the reaction has started, (2) the time interval required for a given fraction of a sample to react, or (3) the time interval required for a reactant concentration to fall to a certain level.

---

**SAMPLE EXERCISE 14.7** | **Using the Integrated First-Order Rate Law**

The decomposition of a certain insecticide in water at 12 °C follows first-order kinetics with a rate constant of 1.45 yr$^{-1}$. A quantity of this insecticide is washed into a lake on June 1, leading to a concentration of $5.0 \times 10^{-7}$ g/cm$^3$. Assume that the average temperature of the lake is 12 °C. **(a)** What is the concentration of the insecticide on June 1 of the following year? **(b)** How long will it take for the insecticide concentration to decrease to $3.0 \times 10^{-7}$ g/cm$^3$ ?

**SOLUTION**

**Analyze** We are given the rate constant for a reaction that obeys first-order kinetics, as well as information about concentrations and times, and asked to calculate how much reactant (insecticide) remains after one year. We must also determine the time interval needed to reach a particular insecticide concentration. Because the exercise gives time in (a) and asks for time in (b), we know that the integrated rate law, Equation 14.13, is required.

**Plan**
**(a)** We are given $k = 1.45$ yr$^{-1}$, $t = 1.00$ yr and $[\text{insecticide}]_0 = 5.0 \times 10^{-7}$ g/cm$^3$, and so Equation 14.13 can be solved for [insecticide]$_t$. **(b)** We have $k = 1.45$ yr$^{-1}$, $[\text{insecticide}]_0 = 5.0 \times 10^{-7}$ g/cm$^3$, and $[\text{insecticide}]_t = 3.0 \times 10^{-7}$ g/cm$^3$, and so we can solve Equation 14.13 for time, $t$.

**Solve**
**(a)** Substituting the known quantities into Equation 14.13, we have

$$\ln[\text{insecticide}]_{t=1\,\text{yr}} = -(1.45\ \text{yr}^{-1})(1.00\ \text{yr}) + \ln(5.0 \times 10^{-7})$$

We use the ln function on a calculator to evaluate the second term on the right, giving

$$\ln[\text{insecticide}]_{t=1\,\text{yr}} = -1.45 + (-14.51) = -15.96$$

To obtain $[\text{insecticide}]_{t=1\,\text{yr}}$, we use the inverse natural logarithm, or $e^x$, function on the calculator:

$$[\text{insecticide}]_{t=1\,\text{yr}} = e^{-15.96} = 1.2 \times 10^{-7}\ \text{g/cm}^3$$

Note that the concentration units for $[A]_t$ and $[A]_0$ must be the same.

**(b)** Again substituting into Equation 14.13, with $[\text{insecticide}]_t = 3.0 \times 10^{-7}$ g/cm$^3$, gives

$$\ln(3.0 \times 10^{-7}) = -(1.45\ \text{yr}^{-1})(t) + \ln(5.0 \times 10^{-7})$$

Solving for $t$ gives

$$t = -[\ln(3.0 \times 10^{-7}) - \ln(5.0 \times 10^{-7})]/1.45\ \text{yr}^{-1}$$
$$= -(-15.02 + 14.51)/1.45\ \text{yr}^{-1} = 0.35\ \text{yr}$$

**Check** In part **(a)** the concentration remaining after 1.00 yr (that is, $1.2 \times 10^{-7}$ g/cm$^3$) is less than the original concentration ($5.0 \times 10^{-7}$ g/cm$^3$), as it should be. In **(b)** the given concentration ($3.0 \times 10^{-7}$ g/cm$^3$) is greater than that remaining after 1.00 yr, indicating that the time must be less than a year. Thus, $t = 0.35$ yr is a reasonable answer.

**PRACTICE EXERCISE**
The decomposition of dimethyl ether, $(CH_3)_2O$, at 510 °C is a first-order process with a rate constant of $6.8 \times 10^{-4}$ s$^{-1}$:

$$(CH_3)_2O(g) \longrightarrow CH_4(g) + H_2(g) + CO(g)$$

If the initial pressure of $(CH_3)_2O$ is 135 torr, what is its pressure after 1420 s?
***Answer:*** 51 torr

---

Equation 14.13 can be used to verify whether a reaction is first order and to determine its rate constant. This equation has the form of the general equation for a straight line, $y = mx + b$, in which $m$ is the slope and $b$ is the $y$-intercept of the line (Appendix A.4):

$$\ln [A]_t = -kt + \ln [A]_0$$

$$y = mx + b$$

For a first-order reaction, therefore, a graph of $\ln[A]_t$ versus time gives a straight line with a slope of $-k$ and a $y$-intercept of $\ln[A]_0$. A reaction that is not first order will not yield a straight line.

As an example, consider the conversion of methyl isonitrile ($CH_3NC$) to its isomer acetonitrile ($CH_3CN$) (▶ FIGURE 14.7). Because experiments show that the reaction is first order, we can write the rate equation:

$$\ln[CH_3NC]_t = -kt + \ln[CH_3NC]_0$$

We run the reaction at a temperature at which methyl isonitrile is a gas (199 °C), and ▼ FIGURE 14.8(a) shows how the pressure of this gas varies with time. We can use pressure as a unit of concentration for a gas because we know from the ideal-gas law the pressure is directly proportional to the number of moles per unit volume. Figure 14.8(b) shows that a plot of the natural logarithm of the pressure versus time is a straight line. The slope of this line is $-5.1 \times 10^{-5} \text{ s}^{-1}$. (You should verify this for yourself, remembering that your result may vary slightly from ours because of inaccuracies associated with reading the graph.) Because the slope of the line equals $-k$, the rate constant for this reaction equals $5.1 \times 10^{-5} \text{ s}^{-1}$.

## Second-Order Reactions

A **second-order reaction** is one whose rate depends either on a reactant concentration raised to the second power or on the concentrations of two reactants each raised to the first power. For simplicity, let's consider reactions of the type A $\longrightarrow$ products or A + B $\longrightarrow$ products that are second order in just one reactant, A:

$$\text{Rate} = -\frac{\Delta[A]}{\Delta t} = k[A]^2$$

With the use of calculus, this differential rate law can be used to derive the integrated rate law

$$\frac{1}{[A]_t} = kt + \frac{1}{[A]_0} \qquad [14.14]$$

This equation, like Equation 14.13, has four variables, $k$, $t$, $[A]_0$, and $[A]_t$, and any one of these can be calculated knowing the other three. Equation 14.14 also has the form of a straight line ($y = mx + b$). If the reaction is second order, a plot of $1/[A]_t$ versus $t$ yields a straight line with slope $k$ and $y$-intercept $1/[A]_0$. One way to distinguish between first- and second-order rate laws is to graph both $\ln[A]_t$ and $1/[A]_t$ against $t$. If the $\ln[A]_t$ plot is linear, the reaction is first order; if the $1/[A]_t$ plot is linear, the reaction is second order.

Methyl isonitrile

Acetonitrile

▲ FIGURE 14.7    **The first-order reaction of $CH_3NC$ conversion into $CH_3CN$.**

GO FIGURE

**What can you conclude from the fact that the plot of ln _P_ versus _t_ is linear?**

(a)

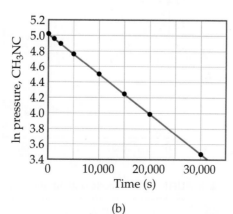

(b)

◀ FIGURE 14.8    **Kinetic data for conversion of methyl isonitrile into acetonitrile.**

**SAMPLE EXERCISE 14.8** Determining Reaction Order from the Integrated Rate Law

The following data were obtained for the gas-phase decomposition of nitrogen dioxide at 300 °C, $NO_2(g) \longrightarrow NO(g) + \frac{1}{2} O_2(g)$:

| Time (s) | [NO$_2$] ($M$) |
| --- | --- |
| 0.0 | 0.01000 |
| 50.0 | 0.00787 |
| 100.0 | 0.00649 |
| 200.0 | 0.00481 |
| 300.0 | 0.00380 |

Is the reaction first or second order in $NO_2$?

### SOLUTION

**Analyze** We are given the concentrations of a reactant at various times during a reaction and asked to determine whether the reaction is first or second order.

**Plan** We can plot $\ln[NO_2]$ and $1/[NO_2]$ against time. One or the other will be linear, indicating whether the reaction is first or second order.

**Solve** To graph $\ln[NO_2]$ and $1/[NO_2]$ against time, we will first prepare the following table from the data given:

| Time (s) | [NO$_2$] ($M$) | ln[NO$_2$] | 1/[NO$_2$] |
| --- | --- | --- | --- |
| 0.0 | 0.01000 | −4.605 | 100 |
| 50.0 | 0.00787 | −4.845 | 127 |
| 100.0 | 0.00649 | −5.037 | 154 |
| 200.0 | 0.00481 | −5.337 | 208 |
| 300.0 | 0.00380 | −5.573 | 263 |

As ▼ **FIGURE 14.9** shows, only the plot of $1/[NO_2]$ versus time is linear. Thus, the reaction obeys a second-order rate law: Rate $= k[NO_2]^2$. From the slope of this straight-line graph, we determine that $k = 0.543 \ M^{-1} s^{-1}$ for the disappearance of $NO_2$.

### PRACTICE EXERCISE

The decomposition of $NO_2$ discussed in the Sample Exercise is second order in $NO_2$ with $k = 0.543 \ M^{-1} s^{-1}$. If the initial concentration of $NO_2$ in a closed vessel is 0.0500, what is the concentration of this reactant after 0.500 hr?

**Answer:** $[NO_2] = 1.00 \times 10^{-3} \ M$

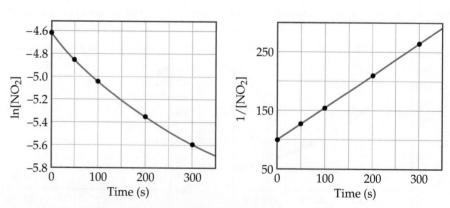

▲ **FIGURE 14.9** Kinetic data for decomposition of $NO_2$.

# Zero-Order Reactions

We've seen that in a first-order reaction the concentration of a reactant A decreases non-linearly, as shown by the red curve in ▶ **FIGURE 14.10**. As [A] declines, the *rate* at which it disappears declines in proportion. A **zero-order reaction** is one in which the rate of disappearance of A is *independent* of [A]. The rate law for a zero-order reaction is

$$\text{Rate} = \frac{-\Delta[A]}{\Delta t} = k$$

The integrated rate law for a zero-order reaction is

$$[A]_t = -kt + [A]_0$$

where $[A]_t$ is the concentration of A at time $t$ and $[A]_0$ is the initial concentration. This is the equation for a straight line with vertical intercept $[A]_0$ and slope $-kt$, as shown in the blue curve in Figure 14.10.

The most common type of zero-order reaction occurs when a gas undergoes decomposition on the surface of a solid. If the surface is completely covered by decomposing molecules, the rate of reaction is constant because the number of reacting surface molecules is constant, so long as there is some gas-phase substance left.

# Half-Life

The **half-life** of a reaction, $t_{1/2}$, is the time required for the concentration of a reactant to reach half its initial value, $[A]_{t_{1/2}} = \frac{1}{2}[A]_0$. Half-life is a convenient way to describe how fast a reaction occurs, especially if it is a first-order process. A fast reaction has a short half-life.

We can determine the half-life of a first-order reaction by substituting $[A]_{t_{1/2}} = \frac{1}{2}[A]_0$ for $[A]_t$ and $t_{1/2}$ for $t$ in Equation 14.12:

$$\ln \frac{\frac{1}{2}[A]_0}{[A]_0} = -kt_{1/2}$$

$$\ln \frac{1}{2} = -kt_{1/2}$$

$$t_{1/2} = -\frac{\ln \frac{1}{2}}{k} = \frac{0.693}{k} \qquad [14.15]$$

From Equation 14.15, we see that $t_{1/2}$ for a first-order rate law does not depend on the initial concentration of any reactant. Consequently, the half-life remains constant throughout the reaction. If, for example, the concentration of a reactant is 0.120 *M* at some instant in the reaction, it will be $\frac{1}{2}(0.120\ M) = 0.060\ M$ after one half-life. After one more half-life passes, the concentration will drop to 0.030 *M*, and so on. Equation 14.15 also indicates that, for a first-order reaction, we can calculate $t_{1/2}$ if we know $k$ and calculate $k$ if we know $t_{1/2}$.

The change in concentration over time for the first-order rearrangement of gaseous methyl isonitrile at 199 °C is graphed in ▶ **FIGURE 14.11**. Because the concentration of this gas is directly proportional to its pressure during the reaction, we have chosen to plot pressure rather than concentration in this graph. The first half-life occurs at 13,600 s (3.78 hr). At a time 13,600 s later, the methyl isonitrile pressure (and therefore, concentration) has decreased to half of one-half, or one-fourth, of the initial value. *In a first-order reaction, the concentration of the reactant decreases by* one-half *in each of a series of regularly spaced time intervals, each interval equal to* $t_{1/2}$.

▲ **GIVE IT SOME THOUGHT**

If a solution containing 10.0 g of a substance reacts by first-order kinetics, how many grams remain after 3 half-lives?

GO FIGURE

At which times during the reaction would you have trouble distinguishing a zero-order reaction from a first-order reaction?

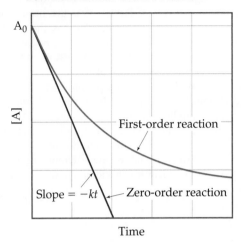

▲ **FIGURE 14.10   Comparison of first-order and zero-order reactions for the disappearance of reactant A with time.**

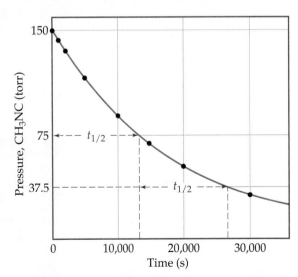

▲ **FIGURE 14.11   Kinetic data for the rearrangment of methyl isonitrile to acetonitrile at 199 °C, showing the half-life of the reaction.**

# CHEMISTRY PUT TO WORK

## Methyl Bromide in the Atmosphere

The compounds known as chlorofluorocarbons (CFCs) are well-known agents responsible for the destruction of Earth's protective ozone layer. Another simple molecule that has the potential to destroy the stratospheric ozone layer is methyl bromide, $CH_3Br$ (▼ FIGURE 14.12). Because this substance has a wide range of uses, including antifungal treatment of plant seeds, it has been produced in large quantities in the past (about 150 million pounds per year worldwide in 1997, at the height of its production). In the stratosphere, the C—Br bond is broken through absorption of short-wavelength radiation. The resultant Br atoms then catalyze decomposition of $O_3$.

Methyl bromide is removed from the lower atmosphere by a variety of mechanisms, including a slow reaction with ocean water:

$$CH_3Br(g) + H_2O(l) \longrightarrow CH_3OH(aq) + HBr(aq) \quad [14.16]$$

Stratosphere

Diffusion to stratosphere

Troposphere

*50% decomposes in 0.8 years*

Lower atmosphere

Methyl bromide applied as antifungal treatment

◀ FIGURE 14.12 **Distribution and fate of methyl bromide in Earth's atmosphere.**

To determine the potential importance of $CH_3Br$ in destruction of the ozone layer, it is important to know how rapidly the reaction in Equation 14.16 and all other reactions remove $CH_3Br$ from the lower atmosphere before it can diffuse into the stratosphere.

The average lifetime of $CH_3Br$ in Earth's lower atmosphere is difficult to measure because the conditions that exist in the atmosphere are too complex to be simulated in the laboratory. Instead, scientists analyzed nearly 4000 atmospheric samples collected above the Pacific Ocean for the presence of several trace organic substances, including methyl bromide. From these measurements, it was possible to estimate the *atmospheric residence time* for $CH_3Br$.

The atmospheric residence time is related to the half-life for $CH_3Br$ in the lower atmosphere, assuming the $CH_3Br$ decomposes by a first-order process. From the experimental data, the half-life for methyl bromide in the lower atmosphere is estimated to be $0.8 \pm 0.1$ year. That is, a collection of $CH_3Br$ molecules present at any given time will, on average, be 50% decomposed after 0.8 year, 75% decomposed after 1.6 years, and so on. A half-life of 0.8 year, while comparatively short, is still sufficiently long so that $CH_3Br$ contributes significantly to the destruction of the ozone layer.

In 1997 an international agreement was reached to phase out use of methyl bromide in developed countries by 2005. However, in recent years exemptions for critical agricultural use have been requested and granted. Nevertheless, worldwide production was down to 25 million pounds in 2009, two-thirds of which is used in the United States.

*RELATED EXERCISE:* 14.124

---

**SAMPLE EXERCISE 14.9** | Determining the Half-Life of a First-Order Reaction

The reaction of $C_4H_9Cl$ with water is a first-order reaction. **(a)** Use Figure 14.4 to estimate the half-life for this reaction. **(b)** Use the half-life from (a) to calculate the rate constant.

### SOLUTION

**Analyze** We are asked to estimate the half-life of a reaction from a graph of concentration versus time and then to use the half-life to calculate the rate constant for the reaction.

### Plan

**(a)** To estimate a half-life, we can select a concentration and then determine the time required for the concentration to decrease to half of that value. **(b)** Equation 14.15 is used to calculate the rate constant from the half-life.

**Solve**
**(a)** From the graph, we see that the initial value of $[C_4H_9Cl]$ is 0.100 $M$. The half-life for this first-order reaction is the time required for $[C_4H_9Cl]$ to decrease to 0.050 $M$, which we can read off the graph. This point occurs at approximately 340 s.

**(b)** Solving Equation 14.15 for $k$, we have

$$k = \frac{0.693}{t_{1/2}} = \frac{0.693}{340 \text{ s}} = 2.0 \times 10^{-3} \text{ s}^{-1}$$

**Check** At the end of the second half-life, which should occur at 680 s, the concentration should have decreased by yet another factor of 2, to 0.025. Inspection of the graph shows that this is indeed the case.

### PRACTICE EXERCISE

**(a)** Using Equation 14.15, calculate $t_{1/2}$ for the decomposition of the insecticide described in Sample Exercise 14.7. **(b)** How long does it take for the concentration of the insecticide to reach one-quarter of the initial value?
**Answers:** **(a)** 0.478 yr $= 1.51 \times 10^7$ s, **(b)** it takes two half-lives, 2(0.478 yr) $= 0.956$ yr

The half-life for second-order and other reactions depends on reactant concentrations and therefore changes as the reaction progresses. We obtained Equation 14.15 for the half-life for a first-order reaction by substituting $[A]_{t_{1/2}} = \frac{1}{2}[A]_0$ for $[A]_t$ and $t_{1/2}$ for $t$ in Equation 14.12. We find the half-life of a second-order reaction by making the same substitutions into Equation 14.14:

$$\frac{1}{\frac{1}{2}[A]_0} = kt_{1/2} + \frac{1}{[A]_0}$$

$$\frac{2}{[A]_0} - \frac{1}{[A]_0} = kt_{1/2}$$

$$t_{1/2} = \frac{1}{k[A]_0} \qquad [14.17]$$

In this case the half-life depends on the initial concentration of reactant—the lower the initial concentration, the longer the half-life.

 **GIVE IT SOME THOUGHT**

How does the half-life of a second-order reaction change as the reaction proceeds?

# 14.5 | TEMPERATURE AND RATE

The rates of most chemical reactions increase as the temperature rises. For example, dough rises faster at room temperature than when refrigerated, and plants grow more rapidly in warm weather than in cold. We can see the effect of temperature on reaction rate by observing a chemiluminescence reaction (one that produces light). The characteristic glow of fireflies is a familiar example of chemiluminescence. Another is the light produced by Cyalume® light sticks, which contain chemicals that produce chemiluminescence when mixed. As seen in ▶ **FIGURE 14.13**, these light sticks produce a brighter light at higher temperature. The amount of light produced is greater because the rate of the reaction is faster at the higher temperature. Although the light stick glows more brightly initially, its luminescence also dies out more rapidly at the higher temperature.

▶ **FIGURE 14.13  Temperature affects the rate of the chemiluminescence reaction in light sticks.**

Hot water          Cold water

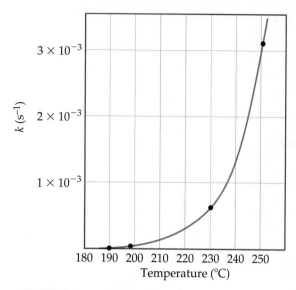

**▲ FIGURE 14.14 Temperature dependence of the rate constant for methyl isonitrile conversion to acetonitrile.** The four points indicated are used in Sample Exercise 14.11.

How is this experimentally observed temperature effect reflected in the rate law? The faster rate at higher temperature is due to an increase in the rate constant with increasing temperature. For example, let's reconsider the first-order reaction $CH_3NC \longrightarrow CH_3CN$. ◄ **FIGURE 14.14** shows the rate constant for this reaction as a function of temperature. The rate constant and, hence, the rate of the reaction increase rapidly with temperature, approximately doubling for each 10 °C rise.

## The Collision Model

Reaction rates are affected both by reactant concentrations and by temperature. The **collision model**, based on the kinetic-molecular theory ∞ (Section 10.7), accounts for both of these effects at the molecular level. The central idea of the collision model is that molecules must collide to react. The greater the number of collisions per second, the greater the reaction rate. As reactant concentration increases, therefore, the number of collisions increases, leading to an increase in reaction rate. According to the kinetic-molecular theory of gases, increasing the temperature increases molecular speeds. As molecules move faster, they collide more forcefully (with more energy) and more frequently, increasing reaction rates.

For a reaction to occur, though, more is required than simply a collision. For most reactions, only a tiny fraction of collisions leads to a reaction. For example, in a mixture of $H_2$ and $I_2$ at ordinary temperatures and pressures, each molecule undergoes about $10^{10}$ collisions per second. If every collision between $H_2$ and $I_2$ resulted in the formation of HI, the reaction would be over in much less than a second. Instead, at room temperature the reaction proceeds very slowly because only about one in every $10^{13}$ collisions produces a reaction. What keeps the reaction from occurring more rapidly?

## The Orientation Factor

In most reactions, molecules must be oriented in a certain way during collision for a reaction to occur. The relative orientations of the molecules during collision determine whether the atoms are suitably positioned to form new bonds. For example, consider the reaction

$$Cl + NOCl \longrightarrow NO + Cl_2$$

which takes place if the collision brings Cl atoms together to form $Cl_2$, as shown at the top in ▼ **FIGURE 14.15**. In contrast, the collision shown at the bottom in this figure is ineffective and does not yield products.

**▼ FIGURE 14.15 Molecular collisions may or may not lead to a chemical reaction between Cl and NOCl.**

◀ **FIGURE 14.16** **Energy is needed to overcome a barrier between initial and final states.**

## Activation Energy

In addition to molecular orientation during collisions, another factor is usually even more important in determining whether a particular collision results in reaction. In 1888 the Swedish chemist Svante Arrhenius suggested that molecules must possess a certain minimum amount of energy to react. According to the collision model, this energy comes from the kinetic energies of the colliding molecules. Upon collision, the kinetic energy of the molecules can be used to stretch, bend, and ultimately break bonds, leading to chemical reactions. That is, the kinetic energy is used to change the potential energy of the molecule. If molecules are moving too slowly—in other words, with too little kinetic energy— they merely bounce off one another without changing. The minimum energy required to initiate a chemical reaction is called the **activation energy**, $E_a$, and its value varies from reaction to reaction.

The situation during reactions is analogous to that shown in ▲ **FIGURE 14.16**. The player needs to move his ball over the hill in the direction of the cup. The hill is a *barrier* between ball and cup. To reach the cup, the player must impart enough kinetic energy with the putter to move the ball to the top of the barrier. If he does not impart enough energy, the ball will roll partway up the hill and then back down toward him. In the same way, molecules require a certain minimum energy to break existing bonds during a chemical reaction. We can think of this minimum energy as an *energy barrier*. In the rearrangement of methyl isonitrile to acetonitrile, for example, we might imagine the reaction passing through an intermediate state in which the N≡C portion of the methyl isonitrile molecule is sideways:

$$H_3C-N\equiv C: \longrightarrow \left[ H_3C\cdots \overset{\ddot{C}}{\underset{\ddot{N}}{|||}} \right] \longrightarrow H_3C-C\equiv N:$$

▶ **FIGURE 14.17** shows that energy must be supplied to stretch the bond between the $H_3C$ group and the N≡C group to allow the N≡C group to rotate. After the N≡C group has twisted sufficiently, the C—C bond begins to form, and the energy of the molecule drops. Thus, the barrier to formation of acetonitrile represents the energy necessary to force the molecule through the relatively unstable intermediate state, analogous to forcing the ball in Figure 14.16 over the hill. The difference between the energy of the starting molecule and the highest energy along the reaction pathway is the activation energy, $E_a$. The molecule having the arrangement of atoms shown at the top of the barrier is called either the **activated complex** or the **transition state**.

The conversion of $H_3C-N\equiv C$ to $H_3C-C\equiv N$ is exothermic. Figure 14.17 therefore shows the product as having a lower energy than the reactant. The energy change for the reaction, $\Delta E$, has no effect on reaction rate, however. *The rate depends on the magnitude of $E_a$; generally, the lower the value of $E_a$ is, the faster the reaction.*

Notice that the reverse reaction is endothermic. The activation energy for the reverse reaction is equal to the energy that must be overcome if approaching the barrier from the right: $\Delta E + E_a$.

△ **GO FIGURE**

How does the energy needed to overcome the energy barrier compare with the overall change in energy for this reaction?

▲ **FIGURE 14.17** **Energy profile for conversion of methyl isonitrile ($H_3CNC$) to its isomer acetonitrile ($H_3CCN$).**

▶ **FIGURE 14.18** The effect of temperature on the distribution of kinetic energies of molecules in a sample.

Any particular methyl isonitrile molecule acquires sufficient energy to overcome the energy barrier through collisions with other molecules. Recall from the kinetic-molecular theory of gases that, at any instant, gas molecules are distributed in energy over a wide range. ∞ (Section 10.7) ▲ **FIGURE 14.18** shows the distribution of kinetic energies for two temperatures, comparing them with the minimum energy needed for reaction, $E_a$. At the higher temperature a much greater fraction of the molecules have kinetic energy greater than $E_a$, which leads to a greater rate of reaction.

 **GIVE IT SOME THOUGHT**

Suppose we have two reactions, A ⟶ B and B ⟶ C. You can isolate B, and it is stable. Is B the transition state for the reaction A ⟶ C?

The fraction of molecules that have an energy equal to or greater than $E_a$ is given by the expression

$$f = e^{-E_a/RT} \quad\quad [14.18]$$

In this equation $R$ is the gas constant (8.314 J/mol-K) and $T$ is the absolute temperature. To get an idea of the magnitude of $f$, let's suppose that $E_a$ is 100 kJ/mol, a value typical of many reactions, and that $T$ is 300 K. The calculated value of $f$ is $3.9 \times 10^{-18}$, an extremely small number! At 310 K, $f = 1.4 \times 10^{-17}$. Thus, a 10-degree increase in temperature produces a 3.6-fold increase in the fraction of molecules possessing at least 100 kJ/mol of energy.

**GIVE IT SOME THOUGHT**

In a chemical reaction, why does not every collision between reactant molecules result in formation of a product molecule?

## The Arrhenius Equation

Arrhenius noted that for most reactions the increase in rate with increasing temperature is nonlinear (Figure 14.14). He found that most reaction-rate data obeyed an equation based on (a) the fraction of molecules possessing energy $E_a$ or greater, (b) the number of collisions per second, and (c) the fraction of collisions that have the appropriate orientation. These three factors are incorporated into the **Arrhenius equation**:

$$k = Ae^{-E_a/RT} \quad\quad [14.19]$$

In this equation $k$ is the rate constant, $E_a$ is the activation energy, $R$ is the gas constant (8.314 J/mol-K), and $T$ is the absolute temperature. The **frequency factor**, $A$, is constant, or nearly so, as temperature is varied. This factor is related to the frequency of collisions and the probability that the collisions are favorably oriented for reaction.* As the magnitude of $E_a$ increases, $k$ decreases because the fraction of molecules that possess the required energy is smaller. Thus, *reaction rates decrease as $E_a$ increases.*

*Because collision frequency increases with temperature, $A$ also has some temperature dependence, but this dependence is much smaller than the exponential term. Therefore, $A$ is considered approximately constant.

**SAMPLE EXERCISE 14.10** | **Relating Energy Profiles to Activation Energies and Speeds of Reaction**

Consider a series of reactions having these energy profiles:

Rank the reactions from slowest to fastest assuming that they have nearly the same value for the frequency factor $A$.

**SOLUTION**

The lower the activation energy, the faster the reaction. The value of $\Delta E$ does not affect the rate. Hence, the order from slowest reaction to fastest is $2 < 3 < 1$.

**PRACTICE EXERCISE**

Rank the reverse reactions from slowest to fastest.

***Answer:*** $2 < 1 < 3$ because, if you approach the barrier from the right, the $E_a$ values are 40 kJ/mol for reverse reaction 2, 25 kJ/mol for reverse reaction 1, and 15 kJ/mol for reverse reaction 3.

# Determining the Activation Energy

We can calculate the activation energy for a reaction by manipulating the Arrhenius equation. Taking the natural log of both sides of Equation 14.19, we obtain

$$\ln k = -\frac{E_a}{RT} + \ln A$$

$$\underset{y}{} \quad = \quad \underset{mx}{} \quad + \quad \underset{b}{}$$

[14.20]

which has the form of the equation for a straight line. A graph of $\ln k$ versus $1/T$ is a line with a slope equal to $-E_a/R$ and a $y$-intercept equal to $\ln A$. Thus, the activation energy can be determined by measuring $k$ at a series of temperatures, graphing $\ln k$ versus $1/T$, and calculating $E_a$ from the slope of the resultant line.

We can also use Equation 14.20 to evaluate $E_a$ in a nongraphical way if we know the rate constant of a reaction at two or more temperatures. For example, suppose that at two different temperatures $T_1$ and $T_2$ a reaction has rate constants $k_1$ and $k_2$. For each condition, we have

$$\ln k_1 = -\frac{E_a}{RT_1} + \ln A \quad \text{and} \quad \ln k_2 = -\frac{E_a}{RT_2} + \ln A$$

Subtracting $\ln k_2$ from $\ln k_1$ gives

$$\ln k_1 - \ln k_2 = \left(-\frac{E_a}{RT_1} + \ln A\right) - \left(-\frac{E_a}{RT_2} + \ln A\right)$$

Simplifying this equation and rearranging give

$$\ln \frac{k_1}{k_2} = \frac{E_a}{R}\left(\frac{1}{T_2} - \frac{1}{T_1}\right)$$ [14.21]

Equation 14.21 provides a convenient way to calculate a rate constant $k_1$ at some temperature $T_1$ when we know the activation energy and the rate constant $k_2$ at some other temperature $T_2$.

---

**SAMPLE EXERCISE 14.11** Determining the Activation Energy

The following table shows the rate constants for the rearrangement of methyl isonitrile at various temperatures (these are the data points in Figure 14.14):

| Temperature (°C) | $k$ (s$^{-1}$) |
|---|---|
| 189.7 | $2.52 \times 10^{-5}$ |
| 198.9 | $5.25 \times 10^{-5}$ |
| 230.3 | $6.30 \times 10^{-4}$ |
| 251.2 | $3.16 \times 10^{-3}$ |

**(a)** From these data, calculate the activation energy for the reaction. **(b)** What is the value of the rate constant at 430.0 K?

**SOLUTION**

**Analyze** We are given rate constants, $k$, measured at several temperatures and asked to determine the activation energy, $E_a$, and the rate constant, $k$, at a particular temperature.

**Plan** We can obtain $E_a$ from the slope of a graph of $\ln k$ versus $1/T$. Once we know $E_a$, we can use Equation 14.21 together with the given rate data to calculate the rate constant at 430.0 K.

**Solve**

**(a)** We must first convert the temperatures from degrees Celsius to kelvins. We then take the inverse of each temperature, $1/T$, and the natural log of each rate constant, $\ln k$. This gives us the table shown at the right:

| $T$ (K) | $1/T$ (K$^{-1}$) | $\ln k$ |
|---|---|---|
| 462.9 | $2.160 \times 10^{-3}$ | $-10.589$ |
| 472.1 | $2.118 \times 10^{-3}$ | $-9.855$ |
| 503.5 | $1.986 \times 10^{-3}$ | $-7.370$ |
| 524.4 | $1.907 \times 10^{-3}$ | $-5.757$ |

A graph of $\ln k$ versus $1/T$ is a straight line (▶**FIGURE 14.19**).

▲ **FIGURE 14.19** Graphical determination of activation energy $E_a$.

The slope of the line is obtained by choosing any two well-separated points and using the coordinates of each:

$$\text{Slope} = \frac{\Delta y}{\Delta x} = \frac{-6.6 - (-10.4)}{0.00195 - 0.00215} = -1.9 \times 10^4$$

Because logarithms have no units, the numerator in this equation is dimensionless. The denominator has the units of $1/T$, namely, K$^{-1}$. Thus, the overall units for the slope are K. The slope equals $-E_a/R$. We use the value for the gas constant $R$ in units of J/mol-K (Table 10.2). We thus obtain

$$\text{Slope} = -\frac{E_a}{R}$$

$$E_a = -(\text{slope})(R) = -(-1.9 \times 10^4 \text{ K})\left(8.314 \frac{J}{\text{mol-K}}\right)\left(\frac{1 \text{ kJ}}{1000 \text{ J}}\right)$$

$$= 1.6 \times 10^2 \text{ kJ/mol} = 160 \text{ kJ/mol}$$

We report the activation energy to only two significant figures because we are limited by the precision with which we can read the graph in Figure 14.19.

**(b)** To determine the rate constant, $k_1$, at $T_1 = 430.0$ K, we can use Equation 14.21 with $E_a = 160$ kJ/mol and one of the rate constants and temperatures from the given data, such as $k_2 = 2.52 \times 10^{-5}\,\text{s}^{-1}$ and $T_2 = 462.9$ K:

$$\ln\left(\frac{k_1}{2.52 \times 10^{-5}\,\text{s}^{-1}}\right) = \left(\frac{160\,\text{kJ/mol}}{8.314\,\text{J/mol-K}}\right)\left(\frac{1}{462.9\,\text{K}} - \frac{1}{430.0\,\text{K}}\right)\left(\frac{1000\,\text{J}}{1\,\text{kJ}}\right) = -3.18$$

Thus,

$$\frac{k_1}{2.52 \times 10^{-5}\,\text{s}^{-1}} = e^{-3.18} = 4.15 \times 10^{-2}$$

$$k_1 = (4.15 \times 10^{-2})(2.52 \times 10^{-5}\,\text{s}^{-1}) = 1.0 \times 10^{-6}\,\text{s}^{-1}$$

Note that the units of $k_1$ are the same as those of $k_2$.

**PRACTICE EXERCISE**

Using the data in Sample Exercise 14.11, calculate the rate constant for the rearrangement of methyl isonitrile at 280 °C.

*Answer:* $2.2 \times 10^{-2}\,\text{s}^{-1}$

# 14.6 | REACTION MECHANISMS

A balanced equation for a chemical reaction indicates the substances present at the start of the reaction and those present at the end of the reaction. It provides no information, however, about the detailed steps that occur at the molecular level as the reactants are turned into products. The steps by which a reaction occurs is called the **reaction mechanism**. At the most sophisticated level, a reaction mechanism describes the order in which bonds are broken and formed and the changes in relative positions of the atoms in the course of the reaction.

## Elementary Reactions

We have seen that reactions take place because of collisions between reacting molecules. For example, the collisions between molecules of methyl isonitrile ($CH_3NC$) can provide the energy to allow the $CH_3NC$ to rearrange to acetonitrile:

$$H_3C-N\equiv C: \longrightarrow \left[\,H_3C\cdots\overset{\ddot{C}}{\underset{\ddot{N}}{\,|\!|\!|}}\,\right] \longrightarrow H_3C-C\equiv N:$$

Similarly, the reaction of NO and $O_3$ to form $NO_2$ and $O_2$ appears to occur as a result of a single collision involving suitably oriented and sufficiently energetic NO and $O_3$ molecules:

$$NO(g) + O_3(g) \longrightarrow NO_2(g) + O_2(g) \qquad [14.22]$$

Both reactions occur in a single event or step and are called **elementary reactions**.

The number of molecules that participate as reactants in an elementary reaction defines the **molecularity** of the reaction. If a single molecule is involved, the reaction is **unimolecular**. The rearrangement of methyl isonitrile is a unimolecular process. Elementary reactions involving the collision of two reactant molecules are **bimolecular**. The reaction between NO and $O_3$ is bimolecular. Elementary reactions involving the simultaneous collision of three molecules are **termolecular**. Termolecular reactions are far less probable than unimolecular or bimolecular processes and are rarely encountered. The chance that four or more molecules will collide simultaneously with any regularity is even more remote; consequently, such collisions are never proposed as part of a reaction mechanism.

 **GIVE IT SOME THOUGHT**

What is the molecularity of the elementary reaction?

$$NO(g) + Cl_2(g) \longrightarrow NOCl(g) + Cl(g)$$

## Multistep Mechanisms

The net change represented by a balanced chemical equation often occurs by a *multistep mechanism* consisting of a sequence of elementary reactions. For example, below 225 °C, the reaction

$$NO_2(g) + CO(g) \longrightarrow NO(g) + CO_2(g) \qquad [14.23]$$

appears to proceed in two elementary reactions (or two *elementary steps*), each of which is bimolecular. First, two $NO_2$ molecules collide, and an oxygen atom is transferred from one to the other. The resultant $NO_3$ then collides with a CO molecule and transfers an oxygen atom to it:

$$NO_2(g) + NO_2(g) \longrightarrow NO_3(g) + NO(g)$$
$$NO_3(g) + CO(g) \longrightarrow NO_2(g) + CO_2(g)$$

Thus, we say that the reaction occurs by a two-step mechanism.

*The chemical equations for the elementary reactions in a multistep mechanism must always add to give the chemical equation of the overall process.* In the present example the sum of the two elementary reactions is

$$2\,NO_2(g) + NO_3(g) + CO(g) \longrightarrow NO_2(g) + NO_3(g) + NO(g) + CO_2(g)$$

Simplifying this equation by eliminating substances that appear on both sides gives Equation 14.23, the net equation for the process.

Because $NO_3$ is neither a reactant nor a product of the reaction—it is formed in one elementary reaction and consumed in the next—it is called an **intermediate**. Multistep mechanisms involve one or more intermediates. Intermediates are not the same as transition states, as shown in ▼ FIGURE 14.20. Intermediates can be stable and can therefore sometimes be identified and even isolated. Transition states, on the other hand, are always inherently unstable and as such can never be isolated. Nevertheless, the use of advanced "ultrafast" techniques sometimes allows us to characterize them.

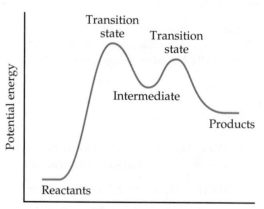

► FIGURE 14.20 **The energy profile of a reaction, showing transition states and an intermediate.**

---

**SAMPLE EXERCISE 14.12** | **Determining Molecularity and Identifying Intermediates**

It has been proposed that the conversion of ozone into $O_2$ proceeds by a two-step mechanism:

$$O_3(g) \longrightarrow O_2(g) + O(g)$$
$$O_3(g) + O(g) \longrightarrow 2\,O_2(g)$$

**(a)** Describe the molecularity of each elementary reaction in this mechanism.
**(b)** Write the equation for the overall reaction. **(c)** Identify the intermediate(s).

### SOLUTION

**Analyze** We are given a two-step mechanism and asked for **(a)** the molecularities of each of the two elementary reactions, **(b)** the equation for the overall process, and **(c)** the intermediate.

**Plan** The molecularity of each elementary reaction depends on the number of reactant molecules in the equation for that reaction. The overall equation is the sum of the equations for the elementary reactions. The intermediate is a substance formed in one step of the mechanism and used in another and therefore not part of the equation for the overall reaction.

**Solve**

**(a)** The first elementary reaction involves a single reactant and is consequently unimolecular. The second reaction, which involves two reactant molecules, is bimolecular.

**(b)** Adding the two elementary reactions gives

$$2\,O_3(g) + O(g) \longrightarrow 3\,O_2(g) + O(g)$$

Because $O(g)$ appears in equal amounts on both sides of the equation, it can be eliminated to give the net equation for the chemical process:

$$2\,O_3(g) \longrightarrow 3\,O_2(g)$$

**(c)** The intermediate is $O(g)$. It is neither an original reactant nor a final product but is formed in the first step of the mechanism and consumed in the second.

**PRACTICE EXERCISE**

For the reaction

$$Mo(CO)_6 + P(CH_3)_3 \longrightarrow Mo(CO)_5\,P(CH_3)_3 + CO$$

the proposed mechanism is

$$Mo(CO)_6 \longrightarrow Mo(CO)_5 + CO$$

$$Mo(CO)_5 + P(CH_3)_3 \longrightarrow Mo(CO)_5\,P(CH_3)_3$$

**(a)** Is the proposed mechanism consistent with the equation for the overall reaction? **(b)** What is the molecularity of each step of the mechanism? **(c)** Identify the intermediate(s).

**Answers:** **(a)** Yes, the two equations add to yield the equation for the reaction. **(b)** The first elementary reaction is unimolecular, and the second one is bimolecular. **(c)** $Mo(CO)_5$

## Rate Laws for Elementary Reactions

In Section 14.3 we stressed that rate laws must be determined experimentally; they cannot be predicted from the coefficients of balanced chemical equations. We are now in a position to understand why this is so. Every reaction is made up of a series of one or more elementary steps, and the rate laws and relative speeds of these steps dictate the overall rate law for the reaction. Indeed, the rate law for a reaction can be determined from its mechanism, as we will see shortly, and compared with the experimental rate law. Thus, our next challenge in kinetics is to arrive at reaction mechanisms that lead to rate laws consistent with those observed experimentally. We start by examining the rate laws of elementary reactions.

Elementary reactions are significant in a very important way: *If a reaction is elementary, its rate law is based directly on its molecularity.* For example, consider the unimolecular reaction

$$A \longrightarrow products$$

As the number of A molecules increases, the number that react in a given time interval increases proportionally. Thus, the rate of a unimolecular process is first order:

$$Rate = k[A]$$

For bimolecular elementary steps, the rate law is second order, as in the reaction

$$A + B \longrightarrow products \qquad Rate = k[A][B]$$

The second-order rate law follows directly from collision theory. If we double the concentration of A, the number of collisions between molecules of A and B doubles; likewise, if we double [B], the number of collisions between A and B doubles. Therefore, the rate law is first order in both [A] and [B] and second order overall.

The rate laws for all feasible elementary reactions are given in ▶ TABLE 14.3. Notice how each rate law follows directly from the molecularity of the reaction. It is important to remember, however, that we cannot tell by merely looking at a balanced, overall chemical equation whether the reaction involves one or several elementary steps.

**TABLE 14.3 • Elementary Reactions and Their Rate Laws**

| Molecularity | Elementary Reaction | Rate Law |
|---|---|---|
| *Uni*molecular | A $\longrightarrow$ products | Rate = $k[A]$ |
| *Bi*molecular | A + A $\longrightarrow$ products | Rate = $k[A]^2$ |
| *Bi*molecular | A + B $\longrightarrow$ products | Rate = $k[A][B]$ |
| *Ter*molecular | A + A + A $\longrightarrow$ products | Rate = $k[A]^3$ |
| *Ter*molecular | A + A + B $\longrightarrow$ products | Rate = $k[A]^2[B]$ |
| *Ter*molecular | A + B + C $\longrightarrow$ products | Rate = $k[A][B][C]$ |

**SAMPLE EXERCISE 14.13** | **Predicting the Rate Law for an Elementary Reaction**

If the following reaction occurs in a single elementary reaction, predict its rate law:

$$H_2(g) + Br_2(g) \longrightarrow 2\ HBr(g)$$

**SOLUTION**

**Analyze** We are given the equation and asked for its rate law, assuming that it is an elementary process.

**Plan** Because we are assuming that the reaction occurs as a single elementary reaction, we are able to write the rate law using the coefficients for the reactants in the equation as the reaction orders.

**Solve** The reaction is bimolecular, involving one molecule of $H_2$ and one molecule of $Br_2$. Thus, the rate law is first order in each reactant and second order overall:

$$Rate = k[H_2][Br_2]$$

**Comment** Experimental studies of this reaction show that the reaction actually has a very different rate law:

$$Rate = k[H_2][Br_2]^{1/2}$$

Because the experimental rate law differs from the one obtained by assuming a single elementary reaction, we can conclude that the mechanism cannot occur by a single elementary step. It must, therefore, involve two or more elementary steps.

**PRACTICE EXERCISE**

Consider the following reaction: $2\ NO(g) + Br_2(g) \longrightarrow 2\ NOBr(g)$. **(a)** Write the rate law for the reaction, assuming it involves a single elementary reaction. **(b)** Is a single-step mechanism likely for this reaction?

**Answers:** **(a)** Rate = $k[NO]^2[Br_2]$, **(b)** No, because termolecular reactions are very rare.

## The Rate-Determining Step for a Multistep Mechanism

As with the reaction in Sample Exercise 14.13, most reactions occur by mechanisms that involve two or more elementary reactions. Each step of the mechanism has its own rate constant and activation energy. Often one step is much slower than the others, and the overall rate of a reaction cannot exceed the rate of the slowest elementary step. Because the slow step limits the overall reaction rate, it is called the **rate-determining step** (or *rate-limiting step*).

To understand the concept of the rate-determining step for a reaction, consider a toll road with two toll plazas (▶ **FIGURE 14.21**). Cars enter the toll road at point 1 and pass through toll plaza A. They then pass an intermediate point 2 before passing through toll plaza B and arriving at point 3. We can envision this trip along the toll road as occurring in two elementary steps:

Step 1:  Point 1 $\longrightarrow$ Point 2   (through toll plaza A)

Step 2:  Point 2 $\longrightarrow$ Point 3   (through toll plaza B)

Overall:  Point 1 $\longrightarrow$ Point 3   (through both toll plazas)

(a) Cars slowed at toll plaza A, rate-determining step is passage through A

(b) Cars slowed at toll plaza B, rate-determining step is passage through B

◀ **FIGURE 14.21  Rate-determining steps in traffic flow on a toll road.**

Now suppose that one or more gates at toll plaza A are malfunctioning, so that traffic backs up behind the gates, as depicted in Figure 14.21(a). The rate at which cars can get to point 3 is limited by the rate at which they can get through the traffic jam at plaza A. Thus, step 1 is the rate-determining step of the journey along the toll road. If, however, all gates at A are functioning but one or more at B are not, traffic flows quickly through A but gets backed up at B, as depicted in Figure 14.21(b). In this case step 2 is the rate-determining step.

In the same way, *the slowest step in a multistep reaction limits the overall rate.* By analogy to Figure 14.21(a), the rate of a fast step following the rate-determining step does not speed up the overall rate. If the slow step is not the first one, as is the case in Figure 14.21(b), the faster preceding steps produce intermediate products that accumulate before being consumed in the slow step. In either case, *the rate-determining step governs the rate law for the overall reaction.*

▲ **GIVE IT SOME THOUGHT**

Why can't the rate law for a reaction generally be deduced from the balanced equation for the reaction?

## Mechanisms with a Slow Initial Step

We can most easily see the relationship between the slow step in a mechanism and the rate law for the overall reaction by considering an example in which the first step in a multistep mechanism is the rate-determining step. Consider the reaction of $NO_2$ and CO to produce NO and $CO_2$ (Equation 14.23). Below 225 °C, it is found experimentally that the rate law for this reaction is second order in $NO_2$ and zero order in CO: Rate $= k[NO_2]^2$. Can we propose a reaction mechanism consistent with this rate law? Consider the two-step mechanism:*

$$\text{Step 1:}\quad NO_2(g) + NO_2(g) \xrightarrow{k_1} NO_3(g) + NO(g) \quad \text{(slow)}$$

$$\text{Step 2:}\quad NO_3(g) + CO(g) \xrightarrow{k_2} NO_2(g) + CO_2(g) \quad \text{(fast)}$$

$$\text{Overall:}\quad NO_2(g) + CO(g) \longrightarrow NO(g) + CO_2(g)$$

Step 2 is much faster than step 1; that is, $k_2 \gg k_1$, telling us that the intermediate $NO_3(g)$ is slowly produced in step 1 and immediately consumed in step 2.

---

*Note the rate constants $k_1$ and $k_2$ written above the reaction arrows. The subscript on each rate constant identifies the elementary step involved. Thus, $k_1$ is the rate constant for step 1, and $k_2$ is the rate constant for step 2. A negative subscript refers to the rate constant for the reverse of an elementary step. For example, $k_{-1}$ is the rate constant for the reverse of the first step.

Because step 1 is slow and step 2 is fast, step 1 is the rate-determining step. Thus, the rate of the overall reaction depends on the rate of step 1, and the rate law of the overall reaction equals the rate law of step 1. Step 1 is a bimolecular process that has the rate law

$$\text{Rate} = k_1[NO_2]^2$$

Thus, the rate law predicted by this mechanism agrees with the one observed experimentally. The reactant CO is absent from the rate law because it reacts in a step that follows the rate-determining step.

A scientist would not, at this point, say that we have "proved" that this mechanism is correct. All we can say is that the rate law predicted by the mechanism is *consistent with experiment*. There could easily be a different sequence of steps that leads to the same rate law. If, however, the predicted rate law of the proposed mechanism disagrees with experiment, we know for certain that the mechanism cannot be correct.

---

**SAMPLE EXERCISE 14.14** | **Determining the Rate Law for a Multistep Mechanism**

The decomposition of nitrous oxide, $N_2O$, is believed to occur by a two-step mechanism:

$$N_2O(g) \longrightarrow N_2(g) + O(g) \quad \text{(slow)}$$

$$N_2O(g) + O(g) \longrightarrow N_2(g) + O_2(g) \quad \text{(fast)}$$

**(a)** Write the equation for the overall reaction. **(b)** Write the rate law for the overall reaction.

**SOLUTION**

**Analyze** Given a multistep mechanism with the relative speeds of the steps, we are asked to write the overall reaction and the rate law for that overall reaction.

**Plan** **(a)** Find the overall reaction by adding the elementary steps and eliminating the intermediates. **(b)** The rate law for the overall reaction will be that of the slow, rate-determining step.

**Solve** **(a)** Adding the two elementary reactions gives

$$2\,N_2O(g) + O(g) \longrightarrow 2\,N_2(g) + 2\,O_2(g) + O(g)$$

Omitting the intermediate, $O(g)$, which occurs on both sides of the equation, gives the overall reaction:

$$2\,N_2O(g) \longrightarrow 2\,N_2(g) + O_2(g)$$

**(b)** The rate law for the overall reaction is just the rate law for the slow, rate-determining elementary reaction. Because that slow step is a unimolecular elementary reaction, the rate law is first order:

$$\text{Rate} = k[N_2O]$$

**PRACTICE EXERCISE**

Ozone reacts with nitrogen dioxide to produce dinitrogen pentoxide and oxygen:

$$O_3(g) + 2\,NO_2(g) \longrightarrow N_2O_5(g) + O_2(g)$$

The reaction is believed to occur in two steps:

$$O_3(g) + NO_2(g) \longrightarrow NO_3(g) + O_2(g)$$

$$NO_3(g) + NO_2(g) \longrightarrow N_2O_5(g)$$

The experimental rate law is rate = $k[O_3][NO_2]$. What can you say about the relative rates of the two steps of the mechanism?

**Answer:** Because the rate law conforms to the molecularity of the first step, that must be the rate-determining step. The second step must be much faster than the first one.

---

## Mechanisms with a Fast Initial Step

It is less straightforward to derive the rate law for a mechanism in which an intermediate is a reactant in the rate-determining step. This situation arises in multistep mechanisms when the first step is fast and therefore *not* the rate-determining step. Let's consider one example: the gas-phase reaction of nitric oxide (NO) with bromine ($Br_2$):

$$2\,NO(g) + Br_2(g) \longrightarrow 2\,NOBr(g) \qquad [14.24]$$

The experimentally determined rate law for this reaction is second order in NO and first order in $Br_2$:

$$\text{Rate} = k[NO]^2[Br_2] \qquad [14.25]$$

We seek a reaction mechanism that is consistent with this rate law. One possibility is that the reaction occurs in a single termolecular step:

$$NO(g) + NO(g) + Br_2(g) \longrightarrow 2\,NOBr(g) \qquad \text{Rate} = k[NO]^2[Br_2] \qquad [14.26]$$

As noted in Practice Exercise 14.13, this does not seem likely because termolecular processes are so rare.

> ⚠ **GIVE IT SOME THOUGHT**
>
> Why are termolecular elementary steps rare in gas-phase reactions?

Let's consider an alternative mechanism that does not involve a termolecular step:

$$\text{Step 1:} \qquad NO(g) + Br_2(g) \underset{k_{-1}}{\overset{k_1}{\rightleftharpoons}} NOBr_2(g) \;\; \text{(fast)}$$
$$[14.27]$$
$$\text{Step 2:} \quad NOBr_2(g) + NO(g) \overset{k_2}{\longrightarrow} 2\,NOBr(g) \;\; \text{(slow)}$$

In this mechanism, step 1 involves two processes: a forward reaction and its reverse.

Because step 2 is the rate-determining step, the rate law for that step governs the rate of the overall reaction:

$$\text{Rate} = k_2[NOBr_2][NO] \qquad [14.28]$$

However, $NOBr_2$ is an intermediate generated in the forward reaction of step 1. Intermediates are usually unstable and have a low, unknown concentration. Thus, the rate law of Equation 14.28 depends on the unknown concentration of an intermediate. This is not desirable. Instead, in general, we want to express the rate law for any reaction in terms of the reactants, or the products if necessary, of the reaction.

With the aid of some assumptions, we can express the concentration of the intermediate $NOBr_2$ in terms of the concentrations of the starting reactants NO and $Br_2$. We first assume that $NOBr_2$ is unstable and does not accumulate to any significant extent in the reaction mixture. Once formed, $NOBr_2$ can be consumed either by reacting with NO to form NOBr or by re-forming NO and $Br_2$. The first of these possibilities is step 2 of our alternative mechanism, a slow process. The second is the reverse of step 1, a unimolecular process:

$$NOBr_2(g) \overset{k_{-1}}{\longrightarrow} NO(g) + Br_2(g)$$

Because step 2 is slow, we assume that most of the $NOBr_2$ falls apart according to this reaction. Thus, we have both the forward and reverse reactions of step 1 occurring much faster than step 2. Because they occur rapidly relative to step 2, the forward and reverse reactions of step 1 establish an equilibrium. As in any other dynamic equilibrium, the rate of the forward reaction equals that of the reverse reaction:

$$\underset{\text{Rate of forward reaction}}{k_1[NO][Br_2]} = \underset{\text{Rate of reverse reaction}}{k_{-1}[NOBr_2]}$$

Solving for $[NOBr_2]$, we have

$$[NOBr_2] = \frac{k_1}{k_{-1}}[NO][Br_2]$$

Substituting this relationship into Equation 14.28, we have

$$\text{Rate} = k_2\frac{k_1}{k_{-1}}[NO][Br_2][NO] = k[NO]^2[Br_2]$$

where the experimental rate constant $k$ equals $k_2 k_1/k_{-1}$. This expression is consistent with the experimental rate law (Equation 14.25). Thus, our alternative mechanism

(Equation 14.27), which involves two steps but only unimolecular and bimolecular processes, is far more probable than the single-step termolecular mechanism of Equation 14.26.

In general, *whenever a fast step precedes a slow one, we can solve for the concentration of an intermediate by assuming that an equilibrium is established in the fast step.*

---

**SAMPLE EXERCISE 14.15** | **Deriving the Rate Law for a Mechanism with a Fast Initial Step**

Show that the following mechanism for Equation 14.24 also produces a rate law consistent with the experimentally observed one:

$$\text{Step 1:} \quad NO(g) + NO(g) \underset{k_{-1}}{\overset{k_1}{\rightleftharpoons}} N_2O_2(g) \qquad \text{(fast, equilibrium)}$$

$$\text{Step 2:} \quad N_2O_2(g) + Br_2(g) \overset{k_2}{\longrightarrow} 2\,NOBr(g) \quad \text{(slow)}$$

**SOLUTION**

**Analyze** We are given a mechanism with a fast initial step and asked to write the rate law for the overall reaction.

**Plan** The rate law of the slow elementary step in a mechanism determines the rate law for the overall reaction. Thus, we first write the rate law based on the molecularity of the slow step. In this case the slow step involves the intermediate $N_2O_2$ as a reactant. Experimental rate laws, however, do not contain the concentrations of intermediates; instead they are expressed in terms of the concentrations of starting substances. Thus, we must relate the concentration of $N_2O_2$ to the concentration of NO by assuming that an equilibrium is established in the first step.

**Solve** The second step is rate determining, so the overall rate is

$$\text{Rate} = k_2[N_2O_2][Br_2]$$

We solve for the concentration of the intermediate $N_2O_2$ by assuming that an equilibrium is established in step 1; thus, the rates of the forward and reverse reactions in step 1 are equal:

$$k_1[NO]^2 = k_{-1}[N_2O_2]$$

Solving for the concentration of the intermediate, $N_2O_2$, gives

$$[N_2O_2] = \frac{k_1}{k_{-1}}[NO]^2$$

Substituting this expression into the rate expression gives

$$\text{Rate} = k_2\frac{k_1}{k_{-1}}[NO]^2[Br_2] = k[NO]^2[Br_2]$$

Thus, this mechanism also yields a rate law consistent with the experimental one.

**PRACTICE EXERCISE**

The first step of a mechanism involving the reaction of bromine is

$$Br_2(g) \underset{k_{-1}}{\overset{k_1}{\rightleftharpoons}} 2\,Br(g) \quad \text{(fast, equilibrium)}$$

What is the expression relating the concentration of Br(g) to that of $Br_2(g)$?

*Answer:* $[Br] = \left(\dfrac{k_1}{k_{-1}}[Br_2]\right)^{1/2}$

---

So far we have considered only three reaction mechanisms: one for a reaction that occurs in a single elementary step and two for simple multistep reactions where there is one rate-determining step. There are other more complex mechanisms, however. If you take a biochemistry class, for example, you will learn about cases in which you have to assume that the concentration of an intermediate cannot be neglected in deriving the rate law. Furthermore, some mechanisms require a large number of steps, sometimes 35 or more, to arrive at a rate law that agrees with experimental data!

# 14.7 | CATALYSIS

A **catalyst** is a substance that changes the speed of a chemical reaction without under-going a permanent chemical change itself. Most reactions in the body, the atmosphere, and the oceans occur with the help of catalysts. Much industrial chemical research is de-voted to the search for more effective catalysts for reactions of commercial importance. Extensive research efforts also are devoted to finding means of inhibiting or removing certain catalysts that promote undesirable reactions, such as those that corrode metals, age our bodies, and cause tooth decay.

## Homogeneous Catalysis

A catalyst that is present in the same phase as the reactants in a reaction mixture is called a **homogeneous catalyst**. Examples abound both in solution and in the gas phase. Consider, for example, the decomposition of aqueous hydrogen peroxide, $H_2O_2(aq)$, into water and oxygen:

$$2\ H_2O_2(aq) \longrightarrow 2\ H_2O(l) + O_2(g) \qquad [14.29]$$

In the absence of a catalyst, this reaction occurs extremely slowly. Many substances are capa-ble of catalyzing the reaction, however, including bromide ion, which reacts with hydrogen peroxide in acidic solution, forming aqueous bromine and water (▼ FIGURE 14.22):

$$2\ Br^-(aq) + H_2O_2(aq) + 2\ H^+ \longrightarrow Br_2(aq) + 2\ H_2O(l) \qquad [14.30]$$

NaBr catalyst about to be added to reaction mixture

$H_2O_2(aq)$ in acidic solution

$2\ Br^-(aq) + H_2O_2(aq) + 2\ H^+(aq)$
$\longrightarrow Br_2(aq) + 2\ H_2O(l)$
brown

$Br_2(aq) + H_2O_2(aq) \longrightarrow$
$2\ Br^-(aq) + 2\ H^+(aq) + O_2(g)$
colorless                          bubbles

▲ **FIGURE 14.22  Homogeneous catalysis.** Effect of catalyst on the speed of hydrogen peroxide decomposition to water and oxygen gas.

If this were the complete reaction, bromide ion would not be a catalyst because it undergoes chemical change during the reaction. However, hydrogen peroxide also reacts with the $Br_2(aq)$ generated in Equation 14.30:

$$Br_2(aq) + H_2O_2(aq) \longrightarrow 2\,Br^-(aq) + 2\,H^+(aq) + O_2(g) \qquad [14.31]$$

The sum of Equations 14.30 and 14.31 is just Equation 14.29, a result which you can check for yourself.

When the $H_2O_2$ has been completely decomposed, we are left with a colorless solution of $Br^-(aq)$, which means that this ion is indeed a catalyst of the reaction because it speeds up the reaction without itself undergoing any net change. In contrast, $Br_2$ is an intermediate because it is first formed (Equation 14.30) and then consumed (Equation 14.31). Neither the catalyst nor the intermediate appears in the equation for the overall reaction. Notice, however, that *the catalyst is there at the start of the reaction, whereas the intermediate is formed during the course of the reaction.*

How does a catalyst work? If we think about the general form of rate laws (Equation 14.7, rate $= k[A]^m[B]^n$), we must conclude that the catalyst must affect the numerical value of $k$, the rate constant. On the basis of the Arrhenius equation (Equation 14.19, $k = Ae^{-E_a/RT}$), $k$ is determined by the activation energy ($E_a$) and the frequency factor ($A$). A catalyst may affect the rate of reaction by altering the value of either $E_a$ or $A$. We can envision this happening in two ways: The catalyst could provide a new mechanism for the reaction that has an $E_a$ value lower than the $E_a$ value for the uncatalyzed reaction, or the catalyst could assist in the orientation of reactants and so increase $A$. The most dramatic catalytic effects come from lowering $E_a$. As a general rule, *a catalyst lowers the overall activation energy for a chemical reaction.*

A catalyst can lower the activation energy for a reaction by providing a different mechanism for the reaction. In the decomposition of hydrogen peroxide, for example, two successive reactions of $H_2O_2$, first with bromide and then with bromine, take place. Because these two reactions together serve as a catalytic pathway for hydrogen peroxide decomposition, *both* of them must have significantly lower activation energies than the uncatalyzed decomposition (◀ **FIGURE 14.23**).

## GO FIGURE

**Where are the intermediates and transition states in this diagram?**

▲ **FIGURE 14.23 Energy profiles for the uncatalyzed and bromide-catalyzed decomposition of $H_2O_2$.**

## GIVE IT SOME THOUGHT

How does a catalyst increase the rate of a reaction?

## Heterogeneous Catalysis

A **heterogeneous catalyst** is one that exists in a phase different from the phase of the reactant molecules, usually as a solid in contact with either gaseous reactants or with reactants in a liquid solution. Many industrially important reactions are catalyzed by the surfaces of solids. For example, hydrocarbon molecules are rearranged to form gasoline with the aid of what are called "cracking" catalysts. Heterogeneous catalysts are often composed of metals or metal oxides. Because the catalyzed reaction occurs on the surface, special methods are often used to prepare catalysts so that they have very large surface areas.

The initial step in heterogeneous catalysis is usually **adsorption** of reactants. *Adsorption* refers to the binding of molecules to a surface, whereas *absorption* refers to the uptake of molecules into the interior of a substance. ∞ (Section 13.6) Adsorption occurs because the atoms or ions at the surface of a solid are extremely reactive. Unlike their counterparts in the interior of the substance, surface atoms and ions have unused bonding capacity that can be used to bond molecules from the gas or solution phase to the surface of the solid.

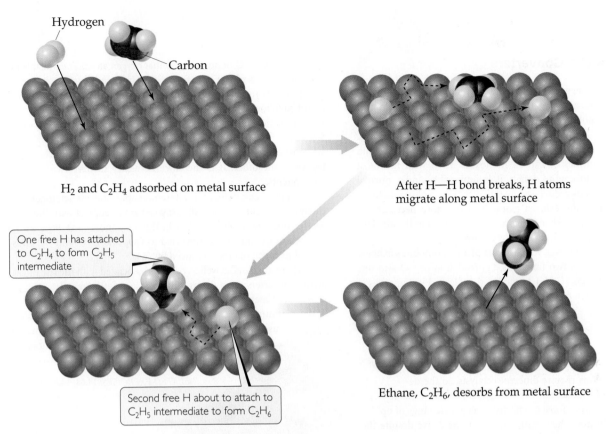

Hydrogen

Carbon

$H_2$ and $C_2H_4$ adsorbed on metal surface

After H—H bond breaks, H atoms migrate along metal surface

One free H has attached to $C_2H_4$ to form $C_2H_5$ intermediate

Second free H about to attach to $C_2H_5$ intermediate to form $C_2H_6$

Ethane, $C_2H_6$, desorbs from metal surface

▲ **FIGURE 14.24  Heterogeneous catalysis.** Mechanism for reaction of ethylene with hydrogen on a catalytic surface.

The reaction of hydrogen gas with ethylene gas to form ethane gas provides an example of heterogeneous catalysis:

$$C_2H_4(g) \ + \ H_2(g) \ \longrightarrow \ C_2H_6(g) \quad \Delta H° = -137 \text{ kJ/mol} \qquad [14.32]$$
Ethylene                    Ethane

Even though this reaction is exothermic, it occurs very slowly in the absence of a catalyst. In the presence of a finely powdered metal, however, such as nickel, palladium, or platinum, the reaction occurs easily at room temperature via the mechanism diagrammed in ▲ **FIGURE 14.24.** Both ethylene and hydrogen are adsorbed on the metal surface. Upon adsorption, the H—H bond of $H_2$ breaks, leaving two H atoms initially bonded to the metal surface but relatively free to move. When a hydrogen encounters an adsorbed ethylene molecule, it can form a $\sigma$ bond to one of the carbon atoms, effectively destroying the C—C $\pi$ bond and leaving an *ethyl group* ($C_2H_5$) bonded to the surface via a metal-to-carbon $\sigma$ bond . This $\sigma$ bond is relatively weak, so when the other carbon atom also encounters a hydrogen atom, a sixth C—H $\sigma$ bond is readily formed, and an ethane molecule ($C_2H_6$) is released from the metal surface.

 GIVE IT SOME THOUGHT

How does a homogeneous catalyst compare with a heterogeneous one regarding the ease of recovery of the catalyst from the reaction mixture?

## Enzymes

The human body is characterized by an extremely complex system of interrelated chemical reactions, all of which must occur at carefully controlled rates to maintain life. A large number of marvelously efficient biological catalysts known as **enzymes** are necessary for many of these reactions to occur at suitable rates. Most enzymes are large

# CHEMISTRY PUT TO WORK

## Catalytic Converters

Heterogeneous catalysis plays a major role in the fight against urban air pollution. Two components of automobile exhausts that help form photochemical smog are nitrogen oxides and unburned hydrocarbons. In addition, automobile exhaust may contain considerable quantities of carbon monoxide. Even with the most careful attention to engine design, it is impossible under normal driving conditions to reduce the quantity of these pollutants to an acceptable level in the exhaust gases. It is therefore necessary to remove them from the exhaust before they are vented to the air. This removal is accomplished in the *catalytic converter*.

The catalytic converter, which is part of an automobile's exhaust system, must perform two functions: (1) oxidation of CO and unburned hydrocarbons ($C_xH_y$) to carbon dioxide and water, and (2) reduction of nitrogen oxides to nitrogen gas:

$$CO, C_xH_y \xrightarrow{O_2} CO_2 + H_2O$$

$$NO, NO_2 \longrightarrow N_2$$

These two functions require different catalysts, so the development of a successful catalyst system is a difficult challenge. The catalysts must be effective over a wide range of operating temperatures. They must continue to be active despite the fact that various components of the exhaust can block the active sites of the catalyst. And the catalysts must be sufficiently rugged to withstand exhaust gas turbulence and the mechanical shocks of driving under various conditions for thousands of miles.

Catalysts that promote the combustion of CO and hydrocarbons are, in general, the transition-metal oxides and the noble metals. These materials are supported on a structure (▶ FIGURE 14.25) that allows the best possible contact between the flowing exhaust gas and the catalyst surface. A honeycomb structure made from alumina ($Al_2O_3$) and impregnated with the catalyst is employed. Such catalysts operate by first adsorbing oxygen gas present in the exhaust gas. This adsorption weakens the O—O bond in $O_2$, so that oxygen atoms are available for reaction with adsorbed CO to form $CO_2$. Hydrocarbon oxidation probably proceeds somewhat similarly, with the hydrocarbons first being adsorbed followed by rupture of a C—H bond.

Transition-metal oxides and noble metals are also the most effective catalysts for reduction of NO to $N_2$ and $O_2$. The catalysts that are most effective in one reaction, however, are usually much less effective in the other. It is therefore necessary to have two catalytic components.

Catalytic converters contain remarkably efficient heterogeneous catalysts. The automotive exhaust gases are in contact with the catalyst for only 100 to 400 ms, but in this very short time, 96% of the hydrocarbons and CO is converted to $CO_2$ and $H_2O$, and the emission of nitrogen oxides is reduced by 76%.

There are costs as well as benefits associated with the use of catalytic converters, one being that some of the metals are very expensive. Catalytic converters currently account for about 35% of the platinum, 65% of the palladium, and 95% of the rhodium used annually. All of these metals, which come mainly from Russia and South Africa, can be far more expensive than gold.

*RELATED EXERCISES: 14.64, 14.87, 14.88*

▲ **FIGURE 14.25** **Cross section of a catalytic converter.**

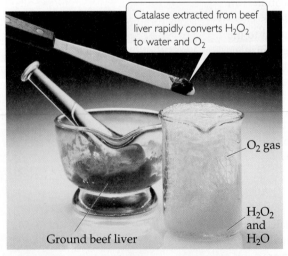

Catalase extracted from beef liver rapidly converts $H_2O_2$ to water and $O_2$

$O_2$ gas

$H_2O_2$ and $H_2O$

Ground beef liver

▲ **FIGURE 14.26** **Enzymes speed up reactions.**

protein molecules with molecular weights ranging from about 10,000 to about 1 million amu. They are very selective in the reactions they catalyze, and some are absolutely specific, operating for only one substance in only one reaction. The decomposition of hydrogen peroxide, for example, is an important biological process. Because hydrogen peroxide is strongly oxidizing, it can be physiologically harmful. For this reason, the blood and liver of mammals contain an enzyme, *catalase*, that catalyzes the decomposition of hydrogen peroxide into water and oxygen (Equation 14.29). ◀ FIGURE 14.26 shows the dramatic acceleration of this chemical reaction by the catalase in beef liver.

Which molecules must bind more tightly to the active site, substrates or products?

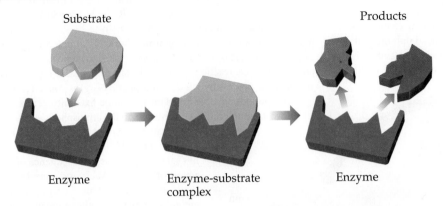

▲ **FIGURE 14.27   Lock-and-key model for enzyme action.**

The reaction any given enzyme catalyzes takes place at a specific location in the enzyme, the **active site**. The substances that react at this site are called **substrates**. The **lock-and-key model** provides a simple explanation for the specificity of an enzyme (▲ FIGURE 14.27). The substrate is pictured as fitting neatly into the active site, much like a key fits into a lock. Although this model oversimplifies the situation, since enzymes can "wiggle" to adjust the shape and size of the active site, the lock-and-key model is a good place to start understanding enzyme activity.

▶ FIGURE 14.28 shows a model of the enzyme lysozyme without and with a bound substrate molecule.

The combination of enzyme and substrate is called the *enzyme-substrate complex.* Although Figure 14.27 shows both the active site and its substrate as having a fixed shape, the active site is often fairly flexible and so may change shape as it binds the substrate. The binding between substrate and active site involves dipole–dipole attractions, hydrogen bonds, and dispersion forces. ∞ (Section 11.2)

As substrate molecules enter the active site, they are somehow activated so that they are capable of reacting rapidly. This activation process may occur, for example, by the withdrawal or donation of electron density from a particular bond or group of atoms in the enzyme's active site. In addition, the substrate may become distorted in the process of fitting into the active site and made more reactive. Once the reaction occurs, the products depart from the active site, allowing another substrate molecule to enter.

The activity of an enzyme is destroyed if some molecule other than the substrate specific to that enzyme binds to the active site and blocks entry of the substrate. Such substances are called *enzyme inhibitors*. Nerve poisons and certain toxic metal ions, such as lead and mercury, are believed to act in this way to inhibit enzyme activity. Some other poisons act by attaching elsewhere on the enzyme, thereby distorting the active site so that the substrate no longer fits.

Enzymes are enormously more efficient than nonbiochemical catalysts. The number of individual catalyzed reaction events occurring at a particular active site, called the *turnover number*, is generally in the range of $10^3$ to $10^7$ per second. Such large turnover numbers correspond to very low activation energies. Compared with a simple chemical catalyst, enzymes can increase the rate constant for a given reaction by a million-fold or more.

▲ **FIGURE 14.28   Molecular model of lysozyme without and with a bound substrate molecule (yellow).**

GIVE IT SOME THOUGHT

Is it reasonable to say that enzymes stabilize the transition state for a reaction? Explain your answer.

# CHEMISTRY AND LIFE

## NITROGEN FIXATION AND NITROGENASE

Nitrogen is one of the most essential elements in living organisms, found in many compounds vital to life, including proteins, nucleic acids, vitamins, and hormones. Nitrogen is continually cycling through the biosphere in various forms, as shown in ◀ **FIGURE 14.29**. For example, certain microorganisms convert the nitrogen in animal waste and dead plants and animals into $N_2(g)$, which then returns to the atmosphere. For the food chain to be sustained, there must be a means of converting atmospheric $N_2(g)$ in a form plants can use. For this reason, if a chemist were asked to name the most important chemical reaction in the world, she might easily say *nitrogen fixation*, the process by which atmospheric $N_2(g)$ is converted into compounds suitable for plant use. Some fixed nitrogen results from the action of lightning on the atmosphere, and some is produced industrially using a process we will discuss in Chapter 15. About 60% of fixed nitrogen, however, is a consequence of the action of the remarkable and complex enzyme *nitrogenase*. This enzyme is *not* present in humans or other animals; rather, it is found in bacteria that live in the root nodules of certain plants, such as the legumes clover and alfalfa.

Nitrogenase converts $N_2$ into $NH_3$, a process that, in the absence of a catalyst, has a very large activation energy. This process is a *reduction* reaction in which the oxidation state of N is reduced from 0 in $N_2$ to $-3$ in $NH_3$. The mechanism by which nitrogenase reduces $N_2$ is not fully understood. Like many other enzymes, including catalase, the active site of nitrogenase contains transition-metal atoms; such enzymes are called *metalloenzymes*. Because transition metals can readily change oxidation state, metalloenzymes are especially useful for effecting transformations in which substrates are either oxidized or reduced.

It has been known for nearly 30 years that a portion of nitrogenase contains iron and molybdenum atoms. This portion, called the *FeMo-cofactor*, is thought to serve as the active site of the enzyme. The FeMo-cofactor of nitrogenase is a cluster of seven Fe atoms and one Mo atom, all linked by sulfur atoms (◀ **FIGURE 14.30**).

It is one of the wonders of life that simple bacteria can contain beautifully complex and vitally important enzymes such as nitrogenase. Because of this enzyme, nitrogen is continually cycled between its comparatively inert role in the atmosphere and its critical role in living organisms. Without nitrogenase, life as we know it could not exist on Earth.

*RELATED EXERCISES:* 14.91, 14.126

▲ **FIGURE 14.29 Simplified picture of the nitrogen cycle.**

◀ **FIGURE 14.30 The FeMo-cofactor of nitrogenase.** Nitrogenase is found in nodules in the roots of certain plants, such as the white clover roots shown at the left. The cofactor, which is thought to be the active site of the enzyme, contains seven Fe atoms and one Mo atom, linked by sulfur atoms. The molecules on the outside of the cofactor connect it to the rest of the protein.

**SAMPLE INTEGRATIVE EXERCISE** Putting Concepts Together

Formic acid (HCOOH) decomposes in the gas phase at elevated temperatures as follows:

$$HCOOH(g) \longrightarrow CO_2(g) + H_2(g)$$

The uncatalyzed decomposition reaction is determined to be first order. A graph of the partial pressure of HCOOH versus time for decomposition at 838 K is shown as the red curve in ▶ FIGURE 14.31. When a small amount of solid ZnO is added to the reaction chamber, the partial pressure of acid versus time varies as shown by the blue curve in Figure 14.31.

**(a)** Estimate the half-life and first-order rate constant for formic acid decomposition.

**(b)** What can you conclude from the effect of added ZnO on the decomposition of formic acid?

**(c)** The progress of the reaction was followed by measuring the partial pressure of formic acid vapor at selected times. Suppose that, instead, we had plotted the concentration of formic acid in units of mol/L. What effect would this have had on the calculated value of $k$?

**(d)** The pressure of formic acid vapor at the start of the reaction is $3.00 \times 10^2$ torr. Assuming constant temperature and ideal-gas behavior, what is the pressure in the system at the end of the reaction? If the volume of the reaction chamber is 436 cm³, how many moles of gas occupy the reaction chamber at the end of the reaction?

**(e)** The standard heat of formation of formic acid vapor is $\Delta H_f^\circ = -378.6$ kJ/mol. Calculate $\Delta H^\circ$ for the overall reaction. If the activation energy ($E_a$) for the reaction is 184 kJ/mol, sketch an approximate energy profile for the reaction, and label $E_a$, $\Delta H^\circ$, and the transition state.

▲ **FIGURE 14.31** **Variation in pressure of HCOOH(*g*) as a function of time at 838 K.**

**SOLUTION**

**(a)** The initial pressure of HCOOH is $3.00 \times 10^2$ torr. On the graph we move to the level at which the partial pressure of HCOOH is $1.50 \times 10^2$ torr, half the initial value. This corresponds to a time of about $6.60 \times 10^2$ s, which is therefore the half-life. The first-order rate constant is given by Equation 14.15: $k = 0.693/t_{1/2} = 0.693/660$ s $= 1.05 \times 10^{-3}$ s$^{-1}$.

**(b)** The reaction proceeds much more rapidly in the presence of solid ZnO, so the surface of the oxide must be acting as a catalyst for the decomposition of the acid. This is an example of heterogeneous catalysis.

**(c)** If we had graphed the concentration of formic acid in units of moles per liter, we would still have determined that the half-life for decomposition is 660 s, and we would have computed the same value for $k$. Because the units for $k$ are s$^{-1}$, the value for $k$ is independent of the units used for concentration.

**(d)** According to the stoichiometry of the reaction, two moles of product are formed for each mole of reactant. When reaction is completed, therefore, the pressure will be 600 torr, just twice the initial pressure, assuming ideal-gas behavior. (Because we are working at quite high temperature and fairly low gas pressure, assuming ideal-gas behavior is reasonable.) The number of moles of gas present can be calculated using the ideal-gas equation: ∞ (Section 10.4)

$$n = \frac{PV}{RT} = \frac{(600/760 \text{ atm})(0.436 \text{ L})}{(0.08206 \text{ L-atm/mol-K})(838 \text{ K})} = 5.00 \times 10^{-3} \text{ mole}$$

**(e)** We first calculate the overall change in energy, $\Delta H^\circ$ (∞ Section 5.7 and Appendix C), as in

$$\Delta H^\circ = \Delta H_f^\circ(CO_2(g)) + \Delta H_f^\circ(H_2(g)) - \Delta H_f^\circ(HCOOH(g))$$

$$= -393.5 \text{ kJ/mol} + 0 - (-378.6 \text{ kJ/mol})$$

$$= -14.9 \text{ kJ/mol}$$

From this and the given value for $E_a$, we can draw an approximate energy profile for the reaction, in analogy to Figure 14.17.

# CHAPTER SUMMARY AND KEY TERMS

**INTRODUCTION AND SECTION 14.1** **Chemical kinetics** is the area of chemistry in which **reaction rates** are studied. Factors that affect reaction rate are the physical state of the reactants; concentration; temperature; and the presence of catalysts.

**SECTION 14.2** Reaction rate are usually expressed as changes in concentration per unit time: Typically, for reactions in solution, rates are given in units of molarity per second $M/s$. For most reactions, a plot of molarity versus time shows that the rate slows down as the reaction proceeds. The **instantaneous rate** is the slope of a line drawn tangent to the concentration-versus-time curve at a specific time. Rates can be written in terms of the appearance of products or the disappearance of reactants; the stoichiometry of the reaction dictates the relationship between rates of appearance and disappearance.

**SECTION 14.3** The quantitative relationship between rate and concentration is expressed by a **rate law**, which usually has the following form:

$$\text{Rate} = k[\text{reactant 1}]^m[\text{reactant 2}]^n \ldots$$

The constant $k$ in the rate law is called the **rate constant**; the exponents $m$, $n$, and so forth are called **reaction orders** for the reactants. The sum of the reaction orders gives the **overall reaction order**. Reaction orders must be determined experimentally. The units of the rate constant depend on the overall reaction order. For a reaction in which the overall reaction order is 1, $k$ has units of $s^{-1}$; for one in which the overall reaction order is 2, $k$ has units of $M^{-1} s^{-1}$. Spectroscopy is one technique that can be used to monitor the course of a reaction. According to Beer's law, the absorption of electromagnetic radiation by a substance at a particular wavelength is directly proportional to its concentration.

**SECTION 14.4** Rate laws can be used to determine the concentrations of reactants or products at any time during a reaction. In a **first-order reaction** the rate is proportional to the concentration of a single reactant raised to the first power: Rate = $k[A]$. In such cases the integrated form of the rate law is $\ln[A]_t = -kt + \ln[A]_0$, where $[A]_t$ is the concentration of reactant A at time $t$, $k$ is the rate constant, and $[A]_0$ is the initial concentration of A. Thus, for a first-order reaction, a graph of $\ln[A]$ versus time yields a straight line of slope $-k$.

A **second-order reaction** is one for which the overall reaction order is 2. If a second-order rate law depends on the concentration of only one reactant, then rate = $k[A]^2$, and the time dependence of $[A]$ is given by the integrated form of the rate law: $1/[A]_t = 1/[A]_0 + kt$. In this case a graph of $1/[A]_t$ versus time yields a straight line. A **zero-order reaction** is one for which the overall reaction order is 0. Rate = $k$ if the reaction is zero order.

The **half-life** of a reaction, $t_{1/2}$, is the time required for the concentration of a reactant to drop to one-half of its original value. For a first-order reaction, the half-life depends only on the rate constant and not on the initial concentration: $t_{1/2} = 0.693/k$. The half-life of a second-order reaction depends on both the rate constant and the initial concentration of A: $t_{1/2} = 1/k[A]_0$.

**SECTION 14.5** The **collision model**, which assumes that reactions occur as a result of collisions between molecules, helps explain why the magnitudes of rate constants increase with increasing temperature.

The greater the kinetic energy of the colliding molecules, the greater is the energy of collision. The minimum energy required for a reaction to occur is called the **activation energy**, $E_a$. A collision with energy $E_a$ or greater can cause the atoms of the colliding molecules to reach the **activated complex** (or **transition state**), which is the highest energy arrangement in the pathway from reactants to products. Even if a collision is energetic enough, it may not lead to reaction; the reactants must also be correctly oriented relative to one another in order for a collision to be effective.

Because the kinetic energy of molecules depends on temperature, the rate constant of a reaction is very dependent on temperature. The relationship between $k$ and temperature is given by the **Arrhenius equation**: $k = Ae^{-E_a/RT}$. The term $A$ is called the **frequency factor**; it relates to the number of collisions that are favorably oriented for reaction. The Arrhenius equation is often used in logarithmic form: $\ln k = \ln A - E_a/RT$. Thus, a graph of $\ln k$ versus $1/T$ yields a straight line with slope $-E_a/R$.

**SECTION 14.6** A **reaction mechanism** details the individual steps that occur in the course of a reaction. Each of these steps, called **elementary reactions**, has a well-defined rate law that depends on the number of molecules (the **molecularity**) of the step. Elementary reactions are defined as either **unimolecular**, **bimolecular**, or **termolecular**, depending on whether one, two, or three reactant molecules are involved, respectively. Termolecular elementary reactions are very rare. Unimolecular, bimolecular, and termolecular reactions follow rate laws that are first order overall, second order overall, and third order overall, respectively. Many reactions occur by a multistep mechanism, involving two or more elementary reactions, or steps. An **intermediate** is produced in one elementary step, is consumed in a later elementary step, and therefore does not appear in the overall equation for the reaction. When a mechanism has several elementary steps, the overall rate is limited by the slowest elementary step, called the **rate-determining step**. A fast elementary step that follows the rate-determining step will have no effect on the rate law of the reaction. A fast step that precedes the rate-determining step often creates an equilibrium that involves an intermediate. For a mechanism to be valid, the rate law predicted by the mechanism must be the same as that observed experimentally.

**SECTION 14.7** A **catalyst** is a substance that increases the rate of a reaction without undergoing a net chemical change itself. It does so by providing a different mechanism for the reaction, one that has a lower activation energy. A **homogeneous catalyst** is one that is in the same phase as the reactants. A **heterogeneous catalyst** has a different phase from the reactants. Finely divided metals are often used as heterogeneous catalysts for solution- and gas-phase reactions. Reacting molecules can undergo binding, or **adsorption**, at the surface of the catalyst. The adsorption of a reactant at specific sites on the surface makes bond breaking easier, lowering the activation energy. Catalysis in living organisms is achieved by **enzymes**, large protein molecules that usually catalyze a very specific reaction. The specific reactant molecules involved in an enzymatic reaction are called **substrates**. The site of the enzyme where the catalysis occurs is called the **active site**. In the **lock-and-key model** for enzyme catalysis, substrate molecules bind very specifically to the active site of the enzyme, after which they can undergo reaction.

## KEY SKILLS

- Understand the factors that affect the rate of chemical reactions. (Section 14.1)
- Determine the rate of a reaction given time and concentration. (Section 14.2)
- Relate the rate of formation of products and the rate of disappearance of reactants given the balanced chemical equation for the reaction. (Section 14.2)
- Understand the form and meaning of a rate law including the ideas of reaction order and rate constant. (Section 14.3)
- Determine the rate law and rate constant for a reaction from a series of experiments given the measured rates for various concentrations of reactants. (Section 14.3)
- Use the integrated form of a rate law to determine the concentration of a reactant at a given time. (Section 14.4)
- Explain how the activation energy affects a rate and be able to use the Arrhenius equation. (Section 14.5)
- Predict a rate law for a reaction having a multistep mechanism given the individual steps in the mechanism. (Section 14.6)
- Explain how a catalyst works. (Section 14.7)

## KEY EQUATIONS

- $\text{Rate} = -\dfrac{1}{a}\dfrac{\Delta[A]}{\Delta t} = -\dfrac{1}{b}\dfrac{\Delta[B]}{\Delta t} = \dfrac{1}{c}\dfrac{\Delta[C]}{\Delta t} = \dfrac{1}{d}\dfrac{\Delta[D]}{\Delta t}$  [14.4]  Relating rates to the components of the balanced chemical equation $a\,A + b\,B \longrightarrow c\,C + d\,D$

- $\text{Rate} = k[A]^m[B]^n$  [14.7]  General form of a rate law for the reaction $A + B \longrightarrow$ products

- $\ln[A]_t - \ln[A]_0 = -kt$  or  $\ln\dfrac{[A]_t}{[A]_0} = -kt$  [14.12]  The integrated form of a first-order rate law for the reaction $A \longrightarrow$ products

- $\dfrac{1}{[A]_t} = kt + \dfrac{1}{[A]_0}$  [14.14]  The integrated form of the second-order rate law for the reaction $A \longrightarrow$ products

- $t_{1/2} = \dfrac{0.693}{k}$  [14.15]  Relating the half-life and rate constant for a first-order reaction

- $k = Ae^{-E_a/RT}$  [14.19]  The Arrhenius equation, which expresses how the rate constant depends on temperature

- $\ln k = -\dfrac{E_a}{RT} + \ln A$  [14.20]  Linear form of the Arrhenius equation

# EXERCISES

## VISUALIZING CONCEPTS

**14.1** For which one of the following vessels for the reaction $A + B \longrightarrow C$ is the reaction the fastest? Assume all vessels are at the same temperature. [Section 4.1]

**14.2** Consider the following graph of the concentration of a substance over time. (**a**) Is X a reactant or product of the reaction? (**b**) Is the reaction speeding up, slowing down, or not changing its rate as time progresses? (**c**) Why is the average rate of the reaction different between points 1 and 2 than between points 2 and 3? [Section 14.2]

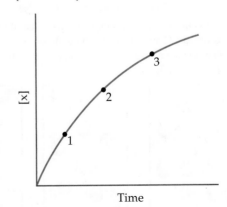

**14.3** You study the rate of a reaction, measuring both the concentration of the reactant and the concentration of the product as a function of time, and obtain the following results:

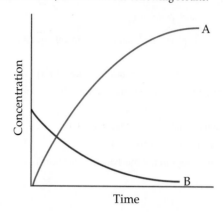

Which chemical equation is consistent with these data: (a) A $\longrightarrow$ B, (b) B $\longrightarrow$ A, (c) A $\longrightarrow$ 2 B, (d) B $\longrightarrow$ 2 A? Explain your choice. [Section 14.2]

**14.4** You perform the reaction K + L $\rightarrow$ M, monitor the production of M over time, and then plot this graph from your data:

(a) Is the reaction occurring at a constant rate from $t = 0$ to $t = 15$ min? Explain. (b) Is the reaction completed at $t = 15$ min? Explain.

**14.5** You perform a series of experiments for the reaction A $\longrightarrow$ B + C and find that the rate law has the form rate $= k[A]^x$. Determine the value of $x$ in each of the following cases: (a) There is no rate change when $[A]_0$ is tripled. (b) The rate increases by a factor of 9 when $[A]_0$ is tripled. (c) When $[A]_0$ is doubled, the rate increases by a factor of 8. [Section 14.3]

**14.6** The following diagrams represent mixtures of NO(g) and $O_2(g)$. These two substances react as follows:

$$2\,NO(g) + O_2(g) \longrightarrow 2\,NO_2(g)$$

It has been determined experimentally that the rate is second order in NO and first order in $O_2$. Based on this fact, which of the following mixtures will have the fastest initial rate? [Section 14.3]

(1)

(2)

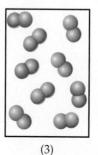

(3)

**14.7** A friend studies a first-order reaction and obtains the following three graphs for experiments done at two different temperatures. (a) Which two graphs represent experiments done at the same temperature? What accounts for the difference in these two graphs? In what way are they the same? (b) Which two graphs represent experiments done with the same starting concentration but at different temperatures? Which graph probably represents the lower temperature? How do you know? [Section 14.4]

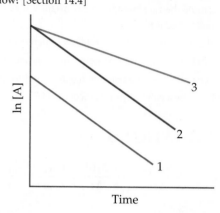

**14.8** (a) Given the following diagrams at $t = 0$ min and $t = 30$ min, what is the half-life of the reaction if it follows first-order kinetics?

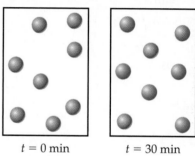

$t = 0$ min $\qquad$ $t = 30$ min

(b) After four half-life periods for a first-order reaction, what fraction of reactant remains? [Section 14.4]

**14.9** The following diagram shows the reaction profile of a reaction. Label the components indicated by the boxes. [Section 14.5]

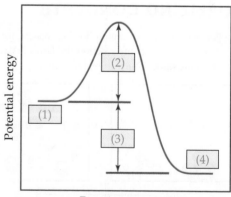

**14.10** You study the effect of temperature on the rate of two reactions and graph the natural logarithm of the rate constant for each reaction as a function of $1/T$. How do the two graphs compare (a) if the activation energy of the second reaction is higher than the activation energy of the first reaction but the two reactions have the same frequency factor, and (b) if the frequency factor of the second reaction is higher than the frequency factor of the first reaction but the two reactions have the same activation energy? [Section 14.5]

**14.11** The following graph shows two different reaction pathways for the same overall reaction at the same temperature. (a) Which pathway is slower? Why? (b) How can there be two different reaction pathways for the same reaction at the same temperature? Discuss. [Section 14.6]

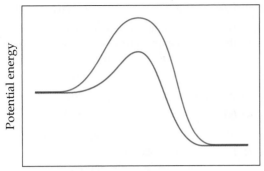

Reaction progress

**14.12** Consider the diagram that follows, which represents two steps in an overall reaction. The red spheres are oxygen, the blue ones nitrogen, and the green ones fluorine. (a) Write the chemical equation for each step in the reaction. (b) Write the equation for the overall reaction. (c) Identify the intermediate in the mechanism. (d) Write the rate law for the overall reaction if the first step is the slow, rate-determining step. [Section 14.6]

**14.13** Based on the following reaction profile, how many intermediates are formed in the reaction A ⟶ C? How many transition states are there? Which step is the fastest? Is the reaction A ⟶ C exothermic or endothermic? [Section 14.6]

Reaction progress

**14.14** Draw a possible transition state for the bimolecular reaction depicted here. (The blue spheres are nitrogen atoms, and the red ones are oxygen atoms.) Use dashed lines to represent the bonds that are in the process of being broken or made in the transition state. [Section 14.6]

**14.15** The following diagram represents an imaginary two-step mechanism. Let the red spheres represent element A, the green ones element B, and the blue ones element C. (a) Write the equation for the net reaction that is occurring. (b) Identify the intermediate. (c) Identify the catalyst. [Sections 14.6 and 14.7]

**14.16** Draw a graph showing the reaction pathway for an overall exothermic reaction with two intermediates that are produced at different rates. On your graph indicate the reactants, products, intermediates, transition states, and activation energies. [Sections 14.6 and 14.7]

# REACTION RATES (sections 14.1 and 14.2)

**14.17** (a) What is meant by the term *reaction rate*? (b) Name three factors that can affect the rate of a chemical reaction. (c) Is the rate of disappearance of reactants always the same as the rate of appearance of products? Explain.

**14.18** (a) What are the units usually used to express the rates of reactions occurring in solution? (b) From your everyday experience, give two examples of the effects of temperature on the rates of reactions. (c) What is the difference between average rate and instantaneous rate?

**14.19** Consider the following hypothetical aqueous reaction: $A(aq) \longrightarrow B(aq)$. A flask is charged with 0.065 mol of A in a total volume of 100.0 mL. The following data are collected:

| Time (min) | 0 | 10 | 20 | 30 | 40 |
|---|---|---|---|---|---|
| Moles of A | 0.065 | 0.051 | 0.042 | 0.036 | 0.031 |

(a) Calculate the number of moles of B at each time in the table, assuming that there are no molecules of B at time zero, and that A cleanly converts to B with no intermediates. (b) Calculate the average rate of disappearance of A for each 10-min interval in units of $M/s$. (c) Between $t = 10$ min and $t = 30$ min, what is the average rate of appearance of B in units of $M/s$? Assume that the volume of the solution is constant.

**14.20** A flask is charged with 0.100 mol of A and allowed to react to form B according to the hypothetical gas-phase reaction $A(g) \longrightarrow B(g)$. The following data are collected:

| Time (s) | 0 | 40 | 80 | 120 | 160 |
|---|---|---|---|---|---|
| Moles of A | 0.100 | 0.067 | 0.045 | 0.030 | 0.020 |

(a) Calculate the number of moles of B at each time in the table, assuming that A is cleanly converted to B with no intermediates. (b) Calculate the average rate of disappearance of A for each 40-s interval in units of mol/s. (c) What additional information would be needed to calculate the rate in units of concentration per time?

**14.21** The isomerization of methyl isonitrile ($CH_3NC$) to acetonitrile ($CH_3CN$) was studied in the gas phase at 215 °C, and the following data were obtained:

| Time (s) | [CH₃NC] (*M*) |
|----------|--------------|
| 0        | 0.0165       |
| 2,000    | 0.0110       |
| 5,000    | 0.00591      |
| 8,000    | 0.00314      |
| 12,000   | 0.00137      |
| 15,000   | 0.00074      |

(a) Calculate the average rate of reaction, in *M*/s, for the time interval between each measurement. (b) Calculate the average rate of reaction over the entire time of the data from $t = 0$ to $t = 15,000$ s. (c) Graph [CH₃NC] versus time and determine the instantaneous rates in *M*/s at $t = 5000$ s and $t = 8000$ s.

**14.22** The rate of disappearance of HCl was measured for the following reaction:

$$CH_3OH(aq) + HCl(aq) \longrightarrow CH_3Cl(aq) + H_2O(l)$$

The following data were collected:

| Time (min) | [HCl] (*M*) |
|-----------|-------------|
| 0.0       | 1.85        |
| 54.0      | 1.58        |
| 107.0     | 1.36        |
| 215.0     | 1.02        |
| 430.0     | 0.580       |

(a) Calculate the average rate of reaction, in *M*/s, for the time interval between each measurement. (b) Calculate the average rate of reaction for the entire time for the data from $t = 0.0$ min to $t = 430.0$ min.

(c) Graph [HCl] versus time and determine the instantaneous rates in *M*/min and *M*/s at $t = 75.0$ min and $t = 250$ min.

**14.23** For each of the following gas-phase reactions, indicate how the rate of disappearance of each reactant is related to the rate of appearance of each product:

(a) $H_2O_2(g) \longrightarrow H_2(g) + O_2(g)$

(b) $2 N_2O(g) \longrightarrow 2 N_2(g) + O_2(g)$

(c) $N_2(g) + 3 H_2(g) \longrightarrow 2 NH_3(g)$

(d) $C_2H_5NH_2(g) \longrightarrow C_2H_4(g) + NH_3(g)$

**14.24** For each of the following gas-phase reactions, write the rate expression in terms of the appearance of each product and disappearance of each reactant:

(a) $2 H_2O(g) \longrightarrow 2 H_2(g) + O_2(g)$

(b) $2 SO_2(g) + O_2(g) \longrightarrow 2 SO_3(g)$

(c) $2 NO(g) + 2 H_2(g) \longrightarrow N_2(g) + 2 H_2O(g)$

(d) $N_2(g) + 2 H_2(g) \longrightarrow N_2H_4(g)$

**14.25** (a) Consider the combustion of $H_2(g)$: $2 H_2(g) + O_2(g) \longrightarrow 2 H_2O(g)$. If hydrogen is burning at the rate of 0.48 mol/s, what is the rate of consumption of oxygen? What is the rate of formation of water vapor? (b) The reaction $2 NO(g) + Cl_2(g) \longrightarrow 2 NOCl(g)$ is carried out in a closed vessel. If the partial pressure of NO is decreasing at the rate of 56 torr/min, what is the rate of change of the total pressure of the vessel?

**14.26** (a) Consider the combustion of ethylene, $C_2H_4(g) + 3 O_2(g) \longrightarrow 2 CO_2(g) + 2 H_2O(g)$. If the concentration of $C_2H_4$ is decreasing at the rate of 0.036 *M*/s, what are the rates of change in the concentrations of $CO_2$ and $H_2O$? (b) The rate of decrease in $N_2H_4$ partial pressure in a closed reaction vessel from the reaction $N_2H_4(g) + H_2(g) \longrightarrow 2 NH_3(g)$ is 74 torr per hour. What are the rates of change of $NH_3$ partial pressure and total pressure in the vessel?

# RATE LAWS (section 14.3)

**14.27** A reaction A + B $\longrightarrow$ C obeys the following rate law: Rate $= k[B]^2$. (a) If [A] is doubled, how will the rate change? Will the rate constant change? Explain. (b) What are the reaction orders for A and B? What is the overall reaction order? (c) What are the units of the rate constant?

**14.28** Consider a hypothetical reaction between A, B, and C that is first order in A, zero order in B, and second order in C. (a) Write the rate law for the reaction. (b) How does the rate change when [A] is doubled and the other reactant concentrations are held constant? (c) How does the rate change when [B] is tripled and the other reactant concentrations are held constant? (d) How does the rate change when [C] is tripled and the other reactant concentrations are held constant? (e) By what factor does the rate change when the concentrations of all three reactants are tripled? (f) By what factor does the rate change when the concentrations of all three reactants are cut in half?

**14.29** The decomposition reaction of $N_2O_5$ in carbon tetrachloride is $2 N_2O_5 \longrightarrow 4 NO_2 + O_2$. The rate law is first order in $N_2O_5$. At 64 °C the rate constant is $4.82 \times 10^{-3}$ s$^{-1}$. (a) Write the rate law for the reaction. (b) What is the rate of reaction when $[N_2O_5] = 0.0240\ M$? (c) What happens to the rate when the concentration of $N_2O_5$ is doubled to $0.0480\ M$? (d) What happens to the rate when the concentration of $N_2O_5$ is halved to $0.0120\ M$?

**14.30** Consider the following reaction:

$$2 NO(g) + 2 H_2(g) \longrightarrow N_2(g) + 2 H_2O(g)$$

(a) The rate law for this reaction is first order in $H_2$ and second order in NO. Write the rate law. (b) If the rate constant for this reaction at 1000 K is $6.0 \times 10^4\ M^{-2} s^{-1}$, what is the reaction rate when $[NO] = 0.035\ M$ and $[H_2] = 0.015\ M$? (c) What is the reaction rate at 1000 K when the concentration of NO is increased to $0.10\ M$, while the concentration of $H_2$ is $0.010\ M$?

**(d)** What is the reaction rate at 1000 K if [NO] is decreased to 0.010 $M$ and [$H_2$] is increased to 0.030 $M$?

**14.31** Consider the following reaction:

$$CH_3Br(aq) + OH^-(aq) \longrightarrow CH_3OH(aq) + Br^-(aq)$$

The rate law for this reaction is first order in $CH_3Br$ and first order in $OH^-$. When [$CH_3Br$] is $5.0 \times 10^{-3}$ $M$ and [$OH^-$] is 0.050 $M$, the reaction rate at 298 K is 0.0432 $M/s$. **(a)** What is the value of the rate constant? **(b)** What are the units of the rate constant? **(c)** What would happen to the rate if the concentration of $OH^-$ were tripled? **(d)** What would happen to the rate if the concentration of both reactants were tripled?

**14.32** The reaction between ethyl bromide ($C_2H_5Br$) and hydroxide ion in ethyl alcohol at 330 K, $C_2H_5Br(alc) + OH^-(alc) \longrightarrow C_2H_5OH(l) + Br^-(alc)$, is first order each in ethyl bromide and hydroxide ion. When [$C_2H_5Br$] is 0.0477 $M$ and [$OH^-$] is 0.100 $M$, the rate of disappearance of ethyl bromide is $1.7 \times 10^{-7}$ $M/s$. **(a)** What is the value of the rate constant? **(b)** What are the units of the rate constant? **(c)** How would the rate of disappearance of ethyl bromide change if the solution were diluted by adding an equal volume of pure ethyl alcohol to the solution?

**14.33** The iodide ion reacts with hypochlorite ion (the active ingredient in chlorine bleaches) in the following way: $OCl^- + I^- \longrightarrow OI^- + Cl^-$. This rapid reaction gives the following rate data:

| [$OCl^-$] ($M$) | [$I^-$] ($M$) | Initial Rate ($M/s$) |
|---|---|---|
| $1.5 \times 10^{-3}$ | $1.5 \times 10^{-3}$ | $1.36 \times 10^{-4}$ |
| $3.0 \times 10^{-3}$ | $1.5 \times 10^{-3}$ | $2.72 \times 10^{-4}$ |
| $1.5 \times 10^{-3}$ | $3.0 \times 10^{-3}$ | $2.72 \times 10^{-4}$ |

**(a)** Write the rate law for this reaction. **(b)** Calculate the rate constant with proper units. **(c)** Calculate the rate when [$OCl^-$] = $2.0 \times 10^{-3}$ $M$ and [$I^-$] = $5.0 \times 10^{-4}$ $M$.

**14.34** The reaction $2 ClO_2(aq) + 2 OH^-(aq) \longrightarrow ClO_3^-(aq) + ClO_2^-(aq) + H_2O(l)$ was studied with the following results:

| Experiment | [$ClO_2$] ($M$) | [$OH^-$] ($M$) | Initial Rate ($M/s$) |
|---|---|---|---|
| 1 | 0.060 | 0.030 | 0.0248 |
| 2 | 0.020 | 0.030 | 0.00276 |
| 3 | 0.020 | 0.090 | 0.00828 |

**(a)** Determine the rate law for the reaction. **(b)** Calculate the rate constant with proper units. **(c)** Calculate the rate when [$ClO_2$] = 0.100 $M$ and [$OH^-$] = 0.050 $M$.

**14.35** The following data were measured for the reaction $BF_3(g) + NH_3(g) \longrightarrow F_3BNH_3(g)$:

| Experiment | [$BF_3$] ($M$) | [$NH_3$] ($M$) | Initial Rate ($M/s$) |
|---|---|---|---|
| 1 | 0.250 | 0.250 | 0.2130 |
| 2 | 0.250 | 0.125 | 0.1065 |
| 3 | 0.200 | 0.100 | 0.0682 |
| 4 | 0.350 | 0.100 | 0.1193 |
| 5 | 0.175 | 0.100 | 0.0596 |

**(a)** What is the rate law for the reaction? **(b)** What is the overall order of the reaction? **(c)** Calculate the rate constant with proper units? **(d)** What is the rate when [$BF_3$] = 0.100 $M$ and [$NH_3$] = 0.500 $M$?

**14.36** The following data were collected for the rate of disappearance of NO in the reaction $2 NO(g) + O_2(g) \longrightarrow 2 NO_2(g)$:

| Experiment | [NO] ($M$) | [$O_2$] ($M$) | Initial Rate ($M/s$) |
|---|---|---|---|
| 1 | 0.0126 | 0.0125 | $1.41 \times 10^{-2}$ |
| 2 | 0.0252 | 0.0125 | $5.64 \times 10^{-2}$ |
| 3 | 0.0252 | 0.0250 | $1.13 \times 10^{-1}$ |

**(a)** What is the rate law for the reaction? **(b)** What are the units of the rate constant? **(c)** What is the average value of the rate constant calculated from the three data sets? **(d)** What is the rate of disappearance of NO when [NO] = 0.0750 $M$ and [$O_2$] = 0.0100 $M$? **(e)** What is the rate of disappearance of $O_2$ at the concentrations given in part (d)?

**[14.37]** Consider the gas-phase reaction between nitric oxide and bromine at 273 °C: $2 NO(g) + Br_2(g) \longrightarrow 2 NOBr(g)$. The following data for the initial rate of appearance of NOBr were obtained:

| Experiment | [NO] ($M$) | [$Br_2$] ($M$) | Initial Rate ($M/s$) |
|---|---|---|---|
| 1 | 0.10 | 0.20 | 24 |
| 2 | 0.25 | 0.20 | 150 |
| 3 | 0.10 | 0.50 | 60 |
| 4 | 0.35 | 0.50 | 735 |

**(a)** Determine the rate law. **(b)** Calculate the average value of the rate constant for the appearance of NOBr from the four data sets. **(c)** How is the rate of appearance of NOBr related to the rate of disappearance of $Br_2$? **(d)** What is the rate of disappearance of $Br_2$ when [NO] = 0.075 $M$ and [$Br_2$] = 0.25 $M$?

**[14.38]** Consider the reaction of peroxydisulfate ion ($S_2O_8^{2-}$) with iodide ion ($I^-$) in aqueous solution:

$$S_2O_8^{2-}(aq) + 3 I^-(aq) \longrightarrow 2 SO_4^{2-}(aq) + I_3^-(aq)$$

At a particular temperature the initial rate of disappearance of $S_2O_8^{2-}$ varies with reactant concentrations in the following manner:

| Experiment | [$S_2O_8^{2-}$] ($M$) | [$I^-$] ($M$) | Initial Rate ($M/s$) |
|---|---|---|---|
| 1 | 0.018 | 0.036 | $2.6 \times 10^{-6}$ |
| 2 | 0.027 | 0.036 | $3.9 \times 10^{-6}$ |
| 3 | 0.036 | 0.054 | $7.8 \times 10^{-6}$ |
| 4 | 0.050 | 0.072 | $1.4 \times 10^{-5}$ |

**(a)** Determine the rate law for the reaction and state the units of the rate constant. **(b)** What is the average value of the rate constant for the disappearance of $S_2O_8^{2-}$ based on the four sets of data? **(c)** How is the rate of disappearance of $S_2O_8^{2-}$ related to the rate of disappearance of $I^-$? **(d)** What is the rate of disappearance of $I^-$ when [$S_2O_8^{2-}$] = 0.025 $M$ and [$I^-$] = 0.050 $M$?

# CHANGE OF CONCENTRATION WITH TIME (section 14.4)

**14.39** (a) Define the following symbols that are encountered in rate equations for the generic reaction A $\longrightarrow$ B: $[A]_0$, $t_{1/2}$ $[A]_t$, $k$. (b) What quantity, when graphed versus time, will yield a straight line for a first-order reaction? (c) How can you calculate the rate constant for a first-order reaction from the graph you made in part (b)?

**14.40** (a) For a generic second-order reaction A $\longrightarrow$ B, what quantity, when graphed versus time, will yield a straight line? (b) What is the slope of the straight line from part (a)? (c) How do the half-lives of first-order and second-order reactions differ?

**14.41** For the generic reaction A $\longrightarrow$ B that is zero order in A, what would you graph in order to obtain the rate constant?

**14.42** Sketch a graph for the generic first-order reaction A $\longrightarrow$ B that has concentration of A on the vertical axis and time on the horizontal axis. (a) Is this graph linear? Explain. (b) Indicate on your graph the half-life for the reaction.

**14.43** (a) The gas-phase decomposition of $SO_2Cl_2$, $SO_2Cl_2(g)$ $\longrightarrow$ $SO_2(g)$ + $Cl_2(g)$, is first order in $SO_2Cl_2$. At 600 K the half-life for this process is $2.3 \times 10^5$ s. What is the rate constant at this temperature? (b) At 320 °C the rate constant is $2.2 \times 10^{-5}\,s^{-1}$. What is the half-life at this temperature?

**14.44** Molecular iodine, $I_2(g)$, dissociates into iodine atoms at 625 K with a first-order rate constant of $0.271\,s^{-1}$. (a) What is the half-life for this reaction? (b) If you start with 0.050 $M$ $I_2$ at this temperature, how much will remain after 5.12 s assuming that the iodine atoms do not recombine to form $I_2$?

**14.45** As described in Exercise 14.43, the decomposition of sulfuryl chloride ($SO_2Cl_2$) is a first-order process. The rate constant for the decomposition at 660 K is $4.5 \times 10^{-2}\,s^{-1}$. (a) If we begin with an initial $SO_2Cl_2$ pressure of 450 torr, what is the pressure of this substance after 60 s? (b) At what time will the pressure of $SO_2Cl_2$ decline to one-tenth its initial value?

**14.46** The first-order rate constant for the decomposition of $N_2O_5$, $2\,N_2O_5(g)$ $\longrightarrow$ $4\,NO_2(g)$ + $O_2(g)$, at 70 °C is $6.82 \times 10^{-3}\,s^{-1}$. Suppose we start with 0.0250 mol of $N_2O_5(g)$ in a volume of 2.0 L. (a) How many moles of $N_2O_5$ will remain after 5.0 min? (b) How many minutes will it take for the quantity of $N_2O_5$ to drop to 0.010 mol? (c) What is the half-life of $N_2O_5$ at 70 °C ?

**14.47** The reaction

$$SO_2Cl_2(g) \longrightarrow SO_2(g) + Cl_2(g)$$

is first order in $SO_2Cl_2$. Using the following kinetic data, determine the magnitude and units of the first-order rate constant:

| Time (s) | Pressure $SO_2Cl_2$ (atm) |
|---|---|
| 0 | 1.000 |
| 2,500 | 0.947 |
| 5,000 | 0.895 |
| 7,500 | 0.848 |
| 10,000 | 0.803 |

**14.48** From the following data for the first-order gas-phase isomerization of $CH_3NC$ at 215 °C, calculate the first-order rate constant and half-life for the reaction:

| Time (s) | Pressure $CH_3NC$ (torr) |
|---|---|
| 0 | 502 |
| 2,000 | 335 |
| 5,000 | 180 |
| 8,000 | 95.5 |
| 12,000 | 41.7 |
| 15,000 | 22.4 |

**14.49** Consider the data presented in Exercise 14.19. (a) By using appropriate graphs, determine whether the reaction is first order or second order. (b) What is the rate constant for the reaction? (c) What is the half-life for the reaction?

**14.50** Consider the data presented in Exercise 14.20. (a) Determine whether the reaction is first order or second order. (b) What is the rate constant? (c) What is the half-life?

**14.51** The gas-phase decomposition of $NO_2$, $2\,NO_2(g)$ $\longrightarrow$ $2\,NO(g)$ + $O_2(g)$, is studied at 383 °C, giving the following data:

| Time (s) | $[NO_2]$ ($M$) |
|---|---|
| 0.0 | 0.100 |
| 5.0 | 0.017 |
| 10.0 | 0.0090 |
| 15.0 | 0.0062 |
| 20.0 | 0.0047 |

(a) Is the reaction first order or second order with respect to the concentration of $NO_2$? (b) What is the rate constant? (c) If you used the method of initial rates to obtain the order for $NO_2$, predict what reaction rates you would measure in the beginning of the reaction for initial concentrations of 0.200 $M$, 0.100 $M$, and 0.050 $M$ $NO_2$.

**14.52** Sucrose ($C_{12}H_{22}O_{11}$), commonly known as table sugar, reacts in dilute acid solutions to form two simpler sugars, glucose and fructose, both of which have the formula $C_6H_{12}O_6$. At 23 °C and in 0.5 $M$ HCl, the following data were obtained for the disappearance of sucrose:

| Time (min) | $[C_{12}H_{22}O_{11}]$ ($M$) |
|---|---|
| 0 | 0.316 |
| 39 | 0.274 |
| 80 | 0.238 |
| 140 | 0.190 |
| 210 | 0.146 |

(a) Is the reaction first order or second order with respect to $[C_{12}H_{22}O_{11}]$? (b) What is the rate constant? (c) Using this rate constant, calculate the concentration of sucrose at 39, 80, 140, and 210 min if the initial sucrose concentration was 0.316 $M$ and the reaction was zero order in sucrose.

# TEMPERATURE AND RATE (section 14.5)

**14.53** (a) What factors determine whether a collision between two molecules will lead to a chemical reaction? (b) According to the collision model, why does temperature affect the value of the rate constant? (c) Does the rate constant for a reaction generally increase or decrease with an increase in reaction temperature?

**14.54** (a) In which of the following reactions would you expect the orientation factor to be least important in leading to reaction: $NO + O \longrightarrow NO_2$ or $H + Cl \longrightarrow HCl$? (b) How does the kinetic-molecular theory help us understand the temperature dependence of chemical reactions?

**14.55** Calculate the fraction of atoms in a sample of argon gas at 400 K that has an energy of 10.0 kJ or greater.

**14.56** (a) The activation energy for the isomerization of methyl isonitrile (Figure 14.7) is 160 kJ/mol. Calculate the fraction of methyl isonitrile molecules that has an energy of 160.0 kJ or greater at 500 K. (b) Calculate this fraction for a temperature of 520 K. What is the ratio of the fraction at 520 K to that at 500 K?

**14.57** The gas-phase reaction $Cl(g) + HBr(g) \longrightarrow HCl(g) + Br(g)$ has an overall enthalpy change of $-66$ kJ. The activation energy for the reaction is 7 kJ. (a) Sketch the energy profile for the reaction, and label $E_a$ and $\Delta E$. (b) What is the activation energy for the reverse reaction?

**14.58** For the elementary process $N_2O_5(g) \longrightarrow NO_2(g) + NO_3(g)$ the activation energy $(E_a)$ and overall $\Delta E$ are 154 kJ/mol and 136 kJ/mol, respectively. (a) Sketch the energy profile for this reaction, and label $E_a$ and $\Delta E$. (b) What is the activation energy for the reverse reaction?

**14.59** Indicate whether each statement is true or false. If it is false, rewrite it so that it is true.
(a) If you compare two reactions with similar collision factors, the one with the larger activation energy will be faster.
(b) A reaction that has a small rate constant must have a small frequency factor.
(c) Increasing the reaction temperature increases the fraction of successful collisions between reactants.

**14.60** Indicate whether each statement is true or false. If it is false, rewrite it so that it is true.
(a) If you measure the rate constant for a reaction at different temperatures, you can calculate the overall enthalpy change for the reaction.
(b) Exothermic reactions are faster than endothermic reactions.
(c) If you double the temperature for a reaction, you cut the activation energy in half.

**14.61** Based on their activation energies and energy changes and assuming that all collision factors are the same, which of the following reactions would be fastest and which would be slowest? Explain your answer.
(a) $E_a = 45$ kJ/mol; $\Delta E = -25$ kJ/mol
(b) $E_a = 35$ kJ/mol; $\Delta E = -10$ kJ/mol
(c) $E_a = 55$ kJ/mol; $\Delta E = 10$ kJ/mol

**14.62** Which of the reactions in Exercise 14.61 will be fastest in the reverse direction? Which will be slowest? Explain.

**14.63** (a) A certain first-order reaction has a rate constant of $2.75 \times 10^{-2}\,s^{-1}$ at 20 °C. What is the value of $k$ at 60 °C if $E_a = 75.5$ kJ/mol? (b) Another first-order reaction also has a rate constant of $2.75 \times 10^{-2}\,s^{-1}$ at 20 °C. What is the value of $k$ at 60 °C if $E_a = 125$ kJ/mol? (c) What assumptions do you need to make in order to calculate answers for parts (a) and (b)?

**14.64** Understanding the high-temperature behavior of nitrogen oxides is essential for controlling pollution generated in automobile engines. The decomposition of nitric oxide (NO) to $N_2$ and $O_2$ is second order with a rate constant of $0.0796\,M^{-1}\,s^{-1}$ at 737 °C and $0.0815\,M^{-1}\,s^{-1}$ at 947 °C. Calculate the activation energy for the reaction.

**14.65** The rate of the reaction
$$CH_3COOC_2H_5(aq) + OH^-(aq) \longrightarrow$$
$$CH_3COO^-(aq) + C_2H_5OH(aq)$$
was measured at several temperatures, and the following data were collected:

| Temperature (°C) | $k\ (M^{-1}\,s^{-1})$ |
|---|---|
| 15 | 0.0521 |
| 25 | 0.101 |
| 35 | 0.184 |
| 45 | 0.332 |

Calculate the value of $E_a$ by constructing an appropriate graph.

**14.66** The temperature dependence of the rate constant for a reaction is tabulated as follows:

| Temperature (K) | $k\ (M^{-1}\,s^{-1})$ |
|---|---|
| 600 | 0.028 |
| 650 | 0.22 |
| 700 | 1.3 |
| 750 | 6.0 |
| 800 | 23 |

Calculate $E_a$ and $A$.

**[14.67]** The activation energy of a certain reaction is 65.7 kJ/mol. How many times faster will the reaction occur at 50 °C than at 0 °C? State the assumptions you need to make in order to perform this calculation.

**[14.68]** The following is a quote from an article in the August 18, 1998, issue of *The New York Times* about the breakdown of cellulose and starch: "A drop of 18 degrees Fahrenheit [from 77 °F to 59 °F] lowers the reaction rate six times; a 36-degree drop [from 77 °F to 41 °F] produces a fortyfold decrease in the rate." (a) Calculate activation energies for the breakdown process based on the two estimates of the effect of temperature on rate. Are the values consistent? (b) Assuming the value of $E_a$ calculated from the 36-degree drop and that the rate of breakdown is first order with a half-life at 25 °C of 2.7 years, calculate the half-life for breakdown at a temperature of $-15$ °C.

# REACTION MECHANISMS (section 14.6)

**14.69** **(a)** What is meant by the term *elementary reaction*? **(b)** What is the difference between a *unimolecular* and a *bimolecular* elementary reaction? **(c)** What is a *reaction mechanism*?

**14.70** **(a)** What is meant by the term *molecularity*? **(b)** Why are termolecular elementary reactions so rare? **(c)** What is an *intermediate* in a mechanism?

**14.71** What are the differences between an intermediate and a transition state?

**14.72** What is meant by the term *rate-determining step*?

**14.73** What is the molecularity of each of the following elementary reactions? Write the rate law for each.
**(a)** $Cl_2(g) \longrightarrow 2\,Cl(g)$
**(b)** $OCl^-(aq) + H_2O(l) \longrightarrow HOCl(aq) + OH^-(aq)$
**(c)** $NO(g) + Cl_2(g) \longrightarrow NOCl_2(g)$

**14.74** What is the molecularity of each of the following elementary reactions? Write the rate law for each.
**(a)** $2\,NO(g) \longrightarrow N_2O_2(g)$
**(b)** $H_2C \overset{\displaystyle CH_2}{\frown} CH_2(g) \longrightarrow CH_2{=}CH{-}CH_3(g)$
**(c)** $SO_3(g) \longrightarrow SO_2(g) + O(g)$

**14.75** **(a)** Based on the following reaction profile, how many intermediates are formed in the reaction A $\longrightarrow$ D? **(b)** How many transition states are there? **(c)** Which step is the fastest? **(d)** Is the reaction A $\longrightarrow$ D exothermic or endothermic?

Reaction progress

**14.76** Consider the following energy profile.

Reaction progess

**(a)** How many elementary reactions are in the reaction mechanism? **(b)** How many intermediates are formed in the reaction? **(c)** Which step is rate limiting? **(d)** Is the overall reaction exothermic or endothermic?

**14.77** The following mechanism has been proposed for the gas-phase reaction of $H_2$ with $ICl$:
$$H_2(g) + ICl(g) \longrightarrow HI(g) + HCl(g)$$
$$HI(g) + ICl(g) \longrightarrow I_2(g) + HCl(g)$$
**(a)** Write the balanced equation for the overall reaction. **(b)** Identify any intermediates in the mechanism. **(c)** If the first step is slow and the second one is fast, which rate law do you expect to be observed for the overall reaction?

**14.78** The decomposition of hydrogen peroxide is catalyzed by iodide ion. The catalyzed reaction is thought to proceed by a two-step mechanism:
$$H_2O_2(aq) + I^-(aq) \longrightarrow H_2O(l) + IO^-(aq) \quad \text{(slow)}$$
$$IO^-(aq) + H_2O_2(aq) \longrightarrow H_2O(l) + O_2(g) + I^-(aq) \quad \text{(fast)}$$
**(a)** Write the chemical equation for the overall process. **(b)** Identify the intermediate, if any, in the mechanism. **(c)** Assuming that the first step of the mechanism is rate determining, predict the rate law for the overall process.

**14.79** The reaction $2\,NO(g) + Cl_2(g) \longrightarrow 2\,NOCl(g)$ was performed and the following data obtained:

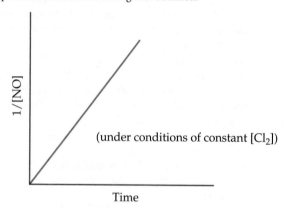

(under conditions of constant $[Cl_2]$)

Is the following mechanism consistent with the data? Explain.
$$NO(g) + Cl_2(g) \longrightarrow NOCl_2(g)$$
$$NOCl_2(g) + NO(g) \longrightarrow 2\,NOCl(g)$$

**14.80** You have studied the gas-phase oxidation of HBr by $O_2$:
$$4\,HBr(g) + O_2(g) \longrightarrow 2\,H_2O(g) + 2\,Br_2(g)$$
You find the reaction to be first order with respect to HBr and first order with respect to $O_2$. You propose the following mechanism:
$$HBr(g) + O_2(g) \longrightarrow HOOBr(g)$$
$$HOOBr(g) + HBr(g) \longrightarrow 2\,HOBr(g)$$
$$HOBr(g) + HBr(g) \longrightarrow H_2O(g) + Br_2(g)$$
**(a)** Confirm that the elementary reactions add to give the overall reaction. **(b)** Based on the experimentally determined rate law, which step is rate determining? **(c)** What are the intermediates in this mechanism? **(d)** If you are unable to detect HOBr or HOOBr among the products, does this disprove your mechanism?

# CATALYSIS (section 14.7)

**14.81** (a) What is a catalyst? (b) What is the difference between a homogeneous and a heterogeneous catalyst? (c) Do catalysts affect the overall enthalpy change for a reaction, the activation energy, or both?

**14.82** (a) Most commercial heterogeneous catalysts are extremely finely divided solid materials. Why is particle size important? (b) What role does adsorption play in the action of a heterogeneous catalyst?

**[14.83]** Platinum nanoparticles of diameter ~2 nm are important catalysts in carbon monoxide oxidation to carbon dioxide. Platinum crystallizes in a face-centered cubic arrangement with an edge length of 3.924 Å. (a) Estimate how many platinum atoms would fit into a 2.0-nm sphere; the volume of a sphere is $(4/3)\pi r^3$. Recall that $1\text{Å} = 1 \times 10^{-10}$ m and $1$ nm $= 1 \times 10^{-9}$ m. (b) Estimate how many platinum atoms are on the surface of a 2.0-nm Pt sphere, using the surface area of a sphere $(4\pi r^2)$ and assuming that the "footprint" of one Pt atom can be estimated from its atomic diameter of 2.8 Å. (c) Using your results from (a) and (b), calculate the percentage of Pt atoms that are on the surface of a 2.0-nm nanoparticle. (d) Repeat these calculations for a 5.0-nm platinum nanoparticle. (e) Which size of nanoparticle would you expect to be more catalytically active and why?

**14.84** In solution, chemical species as simple as $H^+$ and $OH^-$ can serve as catalysts for reactions. Imagine you could measure the $[H^+]$ of a solution containing an acid-catalyzed reaction as it occurs. Assume the reactants and products themselves are neither acids nor bases. Sketch the $[H^+]$ concentration profile you would measure as a function of time for the reaction, assuming $t = 0$ is when you add a drop of acid to the reaction.

**14.85** The oxidation of $SO_2$ to $SO_3$ is catalyzed by $NO_2$. The reaction proceeds according to:

$$NO_2(g) + SO_2(g) \longrightarrow NO(g) + SO_3(g)$$
$$2\,NO(g) + O_2(g) \longrightarrow 2\,NO_2(g)$$

(a) Show that the two reactions can be summed to give the overall oxidation of $SO_2$ by $O_2$ to give $SO_3$. (b) Why do we consider $NO_2$ a catalyst and not an intermediate in this reaction? (c) Is this an example of homogeneous catalysis or heterogeneous catalysis?

**14.86** NO catalyzes the decomposition of $N_2O$, possibly by the following mechanism:

$$NO(g) + N_2O(g) \longrightarrow N_2(g) + NO_2(g)$$
$$2\,NO_2(g) \longrightarrow 2\,NO(g) + O_2(g)$$

(a) What is the chemical equation for the overall reaction? Show how the two steps can be added to give the overall equation. (b) Why is NO considered a catalyst and not an intermediate? (c) If experiments show that during the decomposition of $N_2O$, $NO_2$ does not accumulate in measurable quantities, does this rule out the proposed mechanism? If you think not, suggest what might be going on.

**14.87** Many metallic catalysts, particularly the precious-metal ones, are often deposited as very thin films on a substance of high surface area per unit mass, such as alumina ($Al_2O_3$) or silica ($SiO_2$). (a) Why is this an effective way of utilizing the catalyst material compared to having powdered metals? (b) How does the surface area affect the rate of reaction?

**14.88** (a) If you were going to build a system to check the effectiveness of automobile catalytic converters on cars, what substances would you want to look for in the car exhaust? (b) Automobile catalytic converters have to work at high temperatures, as hot exhaust gases stream through them. In what ways could this be an advantage? In what ways a disadvantage? (c) Why is the rate of flow of exhaust gases over a catalytic converter important?

**14.89** When $D_2$ reacts with ethylene ($C_2H_4$) in the presence of a finely divided catalyst, ethane with two deuteriums, $CH_2D$—$CH_2D$, is formed. (Deuterium, D, is an isotope of hydrogen of mass 2). Very little ethane forms in which two deuteriums are bound to one carbon (for example, $CH_3$—$CHD_2$). Use the sequence of steps involved in the reaction (Figure 14.24) to explain why this is so.

**14.90** Heterogeneous catalysts that perform hydrogenation reactions, as illustrated in Figure 14.24, are subject to "poisoning," which shuts down their catalytic ability. Compounds of sulfur are often poisons. Suggest a mechanism by which such compounds might act as poisons.

**14.91** (a) Explain the importance of enzymes in biological systems. (b) What chemical transformations are catalyzed (*i*) by the enzyme catalase, (*ii*) by nitrogenase? (c) Many enzymes follow this generic reaction mechanism, where E is enzyme, S is substrate, ES is the enzyme-substrate complex (where the substrate is bound to the enzyme's active site), and P is the product:

1. $E + S \rightleftharpoons ES$

2. $ES \longrightarrow E + P$

What assumptions are made in this model with regard to the rate of the bound substrate being chemically transformed into bound product in the active site?

**14.92** There are literally thousands of enzymes at work in complex living systems such as human beings. What properties of enzymes give rise to their ability to distinguish one substrate from another?

**14.93** The enzyme carbonic anhydrase catalyzes the reaction $CO_2(g) + H_2O(l) \longrightarrow HCO_3^-(aq) + H^+(aq)$. In water, without the enzyme, the reaction proceeds with a rate constant of $0.039$ s$^{-1}$ at 25 °C. In the presence of the enzyme in water, the reaction proceeds with a rate constant of $1.0 \times 10^6$ s$^{-1}$ at 25 °C. Assuming the collision factor is the same for both situations, calculate the difference in activation energies for the uncatalyzed versus enzyme-catalyzed reaction.

**14.94** The enzyme urease catalyzes the reaction of urea, ($NH_2CONH_2$), with water to produce carbon dioxide and ammonia. In water, without the enzyme, the reaction proceeds with a first-order rate constant of $4.15 \times 10^{-5}$ s$^{-1}$ at 100 °C. In the presence of the enzyme in water, the reaction proceeds with a rate constant of $3.4 \times 10^4$ s$^{-1}$ at 21 °C. (a) Write out the balanced equation for the reaction catalyzed by urease. (b) Assuming the collision factor is the same for both situations, estimate the difference in activation energies for the uncatalyzed versus enzyme-catalyzed reaction.

**[14.95]** The activation energy of an uncatalyzed reaction is 95 kJ/mol. The addition of a catalyst lowers the activation energy to 55 kJ/mol. Assuming that the collision factor remains the same, by what factor will the catalyst increase the rate of the reaction at (a) 25 °C, (b) 125 °C?

[14.96] Suppose that a certain biologically important reaction is quite slow at physiological temperature (37 °C) in the absence of a catalyst. Assuming that the collision factor remains the same, by how much must an enzyme lower the activation energy of the reaction in order to achieve a $1 \times 10^5$-fold increase in the reaction rate?

## ADDITIONAL EXERCISES

14.97 Explain why rate laws generally cannot be written from balanced equations. Under what circumstance is the rate law related directly to the balanced equation for a reaction?

14.98 Hydrogen sulfide ($H_2S$) is a common and troublesome pollutant in industrial wastewaters. One way to remove $H_2S$ is to treat the water with chlorine, in which case the following reaction occurs:

$$H_2S(aq) + Cl_2(aq) \longrightarrow S(s) + 2 H^+(aq) + 2 Cl^-(aq)$$

The rate of this reaction is first order in each reactant. The rate constant for the disappearance of $H_2S$ at 28 °C is $3.5 \times 10^{-2} M^{-1} s^{-1}$. If at a given time the concentration of $H_2S$ is $2.0 \times 10^{-4} M$ and that of $Cl_2$ is 0.025 $M$, what is the rate of formation of $Cl^-$?

14.99 The reaction $2 NO(g) + O_2(g) \longrightarrow 2 NO_2(g)$ is second order in NO and first order in $O_2$. When [NO] = 0.040 $M$ and [$O_2$] = 0.035 $M$, the observed rate of disappearance of NO is $9.3 \times 10^{-5} M/s$. (a) What is the rate of disappearance of $O_2$ at this moment? (b) What is the value of the rate constant? (c) What are the units of the rate constant? (d) What would happen to the rate if the concentration of NO were increased by a factor of 1.8?

14.100 Consider the following reaction between mercury(II) chloride and oxalate ion:

$$2 HgCl_2(aq) + C_2O_4{}^{2-}(aq) \longrightarrow$$
$$2 Cl^-(aq) + 2 CO_2(g) + Hg_2Cl_2(s)$$

The initial rate of this reaction was determined for several concentrations of $HgCl_2$ and $C_2O_4{}^{2-}$, and the following rate data were obtained for the rate of disappearance of $C_2O_4{}^{2-}$:

| Experiment | [HgCl₂] (M) | [C₂O₄²⁻] (M) | Rate (M/s) |
|---|---|---|---|
| 1 | 0.164 | 0.15 | $3.2 \times 10^{-5}$ |
| 2 | 0.164 | 0.45 | $2.9 \times 10^{-4}$ |
| 3 | 0.082 | 0.45 | $1.4 \times 10^{-4}$ |
| 4 | 0.246 | 0.15 | $4.8 \times 10^{-5}$ |

(a) What is the rate law for this reaction? (b) What is the value of the rate constant with proper units? (c) What is the reaction rate when the initial concentration of $HgCl_2$ is 0.100 $M$ and that of ($C_2O_4{}^{2-}$) is 0.25 $M$ if the temperature is the same as that used to obtain the data shown?

14.101 The reaction $2 NO_2 \longrightarrow 2 NO + O_2$ has the rate constant $k = 0.63 M^{-1} s^{-1}$. Based on the units for $k$, is the reaction first or second order in $NO_2$? If the initial concentration of $NO_2$ is 0.100 $M$, how would you determine how long it would take for the concentration to decrease to 0.025 $M$?

14.102 Consider two reactions. Reaction (1) has a constant half-life, whereas reaction (2) has a half-life that gets longer as the reaction proceeds. What can you conclude about the rate laws of these reactions from these observations?

[14.103] When chemists are performing kinetics experiments, the general rule of thumb is to allow the reaction to proceed for 4 half-lives. (a) Explain how you would be able to tell that the reaction has proceeded for 4 half-lives. (b) Let us suppose a reaction A ⟶ B takes 6 days to proceed for 4 half-lives and is first order in A. However, when your lab partner performs this reaction for the first time, he does not realize how long it takes, and he stops taking kinetic data, monitoring the loss of A, after only 2 hours. Your lab partner concludes the reaction is zero order in A based on the data. Sketch a graph of [A] versus time to convince your lab partner the two of you need to be in the lab for a few days to obtain the proper rate law for the reaction.

14.104 (a) The reaction $H_2O_2(aq) \longrightarrow H_2O(l) + \frac{1}{2} O_2(g)$ is first order. Near room temperature, the rate constant equals $7.0 \times 10^{-4} s^{-1}$. Calculate the half-life at this temperature. (b) At 415 °C, $(CH_2)_2O$ decomposes in the gas phase, $(CH_2)_2O(g) \longrightarrow CH_4(g) + CO(g)$. If the reaction is first order with a half-life of 56.3 min at this temperature, calculate the rate constant in $s^{-1}$.

14.105 Americium-241 is used in smoke detectors. It has a first order rate constant for radioactive decay of $k = 1.6 \times 10^{-3} yr^{-1}$. By contrast, iodine-125, which is used to test for thyroid functioning, has a rate constant for radioactive decay of $k = 0.011 day^{-1}$. (a) What are the half-lives of these two isotopes? (b) Which one decays at a faster rate? (c) How much of a 1.00-mg sample of each isotope remains after 3 half-lives? (d) How much of a 1.00-mg sample of each isotope remains after 4 days?

14.106 Urea ($NH_2CONH_2$) is the end product in protein metabolism in animals. The decomposition of urea in 0.1 $M$ HCl occurs according to the reaction

$$NH_2CONH_2(aq) + H^+(aq) + 2 H_2O(l) \longrightarrow$$
$$2 NH_4{}^+(aq) + HCO_3{}^-(aq)$$

The reaction is first order in urea and first order overall. When [$NH_2CONH_2$] = 0.200 $M$, the rate at 61.05 °C is $8.56 \times 10^{-5} M/s$. (a) What is the rate constant, $k$? (b) What is the concentration of urea in this solution after $4.00 \times 10^3$ s if the starting concentration is 0.500 $M$? (c) What is the half-life for this reaction at 61.05 °C ?

14.107 The rate of a first-order reaction is followed by spectroscopy, monitoring the absorbance of a colored reactant at 520 nm. The reaction occurs in a 1.00-cm sample cell, and the only colored species in the reaction has an extinction coefficient of $5.60 \times 10^3 M^{-1} cm^{-1}$ at 520 nm. (a) Calculate the initial concentration of the colored reactant if the absorbance is 0.605 at the beginning of the reaction. (b) The absorbance falls to 0.250 at 30.0 min. Calculate the rate constant in units of $s^{-1}$. (c) Calculate the half-life of the reaction. (d) How long does it take for the absorbance to fall to 0.100?

**[14.108]** A colored dye compound decomposes to give a colorless product. The original dye absorbs at 608 nm and has an extinction coefficient of $4.7 \times 10^4 \, M^{-1} cm^{-1}$ at that wavelength. You perform the decomposition reaction in a 1-cm cuvette in a spectrometer and obtain the following data:

| Time (min) | Absorbance at 608 nm |
|------------|----------------------|
| 0          | 1.254                |
| 30         | 0.941                |
| 60         | 0.752                |
| 90         | 0.672                |
| 120        | 0.545                |

From these data, determine the rate law for the reaction "dye $\longrightarrow$ product" and determine the rate constant.

**14.109** Cyclopentadiene ($C_5H_6$) reacts with itself to form dicyclopentadiene ($C_{10}H_{12}$). A 0.0400 $M$ solution of $C_5H_6$ was monitored as a function of time as the reaction $2 \, C_5H_6 \longrightarrow C_{10}H_{12}$ proceeded. The following data were collected:

| Time (s) | [$C_5H_6$] ($M$) |
|----------|------------------|
| 0.0      | 0.0400           |
| 50.0     | 0.0300           |
| 100.0    | 0.0240           |
| 150.0    | 0.0200           |
| 200.0    | 0.0174           |

Plot [$C_5H_6$] versus time, ln [$C_5H_6$] versus time, and $1/[C_5H_6]$ versus time. What is the order of the reaction? What is the value of the rate constant?

**14.110** **(a)** Two reactions have identical values for $E_a$. Does this ensure that they will have the same rate constant if run at the same temperature? Explain. **(b)** Two similar reactions have the same rate constant at 25 °C, but at 35 °C one of the reactions has a larger rate constant than the other. Account for these observations.

**14.111** The first-order rate constant for reaction of a particular organic compound with water varies with temperature as follows:

| Temperature (K) | Rate Constant (s$^{-1}$) |
|-----------------|--------------------------|
| 300             | $3.2 \times 10^{-11}$    |
| 320             | $1.0 \times 10^{-9}$     |
| 340             | $3.0 \times 10^{-8}$     |
| 355             | $2.4 \times 10^{-7}$     |

From these data, calculate the activation energy in units of kJ/mol.

**14.112** The following mechanism has been proposed for the reaction of NO with $H_2$ to form $N_2O$ and $H_2O$:

$$NO(g) + NO(g) \longrightarrow N_2O_2(g)$$
$$N_2O_2(g) + H_2(g) \longrightarrow N_2O(g) + H_2O(g)$$

**(a)** Show that the elementary reactions of the proposed mechanism add to provide a balanced equation for the reaction. **(b)** Write a rate law for each elementary reaction in the mechanism. **(c)** Identify any intermediates in the mechanism. **(d)** The observed rate law is rate = $k[NO]^2[H_2]$. If the proposed mechanism is correct, what can we conclude about the relative speeds of the first and second reactions?

**14.113** Ozone in the upper atmosphere can be destroyed by the following two-step mechanism:

$$Cl(g) + O_3(g) \longrightarrow ClO(g) + O_2(g)$$
$$ClO(g) + O(g) \longrightarrow Cl(g) + O_2(g)$$

**(a)** What is the overall equation for this process? **(b)** What is the catalyst in the reaction? How do you know? **(c)** What is the intermediate in the reaction? How do you distinguish it from the catalyst?

**14.114** Using Figure 14.23 as your basis, draw the energy profile for the bromide–catalyzed decomposition of hydrogen peroxide. **(a)** Label the curve with the activation energies for reactions [14.30] and [14.31]. **(b)** Notice from Figure 14.22 that when $Br^-(aq)$ is first added, $Br_2$ accumulates to some extent during the reaction and the solution turns brown. What does this tell us about the relative rates of the reactions represented by Equations 14.30 and 14.31?

**[14.115]** The following mechanism has been proposed for the gas-phase reaction of chloroform ($CHCl_3$) and chlorine:

Step 1: $\quad Cl_2(g) \underset{k_{-1}}{\overset{k_1}{\rightleftharpoons}} 2 \, Cl(g) \quad$ (fast)

Step 2: $\quad Cl(g) + CHCl_3(g) \overset{k_2}{\longrightarrow} HCl(g) + CCl_3(g) \quad$ (slow)

Step 3: $\quad Cl(g) + CCl_3(g) \overset{k_3}{\longrightarrow} CCl_4 \quad$ (fast)

**(a)** What is the overall reaction? **(b)** What are the intermediates in the mechanism? **(c)** What is the molecularity of each of the elementary reactions? **(d)** What is the rate-determining step? **(e)** What is the rate law predicted by this mechanism? (*Hint:* The overall reaction order is not an integer.)

**[14.116]** In a hydrocarbon solution, the gold compound $(CH_3)_3AuPH_3$ decomposes into ethane ($C_2H_6$) and a different gold compound, $(CH_3)AuPH_3$. The following mechanism has been proposed for the decomposition of $(CH_3)_3AuPH_3$:

Step 1: $\quad (CH_3)_3 \, AuPH_3 \underset{k_{-1}}{\overset{k_1}{\rightleftharpoons}} (CH_3)_3Au + PH_3 \quad$ (fast)

Step 2: $\quad (CH_3)_3 \, Au \overset{k_2}{\longrightarrow} C_2H_6 + (CH_3)Au \quad$ (slow)

Step 3: $\quad (CH_3)Au + PH_3 \overset{k_3}{\longrightarrow} (CH_3)AuPH_3 \quad$ (fast)

**(a)** What is the overall reaction? **(b)** What are the intermediates in the mechanism? **(c)** What is the molecularity of each of the elementary steps? **(d)** What is the rate-determining step? **(e)** What is the rate law predicted by this mechanism? **(f)** What would be the effect on the reaction rate of adding $PH_3$ to the solution of $(CH_3)_3AuPH_3$?

**14.117** One of the many remarkable enzymes in the human body is carbonic anhydrase, which catalyzes the interconversion of carbon dioxide and water with bicarbonate ion and protons. If it were not for this enzyme, the body could not rid itself rapidly enough of the $CO_2$ accumulated by cell metabolism. The enzyme catalyzes the dehydration (release to air) of up to $10^7$ $CO_2$ molecules per second. Which components of this description correspond to the terms *enzyme*, *substrate*, and *turnover number*?

**14.118** Enzymes are often described as following the two-step mechanism:

$$E + S \rightleftharpoons ES \quad (fast)$$
$$ES \longrightarrow E + P \quad (slow)$$

where E = enzyme, S = substrate, ES = enzyme-substrate complex, and P = product.

(a) If an enzyme follows this mechanism, what rate law is expected for the reaction? (b) Molecules that can bind to the active site of an enzyme but are not converted into product are called *enzyme inhibitors*. Write an additional elementary step to add into the preceding mechanism to account for the reaction of E with I, an inhibitor.

## INTEGRATIVE EXERCISES

**14.119** Dinitrogen pentoxide ($N_2O_5$) decomposes in chloroform as a solvent to yield $NO_2$ and $O_2$. The decomposition is first order with a rate constant at 45 °C of $1.0 \times 10^{-5}$ $s^{-1}$. Calculate the partial pressure of $O_2$ produced from 1.00 L of 0.600 $M$ $N_2O_5$ solution at 45 °C over a period of 20.0 hr if the gas is collected in a 10.0-L container. (Assume that the products do not dissolve in chloroform.)

**[14.120]** The reaction between ethyl iodide and hydroxide ion in ethanol ($C_2H_5OH$) solution, $C_2H_5I(alc) + OH^-(alc) \longrightarrow C_2H_5OH(l) + I^-(alc)$, has an activation energy of 86.8 kJ/mol and a frequency factor of $2.10 \times 10^{11}$ $M^{-1} s^{-1}$. (a) Predict the rate constant for the reaction at 35 °C. (b) A solution of KOH in ethanol is made up by dissolving 0.335 g KOH in ethanol to form 250.0 mL of solution. Similarly, 1.453 g of $C_2H_5I$ is dissolved in ethanol to form 250.0 mL of solution. Equal volumes of the two solutions are mixed. Assuming the reaction is first order in each reactant, what is the initial rate at 35 °C ? (c) Which reagent in the reaction is limiting, assuming the reaction proceeds to completion? (d) Assuming the frequency factor and activation energy do not change as a function of temperature, calculate the rate constant for the reaction at 50 °C.

**[14.121]** You obtain kinetic data for a reaction at a set of different temperatures. You plot ln $k$ versus $1/T$ and obtain the following graph:

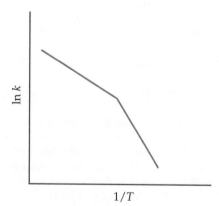

Suggest a molecular-level interpretation of these unusual data.

**14.122** The gas-phase reaction of NO with $F_2$ to form NOF and F has an activation energy of $E_a = 6.3$ kJ/mol and a frequency factor of $A = 6.0 \times 10^8$ $M^{-1} s^{-1}$. The reaction is believed to be bimolecular:

$$NO(g) + F_2(g) \longrightarrow NOF(g) + F(g)$$

(a) Calculate the rate constant at 100 °C. (b) Draw the Lewis structures for the NO and the NOF molecules, given that the chemical formula for NOF is misleading because the nitrogen atom is actually the central atom in the molecule. (c) Predict the shape for the NOF molecule. (d) Draw a possible transition state for the formation of NOF, using dashed lines to indicate the weak bonds that are beginning to form. (e) Suggest a reason for the low activation energy for the reaction.

**14.123** The mechanism for the oxidation of HBr by $O_2$ to form 2 $H_2O$ and $Br_2$ is shown in Exercise 14.80. (a) Calculate the overall standard enthalpy change for the reaction process. (b) HBr does not react with $O_2$ at a measurable rate at room temperature under ordinary conditions. What can you infer from this about the magnitude of the activation energy for the rate-determining step? (c) Draw a plausible Lewis structure for the intermediate HOOBr. To what familiar compound of hydrogen and oxygen does it appear similar?

**[14.124]** The rates of many atmospheric reactions are accelerated by the absorption of light by one of the reactants. For example, consider the reaction between methane and chlorine to produce methyl chloride and hydrogen chloride:

Reaction 1: $CH_4(g) + Cl_2(g) \longrightarrow CH_3Cl(g) + HCl(g)$

This reaction is very slow in the absence of light. However, $Cl_2(g)$ can absorb light to form Cl atoms:

Reaction 2: $Cl_2(g) + h\nu \longrightarrow 2 Cl(g)$

Once the Cl atoms are generated, they can catalyze the reaction of $CH_4$ and $Cl_2$, according to the following proposed mechanism:

Reaction 3: $CH_4(g) + Cl(g) \longrightarrow CH_3(g) + HCl(g)$
Reaction 4: $CH_3(g) + Cl_2(g) \longrightarrow CH_3Cl(g) + Cl(g)$

The enthalpy changes and activation energies for these two reactions are tabulated as follows:

| Reaction | $\Delta H°$ (kJ/mol) | $E_a$ (kJ/mol) |
|----------|---------------------|----------------|
| 3        | +4                  | 17             |
| 4        | −109                | 4              |

(a) By using the bond enthalpy for $Cl_2$ (Table 8.4), determine the longest wavelength of light that is energetic enough to cause reaction 2 to occur. In which portion of the electromagnetic spectrum is this light found? (b) By using the data tabulated here, sketch a quantitative energy profile for the catalyzed reaction represented by reactions 3 and 4. (c) By using bond enthalpies, estimate where the reactants, $CH_4(g) + Cl_2(g)$, should be placed on your diagram in part (b). Use this result to estimate the value of $E_a$ for the reaction $CH_4(g) + Cl_2(g) \longrightarrow CH_3(g) + HCl(g) + Cl(g)$. (d) The species $Cl(g)$ and $CH_3(g)$ in reactions 3 and 4 are radicals, that is, atoms or molecules with unpaired electrons. Draw a Lewis structure of $CH_3$, and verify that it is a radical. (e) The sequence of reactions 3 and 4 comprises a radical chain mechanism. Why do you think this is called a "chain reaction"? Propose a reaction that will terminate the chain reaction.

[14.125] Many primary amines, $RNH_2$, where R is a carbon-containing fragment such as $CH_3$, $CH_3CH_2$, and so on, undergo reactions where the transition state is tetrahedral. (a) Draw a hybrid orbital picture to visualize the bonding at the nitrogen in a primary amine (just use a C atom for "R"). (b) What kind of reactant with a primary amine can produce a tetrahedral intermediate?

[14.126] The $NO_x$ waste stream from automobile exhaust includes species such as NO and $NO_2$. Catalysts that convert these species to $N_2$ are desirable to reduce air pollution. (a) Draw the Lewis dot and VSEPR structures of NO, $NO_2$, and $N_2$. (b) Using a resource such as Table 8.4, look up the energies of the bonds in these molecules. In what region of the electromagnetic spectrum are these energies? (c) Design a spectroscopic experiment to monitor the conversion of $NO_x$ into $N_2$, describing what wavelengths of light need to be monitored as a function of time.

# WHAT'S AHEAD

**15.1 THE CONCEPT OF EQUILIBRIUM**
We begin by examining reversible reactions and the concept of equilibrium.

**15.2 THE EQUILIBRIUM CONSTANT**
We define the *equilibrium constant* based on rates of forward and reverse reactions, and learn how to write *equilibrium-constant expressions* for homogeneous reactions.

**15.3 UNDERSTANDING AND WORKING WITH EQUILIBRIUM CONSTANTS**
We learn to interpret the magnitude of an equilibrium constant and how its value depends on the way the corresponding chemical equation is expressed.

**15.4 HETEROGENEOUS EQUILIBRIA**
We then learn how to write equilibrium-constant expressions for heterogeneous reactions.

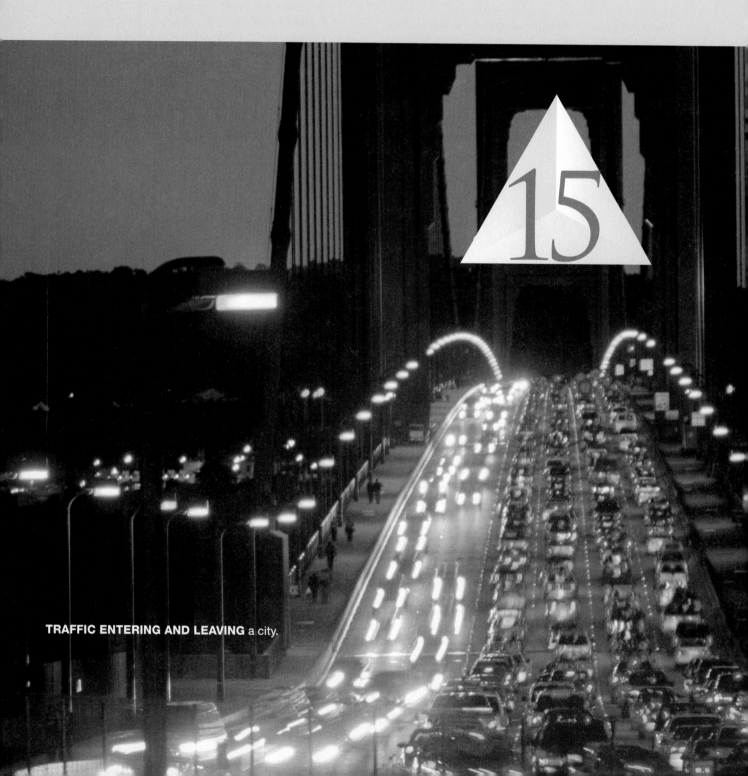

**TRAFFIC ENTERING AND LEAVING** a city.

## 15.5 CALCULATING EQUILIBRIUM CONSTANTS
We see that the value of an equilibrium constant can be calculated from equilibrium concentrations of reactants and products.

## 15.6 APPLICATIONS OF EQUILIBRIUM CONSTANTS
We also see that equilibrium constants can be used to predict equilibrium concentrations of reactants and products and to

determine the direction in which a reaction mixture must proceed to achieve equilibrium.

## 15.7 LE CHÂTELIER'S PRINCIPLE
We discuss *Le Châtelier's principle*, which predicts how a system at equilibrium responds to changes in concentration, volume, pressure, and temperature.

# CHEMICAL EQUILIBRIUM

**TO BE IN EQUILIBRIUM IS** to be in a state of balance. A tug of war in which the two sides pull with equal force so that the rope does not move is an example of a *static* equilibrium, one in which an object is at rest. Equilibria can also be *dynamic*, as illustrated in the chapter-opening photograph, which shows cars traveling

in both directions over a bridge that serves as the entry to a city. If the rate at which cars leave the city equals the rate at which they enter, the two opposing processes are in balance, and the net number of cars in the city is constant.

We have already encountered several instances of dynamic equilibrium. For example, the vapor above a liquid in a closed container is in equilibrium with the liquid phase ∞ (Section 11.5), which means that the rate at which molecules escape from the liquid into the gas phase equals the rate at which molecules in the gas phase become part of the liquid. Similarly, in a saturated sodium chloride solution in contact with undissolved sodium chloride, the solid is in equilibrium with the ions dispersed in water. ∞ (Section 13.2) The rate at which ions leave the solid surface equals the rate at which other ions leave the liquid and become part of the solid.

In this chapter we consider dynamic equilibria in chemical reactions. **Chemical equilibrium** *occurs when opposing reactions proceed at equal rates*: The rate at which the products form from the reactants equals the rate at which the reactants form from the products. As a result, concentrations cease to change, making the reaction appear to be stopped. Chemical equilibria are involved in many natural phenomena and play important roles in many industrial processes. In this and the next two chapters, we will explore chemical equilibrium in some detail. Later, in Chapter 19, we will learn how to relate chemical equilibria to thermodynamics. Here we learn how to express the equilibrium state of a reaction in quantitative terms and study the factors that determine the relative concentrations of reactants and products in equilibrium mixtures.

## 15.1 | THE CONCEPT OF EQUILIBRIUM

Let's examine a simple chemical reaction to see how it reaches an *equilibrium state*—a mixture of reactants and products whose concentrations no longer change with time. We begin with $N_2O_4$, a colorless substance that dissociates to form brown $NO_2$. ▼ FIGURE 15.1 shows a sample of frozen $N_2O_4$ inside a sealed tube. The solid $N_2O_4$ vaporizes as it is warmed above its boiling point (21.2 °C), and the gas turns darker as the colorless $N_2O_4$ gas dissociates into brown $NO_2$ gas. Eventually, even though there is still $N_2O_4$ in the tube, the color stops getting darker because the system reaches equilibrium. We are left with an *equilibrium mixture* of $N_2O_4$ and $NO_2$ in which the concentrations of the gases no longer change as time passes. Because the reaction is in a closed system, where no gases can escape, equilibrium will eventually be reached.

▲ GO FIGURE

How can you tell if you are at equilibrium?

Frozen $N_2O_4$ sample is nearly colorless

Warmed $N_2O_4$ dissociates to brown $NO_2(g)$

Colors stop changing, equilibrium reached: rate of reaction
$N_2O_4(g) \longrightarrow 2 NO_2(g)$ = rate of reaction $2 NO_2(g) \longrightarrow N_2O_4(g)$

▲ FIGURE 15.1   The equilibrium between $NO_2$ and $N_2O_4$.

The equilibrium mixture results because the reaction is *reversible*: $N_2O_4$ can form $NO_2$, and $NO_2$ can form $N_2O_4$. This situation is represented by writing the equation for the reaction with two half arrows pointing in opposite directions: ∞ (Section 4.1)

$$N_2O_4(g) \rightleftharpoons 2\,NO_2(g) \qquad\qquad [15.1]$$
$$\text{Colorless} \qquad\quad \text{Brown}$$

We can analyze this equilibrium using our knowledge of kinetics. Let's call the decomposition of $N_2O_4$ the forward reaction and the formation of $N_2O_4$ the reverse reaction. In this case, both the forward reaction and the reverse reaction are elementary reactions. As we learned in Section 14.6, the rate laws for elementary reactions can be written from their chemical equations:

Forward reaction:  $N_2O_4(g) \longrightarrow 2\,NO_2(g)$   $\text{Rate}_f = k_f[N_2O_4]$   $\qquad [15.2]$

Reverse reaction:  $2\,NO_2(g) \longrightarrow N_2O_4(g)$   $\text{Rate}_r = k_r[NO_2]^2$   $\qquad [15.3]$

At equilibrium, the rate at which $NO_2$ forms in the forward reaction equals the rate at which $N_2O_4$ forms in the reverse reaction:

$$\underbrace{k_f[N_2O_4]}_{\text{Forward reaction}} = \underbrace{k_r[NO_2]^2}_{\text{Reverse reaction}} \qquad\qquad [15.4]$$

Rearranging this equation gives

$$\frac{[NO_2]^2}{[N_2O_4]} = \frac{k_f}{k_r} = \text{a constant} \qquad\qquad [15.5]$$

From Equation 15.5 we see that the quotient of two rate constants is another constant. We also see that, at equilibrium, the ratio of the concentration terms equals this same constant. (We consider this constant, called the equilibrium constant, in Section 15.2.) It makes no difference whether we start with $N_2O_4$ or with $NO_2$, or even with some mixture of the two. At equilibrium, at a given temperature, the ratio equals a specific value. Thus, there is an important constraint on the proportions of $N_2O_4$ and $NO_2$ at equilibrium.

Once equilibrium is established, the concentrations of $N_2O_4$ and $NO_2$ no longer change, as shown in ▼ FIGURE 15.2(a). However, the fact that the composition of the equilibrium mixture remains constant with time does not mean that $N_2O_4$ and $NO_2$ stop reacting. On the contrary, the equilibrium is *dynamic*—which means some $N_2O_4$ is always converting to $NO_2$ and some $NO_2$ is always converting to $N_2O_4$. At equilibrium, however, the two processes occur at the same rate, as shown in Figure 15.2(b).

We learn several important lessons about equilibrium from this example:

- At equilibrium, the concentrations of reactants and products no longer change with time.

- For equilibrium to occur, neither reactants nor products can escape from the system.

- At equilibrium, a particular ratio of concentration terms equals a constant.

◤ **GO FIGURE**

**At equilibrium, are the concentrations of NO₂ and N₂O₄ equal?**

(a)

(b)

◀ **FIGURE 15.2  Achieving chemical equilibrium in the** $N_2O_4(g) \rightleftharpoons 2\,NO_2(g)$ **reaction.** Equilibrium occurs when the rate of the forward reaction equals the rate of the reverse reaction.

GIVE IT SOME THOUGHT

**a.** Which quantities are equal in a dynamic equilibrium?
**b.** If the rate constant for the forward reaction in Equation 15.1 is larger than the rate constant for the reverse reaction, will the constant in Equation 15.5 be greater than 1 or smaller than 1?

# 15.2 | THE EQUILIBRIUM CONSTANT

A reaction in which reactants convert to products and products convert to reactants in the same reaction vessel naturally leads to an equilibrium, regardless of how complicated the reaction is and regardless of the nature of the kinetic processes for the forward and reverse reactions. Consider the synthesis of ammonia from nitrogen and hydrogen:

$$N_2(g) + 3 H_2(g) \rightleftharpoons 2 NH_3(g) \qquad [15.6]$$

This reaction is the basis for the **Haber process**, which is critical for the production of fertilizers and therefore critical to the world's food supply. In the Haber process, $N_2$ and $H_2$ react at high pressure and temperature in the presence of a catalyst to form ammonia. In a closed system, however, the reaction does not lead to complete consumption of the $N_2$ and $H_2$. Rather, at some point the reaction appears to stop with all three components of the reaction mixture present at the same time.

How the concentrations of $H_2$, $N_2$, and $NH_3$ vary with time is shown in ▼ **FIGURE 15.3**. Notice that an equilibrium mixture is obtained regardless of whether we begin with $N_2$ and $H_2$ or with $NH_3$. *The equilibrium condition is reached from either direction.*

GIVE IT SOME THOUGHT

How do we know when equilibrium has been reached in a chemical reaction?

An expression similar to Equation 15.5 governs the concentrations of $N_2$, $H_2$, and $NH_3$ at equilibrium. If we were to systematically change the relative amounts of the three gases in the starting mixture and then analyze each equilibrium mixture, we could determine the relationship among the equilibrium concentrations.

Chemists carried out studies of this kind on other chemical systems in the nineteenth century before Haber's work. In 1864, Cato Maximilian Guldberg (1836–1902) and Peter Waage (1833–1900) postulated their **law of mass action**, which expresses, for any reaction, the relationship between the concentrations of the reactants and products present at equilibrium. Suppose we have the general equilibrium equation

$$a A + b B \rightleftharpoons d D + e E \qquad [15.7]$$

where A, B, D, and E are the chemical species involved and $a$, $b$, $d$, and $e$ are their coefficients in the balanced chemical equation. According to the law of mass action, the equilibrium condition is described by the expression

$$K_c = \frac{[D]^d[E]^e}{[A]^a[B]^b} \quad \begin{array}{l} \longleftarrow \text{ products} \\ \longleftarrow \text{ reactants} \end{array} \qquad [15.8]$$

We call this relationship the **equilibrium-constant expression** (or merely the *equilibrium expression*) for the reaction. The constant $K_c$, the **equilibrium constant**, is the numerical value obtained when we substitute molar equilibrium concentrations

▶ **FIGURE 15.3** **The same equilibrium is reached whether we start with only reactants ($N_2$ and $H_2$) or with only product ($NH_3$).**

# CHEMISTRY PUT TO WORK

## The Haber Process

The quantity of food required to feed the ever-increasing human population far exceeds that provided by nitrogen-fixing plants. ∞ (Section 14.7) Therefore, human agriculture requires substantial amounts of ammonia-based fertilizers for croplands. Of all the chemical reactions that humans have learned to control for their own purposes, the synthesis of ammonia from hydrogen and atmospheric nitrogen is one of the most important.

In 1912 the German chemist Fritz Haber (1868–1934) developed the Haber process (Equation 15.6). The process is sometimes also called the *Haber–Bosch process* to honor Karl Bosch, the engineer who developed the industrial process on a large scale. The engineering needed to implement the Haber process requires the use of temperatures and pressures (approximately 500 °C and 200 to 600 atm) that were difficult to achieve at that time.

The Haber process provides a historically interesting example of the complex impact of chemistry on our lives. At the start of World War I, in 1914, Germany depended on nitrate deposits in Chile for the nitrogen-containing compounds needed to manufacture explosives. During the war, the Allied naval blockade of South America cut off this supply. However, by using the Haber reaction to fix nitrogen from air, Germany was able to continue to produce explosives. Experts have estimated that World War I would have ended before 1918 had it not been for the Haber process.

From these unhappy beginnings as a major factor in international warfare, the Haber process has become the world's principal source of fixed nitrogen. The same process that prolonged World War I has enabled the manufacture of fertilizers that have increased crop yields, thereby saving millions of people from starvation. About 40 billion pounds of ammonia are manufactured annually in the United States, mostly by the Haber process. The ammonia can be applied directly to the soil (▼ FIGURE 15.4), or it can be converted into ammonium salts that are also used as fertilizers.

Haber was a patriotic German who gave enthusiastic support to his nation's war effort. He served as chief of Germany's Chemical Warfare Service during World War I and developed the use of chlorine as a poison-gas weapon. Consequently, the decision to award him the Nobel Prize in Chemistry in 1918 was the subject of considerable controversy and criticism. The ultimate irony, however, came in 1933 when Haber was expelled from Germany because he was Jewish.

*RELATED EXERCISES:* 15.46 and 15.76

◀ FIGURE 15.4  **Liquid ammonia used as fertilizer by direct injection into soil.**

into the equilibrium-constant expression. The subscript $c$ on the $K$ indicates that concentrations expressed in molarity are used to evaluate the constant.

The numerator of the equilibrium-constant expression is the product of the concentrations of all substances on the product side of the equilibrium equation, each raised to a power equal to its coefficient in the balanced equation. The denominator is similarly derived from the reactant side of the equilibrium equation. Thus, for the Haber process, $N_2(g) + 3 H_2(g) \rightleftharpoons 2 NH_3(g)$, the equilibrium-constant expression is

$$K_c = \frac{[NH_3]^2}{[N_2][H_2]^3} \qquad [15.9]$$

Once we know the balanced chemical equation for a reaction that reaches equilibrium, we can write the equilibrium-constant expression even if we do not know the reaction mechanism. *The equilibrium-constant expression depends only on the stoichiometry of the reaction, not on its mechanism.*

The value of the equilibrium constant at any given temperature does not depend on the initial amounts of reactants and products. It also does not matter whether other substances are present, as long as they do not react with a reactant or a product. The value of $K_c$ depends only on the particular reaction and on the temperature.

---

**SAMPLE EXERCISE 15.1**   **Writing Equilibrium-Constant Expressions**

Write the equilibrium expression for $K_c$ for the following reactions:

(a) $2 O_3(g) \rightleftharpoons 3 O_2(g)$

(b) $2 NO(g) + Cl_2(g) \rightleftharpoons 2 NOCl(g)$

(c) $Ag^+(aq) + 2 NH_3(aq) \rightleftharpoons Ag(NH_3)_2^+(aq)$

**SOLUTION**

**Analyze** We are given three equations and are asked to write an equilibrium-constant expression for each.

**Plan** Using the law of mass action, we write each expression as a quotient having the product concentration terms in the numerator and the reactant concentration terms in the denominator. Each concentration term is raised to the power of its coefficient in the balanced chemical equation.

**Solve**

(a) $K_c = \dfrac{[O_2]^3}{[O_3]^2}$    (b) $K_c = \dfrac{[NOCl]^2}{[NO]^2[Cl_2]}$    (c) $K_c = \dfrac{[Ag(NH_3)_2^+]}{[Ag^+][NH_3]^2}$

**PRACTICE EXERCISE**

Write the equilibrium-constant expression $K_c$ for (a) $H_2(g) + I_2(g) \rightleftharpoons 2 HI(g)$, (b) $Cd^{2+}(aq) + 4 Br^-(aq) \rightleftharpoons CdBr_4^{2-}(aq)$.

**Answers:**   (a) $K_c = \dfrac{[HI]^2}{[H_2][I_2]}$    (b) $K_c = \dfrac{[CdBr_4^{2-}]}{[Cd^{2+}][Br^-]^4}$

---

## Evaluating $K_c$

We can illustrate how the law of mass action was discovered empirically and demonstrate that the equilibrium constant is independent of starting concentrations by examining a series of experiments involving dinitrogen tetroxide and nitrogen dioxide:

$$N_2O_4(g) \rightleftharpoons 2 NO_2(g) \qquad K_c = \frac{[NO_2]^2}{[N_2O_4]} \qquad [15.10]$$

We start with several sealed tubes containing different concentrations of $NO_2$ and $N_2O_4$. The tubes are kept at 100 °C until equilibrium is reached. We then analyze the mixtures and determine the equilibrium concentrations of $NO_2$ and $N_2O_4$, which are shown in ▼ TABLE 15.1.

To evaluate $K_c$, we insert the equilibrium concentrations into the equilibrium-constant expression. For example, using Experiment 1 data, $[NO_2] = 0.0172\ M$ and $[N_2O_4] = 0.00140\ M$, we find

$$K_c = \frac{[NO_2]^2}{[N_2O_4]} = \frac{[0.0172]^2}{0.00140} = 0.211$$

**TABLE 15.1 • Initial and Equilibrium Concentrations of $N_2O_4(g)$ and $NO_2(g)$ at 100 °C**

| Experiment | Initial $[N_2O_4]$ ($M$) | Initial $[NO_2]$ ($M$) | Equilibrium $[N_2O_4]$ ($M$) | Equilibrium $[NO_2]$ ($M$) | $K_c$ |
|---|---|---|---|---|---|
| 1 | 0.0 | 0.0200 | 0.00140 | 0.0172 | 0.211 |
| 2 | 0.0 | 0.0300 | 0.00280 | 0.0243 | 0.211 |
| 3 | 0.0 | 0.0400 | 0.00452 | 0.0310 | 0.213 |
| 4 | 0.0200 | 0.0 | 0.00452 | 0.0310 | 0.213 |

Proceeding in the same way, the values of $K_c$ for the other samples are calculated. Note from Table 15.1 that the value for $K_c$ is constant (within the limits of experimental error) even though the initial concentrations vary. Furthermore, Experiment 4 shows that equilibrium can be achieved beginning with $N_2O_4$ rather than with $NO_2$. That is, equilibrium can be approached from either direction. ▶ FIGURE 15.5 shows how Experiments 3 and 4 result in the same equilibrium mixture even though the two experiments start with very different $NO_2$ concentrations.

Notice that no units are given for $K_c$ either in Table 15.1 or in the calculation we just did using Experiment 1 data. It is common practice to write equilibrium constants without units for reasons that we address later in this section.

Recall that we began our discussion of equilibrium in terms of rates. Equation 15.5 shows that $K_c$ is equal to $k_f/k_r$, the ratio of the forward rate constant to the reverse rate constant. For the $N_2O_4/NO_2$ reaction, $K_c = 0.212$, which means that $k_r$ is 4.72 times as large as $k_f$ (since $1/0.212 = 4.72$). It is not possible to obtain the absolute value of either rate constant knowing only the value of $K_c$.

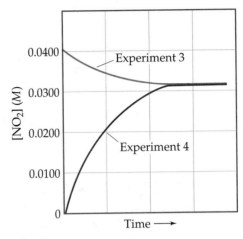

▲ FIGURE 15.5 **The same equilibrium mixture is produced regardless of the initial NO$_2$ concentration.** The concentration of $NO_2$ either increases or decreases until equilibrium is reached.

 GIVE IT SOME THOUGHT

How does the value of $K_c$ in Equation 15.10 depend on the starting concentrations of $NO_2$ and $N_2O_4$?

## Equilibrium Constants in Terms of Pressure, $K_p$

When the reactants and products in a chemical reaction are gases, we can formulate the equilibrium-constant expression in terms of partial pressures. When partial pressures in atmospheres are used in the expression, we denote the equilibrium constant $K_p$ (where the subscript $p$ stands for pressure). For the general reaction in Equation 15.7, we have

$$K_p = \frac{(P_D)^d (P_E)^e}{(P_A)^a (P_B)^b} \qquad [15.11]$$

where $P_A$ is the partial pressure of A in atmospheres, $P_B$ is the partial pressure of B in atmospheres, and so forth. For example, for our $N_2O_4/NO_2$ reaction we have

$$K_p = \frac{(P_{NO_2})^2}{P_{N_2O_4}}$$

 GIVE IT SOME THOUGHT

What is the difference between the equilibrium constant $K_c$ and the equilibrium constant $K_p$?

For a given reaction, the numerical value of $K_c$ is generally different from the numerical value of $K_p$. We must therefore take care to indicate, via subscript $c$ or $p$, which constant we are using. It is possible, however, to calculate one from the other using the ideal-gas equation: ∞ (Section 10.4)

$$PV = nRT, \text{ so } P = \frac{n}{V}RT \qquad [15.12]$$

The usual units for $n/V$ are mol/L, which equals molarity, $M$. For substance A in our generic reaction, we therefore see that

$$P_A = \frac{n_A}{V}RT = [A]RT \qquad [15.13]$$

When we substitute Equation 15.13 and like expressions for the other gaseous components of the reaction into Equation 15.11, we obtain a general expression relating $K_p$ and $K_c$:

$$K_p = K_c(RT)^{\Delta n} \qquad [15.14]$$

The quantity $\Delta n$ is the change in the number of moles of gas in the balanced chemical equation. It equals the sum of the coefficients of the gaseous products minus the sum of the coefficients of the gaseous reactants:

$$\Delta n = (\text{moles of gaseous product}) - (\text{moles of gaseous reactant}) \qquad [15.15]$$

For example, in the $N_2O_4(g) \rightleftharpoons 2\,NO_2(g)$ reaction, there are two moles of product $NO_2$ and one mole of reactant $N_2O_4$. Therefore, $\Delta n = 2 - 1 = 1$, and $K_p = K_c(RT)$ for this reaction.

From Equation 15.14, we see that $K_p = K_c$ only when the same number of moles of gas appears on both sides of the balanced chemical equation, so that $\Delta n = 0$.

---

**SAMPLE EXERCISE 15.2** | **Converting between $K_c$ and $K_p$**

For the Haber process,

$$N_2(g) + 3\,H_2(g) \rightleftharpoons 2\,NH_3(g)$$

$K_c = 9.60$ at 300 °C. Calculate $K_p$ for this reaction at this temperature.

**SOLUTION**

**Analyze** We are given $K_c$ for a reaction and asked to calculate $K_p$.

**Plan** The relationship between $K_c$ and $K_p$ is given by Equation 15.14. To apply that equation, we must determine $\Delta n$ by comparing the number of moles of product with the number of moles of reactants (Equation 15.15).

**Solve** With 2 mol of gaseous products ($2\,NH_3$) and 4 mol of gaseous reactants ($1\,N_2 + 3\,H_2$), $\Delta n = 2 - 4 = -2$. (Remember that $\Delta$ functions are always based on *products minus reactants*.) The temperature is $273 + 300 = 573$ K. The value for the ideal-gas constant, $R$, is 0.08206 L-atm/mol-K. Using $K_c = 9.60$, we therefore have

$$K_p = K_c(RT)^{\Delta n} = (9.60)(0.08206 \times 573)^{-2} = \frac{(9.60)}{(0.08206 \times 573)^2} = 4.34 \times 10^{-3}$$

**PRACTICE EXERCISE**

For the equilibrium $2\,SO_3(g) \rightleftharpoons 2\,SO_2(g) + O_2(g)$, $K_c$ is $4.08 \times 10^{-3}$ at 1000 K. Calculate the value for $K_p$.

*Answer:* 0.335

---

## Equilibrium Constants and Units

You may wonder why equilibrium constants are reported without units. The equilibrium constant is related to the kinetics of a reaction as well as to the thermodynamics. (We explore this latter connection in Chapter 19.) Equilibrium constants derived from thermodynamic measurements are defined in terms of *activities* rather than concentrations or partial pressures.

The activity of any substance in an *ideal* mixture is the ratio of the concentration or pressure of the substance either to a reference concentration (1 *M*) or to a reference pressure (1 atm). For example, if the concentration of a substance in an equilibrium mixture is 0.010 *M*, its activity is 0.010 *M*/1 *M* = 0.010. The units of such ratios always cancel and, consequently, activities have no units. Furthermore, the numerical value of the activity equals the concentration. For pure solids and pure liquids, the situation is even simpler because the activities then merely equal 1 (again with no units).

In real systems, activities are also ratios that have no units. Even though these activities may not be exactly numerically equal to concentrations, we will ignore the differences. All we need to know at this point is that activities have no units. As a result, the *thermodynamic equilibrium constants* derived from them also have no units. It is therefore common practice to write all types of equilibrium constants without units, a practice that we adhere to in this text. In more advanced chemistry courses, you may make more rigorous distinctions between concentrations and activities.

⚠ **GIVE IT SOME THOUGHT**

If the concentration of $N_2O_4$ in an equilibrium mixture is 0.00140 *M,* what is its activity? (Assume the solution is ideal.)

# 15.3 | UNDERSTANDING AND WORKING WITH EQUILIBRIUM CONSTANTS

Before doing calculations with equilibrium constants, it is valuable to understand what the magnitude of an equilibrium constant can tell us about the relative concentrations of reactants and products in an equilibrium mixture. It is also useful to consider how the magnitude of any equilibrium constant depends on how the chemical equation is expressed.

## The Magnitude of Equilibrium Constants

The magnitude of the equilibrium constant for a reaction gives us important information about the composition of the equilibrium mixture. For example, consider the experimental data for the reaction of carbon monoxide gas and chlorine gas at 100 °C to form phosgene ($COCl_2$), a toxic gas used in the manufacture of certain polymers and insecticides:

$$CO(g) + Cl_2(g) \rightleftharpoons COCl_2(g) \qquad K_c = \frac{[COCl_2]}{[CO][Cl_2]} = 4.56 \times 10^9$$

For the equilibrium constant to be so large, the numerator of the equilibrium-constant expression must be approximately a billion ($10^9$) times larger than the denominator. Thus, the equilibrium concentration of $COCl_2$ must be much greater than that of $CO$ or $Cl_2$, and in fact this is just what we find experimentally. We say that this equilibrium *lies to the right* (that is, toward the product side). Likewise, a very small equilibrium constant indicates that the equilibrium mixture contains mostly reactants. We then say that the equilibrium *lies to the left*. In general,

*If K* ≫ 1 *(large K):*   Equilibrium lies to right, products predominate

*If K* ≪ 1 *(small K):*   Equilibrium lies to left, reactants predominate

These situations are summarized in ▶ FIGURE 15.6. Remember, it is forward and reverse *rates* that are equal at equilibrium, not concentrations.

▲ **GO FIGURE**

**What would this figure look like for a reaction in which $K \approx 1$?**

$K \gg 1$, equilibrium "lies to the right"

$K \ll 1$, equilibrium "lies to the left"

▲ **FIGURE 15.6  Relationship between magnitude of $K$ and composition of an equilibrium mixture.**

| SAMPLE EXERCISE 15.3 | Interpreting the Magnitude of an Equilibrium Constant |
|---|---|

The following diagrams represent three systems at equilibrium, all in the same-size containers. **(a)** Without doing any calculations, rank the systems in order of increasing $K_c$. **(b)** If the volume of the containers is 1.0 L and each sphere represents 0.10 mol, calculate $K_c$ for each system.

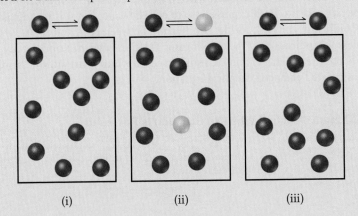

(i)          (ii)          (iii)

## SOLUTION

**Analyze** We are asked to judge the relative magnitudes of three equilibrium constants and then to calculate them.

**Plan** (a) The more product present at equilibrium, relative to reactant, the larger the equilibrium constant. (b) The equilibrium constant is given by Equation 15.8.

**Solve**

(a) Each box contains 10 spheres. The amount of product in each varies as follows: (i) 6, (ii) 1, (iii) 8. Therefore, the equilibrium constant varies in the order (ii) < (i) < (iii), from smallest (most reactant) to largest (most products).

(b) In (i) we have 0.60 mol/L product and 0.40 mol/L reactant, giving $K_c = 0.60/0.40 = 1.5$. (You will get the same result by merely dividing the number of spheres of each kind: 6 spheres/4 spheres = 1.5.) In (ii) we have 0.10 mol/L product and 0.90 mol/L reactant, giving $K_c = 0.10/0.90 = 0.11$ (or 1 sphere/9 spheres = 0.11). In (iii) we have 0.80 mol/L product and 0.20 mol/L reactant, giving $K_c = 0.80/0.20 = 4.0$ (or 8 spheres/2 spheres = 4.0). These calculations verify the order in (a).

**Comment** Imagine a drawing that represents a reaction with a very small or very large value of $K_c$. For example, what would the drawing look like if $K_c = 1 \times 10^{-5}$? In that case there would need to be 100,000 reactant molecules for only 1 product molecule. But then, that would be impractical to draw.

**PRACTICE EXERCISE**

For the reaction $H_2(g) + I_2(g) \rightleftharpoons 2\,HI(g)$, $K_p = 794$ at 298 K and $K_p = 55$ at 700 K. Is the formation of HI favored more at the higher or lower temperature?

***Answer:*** at the lower temperature because $K_p$ is larger at the lower temperature

## The Direction of the Chemical Equation and *K*

We have seen that we can represent the $N_2O_4/NO_2$ equilibrium as

$$N_2O_4(g) \rightleftharpoons 2\,NO_2(g) \quad K_c = \frac{[NO_2]^2}{[N_2O_4]} = 0.212 \quad \text{(at 100 °C)} \qquad [15.16]$$

We could equally well consider this equilibrium in terms of the reverse reaction:

$$2\,NO_2(g) \rightleftharpoons N_2O_4(g)$$

The equilibrium expression is then

$$K_c = \frac{[N_2O_4]}{[NO_2]^2} = \frac{1}{0.212} = 4.72 \quad \text{(at 100 °C)} \qquad [15.17]$$

Equation 15.17 is the reciprocal of the expression in Equation 15.16. *The equilibrium-constant expression for a reaction written in one direction is the reciprocal of the expression for the reaction written in the reverse direction.* Consequently, the numerical value of the equilibrium constant for the reaction written in one direction is the reciprocal of that for the reverse reaction. Both expressions are equally valid, but it is meaningless to say that the equilibrium constant for the equilibrium between $NO_2$ and $N_2O_4$ is "0.212" or "4.72" unless we indicate how the equilibrium reaction is written and specify the temperature. Therefore, whenever you are using an equilibrium constant, you should always write the associated balanced chemical equation.

| **SAMPLE EXERCISE 15.4** | **Evaluating an Equilibrium Constant When an Equation Is Reversed** |

For the reaction

$$N_2(g) + O_2(g) \rightleftharpoons 2\,NO(g)$$

that is run at 25 °C, $K_c = 1 \times 10^{-30}$. Use this information to write the equilibrium-constant expression and calculate the equilibrium constant for the reaction

$$2\,NO(g) \rightleftharpoons N_2(g) + O_2(g)$$

**SOLUTION**

**Analyze** We are asked to write the equilibrium-constant expression for a reaction and to determine the value of $K_c$ given the chemical equation and equilibrium constant for the reverse reaction.

**Plan** The equilibrium-constant expression is a quotient of products over reactants, each raised to a power equal to its coefficient in the balanced equation. The value of the equilibrium constant is the reciprocal of that for the reverse reaction.

**Solve**
Writing products over reactants, we have

$$K_c = \frac{[N_2][O_2]}{[NO]^2}$$

Both the equilibrium-constant expression and the numerical value of the equilibrium constant are the reciprocals of those for the formation of NO from $N_2$ and $O_2$:

$$K_c = \frac{[N_2][O_2]}{[NO]^2} = \frac{1}{1 \times 10^{-30}} = 1 \times 10^{30}$$

**Comment**  Regardless of the way we express the equilibrium among NO, $N_2$, and $O_2$, at 25 °C it lies on the side that favors $N_2$ and $O_2$. Thus, the equilibrium mixture will contain mostly $N_2$ and $O_2$ with very little NO present.

**PRACTICE EXERCISE**
For $N_2(g) + 3 H_2(g) \rightleftharpoons 2 NH_3(g)$, $K_p = 4.34 \times 10^{-3}$ at 300 °C. What is the value of $K_p$ for the reverse reaction?
**Answer:** $2.30 \times 10^2$

# Relating Chemical Equation Stoichiometry and Equilibrium Constants

There are many ways to write a balanced chemical equation for a given reaction. For example, if we multiply Equation 15.1, $N_2O_4(g) \rightleftharpoons 2 NO_2(g)$ by 2, we have

$$2 N_2O_4(g) \rightleftharpoons 4 NO_2(g)$$

This chemical equation is balanced and might be written this way in some contexts. Therefore, the equilibrium-constant expression for this equation is

$$K_c = \frac{[NO_2]^4}{[N_2O_4]^2}$$

which is the square of the equilibrium-constant expression given in Equation 15.10 for the reaction as written in Equation 15.1: $[NO_2]^2/[N_2O_4]$. Because the new equilibrium-constant expression equals the original expression squared, the new equilibrium constant $K_c$ equals the original constant squared: $0.212^2 = 0.0449$ (at 100 °C). Once again, it is important to remember that you must relate each equilibrium constant you work with to a *specific* balanced chemical equation. The concentrations of the substances in the equilibrium mixture will be the same no matter how you write the chemical equation, but the value of $K_c$ you calculate depends completely on how you write the reaction.

⚠ GIVE IT SOME THOUGHT
How does the magnitude of $K_p$ for the reaction $2 HI(g) \rightleftharpoons H_2(g) + I_2(g)$ change if the equilibrium is written $6 HI(g) \rightleftharpoons 3 H_2(g) + 3 I_2(g)$?

It is also possible to calculate the equilibrium constant for a reaction if we know the equilibrium constants for other reactions that add up to give us the one we want, similar to Hess's law. ∞ (Section 5.6) For example, consider the following two reactions, their equilibrium-constant expressions, and their equilibrium constants at 100 °C:

**1.** $2 NOBr(g) \rightleftharpoons 2 NO(g) + Br_2(g)$   $K_c = \dfrac{[NO]^2[Br_2]}{[NOBr]^2} = 0.014$

**2.** $Br_2(g) + Cl_2(g) \rightleftharpoons 2 BrCl(g)$   $K_c = \dfrac{[BrCl]^2}{[Br_2][Cl_2]} = 7.2$

The net sum of these two equations is

**3.** $2 NOBr(g) + Cl_2(g) \rightleftharpoons 2 NO(g) + 2 BrCl(g)$

You can prove algebraically that the equilibrium-constant expression for reaction 3 is the product of the expressions for reactions 1 and 2:

$$K_c = \frac{[NO]^2[BrCl]^2}{[NOBr]^2[Cl_2]} = \frac{[NO]^2[Br_2]}{[NOBr]^2} \times \frac{[BrCl]^2}{[Br_2][Cl_2]}$$

Thus,

$$K_{c3} = (K_{c1})(K_{c2}) = (0.014)(7.2) = 0.10$$

To summarize:

1. The equilibrium constant of a reaction in the *reverse* direction is the *inverse* (or *reciprocal*) of the equilibrium constant of the reaction in the forward direction:

$$A + B \rightleftharpoons C + D \quad K_1$$
$$C + D \rightleftharpoons A + B \quad K = 1/K_1$$

2. The equilibrium constant of a reaction that has been *multiplied* by a number is equal to the original equilibrium constant raised to a *power* equal to that number.

$$A + B \rightleftharpoons C + D \quad K_1$$
$$nA + nB \rightleftharpoons nC + nD \quad K = K_1^n$$

3. The equilibrium constant for a net reaction made up of *two or more reactions* is the *product* of the equilibrium constants for the individual reactions:

$$\begin{aligned}
&1.\ A + B \rightleftharpoons C + D \quad K_1 \\
&2.\ C + F \rightleftharpoons G + A \quad K_2 \\
\hline
&3.\ B + F \rightleftharpoons D + G \quad K_3 = (K_1)(K_2)
\end{aligned}$$

---

**SAMPLE EXERCISE 15.5** | **Combining Equilibrium Expressions**

Given the reactions

$$HF(aq) \rightleftharpoons H^+(aq) + F^-(aq) \qquad K_c = 6.8 \times 10^{-4}$$
$$H_2C_2O_4(aq) \rightleftharpoons 2 H^+(aq) + C_2O_4^{2-}(aq) \quad K_c = 3.8 \times 10^{-6}$$

determine the value of $K_c$ for the reaction

$$2 HF(aq) + C_2O_4^{2-}(aq) \rightleftharpoons 2 F^-(aq) + H_2C_2O_4(aq)$$

**SOLUTION**

**Analyze** We are given two equilibrium equations and the corresponding equilibrium constants and are asked to determine the equilibrium constant for a third equation, which is related to the first two.

**Plan** We cannot simply add the first two equations to get the third. Instead, we need to determine how to manipulate the equations to come up with the steps that will add to give us the desired equation.

**Solve**

If we multiply the first equation by 2 and make the corresponding change to its equilibrium constant (raising to the power 2), we get

$$2 HF(aq) \rightleftharpoons 2 H^+(aq) + 2 F^-(aq) \qquad\qquad K_c = (6.8 \times 10^{-4})^2 = 4.6 \times 10^{-7}$$

Reversing the second equation and again making the corresponding change to its equilibrium constant (taking the reciprocal) gives

$$2 H^+(aq) + C_2O_4^{2-}(aq) \rightleftharpoons H_2C_2O_4(aq) \qquad\qquad K_c = \frac{1}{3.8 \times 10^{-6}} = 2.6 \times 10^5$$

Now we have two equations that sum to give the net equation, and we can multiply the individual $K_c$ values to get the desired equilibrium constant.

$$\begin{aligned}
2 HF(aq) &\rightleftharpoons 2 H^+(aq) + 2 F^-(aq) & K_c &= 4.6 \times 10^{-7} \\
2 H^+(aq) + C_2O_4^{2-}(aq) &\rightleftharpoons H_2C_2O_4(aq) & K_c &= 2.5 \times 10^5 \\
\hline
2 HF(aq) + C_2O_4^{2-}(aq) &\rightleftharpoons 2 F^-(aq) + H_2C_2O_4(aq) & K_c &= (4.6 \times 10^{-7})(2.6 \times 10^5) = 0.12
\end{aligned}$$

**PRACTICE EXERCISE**

Given that, at 700 K, $K_p = 54.0$ for the reaction $H_2(g) + I_2(g) \rightleftharpoons 2 HI(g)$ and $K_p = 1.04 \times 10^{-4}$ for the reaction $N_2(g) + 3 H_2(g) \rightleftharpoons 2 NH_3(g)$, determine the value of $K_p$ for the reaction $2 NH_3(g) + 3 I_2(g) \rightleftharpoons 6 HI(g) + N_2(g)$ at 700 K.

**Answer:** $\dfrac{(54.0)^3}{1.04 \times 10^{-4}} = 1.51 \times 10^9$

# 15.4 | HETEROGENEOUS EQUILIBRIA

Many equilibria involve substances that are all in the same phase, usually gas or liquid. Such equilibria are called **homogeneous equilibria**. In some cases, however, the substances in equilibrium are in different phases, giving rise to **heterogeneous equilibria**. As an example of the latter, consider the equilibrium that occurs when solid lead(II) chloride dissolves in water to form a saturated solution:

$$PbCl_2(s) \rightleftharpoons Pb^{2+}(aq) + 2\,Cl^-(aq) \qquad [15.18]$$

This system consists of a solid in equilibrium with two aqueous species. If we want to write the equilibrium-constant expression for this process, we encounter a problem we have not encountered previously: How do we express the concentration of a solid? Although we can express that concentration in moles per unit volume, it is unnecessary to do so in writing equilibrium-constant expressions. *Whenever a pure solid or a pure liquid is involved in a heterogeneous equilibrium, its concentration is not included in the equilibrium-constant expression.* Thus, the equilibrium-constant expression for the reaction of Equation 15.18 is

$$K_c = [Pb^{2+}][Cl^-]^2 \qquad [15.19]$$

Even though $PbCl_2(s)$ does not appear in the equilibrium-constant expression, it must be present for equilibrium to occur.

The fact that pure solids and pure liquids are excluded from equilibrium-constant expressions can be explained in two ways. First, the concentration of a pure solid or liquid has a constant value. If the mass of a solid is doubled, its volume also doubles. Thus, its concentration, which relates to the ratio of mass to volume, stays the same. Because equilibrium-constant expressions include terms only for reactants and products whose concentrations can change during a chemical reaction, the concentrations of pure solids and pure liquids are omitted.

The omission can also be rationalized in a second way. Recall from Section 15.2 that what is substituted into a thermodynamic equilibrium expression is the activity of each substance, which is a ratio of the concentration to a reference value. For a pure substance, the reference value is the concentration of the pure substance, so that the activity of any pure solid or liquid is always 1.

 GIVE IT SOME THOUGHT

Write the equilibrium-constant expression for the evaporation of water, $H_2O(l) \rightleftharpoons H_2O(g)$, in terms of partial pressures.

Decomposition of calcium carbonate is another example of a heterogeneous reaction:

$$CaCO_3(s) \rightleftharpoons CaO(s) + CO_2(g)$$

Omitting the concentrations of the solids from the equilibrium-constant expression gives

$$K_c = [CO_2] \quad \text{and} \quad K_p = P_{CO_2}$$

These equations tell us that at a given temperature, an equilibrium among $CaCO_3$, $CaO$, and $CO_2$ always leads to the same $CO_2$ partial pressure as long as all three components are present. As shown in ▶ **FIGURE 15.7**, we have the same $CO_2$ pressure regardless of the relative amounts of $CaO$ and $CaCO_3$.

 GO FIGURE

Imagine starting with only CaO in a bell jar and adding $CO_2(g)$ to make its pressure the same as it is in these two bell jars. How does the equilibrium concentration of $CO_2(g)$ in your jar compare with the $CO_2(g)$ equilibrium concentration in these two jars?

$$CaCO_3(s) \rightleftharpoons CaO(s) + CO_2(g)$$

CaCO₃    CaO

Large amount of CaCO₃, small amount of CaO, gas pressure $P$

CaCO₃    CaO

Small amount of CaCO₃, large amount of CaO, gas pressure still $P$

▲ **FIGURE 15.7** **At a given temperature, the equilibrium pressure of $CO_2$ in the bell jars is the same no matter how much of each solid is present.**

---

**SAMPLE EXERCISE 15.6** | **Writing Equilibrium-Constant Expressions for Heterogeneous Reactions**

Write the equilibrium-constant expression $K_c$ for

**(a)** $CO_2(g) + H_2(g) \rightleftharpoons CO(g) + H_2O(l)$

**(b)** $SnO_2(s) + 2\,CO(g) \rightleftharpoons Sn(s) + 2\,CO_2(g)$

## SOLUTION

**Analyze** We are given two chemical equations, both for heterogeneous equilibria, and asked to write the corresponding equilibrium-constant expressions.

**Plan** We use the law of mass action, remembering to omit any pure solids and pure liquids from the expressions.

**Solve**
(a) The equilibrium-constant expression is

$$K_c = \frac{[CO]}{[CO_2][H_2]}$$

Because $H_2O$ appears in the reaction as a liquid, its concentration does not appear in the equilibrium-constant expression.

(b) The equilibrium-constant expression is

$$K_c = \frac{[CO_2]^2}{[CO]^2}$$

Because $SnO_2$ and $Sn$ are pure solids, their concentrations do not appear in the equilibrium-constant expression.

## PRACTICE EXERCISE

Write the following equilibrium-constant expressions:

(a) $K_c$ for $Cr(s) + 3\,Ag^+(aq) \rightleftharpoons Cr^{3+}(aq) + 3\,Ag(s)$
(b) $K_p$ for $3\,Fe(s) + 4\,H_2O(g) \rightleftharpoons Fe_3O_4(s) + 4\,H_2(g)$

**Answers:** (a) $K_c = \dfrac{[Cr^{3+}]}{[Ag^+]^3}$    (b) $K_p = \dfrac{(P_{H_2})^4}{(P_{H_2O})^4}$

---

**SAMPLE EXERCISE 15.7** | **Analyzing a Heterogeneous Equilibrium**

Each of these mixtures was placed in a closed container and allowed to stand:

(a) $CaCO_3(s)$
(b) $CaO(s)$ and $CO_2(g)$ at a pressure greater than the value of $K_p$
(c) $CaCO_3(s)$ and $CO_2(g)$ at a pressure greater than the value of $K_p$
(d) $CaCO_3(s)$ and $CaO(s)$

Determine whether or not each mixture can attain the equilibrium

$$CaCO_3(s) \rightleftharpoons CaO(s) + CO_2(g)$$

## SOLUTION

**Analyze** We are asked which of several combinations of species can establish an equilibrium between calcium carbonate and its decomposition products, calcium oxide and carbon dioxide.

**Plan** For equilibrium to be achieved, it must be possible for both the forward process and the reverse process to occur. For the forward process to occur, there must be some calcium carbonate present. For the reverse process to occur, there must be both calcium oxide and carbon dioxide. In both cases, either the necessary compounds may be present initially or they may be formed by reaction of the other species.

**Solve** Equilibrium can be reached in all cases except (c) as long as sufficient quantities of solids are present. (a) $CaCO_3$ simply decomposes, forming $CaO(s)$ and $CO_2(g)$ until the equilibrium pressure of $CO_2$ is attained. There must be enough $CaCO_3$, however, to allow the $CO_2$ pressure to reach equilibrium. (b) $CO_2$ continues to combine with $CaO$ until the partial pressure of the $CO_2$ decreases to the equilibrium value. (c) There is no $CaO$ present, so equilibrium cannot be attained because there is no way the $CO_2$ pressure can decrease to its equilibrium value (which would require some of the $CO_2$ to react with $CaO$). (d) The situation is essentially the same as in (a): $CaCO_3$ decomposes until equilibrium is attained. The presence of $CaO$ initially makes no difference.

## PRACTICE EXERCISE

When added to $Fe_3O_4(s)$ in a closed container, which one of the following substances — $H_2(g)$, $H_2O(g)$, $O_2(g)$ — allows equilibrium to be established in the reaction $3\,Fe(s) + 4\,H_2O(g) \rightleftharpoons Fe_3O_4(s) + 4\,H_2(g)$?

**Answer:** $H_2(g)$

When a solvent is a reactant or product in an equilibrium, its concentration is omitted from the equilibrium-constant expression, provided the concentrations of reactants and products are low, so that the solvent is essentially a pure substance. Applying this guideline to an equilibrium involving water as a solvent,

$$H_2O(l) + CO_3^{2-}(aq) \rightleftharpoons OH^-(aq) + HCO_3^-(aq) \qquad [15.20]$$

gives an equilibrium-constant expression that does not contain $[H_2O]$:

$$K_c = \frac{[OH^-][HCO_3^-]}{[CO_3^{2-}]} \qquad [15.21]$$

▲ GIVE IT SOME THOUGHT

Write the equilibrium-constant expression for the reaction $NH_3(aq) + H_2O(l) \rightleftharpoons NH_4^+(aq) + OH^-(aq)$

# 15.5 | CALCULATING EQUILIBRIUM CONSTANTS

If we can measure the equilibrium concentrations of all the reactants and products in a chemical reaction, as we did with the data in Table 15.1, calculating the value of the equilibrium constant is straightforward. We simply insert all the equilibrium concentrations into the equilibrium-constant expression for the reaction.

---

**SAMPLE EXERCISE 15.8** | **Calculating $K$ When All Equilibrium Concentrations Are Known**

After a mixture of hydrogen and nitrogen gases in a reaction vessel is allowed to attain equilibrium at 472 °C, it is found to contain 7.38 atm $H_2$, 2.46 atm $N_2$, and 0.166 atm $NH_3$. From these data, calculate the equilibrium constant $K_p$ for the reaction

$$N_2(g) + 3 H_2(g) \rightleftharpoons 2 NH_3(g)$$

**SOLUTION**

**Analyze** We are given a balanced equation and equilibrium partial pressures and are asked to calculate the value of the equilibrium constant.

**Plan** Using the balanced equation, we write the equilibrium-constant expression. We then substitute the equilibrium partial pressures into the expression and solve for $K_p$.

**Solve**

$$K_p = \frac{(P_{NH_3})^2}{P_{N_2}(P_{H_2})^3} = \frac{(0.166)^2}{(2.46)(7.38)^3} = 2.79 \times 10^{-5}$$

**PRACTICE EXERCISE**

An aqueous solution of acetic acid is found to have the following equilibrium concentrations at 25 °C: $[CH_3COOH] = 1.65 \times 10^{-2} M$; $[H^+] = 5.44 \times 10^{-4} M$; and $[CH_3COO^-] = 5.44 \times 10^{-4} M$. Calculate the equilibrium constant $K_c$ for the ionization of acetic acid at 25 °C. The reaction is

$$CH_3COOH(aq) \rightleftharpoons H^+(aq) + CH_3COO^-(aq)$$

**Answer:** $1.79 \times 10^{-5}$

---

Often we do not know the equilibrium concentrations of all species in an equilibrium mixture. If we know the equilibrium concentration of at least one species, however, we can generally use the stoichiometry of the reaction to deduce the equilibrium concentrations of the others. The following steps outline the procedure:

1. Tabulate all known initial and equilibrium concentrations of the species that appear in the equilibrium-constant expression.

2. For those species for which initial and equilibrium concentrations are known, calculate the change in concentration that occurs as the system reaches equilibrium.

3. Use the stoichiometry of the reaction (that is, the coefficients in the balanced chemical equation) to calculate the changes in concentration for all other species in the equilibrium-constant expression.

4. Use initial concentrations from step 1 and changes in concentration from step 3 to calculate any equilibrium concentrations not tabulated in step 1.

5. Determine the value of the equilibrium constant.

---

**SAMPLE EXERCISE 15.9** | **Calculating *K* from Initial and Equilibrium Concentrations**

A closed system initially containing $1.000 \times 10^{-3}\,M\,H_2$ and $2.000 \times 10^{-3}\,M\,I_2$ at 448 °C is allowed to reach equilibrium, and at equilibrium the HI concentration is $1.87 \times 10^{-3}\,M$. Calculate $K_c$ at 448 °C for the reaction taking place, which is

$$H_2(g) + I_2(g) \rightleftharpoons 2\,HI(g)$$

**SOLUTION**

**Analyze** We are given the initial concentrations of $H_2$ and $I_2$ and the equilibrium concentration of HI. We are asked to calculate the equilibrium constant $K_c$ for $H_2(g) + I_2(g) \rightleftharpoons 2\,HI(g)$.

**Plan** We construct a table to find equilibrium concentrations of all species and then use the equilibrium concentrations to calculate the equilibrium constant.

**Solve** First, we tabulate the initial and equilibrium concentrations of as many species as we can. We also provide space in our table for listing the changes in concentrations. As shown, it is convenient to use the chemical equation as the heading for the table.

|  | $H_2(g)$ + | $I_2(g)$ $\rightleftharpoons$ | $2\,HI(g)$ |
|---|---|---|---|
| Initial concentration (*M*) | $1.000 \times 10^{-3}$ | $2.000 \times 10^{-3}$ | 0 |
| Change in concentration (*M*) |  |  |  |
| Equilibrium concentration (*M*) |  |  | $1.87 \times 10^{-3}$ |

Second, we calculate the change in HI concentration, which is the difference between the equilibrium and initial values:

$$\text{Change in [HI]} = 1.87 \times 10^{-3}\,M - 0 = 1.87 \times 10^{-3}\,M$$

Third, we use the coefficients in the balanced equation to relate the change in [HI] to the changes in $[H_2]$ and $[I_2]$:

$$\left(1.87 \times 10^{-3}\,\frac{\text{mol HI}}{\text{L}}\right)\left(\frac{1\,\text{mol}\,H_2}{2\,\text{mol HI}}\right) = 0.935 \times 10^{-3}\,\frac{\text{mol}\,H_2}{\text{L}}$$

$$\left(1.87 \times 10^{-3}\,\frac{\text{mol HI}}{\text{L}}\right)\left(\frac{1\,\text{mol}\,I_2}{2\,\text{mol HI}}\right) = 0.935 \times 10^{-3}\,\frac{\text{mol}\,I_2}{\text{L}}$$

Fourth, we calculate the equilibrium concentrations of $H_2$ and $I_2$, using initial concentrations and changes in concentration. The equilibrium concentration equals the initial concentration minus that consumed:

$$[H_2] = 1.000 \times 10^{-3}\,M - 0.935 \times 10^{-3}\,M = 0.065 \times 10^{-3}\,M$$
$$[I_2] = 2.000 \times 10^{-3}\,M - 0.935 \times 10^{-3}\,M = 1.065 \times 10^{-3}\,M$$

Our table now looks like this (with equilibrium concentrations in blue for emphasis):

|  | $H_2(g)$ + | $I_2(g)$ $\rightleftharpoons$ | $2\,HI(g)$ |
|---|---|---|---|
| Initial concentration (*M*) | $1.000 \times 10^{-3}$ | $2.000 \times 10^{-3}$ | 0 |
| Change in concentration (*M*) | $-0.935 \times 10^{-3}$ | $-0.935 \times 10^{-3}$ | $+1.87 \times 10^{-3}$ |
| Equilibrium concentration (*M*) | $0.065 \times 10^{-3}$ | $1.065 \times 10^{-3}$ | $1.87 \times 10^{-3}$ |

Notice that the entries for the changes are negative when a reactant is consumed and positive when a product is formed.

Finally, we use the equilibrium-constant expression to calculate the equilibrium constant:

$$K_c = \frac{[HI]^2}{[H_2][I_2]} = \frac{(1.87 \times 10^{-3})^2}{(0.065 \times 10^{-3})(1.065 \times 10^{-3})} = 51$$

**Comment** The same method can be applied to gaseous equilibrium problems to calculate $K_p$, in which case partial pressures are used as table entries in place of molar concentrations. Your instructor may refer to this kind of table as an ICE chart, where ICE stands for *I*nitial – *C*hange – *E*quilibrium.

**PRACTICE EXERCISE**

Sulfur trioxide decomposes at high temperature in a sealed container: $2\,SO_3(g) \rightleftharpoons 2\,SO_2(g) + O_2(g)$. Initially, the vessel is charged at 1000 K with $SO_3(g)$ at a partial pressure of 0.500 atm. At equilibrium the $SO_3$ partial pressure is 0.200 atm. Calculate the value of $K_p$ at 1000 K.

*Answer:* 0.338

# 15.6 | APPLICATIONS OF EQUILIBRIUM CONSTANTS

We have seen that the magnitude of $K$ indicates the extent to which a reaction proceeds. If $K$ is very large, the equilibrium mixture contains mostly substances on the product side of the equation for the reaction. (That is, the reaction proceeds far to the right.) If $K$ is very small (that is, much less than 1), the equilibrium mixture contains mainly substances on the reactant side of the equation. The equilibrium constant also allows us to (1) predict the direction in which a reaction mixture achieves equilibrium and (2) calculate equilibrium concentrations of reactants and products.

## Predicting the Direction of Reaction

For the formation of $NH_3$ from $N_2$ and $H_2$ (Equation 15.6), $K_c = 0.105$ at 472 °C. Suppose we place 2.00 mol of $H_2$, 1.00 mol of $N_2$, and 2.00 mol of $NH_3$ in a 1.00-L container at 472 °C. How will the mixture react to reach equilibrium? Will $N_2$ and $H_2$ react to form more $NH_3$, or will $NH_3$ decompose to $N_2$ and $H_2$?

To answer this question, we substitute the starting concentrations of $N_2$, $H_2$, and $NH_3$ into the equilibrium-constant expression and compare its value to the equilibrium constant:

$$\frac{[NH_3]^2}{[N_2][H_2]^3} = \frac{(2.00)^2}{(1.00)(2.00)^3} = 0.500 \quad \text{whereas} \quad K_c = 0.105 \qquad [15.22]$$

To reach equilibrium, the quotient $[NH_3]^2/[N_2][H_2]^3$ must decrease from the starting value of 0.500 to the equilibrium value of 0.105. Because the system is closed, this change can happen only if $[NH_3]$ decreases and $[N_2]$ and $[H_2]$ increase. Thus, the reaction proceeds toward equilibrium by forming $N_2$ and $H_2$ from $NH_3$; that is, the reaction as written in Equation 15.6 proceeds from right to left.

This approach can be formalized by defining a quantity called the reaction quotient. The **reaction quotient**, $Q$, *is a number obtained by substituting reactant and product concentrations or partial pressures at any point during a reaction into an equilibrium-constant expression.* Therefore, for the general reaction

$$a\,A + b\,B \rightleftharpoons d\,D + e\,E$$

the reaction quotient in terms of molar concentrations is

$$Q_c = \frac{[D]^d[E]^e}{[A]^a[B]^b} \qquad [15.23]$$

(A related quantity $Q_p$ can be written for any reaction that involves gases by using partial pressures instead of concentrations.)

Although we use what looks like the equilibrium-constant expression to calculate the reaction quotient, the concentrations we use may or may not be the equilibrium concentrations. For example, when we substituted the starting concentrations into the equilibrium-constant expression of Equation 15.22, we obtained $Q_c = 0.500$ whereas $K_c = 0.105$. The equilibrium constant has only one value at each temperature. The reaction quotient, however, varies as the reaction proceeds.

Of what use is $Q$? One practical thing we can do with $Q$ is tell whether our reaction really is at equilibrium, which is an especially valuable option when a reaction is very slow. We can take samples of our reaction mixture as the reaction proceeds, separate the components, and measure their concentrations. Then we insert these numbers into Equation 15.23 for our reaction. To determine whether or not we are at equilibrium, or in which direction the reaction proceeds to achieve equilibrium, we compare the values of $Q_c$ and $K_c$ or $Q_p$ and $K_p$. Three possible situations arise:

- $Q = K$: The reaction quotient equals the equilibrium constant only if the system is at equilibrium.

At equilibrium

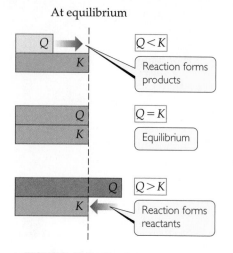

▲ **FIGURE 15.8 Predicting the direction of a reaction by comparing Q and K at a given temperature.**

- $Q > K$: The concentration of products is too large and that of reactants too small. Substances on the right side of the chemical equation react to form substances on the left; the reaction proceeds from right to left to approach equilibrium.

- $Q < K$: The concentration of products is too small and that of reactants too large. The reaction achieves equilibrium by forming more products; it proceeds from left to right.

These relationships are summarized in ◄ **FIGURE 15.8**.

---

**SAMPLE EXERCISE 15.10** | **Predicting the Direction of Approach to Equilibrium**

At 448 °C the equilibrium constant $K_c$ for the reaction

$$H_2(g) + I_2(g) \rightleftharpoons 2\,HI(g)$$

is 50.5. Predict in which direction the reaction proceeds to reach equilibrium if we start with $2.0 \times 10^{-2}$ mol of HI, $1.0 \times 10^{-2}$ mol of $H_2$, and $3.0 \times 10^{-2}$ mol of $I_2$ in a 2.00-L container.

**SOLUTION**

**Analyze** We are given a volume and initial molar amounts of the species in a reaction and asked to determine in which direction the reaction must proceed to achieve equilibrium.

**Plan** We can determine the starting concentration of each species in the reaction mixture. We can then substitute the starting concentrations into the equilibrium-constant expression to calculate the reaction quotient, $Q_c$. Comparing the magnitudes of the equilibrium constant, which is given, and the reaction quotient will tell us in which direction the reaction will proceed.

**Solve**
The initial concentrations are

$$[HI] = 2.0 \times 10^{-2}\ \text{mol}/2.00\ \text{L} = 1.0 \times 10^{-2}\ M$$
$$[H_2] = 1.0 \times 10^{-2}\ \text{mol}/2.00\ \text{L} = 5.0 \times 10^{-3}\ M$$
$$[I_2] = 3.0 \times 10^{-2}\ \text{mol}/2.00\ \text{L} = 1.5 \times 10^{-2}\ M$$

The reaction quotient is therefore

$$Q_c = \frac{[HI]^2}{[H_2][I_2]} = \frac{(1.0 \times 10^{-2})^2}{(5.0 \times 10^{-3})(1.5 \times 10^{-2})} = 1.3$$

Because $Q_c < K_c$, the concentration of HI must increase and the concentrations of $H_2$ and $I_2$ must decrease to reach equilibrium; the reaction as written proceeds left to right to attain equilibrium.

**PRACTICE EXERCISE**

At 1000 K the value of $K_p$ for the reaction $2\,SO_3(g) \rightleftharpoons 2\,SO_2(g) + O_2(g)$ is 0.338. Calculate the value for $Q_p$, and predict the direction in which the reaction proceeds toward equilibrium if the initial partial pressures are $P_{SO_3} = 0.16$ atm; $P_{SO_2} = 0.41$ atm; $P_{O_2} = 2.5$ atm.

**Answer:** $Q_p = 16$; $Q_p > K_p$, and so the reaction will proceed from right to left, forming more $SO_3$.

---

## Calculating Equilibrium Concentrations

Chemists frequently need to calculate the amounts of reactants and products present at equilibrium in a reaction for which they know the equilibrium constant. The approach in solving problems of this type is similar to the one we used for evaluating equilibrium constants: We tabulate initial concentrations or partial pressures, changes in those concentrations or pressures, and final equilibrium concentrations or partial pressures. Usually we end up using the equilibrium-constant expression to derive an equation that must be solved for an unknown quantity, as demonstrated in Sample Exercise 15.11.

---

**SAMPLE EXERCISE 15.11 | Calculating Equilibrium Concentrations**

For the Haber process, $N_2(g) + 3 H_2(g) \rightleftharpoons 2 NH_3(g)$, $K_p = 1.45 \times 10^{-5}$ at 500 °C. In an equilibrium mixture of the three gases at 500 °C, the partial pressure of $H_2$ is 0.928 atm and that of $N_2$ is 0.432 atm. What is the partial pressure of $NH_3$ in this equilibrium mixture?

**SOLUTION**

**Analyze** We are given an equilibrium constant, $K_p$, and the equilibrium partial pressures of two of the three substances in the equation ($N_2$ and $H_2$), and we are asked to calculate the equilibrium partial pressure for the third substance ($NH_3$).

**Plan** We can set $K_p$ equal to the equilibrium-constant expression and substitute in the partial pressures that we know. Then we can solve for the only unknown in the equation.

**Solve** We tabulate the equilibrium pressures:

$$N_2(g) + 3 H_2(g) \rightleftharpoons 2 NH_3(g)$$

| Equilibrium pressure (atm) | 0.432 | 0.928 | $x$ |
| --- | --- | --- | --- |

Because we do not know the equilibrium pressure of $NH_3$, we represent it with $x$. At equilibrium the pressures must satisfy the equilibrium-constant expression:

$$K_p = \frac{(P_{NH_3})^2}{P_{N_2}(P_{H_2})^3} = \frac{x^2}{(0.432)(0.928)^3} = 1.45 \times 10^{-5}$$

We now rearrange the equation to solve for $x$:

$$x^2 = (1.45 \times 10^{-5})(0.432)(0.928)^3 = 5.01 \times 10^{-6}$$

$$x = \sqrt{5.01 \times 10^{-6}} = 2.24 \times 10^{-3} \text{ atm} = P_{NH_3}$$

**Check** We can always check our answer by using it to recalculate the value of the equilibrium constant:

$$K_p = \frac{(2.24 \times 10^{-3})^2}{(0.432)(0.928)^3} = 1.45 \times 10^{-5}$$

**PRACTICE EXERCISE**

At 500 K the reaction $PCl_5(g) \rightleftharpoons PCl_3(g) + Cl_2(g)$ has $K_p = 0.497$. In an equilibrium mixture at 500 K, the partial pressure of $PCl_5$ is 0.860 atm and that of $PCl_3$ is 0.350 atm. What is the partial pressure of $Cl_2$ in the equilibrium mixture?

**Answer:** 1.22 atm

---

In many situations we know the value of the equilibrium constant and the initial amounts of all species. We must then solve for the equilibrium amounts. Solving this type of problem usually entails treating the change in concentration as a variable. The stoichiometry of the reaction gives us the relationship between the changes in the amounts of all the reactants and products, as illustrated in Sample Exercise 15.12. The calculations frequently involve the quadratic formula, as you will see in this exercise.

---

**SAMPLE EXERCISE 15.12 | Calculating Equilibrium Concentrations from Initial Concentrations**

A 1.000-L flask is filled with 1.000 mol of $H_2(g)$ and 2.000 mol of $I_2(g)$ at 448 °C. The value of the equilibrium constant $K_c$ for the reaction

$$H_2(g) + I_2(g) \rightleftharpoons 2 HI(g)$$

at 448 °C is 50.5. What are the equilibrium concentrations of $H_2$, $I_2$, and HI in moles per liter?

**SOLUTION**

**Analyze** We are given the volume of a container, an equilibrium constant, and starting amounts of reactants in the container and are asked to calculate the equilibrium concentrations of all species.

**Plan** In this case we are not given any of the equilibrium concentrations. We must develop some relationships that relate the initial concentrations to those at equilibrium. The procedure is similar in many regards to that outlined in Sample Exercise 15.9, where we calculated an equilibrium constant using initial concentrations.

**Solve** First, we note the initial concentrations of $H_2$ and $I_2$:

$$[H_2] = 1.000 \, M \quad \text{and} \quad [I_2] = 2.000 \, M$$

Second, we construct a table in which we tabulate the initial concentrations:

| | $H_2(g)$ + | $I_2(g)$ $\rightleftharpoons$ | 2 HI(g) |
| --- | --- | --- | --- |
| Initial concentration (M) | 1.000 | 2.000 | 0 |
| Change in concentration (M) | | | |
| Equilibrium concentration (M) | | | |

Third, we use the stoichiometry of the reaction to determine the changes in concentration that occur as the reaction proceeds to equilibrium. The $H_2$ and $I_2$ concentrations will decrease as equilibrium is established and that of HI will increase. Let's represent the change in concentration of $H_2$ by $x$. The balanced chemical equation tells us the relationship between the changes in the concentrations of the three gases. For each $x$ mol of $H_2$ that reacts, $x$ mol of $I_2$ are consumed and $2x$ mol of HI are produced:

Fourth, we use initial concentrations and changes in concentrations, as dictated by stoichiometry, to express the equilibrium concentrations. With all our entries, our table now looks like this:

Fifth, we substitute the equilibrium concentrations into the equilibrium-constant expression and solve for $x$:

If you have an equation-solving calculator, you can solve this equation directly for $x$. If not, expand this expression to obtain a quadratic equation in $x$:

Solving the quadratic equation (Appendix A.3) leads to two solutions for $x$:

When we substitute $x = 2.323$ into the expressions for the equilibrium concentrations, we find *negative* concentrations of $H_2$ and $I_2$. Because a negative concentration is not chemically meaningful, we reject this solution. We then use $x = 0.935$ to find the equilibrium concentrations:

**Check** We can check our solution by putting these numbers into the equilibrium-constant expression to assure that we correctly calculate the equilibrium constant:

|  | $H_2(g)$ | + | $I_2(g)$ | $\rightleftharpoons$ | $2\,HI(g)$ |
|---|---|---|---|---|---|
| Initial concentration (M) | 1.000 |  | 2.000 |  | 0 |
| Change in concentration (M) | $-x$ |  | $-x$ |  | $+2x$ |
| Equilibrium concentration (M) |  |  |  |  |  |

|  | $H_2(g)$ | + | $I_2(g)$ | $\rightleftharpoons$ | $2\,HI(g)$ |
|---|---|---|---|---|---|
| Initial concentration (M) | 1.000 |  | 2.000 |  | 0 |
| Change in concentration (M) | $-x$ |  | $-x$ |  | $+2x$ |
| Equilibrium concentration (M) | $1.000 - x$ |  | $2.000 - x$ |  | $2x$ |

$$K_c = \frac{[HI]^2}{[H_2][I_2]} = \frac{(2x)^2}{(1.000 - x)(2.000 - x)} = 50.5$$

$$4x^2 = 50.5(x^2 - 3.000x + 2.000)$$
$$46.5x^2 - 151.5x + 101.0 = 0$$

$$x = \frac{-(-151.5) \pm \sqrt{(-151.5)^2 - 4(46.5)(101.0)}}{2(46.5)} = 2.323 \text{ or } 0.935$$

$$[H_2] = 1.000 - x = 0.065\ M$$
$$[I_2] = 2.000 - x = 1.065\ M$$
$$[HI] = 2x = 1.87\ M$$

$$K_c = \frac{[HI]^2}{[H_2][I_2]} = \frac{(1.87)^2}{(0.065)(1.065)} = 51$$

**Comment** Whenever you use a quadratic equation to solve an equilibrium problem, one of the solutions to the equation will give you a value that leads to negative concentrations and thus is not chemically meaningful. Reject this solution to the quadratic equation.

### PRACTICE EXERCISE

For the equilibrium $PCl_5(g) \rightleftharpoons PCl_3(g) + Cl_2(g)$, the equilibrium constant $K_p$ is 0.497 at 500 K. A gas cylinder at 500 K is charged with $PCl_5(g)$ at an initial pressure of 1.66 atm. What are the equilibrium pressures of $PCl_5$, $PCl_3$, and $Cl_2$ at this temperature?
*Answer:* $P_{PCl_5} = 0.967$ atm, $P_{PCl_3} = P_{Cl_2} = 0.693$ atm

## 15.7 | LE CHÂTELIER'S PRINCIPLE

Many of the products we use in everyday life are obtained from the chemical industry. Chemists and chemical engineers in industry spend a great deal of time and effort to maximize the yield of valuable products and minimize waste. For example, when Haber developed his process for making ammonia from $N_2$ and $H_2$, he examined how reaction conditions might be varied to increase yield. Using the values of the equilibrium constant at various temperatures, he calculated the equilibrium amounts of $NH_3$ formed under a variety of conditions. Some of Haber's results are shown in ▶ **FIGURE 15.9.**

◢ **GO FIGURE**

**At what combination of pressure and temperature should you run the reaction to maximize NH$_3$ yield?**

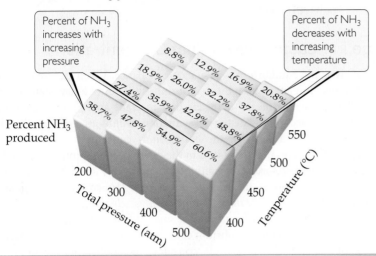

◀ **FIGURE 15.9   Effect of temperature and pressure on NH$_3$ yield in the Haber process.** Each mixture was produced by starting with a 3:1 molar mixture of H$_2$ and N$_2$.

Notice that the percent of NH$_3$ present at equilibrium decreases with increasing temperature and increases with increasing pressure.

We can understand these effects in terms of a principle first put forward by Henri-Louis Le Châtelier* (1850–1936), a French industrial chemist: *If a system at equilibrium is disturbed by a change in temperature, pressure, or a component concentration, the system will shift its equilibrium position so as to counteract the effect of the disturbance.*

**Le Chatelier's Principle**

If a system at equilibrium is disturbed by a change in **concentration, pressure,** or **temperature,** the system will shift its equilibrium position so as to counter the effect of the disturbance.

**Concentration:** adding or removing a reactant or product

*If a substance is added to a system at equilibrium, the system reacts to consume some of the substance. If a substance is removed from a system, the system reacts to produce more of substance.*

**Pressure:** changing the pressure by changing the volume

*At constant temperature, reducing the volume of a gaseous equilibrium mixture causes the system to shift in the direction that reduces the number of moles of gas.*

**Temperature:**

*If the temperature of a system at equilibrium is increased, the system reacts as if we added a reactant to an endothermic reaction or a product to an exothermic reaction. The equilibrium shifts in the direction that consumes the "excess reactant," namely heat.*

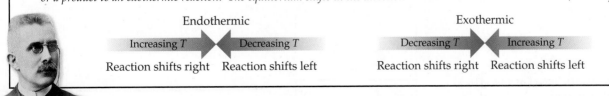

*Pronounced "le-SHOT-lee-ay."

In this section we use Le Châtelier's principle to make qualitative predictions about how a system at equilibrium responds to various changes in external conditions. We consider three ways in which a chemical equilibrium can be disturbed: (1) adding or removing a reactant or product, (2) changing the pressure by changing the volume, and (3) changing the temperature.

## Change in Reactant or Product Concentration

A system at dynamic equilibrium is in a state of balance. When the concentrations of species in the reaction are altered, the equilibrium shifts until a new state of balance is attained. What does *shift* mean? It means that reactant and product concentrations change over time to accommodate the new situation. *Shift* does *not* mean that the equilibrium constant itself is altered; the equilibrium constant remains the same. Le Châtelier's principle states that the shift is in the direction that minimizes or reduces the effect of the change. Therefore, *if a chemical system is already at equilibrium and the concentration of any substance in the mixture is increased (either reactant or product), the system reacts to consume some of that substance. Conversely, if the concentration of a substance is decreased, the system reacts to produce some of that substance.*

There is no change in the equilibrium constant when we change the concentrations of reactants or products. As an example, consider our familiar equilibrium mixture of $N_2$, $H_2$, and $NH_3$:

$$N_2(g) + 3 H_2(g) \rightleftharpoons 2 NH_3(g)$$

Adding $H_2$ causes the system to shift so as to reduce the increased concentration of $H_2$ (▼ **FIGURE 15.10**). This change can occur only if the reaction consumes $H_2$ and simultaneously consumes $N_2$ to form more $NH_3$. Adding $N_2$ to the equilibrium mixture likewise causes the reaction to shift toward forming more $NH_3$. Removing $NH_3$ also causes a shift toward producing more $NH_3$, whereas *adding* $NH_3$ to the system at equilibrium causes the reaction to shift in the direction that reduces the increased $NH_3$ concentration: Some of the added ammonia decomposes to form $N_2$ and $H_2$.

In the Haber reaction, therefore, removing $NH_3$ from an equilibrium mixture of $N_2$, $H_2$, and $NH_3$ causes the reaction to shift right to form more $NH_3$. If the $NH_3$ can be removed continuously as it is produced, the yield can be increased dramatically. In the

**GO FIGURE**

**Why does the nitrogen concentration decrease after hydrogen is added?**

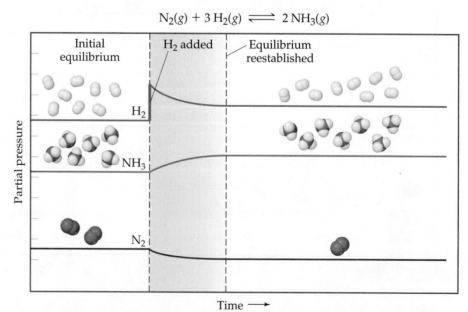

▶ **FIGURE 15.10 Effect of adding H₂ to an equilibrium mixture of N₂, H₂, and NH₃.** Adding $H_2$ causes the reaction as written to shift to the right, consuming some $H_2$ to produce more $NH_3$.

Hot gases

N₂

H₂

**1** Incoming N₂ and H₂ gases

Heat exchanger

**6** Unreacted N₂ and H₂ recycled

Heat exchanger

**4** Gases released from catalyst

**3** Heated gases pass over catalyst, NH₃ forms

**5** As gas mixture cools, NH₃(g) liquifies

**2** N₂ and H₂ gases heated to approximately 500 °C

Liquid NH₃ outlet

▲ **FIGURE 15.11** **Diagram of the industrial production of ammonia.** Incoming N₂(g) and H₂(g) are heated to approximately 500 °C and passed over a catalyst. When the resultant N₂, H₂, and NH₃ mixture is cooled, the NH₃ liquefies and is removed from the mixture, shifting the reaction to produce more NH₃.

industrial production of ammonia, the $NH_3$ is continuously removed by selectively liquefying it (▲ **FIGURE 15.11**). (The boiling point of $NH_3$, $-33\ °C$, is much higher than those of $N_2$, $-196\ °C$, and $H_2$, $-253\ °C$.) The liquid $NH_3$ is removed, and the $N_2$ and $H_2$ are recycled to form more $NH_3$. As a result of the product being continuously removed, the reaction is driven essentially to completion.

 GIVE IT SOME THOUGHT

What happens to the equilibrium $2\ NO(g) + O_2(g) \rightleftharpoons 2\ NO_2(g)$ if
a. $O_2$ is added to the system,
b. NO is removed?

## Effects of Volume and Pressure Changes

If a system containing one or more gases is at equilibrium and its volume is decreased, thereby increasing its total pressure, Le Châtelier's principle indicates that the system responds by shifting its equilibrium position to reduce the pressure. A system can reduce its pressure by reducing the total number of gas molecules (fewer molecules of gas exert a lower pressure). Thus, at constant temperature, *reducing the volume of a gaseous equilibrium mixture causes the system to shift in the direction that reduces the number of moles of gas.* Increasing the volume causes a shift in the direction that produces more gas molecules (▶ **FIGURE 15.12**).

 GIVE IT SOME THOUGHT

What happens to the equilibrium $2\ SO_2(g) + O_2(g) \rightleftharpoons 2\ SO_3(g)$ if the volume of the system is increased?

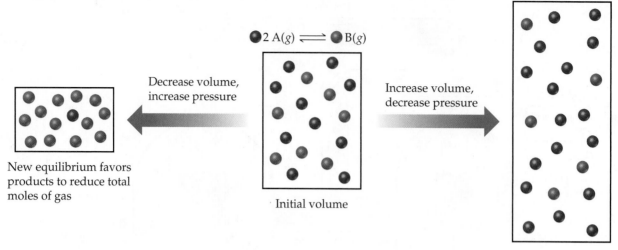

▲ **FIGURE 15.12    Pressure and Le Châtelier's principle.**

In the reaction $N_2(g) + 3\,H_2(g) \rightleftharpoons 2\,NH_3(g)$, four molecules of reactant are consumed for every two molecules of product produced. Consequently, an increase in pressure (caused by a decrease in volume) shifts the reaction in the direction that produces fewer gas molecules, which leads to the formation of more $NH_3$, as indicated in Figure 15.9. In the reaction $H_2(g) + I_2(g) \rightleftharpoons 2\,HI(g)$, the number of molecules of gaseous products (two) equals the number of molecules of gaseous reactants; therefore, changing the pressure does not influence the position of equilibrium.

Keep in mind that, as long as temperature remains constant, pressure-volume changes do *not* change the value of $K$. Rather, these changes alter the partial pressures of the gaseous substances. In Sample Exercise 15.8, we calculated $K_p = 2.79 \times 10^{-5}$ for the Haber reaction, $N_2(g) + 3\,H_2(g) \rightleftharpoons 2\,NH_3(g)$, in an equilibrium mixture at 472 °C containing 7.38 atm $H_2$, 2.46 atm $N_2$, and 0.166 atm $NH_3$. Consider what happens when we suddenly reduce the volume of the system by one-half. If there were no shift in equilibrium, this volume change would cause the partial pressures of all substances to double, giving $P_{H_2} = 14.76$ atm, $P_{N_2} = 4.92$ atm, and $P_{NH_3} = 0.332$ atm. The reaction quotient would then no longer equal the equilibrium constant:

$$Q_p = \frac{(P_{NH_3})^2}{P_{N_2}(P_{H_2})^3} = \frac{(0.332)^2}{(4.92)(14.76)^3} = 6.97 \times 10^{-6} \neq K_p$$

Because $Q_p < K_p$, the system would no longer be at equilibrium. Equilibrium would be reestablished by increasing $P_{NH_3}$ and/or decreasing $P_{N_2}$ and $P_{H_2}$ until $Q_p = K_p = 2.79 \times 10^{-5}$. Therefore, the equilibrium shifts to the right in the reaction as written, as Le Châtelier's principle predicts.

It is possible to change the pressure of a system in which a chemical reaction is running without changing its volume. For example, pressure increases if additional amounts of any reacting components are added to the system. We have already seen how to deal with a change in concentration of a reactant or product. The total pressure in the reaction vessel might also be increased by adding a gas that is not involved in the equilibrium. For example, argon might be added to the ammonia equilibrium system. The argon would not alter the partial pressures of any of the reacting components and therefore would not cause a shift in equilibrium.

## Effect of Temperature Changes

Changes in concentrations or partial pressures shift equilibria without changing the value of the equilibrium constant. In contrast, almost every equilibrium constant changes as the temperature changes. For example, consider the equilibrium established when cobalt(II) chloride ($CoCl_2$) is dissolved in hydrochloric acid, $HCl(aq)$, in the endothermic reaction

$$Co(H_2O)_6^{2+}(aq) + 4\,Cl^-(aq) \rightleftharpoons CoCl_4^{2-}(aq) + 6\,H_2O(l) \qquad \Delta H > 0 \quad [15.24]$$
Pale pink Deep blue

Because $Co(H_2O)_6^{2+}$ is pink and $CoCl_4^{2-}$ is blue, the position of this equilibrium is readily apparent from the color of the solution (▼ **FIGURE 15.13**). When the solution is heated it turns blue, indicating that the equilibrium has shifted to form more $CoCl_4^{2-}$. Cooling the solution leads to a pink solution, indicating that the equilibrium has shifted to produce more $Co(H_2O)_6^{2+}$. We can monitor this reaction by spectroscopic methods, measuring the concentration of all species at the different temperatures. ∞ (Section 14.2) We can then calculate the equilibrium constant at each temperature. How can we explain the fact that the equilibrium constants and therefore the position of equilibrium both depend on temperature?

We can deduce the rules for the relationship between $K$ and temperature from Le Châtelier's principle. We do this by treating heat as a chemical reagent. In an *endothermic* (heat-absorbing) reaction, we consider heat a *reactant*, and in an *exothermic* (heat-releasing) reaction, we consider heat a *product*:

*Endothermic:*      Reactants + *heat* $\rightleftharpoons$ products

*Exothermic:*      Reactants $\rightleftharpoons$ products + *heat*

*When the temperature of a system at equilibrium is increased, the system reacts as if we added a reactant to an endothermic reaction or a product to an exothermic reaction. The equilibrium shifts in the direction that consumes the excess reactant (or product), namely heat.*

---

$\Delta H > 0$, endothermic reaction

$$\text{Heat} + Co(H_2O)_6^{2+}(aq) + 4\,Cl^-(aq) \rightleftharpoons CoCl_4^{2-}(aq) + 6\,H_2O(l)$$
Pink Blue

Heat

Add heat: reaction shifts right to increase blue $CoCl_4^{2-}$ concentration and decrease pink $Co(H_2O)_6^{2+}$ concentration

Cool

At equilibrium, significant amounts of both pink $Co(H_2O)_6^{2+}$ and blue $CoCl_4^{2-}$ are present; solution appears violet

Remove heat: reaction shifts left to decrease blue $CoCl_4^{2-}$ concentration and increase pink $Co(H_2O)_6^{2+}$ concentration

◄ **FIGURE 15.13** **Temperature and Le Châtelier's principle.**

▲ GIVE IT SOME THOUGHT

Use Le Châtelier's principle to explain why the equilibrium vapor pressure of a liquid increases with increasing temperature.

In an endothermic reaction, such as Equation 15.24, heat is absorbed as reactants are converted to products. Thus, increasing the temperature causes the equilibrium to shift to the right, in the direction of making more products, and $K$ increases. In an exothermic reaction, the opposite occurs: Heat is produced as reactants are converted to products. Thus, increasing the temperature in this case causes the equilibrium to shift to the left, in the direction of making more reactants, and $K$ decreases.

> *Endothermic:*      Increasing $T$ results in higher $K$ value
>
> *Exothermic:*      Increasing $T$ results in lower $K$ value

Cooling a reaction has the opposite effect. As we lower the temperature, the equilibrium shifts in the direction that produces heat. Thus, cooling an endothermic reaction shifts the equilibrium to the left, decreasing $K$, as shown in Figure 15.13, and cooling an exothermic reaction shifts the equilibrium to the right, increasing $K$.

---

**SAMPLE EXERCISE 15.13** | **Using Le Châtelier's Principle to Predict Shifts in Equilibrium**

Consider the equilibrium

$$N_2O_4(g) \rightleftharpoons 2\,NO_2(g) \qquad \Delta H° = 58.0\ kJ$$

In which direction will the equilibrium shift when (a) $N_2O_4$ is added, (b) $NO_2$ is removed, (c) the pressure is increased by addition of $N_2(g)$, (d) the volume is increased, (e) the temperature is decreased?

**SOLUTION**

**Analyze** We are given a series of changes to be made to a system at equilibrium and are asked to predict what effect each change will have on the position of the equilibrium.

**Plan** Le Châtelier's principle can be used to determine the effects of each of these changes.

**Solve**
(a) The system will adjust to decrease the concentration of the added $N_2O_4$, so the equilibrium shifts to the right, in the direction of product.

(b) The system will adjust to the removal of $NO_2$ by shifting to the side that produces more $NO_2$; thus, the equilibrium shifts to the right.

(c) Adding $N_2$ will increase the total pressure of the system, but $N_2$ is not involved in the reaction. The partial pressures of $NO_2$ and $N_2O_4$ are therefore unchanged, and there is no shift in the position of the equilibrium.

(d) If the volume is increased, the system will shift in the direction that occupies a larger volume (more gas molecules); thus, the equilibrium shifts to the right.

(e) The reaction is endothermic, so we can imagine heat as a reagent on the reactant side of the equation. Decreasing the temperature will shift the equilibrium in the direction that produces heat, so the equilibrium shifts to the left, toward the formation of more $N_2O_4$. Note that only this last change also affects the value of the equilibrium constant, $K$.

**PRACTICE EXERCISE**

For the reaction

$$PCl_5(g) \rightleftharpoons PCl_3(g) + Cl_2(g) \qquad \Delta H° = 87.9\ kJ$$

in which direction will the equilibrium shift when (a) $Cl_2(g)$ is removed, (b) the temperature is decreased, (c) the volume of the reaction system is increased, (d) $PCl_3(g)$ is added?

**Answers:** (a) right, (b) left, (c) right, (d) left

**SAMPLE EXERCISE 15.14** | Predicting the Effect of Temperature on *K*

**(a)** Using the standard heat of formation data in Appendix C, determine the standard enthalpy change for the reaction

$$N_2(g) + 3 H_2(g) \rightleftharpoons 2 NH_3(g)$$

**(b)** Determine how the equilibrium constant for this reaction should change with temperature.

**SOLUTION**

**Analyze** We are asked to determine the standard enthalpy change of a reaction and how the equilibrium constant for the reaction varies with temperature.

**Plan** **(a)** We can use standard enthalpies of formation to calculate $\Delta H°$ for the reaction. **(b)** We can then use Le Châtelier's principle to determine what effect temperature will have on the equilibrium constant.

**Solve**
**(a)** Recall that the standard enthalpy change for a reaction is given by the sum of the standard molar enthalpies of formation of the products, each multiplied by its coefficient in the balanced chemical equation, less the same quantities for the reactants. ∞ (Section 5.7) At 25 °C, $\Delta H_f°$ for $NH_3(g)$ is $-46.19$ kJ/mol. The $\Delta H_f°$ values for $H_2(g)$ and $N_2(g)$ are zero by definition because the enthalpies of formation of the elements in their normal states at 25 °C are defined as zero. ∞ (Section 5.7) Because 2 mol of $NH_3$ is formed, the total enthalpy change is

$$(2 \text{ mol})(-46.19 \text{ kJ/mol}) - 0 = -92.38 \text{ kJ}$$

**(b)** Because the reaction in the forward direction is exothermic, we can consider heat a product of the reaction. An increase in temperature causes the reaction to shift in the direction of less $NH_3$ and more $N_2$ and $H_2$. This effect is seen in the values for $K_p$ presented in ▶ **TABLE 15.2**. Notice that $K_p$ changes markedly with changes in temperature and that it is larger at lower temperatures.

**Comment** The fact that $K_p$ for the formation of $NH_3$ from $N_2$ and $H_2$ decreases with increasing temperature is a matter of great practical importance. To form $NH_3$ at a reasonable rate requires higher temperatures. At higher temperatures, however, the equilibrium constant is smaller, and so the percentage conversion to $NH_3$ is smaller. To compensate for this, higher pressures are needed because high pressure favors $NH_3$ formation.

**PRACTICE EXERCISE**

Using the thermodynamic data in Appendix C, determine the enthalpy change for the reaction

$$2 POCl_3(g) \rightleftharpoons 2 PCl_3(g) + O_2(g)$$

Use this result to determine how the equilibrium constant for the reaction should change with temperature.
***Answer:*** $\Delta H° = 508.3$ kJ; the equilibrium constant will increase with increasing temperature

**TABLE 15.2 • Variation in $K_p$ with Temperature for $N_2 + 3 H_2 \rightleftharpoons 2 NH_3$**

| Temperature (°C) | $K_p$ |
|---|---|
| 300 | $4.34 \times 10^{-3}$ |
| 400 | $1.64 \times 10^{-4}$ |
| 450 | $4.51 \times 10^{-5}$ |
| 500 | $1.45 \times 10^{-5}$ |
| 550 | $5.38 \times 10^{-6}$ |
| 600 | $2.25 \times 10^{-6}$ |

## The Effect of Catalysts

What happens if we add a catalyst to a chemical system that is at equilibrium? As shown in ▶ **FIGURE 15.14**, ∞ (Figure 14.23) a catalyst lowers the activation barrier between reactants and products. The activation energies for both the forward and reverse reactions are lowered. The catalyst thereby increases the rates of both forward and reverse reactions. Since *K* is the ratio of the forward and reverse rate constants for a reaction, you can predict, correctly, that the presence of a catalyst, even though it changes the reaction *rate*, does not affect the numeric value of *K* (Figure 15.14). As a result, *a catalyst increases the rate at which equilibrium is achieved but does not change the composition of the equilibrium mixture.*

The rate at which a reaction approaches equilibrium is an important practical consideration. As an example, let's again consider the synthesis of ammonia from $N_2$ and $H_2$. In designing his process, Haber had to deal with a rapid decrease in the equilibrium constant with increasing temperature (Table 15.2). At temperatures sufficiently high to

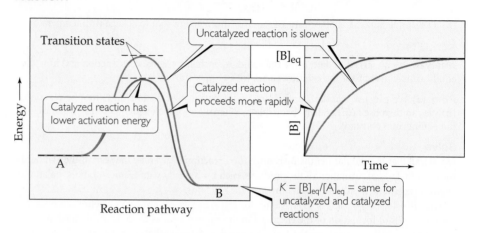

▲ **GO FIGURE**

How much faster is the catalyzed reaction compared to the uncatalyzed reaction?

▲ **FIGURE 15.14** A catalyst increases the rate at which equilibrium is reached but does not change the overall composition of the mixture at equilibrium.

give a satisfactory reaction rate, the amount of ammonia formed was too small. The solution to this dilemma was to develop a catalyst that would produce a reasonably rapid approach to equilibrium at a sufficiently low temperature, so that the equilibrium constant remained reasonably large. The development of a suitable catalyst thus became the focus of Haber's research efforts.

After trying different substances to see which would be most effective, Carl Bosch (see "Chemistry Put to Work: The Haber Process," page 615) settled on iron mixed with metal oxides, and variants of this catalyst formulation are still used today. These catalysts make it possible to obtain a reasonably rapid approach to equilibrium at around 400 to 500 °C and 200 to 600 atm. The high pressures are needed to obtain a satisfactory equilibrium amount of $NH_3$. If chemists and chemical engineers could identify a catalyst that leads to sufficiently rapid reaction at temperatures lower than 400 °C, it would be possible to obtain the same extent of equilibrium conversion at pressures much lower than 200 to 600 atm. This would result in great savings in the cost of the high-pressure equipment used in ammonia synthesis today.

As noted in Section 15.2, our need for nitrogen as fertilizer is growing globally, making the fixation of nitrogen a process of ever-increasing importance.

▲ **GIVE IT SOME THOUGHT**

Does the addition of a catalyst have any effect on the position of an equilibrium?

**SAMPLE INTEGRATIVE EXERCISE** Putting Concepts Together

At temperatures near 800 °C, steam passed over hot coke (a form of carbon obtained from coal) reacts to form CO and $H_2$:

$$C(s) + H_2O(g) \rightleftharpoons CO(g) + H_2(g)$$

The mixture of gases that results is an important industrial fuel called *water gas*. **(a)** At 800 °C the equilibrium constant for this reaction is $K_p = 14.1$. What are the equilibrium partial pressures of $H_2O$, CO, and $H_2$ in the equilibrium mixture at this temperature if we start with solid carbon and 0.100 mol of $H_2O$ in a 1.00-L vessel? **(b)** What is the minimum amount of carbon required to achieve equilibrium under these conditions? **(c)** What is the total pressure in the vessel at equilibrium? **(d)** At 25 °C the value of $K_p$ for this reaction is $1.7 \times 10^{-21}$. Is the reaction exothermic or endothermic? **(e)** To produce the maximum amount of CO and $H_2$ at equilibrium, should the pressure of the system be increased or decreased?

## SOLUTION

**(a)** To determine the equilibrium partial pressures, we use the ideal-gas equation, first determining the starting partial pressure of hydrogen.

$$P_{H_2O} = \frac{n_{H_2O}RT}{V} = \frac{(0.100 \text{ mol})(0.08206 \text{ L-atm/mol-K})(1073 \text{ K})}{1.00 \text{ L}} = 8.81 \text{ atm}$$

We then construct a table of initial partial pressures and their changes as equilibrium is achieved:

|  | C(s) + | H₂O(g) ⇌ | CO(g) + | H₂(g) |
|---|---|---|---|---|
| Initial partial pressure (atm) |  | 8.81 | 0 | 0 |
| Change in partial pressure (atm) |  | $-x$ | $+x$ | $+x$ |
| Equilibrium partial pressure (atm) |  | $8.81 - x$ | $x$ | $x$ |

There are no entries in the table under C(s) because the reactant, being a solid, does not appear in the equilibrium-constant expression. Substituting the equilibrium partial pressures of the other species into the equilibrium-constant expression for the reaction gives

$$K_p = \frac{P_{CO}P_{H_2}}{P_{H_2O}} = \frac{(x)(x)}{(8.81 - x)} = 14.1$$

Multiplying through by the denominator gives a quadratic equation in $x$:

$$x^2 = (14.1)(8.81 - x)$$
$$x^2 + 14.1x - 124.22 = 0$$

Solving this equation for $x$ using the quadratic formula yields $x = 6.14$ atm. Hence, the equilibrium partial pressures are $P_{CO} = x = 6.14$ atm, $P_{H_2} = x = 6.14$ atm, and $P_{H_2O} = (8.81 - x) = 2.67$ atm.

**(b)** Part (a) shows that $x = 6.14$ atm of H₂O must react for the system to achieve equilibrium. We can use the ideal-gas equation to convert this partial pressure into a mole amount.

$$n = \frac{PV}{RT} = \frac{(6.14 \text{ atm})(1.00 \text{ L})}{(0.08206 \text{ L-atm/mol-K})(1073 \text{ K})} = 0.0697 \text{ mol}$$

Thus, 0.0697 mol of H₂O and the same amount of C must react to achieve equilibrium. As a result, there must be at least 0.0697 mol of C (0.836 g C) present among the reactants at the start of the reaction.

**(c)** The total pressure in the vessel at equilibrium is simply the sum of the equilibrium partial pressures:

$$P_{total} = P_{H_2O} + P_{CO} + P_{H_2} = 2.67 \text{ atm} + 6.14 \text{ atm} + 6.14 \text{ atm} = 14.95 \text{ atm}$$

**(d)** In discussing Le Châtelier's principle, we saw that endothermic reactions exhibit an increase in $K_p$ with increasing temperature. Because the equilibrium constant for this reaction increases as temperature increases, the reaction must be endothermic. From the enthalpies of formation given in Appendix C, we can verify our prediction by calculating the enthalpy change for the reaction, $\Delta H^\circ = \Delta H_f^\circ(CO(g)) + \Delta H_f^\circ(H_2(g)) - \Delta H_f^\circ(C(s, \text{graphite})) - \Delta H_f^\circ(H_2O(g)) = +131.3$ KJ. The positive sign for $\Delta H^\circ$ indicates that the reaction is endothermic.

**(e)** According to Le Châtelier's principle, a decrease in the pressure causes a gaseous equilibrium to shift toward the side of the equation with the greater number of moles of gas. In this case there are two moles of gas on the product side and only one on the reactant side. Therefore, the pressure should be decreased to maximize the yield of the CO and H₂.

# CHEMISTRY PUT TO WORK

## Controlling Nitric Oxide Emissions

The formation of NO from $N_2$ and $O_2$,

$$\tfrac{1}{2}N_2(g) + \tfrac{1}{2}O_2(g) \rightleftharpoons NO(g) \qquad \Delta H° = 90.4 \text{ kJ}$$

[15.25]

provides an interesting example of the practical importance of the fact that equilibrium constants and reaction rates change with temperature. By applying Le Châtelier's principle to this endothermic reaction and treating heat as a reactant, we deduce that an increase in temperature shifts the equilibrium in the direction of more NO. The equilibrium constant $K_p$ for formation of 1 mol of NO from its elements at 300 K is only about $1 \times 10^{-15}$ (▶ **FIGURE 15.15**). At 2400 K, however, the equilibrium constant is about 0.05, which is $10^{13}$ times larger than the 300 K value.

Figure 15.15 helps explain why NO is a pollution problem. In the cylinder of a modern high-compression automobile engine, the temperature during the fuel-burning part of the cycle is approximately 2400 K. Also, there is a fairly large excess of air in the cylinder. These conditions favor the formation of NO. After combustion, however, the gases cool quickly. As the temperature drops, the equilibrium in Equation 15.25 shifts to the left (because the reactant heat is being removed). The lower temperature also means that the reaction rate decreases, however, so the NO formed at 2400 K is essentially "frozen" in that form as the gas cools.

The gases exhausting from the cylinder are still quite hot, perhaps 1200 K. At this temperature, as shown in Figure 15.15, the equilibrium constant for formation of NO is about $5 \times 10^{-4}$, much smaller than the value at 2400 K. However, the rate of conversion of NO to $N_2$ and $O_2$ is too slow to permit much loss of NO before the gases are cooled further.

As discussed in the "Chemistry Put to Work" box in Section 14.7, one of the goals of automotive catalytic converters is to achieve rapid conversion of NO to $N_2$ and $O_2$ at the temperature of the exhaust gas. Some catalysts developed for this reaction are reasonably effective under the grueling conditions in automotive exhaust systems. Nevertheless, scientists and engineers are continuously searching for new materials that provide even more effective catalysis of the decomposition of nitrogen oxides.

## GO FIGURE

Estimate the value of $K_p$ at 1200 K, the exhaust gas temperature.

▲ **FIGURE 15.15 Equilibrium and temperature.** The equilibrium constant increases with increasing temperature because the reaction is endothermic. It is necessary to use a log scale for $K_p$ because the values vary over such a large range.

# CHAPTER SUMMARY AND KEY TERMS

**INTRODUCTION AND SECTION 15.1** A chemical reaction can achieve a state in which the forward and reverse processes are occurring at the same rate. This condition is called **chemical equilibrium**, and it results in the formation of an equilibrium mixture of the reactants and products of the reaction. The composition of an equilibrium mixture does not change with time if temperature is held constant.

**SECTION 15.2** An equilibrium that is used throughout this chapter is the reaction $N_2(g) + 3H_2(g) \rightleftharpoons 2NH_3(g)$. This reaction is the basis of the **Haber process** for the production of ammonia. The relationship between the concentrations of the reactants and products of a system at equilibrium is given by the **law of mass action**. For an equilibrium equation of the form $aA + bB \rightleftharpoons dD + eE$, the **equilibrium-constant expression** is written as

$$K_c = \frac{[D]^d[E]^e}{[A]^a[B]^b}$$

where $K_c$ is a constant called the **equilibrium constant**. When the equilibrium system of interest consists of gases, it is often convenient to express the concentrations of reactants and products in terms of gas pressures:

$$K_p = \frac{(P_D)^d(P_E)^e}{(P_A)^a(P_B)^b}$$

$K_c$ and $K_p$ are related by the expression $K_p = K_c(RT)^{\Delta n}$.

**SECTION 15.3** The value of the equilibrium constant changes with temperature. A large value of $K_c$ indicates that the equilibrium mixture contains more products than reactants and therefore lies toward the product side of the equation. A small value for the equilibrium constant means that the equilibrium mixture contains less products than reactants and therefore lies toward the reactant side. The equilibrium-constant expression and the equilibrium constant of the reverse of a reaction are the reciprocals of those of the forward reaction. If a reaction is the sum of two or more reactions, its equilibrium constant will be the product of the equilibrium constants for the individual reactions.

**SECTION 15.4** Equilibria for which all substances are in the same phase are called **homogeneous equilibria**; in **heterogeneous equilibria** two or more phases are present. The concentrations of pure solids and liquids are left out of the equilibrium-constant expression for a heterogeneous equilibrium.

**SECTION 15.5** If the concentrations of all species in an equilibrium are known, the equilibrium-constant expression can be used to calculate the equilibrium constant. The changes in the concentrations of reactants and products on the way to achieving equilibrium are governed by the stoichiometry of the reaction.

**SECTION 15.6** The **reaction quotient**, $Q$, is found by substituting reactant and product concentrations or partial pressures at any point during a reaction into the equilibrium-constant expression. If the system is at equilibrium, $Q = K$. If $Q \neq K$, however, the system is not at equilibrium. When $Q < K$, the reaction will move toward equilibrium by forming more products (the reaction proceeds from left to right); when $Q > K$, the reaction will proceed from right to left. Knowing the value of $K$ makes it possible to calculate the equilibrium amounts of reactants and products, often by the solution of an equation in which the unknown is the change in a partial pressure or concentration.

**SECTION 15.7** **Le Châtelier's principle** states that if a system at equilibrium is disturbed, the equilibrium will shift to minimize the disturbing influence. By this principle, if a reactant or product is added to a system at equilibrium, the equilibrium will shift to consume the added substance. The effects of removing reactants or products and of changing the pressure or volume of a reaction can be similarly deduced. For example, if the volume of the system is reduced, the equilibrium will shift in the direction that decreases the number of gas molecules. The enthalpy change for a reaction indicates how an increase in temperature affects the equilibrium: For an endothermic reaction, an increase in temperature shifts the equilibrium to the right; for an exothermic reaction, a temperature increase shifts the equilibrium to the left. Catalysts affect the speed at which equilibrium is reached but do not affect the magnitude of $K$.

# KEY SKILLS

- Understand what is meant by chemical equilibrium and how it relates to reaction rates (Section 15.1).
- Write the equilibrium-constant expression for any reaction (Section 15.2).
- Relate $K_c$ and $K_p$ (Section 15.2).
- Relate the magnitude of an equilibrium constant to the relative amounts of reactants and products present in an equilibrium mixture (Section 15.3).
- Manipulate the equilibrium constant to reflect changes in the chemical equation (Section 15.3).
- Write the equilibrium-constant expression for a heterogeneous reaction (Section 15.4).
- Calculate an equilibrium constant from concentration measurements (Section 15.5).
- Predict the direction of a reaction given the equilibrium constant and the concentrations of reactants and products (Section 15.6).
- Calculate equilibrium concentrations given the equilibrium constant and all but one equilibrium concentration (Section 15.6).
- Calculate equilibrium concentrations, given the equilibrium constant and the starting concentrations (Section 15.6).
- Understand how changing the concentrations, volume, or temperature of a system at equilibrium affects the equilibrium position (Section 15.7).

# KEY EQUATIONS

- $K_c = \dfrac{[D]^d[E]^e}{[A]^a[B]^b}$  [15.8]  The equilibrium-constant expression for a general reaction of the type $a\,A + b\,B \rightleftharpoons d\,D + e\,E$; the concentrations are equilibrium concentrations only

- $K_p = \dfrac{(P_D)^d(P_E)^e}{(P_A)^a(P_B)^b}$  [15.11]  The equilibrium-constant expression in terms of equilibrium partial pressures

- $K_p = K_c(RT)^{\Delta n}$  [15.14]  Relating the equilibrium constant based on pressures to the equilibrium constant based on concentration

- $Q_c = \dfrac{[D]^d[E]^e}{[A]^a[B]^b}$  [15.23]  The reaction quotient. The concentrations are for any time during a reaction. If the concentrations are equilibrium concentrations, then $Q_c = K_c$.

# EXERCISES

## VISUALIZING CONCEPTS

**15.1** **(a)** Based on the following energy profile, predict whether $k_f > k_r$ or $k_f < k_r$. **(b)** Using Equation 15.5, predict whether the equilibrium constant for the process is greater than 1 or less than 1. [Section 15.1]

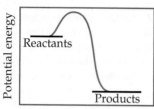

**15.2** The following diagrams represent a hypothetical reaction A $\longrightarrow$ B, with A represented by red spheres and B represented by blue spheres. The sequence from left to right represents the system as time passes. Do the diagrams indicate that the system reaches an equilibrium state? Explain. [Sections 15.1 and 15.2]

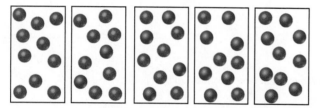

**15.3** The following diagram represents an equilibrium mixture produced for a reaction of the type A + X $\rightleftharpoons$ AX. If the volume is 1 L, is $K$ greater or smaller than 1? [Section 15.2]

**15.4** The following diagram represents a reaction shown going to completion. **(a)** Letting A = red spheres and B = blue spheres, write a balanced equation for the reaction. **(b)** Write the equilibrium-constant expression for the reaction. **(c)** Assuming that all of the molecules are in the gas phase, calculate $\Delta n$, the change in the number of gas molecules that accompanies the reaction. **(d)** How can you calculate $K_p$ if you know $K_c$ at a particular temperature? [Section 15.2]

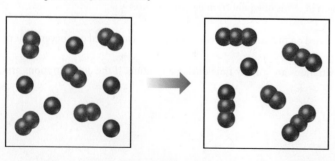

**15.5** A friend says that the faster the reaction, the larger the equilibrium constant. Is your friend correct? Why or why not? [Sections 15.1 and 15.2]

**15.6** A certain chemical reaction has $K_c = 1.5 \times 10^6$. Does this mean that at equilibrium there are $1.5 \times 10^6$ times as many product molecules as reactant molecules? Explain. [Sections 15.1 and 15.2]

**15.7** Ethene ($C_2H_4$) reacts with halogens ($X_2$) by the following reaction:

$$C_2H_4(g) + X_2(g) \rightleftharpoons C_2H_4X_2(g)$$

The following figures represent the concentrations at equilibrium at the same temperature when $X_2$ is $Cl_2$ (green), $Br_2$ (brown), and $I_2$ (purple). List the equilibria from smallest to largest equilibrium constant. [Section 15.3]

(a)                              (b)

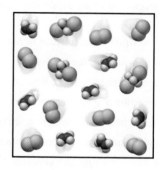

(c)

**15.8** The reaction $A_2 + B_2 \rightleftharpoons 2\,AB$ has an equilibrium constant $K_c = 1.5$. The following diagrams represent reaction mixtures containing $A_2$ molecules (red), $B_2$ molecules (blue), and AB molecules. **(a)** Which reaction mixture is at equilibrium? **(b)** For those mixtures that are not at equilibrium, how will the reaction proceed to reach equilibrium? [Sections 15.5 and 15.6]

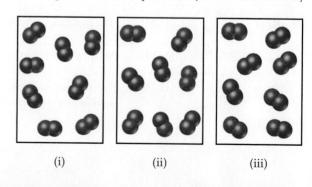

(i)                    (ii)                    (iii)

**15.9** The reaction $A_2(g) + B(g) \rightleftharpoons A(g) + AB(g)$ has an equilibrium constant of $K_p = 2$. The accompanying diagram shows a mixture containing A atoms (red), $A_2$ molecules, and AB molecules (red and blue). How many B atoms should be added to the diagram to illustrate an equilibrium mixture? [Section 15.6]

**15.10** The diagram shown here represents the equilibrium state for the reaction $A_2(g) + 2 B(g) \rightleftharpoons 2 AB(g)$. **(a)** Assuming the volume is 2 L, calculate the equilibrium constant $K_c$ for the reaction. **(b)** If the volume of the equilibrium mixture is decreased, will the number of AB molecules increase or decrease? [Sections 15.5 and 15.7]

**15.11** The following diagrams represent equilibrium mixtures for the reaction $A_2 + B \rightleftharpoons A + AB$ at (a) 300 K and (b) 500 K. The A atoms are red, and the B atoms are blue. Is the reaction exothermic or endothermic? [Section 15.7]

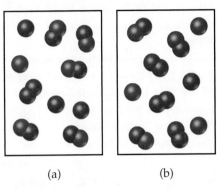

(a)　　　　　(b)

**15.12** The following graph represents the yield of the compound AB at equilibrium in the reaction $A(g) + B(g) \longrightarrow AB(g)$ at two different pressures, $x$ and $y$, as a function of temperature.

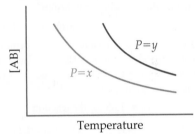

**(a)** Is this reaction exothermic or endothermic? **(b)** Is $P = x$ greater or smaller than $P = y$? [Section 15.7]

# EQUILIBRIUM; THE EQUILIBRIUM CONSTANT (sections 15.1, 15.2, 15.3, 15.4)

**15.13** Suppose that the gas-phase reactions $A \longrightarrow B$ and $B \longrightarrow A$ are both elementary processes with rate constants of $4.7 \times 10^{-3} \text{ s}^{-1}$ and $5.8 \times 10^{-1} \text{ s}^{-1}$, respectively. **(a)** What is the value of the equilibrium constant for the equilibrium $A(g) \rightleftharpoons B(g)$? **(b)** Which is greater at equilibrium, the partial pressure of A or the partial pressure of B? Explain.

**15.14** Consider the reaction $A + B \rightleftharpoons C + D$. Assume that both the forward reaction and the reverse reaction are elementary processes and that the value of the equilibrium constant is very large. **(a)** Which species predominate at equilibrium, reactants or products? **(b)** Which reaction has the larger rate constant, the forward or the reverse? Explain.

**15.15** Write the expression for $K_c$ for the following reactions. In each case indicate whether the reaction is homogeneous or heterogeneous.
  **(a)** $3 NO(g) \rightleftharpoons N_2O(g) + NO_2(g)$
  **(b)** $CH_4(g) + 2 H_2S(g) \rightleftharpoons CS_2(g) + 4 H_2(g)$
  **(c)** $Ni(CO)_4(g) \rightleftharpoons Ni(s) + 4 CO(g)$
  **(d)** $HF(aq) \rightleftharpoons H^+(aq) + F^-(aq)$

  **(e)** $2 Ag(s) + Zn^{2+}(aq) \rightleftharpoons 2 Ag^+(aq) + Zn(s)$
  **(f)** $H_2O(l) \rightleftharpoons H^+(aq) + OH^-(aq)$
  **(g)** $2 H_2O(l) \rightleftharpoons 2 H^+(aq) + 2 OH^-(aq)$

**15.16** Write the expressions for $K_c$ for the following reactions. In each case indicate whether the reaction is homogeneous or heterogeneous.
  **(a)** $2 O_3(g) \rightleftharpoons 3 O_2(g)$
  **(b)** $Ti(s) + 2 Cl_2(g) \rightleftharpoons TiCl_4(l)$
  **(c)** $2 C_2H_4(g) + 2 H_2O(g) \rightleftharpoons 2 C_2H_6(g) + O_2(g)$
  **(d)** $C(s) + 2 H_2(g) \rightleftharpoons CH_4(g)$
  **(e)** $4 HCl(aq) + O_2(g) \rightleftharpoons 2 H_2O(l) + 2 Cl_2(g)$
  **(f)** $2 C_8H_{18}(l) + 25 O_2(g) \rightleftharpoons 16 CO_2(g) + 18 H_2O(g)$
  **(g)** $2 C_8H_{18}(l) + 25 O_2(g) \rightleftharpoons 16 CO_2(g) + 18 H_2O(l)$

**15.17** When the following reactions come to equilibrium, does the equilibrium mixture contain mostly reactants or mostly products?
  **(a)** $N_2(g) + O_2(g) \rightleftharpoons 2 NO(g); K_c = 1.5 \times 10^{-10}$
  **(b)** $2 SO_2(g) + O_2(g) \rightleftharpoons 2 SO_3(g); K_p = 2.5 \times 10^9$

**15.18** Which of the following reactions lies to the right, favoring the formation of products, and which lies to the left, favoring formation of reactants?

(a) $2 NO(g) + O_2(g) \rightleftharpoons 2 NO_2(g)$; $K_p = 5.0 \times 10^{12}$

(b) $2 HBr(g) \rightleftharpoons H_2(g) + Br_2(g)$; $K_c = 5.8 \times 10^{-18}$

**15.19** Can the equilibrium constant ever be a negative number? Explain.

**15.20** Can the equilibrium constant ever be zero? Explain.

**15.21** If $K_c = 0.042$ for $PCl_3(g) + Cl_2(g) \rightleftharpoons PCl_5(g)$ at 500 K, what is the value of $K_p$ for this reaction at this temperature?

**15.22** Calculate $K_c$ at 303 K for $SO_2(g) + Cl_2(g) \rightleftharpoons SO_2Cl_2(g)$ if $K_p = 34.5$ at this temperature.

**15.23** The equilibrium constant for the reaction

$$2 NO(g) + Br_2(g) \rightleftharpoons 2 NOBr(g)$$

is $K_c = 1.3 \times 10^{-2}$ at 1000 K. (a) At this temperature does the equilibrium favor NO and $Br_2$, or does it favor NOBr? (b) Calculate $K_c$ for $2 NOBr(g) \rightleftharpoons 2 NO(g) + Br_2(g)$. (c) Calculate $K_c$ for $NOBr(g) \rightarrow NO(g) + \frac{1}{2} Br_2(g)$.

**15.24** Consider the following equilibrium:

$$2 H_2(g) + S_2(g) \rightleftharpoons 2 H_2S(g) \quad K_c = 1.08 \times 10^7 \text{ at } 700 \text{ °C}$$

(a) Calculate $K_p$. (b) Does the equilibrium mixture contain mostly $H_2$ and $S_2$ or mostly $H_2S$? (c) Calculate the values of $K_c$ and $K_p$ if you rewrote the balanced chemical equation with 1 mol of $H_2(g)$ instead of 2 mol.

**15.25** At 1000 K, $K_p = 1.85$ for the reaction

$$SO_2(g) + \frac{1}{2} O_2(g) \rightleftharpoons SO_3(g)$$

(a) What is the value of $K_p$ for the reaction $SO_3(g) \rightleftharpoons SO_2(g) + \frac{1}{2} O_2(g)$? (b) What is the value of $K_p$ for the reaction $2 SO_2(g) + O_2(g) \rightleftharpoons 2 SO_3(g)$? (c) What is the value of $K_c$ for the reaction in part (b)?

**15.26** Consider the following equilibrium, for which $K_p = 0.0752$ at 480 °C:

$$2 Cl_2(g) + 2 H_2O(g) \rightleftharpoons 4 HCl(g) + O_2(g)$$

(a) What is the value of $K_p$ for the reaction $4 HCl(g) + O_2(g) \rightleftharpoons 2 Cl_2(g) + 2 H_2O(g)$? (b) What is the value of $K_p$ for the reaction $Cl_2(g) + H_2O(g) \rightleftharpoons 2 HCl(g) + \frac{1}{2} O_2(g)$? (c) What is the value of $K_c$ for the reaction in part (b)?

**15.27** The following equilibria were attained at 823 K:

$$CoO(s) + H_2(g) \rightleftharpoons Co(s) + H_2O(g) \quad K_c = 67$$
$$CoO(s) + CO(g) \rightleftharpoons Co(s) + CO_2(g) \quad K_c = 490$$

Based on these equilibria, calculate the equilibrium constant for $H_2(g) + CO_2(g) \rightleftharpoons CO(g) + H_2O(g)$ at 823 K.

**15.28** Consider the equilibrium

$$N_2(g) + O_2(g) + Br_2(g) \rightleftharpoons 2 NOBr(g)$$

Calculate the equilibrium constant $K_p$ for this reaction, given the following information (at 298 K):

$$2 NO(g) + Br_2(g) \rightleftharpoons 2 NOBr(g) \quad K_c = 2.0$$
$$2 NO(g) \rightleftharpoons N_2(g) + O_2(g) \quad K_c = 2.1 \times 10^{30}$$

**15.29** Explain why we normally exclude pure solids and liquids from equilibrium-constant expressions.

**15.30** Explain why we normally exclude solvents from liquid-phase reactions in equilibrium-constant expressions.

**15.31** Mercury(I) oxide decomposes into elemental mercury and elemental oxygen: $2 Hg_2O(s) \rightleftharpoons 4 Hg(l) + O_2(g)$. (a) Write the equilibrium-constant expression for this reaction in terms of partial pressures. (b) Suppose you run this reaction in a solvent that dissolves elemental mercury and elemental oxygen. Rewrite the equilibrium-constant expression in terms of molarities for the reaction, using (solv) to indicate solvation.

**15.32** Consider the equilibrium $Na_2O(s) + SO_2(g) \rightleftharpoons Na_2SO_3(s)$. (a) Write the equilibrium-constant expression for this reaction in terms of partial pressures. (b) All the compounds in this reaction are soluble in water. Rewrite the equilibrium-constant expression in terms of molarities for the aqueous reaction.

# CALCULATING EQUILIBRIUM CONSTANTS (section 15.5)

**15.33** Methanol ($CH_3OH$) is produced commercially by the catalyzed reaction of carbon monoxide and hydrogen: $CO(g) + 2 H_2(g) \rightleftharpoons CH_3OH(g)$. An equilibrium mixture in a 2.00-L vessel is found to contain 0.0406 mol $CH_3OH$, 0.170 mol CO, and 0.302 mol $H_2$ at 500 K. Calculate $K_c$ at this temperature.

**15.34** Gaseous hydrogen iodide is placed in a closed container at 425 °C, where it partially decomposes to hydrogen and iodine: $2 HI(g) \rightleftharpoons H_2(g) + I_2(g)$. At equilibrium it is found that $[HI] = 3.53 \times 10^{-3} M$, $[H_2] = 4.79 \times 10^{-4} M$, and $[I_2] = 4.79 \times 10^{-4} M$. What is the value of $K_c$ at this temperature?

**15.35** The equilibrium $2 NO(g) + Cl_2(g) \rightleftharpoons 2 NOCl(g)$ is established at 500 K. An equilibrium mixture of the three gases has partial pressures of 0.095 atm, 0.171 atm, and 0.28 atm for NO, $Cl_2$, and NOCl, respectively. (a) Calculate $K_p$ for this reaction at 500.0 K. (b) If the vessel has a volume of 5.00 L, calculate $K_c$ at this temperature.

**15.36** Phosphorus trichloride gas and chlorine gas react to form phosphorus pentachloride gas: $PCl_3(g) + Cl_2(g) \rightleftharpoons PCl_5(g)$. A 7.5-L gas vessel is charged with a mixture of $PCl_3(g)$ and $Cl_2(g)$, which is allowed to equilibrate at 450 K. At equilibrium the partial pressures of the three gases are $P_{PCl_3} = 0.124$ atm, $P_{Cl_2} = 0.157$ atm, and $P_{PCl_5} = 1.30$ atm. (a) What is the value of $K_p$ at this temperature? (b) Does the equilibrium favor reactants or products? (c) Calculate $K_c$ for this reaction at 450 K.

**15.37** A mixture of 0.10 mol of NO, 0.050 mol of $H_2$, and 0.10 mol of $H_2O$ is placed in a 1.0-L vessel at 300 K. The following equilibrium is established:

$$2 NO(g) + 2 H_2(g) \rightleftharpoons N_2(g) + 2 H_2O(g)$$

At equilibrium $[NO] = 0.062 M$. (a) Calculate the equilibrium concentrations of $H_2$, $N_2$, and $H_2O$. (b) Calculate $K_c$.

**15.38** A mixture of 1.374 g of $H_2$ and 70.31 g of $Br_2$ is heated in a 2.00-L vessel at 700 K. These substances react according to

$$H_2(g) + Br_2(g) \rightleftharpoons 2 HBr(g)$$

At equilibrium the vessel is found to contain 0.566 g of $H_2$. **(a)** Calculate the equilibrium concentrations of $H_2$, $Br_2$, and HBr. **(b)** Calculate $K_c$.

**15.39** A mixture of 0.2000 mol of $CO_2$, 0.1000 mol of $H_2$, and 0.1600 mol of $H_2O$ is placed in a 2.000-L vessel. The following equilibrium is established at 500 K:

$$CO_2(g) + H_2(g) \rightleftharpoons CO(g) + H_2O(g)$$

**(a)** Calculate the initial partial pressures of $CO_2$, $H_2$, and $H_2O$. **(b)** At equilibrium $P_{H_2O} = 3.51$ atm. Calculate the equilibrium partial pressures of $CO_2$, $H_2$, and CO. **(c)** Calculate $K_p$ for the reaction. **(d)** Calculate $K_c$ for the reaction.

**15.40** A flask is charged with 1.500 atm of $N_2O_4(g)$ and 1.00 atm $NO_2(g)$ at 25 °C, and the following equilibrium is achieved:

$$N_2O_4(g) \rightleftharpoons 2 NO_2(g)$$

After equilibrium is reached, the partial pressure of $NO_2$ is 0.512 atm. **(a)** What is the equilibrium partial pressure of $N_2O_4$? **(b)** Calculate the value of $K_p$ for the reaction. **(c)** Calculate $K_c$ for the reaction.

**15.41** Two different proteins X and Y are dissolved in aqueous solution at 37 °C. The proteins bind in a 1:1 ratio to form XY. A solution that is initially 1.00 m$M$ in each protein is allowed to reach equilibrium. At equilibrium, 0.20 m$M$ of free X and 0.20 m$M$ of free Y remain. What is $K_c$ for the reaction?

**[15.42]** A chemist at a pharmaceutical company is measuring equilibrium constants for reactions in which drug candidate molecules bind to a protein involved in cancer. The drug molecules bind the protein in a 1:1 ratio to form a drug-protein complex. The protein concentration in aqueous solution at 25 °C is $1.50 \times 10^{-6} M$. Drug A is introduced into the protein solution at an initial concentration of $2.00 \times 10^{-6} M$. Drug B is introduced into a separate, identical protein solution at an initial concentration of $2.00 \times 10^{-6} M$. At equilibrium, the drug A-protein solution has an A-protein complex concentration of $1.00 \times 10^{-6} M$, and the drug B solution has a B-protein complex concentration of $1.40 \times 10^{-6} M$. Calculate the $K_c$ value for the A-protein binding reaction and for the B-protein binding reaction. Assuming that the drug that binds more strongly will be more effective, which drug is the better choice for further research?

# APPLICATIONS OF EQUILIBRIUM CONSTANTS (section 15.6)

**15.43** **(a)** How does a reaction quotient differ from an equilibrium constant? **(b)** If $Q_c < K_c$, in which direction will a reaction proceed in order to reach equilibrium? **(c)** What condition must be satisfied so that $Q_c = K_c$?

**15.44** **(a)** How is a reaction quotient used to determine whether a system is at equilibrium? **(b)** If $Q_c > K_c$, how must the reaction proceed to reach equilibrium? **(c)** At the start of a certain reaction, only reactants are present; no products have been formed. What is the value of $Q_c$ at this point in the reaction?

**15.45** At 100 °C the equilibrium constant for the reaction $COCl_2(g) \rightleftharpoons CO(g) + Cl_2(g)$ has the value $K_c = 2.19 \times 10^{-10}$. Are the following mixtures of $COCl_2$, CO, and $Cl_2$ at 100 °C at equilibrium? If not, indicate the direction that the reaction must proceed to achieve equilibrium. **(a)** $[COCl_2] = 2.00 \times 10^{-3} M$, $[CO] = 3.3 \times 10^{-6} M$, $[Cl_2] = 6.62 \times 10^{-6} M$; **(b)** $[COCl_2] = 4.50 \times 10^{-2} M$, $[CO] = 1.1 \times 10^{-7} M$, $[Cl_2] = 2.25 \times 10^{-6} M$; **(c)** $[COCl_2] = 0.0100 M$, $[CO] = [Cl_2] = 1.48 \times 10^{-6} M$

**15.46** As shown in Table 15.2, $K_p$ for the equilibrium

$$N_2(g) + 3 H_2(g) \rightleftharpoons 2 NH_3(g)$$

is $4.51 \times 10^{-5}$ at 450 °C. For each of the mixtures listed here, indicate whether the mixture is at equilibrium at 450 °C. If it is not at equilibrium, indicate the direction (toward product or toward reactants) in which the mixture must shift to achieve equilibrium.
**(a)** 98 atm $NH_3$, 45 atm $N_2$, 55 atm $H_2$
**(b)** 57 atm $NH_3$, 143 atm $N_2$, no $H_2$
**(c)** 13 atm $NH_3$, 27 atm $N_2$, 82 atm $H_2$

**15.47** At 100 °C, $K_c = 0.078$ for the reaction

$$SO_2Cl_2(g) \rightleftharpoons SO_2(g) + Cl_2(g)$$

In an equilibrium mixture of the three gases, the concentrations of $SO_2Cl_2$ and $SO_2$ are 0.108 $M$ and 0.052 $M$, respectively. What is the partial pressure of $Cl_2$ in the equilibrium mixture?

**15.48** At 900 K the following reaction has $K_p = 0.345$:

$$2 SO_2(g) + O_2(g) \rightleftharpoons 2 SO_3(g)$$

In an equilibrium mixture the partial pressures of $SO_2$ and $O_2$ are 0.135 atm and 0.455 atm, respectively. What is the equilibrium partial pressure of $SO_3$ in the mixture?

**15.49** **(a)** At 1285 °C the equilibrium constant for the reaction $Br_2(g) \rightleftharpoons 2 Br(g)$ is $K_c = 1.04 \times 10^{-3}$. A 0.200-L vessel containing an equilibrium mixture of the gases has 0.245 g $Br_2(g)$ in it. What is the mass of $Br(g)$ in the vessel? **(b)** For the reaction $H_2(g) + I_2(g) \rightleftharpoons 2 HI(g)$, $K_c = 55.3$ at 700 K. In a 2.00-L flask containing an equilibrium mixture of the three gases, there are 0.056 g $H_2$ and 4.36 g $I_2$. What is the mass of HI in the flask?

**15.50** **(a)** At 800 K the equilibrium constant for $I_2(g) \rightleftharpoons 2 I(g)$ is $K_c = 3.1 \times 10^{-5}$. If an equilibrium mixture in a 10.0-L vessel contains $2.67 \times 10^{-2}$ g of $I(g)$, how many grams of $I_2$ are in the mixture? **(b)** For $2 SO_2(g) + O_2(g) \rightleftharpoons 2 SO_3(g)$, $K_p = 3.0 \times 10^4$ at 700 K. In a 2.00-L vessel the equilibrium mixture contains 1.17 g of $SO_3$ and 0.105 g of $O_2$. How many grams of $SO_2$ are in the vessel?

**15.51** At 2000 °C the equilibrium constant for the reaction

$$2 NO(g) \rightleftharpoons N_2(g) + O_2(g)$$

is $K_c = 2.4 \times 10^3$. If the initial concentration of NO is 0.175 $M$, what are the equilibrium concentrations of NO, $N_2$, and $O_2$?

**15.52** For the equilibrium

$$Br_2(g) + Cl_2(g) \rightleftharpoons 2 BrCl(g)$$

at 400 K, $K_c = 7.0$. If 0.25 mol of $Br_2$ and 0.55 mol of $Cl_2$ are introduced into a 3.0-L container at 400 K, what will be the equilibrium concentrations of $Br_2$, $Cl_2$, and BrCl?

**15.53** At 373 K, $K_p = 0.416$ for the equilibrium

$$2 NOBr(g) \rightleftharpoons 2 NO(g) + Br_2(g)$$

If the pressures of $NOBr(g)$ and $NO(g)$ are equal, what is the equilibrium pressure of $Br_2(g)$?

**15.54** At 218 °C, $K_c = 1.2 \times 10^{-4}$ for the equilibrium

$$NH_4SH(s) \rightleftharpoons NH_3(g) + H_2S(g)$$

Calculate the equilibrium concentrations of $NH_3$ and $H_2S$ if a sample of solid $NH_4SH$ is placed in a closed vessel at 218 °C and decomposes until equilibrium is reached.

**15.55** Consider the reaction

$$CaSO_4(s) \rightleftharpoons Ca^{2+}(aq) + SO_4^{2-}(aq)$$

At 25 °C the equilibrium constant is $K_c = 2.4 \times 10^{-5}$ for this reaction. (a) If excess $CaSO_4(s)$ is mixed with water at 25 °C to produce a saturated solution of $CaSO_4$, what are the equilibrium concentrations of $Ca^{2+}$ and $SO_4^{2-}$? (b) If the resulting solution has a volume of 1.4 L, what is the minimum mass of $CaSO_4(s)$ needed to achieve equilibrium?

**15.56** At 80 °C, $K_c = 1.87 \times 10^{-3}$ for the reaction

$$PH_3BCl_3(s) \rightleftharpoons PH_3(g) + BCl_3(g)$$

(a) Calculate the equilibrium concentrations of $PH_3$ and $BCl_3$ if a solid sample of $PH_3BCl_3$ is placed in a closed vessel at 80 °C and decomposes until equilibrium is reached. (b) If the flask has a volume of 0.250 L, what is the minimum mass of $PH_3BCl_3(s)$ that must be added to the flask to achieve equilibrium?

**15.57** For the reaction $I_2 + Br_2(g) \rightleftharpoons 2\,IBr(g)$, $K_c = 280$ at 150 °C. Suppose that 0.500 mol IBr in a 2.00-L flask is allowed to reach equilibrium at 150 °C. What are the equilibrium concentrations of IBr, $I_2$, and $Br_2$?

**15.58** At 25 °C the reaction

$$CaCrO_4(s) \rightleftharpoons Ca^{2+}(aq) + CrO_4^{2-}(aq)$$

has an equilibrium constant $K_c = 7.1 \times 10^{-4}$. What are the equilibrium concentrations of $Ca^{2+}$ and $CrO_4^{2-}$ in a saturated solution of $CaCrO_4$?

**15.59** Methane, $CH_4$, reacts with $I_2$ according to the reaction $CH_4(g) + I_2(g) \rightleftharpoons CH_3I(g) + HI(g)$. At 630 K, $K_p$ for this reaction is $2.26 \times 10^{-4}$. A reaction was set up at 630 K with initial partial pressures of methane of 105.1 torr and of 7.96 torr for $I_2$. Calculate the pressures, in torr, of all reactants and products at equilibrium.

**15.60** The reaction of an organic acid with an alcohol, in organic solvent, to produce an ester and water is commonly done in the pharmaceutical industry. This reaction is catalyzed by strong acid (usually $H_2SO_4$). A simple example is the reaction of acetic acid with ethyl alcohol to produce ethyl acetate and water:

$$CH_3COOH(solv) + CH_3CH_2OH(solv) \rightleftharpoons$$
$$CH_3COOCH_2CH_3(solv) + H_2O(solv)$$

where "(*solv*)" indicates that all reactants and products are in solution but not an aqueous solution. The equilibrium constant for this reaction at 55 °C is 6.68. A pharmaceutical chemist makes up 15.0 L of a solution that is initially 0.275 *M* in acetic acid and 3.85 *M* in ethanol. At equilibrium, how many grams of ethyl acetate are formed?

# LE CHÂTELIER'S PRINCIPLE (section 15.7)

**15.61** Consider the following equilibrium for which $\Delta H < 0$

$$2\,SO_2(g) + O_2(g) \rightleftharpoons 2\,SO_3(g)$$

How will each of the following changes affect an equilibrium mixture of the three gases: (a) $O_2(g)$ is added to the system; (b) the reaction mixture is heated; (c) the volume of the reaction vessel is doubled; (d) a catalyst is added to the mixture; (e) the total pressure of the system is increased by adding a noble gas; (f) $SO_3(g)$ is removed from the system?

**15.62** Consider $4\,NH_3(g) + 5\,O_2(g) \rightleftharpoons 4\,NO(g) + 6\,H_2O(g)$, $\Delta H = -904.4$ kJ. How does each of the following changes affect the yield of NO at equilibrium? Answer increase, decrease, or no change: (a) increase $[NH_3]$; (b) increase $[H_2O]$; (c) decrease $[O_2]$; (d) decrease the volume of the container in which the reaction occurs; (e) add a catalyst; (f) increase temperature.

**15.63** How do the following changes affect the value of the equilibrium constant for a gas-phase exothermic reaction: (a) removal of a reactant (b) removal of a product, (c) decrease in the volume, (d) decrease in the temperature, (e) addition of a catalyst?

**15.64** For a certain gas-phase reaction, the fraction of products in an equilibrium mixture is increased by either increasing the temperature or by increasing the volume of the reaction vessel. (a) Is the reaction exothermic or endothermic? (b) Does the balanced chemical equation have more molecules on the reactant side or product side?

**15.65** Consider the following equilibrium between oxides of nitrogen

$$3\,NO(g) \rightleftharpoons NO_2(g) + N_2O(g)$$

(a) Use data in Appendix C to calculate $\Delta H°$ for this reaction. (b) Will the equilibrium constant for the reaction increase or decrease with increasing temperature? Explain. (c) At constant temperature, would a change in the volume of the container affect the fraction of products in the equilibrium mixture?

**15.66** Methanol ($CH_3OH$) can be made by the reaction of CO with $H_2$:

$$CO(g) + 2\,H_2(g) \rightleftharpoons CH_3OH(g)$$

(a) Use thermochemical data in Appendix C to calculate $\Delta H°$ for this reaction. (b) To maximize the equilibrium yield of methanol, would you use a high or low temperature? (c) To maximize the equilibrium yield of methanol, would you use a high or low pressure?

**15.67** Ozone, $O_3$, decomposes to molecular oxygen in the stratosphere according to the reaction $2\,O_3(g) \rightarrow 3\,O_2(g)$. Would an increase in pressure favor the formation of ozone or of oxygen?

**15.68** *Bioremediation* is the use of microorganisms to degrade environmental pollutants. Many pollutants contain only carbon and hydrogen (oil being one example). The chemical reactions are complicated, but in general the microorganisms react the pollutant hydrocarbon with $O_2$ to produce $CO_2$ and other carbon-containing compounds that are incorporated into the organism's biomass. How would increasing levels of $CO_2$ in the environment affect the bioremediation reaction?

# ADDITIONAL EXERCISES

**15.69** Both the forward reaction and the reverse reaction in the following equilibrium are believed to be elementary steps:

$$CO(g) + Cl_2(g) \rightleftharpoons COCl(g) + Cl(g)$$

At 25 °C the rate constants for the forward and reverse reactions are $1.4 \times 10^{-28}\ M^{-1}\ s^{-1}$ and $9.3 \times 10^{10}\ M^{-1}\ s^{-1}$, respectively. **(a)** What is the value for the equilibrium constant at 25 °C ? **(b)** Are reactants or products more plentiful at equilibrium? **(c)** What additional information would you need in order to decide whether the reaction as written is endothermic or exothermic?

**15.70** If $K_c = 1$ for the equilibrium $2\ A(g) \rightleftharpoons B(g)$, what is the relationship between [A] and [B] at equilibrium?

**15.71** A mixture of $CH_4$ and $H_2O$ is passed over a nickel catalyst at 1000 K. The emerging gas is collected in a 5.00-L flask and is found to contain 8.62 g of CO, 2.60 g of $H_2$, 43.0 g of $CH_4$, and 48.4 g of $H_2O$. Assuming that equilibrium has been reached, calculate $K_c$ and $K_p$ for the reaction.

**15.72** When 2.00 mol of $SO_2Cl_2$ is placed in a 2.00-L flask at 303 K, 56% of the $SO_2Cl_2$ decomposes to $SO_2$ and $Cl_2$:

$$SO_2Cl_2(g) \rightleftharpoons SO_2(g) + Cl_2(g)$$

**(a)** Calculate $K_c$ for this reaction at this temperature. **(b)** Calculate $K_p$ for this reaction at 303 K. **(c)** Repeat these calculations for 2.00 mol of $SO_2Cl_2$ in a 15.00-L vessel at 303 K.

**15.73** A mixture of $H_2$, S, and $H_2S$ is held in a 1.0-L vessel at 90 °C and reacts according to the equation:

$$H_2(g) + S(s) \rightleftharpoons H_2S(g)$$

At equilibrium the mixture contains 0.46 g of $H_2S$ and 0.40 g $H_2$. **(a)** Write the equilibrium-constant expression for this reaction. **(b)** What is the value of $K_c$ for the reaction at this temperature? **(c)** Why can we ignore the amount of S when doing the calculation in part (b)?

**15.74** A sample of nitrosyl bromide (NOBr) decomposes according to the equation

$$2\ NOBr(g) \rightleftharpoons 2\ NO(g) + Br_2(g)$$

An equilibrium mixture in a 5.00-L vessel at 100 °C contains 3.22 g of NOBr, 3.08 g of NO, and 4.19 g of $Br_2$. **(a)** Calculate $K_c$. **(b)** What is the total pressure exerted by the mixture of gases? **(c)** What was the mass of the original sample of NOBr?

**15.75** Consider the hypothetical reaction $A(g) \rightleftharpoons 2\ B(g)$. A flask is charged with 0.75 atm of pure A, after which it is allowed to reach equilibrium at 0 °C. At equilibrium the partial pressure of A is 0.36 atm. **(a)** What is the total pressure in the flask at equilibrium? **(b)** What is the value of $K_p$? **(c)** What could we do to maximize the yield of B?

**15.76** As shown in Table 15.2, the equilibrium constant for the reaction $N_2(g) + 3\ H_2(g) \rightleftharpoons 2\ NH_3(g)$ is $K_p = 4.34 \times 10^{-3}$ at 300 °C. Pure $NH_3$ is placed in a 1.00-L flask and allowed to reach equilibrium at this temperature. There are 1.05 g $NH_3$ in the equilibrium mixture. **(a)** What are the masses of $N_2$ and $H_2$ in the equilibrium mixture? **(b)** What was the initial mass of ammonia placed in the vessel? **(c)** What is the total pressure in the vessel?

**15.77** For the equilibrium

$$2\ IBr(g) \rightleftharpoons I_2(g) + Br_2(g)$$

$K_p = 8.5 \times 10^{-3}$ at 150 °C. If 0.025 atm of IBr is placed in a 2.0-L container, what is the partial pressure of all substances after equilibrium is reached?

**15.78** For the equilibrium

$$PH_3BCl_3(s) \rightleftharpoons PH_3(g) + BCl_3(g)$$

$K_p = 0.052$ at 60 °C. **(a)** Calculate $K_c$. **(b)** After 3.00 g of solid $PH_3BCl_3$ is added to a closed 1.500-L vessel at 60 °C, the vessel is charged with 0.0500 g of $BCl_3(g)$. What is the equilibrium concentration of $PH_3$?

**[15.79]** Solid $NH_4SH$ is introduced into an evacuated flask at 24 °C. The following reaction takes place:

$$NH_4SH(s) \rightleftharpoons NH_3(g) + H_2S(g)$$

At equilibrium the total pressure (for $NH_3$ and $H_2S$ taken together) is 0.614 atm. What is $K_p$ for this equilibrium at 24 °C?

**[15.80]** A 0.831-g sample of $SO_3$ is placed in a 1.00-L container and heated to 1100 K. The $SO_3$ decomposes to $SO_2$ and $O_2$:

$$2\ SO_3(g) \rightleftharpoons 2\ SO_2(g) + O_2(g)$$

At equilibrium the total pressure in the container is 1.300 atm. Find the values of $K_p$ and $K_c$ for this reaction at 1100 K.

**15.81** Nitric oxide (NO) reacts readily with chlorine gas as follows:

$$2\ NO(g) + Cl_2(g) \rightleftharpoons 2\ NOCl(g)$$

At 700 K the equilibrium constant $K_p$ for this reaction is 0.26. Predict the behavior of each of the following mixtures at this temperature and indicate whether or not the mixtures are at equilibrium. If not, state whether the mixture will need to produce more products or reactants to reach equilibrium. **(a)** $P_{NO} = 0.15$ atm, $P_{Cl_2} = 0.31$ atm, and $P_{NOCl} = 0.11$ atm; **(b)** $P_{NO} = 0.12$ atm, $P_{Cl_2} = 0.10$ atm, and $P_{NOCl} = 0.050$ atm; **(c)** $P_{NO} = 0.15$ atm, $P_{Cl_2} = 0.20$ atm, and $P_{NOCl} = 5.10 \times 10^{-3}$ atm.

**15.82** At 900 °C, $K_c = 0.0108$ for the reaction

$$CaCO_3(s) \rightleftharpoons CaO(s) + CO_2(g)$$

A mixture of $CaCO_3$, CaO, and $CO_2$ is placed in a 10.0-L vessel at 900 °C. For the following mixtures, will the amount of $CaCO_3$ increase, decrease, or remain the same as the system approaches equilibrium? **(a)** 15.0 g $CaCO_3$, 15.0 g CaO, and 4.25 g $CO_2$ **(b)** 2.50 g $CaCO_3$, 25.0 g CaO, and 5.66 g $CO_2$ **(c)** 30.5 g $CaCO_3$, 25.5 g CaO, and 6.48 g $CO_2$

**15.83** When 1.50 mol $CO_2$ and 1.50 mol $H_2$ are placed in a 3.00-L container at 395 °C, the following reaction occurs: $CO_2(g) + H_2(g) \rightleftharpoons CO(g) + H_2O(g)$. If $K_c = 0.802$, what are the concentrations of each substance in the equilibrium mixture?

**15.84** The equilibrium constant $K_c$ for $C(s) + CO_2(g) \rightleftharpoons 2\ CO(g)$ is 1.9 at 1000 K and 0.133 at 298 K. **(a)** If excess C is allowed to react with 25.0 g of $CO_2$ in a 3.00-L vessel at 1000 K, how many grams of CO are produced? **(b)** How many grams of C are consumed? **(c)** If a smaller vessel is used for the reaction, will the yield of CO be greater or smaller? **(d)** Is the reaction endothermic or exothermic?

**15.85** NiO is to be reduced to nickel metal in an industrial process by use of the reaction

$$NiO(s) + CO(g) \rightleftharpoons Ni(s) + CO_2(g)$$

At 1600 K the equilibrium constant for the reaction is $K_p = 6.0 \times 10^2$. If a CO pressure of 150 torr is to be employed in the furnace and total pressure never exceeds 760 torr, will reduction occur?

**15.86** Le Châtelier noted that many industrial processes of his time could be improved by an understanding of chemical equilibria. For example, the reaction of iron oxide with carbon monoxide was used to produce elemental iron and $CO_2$ according to the reaction

$$Fe_2O_3(s) + 3 CO(g) \rightleftharpoons 2 Fe(s) + 3 CO_2(g)$$

Even in Le Châtelier's time, it was noted that a great deal of CO was wasted, expelled through the chimneys over the furnaces. Le Châtelier wrote, "Because this incomplete reaction was thought to be due to an insufficiently prolonged contact between carbon monoxide and the iron ore [oxide], the dimensions of the furnaces have been increased. In England they have been made as high as thirty meters. But the proportion of carbon monoxide escaping has not diminished, thus demonstrating, by an experiment costing several hundred thousand francs, that the reduction of iron oxide by carbon monoxide is a limited reaction. Acquaintance with the laws of chemical equilibrium would have permitted the same conclusion to be reached more rapidly and far more economically." What does this anecdote tell us about the equilibrium constant for this reaction?

**[15.87]** At 700 K the equilibrium constant for the reaction

$$CCl_4(g) \rightleftharpoons C(s) + 2 Cl_2(g)$$

is $K_p = 0.76$. A flask is charged with 2.00 atm of $CCl_4$, which then reaches equilibrium at 700 K. **(a)** What fraction of the $CCl_4$ is converted into C and $Cl_2$? **(b)** What are the partial pressures of $CCl_4$ and $Cl_2$ at equilibrium?

**[15.88]** The reaction $PCl_3(g) + Cl_2(g) \rightleftharpoons PCl_5(g)$ has $K_p = 0.0870$ at 300 °C. A flask is charged with 0.50 atm $PCl_3$, 0.50 atm $Cl_2$, and 0.20 atm $PCl_5$ at this temperature. **(a)** Use the reaction quotient to determine the direction the reaction must proceed to reach equilibrium. **(b)** Calculate the equilibrium partial pressures of the gases. **(c)** What effect will increasing the volume of the system have on the mole fraction of $Cl_2$ in the equilibrium mixture? **(d)** The reaction is exothermic. What effect will increasing the temperature of the system have on the mole fraction of $Cl_2$ in the equilibrium mixture?

**[15.89]** An equilibrium mixture of $H_2$, $I_2$, and HI at 458 °C contains 0.112 mol $H_2$, 0.112 mol $I_2$, and 0.775 mol HI in a 5.00-L vessel. What are the equilibrium partial pressures when equilibrium is reestablished following the addition of 0.200 mol of HI?

**[15.90]** Consider the hypothetical reaction $A(g) + 2 B(g) \rightleftharpoons 2 C(g)$, for which $K_c = 0.25$ at a certain temperature. A 1.00-L reaction vessel is loaded with 1.00 mol of compound C, which is allowed to reach equilibrium. Let the variable $x$ represent the number of mol/L of compound A present at equilibrium. **(a)** In terms of $x$, what are the equilibrium concentrations of compounds B and C? **(b)** What limits must be placed on the value of $x$ so that all concentrations are positive? **(c)** By putting the equilibrium concentrations (in terms of $x$) into the equilibrium-constant expression, derive an equation that can be solved for $x$. **(d)** The equation from part (c) is a cubic equation (one that has the form $ax^3 + bx^2 + cx + d = 0$). In general, cubic equations cannot be solved in closed form. However, you can estimate the solution by plotting the cubic equation in the allowed range of $x$ that you specified in part (b). The point at which the cubic equation crosses the $x$-axis is the solution. **(e)** From the plot in part (d), estimate the equilibrium concentrations of A, B, and C. (*Hint:* You can check the accuracy of your answer by substituting these concentrations into the equilibrium expression.)

**15.91** At 1200 K, the approximate temperature of automobile exhaust gases (Figure 15.15), $K_p$ for the reaction

$$2 CO_2(g) \rightleftharpoons 2 CO(g) + O_2(g)$$

is about $1 \times 10^{-13}$. Assuming that the exhaust gas (total pressure 1 atm) contains 0.2% CO, 12% $CO_2$, and 3% $O_2$ by volume, is the system at equilibrium with respect to the $CO_2$ reaction? Based on your conclusion, would the CO concentration in the exhaust be decreased or increased by a catalyst that speeds up the $CO_2$ reaction?

**15.92** Suppose that you worked at the U.S. Patent Office and a patent application came across your desk claiming that a newly developed catalyst was much superior to the Haber catalyst for ammonia synthesis because the catalyst led to much greater equilibrium conversion of $N_2$ and $H_2$ into $NH_3$ than the Haber catalyst under the same conditions. What would be your response?

# INTEGRATIVE EXERCISES

**15.93** Consider the reaction $IO_4^-(aq) + 2 H_2O(l) \rightleftharpoons H_4IO_6^-(aq)$; $K_c = 3.5 \times 10^{-2}$. If you start with 25.0 mL of a 0.905 $M$ solution of $NaIO_4$, and then dilute it with water to 500.0 mL, what is the concentration of $H_4IO_6^-$ at equilibrium?

**[15.94]** Silver chloride, AgCl(s), is an "insoluble" strong electrolyte. **(a)** Write the equation for the dissolution of AgCl(s) in $H_2O(l)$. **(b)** Write the expression for $K_c$ for the reaction in part (a). **(c)** Based on the thermochemical data in Appendix C and Le Châtelier's principle, predict whether the solubility of AgCl in $H_2O$ increases or decreases with increasing temperature. **(d)** The equilibrium constant for the dissolution of AgCl in water is $1.6 \times 10^{-10}$ at 25 °C. In addition, $Ag^+(aq)$ can react with $Cl^-(aq)$ according to the reaction

$$Ag^+(aq) + 2 Cl^-(aq) \longrightarrow AgCl_2^-(aq)$$

where $K_c = 1.8 \times 10^5$ at 25 °C. Although AgCl is "not soluble" in water, the complex $AgCl_2^-$ is soluble. At 25 °C, is the solubility of AgCl in a 0.100 $M$ NaCl solution *greater* than the solubility of AgCl in pure water, due to the formation of soluble $AgCl_2^-$ ions? Or is the AgCl solubility in 0.100 $M$ NaCl *less* than in pure water because of a Le Châtelier–type argument? Justify your answer with calculations. (*Hint:* Any form in which silver is in solution counts as "solubility.")

**[15.95]** Consider the equilibrium $A \rightleftharpoons B$ in which both the forward and reverse reactions are elementary (single-step) reactions. Assume that the only effect of a catalyst on the reaction is to lower the activation energies of the forward and reverse reactions, as shown in Figure 15.14. Using the Arrhenius equation (Section 14.5), prove that the equilibrium constant is the same for the catalyzed reaction as for the uncatalyzed one.

[15.96] The phase diagram for $SO_2$ is shown here. (a) What does this diagram tell you about the enthalpy change in the reaction $SO_2(l) \longrightarrow SO_2(g)$? (b) Calculate the equilibrium constant for this reaction at 100 °C and at 0 °C. (c) Why is it not possible to calculate an equilibrium constant between the gas and liquid phases in the supercritical region? (d) At which of the three points marked in red does $SO_2(g)$ most closely approach ideal-gas behavior? (e) At which of the three red points does $SO_2(g)$ behave least ideally?

[15.97] Write the equilibrium-constant expression for the equilibrium

$$C(s) + CO_2(g) \rightleftharpoons 2\, CO(g)$$

The table that follows shows the relative mole percentages of $CO_2(g)$ and $CO(g)$ at a total pressure of 1 atm for several temperatures. Calculate the value of $K_p$ at each temperature. Is the reaction exothermic or endothermic? Explain.

| Temperature (°C) | CO₂ (mol %) | CO (mol %) |
|---|---|---|
| 850 | 6.23 | 93.77 |
| 950 | 1.32 | 98.68 |
| 1050 | 0.37 | 99.63 |
| 1200 | 0.06 | 99.94 |

15.98 In Section 11.5 we defined the vapor pressure of a liquid in terms of an equilibrium. (a) Write the equation representing the equilibrium between liquid water and water vapor and the corresponding expression for $K_p$. (b) By using data in Appendix B, give the value of $K_p$ for this reaction at 30 °C. (c) What is the value of $K_p$ for any liquid in equilibrium with its vapor at the normal boiling point of the liquid?

15.99 Water molecules in the atmosphere can form hydrogen-bonded dimers, $(H_2O)_2$. The presence of these dimers is thought to be important in the nucleation of ice crystals in the atmosphere and in the formation of acid rain. (a) Using VSEPR theory, draw the structure of a water dimer, using dashed lines to indicate intermolecular interactions. (b) What kind of intermolecular forces are involved in water dimer formation? (c) The $K_p$ for water dimer formation in the gas phase is 0.050 at 300 K and 0.020 at 350 K. Is water dimer formation endothermic or exothermic?

15.100 The protein hemoglobin (Hb) transports $O_2$ in mammalian blood. Each Hb can bind 4 $O_2$ molecules. The equilibrium constant for the $O_2$-binding reaction is higher in fetal hemoglobin than in adult hemoglobin. In discussing protein oxygen-binding capacity, biochemists use a measure called the *P50 value*, defined as the partial pressure of oxygen at which 50% of the protein is saturated. Fetal hemoglobin has a P50 value of 19 torr, and adult hemoglobin has a P50 value of 26.8 torr. Use these data to estimate how much larger $K_c$ is for the aqueous reaction $4\, O_2(g) + Hb(aq) \longrightarrow [Hb(O_2)_4(aq)]$.

# WHAT'S AHEAD

**16.1 ACIDS AND BASES: A BRIEF REVIEW**
We start by reviewing the *Arrhenius* definition of acids and bases.

**16.2 BRØNSTED–LOWRY ACIDS AND BASES**
We learn that a Brønsted–Lowry acid is a *proton donor* and a Brønsted–Lowry base is a *proton acceptor*. Two species that differ by the presence or absence of a proton are known as a *conjugate acid–base pair*.

**16.3 THE AUTOIONIZATION OF WATER**
We see that the *autoionization* of water produces small quantities of $H_3O^+$ and $OH^-$ ions. The *equilibrium constant* for

autoionization, $K_w = [H_3O^+][OH^-]$, defines the relationship between $H_3O^+$ and $OH^-$ concentrations in aqueous solutions.

**16.4 THE pH SCALE**
We use the pH scale to describe the acidity or basicity of an aqueous solution. Neutral solutions have a pH = 7 , acidic solutions have pH below 7, and basic solutions have pH above 7.

**16.5 STRONG ACIDS AND BASES**
We categorize acids and bases as being either strong or weak electrolytes. *Strong* acids and bases are strong electrolytes, ionizing or dissociating completely in aqueous solution. *Weak* acids and bases are weak electrolytes and ionize only partially.

**RHUBARB** is a vegetable whose stalks are eaten for their tart flavor. The sour taste comes from the presence of acids in the plant.

# ACID–BASE EQUILIBRIA

**TASTE IS ONE OF THE** five senses we use to experience the world around us. Receptors on the tongue are sensitive to chemical stimuli that lead to five basic taste sensations: sweet, sour, salty, bitter, and umami (from the Japanese word for "delicious" and triggered by the amino acid glutamic acid). The sensation of

sour is a response to the presence of acids, and we associate a sour taste with certain fruits and vegetables because they contain acids. For example, lemons, limes, and grapefruits contain citric acid ($H_3C_6H_5O_7$), and green apples and grapes contain malic acid ($H_2C_4H_4O_5$). The vegetable rhubarb is among the sourest of foods, so sour that eating a fresh stalk of rhubarb is sure to elicit a pucker on the first bite. The sour taste comes from the high acid content of the stalks. One of several acids found in rhubarb is oxalic acid, ($H_2C_2O_4$) (▶ FIGURE 16.1), which in large doses can be lethal. The oxalic acid content in the leaves is much higher than in the stalks, so much so that the leaves are considered toxic.*

Acids and bases are important in numerous chemical processes that occur around us—from industrial processes to biological ones, from reactions in the laboratory to those in our environment. The time required for a metal object immersed in water to corrode, the ability of an aquatic environment to support fish and plant life, the fate of

*It is estimated that a 150-lb person would need to eat approximately 5 kg of rhubarb leaves to receive a lethal dose, although much smaller quantities would probably make you sick.

▲ **FIGURE 16.1 Oxalic acid, $H_2C_2O_4$.**

pollutants washed out of the air by rain, and even the rates of reactions that maintain our lives all critically depend on the acidity or basicity of solutions.

We have encountered acids and bases many times in earlier discussions. For example, a portion of Chapter 4 focused on their reactions. In this chapter we reexamine acids and bases, taking a closer look at how they are identified and characterized. In doing so, we consider their behavior both in terms of their structure and bonding and in terms of the chemical equilibria in which they participate.

# 16.1 | ACIDS AND BASES: A BRIEF REVIEW

From the earliest days of experimental chemistry, scientists have recognized acids and bases by their characteristic properties. Acids have a sour taste and cause certain dyes to change color, whereas bases have a bitter taste and feel slippery (soap is a good example). Use of the term *base* comes from the old English meaning of the word, "to bring low." (We still use the word *debase* in this sense, meaning to lower the value of something.) When a base is added to an acid, the base "lowers" the amount of acid. Indeed, when acids and bases are mixed in certain proportions, their characteristic properties disappear altogether. ∞ ( Section 4.3)

By 1830 it was evident that all acids contain hydrogen but not all hydrogen-containing substances are acids. During the 1880s, the Swedish chemist Svante Arrhenius (1859–1927) defined acids as substances that produce $H^+$ ions in water and bases as substances that produce $OH^-$ ions in water. Over time the Arrhenius concept of acids and bases came to be stated in the following way:

- An *acid* is a substance that, when dissolved in water, increases the concentration of $H^+$ ions.

- A *base* is a substance that, when dissolved in water, increases the concentration of $OH^-$ ions.

Hydrogen chloride is an Arrhenius acid. Hydrogen chloride gas is highly soluble in water because of its chemical reaction with water, which produces hydrated $H^+$ and $Cl^-$ ions:

$$HCl(g) \xrightarrow{H_2O} H^+(aq) + Cl^-(aq) \qquad [16.1]$$

The aqueous solution of HCl is known as hydrochloric acid. Concentrated hydrochloric acid is about 37% HCl by mass and is 12 *M* in HCl.

Sodium hydroxide is an Arrhenius base. Because NaOH is an ionic compound, it dissociates into $Na^+$ and $OH^-$ ions when it dissolves in water, thereby releasing $OH^-$ ions into the solution.

 GIVE IT SOME THOUGHT

What two ions are central to the Arrhenius definitions of acids and bases?

# 16.2 | BRØNSTED–LOWRY ACIDS AND BASES

The Arrhenius concept of acids and bases, while useful, has limitations. For one thing, it is restricted to aqueous solutions. In 1923 the Danish chemist Johannes Brønsted (1879–1947) and the English chemist Thomas Lowry (1874–1936) independently proposed a more general definition of acids and bases. Their concept is based on the fact that *acid–base reactions involve the transfer of $H^+$ ions from one substance to another.*

## The $H^+$ Ion in Water

We might at first imagine that ionization of HCl in water produces just $H^+$ and $Cl^-$. A hydrogen ion is no more than a bare proton, however, and would interact strongly with any source of electron density, such as the nonbonding electron pairs on the oxygen atoms of water molecules. For example, the interaction of a proton with water forms the **hydronium ion**, $H_3O^+(aq)$:

$$H^+ \ + \ :\!\overset{..}{O}\!-\!H \ \longrightarrow \ \left[ H\!-\!\overset{..}{O}\!-\!H \right]^+$$
$$\qquad\qquad\ \ |\qquad\qquad\qquad\ \ | \qquad\quad [16.2]$$
$$\qquad\qquad\ \ H\qquad\qquad\qquad\ H$$

The behavior of $H^+$ ions in liquid water is complex because hydronium ions are not the only polyatomic ions that form when $H^+$ interacts with water molecules. The $H_3O^+$ ion can form hydrogen bonds to additional $H_2O$ molecules to generate such ions as $H_5O_2^+$ and $H_9O_4^+$ (▶ **FIGURE 16.2**)

Chemists use the notations $H^+(aq)$ and $H_3O^+(aq)$ interchangeably to represent the hydrated proton responsible for the characteristic properties of aqueous solutions of acids. We often use the notation $H^+(aq)$ for simplicity and convenience, as we did in Chapter 4 and Equation 16.1. The notation $H_3O^+(aq)$, however, more closely represents reality.

## Proton-Transfer Reactions

In the reaction that occurs when HCl dissolves in water, the HCl molecule transfers an $H^+$ ion (a proton) to a water molecule. Thus, we can represent the reaction as occurring between an HCl molecule and a water molecule to form hydronium and chloride ions:

$$HCl(g) \ + \ H_2O(l) \ \longrightarrow \ Cl^-(aq) \ + \ H_3O^+(aq)$$

$$:\!\overset{..}{\underset{..}{Cl}}\!-\!H \ + \ :\!\overset{..}{O}\!-\!H \ \longrightarrow \ :\!\overset{..}{\underset{..}{Cl}}\!:^- \ + \ \left[ H\!-\!\overset{..}{O}\!-\!H \right]^+$$
$$\qquad\qquad\qquad |\qquad\qquad\qquad\qquad\qquad\quad | \qquad [16.3]$$
$$\qquad\qquad\qquad H\qquad\qquad\qquad\qquad\qquad\ H$$

Acid        Base

The polar $H_2O$ molecule promotes the ionization of acids in water solution by accepting a proton to form $H_3O^+$.

Brønsted and Lowry proposed definitions of acids and bases in terms of their ability to transfer protons:

- An *acid* is a substance (molecule or ion) that donates a proton to another substance.

- A *base* is a substance that accepts a proton.

Thus, when HCl dissolves in water (Equation 16.3), HCl acts as a **Brønsted–Lowry acid** (it donates a proton to $H_2O$), and $H_2O$ acts as a **Brønsted–Lowry base** (it accepts a proton from HCl).

Because the emphasis in the Brønsted–Lowry concept is on proton transfer, the concept also applies to reactions that do not occur in aqueous solution. In the reaction

**GO FIGURE**

Which type of intermolecular force do the dotted lines in this figure represent?

$H_5O_2^+$

$H_9O_4^+$

▲ **FIGURE 16.2  Ball-and-stick models and Lewis structures for two hydrated hydronium ions.**

between gas phase HCl and NH$_3$, for example, a proton is transferred from the acid HCl to the base NH$_3$:

$$\ddot{\underset{\cdot\cdot}{C}}l\text{—H} \quad + \quad :\overset{\overset{\displaystyle H}{|}}{\underset{\underset{\displaystyle H}{|}}{N}}\text{—H} \quad \longrightarrow \quad :\ddot{\underset{\cdot\cdot}{C}}l:^- \quad + \quad \left[\,H\text{—}\overset{\overset{\displaystyle H}{|}}{\underset{\underset{\displaystyle H}{|}}{N}}\text{—H}\,\right]^+ \qquad [16.4]$$

Acid      Base

The hazy film that forms on the windows of general chemistry laboratories and on glassware in the laboratory is largely solid NH$_4$Cl formed by the gas-phase reaction between HCl and NH$_3$.

Let's consider another example that compares the relationship between the Arrhenius and Brønsted–Lowry definitions of acids and bases—an aqueous solution of ammonia, in which we have the equilibrium:

$$\underset{\text{Base}}{NH_3(aq)} + \underset{\text{Acid}}{H_2O(l)} \rightleftharpoons NH_4^+(aq) + OH^-(aq) \qquad [16.5]$$

Ammonia is a Brønsted–Lowry base because it accepts a proton from H$_2$O. Ammonia is also an Arrhenius base because adding it to water leads to an increase in the concentration of OH$^-(aq)$.

An acid and a base always work together to transfer a proton. In other words, a substance can function as an acid only if another substance simultaneously behaves as a base. To be a Brønsted–Lowry acid, a molecule or ion must have a hydrogen atom it can lose as an H$^+$ ion. To be a Brønsted–Lowry base, a molecule or ion must have a non-bonding pair of electrons it can use to bind the H$^+$ ion.

Some substances can act as an acid in one reaction and as a base in another. For example, H$_2$O is a Brønsted–Lowry base in Equation 16.3 and a Brønsted–Lowry acid in Equation 16.5. A substance capable of acting as either an acid or a base is called **amphiprotic**. An amphiprotic substance acts as a base when combined with something more strongly acidic than itself and as an acid when combined with something more strongly basic than itself.

### ▲ GIVE IT SOME THOUGHT

In the forward reaction of this equilibrium, which substance acts as the Brønsted–Lowry base?

$$H_2S(aq) + CH_3NH_2(aq) \rightleftharpoons HS^-(aq) + CH_3NH_3^+(aq)$$

## Conjugate Acid–Base Pairs

In any acid–base equilibrium, both the forward reaction (to the right) and the reverse reaction (to the left) involve proton transfer. For example, consider the reaction of an acid HX with water:

$$HX(aq) + H_2O(l) \rightleftharpoons X^-(aq) + H_3O^+(aq) \qquad [16.6]$$

In the forward reaction, HX donates a proton to H$_2$O. Therefore, HX is the Brønsted–Lowry acid and H$_2$O is the Brønsted–Lowry base. In the reverse reaction, the H$_3$O$^+$ ion donates a proton to the X$^-$ ion, so H$_3$O$^+$ is the acid and X$^-$ is the base. When the acid HX donates a proton, it leaves behind a substance, X$^-$, that can act as a base. Likewise, when H$_2$O acts as a base, it generates H$_3$O$^+$, which can act as an acid.

An acid and a base such as HX and X$^-$ that differ only in the presence or absence of a proton are called a **conjugate acid–base pair**.* Every acid has a **conjugate base**, formed by removing a proton from the acid. For example, OH$^-$ is the conjugate base of H$_2$O, and X$^-$ is the conjugate base of HX. Every base has a **conjugate acid**, formed by adding a proton to the base. Thus, H$_3$O$^+$ is the conjugate acid of H$_2$O, and HX is the conjugate acid of X$^-$.

In any acid–base (proton-transfer) reaction, we can identify two sets of conjugate acid–base pairs. For example, consider the reaction between nitrous acid and water:

$$\text{HNO}_2(aq) + \text{H}_2\text{O}(l) \rightleftharpoons \text{NO}_2^-(aq) + \text{H}_3\text{O}^+(aq) \qquad [16.7]$$

remove H$^+$

Acid      Base      Conjugate base      Conjugate acid

add H$^+$

Likewise, for the reaction between NH$_3$ and H$_2$O (Equation 16.5), we have

$$\text{NH}_3(aq) + \text{H}_2\text{O}(l) \rightleftharpoons \text{NH}_4^+(aq) + \text{OH}^-(aq) \qquad [16.8]$$

add H$^+$

Base      Acid      Conjugate acid      Conjugate base

remove H$^+$

---

## SAMPLE EXERCISE 16.1   Identifying Conjugate Acids and Bases

**(a)** What is the conjugate base of HClO$_4$, H$_2$S, PH$_4^+$, HCO$_3^-$? **(b)** What is the conjugate acid of CN$^-$, SO$_4^{2-}$, H$_2$O, HCO$_3^-$?

### SOLUTION

**Analyze** We are asked to give the conjugate base for several acids and the conjugate acid for several bases.

**Plan** The conjugate base of a substance is simply the parent substance minus one proton, and the conjugate acid of a substance is the parent substance plus one proton.

**Solve**
**(a)** HClO$_4$ less one proton H$^+$ is ClO$_4^-$. The other conjugate bases are HS$^-$, PH$_3$, and CO$_3^{2-}$.
**(b)** CN$^-$ plus one proton H$^+$ is HCN. The other conjugate acids are HSO$_4^-$, H$_3$O$^+$, and H$_2$CO$_3$. Notice that the hydrogen carbonate ion (HCO$_3^-$) is amphiprotic. It can act as either an acid or a base.

### PRACTICE EXERCISE

Write the formula for the conjugate acid of each of the following: HSO$_3^-$, F$^-$, PO$_4^{3-}$, CO.
**Answers:** H$_2$SO$_3$, HF, HPO$_4^{2-}$, HCO$^+$

Once you become proficient at identifying conjugate acid–base pairs it is not difficult to write equations for reactions involving Brønsted–Lowry acids and bases (proton-transfer reactions).

---

*The word *conjugate* means "joined together as a pair."

**SAMPLE EXERCISE 16.2** **Writing Equations for Proton-Transfer Reactions**

The hydrogen sulfite ion ($HSO_3^-$) is amphiprotic. Write an equation for the reaction of $HSO_3^-$ with water (a) in which the ion acts as an acid and (b) in which the ion acts as a base. In both cases identify the conjugate acid–base pairs.

**SOLUTION**

**Analyze and Plan** We are asked to write two equations representing reactions between $HSO_3^-$ and water, one in which $HSO_3^-$ should donate a proton to water, thereby acting as a Brønsted–Lowry acid, and one in which $HSO_3^-$ should accept a proton from water, thereby acting as a base. We are also asked to identify the conjugate pairs in each equation.

**Solve**

(a)
$$HSO_3^-(aq) + H_2O(l) \rightleftharpoons SO_3^{2-}(aq) + H_3O^+(aq)$$

The conjugate pairs in this equation are $HSO_3^-$ (acid) and $SO_3^{2-}$ (conjugate base), and $H_2O$ (base) and $H_3O^+$ (conjugate acid).

(b)
$$HSO_3^-(aq) + H_2O(l) \rightleftharpoons H_2SO_3(aq) + OH^-(aq)$$

The conjugate pairs in this equation are $H_2O$ (acid) and $OH^-$ (conjugate base), and $HSO_3^-$ (base) and $H_2SO_3$ (conjugate acid).

**PRACTICE EXERCISE**

When lithium oxide ($Li_2O$) is dissolved in water, the solution turns basic from the reaction of the oxide ion ($O^{2-}$) with water. Write the equation for this reaction and identify the conjugate acid–base pairs.

**Answer:** $O^{2-}(aq) + H_2O(l) \longrightarrow OH^-(aq) + OH^-(aq)$. The $OH^-$ is both the conjugate acid of $O^{2-}$ and the conjugate base of $H_2O$.

## Relative Strengths of Acids and Bases

Some acids are better proton donors than others, and some bases are better proton acceptors than others. If we arrange acids in order of their ability to donate a proton, we find that the more easily a substance gives up a proton, the less easily its conjugate base accepts a proton. Similarly, the more easily a base accepts a proton, the less easily its conjugate acid gives up a proton. In other words, *the stronger an acid, the weaker its conjugate base*, and *the stronger a base, the weaker its conjugate acid*. Thus, if we know something about the strength of an acid (its ability to donate protons), we also know something about the strength of its conjugate base (its ability to accept protons).

The inverse relationship between the strengths of acids and their conjugate bases is illustrated in ▶ FIGURE 16.3. Here we have grouped acids and bases into three broad categories based on their behavior in water:

1. A *strong acid* completely transfers its protons to water, leaving no undissociated molecules in solution. ∞ (Section 4.3) Its conjugate base has a negligible tendency to be protonated (to accept protons) in aqueous solution. (*The conjugate base of a strong acid shows negligible basicity.*)

2. A *weak acid* only partially dissociates in aqueous solution and therefore exists in the solution as a mixture of the acid and its conjugate base. The conjugate base of a weak acid shows a slight ability to remove protons from water. (*The conjugate base of a weak acid is a weak base.*)

3. A substance with *negligible acidity* contains hydrogen but does not demonstrate any acidic behavior in water. Its conjugate base is a strong base, reacting completely with water, abstracting protons to form $OH^-$ ions. (*The conjugate base of a substance with negligible acidity is a strong base.*)

The ions $H^+(aq)$ and $OH^-(aq)$ are, respectively, the strongest possible acid and strongest possible base that can exist at equilibrium in aqueous solution. Stronger acids react with water to produce $H^+(aq)$ ions, and stronger bases react with water to produce $OH^-(aq)$ ions. This effect is known as the *leveling effect*.

◢ **GO FIGURE**

If O²⁻ ions are added to water, what reaction, if any, occurs?

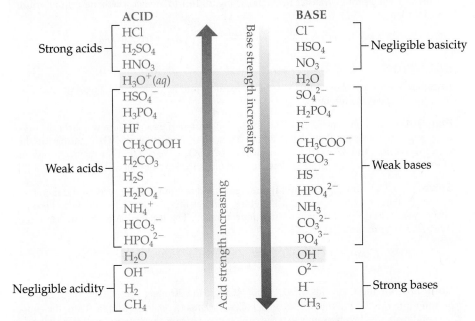

▲ **FIGURE 16.3  Relative strengths of select conjugate acid–base pairs.** The two members of each pair are listed opposite each other in the two columns.

◢ **GIVE IT SOME THOUGHT**

Given that $HClO_4$ is a strong acid, how would you classify the basicity of $ClO_4^-$?

We can think of proton-transfer reactions as being governed by the relative abilities of two bases to abstract protons. For example, consider the proton transfer that occurs when an acid HX dissolves in water:

$$HX(aq) + H_2O(l) \rightleftharpoons H_3O^+(aq) + X^-(aq) \qquad [16.9]$$

If $H_2O$ (the base in the forward reaction) is a stronger base than $X^-$ (the conjugate base of HX), $H_2O$ abstracts the proton from HX to produce $H_3O^+$ and $X^-$. As a result, the equilibrium lies to the right. This describes the behavior of a strong acid in water. For example, when HCl dissolves in water, the solution consists almost entirely of $H_3O^+$ and $Cl^-$ ions with a negligible concentration of HCl molecules:

$$HCl(g) + H_2O(l) \longrightarrow H_3O^+(aq) + Cl^-(aq) \qquad [16.10]$$

$H_2O$ is a stronger base than $Cl^-$ (Figure 16.3), so $H_2O$ acquires the proton to become the hydronium ion.

When $X^-$ is a stronger base than $H_2O$, the equilibrium lies to the left. This situation occurs when HX is a weak acid. For example, an aqueous solution of acetic acid consists mainly of $CH_3COOH$ molecules with only a relatively few $H_3O^+$ and $CH_3COO^-$ ions:

$$CH_3COOH(aq) + H_2O(l) \rightleftharpoons H_3O^+(aq) + CH_3COO^-(aq) \qquad [16.11]$$

The $CH_3COO^-$ ion is a stronger base than $H_2O$ (Figure 16.3) and therefore abstracts the proton from $H_3O^+$.

From these examples, we conclude that *in every acid–base reaction, equilibrium favors transfer of the proton from the stronger acid to the stronger base to form the weaker acid and the weaker base.*

**SAMPLE EXERCISE 16.3** | Predicting the Position of a Proton-Transfer Equilibrium

For the following proton-transfer reaction use Figure 16.3 to predict whether the equilibrium lies to the left $(K_c < 1)$ or to the right $(K_c > 1)$:

$$HSO_4^-(aq) + CO_3^{2-}(aq) \rightleftharpoons SO_4^{2-}(aq) + HCO_3^-(aq)$$

**SOLUTION**

**Analyze** We are asked to predict whether an equilibrium lies to the right, favoring products, or to the left, favoring reactants.

**Plan** This is a proton-transfer reaction, and the position of the equilibrium will favor the proton going to the stronger of two bases. The two bases in the equation are $CO_3^{2-}$, the base in the forward reaction, and $SO_4^{2-}$, the conjugate base of $HSO_4^-$. We can find the relative positions of these two bases in Figure 16.3 to determine which is the stronger base.

**Solve** The $CO_3^{2-}$ ion appears lower in the right-hand column in Figure 16.3 and is therefore a stronger base than $SO_4^{2-}$. $CO_3^{2-}$, therefore, will get the proton preferentially to become $HCO_3^-$, while $SO_4^{2-}$ will remain mostly unprotonated. The resulting equilibrium lies to the right, favoring products (that is, $K_c > 1$):

$$\underset{\text{Acid}}{HSO_4^-(aq)} + \underset{\text{Base}}{CO_3^{2-}(aq)} \rightleftharpoons \underset{\text{Conjugate base}}{SO_4^{2-}(aq)} + \underset{\text{Conjugate acid}}{HCO_3^-(aq)} \qquad K_c > 1$$

**Comment** Of the two acids $HSO_4^-$ and $HCO_3^-$, the stronger one ($HSO_4^-$) gives up a proton more readily, and the weaker one ($HCO_3^-$) tends to retain its proton. Thus, the equilibrium favors the direction in which the proton moves from the stronger acid and becomes bonded to the stronger base.

**PRACTICE EXERCISE**

For each reaction, use Figure 16.3 to predict whether the equilibrium lies to the left or to the right:

**(a)** $HPO_4^{2-}(aq) + H_2O(l) \rightleftharpoons H_2PO_4^-(aq) + OH^-(aq)$
**(b)** $NH_4^+(aq) + OH^-(aq) \rightleftharpoons NH_3(aq) + H_2O(l)$

*Answers:* **(a)** left, **(b)** right

# 16.3 | THE AUTOIONIZATION OF WATER

One of the most important chemical properties of water is its ability to act as either a Brønsted-Lowry acid or a Brønsted-Lowry base. In the presence of an acid, it acts as a proton acceptor; in the presence of a base, it acts as a proton donor. In fact, one water molecule can donate a proton to another water molecule:

$$H_2O(l) + H_2O(l) \rightleftharpoons OH^-(aq) + H_3O^+(aq)$$

$$\text{:} \overset{..}{O}\text{—H} + \text{:} \overset{..}{O}\text{—H} \rightleftharpoons \text{:} \overset{..}{O} \text{:}^- + \left[ H—\overset{..}{O}—H \right]^+ \qquad [16.12]$$

We call this process the **autoionization** of water.

Because the forward and reverse reactions in Equation 16.12 are extremely rapid no water molecule remains ionized for long. At room temperature only about two out of every $10^9$ water molecules are ionized at any given instant. Thus, pure water consists almost entirely of $H_2O$ molecules and is an extremely poor conductor of electricity. Nevertheless, the autoionization of water is very important, as we will soon see.

**Acidic solution**
$[H^+] > [OH^-]$
$[H^+][OH^-] = 1.0 \times 10^{-14}$

**Neutral solution**
$[H^+] = [OH^-]$
$[H^+][OH^-] = 1.0 \times 10^{-14}$

**Basic solution**
$[H^+] < [OH^-]$
$[H^+][OH^-] = 1.0 \times 10^{-14}$

▲ **FIGURE 16.4** Relative concentrations of $H^+$ and $OH^-$ in aqueous solutions at 25 °C.

## The Ion Product of Water

The equilibrium-constant expression for the autoionization of water is

$$K_c = [H_3O^+][OH^-] \qquad [16.13]$$

The term $[H_2O]$ is excluded from the equilibrium-constant expression because we exclude the concentrations of pure solids and liquids. ∞ (Section 15.4) Because this expression refers specifically to the autoionization of water, we use the symbol $K_w$ to denote the equilibrium constant, which we call the **ion-product constant** for water. At 25 °C, $K_w$ equals $1.0 \times 10^{-14}$. Thus, we have

$$K_w = [H_3O^+][OH^-] = 1.0 \times 10^{-14} \quad (\text{at } 25 °C) \qquad [16.14]$$

Because we use $H^+(aq)$ and $H_3O^+(aq)$ interchangeably to represent the hydrated proton, the autoionization reaction for water can also be written as

$$H_2O(l) \rightleftharpoons H^+(aq) + OH^-(aq) \qquad [16.15]$$

Likewise, the expression for $K_w$ can be written in terms of either $H_3O^+$ or $H^+$, and $K_w$ has the same value in either case:

$$K_w = [H_3O^+][OH^-] = [H^+][OH^-] = 1.0 \times 10^{-14} \quad (\text{at } 25 °C) \qquad [16.16]$$

This equilibrium-constant expression and the value of $K_w$ at 25 °C are extremely important, and you should commit them to memory.

A solution in which $[H^+] = [OH^-]$ is said to be *neutral*. In most solutions, however, the $H^+$ and $OH^-$ concentrations are not equal. As the concentration of one of these ions increases, the concentration of the other must decrease, so that the product of their concentrations always equals $1.0 \times 10^{-14}$ (▲ **FIGURE 16.4**).

---

**SAMPLE EXERCISE 16.4** Calculating [H⁺] for Pure Water

Calculate the values of $[H^+]$ and $[OH^-]$ in a neutral solution at 25 °C.

**SOLUTION**

**Analyze** We are asked to determine the concentrations of $H^+$ and $OH^-$ ions in a neutral solution at 25 °C.

**Plan** We will use Equation 16.16 and the fact that, by definition, $[H^+] = [OH^-]$ in a neutral solution.

**Solve** We will represent the concentration of $H^+$ and $OH^-$ in neutral solution with $x$. This gives

$$[H^+][OH^-] = (x)(x) = 1.0 \times 10^{-14}$$

$$x^2 = 1.0 \times 10^{-14}$$

$$x = 1.0 \times 10^{-7} M = [H^+] = [OH^-]$$

In an acid solution $[H^+]$ is greater than $1.0 \times 10^{-7} M$; in a basic solution $[H^+]$ is less than $1.0 \times 10^{-7} M$.

What makes Equation 16.16 particularly useful is that it is applicable both to pure water and to any aqueous solution. Although the equilibrium between $H^+(aq)$ and $OH^-(aq)$ as well as other ionic equilibria are affected somewhat by the presence of additional ions in solution, it is customary to ignore these ionic effects except in work requiring exceptional accuracy. Thus, Equation 16.16 is taken to be valid for any dilute aqueous solution and can be used to calculate either $[H^+]$ (if $[OH^-]$ is known) or $[OH^-]$ (if $[H^+]$ is known).

---

**SAMPLE EXERCISE 16.5** | **Calculating [H⁺] from [OH⁻]**

Calculate the concentration of $H^+(aq)$ in (a) a solution in which $[OH^-]$ is 0.010 M, (b) a solution in which $[OH^-]$ is $1.8 \times 10^{-9}\ M$. *Note:* In this problem and all that follow, we assume, unless stated otherwise, that the temperature is 25 °C.

**SOLUTION**

**Analyze** We are asked to calculate the $[H^+]$ concentration in an aqueous solution where the hydroxide concentration is known.

**Plan** We can use the equilibrium-constant expression for the autoionization of water and the value of $K_w$ to solve for each unknown concentration.

**Solve**

(a) Using Equation 16.16, we have

$$[H^+][OH^-] = 1.0 \times 10^{-14}$$

$$[H^+] = \frac{(1.0 \times 10^{-14})}{[OH^-]} = \frac{1.0 \times 10^{-14}}{0.010} = 1.0 \times 10^{-12}\ M$$

This solution is basic because

$$[OH^-] > [H^+]$$

(b) In this instance

$$[H^+] = \frac{(1.0 \times 10^{-14})}{[OH^-]} = \frac{1.0 \times 10^{-14}}{1.8 \times 10^{-9}} = 5.6 \times 10^{-6}\ M$$

This solution is acidic because

$$[H^+] > [OH^-]$$

**PRACTICE EXERCISE**

Calculate the concentration of $OH^-(aq)$ in a solution in which (a) $[H^+] = 2 \times 10^{-6}\ M$; (b) $[H^+] = [OH^-]$; (c) $[H^+] = 100 \times [OH^-]$.
**Answers:** (a) $5 \times 10^{-9}\ M$, (b) $1.0 \times 10^{-7}\ M$, (c) $1.0 \times 10^{-8}\ M$

---

# 16.4 | THE pH SCALE

The molar concentration of $H^+(aq)$ in an aqueous solution is usually very small. For convenience, we therefore usually express $[H^+]$ in terms of **pH**, which is the negative logarithm in base 10 of $[H^+]$:*

$$pH = -\log[H^+] \qquad [16.17]$$

If you need to review the use of logarithms, see Appendix A.

We can use Equation 16.17 to calculate the pH of a neutral solution at 25 °C (that is, one in which $[H^+] = 1.0 \times 10^{-7}\ M$):

$$pH = -\log(1.0 \times 10^{-7}) = -(-7.00) = 7.00$$

The pH of a neutral solution is 7.00 at 25 °C. Notice that the pH is reported with two decimal places. We do so because only the numbers to the right of the decimal point are the significant

---

*Because $[H^+]$ and $[H_3O^+]$ are used interchangeably, you might see pH defined as $-\log[H_3O^+]$.

**TABLE 16.1 • Relationships among (H⁺), (OH⁻), and pH at 25 °C**

| Solution Type | $[H^+]$ $(M)$ | $[OH^-]$ $(M)$ | pH |
|---|---|---|---|
| Acidic | $>1.0 \times 10^{-7}$ | $<1.0 \times 10^{-7}$ | $<7.00$ |
| Neutral | $1.0 \times 10^{-7}$ | $1.0 \times 10^{-7}$ | $7.00$ |
| Basic | $<1.0 \times 10^{-7}$ | $>1.0 \times 10^{-7}$ | $>7.00$ |

figures in a logarithm. Because our original value for the concentration ($1.0 \times 10^{-7}\ M$) has two significant figures, the corresponding pH has two decimal places (7.00).

What happens to the pH of a solution as we make the solution more and more acidic, so that $[H^+]$ increases? Because of the negative sign in the logarithm term of Equation 16.17, *the pH decreases as* $[H^+]$ *increases.* For example, the pH of a neutral solution ($[H^+] = 1.0 \times 10^{-7}\ M$) is 7.00, but when we add sufficient acid to make $[H^+] = 1.0 \times 10^{-3}\ M$ the pH is

$$pH = -\log(1.0 \times 10^{-3}) = -(-3.00) = 3.00$$

At 25 °C the pH of an acidic solution is less than 7.00.

We can also calculate the pH of a basic solution, one in which $[OH^-] > 1.0 \times 10^{-7}\ M$. Suppose $[OH^-] = 2.0 \times 10^{-3}\ M$. We can use Equation 16.16 to calculate $[H^+]$ for this solution and Equation 16.17 to calculate the pH:

$$[H^+] = \frac{K_w}{[OH^-]} = \frac{1.0 \times 10^{-14}}{2.0 \times 10^{-3}} = 5.0 \times 10^{-12}\ M$$

$$pH = -\log(5.0 \times 10^{-12}) = 11.30$$

At 25 °C the pH of a basic solution is greater than 7.00. The relationships among $[H^+]$, $[OH^-]$, and pH are summarized in ▲ **TABLE 16.1**.

◢ **GIVE IT SOME THOUGHT**

Is it possible for a solution to have a negative pH? If so, would that pH signify a basic or acidic solution?

You might think that when $[H^+]$ is very small, as is often the case, it would be unimportant. Nothing is further from the truth. If $[H^+]$ is part of a kinetic rate law, for example, changing its concentration changes the rate. ∞ (Section 14.3) Thus, if the rate law is first order in $[H^+]$, doubling the $H^+$ concentration doubles the rate even if the change is merely from $1 \times 10^{-7}\ M$ to $2 \times 10^{-7}\ M$. In biological systems, many reactions involve proton transfers and have rates that depend on $[H^+]$. Because the speeds of these reactions are crucial, the pH of biological fluids must be maintained within narrow limits. For example, human blood has a normal pH range of 7.35 to 7.45. Illness and even death can result if the pH varies much from this narrow range.

**SAMPLE EXERCISE 16.6** | **Calculating pH from $[H^+]$**

Calculate the pH values for the two solutions of Sample Exercise 16.5.

**SOLUTION**

**Analyze** We are asked to determine the pH of aqueous solutions for which we have already calculated $[H^+]$.

**Plan** We can calculate pH using its defining equation, Equation 16.17.

**Solve**
(a) In the first instance we found $[H^+]$ to be $1.0 \times 10^{-12}\ M$, so that

$$pH = -\log(1.0 \times 10^{-12}) = -(-12.00) = 12.00$$

Because $1.0 \times 10^{-12}$ has two significant figures, the pH has two decimal places, 12.00.

**(b)** For the second solution, $[H^+] = 5.6 \times 10^{-6}\,M$. Before performing the calculation, it is helpful to estimate the pH. To do so, we note that $[H^+]$ lies between $1 \times 10^{-6}$ and $1 \times 10^{-5}$. Thus, we expect the pH to lie between 6.0 and 5.0. We use Equation 16.17 to calculate the pH:

$$pH = -\log(5.6 \times 10^{-6}) = 5.25$$

**Check** After calculating a pH, it is useful to compare it to your estimate. In this case the pH, as we predicted, falls between 6 and 5. Had the calculated pH and the estimate not agreed, we should have reconsidered our calculation or estimate or both.

**PRACTICE EXERCISE**

**(a)** In a sample of lemon juice, $[H^+] = 3.8 \times 10^{-4}\,M$. What is the pH? **(b)** A commonly available window-cleaning solution has $[OH^-] = 1.9 \times 10^{-6}\,M$. What is the pH?

*Answers:* **(a)** 3.42, **(b)** $[H^+] = 5.3 \times 10^{-9}\,M$, so pH = 8.28

## pOH and Other "p" Scales

The negative logarithm is a convenient way of expressing the magnitudes of other small quantities. We use the convention that the negative logarithm of a quantity is labeled "p" (quantity). Thus, we can express the concentration of $OH^-$ as pOH:

$$pOH = -\log[OH^-] \qquad [16.18]$$

Likewise, $pK_w$ equals $-\log K_w$.

By taking the negative logarithm of both sides of the equilibrium-constant expression for water, $K_w = [H^+][OH^-]$, we obtain

$$-\log[H^+] + (-\log[OH^-]) = -\log K_w \qquad [16.19]$$

from which we obtain the useful expression

$$pH + pOH = 14.00 \quad (\text{at } 25\,°C) \qquad [16.20]$$

The pH and pOH values characteristic of a number of familiar solutions are shown in ▶ **FIGURE 16.5**. Notice that a change in $[H^+]$ by a factor of 10 causes the pH to change by 1. Thus, the concentration of $H^+(aq)$ in a solution of pH 6 is 10 times the $H^+(aq)$ concentration in a solution of pH 7.

 **GIVE IT SOME THOUGHT**

If the pOH for a solution is 3.00, what is the pH? Is the solution acidic or basic?

**SAMPLE EXERCISE 16.7** Calculating [H$^+$] from pOH

A sample of freshly pressed apple juice has a pOH of 10.24. Calculate $[H^+]$.

**SOLUTION**

**Analyze** We need to calculate $[H^+]$ from pOH.

**Plan** We will first use Equation 16.20, $pH + pOH = 14.00$, to calculate pH from pOH. Then we will use Equation 16.17 to determine the concentration of $H^+$.

**Solve** From Equation 16.20, we have

$$pH = 14.00 - pOH$$
$$pH = 14.00 - 10.24 = 3.76$$

Next we use Equation 16.17:

$$pH = -\log[H^+] = 3.76$$

Thus,

$$\log[H^+] = -3.76$$

To find $[H^+]$, we need to determine the *antilogarithm* of $-3.76$. Scientific calculators have an antilogarithm function (sometimes labeled INV log or $10^x$) that allows us to perform the calculation:

$$[H^+] = \text{antilog}(-3.76) = 10^{-3.76} = 1.7 \times 10^{-4}\,M$$

**Comment**  The number of significant figures in [H⁺] is two because the number of decimal places in the pH is two.

**Check**  Because the pH is between 3.0 and 4.0, we know that [H⁺] will be between $1.0 \times 10^{-3}\,M$ and $1.0 \times 10^{-4}\,M$. Our calculated [H⁺] falls within this estimated range.

### PRACTICE EXERCISE
A solution formed by dissolving an antacid tablet has a pH of 9.18. Calculate [OH⁻].
**Answer:**  $[OH^-] = 1.5 \times 10^{-5}$

▲ FIGURE 16.5  **Concentrations of H⁺ and pH values of some common substances at 25 °C.**

## Measuring pH

The pH of a solution can be measured with a *pH meter* (▶ FIGURE 16.6). A complete understanding of how this important device works requires a knowledge of electro-chemistry, a subject we take up in Chapter 20. In brief, a pH meter consists of a pair of electrodes connected to a meter capable of measuring small voltages, on the order of millivolts. A voltage, which varies with pH, is generated when the electrodes are placed in a solution. This voltage is read by the meter, which is calibrated to give pH.

Although less precise, acid–base indicators can be used to measure pH. An acid–base indicator is a colored substance that can exist in either an acid or a base form. The two forms have different colors. Thus, the indicator has one color at lower pH and another at higher pH. If you know the pH at which the indicator turns from one form to the other, you can determine whether a solution has a higher or lower pH than this value. Litmus, for example, changes color in the vicinity of pH 7. The color change, however, is not very sharp. Red litmus indicates a pH of about 5 or lower, and blue litmus indicates a pH of about 8 or higher.

▲ FIGURE 16.6  **A digital pH meter.** The device is a millivoltmeter, and the electrodes immersed in a solution produce a voltage that depends on the pH of the solution.

**Which of these indicators is best suited to distinguish between a solution that is slightly acidic and one that is slightly basic?**

Methyl red

Bromthymol blue

Phenolphthalein

▲ **FIGURE 16.8 Solutions containing three common acid–base indicators at various pH values.**

**If a colorless solution turns pink when we add phenolphthalein, what can we conclude about the pH of the solution?**

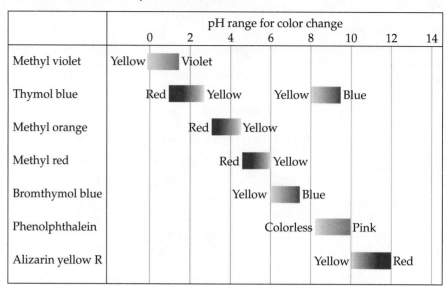

▲ **FIGURE 16.7 pH ranges for common acid–base indicators.** Most indicators have a useful range of about 2 pH units.

Some common indicators are listed in ▲ **FIGURE 16.7.** The chart tells us, for instance, that methyl red changes color over the pH interval from about 4.5 to 6.0. Below pH 4.5 it is in the acid form, which is red. In the interval between 4.5 and 6.0, it is gradually converted to its basic form, which is yellow. Once the pH rises above 6 the conversion is complete, and the solution is yellow. This color change, along with that of the indicators bromthymol blue and phenolphthalein, is shown in ◄ **FIGURE 16.8.** Paper tape impregnated with several indicators is widely used for determining approximate pH values.

## 16.5 | STRONG ACIDS AND BASES

The chemistry of an aqueous solution often depends critically on pH. It is therefore important to examine how pH relates to acid and base concentrations. The simplest cases are those involving strong acids and strong bases. Strong acids and bases are *strong electrolytes*, existing in aqueous solution entirely as ions. There are relatively few common strong acids and bases (see Table 4.2).

### Strong Acids

The seven most common strong acids include six monoprotic acids (HCl, HBr, HI, $HNO_3$, $HClO_3$, and $HClO_4$), and one diprotic acid ($H_2SO_4$). Nitric acid ($HNO_3$) exemplifies the behavior of the monoprotic strong acids. For all practical purposes, an aqueous solution of $HNO_3$ consists entirely of $H_3O^+$ and $NO_3^-$ ions:

$$HNO_3(aq) + H_2O(l) \longrightarrow H_3O^+(aq) + NO_3^-(aq) \quad \text{(complete ionization)} \quad [16.21]$$

We have not used equilibrium arrows for this equation because the reaction lies entirely to the right. ∞ (Section 4.1) As noted in Section 16.3, we use $H_3O^+(aq)$ and $H^+(aq)$ interchangeably to represent the hydrated proton in water. Thus, we can simplify this acid ionization equation to

$$HNO_3(aq) \longrightarrow H^+(aq) + NO_3^-(aq)$$

In an aqueous solution of a strong acid, the acid is normally the only significant source of $H^+$ ions.* As a result, calculating the pH of a solution of a strong monoprotic acid is straightforward because $[H^+]$ equals the original concentration of acid. In a 0.20 $M$ solution of $HNO_3(aq)$, for example, $[H^+] = [NO_3^-] = 0.20$ $M$. The situation with the diprotic acid $H_2SO_4$ is more complex, as we will see in Section 16.6.

---

**SAMPLE EXERCISE 16.8** | **Calculating the pH of a Strong Acid**

What is the pH of a 0.040 $M$ solution of $HClO_4$?

**SOLUTION**

**Analyze and Plan** Because $HClO_4$ is a strong acid, it is completely ionized, giving $[H^+] = [ClO_4^-] = 0.040$ $M$.

**Solve**

$$pH = -\log(0.040) = 1.40.$$

**Check** Because $[H^+]$ lies between $1 \times 10^{-2}$ and $1 \times 10^{-1}$, the pH will be between 2.0 and 1.0. Our calculated pH falls within the estimated range. Furthermore, because the concentration has two significant figures, the pH has two decimal places.

**PRACTICE EXERCISE**

An aqueous solution of $HNO_3$ has a pH of 2.34. What is the concentration of the acid?

**Answer:** 0.0046 $M$

---

## Strong Bases

The most common soluble strong bases are the ionic hydroxides of the alkali metals, such as NaOH, KOH, and the ionic hydroxides heavier alkaline earth metals, such as $Sr(OH)_2$. These compounds completely dissociate into ions in aqueous solution. Thus, a solution labeled 0.30 $M$ NaOH consists of 0.30 $M$ $Na^+(aq)$ and 0.30 $M$ $OH^-(aq)$; there is essentially no undissociated NaOH.

 **GIVE IT SOME THOUGHT**

Which solution has the higher pH, a 0.001 $M$ solution of NaOH or a 0.001 $M$ solution of $Ba(OH)_2$?

---

**SAMPLE EXERCISE 16.9** | **Calculating the pH of a Strong Base**

What is the pH of **(a)** a 0.028 $M$ solution of NaOH, **(b)** a 0.0011 $M$ solution of $Ca(OH)_2$?

**SOLUTION**

**Analyze** We are asked to calculate the pH of two solutions of strong bases.

**Plan** We can calculate each pH by either of two equivalent methods. First, we could use Equation 16.16 to calculate $[H^+]$ and then use Equation 16.17 to calculate the pH. Alternatively, we could use $[OH^-]$ to calculate pOH and then use Equation 16.20 to calculate the pH.

**Solve**
**(a)** NaOH dissociates in water to give one $OH^-$ ion per formula unit. Therefore, the $OH^-$ concentration for the solution in (a) equals the stated concentration of NaOH, namely 0.028 $M$.

*Method 1:*

$$[H^+] = \frac{1.0 \times 10^{-14}}{0.028} = 3.57 \times 10^{-13} \, M \qquad pH = -\log(3.57 \times 10^{-13}) = 12.45$$

*Method 2:*

$$pOH = -\log(0.028) = 1.55 \qquad pH = 14.00 - pOH = 12.45$$

---

*If the concentration of the acid is $10^{-6}$ $M$ or less, we also need to consider $H^+$ ions that result from $H_2O$ autoionization. Normally, the concentration of $H^+$ from $H_2O$ is so small that it can be neglected.

**(b)** $Ca(OH)_2$ is a strong base that dissociates in water to give two $OH^-$ ions per formula unit. Thus, the concentration of $OH^-(aq)$ for the solution in part (b) is $2 \times (0.0011\ M) = 0.0022\ M$.

*Method 1:*

$$[H^+] = \frac{1.0 \times 10^{-14}}{0.0022} = 4.55 \times 10^{-12}\ M \qquad pH = -\log(4.55 \times 10^{-12}) = 11.34$$

*Method 2:*

$$pOH = -\log(0.0022) = 2.66 \qquad pH = 14.00 - pOH = 11.34$$

**PRACTICE EXERCISE**

What is the concentration of a solution of **(a)** KOH for which the pH is 11.89, **(b)** $Ca(OH)_2$ for which the pH is 11.68?

**Answers: (a)** $7.8 \times 10^{-3}\ M$, **(b)** $2.4 \times 10^{-3}\ M$

Although all of the alkali metal hydroxides are strong electrolytes, LiOH, RbOH, and CsOH are not commonly encountered in the laboratory. The hydroxides of the heavier alkaline earth metals—$Ca(OH)_2$, $Sr(OH)_2$, and $Ba(OH)_2$—are also strong electrolytes. They have limited solubility, however, so they are used only when high solubility is not critical.

Strongly basic solutions are also created by certain substances that react with water to form $OH^-(aq)$. The most common of these contain the oxide ion. Ionic metal oxides, especially $Na_2O$ and CaO, are often used in industry when a strong base is needed. The $O^{2-}$ reacts with water to form $OH^-$, leaving virtually no $O^{2-}$ in the solution:

$$O^{2-}(aq) + H_2O(l) \longrightarrow 2\,OH^-(aq) \qquad [16.22]$$

Thus, a solution formed by dissolving 0.010 mol of $Na_2O(s)$ in enough water to form 1.0 L of solution has $[OH^-] = 0.020\ M$ and a pH of 12.30.

 **GIVE IT SOME THOUGHT**

The $CH_3^-$ ion is the conjugate base of $CH_4$, and $CH_4$ shows no evidence of being an acid in water. What happens when $CH_3^-$ is added to water?

# 16.6 | WEAK ACIDS

Most acidic substances are weak acids and therefore only partially ionized in aqueous solution (▶ **FIGURE 16.9**). We can use the equilibrium constant for the ionization reaction to express the extent to which a weak acid ionizes. If we represent a general weak acid as HA, we can write the equation for its ionization in either of the following ways, depending on whether the hydrated proton is represented as $H_3O^+(aq)$ or $H^+(aq)$:

$$HA(aq) + H_2O(l) \rightleftharpoons H_3O^+(aq) + A^-(aq) \qquad [16.23]$$

or

$$HA(aq) \rightleftharpoons H^+(aq) + A^-(aq) \qquad [16.24]$$

Because $H_2O$ is the solvent, it is omitted from the equilibrium-constant expression. ∞ (Section 15.4) Thus, we can write the equilibrium-constant expression as either

$$K_c = \frac{[H_3O^+][A^-]}{[HA]} \quad \text{or} \quad K_c = \frac{[H^+][A^-]}{[HA]}$$

As we did for the ion-product constant for the autoionization of water, we change the subscript on this equilibrium constant to indicate the type of equation to which it corresponds:

$$K_a = \frac{[H_3O^+][A^-]}{[HA]} \quad \text{or} \quad K_a = \frac{[H^+][A^-]}{[HA]} \qquad [16.25]$$

**Strong acid**
HA molecules
completely dissociate

**Weak acid**
HA molecules
partially dissociate

▲ **FIGURE 16.9    Species present in a solution of a strong acid and a weak acid.**

The subscript $a$ denotes that $K_a$ is an equilibrium constant for the ionization of an acid, so $K_a$ is called the **acid-dissociation constant**.

▼ **TABLE 16.2** shows the structural formulas, conjugate bases, and $K_a$ values for a number of weak acids. Appendix D provides a more complete list. Many weak acids are organic compounds composed entirely of carbon, hydrogen, and oxygen. These compounds usually contain some hydrogen atoms bonded to carbon atoms and some bonded to oxygen atoms. In almost all cases, the hydrogen atoms bonded to carbon do not ionize in water; instead, the acidic behavior of these compounds is due to the hydrogen atoms attached to oxygen atoms.

### TABLE 16.2 • Some Weak Acids in Water at 25 °C

| Acid | Structural Formula* | Conjugate Base | $K_a$ |
|---|---|---|---|
| Chlorous ($HClO_2$) | H—O—Cl—O | $ClO_2^-$ | $1.0 \times 10^{-2}$ |
| Hydrofluoric (HF) | H—F | $F^-$ | $6.8 \times 10^{-4}$ |
| Nitrous ($HNO_2$) | H—O—N=O | $NO_2^-$ | $4.5 \times 10^{-4}$ |
| Benzoic ($C_6H_5COOH$) | H—O—C(=O)—⬡ | $C_6H_5COO^-$ | $6.3 \times 10^{-5}$ |
| Acetic ($CH_3COOH$) | H—O—C(=O)—C(H)(H)—H | $CH_3COO^-$ | $1.8 \times 10^{-5}$ |
| Hypochlorous (HOCl) | H—O—Cl | $OCl^-$ | $3.0 \times 10^{-5}$ |
| Hydrocyanic (HCN) | H—C≡N | $CN^-$ | $4.9 \times 10^{-10}$ |
| Phenol ($HOC_6H_5$) | H—O—⬡ | $C_6H_5O^-$ | $1.3 \times 10^{-10}$ |

*The proton that ionizes is shown in red.

The magnitude of $K_a$ indicates the tendency of the acid to ionize in water: *The larger the value of $K_a$, the stronger the acid.* Chlorous acid (HClO$_2$), for example, is the strongest acid in Table 16.2, and phenol (HOC$_6$H$_5$) is the weakest. For most weak acids $K_a$ values range from $10^{-2}$ to $10^{-10}$.

 **GIVE IT SOME THOUGHT**

Based on the entries in Table 16.2, which element is most commonly bonded to the acidic hydrogen?

## Calculating $K_a$ from pH

In order to calculate either the $K_a$ value for a weak acid or the pH of its solutions, we will use many of the skills for solving equilibrium problems developed in Section 15.5. In many cases the small magnitude of $K_a$ allows us to use approximations to simplify the problem. In doing these calculations, it is important to realize that proton-transfer reactions are generally very rapid. As a result, the measured or calculated pH for a weak acid always represents an equilibrium condition.

---

**SAMPLE EXERCISE 16.10** | **Calculating $K_a$ from Measured pH**

A student prepared a 0.10 $M$ solution of formic acid (HCOOH) and found its pH at 25 °C to be 2.38. Calculate $K_a$ for formic acid at this temperature.

**SOLUTION**

**Analyze** We are given the molar concentration of an aqueous solution of weak acid and the pH of the solution, and we are asked to determine the value of $K_a$ for the acid.

**Plan** Although we are dealing specifically with the ionization of a weak acid, this problem is very similar to the equilibrium problems we encountered in Chapter 15. We can solve this problem using the method first outlined in Sample Exercise 15.9, starting with the chemical reaction and a tabulation of initial and equilibrium concentrations.

**Solve** The first step in solving any equilibrium problem is to write the equation for the equilibrium reaction. The ionization of formic acid can be written as

$$\text{HCOOH}(aq) \rightleftharpoons \text{H}^+(aq) + \text{HCOO}^-(aq)$$

The equilibrium-constant expression is

$$K_a = \frac{[\text{H}^+][\text{HCOO}^-]}{[\text{HCOOH}]}$$

From the measured pH, we can calculate [H$^+$]:

$$\text{pH} = -\log[\text{H}^+] = 2.38$$

$$\log[\text{H}^+] = -2.38$$

$$[\text{H}^+] = 10^{-2.38} = 4.2 \times 10^{-3} \, M$$

To determine the concentrations of the species involved in the equilibrium, we imagine that the solution is initially 0.10 $M$ in HCOOH molecules. We then consider the ionization of the acid into H$^+$ and HCOO$^-$. For each HCOOH molecule that ionizes, one H$^+$ ion and one HCOO$^-$ ion are produced in solution. Because the pH measurement indicates that [H$^+$] = $4.2 \times 10^{-3} \, M$ at equilibrium, we can construct the following table:

| | HCOOH($aq$) $\rightleftharpoons$ | H$^+$($aq$) + | HCOO$^-$($aq$) |
|---|---|---|---|
| Initial | 0.10 $M$ | 0 | 0 |
| Change | $-4.2 \times 10^{-3} \, M$ | $+4.2 \times 10^{-3} \, M$ | $+4.2 \times 10^{-3} \, M$ |
| Equilibrium | $(0.10 - 4.2 \times 10^{-3}) \, M$ | $4.2 \times 10^{-3} \, M$ | $4.2 \times 10^{-3} \, M$ |

Notice that we have neglected the very small concentration of H$^+$($aq$) due to H$_2$O autoionization. Notice also that the amount of HCOOH that ionizes is very small compared with the initial concentration of the acid. To the number of significant figures we are using, the subtraction yields 0.10 $M$:

$$(0.10 - 4.2 \times 10^{-3}) \, M \simeq 0.10 \, M$$

We can now insert the equilibrium concentrations into the expression for $K_a$:

$$K_a = \frac{(4.2 \times 10^{-3})(4.2 \times 10^{-3})}{0.10} = 1.8 \times 10^{-4}$$

**Check** The magnitude of our answer is reasonable because $K_a$ for a weak acid is usually between $10^{-2}$ and $10^{-10}$.

**PRACTICE EXERCISE**

Niacin, one of the B vitamins, has the molecular structure

A 0.020 $M$ solution of niacin has a pH of 3.26. What is the acid-dissociation constant for niacin?

***Answer:*** $1.5 \times 10^{-5}$

## Percent Ionization

We have seen that the magnitude of $K_a$ indicates the strength of a weak acid. Another measure of acid strength is **percent ionization**, defined as

$$\text{Percent ionization} = \frac{\text{concentration ionized}}{\text{original concentration}} \times 100\% \qquad [16.26]$$

The stronger the acid, the greater the percent ionization.

For any acid, the concentration of acid that ionizes equals the concentration of $H^+(aq)$ that forms, assuming that $H_2O$ autoionization is negligible. Thus, the percent ionization for an acid HA is also given by

$$\text{Percent ionization} = \frac{[H^+]_{\text{equilibrium}}}{[HA]_{\text{initial}}} \times 100\% \qquad [16.27]$$

For example, a 0.035 $M$ solution of $HNO_2$ contains $3.7 \times 10^{-3}$ $M$ $H^+(aq)$ and its percent ionization is

$$\text{Percent ionization} = \frac{[H^+]_{\text{equilibrium}}}{[HNO_2]_{\text{initial}}} \times 100\% = \frac{3.7 \times 10^{-3}\ M}{0.035\ M} \times 100\% = 11\%$$

**SAMPLE EXERCISE 16.11** | **Calculating Percent Ionization**

As calculated in Sample Exercise 16.10, a 0.10 $M$ solution of formic acid (HCOOH) contains $4.2 \times 10^{-3}$ $M$ $H^+(aq)$. Calculate the percentage of the acid that is ionized.

**SOLUTION**

**Analyze** We are given the molar concentration of an aqueous solution of weak acid and the equilibrium concentration of $H^+(aq)$ and asked to determine the percent ionization of the acid.

**Plan** The percent ionization is given by Equation 16.27.

**Solve**

$$\text{Percent ionization} = \frac{[H^+]_{\text{equilibrium}}}{[HCOOH]_{\text{initial}}} \times 100\% = \frac{4.2 \times 10^{-3}\ M}{0.10\ M} \times 100\% = 4.2\%$$

**PRACTICE EXERCISE**

A 0.020 $M$ solution of niacin has a pH of 3.26. Calculate the percent ionization of the niacin.

***Answer:*** 2.7%

## Using $K_a$ to Calculate pH

Knowing the value of $K_a$ and the initial concentration of a weak acid, we can calculate the concentration of $H^+(aq)$ in a solution of the acid. Let's calculate the pH at 25 °C of a 0.30 $M$ solution of acetic acid ($CH_3COOH$), the weak acid responsible for the characteristic odor and acidity of vinegar.

1. Our first step is to write the ionization equilibrium:

$$CH_3COOH(aq) \rightleftharpoons H^+(aq) + CH_3COO^-(aq) \qquad [16.28]$$

Notice that the hydrogen that ionizes is the one attached to an oxygen atom.

2. The second step is to write the equilibrium-constant expression and the value for the equilibrium constant. Taking $K_a = 1.8 \times 10^{-5}$ from Table 16.2, we write

$$K_a = \frac{[H^+][CH_3COO^-]}{[CH_3COOH]} = 1.8 \times 10^{-5} \qquad [16.29]$$

3. The third step is to express the concentrations involved in the equilibrium reaction. This can be done with a little accounting, as described in Sample Exercise 16.10. Because we want to find the equilibrium value for $[H^+]$, let's call this quantity $x$. The concentration of acetic acid before any of it ionizes is 0.30 $M$. The chemical equation tells us that for each molecule of $CH_3COOH$ that ionizes, one $H^+(aq)$ and one $CH_3COO^-(aq)$ are formed. Consequently, if $x$ moles per liter of $H^+(aq)$ form at equilibrium, $x$ moles per liter of $CH_3COO^-(aq)$ must also form and $x$ moles per liter of $CH_3COOH$ must be ionized:

|  | $CH_3COOH(aq)$ | $\rightleftharpoons$ $H^+(aq)$ | $+$ $CH_3COO^-(aq)$ |
|---|---|---|---|
| Initial | 0.30 $M$ | 0 | 0 |
| Change | $-x\,M$ | $+x\,M$ | $+x\,M$ |
| Equilibrium | $(0.30 - x)\,M$ | $x\,M$ | $x\,M$ |

4. The fourth step is to substitute the equilibrium concentrations into the equilibrium-constant expression and solve for $x$:

$$K_a = \frac{[H^+][CH_3COO^-]}{[CH_3COOH]} = \frac{(x)(x)}{0.30 - x} = 1.8 \times 10^{-5} \qquad [16.30]$$

This expression leads to a quadratic equation in $x$, which we can solve by using either an equation-solving calculator or the quadratic formula. We can simplify the problem, however, by noting that the value of $K_a$ is quite small. As a result, we anticipate that the equilibrium lies far to the left and that $x$ is much smaller than the initial concentration of acetic acid. Thus, we *assume* that $x$ is negligible relative to 0.30, so that $0.30 - x$ is essentially equal to 0.30. We can (and should!) check the validity of this assumption when we finish the problem. By using this assumption, Equation 16.30 becomes

$$K_a = \frac{x^2}{0.30} = 1.8 \times 10^{-5}$$

Solving for $x$, we have

$$x^2 = (0.30)(1.8 \times 10^{-5}) = 5.4 \times 10^{-6}$$
$$x = \sqrt{5.4 \times 10^{-6}} = 2.3 \times 10^{-3}$$
$$[H^+] = x = 2.3 \times 10^{-3}\,M$$
$$pH = -\log(2.3 \times 10^{-3}) = 2.64$$

Now we check the validity of our simplifying assumption that $0.30 - x \simeq 0.30$. The value of $x$ we determined is so small that, for this number of significant figures, the assumption is entirely valid. We are thus satisfied that the assumption was a reasonable one to make. Because $x$ represents the moles per liter of acetic acid that ionize, we see that, in this particular case, less than 1% of the acetic acid molecules ionize:

$$\text{Percent ionization of } CH_3COOH = \frac{0.0023 \ M}{0.30 \ M} \times 100\% = 0.77\%$$

As a general rule, if $x$ is more than about 5% of the initial concentration value, it is better to use the quadratic formula. You should always check the validity of any simplifying assumptions after you have finished solving a problem.

### GIVE IT SOME THOUGHT

Why can we generally assume that the equilibrium concentration of a weak acid equals its initial concentration?

Finally, we can compare the pH value of this weak acid with the pH of a solution of a strong acid of the same concentration. The pH of the 0.30 $M$ acetic acid is 2.64, but the pH of a 0.30 $M$ solution of a strong acid such as HCl is $-\log(0.30) = 0.52$. As expected, the pH of a solution of a weak acid is higher than that of a solution of a strong acid of the same molarity. (Remember, the higher the pH value, the *less* acidic the solution.)

---

**SAMPLE EXERCISE 16.12** | **Using $K_a$ to Calculate pH**

Calculate the pH of a 0.20 $M$ solution of HCN. (Refer to Table 16.2 or Appendix D for the value of $K_a$.)

#### SOLUTION

**Analyze** We are given the molarity of a weak acid and are asked for the pH. From Table 16.2, $K_a$ for HCN is $4.9 \times 10^{-10}$.

**Plan** We proceed as in the example just worked in the text, writing the chemical equation and constructing a table of initial and equilibrium concentrations in which the equilibrium concentration of $H^+$ is our unknown.

**Solve** Writing both the chemical equation for the ionization reaction that forms $H^+(aq)$ and the equilibirium-constant ($K_a$) expression for the reaction:

$$HCN(aq) \rightleftharpoons H^+(aq) + CN^-(aq)$$

$$K_a = \frac{[H^+][CN^-]}{[HCN]} = 4.9 \times 10^{-10}$$

Next, we tabulate the concentrations of the species involved in the equilibrium reaction, letting $x = [H^+]$ at equilibrium:

| | $HCN(aq)$ | $\rightleftharpoons$ | $H^+(aq)$ | $+$ | $CN^-(aq)$ |
|---|---|---|---|---|---|
| Initial | 0.20 $M$ | | 0 | | 0 |
| Change | $-x \ M$ | | $+x \ M$ | | $+x \ M$ |
| Equilibrium | $(0.20 - x) \ M$ | | $x \ M$ | | $x \ M$ |

Substituting the equilibrium concentrations into the equilibrium-constant expression yields

$$K_a = \frac{(x)(x)}{0.20 - x} = 4.9 \times 10^{-10}$$

We next make the simplifying approximation that $x$, the amount of acid that dissociates, is small compared with the initial concentration of acid, $0.20 - x \simeq 0.20$. Thus,

$$\frac{x^2}{0.20} = 4.9 \times 10^{-10}$$

Solving for $x$, we have

$$x^2 = (0.20)(4.9 \times 10^{-10}) = 0.98 \times 10^{-10}$$
$$x = \sqrt{0.98 \times 10^{-10}} = 9.9 \times 10^{-6} \ M = [H^+]$$

A concentration of $9.9 \times 10^{-6} \ M$ is much smaller than 5% of 0.20, the initial HCN concentration. Our simplifying approximation is therefore appropriate. We now calculate the pH of the solution:

$$pH = -\log[H^+] = -\log(9.9 \times 10^{-6}) = 5.00$$

#### PRACTICE EXERCISE

The $K_a$ for niacin (Practice Exercise 16.10) is $1.5 \times 10^{-5}$. What is the pH of a 0.010 $M$ solution of niacin?

***Answer:*** 3.41

Reaction proceeds more rapidly in strong acid, leading to formation of larger H$_2$ bubbles and rapid disappearance of metal

Reaction complete in strong acid

H$_2$ bubbles show reaction still in progress in weak acid

Reaction eventually goes to completion in both acids

1 $M$ HCl($aq$)
[H$^+$] = 1 $M$

1 $M$ CH$_3$COOH($aq$)
[H$^+$] = 0.004 $M$

▲ **FIGURE 16.10** **Rates of the same reaction run in a weak acid and a strong acid.** The bubbles are H$_2$ gas, which along with metal cations, is produced when a metal is oxidized by an acid (Section 4.4).

The properties of an acid solution that relate directly to the concentration of H$^+$($aq$), such as electrical conductivity and rate of reaction with an active metal, are less evident for a solution of a weak acid than for a solution of a strong acid of the same concentration. ▲ **FIGURE 16.10** presents an experiment that demonstrates this difference with 1 $M$ CH$_3$COOH and 1 $M$ HCl. The 1 $M$ CH$_3$COOH contains only 0.004 $M$ H$^+$($aq$), whereas the 1 $M$ HCl solution contains 1 $M$ H$^+$($aq$). As a result, the reaction rate with the metal is much faster in the HCl solution.

As the concentration of a weak acid increases, the equilibrium concentration of H$^+$($aq$) increases, as expected. However, as shown in ▼ **FIGURE 16.11**, *the percent ionization decreases as the concentration increases.* Thus, the concentration of H$^+$($aq$) is not directly proportional to the concentration of the weak acid. For example, doubling the concentration of a weak acid does not double the concentration of H$^+$($aq$).

◢ GO FIGURE

Is the trend observed in this graph consistent with Le Châtelier's principle? Explain.

CH$_3$COOH molecules less prone to dissociate as concentration increases

▲ **FIGURE 16.11** **Effect of concentration on percent ionization in an acetic acid solution.**

**SAMPLE EXERCISE 16.13** | Using $K_a$ to Calculate Percent Ionization

Calculate the percentage of HF molecules ionized in (**a**) a 0.10 $M$ HF solution, (**b**) a 0.010 $M$ HF solution.

**SOLUTION**

**Analyze** We are asked to calculate the percent ionization of two HF solutions of different concentration. From Appendix D, we find $K_a = 6.8 \times 10^{-4}$.

**Plan** We approach this problem as we have previous equilibrium problems. We begin by writing the chemical equation for the equilibrium and tabulating the known and unknown concentrations of all species. We then substitute the equilibrium concentrations into the equilibrium-constant expression and solve for the unknown concentration, that of $H^+$.

**Solve**
(**a**) The equilibrium reaction and equilibrium concentrations are as follows:

|  | $HF(aq)$ | $\rightleftharpoons$ | $H^+(aq)$ | + | $F^-(aq)$ |
|---|---|---|---|---|---|
| Initial | 0.10 M | | 0 | | 0 |
| Change | $-x\, M$ | | $+x\, M$ | | $+x\, M$ |
| Equilibrium | $(0.10 - x)\, M$ | | $x\, M$ | | $x\, M$ |

The equilibrium-constant expression is

$$K_a = \frac{[H^+][F^-]}{[HF]} = \frac{(x)(x)}{0.10 - x} = 6.8 \times 10^{-4}$$

When we try solving this equation using the approximation $0.10 - x \simeq 0.10$ (that is, by neglecting the concentration of acid that ionizes), we obtain

$$x = 8.2 \times 10^{-3}\, M$$

Because this value is greater than 5% of 0.10 $M$, however, we should work the problem without the approximation. Rearranging our equation and writing it in standard quadratic form, we have

$$x^2 = (0.10 - x)(6.8 \times 10^{-4})$$
$$= 6.8 \times 10^{-5} - (6.8 \times 10^{-4})x$$
$$x^2 + (6.8 \times 10^{-4})x - 6.8 \times 10^{-5} = 0$$

Substituting these values in the standard quadratic formula gives

$$x = \frac{-6.8 \times 10^{-4} \pm \sqrt{(6.8 \times 10^{-4})^2 - 4(-6.8 \times 10^{-5})}}{2}$$
$$= \frac{-6.8 \times 10^{-4} \pm 1.6 \times 10^{-2}}{2}$$

Of the two solutions, only the one that gives a positive value for $x$ is chemically reasonable. Thus,

$$x = [H^+] = [F^-] = 7.9 \times 10^{-3}\, M$$

From our result, we can calculate the percent of molecules ionized:

$$\text{Percent ionization of HF} = \frac{\text{concentration ionized}}{\text{original concentration}} \times 100\%$$
$$= \frac{7.9 \times 10^{-3}\, M}{0.10\, M} \times 100\% = 7.9\%$$

(**b**) Proceeding similarly for the 0.010 $M$ solution, we have

$$\frac{x^2}{0.010 - x} = 6.8 \times 10^{-4}$$

Solving the resultant quadratic expression, we obtain

$$x = \left[H^+\right] = \left[F^-\right] = 2.3 \times 10^{-3}\, M$$

The percentage of molecules ionized is

$$\frac{0.0023\, M}{0.010\, M} \times 100\% = 23\%$$

**Comment** Notice that if we do not use the quadratic formula, we calculate 8.2% ionization for (a) and 26% ionization for (b). Notice also that in diluting the solution by a factor of 10, the percentage of molecules ionized increases by a factor of 3. This result is in accord with what we see in Figure 16.11. It is also what we expect from Le Châtelier's principle. ∞ (Section 15.7) There are more "particles" or reaction components on the right side of the equation than on the left. Dilution causes the reaction to shift in the direction of the larger number of particles (toward the product side) because this counters the effect of the decreasing concentration of particles.

**PRACTICE EXERCISE**

In Practice Exercise 16.11, we found that the percent ionization of niacin ($K_a = 1.5 \times 10^{-5}$) in a 0.020 $M$ solution is 2.7%. Calculate the percentage of niacin molecules ionized in a solution that is (**a**) 0.010 $M$, (**b**) $1.0 \times 10^{-3}\, M$.

**Answers:** (**a**) 3.9%, (**b**) 12%

Citric acid has four hydrogens bonded to oxygen. How does the hydrogen that is not an acidic proton differ from the other three?

Citric acid

▲ **FIGURE 16.12** The structure of the polyprotic acid, citric acid.

## Polyprotic Acids

Many acids have more than one ionizable H atom. These acids are known as **polyprotic acids**. For example, with sulfurous acid ($H_2SO_3$) we have the successive ionizations

$$H_2SO_3(aq) \rightleftharpoons H^+(aq) + HSO_3^-(aq) \qquad K_{a1} = 1.7 \times 10^{-2} \qquad [16.31]$$

$$HSO_3^-(aq) \rightleftharpoons H^+(aq) + SO_3^{2-}(aq) \qquad K_{a2} = 6.4 \times 10^{-8} \qquad [16.32]$$

Note that the acid-dissociation constants are labeled $K_{a1}$ and $K_{a2}$. The numbers on the constants refer to the particular proton of the acid that is ionizing. Thus, $K_{a2}$ always refers to the equilibrium involving removal of the second proton of a polyprotic acid.

Note that $K_{a2}$ for sulfurous acid is much smaller than $K_{a1}$. Because of electrostatic attractions, we would expect a positively charged proton to be lost more readily from the neutral $H_2SO_3$ molecule than from the negatively charged $HSO_3^-$ ion. This observation is general: *It is always easier to remove the first proton from a polyprotic acid than to remove the second.* Similarly, for an acid with three ionizable protons, it is easier to remove the second proton than the third. Thus, the $K_a$ values become successively smaller as successive protons are removed.

### GIVE IT SOME THOUGHT

What is meant by the symbol $K_{a3}$ for $H_3PO_4$?

The acid-dissociation constants for common polyprotic acids are listed in ▼ **TABLE 16.3**, and Appendix D provides a more complete list. The structure of citric acid illustrates the presence of multiple ionizable protons ◄ **FIGURE 16.12**.

Notice in Table 16.3 that in most cases the $K_a$ values for successive losses of protons differ by a factor of at least $10^3$. Notice also that the value of $K_{a1}$ for sulfuric acid is listed simply as "large." Sulfuric acid is a strong acid with respect to the removal of the first proton. Thus, the reaction for the first ionization step lies completely to the right:

$$H_2SO_4(aq) \longrightarrow H^+(aq) + HSO_4^-(aq) \quad \text{(complete ionization)}$$

However, $HSO_4^-$ is a weak acid for which $K_{a2} = 1.2 \times 10^{-2}$.

For many polyprotic acids $K_{a1}$ is much larger than subsequent dissociation constants, in which case the $H^+(aq)$ in the solution comes almost entirely from the first ionization reaction. As long as successive $K_a$ values differ by a factor of $10^3$ or more, it is possible to obtain a satisfactory estimate of the pH of polyprotic acid solutions by treating the acids as if they were monoprotic, considering only $K_{a1}$.

**TABLE 16.3** • Acid-Dissociation Constants of Some Common Polyprotic Acids

| Name | Formula | $K_{a1}$ | $K_{a2}$ | $K_{a3}$ |
|---|---|---|---|---|
| Ascorbic | $H_2C_6H_6O_6$ | $8.0 \times 10^{-5}$ | $1.6 \times 10^{-12}$ | |
| Carbonic | $H_2CO_3$ | $4.3 \times 10^{-7}$ | $5.6 \times 10^{-11}$ | |
| Citric | $H_3C_6H_5O_7$ | $7.4 \times 10^{-4}$ | $1.7 \times 10^{-5}$ | $4.0 \times 10^{-7}$ |
| Oxalic | $H_2C_2O_4$ | $5.9 \times 10^{-2}$ | $6.4 \times 10^{-5}$ | |
| Phosphoric | $H_3PO_4$ | $7.5 \times 10^{-3}$ | $6.2 \times 10^{-8}$ | $4.2 \times 10^{-13}$ |
| Sulfurous | $H_2SO_3$ | $1.7 \times 10^{-2}$ | $6.4 \times 10^{-8}$ | |
| Sulfuric | $H_2SO_4$ | Large | $1.2 \times 10^{-2}$ | |
| Tartaric | $H_2C_4H_4O_6$ | $1.0 \times 10^{-3}$ | $4.6 \times 10^{-5}$ | |

**SAMPLE EXERCISE 16.14**  **Calculating the pH of a Polyprotic Acid Solution**

The solubility of $CO_2$ in water at 25 °C and 0.1 atm is 0.0037 $M$. The common practice is to assume that all the dissolved $CO_2$ is in the form of carbonic acid ($H_2CO_3$), which is produced in the reaction

$$CO_2(aq) + H_2O(l) \rightleftharpoons H_2CO_3(aq)$$

What is the pH of a 0.0037 $M$ solution of $H_2CO_3$?

## SOLUTION

**Analyze** We are asked to determine the pH of a 0.0037 $M$ solution of a polyprotic acid.

**Plan** $H_2CO_3$ is a diprotic acid; the two acid-dissociation constants, $K_{a1}$ and $K_{a2}$ (Table 16.3), differ by more than a factor of $10^3$. Consequently, the pH can be determined by considering only $K_{a1}$, thereby treating the acid as if it were a monoprotic acid.

**Solve** Proceeding as in Sample Exercises 16.12 and 16.13, we can write the equilibrium reaction and equilibrium concentrations as

|  | $H_2CO_3(aq)$ | $\rightleftharpoons$ | $H^+(aq)$ | $+$ | $HCO_3^-(aq)$ |
|---|---|---|---|---|---|
| Initial | 0.0037 $M$ | | 0 | | 0 |
| Change | $-x\ M$ | | $+x\ M$ | | $+x\ M$ |
| Equilibrium | $(0.0037 - x)\ M$ | | $x\ M$ | | $x\ M$ |

The equilibrium-constant expression is

$$K_{a1} = \frac{[H^+][HCO_3^-]}{[H_2CO_3]} = \frac{(x)(x)}{0.0037 - x} = 4.3 \times 10^{-7}$$

Solving this equation using an equation-solving calculator, we get

$$x = 4.0 \times 10^{-5}\,M$$

Alternatively, because $K_{a1}$ is small, we can make the simplifying approximation that $x$ is small, so that

$$0.0037 - x \simeq 0.0037$$

Thus,

$$\frac{(x)(x)}{0.0037} = 4.3 \times 10^{-7}$$

Solving for $x$, we have

$$x^2 = (0.0037)(4.3 \times 10^{-7}) = 1.6 \times 10^{-9}$$

$$x = [H^+] = [HCO_3^-] = \sqrt{1.6 \times 10^{-9}} = 4.0 \times 10^{-5}\,M$$

Because we get the same value (to 2 significant figures) our simplifying assumption was justified. The pH is therefore

$$pH = -\log[H^+] = -\log(4.0 \times 10^{-5}) = 4.40$$

**Comment** If we were asked for $[CO_3^{2-}]$, we would need to use $K_{a2}$. Let's illustrate that calculation. Using our calculated values of $[HCO_3^-]$ and $[H^+]$ and setting $[CO_3^{2-}] = y$, we have

|  | $HCO_3^-(aq)$ | $\rightleftharpoons$ | $H^+(aq)$ | $+$ | $CO_3^{2-}(aq)$ |
|---|---|---|---|---|---|
| Initial | $4.0 \times 10^{-5}\ M$ | | $4.0 \times 10^{-5}\ M$ | | 0 |
| Change | $-y\ M$ | | $+y\ M$ | | $+y\ M$ |
| Equilibrium | $(4.0 \times 10^{-5} - y)\ M$ | | $(4.0 \times 10^{-5} + y)\ M$ | | $y\ M$ |

Assuming that $y$ is small relative to $4.0 \times 10^{-5}$, we have

$$K_{a2} = \frac{[H^+][CO_3^{2-}]}{[HCO_3^-]} = \frac{(4.0 \times 10^{-5})(y)}{4.0 \times 10^{-5}} = 5.6 \times 10^{-11}$$

$$y = 5.6 \times 10^{-11}\,M = [CO_3^{2-}]$$

This value is indeed very small compared with $4.0 \times 10^{-5}$, showing that our assumption was justified. It also shows that the ionization of $HCO_3^-$ is negligible relative to that of $H_2CO_3$, as far as production of $H^+$ is concerned. However, it is the *only* source of $CO_3^{2-}$, which has a very low concentration in the solution. Our calculations thus tell us

that in a solution of carbon dioxide in water, most of the $CO_2$ is in the form of $CO_2$ or $H_2CO_3$, only a small fraction ionizes to form $H^+$ and $HCO_3^-$, and an even smaller fraction ionizes to give $CO_3^{2-}$. Notice also that $[CO_3^{2-}]$ is numerically equal to $K_{a2}$.

## PRACTICE EXERCISE

**(a)** Calculate the pH of a 0.020 $M$ solution of oxalic acid ($H_2C_2O_4$). (See Table 16.3 for $K_{a1}$ and $K_{a2}$.) **(b)** Calculate the concentration of oxalate ion, $[C_2O_4^{2-}]$, in this solution.

**Answers:** **(a)** pH = 1.80, **(b)** $[C_2O_4^{2-}] = 6.4 \times 10^{-5}\,M$

# 16.7 | WEAK BASES

Many substances behave as weak bases in water. Weak bases react with water, abstracting protons from $H_2O$, thereby forming the conjugate acid of the base and $OH^-$ ions:

$$B(aq) + H_2O(l) \rightleftharpoons HB^+(aq) + OH^-(aq) \qquad [16.33]$$

The equilibrium-constant expression for this reaction can be written as

$$K_b = \frac{[BH^+][OH^-]}{[B]} \qquad [16.34]$$

Water is the solvent, so it is omitted from the equilibrium-constant expression. The most commonly encountered weak base is ammonia:

$$NH_3(aq) + H_2O(l) \rightleftharpoons NH_4^+(aq) + OH^-(aq) \quad K_b = \frac{[NH_4^+][OH^-]}{[NH_3]} \quad [16.35]$$

As with $K_w$ and $K_a$, the subscript $b$ in $K_b$ denotes that the equilibrium constant refers to a particular type of reaction, namely the ionization of a weak base in water. The constant $K_b$, the **base-dissociation constant**, *always refers to the equilibrium in which a base reacts with $H_2O$ to form the corresponding conjugate acid and $OH^-$.*

▼ **TABLE 16.4** lists the Lewis structures, conjugate acids, and $K_b$ values for a number of weak bases in water. Appendix D includes a more extensive list. These bases contain one or more lone pairs of electrons because a lone pair is necessary to form the bond with $H^+$. Notice that in the neutral molecules in Table 16.4, the lone pairs are on nitrogen atoms. The other bases listed are anions derived from weak acids.

**TABLE 16.4 • Some Weak Bases in Water at 25 °C**

| Base | Structural Formula* | Conjugate Acid | $K_b$ |
|---|---|---|---|
| Ammonia ($NH_3$) | H—N̈—H, H | $NH_4^+$ | $1.8 \times 10^{-5}$ |
| Pyridine ($C_5H_5N$) | ⬡N: | $C_5H_5NH^+$ | $1.7 \times 10^{-9}$ |
| Hydroxylamine ($HONH_2$) | H—N̈—ÖH, H | $HONH_3^+$ | $1.1 \times 10^{-8}$ |
| Methylamine ($CH_3NH_2$) | H—N̈—$CH_3$, H | $CH_3NH_3^+$ | $4.4 \times 10^{-4}$ |
| Hydrosulfide ion ($HS^-$) | $[H—S̈:]^-$ | $H_2S$ | $1.8 \times 10^{-7}$ |
| Carbonate ion ($CO_3^{2-}$) | $\left[\begin{array}{c} :Ö: \\ \| \\ :Ö—C=Ö: \end{array}\right]^{2-}$ | $HCO_3^-$ | $1.8 \times 10^{-4}$ |
| Hypochlorite ion ($ClO^-$) | $[:C̈l—Ö:]^-$ | $HClO$ | $3.3 \times 10^{-7}$ |

*The atom that accepts the proton is shown in blue.

**SAMPLE EXERCISE 16.15** | Using $K_b$ to Calculate $OH^-$

Calculate the concentration of $OH^-$ in a 0.15 $M$ solution of $NH_3$.

**SOLUTION**

**Analyze** We are given the concentration of a weak base and asked to determine the concentration of $OH^-$.

**Plan** We will use essentially the same procedure here as used in solving problems involving the ionization of weak acids, that is, write the chemical equation and tabulate initial and equilibrium concentrations.

**Solve** The ionization reaction and equilibrium-constant expression are

$$NH_3(aq) + H_2O(l) \rightleftharpoons NH_4^+(aq) + OH^-(aq)$$

$$K_b = \frac{[NH_4^+][OH^-]}{[NH_3]} = 1.8 \times 10^{-5}$$

The equilibrium concentrations are (We ignore the concentration of $H_2O$ because it is not involved in the equilibrium-constant expression.)

|  | $NH_3(aq)$ + | $H_2O(l) \rightleftharpoons$ | $NH_4^+(aq)$ + | $OH^-$ |
|---|---|---|---|---|
| Initial | 0.15 $M$ | — | 0 | 0 |
| Change | $-x\ M$ | — | $+x\ M$ | $+x\ M$ |
| Equilibrium | $(0.15 - x)\ M$ | — | $x\ M$ | $x\ M$ |

Inserting these quantities into the equilibrium-constant expression gives

$$K_b = \frac{[NH_4^+][OH^-]}{[NH_3]} = \frac{(x)(x)}{0.15 - x} = 1.8 \times 10^{-5}$$

Because $K_b$ is small, the amount of $NH_3$ that reacts with water is much smaller than the $NH_3$ concentration, and so we can neglect $x$ relative to 0.15 $M$. Then we have

$$\frac{x^2}{0.15} = 1.8 \times 10^{-5}$$

$$x^2 = (0.15)(1.8 \times 10^{-5}) = 2.7 \times 10^{-6}$$

$$x = [NH_4^+] = [OH^-] = \sqrt{2.7 \times 10^{-6}} = 1.6 \times 10^{-3}\ M$$

**Check** The value obtained for $x$ is only about 1% of the $NH_3$ concentration, 0.15 $M$. Therefore, neglecting $x$ relative to 0.15 was justified.

**Comment** You may be asked to find the pH of a solution of a weak base. Once you have found $[OH^-]$, you can proceed as in Sample Exercise 16.9, where we calculated the pH of a strong base. In the present sample exercise, we have seen that the 0.15 $M$ solution of $NH_3$ contains $[OH^-] = 1.6 \times 10^{-3}\ M$. Thus, $pOH = -\log(1.6 \times 10^{-3}) = 2.80$, and $pH = 14.00 - 2.80 = 11.20$. The pH of the solution is above 7 because we are dealing with a solution of a base.

**PRACTICE EXERCISE**

Which of the following compounds should produce the highest pH as a 0.05 $M$ solution: pyridine, methylamine, or nitrous acid?

*Answer:* methylamine (because it has the larger $K_b$ value of the two amine bases in the list)

## Types of Weak Bases

Weak bases fall into two general categories. The first category is neutral substances that have an atom with a nonbonding pair of electrons that can accept a proton. Most of these bases, including all uncharged bases in Table 16.4, contain a nitrogen atom. These substances include ammonia and a related class of compounds called **amines** (► FIGURE 16.13). In organic amines, at least one N—H bond in $NH_3$ is replaced with an N—C bond. Like $NH_3$, amines can abstract a proton from a water molecule by forming an N—H bond, as shown here for methylamine:

$$H{-}\overset{..}{N}{-}CH_3(aq) + H_2O(l) \rightleftharpoons \left[ H{-}\overset{\overset{\displaystyle H}{|}}{\underset{\underset{\displaystyle H}{|}}{N}}{-}CH_3 \right]^+ (aq) + OH^-(aq) \qquad [16.36]$$

▲ GO FIGURE

When hydroxylamine acts as a base, which atom accepts the proton?

Ammonia
$NH_3$

Methylamine
$CH_3NH_2$

Hydroxylamine
$NH_2OH$

▲ **FIGURE 16.13** **Structures of ammonia and two simple amines.**

Anions of weak acids make up the second general category of weak bases. In an aqueous solution of sodium hypochlorite (NaClO), for example, NaClO dissociates to $Na^+$ and $ClO^-$ ions. The $Na^+$ ion is always a spectator ion in acid–base reactions. ∞ (Section 4.3) The $ClO^-$ ion, however, is the conjugate base of a weak acid, hypochlorous acid. Consequently, the $ClO^-$ ion acts as a weak base in water:

$$ClO^-(aq) + H_2O(l) \rightleftharpoons HClO(aq) + OH^-(aq) \qquad K_b = 3.3 \times 10^{-7} \qquad [16.37]$$

In Figure 16.5 we saw that bleach is quite basic (pH values of 12–13). Common chlorine bleach is typically a 5% NaOCl solution.

---

**SAMPLE EXERCISE 16.16** | **Using pH to Determine the Concentration of a Salt**

A solution made by adding solid sodium hypochlorite (NaClO) to enough water to make 2.00 L of solution has a pH of 10.50. Using the information in Equation 16.37, calculate the number of moles of NaClO added to the water.

**SOLUTION**

**Analyze** NaClO is an ionic compound consisting of $Na^+$ and $ClO^-$ ions. As such, it is a strong electrolyte that completely dissociates in solution into $Na^+$, a spectator ion, and $ClO^-$ ion, a weak base with $K_b = 3.3 \times 10^{-7}$ (Equation 16.37). Given this information we must calculate the number of moles of NaClO needed to raise the basicity of 2.00-L of water to 10.50.

**Plan** From the pH, we can determine the equilibrium concentration of $OH^-$. We can then construct a table of initial and equilibrium concentrations in which the initial concentration of $ClO^-$ is our unknown. We can calculate $[ClO^-]$ using the expression for $K_b$.

**Solve** We can calculate $[OH^-]$ by using either Equation 16.16 or Equation 16.20; we will use the latter method here:

$$pOH = 14.00 - pH = 14.00 - 10.50 = 3.50$$
$$[OH^-] = 10^{-3.50} = 3.2 \times 10^{-4}\ M$$

This concentration is high enough that we can assume that Equation 16.37 is the only source of $OH^-$; that is, we can neglect any $OH^-$ produced by the autoionization of $H_2O$. We now assume a value of $x$ for the initial concentration of $ClO^-$ and solve the equilibrium problem in the usual way.

|  | $ClO^-(aq)$ | $+$ | $H_2O(l)$ | $\rightleftharpoons$ | $HClO(aq)$ | $+$ | $OH^-(aq)$ |
|---|---|---|---|---|---|---|---|
| Initial | $x$ M | | — | | 0 | | 0 |
| Change | $-3.2 \times 10^{-4}\ M$ | | — | | $+3.2 \times 10^{-4}\ M$ | | $+3.2 \times 10^{-4}\ M$ |
| Equilibrium | $(x - 3.2 \times 10^{-4})\ M$ | | — | | $3.2 \times 10^{-4}\ M$ | | $3.2 \times 10^{-4}\ M$ |

We now use the expression for the base-dissociation constant to solve for $x$:

$$K_b = \frac{[HClO][OH^-]}{[ClO^-]} = \frac{(3.2 \times 10^{-4})^2}{x - 3.2 \times 10^{-4}} = 3.3 \times 10^{-7}$$

$$x = \frac{(3.2 \times 10^{-4})^2}{3.3 \times 10^{-7}} + (3.2 \times 10^{-4}) = 0.31\ M$$

We say that the solution is 0.31 $M$ in NaClO even though some of the ClO$^-$ ions have reacted with water. Because the solution is 0.31 $M$ in NaClO and the total volume of solution is 2.00 L, 0.62 mol of NaClO is the amount of the salt that was added to the water.

**PRACTICE EXERCISE**
What is the molarity of an aqueous NH$_3$ solution that has a pH of 11.17?
***Answer:*** 0.12 $M$

## 16.8 | RELATIONSHIP BETWEEN $K_a$ AND $K_b$

We have seen in a qualitative way that the stronger acids have the weaker conjugate bases. To see if we can find a corresponding *quantitative* relationship, let's consider the $NH_4^+$ and $NH_3$ conjugate acid–base pair. Each species reacts with water. For the acid, $NH_4^+$ the reaction is:

$$NH_4^+(aq) + H_2O(l) \rightleftharpoons NH_3(aq) + H_3O^+(aq)$$

or written in its simpler form:

$$NH_4^+(aq) \rightleftharpoons NH_3(aq) + H^+(aq) \qquad [16.38]$$

and for the base $NH_3$:

$$NH_3(aq) + H_2O(l) \rightleftharpoons NH_4^+(aq) + OH^-(aq) \qquad [16.39]$$

and each equilibrium is expressed by a dissociation constant:

$$K_a = \frac{[NH_3][H^+]}{[NH_4^+]} \qquad K_b = \frac{[NH_4^+][OH^-]}{[NH_3]}$$

When we add Equations 16.38 and 16.39, the $NH_4^+$ and $NH_3$ species cancel and we are left with the autoionization of water:

$$NH_4^+(aq) \rightleftharpoons NH_3(aq) + H^+(aq)$$

$$\underline{NH_3(aq) + H_2O(l) \rightleftharpoons NH_4^+(aq) + OH^-(aq)}$$

$$H_2O(l) \rightleftharpoons H^+(aq) + OH^-(aq)$$

Recall that when two equations are added to give a third, the equilibrium constant associated with the third equation equals the product of the equilibrium constants of the first two equations. ∞ (Section 15.3)

Applying this rule to our present example, when we multiply $K_a$ and $K_b$, we obtain

$$K_a \times K_b = \left(\frac{[NH_3][H^+]}{[NH_4^+]}\right)\left(\frac{[NH_4^+][OH^-]}{[NH_3]}\right)$$

$$= [H^+][OH^-] = K_w$$

Thus, the product of $K_a$ and $K_b$ is the ion-product constant for water, $K_w$ (Equation 16.16). We expect this result because adding Equations 16.38 and 16.39 gave us the autoionization equilibrium for water, for which the equilibrium constant is $K_w$.

This relationship is so important that it should receive special attention: *The product of the acid-dissociation constant for an acid and the base-dissociation constant for its conjugate base equals the ion-product constant for water:*

$$K_a \times K_b = K_w \qquad [16.40]$$

As the strength of an acid increases ($K_a$ gets larger), the strength of its conjugate base must decrease ($K_b$ gets smaller) so that the product $K_a \times K_b$ remains $1.0 \times 10^{-14}$ at 25 °C. ▶ **TABLE 16.5** demonstrates this relationship. Remember, this important relationship applies *only* to conjugate acid–base pairs.

By using Equation 16.40, we can calculate $K_b$ for any weak base if we know $K_a$ for its conjugate acid. Similarly, we can calculate $K_a$ for a weak acid if we know $K_b$ for its conjugate base. As a practical consequence, ionization constants are often listed for only one member of a conjugate acid–base pair. For example, Appendix D does not contain $K_b$

| TABLE 16.5 • Some Conjugate Acid–Base Pairs | | | |
|---|---|---|---|
| **Acid** | $K_a$ | **Base** | $K_b$ |
| $HNO_3$ | (Strong acid) | $NO_3^-$ | (Negligible basicity) |
| $HF$ | $6.8 \times 10^{-4}$ | $F^-$ | $1.5 \times 10^{-11}$ |
| $HC_2H_3O_2$ | $1.8 \times 10^{-5}$ | $C_2H_3O_2^-$ | $5.6 \times 10^{-10}$ |
| $H_2CO_3$ | $4.3 \times 10^{-7}$ | $HCO_3^-$ | $2.3 \times 10^{-8}$ |
| $NH_4^+$ | $5.6 \times 10^{-10}$ | $NH_3$ | $1.8 \times 10^{-5}$ |
| $HCO_3^-$ | $5.6 \times 10^{-11}$ | $CO_3^{2-}$ | $1.8 \times 10^{-4}$ |
| $OH^-$ | (Negligible acidity) | $O^{2-}$ | (Strong base) |

values for the anions of weak acids because they can be readily calculated from the tabulated $K_a$ values for their conjugate acids.

If you look up the values for acid- or base-dissociation constants in a chemistry handbook, you may find them expressed as $pK_a$ or $pK_b$ (that is, $-\log K_a$ or $-\log K_b$) (Section 16.4). Equation 16.40 can be written in terms of $pK_a$ and $pK_b$ by taking the negative logarithm of both sides:

$$pK_a + pK_b = pK_w = 14.00 \quad \text{at 25 °C} \qquad [16.41]$$

⚠️ **GIVE IT SOME THOUGHT**

What is the $pK_a$ value for HF? What is the $pK_b$ value for $F^-$?

## CHEMISTRY PUT TO WORK

### Amines and Amine Hydrochlorides

Many low-molecular-weight amines have a fishy odor. Amines and $NH_3$ are produced by the anaerobic (absence of $O_2$) decomposition of dead animal or plant matter. Two such amines with very disagreeable odors are $H_2N(CH_2)_4NH_2$, *putrescine*, and $H_2N(CH_2)_5NH_2$, *cadaverine*.

Many drugs, including quinine, codeine, caffeine, and amphetamine, are amines. Like other amines, these substances are weak bases; the amine nitrogen is readily protonated upon treatment with an acid. The resulting products are called *acid salts*. If we use A as the abbreviation for an amine, the acid salt formed by reaction with hydrochloric acid can be written $AH^+Cl^-$. It can also be written as A·HCl and referred to as a hydrochloride. Amphetamine hydrochloride, for example, is the acid salt formed by treating amphetamine with HCl:

Acid salts are much less volatile, more stable, and generally more water soluble than the corresponding amines. For this reason, many drugs that are amines are sold and administered as acid salts. Some examples of over-the-counter medications that contain amine hydrochlorides as active ingredients are shown in ▼ FIGURE 16.14.

*RELATED EXERCISES:* 16.75, 16.76, 16.104, 16.113, and 16.122

◄ FIGURE 16.14 Some over-the-counter medications in which an amine hydrochloride is a major active ingredient.

**SAMPLE EXERCISE 16.17**  **Calculating $K_a$ or $K_b$ for a Conjugate Acid–Base Pair**

Calculate (a) $K_b$ for the fluoride ion, (b) $K_a$ for the ammonium ion.

**SOLUTION**

**Analyze**  We are asked to determine dissociation constants for $F^-$, the conjugate base of HF, and $NH_4^+$, the conjugate acid of $NH_3$.

**Plan**  We can use the tabulated $K$ values for HF and $NH_3$ and the relationship between $K_a$ and $K_b$ to calculate the ionization constants for their conjugates, $F^-$ and $NH_4^+$.

**Solve**
(a)  For the weak acid HF, Table 16.2 and Appendix D give $K_a = 6.8 \times 10^{-4}$. We can use Equation 16.40 to calculate $K_b$ for the conjugate base, $F^-$:

$$K_b = \frac{K_w}{K_a} = \frac{1.0 \times 10^{-14}}{6.8 \times 10^{-4}} = 1.5 \times 10^{-11}$$

(b)  For $NH_3$, Table 16.4 and in Appendix D give $K_b = 1.8 \times 10^{-5}$, and this value in Equation 16.40 gives us $K_a$ for the conjugate acid, $NH_4^+$:

$$K_a = \frac{K_w}{K_b} = \frac{1.0 \times 10^{-14}}{1.8 \times 10^{-5}} = 5.6 \times 10^{-10}$$

**Check**  The respective $K$ values for $F^-$ and $NH_4^+$ are listed in Table 16.5, where we see that the values calculated here agree with those in Table 16.5.

**PRACTICE EXERCISE**

(a)  Which of these anions has the largest base-dissociation constant: $NO_2^-$, $PO_4^{3-}$, or $N_3^-$?
(b)  The base quinoline has the structure

Its conjugate acid is listed in handbooks as having a $pK_a$ of 4.90. What is the base-dissociation constant for quinoline?

**Answers:**  (a) $PO_4^{3-}$ ($K_b = 2.4 \times 10^{-2}$), (b) $K_b = 7.9 \times 10^{-10}$

# 16.9 | ACID–BASE PROPERTIES OF SALT SOLUTIONS

Even before you began this chapter, you were undoubtedly aware of many substances that are acidic, such as $HNO_3$, HCl, and $H_2SO_4$, and others that are basic, such as NaOH and $NH_3$. However, our discussion up to this point in the chapter has indicated that ions can also exhibit acidic or basic properties. For example, we calculated $K_a$ for $NH_4^+$ and $K_b$ for $F^-$ in Sample Exercise 16.17. Such behavior implies that salt solutions can be acidic or basic. Before proceeding with further discussions of acids and bases, let's examine the way dissolved salts can affect pH.

Because nearly all salts are strong electrolytes, we can assume that any salt dissolved in water is completely dissociated. Consequently, the acid–base properties of salt solutions are due to the behavior of the cations and anions. Many ions react with water to generate $H^+(aq)$ or $OH^-(aq)$ ions. This type of reaction is often called **hydrolysis**. The pH of an aqueous salt solution can be predicted qualitatively by considering the salt's cations and anions.

## An Anion's Ability to React with Water

In general, an anion $X^-$ in solution can be considered the conjugate base of an acid. For example, $Cl^-$ is the conjugate base of HCl, and $CH_3COO^-$ is the conjugate base of $CH_3COOH$. Whether or not an anion reacts with water to produce hydroxide ions depends on the strength of the anion's conjugate acid. To identify the acid and assess its strength, we add a proton to the anion's formula. If the acid HX determined in this way is one of the seven strong acids listed on page 664, the anion has a negligible tendency to abstract protons from water and does not affect the pH of the solution. The presence of

$Cl^-$ in an aqueous solution, for example, does not result in the production of any $OH^-$ and does not affect the pH. Thus, $Cl^-$ is always a spectator ion in acid–base chemistry.

If HX is *not* one of the seven strong acids, it is a weak acid. In this case, the conjugate base $X^-$ is a weak base and it reacts to a small extent with water to produce the weak acid and hydroxide ions:

$$X^-(aq) + H_2O(l) \rightleftharpoons HX(aq) + OH^-(aq) \qquad [16.42]$$

The $OH^-$ ion generated in this way increases the pH of the solution, making it basic. Acetate ion, for example, being the conjugate base of a weak acid, reacts with water to produce acetic acid and hydroxide ions, thereby increasing the pH of the solution:

$$CH_3COO^-(aq) + H_2O(l) \rightleftharpoons CH_3COOH(aq) + OH^-(aq) \qquad [16.43]$$

⚠ **GIVE IT SOME THOUGHT**

What effect will $NO_3^-$ ions have on the pH of a solution? What effect will $CO_3^{2-}$ ions have?

The situation is more complicated for salts containing anions that have ionizable protons, such as $HSO_3^-$. These salts are amphiprotic (Section 16.2), and how they behave in water is determined by the relative magnitudes of $K_a$ and $K_b$ for the ion, as shown in Sample Exercise 16.19. If $K_a > K_b$, the ion causes the solution to be acidic. If $K_b > K_a$, the solution is made basic by the ion.

## A Cation's Ability to React with Water

Polyatomic cations containing one or more protons can be considered the conjugate acids of weak bases. The $NH_4^+$ ion, for example, is the conjugate acid of the weak base $NH_3$. Thus, $NH_4^+$ is a weak acid and will donate a proton to water, producing hydronium ions and thereby lowering the pH:

$$NH_4^+(aq) + H_2O(l) \rightleftharpoons NH_3(aq) + H_3O^+(aq) \qquad [16.44]$$

Many metal ions react with water to decrease the pH of an aqueous solution. This effect is most pronounced for small, highly charged cations like $Fe^{3+}$ and $Al^{3+}$, as illustrated by the $K_a$ values for metal cations in ◀ **TABLE 16.6**. A comparison of $Fe^{2+}$ and $Fe^{3+}$ values in the table illustrates how acidity increases as ionic charge increases.

Notice that $K_a$ values for the 3+ ions in Table 16.6 are comparable to the values for familiar weak acids, such as acetic acid ($K_a = 1.8 \times 10^{-5}$). The ions of alkali and alkaline earth metals, being relatively large and not highly charged, do not react with water and therefore do not affect pH. Note that these are the same cations found in the strong bases (Section 16.5). The different tendencies of four cations to lower the pH of a solution are illustrated in ▼ **FIGURE 16.15**.

**TABLE 16.6** • Acid-Dissociation Constants for Metal Cations in Aqueous Solution at 25 °C

| Cation | $K_a$ |
| --- | --- |
| $Fe^{2+}$ | $3.2 \times 10^{-10}$ |
| $Zn^{2+}$ | $2.5 \times 10^{-10}$ |
| $Ni^{2+}$ | $2.5 \times 10^{-11}$ |
| $Fe^{3+}$ | $6.3 \times 10^{-3}$ |
| $Cr^{3+}$ | $1.6 \times 10^{-4}$ |
| $Al^{3+}$ | $1.4 \times 10^{-5}$ |

▶ **FIGURE 16.15 Effect of cations on solution pH.** The pH values of 1.0 *M* solutions of four nitrate salts are estimated using acid–base indicators.

| NaNO₃ | Ca(NO₃)₂ | Zn(NO₃)₂ | Al(NO₃)₃ |
| --- | --- | --- | --- |
| Bromothymol blue | Bromothymol blue | Methyl red | Methyl orange |
| pH = 7.0 | pH = 6.9 | pH = 5.5 | pH = 3.5 |

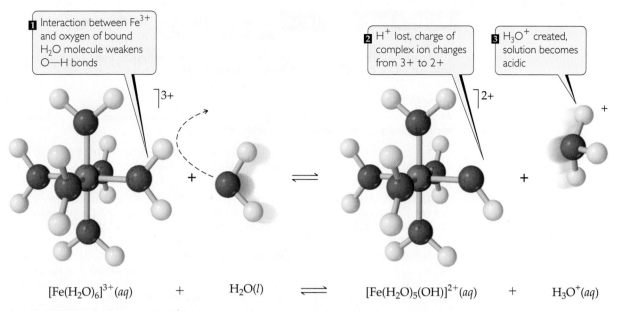

$$[Fe(H_2O)_6]^{3+}(aq) \quad + \quad H_2O(l) \quad \rightleftharpoons \quad [Fe(H_2O)_5(OH)]^{2+}(aq) \quad + \quad H_3O^+(aq)$$

▲ **FIGURE 16.16    A hydrated Fe³⁺ ion acts as an acid by donating an H⁺ to a free H₂O molecule, forming H₃O⁺.**

The mechanism by which metal ions produce acidic solutions is shown in ▲ **FIGURE 16.16**. Because metal ions are positively charged, they attract the unshared electron pairs of water molecules and become hydrated.  ∞ (Section 13.1) The larger the charge on the metal ion, the stronger the interaction between the ion and the oxygen of its hydrating water molecules. As the strength of this interaction increases, the O—H bonds in the hydrating water molecules become weaker. This facilitates transfer of protons from the hydration water molecules to solvent water molecules.

## Combined Effect of Cation and Anion in Solution

To determine whether a salt forms an acidic, a basic, or a neutral solution when dissolved in water, we must consider the action of both cation and anion. There are four possible combinations.

1. If the salt contains an anion that does not react with water and a cation that does not react with water, we expect the pH to be neutral. Such is the case when the anion is a conjugate base of a strong acid and the cation is either from group 1A or one of the heavier members of group 2A ($Ca^{2+}$, $Sr^{2+}$, and $Ba^{2+}$). *Examples*: **NaCl, Ba(NO₃)₂, RbClO₄.**

2. If the salt contains an anion that reacts with water to produce hydroxide ions and a cation that does not react with water, we expect the pH to be basic. Such is the case when the anion is the conjugate base of a weak acid and the cation is either from group 1A or one of the heavier members of group 2A ($Ca^{2+}$, $Sr^{2+}$, and $Ba^{2+}$). *Examples*: **NaClO, RbF, BaSO₃.**

3. If the salt contains a cation that reacts with water to produce hydronium ions and an anion that does not react with water, we expect the pH to be acidic. Such is the case when the cation is a conjugate acid of a weak base or a small cation with a charge of 2+ or greater. *Examples*: **NH₄NO₃, AlCl₃, Fe(NO₃)₃.**

4. If the salt contains an anion and a cation *both* capable of reacting with water, both hydroxide ions and hydronium ions are produced. Whether the solution is basic, neutral, or acidic depends on the relative abilities of the ions to react with water. *Examples*: **NH₄ClO, Al(CH₃COO)₃, CrF₃.**

**SAMPLE EXERCISE 16.18** | Determining Whether Salt Solutions Are Acidic, Basic, or Neutral

Determine whether aqueous solutions of each of these salts are acidic, basic, or neutral: **(a)** $Ba(CH_3COO)_2$, **(b)** $NH_4Cl$, **(c)** $CH_3NH_3Br$, **(d)** $KNO_3$, **(e)** $Al(ClO_4)_3$.

**SOLUTION**

**Analyze** We are given the chemical formulas of five ionic compounds (salts) and asked whether their aqueous solutions will be acidic, basic, or neutral.

**Plan** We can determine whether a solution of a salt is acidic, basic, or neutral by identifying the ions in solution and by assessing how each ion will affect the pH.

**Solve**

**(a)** This solution contains barium ions and acetate ions. The cation is an ion of a heavy alkaline earth metal and will therefore not affect the pH. The anion, $CH_3COO^-$, is the conjugate base of the weak acid $CH_3COOH$ and will hydrolyze to produce $OH^-$ ions, thereby making the solution basic (combination 2).

**(b)** In this solution, $NH_4^+$ is the conjugate acid of a weak base ($NH_3$) and is therefore acidic. $Cl^-$ is the conjugate base of a strong acid (HCl) and therefore has no influence on the pH of the solution. Because the solution contains an ion that is acidic ($NH_4^+$) and one that has no influence on pH ($Cl^-$), the solution of $NH_4Cl$ will be acidic (combination 3).

**(c)** Here $CH_3NH_3^+$ is the conjugate acid of a weak base ($CH_3NH_2$, an amine) and is therefore acidic, and $Br^-$ is the conjugate base of a strong acid (HBr) and therefore pH neutral. Because the solution contains one ion that is acidic and one that has no influence on pH, the solution of $CH_3NH_3Br$ will be acidic (combination 3).

**(d)** This solution contains the $K^+$ ion, which is a cation of group 1A, and the $NO_3^-$ ion, which is the conjugate base of the strong acid $HNO_3$. Neither of the ions will react with water to any appreciable extent, making the solution neutral (combination 1).

**(e)** This solution contains $Al^{3+}$ and $ClO_4^-$ ions. Cations, such as $Al^{3+}$, that have a charge of 3+ or higher are acidic. The $ClO_4^-$ ion is the conjugate base of a strong acid ($HClO_4$) and therefore does not affect pH. Thus, the solution of $Al(ClO_4)_3$ will be acidic (combination 3).

**PRACTICE EXERCISE**

Indicate which salt in each of the following pairs forms the more acidic (or less basic) 0.010 *M* solution: **(a)** $NaNO_3$ or $Fe(NO_3)_3$, **(b)** KBr or KBrO, **(c)** $CH_3NH_3Cl$ or $BaCl_2$, **(d)** $NH_4NO_2$ or $NH_4NO_3$.

***Answers:*** **(a)** $Fe(NO_3)_3$, **(b)** KBr, **(c)** $CH_3NH_3Cl$, **(d)** $NH_4NO_3$

---

**SAMPLE EXERCISE 16.19** | Predicting Whether the Solution of an Amphiprotic Anion Is Acidic or Basic

Predict whether the salt $Na_2HPO_4$ forms an acidic solution or a basic solution when dissolved in water.

**SOLUTION**

**Analyze** We are asked to predict whether a solution of $Na_2HPO_4$ is acidic or basic. This substance is an ionic compound composed of $Na^+$ and $HPO_4^{2-}$ ions.

**Plan** We need to evaluate each ion, predicting whether it is acidic or basic. Because $Na^+$ is a cation of group 1A, it has no influence on pH. Thus, our analysis of whether the solution is acidic or basic must focus on the behavior of the $HPO_4^{2-}$ ion. We need to consider the fact that $HPO_4^{2-}$ can act as either an acid or a base:

$$\text{As acid} \qquad HPO_4^{2-}(aq) \rightleftharpoons H^+(aq) + PO_4^{3-}(aq) \qquad [16.45]$$

$$\text{As base} \qquad HPO_4^{2-}(aq) + H_2O \rightleftharpoons H_2PO_4^-(aq) + OH^-(aq) \qquad [16.46]$$

Of these two reactions, the one with the larger equilibrium constant determines whether the solution is acidic or basic.

**Solve** The value of $K_a$ for Equation 16.45 is $4.2 \times 10^{-13}$ (Table 16.3). For Equation 16.46, we must calculate $K_b$ for the base $HPO_4^{2-}$ from the value of $K_a$ for its conjugate acid, $H_2PO_4^-$, and the relationship $K_a \times K_b = K_w$ (Equation 16.40). Using the value $K_a(H_2PO_4^-) = 6.2 \times 10^{-8}$ from Table 16.3, we have

$$K_b(HPO_4^{2-}) \times K_a(H_2PO_4^-) = K_w = 1.0 \times 10^{-14}.$$

$$K_b(HPO_4^{2-}) = \frac{1.0 \times 10^{-14}}{6.2 \times 10^{-8}} = 1.6 \times 10^{-7}$$

This $K_b$ value is more than $10^5$ times larger than $K_a$ for $HPO_4{}^{2-}$; thus, the reaction in Equation 16.46 predominates over that in Equation 16.45, and the solution is basic.

**PRACTICE EXERCISE**
Predict whether the dipotassium salt of citric acid ($K_2HC_6H_5O_7$) forms an acidic or basic solution in water (see Table 16.3 for data).
*Answer:* acidic

# 16.10 | ACID–BASE BEHAVIOR AND CHEMICAL STRUCTURE

When a substance is dissolved in water, it may behave as an acid, behave as a base, or exhibit no acid–base properties. How does the chemical structure of a substance determine which of these behaviors is exhibited by the substance? For example, why do some substances that contain OH groups behave as bases, releasing $OH^-$ ions into solution, whereas others behave as acids, ionizing to release $H^+$ ions? In this section we discuss briefly the effects of chemical structure on acid–base behavior.

## Factors That Affect Acid Strength

A molecule containing H will act as a proton donor (an acid) only if the H—X bond is polarized in this way:

$$\overset{\longrightarrow}{H—X}$$

In ionic hydrides, such as NaH, the reverse is true: the H atom possesses a negative charge and behaves as a proton acceptor (a base). Nonpolar H—X bonds, such as the H—C bond in $CH_4$, produce neither acidic nor basic aqueous solutions.

A second factor that helps determine whether a molecule containing an H—X bond will donate a proton is the strength of the bond. Very strong bonds are less easily broken than weaker ones. This factor is important, for example, in the hydrogen halides. The H—F bond is the most polar H—X bond. You therefore might expect HF to be a very strong acid if bond polarity were all that mattered. However, the H—X bond strength increases as you move up the group: 299 kJ/mol in HI, 366 kJ/mol in HBr, 431 kJ/mol in HCl, and 567 kJ/mol in HF. Because HF has the highest bond strength among the hydrogen halides, it is a weak acid, whereas all the other hydrogen halides are strong acids in water.

A third factor that affects the ease with which a hydrogen atom ionizes from HX is the stability of the conjugate base, $X^-$. In general, the greater the stability of the conjugate base, the stronger the acid.

The strength of an acid is often a combination of all three factors.

## Binary Acids

For a series of binary acids HX in which X represents members of the same *group* in the periodic table, the strength of the H—X bond is generally the most important factor determining acid strength. The strength of an H—X bond tends to decrease as the element X increases in size. As a result, the bond strength decreases and acidity increases down a group. Thus, HCl is a stronger acid than HF, and $H_2S$ is a stronger acid than $H_2O$.

Bond polarity is the major factor determining acidity for binary acids HX when X represents members of the same *period*. Thus, acidity increases as the electronegativity of the element X increases, as it generally does moving from left to right across a period. For example, the difference in acidity of the period 2 elements is $CH_4 < NH_3 \ll H_2O < HF$. Because the C—H bond is essentially nonpolar, $CH_4$ shows no tendency to form $H^+$ and $CH_3{}^-$ ions. Although the N—H bond is polar, $NH_3$ has a nonbonding pair of electrons on the nitrogen atom that dominates its chemistry, so $NH_3$ acts as a base rather than an acid.

| 4A | 5A | 6A | 7A |
|---|---|---|---|
| **CH$_4$**<br>Neither acid<br>nor base | **NH$_3$**<br>Weak base<br>$K_b = 1.8 \times 10^{-5}$ | **H$_2$O** | **HF**<br>Weak acid<br>$K_a = 6.8 \times 10^{-4}$ |
| **SiH$_4$**<br>Neither acid<br>nor base | **PH$_3$**<br>Very weak base<br>$K_b = 4 \times 10^{-28}$ | **H$_2$S**<br>Weak acid<br>$K_a = 9.5 \times 10^{-8}$ | **HCl**<br>Strong acid |
| | | **H$_2$Se**<br>Weak acid<br>$K_a = 1.3 \times 10^{-4}$ | **HBr**<br>Strong acid |

Increasing acid strength →

(vertical) Increasing acid strength

▶ FIGURE 16.17 **Trends in acid strength for the binary hydrides of periods 2–4.**

The periodic trends in the acid strengths of binary compounds of hydrogen and the nonmetals of periods 2 and 3 are summarized in ▲ **FIGURE 16.17.**

### GIVE IT SOME THOUGHT

What is the major factor determining the increase in acidity of binary acids going down a group? What is the major factor going across a period?

## Oxyacids

Many common acids, such as sulfuric acid, contain one or more O—H bonds:

Acids in which OH groups and possibly additional oxygen atoms are bound to a central atom are called **oxyacids**. At first it may seem confusing that the OH group, which we know behaves as a base, is also present in some acids. Let's take a closer look at what factors determine whether a given OH group behaves as a base or as an acid.

Consider an OH group bound to some atom Y, which might in turn have other groups attached to it:

$$\text{—Y—O—H}$$

At one extreme, Y might be a metal, such as Na or Mg. Because of the low electronegativity of metals, the pair of electrons shared between Y and O is completely transferred to oxygen, and an ionic compound containing OH$^-$ is formed. Such compounds are therefore sources of OH$^-$ ions and behave as bases, as in NaOH and Mg(OH)$_2$.

When Y is a nonmetal, the bond to O is covalent and the substance does not readily lose OH$^-$. Instead, these compounds are either acidic or neutral. *Generally, as the electronegativity of Y increases, so does the acidity of the substance.* This happens for two reasons: First, as electron density is drawn toward Y, the O—H bond becomes weaker and more polar, thereby favoring loss of H$^+$. Second, because the conjugate base of any acid YOH is usually an anion, its stability generally increases as the electronegativity of

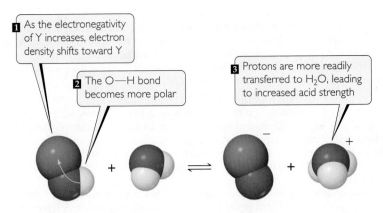

1 As the electronegativity of Y increases, electron density shifts toward Y

2 The O—H bond becomes more polar

3 Protons are more readily transferred to $H_2O$, leading to increased acid strength

| Substance | Y—OH | Electronegativity of Y | Dissociation constant |
|---|---|---|---|
| Hypochlorous acid | Cl—OH | 3.0 | $K_a = 3.0 \times 10^{-8}$ |
| Hypobromous acid | Br—OH | 2.8 | $K_a = 2.5 \times 10^{-9}$ |
| Hypoiodous acid | I—OH | 2.5 | $K_a = 2.3 \times 10^{-11}$ |
| Water | H—OH | 2.1 | $K_w = 1.0 \times 10^{-14}$ |

◀ **FIGURE 16.18   Acidity of the hypohalous oxyacids (YOH) as a function of electronegativity of Y.**

Y increases. This trend is illustrated by the $K_a$ values of the hypohalous acids (YOH acids where Y is a halide ion), which decrease as the electronegativity of the halogen atom decreases (▲ **FIGURE 16.18**).

Many oxyacids contain additional oxygen atoms bonded to the central atom Y. These atoms pull electron density from the O—H bond, further increasing its polarity. Increasing the number of oxygen atoms also helps stabilize the conjugate base by increasing its ability to "spread out" its negative charge. Thus, *the strength of an acid increases as additional electronegative atoms bond to the central atom Y*. For example, the strength of the chlorine oxyacids (Y = Cl) steadily increases as O atoms are added:

Hypochlorous          Chlorous          Chloric          Perchloric

H—Ö—Cl̈:     H—Ö—Cl̈—Ö:     H—Ö—Cl—Ö:     H—Ö—Cl—Ö:

$K_a = 3.0 \times 10^{-8}$     $K_a = 1.1 \times 10^{-2}$     Strong acid     Strong acid

Increasing acid strength

Because the oxidation number of Y increases as the number of attached O atoms increases, this correlation can be stated in an equivalent way: In a series of oxyacids, the acidity increases as the oxidation number of the central atom increases.

 GIVE IT SOME THOUGHT

Which acid has the larger acid-dissociation constant, $HIO_2$ or $HBrO_3$?

**SAMPLE EXERCISE 16.20**   **Predicting Relative Acidities from Composition and Structure**

Arrange the compounds in each series in order of increasing acid strength: **(a)** $AsH_3$, HBr, KH, $H_2Se$; **(b)** $H_2SO_4$, $H_2SeO_3$, $H_2SeO_4$.

**SOLUTION**

**Analyze** We are asked to arrange two sets of compounds in order from weakest acid to strongest acid. In **(a)**, the substances are binary compounds containing H, and in **(b)** the substances are oxyacids.

**Plan** For the binary compounds, we will consider the electronegativities of As, Br, K, and Se relative to the electronegativity of H. The higher the electronegativity of these atoms, the higher the partial positive charge on H and so the more acidic the compound.

For the oxyacids, we will consider both the electronegativities of the central atom and the number of oxygen atoms bonded to the central atom.

**Solve**

**(a)** Because K is on the left side of the periodic table, it has a very low electronegativity (0.8, from Figure 8.7). As a result, the hydrogen in KH carries a negative charge. Thus, KH should be the least acidic (most basic) compound in the series.

Arsenic and hydrogen have similar electronegativities, 2.0 and 2.1, respectively. This means that the As—H bond is nonpolar, and so $AsH_3$ has little tendency to donate a proton in aqueous solution.

The electronegativity of Se is 2.4, and that of Br is 2.8. Consequently, the H—Br bond is more polar than the H—Se bond, giving HBr the greater tendency to donate a proton. (This expectation is confirmed by Figure 16.17, where we see that $H_2Se$ is a weak acid and HBr a strong acid.) Thus, the order of increasing acidity is $KH < AsH_3 < H_2Se < HBr$.

**(b)** The acids $H_2SO_4$ and $H_2SeO_4$ have the same number of O atoms and the same number of OH groups. In such cases, the acid strength increases with increasing electronegativity of the central atom. Because S is slightly more electronegative than Se (2.5 vs 2.4), we predict that $H_2SO_4$ is more acidic than $H_2SeO_4$.

For acids with the same central atom, the acidity increases as the number of oxygen atoms bonded to the central atom increases. Thus, $H_2SeO_4$ should be a stronger acid than $H_2SeO_3$. We predict the order of increasing acidity to be $H_2SeO_3 < H_2SeO_4 < H_2SO_4$.

**PRACTICE EXERCISE**

In each pair, choose the compound that give the more acidic (or less basic) solution: **(a)** HBr, HF; **(b)** $PH_3$, $H_2S$; **(c)** $HNO_2$, $HNO_3$; **(d)** $H_2SO_3$, $H_2SeO_3$.
***Answers:*** **(a)** HBr, **(b)** $H_2S$, **(c)** $HNO_3$, **(d)** $H_2SO_3$

## Carboxylic Acids

Another large group of acids is illustrated by acetic acid, a weak acid ($K_a = 1.8 \times 10^{-5}$):

The portion of the structure shown in red is called the *carboxyl group*, which is often written COOH. Thus, the chemical formula of acetic acid is written as $CH_3COOH$, where only the hydrogen atom in the carboxyl group can be ionized. Acids that contain a carboxyl group are called **carboxylic acids**, and they form the largest category of organic acids. Formic acid and benzoic acid are further examples of this large and important category of acids:

Formic acid                    Benzoic acid

Two factors contribute to the acidic behavior of carboxylic acids. First, the additional oxygen atom attached to the carbon of the carboxyl group draws electron density from the O—H bond, increasing its polarity and helping to stabilize the conjugate base. Second, the conjugate base of a carboxylic acid (a *carboxylate anion*) can exhibit resonance ∞ (Section 8.6), which contributes to the stability of the anion by spreading the negative charge over several atoms:

# CHEMISTRY AND LIFE

## THE AMPHIPROTIC BEHAVIOR OF AMINO ACIDS

The general structure of *amino acids*, the building blocks of proteins, is

Amine group (basic)    Carboxyl group (acidic)

where different amino acids have different R groups attached to the central carbon atom. For example, in *glycine*, the simplest amino acid, R is a hydrogen atom, and in *alanine* R is a $CH_3$ group:

Glycine          Alanine

Amino acids contain a carboxyl group and can therefore serve as acids. They also contain an $NH_2$ group, characteristic of amines (Section 16.7), and thus they can also act as bases. Amino acids, therefore, are amphiprotic. For glycine, we might expect the acid and base reactions with water to be

*Acid:* $H_2N-CH_2-COOH(aq) + H_2O(l) \rightleftharpoons$

$H_2N-CH_2-COO^-(aq) + H_3O^+(aq)$    [16.47]

*Base:* $H_2N-CH_2-COOH(aq) + H_2O(l) \rightleftharpoons$

$^+H_3N-CH_2-COOH(aq) + OH^-(aq)$    [16.48]

The pH of a solution of glycine in water is about 6.0, indicating that it is a slightly stronger acid than base. The acid–base chemistry of amino acids is more complicated than shown in Equations 16.47 and 16.48, however. Because the COOH group can act as an acid and the $NH_2$ group can act as a base, amino acids undergo a "self-contained" Brønsted–Lowry acid–base reaction in which the proton of the carboxyl group is transferred to the basic nitrogen atom:

proton transfer

Neutral molecule          Zwitterion

Although the form of the amino acid on the right in this equation is electrically neutral overall, it has a positively charged end and a negatively charged end. A molecule of this type is called a *zwitterion* (German for "hybrid ion").

Do amino acids exhibit any properties indicating that they behave as zwitterions? If so, their behavior should be similar to that of ionic substances. ∞ (Section 8.2) Crystalline amino acids have relatively high melting points, usually above 200 °C, which is characteristic of ionic solids. Amino acids are far more soluble in water than in nonpolar solvents. In addition, the dipole moments of amino acids are large, consistent with a large separation of charge in the molecule. Thus, the ability of amino acids to act simultaneously as acids and bases has important effects on their properties.

*RELATED EXERCISE:* 16.113

---

 GIVE IT SOME THOUGHT

What group of atoms is present in all carboxylic acids?

---

# 16.11 | LEWIS ACIDS AND BASES

For a substance to be a proton acceptor (a Brønsted–Lowry base), it must have an unshared pair of electrons for binding the proton, as, for example, in $NH_3$. Using Lewis structures, we can write the reaction between $H^+$ and $NH_3$ as

$$H^+ + :N-H \longrightarrow \left[ H-N-H \right]^+$$

G. N. Lewis was the first to notice this aspect of acid–base reactions. He proposed a definition of acid and base that emphasizes the shared electron pair: A **Lewis acid** is an electron-pair acceptor, and a **Lewis base** is an electron-pair donor.

Every base that we have discussed thus far—whether $OH^-$, $H_2O$, an amine, or an anion—is an electron-pair donor. Everything that is a base in the Brønsted–Lowry sense (a proton acceptor) is also a base in the Lewis sense (an electron-pair donor). In the Lewis theory, however, a base can donate its electron pair to something other than $H^+$.

The Lewis definition therefore greatly increases the number of species that can be considered acids; in other words, $H^+$ is a Lewis acid but not the only one. For example, the reaction between $NH_3$ and $BF_3$ occurs because $BF_3$ has a vacant orbital in its valence shell. ∞ (Section 8.7) It therefore acts as an electron-pair acceptor (a Lewis acid) toward $NH_3$, which donates the electron pair:

One electron pair of one of the carbon–oxygen double bonds is moved onto the oxygen, leaving a vacant orbital on the carbon, which means the carbon can accept an electron pair donated by $H_2O$. The initial acid–base product rearranges by transferring a proton from the water oxygen to a carbon dioxide oxygen, forming carbonic acid.

### GIVE IT SOME THOUGHT

What feature must any molecule or ion have in order to act as a Lewis base?

Our emphasis throughout this chapter has been on water as the solvent and on the proton as the source of acidic properties. In such cases we find the Brønsted–Lowry definition of acids and bases to be the most useful. In fact, when we speak of a substance as being acidic or basic, we are usually thinking of aqueous solutions and using these terms in the Arrhenius or Brønsted–Lowry sense. The advantage of the Lewis definitions of acid and base is that they allow us to treat a wider variety of reactions, including those that do not involve proton transfer, as acid–base reactions. To avoid confusion, a substance such as $BF_3$ is rarely called an acid unless it is clear from the context that we are using the term in the sense of the Lewis definition. Instead, substances that function as electron-pair acceptors are referred to explicitly as "Lewis acids."

Lewis acids include molecules that, like $BF_3$, have an incomplete octet of electrons. In addition, many simple cations can function as Lewis acids. For example, $Fe^{3+}$ interacts strongly with cyanide ions to form the ferricyanide ion:

$$Fe^{3+} + 6[:C{\equiv}N:]^- \longrightarrow [Fe(C{\equiv}N:)_6]^{3-}$$

The $Fe^{3+}$ ion has vacant orbitals that accept the electron pairs donated by the cyanide ions. (We will learn more in Chapter 23 about just which orbitals are used by the $Fe^{3+}$ ion.) The metal ion is highly charged, too, which contributes to the interaction with $CN^-$ ions.

Some compounds containing multiple bonds can behave as Lewis acids. For example, the reaction of carbon dioxide with water to form carbonic acid ($H_2CO_3$) can be pictured as an attack by a water molecule on $CO_2$, in which the water acts as an electron-pair donor and the $CO_2$ as an electron-pair acceptor:

One electron pair of one of the carbon–oxygen double bonds is moved onto the oxygen, leaving a vacant orbital on the carbon, which means the carbon can accept an electron pair donated by $H_2O$. The initial acid–base product rearranges by transferring a proton from the water oxygen to a carbon dioxide oxygen, forming carbonic acid.

The hydrated cations we encountered in Section 16.9, such as $[Fe(H_2O)_6]^{3+}$ in Figure 16.16, form through the reaction between the cation acting as a Lewis acid and the water molecules acting as Lewis bases. When a water molecule interacts with the positively charged metal ion, electron density is drawn from the oxygen (▶ FIGURE 16.19). This flow of electron density causes the O—H bond to become more polarized; as a result, water molecules bound to the metal ion are more acidic than those in the bulk solvent. This effect becomes more pronounced as the charge of the cation increases, which explains why 3+ cations are much more acidic than cations with smaller charges.

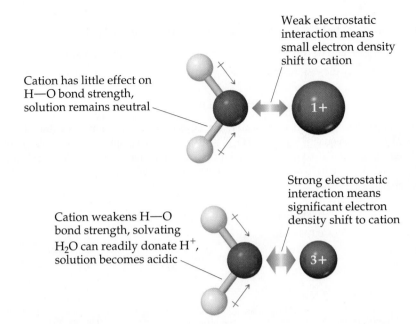

Weak electrostatic interaction means small electron density shift to cation

Cation has little effect on H—O bond strength, solution remains neutral

1+

Strong electrostatic interaction means significant electron density shift to cation

Cation weakens H—O bond strength, solvating $H_2O$ can readily donate $H^+$, solution becomes acidic

3+

◀ **FIGURE 16.19** **The acidity of a hydrated cation depends on cation charge.**

---

**SAMPLE INTEGRATIVE EXERCISE** | **Putting Concepts Together**

Phosphorous acid ($H_3PO_3$) has the Lewis structure

$$\ddot{\text{O}}\text{—P—}\ddot{\text{O}}\text{—H}$$

with H above P and :O—H below P

**(a)** Explain why $H_3PO_3$ is diprotic and not triprotic. **(b)** A 25.0-mL sample of an $H_3PO_3$ solution titrated with 0.102 $M$ NaOH requires 23.3 mL of NaOH to neutralize both acidic protons. What is the molarity of the $H_3PO_3$ solution? **(c)** The original solution from part (b) has a pH of 1.59. Calculate the percent ionization and $K_{a1}$ for $H_3PO_3$, assuming that $K_{a1} \gg K_{a2}$. **(d)** How does the osmotic pressure of a 0.050 $M$ solution of HCl compare qualitatively with that of a 0.050 $M$ solution of $H_3PO_3$? Explain.

**SOLUTION**

We will use what we have learned about molecular structure and its impact on acidic behavior to answer part (a). We will then use stoichiometry and the relationship between pH and [$H^+$] to answer parts (b) and (c). Finally, we will consider percent ionization in order to compare the osmotic pressure of the two solutions in part (d).

**(a)** Acids have polar H—X bonds. From Figure 8.7 we see that the electronegativity of H is 2.1 and that of P is also 2.1. Because the two elements have the same electronegativity, the H—P bond is nonpolar. ∞ (Section 8.4) Thus, this H cannot be acidic. The other two H atoms, however, are bonded to O, which has an electronegativity of 3.5. The H—O bonds are, therefore, polar with H having a partial positive charge. These two H atoms are consequently acidic.

**(b)** The chemical equation for the neutralization reaction is

$$H_3PO_3(aq) + 2\,NaOH(aq) \longrightarrow Na_2HPO_3(aq) + 2\,H_2O(l)$$

From the definition of molarity, $M = \text{mol/L}$, we see that moles $= M \times L$. ∞ (Section 4.5) Thus, the number of moles of NaOH added to the solution is

$$(0.0233 \text{ L})(0.102 \text{ mol/L}) = 2.38 \times 10^{-3} \text{ mol NaOH}$$

The balanced equation indicates that 2 mol of NaOH is consumed for each mole of $H_3PO_3$. Thus, the number of moles of $H_3PO_3$ in the sample is

$$(2.38 \times 10^{-3} \text{ mol NaOH})\left(\frac{1 \text{ mol } H_3PO_3}{2 \text{ mol NaOH}}\right) = 1.19 \times 10^{-3} \text{ mol } H_3PO_3$$

The concentration of the $H_3PO_3$ solution, therefore, equals $(1.19 \times 10^{-3}\text{mol})/(0.0250\,\text{L}) = 0.0476\,M$.

**(c)** From the pH of the solution, 1.59, we can calculate $[H^+]$ at equilibrium:

$$[H^+] = \text{antilog}(-1.59) = 10^{-1.59} = 0.026\ M \text{ (two significant figures)}$$

Because $K_{a1} \gg K_{a2}$, the vast majority of the ions in solution are from the first ionization step of the acid.

$$H_3PO_3(aq) \rightleftharpoons H^+(aq) + H_2PO_3^-(aq)$$

Because one $H_2PO_3^-$ ion forms for each $H^+$ ion formed, the equilibrium concentrations of $H^+$ and $H_2PO_3^-$ are equal: $[H^+] = [H_2PO_3^-] = 0.026\ M$. The equilibrium concentration of $H_3PO_3$ equals the initial concentration minus the amount that ionizes to form $H^+$ and $H_2PO_3^-$: $[H_3PO_3] = 0.0476\ M - 0.026\ M = 0.022\ M$ (two significant figures). These results can be tabulated as follows:

| | $H_3PO_3(aq)$ | $\rightleftharpoons$ | $H^+(aq)$ | + | $H_2PO_3^-(aq)$ |
|---|---|---|---|---|---|
| Initial | $0.0476\ M$ | | 0 | | 0 |
| Change | $-0.026\ M$ | | $+0.026\ M$ | | $+0.026\ M$ |
| Equilibrium | $0.022\ M$ | | $0.026\ M$ | | $0.026\ M$ |

The percent ionization is

$$\text{percent ionization} = \frac{[H^+]_{\text{equilibrium}}}{[H_3PO_3]_{\text{initial}}} \times 100\% = \frac{0.026\ M}{0.0476\ M} \times 100\% = 55\%$$

The first acid-dissociation constant is

$$K_{a1} = \frac{[H^+][H_2PO_3^-]}{[H_3PO_3]} = \frac{(0.026)(0.026)}{0.022} = 0.031$$

**(d)** Osmotic pressure is a colligative property and depends on the total concentration of particles in solution. ∞ (Section 13.5) Because HCl is a strong acid, a 0.050 $M$ solution will contain 0.050 $M$ $H^+(aq)$ and 0.050 $M$ $Cl^-(aq)$, or a total of 0.100 mol/L of particles. Because $H_3PO_3$ is a weak acid, it ionizes to a lesser extent than HCl and, hence, there are fewer particles in the $H_3PO_3$ solution. As a result, the $H_3PO_3$ solution will have the lower osmotic pressure.

# CHAPTER SUMMARY AND KEY TERMS

**SECTION 16.1** Acids and bases were first recognized by the properties of their aqueous solutions. For example, acids turn litmus red, whereas bases turn litmus blue. Arrhenius recognized that the properties of acidic solutions are due to $H^+(aq)$ ions and those of basic solutions are due to $OH^-(aq)$ ions.

**SECTION 16.2** The Brønsted–Lowry concept of acids and bases is more general than the Arrhenius concept and emphasizes the transfer of a proton ($H^+$) from an acid to a base. The $H^+$ ion, which is merely a proton with no surrounding valence electrons, is strongly bound to water. For this reason, the **hydronium ion**, $H_3O^+(aq)$, is often used to represent the predominant form of $H^+$ in water instead of the simpler $H^+(aq)$.

A **Brønsted–Lowry acid** is a substance that donates a proton to another substance; a **Brønsted–Lowry base** is a substance that accepts a proton from another substance. Water is an **amphiprotic** substance, one that can function as either a Brønsted–Lowry acid or base, depending on the substance with which it reacts.

The **conjugate base** of a Brønsted–Lowry acid is the species that remains when a proton is removed from the acid. The **conjugate acid** of a Brønsted–Lowry base is the species formed by adding a proton to the base. Together, an acid and its conjugate base (or a base and its conjugate acid) are called a **conjugate acid–base pair**.

The acid–base strengths of conjugate acid–base pairs are related: The stronger an acid, the weaker is its conjugate base; the weaker an acid, the stronger is its conjugate base. In every acid–base reaction, the position of the equilibrium favors the transfer of the proton from the stronger acid to the stronger base.

**SECTION 16.3** Water ionizes to a slight degree, forming $H^+(aq)$ and $OH^-(aq)$. The extent of this **autoionization** is expressed by the **ion-product constant** for water: $K_w = [H^+][OH^-] = 1.0 \times 10^{-14}$ (25 °C). This relationship describes both pure water and aqueous solutions. The $K_w$ expression indicates that the product of $[H^+]$ and $[OH^-]$ is a constant. Thus, as $[H^+]$ increases, $[OH^-]$ decreases. Acidic solutions are those that contain more $H^+(aq)$ than $OH^-(aq)$, whereas basic solutions contain more $OH^-(aq)$ than $H^+(aq)$.

**SECTION 16.4** The concentration of $H^+(aq)$ can be expressed in terms of **pH**: $pH = -\log[H^+]$. At 25 °C the pH of a neutral solution is 7.00, whereas the pH of an acidic solution is below 7.00, and the pH of a basic solution is above 7.00. The pX notation is also used to represent the negative logarithm of other small quantities, as in pOH and p$K_w$. The pH of a solution can be measured using a pH meter, or it can be estimated using acid–base indicators.

**SECTION 16.5** Strong acids are strong electrolytes, ionizing completely in aqueous solution. The common strong acids are HCl, HBr, HI, $HNO_3$, $HClO_3$, $HClO_4$, and $H_2SO_4$. The conjugate bases of strong acids have negligible basicity.

Common strong bases are the ionic hydroxides of the alkali metals and the heavy alkaline earth metals.

**SECTION 16.6** Weak acids are weak electrolytes; only some of the molecules exist in solution in ionized form. The extent of ionization is expressed by the **acid-dissociation constant**, $K_a$, which is the equilibrium constant for the reaction $HA(aq) \rightleftharpoons H^+(aq) + A^-(aq)$, which can also be written $HA(aq) + H_2O(l) \rightleftharpoons H_3O^+(aq) + A^-(aq)$.

The larger the value of $K_a$, the stronger is the acid. For solutions of the same concentration, a stronger acid also has a larger **percent ionization**. The concentration of a weak acid and its $K_a$ value can be used to calculate the pH of a solution.

  **Polyprotic acids**, such as $H_2SO_3$, have more than one ionizable proton. These acids have acid-dissociation constants that decrease in magnitude in the order $K_{a1} > K_{a2} > K_{a3}$. Because nearly all the $H^+(aq)$ in a polyprotic acid solution comes from the first dissociation step, the pH can usually be estimated satisfactorily by considering only $K_{a1}$.

**SECTION 16.7**    Weak bases include $NH_3$, **amines**, and the anions of weak acids. The extent to which a weak base reacts with water to generate the corresponding conjugate acid and $OH^-$ is measured by the **base-dissociation constant**, $K_b$. This is the equilibrium constant for the reaction $B(aq) + H_2O(l) \rightleftharpoons HB^+(aq) + OH^-(aq)$, where B is the base.

**SECTION 16.8**    The relationship between the strength of an acid and the strength of its conjugate base is expressed quantitatively by the equation $K_a \times K_b = K_w$, where $K_a$ and $K_b$ are dissociation constants for conjugate acid–base pairs.

**SECTION 16.9**    The acid–base properties of salts can be ascribed to the behavior of their respective cations and anions. The reaction of ions with water, with a resultant change in pH, is called **hydrolysis**. The cations of the alkali metals and the alkaline earth metals as well as the anions of strong acids, such as $Cl^-$, $Br^-$, $I^-$, and $NO_3^-$, do not undergo hydrolysis. They are always spectator ions in acid–base chemistry.

**SECTION 16.10**    The tendency of a substance to show acidic or basic characteristics in water can be correlated with its chemical structure. Acid character requires the presence of a highly polar H—X bond. Acidity is also favored when the H—X bond is weak and when the $X^-$ ion is very stable.

  For **oxyacids** with the same number of OH groups and the same number of O atoms, acid strength increases with increasing electronegativity of the central atom. For oxyacids with the same central atom, acid strength increases as the number of oxygen atoms attached to the central atom increases. **Carboxylic acids**, which are organic acids containing the COOH group, are the most important class of organic acids. The presence of delocalized pi bonding in the conjugate base is partially responsible for the acidity of these compounds.

**SECTION 16.11**    The Lewis concept of acids and bases emphasizes the shared electron pair rather than the proton. A **Lewis acid** is an electron-pair acceptor, and a **Lewis base** is an electron-pair donor. The Lewis concept is more general than the Brønsted–Lowry concept because it can apply to cases in which the acid is some substance other than $H^+$.

# KEY SKILLS

- Define and identify Arrhenius acids and bases. (Section 16.1)
- Understand the nature of the hydrated proton, represented as either $H^+(aq)$ or $H_3O^+(aq)$. (Section 16.2)
- Define and identify Brønsted–Lowry acids and bases and identify conjugate acid–base pairs. (Section 16.2)
- Relate the strength of an acid to the strength of its conjugate base. (Section 16.2)
- Understand how the equilibrium position of a proton-transfer reaction relates the strengths of the acids and bases involved. (Section 16.3)
- Describe the autoionization of water and understand how $[H_3O^+]$ and $[OH^-]$ are related. (Section 16.3)
- Calculate the pH of a solution given $[H_3O^+]$ or $[OH^-]$. (Section 16.4)
- Calculate the pH of a strong acid or strong base given its concentration. (Section 16.5)
- Calculate $K_a$ or $K_b$ for a weak acid or weak base given its concentration and the pH of the solution. (Sections 16.6 and 16.7)
- Calculate the pH of a weak acid or weak base or its percent ionization given its concentration and $K_a$ or $K_b$. (Sections 16.6 and 16.7)
- Calculate $K_b$ for a weak base given $K_a$ of its conjugate acid, and similarly calculate $K_a$ from $K_b$. (Section 16.8)
- Predict whether an aqueous solution of a salt will be acidic, basic, or neutral. (Section 16.9)
- Predict the relative strength of a series of acids from their molecular structures. (Section 16.10)
- Define and identify Lewis acids and bases. (Section 16.11)

# KEY EQUATIONS

- $K_w = [H_3O^+][OH^-] = [H^+][OH^-] = 1.0 \times 10^{-14}$    [16.16]    Ion product of water at 25 °C

- $pH = -\log[H^+]$    [16.17]    Definition of pH

- $pOH = -\log[OH^-]$    [16.18]    Definition of pOH

- $pH + pOH = 14.00$    [16.20]    Relationship between pH and pOH

- $K_a = \dfrac{[H_3O^+][A^-]}{[HA]}$ or $K_a = \dfrac{[H^+][A^-]}{[HA]}$    [16.25]    Acid dissociation constant for a weak acid, HA

- Percent ionization $= \dfrac{[H^+]_{equilibrium}}{[HA]_{initial}} \times 100\%$    [16.27]    Percent ionization of a weak acid

- $K_b = \dfrac{[BH^+][OH^-]}{[B]}$    [16.34]    Base-dissociation constant for a weak base, B

- $K_a \times K_b = K_w$    [16.40]    Relationship between acid- and base-dissociation constants of a conjugate acid–base pair

# EXERCISES

## VISUALIZING CONCEPTS

**16.1** **(a)** Identify the Brønsted–Lowry acid and base in the reaction

$$\bigcirc = H \quad \bullet = N \quad \bullet = X$$

**(b)** Identify the Lewis acid and base in the reaction. [Sections 16.2 and 16.11]

**16.2** The following diagrams represent aqueous solutions of two monoprotic acids, HA (A = X or Y). The water molecules have been omitted for clarity. **(a)** Which is the stronger acid, HX or HY? **(b)** Which is the stronger base, X$^-$ or Y$^-$? **(c)** If you mix equal concentrations of HX and NaY, will the equilibrium

$$HX(aq) + Y^-(aq) \rightleftharpoons HY(aq) + X^-(aq)$$

lie mostly to the right ($K_c > 1$) or to the left ($K_c < 1$)? [Section 16.2]

$$\text{= HA} \quad \text{= H}_3\text{O}^+ \quad \text{= A}^-$$

HX        HY

**16.3** The following diagrams represent aqueous solutions of three acids, HX, HY, and HZ. The water molecules have been omitted for clarity, and the hydrated proton is represented as H$^+$ rather than H$_3$O$^+$. **(a)** Which of the acids is a strong acid? Explain. **(b)** Which acid would have the smallest acid-dissociation constant, $K_a$? **(c)** Which solution would have the highest pH? [Sections 16.5 and 16.6]

HX      HY      HZ

**16.4** In which of the following cases is the approximation that the equilibrium concentration of H$^+$(aq) is small relative to the initial concentration of HA likely to be most valid: **(a)** initial [HA] = 0.100 $M$ and $K_a = 1.0 \times 10^{-6}$, **(b)** initial [HA] = 0.100 $M$ and $K_a = 1.0 \times 10^{-4}$, **(c)** initial [HA] = 1.00 $M$ and $K_a = 1.0 \times 10^{-6}$? [Section 16.6]

**16.5** The indicator methyl orange has been added to both of these solutions. Based on the colors, classify each statement as true or false:

**(a)** The pH of solution A is definitely less than 7.00.

**(b)** The pH of solution B is definitely greater than 7.00.

**(c)** The pH of solution B is greater than that of solution A. [Section 16.4]

Solution A     Solution B

**16.6** **(a)** Which of these three lines represents the effect of concentration on the percent ionization of a weak acid? **(b)** Explain in qualitative terms why the curve you chose has the shape it does. [Section 16.6]

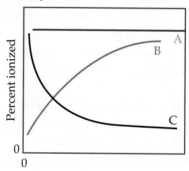

Acid concentration

**16.7** Each of the three molecules shown here contains an OH group, but one molecule acts as a base, one as an acid, and the third is neither acid nor base. **(a)** Which one acts as a base? Why does only this molecule act as a base? **(b)** Which one acts as an acid? **(c)** Why is the remaining molecule neither acidic nor basic? [Sections 16.6 and 16.7]

Molecule A        Molecule B

Molecule C

**16.8** Which of the following diagrams best represents an aqueous solution of NaF? The water molecules are not shown for clarity. Will this solution be acidic, neutral, or basic? [Section 16.9]

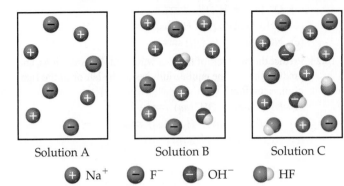

Solution A        Solution B        Solution C

+ Na$^+$    − F$^-$    ◐ OH$^-$    ◐ HF

**16.9** Consider the molecular models shown here, where X represents a halogen atom. **(a)** If X is the same atom in both molecules, which one will be more acidic? **(b)** Does the acidity of each molecule increase or decrease as the electronegativity of the atom X increases? [Section 16.10]

(a)                    (b)

**16.10** **(a)** The following diagram represents the reaction of PCl$_4^+$ with Cl$^-$. Draw the Lewis structures for the reactants and products, and identify the Lewis acid and the Lewis base in the reaction.

**(b)** The following reaction represents a hydrated cation losing a proton. How does the equilibrium constant for the reaction change as the charge of the cation increases? [Sections 16.9 and 16.11]

# ARRHENIUS AND BRØNSTED–LOWRY ACIDS AND BASES (sections 16.1 and 16.2)

**16.11** Although HCl and H$_2$SO$_4$ have very different properties as pure substances, their aqueous solutions possess many common properties. List some general properties of these solutions, and explain their common behavior in terms of the species present.

**16.12** Although pure NaOH and NH$_3$ have very different properties, their aqueous solutions possess many common properties. List some general properties of these solutions, and explain their common behavior in terms of the species present.

**16.13** **(a)** What is the difference between the Arrhenius and the Brønsted–Lowry definitions of an acid? **(b)** NH$_3$(g) and HCl(g) react to form the ionic solid NH$_4$Cl(s). Which substance is the Brønsted–Lowry acid in this reaction? Which is the Brønsted–Lowry base?

**16.14** **(a)** What is the difference between the Arrhenius and the Brønsted–Lowry definitions of a base? **(b)** Can a substance behave as an Arrhenius base if it does not contain an OH group? Explain.

**16.15** **(a)** Give the conjugate base of the following Brønsted–Lowry acids: **(i)** HIO$_3$, **(ii)** NH$_4^+$. **(b)** Give the conjugate acid of the following Brønsted–Lowry bases: **(i)** O$^{2-}$, **(ii)** H$_2$PO$_4^-$.

**16.16** **(a)** Give the conjugate base of the following Brønsted–Lowry acids: **(i)** HCOOH, **(ii)** HPO$_4^{2-}$. **(b)** Give the conjugate acid of the following Brønsted–Lowry bases: **(i)** SO$_4^{2-}$, **(ii)** CH$_3$NH$_2$.

**16.17** Designate the Brønsted–Lowry acid and the Brønsted–Lowry base on the left side of each of the following equations, and also designate the conjugate acid and conjugate base of each on the right side:

**(a)** NH$_4^+$(aq) + CN$^-$(aq) $\rightleftharpoons$ HCN(aq) + NH$_3$(aq)

**(b)** (CH$_3$)$_3$N(aq) + H$_2$O(l) $\rightleftharpoons$
$\qquad\qquad$ (CH$_3$)$_3$NH$^+$(aq) + OH$^-$(aq)

**(c)** HCOOH(aq) + PO$_4^{3-}$(aq) $\rightleftharpoons$
$\qquad\qquad$ HCOO$^-$(aq) + HPO$_4^{2-}$(aq)

**16.18** Designate the Brønsted–Lowry acid and the Brønsted–Lowry base on the left side of each equation, and also designate the conjugate acid and conjugate base of each on the right side.

**(a)** HBrO(aq) + H$_2$O(l) $\rightleftharpoons$ H$_3$O$^+$(aq) + BrO$^-$(aq)

**(b)** HSO$_4^-$(aq) + HCO$_3^-$(aq) $\rightleftharpoons$ SO$_4^{2-}$(aq) + H$_2$CO$_3$(aq)

**(c)** HSO$_3^-$(aq) + H$_3$O$^+$(aq) $\rightleftharpoons$ H$_2$SO$_3$(aq) + H$_2$O(l)

**16.19** **(a)** The hydrogen oxalate ion (HC$_2$O$_4^-$) is amphiprotic. Write a balanced chemical equation showing how it acts as an acid toward water and another equation showing how it acts as a base toward water. **(b)** What is the conjugate acid of HC$_2$O$_4^-$? What is its conjugate base?

**16.20** **(a)** Write an equation for the reaction in which H$_2$C$_6$H$_7$O$_5^-$(aq) acts as a base in H$_2$O(l). **(b)** Write an equation for the reaction in which H$_2$C$_6$H$_7$O$_5^-$(aq) acts as an acid in H$_2$O(l). **(c)** What is the conjugate acid of H$_2$C$_6$H$_7$O$_5^-$(aq)? What is its conjugate base?

**16.21** Label each of the following as being a strong base, a weak base, or a species with negligible basicity. In each case write the formula of its conjugate acid, and indicate whether the conjugate acid is a strong acid, a weak acid, or a species with negligible acidity: **(a)** CH$_3$COO$^-$, **(b)** HCO$_3^-$, **(c)** O$^{2-}$, **(d)** Cl$^-$, **(e)** NH$_3$.

**16.22** Label each of the following as being a strong acid, a weak acid, or a species with negligible acidity. In each case write the formula of its conjugate base, and indicate whether the conjugate base is a strong base, a weak base, or a species with negligible basicity: **(a)** HCOOH, **(b)** $H_2$, **(c)** $CH_4$, **(d)** HF, **(e)** $NH_4^+$.

**16.23** **(a)** Which of the following is the stronger Brønsted–Lowry acid, HBrO or HBr? **(b)** Which is the stronger Brønsted–Lowry base, $F^-$ or $Cl^-$? Briefly explain your choices.

**16.24** **(a)** Which of the following is the stronger Brønsted–Lowry acid, $HClO_3$ or $HClO_2$? **(b)** Which is the stronger Brønsted–Lowry base, $HS^-$ or $HSO_4^-$? Briefly explain your choices.

**16.25** Predict the products of the following acid–base reactions, and predict whether the equilibrium lies to the left or to the right of the equation:
**(a)** $O^{2-}(aq) + H_2O(l) \rightleftharpoons$
**(b)** $CH_3COOH(aq) + HS^-(aq) \rightleftharpoons$
**(c)** $NO_2^-(aq) + H_2O(l) \rightleftharpoons$

**16.26** Predict the products of the following acid–base reactions, and predict whether the equilibrium lies to the left or to the right of the equation:
**(a)** $NH_4^+(aq) + OH^-(aq) \rightleftharpoons$
**(b)** $CH_3COO^-(aq) + H_3O^+(aq) \rightleftharpoons$
**(c)** $HCO_3^-(aq) + F^-(aq) \rightleftharpoons$

# AUTOIONIZATION OF WATER (section 16.3)

**16.27** If a neutral solution of water, with pH = 7.00, is heated to 50 °C, the pH drops to 6.63. Does this mean that the concentration of $[H^+]$ is greater than the concentration of $[OH^-]$? Explain.

**16.28** **(a)** Write a chemical equation that illustrates the autoionization of water. **(b)** Write the expression for the ion-product constant for water, $K_w$. Why is $[H_2O]$ absent from this expression? **(c)** A solution is described as basic. What does this statement mean?

**16.29** Calculate $[H^+]$ for each of the following solutions, and indicate whether the solution is acidic, basic, or neutral: **(a)** $[OH^-] = 0.00045\ M$; **(b)** $[OH^-] = 8.8 \times 10^{-9}\ M$; **(c)** a solution in which $[OH^-]$ is 100 times greater than $[H^+]$.

**16.30** Calculate $[OH^-]$ for each of the following solutions, and indicate whether the solution is acidic, basic, or neutral: **(a)** $[H^+] = 0.0505\ M$; **(b)** $[H^+] = 2.5 \times 10^{-10}\ M$; **(c)** a solution in which $[H^+]$ is 1000 times greater than $[OH^-]$.

**16.31** At the freezing point of water (0 °C), $K_w = 1.2 \times 10^{-15}$. Calculate $[H^+]$ and $[OH^-]$ for a neutral solution at this temperature.

**16.32** Deuterium oxide ($D_2O$, where D is deuterium, the hydrogen-2 isotope) has an ion-product constant, $K_w$, of $8.9 \times 10^{-16}$ at 20 °C. Calculate $[D^+]$ and $[OD^-]$ for pure (neutral) $D_2O$ at this temperature.

# THE pH SCALE (section 16.4)

**16.33** By what factor does $[H^+]$ change for a pH change of **(a)** 2.00 units, **(b)** 0.50 units?

**16.34** Consider two solutions, solution A and solution B. $[H^+]$ in solution A is 250 times greater than that in solution B. What is the difference in the pH values of the two solutions?

**16.35** **(a)** If NaOH is added to water, how does $[H^+]$ change? How does pH change? **(b)** Use the pH values in Figure 16.5 to estimate the pH of a solution with $[H^+] = 0.0006\ M$. Is the solution acidic or basic? **(c)** If the pH of a solution is 5.2, first estimate and then calculate the molar concentrations of $H^+(aq)$ and $OH^-(aq)$ in the solution.

**16.36** **(a)** If $HNO_3$ is added to water, how does $[OH^-]$ change? How does pH change? **(b)** Use the pH values in Figure 16.5 to estimate the pH of a solution with $[OH^-] = 0.014\ M$. Is the solution acidic or basic? **(c)** If pH = 6.6, first estimate and then calculate the molar concentrations of $H^+(aq)$ and $OH^-(aq)$ in the solution.

**16.37** Complete the following table by calculating the missing entries and indicating whether the solution is acidic or basic.

**16.38** Complete the following table by calculating the missing entries. In each case indicate whether the solution is acidic or basic.

| $[H^+]$ | $OH^-(aq)$ | pH | pOH | Acidic or basic? |
|---|---|---|---|---|
| $7.5 \times 10^{-3}\ M$ | | | | |
| | $3.6 \times 10^{-10}\ M$ | | | |
| | | 8.25 | | |
| | | | 5.70 | |

**16.39** The average pH of normal arterial blood is 7.40. At normal body temperature (37 °C), $K_w = 2.4 \times 10^{-14}$. Calculate $[H^+]$, $[OH^-]$, and pOH for blood at this temperature.

| pH | pOH | $[H^+]$ | $[OH^-]$ | Acidic or basic? |
|---|---|---|---|---|
| 5.25 | | | | |
| | 2.02 | | | |
| | | $4.4 \times 10^{-10}\ M$ | | |
| | | | $8.5 \times 10^{-2}\ M$ | |

**16.40** Carbon dioxide in the atmosphere dissolves in raindrops to produce carbonic acid ($H_2CO_3$), causing the pH of clean, unpolluted rain to range from about 5.2 to 5.6. What are the ranges of $[H^+]$ and $[OH^-]$ in the raindrops?

# STRONG ACIDS AND BASES (section 16.5)

**16.41** (a) What is a strong acid? (b) A solution is labeled 0.500 $M$ HCl. What is [$H^+$] for the solution? (c) Which of the following are strong acids: HF, HCl, HBr, HI?

**16.42** (a) What is a strong base? (b) A solution is labeled 0.035 $M$ Sr(OH)$_2$. What is [$OH^-$] for the solution? (c) Is the following statement true or false? Because Mg(OH)$_2$ is not very soluble, it cannot be a strong base. Explain.

**16.43** Calculate the pH of each of the following strong acid solutions: (a) $8.5 \times 10^{-3}$ $M$ HBr, (b) 1.52 g of HNO$_3$ in 575 mL of solution, (c) 5.00 mL of 0.250 $M$ HClO$_4$ diluted to 50.0 mL, (d) a solution formed by mixing 10.0 mL of 0.100 $M$ HBr with 20.0 mL of 0.200 $M$ HCl.

**16.44** Calculate the pH of each of the following strong acid solutions: (a) 0.0167 $M$ HNO$_3$, (b) 0.225 g of HClO$_3$ in 2.00 L of solution, (c) 15.00 mL of 1.00 $M$ HCl diluted to 0.500 L, (d) a mixture formed by adding 50.0 mL of 0.020 $M$ HCl to 125 mL of 0.010 $M$ HI.

**16.45** Calculate [$OH^-$] and pH for (a) $1.5 \times 10^{-3}$ $M$ Sr(OH$_2$), (b) 2.250 g of LiOH in 250.0 mL of solution, (c) 1.00 mL of 0.175 $M$ NaOH diluted to 2.00 L, (d) a solution formed by adding 5.00 mL of 0.105 $M$ KOH to 15.0 mL of $9.5 \times 10^{-2}$ $M$ Ca(OH)$_2$.

**16.46** Calculate [$OH^-$] and pH for each of the following strong base solutions: (a) 0.182 $M$ KOH, (b) 3.165 g of KOH in 500.0 mL of solution, (c) 10.0 mL of 0.0105 $M$ Ca(OH)$_2$ diluted to 500.0 mL, (d) a solution formed by mixing 20.0 mL of 0.015 $M$ Ba(OH)$_2$ with 40.0 mL of $8.2 \times 10^{-3}$ $M$ NaOH.

**16.47** Calculate the concentration of an aqueous solution of NaOH that has a pH of 11.50.

**16.48** Calculate the concentration of an aqueous solution of Ca(OH)$_2$ that has a pH of 10.05.

# WEAK ACIDS (section 16.6)

**16.49** Write the chemical equation and the $K_a$ expression for the ionization of each of the following acids in aqueous solution. First show the reaction with H$^+$(aq) as a product and then with the hydronium ion: (a) HBrO$_2$, (b) C$_2$H$_5$COOH.

**16.50** Write the chemical equation and the $K_a$ expression for the acid dissociation of each of the following acids in aqueous solution. First show the reaction with H$^+$(aq) as a product and then with the hydronium ion: (a) C$_6$H$_5$COOH, (b) HCO$_3^-$.

**16.51** Lactic acid (CH$_3$CH(OH)COOH) has one acidic hydrogen. A 0.10 $M$ solution of lactic acid has a pH of 2.44. Calculate $K_a$.

**16.52** Phenylacetic acid (C$_6$H$_5$CH$_2$COOH) is one of the substances that accumulates in the blood of people with phenylketonuria, an inherited disorder that can cause mental retardation or even death. A 0.085 $M$ solution of C$_6$H$_5$CH$_2$COOH has a pH of 2.68. Calculate the $K_a$ value for this acid.

**16.53** A 0.100 $M$ solution of chloroacetic acid (ClCH$_2$COOH) is 11.0% ionized. Using this information, calculate [ClCH$_2$COO$^-$], [H$^+$], [ClCH$_2$COOH], and $K_a$ for chloroacetic acid.

**16.54** A 0.100 $M$ solution of bromoacetic acid (BrCH$_2$COOH) is 13.2% ionized. Calculate [H$^+$], [BrCH$_2$COO$^-$], [BrCH$_2$COOH] and $K_a$ for bromoacetic acid.

**16.55** A particular sample of vinegar has a pH of 2.90. If acetic acid is the only acid that vinegar contains ($K_a = 1.8 \times 10^{-5}$), calculate the concentration of acetic acid in the vinegar.

**16.56** If a solution of HF ($K_a = 6.8 \times 10^{-4}$) has a pH of 3.65, calculate the concentration of hydrofluoric acid.

**16.57** The acid-dissociation constant for benzoic acid (C$_6$H$_5$COOH) is $6.3 \times 10^{-5}$. Calculate the equilibrium concentrations of H$_3$O$^+$, C$_6$H$_5$COO$^-$, and C$_6$H$_5$COOH in the solution if the initial concentration of C$_6$H$_5$COOH is 0.050 $M$.

**16.58** The acid-dissociation constant for chlorous acid (HClO$_2$) is $1.1 \times 10^{-2}$. Calculate the concentrations of H$_3$O$^+$, ClO$_2^-$, and HClO$_2$ at equilibrium if the initial concentration of HClO$_2$ is 0.0125 $M$.

**16.59** Calculate the pH of each of the following solutions ($K_a$ and $K_b$ values are given in Appendix D): (a) 0.095 $M$ propionic acid (C$_2$H$_5$COOH), (b) 0.100 $M$ hydrogen chromate ion (HCrO$_4^-$), (c) 0.120 $M$ pyridine (C$_5$H$_5$N).

**16.60** Determine the pH of each of the following solutions ($K_a$ and $K_b$ values are given in Appendix D): (a) 0.095 $M$ hypochlorous acid, (b) 0.0085 $M$ hydrazine, (c) 0.165 $M$ hydroxylamine.

**16.61** Saccharin, a sugar substitute, is a weak acid with p$K_a$ = 2.32 at 25 °C. It ionizes in aqueous solution as follows:

$$HNC_7H_4SO_3(aq) \rightleftharpoons H^+(aq) + NC_7H_4SO_3^-(aq)$$

What is the pH of a 0.10 $M$ solution of this substance?

**16.62** The active ingredient in aspirin is acetylsalicylic acid (HC$_9$H$_7$O$_4$), a monoprotic acid with $K_a = 3.3 \times 10^{-4}$ at 25 °C. What is the pH of a solution obtained by dissolving two extra-strength aspirin tablets, containing 500 mg of acetylsalicylic acid each, in 250 mL of water?

**16.63** Calculate the percent ionization of hydrazoic acid (HN$_3$) in solutions of each of the following concentrations ($K_a$ is given in Appendix D): (a) 0.400 $M$, (b) 0.100 $M$, (c) 0.0400 $M$.

**16.64** Calculate the percent ionization of propionic acid (C$_2$H$_5$COOH) in solutions of each of the following concentrations ($K_a$ is given in Appendix D): (a) 0.250 $M$, (b) 0.0800 $M$, (c) 0.0200 $M$.

**16.65** Show that for a weak acid, the percent ionization should vary as the inverse square root of the acid concentration.

**16.66** For solutions of a weak acid, a graph of pH versus the logarithm of the initial acid concentration should be a straight line. What is the magnitude of the slope of that line?

**16.67** Citric acid, which is present in citrus fruits, is a triprotic acid (Table 16.3). Calculate the pH of a 0.040 $M$ solution of citric acid. Explain any approximations or assumptions you make in your calculations. Is the concentration of citrate ion (C$_6$H$_5$O$_7$)$^{3-}$ equal to, less than, or greater than the H$^+$ ion concentration?

**16.68** Tartaric acid is found in many fruits, including grapes, and is partially responsible for the dry texture of certain wines. Calculate the pH and the tartarate ion (C$_4$H$_4$O$_6^{2-}$) concentration for a 0.250 $M$ solution of tartaric acid, for which the acid-dissociation constants are listed in Table 16.3. Explain any approximations or assumptions that you make in your calculation.

# WEAK BASES (section 16.7)

**16.69** Consider the base hydroxylamine, $NH_2OH$. (a) What is the conjugate acid of hydroxylamine? (b) When it acts as a base, which atom in hydroxylamine accepts a proton? (c) There are two atoms in hydroxylamine that have nonbonding electron pairs that could act as proton acceptors. Use Lewis structures and formal charges ∞ (Section 8.5) to rationalize why one of these two atoms is a much better proton acceptor than the other.

**16.70** The hypochlorite ion, $ClO^-$, acts as a weak base. (a) Is $ClO^-$ a stronger or weaker base than hydroxylamine? (b) When $ClO^-$ acts as a base, which atom, Cl or O, acts as the proton acceptor? (c) Can you use formal charges to rationalize your answer to part (b)?

**16.71** Write the chemical equation and the $K_b$ expression for the reaction of each of the following bases with water: (a) dimethylamine, $(CH_3)_2NH$; (b) carbonate ion, $CO_3^{2-}$; (c) formate ion, $CHO_2^-$.

**16.72** Write the chemical equation and the $K_b$ expression for the reaction of each of the following bases with water: (a) propylamine, $C_3H_7NH_2$; (b) monohydrogen phosphate ion, $HPO_4^{2-}$; (c) benzoate ion, $C_6H_5CO_2^-$.

**16.73** Calculate the molar concentration of $OH^-$ ions in a 0.075 $M$ solution of ethylamine ($C_2H_5NH_2$; $K_b = 6.4 \times 10^{-4}$). Calculate the pH of this solution.

**16.74** Calculate the molar concentration of $OH^-$ ions in a 0.724 $M$ solution of hypobromite ion ($BrO^-$; $K_b = 4.0 \times 10^{-6}$). What is the pH of this solution?

**16.75** Ephedrine, a central nervous system stimulant, is used in nasal sprays as a decongestant. This compound is a weak organic base:

$$C_{10}H_{15}ON(aq) + H_2O(l) \rightleftharpoons C_{10}H_{15}ONH^+(aq) + OH^-(aq)$$

A 0.035 $M$ solution of ephedrine has a pH of 11.33. (a) What are the equilibrium concentrations of $C_{10}H_{15}ON$, $C_{10}H_{15}ONH^+$, and $OH^-$? (b) Calculate $K_b$ for ephedrine.

**16.76** Codeine ($C_{18}H_{21}NO_3$) is a weak organic base. A $5.0 \times 10^{-3} M$ solution of codeine has a pH of 9.95. Calculate the value of $K_b$ for this substance. What is the $pK_b$ for this base?

# THE $K_a$–$K_b$ RELATIONSHIP; ACID–BASE PROPERTIES OF SALTS (sections 16.8 and 16.9)

**16.77** Although the acid-dissociation constant for phenol ($C_6H_5OH$) is listed in Appendix D, the base-dissociation constant for the phenolate ion ($C_6H_5O^-$) is not. (a) Explain why it is not necessary to list both $K_a$ for phenol and $K_b$ for the phenolate ion. (b) Calculate $K_b$ for the phenolate ion. (c) Is the phenolate ion a weaker or stronger base than ammonia?

**16.78** Use the acid-dissociation constants in Table 16.3 to arrange these oxyanions from strongest base to weakest: $SO_4^{2-}$, $CO_3^{2-}$, $SO_3^{2-}$, and $PO_4^{3-}$.

**16.79** (a) Given that $K_a$ for acetic acid is $1.8 \times 10^{-5}$ and that for hypochlorous acid is $3.0 \times 10^{-8}$, which is the stronger acid? (b) Which is the stronger base, the acetate ion or the hypochlorite ion? (c) Calculate $K_b$ values for $CH_3COO^-$ and $ClO^-$.

**16.80** (a) Given that $K_b$ for ammonia is $1.8 \times 10^{-5}$ and that for hydroxylamine is $1.1 \times 10^{-8}$, which is the stronger base? (b) Which is the stronger acid, the ammonium ion or the hydroxylammonium ion? (c) Calculate $K_a$ values for $NH_4^+$ and $H_3NOH^+$.

**16.81** Using data from Appendix D, calculate $[OH^-]$ and pH for each of the following solutions: (a) 0.10 $M$ NaBrO, (b) 0.080 $M$ NaHS, (c) a mixture that is 0.10 $M$ in $NaNO_2$ and 0.20 $M$ in $Ca(NO_2)_2$.

**16.82** Using data from Appendix D, calculate $[OH^-]$ and pH for each of the following solutions: (a) 0.105 $M$ NaF, (b) 0.035 $M$ $Na_2S$, (c) a mixture that is 0.045 $M$ in $CH_3COONa$ and 0.055 $M$ in $(CH_3COO)_2Ba$.

**16.83** Predict whether aqueous solutions of the following compounds are acidic, basic, or neutral: (a) $NH_4Br$, (b) $FeCl_3$, (c) $Na_2CO_3$, (d) $KClO_4$, (e) $NaHC_2O_4$.

**16.84** Predict whether aqueous solutions of the following substances are acidic, basic, or neutral: (a) $AlCl_3$, (b) NaBr, (c) NaClO, (d) $[CH_3NH_3]NO_3$, (e) $Na_2SO_3$.

**16.85** An unknown salt is either NaF, NaCl, or NaOCl. When 0.050 mol of the salt is dissolved in water to form 0.500 L of solution, the pH of the solution is 8.08. What is the identity of the salt?

**16.86** An unknown salt is either KBr, $NH_4Cl$, KCN, or $K_2CO_3$. If a 0.100 $M$ solution of the salt is neutral, what is the identity of the salt?

# ACID–BASE CHARACTER AND CHEMICAL STRUCTURE (section 16.10)

**16.87** How does the acid strength of an oxyacid depend on (a) the electronegativity of the central atom; (b) the number of non-protonated oxygen atoms in the molecule?

**16.88** (a) Why is $NH_3$ a stronger base than $H_2O$? (b) Why is $NH_3$ a stronger base than $CH_4$?

**16.89** Explain the following observations: (a) $HNO_3$ is a stronger acid than $HNO_2$; (b) $H_2S$ is a stronger acid than $H_2O$; (c) $H_2SO_4$ is a stronger acid than $HSO_4^-$; (d) $H_2SO_4$ is a stronger acid than $H_2SeO_4$; (e) $CCl_3COOH$ is a stronger acid than $CH_3COOH$.

**16.90** Explain the following observations: (a) HCl is a stronger acid than $H_2S$; (b) $H_3PO_4$ is a stronger acid than $H_3AsO_4$; (c) $HBrO_3$ is a stronger acid than $HBrO_2$; (d) $H_2C_2O_4$ is a stronger acid than $HC_2O_4^-$; (e) benzoic acid ($C_6H_5COOH$) is a stronger acid than phenol ($C_6H_5OH$).

**16.91** Based on their compositions and structures and on conjugate acid–base relationships, select the stronger base in each of the following pairs: (a) $BrO^-$ or $ClO^-$, (b) $BrO^-$ or $BrO_2^-$, (c) $HPO_4^{2-}$ or $H_2PO_4^-$.

**16.92** Based on their compositions and structures and on conjugate acid–base relationships, select the stronger base in each of the following pairs: **(a)** $NO_3^-$ or $NO_2^-$, **(b)** $PO_4^{3-}$ or $AsO_4^{3-}$, **(c)** $HCO_3^-$ or $CO_3^{2-}$.

**16.93** Indicate whether each of the following statements is true or false. For each statement that is false, correct the statement to make it true. **(a)** In general, the acidity of binary acids increases from left to right in a given row of the periodic table. **(b)** In a series of acids that have the same central atom, acid strength increases with the number of hydrogen atoms bonded to the central atom. **(c)** Hydrotelluric acid ($H_2Te$) is a stronger acid than $H_2S$ because Te is more electronegative than S.

**16.94** Indicate whether each of the following statements is true or false. For each statement that is false, correct the statement to make it true. **(a)** Acid strength in a series of H—X molecules increases with increasing size of X. **(b)** For acids of the same general structure but differing electronegativities of the central atoms, acid strength decreases with increasing electronegativity of the central atom. **(c)** The strongest acid known is HF because fluorine is the most electronegative element.

# LEWIS ACIDS AND BASES (section 16.11)

**16.95** If a substance is an Arrhenius base, is it necessarily a Brønsted–Lowry base? Is it necessarily a Lewis base? Explain.

**16.96** If a substance is a Lewis acid, is it necessarily a Brønsted–Lowry acid? Is it necessarily an Arrhenius acid? Explain.

**16.97** Identify the Lewis acid and Lewis base among the reactants in each of the following reactions:

**(a)** $Fe(ClO_4)_3(s) + 6\,H_2O(l) \rightleftharpoons$
$$Fe(H_2O)_6^{3+}(aq) + 3\,ClO_4^-(aq)$$

**(b)** $CN^-(aq) + H_2O(l) \rightleftharpoons HCN(aq) + OH^-(aq)$

**(c)** $(CH_3)_3N(g) + BF_3(g) \rightleftharpoons (CH_3)_3NBF_3(s)$

**(d)** $HIO(lq) + NH_2^-(lq) \rightleftharpoons NH_3(lq) + IO^-(lq)$
($lq$ denotes liquid ammonia as solvent)

**16.98** Identify the Lewis acid and Lewis base in each of the following reactions:

**(a)** $HNO_2(aq) + OH^-(aq) \rightleftharpoons NO_2^-(aq) + H_2O(l)$

**(b)** $FeBr_3(s) + Br^-(aq) \rightleftharpoons FeBr_4^-(aq)$

**(c)** $Zn^{2+}(aq) + 4\,NH_3(aq) \rightleftharpoons Zn(NH_3)_4^{2+}(aq)$

**(d)** $SO_2(g) + H_2O(l) \rightleftharpoons H_2SO_3(aq)$

**16.99** Predict which member of each pair produces the more acidic aqueous solution: **(a)** $K^+$ or $Cu^{2+}$, **(b)** $Fe^{2+}$ or $Fe^{3+}$, **(c)** $Al^{3+}$ or $Ga^{3+}$. Explain.

**16.100** Which member of each pair produces the more acidic aqueous solution: **(a)** $ZnBr_2$ or $CdCl_2$, **(b)** $CuCl$ or $Cu(NO_3)_2$, **(c)** $Ca(NO_3)_2$ or $NiBr_2$? Explain.

# ADDITIONAL EXERCISES

**16.101** Triethylamine, $(C_2H_5)_3N$, has a $pK_b$ value of 2.99. Is triethylamine a stronger base than ammonia, $NH_3$?

**16.102** Indicate whether each of the following statements is correct or incorrect. For those that are incorrect, explain why they are wrong.

**(a)** Every Brønsted–Lowry acid is also a Lewis acid.

**(b)** Every Lewis acid is also a Brønsted–Lowry acid.

**(c)** Conjugate acids of weak bases produce more acidic solutions than conjugate acids of strong bases.

**(d)** $K^+$ ion is acidic in water because it causes hydrating water molecules to become more acidic.

**(e)** The percent ionization of a weak acid in water increases as the concentration of acid decreases.

**16.103** Use Figure 16.3 to predict whether the equilibrium lies to the right or to the left in the following reactions:

**(a)** $NH_4^+(aq) + PO_4^{3-}(aq) \rightleftharpoons NH_3(aq) + HPO_4^{2-}(aq)$

**(b)** $CH_3COOH(aq) + F^-(aq) \rightleftharpoons$
$$CH_3COO^-(aq) + HF(aq)$$

**16.104** The odor of fish is due primarily to amines, especially methylamine ($CH_3NH_2$). Fish is often served with a wedge of lemon, which contains citric acid. The amine and the acid react forming a product with no odor, thereby making the less-than-fresh fish more appetizing. Using data from Appendix D, calculate the equilibrium constant for the reaction of citric acid with methylamine, if only the first proton of the citric acid ($K_{a1}$) is important in the neutralization reaction.

**16.105** Hemoglobin plays a part in a series of equilibria involving protonation-deprotonation and oxygenation-deoxygenation. The overall reaction is approximately as follows:

$$HbH^+(aq) + O_2(aq) \rightleftharpoons HbO_2(aq) + H^+(aq)$$

where Hb stands for hemoglobin and $HbO_2$ for oxyhemoglobin. **(a)** The concentration of $O_2$ is higher in the lungs and lower in the tissues. What effect does high $[O_2]$ have on the position of this equilibrium? **(b)** The normal pH of blood is 7.4. Is the blood acidic, basic, or neutral? **(c)** If the blood pH is lowered by the presence of large amounts of acidic metabolism products, a condition known as acidosis results. What effect does lowering blood pH have on the ability of hemoglobin to transport $O_2$?

**[16.106]** Calculate the pH of a solution made by adding 2.50 g of lithium oxide ($Li_2O$) to enough water to make 1.500 L of solution.

**16.107** Which of the following solutions has the higher pH? **(a)** a 0.1 $M$ solution of a strong acid or a 0.1 $M$ solution of a weak acid, **(b)** a 0.1 $M$ solution of an acid with $K_a = 2 \times 10^{-3}$ or one with $K_a = 8 \times 10^{-6}$, **(c)** a 0.1 $M$ solution of a base with $pK_b = 4.5$ or one with $pK_b = 6.5$.

**16.108** What is the pH of a solution that is $2.5 \times 10^{-9}$ in NaOH? Does your answer make sense? What assumption do we normally make that is not valid in this case?

**16.109** Caproic acid ($C_5H_{11}COOH$) is found in small amounts in coconut and palm oils and is used in making artificial flavors. A saturated solution of the acid contains 11 g/L and has a pH of 2.94. Calculate $K_a$ for the acid.

**16.110** Butyric acid is responsible for the foul smell of rancid butter. The $pK_a$ of butyric acid is 4.84. **(a)** Calculate the $pK_b$ for the butyrate ion. **(b)** Calculate the pH of a 0.050 $M$ solution of butyric acid. **(c)** Calculate the pH of a 0.050 $M$ solution of sodium butyrate.

**16.111** Arrange the following 0.10 $M$ solutions in order of increasing acidity (decreasing pH): (i) $NH_4NO_3$, (ii) $NaNO_3$, (iii) $CH_3COONH_4$, (iv) NaF, (v) $CH_3COONa$.

**[16.112]** Many moderately large organic molecules containing basic nitrogen atoms are not very soluble in water as neutral molecules, but they are frequently much more soluble as their acid salts. Assuming that pH in the stomach is 2.5, indicate whether each of the following compounds would be present in the stomach as the neutral base or in the protonated form: nicotine, $K_b = 7 \times 10^{-7}$; caffeine, $K_b = 4 \times 10^{-14}$; strychnine, $K_b = 1 \times 10^{-6}$; quinine, $K_b = 1.1 \times 10^{-6}$.

**[16.113]** The amino acid glycine ($H_2N$—$CH_2$—COOH) can participate in the following equilibria in water:

$$H_2N\text{—}CH_2\text{—}COOH + H_2O \rightleftharpoons$$
$$H_2N\text{—}CH_2\text{—}COO^- + H_3O^+ \quad K_a = 4.3 \times 10^{-3}$$

$$H_2N\text{—}CH_2\text{—}COOH + H_2O \rightleftharpoons$$
$$^+H_3N\text{—}CH_2\text{—}COOH + OH^- \quad K_b = 6.0 \times 10^{-5}$$

**(a)** Use the values of $K_a$ and $K_b$ to estimate the equilibrium constant for the intramolecular proton transfer to form a zwitterion:

$$H_2N\text{—}CH_2\text{—}COOH \rightleftharpoons \,^+H_3N\text{—}CH_2\text{—}COO^-$$

What assumptions did you need to make? **(b)** What is the pH of a 0.050 $M$ aqueous solution of glycine? **(c)** What would be the predominant form of glycine in a solution with pH 13? With pH 1?

**16.114** The structural formula for acetic acid is shown in Table 16.2. Replacing hydrogen atoms on the carbon with chlorine atoms causes an increase in acidity, as follows:

| Acid | Formula | $K_a$(25 °C) |
|---|---|---|
| Acetic | $CH_3COOH$ | $1.8 \times 10^{-5}$ |
| Chloroacetic | $CH_2ClCOOH$ | $1.4 \times 10^{-3}$ |
| Dichloroacetic | $CHCl_2COOH$ | $3.3 \times 10^{-2}$ |
| Trichloroacetic | $CCl_3COOH$ | $2 \times 10^{-1}$ |

Using Lewis structures as the basis of your discussion, explain the observed trend in acidities in the series. Calculate the pH of a 0.010 $M$ solution of each acid.

# INTEGRATIVE EXERCISES

**16.115** Calculate the number of $H^+ (aq)$ ions in 1.0 mL of pure water at 25 °C.

**16.116** How many milliliters of concentrated hydrochloric acid solution (36.0% HCl by mass, density = 1.18 g/mL) are required to produce 10.0 L of a solution that has a pH of 2.05?

**16.117** The volume of an adult's stomach ranges from about 50 mL when empty to 1 L when full. If the stomach volume is 400 mL and its contents have a pH of 2, how many moles of $H^+$ does the stomach contain? Assuming that all the $H^+$ comes from HCl, how many grams of sodium hydrogen carbonate will totally neutralize the stomach acid?

**16.118** Atmospheric $CO_2$ levels have risen by nearly 20% over the past 40 years from 315 ppm to 380 ppm. **(a)** Given that the average pH of clean, unpolluted rain today is 5.4, determine the pH of unpolluted rain 40 years ago. Assume that carbonic acid ($H_2CO_3$) formed by the reaction of $CO_2$ and water is the only factor influencing pH.

$$CO_2(g) + H_2O(l) \rightleftharpoons H_2CO_3(aq)$$

**(b)** What volume of $CO_2$ at 25 °C and 1.0 atm is dissolved in a 20.0-L bucket of today's rainwater?

**16.119** In many reactions the addition of $AlCl_3$ produces the same effect as the addition of $H^+$. **(a)** Draw a Lewis structure for $AlCl_3$ in which no atoms carry formal charges, and determine its structure using the VSEPR method. **(b)** What characteristic is notable about the structure in part (a) that helps us understand the acidic character of $AlCl_3$? **(c)** Predict the result of the reaction between $AlCl_3$ and $NH_3$ in a solvent that does not participate as a reactant. **(d)** Which acid–base theory is most suitable for discussing the similarities between $AlCl_3$ and $H^+$?

**16.120** What is the boiling point of a 0.10 $M$ solution of $NaHSO_4$ if the solution has a density of 1.002 g/mL?

**16.121** Use average bond enthalpies from Table 8.4 to estimate the enthalpies of the following gas-phase reactions:

*Reaction 1:*    $HF(g) + H_2O(g) \rightleftharpoons F^-(g) + H_3O^+(g)$

*Reaction 2:*    $HCl(g) + H_2O(g) \rightleftharpoons Cl^-(g) + H_3O^+(g)$

Are both reactions exothermic? How do these values relate to the different strengths of hydrofluoric and hydrochloric acid?

**[16.122]** Cocaine is a weak organic base whose molecular formula is $C_{17}H_{21}NO_4$. An aqueous solution of cocaine was found to have a pH of 8.53 and an osmotic pressure of 52.7 torr at 15 °C. Calculate $K_b$ for cocaine.

**[16.123]** The iodate ion is reduced by sulfite according to the following reaction:

$$IO_3^-(aq) + 3 SO_3^{2-}(aq) \longrightarrow I^-(aq) + 3 SO_4^{2-}(aq)$$

The rate of this reaction is found to be first order in $IO_3^-$, first order in $SO_3^{2-}$, and first order in $H^+$. **(a)** Write the rate law for the reaction. **(b)** By what factor will the rate of the reaction change if the pH is lowered from 5.00 to 3.50? Does the reaction proceed more quickly or more slowly at the lower pH? **(c)** By using the concepts discussed in Section 14.6, explain how the reaction can be pH-dependent even though $H^+$ does not appear in the overall reaction.

**16.124** **(a)** Using dissociation constants from Appendix D, determine the value for the equilibrium constant for each of the following reactions.

**(i)** $HCO_3^-(aq) + OH^-(aq) \rightleftharpoons CO_3^{2-}(aq) + H_2O(l)$

**(ii)** $NH_4^+(aq) + CO_3^{2-}(aq) \rightleftharpoons NH_3(aq) + HCO_3^-(aq)$

**(b)** We usually use single arrows for reactions when the forward reaction is appreciable ($K$ much greater than 1) or when products escape from the system, so that equilibrium is never established. If we follow this convention, which of these equilibria might be written with a single arrow?

# WHAT'S AHEAD

**17.1** THE COMMON-ION EFFECT
We begin by considering a specific example of Le Châtelier's principle known as the common-ion effect.

**17.2** BUFFERED SOLUTIONS
We consider the composition of buffered solutions and learn how they resist pH change when small amounts of a strong acid or strong base are added to them.

**17.3** ACID–BASE TITRATIONS
We examine acid–base titrations and explore how to determine pH at any point in an acid–base titration.

**17.4** SOLUBILITY EQUILIBRIA
We learn how to use *solubility-product constants* to determine to what extent a sparingly soluble salt dissolves in water.

**THE GREAT BARRIER REEF** stretches for more than 2600 km off of the eastern coast of Australia. Coral reefs such as this are among the most diverse ecosystems on the planet.

# ADDITIONAL ASPECTS OF AQUEOUS EQUILIBRIA

**WATER, THE MOST COMMON AND** most important solvent on Earth, occupies its position of importance because of its abundance and its exceptional ability to dissolve a wide variety of substances. Coral reefs are a striking example of aqueous chemistry at work in nature. Coral reefs are built by tiny animals called stony corals, which secrete a hard calcium carbonate exoskeleton. Over time, the stony corals build up large networks of calcium carbonate upon which a reef is built. The size of such structures can be immense, as illustrated by the Great Barrier Reef.

Stony corals make their exoskeletons from dissolved $Ca^{2+}$ and $CO_3^{2-}$ ions. This process is aided by the fact that the $CO_3^{2-}$ concentration is supersaturated in most parts of the ocean. However, well-documented increases in the amount of $CO_2$ in the atmosphere threaten to upset the aqueous chemistry that stony corals depend on. As atmospheric $CO_2$ levels increase, the amount of $CO_2$ dissolved in the ocean also increases. This lowers the pH of the ocean and leads to a decrease in the $CO_3^{2-}$ concentration. As a result it becomes more difficult for stony corals and other important ocean creatures to maintain their exoskeletons. We will take a closer look at the consequences of ocean acidification later in the chapter.

To understand the chemistry that underlies coral reef formation, we must understand the concepts of aqueous equilibria. In this chapter we take a step toward understanding such complex solutions by looking first at further applications of acid–base equilibria. The idea is to consider not only solutions in which there is a single solute but also those containing a mixture of solutes. We then broaden our discussion to include two additional types of aqueous equilibria: those involving slightly soluble salts and those involving the formation of metal complexes in solution. For the most part, the discussions and calculations in this chapter are an extension of those in Chapters 15 and 16.

# 17.1 | THE COMMON-ION EFFECT

In Chapter 16 we examined the equilibrium concentrations of ions in solutions containing a weak acid or a weak base. We now consider solutions that contain a weak acid, such as acetic acid ($CH_3COOH$), and a soluble salt of that acid, such as sodium acetate ($CH_3COONa$). Notice that these solutions contain two substances that share a *common ion*, $CH_3COO^-$. It is instructive to view these solutions from the perspective of Le Châtelier's principle. ∞ (Section 15.7)

Sodium acetate is a soluble ionic compound and therefore a strong electrolyte. ∞ (Section 4.1) Consequently, it dissociates completely in aqueous solution to form $Na^+$ and $CH_3COO^-$ ions:

$$CH_3COONa(aq) \longrightarrow Na^+(aq) + CH_3COO^-(aq)$$

In contrast, $CH_3COOH$ is a weak electrolyte that ionizes only partially, represented by the equilibrium

$$CH_3COOH(aq) \rightleftharpoons H^+(aq) + CH_3COO^-(aq) \qquad [17.1]$$

When we have sodium acetate and acetic acid in the same solution, the $CH_3COO^-$ from $CH_3COONa$ causes the equilibrium of Equation 17.1 to shift to the left, thereby decreasing the equilibrium concentration of $H^+(aq)$:

$$CH_3COOH(aq) \rightleftharpoons H^+(aq) + CH_3COO^-(aq)$$

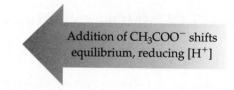

Addition of $CH_3COO^-$ shifts equilibrium, reducing $[H^+]$

In other words, the presence of the added acetate ion causes the acetic acid to ionize less than it normally would.

*Whenever a weak electrolyte and a strong electrolyte containing a common ion are together in solution, the weak electrolyte ionizes less than it would if it were alone in solution.* We call this observation the **common-ion effect**.

---

**SAMPLE EXERCISE 17.1** | Calculating the pH When a Common Ion Is Involved

What is the pH of a solution made by adding 0.30 mol of acetic acid and 0.30 mol of sodium acetate to enough water to make 1.0 L of solution?

### SOLUTION

**Analyze** We are asked to determine the pH of a solution of a weak electrolyte ($CH_3COOH$) and a strong electrolyte ($CH_3COONa$) that share a common ion, $CH_3COO^-$.

**Plan** In any problem in which we must determine the pH of a solution containing a mixture of solutes, it is helpful to proceed by a series of logical steps:

1. Consider which solutes are strong electrolytes and which are weak electrolytes, and identify the major species in solution.

2. Identify the important equilibrium that is the source of $H^+$ and therefore determines pH.

3. Tabulate the concentrations of ions involved in the equilibrium.

4. Use the equilibrium-constant expression to calculate $[H^+]$ and then pH.

**Solve** First, because $CH_3COOH$ is a weak electrolyte and $CH_3COONa$ is a strong electrolyte, the major species in the solution are $CH_3COOH$ (a weak acid), $Na^+$ (which is neither acidic nor basic and is therefore a spectator in the acid–base chemistry), and $CH_3COO^-$ (which is the conjugate base of $CH_3COOH$).

Second, $[H^+]$ and, therefore, the pH are controlled by the dissociation equilibrium of $CH_3COOH$:

[We have written the equilibrium using $H^+(aq)$ rather than $H_3O^+(aq)$, but both representations of the hydrated hydrogen ion are equally valid.]

$$CH_3COOH(aq) \rightleftharpoons H^+(aq) + CH_3COO^-(aq)$$

Third, we tabulate the initial and equilibrium concentrations as we did in solving other equilibrium problems in Chapters 15 and 16:

|  | $CH_3COOH(aq)$ $\rightleftharpoons$ | $H^+(aq)$ + | $CH_3COO^-(aq)$ |
|---|---|---|---|
| Initial | $0.30\ M$ | $0$ | $0.30\ M$ |
| Change | $-x\ M$ | $+x\ M$ | $+x\ M$ |
| Equilibrium | $(0.30 - x)\ M$ | $x\ M$ | $(0.30 + x)\ M$ |

The equilibrium concentration of $CH_3COO^-$ (the common ion) is the initial concentration that is due to $CH_3COONa$ ($0.30\ M$) plus the change in concentration ($x$) that is due to the ionization of $CH_3COOH$.

Now we can use the equilibrium-constant expression:

$$K_a = 1.8 \times 10^{-5} = \frac{[H^+][CH_3COO^-]}{[CH_3COOH]}$$

The dissociation constant for $CH_3COOH$ at 25 °C is from Appendix D; addition of $CH_3COONa$ does not change the value of this constant. Substituting the equilibrium-constant concentrations from our table into the equilibrium expression gives:

$$K_a = 1.8 \times 10^{-5} = \frac{x(0.30 + x)}{0.30 - x}$$

Because $K_a$ is small, we assume that $x$ is small compared to the original concentrations of $CH_3COOH$ and $CH_3COO^-$ ($0.30\ M$ each). Thus, we can ignore the very small $x$ relative to $0.30\ M$, giving:

$$K_a = 1.8 \times 10^{-5} = \frac{x(0.30)}{0.30}$$

The resulting value of $x$ is indeed small relative to $0.30$, justifying the approximation made in simplifying the problem.

$$x = 1.8 \times 10^{-5}\ M = [H^+]$$

Finally, we calculate the pH from the equilibrium concentration of $H^+(aq)$:

$$pH = -\log(1.8 \times 10^{-5}) = 4.74$$

**Comment** In Section 16.6 we calculated that a $0.30\ M$ solution of $CH_3COOH$ has a pH of 2.64, corresponding to $[H^+] = 2.3 \times 10^{-3}\ M$. Thus, the addition of $CH_3COONa$ has substantially decreased $[H^+]$, as we expect from Le Châtelier's principle.

**PRACTICE EXERCISE**

Calculate the pH of a solution containing $0.085\ M$ nitrous acid ($HNO_2$, $K_a = 4.5 \times 10^{-4}$) and $0.10\ M$ potassium nitrite ($KNO_2$).

*Answer:* 3.42

**SAMPLE EXERCISE 17.2** | Calculating Ion Concentrations When a Common Ion Is Involved

Calculate the fluoride ion concentration and pH of a solution that is 0.20 $M$ in HF and 0.10 $M$ in HCl.

**SOLUTION**

**Analyze** We are asked to determine the concentration of $F^-$ and the pH in a solution containing the weak acid HF and the strong acid HCl. In this case the common ion is $H^+$.

**Plan** We can again use the four steps outlined in Sample Exercise 17.1.

**Solve** Because HF is a weak acid and HCl is a strong acid, the major species in solution are HF, $H^+$, and $Cl^-$. The $Cl^-$, which is the conjugate base of a strong acid, is merely a spectator ion in any acid–base chemistry. The problem asks for $[F^-]$, which is formed by ionization of HF. Thus, the important equilibrium is

$$HF(aq) \rightleftharpoons H^+(aq) + F^-(aq)$$

The common ion in this problem is the hydrogen (or hydronium) ion. Now we can tabulate the initial and equilibrium concentrations of each species involved in this equilibrium:

| | HF(aq) $\rightleftharpoons$ | $H^+(aq)$ + | $F^-(aq)$ |
|---|---|---|---|
| Initial | 0.20 $M$ | 0.10 $M$ | 0 |
| Change | $-x\,M$ | $+x\,M$ | $+x\,M$ |
| Equilibrium | $(0.20 - x)\,M$ | $(0.10 + x)\,M$ | $x\,M$ |

The equilibrium constant for the ionization of HF, from Appendix D, is $6.8 \times 10^{-4}$. Substituting the equilibrium-constant concentrations into the equilibrium expression gives

$$K_a = 6.8 \times 10^{-4} = \frac{[H^+][F^-]}{[HF]} = \frac{(0.10 + x)(x)}{0.20 - x}$$

If we assume that $x$ is small relative to 0.10 or 0.20 $M$, this expression simplifies to

$$\frac{(0.10)(x)}{0.20} = 6.8 \times 10^{-4}$$

$$x = \frac{0.20}{0.10}(6.8 \times 10^{-4}) = 1.4 \times 10^{-3}\,M = [F^-]$$

This $F^-$ concentration is substantially smaller than it would be in a 0.20 $M$ solution of HF with no added HCl. The common ion, $H^+$, suppresses the ionization of HF. The concentration of $H^+(aq)$ is

$$[H^+] = (0.10 + x)\,M \simeq 0.10\,M$$

Thus,

$$pH = 1.00$$

**Comment** Notice that for all practical purposes, the hydrogen ion concentration is due entirely to the HCl; the HF makes a negligible contribution by comparison.

**PRACTICE EXERCISE**

Calculate the formate ion concentration and pH of a solution that is 0.050 $M$ in formic acid (HCOOH, $K_a = 1.8 \times 10^{-4}$) and 0.10 $M$ in HNO₃.

**Answer:** $[HCOO^-] = 9.0 \times 10^{-5}$, pH = 1.00

Sample Exercises 17.1 and 17.2 both involve weak acids. The ionization of a weak base is also decreased by the addition of a common ion. For example, the addition of $NH_4^+$ (as from the strong electrolyte $NH_4Cl$) causes the base-dissociation equilibrium of $NH_3$ to shift to the left, decreasing the equilibrium concentration of $OH^-$ and lowering the pH:

$$NH_3(aq) + H_2O(l) \rightleftharpoons NH_4^+(aq) + OH^-(aq) \qquad [17.2]$$

Addition of $NH_4^+$ shifts equilibrium, reducing $[OH^-]$

GIVE IT SOME THOUGHT

If solutions of $NH_4Cl(aq)$ and $NH_3(aq)$ are mixed, which ions in the resulting
solution are spectator ions in any acid–base chemistry occurring in the solution?
What equilibrium reaction determines $[OH^-]$ and, therefore, the pH of the solution?

# 17.2 | BUFFERED SOLUTIONS

Solutions that contain a weak conjugate acid–base pair, such as those discussed in
Section 17.1, resist drastic changes in pH when small amounts of strong acid or strong
base are added to them. These solutions are called **buffered solutions** (or merely
**buffers**). Human blood, for example, is a complex buffered solution that maintains the
blood pH at about 7.4 (see the "Chemistry and Life" box on page 713). Much of the
chemical behavior of seawater is determined by its pH, buffered at about 8.1 to 8.3 near
the surface (see "Chemistry and Life" box on page 728). Buffered solutions find many
important applications in the laboratory and in medicine (▶ FIGURE 17.1).

2    4    6        9    12

▲ **FIGURE 17.1  Buffered solutions.** For
laboratory work, prepackaged buffered
solutions can be purchased.

## Composition and Action of Buffered Solutions

A buffer resists changes in pH because it contains both an acid to neutralize added $OH^-$
ions and a base to neutralize added $H^+$ ions. The acid and base that make up the
buffer, however, must not consume each other through a neutralization reaction.
These requirements are fulfilled by a weak acid–base conjugate pair, such as
$CH_3COOH$–$CH_3COO^-$ or $NH_4^+$–$NH_3$. Thus, buffers are often prepared by mixing a
weak acid or a weak base with a salt of that acid or base. The $CH_3COOH$–$CH_3COO^-$
buffer can be prepared, for example, by adding $CH_3COONa$ to a solution of
$CH_3COOH$. The $NH_4^+$–$NH_3$ buffer can be prepared by adding $NH_4Cl$ to a solution of
$NH_3$. By choosing appropriate components and adjusting their relative concentrations,
we can buffer a solution at virtually any pH.

 GIVE IT SOME THOUGHT

Which of these conjugate acid–base pairs will *not* function as a buffer:
$C_2H_5COOH$ and $C_2H_5COO^-$, $HCO_3^-$ and $CO_3^{2-}$, or $HNO_3$ and $NO_3^-$? Explain.

To understand how a buffer works, let's consider one composed of a weak acid HX
and one of its salts MX, where $M^+$ could be $Na^+$, $K^+$, or any other cation that does not
react with water. The acid-dissociation equilibrium in this buffered solution involves
both the acid and its conjugate base:

$$HX(aq) \rightleftharpoons H^+(aq) + X^-(aq) \qquad [17.3]$$

The corresponding acid-dissociation-constant expression is

$$K_a = \frac{[H^+][X^-]}{[HX]} \qquad [17.4]$$

Solving this expression for $[H^+]$, we have

$$[H^+] = K_a\frac{[HX]}{[X^-]} \qquad [17.5]$$

We see from this expression that $[H^+]$ and, thus, the pH are determined by two factors:
the value of $K_a$ for the weak-acid component of the buffer and the ratio of the concentrations of the conjugate acid–base pair, $[HX]/[X^-]$.

If $OH^-$ ions are added to the buffered solution, they react with the buffer acid component to produce water and $X^-$:

$$\underset{\text{added base}}{OH^-(aq)} + HX(aq) \longrightarrow H_2O(l) + X^-(aq) \qquad [17.6]$$

▲ FIGURE 17.2 **Buffer action.** The pH of an HF/F⁻ buffered solution changes by only a small amount in response to addition of an acid or base.

This reaction causes [HX] to decrease and [X⁻] to increase. As long as the amounts of HX and X⁻ in the buffer are large relative to the amount of OH⁻ added, the ratio [HX]/[X⁻] does not change much and, thus, the change in pH is small.

If H⁺ ions are added, they react with the base component of the buffer:

$$H^+(aq) + X^-(aq) \longrightarrow HX(aq) \qquad [17.7]$$

added acid

This reaction can also be represented using $H_3O^+$:

$$H_3O^+(aq) + X^-(aq) \longrightarrow HX(aq) + H_2O(l)$$

Using either equation, we see that the reaction causes [X⁻] to decrease and [HX] to increase. As long as the change in the ratio [HX]/[X⁻] is small, the change in pH will be small.

▲ FIGURE 17.2 shows an HX/MX buffer consisting of equal concentrations of hydrofluoric acid and fluoride ion (center). The addition of OH⁻ reduces [HF] and increases [F⁻], whereas the addition of [H⁺] reduces [F⁻] and increases [HF].

### ▲ GIVE IT SOME THOUGHT

**a.** What happens when NaOH is added to a buffer composed of $CH_3COOH$ and $CH_3COO^-$?

**b.** What happens when HCl is added to this buffer?

## Calculating the pH of a Buffer

Because conjugate acid–base pairs share a common ion, we can use the same procedures to calculate the pH of a buffer that we used to treat the common-ion effect in Sample Exercise 17.1. Alternatively, we can take an approach based on an equation derived from Equation 17.5. Taking the negative logarithm of both sides of Equation 17.5, we have

$$-\log[H^+] = -\log\left(K_a \frac{[HX]}{[X^-]}\right) = -\log K_a - \log \frac{[HX]}{[X^-]}$$

Because $-\log[H^+] = pH$ and $-\log K_a = pK_a$, we have

$$pH = pK_a - \log\frac{[HX]}{[X^-]} = pK_a + \log\frac{[X^-]}{[HX]} \qquad [17.8]$$

In general,

$$pH = pK_a + \log\frac{[base]}{[acid]} \qquad [17.9]$$

where [acid] and [base] refer to the equilibrium concentrations of the *conjugate acid–base pair*. Note that when [base] = [acid], we have pH = $pK_a$.

Equation 17.9 is known as the **Henderson–Hasselbalch equation**. Biologists, biochemists, and others who work frequently with buffers often use this equation to calculate the pH of buffers. In doing equilibrium calculations, we have seen that we can normally neglect the amounts of the acid and base of the buffer that ionize. Therefore, we can usually use the starting concentrations of the acid and base components of the buffer directly in Equation 17.9.

---

**SAMPLE EXERCISE 17.3**  **Calculating the pH of a Buffer**

What is the pH of a buffer that is 0.12 $M$ in lactic acid [$CH_3CH(OH)COOH$, or $HC_3H_5O_3$] and 0.10 $M$ in sodium lactate [$CH_3CH(OH)COONa$, or $NaC_3H_5O_3$]? For lactic acid, $K_a = 1.4 \times 10^{-4}$.

**SOLUTION**

**Analyze** We are asked to calculate the pH of a buffer containing lactic acid ($HC_3H_5O_3$) and its conjugate base, the lactate ion ($C_3H_5O_3^-$).

**Plan** We will first determine the pH using the method described in Section 17.1. Because $HC_3H_5O_3$ is a weak electrolyte and $NaC_3H_5O_3$ is a strong electrolyte, the major species in solution are $HC_3H_5O_3$, $Na^+$, and $C_3H_5O_3^-$. The $Na^+$ ion is a spectator ion. The $HC_3H_5O_3$–$C_3H_5O_3^-$ conjugate acid–base pair determines [$H^+$] and, thus, pH; [$H^+$] can be determined using the acid-dissociation equilibrium of lactic acid.

**Solve** The initial and equilibrium concentrations of the species involved in this equilibrium are

|  | $HC_3H_5O_3(aq)$ | $\rightleftharpoons$ | $H^+(aq)$ | + | $C_3H_5O_3^-(aq)$ |
|---|---|---|---|---|---|
| Initial | 0.12 $M$ | | 0 | | 0.10 $M$ |
| Change | $-x\,M$ | | $+x\,M$ | | $+x\,M$ |
| Equilibrium | $(0.12 - x)\,M$ | | $x\,M$ | | $(0.10 + x)\,M$ |

The equilibrium concentrations are governed by the equilibrium expression:

$$K_a = 1.4 \times 10^{-4} = \frac{[H^+][C_3H_5O_3^-]}{[HC_3H_5O_3]} = \frac{x(0.10 + x)}{(0.12 - x)}$$

Because $K_a$ is small and a common ion is present, we expect $x$ to be small relative to either 0.12 or 0.10 $M$. Thus, our equation can be simplified to give

$$K_a = 1.4 \times 10^{-4} = \frac{x(0.10)}{0.12}$$

Solving for $x$ gives a value that justifies our approximation:

$$[H^+] = x = \left(\frac{0.12}{0.10}\right)(1.4 \times 10^{-4}) = 1.7 \times 10^{-4}\,M$$

$$pH = -\log(1.7 \times 10^{-4}) = 3.77$$

Alternatively, we can use the Henderson–Hasselbalch equation to calculate pH directly:

$$pH = pK_a + \log\frac{[base]}{[acid]} = 3.85 + \log\left(\frac{0.10}{0.12}\right)$$

$$= 3.85 + (-0.08) = 3.77$$

**PRACTICE EXERCISE**

Calculate the pH of a buffer composed of 0.12 $M$ benzoic acid and 0.20 $M$ sodium benzoate. (Refer to Appendix D.)

***Answer:*** 4.42

In Sample Exercise 17.3 we calculated the pH of a buffered solution. Often we will need to work in the opposite direction by calculating the amounts of the acid and its conjugate base needed to achieve a specific pH. This calculation is illustrated in Sample Exercise 17.4.

---

**SAMPLE EXERCISE 17.4** | **Preparing a Buffer**

How many moles of $NH_4Cl$ must be added to 2.0 L of 0.10 $M$ $NH_3$ to form a buffer whose pH is 9.00? (Assume that the addition of $NH_4Cl$ does not change the volume of the solution.)

**SOLUTION**

**Analyze** We are asked to determine the amount of $NH_4^+$ ion required to prepare a buffer of a specific pH.

**Plan** The major species in the solution will be $NH_4^+$, $Cl^-$, and $NH_3$. Of these, the $Cl^-$ ion is a spectator (it is the conjugate base of a strong acid). Thus, the $NH_4^+$–$NH_3$ conjugate acid–base pair will determine the pH of the buffer. The equilibrium relationship between $NH_4^+$ and $NH_3$ is given by the base-dissociation reaction for $NH_3$:

$$NH_3(aq) + H_2O(l) \rightleftharpoons NH_4^+(aq) + OH^-(aq) \qquad K_b = \frac{[NH_4^+][OH^-]}{[NH_3]} = 1.8 \times 10^{-5}$$

The key to this exercise is to use this $K_b$ expression to calculate $[NH_4^+]$.

**Solve** We obtain $[OH^-]$ from the given pH:

$$pOH = 14.00 - pH = 14.00 - 9.00 = 5.00$$

and so

$$[OH^-] = 1.0 \times 10^{-5}\,M$$

Because $K_b$ is small and the common ion $[NH_4^+]$ is present, the equilibrium concentration of $NH_3$ essentially equals its initial concentration:

$$[NH_3] = 0.10\,M$$

We now use the expression for $K_b$ to calculate $[NH_4^+]$:

$$[NH_4^+] = K_b \frac{[NH_3]}{[OH^-]} = (1.8 \times 10^{-5}) \frac{(0.10\,M)}{(1.0 \times 10^{-5}\,M)} = 0.18\,M$$

Thus, for the solution to have pH = 9.00, $[NH_4^+]$ must equal 0.18 $M$. The number of moles of $NH_4Cl$ needed to produce this concentration is given by the product of the volume of the solution and its molarity:

$$(2.0\,L)(0.18\,\text{mol } NH_4Cl/L) = 0.36\,\text{mol } NH_4Cl$$

---

**Comment** Because $NH_4^+$ and $NH_3$ are a conjugate acid–base pair, we could use the Henderson–Hasselbalch equation (Equation 17.9) to solve this problem. To do so requires first using Equation 16.41 to calculate $pK_a$ for $NH_4^+$ from the value of $pK_a$ for $NH_3$. We suggest you try this approach to convince yourself that you can use the Henderson–Hasselbalch equation for buffers for which you are given $K_b$ for the conjugate base rather than $K_a$ for the conjugate acid.

**PRACTICE EXERCISE**

Calculate the concentration of sodium benzoate that must be present in a 0.20 $M$ solution of benzoic acid ($C_6H_5COOH$) to produce a pH of 4.00.
*Answer:* 0.13 $M$

---

## Buffer Capacity and pH Range

Two important characteristics of a buffer are its capacity and its effective pH range. **Buffer capacity** is the amount of acid or base the buffer can neutralize before the pH begins to change to an appreciable degree. The buffer capacity depends on the amount of acid and base used to prepare the buffer. According to Equation 17.5, for example, the pH of a 1-L solution that is 1 $M$ in $CH_3COOH$ and 1 $M$ in $CH_3COONa$ is the same as the pH of a 1-L solution that is 0.1 $M$ in $CH_3COOH$ and 0.1 $M$ in $CH_3COONa$. The first solution has a greater buffering capacity, however, because it contains more $CH_3COOH$ and $CH_3COO^-$.

The **pH range** of any buffer is the pH range over which the buffer acts effectively. Buffers most effectively resist a change in pH in *either* direction when the concentrations of weak acid and conjugate base are about the same. From Equation 17.9 we see that when the concentrations of weak acid and conjugate base are equal, $pH = pK_a$. This relationship gives the optimal pH of any buffer. Thus, we usually try to select a buffer whose acid form has a $pK_a$ close to the desired pH. In practice, we find that if the concentration of one component of the buffer is more than 10 times the concentration of the other component, the buffering action is poor. Because $\log 10 = 1$, *buffers usually have a usable range within ±1 pH unit of* $pK_a$ (that is, a range of $pH = pK_a \pm 1$).

 **GIVE IT SOME THOUGHT**

The $K_a$ values for nitrous acid ($HNO_2$) and hypochlorous ($HClO$) acid are $4.5 \times 10^{-4}$ and $3.0 \times 10^{-8}$, respectively. Which one would be more suitable for use in a solution buffered at $pH = 7.0$? What other substance would be needed to make the buffer?

## Addition of Strong Acids or Bases to Buffers

Let's now consider in a more quantitative way how a buffered solution responds to addition of a strong acid or base. In this discussion, it is important to understand that *reactions between strong acids and weak bases proceed essentially to completion, as do those between strong bases and weak acids.* Thus, as long as we do not exceed the buffering capacity of the buffer, we can assume that the strong acid or strong base is completely consumed by reaction with the buffer.

Consider a buffer that contains a weak acid HX and its conjugate base $X^-$. When a strong acid is added to this buffer, the added $H^+$ is consumed by $X^-$ to produce HX; thus, [HX] increases and $[X^-]$ decreases. (See Equation 17.7.) Upon addition of a strong base, the added $OH^-$ is consumed by HX to produce $X^-$; in this case [HX] decreases and $[X^-]$ increases. (See Equation 17.6.) These two situations are summarized in Figure 17.2.

To calculate how the pH of the buffer responds to the addition of a strong acid or a strong base, we follow the strategy outlined in ▼ **FIGURE 17.3**:

1. Consider the acid–base neutralization reaction and determine its effect on [HX] and $[X^-]$. This step is a *stoichiometry calculation.* ∞ (Section 3.6)

2. Use the calculated values of [HX] and $[X^-]$ along with $K_a$ to calculate $[H^+]$. This step is an *equilibrium calculation* and is most easily done using the Henderson–Hasselbalch equation.

▲ **FIGURE 17.3**  **Calculating the pH of a buffer after addition of an acid or base.**

1.000 L buffer
0.300 M CH$_3$COOH
0.300 M CH$_3$COO$^-$  pH = 4.74

Add 5.0 mL of
4.0 M NaOH(aq)

pH = 4.80

**pH increases by
0.06 pH units**

1.000 L H$_2$O   pH = 7.00

Add 5.0 mL of
4.0 M NaOH(aq)

pH = 12.30

**pH increases by
5.30 pH units**

▲ **FIGURE 17.4** **Effect of adding a
strong base to a buffered solution and
to water.**

## SAMPLE EXERCISE 17.5 | Calculating pH Changes in Buffers

A buffer is made by adding 0.300 mol CH$_3$COOH and 0.300 mol CH$_3$COONa to enough water to make 1.000 L of solution. The pH of the buffer is 4.74 (Sample Exercise 17.1). **(a)** Calculate the pH of this solution after 5.0 mL of 4.0 M NaOH(aq) solution is added. **(b)** For comparison, calculate the pH of a solution made by adding 5.0 mL of 4.0 M NaOH(aq) solution to 1.000 L of pure water.

### SOLUTION

**Analyze** We are asked to determine the pH of a buffer after addition of a small amount of strong base and to compare the pH change with the pH that would result if we were to add the same amount of strong base to pure water.

**Plan** Solving this problem involves the two steps outlined in Figure 17.3. First we do a stoichiometry calculation to determine how the added OH$^-$ affects the buffer composition. Then we use the resultant buffer composition and either the Henderson–Hasselbalch equation or the equilibrium-constant expression for the buffer to determine the pH.

**Solve** **(a)** *Stoichiometry Calculation:* The OH$^-$ provided by NaOH reacts with CH$_3$COOH, the weak acid component of the buffer. Prior to this neutralization reaction, there are 0.300 mol each of CH$_3$COOH and CH$_3$COO$^-$. The amount of base added is 0.0050 L × 4.0 mol/L = 0.020 mol. Neutralizing the 0.020 mol OH$^-$ requires 0.020 mol of CH$_3$COOH. Consequently, the amount of CH$_3$COOH *decreases* by 0.020 mol, and the amount of the product of the neutralization, CH$_3$COO$^-$, *increases* by 0.020 mol. We can create a table to see how the composition of the buffer changes as a result of its reaction with OH$^-$:

$$CH_3COOH(aq) + OH^-(aq) \longrightarrow H_2O(l) + CH_3COO^-(aq)$$

|  | | | | |
|---|---|---|---|---|
| Buffer before addition | 0.300 mol | 0 | — | 0.300 mol |
| Addition | | 0.020 mol | — | |
| Buffer after addition | 0.280 mol | 0 | — | 0.320 mol |

*Equilibrium Calculation:* We now turn our attention to the equilibrium for the ionization of acetic acid, the relationship that determines the buffer pH:

$$CH_3COOH(aq) \rightleftharpoons H^+(aq) + CH_3COO^-(aq)$$

Using the quantities of CH$_3$COOH and CH$_3$COO$^-$ remaining in the buffer, we determine the pH using the Henderson–Hasselbalch equation. The volume of the solution is now 1.000 L + 0.0050 L = 1.005 L due to addition of the NaOH solution:

$$pH = 4.74 + \log\frac{0.320 \text{ mol}/1.005 \text{ L}}{0.280 \text{ mol}/1.005 \text{ L}} = 4.80$$

**(b)** To determine the pH of a solution made by adding 0.020 mol of NaOH to 1.000 L of pure water, we first determine the concentration of OH$^-$ ions in solution,

$$[OH^-] = 0.020 \text{ mol}/(1.005 \text{ L}) = 0.020 \text{ M}$$

We use this value in Equation 16.18 to calculate pOH and then use our calculated pOH value in Equation 16.20 to obtain pH:

$$pOH = -\log[OH^-] = -\log(0.020) = +1.70$$

$$pH = 14 - (+1.70) = 12.30$$

**Comment** Note that the small amount of added NaOH changes the pH of water significantly. In contrast, the pH of the buffer changes very little when the NaOH is added, as summarized in ◄ **FIGURE 17.4**.

### PRACTICE EXERCISE

Determine **(a)** the pH of the original buffer described in Sample Exercise 17.5 after the addition of 0.020 mol HCl and **(b)** the pH of the solution that would result from the addition of 0.020 mol HCl to 1.000 L of pure water.

***Answers:*** **(a)** 4.68, **(b)** 1.70

# CHEMISTRY AND LIFE

## BLOOD AS A BUFFERED SOLUTION

Chemical reactions that occur in living systems are often extremely sensitive to pH. Many of the enzymes that catalyze important biochemical reactions, for example, are effective only within a narrow pH range. For this reason, the human body maintains a remarkably intricate system of buffers, both within cells and in the fluids that transport cells. Blood, the fluid that transports oxygen to all parts of the body, is one of the most prominent examples of the importance of buffers in living beings.

Human blood has a normal pH of 7.35 to 7.45. Any deviation from this range can have extremely disruptive effects on the stability of cell membranes, the structures of proteins, and the activities of enzymes. Death may result if the blood pH falls below 6.8 or rises above 7.8. When the pH falls below 7.35, the condition is called *acidosis*; when it rises above 7.45, the condition is called *alkalosis*. Acidosis is the more common tendency because metabolism generates several acids in the body.

The major buffer system used to control blood pH is the *carbonic acid–bicarbonate buffer system*. Carbonic acid ($H_2CO_3$) and bicarbonate ion ($HCO_3^-$) are a conjugate acid–base pair. In addition, carbonic acid decomposes into carbon dioxide gas and water. The important equilibria in this buffer system are

$$H^+(aq) + HCO_3^-(aq) \rightleftharpoons H_2CO_3(aq) \rightleftharpoons H_2O(l) + CO_2(g)$$
$$[17.10]$$

Several aspects of these equilibria are notable. First, although carbonic acid is diprotic, the carbonate ion ($CO_3^{2-}$) is unimportant in this system. Second, one component of this equilibrium, $CO_2$, is a gas, which provides a mechanism for the body to adjust the equilibria. Removal of $CO_2$ via exhalation shifts the equilibria to the right, consuming $H^+$ ions. Third, the buffer system in blood operates at pH 7.4, which is fairly far removed from the $pK_{a1}$ value of $H_2CO_3$ (6.1 at physiological temperatures). For the buffer to have a pH of 7.4, the ratio [base]/[acid] must be about 20. In normal blood plasma the concentrations of $HCO_3^-$ and $H_2CO_3$ are about 0.024 $M$ and 0.0012 $M$, respectively. Consequently, the buffer has a high capacity to neutralize additional acid but only a low capacity to neutralize additional base.

The principal organs that regulate the pH of the carbonic acid–bicarbonate buffer system are the lungs and kidneys. When the concentration of $CO_2$ rises, the equilibria in Equation 17.10 shift to the left, which leads to the formation of more $H^+$ and a drop in pH. This change is detected by receptors in the brain that trigger a reflex to breathe faster and deeper, increasing the rate at which $CO_2$ is expelled from the lungs and thereby shifting the equilibria back to the right. When the blood pH becomes too high, the kidneys remove $HCO_3^-$ from the blood. This shifts the equilibria to the left, increasing the concentration of $H^+$. As a result, the pH decreases.

Regulation of blood pH relates directly to the effective transport of $O_2$ throughout the body. The protein hemoglobin, found in red blood cells (▶ FIGURE 17.5), carries oxygen. Hemoglobin (Hb)

reversibly binds both $H^+$ and $O_2$. These two substances compete for the Hb, which can be represented approximately by the equilibrium

$$HbH^+ + O_2 \rightleftharpoons HbO_2 + H^+ \qquad [17.11]$$

Oxygen enters the blood through the lungs, where it passes into the red blood cells and binds to Hb. When the blood reaches tissue in which the concentration of $O_2$ is low, the equilibrium in Equation 17.11 shifts to the left and $O_2$ is released.

During periods of strenuous exertion, three factors work together to ensure delivery of $O_2$ to active tissues. The role of each factor can be understood by applying Le Châtelier's principle to Equation 17.11:

1. $O_2$ is consumed, causing the equilibrium to shift to the left, releasing more $O_2$.

2. Large amounts of $CO_2$ are produced by metabolism, which increases $[H^+]$ and causes the equilibrium to shift to the left, releasing $O_2$.

3. Body temperature rises. Because Equation 17.11 is exothermic, the increase in temperature shifts the equilibrium to the left, releasing $O_2$.

In addition to the factors causing release of $O_2$ to tissues, the decrease in pH stimulates an increase in breathing rate, which furnishes more $O_2$ and eliminates $CO_2$. Without this elaborate series of equilibrium shifts and pH changes, the $O_2$ in tissues would be rapidly depleted, making further activity impossible. Under such conditions the buffering capacity of the blood and the exhalation of $CO_2$ through the lungs are essential to keep the pH from dropping too low, thereby triggering acidosis.

*RELATED EXERCISES: 17.29 and 17.95*

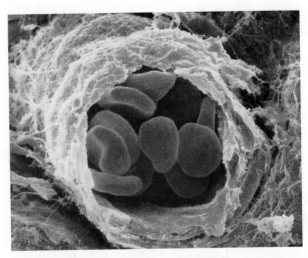

▲ FIGURE 17.5  **Red blood cells.** A scanning electromicrograph of red blood cells traveling through a small branch of an artery.

**GO FIGURE**

**In which direction do you expect the pH to change as NaOH is added to the HCl solution?**

Buret containing NaOH(aq) of known concentration

pH meter

Beaker containing HCl(aq) of unknown concentration

▲ **FIGURE 17.6** **Measuring pH during a titration.**

# 17.3 | ACID–BASE TITRATIONS

In an acid–base titration, a solution containing a known concentration of base is slowly added to an acid (or the acid is added to the base). ∞ (Section 4.6) Acid–base indicators can be used to signal the *equivalence point* of a titration (the point at which stoichiometrically equivalent quantities of acid and base have been brought together). Alternatively, a pH meter can be used to monitor the progress of the reaction (◄ **FIGURE 17.6**), producing a **pH titration curve**, a graph of the pH as a function of the volume of titrant added. The shape of the titration curve makes it possible to determine the equivalence point. The curve can also be used to select suitable indicators and to determine the $K_a$ of the weak acid or the $K_b$ of the weak base being titrated.

To understand why titration curves have certain characteristic shapes, we will examine the curves for three kinds of titrations: (1) strong acid–strong base, (2) weak acid–strong base, and (3) polyprotic acid–strong base. We will also briefly consider how these curves relate to those involving weak bases.

## Strong Acid–Strong Base Titrations

The titration curve produced when a strong base is added to a strong acid has the general shape shown in ▼ **FIGURE 17.7**, which depicts the pH change that occurs as

**GO FIGURE**

**What volume of NaOH(aq) would be needed to reach the equivalence point if the concentration of the added base were 0.200 M?**

pH = 7.0 at equivalence point, NaCl(aq) salt solution

Equivalence point

Equivalence point occurs when moles base = moles acid

Only HCl(aq) present before titration

H⁺ consumed as OH⁻ added, forming H₂O (pH < 7.0)

H⁺ completely neutralized by OH⁻ (pH = 7.0)

No H⁺ left to react with excess OH⁻ (pH > 7.0)

▲ **FIGURE 17.7** **Titration of a strong acid with a strong base.** The pH curve for titration of 50.0 mL of a 0.100 $M$ solution of hydrochloric acid with a 0.100 $M$ solution of NaOH(aq). For clarity, water molecules have been omitted from the molecular art.

0.100 $M$ NaOH is added to 50.0 mL of 0.100 $M$ HCl. The pH can be calculated at various stages of the titration. To help understand these calculations, we can divide the curve into four regions:

1. **Initial pH:** The pH of the solution before the addition of any base is determined by the initial concentration of the strong acid. For a solution of 0.100 $M$ HCl, $[H^+] = 0.100\ M$ and pH $= -\log(0.100) = 1.000$. Thus, the initial pH is low.

2. **Between initial pH and equivalence point:** As NaOH is added, the pH increases slowly at first and then rapidly in the vicinity of the equivalence point. The pH before the equivalence point is determined by the concentration of acid not yet neutralized. This calculation is illustrated in Sample Exercise 17.6(a).

3. **Equivalence point:** At the equivalence point an equal number of moles of NaOH and HCl have reacted, leaving only a solution of their salt, NaCl. The pH of the solution is 7.00 because the cation of a strong base (in this case Na$^+$) and the anion of a strong acid (in this case Cl$^-$) are neither acids nor bases and, therefore, have no appreciable effect on pH. ∞ (Section 16.9)

4. **After equivalence point:** The pH of the solution after the equivalence point is determined by the concentration of excess NaOH in the solution. This calculation is illustrated in Sample Exercise 17.6(b).

---

**SAMPLE EXERCISE 17.6** | **Calculating pH for a Strong Acid–Strong Base Titration**

Calculate the pH when (**a**) 49.0 mL and (**b**) 51.0 mL of 0.100 $M$ NaOH solution have been added to 50.0 mL of 0.100 $M$ HCl solution.

**SOLUTION**

**Analyze** We are asked to calculate the pH at two points in the titration of a strong acid with a strong base. The first point is just before the equivalence point, so we expect the pH to be determined by the small amount of strong acid that has not yet been neutralized. The second point is just after the equivalence point, so we expect this pH to be determined by the small amount of excess strong base.

**Plan** (**a**) As the NaOH solution is added to the HCl solution, $H^+(aq)$ reacts with $OH^-(aq)$ to form $H_2O$. Both Na$^+$ and Cl$^-$ are spectator ions, having negligible effect on the pH. To determine the pH of the solution, we must first determine how many moles of $H^+$ were originally present and how many moles of $OH^-$ were added. We can then calculate how many moles of each ion remain after the neutralization reaction. To calculate $[H^+]$, and hence pH, we must also remember that the volume of the solution increases as we add titrant, thus diluting the concentration of all solutes present.

**Solve** The number of moles of $H^+$ in the original HCl solution is given by the product of the volume of the solution and its molarity:

$$(0.0500\ \text{L soln})\left(\frac{0.100\ \text{mol}\ H^+}{1\ \text{L soln}}\right) = 5.00 \times 10^{-3}\ \text{mol}\ H^+$$

Likewise, the number of moles of $OH^-$ in 49.0 mL of 0.100 $M$ NaOH is

$$(0.0490\ \text{L soln})\left(\frac{0.100\ \text{mol}\ OH^-}{1\ \text{L soln}}\right) = 4.90 \times 10^{-3}\ \text{mol}\ OH^-$$

Because we have not reached the equivalence point, there are more moles of $H^+$ present than $OH^-$. Each mole of $OH^-$ reacts with 1 mol of $H^+$. Using the convention introduced in Sample Exercise 17.5, we have

| | $H^+(aq)$ | $+$ | $OH^-(aq)$ | $\longrightarrow$ | $H_2O(l)$ |
|---|---|---|---|---|---|
| Before addition | $5.00 \times 10^{-3}$ mol | | 0 | | — |
| Addition | | | $4.90 \times 10^{-3}$ mol | | |
| After addition | $0.10 \times 10^{-3}$ mol | | 0 | | — |

The volume of the reaction mixture increases as the NaOH solution is added to the HCl solution. Thus, at this point in the titration, the volume in the titration flask is

$$50.0\ \text{mL} + 49.0\ \text{mL} = 99.0\ \text{mL} = 0.0990\ \text{L}$$

Thus, the concentration of $H^+(aq)$ in the flask is

$$[H^+] = \frac{\text{moles}\ H^+(aq)}{\text{liters soln}} = \frac{0.10 \times 10^{-3}\ \text{mol}}{0.09900\ \text{L}} = 1.0 \times 10^{-3}\ M$$

The corresponding pH is

$$-\log(1.0 \times 10^{-3}) = 3.00$$

**Plan (b)** We proceed in the same way as we did in part (a) except we are now past the equivalence point and have more $OH^-$ in the solution than $H^+$. As before, the initial number of moles of each reactant is determined from their volumes and concentrations. The reactant present in smaller stoichiometric amount (the limiting reactant) is consumed completely, leaving an excess of hydroxide ion.

**Solve**

| | $H^+(aq)$ | $+$ | $OH^-(aq)$ | $\longrightarrow$ | $H_2O(l)$ |
|---|---|---|---|---|---|
| Before addition | $5.00 \times 10^{-3}$ mol | | 0 | | — |
| Addition | | | $5.10 \times 10^{-3}$ mol | | |
| After addition | 0 | | $0.10 \times 10^{-3}$ mol | | — |

In this case the volume in the titration flask is

$$50.0 \text{ mL} + 51.0 \text{ mL} = 101.0 \text{ mL} = 0.1010 \text{ L}$$

Hence, the concentration of $OH^-(aq)$ in the flask is

$$[OH^-] = \frac{\text{moles } OH^-(aq)}{\text{liters soln}} = \frac{0.10 \times 10^{-3} \text{ mol}}{0.1010 \text{ L}} = 1.0 \times 10^{-3} M$$

and we have

$$pOH = -\log(1.0 \times 10^{-3}) = 3.00$$

$$pH = 14.00 - pOH = 14.00 - 3.00 = 11.00$$

**Comment** Note that the pH increased by only two pH units, from 1.00 (Figure 17.7) to 3.00, after the first 49.0 mL of NaOH solution was added, but jumped by eight pH units, from 3.00 to 11.00, as 2.0 mL of base solution was added near the equivalence point. Such a rapid rise in pH near the equivalence point is a characteristic of titrations involving strong acids and strong bases.

**PRACTICE EXERCISE**
Calculate the pH when **(a)** 24.9 mL and **(b)** 25.1 mL of 0.100 $M$ $HNO_3$ have been added to 25.0 mL of 0.100 $M$ KOH solution.
**Answers: (a)** 10.30, **(b)** 3.70

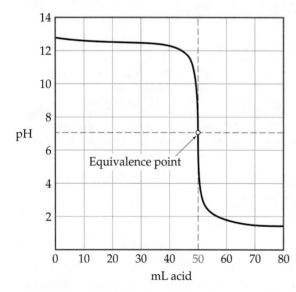

▲ **FIGURE 17.8 Titration of a strong base with a strong acid.** The pH curve for titration of 50.0 mL of a 0.100 $M$ solution of a strong base with a 0.100 $M$ solution of a strong acid.

Titration of a solution of a strong base with a solution of a strong acid yields an analogous curve of pH versus added acid. In this case, however, the pH is high at the outset of the titration and low at its completion (◀ **FIGURE 17.8**).

▲ **GIVE IT SOME THOUGHT**
What is the pH at the equivalence point when 0.10 $M$ $HNO_3$ is used to titrate a volume of solution containing 0.30 g of KOH?

## Weak Acid–Strong Base Titrations

The curve for titration of a weak acid by a strong base is similar to the curve in Figure 17.7. Consider, for example, the curve for titration of 50.0 mL of 0.100 $M$ acetic acid with 0.100 $M$ NaOH shown in ▶ **FIGURE 17.9**. We can calculate the pH at points along this curve, using principles we discussed earlier, which means again dividing the curve into four regions:

1. **Initial pH:** We use $K_a$ to calculate this pH, as shown in Section 16.6. The calculated pH of 0.100 $M$ $CH_3COOH$ is 2.89.

2. **Between initial pH and equivalence point:** Prior to reaching the equivalence point, the acid is being neutralized, and its conjugate base is being formed:

$$CH_3COOH(aq) + OH^-(aq) \longrightarrow CH_3COO^-(aq) + H_2O(l) \qquad [17.12]$$

Thus, the solution contains a mixture of $CH_3COOH$ and $CH_3COO^-$. Calculating the pH in this region involves two steps. First, we consider the neutralization reaction between $CH_3COOH$ and $OH^-$ to determine $[CH_3COOH]$ and $[CH_3COO^-]$. Next, we calculate the pH of this buffer pair using procedures developed in Sections 17.1 and 17.2. The general procedure is diagrammed in ▶ **FIGURE 17.10** and illustrated in Sample Exercise 17.7.

If the acetic acid being titrated here were replaced by hydrochloric acid, would the amount of base needed to reach the equivalence point change? Would the pH at the equivalence point change?

▲ **FIGURE 17.9**   **Titration of a weak acid with a strong base.**  The pH curve for titration of 50.0 mL of a 0.100 $M$ solution of acetic acid with a 0.100 $M$ solution of NaOH($aq$). For clarity, water molecules have been omitted from the molecular art.

▲ **FIGURE 17.10**   **Procedure for calculating pH when a weak acid is partially neutralized by a strong base.**

3. **Equivalence point:** The equivalence point is reached when 50.0 mL of 0.100 $M$ NaOH has been added to the 50.0 mL of 0.100 $M$ CH$_3$COOH. At this point, the $5.00 \times 10^{-3}$ mol of NaOH completely reacts with the $5.00 \times 10^{-3}$ mol of CH$_3$COOH to form $5.00 \times 10^{-3}$ mol of CH$_3$COONa. The Na$^+$ ion of this salt has no significant effect on the pH. The CH$_3$COO$^-$ ion, however, is a weak base, and the pH at the equivalence point is therefore greater than 7. In general, the pH at the equivalence point is always above 7 in a weak acid–strong base titration because the anion of the salt formed is a weak base. The procedure for calculating the pH of the solution of a weak base is described in Section 16.7 and is shown in Sample Exercise 17.8.

4. **After equivalence point (excess base):** In this region, [OH$^-$] from the reaction of CH$_3$COO$^-$ with water is negligible relative to [OH$^-$] from the excess NaOH. Thus, the pH is determined by the concentration of OH$^-$ from the excess NaOH. The method for calculating pH in this region is therefore like that illustrated in Sample Exercise 17.6(b). Thus, the addition of 51.0 mL of 0.100 $M$ NaOH to 50.0 mL of either 0.100 $M$ HCl or 0.100 $M$ CH$_3$COOH yields the same pH, 11.00. Notice by comparing Figures 17.7 and 17.9 that the titration curves for a strong acid and a weak acid are the same after the equivalence point.

---

**SAMPLE EXERCISE 17.7** | **Calculating pH for a Weak Acid–Strong Base Titration**

Calculate the pH of the solution formed when 45.0 mL of 0.100 $M$ NaOH is added to 50.0 mL of 0.100 $M$ CH$_3$COOH ($K_a = 1.8 \times 10^{-5}$).

**SOLUTION**

**Analyze** We are asked to calculate the pH before the equivalence point of the titration of a weak acid with a strong base.

**Plan** We first must determine the number of moles of CH$_3$COOH and CH$_3$COO$^-$ present after the neutralization reaction. We then calculate pH using $K_a$, [CH$_3$COOH], and [CH$_3$COO$^-$].

**Solve** *Stoichiometry Calculation:* The product of the volume and concentration of each solution gives the number of moles of each reactant present before the neutralization:

$$(0.0500 \text{ L soln})\left(\frac{0.100 \text{ mol CH}_3\text{COOH}}{1 \text{ L soln}}\right) = 5.00 \times 10^{-3} \text{ mol CH}_3\text{COOH}$$

$$(0.0450 \text{ L soln})\left(\frac{0.100 \text{ mol NaOH}}{1 \text{ L soln}}\right) = 4.50 \times 10^{-3} \text{ mol NaOH}$$

The $4.50 \times 10^{-3}$ of NaOH consumes $4.50 \times 10^{-3}$ of CH$_3$COOH:

| | CH$_3$COOH($aq$) | + OH$^-$($aq$) | $\longrightarrow$ CH$_3$COO$^-$($aq$) | + H$_2$O($l$) |
|---|---|---|---|---|
| Before addition | $5.00 \times 10^{-3}$ mol | 0 | 0 | — |
| Addition | | $4.50 \times 10^{-3}$ mol | | |
| After addition | $0.50 \times 10^{-3}$ mol | 0 | $4.50 \times 10^{-3}$ mol | — |

The total volume of the solution is

$$45.0 \text{ mL} + 50.0 \text{ mL} = 95.0 \text{ mL} = 0.0950 \text{ L}$$

The resulting molarities of CH$_3$COOH and CH$_3$COO$^-$ after the reaction are therefore

$$[\text{CH}_3\text{COOH}] = \frac{0.50 \times 10^{-3} \text{ mol}}{0.0950 \text{ L}} = 0.0053 \ M$$

$$[\text{CH}_3\text{COO}^-] = \frac{4.50 \times 10^{-3} \text{ mol}}{0.0950 \text{ L}} = 0.0474 \ M$$

*Equilibrium Calculation:* The equilibrium between CH$_3$COOH and CH$_3$COO$^-$ must obey the equilibrium-constant expression for CH$_3$COOH:

$$K_a = \frac{[\text{H}^+][\text{CH}_3\text{COO}^-]}{[\text{CH}_3\text{COOH}]} = 1.8 \times 10^{-5}$$

Solving for $[H^+]$ gives

$$[H^+] = K_a \times \frac{[CH_3COOH]}{[CH_3COO^-]} = (1.8 \times 10^{-5}) \times \left(\frac{0.0053}{0.0474}\right) = 2.0 \times 10^{-6} \, M$$

$$pH = -\log(2.0 \times 10^{-6}) = 5.70$$

**Comment** We could have solved for pH equally well using the Henderson–Hasselbalch equation.

### PRACTICE EXERCISE

(a) Calculate the pH in the solution formed by adding 10.0 mL of 0.050 $M$ NaOH to 40.0 mL of 0.0250 $M$ benzoic acid ($C_6H_5COOH$, $K_a = 6.3 \times 10^{-5}$. (b) Calculate the pH in the solution formed by adding 10.0 mL of 0.100 $M$ HCl to 20.0 mL of 0.100 $M$ NH_3.

*Answers:* (a) 4.20, (b) 9.26

In order to follow the evolution of pH as a function of added base further, we can calculate the pH at the equivalence point.

### SAMPLE EXERCISE 17.8   Calculating the pH at the Equivalence Point

Calculate the pH at the equivalence point in the titration of 50.0 mL of 0.100 $M$ $CH_3COOH$ with 0.100 $M$ NaOH.

### SOLUTION

**Analyze** We are asked to determine the pH at the equivalence point of the titration of a weak acid with a strong base. Because the neutralization of a weak acid produces its anion, which is a weak base, we expect the pH at the equivalence point to be greater than 7.

**Plan** The initial number of moles of acetic acid equals the number of moles of acetate ion at the equivalence point. We use the volume of the solution at the equivalence point to calculate the concentration of acetate ion. Because the acetate ion is a weak base, we can calculate the pH using $K_b$ and $[CH_3COO^-]$.

**Solve** The number of moles of acetic acid in the initial solution is obtained from the volume and molarity of the solution:

$$\text{Moles} = M \times L = (0.100 \, \text{mol})/L(0.0500 \, L) = 5.00 \times 10^{-3} \, \text{mol} \, CH_3COOH$$

Hence, $5.00 \times 10^{-3}$ mol of $[CH_3COO^-]$ is formed. It will take 50.0 mL of NaOH to reach the equivalence point (Figure 17.9). The volume of this salt solution at the equivalence point is the sum of the volumes of the acid and base, 50.0 mL + 50.0 mL = 100.0 mL = 0.1000 L. Thus, the concentration of $CH_3COO^-$ is

$$[CH_3COO^-] = \frac{5.00 \times 10^{-3} \, \text{mol}}{0.1000 \, L} = 0.0500 \, M$$

The $CH_3COO^-$ ion is a weak base:

$$CH_3COO^-(aq) + H_2O(l) \rightleftharpoons CH_3COOH(aq) + OH^-(aq)$$

The $K_b$ for $CH_3COO^-$ can be calculated from the $K_a$ value of its conjugate acid, $K_b = K_w/K_a = (1.0 \times 10^{-14})/(1.8 \times 10^{-5}) = 5.6 \times 10^{-10}$. Using the $K_b$ expression, we have

$$K_b = \frac{[CH_3COOH][OH^-]}{[CH_3COO^-]} = \frac{(x)(x)}{0.0500-x} = 5.6 \times 10^{-10}$$

Making the approximation that $0.0500 - x \approx 0.0500$, and then solving for $x$, we have $x = [OH^-] = 5.3 \times 10^{-6} \, M$, which gives pOH = 5.28 and pH = 8.72.

**Check** The pH is above 7, as expected for the salt of a weak acid and strong base.

### PRACTICE EXERCISE

Calculate the pH at the equivalence point when (a) 40.0 mL of 0.025 $M$ benzoic acid ($C_6H_5COOH$, $K_a = 6.3 \times 10^{-5}$) is titrated with 0.050 $M$ NaOH; (b) 40.0 mL of 0.100 $M$ NH_3 is titrated with 0.100 $M$ HCl.

*Answers:* (a) 8.21, (b) 5.28

▲ GO FIGURE

**How does the pH at the equivalence point change as the acid being titrated becomes weaker? How does the volume of NaOH(aq) needed to reach the equivalence point change?**

▲ **FIGURE 17.11 A set of curves showing the effect of acid strength on the characteristics of the titration curve when a weak acid is titrated by a strong base.** Each curve represents titration of 50.0 mL of 0.10 *M* acid with 0.10 *M* NaOH.

The titration curve for a weak acid–strong base titration (Figure 17.9) differs from the curve for a strong acid–strong base titration (Figure 17.7) in three noteworthy ways:

1. The solution of the weak acid has a higher initial pH than a solution of a strong acid of the same concentration.

2. The pH change in the rapid-rise portion of the curve near the equivalence point is smaller for the weak acid than for the strong acid.

3. The pH at the equivalence point is above 7.00 for the weak acid titration.

The weaker the acid, the more pronounced these differences become. To illustrate this consider the family of titration curves shown in ◀ **FIGURE 17.11**. Notice that as the acid becomes weaker (that is, as $K_a$ becomes smaller), the initial pH increases and the pH change near the equivalence point becomes less marked. Furthermore, the pH at the equivalence point steadily increases as $K_a$ decreases, because the strength of the conjugate base of the weak acid increases. It is virtually impossible to determine the equivalence point when $pK_a$ is 10 or higher because the pH change is too small and gradual.

## Titrations of Polyprotic Acids

When weak acids contain more than one ionizable H atom, the reaction with $OH^-$ occurs in a series of steps. Neutralization of $H_3PO_3$, for example, proceeds in two steps (Chapter 16 Sample Integrative Exercise):

$$H_3PO_3(aq) + OH^-(aq) \longrightarrow H_2PO_3^-(aq) + H_2O(l) \quad [17.13]$$

$$H_2PO_3^-(aq) + OH^-(aq) \longrightarrow HPO_3^{2-}(aq) + H_2O(l) \quad [17.14]$$

When the neutralization steps of a polyprotic acid or polybasic base are sufficiently separated, the titration has multiple equivalence points. ▼ **FIGURE 17.12** shows the two equivalence points corresponding to Equations 17.13 and 17.14.

▶ **FIGURE 17.12 Titration curve for a diprotic acid.** The curve shows the pH change when 50.0 mL of 0.10 *M* $H_3PO_3$ is titrated with 0.10 *M* NaOH.

▲ GIVE IT SOME THOUGHT

Sketch an approximate titration curve for the titration of $Na_2CO_3$ with HCl.

## Titrating with an Acid–Base Indicator

Oftentimes in an acid–base titration, an indicator is used rather than a pH meter. Optimally, an indicator should change color at the equivalence point in a titration. In practice, however, that is unnecessary. The pH changes very rapidly near the equivalence point, and in this region one drop of titrant can change the pH by several units. Thus, an indicator beginning and ending its color change anywhere on the rapid-rise portion of the titration curve gives a sufficiently accurate measure of the titrant volume needed to reach the equivalence point. The point in a titration where the indicator changes color is called the *end point* to distinguish it from the equivalence point that it closely approximates.

▶ FIGURE 17.13 shows the curve for titration of a strong base (NaOH) with a strong acid (HCl). We see from the vertical part of the curve that the pH changes rapidly from roughly 11 to 3 near the equivalence point. Consequently, an indicator for this titration can change color anywhere in this range. Most strong acid–strong base titrations are carried out using phenolphthalein as an indicator because it changes color in this range (see Figure 16.8, page 664). Several other indicators would also be satisfactory, including methyl red, which, as the lower color band in Figure 17.13 shows, changes color in the pH range from about 4.2 to 6.0. (see Figure 16.8, page 664).

As noted in our discussion of Figure 17.11, because the pH change near the equivalence point becomes smaller as $K_a$ decreases, the choice of indicator for a weak acid–strong base titration is more critical than it is for titrations where both acid and base are strong. When $0.100\ M\ CH_3COOH\ (K_a = 1.8 \times 10^{-5})$ is titrated with $0.100\ M$ NaOH, for example, the pH increases rapidly only over the pH range from about 7 to 11 (▼ FIGURE 17.14). Phenolphthalein is therefore an ideal indicator because it changes

GO FIGURE

Is methyl red a suitable indicator when you are titrating a strong acid with a strong base? Explain your answer.

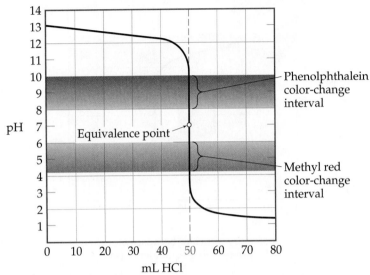

▲ FIGURE 17.13  **Using color indicators for titration of a strong base with a strong acid.** Both phenolphthalein and methyl red change color in the rapid-rise portion of the titration curve.

Phenolphthalein indicator
Color-change interval 8.3 < pH < 10.0

Suitable indicator because equivalence point falls within the color-change interval

Methyl red indicator
Color-change interval 4.2 < pH < 6.0

Unsatisfactory indicator because color changes before reaching equivalence point

▲ FIGURE 17.14  **Good and poor indicators for titration of a weak acid with a strong base.**

▲ **FIGURE 17.15** **Good and poor indicators for titration of a weak base with a strong acid.**

color from pH 8.3 to 10.0, close to the pH at the equivalence point. Methyl red is a poor choice, however, because its color change, from 4.2 to 6.0, begins well before the equivalence point is reached.

Titration of a weak base (such as 0.100 $M$ $NH_3$) with a strong acid solution (such as 0.100 $M$ HCl) leads to the titration curve shown in ▲ **FIGURE 17.15**. In this example, the equivalence point occurs at pH 5.28. Thus, methyl red is an ideal indicator but phenolphthalein would be a poor choice.

### ▲ GIVE IT SOME THOUGHT

Why is the choice of indicator more crucial for a weak acid–strong base titration than for a strong acid–strong base titration?

## 17.4 | SOLUBILITY EQUILIBRIA

The equilibria we have considered thus far in this chapter have involved acids and bases. Furthermore, they have been homogeneous; that is, all the species have been in the same phase. Through the rest of the chapter, we will consider the equilibria involved in the dissolution or precipitation of ionic compounds. These reactions are heterogeneous.

Dissolution and precipitation occur both within us and around us. Tooth enamel dissolves in acidic solutions, for example, causing tooth decay, and the precipitation of certain salts in our kidneys produces kidney stones. The waters of Earth contain salts dissolved as water passes over and through the ground. Precipitation of $CaCO_3$ from groundwater is responsible for the formation of stalactites and stalagmites within limestone caves.

In our earlier discussion of precipitation reactions, we considered general rules for predicting the solubility of common salts in water. ∞ (Section 4.2) These rules give us a qualitative sense of whether a compound has a low or high solubility in water. By considering solubility equilibria, however, we can make quantitative predictions about solubility.

### The Solubility-Product Constant, $K_{sp}$

Recall that a *saturated solution* is one in which the solution is in contact with undissolved solute. ∞ (Section 13.2) Consider, for example, a saturated aqueous solution of

$BaSO_4$ in contact with solid $BaSO_4$. Because the solid is an ionic compound, it is a strong electrolyte and yields $Ba^{2+}(aq)$ and $SO_4^{2-}(aq)$ ions when dissolved in water, readily establishing the equilibrium

$$BaSO_4(s) \rightleftharpoons Ba^{2+}(aq) + SO_4^{2-}(aq) \qquad [17.15]$$

As with any other equilibrium, the extent to which this dissolution reaction occurs is expressed by the magnitude of the equilibrium constant. Because this equilibrium equation describes the dissolution of a solid, the equilibrium constant indicates how soluble the solid is in water and is referred to as the **solubility-product constant** (or simply the **solubility product**). It is denoted $K_{sp}$, where *sp* stands for solubility product.

The equilibrium-constant expression for the equilibrium between a solid and an aqueous solution of its component ions is written according to the rules that apply to any other equilibrium-constant expression. Remember, however, that solids do not appear in the equilibrium-constant expressions for heterogeneous equilibrium. ∞ (Section 15.4) Thus, the solubility-product expression for $BaSO_4$, which is based on Equation 17.15, is

$$K_{sp} = [Ba^{2+}][SO_4^{2-}] \qquad [17.16]$$

In general, *the solubility product $K_{sp}$ of a compound equals the product of the concentration of the ions involved in the equilibrium, each raised to the power of its coefficient in the equilibrium equation.* The coefficient for each ion in the equilibrium equation also equals its subscript in the compound's chemical formula.

The values of $K_{sp}$ at 25 °C for many ionic solids are tabulated in Appendix D. The value of $K_{sp}$ for $BaSO_4$ is $1.1 \times 10^{-10}$, a very small number indicating that only a very small amount of the solid dissolves in 25 °C water.

---

**SAMPLE EXERCISE 17.9**  **Writing Solubility-Product ($K_{sp}$) Expressions**

Write the expression for the solubility-product constant for $CaF_2$, and look up the corresponding $K_{sp}$ value in Appendix D.

**SOLUTION**

**Analyze**  We are asked to write an equilibrium-constant expression for the process by which $CaF_2$ dissolves in water.

**Plan**  We apply the general rules for writing an equilibrium-constant expression, excluding the solid reactant from the expression. We assume that the compound dissociates completely into its component ions:

$$CaF_2(s) \rightleftharpoons Ca^{2+}(aq) + 2\,F^-(aq)$$

**Solve**  The expression for $K_{sp}$ is

$$K_{sp} = [Ca^{2+}][F^-]^2$$

Appendix D gives $3.9 \times 10^{-11}$ for this $K_{sp}$.

**PRACTICE EXERCISE**

Give the solubility-product-constant expressions and $K_{sp}$ values (from Appendix D) for **(a)** barium carbonate, **(b)** silver sulfate.

**Answers:** **(a)** $K_{sp} = [Ba^{2+}][CO_3^{2-}] = 5.0 \times 10^{-9}$, **(b)** $K_{sp} = [Ag^+]^2[SO_4^{2-}] = 1.5 \times 10^{-5}$

---

## Solubility and $K_{sp}$

It is important to distinguish carefully between solubility and the solubility-product constant. The solubility of a substance is the quantity that dissolves to form a saturated solution. ∞ (Section 13.2) Solubility is often expressed as grams of solute per liter of solution (g/L). *Molar solubility* is the number of moles of solute that dissolve in forming 1 L of saturated solution of the solute (mol/L). The solubility-product constant ($K_{sp}$) is the equilibrium constant for the equilibrium between an ionic solid and its saturated solution and is a unitless number. Thus, the magnitude of $K_{sp}$ is a measure of how much of the solid dissolves to form a saturated solution.

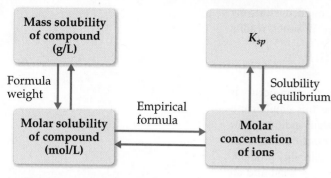

▲ FIGURE 17.16 **Procedure for converting between solubility and $K_{sp}$.** Starting from the mass solubility, follow the green arrows to determine $K_{sp}$. Starting from $K_{sp}$, follow the red arrows to determine either molar solubility or mass solubility.

▲ GIVE IT SOME THOUGHT

Without doing a calculation, predict which of these compounds has the greatest molar solubility in water: AgCl ($K_{sp} = 1.8 \times 10^{-10}$), AgBr ($K_{sp} = 5.0 \times 10^{-13}$), or AgI ($K_{sp} = 8.3 \times 10^{-17}$).

The solubility of a substance can change considerably in response to a number of factors. For example, the solubilities of hydroxide salts, like $Mg(OH)_2$, are dependent upon the pH of the solution. The solubility is also affected by concentrations of other ions in solution, especially common ions. In other words, the numeric value of the solubility of a given solute can and does change as the other species in solution change. In contrast, the solubility-product constant, $K_{sp}$, has only one value for a given solute at any specific temperature.* ◄ FIGURE 17.16 summarizes the relationships among various expressions of solubility and $K_{sp}$.

---

**SAMPLE EXERCISE 17.10** | Calculating $K_{sp}$ from Solubility

Solid silver chromate is added to pure water at 25 °C, and some of the solid remains undissolved. The mixture is stirred for several days to ensure that equilibrium is achieved between the undissolved $Ag_2CrO_4(s)$ and the solution. Analysis of the equilibrated solution shows that its silver ion concentration is $1.3 \times 10^{-4}$ M. Assuming that $Ag_2CrO_4$ dissociates completely in water and that there are no other important equilibria involving $Ag^+$ or $CrO_4^{2-}$ ions in the solution, calculate $K_{sp}$ for this compound.

**SOLUTION**

**Analyze** We are given the equilibrium concentration of $Ag^+$ in a saturated solution of $Ag_2CrO_4$ and asked to determine the value of $K_{sp}$ for $Ag_2CrO_4$.

**Plan** The equilibrium equation and the expression for $K_{sp}$ are

$$Ag_2CrO_4(s) \rightleftharpoons 2\,Ag^+(aq) + CrO_4^{2-}(aq) \qquad K_{sp} = [Ag^+]^2[CrO_4^{2-}]$$

To calculate $K_{sp}$, we need the equilibrium concentrations of $Ag^+$ and $CrO_4^{2-}$. We know that at equilibrium $[Ag^+] = 1.3 \times 10^{-4}$ M. All the $Ag^+$ and $CrO_4^{2-}$ ions in the solution come from the $Ag_2CrO_4$ that dissolves. Thus, we can use $[Ag^+]$ to calculate $[CrO_4^{2-}]$.

**Solve** From the chemical formula of silver chromate, we know that there must be 2 $Ag^+$ ions in solution for each $CrO_4^{2-}$ ion in solution. Consequently, the concentration of $CrO_4^{2-}$ is half the concentration of $Ag^+$:

$$[CrO_4^{2-}] = \left(\frac{1.3 \times 10^{-4}\ mol\ Ag^+}{L}\right)\left(\frac{1\ mol\ CrO_4^{2-}}{2\ mol\ Ag^+}\right) = 6.5 \times 10^{-5}\ M$$

and $K_{sp}$ is

$$K_{sp} = [Ag^+]^2[CrO_4^{2-}] = (1.3 \times 10^{-4})^2(6.5 \times 10^{-5}) = 1.1 \times 10^{-12}$$

**Check** We obtain a small value, as expected for a slightly soluble salt. Furthermore, the calculated value agrees well with the one given in Appendix D, $1.2 \times 10^{-12}$.

**PRACTICE EXERCISE**

A saturated solution of $Mg(OH)_2$ in contact with undissolved $Mg(OH)_2(s)$ is prepared at 25 °C. The pH of the solution is found to be 10.17. Assuming that $Mg(OH)_2$ dissociates completely in water and that there are no other simultaneous equilibria involving the $Mg^{2+}$ or $OH^-$ ions, calculate $K_{sp}$ for this compound.
**Answer:** $1.6 \times 10^{-12}$

---

*This is strictly true only for very dilute solutions, for $K_{sp}$ values change somewhat when the concentration of ionic substances in water is increased. However, we will ignore these effects, which are taken into consideration only for work that requires exceptional accuracy.

In principle, it is possible to use the $K_{sp}$ value of a salt to calculate solubility under a variety of conditions. In practice, great care must be taken in doing so for the reasons indicated in "A Closer Look: Limitations of Solubility Products" at the end of this section. Agreement between the measured solubility and that calculated from $K_{sp}$ is usually best for salts whose ions have low charges (1+ and 1−) and do not hydrolyze.

---

**SAMPLE EXERCISE 17.11**  Calculating Solubility from $K_{sp}$

The $K_{sp}$ for $CaF_2$ is $3.9 \times 10^{-11}$ at 25 °C. Assuming that $CaF_2$ dissociates completely upon dissolving and that there are no other important equilibria affecting its solubility, calculate the solubility of $CaF_2$ in grams per liter.

**SOLUTION**

**Analyze** We are given $K_{sp}$ for $CaF_2$ and asked to determine solubility. Recall that the solubility of a substance is the quantity that can dissolve in solvent, whereas the solubility-product constant, $K_{sp}$, is an equilibrium constant.

**Plan** To go from $K_{sp}$ to solubility, we follow the steps indicated by the red arrows in Figure 17.16. We first write the chemical equation for the dissolution and set up a table of initial and equilibrium concentrations. We then use the equilibrium-constant expression. In this case we know $K_{sp}$, and so we solve for the concentrations of the ions in solution. Once we know these concentrations, we use the formula weight to determine solubility in g/L.

**Solve** Assume that initially no salt has dissolved, and then allow $x$ mol/L of $CaF_2$ to dissociate completely when equilibrium is achieved:

|  | $CaF_2(s)$ $\rightleftharpoons$ | $Ca^{2+}(aq)$ + | $2 F^-(aq)$ |
|---|---|---|---|
| Initial | — | 0 | 0 |
| Change | — | $+x\,M$ | $+2x\,M$ |
| Equilibrium | — | $x\,M$ | $2x\,M$ |

The stoichiometry of the equilibrium dictates that $2x$ mol/L of $F^-$ are produced for each $x$ mol/L of $CaF_2$ that dissolve. We now use the expression for $K_{sp}$ and substitute the equilibrium concentrations to solve for the value of $x$:

$$K_{sp} = [Ca^{2+}][F^-]^2 = (x)(2x)^2 = 4x^3 = 3.9 \times 10^{-11}$$

(Remember that $\sqrt[3]{y} = y^{1/3}$. To calculate the cube root of a number, use the $y^x$ function on your calculator, with $x = \frac{1}{3}$.) Thus, the molar solubility of $CaF_2$ is $2.1 \times 10^{-4}$ mol/L.

$$x = \sqrt[3]{\frac{3.9 \times 10^{-11}}{4}} = 2.1 \times 10^{-4}$$

The mass of $CaF_2$ that dissolves in water to form 1 L of solution is

$$\left(\frac{2.1 \times 10^{-4} \text{ mol } CaF_2}{1 \text{ L soln}}\right)\left(\frac{78.1 \text{ g } CaF_2}{1 \text{ mol } CaF_2}\right) = 1.6 \times 10^{-2} \text{ g } CaF_2/\text{L soln}$$

**Check** We expect a small number for the solubility of a slightly soluble salt. If we reverse the calculation, we should be able to recalculate the solubility product: $K_{sp} = (2.1 \times 10^{-4})(4.2 \times 10^{-4})^2 = 3.7 \times 10^{-11}$, close to the value given in the problem statement, $3.9 \times 10^{-11}$.

**Comment** Because $F^-$ is the anion of a weak acid, you might expect hydrolysis of the ion to affect the solubility of $CaF_2$. The basicity of $F^-$ is so small ($K_b = 1.5 \times 10^{-11}$), however, that the hydrolysis occurs to only a slight extent and does not significantly influence the solubility. The reported solubility is 0.017 g/L at 25 °C, in good agreement with our calculation.

**PRACTICE EXERCISE**
The $K_{sp}$ for $LaF_3$ is $2 \times 10^{-19}$. What is the solubility of $LaF_3$ in water in moles per liter?
**Answer:** $9 \times 10^{-6}$ mol/L

## A CLOSER LOOK

### LIMITATIONS OF SOLUBILITY PRODUCTS

Ion concentrations calculated from $K_{sp}$ values sometimes deviate appreciably from those found experimentally. In part, these deviations are due to electrostatic interactions between ions in solution, which can lead to ion pairs. (See Section 13.5, "A Closer Look: Colligative Properties of Electrolyte Solutions.") These interactions increase in magnitude both as the concentrations of the ions increase and as their charges increase. The solubility calculated from $K_{sp}$ tends to be low unless corrected to account for these interactions.

As an example of the effect of these interactions, consider CaCO$_3$ (calcite), whose solubility product, $K_{sp} = 4.5 \times 10^{-9}$, gives a calculated solubility of $6.7 \times 10^{-5}$ mol/L, and correcting for ionic interactions in the solution yields $7.3 \times 10^{-5}$ mol/L. The reported solubility, however, is $1.4 \times 10^{-4}$ mol/L, indicating that there must be additional factors involved.

Another common source of error in calculating ion concentrations from $K_{sp}$ is ignoring other equilibria that occur simultaneously in the solution. It is possible, for example, that acid–base equilibria take place simultaneously with solubility equilibria. In particular, both basic anions and cations with high charge-to-size ratios undergo hydrolysis reactions that can measurably increase the solubilities of their salts. For example, CaCO$_3$ contains the basic carbonate ion ($K_b = 1.8 \times 10^{-4}$), which hydrolyzes in water:

$$CO_3{}^{2-}(aq) + H_2O(l) \rightleftharpoons HCO_3{}^-(aq) + OH^-(aq)$$

If we consider the effect of ion-ion interactions as well as simultaneous solubility and hydrolysis equilibria, we calculate a solubility of $1.4 \times 10^{-4}$ mol/L, in agreement with the measured value.

Finally, we generally assume that ionic compounds dissociate completely when they dissolve, but this assumption is not always valid. When MgF$_2$ dissolves, for example, it yields not only Mg$^{2+}$ and F$^-$ ions but also MgF$^+$ ions.

## 17.5 | FACTORS THAT AFFECT SOLUBILITY

Solubility is affected by temperature and by the presence of other solutes. The presence of an acid, for example, can have a major influence on the solubility of a substance. In Section 17.4 we considered the dissolving of ionic compounds in pure water. In this section we examine three factors that affect the solubility of ionic compounds: (1) presence of common ions, (2) solution pH, and (3) presence of complexing agents. We will also examine the phenomenon of *amphoterism*, which is related to the effects of both pH and complexing agents.

### Common-Ion Effect

Solubility of CaF$_2$ decreases sharply as a common ion (F$^-$) is added to the solution

▲ **FIGURE 17.17 Common-ion effect.** Notice that the CaF$_2$ solubility is on a logarithmic scale.

The presence of either Ca$^{2+}(aq)$ or F$^-(aq)$ in a solution reduces the solubility of CaF$_2$, shifting the solubility equilibrium to the left:

$$CaF_2(s) \rightleftharpoons Ca^{2+}(aq) + 2\,F^-(aq)$$

Addition of Ca$^{2+}$ or F$^-$ shifts equilibrium, reducing solubility

This reduction in solubility is another manifestation of the common-ion effect we looked at in Section 17.1. In general, *the solubility of a slightly soluble salt is decreased by the presence of a second solute that furnishes a common ion,* as ◄ **FIGURE 17.17** shows for CaF$_2$.

**SAMPLE EXERCISE 17.12**   **Calculating the Effect of a Common Ion on Solubility**

Calculate the molar solubility of $CaF_2$ at 25 °C in a solution that is (a) 0.010 $M$ in $Ca(NO_3)_2$, (b) 0.010 $M$ in NaF.

## SOLUTION

**Analyze** We are asked to determine the solubility of $CaF_2$ in the presence of two strong electrolytes, each containing an ion common to $CaF_2$. In (a) the common ion is $Ca^{2+}$, and $NO_3^-$ is a spectator ion. In (b) the common ion is $F^-$, and $Na^+$ is a spectator ion.

**Plan** Because the slightly soluble compound is $CaF_2$, we need to use $K_{sp}$ for this compound, which Appendix D gives as $3.9 \times 10^{-11}$. *The value of $K_{sp}$ is unchanged by the presence of additional solutes.* Because of the common-ion effect, however, the solubility of the salt decreases in the presence of common ions. We use our standard equilibrium techniques of starting with the equation for $CaF_2$ dissolution, setting up a table of initial and equilibrium concentrations, and using the $K_{sp}$ expression to determine the concentration of the ion that comes only from $CaF_2$.

**Solve**

(a) The initial concentration of $Ca^{2+}$ is 0.010 $M$ because of the dissolved $Ca(NO_3)_2$:

|  | $CaF_2(s)$ | $\rightleftharpoons$ | $Ca^{2+}(aq)$ | + | $2\,F^-(aq)$ |
|---|---|---|---|---|---|
| Initial | — | | 0.010 $M$ | | 0 |
| Change | — | | $+x\,M$ | | $+2x\,M$ |
| Equilibrium | — | | $(0.010 + x)\,M$ | | $2x\,M$ |

Substituting into the solubility-product expression gives

$$K_{sp} = 3.9 \times 10^{-11} = [Ca^{2+}][F^-]^2 = (0.010 + x)(2x)^2$$

This would be a messy problem to solve exactly, but fortunately it is possible to simplify matters. Even without the common-ion effect, the solubility of $CaF_2$ is very small ($2.1 \times 10^{-4}\,M$). Thus, we assume that the 0.010 $M$ concentration of $Ca^{2+}$ from $Ca(NO_3)_2$ is very much greater than the small additional concentration resulting from the solubility of $CaF_2$; that is, $x$ is much smaller than 0.010 $M$, and $0.010 + x \simeq 0.010$. We then have

$$3.9 \times 10^{-11} = (0.010)(2x)^2$$
$$x^2 = \frac{3.9 \times 10^{-11}}{4(0.010)} = 9.8 \times 10^{-10}$$
$$x = \sqrt{9.8 \times 10^{-10}} = 3.1 \times 10^{-5}\,M$$

This very small value for $x$ validates the simplifying assumption we made. Our calculation indicates that $3.1 \times 10^{-5}$ mol of solid $CaF_2$ dissolves per liter of 0.010 $M$ $Ca(NO_3)_2$ solution.

(b) The common ion is $F^-$, and at equilibrium we have

$$[Ca^{2+}] = x \quad \text{and} \quad [F^-] = 0.010 + 2x$$

Assuming that $2x$ is much smaller than 0.010 $M$ (that is, $0.010 + 2x \simeq 0.010$), we have

$$3.9 \times 10^{-11} = (x)(0.010 + 2x)^2 \simeq x(0.010)^2$$
$$x = \frac{3.9 \times 10^{-11}}{(0.010)^2} = 3.9 \times 10^{-7}\,M$$

Thus, $3.9 \times 10^{-7}$ mol of solid $CaF_2$ should dissolve per liter of 0.010 $M$ NaF solution.

**Comment** The molar solubility of $CaF_2$ in water is $2.1 \times 10^{-4}\,M$ (Sample Exercise 17.11). By comparison, our calculations here give a $CaF_2$ solubility of $3.1 \times 10^{-5}\,M$ in the presence of 0.010 $M$ $Ca^{2+}$ and $3.9 \times 10^{-7}\,M$ in the presence of 0.010 $M$ $F^-$ ion. Thus, the addition of either $Ca^{2+}$ or $F^-$ to a solution of $CaF_2$ decreases the solubility. However, the effect of $F^-$ on the solubility is more pronounced than that of $Ca^{2+}$ because $[F^-]$ appears to the second power in the $K_{sp}$ expression for $CaF_2$, whereas $[Ca^{2+}]$ appears to the first power.

## PRACTICE EXERCISE

For manganese(II) hydroxide, $Mn(OH)_2$, $K_{sp} = 1.6 \times 10^{-13}$. Calculate the molar solubility of $Mn(OH)_2$ in a solution that contains 0.020 $M$ NaOH.

***Answer:*** $4.0 \times 10^{-10}\,M$

## Solubility and pH

The pH of a solution affects the solubility of any substance whose anion is basic. Consider $Mg(OH)_2$, for which the solubility equilibrium is

$$Mg(OH)_2(s) \rightleftharpoons Mg^{2+}(aq) + 2\,OH^-(aq) \quad K_{sp} = 1.8 \times 10^{-11} \quad [17.17]$$

A saturated solution of $Mg(OH)_2$ has a calculated pH of 10.52 and its $Mg^{2+}$ concentration is $1.7 \times 10^{-4}$ $M$. Now suppose that solid $Mg(OH)_2$ is equilibrated with a solution buffered at pH 9.0. The pOH, therefore, is 5.0, so $[OH^-] = 1.0 \times 10^{-5}$. Inserting this value for $[OH^-]$ into the solubility-product expression, we have

$$K_{sp} = [Mg^{2+}][OH^-]^2 = 1.8 \times 10^{-11}$$

$$[Mg^{2+}](1.0 \times 10^{-5})^2 = 1.8 \times 10^{-11}$$

$$[Mg^{2+}] = \frac{1.8 \times 10^{-11}}{(1.0 \times 10^{-5})^2} = 0.18\ M$$

Thus, the $Mg(OH)_2$ dissolves until $[Mg^{2+}] = 0.18\ M$. It is apparent that $Mg(OH)_2$ is much more soluble in this solution.

## CHEMISTRY AND LIFE

### OCEAN ACIDIFICATION

Seawater is a weakly basic solution, with pH values typically between 8.0 and 8.3. This pH range is maintained through a carbonic acid buffer system similar to the one in blood (see Equation 17.10). Because the pH of seawater is higher than in blood (7.35–7.45), however, the second dissociation of carbonic acid cannot be neglected and $CO_3^{2-}$ becomes an important aqueous species.

The availability of carbonate ions plays an important role in shell formation for a number of marine organisms, including stony corals (▶ **FIGURE 17.18**). These organisms, which are referred to as marine *calcifiers* and play an important role in the food chains of nearly all oceanic ecosystems, depend on dissolved $Ca^{2+}$ and $CO_3^{2-}$ ions to form their shells and exoskeletons. The relatively low solubility-product constant of $CaCO_3$,

$$CaCO_3(s) \rightleftharpoons Ca^{2+}(aq) + CO_3^{2-}(aq) \quad K_{sp} = 4.5 \times 10^{-9}$$

and the fact that the ocean contains saturated concentrations of $Ca^{2+}$ and $CO_3^{2-}$ mean that $CaCO_3$ is usually quite stable once formed. In fact, calcium carbonate skeletons of creatures that died millions of years ago are not uncommon in the fossil record.

Just as in our bodies, the carbonic acid buffer system can be perturbed by removing or adding $CO_2(g)$. The concentration of dissolved $CO_2$ in the ocean is sensitive to changes in atmospheric $CO_2$ levels. As discussed in Chapter 18, the atmospheric $CO_2$ concentration has risen by approximately 30% over the past three centuries to the present level of 386 ppm. Human activity has played a prominent role in this increase. Scientists estimate that one-third to one-half of the $CO_2$ emissions resulting from human activity have been absorbed by Earth's oceans. While this absorption helps miti-

gate the greenhouse gas effects of $CO_2$, the extra $CO_2$ in the ocean produces carbonic acid, which lowers the pH. Because $CO_3^{2-}$ is the conjugate base of the weak acid $HCO_3^-$, the carbonate ion readily combines with the hydrogen ion:

$$CO_3^{2-}(aq) + H^+(aq) \longrightarrow HCO_3^-(aq)$$

This consumption of carbonate ion shifts the dissolution equilibrium to the right, increasing the solubility of $CaCO_3$. This can lead to partial dissolution of calcium carbonate shells and exoskeletons. If the amount of atmospheric $CO_2$ continues to increase at the present rate, scientists estimate that seawater pH will fall to 7.9 sometime over the next 50 years. While this change might sound small, it has dramatic ramifications for oceanic ecosystems.

*RELATED EXERCISES: 17.97*

▲ **FIGURE 17.18    Marine calcifiers.** Many sea-dwelling organisms use $CaCO_3$ for their shells and exoskeletons. Examples include stony coral, crustaceans, some phytoplankton, and echinoderms, such as sea urchins and starfish.

If [OH⁻] were reduced further by making the solution even more acidic, the $Mg^{2+}$ concentration would have to increase to maintain the equilibrium condition. Thus, a sample of $Mg(OH)_2(s)$ dissolves completely if sufficient acid is added, as we saw in Figure 4.9 (page 128).

The solubility of almost any ionic compound is affected if the solution is made sufficiently acidic or basic. The effects are noticeable, however, only when one (or both) ions in the compound are at least moderately acidic or basic. The metal hydroxides, such as $Mg(OH)_2$, are examples of compounds containing a strongly basic ion, the hydroxide ion.

In general, *the solubility of a compound containing a basic anion (that is, the anion of a weak acid) increases as the solution becomes more acidic.* As we have seen, the solubility of $Mg(OH)_2$ greatly increases as the acidity of the solution increases. The solubility of $PbF_2$ increases as the solution becomes more acidic, too, because $F^-$ is a weak base (it is the conjugate base of the weak acid HF). As a result, the solubility equilibrium of $PbF_2$ is shifted to the right as the concentration of $F^-$ is reduced by protonation to form HF. Thus, the solution process can be understood in terms of two consecutive reactions:

$$PbF_2(s) \rightleftharpoons Pb^{2+}(aq) + 2\,F^-(aq) \qquad [17.18]$$

$$F^-(aq) + H^+(aq) \rightleftharpoons HF(aq) \qquad [17.19]$$

The equation for the overall process is

$$PbF_2(s) + 2\,H^+(aq) \rightleftharpoons Pb^{2+}(aq) + 2\,HF(aq) \qquad [17.20]$$

The processes responsible for the increase in solubility of $PbF_2$ in acidic solution are illustrated in ▼ **FIGURE 17.19**(a).

Other salts that contain basic anions, such as $CO_3^{2-}$, $PO_4^{3-}$, $CN^-$, or $S^{2-}$, behave similarly. These examples illustrate a general rule: *The solubility of slightly soluble salts containing basic anions increases as [H⁺] increases (as pH is lowered).* The more basic the anion, the more the solubility is influenced by pH. The solubility of salts with anions of negligible basicity (the anions of strong acids), such as $Cl^-$, $Br^-$, $I^-$ and $NO_3^-$, is unaffected by pH changes, as shown in Figure 17.19(b).

Salt whose anion is conjugate
base of weak acid
*Solubility increases as pH decreases*

Salt whose anion is conjugate
base of strong acid
*Solubility unaffected by changes in pH*

(a)

(b)

▲ **FIGURE 17.19 Response of two ionic compounds to addition of a strong acid.** (a) The solubility of $PbF_2$ increases on addition of acid. (b) The solubility of $PbI_2$ is not affected by addition of acid. The water molecules and the anion of the strong acid have been omitted for clarity.

**SAMPLE EXERCISE 17.13** | Predicting the Effect of Acid on Solubility

Which of these substances are more soluble in acidic solution than in basic solution: **(a)** $Ni(OH)_2(s)$, **(b)** $CaCO_3(s)$, **(c)** $BaF_2(s)$, **(d)** $AgCl(s)$?

**SOLUTION**

**Analyze** The problem lists four sparingly soluble salts, and we are asked to determine which are more soluble at low pH than at high pH.

**Plan** Ionic compounds that dissociate to produce a basic anion are more soluble in acid solution.

**Solve**

**(a)** $Ni(OH)_2(s)$ is more soluble in acidic solution because of the basicity of $OH^-$; the $H^+$ reacts with the $OH^-$ ion, forming water:

$$Ni(OH)_2(s) \rightleftharpoons Ni^{2+}(aq) + 2\,OH^-(aq)$$

$$\underline{2\,OH^-(aq) + 2\,H^+(aq) \rightleftharpoons 2\,H_2O(l)}$$

$$\text{Overall:}\quad Ni(OH)_2(s) + 2\,H^+(aq) \rightleftharpoons Ni^{2+}(aq) + 2\,H_2O(l)$$

**(b)** Similarly, $CaCO_3(s)$ dissolves in acid solutions because $CO_3^{2-}$ is a basic anion:

$$CaCO_3(s) \rightleftharpoons Ca^{2+}(aq) + CO_3^{2-}(aq)$$

$$CO_3^{2-}(aq) + 2\,H^+(aq) \rightleftharpoons H_2CO_3(aq)$$

$$\underline{H_2CO_3(aq) \rightleftharpoons CO_2(g) + H_2O(l)}$$

$$\text{Overall:}\quad CaCO_3(s) + 2\,H^+(aq) \rightleftharpoons Ca^{2+}(aq) + CO_2(g) + H_2O(l)$$

The reaction between $CO_3^{2-}$ and $H^+$ occurs in steps, with $HCO_3^-$ forming first and $H_2CO_3$ forming in appreciable amounts only when $[H^+]$ is sufficiently high.

**(c)** The solubility of $BaF_2$ is enhanced by lowering the pH because $F^-$ is a basic anion:

$$BaF_2(s) \rightleftharpoons Ba^{2+}(aq) + 2\,F^-(aq)$$

$$\underline{2\,F^-(aq) + 2\,H^+(aq) \rightleftharpoons 2\,HF(aq)}$$

$$\text{Overall:}\quad BaF_2(s) + 2\,H^+(aq) \rightleftharpoons Ba^{2+}(aq) + 2\,HF(aq)$$

**(d)** The solubility of $AgCl$ is unaffected by changes in pH because $Cl^-$ is the anion of a strong acid and therefore has negligible basicity.

**PRACTICE EXERCISE**

Write the net ionic equation for the reaction between an acid and **(a)** $CuS$, **(b)** $Cu(N_3)_2$.

*Answers:* **(a)** $CuS(s) + H^+(aq) \rightleftharpoons Cu^{2+}(aq) + HS^-(aq)$
**(b)** $Cu(N_3)_2(s) + 2\,H^+(aq) \rightleftharpoons Cu^{2+}(aq) + 2\,HN_3(aq)$

---

## CHEMISTRY AND LIFE

### TOOTH DECAY AND FLUORIDATION

Tooth enamel consists mainly of the mineral hydroxy-apatite, $Ca_{10}(PO_4)_6(OH)_2$, the hardest substance in the body. Tooth cavities form when acids dissolve tooth enamel:

$$Ca_{10}(PO_4)_6(OH)_2(s) + 8\,H^+(aq) \longrightarrow$$
$$10\,Ca^{2+}(aq) + 6\,HPO_4^{2-}(aq) + 2\,H_2O(l)$$

The $Ca^{2+}$ and $HPO_4^{2-}$ ions diffuse out of the enamel and are washed away by saliva. The acids that attack the hydroxyapatite are formed by the action of bacteria on sugars and other carbohydrates present in the plaque adhering to the teeth.

Fluoride ion, which is added to municipal water systems and toothpastes, can react with hydroxyapatite to form fluoroapatite, $Ca_{10}(PO_4)_6F_2$. This mineral, in which $F^-$ has replaced $OH^-$, is much more resistant to attack by acids because the fluoride ion is a much weaker Brønsted–Lowry base than the hydroxide ion.

The usual concentration of $F^-$ in municipal water systems is 1 mg/L (1 ppm). The compound added may be NaF or $Na_2SiF_6$. The silicon-fluorine anion reacts with water to release fluoride ions:

$$SiF_6^{2-}(aq) + 2\,H_2O(l) \longrightarrow 6\,F^-(aq) + 4\,H^+(aq) + SiO_2(s)$$

About 80% of all toothpastes now sold in the United States contain fluoride compounds, usually at the level of 0.1% fluoride by mass. The most common compounds in toothpastes are sodium fluoride (NaF), sodium monofluorophosphate ($Na_2PO_3F$), and stannous fluoride ($SnF_2$).

*RELATED EXERCISES: 17.98 and 17.116*

## Formation of Complex Ions

A characteristic property of metal ions is their ability to act as Lewis acids toward water molecules, which act as Lewis bases. ∞ (Section 16.11) Lewis bases other than water can also interact with metal ions, particularly transition-metal ions. Such interactions can dramatically affect the solubility of a metal salt. For example, AgCl ($K_{sp} = 1.8 \times 10^{-10}$) dissolves in the presence of aqueous ammonia because $Ag^+$ interacts with the Lewis base $NH_3$, as shown in ▼ FIGURE 17.20. This process can be viewed as the sum of two reactions:

$$AgCl(s) \rightleftharpoons Ag^+(aq) + Cl^-(aq) \qquad [17.21]$$

$$\underline{Ag^+(aq) + 2\,NH_3(aq) \rightleftharpoons Ag(NH_3)_2^+(aq) \qquad [17.22]}$$

$$\text{Overall:} \quad AgCl(s) + 2\,NH_3(aq) \rightleftharpoons Ag(NH_3)_2^+(aq) + Cl^-(aq) \quad [17.23]$$

The presence of $NH_3$ drives the reaction, the dissolution of AgCl, to the right as $Ag^+(aq)$ is consumed to form $Ag(NH_3)_2^+$.

$NH_3$ reacts with $Ag^+$, forming $Ag(NH_3)_2^+$

Addition of sufficient $NH_3$ leads to complete dissolution of AgCl

$Ag^+$

$Cl^-$

AgCl

Reaction with $NH_3$ reduces concentration of free $Ag^+$ and increases solubility of AgCl

$Cl^-$

$Ag(NH_3)_2^+$

$NH_3$

$$AgCl(s) + 2\,NH_3(aq) \rightleftharpoons Ag(NH_3)_2^+(aq) + Cl^-(aq)$$

▲ **FIGURE 17.20 Using concentrated NH₃(aq) to dissolve AgCl(s), which has very low solubility in water.**

For a Lewis base such as $NH_3$ to increase the solubility of a metal salt, the base must be able to interact more strongly with the metal ion than water does. In other words, the $NH_3$ must displace solvating $H_2O$ molecules ∞ (Sections 13.1 and 16.11) in order to form $Ag(NH_3)_2^+$:

$$Ag^+(aq) + 2\,NH_3(aq) \rightleftharpoons Ag(NH_3)_2^+(aq) \qquad [17.24]$$

**TABLE 17.1 • Formation Constants for Some Metal Complex Ions in Water at 25 °C**

| Complex Ion | $K_f$ | Equilibrium Equation |
|---|---|---|
| $Ag(NH_3)_2{}^+$ | $1.7 \times 10^7$ | $Ag^+(aq) + 2\,NH_3(aq) \rightleftharpoons Ag(NH_3)_2{}^+(aq)$ |
| $Ag(CN)_2{}^-$ | $1 \times 10^{21}$ | $Ag^+(aq) + 2\,CN^-(aq) \rightleftharpoons Ag(CN)_2{}^-(aq)$ |
| $Ag(S_2O_3)_2{}^{3-}$ | $2.9 \times 10^{13}$ | $Ag^+(aq) + 2\,S_2O_3{}^{2-}(aq) \rightleftharpoons Ag(S_2O_3)_2{}^{3-}(aq)$ |
| $CdBr_4{}^{2-}$ | $5 \times 10^3$ | $Cd^{2+}(aq) + 4\,Br^-(aq) \rightleftharpoons CdBr_4{}^{2-}(aq)$ |
| $Cr(OH)_4{}^-$ | $8 \times 10^{29}$ | $Cr^{3+}(aq) + 4\,OH^-(aq) \rightleftharpoons Cr(OH)_4{}^-(aq)$ |
| $Co(SCN)_4{}^{2-}$ | $1 \times 10^3$ | $Co^{2+}(aq) + 4\,SCN^-(aq) \rightleftharpoons Co(SCN)_4{}^{2-}(aq)$ |
| $Cu(NH_3)_4{}^{2+}$ | $5 \times 10^{12}$ | $Cu^{2+}(aq) + 4\,NH_3(aq) \rightleftharpoons Cu(NH_3)_4{}^{2+}(aq)$ |
| $Cu(CN)_4{}^{2-}$ | $1 \times 10^{25}$ | $Cu^{2+}(aq) + 4\,CN^-(aq) \rightleftharpoons Cu(CN)_4{}^{2-}(aq)$ |
| $Ni(NH_3)_6{}^{2+}$ | $1.2 \times 10^9$ | $Ni^{2+}(aq) + 6\,NH_3(aq) \rightleftharpoons Ni(NH_3)_6{}^{2+}(aq)$ |
| $Fe(CN)_6{}^{4-}$ | $1 \times 10^{35}$ | $Fe^{2+}(aq) + 6\,CN^-(aq) \rightleftharpoons Fe(CN_3)_6{}^{4-}(aq)$ |
| $Fe(CN)_6{}^{3-}$ | $1 \times 10^{42}$ | $Fe^{3+}(aq) + 6\,CN^-(aq) \rightleftharpoons Fe(CN)_6{}^{3-}(aq)$ |

An assembly of a metal ion and the Lewis bases bonded to it, such as $Ag(NH_3)_2{}^+$, is called a **complex ion**. The stability of a complex ion in aqueous solution can be judged by the size of the equilibrium constant for its formation from the hydrated metal ion. For example, the equilibrium constant for Equation 17.24 is

$$K_f = \frac{[Ag(NH_3)_2{}^+]}{[Ag^+][NH_3]^2} = 1.7 \times 10^7 \qquad [17.25]$$

Note that the equilibrium constant for this kind of reaction is called a **formation constant**, $K_f$. The formation constants for several complex ions are listed in ▲ TABLE 17.1.

---

**SAMPLE EXERCISE 17.14** | **Evaluating an Equilibrium Involving a Complex Ion**

Calculate the concentration of $Ag^+$ present in solution at equilibrium when concentrated ammonia is added to a 0.010 *M* solution of $AgNO_3$ to give an equilibrium concentration of $[NH_3] = 0.20$ *M*. Neglect the small volume change that occurs when $NH_3$ is added.

**SOLUTION**

**Analyze** Addition of $NH_3(aq)$ to $Ag^+(aq)$ forms $Ag(NH_3)_2{}^+$, as shown in Equation 17.22. We are asked to determine what concentration of $Ag^+(aq)$ remains uncombined when the $NH_3$ concentration is brought to 0.20 *M* in a solution originally 0.010 *M* in $AgNO_3$.

**Plan** We assume that the $AgNO_3$ is completely dissociated, giving 0.010 *M* $Ag^+$. Because $K_f$ for the formation of $Ag(NH_3)_2{}^+$ is quite large, we assume that essentially all the $Ag^+$ is converted to $Ag(NH_3)_2{}^+$ and approach the problem as though we are concerned with the dissociation of $Ag(NH_3)_2{}^+$ rather than its formation. To facilitate this approach, we need to reverse Equation 17.22 and make the corresponding change to the equilibrium constant:

$$Ag(NH_3)_2{}^+(aq) \rightleftharpoons Ag^+(aq) + 2\,NH_3(aq)$$

$$\frac{1}{K_f} = \frac{1}{1.7 \times 10^7} = 5.9 \times 10^{-8}$$

**Solve** If $[Ag^+]$ is 0.010 *M* initially, $[Ag(NH_3)_2{}^+]$ will be 0.010 *M* following addition of the $NH_3$. We construct a table to solve this equilibrium problem. Note that the $NH_3$ concentration given in the problem is an equilibrium concentration rather than an initial concentration.

| | $Ag(NH_3)_2{}^+(aq)$ $\rightleftharpoons$ | $Ag^+(aq)$ + | $2\,NH_3(aq)$ |
|---|---|---|---|
| Initial | 0.010 *M* | 0 *M* | |
| Change | $-x$ *M* | $+x$ *M* | |
| Equilibrium | 0.010 − *x M* | *x M* | 0.20 *M* |

Because $[Ag^+]$ is very small, we can ignore $x$, so that $0.010 - x \simeq 0.010\,M$. Substituting these values into the equilibrium-constant expression for the dissociation of $Ag(NH_3)_2^+$, we obtain

$$\frac{[Ag^+][NH_3]^2}{[Ag(NH_3)_2^+]} = \frac{(x)(0.20)^2}{0.010} = 5.9 \times 10^{-8}$$

$$x = 1.5 \times 10^{-8}\,M = [Ag^+]$$

Formation of the $Ag(NH_3)_2^+$ complex drastically reduces the concentration of free $Ag^+$ ion in solution.

### PRACTICE EXERCISE

Calculate $[Cr^{3+}]$ in equilibrium with $Cr(OH)_4^-$ when 0.010 mol of $Cr(NO_3)_3$ is dissolved in 1 L of solution buffered at pH 10.0.

**Answer:** $1 \times 10^{-16}\,M$

The general rule is that the solubility of metal salts increases in the presence of suitable Lewis bases, such as $NH_3$, $CN^-$, or $OH^-$, provided the metal forms a complex with the base. The ability of metal ions to form complexes is an extremely important aspect of their chemistry.

## Amphoterism

Some metal oxides and hydroxides that are relatively insoluble in water dissolve in strongly acidic and strongly basic solutions. These substances, called **amphoteric oxides** and **amphoteric hydroxides**, * are soluble in strong acids and bases because they themselves are capable of behaving as either an acid or base. Examples of amphoteric substances include the oxides and hydroxides of $Al^{3+}$, $Cr^{3+}$, $Zn^{2+}$, and $Sn^{2+}$.

Like other metal oxides and hydroxides, amphoteric species dissolve in acidic solutions because their anions, $O^{2-}$ or $OH^-$, react with acids. What makes amphoteric oxides and hydroxides special, though, is that they also dissolve in strongly basic solutions. This behavior results from the formation of complex anions containing several (typically four) hydroxides bound to the metal ion (▼ **FIGURE 17.21**):

$$Al(OH)_3(s) + OH^-(aq) \rightleftharpoons Al(OH)_4^-(aq) \qquad [17.26]$$

The extent to which an insoluble metal hydroxide reacts with either acid or base varies with the particular metal ion involved. Many metal hydroxides—such as $Ca(OH)_2$, $Fe(OH)_2$, and $Fe(OH)_3$—are capable of dissolving in acidic solution but do not react with excess base. These hydroxides are not amphoteric.

The purification of aluminum ore in the manufacture of aluminum metal provides an interesting application of amphoterism. As we have seen, $Al(OH)_3$ is amphoteric,

▲ **FIGURE 17.21  Amphoterism.** Some metal oxides and hydroxides, such as $Al(OH)_3$, are amphoteric, which means they dissolve in both strongly acidic and strongly basic solutions.

*Notice that the term *amphoteric* is applied to the behavior of insoluble oxides and hydroxides that dissolve in acidic or basic solutions. The similar term *amphiprotic* (Section 16.2) relates more generally to any molecule or ion that can either gain or lose a proton.

whereas $Fe(OH)_3$ is not. Aluminum occurs in large quantities as the ore *bauxite*, which is essentially hydrated $Al_2O_3$ contaminated with $Fe_2O_3$. When bauxite is added to a strongly basic solution, the $Al_2O_3$ dissolves because the aluminum forms complex ions, such as $Al(OH)_4^-$. The $Fe_2O_3$ impurity, however, is not amphoteric and remains as a solid. The solution is filtered, getting rid of the iron impurity. Aluminum hydroxide is then precipitated by addition of acid. The purified hydroxide receives further treatment and eventually yields aluminum metal.

## ▲ GIVE IT SOME THOUGHT

What is the difference between an amphoteric substance and an amphiprotic substance?

# 17.6 | PRECIPITATION AND SEPARATION OF IONS

Equilibrium can be achieved starting with the substances on either side of a chemical equation. For example, the equilibrium that exists between $BaSO_4(s)$, $Ba^{2+}(aq)$, and $SO_4^{2-}(aq)$ (Equation 17.15), can be achieved either by starting with $BaSO_4(s)$ or by starting with solutions containing $Ba^{2+}$ and $SO_4^{2-}$. If we mix, say, a $BaCl_2$ aqueous solution and a $Na_2SO_4$ aqueous solution, $BaSO_4$ precipitates if the product of the initial ion concentrations, $Q = [Ba^{2+}][SO_4^{2-}]$, is greater than $K_{sp}$.

The use of the reaction quotient $Q$ to determine the direction in which a reaction must proceed to reach equilibrium was discussed in Section 15.6. The possible relationships between $Q$ and $K_{sp}$ are as follows:

- If $Q > K_{sp}$, precipitation occurs, reducing ion concentrations until $Q = K_{sp}$.
- If $Q = K_{sp}$, equilibrium exists (saturated solution).
- If $Q < K_{sp}$, solid dissolves, increasing ion concentrations until $Q = K_{sp}$.

---

**SAMPLE EXERCISE 17.15** | **Predicting Whether a Precipitate Forms**

Does a precipitate form when 0.10 L of $8.0 \times 10^{-3}\,M\,Pb(NO_3)_2$ is added to 0.40 L of $5.0 \times 10^{-3}\,M\,Na_2SO_4$?

### SOLUTION

**Analyze** The problem asks us to determine whether a precipitate forms when two salt solutions are combined.

**Plan** We should determine the concentrations of all ions just after the solutions are mixed and compare the value of $Q$ with $K_{sp}$ for any potentially insoluble product. The possible metathesis products are $PbSO_4$ and $NaNO_3$. Like all sodium salts $NaNO_3$ is soluble, but $PbSO_4$ has a $K_{sp}$ of $6.3 \times 10^{-7}$ (Appendix D) and will precipitate if the $Pb^{+2}$ and $SO_4^{2-}$ concentrations are high enough for $Q$ to exceed $K_{sp}$.

**Solve** When the two solutions are mixed, the volume is $0.10\,L + 0.40\,L = 0.50\,L$. The number of moles of $Pb^{2+}$ in 0.10 L of $8.0 \times 10^{-3}\,M\,Pb(NO_3)_2$ is

$$(0.10\,L)\left(\frac{8.0 \times 10^{-3}\,mol}{L}\right) = 8.0 \times 10^{-4}\,mol$$

The concentration of $Pb^{2+}$ in the 0.50-L mixture is therefore

$$[Pb^{2+}] = \frac{8.0 \times 10^{-4}\,mol}{0.50\,L} = 1.6 \times 10^{-3}\,M$$

The number of moles of $SO_4^{2-}$ in 0.40 L of $5.0 \times 10^{-3}\,M\,Na_2SO_4$ is

$$(0.40\,L)\left(\frac{5.0 \times 10^{-3}\,mol}{L}\right) = 2.0 \times 10^{-3}\,mol$$

Therefore

$$[SO_4^{2-}] = \frac{2.0 \times 10^{-3}\,mol}{0.50\,L} = 4.0 \times 10^{-3}\,M$$

and

$$Q = [Pb^{2+}][SO_4^{2-}] = (1.6 \times 10^{-3})(4.0 \times 10^{-3}) = 6.4 \times 10^{-6}$$

Because $Q > K_{sp}$, $PbSO_4$ precipitates.

### PRACTICE EXERCISE

Does a precipitate form when 0.050 L of $2.0 \times 10^{-2}\,M\,NaF$ is mixed with 0.010 L of $1.0 \times 10^{-2}\,M\,Ca(NO_3)_2$?

**Answer:** Yes, $CaF_2$ precipitates because $Q = 4.6 \times 10^{-8}$ is larger than $K_{sp} = 3.9 \times 10^{-11}$

# Selective Precipitation of Ions

Ions can be separated from each other based on the solubilities of their salts. Consider a solution containing both $Ag^+$ and $Cu^{2+}$. If HCl is added to the solution, AgCl ($K_{sp} = 1.8 \times 10^{-10}$) precipitates, while $Cu^{2+}$ remains in solution because $CuCl_2$ is soluble. Separation of ions in an aqueous solution by using a reagent that forms a precipitate with one or more (but not all) of the ions is called *selective precipitation*.

---

**SAMPLE EXERCISE 17.16**   **Calculating Ion Concentrations for Precipitation**

A solution contains $1.0 \times 10^{-2}\, M\, Ag^+$ and $2.0 \times 10^{-2}\, M\, Pb^{2+}$. When $Cl^-$ is added, both AgCl ($K_{sp} = 1.8 \times 10^{-10}$) and $PbCl_2$ ($K_{sp} = 1.7 \times 10^{-5}$) can precipitate. What concentration of $Cl^-$ is necessary to begin the precipitation of each salt? Which salt precipitates first?

## SOLUTION

**Analyze** We are asked to determine the concentration of $Cl^-$ necessary to begin the precipitation from a solution containing $Ag^+$ and $Pb^{2+}$ ions, and to predict which metal chloride will begin to precipitate first.

**Plan** We are given $K_{sp}$ values for the two precipitates. Using these and the metal ion concentrations, we can calculate what $Cl^-$ concentration is necessary to precipitate each salt. The salt requiring the lower $Cl^-$ ion concentration precipitates first.

**Solve** For AgCl we have   $K_{sp} = [Ag^+][Cl^-] = 1.8 \times 10^{-10}$

Because $[Ag^+] = 1.0 \times 10^{-2}\, M$, the greatest concentration of $Cl^-$ that can be present without causing precipitation of AgCl can be calculated from the $K_{sp}$ expression:

$$K_{sp} = (1.0 \times 10^{-2})[Cl^-] = 1.8 \times 10^{-10}$$

$$[Cl^-] = \frac{1.8 \times 10^{-10}}{1.0 \times 10^{-2}} = 1.8 \times 10^{-8}\, M$$

Any $Cl^-$ in excess of this very small concentration will cause AgCl to precipitate from solution. Proceeding similarly for $PbCl_2$, we have

$$K_{sp} = [Pb^{2+}][Cl^-]^2 = 1.7 \times 10^{-5}$$

$$[2.0 \times 10^{-2}][Cl^-]^2 = 1.7 \times 10^{-5}$$

$$[Cl^-]^2 = \frac{1.7 \times 10^{-5}}{2.0 \times 10^{-2}} = 8.5 \times 10^{-4}$$

$$[Cl^-] = \sqrt{8.5 \times 10^{-4}} = 2.9 \times 10^{-2}\, M$$

Thus, a concentration of $Cl^-$ in excess of $2.9 \times 10^{-2}\, M$ causes $PbCl_2$ to precipitate.

Comparing the $Cl^-$ concentration required to precipitate each salt, we see that as $Cl^-$ is added, AgCl precipitates first because it requires a much smaller concentration of $Cl^-$. Thus, $Ag^+$ can be separated from $Pb^{2+}$ by slowly adding $Cl^-$ so that the chloride ion concentration remains between $1.8 \times 10^{-8}\, M$ and $2.9 \times 10^{-2}\, M$.

**Comment** Precipitation of AgCl will keep the $Cl^-$ concentration low until the number of moles of $Cl^-$ added exceeds the number of moles of $Ag^+$ in the solution. Once past this point, $[Cl^-]$ rises sharply and $PbCl_2$ will soon begin to precipitate.

## PRACTICE EXERCISE

A solution consists of $0.050\, M\, Mg^{2+}$ and $Cu^{2+}$. Which ion precipitates first as $OH^-$ is added? What concentration of $OH^-$ is necessary to begin the precipitation of each cation? [$K_{sp} = 1.8 \times 10^{-11}$ for $Mg(OH)_2$, and $K_{sp} = 4.8 \times 10^{-20}$ for $Cu(OH)_2$.]

***Answer:*** $Cu(OH)_2$ precipitates first, beginning when $[OH^-] > 1.5 \times 10^{-9}\, M$. $Mg(OH)_2$ begins to precipitate when $[OH^-] > 1.9 \times 10^{-5}\, M$.

◢ GO FIGURE

**What would happen if the pH were raised to 8 first and then H₂S were added?**

Add H₂S

Remove CuS and increase pH

pH ≈ 1

pH ≈ 1

pH ≈ 8

Cu²⁺

Zn²⁺

H⁺

H₂S

HS⁻

CuS(s)

ZnS(s)

▶ **FIGURE 17.22**
**Selective precipitation.** In this example Cu²⁺ ions are separated from Zn²⁺ ions.

Solution containing Zn²⁺(aq) and Cu²⁺(aq)

When H₂S is added to a solution whose pH exceeds 0.6, CuS precipitates

After CuS is removed, the pH is increased, allowing ZnS to precipitate

Sulfide ion is often used to separate metal ions because the solubilities of sulfide salts span a wide range and depend greatly on solution pH. For example, $Cu^{2+}$ and $Zn^{2+}$ can be separated by bubbling $H_2S$ gas through an acidified solution containing these two cations. Because CuS ($K_{sp} = 6 \times 10^{-37}$) is less soluble than ZnS ($K_{sp} = 2 \times 10^{-25}$), CuS precipitates from an acidified solution pH $\approx$ 1 while ZnS does not (▲ **FIGURE 17.22**):

$$Cu^{2+}(aq) + H_2S(aq) \rightleftharpoons CuS(s) + 2 H^+(aq) \qquad [17.27]$$

The CuS can be separated from the $Zn^{2+}$ solution by filtration. The CuS can then be dissolved by raising the concentration of $H^+$ even further, shifting the equilibrium of Equation 17.27 to the left.

# 17.7 | QUALITATIVE ANALYSIS FOR METALLIC ELEMENTS

In this final section, we look at how solubility equilibria and complex-ion formation can be used to detect the presence of particular metal ions in solution. Before the development of modern analytical instrumentation, it was necessary to analyze mixtures of metals in a sample by what were called *wet chemical methods*. For example, an ore sample that might contain several metallic elements was dissolved in a concentrated acid solution that was then tested in a systematic way for the presence of various metal ions.

**Qualitative analysis** determines only the presence or absence of a particular metal ion, whereas **quantitative analysis** determines how much of a given substance is present. Even though wet methods of qualitative analysis have become less important in the chemical industry, they are frequently used in general chemistry laboratory programs to illustrate equilibria, to teach the properties of common metal ions in solution, and to develop laboratory skills. Typically, such analyses proceed in three stages: (1) The ions are separated into broad groups on the basis of solubility properties. (2) The ions in each group are separated by selectively dissolving members in the group. (3) The ions are identified by means of specific tests.

A scheme in general use divides the common cations into five groups (▼ **FIGURE 17.23**). The order in which reagents are added is important in this scheme. The most selective separations—those that involve the smallest number of ions—are carried out first. The reactions used must proceed so far toward completion that any concentration of cations remaining in the solution is too small to interfere with subsequent tests.

Let's look at each of these five groups of cations, briefly examining the logic used in this qualitative analysis scheme.

**Group 1.** *Insoluble chlorides:* Of the common metal ions, only $Ag^+$, $Hg_2^{2+}$, and $Pb^{2+}$ form insoluble chlorides. When HCl is added to a mixture of cations, therefore, only AgCl, $Hg_2Cl_2$, and $PbCl_2$ precipitate, leaving the other cations in solution. The absence of a precipitate indicates that the starting solution contains no $Ag^+$, $Hg_2^{2+}$, or $Pb^{2+}$.

---

**GO FIGURE**

**If a solution contained a mixture of $Cu^{2+}$ and $Zn^{2+}$ ions, would this separation scheme work? After which step would the first precipitate be observed?**

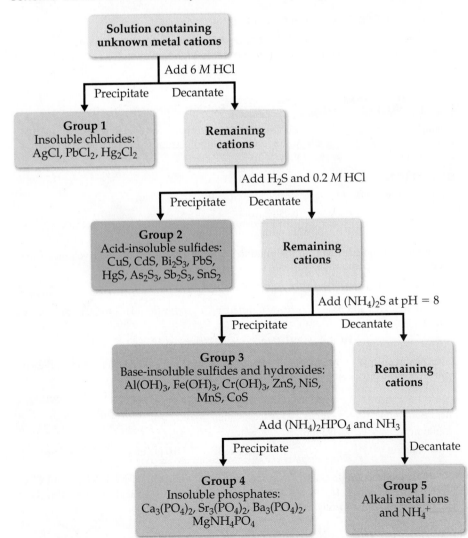

◄ **FIGURE 17.23   Qualitative analysis.** A flowchart showing a common scheme for identifying cations.

**Group 2.** *Acid-insoluble sulfides:* After any insoluble chlorides have been removed, the remaining solution, now acidic, is treated with $H_2S$. Only the most insoluble metal sulfides—CuS, $Bi_2S_3$, CdS, PbS, HgS, $As_2S_3$, $Sb_2S_3$, and $SnS_2$—precipitate. (Note the very small values of $K_{sp}$ for some of these sulfides in Appendix D.) Those metal ions whose sulfides are somewhat more soluble—for example, ZnS or NiS—remain in solution.

**Group 3.** *Base-insoluble sulfides and hydroxides:* After the solution is filtered to remove any acid-insoluble sulfides, it is made slightly basic, and $(NH_4)_2S$ is added. In basic solutions the concentration of $S^{2-}$ is higher than in acidic solutions. Thus, the ion products for many of the more soluble sulfides are made to exceed their $K_{sp}$ values and precipitation occurs. The metal ions precipitated at this stage are $Al^{3+}$, $Cr^{3+}$, $Fe^{3+}$, $Zn^{2+}$, $Ni^{2+}$, $Co^{2+}$, and $Mn^{2+}$ (The $Al^{3+}$, $Fe^{3+}$, and $Cr^{3+}$ ions do not form insoluble sulfides; instead they precipitate as insoluble hydroxides, as Figure 17.23 shows.)

**Group 4.** *Insoluble phosphates:* At this point the solution contains only metal ions from groups 1A and 2A of the periodic table. Adding $(NH_4)_2HPO_4$ to a basic solution precipitates the group 2A elements $Mg^{2+}$, $Ca^{2+}$, $Sr^{2+}$, and $Ba^{2+}$ because these metals form insoluble phosphates.

**Group 5.** *The alkali metal ions and $NH_4^+$:* The ions that remain after removing the insoluble phosphates are tested for individually. A flame test can be used to determine the presence of $K^+$, for example, because the flame turns a characteristic violet color if $K^+$ is present.

 **GIVE IT SOME THOUGHT**

If a precipitate forms when HCl is added to an aqueous solution, what conclusions can you draw about the contents of the solution?

---

**SAMPLE INTEGRATIVE EXERCISE** Putting Concepts Together

A sample of 1.25 L of HCl gas at 21 °C and 0.950 atm is bubbled through 0.500 L of 0.150 $M$ $NH_3$ solution. Calculate the pH of the resulting solution assuming that all the HCl dissolves and that the volume of the solution remains 0.500 L.

**SOLUTION**

The number of moles of HCl gas is calculated from the ideal-gas law,

$$n = \frac{PV}{RT} = \frac{(0.950 \text{ atm})(1.25 \text{ L})}{(0.0821 \text{ L-atm/mol-K})(294 \text{ K})} = 0.0492 \text{ mol HCl}$$

The number of moles of $NH_3$ in the solution is given by the product of the volume of the solution and its concentration,

$$\text{Moles } NH_3 = (0.500 \text{ L})(0.150 \text{ mol } NH_3/\text{L}) = 0.0750 \text{ mol } NH_3$$

The acid HCl and base $NH_3$ react, transferring a proton from HCl to $NH_3$, producing $NH_4^+$ and $Cl^-$ ions,

$$HCl(g) + NH_3(aq) \longrightarrow NH_4^+(aq) + Cl^-(aq)$$

To determine the pH of the solution, we first calculate the amount of each reactant and each product present at the completion of the reaction,

| | $HCl(g)$ + | $NH_3(aq)$ $\longrightarrow$ | $NH_4^+(aq)$ + | $Cl^-(aq)$ |
|---|---|---|---|---|
| Before addition | 0 | 0.0750 mol | 0 | 0 |
| Addition | 0.0492 mol | | | |
| After addition | 0 | 0.0258 mol | 0.0492 mol | 0.0492 mol |

Thus, the reaction produces a solution containing a mixture of $NH_3$, $NH_4^+$, and $Cl^-$. The $NH_3$ is a weak base ($K_b = 1.8 \times 10^{-5}$), $NH_4^+$ is its conjugate acid, and $Cl^-$ is neither acidic nor basic. Consequently, the pH depends on $[NH_3]$ and $[NH_4^+]$,

$$[NH_3] = \frac{0.0258 \text{ mol } NH_3}{0.500 \text{ L soln}} = 0.0516 \text{ } M$$

$$[NH_4^+] = \frac{0.0492 \text{ mol NH}_4^+}{0.500 \text{ L soln}} = 0.0984 \, M$$

We can calculate the pH using either $K_b$ for $NH_3$ or $K_a$ for $NH_4^+$. Using the $K_b$ expression, we have

$$NH_3(aq) \quad + \quad H_2O(l) \rightleftharpoons \quad NH_4^+(aq) \quad + \quad OH^-(aq)$$

|  | | | |
|---|---|---|---|
| Initial | 0.0516 $M$ | — | 0.0984 $M$ | 0 |
| Change | $-x\,M$ | — | $+x\,M$ | $+x\,M$ |
| Equilibrium | $(0.0516 - x)\,M$ | — | $(0.0984 + x)\,M$ | $x\,M$ |

$$K_b = \frac{[NH_4^+][OH^-]}{[NH_3]} = \frac{(0.0984 + x)(x)}{(0.0516 - x)} \simeq \frac{(0.0984)x}{0.0516} = 1.8 \times 10^{-5}$$

$$x = [OH^-] = \frac{(0.0516)(1.8 \times 10^{-5})}{0.0984} = 9.4 \times 10^{-6} \, M$$

Hence, pOH $= -\log(9.4 \times 10^{-6}) = 5.03$ and pH $= 14.00 - \text{pOH} = 14.00 - 5.03 = 8.97$.

# CHAPTER SUMMARY AND KEY TERMS

**SECTION 17.1** In this chapter we have considered several types of important equilibria that occur in aqueous solution. Our primary emphasis has been on acid–base equilibria in solutions containing two or more solutes and on solubility equilibria. The dissociation of a weak acid or weak base is repressed by the presence of a strong electrolyte that provides an ion common to the equilibrium. This phenomenon is called the **common-ion effect**.

**SECTION 17.2** A particularly important type of acid–base mixture is that of a weak conjugate acid–base pair. Such mixtures function as **buffered solutions (buffers)**. Addition of small amounts of a strong acid or a strong base to a buffered solution causes only small changes in pH because the buffer reacts with the added acid or base. (Strong acid–strong base, strong acid–weak base, and weak acid–strong base reactions proceed essentially to completion.) Buffered solutions are usually prepared from a weak acid and a salt of that acid or from a weak base and a salt of that base. Two important characteristics of a buffered solution are its **buffer capacity** and its **pH range**. The optimal pH of a buffer is equal to p$K_a$ (or p$K_b$) of the acid (or base) used to prepare the buffer. The relationship between pH, p$K_a$, and the concentrations of an acid and its conjugate base can be expressed by the **Henderson–Hasselbalch equation**.

**SECTION 17.3** The plot of the pH of an acid (or base) as a function of the volume of added base (or acid) is called a **pH titration curve**. The titration curve of a strong acid–strong base titration exhibits a large change in pH in the immediate vicinity of the equivalence point; at the equivalence point for such a titration pH = 7. For strong acid–weak base or weak acid–strong base titrations, the pH change in the vicinity of the equivalence point is not as large. Furthermore, the pH at the equivalence point is not 7 in either of these cases. Rather, it is the pH of the salt solution that results from the neutralization reaction. For this reason it is important to choose an indicator whose color change is near the pH at the equivalence point for titrations involving either weak acids or weak bases. It is possible to calculate the pH at any point of the titration curve by first considering the effects of the acid–base reaction on solution concentrations and then examining equilibria involving the remaining solute species.

**SECTION 17.4** The equilibrium between a solid compound and its ions in solution provides an example of heterogeneous equilibrium.

The **solubility-product constant** (or simply the **solubility product**), $K_{sp}$, is an equilibrium constant that expresses quantitatively the extent to which the compound dissolves. The $K_{sp}$ can be used to calculate the solubility of an ionic compound, and the solubility can be used to calculate $K_{sp}$.

**SECTION 17.5** Several experimental factors, including temperature, affect the solubilities of ionic compounds in water. The solubility of a slightly soluble ionic compound is decreased by the presence of a second solute that furnishes a common ion (the common-ion effect). The solubility of compounds containing basic anions increases as the solution is made more acidic (as pH decreases). Salts with anions of negligible basicity (the anions of strong acids) are unaffected by pH changes.

The solubility of metal salts is also affected by the presence of certain Lewis bases that react with metal ions to form stable **complex ions**. Complex-ion formation in aqueous solution involves the displacement by Lewis bases (such as $NH_3$ and $CN^-$) of water molecules attached to the metal ion. The extent to which such complex formation occurs is expressed quantitatively by the **formation constant** for the complex ion. **Amphoteric oxides** and **hydroxides** are those that are only slightly soluble in water but dissolve on addition of either acid or base.

**SECTION 17.6** Comparison of the ion product, $Q$, with the value of $K_{sp}$ can be used to judge whether a precipitate will form when solutions are mixed or whether a slightly soluble salt will dissolve under various conditions. Precipitates form when $Q > K_{sp}$. If two salts have sufficiently different solubilities, selective precipitation can be used to precipitate one ion while leaving the other in solution, effectively separating the two ions.

**SECTION 17.7** Metallic elements vary a great deal in the solubilities of their salts, in their acid–base behavior, and in their tendencies to form complex ions. These differences can be used to separate and detect the presence of metal ions in mixtures. **Qualitative analysis** determines the presence or absence of species in a sample, whereas **quantitative analysis** determines how much of each species is present. The qualitative analysis of metal ions in solution can be carried out by separating the ions into groups on the basis of precipitation reactions and then analyzing each group for individual metal ions.

# KEY SKILLS

- Describe the common-ion effect. (Section 17.1)
- Explain how a buffer functions. (Section 17.2)
- Calculate the pH of a buffered solution. (Section 17.2)
- Calculate the pH of a buffer after the addition of small amounts of a strong acid or a strong base. (Section 17.2)
- Calculate the pH at any point in a strong acid-strong base titration. (Section 17.3)
- Calculate the pH at any point in a weak acid-strong base or weak base-strong acid titration. (Section 17.3)
- Understand the differences between the titration curves for a strong acid–strong base titration and those when either the acid or base is weak. (Section 17.3)
- Given either $K_{sp}$, molar solubility or mass solubility for a substance calculate the other two quantities. (Section 17.4)
- Calculate molar solubility in the presence of a common ion. (Section 17.5)
- Predict the effect of pH on solubility. (Section 17.5)
- Predict whether a precipitate will form when solutions are mixed by comparing Q and $K_{sp}$. (Section 17.6)
- Calculate the ion concentrations required to begin precipitation. (Section 17.6)
- Explain the effect of complex-ion formation on solubility. (Section 17.6)

# KEY EQUATION

- $$pH = pK_a + \log\frac{[base]}{[acid]} \qquad [17.9]$$  The Henderson–Hasselbalch equation, used to calculate the pH of a buffer from the concentrations of a conjugate acid–base pair

# EXERCISES

## VISUALIZING CONCEPTS

**17.1** The following boxes represent aqueous solutions containing a weak acid, HX, and its conjugate base, X⁻. Water molecules, hydronium ions and cations are not shown. Which solution has the highest pH? Explain. [Section 17.1]

**17.2** The beaker on the right contains 0.1 *M* acetic acid solution with methyl orange as an indicator. The beaker on the left contains a mixture of 0.1 *M* acetic acid and 0.1 *M* sodium acetate with methyl orange. **(a)** Using Figure 16.7, what can you say about the pH of each solution? **(b)** Which solution is better able to maintain its pH when small amounts of NaOH are added? Explain. [Sections 17.1 and 17.2]

**17.3** A buffer contains a weak acid, HX, and its conjugate base. The weak acid has a p$K_a$ of 4.5, and the buffer has a pH of 4.3. Without doing a calculation, predict whether [HX] = [X⁻], [HX] > [X⁻], or [HX] < [X⁻]. Explain. [Section 17.2]

**17.4** The drawing on the left represents a buffer composed of equal concentrations of a weak acid, HX, and its conjugate base, X⁻. The heights of the columns are proportional to the concentrations of the components of the buffer. **(a)** Which of the three drawings, (1), (2), or (3), represents the buffer after the addition of a strong acid? **(b)** Which of the three represents the buffer after the addition of a strong base? **(c)** Which of the three represents a situation that cannot arise from the addition of either an acid or a base? [Section 17.2]

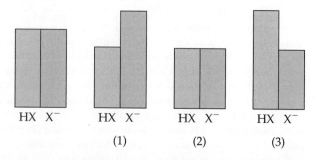

**17.5** The following drawings represent solutions at various stages of the titration of a weak acid, HA, with NaOH. (The Na⁺ ions and water molecules have been omitted for clarity.) To which of the following regions of the titration curve does each drawing correspond: **(a)** before addition of NaOH, **(b)** after addition of NaOH but before equivalence point, (c) at equivalence point, (d) after equivalence point? [Section 17.3]

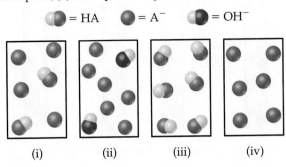

= HA     = A⁻     = OH⁻

(i)          (ii)          (iii)          (iv)

**17.6** Match the following descriptions of titration curves with the diagrams: (a) strong acid added to strong base, (b) strong base added to weak acid, (c) strong base added to strong acid, (d) strong base added to polyprotic acid. [Section 17.3]

mL titrant     mL titrant     mL titrant     mL titrant

(i)          (ii)          (iii)          (iv)

**17.7** Equal volumes of two acids are titrated with 0.10 $M$ NaOH resulting in the two titration curves shown in the following figure. (a) Which curve corresponds to the more concentrated acid solution? (b) Which corresponds to the acid with the larger $K_a$? Explain. [Section 17.3]

**17.8** A saturated solution of $Cd(OH)_2$ is shown in the middle beaker. If hydrochloric acid solution is added, the solubility of

**Saturated solution**

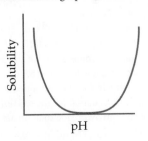

$Cd^{2+}(aq)$     $OH^-(aq)$

Add HCl($aq$)     Add HCl($aq$)

**Beaker A**     **Beaker B**

$Cd(OH)_2(s)$

$Cd(OH)_2(s)$     $Cd(OH)_2(s)$

$Cd(OH)_2$ will increase, causing additional solid to dissolve. Which of the two choices, Beaker A or Beaker B, accurately represents the solution after equilibrium is reestablished? Explain. (The water molecules and Cl⁻ ions are omitted for clarity). [Sections 17.4 and 17.5]

**17.9** The following graphs represent the behavior of $BaCO_3$ under different circumstances. In each case the vertical axis indicates the solubility of the $BaCO_3$ and the horizontal axis represents the concentration of some other reagent. (a) Which graph represents what happens to the solubility of $BaCO_3$ as $HNO_3$ is added? (b) Which graph represents what happens to the $BaCO_3$ solubility as $Na_2CO_3$ is added? (c) Which represents what happens to the $BaCO_3$ solubility as $NaNO_3$ is added? [Section 17.5]

Conc          Conc          Conc

**17.10** $Ca(OH)_2$ has a $K_{sp}$ of $6.5 \times 10^{-6}$. (a) If 0.370 g of $Ca(OH)_2$ is added to 500 mL of water and the mixture is allowed to come to equilibrium, will the solution be saturated? (b) If 50 mL of the solution from part (a) is added to each of the beakers shown here, in which beakers, if any, will a precipitate form? In those cases where a precipitate forms, what is its identity? [Section 17.6]

**(i)** 50 mL
1.0 $M$ HCl($aq$)

**(ii)** 50 mL
1.0 $M$ NaCl($aq$)

**(iii)** 50 mL
1.0 $M$ CaCl₂($aq$)

**(iv)** 50 mL
0.10 $M$ CaCl₂($aq$)

**17.11** What is the name given to the kind of behavior demonstrated by a metal hydroxide in this graph? [Section 17.5]

**17.12** Three cations, $Ni^{2+}$, $Cu^{2+}$, and $Ag^+$, are separated using two different precipitating agents. Based on Figure 17.23, what two precipitating agents could be used? Using these agents, indicate which of the cations is A, which is B, and which is C. [Section 17.7]

Cation A ●    Cation B ●    Cation C ●

# COMMON-ION EFFECT (section 17.1)

**17.13** (a) What is the common-ion effect? (b) Give an example of a salt that can decrease the ionization of $HNO_2$ in solution.

**17.14** (a) Consider the equilibrium $B(aq) + H_2O(l) \rightleftharpoons HB^+(aq) + OH^-(aq)$. Using Le Châtelier's principle, explain the effect of the presence of a salt of $HB^+$ on the ionization of B. (b) Give an example of a salt that can decrease the ionization of $NH_3$ in solution.

**17.15** Use information from Appendix D to calculate the pH of (a) a solution that is 0.060 $M$ in potassium propionate ($C_2H_5COOK$ or $KC_3H_5O_2$) and 0.085 $M$ in propionic acid ($C_2H_5COOH$ or $HC_3H_5O_2$); (b) a solution that is 0.075 $M$ in trimethylamine, $(CH_3)_3N$, and 0.10 $M$ in trimethylammonium chloride, $(CH_3)_3NHCl$; (c) a solution that is made by mixing 50.0 mL of 0.15 $M$ acetic acid and 50.0 mL of 0.20 $M$ sodium acetate.

**17.16** Use information from Appendix D to calculate the pH of (a) a solution that is 0.250 $M$ in sodium formate (HCOONa) and 0.100 $M$ in formic acid (HCOOH); (b) a solution that is 0.510 $M$ in pyridine ($C_5H_5N$) and 0.450 $M$ in pyridinium chloride ($C_5H_5NHCl$); (c) a solution that is made by combining 55 mL of 0.050 $M$ hydrofluoric acid with 125 mL of 0.10 $M$ sodium fluoride.

**17.17** (a) Calculate the percent ionization of 0.0075 $M$ butanoic acid ($K_a = 1.5 \times 10^{-5}$). (b) Calculate the percent ionization of 0.0075 $M$ butanoic acid in a solution containing 0.085 $M$ sodium butanoate.

**17.18** (a) Calculate the percent ionization of 0.125 $M$ lactic acid ($K_a = 1.4 \times 10^{-4}$). (b) Calculate the percent ionization of 0.125 $M$ lactic acid in a solution containing 0.0075 $M$ sodium lactate.

# BUFFERED SOLUTIONS (section 17.2)

**17.19** Explain why a mixture of $CH_3COOH$ and $CH_3COONa$ can act as a buffer while a mixture of HCl and NaCl cannot.

**17.20** Explain why a mixture formed by mixing 100 mL of 0.100 $M$ $CH_3COOH$ and 50 mL of 0.100 $M$ NaOH will act as a buffer.

**17.21** (a) Calculate the pH of a buffer that is 0.12 $M$ in lactic acid and 0.11 $M$ in sodium lactate. (b) Calculate the pH of a buffer formed by mixing 85 mL of 0.13 $M$ lactic acid with 95 mL of 0.15 $M$ sodium lactate.

**17.22** (a) Calculate the pH of a buffer that is 0.105 $M$ in $NaHCO_3$ and 0.125 $M$ in $Na_2CO_3$. (b) Calculate the pH of a solution formed by mixing 65 mL of 0.20 $M$ $NaHCO_3$ with 75 mL of 0.15 $M$ $Na_2CO_3$.

**17.23** A buffer is prepared by adding 20.0 g of sodium acetate ($CH_3COONa$) to 500 mL of a 0.150 $M$ acetic acid ($CH_3COOH$) solution. (a) Determine the pH of the buffer. (b) Write the complete ionic equation for the reaction that occurs when a few drops of hydrochloric acid are added to the buffer. (c) Write the complete ionic equation for the reaction that occurs when a few drops of sodium hydroxide solution are added to the buffer.

**17.24** A buffer is prepared by adding 10.0 g of ammonium chloride ($NH_4Cl$) to 250 mL of 1.00 $M$ $NH_3$ solution. (a) What is the pH of this buffer? (b) Write the complete ionic equation for the reaction that occurs when a few drops of nitric acid are

added to the buffer. (c) Write the complete ionic equation for the reaction that occurs when a few drops of potassium hydroxide solution are added to the buffer.

**17.25** You are asked to prepare a pH = 3.00 buffer solution starting from 1.25 L of a 1.00 $M$ solution of hydrofluoric acid (HF) and an excess of sodium fluoride (NaF). (a) What is the pH of the hydrofluoric acid solution prior to adding sodium fluoride? (b) How many grams of sodium fluoride should be added to prepare the buffer solution? Neglect the small volume change that occurs when the sodium fluoride is added.

**17.26** You are asked to prepare a pH = 4.00 buffer starting from 1.50 L of 0.0200 $M$ solution of benzoic acid ($C_6H_5COOH$) and an excess of sodium benzoate ($C_6H_5COONa$). (a) What is the pH of the benzoic acid solution prior to adding sodium benzoate? (b) How many grams of sodium benzoate should be added to prepare the buffer? Neglect the small volume change that occurs when the sodium benzoate is added.

**17.27** A buffer contains 0.10 mol of acetic acid and 0.13 mol of sodium acetate in 1.00 L. (a) What is the pH of this buffer? (b) What is the pH of the buffer after the addition of 0.02 mol of KOH? (c) What is the pH of the buffer after the addition of 0.02 mol of $HNO_3$?

**17.28** A buffer contains 0.15 mol of propionic acid ($C_2H_5COOH$) and 0.10 mol of sodium propionate ($C_2H_5COONa$) in 1.20 L. **(a)** What is the pH of this buffer? **(b)** What is the pH of the buffer after the addition of 0.01 mol of NaOH? **(c)** What is the pH of the buffer after the addition of 0.01 mol of HI?

**17.29** **(a)** What is the ratio of $HCO_3^-$ to $H_2CO_3$ in blood of pH 7.4? **(b)** What is the ratio of $HCO_3^-$ to $H_2CO_3$ in an exhausted marathon runner whose blood pH is 7.1?

**17.30** A buffer, consisting of $H_2PO_4^-$ and $HPO_4^{2-}$, helps control the pH of physiological fluids. Many carbonated soft drinks also use this buffer system. What is the pH of a soft drink in which the major buffer ingredients are 6.5 g of $NaH_2PO_4$ and 8.0 g of $Na_2HPO_4$ per 355 mL of solution?

**17.31** You have to prepare a pH 3.50 buffer, and you have the following 0.10 $M$ solutions available: HCOOH, $CH_3COOH$, $H_3PO_4$, HCOONa, $CH_3COONa$, and $NaH_2PO_4$. Which solutions would you use? How many milliliters of each solution would you use to make approximately a liter of the buffer?

**17.32** You have to prepare a pH 5.00 buffer, and you have the following 0.10 $M$ solutions available: HCOOH, HCOONa, $CH_3COOH$, $CH_3COONa$, HCN, and NaCN. Which solutions would you use? How many milliliters of each solution would you use to make approximately a liter of the buffer?

# ACID–BASE TITRATIONS (section 17.3)

**17.33** The accompanying graph shows the titration curves for two monoprotic acids. **(a)** Which curve is that of a strong acid? **(b)** What is the approximate pH at the equivalence point of each titration? **(c)** 40.0 mL of each acid was titrated with 0.100 $M$ base. Which acid is more concentrated?

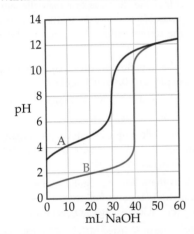

**17.34** How does titration of a strong, monoprotic acid with a strong base differ from titration of a weak, monoprotic acid with a strong base with respect to the following: **(a)** quantity of base required to reach the equivalence point, **(b)** pH at the beginning of the titration, **(c)** pH at the equivalence point, **(d)** pH after addition of a slight excess of base, **(e)** choice of indicator for determining the equivalence point?

**17.35** The samples of nitric and acetic acid shown here are both titrated with a 0.100 $M$ solution of NaOH($aq$).

25.0 mL of 1.0 $M$ HNO$_3$($aq$)    25.0 mL of 1.0 $M$ CH$_3$COOH($aq$)

Determine whether each of the following statements concerning these titrations is true or false.
**(a)** A larger volume of NaOH($aq$) is needed to reach the equivalence point in the titration of HNO$_3$.

**(b)** The pH at the equivalence point in the HNO$_3$ titration will be lower than the pH at the equivalence point in the $CH_3COOH$ titration.
**(c)** Phenolphthalein would be a suitable indicator for both titrations.

**17.36** Determine whether each of the following statements concerning the titrations in Problem 17.35 is true or false.
**(a)** The pH at the beginning of the two titrations will be the same.
**(b)** The titration curves will both be essentially the same after passing the equivalence point.
**(c)** Methyl red would be a suitable indicator for both titrations.

**17.37** Predict whether the equivalence point of each of the following titrations is below, above, or at pH 7: **(a)** $NaHCO_3$ titrated with NaOH, **(b)** $NH_3$ titrated with HCl, **(c)** KOH titrated with HBr.

**17.38** Predict whether the equivalence point of each of the following titrations is below, above, or at pH 7: **(a)** formic acid titrated with NaOH, **(b)** calcium hydroxide titrated with perchloric acid, **(c)** pyridine titrated with nitric acid.

**17.39** As shown in Figure 16.7, the indicator thymol blue has two color changes. Which color change will generally be more suitable for titration of a weak acid with a strong base?

**17.40** Assume that 30.0 mL of a 0.10 $M$ solution of a weak base B that accepts one proton is titrated with a 0.10 $M$ solution of the monoprotic strong acid HX. **(a)** How many moles of HX have been added at the equivalence point? **(b)** What is the predominant form of B at the equivalence point? **(c)** What factor determines the pH at the equivalence point? **(d)** Which indicator, phenolphthalein or methyl red, is likely to be the better choice for this titration?

**17.41** How many milliliters of 0.0850 $M$ NaOH are required to titrate each of the following solutions to the equivalence point: **(a)** 40.0 mL of 0.0900 $M$ HNO$_3$, **(b)** 35.0 mL of 0.0850 $M$ CH$_3$COOH, **(c)** 50.0 mL of a solution that contains 1.85 g of HCl per liter?

**17.42** How many milliliters of 0.105 $M$ HCl are needed to titrate each of the following solutions to the equivalence point: **(a)** 45.0 mL of 0.0950 $M$ NaOH, **(b)** 22.5 mL of 0.118 $M$ NH$_3$, **(c)** 125.0 mL of a solution that contains 1.35 g of NaOH per liter?

**17.43** A 20.0-mL sample of 0.200 $M$ HBr solution is titrated with 0.200 $M$ NaOH solution. Calculate the pH of the solution after the following volumes of base have been added: **(a)** 15.0 mL, **(b)** 19.9 mL, **(c)** 20.0 mL, **(d)** 20.1 mL, **(e)** 35.0 mL.

**17.44** A 20.0-mL sample of 0.150 $M$ KOH is titrated with 0.125 $M$ HClO$_4$ solution. Calculate the pH after the following volumes of acid have been added: **(a)** 20.0 mL, **(b)** 23.0 mL, **(c)** 24.0 mL, **(d)** 25.0 mL, **(e)** 30.0 mL.

**17.45** A 35.0-mL sample of 0.150 $M$ acetic acid (CH$_3$COOH) is titrated with 0.150 $M$ NaOH solution. Calculate the pH after the following volumes of base have been added: **(a)** 0 mL, **(b)** 17.5 mL, **(c)** 34.5 mL, **(d)** 35.0 mL, **(e)** 35.5 mL, **(f)** 50.0 mL.

**17.46** Consider the titration of 30.0 mL of 0.050 $M$ NH$_3$ with 0.025 $M$ HCl. Calculate the pH after the following volumes of titrant have been added: **(a)** 0 mL, **(b)** 20.0 mL, **(c)** 59.0 mL, **(d)** 60.0 mL, **(e)** 61.0 mL, **(f)** 65.0 mL.

**17.47** Calculate the pH at the equivalence point for titrating 0.200 $M$ solutions of each of the following bases with 0.200 $M$ HBr: **(a)** sodium hydroxide (NaOH), **(b)** hydroxylamine (NH$_2$OH), **(c)** aniline (C$_6$H$_5$NH$_2$).

**17.48** Calculate the pH at the equivalence point in titrating 0.100 $M$ solutions of each of the following with 0.080 $M$ NaOH: **(a)** hydrobromic acid (HBr), **(b)** chlorous acid (HClO$_2$), **(c)** benzoic acid (C$_6$H$_5$COOH).

# SOLUBILITY EQUILIBRIA AND FACTORS AFFECTING SOLUBILITY (sections 17.4 and 17.5)

**17.49** **(a)** Why is the concentration of undissolved solid not explicitly included in the expression for the solubility-product constant? **(b)** Write the expression for the solubility-product constant for each of the following strong electrolytes: AgI, SrSO$_4$, Fe(OH)$_2$, and Hg$_2$Br$_2$.

**17.50** **(a)** Explain the difference between solubility and solubility-product constant. **(b)** Write the expression for the solubility-product constant for each of the following ionic compounds: MnCO$_3$, Hg(OH)$_2$, and Cu$_3$(PO$_4$)$_2$.

**17.51** **(a)** If the molar solubility of CaF$_2$ at 35 °C is $1.24 \times 10^{-3}$ mol/L, what is $K_{sp}$ at this temperature? **(b)** It is found that $1.1 \times 10^{-2}$ of SrF$_2$ dissolves per 100 mL of aqueous solution at 25 °C. Calculate the solubility product for SrF$_2$. **(c)** The $K_{sp}$ of Ba(IO$_3$)$_2$ at 25 °C is $6.0 \times 10^{-10}$. What is the molar solubility of Ba(IO$_3$)$_2$?

**17.52** **(a)** The molar solubility of PbBr$_2$ at 25 °C is $1.0 \times 10^{-2}$ mol/L. Calculate $K_{sp}$. **(b)** If 0.0490 g of AgIO$_3$ dissolves per liter of solution, calculate the solubility-product constant. **(c)** Using the appropriate $K_{sp}$ value from Appendix D, calculate the pH of a saturated solution of Ca(OH)$_2$.

**17.53** A 1.00-L solution saturated at 25 °C with calcium oxalate (CaC$_2$O$_4$) contains 0.0061 g of CaC$_2$O$_4$. Calculate the solubility-product constant for this salt at 25 °C.

**17.54** A 1.00-L solution saturated at 25 °C with lead(II) iodide contains 0.54 g of PbI$_2$. Calculate the solubility-product constant for this salt at 25 °C.

**17.55** Using Appendix D, calculate the molar solubility of AgBr in **(a)** pure water, **(b)** $3.0 \times 10^{-2}$ $M$ AgNO$_3$ solution, **(c)** 0.10 $M$ NaBr solution.

**17.56** Calculate the solubility of LaF$_3$ in grams per liter in **(a)** pure water, **(b)** 0.010 $M$ KF solution, **(c)** 0.050 $M$ LaCl$_3$ solution.

**17.57** Consider a beaker containing a saturated solution of CaF$_2$ in equilibrium with undissolved CaF$_2$(s). **(a)** If solid CaCl$_2$ is added to this solution, will the amount of solid CaF$_2$ at the bottom of the beaker increase, decrease, or remain the same? **(b)** Will the concentration of Ca$^{2+}$ ions in solution increase or decrease? **(c)** Will the concentration of F$^-$ ions in solution increase or decrease?

**17.58** Consider a beaker containing a saturated solution of PbI$_2$ in equilibrium with undissolved PbI$_2$(s). **(a)** If solid KI is added to this solution, will the amount of solid PbI$_2$ at the bottom of the beaker increase, decrease, or remain the same? **(b)** Will the concentration of Pb$^{2+}$ ions in solution increase or decrease? **(c)** Will the concentration of I$^-$ ions in solution increase or decrease?

**17.59** Calculate the solubility of Mn(OH)$_2$ in grams per liter when buffered at pH **(a)** 7.0, **(b)** 9.5, **(c)** 11.8.

**17.60** Calculate the molar solubility of Ni(OH)$_2$ when buffered at pH **(a)** 8.0, **(b)** 10.0, **(c)** 12.0.

**17.61** Which of the following salts will be substantially more soluble in acidic solution than in pure water: **(a)** ZnCO$_3$, **(b)** ZnS, **(c)** BiI$_3$, **(d)** AgCN, **(e)** Ba$_3$(PO$_4$)$_2$?

**17.62** For each of the following slightly soluble salts, write the net ionic equation, if any, for reaction with acid: **(a)** MnS, **(b)** PbF$_2$, **(c)** AuCl$_3$, **(d)** Hg$_2$C$_2$O$_4$, **(e)** CuBr.

**17.63** From the value of $K_f$ listed in Table 17.1, calculate the concentration of Ni$^{2+}$ in 1.0 L of a solution that contains a total of $1 \times 10^{-3}$ mol of nickel(II) ion and that is 0.20 $M$ in NH$_3$.

**17.64** To what final concentration of NH$_3$ must a solution be adjusted to just dissolve 0.020 mol of NiC$_2$O$_4$ ($K_{sp} = 4 \times 10^{-10}$) in 1.0 L of solution? (*Hint:* You can neglect the hydrolysis of C$_2$O$_4^{2-}$ because the solution will be quite basic.)

**17.65** Use values of $K_{sp}$ for AgI and $K_f$ for Ag(CN)$_2^-$ to **(a)** calculate the molar solubility of AgI in pure water, **(b)** calculate the equilibrium constant for the reaction

$$\text{AgI}(s) + 2\,\text{CN}^-(aq) \rightleftharpoons \text{Ag(CN)}_2^-(aq) + \text{I}^-(aq)$$

**(c)** Determine the molar solubility of AgI in a 0.100 $M$ NaCN solution.

**17.66** Using the value of $K_{sp}$ for Ag$_2$S, $K_{a1}$ and $K_{a2}$ for H$_2$S, and $K_f = 1.1 \times 10^5$ for AgCl$_2^-$, calculate the equilibrium constant for the following reaction:

$$\text{Ag}_2\text{S}(s) + 4\,\text{Cl}^-(aq) + 2\,\text{H}^+(aq) \rightleftharpoons 2\,\text{AgCl}_2^-(aq) + \text{H}_2\text{S}(aq)$$

# PRECIPITATION AND SEPARATION OF IONS (section 17.6)

**17.67** **(a)** Will $Ca(OH)_2$ precipitate from solution if the pH of a 0.050 $M$ solution of $CaCl_2$ is adjusted to 8.0? **(b)** Will $Ag_2SO_4$ precipitate when 100 mL of 0.050 $M$ $AgNO_3$ is mixed with 10 mL of $5.0 \times 10^{-2} M$ $Na_2SO_4$ solution?

**17.68** **(a)** Will $Co(OH)_2$ precipitate from solution if the pH of a 0.020 $M$ solution of $Co(NO_3)_2$ is adjusted to 8.5? **(b)** Will $AgIO_3$ precipitate when 20 mL of 0.010 $M$ $AgNO_3$ is mixed with 10 mL of 0.015 $M$ $NaIO_3$? ($K_{sp}$ of $AgIO_3$ is $3.1 \times 10^{-8}$.)

**17.69** Calculate the minimum pH needed to precipitate $Mn(OH)_2$ so completely that the concentration of $Mn^{2+}$ is less than 1 $\mu$g per liter [1 part per billion (ppb)].

**17.70** Suppose that a 10-mL sample of a solution is to be tested for $I^-$ ion by addition of 1 drop (0.2 mL) of 0.10 $M$ $Pb(NO_3)_2$. What is the minimum number of grams of $I^-$ that must be present for $PbI_2(s)$ to form?

**17.71** A solution contains $2.0 \times 10^{-4} M$ $Ag^+$ and $1.5 \times 10^{-3} M$ $Pb^{2+}$. If NaI is added, will AgI ($K_{sp} = 8.3 \times 10^{-17}$) or $PbI_2$ ($K_{sp} = 7.9 \times 10^{-9}$) precipitate first? Specify the concentration of $I^-$ needed to begin precipitation.

**17.72** A solution of $Na_2SO_4$ is added dropwise to a solution that is 0.010 $M$ in $Ba^{2+}$ and 0.010 $M$ in $Sr^{2+}$. **(a)** What concentration of $SO_4^{2-}$ is necessary to begin precipitation? (Neglect volume changes. $BaSO_4$: $K_{sp} = 1.1 \times 10^{-10}$; $SrSO_4$: $K_{sp} = 3.2 \times 10^{-7}$.) **(b)** Which cation precipitates first? **(c)** What is the concentration of $SO_4^{2-}$ when the second cation begins to precipitate?

**17.73** A solution contains three anions with the following concentrations: 0.20 $M$ $CrO_4^{2-}$, 0.10 $M$ $CO_3^{2-}$, and 0.010 $M$ $Cl^-$. If a dilute $AgNO_3$ solution is slowly added to the solution, what is the first compound to precipitate: $Ag_2CrO_4$ ($K_{sp} = 1.2 \times 10^{-12}$), $Ag_2CO_3$ ($K_{sp} = 8.1 \times 10^{-12}$), or AgCl ($K_{sp} = 1.8 \times 10^{-10}$)?

**17.74** A 1.0 $M$ $Na_2SO_4$ solution is slowly added to 10.0 mL of a solution that is 0.20 $M$ in $Ca^{2+}$ and 0.30 $M$ in $Ag^+$. **(a)** Which compound will precipitate first: $CaSO_4$ ($K_{sp} = 2.4 \times 10^{-5}$) or $Ag_2SO_4$ ($K_{sp} = 1.5 \times 10^{-5}$)? **(b)** How much $Na_2SO_4$ solution must be added to initiate the precipitation?

# QUALITATIVE ANALYSIS FOR METALLIC ELEMENTS (section 17.7)

**17.75** A solution containing an unknown number of metal ions is treated with dilute HCl; no precipitate forms. The pH is adjusted to about 1, and $H_2S$ is bubbled through. Again, no precipitate forms. The pH of the solution is then adjusted to about 8. Again, $H_2S$ is bubbled through. This time a precipitate forms. The filtrate from this solution is treated with $(NH_4)_2HPO_4$. No precipitate forms. Which metal ions discussed in Section 17.7 are possibly present? Which are definitely absent within the limits of these tests?

**17.76** An unknown solid is entirely soluble in water. On addition of dilute HCl, a precipitate forms. After the precipitate is filtered off, the pH is adjusted to about 1 and $H_2S$ is bubbled in; a precipitate again forms. After filtering off this precipitate, the pH is adjusted to 8 and $H_2S$ is again added; no precipitate forms. No precipitate forms upon addition of $(NH_4)_2HPO_4$. The remaining solution shows a yellow color in a flame test (see Figure 7.21). Based on these observations, which of the following compounds might be present, which are definitely present, and which are definitely absent: CdS, $Pb(NO_3)_2$, HgO, $ZnSO_4$, $Cd(NO_3)_2$, and $Na_2SO_4$?

**17.77** In the course of various qualitative analysis procedures, the following mixtures are encountered: **(a)** $Zn^{2+}$ and $Cd^{2+}$, **(b)** $Cr(OH)_3$ and $Fe(OH)_3$, **(c)** $Mg^{2+}$ and $K^+$, **(d)** $Ag^+$ and $Mn^{2+}$. Suggest how each mixture might be separated.

**17.78** Suggest how the cations in each of the following solution mixtures can be separated: **(a)** $Na^+$ and $Cd^{2+}$, **(b)** $Cu^{2+}$ and $Mg^{2+}$, **(c)** $Pb^{2+}$ and $Al^{3+}$, **(d)** $Ag^+$ and $Hg^{2+}$.

**17.79** **(a)** Precipitation of the group 4 cations of Figure 17.23 requires a basic medium. Why is this so? **(b)** What is the most significant difference between the sulfides precipitated in group 2 and those precipitated in group 3? **(c)** Suggest a procedure that would serve to redissolve the group 3 cations following their precipitation.

**17.80** A student who is in a great hurry to finish his laboratory work decides that his qualitative analysis unknown contains a metal ion from group 4 of Figure 17.23. He therefore tests his sample directly with $(NH_4)_2HPO_4$, skipping earlier tests for the metal ions in groups 1, 2, and 3. He observes a precipitate and concludes that a metal ion from group 4 is indeed present. Why is this possibly an erroneous conclusion?

## ADDITIONAL EXERCISES

**17.81** Derive an equation similar to the Henderson–Hasselbalch equation relating the pOH of a buffer to the $pK_b$ of its base component.

**17.82** Benzenesulfonic acid is a monoprotic acid with $pK_a = 2.25$. Calculate the pH of a buffer composed of 0.150 $M$ benzenesulfonic acid and 0.125 $M$ sodium benzenesulfonate.

**17.83** Furoic acid ($HC_5H_3O_3$) has a $K_a$ value of $6.76 \times 10^{-4}$ at 25 °C. Calculate the pH at 25 °C of **(a)** a solution formed by adding 25.0 g of furoic acid and 30.0 g of sodium furoate ($NaC_5H_3O_3$) to enough water to form 0.250 L of solution; **(b)** a solution formed by mixing 30.0 mL of 0.250 $M$ $HC_5H_3O_3$ and 20.0 mL of 0.22 $M$ $NaC_5H_3O_3$ and diluting the total volume to 125 mL; **(c)** a solution prepared by adding 50.0 mL of 1.65 $M$ NaOH solution to 0.500 L of 0.0850 $M$ $HC_5H_3O_3$.

**17.84** The acid–base indicator bromcresol green is a weak acid. The yellow acid and blue base forms of the indicator are present in equal concentrations in a solution when the pH is 4.68. What is the $pK_a$ for bromcresol green?

**17.85** Equal quantities of 0.010 $M$ solutions of an acid HA and a base B are mixed. The pH of the resulting solution is 9.2. **(a)** Write the equilibrium equation and equilibrium-constant expression for the reaction between HA and B. **(b)** If $K_a$ for HA is $8.0 \times 10^{-5}$, what is the value of the equilibrium constant for the reaction between HA and B? **(c)** What is the value of $K_b$ for B?

**17.86** Two buffers are prepared by adding an equal number of moles of formic acid (HCOOH) and sodium formate (HCOONa) to enough water to make 1.00 L of solution. Buffer A is prepared using 1.00 mol each of formic acid and sodium formate. Buffer B is prepared by using 0.010 mol of each. **(a)** Calculate the pH of each buffer, and explain why they are equal. **(b)** Which buffer will have the greater buffer capacity? Explain. **(c)** Calculate the change in pH for each buffer upon the addition of 1.0 mL of 1.00 $M$ HCl. **(d)** Calculate the change in pH for each buffer upon the addition of 10 mL of 1.00 $M$ HCl. **(e)** Discuss your answers for parts (c) and (d) in light of your response to part (b).

**17.87** A biochemist needs 750 mL of an acetic acid–sodium acetate buffer with pH 4.50. Solid sodium acetate ($CH_3COONa$) and glacial acetic acid ($CH_3COOH$) are available. Glacial acetic acid is 99% $CH_3COOH$ by mass and has a density of 1.05 g/mL. If the buffer is to be 0.15 $M$ in $CH_3COOH$, how many grams of $CH_3COONa$ and how many milliliters of glacial acetic acid must be used?

**17.88** A sample of 0.2140 g of an unknown monoprotic acid was dissolved in 25.0 mL of water and titrated with 0.0950 $M$ NaOH. The acid required 27.4 mL of base to reach the equivalence point. **(a)** What is the molar mass of the acid? **(b)** After 15.0 mL of base had been added in the titration, the pH was found to be 6.50. What is the $K_a$ for the unknown acid?

**17.89** A sample of 0.1687 g of an unknown monoprotic acid was dissolved in 25.0 mL of water and titrated with 0.1150 $M$ NaOH. The acid required 15.5 mL of base to reach the equivalence point. **(a)** What is the molecular weight of the acid? **(b)** After 7.25 mL of base had been added in the titration, the pH was found to be 2.85. What is the $K_a$ for the unknown acid?

**17.90** Show that the pH at the halfway point of a titration of a weak acid with a strong base (where the volume of added base is half of that needed to reach the equivalence point) is equal to $pK_a$ for the acid.

**17.91** A hypothetical weak acid, HA, was combined with NaOH in the following proportions: 0.20 mol of HA, 0.080 mol of NaOH. The mixture was diluted to a total volume of 1.0 L and the pH measured. **(a)** If pH = 4.80, what is the $pK_a$ of the acid? **(b)** How many additional moles of NaOH should be added to the solution to increase the pH to 5.00?

**[17.92]** What is the pH of a solution made by mixing 0.30 mol NaOH, 0.25 mol $Na_2HPO_4$, and 0.20 mol $H_3PO_4$ with water and diluting to 1.00 L?

**[17.93]** Suppose you want to do a physiological experiment that calls for a pH 6.50 buffer. You find that the organism with which you are working is not sensitive to the weak acid $H_2X$ ($K_{a1} = 2 \times 10^{-2}$; $K_{a2} = 5.0 \times 10^{-7}$) or its sodium salts. You have available a 1.0 $M$ solution of this acid and a 1.0 $M$ solution of NaOH. How much of the NaOH solution should be added to 1.0 L of the acid to give a buffer at pH 6.50? (Ignore any volume change.)

**[17.94]** How many microliters of 1.000 $M$ NaOH solution must be added to 25.00 mL of a 0.1000 $M$ solution of lactic acid [$CH_3CH(OH)COOH$ or $HC_3H_5O_3$] to produce a buffer with pH = 3.75?

**17.95** A person suffering from anxiety begins breathing rapidly and as a result suffers alkalosis, an increase in blood pH. **(a)** Using Equation 17.10, explain how rapid breathing can cause the pH of blood to increase. **(b)** One cure for this problem is breathing in a paper bag. Why does this procedure lower blood pH?

**17.96** For each pair of compounds, use $K_{sp}$ values to determine which has the greater molar solubility: **(a)** CdS or CuS, **(b)** $PbCO_3$ or $BaCrO_4$, **(c)** $Ni(OH)_2$ or $NiCO_3$, **(d)** AgI or $Ag_2SO_4$.

**17.97** The solubility of $CaCO_3$ is pH dependent. **(a)** Calculate the molar solubility of $CaCO_3$ ($K_{sp} = 4.5 \times 10^{-9}$) neglecting the acid–base character of the carbonate ion. **(b)** Use the $K_b$ expression for the $CO_3^{2-}$ ion to determine the equilibrium constant for the reaction

$$CaCO_3(s) + H_2O(l) \rightleftharpoons Ca^{2+}(aq) + HCO_3^-(aq) + OH^-(aq)$$

**(c)** If we assume that the only sources of $Ca^{2+}$, $HCO_3^-$, and $OH^-$ ions are from the dissolution of $CaCO_3$, what is the molar solubility of $CaCO_3$ using the preceding expression? What is the pH? **(d)** If the pH is buffered at 8.2 (as is historically typical for the ocean), what is the molar solubility of $CaCO_3$? **(e)** If the pH is buffered at 7.5, what is the molar solubility of $CaCO_3$? How much does this drop in pH increase solubility?

**17.98** Tooth enamel is composed of hydroxyapatite, whose simplest formula is $Ca_5(PO_4)_3OH$, and whose corresponding $K_{sp} = 6.8 \times 10^{-27}$. As discussed in the "Chemistry and Life" box on page 730, fluoride in fluorinated water or in toothpaste reacts with hydroxyapatite to form fluoroapatite, $Ca_5(PO_4)_3F$, whose $K_{sp} = 1.0 \times 10^{-60}$. **(a)** Write the expression for the solubility-constant for hydroxyapatite and for fluoroapatite. **(b)** Calculate the molar solubility of each of these compounds.

**17.99** Use the solubility-product constant for $Cr(OH)_3$ ($K_{sp} = 6.7 \times 10^{-31}$) and the formation constant for $Cr(OH)_4^-$ from Table 17.1 to determine the concentration of $Cr(OH)_4^-$ in a solution that is buffered at pH = 10.0 and is in equilibrium with solid $Cr(OH)_3$.

**17.100** Calculate the solubility of $Mg(OH)_2$ in 0.50 $M$ $NH_4Cl$.

**17.101** The solubility-product constant for barium permanganate, $Ba(MnO_4)_2$, is $2.5 \times 10^{-10}$. Assume that solid $Ba(MnO_4)_2$ is in equilibrium with a solution of $KMnO_4$. What concentration of $KMnO_4$ is required to establish a concentration of $2.0 \times 10^{-8}$ $M$ for the $Ba^{2+}$ ion in solution?

**17.102** Calculate the ratio of $[Ca^{2+}]$ to $[Fe^{2+}]$ in a lake in which the water is in equilibrium with deposits of both $CaCO_3$ and $FeCO_3$. Assume that the water is slightly basic and that the hydrolysis of the carbonate ion can therefore be ignored.

**[17.103]** The solubility products of $PbSO_4$ and $SrSO_4$ are $6.3 \times 10^{-7}$ and $3.2 \times 10^{-7}$, respectively. What are the values of $[SO_4^{2-}]$, $[Pb^{2+}]$, and $[Sr^{2+}]$ in a solution at equilibrium with both substances?

**[17.104]** A buffer of what pH is needed to give a $Mg^{2+}$ concentration of $3.0 \times 10^{-2}$ $M$ in equilibrium with solid magnesium oxalate?

**[17.105]** The value of $K_{sp}$ for $Mg_3(AsO_4)_2$ is $2.1 \times 10^{-20}$. The $AsO_4^{3-}$ ion is derived from the weak acid $H_3AsO_4$ ($pK_{a1} = 2.22$; $pK_{a2} = 6.98$; $pK_{a3} = 11.50$). When asked to calculate the molar solubility of $Mg_3(AsO_4)_2$ in water, a student used the $K_{sp}$ expression and assumed that $[Mg^{2+}] = 1.5[AsO_4^{3-}]$. Why was this a mistake?

**[17.106]** The solubility product for $Zn(OH)_2$ is $3.0 \times 10^{-16}$. The formation constant for the hydroxo complex, $Zn(OH)_4^{2-}$, is $4.6 \times 10^{17}$. What concentration of $OH^-$ is required to dissolve 0.015 mol of $Zn(OH)_2$ in a liter of solution?

**[17.107]** The value of $K_{sp}$ for $Cd(OH)_2$ is $2.5 \times 10^{-14}$. **(a)** What is the molar solubility of $Cd(OH)_2$? **(b)** The solubility of $Cd(OH)_2$ can be increased through formation of the complex ion $CdBr_4^{2-}$ ($K_f = 5 \times 10^3$). If solid $Cd(OH)_2$ is added to a NaBr solution, what would the initial concentration of NaBr need to be in order to increase the molar solubility of $Cd(OH)_2$ to $1.0 \times 10^{-3}$ moles per liter?

# INTEGRATIVE EXERCISES

**17.108** **(a)** Write the net ionic equation for the reaction that occurs when a solution of hydrochloric acid (HCl) is mixed with a solution of sodium formate ($NaCHO_2$). **(b)** Calculate the equilibrium constant for this reaction. **(c)** Calculate the equilibrium concentrations of $Na^+$, $Cl^-$, $H^+$, $CHO_2^-$, and $HCHO_2$ when 50.0 mL of 0.15 $M$ HCl is mixed with 50.0 mL of 0.15 $M$ $NaCHO_2$.

**17.109** **(a)** A 0.1044-g sample of an unknown monoprotic acid requires 22.10 mL of 0.0500 $M$ NaOH to reach the end point. What is the molecular weight of the unknown? **(b)** As the acid is titrated, the pH of the solution after the addition of 11.05 mL of the base is 4.89. What is the $K_a$ for the acid? **(c)** Using Appendix D, suggest the identity of the acid. Do both the molecular weight and $K_a$ value agree with your choice?

**17.110** A sample of 7.5 L of $NH_3$ gas at 22 °C and 735 torr is bubbled into a 0.50-L solution of 0.40 $M$ HCl. Assuming that all the $NH_3$ dissolves and that the volume of the solution remains 0.50 L, calculate the pH of the resulting solution.

**17.111** Aspirin has the structural formula

At body temperature (37 °C), $K_a$ for aspirin equals $3 \times 10^{-5}$. If two aspirin tablets, each having a mass of 325 mg, are dissolved in a full stomach whose volume is 1 L and whose pH is 2, what percent of the aspirin is in the form of neutral molecules?

**17.112** What is the pH at 25 °C of water saturated with $CO_2$ at a partial pressure of 1.10 atm? The Henry's law constant for $CO_2$ at 25 °C is $3.1 \times 10^{-2}$ mol/L-atm. The $CO_2$ is an acidic oxide, reacting with $H_2O$ to form $H_2CO_3$.

**17.113** Excess $Ca(OH)_2$ is shaken with water to produce a saturated solution. The solution is filtered, and a 50.00-mL sample titrated with HCl requires 11.23 mL of 0.0983 $M$ HCl to reach the end point. Calculate $K_{sp}$ for $Ca(OH)_2$. Compare your result with that in Appendix D. Do you think the solution was kept at 25 °C?

**17.114** The osmotic pressure of a saturated solution of strontium sulfate at 25 °C is 21 torr. What is the solubility product of this salt at 25 °C?

**17.115** A concentration of 10–100 parts per billion (by mass) of $Ag^+$ is an effective disinfectant in swimming pools. However, if the concentration exceeds this range, the $Ag^+$ can cause adverse health effects. One way to maintain an appropriate concentration of $Ag^+$ is to add a slightly soluble salt to the pool. Using $K_{sp}$ values from Appendix D, calculate the equilibrium concentration of $Ag^+$ in parts per billion that would exist in equilibrium with **(a)** AgCl, **(b)** AgBr, **(c)** AgI.

**[17.116]** Fluoridation of drinking water is employed in many places to aid in the prevention of tooth decay. Typically the $F^-$ ion concentration is adjusted to about 1 ppb. Some water supplies are also "hard"; that is, they contain certain cations such as $Ca^{2+}$ that interfere with the action of soap. Consider a case where the concentration of $Ca^{2+}$ is 8 ppb. Could a precipitate of $CaF_2$ form under these conditions? (Make any necessary approximations.)

# WHAT'S AHEAD

**18.1** EARTH'S ATMOSPHERE
We begin with a look at the temperature profile, pressure profile, and chemical composition of Earth's atmosphere. We then examine *photoionization* and *photodissociation*, reactions that result from atmospheric absorption of solar radiation.

**18.2** HUMAN ACTIVITIES AND EARTH'S ATMOSPHERE
We next examine the effect human activities have on the atmosphere. We discuss how atmospheric ozone is depleted by reactions involving human-made gases and how acid rain and smog are the result of atmospheric reactions involving compounds produced by human activity.

**18.3** EARTH'S WATER
We examine the global water cycle, which describes how water moves from the ground to surface water to the atmosphere and back into the ground. We compare the chemical compositions of *seawater, freshwater,* and *groundwater.*

**THE BIG ISLAND** of Hawaii.

# CHEMISTRY OF THE ENVIRONMENT

**THE RICHNESS OF LIFE ON** Earth, represented in the chapter-opening photograph, is, as far as we know, unique. Earth's atmosphere, the energy received from the Sun, and the abundance of water on our planet are all features currently believed to be necessary for life.

As technology has advanced and the world human population has increased, humans have put new and greater stresses on the environment. Paradoxically, the very technology that can cause pollution also provides the tools to help understand and manage the environment in a beneficial way. Chemistry is often at the heart of environmental issues. The economic growth of both developed and developing nations depends critically on chemical processes that range from treatment of water supplies to industrial processes. Some of these processes produce products or by-products that are harmful to the environment.

We are now in a position to apply the principles we have learned in preceding chapters to an understanding of how our environment operates and how human activities affect it. To understand and protect the environment in which we live, we must understand how human-made and natural chemical compounds interact on land and in the sea and sky. Our daily decisions as consumers mirror those of leading experts and governmental leaders: In making each decision, we must weigh the costs versus the benefits of our actions. Unfortunately, the environmental impacts of our decisions are often subtle and not immediately evident.

## 18.1 | EARTH'S ATMOSPHERE

Because most of us have never been very far from Earth's surface, we often take for granted the many ways in which the atmosphere determines the environment in which we live. In this section we examine some of the important characteristics of our planet's atmosphere.

The temperature of the atmosphere varies with altitude (◄ **FIGURE 18.1**), and the atmosphere is divided into four regions based on this temperature profile. Just above the surface, in the **troposphere**, the temperature normally decreases with increasing altitude, reaching a minimum of about 215 K at about 10 km. Nearly all of us live our entire lives in the troposphere. Howling winds and soft breezes, rain, and sunny skies—all that we normally think of as "weather"—occur in this region. Commercial jet aircraft typically fly about 10 km (33,000 ft) above Earth, an altitude that defines the upper limit of the troposphere, which we call the *tropopause*.

Above the tropopause, air temperature increases with altitude, reaching a maximum of about 275 K at about 50 km. The region from 10 km to 50 km is the **stratosphere**, and above it are the *mesosphere* and *thermosphere*. Notice in Figure 18.1 that the temperature extremes that form the boundaries between adjacent regions are denoted by the suffix *-pause*. The boundaries are important because gases mix across them relatively slowly. For example, pollutant gases generated in the troposphere pass through the tropopause and find their way into the stratosphere only very slowly.

Atmospheric pressure decreases with increasing elevation (Figure 18.1), declining much more rapidly at lower elevations than at higher ones because of the atmosphere's compressibility. Thus, the pressure decreases from an average value of 760 torr (101 kPa) at sea level to $2.3 \times 10^{-3}$ torr ($3.1 \times 10^{-4}$ kPa) at 100 km, to only $1.0 \times 10^{-6}$ torr ($1.3 \times 10^{-7}$ kPa) at 200 km.

The troposphere and stratosphere together account for 99.9% of the mass of the atmosphere, 75% of which is the mass in the troposphere. Consequently, most of the chemistry that follows focuses on these two regions.

**GO FIGURE**

**At what altitude is the atmospheric temperature lowest?**

▲ **FIGURE 18.1** **Temperature and pressure in the atmosphere vary as a function of altitude above sea level.**

## Composition of the Atmosphere

Earth's atmosphere is constantly bombarded by radiation and energetic particles from the Sun. This barrage of energy has profound chemical and physical effects, especially in the upper regions of the atmosphere, above about 80 km (▶ **FIGURE 18.2**). In addition, because of Earth's gravitational field, heavier atoms and molecules tend to sink in the atmosphere, leaving lighter atoms and molecules at the top of the atmosphere. (This is why, as just noted, 75 percent of the atmosphere's mass is in the troposphere.) Because of all these factors, the composition of the atmosphere is not uniform.

▶ **TABLE 18.1** shows the composition of dry air near sea level. Note that although traces of many substances are present, $N_2$ and $O_2$ make up about 99% of sea-level air. The noble gases and $CO_2$ make up most of the remainder.

| TABLE 18.1 • The Major Components of Dry Air Near Sea Level | | |
|---|---|---|
| **Component\*** | **Content (mole fraction)** | **Molar Mass (g/mol)** |
| Nitrogen | 0.78084 | 28.013 |
| Oxygen | 0.20948 | 31.998 |
| Argon | 0.00934 | 39.948 |
| Carbon dioxide | 0.000382 | 44.0099 |
| Neon | 0.00001818 | 20.183 |
| Helium | 0.00000524 | 4.003 |
| Methane | 0.000002 | 16.043 |
| Krypton | 0.00000114 | 83.80 |
| Hydrogen | 0.0000005 | 2.0159 |
| Nitrous oxide | 0.0000005 | 44.0128 |
| Xenon | 0.000000087 | 131.30 |

\*Ozone, sulfur dioxide, nitrogen dioxide, ammonia, and carbon monoxide are present as trace gases in variable amounts.

High-energy solar particles create excited N and O atoms; visible light results as electrons in these atoms fall from upper-level states to lower-level states

▲ **FIGURE 18.2**  **The aurora borealis (northern lights).**

When applied to substances in aqueous solution, the concentration unit *parts per million* refers to grams of substance per million grams of solution. ⚭ (Section 13.4) When dealing with gases, however, 1 ppm means one part by *volume* in 1 million volumes of the whole. Because volume is proportional to number of moles of gas via the ideal-gas equation ($PV = nRT$), volume fraction and mole fraction are the same. Thus, 1 ppm of a trace constituent of the atmosphere amounts to 1 mol of that constituent in 1 million moles of air; that is, the concentration in parts per million is equal to the mole fraction times $10^6$. For example, Table 18.1 lists the mole fraction of $CO_2$ in the atmosphere as 0.000382, which means its concentration in parts per million is $0.000382 \times 10^6 = 382$ ppm.

Other minor constituents of the troposphere, in addition to $CO_2$, are listed in ▼ TABLE 18.2.

Before we consider the chemical processes that occur in the atmosphere, let's review some of the properties of the two major components, $N_2$ and $O_2$. Recall that the $N_2$ molecule possesses a triple bond between the nitrogen atoms. ⚭ (Section 8.3) This very strong bond (bond energy 941 kJ/mol) is largely responsible for the very low reactivity of $N_2$. The bond energy in $O_2$ is only 495 kJ/mol, making $O_2$ much more reactive than $N_2$. For example, oxygen reacts with many substances to form oxides. The oxides of nonmetals, such as $SO_2$, usually form acidic solutions when dissolved in water. The oxides of active metals, such as CaO, form basic solutions when dissolved in water. ⚭ (Section 7.7)

| TABLE 18.2 • Sources and Typical Concentrations of Some Minor Atmospheric Constituents | | |
|---|---|---|
| **Constituent** | **Sources** | **Typical Concentration** |
| Carbon dioxide, $CO_2$ | Decomposition of organic matter, release from oceans, fossil-fuel combustion | 382 ppm throughout troposphere |
| Carbon monoxide, CO | Decomposition of organic matter, industrial processes, fossil-fuel combustion | 0.05 ppm in unpolluted air; 1–50 ppm in urban areas |
| Methane, $CH_4$ | Decomposition of organic matter, natural-gas seepage, livestock emissions | 1.77 ppm throughout troposphere |
| Nitric oxide, NO | Atmospheric electrical discharges, internal combustion engines, combustion of organic matter | 0.01 ppm in unpolluted air; 0.2 ppm in smog |
| Ozone, $O_3$ | Atmospheric electrical discharges, diffusion from the stratosphere, photochemical smog | 0 to 0.01 ppm in unpolluted air; 0.5 ppm in photochemical smog |
| Sulfur dioxide, $SO_2$ | Volcanic gases, forest fires, bacterial action, fossil-fuel combustion, industrial processes | 0 to 0.01 ppm in unpolluted air; 0.1–2 ppm in polluted urban areas |

---

**SAMPLE EXERCISE 18.1** Calculating the Concentration of Water in Air

What is the concentration, in parts per million, of water vapor in a sample of air if the partial pressure of the water is 0.80 torr and the total pressure of the air is 735 torr?

**SOLUTION**

**Analyze** We are given the partial pressure of water vapor and the total pressure of an air sample and asked to determine the water vapor concentration.

**Plan** Recall that the partial pressure of a component in a mixture of gases is given by the product of its mole fraction and the total pressure of the mixture ⚬⚬⚬ (Section 10.6):

$$P_{H_2O} = X_{H_2O}P_t$$

**Solve** Solving for the mole fraction of water vapor in the mixture, $X_{H_2O}$, gives

$$X_{H_2O} = \frac{P_{H_2O}}{P_t} = \frac{0.80 \text{ torr}}{735 \text{ torr}} = 0.0011$$

The concentration in ppm is the mole fraction times $10^6$:

$$0.0011 \times 10^6 = 1100 \text{ ppm}$$

**PRACTICE EXERCISE**

The concentration of CO in a sample of air is 4.3 ppm. What is the partial pressure of the CO if the total air pressure is 695 torr?

**Answer:** $3.0 \times 10^{-3}$ torr

## Photochemical Reactions in the Atmosphere

Although the atmosphere beyond the stratosphere contains only a small fraction of the atmospheric mass, it forms the outer defense against the hail of radiation and high-energy particles that continuously bombard Earth. As the bombarding radiation passes through the upper atmosphere, it causes two kinds of chemical changes: *photodissociation* and *photoionization*. These processes protect us from high-energy radiation by absorbing most of the radiation before it reaches the troposphere. If it were not for these photochemical processes, plant and animal life as we know it could not exist on Earth.

The Sun emits radiant energy over a wide range of wavelengths (▼ **FIGURE 18.3**). To understand the connection between the wavelength of radiation and its effect on

---

⚠️ GO FIGURE

**Why doesn't the solar spectrum at sea level perfectly match the solar spectrum outside the atmosphere?**

▶ **FIGURE 18.3 The solar spectrum above Earth's atmosphere compared to that at sea level.** The more structured curve at sea level is due to gases in the atmosphere absorbing specific wavelengths of light. "Flux," the unit on the vertical axis, is light energy per area per unit of time.

atoms and molecules, recall that electromagnetic radiation can be pictured as a stream of photons. ∞ (Section 6.2) The energy of each photon is given by $E = h\nu$, where $h$ is Planck's constant and $\nu$ is the radiation frequency. For a chemical change to occur when radiation strikes atoms or molecules, two conditions must be met. First, the incoming photons must have sufficient energy to break a chemical bond or remove an electron from the atom or molecule. Second, the atoms or molecules being bombarded must absorb these photons. When these requirements are met, the energy of the photons is used to do the work associated with some chemical change.

The rupture of a chemical bond resulting from absorption of a photon by a molecule is called **photodissociation**. No ions are formed when the bond between two atoms is cleaved by photodissociation. Instead, half the bonding electrons stay with one atom and half stay with the other atom. The result is two electrically neutral particles.

One of the most important processes occurring above an altitude of about 120 km is photodissociation of the oxygen molecule:

$$\ddot{\text{O}}{=}\ddot{\text{O}} + h\nu \longrightarrow \ddot{\ddot{\text{O}}} + \ddot{\ddot{\text{O}}} \qquad [18.1]$$

The minimum energy required to cause this change is determined by the bond energy (or *dissociation energy*) of $O_2$, 495 kJ/mol.

---

**SAMPLE EXERCISE 18.2** | **Calculating the Wavelength Required to Break a Bond**

What is the maximum wavelength of light, in nanometers, that has enough energy per photon to dissociate the $O_2$ molecule?

**SOLUTION**

**Analyze** We are asked to determine the wavelength of a photon that has just enough energy to break the O=O double bond in $O_2$.

**Plan** We first need to calculate the energy required to break the O=O double bond in one molecule and then find the wavelength of a photon of this energy.

**Solve** The dissociation energy of $O_2$ is 495 kJ/mol. Using this value and Avogadro's number, we can calculate the amount of energy needed to break the bond in a single $O_2$ molecule:

$$\left(495 \times 10^3 \, \frac{\text{J}}{\text{mol}}\right)\left(\frac{1 \, \text{mol}}{6.022 \times 10^{23} \, \text{molecules}}\right) = 8.22 \times 10^{-19} \, \frac{\text{J}}{\text{molecule}}$$

We next use the Planck relationship, $E = h\nu$, ∞ (Equation 6.2) to calculate the frequency $\nu$ of a photon that has this amount of energy:

$$\nu = \frac{E}{h} = \frac{8.22 \times 10^{-19} \, \text{J}}{6.626 \times 10^{-34} \, \text{J-s}} = 1.24 \times 10^{15} \, \text{s}^{-1}$$

Finally, we use the relationship between frequency and wavelength ∞ (Section 6.1) to calculate the wavelength of the light:

$$\lambda = \frac{c}{\nu} = \left(\frac{3.00 \times 10^8 \, \text{m/s}}{1.24 \times 10^{15}/\text{s}}\right)\left(\frac{10^9 \, \text{nm}}{1 \, \text{m}}\right) = 242 \, \text{nm}$$

Thus, light of wavelength 242 nm, which is in the ultraviolet region of the electromagnetic spectrum, has sufficient energy per photon to photodissociate an $O_2$ molecule. Because photon energy increases as wavelength *decreases*, any photon of wavelength *shorter* than 242 nm will have sufficient energy to dissociate $O_2$.

**PRACTICE EXERCISE**

The bond energy in $N_2$ is 941 kJ/mol. What is the longest wavelength a photon can have and still have sufficient energy to dissociate $N_2$?

*Answer:* 127 nm

---

Fortunately for us, $O_2$ absorbs much of the high-energy, short-wavelength radiation from the solar spectrum before that radiation reaches the lower atmosphere. As it does, atomic oxygen, O, is formed. The dissociation of $O_2$ is very extensive at higher elevations. At 400 km, for example, only 1% of the oxygen is in the form of $O_2$; 99% is atomic oxygen. At 130 km, $O_2$ and atomic oxygen are just about equally abundant.

Below 130 km, $O_2$ is more abundant than atomic oxygen because most of the solar energy has been absorbed in the upper atmosphere.

The dissociation energy of $N_2$ is very high, 941 kJ/mol. Analogous to Practice Exercise 18.2, only photons having a wavelength shorter than 127 nm possess sufficient energy to dissociate $N_2$. Furthermore, $N_2$ does not readily absorb photons, even when they possess sufficient energy. As a result, very little atomic nitrogen is formed in the upper atmosphere by photodissociation of $N_2$.

Other photochemical processes besides photodissociation occur in the upper atmosphere, although their discovery has taken many twists and turns. In 1901 Guglielmo Marconi received a radio signal in St. John's, Newfoundland, that had been transmitted from Land's End, England, 2900 km away. Because people at the time thought radio waves traveled in straight lines, they assumed that the curvature of Earth's surface would make radio communication over large distances impossible. Marconi's successful experiment suggested that Earth's atmosphere in some way substantially affects radio-wave propagation. His discovery led to intensive study of the upper atmosphere. In about 1924, the existence of electrons in the upper atmosphere was established by experimental studies.

The electrons in the upper atmosphere result mainly from **photoionization**, which occurs when a molecule in the upper atmosphere absorbs solar radiation and the absorbed energy causes an electron to be ejected from the molecule. The molecule then becomes a positively charged ion. For photoionization to occur, therefore, a molecule must absorb a photon, and the photon must have enough energy to remove an electron.  (Section 7.4)

Four important photoionization processes occurring in the atmosphere above about 90 km are shown in ▼ TABLE 18.3. Photons of any wavelength shorter than the maximum lengths given in the table have enough energy to cause photoionization. A look back at Figure 18.3, however, shows you that virtually all of these high-energy photons are filtered out of the radiation reaching Earth because they are absorbed by the upper atmosphere.

### ▲ GIVE IT SOME THOUGHT

Explain the difference between photoionization and photodissociation.

## Ozone in the Stratosphere

Although $N_2$, $O_2$, and atomic oxygen absorb photons having wavelengths shorter than 240 nm, ozone, $O_3$, is the key absorber of photons having wavelengths ranging from 240 to 310 nm, in the ultraviolet region of the electromagnetic spectrum. Ozone in the upper atmosphere protects us from these harmful high-energy photons, which would otherwise penetrate to Earth's surface. Let's consider how ozone forms in the upper atmosphere and how it absorbs photons.

By the time radiation from the Sun reaches an altitude of 90 km above Earth's surface, most of the short-wavelength radiation capable of photoionization has been absorbed. At this altitude, however, radiation capable of dissociating the $O_2$ molecule is sufficiently intense for photodissociation of $O_2$ (Equation 18.1) to remain important down to an altitude of 30 km. In the region between 30 and 90 km, however, the concentration of

**TABLE 18.3 • Photoionization Reactions for Four Components of the Atmosphere**

| Process | Ionization Energy (kJ/mol) | $\lambda_{max}$ (nm) |
|---|---|---|
| $N_2 + h\nu \longrightarrow N_2^+ + e^-$ | 1495 | 80.1 |
| $O_2 + h\nu \longrightarrow O_2^+ + e^-$ | 1205 | 99.3 |
| $O + h\nu \longrightarrow O^+ + e^-$ | 1313 | 91.2 |
| $NO + h\nu \longrightarrow NO^+ + e^-$ | 890 | 134.5 |

$O_2$ is much greater than the concentration of atomic oxygen. From this finding, we conclude that the oxygen atoms formed by photodissociation of $O_2$ in this region frequently collide with $O_2$ molecules and form ozone:

$$:\overset{..}{O} + O_2 \longrightarrow O_3^* \qquad [18.2]$$

The asterisk on $O_3$ denotes that the molecule contains an excess of energy. This reaction releases 105 kJ/mol. This energy must be transferred away from the $O_3^*$ molecule quickly or else the molecule will fly apart into $O_2$ and atomic O —a decomposition that is the reverse of the reaction by which $O_3^*$ is formed.

An energy-rich $O_3^*$ molecule can release its excess energy by colliding with another atom or molecule and transferring some of the excess energy to it. Let's use M to represent the atom or molecule with which $O_3^*$ collides. (Usually M is $N_2$ or $O_2$ because these are the most abundant molecules in the atmosphere.) The formation of $O_3^*$ and the transfer of excess energy to M are summarized by the equations

$$O(g) + O_2(g) \rightleftharpoons O_3^*(g) \qquad [18.3]$$

$$\underline{O_3^*(g) + M(g) \longrightarrow O_3(g) + M^*(g)} \qquad [18.4]$$

$$O(g) + O_2(g) + M(g) \longrightarrow O_3(g) + M^*(g) \qquad [18.5]$$

The rate at which the reactions of Equations 18.3 and 18.4 proceed depends on two factors that vary in opposite directions with increasing altitude. First, the Equation 18.3 reaction depends on the presence of O atoms. At low altitudes, most of the radiation energetic enough to dissociate $O_2$ into O atoms has been absorbed; thus, O atoms are more plentiful at higher altitudes. Second, Equations 18.3 and 18.4 both depend on molecular collisions. ∞ (Section 14.5) The concentration of molecules is greater at low altitudes, and so the rates of both reactions are greater at lower altitudes. Because these two reactions vary with altitude in opposite directions, the highest rate of $O_3$ formation occurs in a band at an altitude of about 50 km, near the stratopause (Figure 18.1). Overall, roughly 90% of Earth's ozone is found in the stratosphere.

◢ GIVE IT SOME THOUGHT

Why don't $O_2$ and $N_2$ molecules filter out ultraviolet light with wavelengths between 240 and 310 nm?

The photodissociation of ozone reverses the reaction that forms it. We thus have a cycle of ozone formation and decomposition, summarized as follows:

$$O_2(g) + h\nu \longrightarrow O(g) + O(g)$$

$$O(g) + O_2(g) + M(g) \longrightarrow O_3(g) + M^*(g) \quad \text{(heat released)}$$

$$O_3(g) + h\nu \longrightarrow O_2(g) + O(g)$$

$$O(g) + O(g) + M(g) \longrightarrow O_2(g) + M^*(g) \quad \text{(heat released)}$$

The first and third processes are photochemical; they use a solar photon to initiate a chemical reaction. The second and fourth are exothermic chemical reactions. The net result of the four reactions is a cycle in which solar radiant energy is converted into thermal energy. The ozone cycle in the stratosphere is responsible for the rise in temperature that reaches its maximum at the stratopause (Figure 18.1).

The reactions of the ozone cycle account for some, but not all, of the facts about the ozone layer. Many chemical reactions occur that involve substances other than oxygen. We must also consider the effects of turbulence and winds that mix up the stratosphere. A complicated picture results. The overall result of ozone formation and removal reactions, coupled with atmospheric turbulence and other factors, is to produce the upper-atmosphere ozone profile shown in ▶ FIGURE 18.4, with a maximum ozone concentration occurring at an altitude of about 25 km. This band of relatively high ozone concentration is referred to as the "ozone layer" or the "ozone shield."

◢ GO FIGURE

Estimate the ozone concentration in moles per liter for the peak value in this graph.

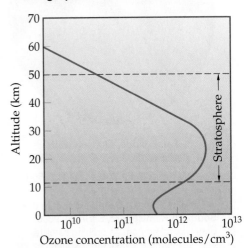

▲ FIGURE 18.4   **Variation in ozone concentration in the atmosphere as a function of altitude.**

Photons with wavelengths shorter than about 300 nm are energetic enough to break many kinds of single chemical bonds. Thus, the "ozone shield" is essential for our continued well-being. The ozone molecules that form this essential shield against high-energy radiation represent only a tiny fraction of the oxygen atoms present in the stratosphere, however, because these molecules are continually destroyed even as they are formed.

# 18.2 | HUMAN ACTIVITIES AND EARTH'S ATMOSPHERE

Both natural and *anthropogenic* (human-caused) events can modify Earth's atmosphere. One impressive natural event was the eruption of Mount Pinatubo in June 1991 (◀ FIGURE 18.5). The volcano ejected approximately 10 km³ of material into the stratosphere, causing a 10% drop in the amount of sunlight reaching Earth's surface during the next 2 years. That drop in sunlight led to a temporary 0.5 °C drop in Earth's surface temperature. The volcanic particles that made it to the stratosphere remained there for approximately 3 years, *raising* the temperature of the stratosphere by several degrees due to light absorption. Measurements of the stratospheric ozone concentration showed significantly increased ozone decomposition in this 3-year period.

Eruption of the Icelandic volcano Eyjafjallajökull in 2010, though not as large as the Pinatubo eruption, has similarly affected the atmosphere over large regions of the Northern Hemisphere.

▲ FIGURE 18.5 **Mount Pinatubo erupts, June 1991.**

## The Ozone Layer and Its Depletion

The ozone layer protects Earth's surface from damaging ultraviolet (UV) radiation. Therefore, if the concentration of ozone in the stratosphere decreases substantially, more UV radiation will reach Earth's surface, causing unwanted photochemical reactions, including reactions correlated with skin cancer. Satellite monitoring of ozone, which began in 1978, has revealed a depletion of ozone in the stratosphere that is particularly severe over Antarctica, a phenomenon known as the *ozone hole* (◀ FIGURE 18.6). The first scientific paper on this phenomenon appeared in 1985, and the National Aeronautics and Space Administration (NASA) maintains an "Ozone Hole Watch" website with daily updates and data from 1999 to the present.

In 1995 the Nobel Prize in Chemistry was awarded to F. Sherwood Rowland, Mario Molina, and Paul Crutzen for their studies of ozone depletion. In 1970 Crutzen showed that naturally occurring nitrogen oxides catalytically destroy ozone. Rowland and Molina recognized in 1974 that chlorine from **chlorofluorocarbons** (CFCs) may deplete the ozone layer. These substances, principally $CFCl_3$ and $CF_2Cl_2$, do not occur in nature and have been widely used as propellants in spray cans, as refrigerant and air-conditioner gases, and as foaming agents for plastics. They are virtually unreactive in the lower atmosphere. Furthermore, they are relatively insoluble in water and are therefore not removed from the atmosphere by rainfall or by dissolution in the oceans. Unfortunately, the lack of reactivity that makes them commercially useful also allows them to survive in the atmosphere and to diffuse into the stratosphere. It is estimated that several million tons of chlorofluorocarbons are now present in the atmosphere.

Total ozone (Dobson units)

| 110 | 220 | 330 | 440 | 550 |

▲ FIGURE 18.6 **Ozone present in the Southern Hemisphere, Sept. 24, 2006.** This data was taken from an orbiting satellite. This day had the lowest stratospheric ozone concentration yet recorded. One "Dobson unit" corresponds to $2.69 \times 10^{16}$ ozone molecules in a 1 cm² column of atmosphere.

As CFCs diffuse into the stratosphere, they are exposed to high-energy radiation, which can cause photodissociation. Because C—Cl bonds are considerably weaker than C—F bonds, free chlorine atoms are formed readily in the presence of light with wavelengths in the range from 190 to 225 nm, as shown in this typical reaction:

$$CF_2Cl_2(g) + h\nu \longrightarrow CF_2Cl(g) + Cl(g) \qquad [18.6]$$

Calculations suggest that chlorine atom formation occurs at the greatest rate at an altitude of about 30 km, the altitude at which ozone is at its highest concentration.

Atomic chlorine reacts rapidly with ozone to form chlorine monoxide and molecular oxygen:

$$Cl(g) + O_3(g) \longrightarrow ClO(g) + O_2(g) \qquad [18.7]$$

This reaction follows a second-order rate law with a very large rate constant:

$$\text{Rate} = k[Cl][O_3] \qquad k = 7.2 \times 10^9 \, M^{-1} s^{-1} \text{ at 298 K} \qquad [18.8]$$

Under certain conditions, the ClO generated in Equation 18.7 can react to regenerate free Cl atoms. One way that this can happen is by photodissociation of ClO:

$$ClO(g) + h\nu \longrightarrow Cl(g) + O(g) \qquad [18.9]$$

The Cl atoms generated in Equations 18.6 and 18.9 can react with more $O_3$, according to Equation 18.7. The result is a sequence of reactions that accomplishes the Cl-catalyzed decomposition of $O_3$ to $O_2$:

$$2\,Cl(g) + 2\,O_3(g) \longrightarrow 2\,ClO(g) + 2\,O_2(g)$$

$$2\,ClO(g) + h\nu \longrightarrow 2\,Cl(g) + 2\,O(g)$$

$$O(g) + O(g) \longrightarrow O_2(g)$$

$$\overline{2\,Cl(g) + 2\,O_3(g) + 2\,ClO(g) + 2\,O(g) \longrightarrow 2\,Cl(g) + 2\,ClO(g) + 3\,O_2(g) + 2\,O(g)}$$

The equation can be simplified by eliminating like species from each side to give

$$2\,O_3(g) \xrightarrow{\text{Cl}} 3\,O_2(g) \qquad [18.10]$$

Because the rate of Equation 18.7 increases linearly with [Cl], the rate at which ozone is destroyed increases as the quantity of Cl atoms increases. Thus, the greater the amount of CFCs that diffuse into the stratosphere, the faster the destruction of the ozone layer. Even though troposphere-to-stratosphere diffusion rates are slow, a thinning of the ozone layer over the South Pole has been observed, particularly during September and October (Figure 18.6).

### ▲ GIVE IT SOME THOUGHT

Since the rate of ozone destruction depends on [Cl], can Cl be considered a catalyst for the reaction of Equation 18.10?

Because of the environmental problems associated with CFCs, steps have been taken to limit their manufacture and use. A major step was the signing in 1987 of the Montreal Protocol on Substances That Deplete the Ozone Layer, in which participating nations agreed to reduce CFC production. More stringent limits were set in 1992, when representatives of approximately 100 nations agreed to ban the production and use of CFCs by 1996, with some exceptions for "essential uses." Since then, the production of CFCs has indeed dropped precipitously, and the size of the ozone hole has leveled off. Nevertheless, because CFCs are unreactive and because they diffuse so slowly into the stratosphere, scientists estimate that ozone depletion will continue for many years to come. What substances have replaced CFCs? At this time, the main alternatives are hydrofluorocarbons, compounds in which C—H bonds replace the C—Cl bonds of CFCs. One such compound in current use is $CH_2FCF_3$, known as HFC-134a.

There are no naturally occurring CFCs, but some natural sources contribute chlorine and bromine to the atmosphere, and, just like halogens from CFC, these naturally occurring Cl and Br atoms can participate in ozone-depleting reactions. The principal natural sources are methyl bromide and methyl chloride, which are emitted from the oceans. It is estimated that these molecules contribute less than a third of the total Cl and Br in the atmosphere; the remaining two-thirds is a result of human activities.

Volcanoes are a source of HCl, but generally the HCl they release reacts with water in the troposphere and does not make it to the upper atmosphere.

## Sulfur Compounds and Acid Rain

**TABLE 18.4 • Median Concentrations of Atmospheric Pollutants in a Typical Urban Atmosphere**

| Pollutant | Concentration (ppm) |
|---|---|
| Carbon monoxide | 10 |
| Hydrocarbons | 3 |
| Sulfur dioxide | 0.08 |
| Nitrogen oxides | 0.05 |
| Total oxidants (ozone and others) | 0.02 |

Sulfur-containing compounds are present to some extent in the natural, unpolluted atmosphere. They originate in the bacterial decay of organic matter, in volcanic gases, and from other sources listed in Table 18.2. The amount of these compounds released into the atmosphere worldwide from natural sources is about $24 \times 10^{12}$ g per year, less than the amount from human activities, about $79 \times 10^{12}$ g per year (principally related to combustion of fuels).

Sulfur compounds, chiefly sulfur dioxide, $SO_2$, are among the most unpleasant and harmful of the common pollutant gases. ◀ **TABLE 18.4** shows the concentrations of several pollutant gases in a *typical* urban environment (where by *typical* we mean one that is not particularly affected by smog). According to these data, the level of sulfur dioxide is 0.08 ppm or higher about half the time. This concentration is considerably lower than that of other pollutants, notably carbon monoxide. Nevertheless, $SO_2$ is regarded as the most serious health hazard among the pollutants shown, especially for people with respiratory difficulties.

Combustion of coal accounts for about 65% of the $SO_2$ released annually in the United States, and combustion of oil accounts for another 20%. The majority of this amount is from coal-burning electrical power plants, which generate about 50% of our electricity. The extent to which $SO_2$ emissions are a problem when coal is burned depends on the amount of sulfur in the coal. Because of concern about $SO_2$ pollution, low-sulfur coal is in greater demand and is thus more expensive. Much of the coal from east of the Mississippi is relatively high in sulfur content, up to 6% by mass. Much of the coal from the western states has a lower sulfur content, but also a lower heat content per unit mass, so the difference in sulfur content per unit of heat produced is not as large as is often assumed.

China, which gets 70 percent of its energy from coal, is the world's largest generator of $SO_2$, producing about 22 million tons annually. As a result, that nation has a major problem with $SO_2$ pollution and has set targets to reduce emissions with some success. In 2010, the U.S. Environmental Protection Agency set new standards to reduce $SO_2$ emissions, the first change in nearly 40 years. The old standard of 140 parts per billion, measured over 24 hours, will be replaced by a standard of 75 parts per billion, measured over 1 hour.

Sulfur dioxide is harmful to both human health and property; furthermore, atmospheric $SO_2$ can be oxidized to $SO_3$ by several pathways (such as reaction with $O_2$ or $O_3$). When $SO_3$ dissolves in water, it produces sulfuric acid:

$$SO_3(g) + H_2O(l) \longrightarrow H_2SO_4(aq)$$

Many of the environmental effects ascribed to $SO_2$ are actually due to $H_2SO_4$.

The presence of $SO_2$ in the atmosphere and the sulfuric acid it produces result in the phenomenon of **acid rain**. (Nitrogen oxides, which form nitric acid, are also major contributors to acid rain.) Uncontaminated rainwater generally has a pH value of about 5.6. The primary source of this natural acidity is $CO_2$, which reacts with water to form carbonic acid, $H_2CO_3$. Acid rain typically has a pH value of about 4. This acidity has affected many lakes in northern Europe, the northern United States, and Canada, reducing fish populations and affecting other parts of the ecological network in the lakes and surrounding forests.

The pH of most natural waters containing living organisms is between 6.5 and 8.5, but as ▶ **FIGURE 18.7** shows, freshwater pH values are far below 6.5 in many parts of the continental United States. At pH levels below 4.0, all vertebrates, most invertebrates, and many microorganisms are destroyed. The lakes most susceptible to damage are those with low concentrations of basic ions, such as $HCO_3^-$, that would act as a buffer to minimize changes in pH. Some of these lakes are recovering as sulfur emissions from fossil fuel combustion decrease, in part because of the Clean Air Act, which has resulted in a reduction of more than 40% in $SO_2$ emissions from power plants since 1980.

Because acids react with metals and with carbonates, acid rain is corrosive both to metals and to stone building materials. Marble and limestone, for example, whose major constituent is $CaCO_3$, are readily attacked by acid rain (▶ **FIGURE 18.8**). Billions of dollars each year are lost because of corrosion due to $SO_2$ pollution.

One way to reduce the quantity of $SO_2$ released into the environment is to remove sulfur from coal and oil before these fuels are burned. Although difficult and expensive,

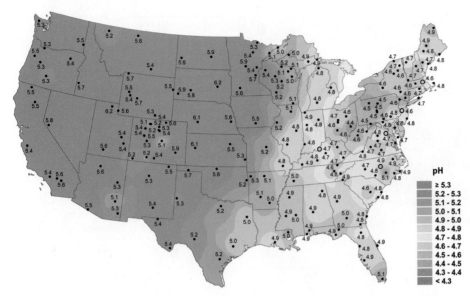

▲ **FIGURE 18.7 Water pH values from freshwater sites across the United States, 2008.** The numbered dots indicate the locations of monitoring stations.

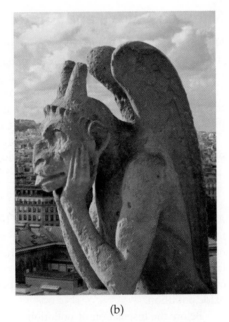

(a)                                          (b)

▲ **FIGURE 18.8 Damage from acid rain.** The right photograph, recently taken, shows how the statue has lost detail in its carvings.

several methods have been developed. Powdered limestone ($CaCO_3$), for example, can be injected into the furnace of a power plant, where it decomposes into lime (CaO) and carbon dioxide:

$$CaCO_3(s) \longrightarrow CaO(s) + CO_2(g)$$

The CaO then reacts with $SO_2$ to form calcium sulfite:

$$CaO(s) + SO_2(g) \longrightarrow CaSO_3(s)$$

The solid particles of $CaSO_3$, as well as much of the unreacted $SO_2$, can be removed from the furnace gas by passing it through an aqueous suspension of CaO (▶ **FIGURE 18.9**). Not all the $SO_2$ is removed, however, and given the enormous quantities of coal and oil burned worldwide, pollution by $SO_2$ will probably remain a problem for some time.

1 Powdered limestone ($CaCO_3$) and air injected into furnace

3 CaO reacts with $SO_2$ from reaction $S + O_2 \longrightarrow SO_2$ to form $CaSO_3$

4 $CaSO_3$ and unreacted $SO_2$ removed by passing through aqueous suspension of CaO

6 Cleaner air expelled through stack

High-sulfur coal

$CaCO_3(s) \longrightarrow$
$CaO(s) + CO_2(g)$

Furnace

$CaO(s) + SO_2(g) \longrightarrow CaSO_3(s)$

Water slurry removed

2 $CaCO_3$ decomposes to CaO (lime) and $CO_2$

5 $CaSO_3$ precipitated into watery slurry

▲ **FIGURE 18.9** **One method for removing $SO_2$ from combusted fuel.**

▲ **FIGURE 18.10** **Photochemical smog is produced largely by the action of sunlight on vehicle exhaust gases.**

▲ **GIVE IT SOME THOUGHT**

What chemical behavior associated with sulfur oxides gives rise to acid rain?

## Nitrogen Oxides and Photochemical Smog

Nitrogen oxides are primary components of smog, a phenomenon with which city dwellers are all too familiar. The term *smog* refers to the pollution condition that occurs in certain urban environments when weather conditions produce a relatively stagnant air mass. The smog made famous by Los Angeles, but now common in many other urban areas as well, is more accurately described as **photochemical smog** because photochemical processes play a major role in its formation (◀ **FIGURE 18.10**).

The majority of nitrogen oxide emissions (about 50%) comes from cars, buses, and other forms of transportation. Nitric oxide, NO, forms in small quantities in the cylinders of internal combustion engines in the reaction

$$N_2(g) + O_2(g) \rightleftharpoons 2\,NO(g) \quad \Delta H = 180.8 \text{ kJ} \qquad [18.11]$$

As noted in the "Chemistry Put to Work" box in Section 15.7, the equilibrium constant for this reaction increases from about $10^{-15}$ at 300 K to about 0.05 at 2400 K (approximate temperature in the cylinder of an engine during combustion). Thus, the reaction is more favorable at higher temperatures. In fact, some NO is formed in any high-temperature combustion. As a result, electrical power plants are also major contributors to nitrogen oxide pollution.

Before the installation of pollution-control devices on automobiles, typical emission levels of $NO_x$ were 4 grams per mile. (The $x$ is either 1 or 2 because both NO and $NO_2$ are formed, although NO predominates.) Starting in 2004, the auto emission standards for $NO_x$ called for a phased-in reduction to 0.07 g/mi by 2009, which was achieved.

In air, nitric oxide is rapidly oxidized to nitrogen dioxide:

$$2\,NO(g) + O_2(g) \rightleftharpoons 2\,NO_2(g) \quad \Delta H = -113.1 \text{ kJ} \qquad [18.12]$$

The equilibrium constant for this reaction decreases from about $10^{12}$ at 300 K to about $10^{-5}$ at 2400 K.

The photodissociation of $NO_2$ initiates the reactions associated with photochemical smog. Dissociation of $NO_2$ requires 304 kJ/mol, which corresponds to a photon wavelength of 393 nm. In sunlight, therefore, $NO_2$ dissociates to NO and O:

$$NO_2(g) + h\nu \longrightarrow NO(g) + O(g) \qquad [18.13]$$

The atomic oxygen formed undergoes several reactions, one of which gives ozone, as described earlier:

$$O(g) + O_2 + M(g) \longrightarrow O_3(g) + M^*(g) \qquad [18.14]$$

Although it is an essential UV screen in the upper atmosphere, ozone is an undesirable pollutant in the troposphere. It is extremely reactive and toxic, and breathing air that contains appreciable amounts of ozone can be especially dangerous for asthma sufferers, exercisers, and the elderly. We therefore have two ozone problems: excessive amounts in many urban environments, where it is harmful, and depletion in the stratosphere, where its presence is vital.

In addition to nitrogen oxides and carbon monoxide, an automobile engine also emits unburned *hydrocarbons* as pollutants. These organic compounds are the principal components of gasoline and of many compounds we use as fuel (propane, $C_3H_8$, and butane, $C_4H_{10}$; for example), but are major ingredients of smog. A typical engine without effective emission controls emits about 10 to 15 g of hydrocarbons per mile. Current standards require that hydrocarbon emissions be less than 0.075 g per mile. Hydrocarbons are also emitted naturally from living organisms (see "A Closer Look" box later in this section).

Reduction or elimination of smog requires that the ingredients essential to its formation be removed from automobile exhaust. Catalytic converters reduce the levels of $NO_x$ and hydrocarbons, two of the major ingredients of smog. (See the "Chemistry Put to Work: Catalytic Converters" in Section 14.7.)

## GIVE IT SOME THOUGHT

What photochemical reaction involving nitrogen oxides initiates the formation of photochemical smog?

## Greenhouse Gases: Water Vapor, Carbon Dioxide, and Climate

In addition to screening out harmful short-wavelength radiation, the atmosphere is essential in maintaining a reasonably uniform and moderate temperature on Earth's surface. Earth is in overall thermal balance with its surroundings. This means that the planet radiates energy into space at a rate equal to the rate at which it absorbs energy from the Sun. ▼ FIGURE 18.11 shows the distribution of radiation to and from Earth's

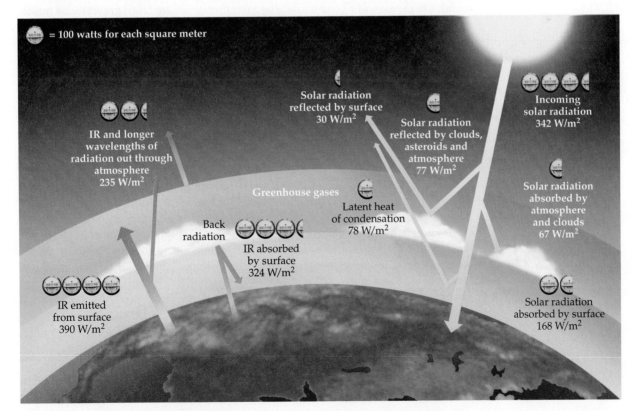

▲ FIGURE 18.11   **Earth's thermal balance.** The amount of radiation reaching the surface of the planet is approximately equal to the amount radiated back into space.

▲ **FIGURE 18.12** **Portions of the infrared radiation emitted by Earth's surface that are absorbed by atmospheric CO₂ and H₂O.**

surface, and ▲ **FIGURE 18.12** shows which portion of the infrared radiation leaving the surface is absorbed by atmospheric water vapor and carbon dioxide. In absorbing this radiation, these two atmospheric gases help maintain a livable uniform temperature at the surface by holding in, as it were, the infrared radiation, which we feel as heat.

The influence of $H_2O$, $CO_2$, and certain other atmospheric gases on Earth's temperature is called the *greenhouse effect* because in trapping infrared radiation these gases act much like the glass of a greenhouse. The gases themselves are called **greenhouse gases**.

Water vapor makes the largest contribution to the greenhouse effect. The partial pressure of water vapor in the atmosphere varies greatly from place to place and time to time but is generally highest near Earth's surface and drops off with increasing elevation. Because water vapor absorbs infrared radiation so strongly, it plays the major role in maintaining the atmospheric temperature at night, when the surface is emitting radiation into space and not receiving energy from the Sun. In very dry desert climates, where the water-vapor concentration is low, it may be extremely hot during the day but very cold at night. In the absence of a layer of water vapor to absorb and then radiate part of the infrared radiation back to Earth, the surface loses this radiation into space and cools off very rapidly.

Carbon dioxide plays a secondary but very important role in maintaining the surface temperature. The worldwide combustion of fossil fuels, principally coal and oil, on a prodigious scale in the modern era has sharply increased carbon dioxide levels in the atmosphere. To get a sense of the amount of $CO_2$ produced—for example, by the combustion of hydrocarbons and other carbon-containing substances, which are the components of fossil fuels—consider the combustion of butane, $C_4H_{10}$. Combustion of 1.00 g of $C_4H_{10}$ produces 3.03 g of $CO_2$. ∞ (Section 3.6) Similarly, a gallon (3.78 L) of gasoline (density 0.7 g/mL, approximate composition $C_8H_{18}$) produces about 8 kg of $CO_2$. Combustion of fossil fuels releases about $2.2 \times 10^{16}$ g (22 billion tons) of $CO_2$ into the atmosphere annually, with the largest quantity coming from transportation vehicles.

Much $CO_2$ is absorbed into oceans or used by plants. Nevertheless, we are now generating $CO_2$ much faster than it is being absorbed or used. Analysis of air trapped in ice cores taken from Antarctica and Greenland makes it possible to determine the

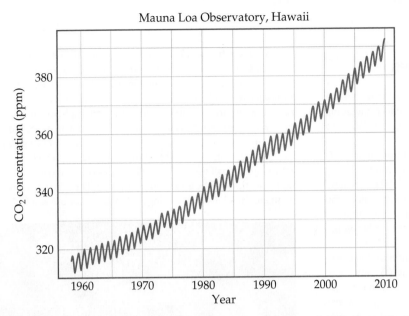

▲ **FIGURE 18.13   Rising CO₂ levels.** The sawtooth shape of the graph is due to regular seasonal variations in $CO_2$ concentration for each year.

atmospheric levels of $CO_2$ during the past 160,000 years. These measurements reveal that the level of $CO_2$ remained fairly constant from the last Ice Age, some 10,000 years ago, until roughly the beginning of the Industrial Revolution, about 300 years ago. Since that time, the concentration of $CO_2$ has increased by about 30% to a current high of about 386 ppm (▲ **FIGURE 18.13**).

A consensus is emerging among scientists that this increase in atmospheric $CO_2$ is perturbing Earth's climate and may be responsible for the observed increase in the average global air temperature of 0.3 °C to 0.6 °C over the past century. Scientists often use the term *climate change* instead of *global warming* to refer to this effect because as the Earth's temperature increases, it affects winds and ocean currents in ways that can cool some areas and warm others.

On the basis of present and expected future rates of fossil-fuel use, the atmospheric $CO_2$ level is expected to double from its present level sometime between 2050 and 2100. Computer models predict that this increase will result in an average global temperature increase of 1 °C to 3 °C. Because so many factors go into determining climate, we cannot predict with certainty what changes will occur because of this warming. Clearly, however, humanity has acquired the potential, by changing the concentrations of $CO_2$ and other heat-trapping gases in the atmosphere, to substantially alter the climate of the planet.

The climate change threat posed by atmospheric $CO_2$ has sparked considerable research into ways of capturing the gas at its largest combustion sources and storing it under ground or under the seafloor. There is also much interest in developing new ways to use $CO_2$ as a chemical feedstock. However, the approximately 115 million tons of $CO_2$ used annually by the global chemical industry is but a small fraction of the approximately 24 billion tons of annual $CO_2$ emissions. The use of $CO_2$ as a raw material will probably never be great enough to reduce its atmospheric concentration.

▲ **GIVE IT SOME THOUGHT**

Explain why nighttime temperatures remain higher in locations where there is higher humidity.

# A CLOSER LOOK

## OTHER GREENHOUSE GASES

Although $CO_2$ receives most of the attention, other gases contribute to the greenhouse effect, including methane, $CH_4$, hydrofluorocarbons (HFCs), and chlorofluorocarbons (CFCs).

HFCs have replaced CFCs in a host of applications, including refrigerants and air-conditioner gases. Although they do not contribute to the depletion of the ozone layer, HFCs are nevertheless strong greenhouse gases. Their total concentration in the atmosphere is still small (40 parts per trillion), but this amount is increasing about 10% per year. Thus, these substances are becoming increasingly important contributors to the greenhouse effect.

Methane already makes a significant contribution to the greenhouse effect. Each methane molecule has about 25 times the greenhouse effect of a $CO_2$ molecule. Studies of atmospheric gas trapped long ago in the Greenland and Antarctic ice sheets show that the atmospheric methane concentration has increased from pre-industrial values of 0.3 to 0.7 ppm to the present value of about 1.8 ppm. The major sources of methane are associated with agriculture and fossil-fuel use.

Methane is formed in biological processes that occur in low-oxygen environments. Anaerobic bacteria, which flourish in swamps and landfills, near the roots of rice plants, and in the digestive systems of cows and other ruminant animals, produce methane (▶ FIGURE 18.14). It also leaks into the atmosphere during natural-gas extraction and transport. It is estimated that about two-thirds of present-day methane emissions, which are increasing by about 1% per year, are related to human activities.

Methane has a half-life in the atmosphere of about 10 years, whereas $CO_2$ is much longer-lived. This might seem a good thing, but there are indirect effects to consider. Methane is oxidized in the stratosphere, producing water vapor, a powerful greenhouse gas that is otherwise virtually absent from the stratosphere. In the troposphere, methane is attacked by reactive species such as OH radicals or nitrogen oxides, eventually producing other greenhouse gases, such as $O_3$. It has been estimated that the climate-changing effects of $CH_4$ are more than half those of $CO_2$. Given this large contribution, important reductions of the greenhouse effect could be achieved by reducing methane emissions or capturing the emissions for use as a fuel.

▲ FIGURE 18.14 **Methane production.** Ruminant animals, such as cows and sheep, produce methane in their digestive systems.

# 18.3 | EARTH'S WATER

Water covers 72% of Earth's surface and is essential to life. Our bodies are about 65% water by mass. Because of extensive hydrogen bonding, water has unusually high melting and boiling points and a high heat capacity. ∞ (Section 11.2) Water's highly polar character is responsible for its exceptional ability to dissolve a wide range of ionic and polar-covalent substances. Many reactions occur in water, including reactions in which $H_2O$ itself is a reactant. Recall, for example, that $H_2O$ can participate in acid–base reactions as either a proton donor or a proton acceptor. ∞ (Section 16.3) All these properties play a role in our environment.

## The Global Water Cycle

All the water on Earth is connected in a global water cycle (▶ FIGURE 18.15). Most of the processes depicted here rely on the phase changes of water. For instance, warmed by the Sun, liquid water in the oceans evaporates into the atmosphere as water vapor and condenses into liquid water droplets that we see as clouds. Water droplets in the clouds can crystallize to ice, which can precipitate as hail or snow. Once on the ground, the hail or snow melts to liquid water, which soaks into the ground. If conditions are right, it is also possible for ice on the ground to sublime to water vapor in the atmosphere.

 GIVE IT SOME THOUGHT

Consider the phase diagram for water shown in Figure 11.28 (page 446). In what pressure range and in what temperature range must $H_2O$ exist in order for $H_2O(s)$ to sublime to $H_2O(g)$?

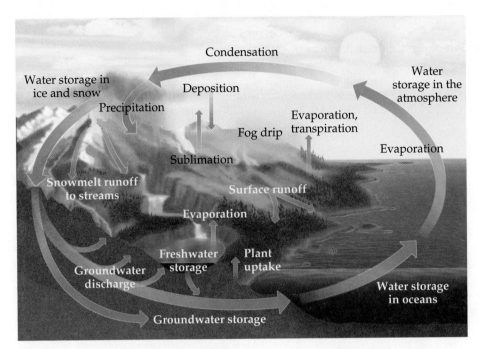

◀ **FIGURE 18.15  The global water cycle.**

## Salt Water: Earth's Oceans and Seas

The vast layer of salty water that covers so much of the planet is in actuality one large connected body and is generally constant in composition. For this reason, oceanographers speak of a *world ocean* rather than of the separate oceans we learn about in geography books.

The world ocean is huge, having a volume of $1.35 \times 10^9 \text{ km}^3$ and containing 97.2% of all the water on Earth. Of the remaining 2.8%, 2.1% is in the form of ice caps and glaciers. All the freshwater—in lakes, in rivers, and in the ground—amounts to only 0.6%. Most of the remaining 0.1% is in brackish (salty) water, such as that in the Great Salt Lake in Utah.

Seawater is often referred to as saline water. The **salinity** of seawater is the mass in grams of dry salts present in 1 kg of seawater. In the world ocean, salinity averages about 35. To put it another way, seawater contains about 3.5% dissolved salts by mass. The list of elements present in seawater is very long. Most, however, are present only in very low concentrations. ▼ TABLE 18.5 lists the 11 ionic species most abundant in seawater.

| **TABLE 18.5 • Ionic Constituents of Seawater Present in Concentrations Greater Than 0.001 g/kg (1 ppm)** | | |
|---|---|---|
| **Ionic Constituent** | **Salinity** | **Concentration ($M$)** |
| Chloride, $Cl^-$ | 19.35 | 0.55 |
| Sodium, $Na^+$ | 10.76 | 0.47 |
| Sulfate, $SO_4^{2-}$ | 2.71 | 0.028 |
| Magnesium, $Mg^{2+}$ | 1.29 | 0.054 |
| Calcium, $Ca^{2+}$ | 0.412 | 0.010 |
| Potassium, $K^+$ | 0.40 | 0.010 |
| Carbon dioxide* | 0.106 | $2.3 \times 10^{-3}$ |
| Bromide, $Br^-$ | 0.067 | $8.3 \times 10^{-4}$ |
| Boric acid, $H_3BO_3$ | 0.027 | $4.3 \times 10^{-4}$ |
| Strontium, $Sr^{2+}$ | 0.0079 | $9.1 \times 10^{-5}$ |
| Fluoride, $F^-$ | 0.0013 | $7.0 \times 10^{-5}$ |

*$CO_2$ is present in seawater as $HCO_3^-$ and $CO_3^{2-}$.

⚠ GO FIGURE

**Look at the trend in density as a function of depth; does it mirror the trend in salinity or in temperature?**

▲ **FIGURE 18.16** **Average temperature, salinity, and density of seawater as a function of depth.** (From Windows to the Universe, University Corporation for Atmospheric Research. Copyright © 2004 University Corporation for Atmospheric Research. All rights reserved.)

Seawater temperature, salinity, and density vary as a function of depth (▲ **FIGURE 18.16**). Sunlight penetrates well only 200 m into the water; the region between 200 m and 1000 m deep is the "twilight zone," where visible light is faint. Below 1000 m, the ocean is pitch-black and cold, about 4 °C. The transport of heat, salt, and other chemicals throughout the ocean is influenced by these changes in the physical properties of seawater, and in turn the changes in the way heat and substances are transported affects ocean currents and the global climate.

The sea is so vast that if the concentration of a substance in seawater is 1 part per billion ($1 \times 10^{-6}$ g per kilogram of water), there is $1 \times 10^{12}$ kg of the substance in the world ocean. Nevertheless, because of high extracting costs, only three substances are obtained from seawater in commercially important amounts: sodium chloride, bromine (from bromide salts), and magnesium (from its salts).

Absorption of $CO_2$ by the ocean plays a large role in global climate. Because carbon dioxide and water form carbonic acid, the $H_2CO_3$ concentration in the ocean increases as the water absorbs atmospheric $CO_2$. Most of the carbon in the ocean, however, is in the form of $HCO_3^-$ and $CO_3^{2-}$ ions, which form a buffer system that maintains the ocean's pH between 8.0 and 8.3. The pH of the ocean is predicted to decrease as the concentration of $CO_2$ in the atmosphere increases, as discussed in the "Chemistry and Life" box on ocean acidification in Section 17.5.

## Freshwater and Groundwater

*Freshwater* is the term used to denote natural waters that have low concentrations (less than 500 ppm) of dissolved salts and solids. Freshwater includes the waters of lakes, rivers, ponds, and streams. The United States is fortunate in its abundance of freshwater—$1.7 \times 10^{15}$ L (660 trillion gallons) is the estimated reserve, which is renewed by rainfall. An estimated $9 \times 10^{11}$ L of freshwater is used every day in the United States. Most of this is used for agriculture (41%) and hydroelectric power (39%), with small amounts for industry (6%), household needs (6%), and drinking water (1%). An adult drinks about 2 L of water per day. In the United States, our daily use of

▲ GO FIGURE

**What factors influence how long it takes for water to migrate from a deep aquifer to the surface?**

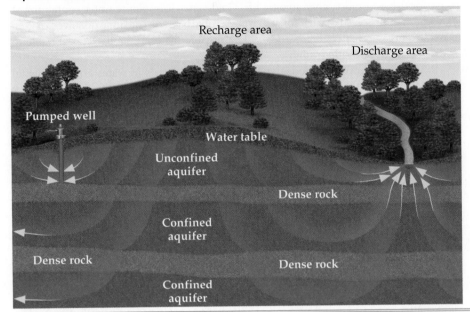

◄ **FIGURE 18.17  Groundwater is water located in aquifers below the soil.** An unconfined aquifer, that has no dense rock between it and the water table, can hold water for days or years. Confined aquifers can hold water for centuries or millenia, depending on their depth. Aquifers are discharged through wells or rivers, and are recharged from water flowing through the soil (e.g., from rain).

water per person far exceeds this subsistence level, amounting to an average of about 300 L/day for personal consumption and hygiene. We use about 8 L/person for cooking and drinking, about 120 L/person for cleaning (bathing, laundering, and housecleaning), 80 L/person for flushing toilets, and 80 L/person for watering lawns.

The total amount of freshwater on Earth is not a very large fraction of the total water present. Indeed, freshwater is one of our most precious resources. It forms by evaporation from the oceans and the land. The water vapor that accumulates in the atmosphere is transported by global atmospheric circulation, eventually returning to Earth as rain, snow, and other forms of precipitation (Figure 18.15).

As water runs off the land on its way to the oceans, it dissolves a variety of cations (mainly $Na^+$, $K^+$, $Mg^{2+}$, $Ca^{2+}$, and $Fe^{2+}$), anions (mainly $Cl^-$, $SO_4^{2-}$, and $HCO_3^-$), and gases (principally $O_2$, $N_2$, and $CO_2$). As we use water, it becomes laden with additional dissolved material, including the wastes of human society. As our population and output of environmental pollutants increase, we find that we must spend ever-increasing amounts of money and resources to guarantee a supply of freshwater.

Approximately 20% of the world's freshwater is under the soil, in the form of *groundwater*. Groundwater resides in *aquifers*, which are layers of porous rock that hold water. The water in aquifers can be very pure and accessible for human consumption if near the surface (▲ **FIGURE 18.17**). Dense rock that does not allow water to readily penetrate can hold groundwater for years or even millennia.

The nature of the rock that contains the groundwater has a large influence on the water's chemical composition. If minerals in the rock are water soluble to some extent, ions can leach out of the rock and remain dissolved in the groundwater. Arsenic in the form of $HAsO_4^{2-}$, $H_2AsO_4^-$, and $H_3AsO_3$ are found in groundwater across the world, most infamously in Bangladesh, at concentrations poisonous to humans.

# 18.4 | HUMAN ACTIVITIES AND EARTH'S WATER

All life on Earth depends on the availability of suitable water. Some organisms can thrive under temperature, pH, and ionic conditions where other organisms would die. Many human activities rely on waste disposal via Earth's waters, even today, and this practice can be detrimental to aquatic organisms.

▲ **FIGURE 18.18 Eutrophication.** This rapid accumulation of dead and decaying plant matter in a body of water uses up the water's oxygen supply, making the water unsuitable for aquatic animals.

## GO FIGURE

**What feature of this process is responsible for its being called *reverse* osmosis?**

Permeator

Hollow fibers of semipermeable membrane

Seawater pumped through at high pressure

Pure water to collector

Fiber

Water molecules pushed into hollow fibers

Solute particles cannot enter hollow fibers

▲ **FIGURE 18.19 Reverse osmosis.**

## Dissolved Oxygen and Water Quality

The amount of $O_2$ dissolved in water is an important indicator of water quality. Water fully saturated with air at 1 atm and 20 °C contains about 9 ppm of $O_2$. Oxygen is necessary for fish and most other aquatic life. Cold-water fish require water containing at least 5 ppm of dissolved oxygen for survival. Aerobic bacteria consume dissolved oxygen to oxidize organic materials for energy. The organic material the bacteria are able to oxidize is said to be **biodegradable**.

Excessive quantities of biodegradable organic materials in water are detrimental because they remove the oxygen necessary to sustain normal animal life. Typical sources of these biodegradable materials, which are called *oxygen-demanding wastes*, include sewage, industrial wastes from food-processing plants and paper mills, and liquid waste from meatpacking plants.

In the presence of oxygen, the carbon, hydrogen, nitrogen, sulfur, and phosphorus in biodegradable material end up mainly as $CO_2$, $HCO_3^-$, $H_2O$, $NO_3^-$, $SO_4^{2-}$, and phosphates. The formation of these oxidation products sometimes reduces the amount of dissolved oxygen to the point where aerobic bacteria can no longer survive. Anaerobic bacteria then take over the decomposition process, forming $CH_4$, $NH_3$, $H_2S$, $PH_3$, and other products, several of which contribute to the offensive odors of some polluted waters.

Plant nutrients, particularly nitrogen and phosphorus, contribute to water pollution by stimulating excessive growth of aquatic plants. The most visible results of excessive plant growth are floating algae and murky water. What is more significant, however, is that as plant growth becomes excessive, the amount of dead and decaying plant matter increases rapidly, a process called *eutrophication* (◄ FIGURE 18.18). The processes by which plants decay consumes $O_2$, and without sufficient oxygen, the water cannot sustain animal life.

The most significant sources of nitrogen and phosphorus compounds in water are domestic sewage (phosphate-containing detergents and nitrogen-containing body wastes), runoff from agricultural land (fertilizers contain both nitrogen and phosphorus), and runoff from livestock areas (animal wastes contain nitrogen).

## GIVE IT SOME THOUGHT

If a test on a sample of polluted water shows a considerable decrease in dissolved oxygen over a five-day period, what can we conclude about the nature of the pollutants present?

## Water Purification: Desalination

Because of its high salt content, seawater is unfit for human consumption and for most of the uses to which we put water. In the United States the salt content of municipal water supplies is restricted by health codes to no more than about 0.05% by mass. This amount is much lower than the 3.5% dissolved salts present in seawater and the 0.5% or so present in brackish water found underground in some regions. The removal of salts from seawater or brackish water to make the water usable is called **desalination**.

Water can be separated from dissolved salts by *distillation* because water is a volatile substance and the salts are nonvolatile. ∞ (Section 13.5: "A Closer Look: Ideal Solutions with Two or More Volatile Components") The principle of distillation is simple enough, but carrying out the process on a large scale presents many problems. As water is distilled from seawater, for example, the salts become more and more concentrated and eventually precipitate out. Distillation is also an energy-intensive process.

Seawater can also be desalinated using **reverse osmosis**. Recall that osmosis is the net movement of solvent molecules, but not solute molecules, through a semipermeable membrane. ∞ (Section 13.5) In osmosis, the solvent passes from the more dilute solution into the more concentrated one. However, if sufficient external pressure is applied, osmosis can be stopped and, at still higher pressures, reversed. When reverse osmosis occurs, solvent passes from the more concentrated into the more dilute solution. In a modern reverse-osmosis facility, hollow fibers are used as the semipermeable membrane (◄ FIGURE 18.19). Water is introduced under pressure into the fibers, and desalinated water is recovered.

▲ **FIGURE 18.20**  **Common steps in treating water for a public water system.**

The world's largest desalination plant, in Jubail, Saudi Arabia, provides 50% of that country's drinking water by using reverse osmosis to desalinate seawater from the Persian Gulf. Such plants are becoming increasingly common in the United States. The largest, near Tampa Bay, Florida, has been operating since 2007 and produces 35 million gallons of drinking water a day by reverse osmosis. Small-scale, manually operated reverse-osmosis desalinators are used in camping, traveling, and at sea.

## Water Purification: Municipal Treatment

The water needed for domestic, agricultural, and industrial use is taken either from lakes, rivers, and underground sources or from reservoirs. Much of the water that finds its way into municipal water systems is "used" water, meaning it has already passed through one or more sewage systems or industrial plants. Consequently, this water must be treated before it is distributed to our faucets.

Municipal water treatment usually involves five steps (▲ **FIGURE 18.20**). After coarse filtration through a screen, the water is allowed to stand in large sedimentation tanks where sand and other minute particles settle out. To aid in removing very small particles, the water may first be made slightly basic with CaO. Then $Al_2(SO_4)_3$ is added and reacts with $OH^-$ ions to form a spongy, gelatinous precipitate of $Al(OH)_3$ ($K_{sp} = 1.3 \times 10^{-33}$). This precipitate settles slowly, carrying suspended particles down with it, thereby removing nearly all finely divided matter and most bacteria. The water is then filtered through a sand bed. Following filtration, the water may be sprayed into the air (aeration) to hasten oxidation of dissolved organic substances.

The final step normally involves treating the water with a chemical agent to ensure the destruction of bacteria. Ozone is more effective, but chlorine is less expensive. Liquefied $Cl_2$ is dispensed from tanks through a metering device directly into the water supply. The amount used depends on the presence of other substances with which the chlorine might react and on the concentrations of bacteria and viruses to be removed. The sterilizing action of chlorine is probably due not to $Cl_2$ itself but to hypochlorous acid, which forms when chlorine reacts with water:

$$Cl_2(aq) + H_2O(l) \longrightarrow HClO(aq) + H^+(aq) + Cl^-(aq) \qquad [18.15]$$

As many as a billion people worldwide lack access to clean water. According to the United Nations, 95% of the world's cities still dump raw sewage into their water supplies. Thus, it should come as no surprise that 80% of all the health maladies in developing countries can be traced to waterborne diseases associated with unsanitary water.

One promising development is a device called the LifeStraw (▶ **FIGURE 18.21**). When a person sucks water through the straw, the water first encounters a textile filter

Carbon removes iodine smells and parasites

Iodine-impregnated beads kill bacteria, viruses, and parasites

15-μm textile filter removes debris

100-μm textile filter removes debris

▲ **FIGURE 18.21**  **A LifeStraw purifies water as it is drunk.**

# A CLOSER LOOK

## WATER SOFTENING

Water containing a relatively high concentration of $Ca^{2+}$, $Mg^{2+}$, and other divalent cations is called *hard water*. Although the presence of these ions is generally not a health threat, they can make water unsuitable for some household and industrial uses. For example, these ions react with soap to form an insoluble soap scum, the stuff of bathtub rings.

In addition, mineral deposits may form when water containing these ions is heated. When water containing calcium ions and bicarbonate ions is heated, some carbon dioxide is driven off. As a result, the solution becomes less acidic and insoluble calcium carbonate forms:

$$Ca^{2+}(aq) + 2\,HCO_3^-(aq) \longrightarrow CaCO_3(s) + CO_2(g) + H_2O(l)$$

The solid $CaCO_3$ coats the surface of hot-water systems and teakettles, reducing heating efficiency (▼ FIGURE 18.22). These deposits, called *scale*, can be especially serious in boilers where water is heated under pressure in pipes running through a furnace.

▲ FIGURE 18.22 **Scale formation.** The interior of this water pipe has been coated with $CaCO_3$ and other insoluble salts deposited from hard water.

Removal of the ions that cause hard water is called *water softening*. In the *lime-soda process* used for large-scale municipal water-softening operations, the water is treated with calcium hydroxide (prepared from lime) and, sodium carbonate (sometimes called soda ash) to precipitate $Ca^{2+}$ as $CaCO_3$ and $Mg^{2+}$ as $Mg(OH)_2$:

$$Ca^{2+}(aq) + CO_3^{2-}(aq) \longrightarrow CaCO_3(s)$$
$$Mg^{2+}(aq) + 2\,OH^-(aq) \longrightarrow Mg(OH)_2(s)$$

In *ion exchange*, a typical household method for softening water, hard water is passed through an ion-exchange resin made up of plastic beads with covalently bound anion groups such as $-COO^-$ or $-SO_3^-$. These negatively charged groups have $Na^+$ ions to balance their charges. The $Ca^{2+}$ and other cations in the hard water are attracted to the anionic groups and displace the lower-charged $Na^+$ into the water. Thus, one type of ion is exchanged for another. To maintain charge balance, $2\,Na^+$ enter the water for each $Ca^{2+}$ removed. If we represent the resin with its anionic site as $R-COO^-$, we can write the equation for the process as

$$2\,Na(R-COO)(s) + Ca^{2+}(aq) \rightleftharpoons$$
$$Ca(R-COO)_2(s) + 2\,Na^+(aq)$$

Water softened in this way contains an increased concentration of $Na^+$. Although $Na^+$ does not form precipitates or cause other problems associated with hard-water cations, individuals concerned about their sodium intake, such as those who have high blood pressure (hypertension), should avoid drinking water softened in this way.

When all the available $Na^+$ ions have been displaced from the ion-exchange resin, the resin is regenerated by flushing it with a concentrated solution of NaCl. The high concentration of $Na^+$ forces the equilibrium in the preceding equation to shift to the left, causing the $Na^+$ to displace the hard-water cations, which are flushed down the drain.

with a mesh opening of 100 μm followed by a second textile filter with a mesh opening of 15 μm. These filters remove debris and even clusters of bacteria. The water next encounters a chamber of iodine-impregnated beads, where bacteria, viruses, and parasites are killed. Finally, the water passes through granulated active carbon, which removes the smell of iodine as well as the parasites that have not been taken by the filters or killed by the iodine.

Water disinfection is one of the greatest public health innovations in human history. It has dramatically decreased the incidences of waterborne bacterial diseases such as cholera and typhus. However, this great benefit comes at a price.

In 1974 scientists in Europe and the United States discovered that chlorination of water produces a group of by-products previously undetected. These by-products are called *trihalomethanes* (THMs) because all have a single carbon atom and three halogen atoms: $CHCl_3$, $CHCl_2Br$, $CHClBr_2$, and $CHBr_3$. These and many other chlorine- and bromine-containing organic substances are produced by the reaction of dissolved chlorine with the organic materials present in nearly all natural waters, as well as with substances that are by-products of human activity. Recall that chlorine dissolves in water to form the oxidizing agent HClO:

$$Cl_2(g) + H_2O(l) \longrightarrow HClO(aq) + H^+(aq) + Cl^-(aq) \qquad [18.16]$$

The HClO in turn reacts with organic substances to form THMs. Bromine enters the reaction sequence through the reaction of HClO with dissolved bromide ion:

$$HOCl(aq) + Br^-(aq) \longrightarrow HBrO(aq) + Cl^-(aq) \qquad [18.17]$$

Then both HBrO($aq$) and HClO($aq$) can halogenate organic substances to form the THMs.

Some THMs and other halogenated organic substances are suspected carcinogens; others interfere with the body's endocrine system. As a result, the World Health Organization and the U.S. Environmental Protection Agency have placed concentration limits of 80 $\mu$g/L (80 ppb) on the total quantity of THMs in drinking water. The goal is to reduce the levels of THMs and other disinfection by-products in the drinking water supply while preserving the antibacterial effectiveness of the water treatment. In some cases, lowering the concentration of chlorine may provide adequate disinfection while reducing the concentrations of THMs formed. Alternative oxidizing agents, such as ozone or chlorine dioxide, produce less of the halogenated substances but have their own disadvantages. For example, each is capable of oxidizing dissolved bromide, as shown here for ozone:

$$O_3(aq) + Br^-(aq) + H_2O(l) \longrightarrow HBrO(aq) + O_2(aq) + OH^-(aq) \qquad [18.18]$$

$$HBrO(aq) + 2\,O_3(aq) \longrightarrow BrO_3^-(aq) + 2\,O_2(aq) + H^+(aq) \qquad [18.19]$$

Bromate ion, $BrO_3^-$, has been shown to cause cancer in animal tests. Bromate's cancer-causing potential has led Los Angeles, for example, to add 3 million black plastic balls to one of its drinking water reservoirs to prevent bromate from forming via photochemical processes (▶ FIGURE 18.23).

At present, there seem to be no completely satisfactory alternatives to chlorination or ozonation, and we are faced with a consideration of benefit versus risk. In this case, the risks of cancer from THMs and related substances in municipal water are very low relative to the risks of cholera, typhus, and gastrointestinal disorders from untreated water. When the water supply is cleaner to begin with, less disinfectant is needed and thus the risk of THMs is lowered. Once THMs form, their concentrations in the water supply can be reduced by aeration because the THMs are more volatile than water. Alternatively, they can be removed by adsorption onto activated charcoal or other adsorbents.

▲ **FIGURE 18.23  Preventing photochemical bromate reactions.** The black plastic balls added to this Los Angeles drinking water reservoir keep sunlight from entering the water and initiating reactions that form harmful bromate ions.

# 18.5 | GREEN CHEMISTRY

The planet on which we live is, to a large extent, a *closed system*, one that exchanges energy but not matter with its environment. If humankind is to thrive in the future, all the processes we carry out should be in balance with Earth's natural processes and physical resources. This goal requires that no toxic materials be released to the environment, that our needs be met with renewable resources, and that we consume the least possible amount of energy. Although the chemical industry is but a small part of human activity, chemical processes are involved in nearly all aspects of modern life. Chemistry is therefore at the heart of efforts to accomplish these goals.

**Green chemistry** is an initiative that promotes the design and application of chemical products and processes that are compatible with human health and that preserve the environment. The founders of the initiative have developed a set of 12 principles to guide work in this area:

1. **Prevention** It is better to prevent waste than to clean it up after it has been created.

2. **Atom Economy** Methods to make chemical compounds should be designed to maximize the incorporation of all starting atoms into the final product.

3. **Less Hazardous Chemical Syntheses** Wherever practical, synthetic methods should be designed to use and generate substances that possess little or no toxicity to human health and the environment.

4. **Design of Safer Chemicals** Chemical products should be designed to minimze toxicity and yet maintain their desired function.

5. **Safer Solvents and Auxiliaries** The use of auxiliary substances (e.g., solvents, separation agents, etc.) should be eliminated wherever possible and, if used, should be as nontoxic as possible.

6. **Design for Energy Efficiency** Energy requirements of chemical processes should be recognized for their environmental and economic impacts and should be minimized. If possible, chemical reactions should be conducted at room temperature and pressure.

7. **Use of Renewable Feedstocks** A raw material or feedstock should be renewable whenever technically and economically practical.

8. **Reduction of Derivatives** Unnecessary derivatization (intermediate compound formation, temporary modification of physical/chemical processes) should be minimized or avoided if possible, because such steps require additional reagents and can generate waste.

9. **Catalysis** Catalytic reagents (as selective as possible) improve product yields within a given time and with a lower energy cost compared to noncatalytic processes and are, therefore, preferred to noncatalytic alternatives.

10. **Design for Degradation** Chemical products should be designed so that at the end of their function they break down into innocuous degradation products and do not persist in the environment.

11. **Real-Time Analysis for Pollution Prevention** Analytical methods need to be developed that allow for real-time, in-process monitoring and control prior to the formation of hazardous substances.

12. **Inherently Safer Chemistry for Accident Prevention** Reagents and solvents used in a chemical process should be chosen to minimize the potential for chemical accidents, including releases, explosions, and fires.*

▲ GIVE IT SOME THOUGHT

Explain how a chemical reaction that uses a catalyst is "greener" than the same reaction run without a catalyst.

To illustrate how green chemistry works, consider the manufacture of styrene, an important building block for many polymers, including the expanded polystyrene packages used to pack eggs and restaurant takeout food. The global demand for styrene is more than 25 million metric tons per year. For many years, styrene has been produced in a two-step process: Benzene and ethylene react to form ethyl benzene, followed by the ethyl benzene being mixed with high-temperature steam and passed over an iron oxide catalyst to form styrene:

Benzene    Ethylene                          Ethyl benzene                         Styrene

This process has several shortcomings. One is that both benzene, which is formed from crude oil, and ethylene, formed from natural gas, are high-priced starting materials for a product that should be a low-priced commodity, and another is that benzene is a known carcinogen. In a recently-developed process that bypasses some of

*Adapted from P. T. Anastas and J. C. Warner, *Green Chemistry: Theory and Practice.* New York: Oxford University Press 1998, p. 30.

these shortcomings, the two-step process is replaced by a one-step process in which toluene is reacted with methanol at 425 °C over a special catalyst:

$$\text{Toluene} + CH_3OH \xrightarrow[-H_2, -H_2O]{\text{Base catalyst}} \text{Styrene}$$

Toluene    Methanol    Styrene

The one-step process saves money both because toluene and methanol are less expensive than benzene and ethylene, and because the reaction requires less energy input. Additional benefits are that the methanol could be produced from biomass and that benzene is replaced by less-toxic toluene. The hydrogen formed in the reaction can be recycled as a source of energy. (This example demonstrates how finding the right catalyst is often key in discovering a new process.)

Let's consider some other examples in which green chemistry can operate to improve environmental quality.

## Supercritical Solvents

A major area of concern in chemical processes is the use of volatile organic compounds as solvents. Generally, the solvent in which a reaction is run is not consumed in the reaction, and there are unavoidable releases of solvent into the atmosphere even in the most carefully controlled processes. Further, the solvent may be toxic or may decompose to some extent during the reaction, thus creating waste products.

The use of supercritical fluids represents a way to replace conventional solvents. Recall that a supercritical fluid is an unusual state of matter that has properties of both a gas and a liquid. ∞ (Section 11.4) Water and carbon dioxide are the two most popular choices as supercritical fluid solvents. One recently developed industrial process, for example, replaces chlorofluorocarbon solvents with liquid or supercritical $CO_2$ in the production of polytetrafluoroethylene ($[CF_2CF_2]_n$, sold as Teflon®). Though $CO_2$ is a greenhouse gas, no new $CO_2$ need be manufactured for use as a supercritical fluid solvent.

As a further example, *para*-xylene is oxidized to form terephthalic acid, which is used to make polyethylene terephthalate (PET) plastic and polyester fiber ∞ (Section 12.8, Table 12.5):

$$CH_3\text{—}\langle\bigcirc\rangle\text{—}CH_3 + 3\,O_2 \xrightarrow[\text{Catalyst}]{190\,°C,\,20\,\text{atm}} HO\text{—}\overset{O}{\overset{\|}{C}}\text{—}\langle\bigcirc\rangle\text{—}\overset{O}{\overset{\|}{C}}\text{—}OH + 2\,H_2O$$

*para*-Xylene                    Terephthalic acid

This commercial process requires pressurization and a relatively high temperature. Oxygen is the oxidizing agent, and acetic acid ($CH_3COOH$) is the solvent. An alternative route employs supercritical water as the solvent and hydrogen peroxide as the oxidant. This alternative process has several potential advantages, most particularly the elimination of acetic acid as solvent.

### ▲ GIVE IT SOME THOUGHT

We noted earlier that increasing carbon dioxide levels contribute to global climate change, which seems like a bad thing, but now we are saying that using carbon dioxide in industrial processes is a good thing for the environment. Explain this seeming contradiction.

## Greener Reagents and Processes

Let us examine two more examples of green chemistry in action.

Hydroquinone, $HO-C_6H_4-OH$, is a common intermediate used to make polymers. The standard industrial route to hydroquinone, used until recently, yields many by-products that are treated as waste:

Using the principles of green chemistry, researchers have improved this process. The new process for hydroquinone production uses a new starting material. Two of the by-products of the new reaction (shown in green) can be isolated and used to make the new starting material.

By-products recycled to make starting material

The new process is an example of "atom economy," a phrase that means that a high percentage of the atoms from the starting materials end up in the product.

### GIVE IT SOME THOUGHT

What other reaction conditions could you change to make hydroquinone production even greener?

Another example of atom economy is a reaction in which, at room temperature and in the presence of a copper(I) catalyst, an organic *azide* and an *alkyne* form one product molecule:

Azide          Alkyne

This reaction is informally called a *click reaction*. The yield—actual, not just theoretical—is close to 100%, and there are no by-products. Depending on the type of azide and type of alkyne we start with, this very efficient click reaction can be used to create any number of valuable product molecules.

## GIVE IT SOME THOUGHT

What are the hybridizations of the two alkyne C atoms before and after the click reaction?

---

**SAMPLE INTEGRATIVE EXERCISE**  **Putting Concepts Together**

(a) Acid rain is no threat to lakes in areas where the rock is limestone (calcium carbonate), which can neutralize the acid. Where the rock is granite, however, no neutralization occurs. How does limestone neutralize acid? (b) Acidic water can be treated with basic substances to increase the pH, although such a procedure is usually only a temporary cure. Calculate the minimum mass of lime, CaO, needed to adjust the pH of a small lake ($V = 4 \times 10^9$ L) from 5.0 to 6.5. Why might more lime be needed?

### SOLUTION

**Analyze**  We need to remember what a neutralization reaction is and calculate the amount of a substance needed to effect a certain change in pH.

**Plan**  For (a), we need to think about how acid can react with calcium carbonate, a reaction that evidently does not happen with acid and granite. For (b), we need to think about what reaction between an acid and CaO is possible and do stoichiometric calculations. From the proposed change in pH, we can calculate the change in proton concentration needed and then figure out how much CaO is needed.

### Solve

(a)  The carbonate ion, which is the anion of a weak acid, is basic ∞ (Sections 16.2 and 16.7) and so reacts with $H^+(aq)$. If the concentration of $H^+(aq)$ is low, the major product is the bicarbonate ion, $HCO_3^-$. If the concentration of $H^+(aq)$ is high, $H_2CO_3$ forms and decomposes to $CO_2$ and $H_2O$. ∞ (Section 4.3)

(b)  The initial and final concentrations of $H^+(aq)$ in the lake are obtained from their pH values:

$$[H^+]_{\text{initial}} = 10^{-5.0} = 1 \times 10^{-5}\,M \quad \text{and} \quad [H^+]_{\text{final}} = 10^{-6.5} = 3 \times 10^{-7}\,M$$

Using the lake volume, we can calculate the number of moles of $H^+(aq)$ at both pH values:

$$(1 \times 10^{-5}\,\text{mol/L})(4.0 \times 10^9\,\text{L}) = 4 \times 10^4\,\text{mol}$$

$$(3 \times 10^{-7}\,\text{mol/L})(4.0 \times 10^9\,\text{L}) = 1 \times 10^3\,\text{mol}$$

Hence, the change in the amount of $H^+(aq)$ is $4 \times 10^4$ mol $- 1 \times 10^3$ mol $\approx 4 \times 10^4$ mol.

Let's assume that all the acid in the lake is completely ionized, so that only the free $H^+(aq)$ contributing to the pH needs to be neutralized. We need to neutralize at least that much acid, although there may be a great deal more than that amount in the lake.

The oxide ion of CaO is very basic. ∞ (Section 16.5) In the neutralization reaction, 1 mol of $O^{2-}$ reacts with 2 mol of $H^+$ to form $H_2O$. Thus, $4 \times 10^4$ mol of $H^+$ requires

$$(4 \times 10^4\,\text{mol H}^+)\left(\frac{1\,\text{mol CaO}}{2\,\text{mol H}^+}\right)\left(\frac{56.1\,\text{g CaO}}{1\,\text{mol CaO}}\right) = 1 \times 10^6\,\text{g CaO}$$

This is slightly more than a ton of CaO. That would not be very costly because CaO is inexpensive, selling for less than $100 per ton when purchased in large quantities. This amount of CaO is the minimum amount needed, however, because there are likely to be weak acids in the water that must also be neutralized.

This liming procedure has been used to bring the pH of some small lakes into the range necessary for fish to live. The lake in our example would be about a half mile long and a half mile wide and have an average depth of 20 ft.

# CHAPTER SUMMARY AND KEY TERMS

**SECTION 18.1** In this section we examined the physical and chemical properties of Earth's atmosphere. The complex temperature variations in the atmosphere give rise to four regions, each with characteristic properties. The lowest of these regions, the **troposphere**, extends from Earth's surface up to an altitude of about 12 km. Above the troposphere, in order of increasing altitude, are the **stratosphere**, mesosphere, and thermosphere. In the upper reaches of the atmosphere, only the simplest chemical species can survive the bombardment of highly energetic particles and radiation from the Sun. The average molecular weight of the atmosphere at high elevations is lower than that at Earth's surface because the lightest atoms and molecules diffuse upward and also because of **photodissociation**, which is the breaking of bonds in molecules because of the absorption of light. Absorption of radiation may also lead to the formation of ions via **photoionization.**

**SECTION 18.2** Ozone is produced in the upper atmosphere from the reaction of atomic oxygen with $O_2$. Ozone is itself decomposed by absorption of a photon or by reaction with an active species such as Cl. **Chlorofluorocarbons** can undergo photodissociation in the stratosphere, introducing atomic chlorine, which is capable of catalytically destroying ozone. A marked reduction in the ozone level in the upper atmosphere would have serious adverse consequences because the ozone layer filters out certain wavelengths of ultraviolet light that are not removed by any other atmospheric component. In the troposphere the chemistry of trace atmospheric components is of major importance. Many of these minor components are pollutants. Sulfur dioxide is one of the more noxious and prevalent examples. It is oxidized in air to form sulfur trioxide, which, upon dissolving in water, forms sulfuric acid. The oxides of sulfur are major contributors to **acid rain**. One method of preventing the escape of $SO_2$ from industrial operations is to react it with CaO to form calcium sulfite ($CaSO_3$).

**Photochemical smog** is a complex mixture in which both nitrogen oxides and ozone play important roles. Smog components are generated mainly in automobile engines, and smog control consists largely of controlling auto emissions.

Carbon dioxide and water vapor are the major components of the atmosphere that strongly absorb infrared radiation. $CO_2$ and $H_2O$ are therefore critical in maintaining Earth's surface temperature. The concentrations of $CO_2$ and other so-called **greenhouse gases** in the atmosphere are thus important in determining worldwide climate. Because of the extensive combustion of fossil fuels (coal, oil, and natural gas), the concentration of carbon dioxide in the atmosphere is steadily increasing.

**SECTION 18.3** Earth's water is largely in the oceans and seas; only a small fraction is freshwater. Seawater contains about 3.5% by mass of dissolved salts and is described as having a **salinity** (grams of dry salts per 1 kg seawater) of 35. Seawater's density and salinity vary with depth. Because most of the world's water is in the oceans, humans may eventually need to recover freshwater from seawater. The global water cycle involves continuous phase changes of water.

**SECTION 18.4** Freshwater contains many dissolved substances including dissolved oxygen, which is necessary for fish and other aquatic life. Substances that are decomposed by bacteria are said to be **biodegradable**. Because the oxidation of biodegradable substances by aerobic bacteria consumes dissolved oxygen, these substances are called oxygen-demanding wastes. The presence of an excess amount of oxygen-demanding wastes in water can sufficiently deplete the dissolved oxygen to kill fish and produce offensive odors. Plant nutrients can contribute to the problem by stimulating the growth of plants that become oxygen-demanding wastes when they die.

**Desalination** is the removal of dissolved salts from seawater or brackish water to make it fit for human consumption. Desalination may be accomplished by distillation or by **reverse osmosis.**

The water available from freshwater sources may require treatment before it can be used domestically. The several steps generally used in municipal water treatment include coarse filtration, sedimentation, sand filtration, aeration, sterilization, and sometimes water softening. Water softening is required when the water contains significant concentrations of ions such as $Mg^{2+}$ and $Ca^{2+}$, which react with soap to form soap scum. Water containing such ions is called hard water. The lime-soda process, which involves adding CaO and $Na_2CO_3$ to hard water, is sometimes used for large-scale municipal water softening. Individual homes usually rely on ion exchange, a process by which hard-water ions are exchanged for $Na^+$ ions.

**SECTION 18.5** The **green chemistry** initiative promotes the design and application of chemical products and processes that are compatible with human health and that preserve the environment. The areas in which the principles of green chemistry can operate to improve environmental quality include choices of solvents and reagents for chemical reactions, development of alternative processes, and improvements in existing systems and practices.

# KEY SKILLS

- Describe the regions of Earth's atmosphere in terms of how temperature varies with altitude. (Section 18.1)

- Describe the composition of the atmosphere in terms of the major components in dry air at sea level. (Section 18.1)

- Calculate concentrations of gases in parts per million (ppm). (Section 18.1)

- Describe the processes of photodissociation and photoionization and their role in the upper atmosphere. (Section 18.1)

- Use bond energies and ionization energies to calculate the minimum frequency or maximum wavelength needed to cause photodissociation or photoionization. (Section 18.1)

- Explain the role of ozone in the upper atmosphere. (Section 18.1)

- Explain how chlorofluorocarbons (CFCs) are involved in depleting the ozone layer. (Section 18.2)

- Describe the origins and behavior of sulfur oxides and nitrogen oxides as air pollutants, including the generation of acid rain and photochemical smog. (Section 18.2)

- Describe how water and carbon dioxide in the atmosphere affect atmospheric temperature via the greenhouse effect. (Section 18.2)
- Describe the global water cycle. (Section 18.3)
- Explain what is meant by the salinity of water and describe the process of reverse osmosis as a means of desalination. (Section 18.4)
- List the major cations, anions, and gases present in natural waters and describe the relationship between dissolved oxygen and water quality. (Section 18.4)
- List the main steps involved in treating water for domestic uses. (Section 18.4)
- Describe the main goals of green chemistry. (Section 18.5)
- Be able to compare reactions and decide which reaction is greener. (Section 18.5)

# EXERCISES

## VISUALIZING CONCEPTS

**18.1** At 273 K and 1 atm pressure, one mole of an ideal gas occupies 22.4 L. ∞ (Section 10.4) **(a)** Looking back at Figure 18.1, do you predict that 1 mole of an ideal gas in the middle of the stratosphere would occupy a greater or smaller volume than 22.4 L? **(b)** Looking at Figure 18.1, we see that the temperature is lower at 85 km altitude than at 50 km. Does this mean that one mole of an ideal gas would occupy less volume at 85 km than at 50 km? Explain. **(c)** In which parts of the atmosphere would you expect gases to behave most ideally (ignoring any photochemical reactions)? [Section 18.1]

**18.2** Molecules in the upper atmosphere tend to contain double and triple bonds rather than single bonds. Suggest an explanation. [Section 18.1]

**18.3** The figure shows the three lowest regions of Earth's atmosphere. **(a)** Name each and indicate the approximate elevations at which the boundaries occur. **(b)** In which region is ozone a pollutant? In which region does it filter UV solar radiation? **(c)** In which region is infrared radiation from Earth's surface most strongly reflected back? **(d)** An aurora borealis is due to excitation of atoms and molecules in the atmosphere 55–95 km above Earth's surface. Which regions in the figure are involved in an aurora borealis? **(e)** Compare the changes in relative concentrations of water vapor and carbon dioxide with increasing elevation in these three regions.

C

B

A

**18.4** You are working with an artist who has been commissioned to make a sculpture for a big city in the eastern United States. The artist is wondering what material to use to make her sculpture because she has heard that acid rain in the eastern United States might destroy it over time. You take samples of granite, marble, bronze, and other materials, and place them outdoors for a long time in the big city. You periodically examine the appearance and measure the mass of the samples. **(a)** What observations would lead you to conclude that one or more of the materials are well-suited for the sculpture? **(b)** What chemical process (or processes) is (are) the most likely responsible for any observed changes in the materials? [Section 18.2]

**18.5** Where does the energy come from to evaporate the estimated 425,000 km$^3$ of water that annually leaves the oceans? [Section 18.3]

**18.6** Distinguish among salt water, freshwater, and groundwater. [Section 18.3]

**18.7** How does carbon dioxide interact with the world ocean? [Section 18.3]

**18.8** The following picture represents an ion-exchange column, in which water containing "hard" ions, such as Ca$^{2+}$, is added to the top of the column, and water containing "soft" ions, such as Na$^+$, comes out the bottom. Explain what is happening in the column. [Section 18.4]

Add hard water to top of column

Ion-exchange resin

Soft water comes out the bottom

**18.9** Describe the basic goals of green chemistry. [Section 18.5]

**18.10** One mystery in environmental science is the imbalance in the "carbon dioxide budget." Considering only human activities, scientists have estimated that 1.6 billion metric tons of $CO_2$ is added to the atmosphere every year because of deforestation (plants use $CO_2$, and fewer plants will leave more $CO_2$ in the atmosphere). Another 5.5 billion tons per year is put into the atmosphere because of burning fossil fuels. It is further estimated (again, considering only human activities) that the atmosphere actually takes up about 3.3 billion tons of this $CO_2$ per year, while the oceans take up 2 billion tons per year, leaving about 1.8 billion tons of $CO_2$ per year unaccounted for. This "missing" $CO_2$ is assumed to be taken up by the "land." What do you think might be happening? [Sections 18.1–18.3]

# EARTH'S ATMOSPHERE (section 18.1)

**18.11** (a) What is the primary basis for the division of the atmosphere into different regions? (b) Name the regions of the atmosphere, indicating the altitude interval for each one.

**18.12** (a) How are the boundaries between the regions of the atmosphere determined? (b) Explain why the stratosphere, which is more than 20 miles thick, has a smaller total mass than the troposphere, which is less than 10 miles thick.

**18.13** Air pollution in the Mexico City metropolitan area is among the worst in the world. The concentration of ozone in Mexico City has been measured at 441 ppb (0.441 ppm). Mexico City sits at an altitude of 7400 feet, which means its atmospheric pressure is only 0.67 atm. (a) Calculate the partial pressure of ozone at 441 ppb if the atmospheric pressure is 0.67 atm. (b) How many ozone molecules are in 1.0 L of air in Mexico City? Assume $T = 25\,°C$.

**18.14** From the data in Table 18.1, calculate the partial pressures of carbon dioxide and argon when the total atmospheric pressure is 1.05 bar.

**18.15** The average concentration of carbon monoxide in air in an Ohio city in 2006 was 3.5 ppm. Calculate the number of CO molecules in 1.0 L of this air at a pressure of 759 torr and a temperature of 22 °C.

**18.16** (a) From the data in Table 18.1, what is the concentration of neon in the atmosphere in ppm? (b) What is the concentration of neon in the atmosphere in molecules per L, assuming an atmospheric pressure of 730 torr and a temperature of 296 K?

**18.17** The dissociation energy of a carbon–bromine bond is typically about 210 kJ/mol. (a) What is the maximum wavelength of photons that can cause C—Br bond dissociation? (b) Which kind of electromagnetic radiation—ultraviolet, visible, or infrared—does the wavelength you calculated in part (a) correspond to?

**18.18** In $CF_3Cl$ the C—Cl bond-dissociation energy is 339 kJ/mol. In $CCl_4$ the C—Cl bond-dissociation energy is 293 kJ/mol. What is the range of wavelengths of photons that can cause C—Cl bond rupture in one molecule but not in the other?

**18.19** (a) Distinguish between *photodissociation* and *photoionization*. (b) Use the energy requirements of these two processes to explain why photodissociation of oxygen is more important than photoionization of oxygen at altitudes below about 90 km.

**18.20** Why is the photodissociation of $N_2$ in the atmosphere relatively unimportant compared with the photodissociation of $O_2$?

# HUMAN ACTIVITIES AND EARTH'S ATMOSPHERE (section 18.2)

**18.21** Do the reactions involved in ozone depletion involve changes in oxidation state of the O atoms? Explain.

**18.22** Explain how the reactions of ozone in the stratosphere are responsible for the relatively warm temperatures of the stratosphere.

**18.23** (a) What is the difference between chlorofluorocarbons and hydrofluorocarbons? (b) Why are hydrofluorocarbons potentially less harmful to the ozone layer than CFCs?

**18.24** Draw the Lewis structure for the chlorofluorocarbon CFC-11, $CFCl_3$. What chemical characteristics of this substance allow it to effectively deplete stratospheric ozone?

**18.25** (a) Why is the fluorine present in chlorofluorocarbons not a major contributor to depletion of the ozone layer? (b) What are the chemical forms in which chlorine exists in the stratosphere following cleavage of the carbon–chlorine bond?

**18.26** Would you expect the substance $CFBr_3$ to be effective in depleting the ozone layer, assuming that it is present in the stratosphere? Explain.

**18.27** For each of the following gases, make a list of known or possible naturally occurring sources: (a) $CH_4$, (b) $SO_2$, (c) NO.

**18.28** Why is rainwater naturally acidic, even in the absence of polluting gases such as $SO_2$?

**18.29** (a) Write a chemical equation that describes the attack of acid rain on limestone, $CaCO_3$. (b) If a limestone sculpture were treated to form a surface layer of calcium sulfate, would this help to slow down the effects of acid rain? Explain.

**18.30** The first stage in corrosion of iron upon exposure to air is oxidation to $Fe^{2+}$. (a) Write a balanced chemical equation to show the reaction of iron with oxygen and protons from acid rain. (b) Would you expect the same sort of reaction to occur with a silver surface? Explain.

**18.31** Alcohol-based fuels for automobiles lead to the production of formaldehyde ($CH_2O$) in exhaust gases. Formaldehyde undergoes photodissociation, which contributes to photochemical smog:

$$CH_2O + h\nu \longrightarrow CHO + H$$

The maximum wavelength of light that can cause this reaction is 335 nm. (a) In what part of the electromagnetic spectrum is light with this wavelength found? (b) What is the maximum strength of a bond, in kJ/mol, that can be broken by absorption of a photon of 335-nm light? (c) Compare your answer from part (b) to the appropriate value from Table 8.4. What do you conclude about C—H bond energy in formaldehyde? (d) Write out the formaldehyde photodissociation reaction, showing Lewis-dot structures.

**18.32** An important reaction in the formation of photochemical smog is the photodissociation of $NO_2$:

$$NO_2 + h\nu \longrightarrow NO(g) + O(g)$$

The maximum wavelength of light that can cause this reaction is 420 nm. **(a)** In what part of the electromagnetic spectrum is light with this wavelength found? **(b)** What is the maximum strength of a bond, in kJ/mol, that can be broken by absorption of a photon of 420-nm light? **(c)** Write out the photodissociation reaction showing Lewis-dot structures.

**18.33** Explain why increasing concentrations of $CO_2$ in the atmosphere affect the quantity of energy leaving Earth but do not affect the quantity of energy entering from the Sun.

**18.34** **(a)** With respect to absorption of radiant energy, what distinguishes a greenhouse gas from a nongreenhouse gas? **(b)** $CH_4$ is a greenhouse gas, but $N_2$ is not. How might the molecular structure of $CH_4$ explain why it is a greenhouse gas?

# EARTH'S WATER (section 18.3)

**18.35** What is the molarity of $Na^+$ in a solution of NaCl whose salinity is 5.6 if the solution has a density of 1.03 g/mol?

**18.36** Phosphorus is present in seawater to the extent of 0.07 ppm by mass. If the phosphorus is present as phosphate, $PO_4^{3-}$, calculate the corresponding molar concentration of phosphate in seawater.

**18.37** The enthalpy of evaporation of water is 40.67 kJ/mol. Sunlight striking Earth's surface supplies 168 W per square meter (1 W = 1 watt = 1 J/s). **(a)** Assuming that evaporation of water is only due to energy input from the Sun, calculate how many grams of water could be evaporated from a 1.00 square meter patch of ocean over a 12-hour day. **(b)** The specific heat capacity of liquid water is 4.184 J/g °C. If the initial temperature of a 1.00 square meter patch of ocean is 26 °C, what is its final temperature after being in sunlight for 12 hours, assuming no phase changes and assuming that sunlight penetrates uniformly to depth of 10.0 cm?

**[18.38]** The enthalpy of fusion of water is 6.01 kJ/mol. Sunlight striking Earth's surface supplies 168 W per square meter (1 W = 1 watt = 1 J/s). **(a)** Assuming that melting of ice is only due to energy input from the Sun, calculate how many grams of ice could be melted from a 1.00 square meter patch of ice over a 12-hour day. **(b)** The specific heat capacity of ice is 2.032 J/g °C. If the initial temperature of a 1.00 square meter patch of ice is −5.0 °C, what is its final temperature after being in sunlight for

12 hours, assuming no phase changes and assuming that sunlight penetrates uniformly to a depth of 1.00 cm?

**18.39** A first-stage recovery of magnesium from seawater is precipitation of $Mg(OH)_2$ with CaO:

$$Mg^{2+}(aq) + CaO(s) + H_2O(l) \longrightarrow Mg(OH)_2(s) + Ca^{2+}(aq)$$

What mass of CaO, in grams, is needed to precipitate 1000 lb of $Mg(OH)_2$?

**18.40** Gold is found in seawater at very low levels, about 0.05 ppb by mass. Assuming that gold is worth about $800 per troy ounce, how many liters of seawater would you have to process to obtain $1,000,000 worth of gold? Assume the density of seawater is 1.03 g/mL and that your gold recovery process is 50% efficient.

**18.41** **(a)** What is *groundwater*? **(b)** What is an *aquifer*?

**18.42** The Ogallala aquifer is the largest in the United States, covering 450,000 $km^2$ across eight states, from South Dakota to Texas. This aquifer provides 82% of the drinking water for the people who live in this region, although most (>75%) of the water that is pumped from it is for irrigation. Irrigation withdrawals are approximately 18 billion gallons per day. **(a)** The Ogallala aquifer might run dry, according to some estimates, in 25 years. How many cubic kilometers of water would be withdrawn in a 25-year period? **(b)** Explain the processes that would recharge the aquifer.

# HUMAN ACTIVITIES AND EARTH'S WATER (section 18.4)

**18.43** Suppose that one wishes to use reverse osmosis to reduce the salt content of brackish water containing 0.22 *M* total salt concentration to a value of 0.01 *M*, thus rendering it usable for human consumption. What is the minimum pressure that needs to be applied in the permeators (Figure 18.19) to achieve this goal, assuming that the operation occurs at 298 K? (*Hint:* Refer to Section 13.5.)

**18.44** Assume that a portable reverse-osmosis apparatus operates on seawater, whose concentrations of constituent ions are listed in Table 18.5, and that the desalinated water output has an effective molarity of about 0.02 *M*. What minimum pressure must be applied by hand pumping at 297 K to cause reverse osmosis to occur? (*Hint:* Refer to Section 13.5.)

**18.45** List the common products formed when an organic material containing the elements carbon, hydrogen, oxygen, sulfur, and nitrogen decomposes **(a)** under aerobic conditions, **(b)** under anaerobic conditions.

**18.46** **(a)** Explain why the concentration of dissolved oxygen in freshwater is an important indicator of the quality of the

water. **(b)** How is the solubility of oxygen in water affected by increasing temperature?

**18.47** The organic anion

is found in most detergents. Assume that the anion undergoes aerobic decomposition in the following manner:

$$2 C_{18}H_{29}SO_3^-(aq) + 51 O_2(aq) \longrightarrow$$
$$36 CO_2(aq) + 28 H_2O(l) + 2 H^+(aq) + 2 SO_4^{2-}(aq)$$

What is the total mass of $O_2$ required to biodegrade 10.0 g of this substance?

**18.48** The average daily mass of $O_2$ taken up by sewage discharged in the United States is 59 g per person. How many liters of water at 9 ppm $O_2$ are totally depleted of oxygen in 1 day by a population of 1,200,000 people?

18.49 Write a balanced chemical equation to describe how magnesium ions are removed in water treatment by the addition of slaked lime, $Ca(OH)_2$.

18.50 (a) Which of the following ionic species could be responsible for hardness in a water supply: $Ca^{2+}$, $K^+$, $Mg^{2+}$, $Fe^{2+}$, $Na^+$? (b) What properties of an ion determine whether it will contribute to water hardness?

18.51 How many moles of $Ca(OH)_2$ and $Na_2CO_3$ should be added to soften 1200 L of water in which $[Ca^{2+}] = 5.0 \times 10^{-4}\ M$ and $[HCO_3^-] = 7.0 \times 10^{-4}\ M$?

18.52 The concentration of $Ca^{2+}$ in a particular water supply is $5.7 \times 10^{-3}\ M$. The concentration of bicarbonate ion, $HCO_3^-$, in the same water is $1.7 \times 10^{-3}\ M$. What masses of $Ca(OH)_2$ and $Na_2CO_3$ must be added to $5.0 \times 10^7$ L of this water to reduce the level of $Ca^{2+}$ to 20% of its original level?

18.53 Ferrous sulfate ($FeSO_4$) is often used as a coagulant in water purification. The iron(II) salt is dissolved in the water to be purified, then oxidized to the iron(III) state by dissolved oxygen, at which time gelatinous $Fe(OH)_3$ forms, assuming the pH is above approximately 6. Write balanced chemical equations for the oxidation of $Fe^{2+}$ to $Fe^{3+}$ by dissolved oxygen and for the formation of $Fe(OH)_3(s)$ by reaction of $Fe^{3+}(aq)$ with $HCO_3^-(aq)$.

18.54 What properties make a substance a good coagulant for water purification?

18.55 (a) What are *trihalomethanes* (THMs)? (b) Draw the Lewis structures of two example THMs.

18.56 If trihalomethanes are easily removed from water by aeration (bubbling with air), what does this imply about the vapor pressure of THMs compared to water?

# GREEN CHEMISTRY (section 18.5)

18.57 One of the principles of green chemistry is that it is better to use as few steps as possible in making new chemicals. How does this principle relate to energy efficiency?

18.58 Discuss how catalysts can make processes more energy efficient.

18.59 A reaction for converting ketones to lactones, called the Baeyer–Villiger reaction,

is used in the manufacture of plastics and pharmaceuticals. 3-Chloroperbenzoic acid is shock-sensitive, however, and prone to explode. Also, 3-chlorobenzoic acid is a waste product. An alternative process being developed uses hydrogen peroxide and a catalyst consisting of tin deposited within a solid support. The catalyst is readily recovered from the reaction mixture. (a) What would you expect to be the other product of oxidation of the ketone to lactone by hydrogen peroxide? (b) What principles of green chemistry are addressed by use of the proposed process?

18.60 The reaction shown here was performed with an iridium catalyst, both in supercritical $CO_2$ ($scCO_2$) and in the chlorinated solvent $CH_2Cl_2$. The kinetic data for the reaction in both solvents are plotted in the graph. Why is this a good example of a green chemical reaction?

18.61 Which choice is greener in a chemical process? Explain. (a) Benzene as a solvent or water as a solvent. (b) The reaction temperature is 500 K, or 1000 K. (c) Sodium chloride as a by-product or chloroform ($CHCl_3$) as a by-product.

18.62 Which choice is greener in a chemical process? Explain. (a) A reaction that can be run at 350 K for 12 hours without a catalyst or one that can be run at 300 K for 1 hour with a catalyst. (b) A reagent for the reaction that can be obtained from corn husks or one that can be obtained from petroleum. (c) A process that produces no by-products or one in which the by-products are recycled for another process.

# ADDITIONAL EXERCISES

**18.63** A friend of yours has seen each of the following items in newspaper articles and would like an explanation: **(a)** acid rain, **(b)** greenhouse gas, **(c)** photochemical smog, **(d)** ozone depletion. Give a brief explanation of each term and identify one or two of the chemicals associated with each.

**18.64** Suppose that on another planet the atmosphere consists of 17% Kr, 38% $CH_4$, and 45% $O_2$. What is the average molar mass at the surface? What is the average molar mass at an altitude at which all the $O_2$ is photodissociated?

**18.65** If an average $O_3$ molecule "lives" only 100–200 seconds in the stratosphere before undergoing dissociation, how can $O_3$ offer any protection from ultraviolet radiation?

**18.66** Show how Equations 18.7 and 18.9 can be added to give Equation 18.10.

**18.67** What properties of CFCs make them ideal for various commercial applications but also make them a long-term problem in the stratosphere?

**18.68** *Halons* are fluorocarbons that contain bromine, such as $CBrF_3$. They are used extensively as foaming agents for fighting fires. Like CFCs, halons are very unreactive and ultimately can diffuse into the stratosphere. **(a)** Based on the data in Table 8.4, would you expect photodissociation of Br atoms to occur in the stratosphere? **(b)** Propose a mechanism by which the presence of halons in the stratosphere could lead to the depletion of stratospheric ozone.

**18.69** It is estimated that the lifetime for HFCs in the stratosphere is 2–7 years. If HFCs have such long lifetimes, why are they being used to replace CFCs?

**[18.70]** The *hydroxyl radical*, OH, is formed at low altitudes via the reaction of excited oxygen atoms with water:

$$O^*(g) + H_2O(g) \longrightarrow 2\,OH(g)$$

**(a)** Write the Lewis structure for the hydroxyl radical. (*Hint:* It has one unpaired electron.)
Once produced, the hydroxyl radical is very reactive. Explain why each of the following series of reactions affects the pollution in the troposphere:

**(b)** $OH + NO_2 \longrightarrow HNO_3$

**(c)** $OH + CO + O_2 \longrightarrow CO_2 + OOH$
$OOH + NO \longrightarrow OH + NO_2$

**(d)** $OH + CH_4 \longrightarrow H_2O + CH_3$
$CH_3 + O_2 \longrightarrow OOCH_3$
$OOCH_3 + NO \longrightarrow OCH_3 + NO_2$

**(e)** The concentration of hydroxyl radicals in the troposphere is approximately $2 \times 10^6$ radicals per $cm^3$. This estimate is based on a method called long path absorption spectroscopy (LPAS), similar in principle to the Beer's law measurement discussed in the Closer Look essay on p. 564, except that the path length in the LPAS measurement is 20 km. Why must the path length be so large?

**18.71** Explain, using Le Châtelier's principle, why the equilibrium constant for the formation of NO from $N_2$ and $O_2$ increases with increasing temperature, whereas the equilibrium constant for the formation of $NO_2$ from NO and $O_2$ decreases with increasing temperature.

**18.72** Natural gas consists primarily of methane, $CH_4(g)$. **(a)** Write a balanced chemical equation for the complete combustion of methane to produce $CO_2(g)$ as the only carbon-containing product. **(b)** Write a balanced chemical equation for the incomplete combustion of methane to produce $CO(g)$ as the only carbon-containing product. **(c)** At 25 °C and 1.0 atm pressure, what is the minimum quantity of dry air needed to combust 1.0 L of $CH_4(g)$ completely to $CO_2(g)$?

**18.73** One of the possible consequences of climate change is an increase in the temperature of ocean water. The oceans serve as a "sink" for $CO_2$ by dissolving large amounts of it. **(a)** How would the solubility of $CO_2$ in the oceans be affected by an increase in the temperature of the water? **(b)** Discuss the implications of your answer to part (a) for the problem of climate change.

**18.74** The rate of solar energy striking Earth averages 168 watts per square meter. The rate of energy radiated from Earth's surface averages 390 watts per square meter. Comparing these numbers, one might expect that the planet would cool quickly, yet it does not. Why not?

**18.75** The solar power striking Earth every day averages 168 watts per square meter. The peak electrical power usage in New York City is 12,000 megawatts. Considering that present technology for solar energy conversion is only about 10% efficient, from how many square meters of land must sunlight be collected in order to provide this peak power? (For comparison, the total area of the city is 830 $km^2$.)

**18.76** Write balanced chemical equations for each of the following reactions: **(a)** The nitric oxide molecule undergoes photodissociation in the upper atmosphere. **(b)** The nitric oxide molecule undergoes photoionization in the upper atmosphere. **(c)** Nitric oxide undergoes oxidation by ozone in the stratosphere. **(d)** Nitrogen dioxide dissolves in water to form nitric acid and nitric oxide.

**18.77** **(a)** Explain why $Mg(OH)_2$ precipitates when $CO_3^{2-}$ ion is added to a solution containing $Mg^{2+}$. **(b)** Will $Mg(OH)_2$ precipitate when 4.0 g of $Na_2CO_3$ is added to 1.00 L of a solution containing 125 ppm of $Mg^{2+}$?

**[18.78]** It has been pointed out that there may be increased amounts of NO in the troposphere as compared with the past because of massive use of nitrogen-containing compounds in fertilizers. Assuming that NO can eventually diffuse into the stratosphere, how might it affect the conditions of life on Earth? Using the index to this text, look up the chemistry of nitrogen oxides. What chemical pathways might NO in the troposphere follow?

**[18.79]** As of the writing of this text, EPA standards limit atmospheric ozone levels in urban environments to 84 ppb. How many moles of ozone would there be in the air above Los Angeles County (area about 4000 square miles; consider a height of 10 m above the ground) if ozone was at this concentration?

# INTEGRATIVE EXERCISES

**18.80** The estimated average concentration of $NO_2$ in air in the United States in 2006 was 0.016 ppm. **(a)** Calculate the partial pressure of the $NO_2$ in a sample of this air when the atmospheric pressure is 755 torr (99.1 kPa). **(b)** How many molecules of $NO_2$ are present under these conditions at 20 °C in a room that measures $15 \times 14 \times 8$ ft?

**[18.81]** In 1986 an electrical power plant in Taylorsville, Georgia, burned 8,376,726 tons of coal, a national record at that time. **(a)** Assuming that the coal was 83% carbon and 2.5% sulfur and that combustion was complete, calculate the number of tons of carbon dioxide and sulfur dioxide produced by the plant during the year. **(b)** If 55% of the $SO_2$ could be removed by reaction with powdered CaO to form $CaSO_3$, how many tons of $CaSO_3$ would be produced?

**18.82** The water supply for a midwestern city contains the following impurities: coarse sand, finely divided particulates, nitrate ion, trihalomethanes, dissolved phosphorus in the form of phosphates, potentially harmful bacterial strains, dissolved organic substances. Which of the following processes or agents, if any, is effective in removing each of these impurities: coarse sand filtration, activated carbon filtration, aeration, ozonization, precipitation with aluminum hydroxide?

**18.83** An impurity in water has an extinction coefficient of $3.45 \times 10^3\ M^{-1}\,cm^{-1}$ at 280 nm, its absorption maximum (A Closer Look, p. 564). Below 50 ppb, the impurity is not a problem for human health. Given that most spectrometers cannot detect absorbances less than 0.0001 with good reliability, is measuring the absorbance of water at 280 nm a good way to detect concentrations of the impurity above the 50-ppb threshold?

**18.84** The concentration of $H_2O$ in the stratosphere is about 5 ppm. It undergoes photodissociation according to:

$$H_2O(g) \longrightarrow H(g) + OH(g)$$

**(a)** Write out the Lewis-dot structures for both products and reactant.

**(b)** Using Table 8.4, calculate the wavelength required to cause this dissociation.

**(c)** The hydroxyl radicals, OH, can react with ozone, giving the following reactions:

$$OH(g) + O_3(g) \longrightarrow HO_2(g) + O_2(g)$$
$$HO_2(g) + O(g) \longrightarrow OH(g) + O_2(g)$$

What overall reaction results from these two elementary reactions? What is the catalyst in the overall reaction? Explain.

**18.85** Bioremediation is the process by which bacteria repair their environment in response, for example, to an oil spill. The efficiency of bacteria for "eating" hydrocarbons depends on the amount of oxygen in the system, pH, temperature, and many other factors. In a certain oil spill, hydrocarbons from the oil disappeared with a first-order rate constant of $2 \times 10^{-6}\,s^{-1}$. How many days did it take for the hydrocarbons to decrease to 10% of their initial value?

**18.86** The standard enthalpies of formation of ClO and $ClO_2$ are 101 and 102 kJ/mol, respectively. Using these data and the thermodynamic data in Appendix C, calculate the overall enthalpy change for each step in the following catalytic cycle:

$$ClO(g) + O_3(g) \longrightarrow ClO_2(g) + O_2(g)$$
$$ClO_2(g) + O(g) \longrightarrow ClO(g) + O_2(g)$$

What is the enthalpy change for the overall reaction that results from these two steps?

**18.87** The main reason that distillation is a costly method for purifying water is the high energy required to heat and vaporize water. **(a)** Using the density, specific heat, and heat of vaporization of water from Appendix B, calculate the amount of energy required to vaporize 1.00 gal of water beginning with water at 20 °C. **(b)** If the energy is provided by electricity costing \$0.085 / kWh, calculate its cost. **(c)** If distilled water sells in a grocery store for \$1.26 per gal, what percentage of the sales price is represented by the cost of the energy?

**[18.88]** A reaction that contributes to the depletion of ozone in the stratosphere is the direct reaction of oxygen atoms with ozone:

$$O(g) + O_3(g) \longrightarrow 2\,O_2(g)$$

At 298 K the rate constant for this reaction is $4.8 \times 10^5\ M^{-1}\,s^{-1}$. **(a)** Based on the units of the rate constant, write the likely rate law for this reaction. **(b)** Would you expect this reaction to occur via a single elementary process? Explain why or why not. **(c)** From the magnitude of the rate constant, would you expect the activation energy of this reaction to be large or small? Explain. **(d)** Use $\Delta H_f^\circ$ values from Appendix C to estimate the enthalpy change for this reaction. Would this reaction raise or lower the temperature of the stratosphere?

**18.89** Nitrogen dioxide ($NO_2$) is the only important gaseous species in the lower atmosphere that absorbs visible light. **(a)** Write the Lewis structure(s) for $NO_2$. **(b)** How does this structure account for the fact that $NO_2$ dimerizes to form $N_2O_4$? Based on what you can find about this dimerization reaction in the text, would you expect to find the $NO_2$ that forms in an urban environment to be in the form of dimer? Explain. **(c)** What would you expect as products, if any, for the reaction of $NO_2$ with CO? **(d)** Would you expect $NO_2$ generated in an urban environment to migrate to the stratosphere? Explain.

**18.90** The following data were collected for the destruction of $O_3$ by H ($O_3 + H \longrightarrow O_2 + OH$) at very low concentrations:

| Trial | [$O_3$] ($M$) | [H] ($M$) | Initial Rate ($M/s$) |
|---|---|---|---|
| 1 | $5.17 \times 10^{-33}$ | $3.22 \times 10^{-26}$ | $1.88 \times 10^{-14}$ |
| 2 | $2.59 \times 10^{-33}$ | $3.25 \times 10^{-26}$ | $9.44 \times 10^{-15}$ |
| 3 | $5.19 \times 10^{-33}$ | $6.46 \times 10^{-26}$ | $3.77 \times 10^{-14}$ |

**(a)** Write the rate law for the reaction.
**(b)** Calculate the rate constant.

**18.91** The degradation of $CF_3CH_2F$ (an HFC) by OH radicals in the troposphere is first order in each reactant and has a rate constant of $k = 1.6 \times 10^8\ M^{-1}\,s^{-1}$ at 4 °C. If the tropospheric concentrations of OH and $CF_3CH_2F$ are $8.1 \times 10^5$ and $6.3 \times 10^8$ molecules/cm$^3$, respectively, what is the rate of reaction at this temperature in $M/s$?

**[18.92]** The Henry's law constant for $CO_2$ in water at 25 °C is $3.1 \times 10^{-2}\ M$ atm$^{-1}$. **(a)** What is the solubility of $CO_2$ in water at this temperature if the solution is in contact with air at normal atmospheric pressure? **(b)** Assume that all of this $CO_2$ is in the form of $H_2CO_3$ produced by the reaction between $CO_2$ and $H_2O$:

$$CO_2(aq) + H_2O(l) \longrightarrow H_2CO_3(aq)$$

What is the pH of this solution?

[18.93] If the pH of a 1.0-in. rainfall over 1500 $mi^2$ is 3.5, how many kilograms of $H_2SO_4$ are present, assuming that it is the only acid contributing to the pH?

18.94 The precipitation of $Al(OH)_3$ ($K_{sp} = 1.3 \times 10^{-33}$) is sometimes used to purify water. **(a)** Estimate the pH at which precipitation of $Al(OH)_3$ will begin if 5.0 lb of $Al_2(SO_4)_3$ is added to 2000 gal of water. **(b)** Approximately how many pounds of CaO must be added to the water to achieve this pH?

18.95 The valuable polymer polyurethane is made by a condensation reaction of alcohols (ROH) with compounds that contain an isocyanate group (RNCO). Two reactions that can generate a urethane monomer are shown here:

(i)  $RNH_2 + CO_2 \longrightarrow R-N=C=O + 2H_2O$

(ii)

**(a)** Which process, i or ii, is greener? Explain.

**(b)** What are the hybridization and geometry of the carbon atoms in each C-containing compound in each reaction?

**(c)** If you wanted to promote the formation of the isocyanate intermediate in each reaction, what could you do, using Le Châtelier's principle?

[18.96] The pH of a particular raindrop is 5.6. **(a)** Assuming the major species in the raindrop are $H_2CO_3(aq)$, $HCO_3^-(aq)$, and $CO_3^{2-}(aq)$, calculate the concentrations of these species in the raindrop, assuming the total carbonate concentration is $1.0 \times 10^{-5} M$. The appropriate $K_a$ values are given in Table 16.3. **(b)** What experiments could you do to test the hypothesis that the rain also contains sulfur-containing species that contribute to its pH? Assume you have a large sample of rain to test.

# WHAT'S AHEAD

### 19.1 SPONTANEOUS PROCESSES
We see that changes that occur in nature have a directional character. They move *spontaneously* in one direction but not in the reverse direction.

### 19.2 ENTROPY AND THE SECOND LAW OF THERMODYNAMICS
We discuss *entropy*, a thermodynamic state function that is important in determining whether a process is spontaneous. The *second law of thermodynamics* tells us that in any spontaneous process the entropy of the universe (system plus surroundings) increases.

### 19.3 MOLECULAR INTERPRETATION OF ENTROPY
On the molecular level, the entropy of a system is related to the number of accessible *microstates*. The entropy of the system increases as the randomness of the system increases. The *third law of thermodynamics* states that, at 0 K, the entropy of a perfect crystalline solid is zero.

### 19.4 ENTROPY CHANGES IN CHEMICAL REACTIONS
Using tabulated *standard molar entropies*, we can calculate the standard entropy changes for systems undergoing reaction.

**THE SKYLINE OF HONG KONG** The construction of our human environment entails the use of enormous amounts of energy to create complex ordered structures, such as modern skyscrapers.

**19.5 GIBBS FREE ENERGY**
We encounter another thermodynamic state function, *free energy* (or *Gibbs free energy*), a measure of how far removed a system is from equilibrium. The change in free energy measures the maximum amount of useful work obtainable from a process and tells us the direction in which a chemical reaction is spontaneous.

**19.6 FREE ENERGY AND TEMPERATURE**
We consider how the relationship among free-energy change, enthalpy change, and entropy change provides insight into how temperature affects the spontaneity of a process.

**19.7 FREE ENERGY AND THE EQUILIBRIUM CONSTANT**
Finally, we consider how the standard free-energy change for a chemical reaction can be used to calculate the equilibrium constant for the reaction.

# CHEMICAL THERMO-DYNAMICS

**HUMANKIND HAS LEARNED TO HARNESS** Earth's resources to create impressive, highly ordered structures, such as the beautiful skyline in the chapter-opening photograph. Our modern society depends heavily on the design of chemical reactions that produce specific useful substances from natural and synthetic materials.

Two of the most important questions chemists ask when designing and using chemical reactions are "How fast is the reaction?" and "How far does it proceed?" The first question is addressed by chemical kinetics, which we discussed in Chapter 14. The second question involves the equilibrium constant, the focus of Chapter 15. Let's briefly review how these concepts are related.

In Chapter 14 we learned that the rate of any chemical reaction is controlled largely by a factor related to energy, namely, the activation energy of the reaction. ∞ (Section 14.5) In general, the lower the activation energy, the faster a reaction proceeds. In Chapter 15 we saw that chemical equilibrium is reached when a given reaction and its reverse reaction occur at the same rate. ∞ (Section 15.1)

Because reaction rates are closely tied to energy, it is logical that equilibrium also depends in some way on energy. In this chapter we explore the connection between energy and the extent of a reaction. Doing so requires a deeper look at *chemical thermodynamics*, the area of chemistry that deals with energy relationships. We first encountered thermodynamics in Chapter 5, where we discussed the nature of energy, the first law of thermodynamics, and the concept of enthalpy. Recall that the enthalpy change for any system is the heat transferred between the system and its surroundings during a constant-pressure process. ∞ (Section 5.3)

In the "Strategies in Chemistry" box in Section 5.4, we pointed out that the enthalpy change that takes place during a reaction is an important guide as to whether the reaction is likely to proceed. Now we will see that reactions involve not only changes in enthalpy but also changes in *entropy*—another important thermodynamic quantity. Our discussion of entropy will lead us to the second law of thermodynamics, which provides insight into why physical and chemical changes tend to favor one direction over another. We drop a brick, for example, and it falls to the ground. We do not expect the brick to spontaneously rise from the ground to our outstretched hand. We light a candle, and it burns down. We do not expect a half-consumed candle to regenerate itself spontaneously, even if we have captured all the gases produced when the candle burned. Thermodynamics helps us understand the significance of this directional character of processes, regardless of whether they are exothermic or endothermic.

▲ GO FIGURE

**Does the potential energy of the eggs change during this process?**

Spontaneous          Not spontaneous

▲ **FIGURE 19.1 A spontaneous process!**

# 19.1 | SPONTANEOUS PROCESSES

The first law of thermodynamics states that *energy is conserved.* ∞ (Section 5.2) In other words, energy is neither created nor destroyed in any process, whether that process is a brick falling, a candle burning, or an ice cube melting. Energy can be transferred between a system and the surroundings and can be converted from one form to another, but the total energy of the universe remains constant. We expressed this law mathematically as $\Delta E = q + w$, where $\Delta E$ is the change in the internal energy of a system, $q$ is the heat absorbed (or released) by the system from (or to) the surroundings, and $w$ is the work done on the system by the surroundings, or on the surroundings by the system. Remember that $q > 0$ means that the system is absorbing heat from the surroundings, and $w > 0$ means that the surroundings are doing work on the system.

The first law helps us balance the books, so to speak, on the heat transferred between a system and its surroundings and the work done by or on a system. However, because energy is conserved, we can't simply use the value of $\Delta E$ to tell us whether a process is favored to occur because anything we do to lower the energy of the system raises the energy of the surroundings, and vice versa. Nevertheless, experience tells us that certain processes *always* occur, even though the energy of the universe is conserved. Water placed in a freezer turns into ice, for instance, and if you touch a hot object, heat is transferred to your hand. The first law guarantees that energy is conserved in these processes, and yet they occur without any outside intervention. We say they are *spontaneous*. A **spontaneous process** is one that proceeds on its own without any outside assistance.

A spontaneous process occurs in one direction only, and the reverse of any spontaneous process is always *nonspontaneous*. Drop an egg above a hard surface, for example, and it breaks on impact (◄ **FIGURE 19.1**). Now, imagine seeing a video clip in which a broken egg rises from the floor, reassembles itself, and ends up in someone's hand. You would conclude that the video is running in reverse because you know that broken eggs simply do not magically rise and reassemble themselves! An egg falling and breaking is spontaneous. The reverse process is *nonspontaneous*, even though energy is conserved in both processes.

We know other spontaneous and nonspontaneous processes that relate more directly to our study of chemistry. For example, a gas spontaneously expands into a vacuum (► **FIGURE 19.2**), but the reverse process, in which the gas moves back entirely into one of the flasks, does not happen. In other words, expansion of the gas is spontaneous, but the reverse process is nonspontaneous. In general, *processes that are spontaneous in one direction are nonspontaneous in the opposite direction.*

Experimental conditions, such as temperature and pressure, are often important in determining whether a process is spontaneous. We are all familiar with situations in which a forward process is spontaneous at one temperature but the reverse process is spontaneous at a different temperature. Consider, for example, ice melting. At atmospheric pressure, when the temperature of the surroundings is above 0 °C, ice melts spontaneously, and the reverse process— liquid water turning into ice—is not spontaneous. However, when the temperature of the surroundings is below 0 °C, the opposite is true—liquid water turns to ice spontaneously, but the reverse process is *not* spontaneous (▼ **FIGURE 19.3**).

What happens at $T = 0$ °C, the normal melting point of water, when the flask of Figure 19.3 contains both water and ice? At the normal melting point of a substance, the solid and liquid phases are in equilibrium. ∞ (Section 11.6) At this temperature, the two phases are interconverting at the same rate and there is no preferred direction for the process.

It is important to realize that the fact that a process is spontaneous does not necessarily mean that it will occur at an observable rate. A chemical reaction is spontaneous if it occurs on its own accord, regardless of its speed. A spontaneous reaction can be very fast, as in the case of acid–base neutralization, or very slow, as in the rusting of iron. Thermodynamics tells us the *direction* and *extent* of a reaction but nothing about the *speed*.

**⚠ GIVE IT SOME THOUGHT**

If a process is nonspontaneous, does that mean the process cannot occur under any circumstances?

**⚠ GO FIGURE**

In which direction is this process exothermic?

Spontaneous for $T > 0$ °C

Spontaneous for $T < 0$ °C

▲ **FIGURE 19.3   Spontaneity can depend on temperature.** At $T > 0$ °C, ice melts spontaneously to liquid water. At $T < 0$ °C, the reverse process, water freezing to ice, is spontaneous. At $T = 0$ °C the two states are in equilibrium.

**⚠ GO FIGURE**

If flask B were smaller than flask A, would the final pressure after the stopcock is opened be greater than, equal to, or less than 0.5 atm?

Closed stopcock

A        B

Gas at        Evacuated flask
1 atm        0 atm

When stopcock opens, gas expands to occupy both flasks

A →        → B

0.5 atm        0.5 atm

**This process is spontaneous**

All gas molecules move back into flask A

A ←        ← B

1 atm        0 atm

**This process is not spontaneous**

▲ **FIGURE 19.2   Expansion of a gas into an evacuated space is a spontaneous process.** The reverse process—gas molecules initially distributed evenly in two flasks all moving into one flask—is not spontaneous.

---

**SAMPLE EXERCISE 19.1   Identifying Spontaneous Processes**

Predict whether each process is spontaneous as described, spontaneous in the reverse direction, or in equilibrium: (**a**) Water at 40 °C gets hotter when a piece of metal heated to 150 °C is added. (**b**) Water at room temperature decomposes into $H_2(g)$ and $O_2(g)$. (**c**) Benzene vapor, $C_6H_6(g)$, at a pressure of 1 atm condenses to liquid benzene at the normal boiling point of benzene, 80.1 °C.

**SOLUTION**

**Analyze** We are asked to judge whether each process is spontaneous in the direction indicated, in the reverse direction, or in neither direction.

**Plan** We need to think about whether each process is consistent with our experience about the natural direction of events or whether we expect the reverse process to occur.

**Solve**
(**a**) This process is spontaneous. Whenever two objects at different temperatures are brought into contact, heat is transferred from the hotter object to the colder one. ∞ (Section 5.1) Thus, heat is transferred from the hot metal to the cooler water. The final temperature, after the metal and water achieve the same temperature (thermal equilibrium), will be somewhere

between the initial temperatures of the metal and the water. **(b)** Experience tells us that this process is not spontaneous—we certainly have never seen hydrogen and oxygen gases spontaneously bubbling up out of water! Rather, the *reverse* process—the reaction of $H_2$ and $O_2$ to form $H_2O$—is spontaneous. **(c)** The normal boiling point is the temperature at which a vapor at 1 atm is in equilibrium with its liquid. Thus, this is an equilibrium situation. If the temperature were below 80.1 °C, condensation would be spontaneous.

**PRACTICE EXERCISE**

At 1 atm pressure, $CO_2(s)$ sublimes at −78 °C. Is this process spontaneous at −100 °C and 1 atm pressure?

*Answer:* No, the reverse process is spontaneous at this temperature.

## Seeking a Criterion for Spontaneity

A marble rolling down an incline or a brick falling from your hand loses potential energy. The loss of some form of energy is a common feature of spontaneous change in mechanical systems. During the 1870s Marcellin Bertholet (1827–1907), a famous chemist of that era, suggested that the direction of spontaneous changes in chemical systems is determined by the loss of energy. He proposed that all spontaneous chemical and physical changes are exothermic. It takes only a few moments, however, to find exceptions to this generalization. For example, the melting of ice at room temperature is spontaneous and endothermic. Similarly, many spontaneous dissolution processes, such as the dissolving of $NH_4NO_3$, are endothermic, as we discovered in Section 13.1. We conclude that although the majority of spontaneous reactions are exothermic, there are spontaneous endothermic ones as well. Clearly, some other factor must be at work in determining the natural direction of processes.

To understand why certain processes are spontaneous, we need to consider more closely the ways in which the state of a system can change. Recall from Section 5.2 that quantities such as temperature, internal energy, and enthalpy are *state functions*, properties that define a state and do not depend on how we reach that state. The heat transferred between a system and its surroundings, $q$, and the work done by or on the system, $w$, are *not* state functions—their values depend on the specific path taken between states. One key to understanding spontaneity is understanding differences in the paths between states.

## Reversible and Irreversible Processes

In 1824 a 28-year-old French engineer named Sadi Carnot (1796–1832) published an analysis of the factors that determine how efficiently a steam engine can convert heat to work. Carnot considered what an *ideal engine*, one with the highest possible efficiency, would be like. He observed that it is impossible to convert the energy content of a fuel completely to work because a significant amount of heat is always lost to the surroundings. Carnot's analysis gave insight into how to build better, more efficient engines, and it was one of the earliest studies in what has developed into the discipline of thermodynamics.

An ideal engine operates under an ideal set of conditions in which all the processes are reversible. A **reversible process** is a specific way in which a system changes its state. In a reversible process, the change occurs in such a way that the system and surroundings can be restored to their original states by *exactly* reversing the change. In other words, we can restore the system to its original condition with no net change to either the system or its surroundings. An **irreversible process** is one that cannot simply be reversed to restore the system and its surroundings to their original states. What Carnot discovered is that the amount of work we can extract from any process depends on the manner in which the process is carried out. He concluded that *a reversible change produces the maximum amount of work that can be done by a system on its surroundings.*

## ◢ GO FIGURE

**If the flow of heat into or out of the system is to be reversible, what must be true of $\delta T$?**

Surroundings at temperature $T$

(a)

Surroundings at temperature $T$

(b)

◀ **FIGURE 19.4** **Reversible flow of heat.** Heat can flow reversibly between a system and its surroundings only if the two have an infinitesimally small difference in temperature $\delta T$. (a) Increasing the temperature of the system by $\delta T$ causes heat to flow from the hotter system to the colder surroundings. (b) Decreasing the temperature of the system by $\delta T$ causes heat to flow from the hotter surroundings to the colder system.

## ◢ GIVE IT SOME THOUGHT

Suppose you have a system made up of water only, with the container and everything beyond being the surroundings. Consider a process in which the water is first evaporated and then condensed back into its original container. Is this two-step process necessarily reversible?

Let's next examine some aspects of reversible and irreversible processes, first with respect to the transfer of heat. When two objects at different temperatures are in contact, heat flows spontaneously from the hotter object to the colder one. Because it is impossible to make heat flow in the opposite direction, from colder object to hotter one, the flow of heat is an irreversible process. Given these facts, can we imagine any conditions under which heat transfer can be made reversible?

To answer this question, we must consider temperature differences that are infinitesimally small, as opposed to the discrete temperature differences with which we are most familiar. For example, consider a system and its surroundings at essentially the same temperature, with just an infinitesimal temperature difference $\delta T$ between them (▲ **FIGURE 19.4**). If the surroundings are at temperature $T$ and the system is at the infinitesimally higher temperature $T + \delta T$, then an infinitesimal amount of heat flows from system to surroundings. We can reverse the direction of heat flow by making an infinitesimal change of temperature in the opposite direction, lowering the system temperature to $T - \delta T$. Now the direction of heat flow is from surroundings to system. *Reversible processes are those that reverse direction whenever an infinitesimal change is made in some property of the system.**

Now let's consider another example, the expansion of an ideal gas at constant temperature (referred to as an **isothermal process**). In the cylinder-piston arrangement of ▼ **FIGURE 19.5**, when the partition is removed, the gas expands spontaneously to fill the

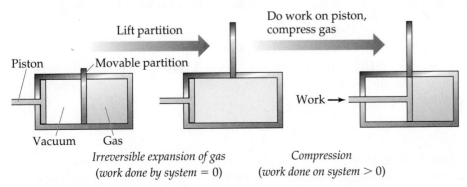

Lift partition

Do work on piston, compress gas

Piston

Movable partition

Work →

Vacuum   Gas

*Irreversible expansion of gas*
*(work done by system = 0)*

*Compression*
*(work done on system > 0)*

◀ **FIGURE 19.5** **An irreversible process.** Initially an ideal gas is confined to the right half of a cylinder. When the partition is removed, the gas spontaneously expands to fill the whole cylinder. No work is done by the system during this expansion. Using the piston to compress the gas back to its original state requires the surroundings to do work on the system.

*For a process to be truly reversible, the amounts of heat must be infinitesimally small and the transfer of heat must occur infinitely slowly; thus, no process that we can observe is truly reversible. The notion of infinitesimal amounts are related to the infinitesimals that you may have studied in a calculus course.

evacuated space. Can we determine whether this particular isothermal expansion is reversible or irreversible? Because the gas expands into a vacuum with no external pressure, it does no *P-V* work on the surroundings. ∞ (Section 5.3) Thus, for the expansion, $w = 0$. We can use the piston to compress the gas back to its original state, but doing so requires that the surroundings do work on the system, meaning that $w > 0$ for the compression. In other words, the path that restores the system to its original state requires a different value of $w$ (and, by the first law, a different value of $q$) than the path by which the system was first changed. The fact that the same path can't be followed to restore the system to its original state indicates that the process is irreversible.

What might a *reversible* isothermal expansion of an ideal gas be? This process will occur only if initially, when the gas is confined to half the cylinder, the external pressure acting on the piston exactly balances the pressure exerted by the gas on the piston. If the external pressure is reduced infinitely slowly, the piston will move outward, allowing the pressure of the confined gas to readjust to maintain the pressure balance. This infinitely slow process in which the external pressure and internal pressure are always in equilibrium is reversible. If we reverse the process and compress the gas in the same infinitely slow manner, we can return the gas to its original volume. The complete cycle of expansion and compression in this hypothetical process, moreover, is accomplished without any net change to the surroundings.

Because real processes can at best only approximate the infinitely slow change associated with reversible processes, all real processes are irreversible. Further, as noted earlier in this discussion, the reverse of any spontaneous process is a nonspontaneous process. A nonspontaneous process can occur only if the surroundings do work on the system. Thus, *any spontaneous process is irreversible.* Even if we return the system to the original condition, the surroundings will have changed.

## 19.2 | ENTROPY AND THE SECOND LAW OF THERMODYNAMICS

How can we use the fact that any spontaneous process is irreversible to make predictions about the spontaneity of an unfamiliar process? Understanding spontaneity requires us to examine the thermodynamic quantity called **entropy**, which was first mentioned in Section 13.1. In general, entropy is associated either with the extent of *randomness* in a system or with the extent to which energy is distributed among the various motions of the molecules of the system. In this section we consider how we can relate entropy changes to heat transfer and temperature. Our analysis will bring us to a profound statement about spontaneity that we call the second law of thermodynamics.

### Entropy Change

The entropy, $S$, of a system is a state function just like internal energy, $E$, and enthalpy, $H$. As with these other quantities, the value of $S$ is a characteristic of the state of a system. ∞ (Section 5.2) Thus, the change in entropy, $\Delta S$, in a system depends only on the initial and final states of the system and not on the path taken from one state to the other:

$$\Delta S = S_{\text{final}} - S_{\text{initial}} \qquad [19.1]$$

For the special case of an isothermal process, $\Delta S$ is equal to the heat that would be transferred if the process were reversible, $q_{\text{rev}}$, divided by the absolute temperature at which the process occurs:

$$\Delta S = \frac{q_{\text{rev}}}{T} \qquad (\text{constant } T) \qquad [19.2]$$

Although there are many possible paths that can take the system from one state to another, only one path is associated with a reversible process. Thus, the value of $q_{\text{rev}}$ is uniquely defined for any two states of the system. Because $S$ is a state function, we can use Equation 19.2 to calculate $\Delta S$ for *any* isothermal process between states, not just the reversible one.

GIVE IT SOME THOUGHT

How do we reconcile the fact that $S$ is a state function but $\Delta S$ depends on $q$, which is not a state function?

## $\Delta S$ for Phase Changes

The melting of a substance at its melting point and the vaporization of a substance at its boiling point are isothermal processes. ∞ (Section 11.4) Consider the melting of ice. At 1 atm pressure, ice and liquid water are in equilibrium at 0 °C. Imagine melting 1 mol of ice at 0 °C, 1 atm to form 1 mol of liquid water at 0 °C, 1 atm. We can achieve this change by adding a certain amount of heat to the system from the surroundings: $q = \Delta H_{fusion}$. Now imagine that we add the heat infinitely slowly, raising the temperature of the surroundings only infinitesimally above 0 °C. When we make the change in this fashion, the process is reversible because we can reverse it by infinitely slowly removing the same amount of heat, $\Delta H_{fusion}$, from the system, using immediate surroundings that are infinitesimally below 0 °C. Thus, $q_{rev} = \Delta H_{fusion}$ for the melting of ice at $T = 0\,°C = 273$ K.

The enthalpy of fusion for $H_2O$ is $\Delta H_{fusion} = 6.01$ kJ/mol (a positive value because melting is an endothermic process). Thus, we can use Equation 19.2 to calculate $\Delta S_{fusion}$ for melting 1 mol of ice at 273 K:

$$\Delta S_{fusion} = \frac{q_{rev}}{T} = \frac{\Delta H_{fusion}}{T} = \frac{(1\ \text{mol})(6.01 \times 10^3\ \text{J/mol})}{273\ \text{K}} = 22.0\ \text{J/K}$$

Notice (a) that we must use the absolute temperature in Equation 19.2 and (b) that the units for $\Delta S$, J/K, are energy divided by absolute temperature, as we expect from Equation 19.2.

---

**SAMPLE EXERCISE 19.2**   **Calculating $\Delta S$ for a Phase Change**

Elemental mercury is a silver liquid at room temperature. Its normal freezing point is −38.9 °C, and its molar enthalpy of fusion is $\Delta H_{fusion} = 2.29$ kJ/mol. What is the entropy change of the system when 50.0 g of Hg($l$) freezes at the normal freezing point?

### SOLUTION

**Analyze** We first recognize that freezing is an *exothermic* process, which means heat is transferred from system to surroundings and $q < 0$. The enthalpy of fusion refers to the process of melting. Because freezing is the reverse of melting, the enthalpy change that accompanies the freezing of 1 mol of Hg is $-\Delta H_{fusion} = -2.29$ kJ/mol.

**Plan** We can use $-\Delta H_{fusion}$ and the atomic weight of Hg to calculate $q$ for freezing 50.0 g of Hg. Then we use this value of $q$ as $q_{rev}$ in Equation 19.2 to determine $\Delta S$ for the system.

**Solve**
For $q$ we have

$$q = (50.0\ \text{g Hg})\left(\frac{1\ \text{mol Hg}}{200.59\ \text{g Hg}}\right)\left(\frac{-2.29\ \text{kJ}}{1\ \text{mol Hg}}\right)\left(\frac{1000\ \text{J}}{1\ \text{kJ}}\right) = -571$$

Before using Equation 19.2, we must first convert the given Celsius temperature to kelvins:

$$-38.9\,°C = (-38.9 + 273.15)\ \text{K} = 234.3\ \text{K}$$

We can now calculate $\Delta S_{sys}$:

$$\Delta S_{sys} = \frac{q_{rev}}{T} = \frac{-571\ \text{J}}{234.3\ \text{K}} = -2.44\ \text{J/K}$$

**Check** The entropy change is negative because our $q_{rev}$ value is negative, which it must be because heat flows out of the system in this exothermic process.

**Comment** This procedure can be used to calculate $\Delta S$ for other isothermal phase changes, such as the vaporization of a liquid at its boiling point.

### PRACTICE EXERCISE

The normal boiling point of ethanol, $C_2H_5OH$, is 78.3 °C, and its molar enthalpy of vaporization is 38.56 kJ/mol. What is the change in entropy in the system when 68.3 g of $C_2H_5OH(g)$ at 1 atm condenses to liquid at the normal boiling point?
*Answer:* −163 J/K

## A CLOSER LOOK

### THE ENTROPY CHANGE WHEN A GAS EXPANDS ISOTHERMALLY

In general, the entropy of any system increases as the system becomes more random or more spread out. Thus, we expect the spontaneous expansion of a gas to result in an increase in entropy. To see how this entropy increase can be calculated, consider the expansion of an ideal gas that is initially constrained by a piston, as in the rightmost part of Figure 19.5. Imagine that we allow the gas to undergo a reversible isothermal expansion by infinitesimally decreasing the external pressure on the piston. The work done on the surroundings by the reversible expansion of the system against the piston can be calculated with the aid of calculus (we do not show the derivation):

$$w_{rev} = -nRT \ln \frac{V_2}{V_1}$$

In this equation, $n$ is the number of moles of gas, $R$ is the gas constant ∞ (Section 10.4), $T$ is the absolute temperature, $V_1$ is the initial volume, and $V_2$ is the final volume. Notice that if $V_2 > V_1$, as it must be in our expansion, then $w_{rev} < 0$, meaning that the expanding gas does work on the surroundings.

One characteristic of an ideal gas is that its internal energy depends only on temperature, not on pressure. Thus, when an ideal gas expands isothermally, $\Delta E = 0$. Because $\Delta E = q_{rev} + w_{rev} = 0$, we see that $q_{rev} = -w_{rev} = nRT \ln(V_2/V_1)$. Then, using Equation 19.2, we can calculate the entropy change in the system:

$$\Delta S_{sys} = \frac{q_{rev}}{T} = \frac{nRT \ln \dfrac{V_2}{V_1}}{T} = nR \ln \frac{V_2}{V_1} \qquad [19.3]$$

From the ideal-gas equation, we can calculate the number of moles in 1.00 L of an ideal gas at 1.00 atm and 0 °C by using the value 0.08206 L-atm/mol-K for $R$:

$$n = \frac{PV}{RT} = \frac{(1.00 \text{ atm})(1.00 \text{ L})}{(0.08206 \text{ L-atm/mol-K})(273 \text{ K})} = 4.46 \times 10^{-2} \text{ mol}$$

The gas constant, $R$, can also be expressed as 8.314 J/mol-K (Table 10.2), and this is the value we must use in Equation 19.3 because we want our answer to be expressed in terms of J rather than in L-atm. Thus, for the expansion of the gas from 1.00 L to 2.00 L, we have

$$\Delta S_{sys} = (4.46 \times 10^{-2} \text{ mol})\left(8.314 \frac{J}{\text{mol-K}}\right)\left(\ln \frac{2.00 \text{ L}}{1.00 \text{ L}}\right)$$

$$= 0.26 \text{ J/K}$$

In Section 19.3 we will see that this increase in entropy is a measure of the increased randomness of the molecules because of the expansion.

*RELATED EXERCISES:* 19.29, 19.30, and 19.106

## The Second Law of Thermodynamics

The key idea of the first law of thermodynamics is that energy is conserved in any process. ∞ (Section 5.2) Entropy, however, is not conserved. For any spontaneous process, the total change in entropy, which is the sum of the entropy change of the system plus the entropy change of the surroundings, is greater than zero.

Let's illustrate this generalization by calculating the entropy change of a system and the entropy change of its surroundings when our system is 1 mol of ice (a piece roughly the size of an ice cube) melting in the palm of your hand, which is part of the surroundings. The process is not reversible because the system and surroundings are at different temperatures. Nevertheless, because $\Delta S$ is a state function, its value is the same regardless of whether the process is reversible or irreversible. We calculated the entropy change of the system just before Sample Exercise 19.2:

$$\Delta S_{sys} = \frac{q_{rev}}{T} = \frac{(1 \text{ mol})(6.01 \times 10^3 \text{ J/mol})}{273 \text{ K}} = 22.0 \text{ J/K}$$

The surroundings immediately in contact with the ice are your hand, which we assume is at body temperature, 37 °C = 310 K. The quantity of heat lost by your hand is $-6.01 \times 10^3$ J/mol, which is equal in magnitude to the quantity of heat gained by the ice but has the opposite sign. Hence, the entropy change of the surroundings is

$$\Delta S_{surr} = \frac{q_{rev}}{T} = \frac{(1 \text{ mol})(-6.01 \times 10^3 \text{ J/mol})}{310 \text{ K}} = -19.4 \text{ J/K}$$

Thus, the total entropy change is positive:

$$\Delta S_{total} = \Delta S_{sys} + \Delta S_{surr} = (22.0 \text{ J/K}) + (-19.4 \text{ J/K}) = 2.6 \text{ J/K}$$

If the temperature of the surroundings were not 310 K but rather some temperature infinitesimally above 273 K, the melting would be reversible instead of irreversible. In that case the entropy change of the surroundings would equal $-22.0$ J/K and $\Delta S_{total}$ would be zero.

In general, any irreversible process results in an increase in total entropy, whereas any reversible process results in no overall change in entropy. This statement is known as the **second law of thermodynamics**.

The sum of the entropy of a system plus the entropy of the surroundings is everything there is, and so we refer to the total entropy change as the entropy change of the universe, $\Delta S_{univ}$. We can therefore state the second law of thermodynamics in terms of two equations:

$$\text{Reversible Process: } \Delta S_{univ} = \Delta S_{sys} + \Delta S_{surr} = 0$$

$$\text{Irreversible Process: } \Delta S_{univ} = \Delta S_{sys} + \Delta S_{surr} > 0 \qquad [19.4]$$

Because spontaneous processes are irreversible, we can say that *the entropy of the universe increases in any spontaneous process*. This profound generalization is yet another way of expressing the second law of thermodynamics.

### GIVE IT SOME THOUGHT

The rusting of iron is spontaneous and is accompanied by a decrease in the entropy of the system (the iron and oxygen). What can we conclude about the entropy change of the surroundings?

The second law of thermodynamics tells us the essential character of any spontaneous change—it is always accompanied by an increase in the entropy of the universe. We can use this criterion to predict whether a given process is spontaneous or not. Before seeing how this is done, however, we will find it useful to explore entropy from a molecular perspective.

A word on notation before we proceed. Throughout most of the remainder of this chapter, we will focus on systems rather than surroundings. To simplify the notation, we will usually refer to the entropy change of the system as $\Delta S$ rather than explicitly indicating $\Delta S_{sys}$.

## 19.3 | MOLECULAR INTERPRETATION OF ENTROPY

As chemists, we are interested in molecules. What does entropy have to do with them and with their transformations? What molecular property does entropy reflect? Ludwig Boltzmann (1844–1906) gave conceptual meaning to the notion of entropy, and to understand his contribution, we need to examine the ways in which we can interpret entropy at the molecular level.

### Expansion of a Gas at the Molecular Level

In discussing Figure 19.2, we talked about the expansion of a gas into a vacuum as a spontaneous process. We now understand that it is an irreversible process and that the entropy of the universe increases during the expansion. How can we explain the spontaneity of this process at the molecular level? We can get a sense of what makes this expansion spontaneous by envisioning the gas as a collection of particles in constant motion, as we did in discussing the kinetic-molecular theory of gases. ∞ (Section 10.7) When the stopcock in Figure 19.2 is opened, we can view the expansion of the gas as the ultimate result of the gas molecules moving randomly throughout the larger volume.

Let's look at this idea more closely by tracking two of the gas molecules as they move around. Before the stopcock is opened, both molecules are confined to the left flask, as shown in ▶ FIGURE 19.6(a). After the stopcock is opened, the molecules travel randomly throughout the entire apparatus. As Figure 19.6(b) shows, there are four possible arrangements for the two molecules once both flasks are available to them. Because the molecular motion is random, all four arrangements are equally likely. Note that now only one arrangement corresponds to the situation before the stopcock was opened: both molecules in the left flask.

(a)

The two molecules are colored
red and blue to keep track of them.

(b)

Four possible arrangements (microstates)
once the stopcock is opened.

▲ **FIGURE 19.6** **Possible arrangements of two gas molecules in two flasks.** (a) Before the stopcock is opened, both molecules are in the left flask. (b) After the stopcock is opened, there are four possible arrangements of the two molecules.

Figure 19.6(b) shows that with both flasks available to the molecules, the probability of the red molecule being in the left flask is two in four (top right and bottom left arrangements), and the probability of the blue molecule being in the left flask is the same (top left and bottom left arrangements). Because the probability is $^2/_4 = ^1/_2$ that each molecule is in the left flask, the probability that *both* are there is $(^1/_2)^2 = ^1/_4$. If we apply the same analysis to *three* gas molecules, we find that the probability that all three are in the left flask at the same time is $(^1/_2)^3 = 1/8$.

Now let's consider a *mole* of gas. The probability that all the molecules are in the left flask at the same time is $(^1/_2)^N$, where $N = 6.02 \times 10^{23}$. This is a vanishingly small number! Thus, there is essentially zero likelihood that all the gas molecules will be in the left flask at the same time. This analysis of the microscopic behavior of the gas molecules leads to the expected macroscopic behavior: The gas spontaneously expands to fill both the left and right flasks, and it does not spontaneously all go back in the left flask.

This molecular view of gas expansion shows the tendency of the molecules to "spread out" among the different arrangements they can take. Before the stopcock is opened, there is only one possible arrangement: all molecules in the left flask. When the stopcock is opened, the arrangement in which all the molecules are in the left flask is but one of an extremely large number of possible arrangements. The most probable arrangements by far are those in which there are essentially equal numbers of molecules in the two flasks. When the gas spreads throughout the apparatus, any given molecule can be in either flask rather than confined to the left flask. We say that with the stopcock opened, the arrangement of gas molecules is more random or disordered than when the molecules are all confined in the left flask.

We will see this notion of increasing randomness helps us understand entropy at the molecular level.

## Boltzmann's Equation and Microstates

The science of thermodynamics developed as a means of describing the properties of matter in our macroscopic world without regard to microscopic structure. In fact, thermodynamics was a well-developed field before the modern view of atomic and molecular structure was even known. The thermodynamic properties of water, for example, addressed the behavior of bulk water (or ice or water vapor) as a substance without considering any specific properties of individual $H_2O$ molecules.

To connect the microscopic and macroscopic descriptions of matter, scientists have developed the field of *statistical thermodynamics*, which uses the tools of statistics and probability to link the microscopic and macroscopic worlds. Here we show how entropy, which is a property of bulk matter, can be connected to the behavior of atoms and molecules. Because the mathematics of statistical thermodynamics is complex, our discussion will be largely conceptual.

In our discussion of two gas molecules in the two-flask system in Figure 19.6, we saw that the number of possible arrangements helped explain why the gas expands.

Suppose we now consider one mole of an ideal gas in a particular thermodynamic state, which we can define by specifying the temperature, $T$, and volume, $V$, of the gas. What is happening to this gas at the microscopic level, and how does what is going on at the microscopic level relate to the entropy of the gas?

Imagine taking a snapshot of the positions and speeds of all the molecules at a given instant. The speed of each molecule tells us its kinetic energy. That particular set of $6 \times 10^{23}$ positions and kinetic energies of the individual gas molecules is what we call a *microstate* of the system. A **microstate** is a single possible arrangement of the positions and kinetic energies of the gas molecules when the gas is in a specific thermodynamic state. We could envision continuing to take snapshots of our system to see other possible microstates.

As you no doubt see, there would be such a staggeringly large number of microstates that taking individual snapshots of all of them is not feasible. Because we are examining such a large number of particles, however, we can use the tools of statistics and probability to determine the total number of microstates for the thermodynamic state. (That is where the *statistical* part of the name *statistical thermodynamics* comes in.) Each thermodynamic state has a characteristic number of microstates associated with it, and we will use the symbol $W$ for that number.

▲ **FIGURE 19.7 Ludwig Boltzmann's gravestone.** Boltzmann's gravestone in Vienna is inscribed with his famous relationship between the entropy of a state, $S$, and the number of available microstates, $W$. (In Boltzmann's time, "log" was used to represent the natural logarithm.)

Students sometimes have difficulty distinguishing between the state of a system and the microstates associated with the state. The difference is that *state* is used to describe the macroscopic view of our system as characterized, for example, by the pressure or temperature of a sample of gas. A *microstate* is a particular microscopic arrangement of the atoms or molecules of the system that corresponds to the given state of the system. Each of the snapshots we described is a microstate—the positions and kinetic energies of individual gas molecules will change from snapshot to snapshot, but each one is a possible arrangement of the collection of molecules corresponding to a single state. For macroscopically sized systems, such as a mole of gas, there is a very large number of microstates for each state—that is, $W$ is generally an extremely large number.

The connection between the number of microstates of a system, $W$, and the entropy of the system, $S$, is expressed in a beautifully simple equation developed by Boltzmann and engraved on his tombstone (▶ **FIGURE 19.7**):

$$S = k \ln W \qquad [19.5]$$

In this equation, $k$ is Boltzmann's constant, $1.38 \times 10^{-23}$ J/K. Thus, *entropy is a measure of how many microstates are associated with a particular macroscopic state.*

### ◢ GIVE IT SOME THOUGHT

What is the entropy of a system that has only a single microstate?

From Equation 19.5, we see that the entropy change accompanying any process is

$$\Delta S = k \ln W_{final} - k \ln W_{initial} = k \ln \frac{W_{final}}{W_{initial}} \qquad [19.6]$$

Any change in the system that leads to an increase in the number of microstates ($W_{final} > W_{initial}$) leads to a positive value of $\Delta S$: *Entropy increases with the number of microstates of the system.*

Let's consider two modifications to our ideal-gas sample and see how the entropy changes in each case. First, suppose we increase the volume of the system, which is analogous to allowing the gas to expand isothermally. A greater volume means a greater number of positions available to the gas atoms and therefore a greater number of microstates. The entropy therefore increases as the volume increases, as we saw in the "A Closer Look" box in Section 19.2.

Second, suppose we keep the volume fixed but increase the temperature. How does this change affect the entropy of the system? Recall the distribution of molecular speeds presented in Figure 10.17(a). An increase in temperature increases the most probable speed of the molecules and also broadens the distribution of speeds. Hence, the molecules have a greater number of possible kinetic energies, and the number of microstates increases. Thus, the entropy of the system increases with increasing temperature.

## Molecular Motions and Energy

When a substance is heated, the motion of its molecules increases. In Section 10.7, we found that the average kinetic energy of the molecules of an ideal gas is directly proportional to the absolute temperature of the gas. That means the higher the temperature, the faster the molecules move and the more kinetic energy they possess. Moreover, hotter systems have a *broader distribution* of molecular speeds, as Figure 10.17(a) shows.

The particles of an ideal gas are idealized points with no volume and no bonds, however, points that we visualize as flitting around through space. Any real molecule can undergo three kinds of more complex motion. The entire molecule can move in one direction, which is the simple motion we visualize for an ideal particle and see in a macroscopic object, such as a thrown baseball. We call such movement **translational motion**. The molecules in a gas have more freedom of translational motion than those in a liquid, which have more freedom of translational motion than the molecules of a solid.

A real molecule can also undergo **vibrational motion**, in which the atoms in the molecule move periodically toward and away from one another, and **rotational motion**, in which the molecule spins about an axis. ▼ FIGURE 19.8 shows the vibrational motions and one of the rotational motions possible for the water molecule. These different forms of motion are ways in which a molecule can store energy, and we refer to the various forms collectively as the *motional energy* of the molecule.

### ⚠ GIVE IT SOME THOUGHT

What kinds of motion can a molecule undergo that a single atom cannot?

The vibrational and rotational motions possible in real molecules lead to arrangements that a single atom can't have. A collection of real molecules therefore has a greater number of possible microstates than does the same number of ideal-gas particles. In general, *the number of microstates possible for a system increases with an increase in volume, an increase in temperature, or an increase in the number of molecules because any of these changes increases the possible positions and kinetic energies of the molecules making up the system.* We will also see that the number of microstates increases as the complexity of the molecule increases because there are more vibrational motions available.

Chemists have several ways of describing an increase in the number of microstates possible for a system and therefore an increase in the entropy for the system. Each way seeks to capture a sense of the increased freedom of motion that causes molecules to spread out when not restrained by physical barriers or chemical bonds.

### ⚠ GO FIGURE

Describe another possible rotational motion for this molecule.

▶ FIGURE 19.8  Vibrational and rotational motions in a water molecule.

— Vibrations —                        — Rotation —

The most common way for describing an increase in entropy is as an increase in the *randomness*, or *disorder*, of the system. Another way likens an entropy increase to an increased *dispersion (spreading out) of energy* because there is an increase in the number of ways the positions and energies of the molecules can be distributed throughout the system. Each description (randomness or energy dispersal) is conceptually helpful if applied correctly.

## Making Qualitative Predictions About ΔS

It is usually not difficult to estimate qualitatively how the entropy of a system changes during a simple process. As noted earlier, an increase in either the temperature or the volume of a system leads to an increase in the number of microstates, and hence an increase in the entropy. One more factor that correlates with number of microstates is the number of independently moving particles.

We can usually make qualitative predictions about entropy changes by focusing on these factors. For example, when water vaporizes, the molecules spread out into a larger volume. Because they occupy a larger volume, there is an increase in their freedom of motion, giving rise to a greater number of possible microstates, and hence an increase in entropy.

Now consider the phases of water. In ice, hydrogen bonding leads to the rigid structure shown in ▼ FIGURE 19.9. Each molecule in the ice is free to vibrate, but its translational and rotational motions are much more restricted than in liquid water. Although there are hydrogen bonds in liquid water, the molecules can more readily move about relative to one another (translation) and tumble around (rotation). During melting, therefore, the number of possible microstates increases and so does the entropy. In water vapor, the molecules are essentially independent of one another and have their full range of translational, vibrational, and rotational motions. Thus, water vapor has an even greater number of possible microstates and therefore a higher entropy than liquid water or ice.

GO FIGURE

**In which phase are water molecules least able to have rotational motion?**

Increasing entropy

Ice

Liquid water

Water vapor

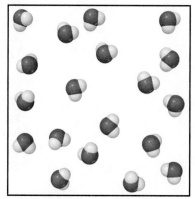

Rigid, crystalline structure

Motion restricted to **vibration** only

Smallest number of microstates

Increased freedom with respect to **translation**

Free to **vibrate** and **rotate**

Larger number of microstates

Molecules spread out, essentially independent of one another

Complete freedom for **translation**, **vibration**, and **rotation**

Largest number of microstates

▲ FIGURE 19.9  **Entropy and the phases of water.** The larger the number of possible microstates, the higher the entropy of the system.

▲ **FIGURE 19.10** **Entropy changes when an ionic solid dissolves in water.** The ions become more spread out and disordered, but the water molecules that hydrate the ions become less disordered.

When an ionic solid dissolves in water, a mixture of water and ions replaces the pure solid and pure water, as shown for KCl in ◄ **FIGURE 19.10**. The ions in the liquid move in a volume that is larger than the volume in which they were able to move in the crystal lattice and so possess more motional energy. This increased motion might lead us to conclude that the entropy of the system has increased. We have to be careful, however, because some of the water molecules have lost some freedom of motion because they are now held around the ions as water of hydration. ∞ (Section 13.1) These water molecules are in a *more* ordered state than before because they are now confined to the immediate environment of the ions. Therefore, the dissolving of a salt involves both a disordering process (the ions become less confined) and an ordering process (some water molecules become more confined). The disordering processes are usually dominant, and so the overall effect is an increase in the randomness of the system when most salts dissolve in water.

The same ideas apply to chemical reactions. Consider the reaction between nitric oxide gas and oxygen gas to form nitrogen dioxide gas:

$$2\,NO(g) + O_2(g) \longrightarrow 2\,NO_2(g) \qquad [19.7]$$

which results in a decrease in the number of molecules—three molecules of gaseous reactants form two molecules of gaseous products (► **FIGURE 19.11**). The formation of new N—O bonds reduces the motions of the atoms in the system. The formation of new bonds decreases the *number of degrees of freedom*, or forms of motion, available to the atoms. That is, the atoms are less free to move in random fashion because of the formation of new bonds. The decrease in the number of molecules and the resultant decrease in motion result in fewer possible microstates and therefore a decrease in the entropy of the system.

In summary, we generally expect the entropy of a system to increase for processes in which

1. Gases form from either solids or liquids.

2. Liquids or solutions form from solids.

3. The number of gas molecules increases during a chemical reaction.

---

**SAMPLE EXERCISE 19.3**    **Predicting the Sign of ΔS**

Predict whether $\Delta S$ is positive or negative for each process, assuming each occurs at constant temperature:

**(a)** $H_2O(l) \longrightarrow H_2O(g)$

**(b)** $Ag^+(aq) + Cl^-(aq) \longrightarrow AgCl(s)$

**(c)** $4\,Fe(s) + 3\,O_2(g) \longrightarrow 2\,Fe_2O_3(s)$

**(d)** $N_2(g) + O_2(g) \longrightarrow 2\,NO(g)$

**SOLUTION**

**Analyze** We are given four reactions and asked to predict the sign of $\Delta S$ for each.

**Plan** We expect $\Delta S$ to be positive if there is an increase in temperature, increase in volume, or increase in number of gas particles. The question states that the temperature is constant, and so we need to concern ourselves only with volume and number of particles.

**Solve**
**(a)** Evaporation involves a large increase in volume as liquid changes to gas. One mole of water (18 g) occupies about 18 mL as a liquid and if it could exist as a gas at STP it would occupy 22.4 L. Because the molecules are distributed throughout a much larger volume in the gaseous state, an increase in motional freedom accompanies vaporization and $\Delta S$ is positive.

**(b)** In this process, ions, which are free to move throughout the volume of the solution, form a solid, in which they are confined to a smaller volume and restricted to more highly constrained positions. Thus, $\Delta S$ is negative.

**(c)** The particles of a solid are confined to specific locations and have fewer ways to move (fewer microstates) than do the molecules of a gas. Because $O_2$ gas is converted into part of the solid product $Fe_2O_3$, $\Delta S$ is negative.

**(d)** The number of moles of reactant gases is the same as the number of moles of product gases, and so the entropy change is expected to be small. The sign of $\Delta S$ is impossible to predict based on our discussions thus far, but we can predict that $\Delta S$ will be close to zero.

**PRACTICE EXERCISE**

Indicate whether each process produces an increase or decrease in the entropy of the system:

**(a)** $CO_2(s) \longrightarrow CO_2(g)$
**(b)** $CaO(s) + CO_2(g) \longrightarrow CaCO_3(s)$
**(c)** $HCl(g) + NH_3(g) \longrightarrow NH_4Cl(s)$
**(d)** $2\,SO_2(g) + O_2(g) \longrightarrow 2\,SO_3(g)$

**Answers:** **(a)** increase, **(b)** decrease, **(c)** decrease, **(d)** decrease

---

**SAMPLE EXERCISE 19.4**  **Predicting Relative Entropies**

In each pair, choose the system that has greater entropy and explain your choice: **(a)** 1 mol of $NaCl(s)$ or 1 mol of $HCl(g)$ at 25 °C, **(b)** 2 mol of $HCl(g)$ or 1 mol of $HCl(g)$ at 25 °C, **(c)** 1 mol of $HCl(g)$ or 1 mol of $Ar(g)$ at 298 K.

**SOLUTION**

**Analyze**  We need to select the system in each pair that has the greater entropy.

**Plan**  We examine the state of each system and the complexity of the molecules it contains.

**Solve**
**(a)** $HCl(g)$ has the higher entropy because the particles in gases are more disordered and have more freedom of motion than the particles in solids. **(b)** When these two systems are at the same pressure, the sample containing 2 mol of HCl has twice the number of molecules as the sample containing 1 mol. Thus, the 2-mol sample has twice the number of microstates and twice the entropy. **(c)** The HCl system has the higher entropy because the number of ways in which an HCl molecule can store energy is greater than the number of ways in which an Ar atom can store energy. (Molecules can rotate and vibrate; atoms cannot.)

**PRACTICE EXERCISE**

Choose the system with the greater entropy in each case: **(a)** 1 mol of $H_2(g)$ at STP or 1 mol of $H_2(g)$ at 100 °C and 0.5 atm, **(b)** 1 mol of $H_2O(s)$ at 0 °C or 1 mol of $H_2O(l)$ at 25 °C, **(c)** 1 mol of $H_2(g)$ at STP or 1 mol of $SO_2(g)$ at STP, **(d)** 1 mol of $N_2O_4(g)$ at STP or 2 mol of $NO_2(g)$ at STP.

**Answers:** **(a)** 1 mol of $H_2(g)$ at 100 °C and 0.5 atm, **(b)** 1 mol of $H_2O(l)$ at 25 °C, **(c)** 1 mol of $SO_2(g)$ at STP, **(d)** 2 mol of $NO_2(g)$ at STP

**GO FIGURE**

What major factor leads to a decrease in entropy as the reaction shown takes place?

$2\,NO(g) + O_2(g)$           $2\,NO_2(g)$

▲ **FIGURE 19.11**  **Entropy decreases when NO(g) is oxidized by $O_2(g)$ to $NO_2(g)$.** A decrease in the number of gaseous molecules leads to a decrease in the entropy of the system.

---

# The Third Law of Thermodynamics

If we decrease the thermal energy of a system by lowering the temperature, the energy stored in translational, vibrational, and rotational motion decreases. As less energy is stored, the entropy of the system decreases. If we keep lowering the temperature, do we reach a state in which these motions are essentially shut down, a point described by a single microstate? This question is addressed by the **third law of thermodynamics**, which states that *the entropy of a pure crystalline substance at absolute zero is zero*: $S(0\,K) = 0$.

Consider a pure crystalline solid. At absolute zero, the individual atoms or molecules in the lattice would be perfectly ordered and as well defined in position as they could be. Because none of them would have thermal motion, there is only one possible microstate. As a result, Equation 19.5 becomes $S = k \ln W = k \ln 1 = 0$. As the temperature is increased from absolute zero, the atoms or molecules in the crystal gain energy in the form of vibrational motion about their lattice positions. This means that the degrees of freedom and the entropy both increase. What happens to the entropy, however, as we continue to heat the crystal? We consider this important question in the next section.

▲ **GIVE IT SOME THOUGHT**

If you are told that the entropy of a system is zero, what do you know about the system?

# CHEMISTRY AND LIFE

## ENTROPY AND HUMAN SOCIETY

The laws of thermodynamics have profound implications for our existence. In the "Chemistry Put to Work" box on page 192, we examined some of the scientific and political challenges of using biofuels as a major energy source to maintain our lifestyles. That discussion builds around the first law of thermodynamics, namely, that energy is conserved. We therefore have important decisions to make as to energy production and consumption.

The second law of thermodynamics is also relevant in discussions about our existence and about our ability and desire to advance as a civilization. Any living organism is a complex, highly organized, well-ordered system. Our entropy content is much lower than it would be if we were completely decomposed into carbon dioxide, water, and several other simple chemicals. Does this mean that our existence is a violation of the second law? No, because the thousands of chemical reactions necessary to produce and maintain human life have caused a very large increase in the entropy of the rest of the universe. Thus, as the second law requires, the overall entropy change during the lifetime of a human, or any other living system, is positive.

In addition to being complex living systems ourselves, we humans are masters of producing order in the world around us. As shown in the chapter-opening photograph, we build impressive, highly ordered structures and buildings. We manipulate and order matter at the nanoscale level in order to produce the technological breakthroughs that have become so commonplace in the twenty-first century (▶ **FIGURE 19.12**). We use tremendous quantities of raw materials to produce highly ordered materials—iron, copper, and a host of other metals from their ores, silicon for computer chips from sand, polymers from fossil fuel feedstocks, and so forth. In so doing, we expend a great deal of energy to, in essence, "fight" the second law of thermodynamics.

For every bit of order we produce, however, we produce an even greater amount of disorder. Petroleum, coal, and natural gas are burned to provide the energy necessary for us to achieve highly ordered structures, but their combustion increases the entropy of the universe by releasing $CO_2(g)$, $H_2O(g)$, and heat. Oxide and sulfide ores release $CO_2(g)$ and $SO_2(g)$ that spread throughout our atmosphere. Thus, even as we strive to create more impressive discoveries and greater order in our society, we drive the entropy of the universe higher, as the second law says we must.

We humans are, in effect, using up our storehouse of energy-rich materials to create order and advance technology. As noted in Chapter 5, we must learn to harness new energy sources, such as solar energy, before we exhaust the supplies of readily available energy of other kinds.

▲ **FIGURE 19.12** **Fighting the second law.** Creating complex structures, such as the skyscrapers in the chapter-opening photograph, requires that we use energy to produce order while knowing that we are increasing the entropy of the universe. Modern cellular telephones, with their detailed displays and complex circuitry are an example on a smaller scale of the impressive order that human ingenuity achieves.

# 19.4 | ENTROPY CHANGES IN CHEMICAL REACTIONS

In Section 5.5 we discussed how calorimetry can be used to measure $\Delta H$ for chemical reactions. No comparable method exists for measuring $\Delta S$ for a reaction. However, because the third law establishes a zero point for entropy, we can use experimental measurements to determine the *absolute value of the entropy, S.* To see schematically how this is done, let's review in greater detail the variation in the entropy of a substance with temperature.

We know that the entropy of a pure crystalline solid at 0 K is zero and that the entropy increases as the temperature of the crystal is increased. ▶ **FIGURE 19.13** shows that the entropy of the solid increases steadily with increasing temperature up to the melting point of the solid. When the solid melts, the atoms or molecules are free to move about the entire volume of the sample. The added degrees of freedom increase the randomness of the substance, thereby increasing its entropy. We therefore see a sharp increase in the entropy at the melting point. After all the solid has melted, the temperature again increases and with it, the entropy.

GO FIGURE

**Why does the plot show vertical jumps at the melting and boiling points?**

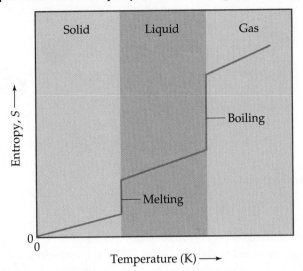

▲ FIGURE 19.13  **Entropy increases with increasing temperature.**

At the boiling point of the liquid, another abrupt increase in entropy occurs. We can understand this increase as resulting from the increased volume available to the atoms or molecules as they enter the gaseous state. When the gas is heated further, the entropy increases steadily as more energy is stored in the translational motion of the gas atoms or molecules.

Another change that occurs at higher temperatures is that the distribution of molecular speeds is skewed toward higher values. ∞ [Figure 10.17(a)] The expansion of the range of speeds leads to increased kinetic energy and increased disorder and, hence, increased entropy. The conclusions we reach in examining Figure 19.13 are consistent with what we noted earlier: Entropy generally increases with increasing temperature because the increased motional energy leads to a greater number of possible microstates.

Entropy plots such as Figure 19.13 can be obtained by carefully measuring how the heat capacity of a substance ∞ (Section 5.5) varies with temperature, and we can use the data to obtain the absolute entropies at different temperatures. (The theory and methods used for these measurements and calculations are beyond the scope of this text.) Entropies are usually tabulated as molar quantities, in units of joules per mole-kelvin (J/mol-K).

Molar entropies for substances in their standard states are known as **standard molar entropies** and denoted $S°$. The standard state for any substance is defined as the pure substance at 1 atm pressure.* ▶ TABLE 19.1 lists the values of $S°$ for a number of substances at 298 K; Appendix C gives a more extensive list.

We can make several observations about the $S°$ values in Table 19.1:

1. Unlike enthalpies of formation, standard molar entropies of elements at the reference temperature of 298 K are *not* zero.

2. The standard molar entropies of gases are greater than those of liquids and solids, consistent with our interpretation of experimental observations, as represented in Figure 19.13.

3. Standard molar entropies generally increase with increasing molar mass.

4. Standard molar entropies generally increase with an increasing number of atoms in the formula of a substance.

Point 4 is related to the molecular motion discussed in Section 19.3. In general, the number of degrees of freedom for a molecule increases with increasing number of

**TABLE 19.1 • Standard Molar Entropies of Selected Substances at 298 K**

| Substance | $S°$ (J/mol-K) |
|---|---|
| $H_2(g)$ | 130.6 |
| $N_2(g)$ | 191.5 |
| $O_2(g)$ | 205.0 |
| $H_2O(g)$ | 188.8 |
| $NH_3(g)$ | 192.5 |
| $CH_3OH(g)$ | 237.6 |
| $C_6H_6(g)$ | 269.2 |
| | |
| $H_2O(l)$ | 69.9 |
| $CH_3OH(l)$ | 126.8 |
| $C_6H_6(l)$ | 172.8 |
| | |
| $Li(s)$ | 29.1 |
| $Na(s)$ | 51.4 |
| $K(s)$ | 64.7 |
| $Fe(s)$ | 27.23 |
| $FeCl_3(s)$ | 142.3 |
| $NaCl(s)$ | 72.3 |

*The standard pressure used in thermodynamics is no longer 1 atm but rather is based on the SI unit for pressure, the pascal (Pa). The standard pressure is $10^5$ Pa, a quantity known as a *bar*: 1 bar = $10^5$ Pa = 0.987 atm. Because 1 bar differs from 1 atm by only 1.3%, we will continue to refer to the standard pressure as 1 atm.

**GO FIGURE**

What might you expect for the value of $S°$ for butane, $C_4H_{10}$?

Methane, $CH_4$
$S° = 186.3$ J/mol-K

Ethane, $C_2H_6$
$S° = 229.6$ J/mol-K

Propane, $C_3H_8$
$S° = 270.3$ J/mol-K

▲ **FIGURE 19.14** **Entropy increases with increasing molecular complexity.**

atoms, and thus the number of possible microstates also increases. ▲ **FIGURE 19.14** compares the standard molar entropies of three hydrocarbons in the gas phase. Notice how the entropy increases as the number of atoms in the molecule increases.

The entropy change in a chemical reaction equals the sum of the entropies of the products minus the sum of the entropies of the reactants:

$$\Delta S° = \sum nS°(\text{products}) - \sum mS°(\text{reactants}) \qquad [19.8]$$

As in Equation 5.31, the coefficients $n$ and $m$ are the coefficients in the balanced chemical equation for the reaction.

---

**SAMPLE EXERCISE 19.5** | **Calculating $\Delta S°$ from Tabulated Entropies**

Calculate the change in the standard entropy of the system, $\Delta S°$, for the synthesis of ammonia from $N_2(g)$ and $H_2(g)$ at 298 K:

$$N_2(g) + 3 H_2(g) \longrightarrow 2 NH_3(g)$$

**SOLUTION**

**Analyze** We are asked to calculate the standard entropy change for the synthesis of $NH_3(g)$ from its constituent elements.

**Plan** We can make this calculation using Equation 19.8 and the standard molar entropy values in Table 19.1 and Appendix C.

**Solve**

Using Equation 19.8, we have

$$\Delta S° = 2S°(NH_3) - [S°(N_2) + 3S°(H_2)]$$

Substituting the appropriate $S°$ values from Table 19.1 yields

$$\Delta S° = (2 \text{ mol})(192.5 \text{ J/mol-K}) - [(1 \text{ mol})(191.5 \text{ J/mol-K}) + (3 \text{ mol})(130.6 \text{ J/mol-K})]$$
$$= -198.3 \text{ J/K}$$

**Check:** The value for $\Delta S°$ is negative, in agreement with our qualitative prediction based on the decrease in the number of molecules of gas during the reaction.

**PRACTICE EXERCISE**

Using the standard molar entropies in Appendix C, calculate the standard entropy change, $\Delta S°$, for the following reaction at 298 K:

$$Al_2O_3(s) + 3 H_2(g) \longrightarrow 2 Al(s) + 3 H_2O(g)$$

***Answer:*** 180.39 J/K

---

## Entropy Changes in the Surroundings

We can use tabulated absolute entropy values to calculate the standard entropy change in a system, such as a chemical reaction, as just described. But what about the entropy change in the surroundings? We encountered this situation in Section 19.2, but it is good to revisit it now that we are examining chemical reactions.

We should recognize that the surroundings for any system serve essentially as a large, constant-temperature heat source (or heat sink if the heat flows from the system to the surroundings). The change in entropy of the surroundings depends on how much heat is absorbed or given off by the system.

For an isothermal process, the entropy change of the surroundings is given by

$$\Delta S_{surr} = \frac{-q_{sys}}{T}$$

Because in a constant-pressure process, $q_{sys}$ is simply the enthalpy change for the reaction, $\Delta H$, we can write

$$\Delta S_{surr} = \frac{-\Delta H_{sys}}{T} \qquad [19.9]$$

For the reaction in Sample Exercise 19.5, $q_{sys}$ is the enthalpy change for the reaction under standard conditions, $\Delta H°$, so the changes in entropy will be standard entropy changes, $\Delta S°$. Therefore, using the procedures described in Section 5.7, we have

$$\Delta H°_{rxn} = 2\Delta H°_f[NH_3(g)] - 3\Delta H°_f[H_2(g)] - \Delta H°_f[N_2(g)]$$
$$= 2(-46.19 \text{ kJ}) - 3(0 \text{ kJ}) - (0 \text{ kJ}) = -92.38 \text{ kJ}$$

The negative value tells us that at 298 K the formation of ammonia from $H_2(g)$ and $N_2(g)$ is exothermic. The surroundings absorb the heat given off by the system, which means an increase in the entropy of the surroundings:

$$\Delta S°_{surr} = \frac{92.38 \text{ kJ}}{298 \text{ K}} = 0.310 \text{ kJ/K} = 310 \text{ J/K}$$

Notice that the magnitude of the entropy gained by the surroundings is greater than that lost by the system, calculated as $-198.3$ J/K in Sample Exercise 19.5.

The overall entropy change for the reaction is

$$\Delta S°_{univ} = \Delta S°_{sys} + \Delta S°_{surr} = -198.3 \text{ J/K} + 310 \text{ J/K} = 112 \text{ J/K}$$

Because $\Delta S°_{univ}$ is positive for any spontaneous reaction, this calculation indicates that when $NH_3(g)$, $H_2(g)$, and $N_2(g)$ are together at 298 K in their standard states (each at 1 atm pressure), the reaction moves spontaneously toward formation of $NH_3(g)$.

Keep in mind that while the thermodynamic calculations indicate that formation of ammonia is spontaneous, they do not tell us anything about the rate at which ammonia is formed. Establishing equilibrium in this system within a reasonable period requires a catalyst, as discussed in Section 15.7.

 GIVE IT SOME THOUGHT

If a process is exothermic, does the entropy of the surroundings (1) always increase, (2) always decrease, or (3) sometimes increase and sometimes decrease, depending on the process?

# 19.5 | GIBBS FREE ENERGY

We have seen examples of endothermic processes that are spontaneous, such as the dissolution of ammonium nitrate in water. ∞ (Section 13.1) We learned in our discussion of the solution process that a spontaneous process that is endothermic must be accompanied by an increase in the entropy of the system. However, we have also encountered processes that are spontaneous and yet proceed with a *decrease* in the entropy of the system, such as the highly exothermic formation of sodium chloride from its constituent elements. ∞ (Section 8.2) Spontaneous processes that result in a decrease in the system's entropy are always exothermic. Thus, the spontaneity of a reaction seems to involve two thermodynamic concepts, enthalpy and entropy.

How can we use $\Delta H$ and $\Delta S$ to predict whether a given reaction occurring at constant temperature and pressure will be spontaneous? The means for doing so was first developed by the American mathematician J. Willard Gibbs (1839–1903). Gibbs (▶ FIGURE 19.15)

▲ FIGURE 19.15 Josiah Willard Gibbs. Gibbs was the first person to be awarded a Ph.D. in science from an American university (Yale, 1863). From 1871 until his death, he held the chair of mathematical physics at Yale. He developed much of the theoretical foundation that led to the development of chemical thermodynamics.

proposed a new state function, now called the **Gibbs free energy** (or just **free energy**), $G$, and defined as

$$G = H - TS \qquad [19.10]$$

where $T$ is the absolute temperature. For an isothermal process, the change in the free energy of the system, $\Delta G$, is

$$\Delta G = \Delta H - T\Delta S \qquad [19.11]$$

Under standard conditions, this equation becomes

$$\Delta G° = \Delta H° - T\Delta S° \qquad [19.12]$$

To see how the state function $G$ relates to reaction spontaneity, recall that for a reaction occurring at constant temperature and pressure

$$\Delta S_{univ} = \Delta S_{sys} + \Delta S_{surr} = \Delta S_{sys} + \left( \frac{-\Delta H_{sys}}{T} \right)$$

where we have used Equation 19.9 to substitute for $\Delta S_{surr}$. Multiplying both sides by $-T$ gives us

$$-T\Delta S_{univ} = \Delta H_{sys} - T\Delta S_{sys} \qquad [19.13]$$

Comparing Equations 19.11 and 19.13, we see that in a process occurring at constant temperature and pressure, the free-energy change, $\Delta G$, is equal to $-T\Delta S_{univ}$. We know that for spontaneous processes, $\Delta S_{univ}$ is always positive and, therefore, $-T\Delta S_{univ}$ is always negative. Thus, the sign of $\Delta G$ provides us with extremely valuable information about the spontaneity of processes that occur at constant temperature and pressure. If both $T$ and $P$ are constant, the relationship between the sign of $\Delta G$ and the spontaneity of a reaction is as follows:

1. If $\Delta G < 0$, the reaction is spontaneous in the forward direction.
2. If $\Delta G = 0$, the reaction is at equilibrium.
3. If $\Delta G > 0$, the reaction in the forward direction is nonspontaneous (work must be done to make it occur) but the reverse reaction is spontaneous.

It is more convenient to use $\Delta G$ as a criterion for spontaneity than to use $\Delta S_{univ}$ because $\Delta G$ relates to the system alone and avoids the complication of having to examine the surroundings.

An analogy is often drawn between the free-energy change during a spontaneous reaction and the potential-energy change when a boulder rolls down a hill (◄ **FIGURE 19.16**). Potential energy in a gravitational field "drives" the boulder until it reaches a state of minimum potential energy in the valley. Similarly, the free energy of a chemical system decreases until it reaches a minimum value. When this minimum is reached, a state of equilibrium exists. *In any spontaneous process carried out at constant temperature and pressure, the free energy always decreases.*

To illustrate these ideas, let's return to the Haber process for the synthesis of ammonia from nitrogen and hydrogen, which we discussed extensively in Chapter 15:

$$N_2(g) + 3\,H_2(g) \rightleftharpoons 2\,NH_3(g)$$

Imagine that we have a reaction vessel that allows us to maintain a constant temperature and pressure and that we have a catalyst that allows the reaction to proceed at a reasonable rate. What happens when we charge the vessel with a certain number of moles of $N_2$ and three times that number of moles of $H_2$? As we saw in Figure 15.3, the $N_2$ and $H_2$ react spontaneously to form $NH_3$ until equilibrium is achieved. Similarly, Figure 15.3 shows that if we charge the vessel with pure $NH_3$, it decomposes spontaneously to $N_2$ and $H_2$ until equilibrium is reached. In each case the free energy of the system gets progressively lower and lower as the reaction moves toward equilibrium, which represents a minimum in the free energy. We illustrate these cases in ► **FIGURE 19.17**.

▲ **GO FIGURE**

Are the processes that move a system toward equilibrium spontaneous or nonspontaneous?

▲ **FIGURE 19.16 Potential energy and free energy.** An analogy is shown between the gravitational potential-energy change of a boulder rolling down a hill and the free-energy change in a spontaneous reaction.

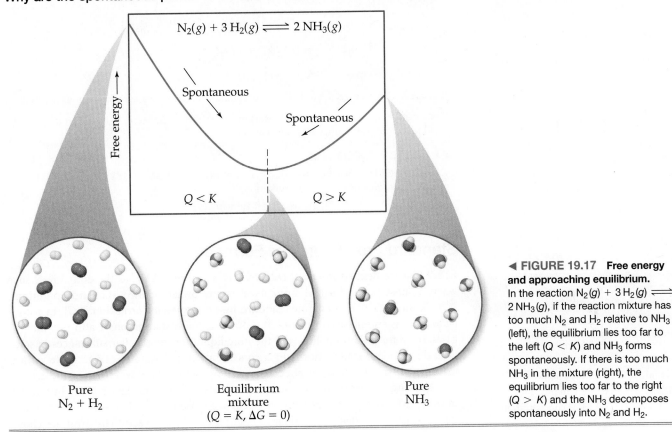

▲ **GO FIGURE**

**Why are the spontaneous processes shown sometimes said to be "downhill" in free energy?**

◀ **FIGURE 19.17 Free energy and approaching equilibrium.** In the reaction $N_2(g) + 3 H_2(g) \rightleftharpoons 2 NH_3(g)$, if the reaction mixture has too much $N_2$ and $H_2$ relative to $NH_3$ (left), the equilibrium lies too far to the left ($Q < K$) and $NH_3$ forms spontaneously. If there is too much $NH_3$ in the mixture (right), the equilibrium lies too far to the right ($Q > K$) and the $NH_3$ decomposes spontaneously into $N_2$ and $H_2$.

▲ **GIVE IT SOME THOUGHT**

What are the criteria for spontaneity
**a.** in terms of entropy and
**b.** in terms of free energy?

This is a good time to remind ourselves of the significance of the reaction quotient, $Q$, for a system that is not at equilibrium. ∞ (Section 15.6) Recall that when $Q < K$, there is an excess of reactants relative to products and the reaction proceeds spontaneously in the forward direction to reach equilibrium, as noted in Figure 19.17. When $Q > K$, the reaction proceeds spontaneously in the reverse direction. At equilibrium $Q = K$.

| SAMPLE EXERCISE 19.6 | Calculating Free-Energy Change from $\Delta H°$, $T$, and $\Delta S°$ |
|---|---|

Calculate the standard free-energy change for the formation of $NO(g)$ from $N_2(g)$ and $O_2(g)$ at 298 K:

$$N_2(g) + O_2(g) \longrightarrow 2 NO(g)$$

given that $\Delta H° = 180.7$ kJ and $\Delta S° = 24.7$ J/K. Is the reaction spontaneous under these conditions?

**SOLUTION**

**Analyze** We are asked to calculate $\Delta G°$ for the indicated reaction (given $\Delta H°$, $\Delta S°$, and $T$) and to predict whether the reaction is spontaneous under standard conditions at 298 K.

**Plan** To calculate $\Delta G°$, we use Equation 19.12, $\Delta G° = \Delta H° - T\Delta S°$. To determine whether the reaction is spontaneous under standard conditions, we look at the sign of $\Delta G°$.

**Solve**

$$\Delta G° = \Delta H° - T\Delta S°$$

$$= 180.7 \text{ kJ} - (298 \text{ K})(24.7 \text{ J/K})\left(\frac{1 \text{ kJ}}{10^3 \text{ J}}\right)$$

$$= 180.7 \text{ kJ} - 7.4 \text{ kJ}$$

$$= 173.3 \text{ kJ}$$

Because $\Delta G°$ is positive, the reaction is not spontaneous under standard conditions at 298 K.

**Comment** Notice that we had to convert the units of the $T\Delta S°$ term to kJ so that they could be added to the $\Delta H°$ term, whose units are kJ.

**PRACTICE EXERCISE**

Calculate $\Delta G°$ for a reaction for which $\Delta H° = 24.6$ kJ and $\Delta S° = 132$ J/K at 298 K. Is the reaction spontaneous under these conditions?

***Answer:*** $\Delta G° = -14.7$ kJ; the reaction is spontaneous.

## Standard Free Energy of Formation

| **TABLE 19.2 · Conventions Used in Establishing Standard Free Energies** | |
|---|---|
| **State of Matter** | **Standard State** |
| Solid | Pure solid |
| Liquid | Pure liquid |
| Gas | 1 atm pressure |
| Solution | 1 $M$ concentration |
| Element | $\Delta G_f° = 0$ for element in standard state |

Recall that we defined *standard enthalpies of formation*, $\Delta H_f°$, as the enthalpy change when a substance is formed from its elements under defined standard conditions. ∞ (Section 5.7) We can define **standard free energies of formation**, $\Delta G_f°$, in a similar way. As is summarized in ◄ TABLE 19.2, standard state means 1 atm pressure for gases, the pure solid for solids, and the pure liquid for liquids. For substances in solution, the standard state is normally a concentration of 1 $M$. (In very accurate work it may be necessary to make certain corrections, but we need not worry about these.)

The temperature usually chosen for purposes of tabulating data is 25 °C, but we will calculate $\Delta G°$ at other temperatures as well. Just as for the standard heats of formation, the free energies of elements in their standard states are set to zero. This arbitrary choice of a reference point has no effect on the quantity in which we are interested, which is the *difference* in free energy between reactants and products.

A listing of standard free energies of formation is given in Appendix C.

 **GIVE IT SOME THOUGHT**

What does the superscript ° indicate when associated with a thermodynamic quantity, as in $\Delta H°, \Delta S°$, or $\Delta G°$?

Standard free energies of formation are useful in calculating the *standard free-energy change* for chemical processes. The procedure is analogous to the calculation of $\Delta H°$ (Equation 5.31) and $\Delta S°$ (Equation 19.8):

$$\Delta G° = \sum n\Delta G_f°(\text{products}) - \sum m\Delta G_f°(\text{reactants}) \qquad [19.14]$$

**SAMPLE EXERCISE 19.7** Calculating Standard Free-Energy Change from Free Energies of Formation

**(a)** Use data from Appendix C to calculate the standard free-energy change for the reaction $P_4(g) + 6 Cl_2(g) \longrightarrow 4 PCl_3(g)$ run at 298 K.

**(b)** What is $\Delta G°$ for the reverse of this reaction?

**SOLUTION**

**Analyze** We are asked to calculate the free-energy change for a reaction and then to determine the free-energy change for the reverse reaction.

**Plan** We look up the free-energy values for the products and reactants and use Equation 19.14: We multiply the molar quantities by the coefficients in the balanced equation and subtract the total for the reactants from that for the products.

**Solve**

**(a)** $Cl_2(g)$ is in its standard state, so $\Delta G_f^\circ$ is zero for this reactant. $P_4(g)$, however, is not in its standard state, so $\Delta G_f^\circ$ is not zero for this reactant. From the balanced equation and values from Appendix C, we have

$$\Delta G_{rxn}^\circ = 4\, \Delta G_f^\circ[PCl_3(g)] - \Delta G_f^\circ[P_4(g)] - 6\, \Delta G_f^\circ[Cl_2(g)]$$
$$= (4\ mol)(-269.6\ kJ/mol) - (1\ mol)(24.4\ kJ/mol) - 0$$
$$= -1102.8\ kJ$$

That $\Delta G^\circ$ is negative tells us that a mixture of $P_4(g)$, $Cl_2(g)$, and $PCl_3(g)$ at 25 °C, each present at a partial pressure of 1 atm, would react spontaneously in the forward direction to form more $PCl_3$. Remember, however, that the value of $\Delta G^\circ$ tells us nothing about the rate at which the reaction occurs.

**(b)** When we reverse the reaction, we reverse the roles of the reactants and products. Thus, reversing the reaction changes the sign of $\Delta G$ in Equation 19.14, just as reversing the reaction changes the sign of $\Delta H$. ∞ (Section 5.4) Hence, using the result from part (a), we have

$$4\ PCl_3(g) \longrightarrow P_4(g) + 6\ Cl_2(g) \quad \Delta G^\circ = +1102.8\ kJ$$

**PRACTICE EXERCISE**

Use data from Appendix C to calculate $\Delta G^\circ$ at 298 K for the combustion of methane: $CH_4(g) + 2\ O_2(g) \longrightarrow CO_2(g) + 2\ H_2O(g)$.
**Answer:** $-800.7\ kJ$

---

**SAMPLE EXERCISE 19.8**    **Estimating and Calculating $\Delta G^\circ$**

In Section 5.7 we used Hess's law to calculate $\Delta H^\circ$ for the combustion of propane gas at 298 K:

$$C_3H_8(g) + 5\ O_2(g) \longrightarrow 3\ CO_2(g) + 4\ H_2O(l) \quad \Delta H^\circ = -2220\ kJ$$

**(a)** *Without using data from Appendix C*, predict whether $\Delta G^\circ$ for this reaction is more negative or less negative than $\Delta H^\circ$. **(b)** Use data from Appendix C to calculate $\Delta G^\circ$ for the reaction at 298 K. Is your prediction from part (a) correct?

**SOLUTION**

**Analyze** In part (a) we must predict the value for $\Delta G^\circ$ relative to that for $\Delta H^\circ$ on the basis of the balanced equation for the reaction. In part (b) we must calculate the value for $\Delta G^\circ$ and compare this value with our qualitative prediction.

**Plan** The free-energy change incorporates both the change in enthalpy and the change in entropy for the reaction (Equation 19.11), so under standard conditions

$$\Delta G^\circ = \Delta H^\circ - T\Delta S^\circ$$

To determine whether $\Delta G^\circ$ is more negative or less negative than $\Delta H^\circ$, we need to determine the sign of the term $T\Delta S^\circ$. Because $T$ is the absolute temperature, 298 K, it is always a positive number. We can predict the sign of $\Delta S^\circ$ by looking at the reaction.

**Solve**

**(a)** The reactants are six molecules of gas, and the products are three molecules of gas and four molecules of liquid. Thus, the number of molecules of gas has decreased significantly during the reaction. By using the general rules discussed in Section 19.3, we expect a decrease in the number of gas molecules to lead to a decrease in the entropy of the system—the products have fewer possible microstates than the reactants. We therefore expect $\Delta S^\circ$ and $T\Delta S^\circ$ to be negative. Because we are subtracting $T\Delta S^\circ$, which is a negative number, we predict that $\Delta G^\circ$ is *less negative* than $\Delta H^\circ$.

**(b)** Using Equation 19.14 and values from Appendix C, we have

$$\Delta G^\circ = 3\Delta G_f^\circ[CO_2(g)] + 4\Delta G_f^\circ[H_2O(l)] - \Delta G_f^\circ[C_3H_8(g)] - 5\Delta G_f^\circ[O_2(g)]$$
$$= 3\ mol(-394.4\ kJ/mol) + 4\ mol(-237.13\ kJ/mol) -$$
$$1\ mol(-23.47\ kJ/mol) - 5\ mol(0\ kJ/mol) = -2108\ kJ$$

Notice that we have been careful to use the value of $\Delta G_f^\circ$ for $H_2O(l)$. As in calculating $\Delta H$ values, the phases of the reactants and products are important. As we predicted, $\Delta G^\circ$ is less negative than $\Delta H^\circ$ because of the decrease in entropy during the reaction.

**PRACTICE EXERCISE**

For the combustion of propane at 298 K, $C_3H_8(g) + 5\ O_2(g) \longrightarrow 3\ CO_2(g) + 4\ H_2O(g)$, do you expect $\Delta G^\circ$ to be more negative or less negative than $\Delta H^\circ$?
**Answer:** more negative

# A CLOSER LOOK

## WHAT'S "FREE" ABOUT FREE ENERGY?

The Gibbs free energy is a remarkable thermodynamic quantity. Because so many chemical reactions are carried out under conditions of near-constant pressure and temperature, chemists, biochemists, and engineers use the sign and magnitude of $\Delta G$ as exceptionally useful tools in the design of chemical and biochemical reactions. We will see examples of the usefulness of $\Delta G$ throughout the remainder of this chapter and this text.

Two common questions often arise when one first learns about the Gibbs free energy: Why does the sign of $\Delta G$ tell us about the spontaneity of reactions? And what is "free" about free energy? We address these two questions here by using concepts discussed in Chapter 5 and earlier in this chapter.

In Section 19.2 we saw that the second law of thermodynamics governs the spontaneity of processes. In order to apply the second law (Equations 19.4), however, we must determine $\Delta S_{univ}$, which is often difficult to evaluate. When $T$ and $P$ are constant, however, we can relate $\Delta S_{univ}$ to the changes in entropy and enthalpy of just the *system* by substituting the Equation 19.9 expression for $\Delta S_{surr}$ in Equation 19.4:

$$\Delta S_{univ} = \Delta S_{sys} + \Delta S_{surr} = \Delta S_{sys} + \left(\frac{-\Delta H_{sys}}{T}\right) \qquad [19.15]$$

(constant $T$, $P$)

Thus, at constant temperature and pressure, the second law becomes

Reversible process: $\quad \Delta S_{univ} = \Delta S_{sys} - \dfrac{\Delta H_{sys}}{T} = 0$

Irreversible process: $\quad \Delta S_{univ} = \Delta S_{sys} - \dfrac{\Delta H_{sys}}{T} > 0$ $\qquad [19.16]$

(constant $T$, $P$)

Now we can see the relationship between $\Delta G_{sys}$ (which we call simply $\Delta G$) and the second law. From Equation 19.11 we know that $\Delta G = \Delta H_{sys} - T\Delta S_{sys}$. If we multiply Equations 19.16 by $-T$ and rearrange, we reach the following conclusion:

Reversible process: $\quad \Delta G = \Delta H_{sys} - T\,\Delta S_{sys} = 0$

Irrversible process: $\quad \Delta G = \Delta H_{sys} - T\,\Delta S_{sys} < 0$ $\qquad [19.17]$

(constant $T$, $P$)

Equations 19.17 allow us to use the sign of $\Delta G$ to conclude whether a reaction is spontaneous, nonspontaneous, or at equilibrium. When $\Delta G < 0$, a process is irreversible and, therefore, spontaneous. When $\Delta G = 0$, the process is reversible and, therefore, at equilibrium. If a process has $\Delta G > 0$, then the reverse process will have $\Delta G < 0$; thus, the process as written is nonspontaneous but its reverse reaction will be irreversible and spontaneous.

The magnitude of $\Delta G$ is also significant. A reaction for which $\Delta G$ is large and negative, such as the burning of gasoline, is much more capable of doing work on the surroundings than is a reaction for which $\Delta G$ is small and negative, such as ice melting at room temperature. In fact, thermodynamics tells us that *the change in free energy for a process, $\Delta G$, equals the maximum useful work that can be done by the system on its surroundings in a spontaneous process occurring at constant temperature and pressure:*

$$\Delta G = -w_{max} \qquad [19.18]$$

(Remember our sign convention from Table 5.1: Work done *by* a system is negative.) In other words, $\Delta G$ gives the theoretical limit to how much work can be done by a process.

The relationship in Equation 19.18 explains why $\Delta G$ is called *free* energy—it is the portion of the energy change of a spontaneous reaction that is free to do useful work. The remainder of the energy enters the environment as heat. For example, the theoretical maximum work obtained for the combustion of gasoline is given by the value of $\Delta G$ for the combustion reaction. On average, standard internal combustion engines are inefficient in utilizing this potential work—more than 60% of the potential work is lost (primarily as heat) in converting the chemical energy of the gasoline to mechanical energy to move the vehicle (▼ **FIGURE 19.18**). When other losses are considered—idling time, braking, aerodynamic drag, and so forth—only about 15% of the potential work from the gasoline is used to move the car. Advances in automobile design—such as hybrid technology, efficient diesel engines, and new lightweight materials—have the potential to increase the percentage of useful work obtained from the gasoline.

For nonspontaneous processes $(\Delta G > 0)$, the free-energy change is a measure of the *minimum* amount of work that must be done to cause the process to occur. In actuality, we always need to do more than this theoretical minimum amount because of the inefficiencies in the way the changes occur.

Chemical energy of gasoline, $\Delta G$

Useful work (15%)

Wasted energy 85% (heat loss from engine, braking, air resistance, and so forth)

▶ **FIGURE 19.18 Energy losses in automobiles.** Very little of the chemical energy of gasoline is actually used as work to move a typical automobile.

# 19.6 | FREE ENERGY AND TEMPERATURE

Tabulations of $\Delta G_f^\circ$, such as those in Appendix C, make it possible to calculate $\Delta G^\circ$ for reactions at the standard temperature of 25 °C, but we are often interested in examining reactions at other temperatures. To see how $\Delta G$ is affected by temperature, let's look again at Equation 19.11:

$$\Delta G = \Delta H - T\Delta S = \Delta H + (-T\Delta S)$$

$$\underset{\substack{\text{Enthalpy} \\ \text{term}}}{\phantom{\Delta H}} \qquad \underset{\substack{\text{Entropy} \\ \text{term}}}{\phantom{(-T\Delta S)}}$$

Notice that we have written the expression for $\Delta G$ as a sum of two contributions, an enthalpy term, $\Delta H$, and an entropy term, $-T\Delta S$. Because the value of $-T\Delta S$ depends directly on the absolute temperature $T$, $\Delta G$ varies with temperature. We know that the enthalpy term, $\Delta H$, can be either positive or negative and that $T$ is positive at all temperatures other than absolute zero. The entropy term, $-T\Delta S$, can also be positive or negative. When $\Delta S$ is positive, which means the final state has greater randomness (a greater number of microstates) than the initial state, the term $-T\Delta S$ is negative. When $\Delta S$ is negative, $-T\Delta S$ is positive.

The sign of $\Delta G$, which tells us whether a process is spontaneous, depends on the signs and magnitudes of $\Delta H$ and $-T\Delta S$. The various combinations of $\Delta H$ and $-T\Delta S$ signs are given in ▼ TABLE 19.3.

Note in Table 19.3 that when $\Delta H$ and $-T\Delta S$ have opposite signs, the sign of $\Delta G$ depends on the magnitudes of these two terms. In these instances temperature is an important consideration. Generally, $\Delta H$ and $\Delta S$ change very little with temperature. However, the value of $T$ directly affects the magnitude of $-T\Delta S$. As the temperature increases, the magnitude of $-T\Delta S$ increases, and this term becomes relatively more important in determining the sign and magnitude of $\Delta G$.

As an example, let's consider once more the melting of ice to liquid water at 1 atm:

$$H_2O(s) \longrightarrow H_2O(l) \quad \Delta H > 0, \Delta S > 0$$

This process is endothermic, which means that $\Delta H$ is positive. Because the entropy increases during the process, $\Delta S$ is positive, which makes $-T\Delta S$ negative. At temperatures below 0 °C (273 K), the magnitude of $\Delta H$ is greater than that of $-T\Delta S$. Hence, the positive enthalpy term dominates, and $\Delta G$ is positive. This positive value of $\Delta G$ means that ice melting is not spontaneous at $T < 0$ °C, just as our everyday experience tells us; rather, the reverse process, the freezing of liquid water into ice, is spontaneous at these temperatures.

What happens at temperatures greater than 0 °C? As $T$ increases, so does the magnitude of $-T\Delta S$. When $T > 0$ °C, the magnitude of $-T\Delta S$ is greater than the magnitude of $\Delta H$, which means that the $-T\Delta S$ term dominates and $\Delta G$ is negative. The negative value of $\Delta G$ tells us that ice melting is spontaneous at $T > 0$ °C.

At the normal melting point of water, $T = 0$ °C, the two phases are in equilibrium. Recall that $\Delta G = 0$ at equilibrium; at $T = 0$ °C, $\Delta H$ and $-T\Delta S$ are equal in magnitude and opposite in sign, so they cancel and give $\Delta G = 0$.

**TABLE 19.3 • How Signs of $\Delta H$ and $\Delta S$ Affect Reaction Spontaneity**

| $\Delta H$ | $\Delta S$ | $-T\Delta S$ | $\Delta G = \Delta H - T\Delta S$ | Reaction Characteristics | Example |
|---|---|---|---|---|---|
| − | + | − | − | Spontaneous at all temperatures | $2\,O_3(g) \longrightarrow 3\,O_2(g)$ |
| + | − | + | + | Nonspontaneous at all temperatures | $3\,O_2(g) \longrightarrow 2\,O_3(g)$ |
| − | − | + | + or − | Spontaneous at low $T$; nonspontaneous at high $T$ | $H_2O(l) \longrightarrow H_2O(s)$ |
| + | + | − | + or − | Spontaneous at high $T$; nonspontaneous at low $T$ | $H_2O(s) \longrightarrow H_2O(l)$ |

▲ **GIVE IT SOME THOUGHT**

The normal boiling point of benzene is 80 °C. At 100 °C and 1 atm, which term is greater in magnitude for the vaporization of benzene, $\Delta H$ or $T\Delta S$?

Our discussion of the temperature dependence of $\Delta G$ is also relevant to standard free-energy changes. We can calculate the values of $\Delta H°$ and $\Delta S°$ at 298 K from the data in Appendix C. If we assume that these values do not change with temperature, we can then use Equation 19.12 to estimate $\Delta G°$ at temperatures other than 298 K.

---

**SAMPLE EXERCISE 19.9** | **Determining the Effect of Temperature on Spontaneity**

The Haber process for the production of ammonia involves the equilibrium

$$N_2(g) + 3\,H_2(g) \rightleftharpoons 2\,NH_3(g)$$

Assume that $\Delta H°$ and $\Delta S°$ for this reaction do not change with temperature. **(a)** Predict the direction in which $\Delta G°$ for the reaction changes with increasing temperature. **(b)** Calculate $\Delta G°$ at 25 °C and 500 °C.

**SOLUTION**

**Analyze** In part (a) we are asked to predict the direction in which $\Delta G°$ changes as temperature increases. In part (b) we need to determine $\Delta G°$ for the reaction at two temperatures.

**Plan** We can answer part (a) by determining the sign of $\Delta S$ for the reaction and then using that information to analyze Equation 19.12. In part (b) we first calculate $\Delta H°$ and $\Delta S°$ for the reaction using data in Appendix C and then use Equation 19.12 to calculate $\Delta G°$.

**Solve**

**(a)** The temperature dependence of $\Delta G°$ comes from the entropy term in Equation 19.12, $\Delta G° = \Delta H° - T\Delta S°$. We expect $\Delta S°$ for this reaction to be negative because the number of molecules of gas is smaller in the products. Because $\Delta S°$ is negative, $-T\Delta S°$ is positive and increases with increasing temperature. As a result, $\Delta G°$ becomes less negative (or more positive) with increasing temperature. Thus, the driving force for the production of $NH_3$ becomes smaller with increasing temperature.

**(b)** We calculated $\Delta H°$ for this reaction in Sample Exercise 15.14 and $\Delta S°$ in Sample Exercise 19.5: $\Delta H° = -92.38$ kJ and $\Delta S° = -198.3$ J/K. If we assume that these values do not change with temperature, we can calculate $\Delta G°$ at any temperature by using Equation 19.12. At $T = 25\ °C = 298$ K, we have

$$\Delta G° = -92.38\text{ kJ} - (298\text{ K})(-198.3\text{ J/K})\left(\frac{1\text{ kJ}}{1000\text{ J}}\right)$$

$$= -92.38\text{ kJ} + 59.1\text{ kJ} = -33.3\text{ kJ}$$

At $T = 500\ °C = 773$ K, we have

$$\Delta G° = -92.38\text{ kJ} - (773\text{ K})\left(-198.3\ \frac{\text{J}}{\text{K}}\right)\left(\frac{1\text{ kJ}}{1000\text{ J}}\right)$$

$$= -92.38\text{ kJ} + 153\text{ kJ} = 61\text{ kJ}$$

Notice that we had to convert the units of $-T\Delta S°$ to kJ in both calculations so that this term can be added to the $\Delta H°$ term, which has units of kJ.

**Comment** Increasing the temperature from 298 K to 773 K changes $\Delta G°$ from $-33.3$ kJ to $+61$ kJ. Of course, the result at 773 K assumes that $\Delta H°$ and $\Delta S°$ do not change with temperature. Although these values do change slightly with temperature, the result at 773 K should be a reasonable approximation.

The positive increase in $\Delta G°$ with increasing $T$ agrees with our prediction in part (a). Our result indicates that in a mixture of $N_2(g)$, $H_2(g)$, and $NH_3(g)$, each present at a partial pressure of 1 atm, the $N_2(g)$ and $H_2(g)$ react spontaneously at 298 K to form more $NH_3(g)$. At 773 K, the positive value of $\Delta G°$ tells us that the reverse reaction is spontaneous. Thus, when the mixture of these gases, each at a partial pressure of 1 atm, is heated to 773 K, some of the $NH_3(g)$ spontaneously decomposes into $N_2(g)$ and $H_2(g)$.

**PRACTICE EXERCISE**

**(a)** Using standard enthalpies of formation and standard entropies in Appendix C, calculate $\Delta H°$ and $\Delta S°$ at 298 K for the reaction $2\,SO_2(g) + O_2(g) \longrightarrow 2\,SO_3(g)$. **(b)** Use your values from part (a) to estimate $\Delta G°$ at 400 K.

*Answers:* **(a)** $\Delta H° = -196.6$ kJ, $\Delta S° = -189.6$ J/K; **(b)** $\Delta G° = -120.8$ kJ

# 19.7 FREE ENERGY AND THE EQUILIBRIUM CONSTANT

In Section 19.5 we saw a special relationship between $\Delta G$ and equilibrium: For a system at equilibrium, $\Delta G = 0$. We have also seen how to use tabulated thermodynamic data to calculate values of the standard free-energy change, $\Delta G°$. In this final section, we learn two more ways in which we can use free energy to analyze chemical reactions: using $\Delta G°$ to calculate $\Delta G$ under *nonstandard* conditions and relating the values of $\Delta G°$ and $K$ for a reaction.

## Free Energy Under Nonstandard Conditions

The set of standard conditions for which $\Delta G°$ values pertain is given in Table 19.2. Most chemical reactions occur under nonstandard conditions. For any chemical process, the relationship between the free-energy change under standard conditions, $\Delta G°$, and the free-energy change under any other conditions, $\Delta G$, is given by

$$\Delta G = \Delta G° + RT \ln Q \qquad [19.19]$$

In this equation $R$ is the ideal-gas constant, 8.314 J/mol-K; $T$ is the absolute temperature; and $Q$ is the reaction quotient for the reaction mixture of interest. ∞ (Section 15.6) Under standard conditions, the concentrations of all the reactants and products are equal to 1. Thus, under standard conditions $Q = 1$, $\ln Q = 0$, and Equation 19.19 reduces to $\Delta G = \Delta G°$ under standard conditions, as it should.

---

**SAMPLE EXERCISE 19.10** | **Relating $\Delta G$ to a Phase Change at Equilibrium**

**(a)** Write the chemical equation that defines the normal boiling point of liquid carbon tetrachloride, $CCl_4(l)$.
**(b)** What is the value of $\Delta G°$ for the equilibrium in part (a)? **(c)** Use data from Appendix C and Equation 19.12 to estimate the normal boiling point of $CCl_4$.

### SOLUTION

**Analyze** **(a)** We must write a chemical equation that describes the physical equilibrium between liquid and gaseous $CCl_4$ at the normal boiling point. **(b)** We must determine the value of $\Delta G°$ for $CCl_4$, in equilibrium with its vapor at the normal boiling point. **(c)** We must estimate the normal boiling point of $CCl_4$, based on available thermodynamic data.

**Plan** **(a)** The chemical equation is the change of state from liquid to gas. For **(b)**, we need to analyze Equation 19.19 at equilibrium ($\Delta G = 0$), and for **(c)** we can use Equation 19.12 to calculate $T$ when $\Delta G = 0$.

### Solve

**(a)** The normal boiling point is the temperature at which a pure liquid is in equilibrium with its vapor at a pressure of 1 atm:   $CCl_4(l) \rightleftharpoons CCl_4(g)$   $P = 1$ atm

**(b)** At equilibrium, $\Delta G = 0$. In any normal boiling-point equilibrium, both liquid and vapor are in their standard state of pure liquid and vapor at 1 atm (Table 19.2). Consequently, $Q = 1$, $\ln Q = 0$, and $\Delta G = \Delta G°$ for this process. We conclude that $\Delta G° = 0$ for the equilibrium representing the normal boiling point of any liquid. (We would also find that $\Delta G° = 0$ for the equilibria relevant to normal melting points and normal sublimation points.)

**(c)** Combining Equation 19.12 with the result from part (b), we see that the equality at the normal boiling point, $T_b$, of $CCl_4(l)$ (or any other pure liquid) is

$$\Delta G° = \Delta H° - T_b \Delta S° = 0$$

Solving the equation for $T_b$, we obtain

$$T_b = \Delta H° / \Delta S°$$

Strictly speaking, we need the values of $\Delta H°$ and $\Delta S°$ for the $CCl_4(l)$–$CCl_4(g)$ equilibrium at the normal boiling point to do this calculation. However, we can *estimate* the boiling point by using the values of $\Delta H°$ and $\Delta S°$ for $CCl_4$ at 298 K, which we obtain from Appendix C and Equations 5.31 and 19.8:

$$\Delta H° = (1 \text{ mol})(-106.7 \text{ kJ/mol}) - (1 \text{ mol})(-139.3 \text{ kJ/mol}) = +32.6 \text{ kJ}$$
$$\Delta S° = (1 \text{ mol})(309.4 \text{ J/mol-K}) - (1 \text{ mol})(214.4 \text{ J/mol-K}) = +95.0 \text{ J/K}$$

As expected, the process is endothermic ($\Delta H > 0$) and produces a gas, thus increasing the entropy ($\Delta S > 0$). We now use these values to estimate $T_b$ for $CCl_4(l)$:

$$T_b = \frac{\Delta H°}{\Delta S°} = \left(\frac{32.6 \text{ kJ}}{95.0 \text{ J/K}}\right)\left(\frac{1000 \text{ J}}{1 \text{ kJ}}\right) = 343 \text{ K} = 70 \text{ °C}$$

Note that we have used the conversion factor between joules and kilojoules to make the units of $\Delta H^\circ$ and $\Delta S^\circ$ match.

**Check** The experimental normal boiling point of $CCl_4(l)$ is 76.5 °C. The small deviation of our estimate from the experimental value is due to the assumption that $\Delta H^\circ$ and $\Delta S^\circ$ do not change with temperature.

### PRACTICE EXERCISE

Use data in Appendix C to estimate the normal boiling point, in K, for elemental bromine, $Br_2(l)$. (The experimental value is given in Figure 11.5.)

*Answer:* 330 K

When the concentrations of reactants and products are nonstandard, we must calculate $Q$ in order to determine $\Delta G$. We illustrate how this is done in Sample Exercise 19.11. At this stage in our discussion, therefore, it becomes important to note the units used to calculate $Q$ when using Equation 19.19. The convention used for standard states is used when applying this equation: In determining the value of $Q$, the concentrations of gases are always expressed as partial pressures in atmospheres and solutes are expressed as their concentrations in molarities.

---

**SAMPLE EXERCISE 19.11** | **Calculating the Free-Energy Change under Nonstandard Conditions**

Calculate $\Delta G$ at 298 K for a mixture of 1.0 atm $N_2$, 3.0 atm $H_2$, and 0.50 atm $NH_3$ being used in the Haber process:

$$N_2(g) + 3H_2(g) \rightleftharpoons 2NH_3(g)$$

### SOLUTION

**Analyze** We are asked to calculate $\Delta G$ under nonstandard conditions.

**Plan** We can use Equation 19.19 to calculate $\Delta G$. Doing so requires that we calculate the value of the reaction quotient $Q$ for the specified partial pressures, for which we use the partial-pressures form of Equation 15.23: $Q = [D]^d[E]^e/[A]^a[B]^b$. We then use a table of standard free energies of formation to evaluate $\Delta G^\circ$.

**Solve** The partial-pressures form of Equation 15.23 gives

$$Q = \frac{P_{NH_3}{}^2}{P_{N_2}P_{H_2}{}^3} = \frac{(0.50)^2}{(1.0)(3.0)^3} = 9.3 \times 10^{-3}$$

In Sample Exercise 19.9 we calculated $\Delta G^\circ = -33.3$ kJ for this reaction. We will have to change the units of this quantity in applying Equation 19.19, however. For the units in Equation 19.19 to work out, we will use kJ/mol as our units for $\Delta G^\circ$, where "per mole" means "per mole of the reaction as written." Thus, $\Delta G^\circ = -33.3$ kJ/mol implies per 1 mol of $N_2$, per 3 mol of $H_2$, and per 2 mol of $NH_3$.

We now use Equation 19.19 to calculate $\Delta G$ for these nonstandard conditions:

$$\Delta G = \Delta G^\circ + RT \ln Q$$
$$= (-33.3 \text{ kJ/mol}) + (8.314 \text{ J/mol-K})(298 \text{ K})(1 \text{ kJ}/1000 \text{ J}) \ln(9.3 \times 10^{-3})$$
$$= (-33.3 \text{ kJ/mol}) + (-11.6 \text{ kJ/mol}) = -44.9 \text{ kJ/mol}$$

**Comment** We see that $\Delta G$ becomes more negative as the pressures of $N_2$, $H_2$, and $NH_3$ are changed from 1.0 atm (standard conditions, $\Delta G^\circ$) to 1.0 atm, 3.0 atm, and 0.50 atm, respectively. The larger negative value for $\Delta G$ indicates a larger "driving force" to produce $NH_3$.

We would make the same prediction based on Le Châtelier's principle. ∞ (Section 15.7) Relative to standard conditions, we have increased the pressure of a reactant ($H_2$) and decreased the pressure of the product ($NH_3$). Le Châtelier's principle predicts that both changes shift the reaction to the product side, thereby forming more $NH_3$.

### PRACTICE EXERCISE

Calculate $\Delta G$ at 298 K for the Haber reaction if the reaction mixture consists of 0.50 atm $N_2$, 0.75 atm $H_2$, and 2.0 atm $NH_3$.

*Answer:* −26.0 kJ/mol

# Relationship Between $\Delta G°$ and $K$

We can now use Equation 19.19 to derive the relationship between $\Delta G°$ and the equilibrium constant, $K$. At equilibrium, $\Delta G = 0$ and $Q = K$. Thus, at equilibrium, Equation 19.19 transforms as follows:

$$\Delta G = \Delta G° + RT \ln Q$$

$$0 = \Delta G° + RT \ln K$$

$$\Delta G° = -RT \ln K \qquad [19.20]$$

By solving Equation 19.20 for $K$, we obtain an expression that allows us to calculate $K$ if we know the value of $\Delta G°$:

$$\ln K = \frac{\Delta G°}{-RT}$$

$$K = e^{-\Delta G°/RT} \qquad [19.21]$$

As usual, we must be careful in our choice of units. In Equations 19.20 and 19.21 we again express $\Delta G°$ in kJ/mol. In the equilibrium-constant expression, we use atmospheres for gas pressures, molarities for solutions, and solids, liquids, and solvents do not appear in the expression. ∞ (Section 15.4) Thus, the equilibrium constant is $K_p$ for gas-phase reactions and $K_c$ for reactions in solution. ∞ (Section 15.2)

From Equation 19.20 we see that if $\Delta G°$ is negative, $\ln K$ must be positive, which means $K > 1$. Therefore, the more negative $\Delta G°$ is, the larger $K$ is. Conversely, if $\Delta G°$ is positive, $\ln K$ is negative, which means $K < 1$. ▶ TABLE 19.4 summarizes these relationships.

**TABLE 19.4 • Relationship between $\Delta G°$ and $K$ at 298 K**

| $\Delta G°$ (kJ/mol) | $K$ |
|---|---|
| +200 | $8.7 \times 10^{-36}$ |
| +100 | $3.0 \times 10^{-18}$ |
| +50 | $1.7 \times 10^{-9}$ |
| +10 | $1.8 \times 10^{-2}$ |
| +1.0 | $6.7 \times 10^{-1}$ |
| 0 | 1.0 |
| −1.0 | 1.5 |
| −10 | $5.7 \times 10^{1}$ |
| −50 | $5.8 \times 10^{8}$ |
| −100 | $3.4 \times 10^{17}$ |
| −200 | $1.1 \times 10^{35}$ |

---

**SAMPLE EXERCISE 19.12** | **Calculating an Equilibrium Constant from $\Delta G°$**

The standard free-energy change for the Haber process at 25 °C was obtained in Sample Exercise 19.9 for the Haber reaction:

$$N_2(g) + 3H_2(g) \rightleftharpoons 2NH_3(g) \qquad \Delta G° = -33.3 \text{ kJ/mol} = -33,300 \text{ J/mol}$$

Use this value of $\Delta G°$ to calculate the equilibrium constant for the process at 25 °C.

**SOLUTION**

**Analyze** We are asked to calculate $K$ for a reaction, given $\Delta G°$.

**Plan** We can use Equation 19.21 to calculate $K$.

**Solve** Remembering to use the absolute temperature for $T$ in Equation 19.21 and the form of $R$ that matches our units, we have $\quad K = e^{-\Delta G°/RT} = e^{-(-33,300 \text{ J/mol})/(8.314 \text{ J/mol-K})(298 \text{ K})} = e^{13.4} = 7 \times 10^5$

**Comment** This is a large equilibrium constant, which indicates that the product, $NH_3$, is greatly favored in the equilibrium mixture at 25 °C. The equilibrium constants for the Haber reaction at temperatures in the range 300 °C to 600 °C, given in Table 15.2, are much smaller than the value at 25 °C. Clearly, a low-temperature equilibrium favors the production of ammonia more than a high-temperature one. Nevertheless, the Haber process is carried out at high temperatures because the reaction is extremely slow at room temperature.

**Remember** Thermodynamics can tell us the direction and extent of a reaction but tells us nothing about the rate at which it will occur. If a catalyst were found that would permit the reaction to proceed at a rapid rate at room temperature, high pressures would not be needed to force the equilibrium toward $NH_3$.

**PRACTICE EXERCISE**

Use data from Appendix C to calculate $\Delta G°$ and $K$ at 298 K for the reaction $H_2(g) + Br_2(l) \rightleftharpoons 2HBr(g)$.

**Answer:** $\Delta G° = -106.4 \text{ kJ/mol}$, $K = 4 \times 10^{18}$

# CHEMISTRY AND LIFE

## DRIVING NONSPONTANEOUS REACTIONS

Many desirable chemical reactions, including a large number that are central to living systems, are nonspontaneous as written. For example, consider the extraction of copper metal from the mineral *chalcocite*, which contains $Cu_2S$. The decomposition of $Cu_2S$ to its elements is nonspontaneous:

$$Cu_2S(s) \longrightarrow 2\,Cu(s) + S(s) \qquad \Delta G° = +86.2\text{ kJ}$$

Because $\Delta G°$ is very positive, we cannot obtain $Cu(s)$ directly via this reaction. Instead, we must find some way to "do work" on the reaction to force it to occur as we wish. We can do this by coupling the reaction to another one so that the overall reaction *is* spontaneous. For example, we can envision the $S(s)$ reacting with $O_2(g)$ to form $SO_2(g)$:

$$S(s) + O_2(g) \longrightarrow SO_2(g) \qquad \Delta G° = -300.4\text{ kJ}$$

By coupling these reactions, we can extract much of the copper metal via a spontaneous reaction:

$$Cu_2S(s) + O_2(g) \longrightarrow 2\,Cu(s) + SO_2(g)$$
$$\Delta G° = (+86.2\text{ kJ}) + (-300.4\text{ kJ}) = -214.2\text{ kJ}$$

In essence, we have used the spontaneous reaction of $S(s)$ with $O_2(g)$ to provide the free energy needed to extract the copper metal from the mineral.

Biological systems employ the same principle of using spontaneous reactions to drive nonspontaneous ones. Many of the biochemical reactions that are essential for the formation and maintenance of highly ordered biological structures are not spontaneous. These necessary reactions are made to occur by coupling them with spontaneous reactions that release energy. The metabolism of food is the usual source of the free energy needed to do the work of maintaining biological systems. For example, complete oxidation of the sugar *glucose*, $C_6H_{12}O_6$, to $CO_2$ and $H_2O$ yields substantial free energy:

$$C_6H_{12}O_6(s) + 6\,O_2(g) \longrightarrow 6\,CO_2(g) + 6\,H_2O(l)$$
$$\Delta G° = -2880\text{ kJ}$$

This energy can be used to drive nonspontaneous reactions in the body. However, a means is necessary to transport the energy released by glucose metabolism to the reactions that require energy. One way, shown in ▼ **FIGURE 19.19**, involves the interconversion of adenosine triphosphate (ATP) and adenosine diphosphate (ADP), molecules that are related to the building blocks of nucleic acids. The conversion of ATP to ADP releases free energy ($\Delta G° = -30.5$ kJ) that can be used to drive other reactions.

In the human body the metabolism of glucose occurs via a complex series of reactions, most of which release free energy. The free energy released during these steps is used in part to reconvert lower-energy ADP back to higher-energy ATP. Thus, the ATP–ADP interconversions are used to store energy during metabolism and to release it as needed to drive nonspontaneous reactions in the body. If you take a course in biochemistry, you will have the opportunity to learn more about the remarkable sequence of reactions used to transport free energy throughout the human body.

*RELATED EXERCISES:* 19.102 and 19.103

▶ **FIGURE 19.19 Schematic representation of free-energy changes during cell metabolism.** The oxidation of glucose to $CO_2$ and $H_2O$ produces free energy that is then used to convert ADP into the more energetic ATP. The ATP is then used, as needed, as an energy source to drive nonspontaneous reactions, such as the conversion of simple molecules into more complex cell constituents.

**SAMPLE INTEGRATIVE EXERCISE** Putting Concepts Together

Consider the simple salts NaCl(*s*) and AgCl(*s*). We will examine the equilibria in which these salts dissolve in water to form aqueous solutions of ions:

$$NaCl(s) \rightleftharpoons Na^+(aq) + Cl^-(aq)$$

$$AgCl(s) \rightleftharpoons Ag^+(aq) + Cl^-(aq)$$

**(a)** Calculate the value of $\Delta G°$ at 298 K for each of the preceding reactions. **(b)** The two values from part (a) are very different. Is this difference primarily due to the enthalpy term or the entropy term of the standard free-energy change? **(c)** Use the values of $\Delta G°$ to calculate the $K_{sp}$ values for the two salts at 298 K. **(d)** Sodium chloride is considered a soluble salt, whereas silver chloride is considered insoluble. Are these descriptions consistent with the answers to part (c)? **(e)** How will $\Delta G°$ for the solution process of these salts change with increasing *T*? What effect should this change have on the solubility of the salts?

## SOLUTION

**(a)** We will use Equation 19.14 along with $\Delta G_f°$ values from Appendix C to calculate the $\Delta G°_{soln}$ values for each equilibrium. (As we did in Section 13.1, we use the subscript "soln" to indicate that these are thermodynamic quantities for the formation of a solution.) We find

$$\Delta G°_{soln}(NaCl) = (-261.9 \text{ kJ/mol}) + (-131.2 \text{ kJ/mol}) - (-384.0 \text{ kJ/mol})$$

$$= -9.1 \text{ kJ/mol}$$

$$\Delta G°_{soln}(AgCl) = (+77.11 \text{ kJ/mol}) + (-131.2 \text{ kJ/mol}) - (-109.70 \text{ kJ/mol})$$

$$= +55.6 \text{ kJ/mol}$$

**(b)** We can write $\Delta G°_{soln}$ as the sum of an enthalpy term, $\Delta H°_{soln}$, and an entropy term, $-T\Delta S°_{soln}$: $\Delta G°_{soln} = \Delta H°_{soln} + (-T\Delta S°_{soln})$. We can calculate the values of $\Delta H°_{soln}$ and $\Delta S°_{soln}$ by using Equations 5.31 and 19.8. We can then calculate $-T\Delta S°_{soln}$ at $T = 298$ K. All these calculations are now familiar to us. The results are summarized in the following table:

| Salt | $\Delta H°_{soln}$ | $\Delta S°_{soln}$ | $T\Delta S°_{soln}$ |
|------|--------|--------|--------|
| NaCl | +3.6 kJ/mol | +43.2 kJ/mol-K | −12.9 kJ/mol |
| AgCl | +65.7 kJ/mol | +34.3 kJ/mol-K | −10.2 kJ/mol |

The entropy terms for the solution of the two salts are very similar. That seems sensible because each solution process should lead to a similar increase in randomness as the salt dissolves, forming hydrated ions. ⊙⊙⊙ (Section 13.1) In contrast, we see a very large difference in the enthalpy term for the solution of the two salts. The difference in the values of $\Delta G°_{soln}$ is dominated by the difference in the values of $\Delta H°_{soln}$.

**(c)** The solubility product, $K_{sp}$, is the equilibrium constant for the solution process. ⊙⊙⊙ (Section 17.4) As such, we can relate $K_{sp}$ directly to $\Delta G°_{soln}$ by using Equation 19.21:

$$K_{sp} = e^{-\Delta G°_{soln}/RT}$$

We can calculate the $K_{sp}$ values in the same way we applied Equation 19.21 in Sample Exercise 19.12. We use the $\Delta G°_{soln}$ values we obtained in part (a), remembering to convert them from kJ/mol to J/mol:

NaCl: $K_{sp} = [Na^+(aq)][Cl^-(aq)] = e^{-(-9100)/[(8.314)(298)]} = e^{+3.7} = 40$

AgCl: $K_{sp} = [Ag^+(aq)][Cl^-(aq)] = e^{-(+55,600)/[(8.314)(298)]} = e^{-22.4} = 1.9 \times 10^{-10}$

The value calculated for the $K_{sp}$ of AgCl is very close to that listed in Appendix D.

**(d)** A soluble salt is one that dissolves appreciably in water. ⊙⊙⊙ (Section 4.2) The $K_{sp}$ value for NaCl is greater than 1, indicating that NaCl dissolves to a great extent. The $K_{sp}$ value for AgCl is very small, indicating that very little dissolves in water. Silver chloride should indeed be considered an insoluble salt.

**(e)** As we expect, the solution process has a positive value of $\Delta S$ for both salts (see the table in part b). As such, the entropy term of the free-energy change, $-T\Delta S°_{soln}$, is negative. If we assume that $\Delta H°_{soln}$ and $\Delta S°_{soln}$ do not change much with temperature, then an increase in *T* will serve to make $\Delta G°_{soln}$ more negative. Thus, the driving force for dissolution of the salts will increase with increasing *T*, and we therefore expect the solubility of the salts to increase with increasing *T*. In Figure 13.18 we see that the solubility of NaCl (and that of nearly any other salt) increases with increasing temperature. ⊙⊙⊙ (Section 13.3)

# CHAPTER SUMMARY AND KEY TERMS

**SECTION 19.1** Most reactions and chemical processes have an inherent directionality: They are **spontaneous** in one direction and nonspontaneous in the reverse direction. The spontaneity of a process is related to the thermodynamic path the system takes from the initial state to the final state. In a **reversible process**, both the system and its surroundings can be restored to their original state by exactly reversing the change. In an **irreversible process** the system cannot return to its original state without there being a permanent change in the surroundings. Any spontaneous process is irreversible. A process that occurs at a constant temperature is said to be **isothermal**.

**SECTION 19.2** The spontaneous nature of processes is related to a thermodynamic state function called **entropy**, denoted $S$. For a process that occurs at constant temperature, the entropy change of the system is given by the heat absorbed by the system along a reversible path, divided by the temperature: $\Delta S = q_{rev}/T$. The way entropy controls the spontaneity of processes is given by the **second law of thermodynamics**, which governs the change in the entropy of the universe, $\Delta S_{univ} = \Delta S_{sys} + \Delta S_{surr}$. The second law states that in a reversible process $\Delta S_{univ} = 0$; in an irreversible (spontaneous) process $\Delta S_{univ} > 0$. Entropy values are usually expressed in units of joules per kelvin, J/K.

**SECTION 19.3** A particular combination of motions and locations of the atoms and molecules of a system at a particular instant is called a **microstate**. The entropy of a system is a measure of its randomness or disorder. The entropy is related to the number of microstates, $W$, corresponding to the state of the system: $S = k \ln W$. Molecules can undergo three kinds of motion: In **translational motion** the entire molecule moves in space. Molecules can also undergo **vibrational motion**, in which the atoms of the molecule move toward and away from one another in periodic fashion, and **rotational motion**, in which the entire molecule spins like a top. The number of available microstates, and therefore the entropy, increases with an increase in volume, temperature, or motion of molecules because any of these changes increases the possible motions and locations of the molecules. As a result, entropy generally increases when liquids or solutions are formed from solids, gases are formed from either solids or liquids, or the number of molecules of gas increases during a chemical reaction. The **third law of thermodynamics** states that the entropy of a pure crystalline solid at 0 K is zero.

**SECTION 19.4** The third law allows us to assign entropy values for substances at different temperatures. Under standard conditions the entropy of a mole of a substance is called its **standard molar entropy**, denoted $S°$. From tabulated values of $S°$, we can calculate the entropy change for any process under standard conditions. For an isothermal process, the entropy change in the surroundings is equal to $-\Delta H/T$.

**SECTION 19.5** The **Gibbs free energy** (or just **free energy**), $G$, is a thermodynamic state function that combines the two state functions enthalpy and entropy: $G = H - TS$. For processes that occur at constant temperature, $\Delta G = \Delta H - T\Delta S$. For a process occurring at constant temperature and pressure, the sign of $\Delta G$ relates to the spontaneity of the process. When $\Delta G$ is negative, the process is spontaneous. When $\Delta G$ is positive, the process is nonspontaneous but the reverse process is spontaneous. At equilibrium the process is reversible and $\Delta G$ is zero. The free energy is also a measure of the maximum useful work that can be performed by a system in a spontaneous process. The standard free-energy change, $\Delta G°$, for any process can be calculated from tabulations of **standard free energies of formation**, $\Delta G_f°$, which are defined in a fashion analogous to standard enthalpies of formation, $\Delta H_f°$. The value of $\Delta G_f°$ for a pure element in its standard state is defined to be zero.

**SECTIONS 19.6 AND 19.7** The values of $\Delta H$ and $\Delta S$ generally do not vary much with temperature. Therefore, the dependence of $\Delta G$ with temperature is governed mainly by the value of $T$ in the expression $\Delta G = \Delta H - T\Delta S$. The entropy term $-T\Delta S$ has the greater effect on the temperature dependence of $\Delta G$ and, hence, on the spontaneity of the process. For example, a process for which $\Delta H > 0$ and $\Delta S > 0$, such as the melting of ice, can be nonspontaneous ($\Delta G > 0$) at low temperatures and spontaneous ($\Delta G < 0$) at higher temperatures. Under nonstandard conditions $\Delta G$ is related to $\Delta G°$ and the value of the reaction quotient, $Q$: $\Delta G = \Delta G° + RT \ln Q$. At equilibrium ($\Delta G = 0$, $Q = K$), $\Delta G° = -RT \ln K$. Thus, the standard free-energy change is directly related to the equilibrium constant for the reaction. This relationship expresses the temperature dependence of equilibrium constants.

# KEY SKILLS

- Understand the meaning of spontaneous process, reversible process, irreversible process, and isothermal process. (Section 19.1)

- State the second law of thermodynamics. (Section 19.2)

- Explain how the entropy of a system is related to the number of possible microstates. (Section 19.3)

- Describe the kinds of molecular motion that a molecule can possess. (Section 19.3)

- Predict the sign of $\Delta S$ for physical and chemical processes. (Section 19.3)

- State the third law of thermodynamics. (Section 19.3)

- Calculate standard entropy changes for a system from standard molar entropies. (Section 19.4)

- Calculate entropy changes in the surroundings for isothermal processes. (Section 19.4)

- Calculate the Gibbs free energy from the enthalpy change and entropy change at a given temperature. (Section 19.5)

- Use free-energy changes to predict whether reactions are spontaneous. (Section 19.5)

- Calculate standard free-energy changes using standard free energies of formation. (Section 19.5)

- Predict the effect of temperature on spontaneity given $\Delta H$ and $\Delta S$. (Section 19.6)

- Calculate $\Delta G$ under nonstandard conditions. (Section 19.7)

- Relate $\Delta G°$ and equilibrium constant. (Section 19.7)

## KEY EQUATIONS

- $\Delta S = \dfrac{q_{rev}}{T}$ (constant $T$)      [19.2]      Relating entropy change to the heat absorbed or released in a reversible process

- Reversible process: $\quad \Delta S_{univ} = \Delta S_{sys} + \Delta S_{surr} = 0$
  Irreversible process: $\quad \Delta S_{univ} = \Delta S_{sys} + \Delta S_{surr} > 0$    [19.4]    The second law of thermodynamics

- $S = k \ln W$      [19.5]      Relating entropy to the number of microstates

- $\Delta S^{\circ} = \sum nS^{\circ}(\text{products}) - \sum mS^{\circ}(\text{reactants})$      [19.8]      Calculating the standard entropy change from standard molar entropies

- $\Delta S_{surr} = \dfrac{-\Delta H_{sys}}{T}$      [19.9]      The entropy change of the surroundings for a process at constant temperature and pressure

- $\Delta G = \Delta H - T\Delta S$      [19.11]      Calculating the Gibbs free-energy change from enthalpy and entropy changes at constant temperature

- $\Delta G^{\circ} = \sum n\Delta G_f^{\circ}(\text{products}) - \sum m\Delta G_f^{\circ}(\text{reactants})$      [19.14]      Calculating the standard free-energy change from standard free energies of formation

- Reversible process: $\quad \Delta G = \Delta H_{sys} - T\Delta S_{sys} = 0$
  Irreversible process: $\quad \Delta G = \Delta H_{sys} - T\Delta S_{sys} < 0$    [19.17]    Relating the free-energy change to the reversibility of a process at constant temperature and pressure

- $\Delta G = -w_{max}$      [19.18]      Relating the free-energy change to the maximum work a process can perform

- $\Delta G = \Delta G^{\circ} + RT \ln Q$      [19.19]      Calculating free-energy change under nonstandard conditions

- $\Delta G^{\circ} = -RT \ln K$      [19.20]      Relating the standard free-energy change and the equilibrium constant

# EXERCISES

## VISUALIZING CONCEPTS

**19.1** Two different gases occupy the two bulbs shown here. Consider the process that occurs when the stopcock is opened, assuming the gases behave ideally. (a) Draw the final (equilibrium) state. (b) Predict the signs of $\Delta H$ and $\Delta S$ for the process. (c) Is the process that occurs when the stopcock is opened a reversible one? (d) How does the process affect the entropy of the surroundings? [Sections 19.1 and 19.2]

**19.2** As shown here, one type of computer keyboard cleaner contains liquefied 1,1-difluoroethane ($C_2H_4F_2$), which is a gas at atmospheric pressure. When the nozzle is squeezed, the 1,1-difluoroethane vaporizes out of the nozzle at high pressure, blowing dust out of objects. (a) Based on your experience, is the vaporization a spontaneous process at room temperature? (b) Defining the 1,1-difluoroethane as the system, do you expect $q_{sys}$ for the process to be positive or negative? Explain. (c) Predict whether $\Delta S$ is positive or negative for this process. (d) Given your answers to (a), (b), and (c), do you think the operation of this product depends more on heat flow or more on entropy change?

Vaporized $C_2H_4F_2$

Liquefied $C_2H_4F_2$

**19.3 (a)** What are the signs of $\Delta S$ and $\Delta H$ for the process depicted here? **(b)** How might temperature affect the sign of $\Delta G$? **(c)** If energy can flow in and out of the system to maintain a constant temperature during the process, what can you say about the entropy change of the surroundings as a result of this process? [Sections 19.2 and 19.5]

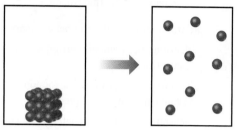

**19.4** Predict the sign of $\Delta S$ accompanying this reaction. Explain your choice. [Section 19.3]

**19.5** The accompanying diagram shows how entropy varies with temperature for a substance that is a gas at the highest temperature shown. **(a)** What processes correspond to the entropy increases along the vertical lines labeled 1 and 2? **(b)** Why is the entropy change for 2 larger than that for 1? [Section 19.3]

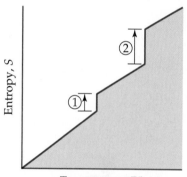

**19.6** *Isomers* are molecules that have the same chemical formula but different arrangements of atoms, as shown here for two isomers of pentane, $C_5H_{12}$. **(a)** Do you expect a significant difference in the enthalpy of combustion of the two isomers? Explain. **(b)** Which isomer do you expect to have the higher standard molar entropy? Explain. [Section 19.4]

$$CH_3-CH_2-CH_2-CH_2-CH_3 \qquad CH_3-\underset{\underset{CH_3}{|}}{\overset{\overset{CH_3}{|}}{C}}-CH_3$$

*n*-pentane           neopentane

**19.7** The accompanying diagram shows how $\Delta H$ (red line) and $T\Delta S$ (blue line) change with temperature for a hypothetical reaction. **(a)** What is the significance of the point at 300 K, where $\Delta H$ and $T\Delta S$ are equal? **(b)** In what temperature range is this reaction spontaneous? [Section 19.6]

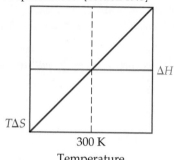

**19.8** The accompanying diagram shows how $\Delta G$ for a hypothetical reaction changes as temperature changes. **(a)** At what temperature is the system at equilibrium? **(b)** In what temperature range is the reaction spontaneous? **(c)** Is $\Delta H$ positive or negative? **(d)** Is $\Delta S$ positive or negative? [Sections 19.5 and 19.6]

**19.9** Consider a reaction $A_2(g) + B_2(g) \rightleftharpoons 2\,AB(g)$, with atoms of A shown in red in the diagram and atoms of B shown in blue. **(a)** If $K_c = 1$, which box represents the system at equilibrium? **(b)** What is the sign of $\Delta G$ for any process in which the contents of a reaction vessel move to equilibrium? **(c)** Rank the boxes in order of increasing magnitude of $\Delta G$ for the reaction. [Sections 19.5 and 19.7]

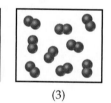

(1)                    (2)                    (3)

**19.10** The accompanying diagram shows how the free energy, $G$, changes during a hypothetical reaction $A(g) + B(g) \longrightarrow C(g)$. On the left are pure reactants, each at 1 atm, and on the right is the pure product, also at 1 atm. **(a)** What is the significance of the minimum in the plot? **(b)** What does the quantity $x$, shown on the right side of the diagram, represent? [Section 19.7]

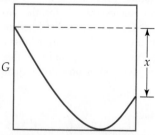

# SPONTANEOUS PROCESSES (section 19.1)

**19.11** Which of the following processes are spontaneous and which are nonspontaneous: (a) the ripening of a banana, (b) dissolution of sugar in a cup of hot coffee, (c) the reaction of nitrogen atoms to form $N_2$ molecules at 25 °C and 1 atm, (d) lightning, (e) formation of $CH_4$ and $O_2$ molecules from $CO_2$ and $H_2O$ at room temperature and 1 atm of pressure?

**19.12** Which of the following processes are spontaneous: (a) the melting of ice cubes at −10 °C and 1 atm pressure; (b) separating a mixture of $N_2$ and $O_2$ into two separate samples, one that is pure $N_2$ and one that is pure $O_2$; (c) alignment of iron filings in a magnetic field; (d) the reaction of hydrogen gas with oxygen gas to form water vapor; (e) the dissolution of HCl(g) in water to form concentrated hydrochloric acid?

**19.13** (a) Give two examples of endothermic processes that are spontaneous. (b) Give an example of a process that is spontaneous at one temperature but nonspontaneous at a different temperature.

**19.14** The crystalline hydrate $Cd(NO_3)_2 \cdot 4\,H_2O(s)$ loses water when placed in a large, closed, dry vessel:

$$Cd(NO_3)_2 \cdot 4\,H_2O(s) \longrightarrow Cd(NO_3)_2(s) + 4\,H_2O(g)$$

This process is spontaneous and $\Delta H$ is positive. Is this process an exception to Bertholet's generalization that all spontaneous changes are exothermic? Explain.

**19.15** Consider the vaporization of liquid water to steam at a pressure of 1 atm. (a) Is this process endothermic or exothermic? (b) In what temperature range is it a spontaneous process? (c) In what temperature range is it a nonspontaneous process? (d) At what temperature are the two phases in equilibrium?

**19.16** The normal freezing point of *n*-octane ($C_8H_{18}$) is −57 °C. (a) Is the freezing of *n*-octane an endothermic or exothermic process? (b) In what temperature range is the freezing of *n*-octane a spontaneous process? (c) In what temperature range is it a nonspontaneous process? (d) Is there any temperature at which liquid *n*-octane and solid *n*-octane are in equilibrium? Explain.

**19.17** (a) What is special about a *reversible* process? (b) Suppose a reversible process is reversed, restoring the system to its original

state. What can be said about the surroundings after the process is reversed? (c) Under what circumstances will the vaporization of water to steam be a reversible process? (d) Are any of the processes that occur in the world around us reversible in nature? Explain.

**19.18** (a) What is meant by calling a process *irreversible*? (b) After a particular irreversible process, the system is restored to its original state. What can be said about the condition of the surroundings after the system is restored to its original state? (c) Under what conditions will the condensation of a liquid be an irreversible process?

**19.19** Consider a process in which an ideal gas changes from state 1 to state 2 in such a way that its temperature changes from 300 K to 200 K. (a) Describe how this change might be carried out while keeping the volume of the gas constant. (b) Describe how it might be carried out while keeping the pressure of the gas constant. (c) Does the change in $\Delta E$ depend on the particular pathway taken to carry out this change of state? Explain.

**19.20** A system goes from state 1 to state 2 and back to state 1. (a) What is the relationship between the value of $\Delta E$ for going from state 1 to state 2 to that for going from state 2 back to state 1? (b) Without further information, can you conclude anything about the amount of heat transferred to the system as it goes from state 1 to state 2 as compared to that upon going from state 2 back to state 1? (c) Suppose the changes in state are reversible processes. Can you conclude anything about the work done by the system upon going from state 1 to state 2 as compared to that upon going from state 2 back to state 1?

**19.21** Consider a system consisting of an ice cube. (a) Under what conditions can the ice cube melt reversibly? (b) If the ice cube melts reversibly, is $\Delta E$ zero for the process? Explain.

**19.22** Consider what happens when a sample of the explosive TNT (Section 8.8: "Chemistry Put to Work: Explosives and Alfred Nobel") is detonated under atmospheric pressure. (a) Is the detonation a spontaneous process? (b) What is the sign of $q$ for this process? (c) Can you determine whether $w$ is positive, negative, or zero for the process? Explain. (d) Can you determine the sign of $\Delta E$ for the process? Explain.

# ENTROPY AND THE SECOND LAW OF THERMODYNAMICS (section 19.2)

**19.23** (a) How can we calculate $\Delta S$ for an isothermal process? (b) Does $\Delta S$ for a process depend on the path taken from the initial state to the final state of the system? Explain.

**19.24** Suppose we vaporize a mole of liquid water at 25 °C and another mole of water at 100 °C. (a) Assuming that the enthalpy of vaporization of water does not change much between 25 °C and 100 °C, which process involves the larger change in entropy? (b) Does the entropy change in either process depend on whether we carry out the process reversibly or not? Explain.

**19.25** The normal boiling point of $Br_2(l)$ is 58.8 °C, and its molar enthalpy of vaporization is $\Delta H_{vap} = 29.6$ kJ/mol. (a) When $Br_2(l)$ boils at its normal boiling point, does its entropy increase or decrease? (b) Calculate the value of $\Delta S$ when 1.00 mol of $Br_2(l)$ is vaporized at 58.8 °C.

**19.26** The element gallium (Ga) freezes at 29.8 °C, and its molar enthalpy of fusion is $\Delta H_{fus} = 5.59$ kJ/mol. (a) When molten

gallium solidifies to Ga(s) at its normal melting point, is $\Delta S$ positive or negative? (b) Calculate the value of $\Delta S$ when 60.0 g of Ga(l) solidifies at 29.8 °C.

**19.27** (a) Express the second law of thermodynamics in words. (b) If the entropy of the system increases during a reversible process, what can you say about the entropy change of the surroundings? (c) In a certain spontaneous process the system undergoes an entropy change, $\Delta S = 42$ J/K. What can you conclude about $\Delta S_{surr}$?

**19.28** (a) Express the second law of thermodynamics as a mathematical equation. (b) In a particular spontaneous process the entropy of the system decreases. What can you conclude about the sign and magnitude of $\Delta S_{surr}$? (c) During a certain reversible process, the surroundings undergo an entropy change, $\Delta S_{surr} = -78$ J/K. What is the entropy change of the system for this process?

**19.29** (a) What sign for $\Delta S$ do you expect when the volume of 0.200 mol of an ideal gas at 27 °C is increased isothermally from an initial volume of 10.0 L? (b) If the final volume is 18.5 L, calculate the entropy change for the process. (c) Do you need to specify the temperature to calculate the entropy change? Explain.

**19.30** (a) What sign for $\Delta S$ do you expect when the pressure on 0.600 mol of an ideal gas at 350 K is increased isothermally from an initial pressure of 0.750 atm? (b) If the final pressure on the gas is 1.20 atm, calculate the entropy change for the process. (c) Do you need to specify the temperature to calculate the entropy change? Explain.

# THE MOLECULAR INTERPRETATION OF ENTROPY (section 19.3)

**19.31** For the isothermal expansion of a gas into a vacuum, $\Delta E = 0$, $q = 0$, and $w = 0$. (a) Is this a spontaneous process? (b) Explain why no work is done by the system during this process. (c) In thermodynamics, what is the "driving force" for the expansion of the gas?

**19.32** (a) What is the difference between a *state* and a *microstate* of a system? (b) As a system goes from state A to state B, its entropy decreases. What can you say about the number of microstates corresponding to each state? (c) In a particular spontaneous process, the number of microstates available to the system decreases. What can you conclude about the sign of $\Delta S_{surr}$?

**19.33** How would each of the following changes affect the number of microstates available to a system: (a) increase in temperature, (b) decrease in volume, (c) change of state from liquid to gas?

**19.34** (a) Using the heat of vaporization in Appendix B, calculate the entropy change for the vaporization of water at 25 °C and at 100 °C. (b) From your knowledge of microstates and the structure of liquid water, explain the difference in these two values.

**19.35** (a) What do you expect for the sign of $\Delta S$ in a chemical reaction in which two moles of gaseous reactants are converted to three moles of gaseous products? (b) For which of the processes in Exercise 19.11 does the entropy of the system increase?

**19.36** (a) In a chemical reaction two gases combine to form a solid. What do you expect for the sign of $\Delta S$? (b) How does the entropy of the system change in the processes described in Exercise 19.12?

**19.37** How does the entropy of the system change when (a) a solid melts, (b) a gas liquefies, (c) a solid sublimes?

**19.38** How does the entropy of the system change when (a) the temperature of the system increases, (b) the volume of a gas increases, (c) equal volumes of ethanol and water are mixed to form a solution?

**19.39** (a) State the third law of thermodynamics. (b) Distinguish between translational motion, vibrational motion, and rotational motion of a molecule. (c) Illustrate these three kinds of motion with sketches for the HCl molecule.

**19.40** (a) If you are told that the entropy of a certain system is zero, what do you know about the system and the temperature? (b) The energy of a gas is increased by heating it. Using $CO_2$ as an example, illustrate the different ways in which additional energy can be distributed among the molecules of the gas. (c) $CO_2(g)$ and $Ar(g)$ have nearly the same molar mass. At a given temperature, will they have the same number of microstates? Explain.

**19.41** For each of the following pairs, choose the substance with the higher entropy per mole at a given temperature: (a) $Ar(l)$ or $Ar(g)$, (b) $He(g)$ at 3 atm pressure or $He(g)$ at 1.5 atm pressure, (c) 1 mol of $Ne(g)$ in 15.0 L or 1 mol of $Ne(g)$ in 1.50 L, (d) $CO_2(g)$ or $CO_2(s)$.

**19.42** For each of the following pairs, indicate which substance possesses the larger standard entropy: (a) 1 mol of $P_4(g)$ at 300 °C, 0.01 atm, or 1 mol of $As_4(g)$ at 300 °C, 0.01 atm; (b) 1 mol of $H_2O(g)$ at 100 °C, 1 atm, or 1 mol of $H_2O(l)$ at 100 °C, 1 atm; (c) 0.5 mol of $N_2(g)$ at 298 K, 20-L volume, or 0.5 mol $CH_4(g)$ at 298 K, 20-L volume; (d) 100 g $Na_2SO_4(s)$ at 30 °C or 100 g $Na_2SO_4(aq)$ at 30 °C.

**19.43** Predict the sign of the entropy change of the system for each of the following reactions:
(a) $N_2(g) + 3 H_2(g) \longrightarrow 2 NH_3(g)$
(b) $CaCO_3(s) \longrightarrow CaO(s) + CO_2(g)$
(c) $3 C_2H_2(g) \longrightarrow C_6H_6(g)$
(d) $Al_2O_3(s) + 3 H_2(g) \longrightarrow 2 Al(s) + 3 H_2O(g)$

**19.44** Predict the sign of $\Delta S_{sys}$ for each of the following processes: (a) Molten gold solidifies. (b) Gaseous $Cl_2$ dissociates in the stratosphere to form gaseous Cl atoms. (c) Gaseous CO reacts with gaseous $H_2$ to form liquid methanol, $CH_3OH$. (d) Calcium phosphate precipitates upon mixing $Ca(NO_3)_2(aq)$ and $(NH_4)_3PO_4(aq)$.

# ENTROPY CHANGES IN CHEMICAL REACTIONS (section 19.4)

**19.45** (a) Using Figure 19.13 as a model, sketch how the entropy of water changes as it is heated from −50 °C to 110 °C at sea level. Show the temperatures at which there are vertical increases in entropy. (b) Which process has the larger entropy change: melting ice or boiling water? Explain.

**19.46** Propanol ($C_3H_7OH$) melts at −126.5 °C and boils at 97.4 °C. Draw a qualitative sketch of how the entropy changes as propanol vapor at 150 °C and 1 atm is cooled to solid propanol at −150 °C and 1 atm.

**19.47** In each of the following pairs, which compound would you expect to have the higher standard molar entropy: (a) $C_2H_2(g)$ or $C_2H_6(g)$, (b) $CO_2(g)$ or $CO(g)$? Explain.

**19.48** Cyclopropane and propylene are isomers (see Exercise 19.6) that both have the formula $C_3H_6$. Based on the molecular structures shown, which of these isomers would you expect to have the higher standard molar entropy at 25 °C?

Cyclopropane          Propylene

**19.49** Use Appendix C to compare the standard entropies at 25 °C for the following pairs of substances: (a) $Sc(s)$ and $Sc(g)$, (b) $NH_3(g)$ and $NH_3(aq)$, (c) 1 mol $P_4(g)$ and 2 mol $P_2(g)$, (d) C(graphite) and C(diamond). In each case explain the difference in the entropy values.

**19.50** Using Appendix C, compare the standard entropies at 25 °C for the following pairs of substances: (a) $CuO(s)$ and $Cu_2O(s)$, (b) 1 mol $N_2O_4(g)$ and 2 mol $NO_2(g)$, (c) $SiO_2(s)$ and $CO_2(g)$, (d) $CO(g)$ and $CO_2(g)$. For each pair, explain the difference in the entropy values.

**[19.51]** The standard entropies at 298 K for certain of the group 4A elements are as follows: C(s, diamond) = 2.43 J/mol-K, Si(s) = 18.81 J/mol-K, Ge(s) = 31.09 J/mol-K, and Sn(s) = 51.818 J/mol-K. All but Sn have the diamond structure. How do you account for the trend in the $S°$ values?

**[19.52]** Three of the forms of elemental carbon are graphite, diamond, and buckminsterfullerene. The entropies at 298 K for graphite and diamond are listed in Appendix C. (a) Account for the difference in the $S°$ values of graphite and diamond in light of their structures (Figure 12.30). (b) What would you expect for the $S°$ value of buckminsterfullerene (Figure 12.47) relative to the values for graphite and diamond? Explain.

**19.53** Using $S°$ values from Appendix C, calculate $\Delta S°$ values for the following reactions. In each case account for the sign of $\Delta S°$.
(a) $C_2H_4(g) + H_2(g) \longrightarrow C_2H_6(g)$
(b) $N_2O_4(g) \longrightarrow 2\,NO_2(g)$
(c) $Be(OH)_2(s) \longrightarrow BeO(s) + H_2O(g)$
(d) $2\,CH_3OH(g) + 3\,O_2(g) \longrightarrow 2\,CO_2(g) + 4\,H_2O(g)$

**19.54** Calculate $\Delta S°$ values for the following reactions by using tabulated $S°$ values from Appendix C. In each case explain the sign of $\Delta S°$.
(a) $HNO_3(g) + NH_3(g) \longrightarrow NH_4NO_3(s)$
(b) $2\,Fe_2O_3(s) \longrightarrow 4\,Fe(s) + 3\,O_2(g)$
(c) $CaCO_3(s, calcite) + 2\,HCl(g) \longrightarrow$
$$CaCl_2(s) + CO_2(g) + H_2O(l)$$
(d) $3\,C_2H_6(g) \longrightarrow C_6H_6(l) + 6\,H_2(g)$

# GIBBS FREE ENERGY (sections 19.5 and 19.6)

**19.55** (a) For a process that occurs at constant temperature, express the change in Gibbs free energy in terms of changes in the enthalpy and entropy of the system. (b) For a certain process that occurs at constant $T$ and $P$, the value of $\Delta G$ is positive. What can you conclude? (c) What is the relationship between $\Delta G$ for a process and the rate at which it occurs?

**19.56** (a) What is the meaning of the standard free-energy change, $\Delta G°$, as compared with $\Delta G$? (b) For any process that occurs at constant temperature and pressure, what is the significance of $\Delta G = 0$? (c) For a certain process, $\Delta G$ is large and negative. Does this mean that the process necessarily occurs rapidly?

**19.57** For a certain chemical reaction, $\Delta H° = -35.4$ kJ and $\Delta S° = -85.5$ J/K. (a) Is the reaction exothermic or endothermic? (b) Does the reaction lead to an increase or decrease in the randomness or disorder of the system? (c) Calculate $\Delta G°$ for the reaction at 298 K. (d) Is the reaction spontaneous at 298 K under standard conditions?

**19.58** A certain reaction has $\Delta H° = +23.7$ kJ and $\Delta S° = +52.4$ J/K. (a) Is the reaction exothermic or endothermic? (b) Does the reaction lead to an increase or decrease in the randomness or disorder of the system? (c) Calculate $\Delta G°$ for the reaction at 298 K. (d) Is the reaction spontaneous at 298 K under standard conditions?

**19.59** Using data in Appendix C, calculate $\Delta H°$, $\Delta S°$, and $\Delta G°$ at 298 K for each of the following reactions. In each case show that $\Delta G° = \Delta H° - T\Delta S°$.
(a) $H_2(g) + F_2(g) \longrightarrow 2\,HF(g)$
(b) $C(s, graphite) + 2\,Cl_2(g) \longrightarrow CCl_4(g)$
(c) $2\,PCl_3(g) + O_2(g) \longrightarrow 2\,POCl_3(g)$
(d) $2\,CH_3OH(g) + H_2(g) \longrightarrow C_2H_6(g) + 2\,H_2O(g)$

**19.60** Use data in Appendix C to calculate $\Delta H°$, $\Delta S°$, and $\Delta G°$ at 25 °C for each of the following reactions. In each case show that $\Delta G° = \Delta H° - T\Delta S°$.
(a) $2\,Cr(s) + 3\,O_2(g) \longrightarrow 2\,CrO_3(s)$
(b) $BaCO_3(s) \longrightarrow BaO(s) + CO_2(g)$
(c) $2\,P(s) + 10\,HF(g) \longrightarrow 2\,PF_5(g) + 5\,H_2(g)$
(d) $K(s) + O_2(g) \longrightarrow KO_2(s)$

**19.61** Using data from Appendix C, calculate $\Delta G°$ for the following reactions. Indicate whether each reaction is spontaneous at 298 K under standard conditions.
(a) $2\,SO_2(g) + O_2(g) \longrightarrow 2\,SO_3(g)$
(b) $NO_2(g) + N_2O(g) \longrightarrow 3\,NO(g)$
(c) $6\,Cl_2(g) + 2\,Fe_2O_3(s) \longrightarrow 4\,FeCl_3(s) + 3\,O_2(g)$
(d) $SO_2(g) + 2\,H_2(g) \longrightarrow S(s) + 2\,H_2O(g)$

**19.62** Using data from Appendix C, calculate the change in Gibbs free energy for each of the following reactions. In each case indicate whether the reaction is spontaneous at 298 K under standard conditions.
(a) $2\,Ag(s) + Cl_2(g) \longrightarrow 2\,AgCl(s)$
(b) $P_4O_6(s) + 12\,H_2(g) \longrightarrow 4\,PH_3(g) + 6\,H_2O(g)$
(c) $CH_4(g) + 4\,F_2(g) \longrightarrow CF_4(g) + 4\,HF(g)$
(d) $2\,H_2O_2(l) \longrightarrow 2\,H_2O(l) + O_2(g)$

**19.63** Octane ($C_8H_{18}$) is a liquid hydrocarbon at room temperature that is the primary constituent of gasoline. (a) Write a balanced equation for the combustion of $C_8H_{18}(l)$ to form $CO_2(g)$ and $H_2O(l)$. (b) Without using thermochemical data, predict whether $\Delta G°$ for this reaction is more negative or less negative than $\Delta H°$.

**19.64** Sulfur dioxide reacts with strontium oxide as follows:

$$SO_2(g) + SrO(s) \longrightarrow SrSO_3(s)$$

(a) Without using thermochemical data, predict whether $\Delta G°$ for this reaction is more negative or less negative than $\Delta H°$. (b) If you had only standard enthalpy data for this reaction, how would you go about making a rough estimate of the value of $\Delta G°$ at 298 K, using data from Appendix C on other substances?

**19.65** Classify each of the following reactions as one of the four possible types summarized in Table 19.3:
(a) $N_2(g) + 3\,F_2(g) \longrightarrow 2\,NF_3(g)$
$$\Delta H° = -249\text{ kJ}; \Delta S° = -278\text{ J/K}$$
(b) $N_2(g) + 3\,Cl_2(g) \longrightarrow 2\,NCl_3(g)$
$$\Delta H° = 460\text{ kJ}; \Delta S° = -275\text{ J/K}$$
(c) $N_2F_4(g) \longrightarrow 2\,NF_2(g)$
$$\Delta H° = 85\text{ kJ}; \Delta S° = 198\text{ J/K}$$

**19.66** From the values given for $\Delta H°$ and $\Delta S°$, calculate $\Delta G°$ for each of the following reactions at 298 K. If the reaction is not spontaneous under standard conditions at 298 K, at what temperature (if any) would the reaction become spontaneous?

(a) $2\,PbS(s) + 3\,O_2(g) \longrightarrow 2\,PbO(s) + 2\,SO_2(g)$
$$\Delta H° = -844 \text{ kJ}; \Delta S° = -165 \text{ J/K}$$

(b) $2\,POCl_3(g) \longrightarrow 2\,PCl_3(g) + O_2(g)$
$$\Delta H° = 572 \text{ kJ}; \Delta S° = 179 \text{ J/K}$$

**19.67** A particular constant-pressure reaction is spontaneous at 390 K. The enthalpy change for the reaction is +23.7 kJ. What can you conclude about the sign and magnitude of $\Delta S$ for the reaction?

**19.68** A certain constant-pressure reaction is nonspontaneous at 45 °C. The entropy change for the reaction is 72 J/K. What can you conclude about the sign and magnitude of $\Delta H$?

**19.69** For a particular reaction, $\Delta H = -32$ kJ and $\Delta S = -98$ J/K. Assume that $\Delta H$ and $\Delta S$ do not vary with temperature. (a) At what temperature will the reaction have $\Delta G = 0$? (b) If $T$ is increased from that in part (a), will the reaction be spontaneous or nonspontaneous?

**19.70** Reactions in which a substance decomposes by losing CO are called *decarbonylation* reactions. The decarbonylation of acetic acid proceeds as follows:
$$CH_3COOH(l) \longrightarrow CH_3OH(g) + CO(g)$$

By using data from Appendix C, calculate the minimum temperature at which this process will be spontaneous under standard conditions. Assume that $\Delta H°$ and $\Delta S°$ do not vary with temperature.

**19.71** Consider the following reaction between oxides of nitrogen:
$$NO_2(g) + N_2O(g) \longrightarrow 3\,NO(g)$$

(a) Use data in Appendix C to predict how $\Delta G°$ for the reaction varies with increasing temperature. (b) Calculate $\Delta G°$ at 800 K, assuming that $\Delta H°$ and $\Delta S°$ do not change with temperature. Under standard conditions is the reaction spontaneous at 800 K? (c) Calculate $\Delta G°$ at 1000 K. Is the reaction spontaneous under standard conditions at this temperature?

**19.72** Methanol ($CH_3OH$) can be made by the controlled oxidation of methane:
$$CH_4(g) + \tfrac{1}{2}O_2(g) \longrightarrow CH_3OH(g)$$

(a) Use data in Appendix C to calculate $\Delta H°$ and $\Delta S°$ for this reaction. (b) How is $\Delta G°$ for the reaction expected to vary with increasing temperature? (c) Calculate $\Delta G°$ at 298 K. Under standard conditions, is the reaction spontaneous at this temperature? (d) Is there a temperature at which the reaction would be at equilibrium under standard conditions and that is low enough so that the compounds involved are likely to be stable?

**19.73** (a) Use data in Appendix C to estimate the boiling point of benzene, $C_6H_6(l)$. (b) Use a reference source, such as the *CRC Handbook of Chemistry and Physics*, to find the experimental boiling point of benzene. How do you explain any deviation between your answer in part (a) and the experimental value?

**19.74** (a) Using data in Appendix C, estimate the temperature at which the free-energy change for the transformation from $I_2(s)$ to $I_2(g)$ is zero. What assumptions must you make in arriving at this estimate? (b) Use a reference source, such as Web Elements (www.webelements.com), to find the experimental melting and boiling points of $I_2$. (c) Which of the values in part (b) is closer to the value you obtained in part (a)? Can you explain why this is so?

**19.75** Acetylene gas, $C_2H_2(g)$, is used in welding. (a) Write a balanced equation for the combustion of acetylene gas to $CO_2(g)$ and $H_2O(l)$. (b) How much heat is produced in burning 1 mol of $C_2H_2$ under standard conditions if both reactants and products are brought to 298 K? (c) What is the maximum amount of useful work that can be accomplished under standard conditions by this reaction?

**19.76** The fuel in high-efficiency natural gas vehicles consists primarily of methane ($CH_4$). (a) How much heat is produced in burning 1 mol of $CH_4(g)$ under standard conditions if reactants and products are brought to 298 K and $H_2O(l)$ is formed? (b) What is the maximum amount of useful work that can be accomplished under standard conditions by this system?

# FREE ENERGY AND EQUILIBRIUM (section 19.7)

**19.77** Explain qualitatively how $\Delta G$ changes for each of the following reactions as the partial pressure of $O_2$ is increased:

(a) $2\,CO(g) + O_2(g) \longrightarrow 2\,CO_2(g)$
(b) $2\,H_2O_2(l) \longrightarrow 2\,H_2O(l) + O_2(g)$
(c) $2\,KClO_3(s) \longrightarrow 2\,KCl(s) + 3\,O_2(g)$

**19.78** Indicate whether $\Delta G$ increases, decreases, or does not change when the partial pressure of $H_2$ is increased in each of the following reactions:

(a) $N_2(g) + 3\,H_2(g) \longrightarrow 2\,NH_3(g)$
(b) $2\,HBr(g) \longrightarrow H_2(g) + Br_2(g)$
(c) $2\,H_2(g) + C_2H_2(g) \longrightarrow C_2H_6(g)$

**19.79** Consider the reaction $2\,NO_2(g) \longrightarrow N_2O_4(g)$. (a) Using data from Appendix C, calculate $\Delta G°$ at 298 K. (b) Calculate $\Delta G$ at 298 K if the partial pressures of $NO_2$ and $N_2O_4$ are 0.40 atm and 1.60 atm, respectively.

**19.80** Consider the reaction $3\,CH_4(g) \longrightarrow C_3H_8(g) + 2\,H_2(g)$. (a) Using data from Appendix C, calculate $\Delta G°$ at 298 K. (b) Calculate $\Delta G$ at 298 K if the reaction mixture consists of 40.0 atm of $CH_4$, 0.0100 atm of $C_3H_8(g)$, and 0.0180 atm of $H_2$.

**19.81** Use data from Appendix C to calculate the equilibrium constant, $K$, at 298 K for each of the following reactions:

(a) $H_2(g) + I_2(g) \rightleftharpoons 2\,HI(g)$
(b) $C_2H_5OH(g) \rightleftharpoons C_2H_4(g) + H_2O(g)$
(c) $3\,C_2H_2(g) \rightleftharpoons C_6H_6(g)$

**19.82** Using data from Appendix C, write the equilibrium-constant expression and calculate the value of the equilibrium constant for these reactions at 298 K:

(a) $NaHCO_3(s) \rightleftharpoons NaOH(s) + CO_2(g)$
(b) $2\,HBr(g) + Cl_2(g) \rightleftharpoons 2\,HCl(g) + Br_2(g)$
(c) $2\,SO_2(g) + O_2(g) \rightleftharpoons 2\,SO_3(g)$

**19.83** Consider the decomposition of barium carbonate:
$$BaCO_3(s) \rightleftharpoons BaO(s) + CO_2(g)$$

Using data from Appendix C, calculate the equilibrium pressure of $CO_2$ at (a) 298 K and (b) 1100 K.

**19.84** Consider the reaction
$$PbCO_3(s) \rightleftharpoons PbO(s) + CO_2(g)$$

Using data in Appendix C, calculate the equilibrium pressure of $CO_2$ in the system at (a) 400 °C and (b) 180 °C.

**19.85** The value of $K_a$ for nitrous acid (HNO$_2$) at 25 °C is given in Appendix D. **(a)** Write the chemical equation for the equilibrium that corresponds to $K_a$. **(b)** By using the value of $K_a$, calculate $\Delta G°$ for the dissociation of nitrous acid in aqueous solution. **(c)** What is the value of $\Delta G$ at equilibrium? **(d)** What is the value of $\Delta G$ when [H$^+$] = 5.0 × 10$^{-2}$ M, [NO$_2$$^-$] = 6.0 × 10$^{-4}$ M, and [HNO$_2$] = 0.20 M?

**19.86** The $K_b$ for methylamine (CH$_3$NH$_2$) at 25 °C is given in Appendix D. **(a)** Write the chemical equation for the equilibrium that corresponds to $K_b$. **(b)** By using the value of $K_b$, calculate $\Delta G°$ for the equilibrium in part (a). **(c)** What is the value of $\Delta G$ at equilibrium? **(d)** What is the value of $\Delta G$ when [H$^+$] = 6.7 × 10$^{-9}$ M, [CH$_3$NH$_3$$^+$] = 2.4 × 10$^{-3}$ M, and [CH$_3$NH$_2$] = 0.098 M?

# ADDITIONAL EXERCISES

**19.87** **(a)** Which of the thermodynamic quantities $T$, $E$, $q$, $w$, and $S$ are state functions? **(b)** Which depend on the path taken from one state to another? **(c)** How many *reversible* paths are there between two states of a system? **(d)** For a reversible isothermal process, write an expression for $\Delta E$ in terms of $q$ and $w$ and an expression for $\Delta S$ in terms of $q$ and $T$.

**19.88** Indicate whether each of the following statements is true or false. If it is false, correct it. **(a)** The feasibility of manufacturing NH$_3$ from N$_2$ and H$_2$ depends entirely on the value of $\Delta H$ for the process N$_2$(g) + 3 H$_2$(g) $\longrightarrow$ 2 NH$_3$(g). **(b)** The reaction of Na(s) with Cl$_2$(g) to form NaCl(s) is a spontaneous process. **(c)** A spontaneous process can in principle be conducted reversibly. **(d)** Spontaneous processes in general require that work be done to force them to proceed. **(e)** Spontaneous processes are those that are exothermic and that lead to a higher degree of order in the system.

**19.89** For each of the following processes, indicate whether the signs of $\Delta S$ and $\Delta H$ are expected to be positive, negative, or about zero. **(a)** A solid sublimes. **(b)** The temperature of a sample of Co(s) is lowered from 60 °C to 25 °C. **(c)** Ethyl alcohol evaporates from a beaker. **(d)** A diatomic molecule dissociates into atoms. **(e)** A piece of charcoal is combusted to form CO$_2$(g) and H$_2$O(g).

**19.90** The reaction 2 Mg(s) + O$_2$(g) $\longrightarrow$ 2 MgO(s) is highly spontaneous and has a negative value for $\Delta S°$. The second law of thermodynamics states that in any spontaneous process there is always an increase in the entropy of the universe. Is there an inconsistency between this reaction and the second law?

**[19.91]** Suppose four gas molecules are placed in the left flask in Figure 19.6(a). Initially, the right flask is evacuated and the stopcock is closed. **(a)** After the stopcock is opened, how many different arrangements of the molecules are possible? **(b)** How many of the arrangements from part (a) have all the molecules in the left flask? **(c)** How does the answer to part (b) explain the spontaneous expansion of the gas?

**[19.92]** Consider a system that consists of two standard playing dice, with the state of the system defined by the sum of the values shown on the top faces. **(a)** The two arrangements of top faces shown here can be viewed as two possible microstates of the system. Explain. **(b)** To which state does each microstate correspond? **(c)** How many possible states are there for the system? **(d)** Which state or states have the highest entropy? Explain. **(e)** Which state or states have the lowest entropy? Explain.

**19.93** Ammonium nitrate dissolves spontaneously and endothermally in water at room temperature. What can you deduce about the sign of $\Delta S$ for this solution process?

**[19.94]** A standard air conditioner involves a *refrigerant* that is typically now a fluorinated hydrocarbon, such as CH$_2$F$_2$. An air-conditioner refrigerant has the property that it readily vaporizes at atmospheric pressure and is easily compressed to its liquid phase under increased pressure. The operation of an air conditioner can be thought of as a closed system made up of the refrigerant going through the two stages shown here (the air circulation is not shown in this diagram).

Expansion chamber

Expansion (low pressure)

Compression chamber

Compression (high pressure)

During *expansion*, the liquid refrigerant is released into an expansion chamber at low pressure, where it vaporizes. The vapor then undergoes *compression* at high pressure back to its liquid phase in a compression chamber. **(a)** What is the sign of $q$ for the expansion? **(b)** What is the sign of $q$ for the compression? **(c)** In a central air-conditioning system, one chamber is inside the home and the other is outside. Which chamber is where, and why? **(d)** Imagine that a sample of liquid refrigerant undergoes expansion followed by compression, so that it is back to its original state. Would you expect that to be a reversible process? **(e)** Suppose that a house and its exterior are both initially at 31 °C. Some time after the air conditioner is turned on, the house is cooled to 24 °C. Is this process spontaneous or nonspontaneous?

**[19.95]** *Trouton's rule* states that for many liquids at their normal boiling points, the standard molar entropy of vaporization is about 88 J/mol-K. **(a)** Estimate the normal boiling point of bromine, Br$_2$, by determining $\Delta H°_{vap}$ for Br$_2$ using data from Appendix C. Assume that $\Delta H°_{vap}$ remains constant with temperature and that Trouton's rule holds. **(b)** Look up the normal boiling point of Br$_2$ in a chemistry handbook or at the WebElements Web site (www.webelements.com).

**[19.96]** For the majority of the compounds listed in Appendix C, the value of $\Delta G°_f$ is more positive (or less negative) than the value of $\Delta H°_f$. **(a)** Explain this observation, using NH$_3$(g), CCl$_4$(l), and KNO$_3$(s) as examples. **(b)** An exception to this observation is CO(g). Explain the trend in the $\Delta H°_f$ and $\Delta G°_f$ values for this molecule.

**19.97** Consider the following three reactions:

(i) $Ti(s) + 2 Cl_2(g) \longrightarrow TiCl_4(g)$

(ii) $C_2H_6(g) + 7 Cl_2(g) \longrightarrow 2 CCl_4(g) + 6 HCl(g)$

(iii) $BaO(s) + CO_2(g) \longrightarrow BaCO_3(s)$

(a) For each of the reactions, use data in Appendix C to calculate $\Delta H°$, $\Delta G°$, and $\Delta S°$ at 25 °C. (b) Which of these reactions are spontaneous under standard conditions at 25 °C? (c) For each of the reactions, predict the manner in which the change in free energy varies with an increase in temperature.

**19.98** Using the data in Appendix C and given the pressures listed, calculate $\Delta G°$ for each of the following reactions:

(a) $N_2(g) + 3 H_2(g) \longrightarrow 2 NH_3(g)$

$P_{N_2} = 2.6$ atm, $P_{H_2} = 5.9$ atm, $P_{NH_3} = 1.2$ atm

(b) $2 N_2H_4(g) + 2 NO_2(g) \longrightarrow 3 N_2(g) + 4 H_2O(g)$

$P_{N_2H_4} = P_{NO_2} = 5.0 \times 10^{-2}$ atm,

$P_{N_2} = 0.5$ atm, $P_{H_2O} = 0.3$ atm

(c) $N_2H_4(g) \longrightarrow N_2(g) + 2 H_2(g)$

$P_{N_2H_4} = 0.5$ atm, $P_{N_2} = 1.5$ atm, $P_{H_2} = 2.5$ atm

**19.99** (a) For each of the following reactions, predict the sign of $\Delta H°$ and $\Delta S°$ and discuss briefly how these factors determine the magnitude of $K$. (b) Based on your general chemical knowledge, predict which of these reactions will have $K > 0$. (c) In each case indicate whether $K$ should increase or decrease with increasing temperature.

(i) $2 Mg(s) + O_2(g) \rightleftharpoons 2 MgO(s)$

(ii) $2 KI(s) \rightleftharpoons 2 K(g) + I_2(g)$

(iii) $Na_2(g) \rightleftharpoons 2 Na(g)$

(iv) $2 V_2O_5(s) \rightleftharpoons 4 V(s) + 5 O_2(g)$

**19.100** Acetic acid can be manufactured by combining methanol with carbon monoxide, an example of a *carbonylation* reaction:

$$CH_3OH(l) + CO(g) \longrightarrow CH_3COOH(l)$$

(a) Calculate the equilibrium constant for the reaction at 25 °C. (b) Industrially, this reaction is run at temperatures above 25 °C. Will an increase in temperature produce an increase or decrease in the mole fraction of acetic acid at equilibrium? Why are elevated temperatures used? (c) At what temperature will this reaction have an equilibrium constant equal to 1? (You may assume that $\Delta H°$ and $\Delta S°$ are temperature independent, and you may ignore any phase changes that might occur.)

**19.101** The oxidation of glucose ($C_6H_{12}O_6$) in body tissue produces $CO_2$ and $H_2O$. In contrast, anaerobic decomposition, which occurs during fermentation, produces ethanol ($C_2H_5OH$) and $CO_2$. (a) Using data given in Appendix C, compare the equilibrium constants for the following reactions:

$$C_6H_{12}O_6(s) + 6 O_2(g) \rightleftharpoons 6 CO_2(g) + 6 H_2O(l)$$

$$C_6H_{12}O_6(s) \rightleftharpoons 2 C_2H_5OH(l) + 2 CO_2(g)$$

(b) Compare the maximum work that can be obtained from these processes under standard conditions.

**[19.102]** The conversion of natural gas, which is mostly methane, into products that contain two or more carbon atoms, such as ethane ($C_2H_6$), is a very important industrial chemical process. In principle, methane can be converted into ethane and hydrogen:

$$2 CH_4(g) \longrightarrow C_2H_6(g) + H_2(g)$$

In practice, this reaction is carried out in the presence of oxygen:

$$2 CH_4(g) + \tfrac{1}{2} O_2(g) \longrightarrow C_2H_6(g) + H_2O(g)$$

(a) Using the data in Appendix C, calculate $K$ for these reactions at 25 °C and 500 °C. (b) Is the difference in $\Delta G°$ for the two reactions due primarily to the enthalpy term ($\Delta H$) or the entropy term ($-T\Delta S$)? (c) Explain how the preceding reactions are an example of driving a nonspontaneous reaction, as discussed in the "Chemistry and Life" box in Section 19.7. (d) The reaction of $CH_4$ and $O_2$ to form $C_2H_6$ and $H_2O$ must be carried out carefully to avoid a competing reaction. What is the most likely competing reaction?

**[19.103]** Cells use the hydrolysis of adenosine triphosphate (ATP) as a source of energy (Figure 19.19). The conversion of ATP to ADP has a standard free-energy change of $-30.5$ kJ/mol. If all the free energy from the metabolism of glucose,

$$C_6H_{12}O_6(s) + 6 O_2(g) \longrightarrow 6 CO_2(g) + 6 H_2O(l)$$

goes into the conversion of ADP to ATP, how many moles of ATP can be produced for each mole of glucose?

**[19.104]** The potassium-ion concentration in blood plasma is about $5.0 \times 10^{-3}$ $M$, whereas the concentration in muscle-cell fluid is much greater (0.15 $M$). The plasma and intracellular fluid are separated by the cell membrane, which we assume is permeable only to $K^+$. (a) What is $\Delta G$ for the transfer of 1 mol of $K^+$ from blood plasma to the cellular fluid at body temperature 37 °C? (b) What is the minimum amount of work that must be used to transfer this $K^+$?

**[19.105]** The relationship between the temperature of a reaction, its standard enthalpy change, and the equilibrium constant at that temperature can be expressed as the following linear equation:

$$\ln K = \frac{-\Delta H°}{RT} + \text{constant}$$

(a) Explain how this equation can be used to determine $\Delta H°$ experimentally from the equilibrium constants at several different temperatures. (b) Derive the preceding equation using relationships given in this chapter. To what is the constant equal?

**[19.106]** One way to derive Equation 19.3 depends on the observation that at constant $T$ the number of ways, $W$, of arranging $m$ ideal-gas particles in a volume $V$ is proportional to the volume raised to the $m$ power:

$$W \propto V^m$$

Use this relationship and Boltzmann's relationship between entropy and number of arrangements (Equation 19.5) to derive the equation for the entropy change for the isothermal expansion or compression of $n$ moles of an ideal gas.

**[19.107]** About 86% of the world's electrical energy is produced by using steam turbines, a form of heat engine. In his analysis of an ideal heat engine, Sadi Carnot concluded that the maximum possible efficiency is defined by the total work that could be done by the engine, divided by the quantity of heat available to do the work (for example, from hot steam produced by combustion of a fuel such as coal or methane). This efficiency is given by the ratio $(T_{high} - T_{low})/T_{high}$, where $T_{high}$ is the temperature of the heat going into the engine and $T_{low}$ is that of the heat leaving the engine. (a) What is the maximum possible efficiency of a heat engine operating between an input temperature of 700 K and an exit temperature of 288 K? (b) Why is it important that electrical power plants be located near bodies of relatively cool water? (c) Under what conditions could a heat engine operate at or near 100% efficiency? (d) It is often said that if the energy of combustion of a fuel such as methane were captured in an electrical fuel cell instead of by burning the fuel in a heat engine, a greater fraction of the energy could be put to useful work. Make a qualitative drawing like that in Figure 5.10 that illustrates the fact that in principle the fuel cell route will produce more useful work than the heat engine route from combustion of methane.

# INTEGRATIVE EXERCISES

**19.108** Most liquids follow Trouton's rule, which states that the molar entropy of vaporization lies in the range of $88 \pm 5$ J/mol-K. The normal boiling points and enthalpies of vaporization of several organic liquids are as follows:

| Substance | Normal Boiling Point (°C) | $\Delta H_{vap}$ (kJ/mol) |
|---|---|---|
| Acetone, $(CH_3)_2CO$ | 56.1 | 29.1 |
| Dimethyl ether, $(CH_3)_2O$ | −24.8 | 21.5 |
| Ethanol, $C_2H_5OH$ | 78.4 | 38.6 |
| Octane, $C_8H_{18}$ | 125.6 | 34.4 |
| Pyridine, $C_5H_5N$ | 115.3 | 35.1 |

**(a)** Calculate $\Delta S_{vap}$ for each of the liquids. Do all the liquids obey Trouton's rule? **(b)** With reference to intermolecular forces (Section 11.2), can you explain any exceptions to the rule? **(c)** Would you expect water to obey Trouton's rule? By using data in Appendix B, check the accuracy of your conclusion. **(d)** Chlorobenzene ($C_6H_5Cl$) boils at 131.8 °C. Use Trouton's rule to estimate $\Delta H_{vap}$ for this substance.

**19.109** In chemical kinetics the *entropy of activation* is the entropy change for the process in which the reactants reach the activated complex. The entropy of activation for bimolecular processes is usually negative. Explain this observation with reference to Figure 14.17.

**19.110** The following processes were all discussed in Chapter 18, "Chemistry of the Environment." Estimate whether the entropy of the system increases or decreases during each process: **(a)** photodissociation of $O_2(g)$, **(b)** formation of ozone from oxygen molecules and oxygen atoms, **(c)** diffusion of CFCs into the stratosphere, **(d)** desalination of water by reverse osmosis.

**19.111** Carbon disulfide ($CS_2$) is a toxic, highly flammable substance. The following thermodynamic data are available for $CS_2(l)$ and $CS_2(g)$ at 298 K:

| | $\Delta H_f^\circ$ (kJ/mol) | $\Delta G_f^\circ$ (kJ/mol) |
|---|---|---|
| $CS_2(l)$ | 89.7 | 65.3 |
| $CS_2(g)$ | 117.4 | 67.2 |

**(a)** Draw the Lewis structure of the molecule. What do you predict for the bond order of the C—S bonds? **(b)** Use the VSEPR method to predict the structure of the $CS_2$ molecule. **(c)** Liquid $CS_2$ burns in $O_2$ with a blue flame, forming $CO_2(g)$ and $SO_2(g)$. Write a balanced equation for this reaction. **(d)** Using the data in the preceding table and in Appendix C, calculate $\Delta H^\circ$ and $\Delta G^\circ$ for the reaction in part (c). Is the reaction exothermic? Is it spontaneous at 298 K? **(e)** Use the data in the table to calculate $\Delta S^\circ$ at 298 K for the vaporization of $CS_2(l)$. Is the sign of $\Delta S^\circ$ as you would expect for a vaporization? **(f)** Using data in the table and your answer to part (e), estimate the boiling point of $CS_2(l)$. Do you predict that the substance will be a liquid or a gas at 298 K and 1 atm?

**[19.112]** The following data compare the standard enthalpies and free energies of formation of some crystalline ionic substances and aqueous solutions of the substances:

| Substance | $\Delta H_f^\circ$ (kJ/mol) | $\Delta G_f^\circ$ (kJ/mol) |
|---|---|---|
| $AgNO_3(s)$ | −124.4 | −33.4 |
| $AgNO_3(aq)$ | −101.7 | −34.2 |
| $MgSO_4(s)$ | −1283.7 | −1169.6 |
| $MgSO_4(aq)$ | −1374.8 | −1198.4 |

**(a)** Write the formation reaction for $AgNO_3(s)$. Based on this reaction, do you expect the entropy of the system to increase or decrease upon the formation of $AgNO_3(s)$? **(b)** Use $\Delta H_f^\circ$ and $\Delta G_f^\circ$ of $AgNO_3(s)$ to determine the entropy change upon formation of the substance. Is your answer consistent with your reasoning in part (a)? **(c)** Is dissolving $AgNO_3$ in water an exothermic or endothermic process? What about dissolving $MgSO_4$ in water? **(d)** For both $AgNO_3$ and $MgSO_4$, use the data to calculate the entropy change when the solid is dissolved in water. **(e)** Discuss the results from part (d) with reference to material presented in this chapter and in the "A Closer Look" box on page 540.

**[19.113]** Consider the following equilibrium:

$$N_2O_4(g) \rightleftharpoons 2\,NO_2(g)$$

Thermodynamic data on these gases are given in Appendix C. You may assume that $\Delta H^\circ$ and $\Delta S^\circ$ do not vary with temperature. **(a)** At what temperature will an equilibrium mixture contain equal amounts of the two gases? **(b)** At what temperature will an equilibrium mixture of 1 atm total pressure contain twice as much $NO_2$ as $N_2O_4$? **(c)** At what temperature will an equilibrium mixture of 10 atm total pressure contain twice as much $NO_2$ as $N_2O_4$? **(d)** Rationalize the results from parts (b) and (c) by using Le Châtelier's principle. [Section 15.7]

**[19.114]** The reaction

$$SO_2(g) + 2\,H_2S(g) \rightleftharpoons 3\,S(s) + 2\,H_2O(g)$$

is the basis of a suggested method for removal of $SO_2$ from power-plant stack gases. The standard free energy of each substance is given in Appendix C. **(a)** What is the equilibrium constant for the reaction at 298 K? **(b)** In principle, is this reaction a feasible method of removing $SO_2$? **(c)** If $P_{SO_2} = P_{H_2S}$ and the vapor pressure of water is 25 torr, calculate the equilibrium $SO_2$ pressure in the system at 298 K. **(d)** Would you expect the process to be more or less effective at higher temperatures?

**19.115** When most elastomeric polymers (e.g., a rubber band) are stretched, the molecules become more ordered, as illustrated here:

Suppose you stretch a rubber band. **(a)** Do you expect the entropy of the system to increase or decrease? **(b)** If the rubber band were stretched isothermally, would heat need to be absorbed or emitted to maintain constant temperature? **(c)** Try this experiment: Stretch a rubber band and wait a moment. Then place the stretched rubber band on your upper lip, and let it return suddenly to its unstretched state (remember to keep holding on). What do you observe? Are your observations consistent with your answer to part (b)?

# WHAT'S AHEAD

**20.1 OXIDATION STATES AND OXIDATION-REDUCTION REACTIONS**
We review oxidation states and *oxidation-reduction (redox) reactions*.

**20.2 BALANCING REDOX EQUATIONS**
We learn how to balance redox equations using the method of *half-reactions*.

**20.3 VOLTAIC CELLS**
We consider *voltaic cells*, which produce electricity from spontaneous redox reactions. Solid electrodes serve as the

surfaces at which oxidation and reduction take place. The electrode where oxidation occurs is the *anode*, and the electrode where reduction occurs is the *cathode*.

**20.4 CELL POTENTIALS UNDER STANDARD CONDITIONS**
We see that an important characteristic of a voltaic cell is its *cell potential*, which is the difference in the electrical potentials at the two electrodes and is measured in units of volts. Half-cell potentials are tabulated for reduction half-reactions under standard conditions (*standard reduction potentials*).

**20.5 FREE ENERGY AND REDOX REACTIONS**
We relate the Gibbs free energy, $\Delta G°$, to cell potential.

20

**A VARIETY OF BATTERIES** of different sizes, composition, and voltages.

# ELECTRO-CHEMISTRY

**WE ARE SURROUNDED BY AN** amazing array of portable electronic gadgets, including cell phones, portable music players, laptop computers, and gaming devices. In the absence of batteries, however, our electronic gadgetry would be nothing more than extra weight. Thus, a variety of batteries of different sizes, compositions, and voltages have been developed, some of which are shown in the chapter-opening photograph. Considerable research is in progress to develop new batteries with more power, faster recharging ability, lighter weight, or cheaper price. At the heart of such development are the oxidation-reduction reactions that power batteries.

As we discussed in Chapter 4, *oxidation* is the loss of electrons in a chemical reaction, and *reduction* is the gain of electrons. ∞ (Section 4.4) Thus, oxidation-reduction (redox) reactions occur when electrons are transferred from an atom that is oxidized to an atom that is reduced. Redox reactions are involved not only in the operation of batteries but also in a wide variety of important natural processes, including the rusting of iron, the browning of foods, and the respiration of animals. **Electrochemistry** is the study of the relationships between electricity and chemical reactions. It includes the study of both spontaneous and nonspontaneous processes.

## 20.1 | OXIDATION STATES AND OXIDATION-REDUCTION REACTIONS

We determine whether a given chemical reaction is an oxidation-reduction reaction by keeping track of the *oxidation numbers* (*oxidation states*) of the elements involved in the reaction. ∞ (Section 4.4) This procedure identifies whether the oxidation state changes for any elements involved in the reaction. For example, consider the reaction that occurs spontaneously when zinc metal is added to a strong acid (▼ **FIGURE 20.1**):

$$Zn(s) + 2\,H^+(aq) \longrightarrow Zn^{2+}(aq) + H_2(g) \qquad [20.1]$$

The chemical equation for this reaction can be written

$$Zn(s) + 2\,H^+(aq) \longrightarrow Zn^{2+}(aq) + H_2(g) \qquad [20.2]$$

H⁺ reduced

Zn oxidized

0   +1   +2   0

From the oxidation numbers below the equation, we see that the oxidation number of Zn changes from 0 to +2 and that of H changes from +1 to 0. Thus, this is an oxidation-reduction reaction. Electrons are transferred from zinc atoms to hydrogen ions and, therefore, Zn is oxidized and $H^+$ is reduced.

▲ **GO FIGURE**

Explain (a) the vigorous bubbling in the beaker on the right and (b) the formation of steam above that beaker.

▶ **FIGURE 20.1 Oxidation of zinc by hydrochloric acid.**

$Zn(s)$      $2\,HCl(aq)$      $ZnCl_2(aq)$      $H_2(g)$

In a reaction such as Equation 20.2, a clear transfer of electrons occurs. In some reactions, however, the oxidation numbers change, but we cannot say that any substance literally gains or loses electrons. For example, in the combustion of hydrogen gas,

$$2 \text{ H}_2(g) + \text{O}_2(g) \longrightarrow 2 \text{ H}_2\text{O}(g) \qquad [20.3]$$

hydrogen is oxidized from the 0 to the $+1$ oxidation state and oxygen is reduced from the 0 to the $-2$ oxidation state. Therefore, Equation 20.3 is an oxidation-reduction reaction. Water is not an ionic substance, however, and so there is not a complete transfer of electrons from hydrogen to oxygen as water is formed. Thus, keeping track of oxidation states is a convenient form of "bookkeeping," but you should not generally equate the oxidation state of an atom with its actual charge in a chemical compound. ∞ (Section 8.5 "A Closer Look: Oxidation Numbers, Formal Charges, and Actual Partial Charges")

### ▲ GIVE IT SOME THOUGHT

What are the oxidation numbers of the elements in the nitrite ion, $NO_2^-$?

In any redox reaction, both oxidation and reduction must occur. If one substance is oxidized, another must be reduced. The substance that makes it possible for another substance to be oxidized is called either the **oxidizing agent** or the **oxidant**. The oxidizing agent acquires electrons from the other substance and so is itself reduced. A **reducing agent**, or **reductant**, is a substance that gives up electrons, thereby causing another substance to be reduced. The reducing agent is therefore oxidized in the process. In Equation 20.2, $H^+(aq)$, the species that is reduced, is the oxidizing agent and $Zn(s)$, the species that is oxidized, is the reducing agent.

---

**SAMPLE EXERCISE 20.1** | **Identifying Oxidizing and Reducing Agents**

The nickel-cadmium (nicad) battery uses the following redox reaction to generate electricity:

$$Cd(s) + NiO_2(s) + 2 \text{ H}_2\text{O}(l) \longrightarrow Cd(OH)_2(s) + Ni(OH)_2(s)$$

Identify the substances that are oxidized and reduced, and indicate which is the oxidizing agent and which is the reducing agent.

#### SOLUTION

**Analyze** We are given a redox equation and asked to identify the substance oxidized and the substance reduced and to label the oxidizing agent and the reducing agent.

**Plan** First, we assign oxidation states, or numbers, to all the atoms and determine which elements change oxidation state. Second, we apply the definitions of oxidation and reduction.

**Solve** $Cd(s) + NiO_2(s) + 2H_2O(l) \longrightarrow Cd(OH)_2(s) + Ni(OH)_2(s)$

The oxidation state of Cd increases from 0 to $+2$, and that of Ni decreases from $+4$ to $+2$. Thus, the Cd atom is oxidized (loses electrons) and is the reducing agent. The oxidation state of Ni decreases as $NiO_2$ is converted into $Ni(OH)_2$. Thus, $NiO_2$ is reduced (gains electrons) and is the oxidizing agent.

**Comment** A common mnemonic for remembering oxidation and reduction is "LEO the lion says GER": *l*osing *e*lectrons is *o*xidation; *g*aining *e*lectrons is *r*eduction.

#### PRACTICE EXERCISE

Identify the oxidizing and reducing agents in the reaction

$$2 \text{ H}_2\text{O}(l) + Al(s) + MnO_4^-(aq) \longrightarrow Al(OH)_4^-(aq) + MnO_2(s)$$

**Answer:** $Al(s)$ is the reducing agent; $MnO_4^-(aq)$ is the oxidizing agent.

# 20.2 | BALANCING REDOX EQUATIONS

Whenever we balance a chemical equation, we must obey the law of conservation of mass: The amount of each element must be the same on both sides of the equation. (Atoms are neither created nor destroyed in any chemical reaction.) As we balance oxidation-reduction reactions, there is an additional requirement: The gains and losses of electrons must be balanced. If a substance loses a certain number of electrons during a reaction, another substance must gain that same number of electrons. (Electrons are neither created nor destroyed in any chemical reaction.)

In many simple chemical equations, such as Equation 20.2, balancing the electrons is handled "automatically" in the sense that we can balance the equation without explicitly considering the transfer of electrons. Many redox equations are more complex than Equation 20.2, however, and cannot be balanced easily without taking into account the number of electrons lost and gained. In this section we examine the *method of half-reactions*, a systematic procedure for balancing redox equations.

## Half-Reactions

Although oxidation and reduction must take place simultaneously, it is often convenient to consider them as separate processes. For example, the oxidation of $Sn^{2+}$ by $Fe^{3+}$,

$$Sn^{2+}(aq) + 2\,Fe^{3+}(aq) \longrightarrow Sn^{4+}(aq) + 2\,Fe^{2+}(aq)$$

can be considered as consisting of two processes: oxidation of $Sn^{2+}$ and reduction of $Fe^{3+}$:

| | | |
|---|---|---|
| *Oxidation:* | $Sn^{2+}(aq) \longrightarrow Sn^{4+}(aq) + 2\,e^-$ | [20.4] |
| *Reduction:* | $2\,Fe^{3+}(aq) + 2\,e^- \longrightarrow 2\,Fe^{2+}(aq)$ | [20.5] |

Notice that electrons are shown as products in the oxidation process and as reactants in the reduction process.

Equations that show either oxidation or reduction alone, such as Equations 20.4 and 20.5, are called **half-reactions**. In the overall redox reaction, the number of electrons lost in the oxidation half-reaction must equal the number of electrons gained in the reduction half-reaction. When this condition is met and each half-reaction is balanced, the electrons on the two sides cancel when the two half-reactions are added to give the balanced oxidation-reduction equation.

## Balancing Equations by the Method of Half-Reactions

In using the half-reaction method, we usually begin with a "skeleton" ionic equation showing only the substances undergoing oxidation and reduction. In such cases, we usually do not need to assign oxidation numbers unless we are unsure whether the reaction involves oxidation-reduction. We will find that $H^+$ (for acidic solutions), $OH^-$ (for basic solutions), and $H_2O$ are often involved as reactants or products in redox reactions. Unless $H^+$, $OH^-$, or $H_2O$ is being oxidized or reduced, these species do not appear in the skeleton equation. Their presence, however, can be deduced as we balance the equation.

For balancing a redox reaction that occurs *in acidic aqueous* solution, the procedure is as follows:

1. Divide the equation into one oxidation half-reaction and one reduction half-reaction.

2. Balance each half-reaction.

   (a) First, balance elements other than H and O.

   (b) Next, balance O atoms by adding $H_2O$ as needed.

   (c) Then balance H atoms by adding $H^+$ as needed.

   (d) Finally, balance charge by adding $e^-$ as needed.

This specific sequence (a)–(d) is important, and it is summarized in the diagram in the margin. At this point, you can check whether the number of electrons in each half-reaction corresponds to the changes in oxidation state.

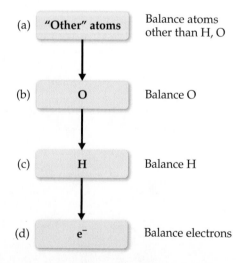

(a) "Other" atoms — Balance atoms other than H, O

(b) O — Balance O

(c) H — Balance H

(d) $e^-$ — Balance electrons

3. Multiply half-reactions by integers as needed to make the number of electrons lost in the oxidation half-reaction equal the number of electrons gained in the reduction half-reaction.

4. Add half-reactions and, if possible, simplify by canceling species appearing on both sides of the combined equation.

5. Check to make sure that atoms and charges are balanced.

As an example, let's consider the reaction between permanganate ion ($MnO_4^-$) and oxalate ion ($C_2O_4^{2-}$) in acidic aqueous solution (▼ **FIGURE 20.2**). When $MnO_4^-$ is added to an acidified solution of $C_2O_4^{2-}$, the deep purple color of the $MnO_4^-$ ion fades, bubbles of $CO_2$ form, and the solution takes on the pale pink color of $Mn^{2+}$. We can therefore write the skeleton equation as

$$MnO_4^-(aq) + C_2O_4^{2-}(aq) \longrightarrow Mn^{2+}(aq) + CO_2(aq) \qquad [20.6]$$

Experiments show that $H^+$ is consumed and $H_2O$ is produced in the reaction. We will see that their involvement in the reaction is deduced in the course of balancing the equation.

To complete and balance Equation 20.6, we first write the two half-reactions (step 1). One half-reaction must have Mn on both sides of the arrow, and the other must have C on both sides of the arrow:

$$MnO_4^-(aq) \longrightarrow Mn^{2+}(aq)$$

$$C_2O_4^{2-}(aq) \longrightarrow CO_2(g)$$

We next complete and balance each half-reaction. First, we balance all the atoms except H and O (step 2a). In the permanganate half-reaction, we have one manganese atom on each side of the equation and so need to do nothing. In the oxalate half-reaction, we add a coefficient 2 on the right to balance the two carbons on the left:

$$MnO_4^-(aq) \longrightarrow Mn^{2+}(aq)$$

$$C_2O_4^{2-}(aq) \longrightarrow 2\ CO_2(g)$$

Next we balance O (step 2b). The permanganate half-reaction has four oxygens on the left and none on the right; therefore we need four $H_2O$ molecules on the right to balance the oxygen atoms:

$$MnO_4^-(aq) \longrightarrow Mn^{2+}(aq) + 4\ H_2O(l)$$

---

**GO FIGURE**

**Which species is reduced in this reaction? Which species is the reducing agent?**

$MnO_4^-(aq)$

The purple color of $MnO_4^-$ disappears immediately as reaction with $C_2O_4^{2-}$ occurs

At end point, purple color of $MnO_4^-$ remains because all $C_2O_4^{2-}$ consumed

$C_2O_4^{2-}(aq)$

(a)　　　　　　　　　　　　　　　　　　　　(b)

◀ **FIGURE 20.2**  Titration of an acidic solution of $Na_2C_2O_4$ with $KMnO_4(aq)$.

The eight hydrogen atoms now in the products must be balanced by adding 8 $H^+$ to the reactants (step 2c):

$$8\,H^+(aq) + MnO_4^-(aq) \longrightarrow Mn^{2+}(aq) + 4\,H_2O(l)$$

There are now equal numbers of each type of atom on the two sides of the equation, but the charge still needs to be balanced. The charge of the reactants is $8(1+) + 1(1-) = 7+$, and that of the products is $1(2+) + 4(0) = 2+$. To balance the charge, we add five electrons to the reactant side (step 2d):

$$5\,e^- + 8\,H^+(aq) + MnO_4^-(aq) \longrightarrow Mn^{2+}(aq) + 4\,H_2O(l)$$

We can use oxidation states to check our result. In this half-reaction Mn goes from the +7 oxidation state in $MnO_4^-$ to the +2 oxidation state of $Mn^{2+}$. Therefore, each Mn atom gains five electrons, in agreement with our balanced half-reaction.

In the oxalate half-reaction, we have C and O balanced (step 2a). We balance the charge (step 2d) by adding two electrons to the products:

$$C_2O_4^{2-}(aq) \longrightarrow 2\,CO_2(g) + 2\,e^-$$

We can check this result using oxidation states. Carbon goes from the +3 oxidation state in $C_2O_4^{2-}$ to the +4 oxidation state in $CO_2$. Thus, each C atom loses one electron; therefore, the two C atoms in $C_2O_4^{2-}$ lose two electrons, in agreement with our balanced half-reaction.

Now we multiply each half-reaction by an appropriate integer so that the number of electrons gained in one half-reaction equals the number of electrons lost in the other (step 3). We multiply the $MnO_4^-$ half-reaction by 2 and the $C_2O_4^{2-}$ half-reaction by 5:

$$10\,e^- + 16\,H^+(aq) + 2\,MnO_4^-(aq) \longrightarrow 2\,Mn^{2+}(aq) + 8\,H_2O(l)$$

$$5\,C_2O_4^{2-}(aq) \longrightarrow 10\,CO_2(g) + 10\,e^-$$

$$\overline{\phantom{xxxxxxxxxxxxxxxxxxxxxxxxxxxxxxxxxxxxxxxxxxxxxxxxxxx}}$$

$$16\,H^+(aq) + 2\,MnO_4^-(aq) + 5\,C_2O_4^{2-}(aq) \longrightarrow$$
$$2\,Mn^{2+}(aq) + 8\,H_2O(l) + 10\,CO_2(g)$$

The balanced equation is the sum of the balanced half-reactions (step 4). Note that the electrons on the reactant and product sides of the equation cancel each other.

We check the balanced equation by counting atoms and charges (step 5): There are 16 H, 2 Mn, 28 O, 10 C, and a net charge of 4+ on each side of the equation, confirming that the equation is correctly balanced.

 **GIVE IT SOME THOUGHT**

Do free electrons appear anywhere in the balanced equation for a redox reaction?

---

**SAMPLE EXERCISE 20.2** | **Balancing Redox Equations in Acidic Solution**

Complete and balance this equation by the method of half-reactions:

$$Cr_2O_7^{2-}(aq) + Cl^-(aq) \longrightarrow Cr^{3+}(aq) + Cl_2(g) \quad \text{(acidic solution)}$$

**SOLUTION**

**Analyze** We are given an incomplete, unbalanced (skeleton) equation for a redox reaction occurring in acidic solution and asked to complete and balance it.

**Plan** We use the half-reaction procedure we just learned.

**Solve**

**Step 1:** We divide the equation into two half-reactions: $Cr_2O_7^{2-}(aq) \longrightarrow Cr^{3+}(aq)$
$$Cl^-(aq) \longrightarrow Cl_2(g)$$

**Step 2:** We balance each half-reaction. In the first half-reaction the presence of one $Cr_2O_7^{2-}$ among the reactants requires two $Cr^{3+}$ among the products. The seven oxygen atoms in $Cr_2O_7^{2-}$ are balanced by adding seven $H_2O$ to the products. The 14 hydrogen atoms in 7 $H_2O$ are then balanced by adding 14 $H^+$ to the reactants:

$$14\,H^+(aq) + Cr_2O_7^{2-}(aq) \longrightarrow 2\,Cr^{3+}(aq) + 7\,H_2O(l)$$

We then balance the charge by adding electrons to the left side of the equation so that the total charge is the same on the two sides:

$$6\,e^- + 14\,H^+(aq) + Cr_2O_7^{2-}(aq) \longrightarrow 2\,Cr^{3+}(aq) + 7\,H_2O(l)$$

We can check this result by looking at the oxidation state changes. Each chromium atom goes from +6 to +3, gaining three electrons; therefore, the two Cr atoms in $Cr_2O_7^{2-}$ gain six electrons, in agreement with our half-reaction.

In the second half-reaction, two $Cl^-$ are required to balance one $Cl_2$:

$$2\,Cl^-(aq) \longrightarrow Cl_2(g)$$

We add two electrons to the right side to attain charge balance:

$$2\,Cl^-(aq) \longrightarrow Cl_2(g) + 2\,e^-$$

This result agrees with the oxidation state changes. Each chlorine atom goes from −1 to 0, losing one electron; therefore, the two chlorine atoms lose two electrons.

**Step 3:** We equalize the number of electrons transferred in the two half-reactions. To do so, we multiply the Cl half-reaction by 3 so that the number of electrons gained in the Cr half-reaction (6) equals the number lost in the Cl half-reaction, allowing the electrons to cancel when the half-reactions are added:

$$6\,Cl^-(aq) \longrightarrow 3\,Cl_2(g) + 6\,e^-$$

**Step 4:** The equations are added to give the balanced equation:

$$14\,H^+(aq) + Cr_2O_7^{2-}(aq) + 6\,Cl^-(aq) \longrightarrow 2\,Cr^{3+}(aq) + 7\,H_2O(l) + 3\,Cl_2(g)$$

**Step 5:** There are equal numbers of atoms of each kind on the two sides of the equation (14 H, 2 Cr, 7 O, 6 Cl). In addition, the charge is the same on the two sides (6+). Thus, the equation is balanced.

**PRACTICE EXERCISE**

Complete and balance the following equations using the method of half-reactions. Both reactions occur in acidic solution.

(a) $Cu(s) + NO_3^-(aq) \longrightarrow Cu^{2+}(aq) + NO_2(g)$

(b) $Mn^{2+}(aq) + NaBiO_3(s) \longrightarrow Bi^{3+}(aq) + MnO_4^-(aq)$

**Answers:** (a) $Cu(s) + 4\,H^+(aq) + 2\,NO_3^-(aq) \longrightarrow Cu^{2+}(aq) + 2\,NO_2(g) + 2\,H_2O(l)$

(b) $2\,Mn^{2+}(aq) + 5\,NaBiO_3(s) + 14\,H^+(aq) \longrightarrow 2\,MnO_4^-(aq) + 5\,Bi^{3+}(aq) + 5\,Na^+(aq) + 7\,H_2O(l)$

# Balancing Equations for Reactions Occurring in Basic Solution

If a redox reaction occurs in basic solution, the equation must be balanced by using $OH^-$ and $H_2O$ rather than $H^+$ and $H_2O$. One approach is to first balance the half-reactions as if they occurred in acidic solution and then count the number of $H^+$ in each half-reaction and add the same number of $OH^-$ *to each side* of the half-reaction. This way, the reaction is mass-balanced because you are adding the same thing to both sides. In essence, what you are doing is "neutralizing" the protons to form water ($H^+ + OH^- \longrightarrow H_2O$) on the side containing $H^+$, and the other side ends up with the $OH^-$. The resulting water molecules can be canceled as needed.

| SAMPLE EXERCISE 20.3 | Balancing Redox Equations in Basic Solution |

Complete and balance this equation for a redox reaction that takes place in basic solution:

$$CN^-(aq) + MnO_4^-(aq) \longrightarrow CNO^-(aq) + MnO_2(s) \quad \text{(basic solution)}$$

## SOLUTION

**Analyze** We are given an incomplete equation for a basic redox reaction and asked to balance it.

**Plan** We go through the first steps of our procedure as if the reaction were occurring in acidic solution. We then add the appropriate number of $OH^-$ ions to each side of the equation, combining $H^+$ and $OH^-$ to form $H_2O$. We complete the process by simplifying the equation.

**Solve**

**Step 1:** We write the incomplete, unbalanced half-reactions:

$$CN^-(aq) \longrightarrow CNO^-(aq)$$
$$MnO_4^-(aq) \longrightarrow MnO_2(s)$$

**Step 2:** We balance each half-reaction as if it took place in acidic solution:

$$CN^-(aq) + H_2O(l) \longrightarrow CNO^-(aq) + 2\,H^+(aq) + 2\,e^-$$
$$3\,e^- + 4\,H^+(aq) + MnO_4^-(aq) \longrightarrow MnO_2(s) + 2\,H_2O(l)$$

Now we must take into account that the reaction occurs in basic solution, adding $OH^-$ to both sides of both half-reactions to neutralize $H^+$:

$$CN^-(aq) + H_2O(l) + 2\,OH^-(aq) \longrightarrow CNO^-(aq) + 2\,H^+(aq) + 2\,e^- + 2\,OH^-(aq)$$
$$3\,e^- + 4\,H^+(aq) + MnO_4^-(aq) + 4\,OH^-(aq) \longrightarrow MnO_2(s) + 2\,H_2O(l) + 4\,OH^-(aq)$$

We "neutralize" $H^+$ and $OH^-$ by forming $H_2O$ when they are on the same side of either half-reaction:

$$CN^-(aq) + H_2O(l) + 2\,OH^-(aq) \longrightarrow CNO^-(aq) + 2\,H_2O(l) + 2\,e^-$$
$$3\,e^- + 4\,H_2O(l) + MnO_4^-(aq) \longrightarrow MnO_2(s) + 2\,H_2O(l) + 4\,OH^-(aq)$$

Next, we cancel water molecules that appear as both reactants and products:

$$CN^-(aq) + 2\,OH^-(aq) \longrightarrow CNO^-(aq) + H_2O(l) + 2\,e^-$$
$$3\,e^- + 2\,H_2O(l) + MnO_4^-(aq) \longrightarrow MnO_2(s) + 4\,OH^-(aq)$$

Both half-reactions are now balanced. You can check the atoms and the overall charge.

**Step 3:** We multiply the cyanide half-reaction by 3, which gives 6 electrons on the product side, and multiply the permanganate half-reaction by 2, which gives 6 electrons on the reactant side:

$$3\,CN^-(aq) + 6\,OH^-(aq) \longrightarrow 3\,CNO^-(aq) + 3\,H_2O(l) + 6\,e^-$$
$$6\,e^- + 4\,H_2O(l) + 2\,MnO_4^-(aq) \longrightarrow 2\,MnO_2(s) + 8\,OH^-(aq)$$

**Step 4:** We add the two half-reactions together and simplify by canceling species that appear as both reactants and products:

$$3\,CN^-(aq) + H_2O(l) + 2\,MnO_4^-(aq) \longrightarrow 3\,CNO^-(aq) + 2\,MnO_2(s) + 2\,OH^-(aq)$$

**Step 5:** Check that the atoms and charges are balanced.

There are 3 C, 3 N, 2 H, 9 O, 2 Mn, and a charge of $5-$ on both sides of the equation.

**Comment** It is important to remember that this procedure doesn't imply that $H^+$ ions are involved in the chemical reaction. Recall that in aqueous solutions at 20 °C, $K_w = [H^+][OH^-] = 1.0 \times 10^{-14}$. Thus, $[H^+]$ is very small in this basic solution. ∞ (Section 16.3)

## PRACTICE EXERCISE

Complete and balance the following equations for oxidation-reduction reactions that occur in basic solution:

**(a)** $NO_2^-(aq) + Al(s) \longrightarrow NH_3(aq) + Al(OH)_4^-(aq)$

**(b)** $Cr(OH)_3(s) + ClO^-(aq) \longrightarrow CrO_4^{2-}(aq) + Cl_2(g)$

**Answers:** **(a)** $NO_2^-(aq) + 2\,Al(s) + 5\,H_2O(l) + OH^-(aq) \longrightarrow NH_3(aq) + 2\,Al(OH)_4^-(aq)$

**(b)** $2\,Cr(OH)_3(s) + 6\,ClO^-(aq) \longrightarrow 2\,CrO_4^{2-}(aq) + 3\,Cl_2(g) + 2\,OH^-(aq) + 2\,H_2O(l)$

Why does the intensity of the blue solution color lessen as the reaction proceeds?

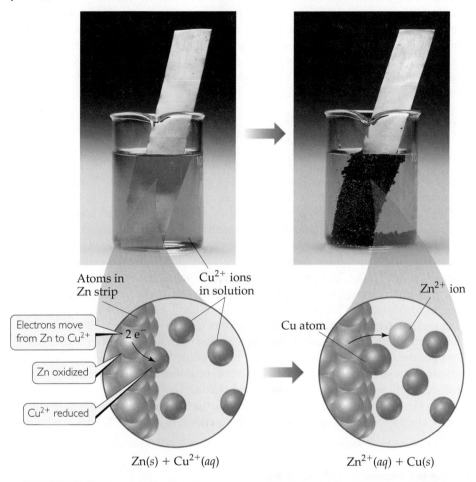

Atoms in
Zn strip

$Cu^{2+}$ ions
in solution

$Zn^{2+}$ ion

Electrons move
from Zn to $Cu^{2+}$

$2\ e^-$

Cu atom

Zn oxidized

$Cu^{2+}$ reduced

$Zn(s) + Cu^{2+}(aq)$

$Zn^{2+}(aq) + Cu(s)$

▲ **FIGURE 20.3   A spontaneous oxidation-reduction reaction involving zinc and copper.**

# 20.3 | VOLTAIC CELLS

The energy released in a spontaneous redox reaction can be used to perform electrical work. This task is accomplished through a **voltaic** (or **galvanic**) **cell**, a device in which the transfer of electrons takes place through an external pathway rather than directly between reactants present in the same reaction vessel.

One such spontaneous reaction occurs when a strip of zinc is placed in contact with a solution containing $Cu^{2+}$. As the reaction proceeds, the blue color of $Cu^{2+}(aq)$ ions fades, and copper metal deposits on the zinc. At the same time, the zinc begins to dissolve. These transformations, shown in ▲ **FIGURE 20.3**, are summarized by the equation

$$Zn(s) + Cu^{2+}(aq) \longrightarrow Zn^{2+}(aq) + Cu(s) \qquad [20.7]$$

▶ **FIGURE 20.4** shows a voltaic cell that uses the redox reaction given in Equation 20.7. Although the setup in Figure 20.4 is more complex than that in Figure 20.3, the reaction is the same in both cases. The significant difference is that in the voltaic cell the Zn metal and $Cu^{2+}(aq)$ are not in direct contact with each other. Instead, Zn metal is in contact with $Zn^{2+}(aq)$ in one compartment, and Cu metal is in contact with $Cu^{2+}(aq)$ in the other compartment. Consequently, $Cu^{2+}$ reduction can occur only by the flow of electrons through an external circuit, namely, a wire connecting the Zn and Cu strips. Electrons flowing through a wire and ions moving in solution both constitute an *electrical current*. This flow of electrical charge can be used to accomplish electrical work.

Which metal, Cu or Zn, is oxidized in this voltaic cell?

Zn electrode in
$1\ M$ ZnSO$_4$ solution

Cu electrode in
$1\ M$ CuSO$_4$ solution

Solutions in contact with each other through porous glass disc

▲ **FIGURE 20.4   A Cu-Zn voltaic cell based on the reaction in Equation 20.7.**

The two solid metals connected by the external circuit are called *electrodes*. By definition, the electrode at which oxidation occurs is the **anode** and the electrode at which reduction occurs is the **cathode**.* The electrodes can be made of materials that participate in the reaction, as in the present example. Over the course of the reaction, the Zn electrode gradually disappears and the copper electrode gains mass. More typically, the electrodes are made of a conducting material, such as platinum or graphite, that does not gain or lose mass during the reaction but serves as a surface at which electrons are transferred.

Each compartment of a voltaic cell is called a *half-cell*. One half-cell is the site of the oxidation half-reaction, and the other is the site of the reduction half-reaction. In our present example, Zn is oxidized and $Cu^{2+}$ is reduced:

Anode (oxidation half-reaction) $\qquad\qquad\qquad Zn(s) \longrightarrow Zn^{2+}(aq) + 2\,e^{-}$

Cathode (reduction half-reaction) $\quad Cu^{2+}(aq) + 2\,e^{-} \longrightarrow Cu(s)$

Electrons become available as zinc metal is oxidized at the anode. They flow through the external circuit to the cathode, where they are consumed as $Cu^{2+}(aq)$ is reduced. Because $Zn(s)$ is oxidized in the cell, the zinc electrode loses mass, and the concentration of the $Zn^{2+}$ solution increases as the cell operates. At the same time, the Cu electrode gains mass, and the $Cu^{2+}$ solution becomes less concentrated as $Cu^{2+}$ is reduced to $Cu(s)$.

For a voltaic cell to work, the solutions in the two half-cells must remain electrically neutral. As Zn is oxidized in the anode half-cell, $Zn^{2+}$ ions enter the solution, upsetting the initial $Zn^{2+}/SO_4^{2-}$ charge balance. To keep the solution electrically neutral, there must be some means for $Zn^{2+}$ cations to migrate out of the anode half-cell and for anions to migrate in. Similarly, the reduction of $Cu^{2+}$ at the cathode removes these cations from the solution, leaving an excess of $SO_4^{2-}$ anions in that half-cell. To maintain electrical neutrality, some of these anions must migrate out of the cathode half-cell, and positive ions must migrate in. In fact, no measurable electron flow occurs between electrodes unless a means is provided for ions to migrate through the solution from one half-cell to the other, thereby completing the circuit.

In Figure 20.4, a porous glass disc separating the two half-cells allows ions to migrate and maintain the electrical neutrality of the solutions. In ▼ **FIGURE 20.5**, a *salt bridge*

---

▲ **GO FIGURE**

How is electrical balance maintained in the left beaker as $Zn^{2+}$ ions are formed at the anode?

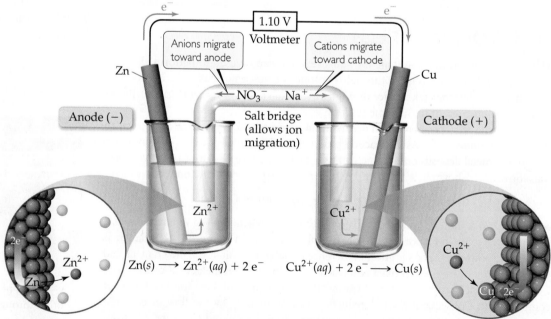

▲ **FIGURE 20.5** **A voltaic cell that uses a salt bridge to complete the electrical circuit.**

---

*To help remember these definitions, note that *anode* and *oxidation* both begin with a vowel, and *cathode* and *reduction* both begin with a consonant.

serves this purpose. The salt bridge consists of a U-shaped tube containing an electrolyte solution, such as $NaNO_3(aq)$, whose ions will not react with other ions in the voltaic cell or with the electrodes. The electrolyte is often incorporated into a paste or gel so that the electrolyte solution does not pour out when the U-tube is inverted. As oxidation and reduction proceed at the electrodes, ions from the salt bridge migrate into the two half-cells—cations migrating to the cathode half-cell and anions migrating to the anode half-cell—to neutralize charge in the half-cell solutions. Whichever device is used to allow ions to migrate between half-cells, *anions always migrate toward the anode and cations toward the cathode.*

▶ FIGURE 20.6 summarizes the various relationships in a voltaic cell. Notice in particular that *electrons flow from the anode through the external circuit to the cathode.* Because of this directional flow, the anode in a voltaic cell is labeled with a negative sign and the cathode is labeled with a positive sign. We can envision the electrons as being attracted to the positive cathode from the negative anode through the external circuit.

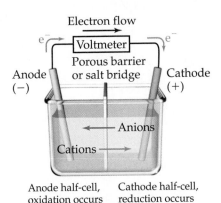

▲ FIGURE 20.6 **Summary of reactions occurring in a voltaic cell.** The half-cells can be separated by either a porous glass disc (as in Figure 20.4) or by a salt bridge (as in Figure 20.5).

---

### SAMPLE EXERCISE 20.4 | Describing a Voltaic Cell

The oxidation-reduction reaction

$$Cr_2O_7^{2-}(aq) + 14\,H^+(aq) + 6\,I^-(aq) \longrightarrow 2\,Cr^{3+}(aq) + 3\,I_2(s) + 7\,H_2O(l)$$

is spontaneous. A solution containing $K_2Cr_2O_7$ and $H_2SO_4$ is poured into one beaker, and a solution of KI is poured into another. A salt bridge is used to join the beakers. A metallic conductor that will not react with either solution (such as platinum foil) is suspended in each solution, and the two conductors are connected with wires through a voltmeter or some other device to detect an electric current. The resultant voltaic cell generates an electric current. Indicate the reaction occurring at the anode, the reaction at the cathode, the direction of electron migration, the direction of ion migration, and the signs of the electrodes.

#### SOLUTION

**Analyze** We are given the equation for a spontaneous reaction that takes place in a voltaic cell and a description of how the cell is constructed. We are asked to write the half-reactions occurring at the anode and at the cathode, as well as the directions of electron and ion movements and the signs assigned to the electrodes.

**Plan** Our first step is to divide the chemical equation into half-reactions so that we can identify the oxidation and the reduction processes. We then use the definitions of anode and cathode and the other terminology summarized in Figure 20.6.

**Solve** In one half-reaction, $Cr_2O_7^{2-}(aq)$ is converted into $Cr^{3+}(aq)$. Starting with these ions and then completing and balancing the half-reaction, we have

$$Cr_2O_7^{2-}(aq) + 14\,H^+(aq) + 6\,e^- \longrightarrow 2\,Cr^{3+}(aq) + 7\,H_2O(l)$$

In the other half-reaction, $I^-(aq)$ is converted to $I_2(s)$:

$$6\,I^-(aq) \longrightarrow 3\,I_2(s) + 6\,e^-$$

Now we can use the summary in Figure 20.6 to help us describe the voltaic cell. The first half-reaction is the reduction process (electrons on the reactant side of the equation). By definition, the reduction process occurs at the cathode. The second half-reaction is the oxidation process (electrons on the product side of the equation), which occurs at the anode.

The $I^-$ ions are the source of electrons, and the $Cr_2O_7^{2-}$ ions accept the electrons. Hence, the electrons flow through the external circuit from the electrode immersed in the KI solution (the anode) to the electrode immersed in the $K_2Cr_2O_7$–$H_2SO_4$ solution (the cathode). The electrodes themselves do not react in any way; they merely provide a means of transferring electrons from or to the solutions. The cations move through the solutions toward the cathode, and the anions move toward the anode. The anode (from which the electrons move) is the negative electrode, and the cathode (toward which the electrons move) is the positive electrode.

#### PRACTICE EXERCISE

The two half-reactions in a voltaic cell are

$$Zn(s) \longrightarrow Zn^{2+}(aq) + 2\,e^-$$

$$ClO_3^-(aq) + 6\,H^+(aq) + 6\,e^- \longrightarrow Cl^-(aq) + 3\,H_2O(l)$$

**(a)** Indicate which reaction occurs at the anode and which at the cathode. **(b)** Which electrode is consumed in the cell reaction? **(c)** Which electrode is positive?

*Answers:* **(a)** The first reaction occurs at the anode and the second reaction at the cathode. **(b)** The anode (Zn) is consumed in the cell reaction. **(c)** The cathode is positive.

## 20.4 | CELL POTENTIALS UNDER STANDARD CONDITIONS

Why do electrons transfer spontaneously from a Zn atom to a $Cu^{2+}$ ion, either directly as in Figure 20.3 or through an external circuit as in Figure 20.4? In a simple sense, we can compare the electron flow to the flow of water in a waterfall (▼ FIGURE 20.7). Water flows spontaneously over a waterfall because of a difference in potential energy between the top of the falls and the bottom. ∞ (Section 5.1) In a similar fashion, electrons flow spontaneously through an external circuit from the anode of a voltaic cell to the cathode because of a difference in potential energy. The potential energy of electrons is higher in the anode than in the cathode. Thus, electrons flow spontaneously toward the electrode with the more positive electrical potential.

The difference in potential energy per electrical charge (the *potential difference*) between two electrodes is measured in volts. One volt (V) is the potential difference required to impart 1 joule (J) of energy to a charge of 1 coulomb (C):

$$1\ V = 1\ \frac{J}{C}$$

Recall that one electron has a charge of $1.60 \times 10^{-19}$ C. ∞ (Section 2.2)

The potential difference between the two electrodes of a voltaic cell is called the **cell potential**, denoted $E_{cell}$. Because the potential difference provides the driving force that pushes electrons through the external circuit, we also call it the **electromotive** ("causing electron motion") **force**, or **emf**. Because $E_{cell}$ is measured in volts, it is also commonly called the *voltage* of the cell.

The cell potential of any voltaic cell is positive. The magnitude of the cell potential depends on the reactions that occur at the cathode and anode, the concentrations of reactants and products, and the temperature, which we will assume to be 25 °C unless otherwise noted. In this section we focus on cells that are operated at 25 °C under *standard conditions*. Recall from Table 19.2 that standard conditions include 1 $M$ concentrations for reactants and products in solution and 1 atm pressure for gaseous reactants and products. The cell potential under standard conditions is called either the **standard cell potential** or **standard emf** and is denoted $E^{\circ}_{cell}$. For the Zn-Cu voltaic cell in Figure 20.5, for example, the standard cell potential at 25 °C is +1.10 V:

$$Zn(s) + Cu^{2+}(aq, 1\ M) \longrightarrow Zn^{2+}(aq, 1\ M) + Cu(s) \quad E^{\circ}_{cell} = +1.10\ V$$

Recall that the superscript ° indicates standard-state conditions. ∞ (Section 5.7)

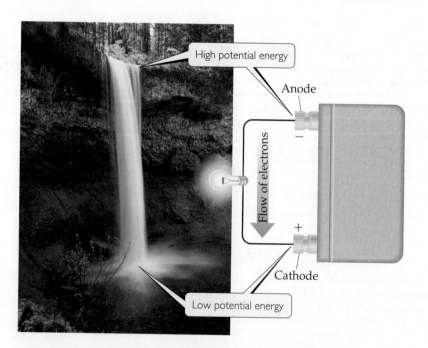

▶ FIGURE 20.7  **Water analogy for electron flow.**

⚠ **GIVE IT SOME THOUGHT**

If a standard cell potential is $E^\circ_{cell}$ = +0.85 V at 25 °C, is the redox reaction of the cell spontaneous?

## Standard Reduction Potentials

The standard cell potential of a voltaic cell, $E^\circ_{cell}$, depends on the particular cathode and anode half-cells. We could, in principle, tabulate the standard cell potentials for all possible cathode/anode combinations. However, it is not necessary to undertake this arduous task. Rather, we can assign a standard potential to each half-cell and then use these half-cell potentials to determine $E^\circ_{cell}$. The cell potential is the difference between two half-cell potentials. By convention, the potential associated with each electrode is chosen to be the potential for *reduction* at that electrode. Thus, standard half-cell potentials are tabulated for reduction reactions, which means they are **standard reduction potentials**, denoted $E^\circ_{red}$. The standard cell potential, $E^\circ_{cell}$, is the standard reduction potential of the cathode reaction, $E^\circ_{red}$ (cathode), *minus* the standard reduction potential of the anode reaction, $E^\circ_{red}$ (anode):

$$E^\circ_{cell} = E^\circ_{red} \text{ (cathode)} - E^\circ_{red} \text{ (anode)} \qquad [20.8]$$

It is not possible to measure the standard reduction potential of a half-reaction directly. If we assign a standard reduction potential to a certain reference half-reaction, however, we can then determine the standard reduction potentials of other half-reactions relative to that reference value. The reference half-reaction is the reduction of $H^+(aq)$ to $H_2(g)$ under standard conditions, which is assigned a standard reduction potential of exactly 0 V:

$$2\,H^+(aq, 1\,M) + 2\,e^- \longrightarrow H_2(g, 1\,atm) \quad E^\circ_{red} = 0\,V \qquad [20.9]$$

An electrode designed to produce this half-reaction is called a **standard hydrogen electrode** (SHE). An SHE consists of a platinum wire connected to a piece of platinum foil covered with finely divided platinum that serves as an inert surface for the reaction (▼ **FIGURE 20.8**). The SHE allows the platinum to be in contact with both 1 $M$ $H^+(aq)$ and a stream of hydrogen gas at 1 atm. The SHE can operate as either the anode or cathode of a cell, depending on the nature of the other electrode.

▶ **FIGURE 20.9** shows a voltaic cell using an SHE. The spontaneous reaction is the one shown in Figure 20.1, namely, oxidation of Zn and reduction of $H^+$:

$$Zn(s) + 2\,H^+(aq) \longrightarrow Zn^{2+}(aq) + H_2(g)$$

Pt atom   H$^+$ ion   H$_2$ molecule

Reduction

1 atm
H$_2$(g)

Pt wire

Pt

1 $M$ H$^+$

SHE as cathode
(H$^+$ reduced to H$_2$)

H$_2$ molecule   H$^+$ ion

Oxidation

SHE as anode
(H$_2$ oxidized to H$^+$)

◀ **FIGURE 20.8   The standard hydrogen electrode (SHE)** is used as a reference electrode.

**GO FIGURE**

**Why does Na⁺ migrate into the cathode half-cell as the cell reaction proceeds?**

▶ **FIGURE 20.9** **A voltaic cell using a standard hydrogen electrode (SHE).** The anode half-cell is Zn metal in a $Zn(NO_3)_2(aq)$ solution, and the cathode half-cell is the SHE in a $HNO_3(aq)$ solution.

$$Zn(s) \longrightarrow Zn^{2+}(aq) + 2\,e^- \qquad 2\,H^+(aq) + 2\,e^- \longrightarrow H_2(g)$$

When the cell is operated under standard conditions, the cell potential is +0.76 V. By using the standard cell potential ($E°_{cell} = 0.76$ V), the defined standard reduction potential of $H^+$ ($E°_{red} = 0$ V) and Equation 20.8, we can determine the standard reduction potential for the $Zn^{2+}/Zn$ half-reaction:

$$E°_{cell} = E°_{red}\,(\text{cathode}) - E°_{red}\,(\text{anode})$$

$$+0.76\text{ V} = 0\text{ V} - E°_{red}\,(\text{anode})$$

$$E°_{red}\,(\text{anode}) = -0.76\text{ V}$$

Thus, a standard reduction potential of −0.76 V can be assigned to the reduction of $Zn^{2+}$ to Zn:

$$Zn^{2+}(aq, 1\ M) + 2\,e^- \longrightarrow Zn(s) \qquad E°_{red} = -0.76\text{ V}$$

We write the reaction as a reduction even though the Zn reaction in Figure 20.9 is an oxidation. *Whenever we assign an electrical potential to a half-reaction, we write the reaction as a reduction.* Half-reactions, however, are reversible, being able to operate as either reductions or oxidations. Consequently, half-reactions are sometimes written using two arrows (⇌) between reactants and products, as in equilibrium reactions.

The standard reduction potentials for other half-reactions can be determined in a fashion analogous to that used for the $Zn^{2+}/Zn$ half-reaction. ▶ **TABLE 20.1** lists some standard reduction potentials; a more complete list is found in Appendix E. These standard reduction potentials, often called *half-cell potentials*, can be combined to calculate $E°_{cell}$ values for a large variety of voltaic cells.

**GIVE IT SOME THOUGHT**

For the half-reaction $Cl_2(g) + 2\,e^- \longrightarrow 2\,Cl^-(aq)$, what are the standard conditions for the reactant and product?

Because electrical potential measures potential energy per electrical charge, standard reduction potentials are intensive properties. ∞ (Section 1.3) In other words, if we increase the amount of substances in a redox reaction, we increase both the energy and the charges involved, but the ratio of energy (joules) to electrical charge (coulombs) remains constant (V = J/C). Thus, *changing the stoichiometric coefficient in a half-reaction does not affect the value of the standard reduction potential.* For example, $E°_{red}$ for the reduction of 10 mol $Zn^{2+}$ is the same as that for the reduction of 1 mol $Zn^{2+}$:

$$10\,Zn^{2+}(aq, 1\ M) + 20\,e^- \longrightarrow 10\,Zn(s) \quad E°_{red} = -0.76\text{ V}$$

## TABLE 20.1 • Standard Reduction Potentials in Water at 25 °C

| $E_{red}^{\circ}$ (V) | Reduction Half-Reaction |
| --- | --- |
| +2.87 | $F_2(g) + 2\,e^- \longrightarrow 2\,F^-(aq)$ |
| +1.51 | $MnO_4^-(aq) + 8\,H^+(aq) + 5\,e^- \longrightarrow Mn^{2+}(aq) + 4\,H_2O(l)$ |
| +1.36 | $Cl_2(g) + 2\,e^- \longrightarrow 2\,Cl^-(aq)$ |
| +1.33 | $Cr_2O_7^{2-}(aq) + 14\,H^+(aq) + 6\,e^- \longrightarrow 2\,Cr^{3+}(aq) + 7\,H_2O(l)$ |
| +1.23 | $O_2(g) + 4\,H^+(aq) + 4\,e^- \longrightarrow 2\,H_2O(l)$ |
| +1.06 | $Br_2(l) + 2\,e^- \longrightarrow 2\,Br^-(aq)$ |
| +0.96 | $NO_3^-(aq) + 4\,H^+(aq) + 3\,e^- \longrightarrow NO(g) + 2\,H_2O(l)$ |
| +0.80 | $Ag^+(aq) + e^- \longrightarrow Ag(s)$ |
| +0.77 | $Fe^{3+}(aq) + e^- \longrightarrow Fe^{2+}(aq)$ |
| +0.68 | $O_2(g) + 2\,H^+(aq) + 2\,e^- \longrightarrow H_2O_2(aq)$ |
| +0.59 | $MnO_4^-(aq) + 2\,H_2O(l) + 3\,e^- \longrightarrow MnO_2(s) + 4\,OH^-(aq)$ |
| +0.54 | $I_2(s) + 2\,e^- \longrightarrow 2\,I^-(aq)$ |
| +0.40 | $O_2(g) + 2\,H_2O(l) + 4\,e^- \longrightarrow 4\,OH^-(aq)$ |
| +0.34 | $Cu^{2+}(aq) + 2\,e^- \longrightarrow Cu(s)$ |
| 0 [defined] | $2\,H^+(aq) + 2\,e^- \longrightarrow H_2(g)$ |
| −0.28 | $Ni^{2+}(aq) + 2\,e^- \longrightarrow Ni(s)$ |
| −0.44 | $Fe^{2+}(aq) + 2\,e^- \longrightarrow Fe(s)$ |
| −0.76 | $Zn^{2+}(aq) + 2\,e^- \longrightarrow Zn(s)$ |
| −0.83 | $2\,H_2O(l) + 2\,e^- \longrightarrow H_2(g) + 2\,OH^-(aq)$ |
| −1.66 | $Al^{3+}(aq) + 3\,e^- \longrightarrow Al(s)$ |
| −2.71 | $Na^+(aq) + e^- \longrightarrow Na(s)$ |
| −3.05 | $Li^+(aq) + e^- \longrightarrow Li(s)$ |

## SAMPLE EXERCISE 20.5 Calculating $E_{red}^{\circ}$ from $E_{cell}^{\circ}$

For the Zn-$Cu^{2+}$ voltaic cell shown in Figure 20.5, we have

$$Zn(s) + Cu^{2+}(aq, 1\,M) \longrightarrow Zn^{2+}(aq, 1\,M) + Cu(s) \quad E_{cell}^{\circ} = 1.10\,V$$

Given that the standard reduction potential of $Zn^{2+}$ to $Zn(s)$ is −0.76 V, calculate the $E_{red}^{\circ}$ for the reduction of $Cu^{2+}$ to Cu:

$$Cu^{2+}(aq, 1\,M) + 2\,e^- \longrightarrow Cu(s)$$

### SOLUTION

**Analyze** We are given $E_{cell}^{\circ}$ and $E_{red}^{\circ}$ for $Zn^{2+}$ and asked to calculate $E_{red}^{\circ}$ for $Cu^{2+}$.

**Plan** In the voltaic cell, Zn is oxidized and is therefore the anode. Thus, the given $E_{red}^{\circ}$ for $Zn^{2+}$ is $E_{red}^{\circ}$ (anode). Because $Cu^{2+}$ is reduced, it is in the cathode half-cell. Thus, the unknown reduction potential for $Cu^{2+}$ is $E_{red}^{\circ}$ (cathode). Knowing $E_{cell}^{\circ}$ and $E_{red}^{\circ}$ (anode), we can use Equation 20.8 to solve for $E_{red}^{\circ}$ (cathode).

**Solve**

$$E_{cell}^{\circ} = E_{red}^{\circ}\,(cathode) - E_{red}^{\circ}\,(anode)$$

$$1.10\,V = E_{red}^{\circ}\,(cathode) - (-0.76\,V)$$

$$E_{red}^{\circ}\,(cathode) = 1.10\,V - 0.76\,V = 0.34\,V$$

**Check** This standard reduction potential agrees with the one listed in Table 20.1.

**Comment:** The standard reduction potential for $Cu^{2+}$ can be represented as $E_{Cu^{2+}}^{\circ} = 0.34$ V and that for $Zn^{2+}$ as $E_{Zn^{2+}}^{\circ} = -0.76$ V. The subscript identifies the ion that is reduced in the reduction half-reaction.

Given $E^\circ_{red}$ values for the two electrodes in a standard voltaic cell, how do you determine which electrode is the cathode?

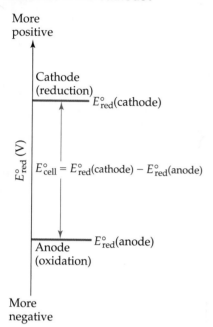

▲ **FIGURE 20.10** Graphical representation of standard cell potential of a voltaic cell.

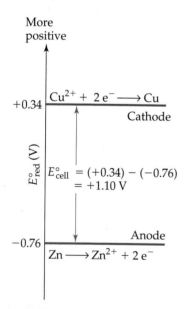

▲ **FIGURE 20.11** Half-cell potentials and standard cell potential for the Zn-Cu voltaic cell.

**PRACTICE EXERCISE**

The standard cell potential is 1.46 V for a voltaic cell based on the following half-reactions:

$$In^+(aq) \longrightarrow In^{3+}(aq) + 2\,e^-$$

$$Br_2(l) + 2\,e^- \longrightarrow 2\,Br^-(aq)$$

Using Table 20.1, calculate $E^\circ_{red}$ for the reduction of $In^{3+}$ to $In^+$.
**Answer:** $-0.40$ V

**SAMPLE EXERCISE 20.6** Calculating $E^\circ_{cell}$ from $E^\circ_{red}$

Use Table 20.1 to calculate $E^\circ_{cell}$ for the voltaic cell described in Sample Exercise 20.4, which is based on the reaction

$$Cr_2O_7^{2-}(aq) + 14\,H^+(aq) + 6\,I^-(aq) \longrightarrow 2\,Cr^{3+}(aq) + 3\,I_2(s) + 7\,H_2O(l)$$

**SOLUTION**

**Analyze** We are given the equation for a redox reaction and asked to use data in Table 20.1 to calculate the standard cell potential for the associated voltaic cell.

**Plan** Our first step is to identify the half-reactions that occur at the cathode and anode, which we did in Sample Exercise 20.4. Then we use Table 20.1 and Equation 20.8 to calculate the standard cell potential.

**Solve** The half-reactions are

$$Cathode:\quad Cr_2O_7^{2-}(aq) + 14\,H^+(aq) + 6\,e^- \longrightarrow 2\,Cr^{3+}(aq) + 7\,H_2O(l)$$

$$Anode:\quad 6\,I^-(aq) \longrightarrow 3\,I_2(s) + 6\,e^-$$

According to Table 20.1, the standard reduction potential for the reduction of $Cr_2O_7^{2-}$ to $Cr^{3+}$ is $+1.33$ V and the standard reduction potential for the reduction of $I_2$ to $I^-$ (the reverse of the oxidation half-reaction) is $+0.54$ V. We use these values in Equation 20.8:

$$E^\circ_{cell} = E^\circ_{red}(cathode) - E^\circ_{red}(anode) = 1.33\ V - 0.54\ V = 0.79\ V$$

Although we must multiply the iodide half-reaction by 3 to obtain a balanced equation, we do *not* multiply the $E^\circ_{red}$ value by 3. As we have noted, the standard reduction potential is an intensive property and so is independent of the stoichiometric coefficients.

**Check** The cell potential, 0.79 V, is a positive number. As noted earlier, a voltaic cell must have a positive potential.

**PRACTICE EXERCISE**

Using data in Table 20.1, calculate the standard emf for a cell that employs the overall cell reaction $2\,Al(s) + 3\,I_2(s) \longrightarrow 2\,Al^{3+}(aq) + 6\,I^-(aq)$.
**Answer:** $0.54\ V - (-1.66\ V) = 2.20\ V$

For each half-cell in a voltaic cell, the standard reduction potential provides a measure of the tendency for reduction to occur: *The more positive the value of $E^\circ_{red}$, the greater the tendency for reduction under standard conditions.* In any voltaic cell operating under standard conditions, the $E^\circ_{red}$ value for the reaction at the cathode is more positive than the $E^\circ_{red}$ value for the reaction at the anode. Thus, electrons flow spontaneously through the external circuit from the electrode with the more negative value of $E^\circ_{red}$ to the electrode with the more positive value of $E^\circ_{red}$.

The fact that the standard cell potential is the difference between the standard reduction potentials of cathode and anode is illustrated graphically in ◀ **FIGURE 20.10**. The more positive $E^\circ_{red}$ value identifies the cathode, and the difference between the two standard reduction potentials is the standard cell potential. ◀ **FIGURE 20.11** shows $E^\circ_{red}$ values for the two half-reactions in the Zn-Cu voltaic cell of Figure 20.5.

| SAMPLE EXERCISE 20.7 | Determining Half-Reactions at Electrodes and Calculating Cell Potentials |

A voltaic cell is based on the two standard half-reactions

$$Cd^{2+}(aq) + 2\,e^- \longrightarrow Cd(s)$$

$$Sn^{2+}(aq) + 2\,e^- \longrightarrow Sn(s)$$

Use data in Appendix E to determine (a) which half-reaction occurs at the cathode and which occurs at the anode and (b) the standard cell potential.

### SOLUTION

**Analyze** We have to look up $E^\circ_{red}$ for two half-reactions. We then use these values first to determine the cathode and the anode and then to calculate the standard cell potential, $E^\circ_{cell}$.

**Plan** The cathode will have the reduction with the more positive $E^\circ_{red}$ value, and the anode will have the less positive $E^\circ_{red}$. To write the half-reaction at the anode, we reverse the half-reaction written for the reduction, so that the half-reaction is written as an oxidation.

**Solve**
(a) According to Appendix E, $E^\circ_{red}(Cd^{2+}/Cd) = -0.403$ V and $E^\circ_{red}(Sn^{2+}/Sn) = -0.136$ V. The standard reduction potential for $Sn^{2+}$ is more positive (less negative) than that for $Cd^{2+}$. Hence, the reduction of $Sn^{2+}$ is the reaction that occurs at the cathode:

*Cathode:*  $\qquad Sn^{2+}(aq) + 2\,e^- \longrightarrow Sn(s)$

The anode reaction, therefore, is the loss of electrons by Cd:

*Anode:*  $\qquad Cd(s) \longrightarrow Cd^{2+}(aq) + 2\,e^-$

(b) The cell potential is given by the difference in the standard reduction potentials at the cathode and anode (Equation 20.8):

$$E^\circ_{cell} = E^\circ_{red}\text{ (cathode)} - E^\circ_{red}\text{ (anode)} = (-0.136\text{ V}) - (-0.403\text{ V}) = 0.267\text{ V}$$

Notice that it is unimportant that the $E^\circ_{red}$ values of both half-reactions are negative; the negative values merely indicate how these reductions compare to the reference reaction, the reduction of $H^+(aq)$.

**Check:**  The cell potential is positive, as it must be for a voltaic cell.

### PRACTICE EXERCISE

A voltaic cell is based on a $Co^{2+}/Co$ half-cell and an $AgCl/Ag$ half-cell.
(a) What half-reaction occurs at the anode? (b) What is the standard cell potential?

*Answers:* (a) $Co \longrightarrow Co^{2+} + 2\,e^-$; (b) $+0.499$ V

## Strengths of Oxidizing and Reducing Agents

Table 20.1 lists half-reactions in order of decreasing tendency to undergo reduction. For example, $F_2$ is located at the top of the table, having the most positive value for $E^\circ_{red}$. Thus, $F_2$ is the most easily reduced species in Table 20.1 and therefore the strongest oxidizing agent listed.

Among the most frequently used oxidizing agents are the halogens, $O_2$, and oxyanions such as $MnO_4^-$, $Cr_2O_7^{2-}$, and $NO_3^-$, whose central atoms have high positive oxidation states. As seen in Table 20.1, all these species have large positive values of $E^\circ_{red}$ and therefore easily undergo reduction.

The lower the tendency for a half-reaction to occur in one direction, the greater the tendency for it to occur in the opposite direction. Thus, *the half-reaction with the most negative reduction potential in Table 20.1 is the one most easily reversed and run as an oxidation*. Being at the bottom of Table 20.1, $Li^+(aq)$ is the most difficult species in the list to reduce and is therefore the poorest oxidizing agent listed. Although $Li^+(aq)$ has little tendency to gain electrons, the reverse reaction, oxidation of $Li(s)$ to $Li^+(aq)$, is highly favorable. Thus, Li is the strongest reducing agent among the substances listed in Table 20.1. (Note that, because Table 20.1 lists half-reactions as reductions, only the substances on the reactant side of these equations can serve as oxidizing agents; only those on the product side can serve as reducing agents.)

Commonly used reducing agents include $H_2$ and the active metals, such as the alkali metals and the alkaline earth metals. Other metals whose cations have negative $E°_{red}$ values—Zn and Fe, for example—are also used as reducing agents. Solutions of reducing agents are difficult to store for extended periods because of the ubiquitous presence of $O_2$, a good oxidizing agent.

The information contained in Table 20.1 is summarized graphically in ▼ FIGURE 20.12. The reactants in half-reactions at the top of Table 20.1 are the most readily reduced species in the table and are therefore the strongest oxidizing agents. Thus, Figure 20.12 shows $F_2(g)$ as the strongest oxidizing agent (the position at the top of the red arrow). The products in half-reactions at the top of Table 20.1 are the most difficult to oxidize and are therefore the weakest reducing agents in the table. The reactants in half-reactions at the bottom of Table 20.1 are the most difficult to reduce and so are the weakest oxidizing agents. The products in half-reactions at the bottom of Table 20.1 are the most readily oxidized species in the table and so are the strongest reducing agents.

This inverse relationship between oxidizing and reducing strength is similar to the inverse relationship between the strengths of conjugate acids and bases. ∞ (Section 16.2 and Figure 16.3)

GO FIGURE

**Why is a strong oxidizing agent easy to reduce?**

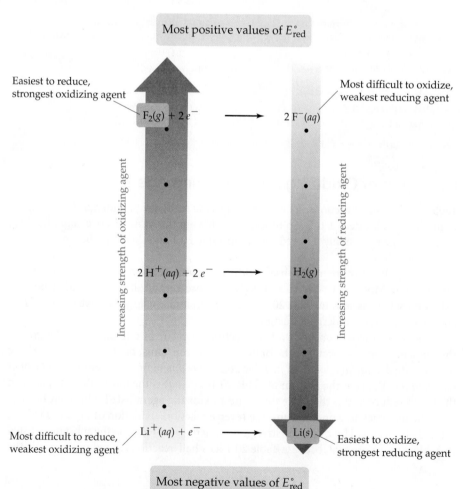

▶ FIGURE 20.12  **Relative strengths of oxidizing and reducing agents.** The standard reduction potentials in Table 20.1 are related to the ability of substances to serve as oxidizing or reducing agents. Species on the left side of the half-reactions can act as oxidizing agents, and those on the right side can act as reducing agents.

**SAMPLE EXERCISE 20.8** | Determining Relative Strengths of Oxidizing Agents

Using Table 20.1, rank the following ions in order of increasing strength as oxidizing agents: $NO_3^-(aq)$, $Ag^+(aq)$, $Cr_2O_7^{2-}(aq)$.

**SOLUTION**

**Analyze** We are asked to rank the abilities of several ions to act as oxidizing agents.

**Plan** The more readily an ion is reduced (the more positive its $E_{red}^\circ$ value), the stronger it is as an oxidizing agent.

**Solve** From Table 20.1, we have

$$NO_3^-(aq) + 4\,H^+(aq) + 3\,e^- \longrightarrow NO(g) + 2\,H_2O(l) \qquad E_{red}^\circ = +0.96\text{ V}$$

$$Ag^+(aq) + e^- \longrightarrow Ag(s) \qquad E_{red}^\circ = +0.80\text{ V}$$

$$Cr_2O_7^{2-}(aq) + 14\,H^+(aq) + 6\,e^- \longrightarrow 2\,Cr^{3+}(aq) + 7\,H_2O(l) \qquad E_{red}^\circ = +1.33\text{ V}$$

Because the standard reduction potential of $Cr_2O_7^{2-}$ is the most positive, $Cr_2O_7^{2-}$ is the strongest oxidizing agent of the three. The rank order is $Ag^+ < NO_3^- < Cr_2O_7^{2-}$.

**PRACTICE EXERCISE**

Using Table 20.1, rank the following species from the strongest to the weakest reducing agent: $I^-(aq)$, $Fe(s)$, $Al(s)$.

**Answer:** $Al(s) > Fe(s) > I^-(aq)$

# 20.5 | FREE ENERGY AND REDOX REACTIONS

We have observed that voltaic cells use spontaneous redox reactions to produce a positive cell potential. We can use this fact together with half-cell potentials to decide whether a given redox reaction is spontaneous. In doing so, it is useful to make Equation 20.8 more general so that we can see how it pertains to general redox reactions, not just reactions in voltaic cells:

$$E^\circ = E_{red}^\circ \text{ (reduction process)} - E_{red}^\circ \text{ (oxidation process)} \qquad [20.10]$$

In writing the equation this way, we have dropped the subscript "cell" to indicate that the calculated emf does not necessarily refer to a voltaic cell. Also, we have generalized the standard reduction potentials by using the general terms *reduction* and *oxidation* rather than the terms specific to voltaic cells, *cathode* and *anode*. We can now make a general statement about the spontaneity of a reaction and its associated emf, E: *A positive value of E indicates a spontaneous process; a negative value of E indicates a nonspontaneous process.* We use E to represent the emf under nonstandard conditions and $E^\circ$ to indicate the standard emf.

**SAMPLE EXERCISE 20.9** | Determining Spontaneity

Use Table 20.1 to determine whether the following reactions are spontaneous under standard conditions.

**(a)** $Cu(s) + 2\,H^+(aq) \longrightarrow Cu^{2+}(aq) + H_2(g)$

**(b)** $Cl_2(g) + 2\,I^-(aq) \longrightarrow 2\,Cl^-(aq) + I_2(s)$

**SOLUTION**

**Analyze** We are given two reactions and must determine whether each is spontaneous.

**Plan** To determine whether a redox reaction is spontaneous under standard conditions, we first need to write its reduction and oxidation half-reactions. We can then use the standard reduction potentials and Equation 20.10 to calculate the standard emf, $E^\circ$, for the reaction. If a reaction is spontaneous, its standard emf must be a positive number.

**Solve**

**(a)** For oxidation of Cu to $Cu^{2+}$ and reduction of $H^+$ to $H_2$, the half-reactions and standard reduction potentials are

| | | |
|---|---|---|
| *Reduction:* | $2\,H^+(aq) + 2\,e^- \longrightarrow H_2(g)$ | $E^\circ_{red} = 0\,V$ |
| *Oxidation:* | $Cu(s) \longrightarrow Cu^{2+}(aq) + 2\,e^-$ | $E^\circ_{red} = +0.34\,V$ |

Notice that for the oxidation, we use the standard reduction potential from Table 20.1 for the reduction of $Cu^{2+}$ to Cu. We now calculate $E^\circ$ by using Equation 20.10:

$$E^\circ = E^\circ_{red}\ (\text{reduction process}) - E^\circ_{red}\ (\text{oxidation process})$$
$$= (0\,V) - (0.34\,V) = -0.34\,V$$

Because $E^\circ$ is negative, the reaction is not spontaneous in the direction written. Copper metal does not react with acids in this fashion. The reverse reaction, however, *is* spontaneous and has a positive $E^\circ$ value:

$$Cu^{2+}(aq) + H_2(g) \longrightarrow Cu(s) + 2\,H^+(aq) \quad E^\circ = +0.34\,V$$

Thus, $Cu^{2+}$ can be reduced by $H_2$.

**(b)** We follow a procedure analogous to that in (a):

| | | |
|---|---|---|
| *Reduction:* | $Cl_2(g) + 2\,e^- \longrightarrow 2\,Cl^-(aq)$ | $E^\circ_{red} = +1.36\,V$ |
| *Oxidation:* | $2\,I^-(aq) \longrightarrow I_2(s) + 2\,e^-$ | $E^\circ_{red} = +0.54\,V$ |

In this case

$$E^\circ = (1.36\,V) - (0.54\,V) = +0.82\,V$$

Because the value of $E^\circ$ is positive, this reaction is spontaneous and could be used to build a voltaic cell.

## PRACTICE EXERCISE

Using the standard reduction potentials listed in Appendix E, determine which of the following reactions are spontaneous under standard conditions:

**(a)** $I_2(s) + 5\,Cu^{2+}(aq) + 6\,H_2O(l) \longrightarrow 2\,IO_3^-(aq) + 5\,Cu(s) + 12\,H^+(aq)$
**(b)** $Hg^{2+}(aq) + 2\,I^-(aq) \longrightarrow Hg(l) + I_2(s)$
**(c)** $H_2SO_3(aq) + 2\,Mn(s) + 4\,H^+(aq) \longrightarrow S(s) + 2\,Mn^{2+}(aq) + 3\,H_2O(l)$

**Answer:** Reactions (b) and (c) are spontaneous.

We can use standard reduction potentials to understand the activity series of metals. ∞ (Section 4.4) Recall that any metal in the activity series (Table 4.5) is oxidized by the ions of any metal below it. We can now recognize the origin of this rule based on standard reduction potentials. The activity series is based on the oxidation reactions of the metals, ordered from strongest reducing agent at the top to weakest reducing agent at the bottom. (Thus, the ordering is inverted relative to that in Table 20.1.) For example, nickel lies above silver in the activity series, making nickel the stronger reducing agent. Because a reducing agent is oxidized in any redox reaction, nickel is more easily oxidized than silver. In a mixture of nickel metal and silver cations, therefore, we expect a displacement reaction in which the silver ions are displaced in the solution by nickel ions:

$$Ni(s) + 2\,Ag^+(aq) \longrightarrow Ni^{2+}(aq) + 2\,Ag(s)$$

In this reaction Ni is oxidized and $Ag^+$ is reduced. Therefore, the standard emf for the reaction is

$$E^\circ = E^\circ_{red}\ (Ag^+/Ag) - E^\circ_{red}\ (Ni^{2+}/Ni)$$
$$= (+0.80\,V) - (-0.28\,V) = +1.08\,V$$

The positive value of $E^\circ$ indicates that the displacement of silver by nickel resulting from oxidation of Ni metal and reduction of $Ag^+$ is a spontaneous process. Remember that although we multiply the silver half-reaction by 2, the reduction potential is not multiplied.

## ⚠ GIVE IT SOME THOUGHT

Based on Table 4.5, which is the stronger reducing agent, Hg(l) or Pb(s)?

# Emf, Free Energy, and the Equilibrium Constant

The change in the Gibbs free energy, $\Delta G$, is a measure of the spontaneity of a process that occurs at constant temperature and pressure. ∞ (Section 19.5) The emf, $E$, of a redox reaction also indicates whether the reaction is spontaneous. The relationship between emf and the free-energy change is

$$\Delta G = -nFE \qquad [20.11]$$

In this equation, $n$ is a positive number without units that represents the number of moles of electrons transferred according to the balanced equation for the reaction, and $F$ is **Faraday's constant**, named after Michael Faraday (▶ FIGURE 20.13):

$$F = 96{,}485 \text{ C/mol} = 96{,}485 \text{ J/V-mol}$$

Faraday's constant is the quantity of electrical charge on 1 mol of electrons.

The units of $\Delta G$ calculated with Equation 20.11 are J/mol. As in Equation 19.19, we use "per mole" to mean per mole of reaction as indicated by the coefficients in the balanced equation. ∞ (Section 19.7)

Because both $n$ and $F$ are positive numbers, a positive value of $E$ in Equation 20.11 leads to a negative value of $\Delta G$. Remember: *A positive value of* E *and a negative value of* $\Delta G$ *both indicate a spontaneous reaction.* When the reactants and products are all in their standard states, Equation 20.11 can be modified to relate $\Delta G°$ and $E°$:

$$\Delta G° = -nFE° \qquad [20.12]$$

Because $\Delta G°$ is related to the equilibrium constant, $K$, for a reaction by the expression $\Delta G° = -RT \ln K$ (Equation 19.20), we can relate $E°$ to $K$ by solving Equation 20.12 for $E°$ and then substituting the Equation 19.20 expression for $\Delta G°$:

$$E° = \frac{\Delta G°}{-nF} = \frac{-RT \ln K}{-nF} = \frac{RT}{nF} \ln K \qquad [20.13]$$

▼ FIGURE 20.14 summarizes the relationships among $E°$, $\Delta G°$, and $K$.

▲ **FIGURE 20.13   Michael Faraday.** Faraday (1791–1867) was born in England, a child of a poor blacksmith. At the age of 14 he was apprenticed to a bookbinder who gave him time to read and to attend lectures. In 1812 he became an assistant in Humphry Davy's laboratory at the Royal Institution. He succeeded Davy as the most famous and influential scientist in England, making an amazing number of important discoveries, including his formulation of the quantitative relationships between electrical current and the extent of chemical reaction in electrochemical cells.

## GO FIGURE

**What does the variable *n* represent in the $\Delta G°$ and $E°$ equations?**

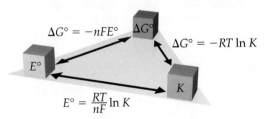

▲ **FIGURE 20.14   Relationships of $E°$, $\Delta G°$, and $K$.** Any one of these important parameters can be used to calculate the other two. The signs of $E°$ and $\Delta G°$ determine the direction that the reaction proceeds under standard conditions. The magnitude of $K$ determines the relative amounts of reactants and products in an equilibrium mixture.

---

**SAMPLE EXERCISE 20.10**   **Using Standard Reduction Potentials to Calculate $\Delta G°$ and $K$**

**(a)** Use the standard reduction potentials in Table 20.1 to calculate the standard free-energy change, $\Delta G°$, and the equilibrium constant, $K$, at 298 K for the reaction

$$4 \text{ Ag}(s) + \text{O}_2(g) + 4 \text{ H}^+(aq) \longrightarrow 4 \text{ Ag}^+(aq) + 2 \text{ H}_2\text{O}(l)$$

**(b)** Suppose the reaction in part (a) is written

$$2 \text{ Ag}(s) + \tfrac{1}{2} \text{O}_2(g) + 2 \text{ H}^+(aq) \longrightarrow 2 \text{ Ag}^+(aq) + \text{H}_2\text{O}(l)$$

What are the values of $E°$, $\Delta G°$, and $K$ when the reaction is written in this way?

## SOLUTION

**Analyze** We are asked to determine $\Delta G°$ and $K$ for a redox reaction, using standard reduction potentials.

**Plan** We use the data in Table 20.1 and Equation 20.10 to determine $E°$ for the reaction and then use $E°$ in Equation 20.12 to calculate $\Delta G°$. We can then use Equation 19.20, $\Delta G° = -RT \ln K$, to calculate $K$.

Alternatively, we can calculate $K$ using Equation 20.13, $E° = \dfrac{RT}{nF} \ln K$.

## Solve

**(a)** We first calculate $E°$ by breaking the equation into two half-reactions and obtaining $E°_{red}$ values from Table 20.1 (or Appendix E):

| | | |
|---|---|---|
| *Reduction:* | $O_2(g) + 4\,H^+(aq) + 4\,e^- \longrightarrow 2\,H_2O(l)$ | $E°_{red} = +1.23$ V |
| *Oxidation:* | $4\,Ag(s) \longrightarrow 4\,Ag^+(aq) + 4\,e^-$ | $E°_{red} = +0.80$ V |

Even though the second half-reaction has 4 Ag, we use the $E°_{red}$ value directly from Table 20.1 because emf is an intensive property.

Using Equation 20.10, we have

$$E° = (1.23\ \text{V}) - (0.80\ \text{V}) = 0.43\ \text{V}$$

The half-reactions show the transfer of four electrons. Thus, for this reaction $n = 4$. We now use Equation 20.12 to calculate $\Delta G°$:

$$\Delta G° = -nFE°$$
$$= -(4)(96{,}485\ \text{J/V-mol})(+0.43\ \text{V})$$
$$= -1.7 \times 10^5\ \text{J/mol} = -170\ \text{kJ/mol}$$

The positive value of $E°$ leads to a negative value of $\Delta G°$. The per mol part of the unit relates to the balanced equation, $4\,Ag(s) + O_2(g) + 4\,H^+(aq) \longrightarrow 4\,Ag^+(aq) + 2\,H_2O(l)$. Thus, $-170$ kJ is associated with 4 mol Ag, 1 mol $O_2$ and 4 mol $H^+$, and so forth, corresponding to the coefficients in the balanced equation.

Now we need to calculate the equilibrium constant, $K$, using $\Delta G° = RT \ln K$. Because $\Delta G°$ is a large negative number, which means the reaction is thermodynamically very favorable, we expect $K$ to be large.

$$\Delta G° = -RT \ln K$$
$$-1.7 \times 10^5\ \text{J/mol} = -(8.314\ \text{J/K mol})\,(298\ \text{K}) \ln K$$
$$\ln K = \frac{-1.7 \times 10^5\ \text{J/mol}}{-(8.314\ \text{J/K mol})(298\ \text{K})}$$
$$\ln K = 69$$
$$K = 9 \times 10^{29}$$

$K$ is indeed very large! This means that we expect silver metal to oxidize in acidic aqueous environments, in air, to $Ag^+$.

Notice that the emf calculated for the reaction was $E° = 0.43$ V, which is easy to measure. Directly measuring such a large equilibrium constant by measuring reactant and product concentrations at equilibrium, on the other hand, would be very difficult.

**(b)** The overall equation is the same as that in part (a), multiplied by $\frac{1}{2}$. The half-reactions are

| | | |
|---|---|---|
| *Reduction:* | $\frac{1}{2}\,O_2(g) + 2\,H^+(aq) + 2\,e^- \longrightarrow H_2O(l)$ | $E°_{red} = +1.23$ V |
| *Oxidation:* | $2\,Ag(s) \longrightarrow 2\,Ag^+(aq) + 2\,e^-$ | $E°_{red} = +0.80$ V |

The values of $E°_{red}$ are the same as they were in part (a); they are not changed by multiplying the half-reactions by $\frac{1}{2}$. Thus, $E°$ has the same value as in part (a):

$$E° = +0.43\ \text{V}$$

Notice, though, that the value of $n$ has changed to $n = 2$, which is one-half the value in part (a). Thus, $\Delta G°$ is half as large as in part (a):

$$\Delta G° = -(2)(96{,}485\ \text{J/V-mol})(+0.43\ \text{V}) = -83\ \text{kJ/mol}$$

The value of $\Delta G°$ is half that in part (a) because the coefficients in the chemical equation are half those in (a).

Now we can calculate $K$ as before:

$$-8.3 \times 10^4\ \text{J/mol} = -(8.314\ \text{J/K mol})(298\ \text{K}) \ln K$$
$$K = 4 \times 10^{14}$$

**Comment** $E°$ is an *intensive* quantity, so multiplying a chemical equation by a certain factor will not affect the value of $E°$. Multiplying an equation will change the value of $n$, however, and hence the value of $\Delta G°$. The change in free energy, in units of J/mol of reaction as written, is an *extensive* quantity. The equilibrium constant is also an extensive quantity.

**PRACTICE EXERCISE**

For the reaction

$$3 Ni^{2+}(aq) + 2 Cr(OH)_3(s) + 10 OH^-(aq) \longrightarrow 3 Ni(s) + 2 CrO_4{}^{2-}(aq) + 8 H_2O(l)$$

**(a)** What is the value of $n$? **(b)** Use the data in Appendix E to calculate $\Delta G°$. **(c)** Calculate $K$ at $T = 298$ K.
***Answers:*** **(a)** 6, **(b)** +87 kJ/mol, **(c)** $K = 6 \times 10^{-16}$

---

## A CLOSER LOOK

### ELECTRICAL WORK

For any spontaneous process, $\Delta G$ is a measure of the maximum useful work, $w_{max}$, that can be extracted from the process: $\Delta G = w_{max}$. ∞ (Section 19.5) Because $\Delta G = -nFE$, the maximum useful electrical work obtainable from a voltaic cell is

$$w_{max} = -nFE_{cell} \qquad [20.14]$$

Because cell emf, $E_{cell}$, is always positive for a voltaic cell, $w_{max}$ is negative, indicating that work is done *by* a system *on* its surroundings, as we expect for a voltaic cell. ∞ (Section 5.2)

As Equation 20.14 shows, the more charge a voltaic cell moves through a circuit (that is, the larger $nF$ is) and the larger the emf pushing the electrons through the circuit (that is, the larger $E_{cell}$ is), the more work the cell can accomplish. In Sample Exercise 20.10, we calculated $\Delta G° = -170$ kJ/mol for the reaction $4 Ag(s) + O_2(g) + 4 H^+(aq) \longrightarrow 4 Ag^+(aq) + 2 H_2O(l)$. Thus, a voltaic cell utilizing this reaction could perform a maximum of 170 kJ of work in consuming 4 mol Ag, 1 mol $O_2$, and 4 mol $H^+$.

If a reaction is not spontaneous, $\Delta G$ is positive and $E$ is negative. To force a nonspontaneous reaction to occur in an electrochemical cell, we need to apply an external potential, $E_{ext}$, that exceeds $|E_{cell}|$. For example, if a nonspontaneous process has $E = -0.9$ V, then the external potential $E_{ext}$ must be greater than $+0.9$ V in order for the process to occur. We will examine such nonspontaneous processes in Section 20.9.

Electrical work can be expressed in energy units of watts times time. The *watt* (W) is a unit of electrical power (that is, rate of energy expenditure):

$$1 W = 1 J/s$$

Thus, a watt-second is a joule. The unit employed by electric utilities is the kilowatt-hour (kWh), which equals $3.6 \times 10^6$ J:

$$1 \text{ kWh} = (1000 \text{ W})(1 \text{ hr})\left(\frac{3600 \text{ s}}{1 \text{ hr}}\right)\left(\frac{1 \text{ J/s}}{1 \text{ W}}\right) = 3.6 \times 10^6 \text{ J}$$

*RELATED EXERCISES:* 20.59, 20.60

---

## 20.6 | CELL POTENTIALS UNDER NONSTANDARD CONDITIONS

We have seen how to calculate the emf of a cell when the reactants and products are under standard conditions. As a voltaic cell is discharged, however, reactants are consumed and products are generated, so concentrations change. The emf progressively drops until $E = 0$, at which point we say the cell is "dead." In this section we examine how the emf generated under nonstandard conditions can be calculated by using an equation first derived by Walther Nernst (1864–1941), a German chemist who established many of the theoretical foundations of electrochemistry.

### The Nernst Equation

The effect of concentration on cell emf can be obtained from the effect of concentration on free-energy change. ∞ (Section 19.7) Recall that the free-energy change for any chemical reaction, $\Delta G$, is related to the standard free-energy change for the reaction, $\Delta G°$:

$$\Delta G = \Delta G° + RT \ln Q \qquad [20.15]$$

The quantity $Q$ is the reaction quotient, which has the form of the equilibrium-constant expression except that the concentrations are those that exist in the reaction mixture at a given moment. ∞ (Section 15.6)

Substituting $\Delta G = -nFE$ (Equation 20.11) into Equation 20.15 gives

$$-nFE = -nFE° + RT \ln Q$$

Solving this equation for $E$ gives the **Nernst equation:**

$$E = E° - \frac{RT}{nF} \ln Q \qquad [20.16]$$

This equation is customarily expressed in terms of the base-10 logarithm:

$$E = E° - \frac{2.303\, RT}{nF} \log Q \qquad [20.17]$$

At $T = 298$ K the quantity $2.303\, RT/F$ equals 0.0592, with units of volts, and so the Nernst equation simplifies to

$$E = E° - \frac{0.0592\text{ V}}{n} \log Q \qquad (T = 298 \text{ K}) \qquad [20.18]$$

We can use this equation to find the emf $E$ produced by a cell under nonstandard conditions or to determine the concentration of a reactant or product by measuring $E$ for the cell. For example, consider the following reaction:

$$Zn(s) + Cu^{2+}(aq) \longrightarrow Zn^{2+}(aq) + Cu(s)$$

In this case $n = 2$ (two electrons are transferred from Zn to $Cu^{2+}$), and the standard emf is $+1.10$ V (Section 20.4). Thus, at 298 K the Nernst equation gives

$$E = 1.10 \text{ V} - \frac{0.0592\text{ V}}{2} \log \frac{[Zn^{2+}]}{[Cu^{2+}]} \qquad [20.19]$$

Recall that pure solids are excluded from the expression for $Q$. ∞ (Section 15.6) According to Equation 20.19, the emf increases as $[Cu^{2+}]$ increases and as $[Zn^{2+}]$ decreases. For example, when $[Cu^{2+}]$ is 5.0 $M$ and $[Zn^{2+}]$ is 0.050 $M$, we have

$$E = 1.10 \text{ V} - \frac{0.0592\text{ V}}{2} \log \left( \frac{0.050}{5.0} \right)$$

$$= 1.10 \text{ V} - \frac{0.0592\text{ V}}{2} (-2.00) = 1.16 \text{ V}$$

Thus, increasing the concentration of reactant $Cu^{2+}$ and decreasing the concentration of product $Zn^{2+}$ relative to standard conditions increases the emf of the cell relative to standard conditions ($E° = +1.10$ V).

The Nernst equation helps us understand why the emf of a voltaic cell drops as the cell discharges. As reactants are converted to products, the value of $Q$ increases, so the value of $E$ decreases, eventually reaching $E = 0$. Because $\Delta G = -nFE$ (Equation 20.11), it follows that $\Delta G = 0$ when $E = 0$. Recall that a system is at equilibrium when $\Delta G = 0$. ∞ (Section 19.7) Thus, when $E = 0$, the cell reaction has reached equilibrium, and no net reaction occurs.

In general, increasing the concentration of reactants or decreasing the concentration of products increases the driving force for the reaction, resulting in a higher emf. Conversely, decreasing the concentration of reactants or increasing the concentration of products causes the emf to decrease from its value under standard conditions.

---

**SAMPLE EXERCISE 20.11** | **Cell Potential under Nonstandard Conditions**

Calculate the emf at 298 K generated by a voltaic cell in which the reaction is

$$Cr_2O_7^{2-}(aq) + 14\,H^+(aq) + 6\,I^-(aq) \longrightarrow 2\,Cr^{3+}(aq) + 3\,I_2(s) + 7\,H_2O(l)$$

when $[Cr_2O_7^{2-}] = 2.0$ $M$, $[H^+] = 1.0$ $M$, $[I^-] = 1.0$ $M$, and $[Cr^{3+}] = 1.0 \times 10^{-5}$ $M$.

**SOLUTION**

**Analyze** We are given a chemical equation for a voltaic cell and the concentrations of reactants and products under which it operates. We are asked to calculate the emf of the cell under these nonstandard conditions.

**Plan** To calculate the emf of a cell under nonstandard conditions, we use the Nernst equation in the form of Equation 20.18.

**Solve** We calculate $E°$ for the cell from standard reduction potentials (Table 20.1 or Appendix E). The standard emf for this reaction was calculated in Sample Exercise 20.6: $E° = 0.79$ V. As that exercise shows, six electrons are transferred from reducing agent to oxidizing agent, so $n = 6$. The reaction quotient, $Q$, is

$$Q = \frac{[Cr^{3+}]^2}{[Cr_2O_7^{2-}][H^+]^{14}[I^-]^6} = \frac{(1.0 \times 10^{-5})^2}{(2.0)(1.0)^{14}(1.0)^6} = 5.0 \times 10^{-11}$$

Using Equation 20.18, we have

$$E = 0.79 \text{ V} - \left(\frac{0.0592 \text{ V}}{6}\right)\log(5.0 \times 10^{-11})$$

$$= 0.79 \text{ V} - \left(\frac{0.0592 \text{ V}}{6}\right)(-10.30)$$

$$= 0.79 \text{ V} + 0.10 \text{ V} = 0.89 \text{ V}$$

**Check** This result is qualitatively what we expect: Because the concentration of $Cr_2O_7^{2-}$ (a reactant) is greater than 1 $M$ and the concentration of $Cr^{3+}$ (a product) is less than 1 $M$, the emf is greater than $E°$. Because $Q$ is about $10^{-10}$, $\log Q$ is about $-10$. Thus, the correction to $E°$ is about $0.06 \times 10/6$, which is 0.1, in agreement with the more detailed calculation.

**PRACTICE EXERCISE**

Calculate the emf generated by the cell described in the practice exercise accompanying Sample Exercise 20.6 when $[Al^{3+}] = 4.0 \times 10^{-3}$ $M$ and $[I^-] = 0.010$ $M$.

**Answer:** $E = +2.36$ V

---

**SAMPLE EXERCISE 20.12** | **Calculating Concentrations in a Voltaic Cell**

If the potential of a Zn-$H^+$ cell (like that in Figure 20.9) is 0.45 V at 25 °C when $[Zn^{2+}] = 1.0$ $M$ and $P_{H_2} = 1.0$ atm, what is the $H^+$ concentration?

**SOLUTION**

**Analyze** We are given a description of a voltaic cell, its emf, and the concentration of $Zn^{2+}$ and the partial pressure of $H_2$ (both products in the cell reaction). We are asked to calculate the concentration of $H^+$, a reactant.

**Plan** We write the equation for the cell reaction and use standard reduction potentials to calculate $E°$ for the reaction. After determining the value of $n$ from our reaction equation, we solve the Nernst equation, Equation 20.18, for $Q$. Finally, we use the equation for the cell reaction to write an expression for $Q$ that contains $[H^+]$ to determine $[H^+]$.

**Solve** The cell reaction is

$$Zn(s) + 2 H^+(aq) \longrightarrow Zn^{2+}(aq) + H_2(g)$$

The standard emf is

$$E° = E°_{red} \text{ (reduction)} - E°_{red} \text{ (oxidation)}$$
$$= 0 \text{ V} - (-0.76 \text{ V}) = +0.76 \text{ V}$$

Because each Zn atom loses two electrons,

$$n = 2$$

Using Equation 20.18, we can solve for $Q$:

$$0.45 \text{ V} = 0.76 \text{ V} - \frac{0.0592 \text{ V}}{2}\log Q$$
$$Q = 10^{10.5} = 3 \times 10^{10}$$

$Q$ has the form of the equilibrium constant for the reaction:

$$Q = \frac{[Zn^{2+}]P_{H_2}}{[H^+]^2} = \frac{(1.0)(1.0)}{[H^+]^2} = 3 \times 10^{10}$$

Solving for $[H^+]$, we have

$$[H^+]^2 = \frac{1.0}{3 \times 10^{10}} = 3 \times 10^{-11}$$
$$[H^+] = \sqrt{3 \times 10^{-11}} = 6 \times 10^{-6} M$$

**Comment** A voltaic cell whose cell reaction involves $H^+$ can be used to measure $[H^+]$ or pH. A pH meter is a specially designed voltaic cell with a voltmeter calibrated to read pH directly. ∞ (Section 16.4)

**PRACTICE EXERCISE**

What is the pH of the solution in the cathode half-cell in Figure 20.9 when $P_{H_2} = 1.0$ atm, $[Zn^{2+}]$ in the anode half-cell is 0.10 $M$, and the cell emf is 0.542 V?

**Answer:** pH = 4.23 (using data from Appendix E to obtain $E°$ to three significant figures)

## Concentration Cells

In the voltaic cells we have looked at thus far, the reactive species at the anode has been different from the reactive species at the cathode. Cell emf depends on concentration, however, so a voltaic cell can be constructed using the *same* species in both half-cells as long as the concentrations are different. A cell based solely on the emf generated because of a difference in a concentration is called a **concentration cell**.

An example of a concentration cell is diagrammed in ▼ **FIGURE 20.15**(a). One half-cell consists of a strip of nickel metal immersed in a $1.00 \times 10^{-3} M$ solution of $Ni^{2+}(aq)$. The other half-cell also has an $Ni(s)$ electrode, but it is immersed in a $1.00 M$ solution of $Ni^{2+}(aq)$. The two half-cells are connected by a salt bridge and by an external wire running through a voltmeter. The half-cell reactions are the reverse of each other:

| | | |
|---|---|---|
| Anode: | $Ni(s) \longrightarrow Ni^{2+}(aq) + 2 e^-$ | $E^{\circ}_{red} = -0.28$ V |
| Cathode: | $Ni^{2+}(aq) + 2 e^- \longrightarrow Ni(s)$ | $E^{\circ}_{red} = -0.28$ V |

Although the *standard* emf for this cell is zero,

$$E^{\circ}_{cell} = E^{\circ}_{red} \text{(cathode)} - E^{\circ}_{red} \text{(anode)} = (-0.28 \text{ V}) - (-0.28 \text{ V}) = 0 \text{ V}$$

the cell operates under *nonstandard* conditions because the concentration of $Ni^{2+}(aq)$ is not 1 $M$ in both half-cells. In fact, the cell operates until $[Ni^{2+}]_{anode} = [Ni^{2+}]_{cathode}$. Oxidation of $Ni(s)$ occurs in the half-cell containing the more dilute solution, which means this is the anode of the cell. Reduction of $Ni^{2+}(aq)$ occurs in the half-cell containing the more concentrated solution, making it the cathode. The *overall* cell reaction is therefore

| | |
|---|---|
| Anode: | $Ni(s) \longrightarrow Ni^{2+}(aq, \text{dilute}) + 2 e^-$ |
| Cathode: | $Ni^{2+}(aq, \text{concentrated}) + 2 e^- \longrightarrow Ni(s)$ |
| Overall: | $Ni^{2+}(aq, \text{concentrated}) \longrightarrow Ni^{2+}(aq, \text{dilute})$ |

We can calculate the emf of a concentration cell by using the Nernst equation. For this particular cell, we see that $n = 2$. The expression for the reaction quotient for the overall reaction is $Q = [Ni^{2+}]_{dilute}/[Ni^{2+}]_{concentrated}$. Thus, the emf at 298 K is

$$E = E^{\circ} - \frac{0.0592 \text{ V}}{n} \log Q$$

$$= 0 - \frac{0.0592 \text{ V}}{2} \log \frac{[Ni^{2+}]_{dilute}}{[Ni^{2+}]_{concentrated}} = -\frac{0.0592 \text{ V}}{2} \log \frac{1.00 \times 10^{-3} M}{1.00 M}$$

$$= +0.0888 \text{ V}$$

---

**⚠ GO FIGURE**

Assuming that the solutions are made from $Ni(NO_3)_2$, how do the ions migrate as the cell operates?

[Ni²⁺] = 1.00 × 10⁻³ M   [Ni²⁺] = 1.00 M

[Ni²⁺] = 0.5 M   [Ni²⁺] = 0.5 M

(a)    (b)

▲ **FIGURE 20.15   Concentration cell based on the Ni²⁺-Ni cell reaction.** (a) Concentrations of Ni²⁺(aq) in the two half-cells are unequal, and the cell generates an electrical current. (b) The cell operates until [Ni²⁺(aq)] is the same in the two half-cells, at which point the cell has reached equilibrium and is "dead."

This concentration cell generates an emf of nearly 0.09 V even though $E° = 0$. The difference in concentration provides the driving force for the cell. When the concentrations in the two half-cells become the same, $Q = 1$ and $E = 0$.

The idea of generating a potential by a concentration difference is the basis for the operation of pH meters. It is also a critical aspect in biology. For example, nerve cells in the brain generate a potential across the cell membrane by having different concentrations of ions on the two sides of the membrane. The regulation of the heartbeat in mammals, as discussed in the following "Chemistry and Life" box, is another example of the importance of electrochemistry to living organisms.

## CHEMISTRY AND LIFE

### HEARTBEATS AND ELECTROCARDIOGRAPHY

The human heart is a marvel of efficiency and dependability. In a typical day an adult's heart pumps more than 7000 L of blood through the circulatory system, usually with no maintenance required beyond a sensible diet and lifestyle. We generally think of the heart as a mechanical device, a muscle that circulates blood via regularly spaced muscular contractions. However, more than two centuries ago, two pioneers in electricity, Luigi Galvani (1729–1787) and Alessandro Volta (1745–1827), discovered that the contractions of the heart are controlled by electrical phenomena, as are nerve impulses throughout the body. The pulses of electricity that cause the heart to beat result from a remarkable combination of electrochemistry and the properties of semipermeable membranes. ∞ (Section 13.5)

Cell walls are membranes with variable permeability with respect to a number of physiologically important ions (especially $Na^+$, $K^+$, and $Ca^{2+}$). The concentrations of these ions are different for the fluids inside the cells (the *intracellular fluid*, or ICF) and outside the cells (the *extracellular fluid*, or ECF). In cardiac muscle cells, for example, the concentrations of $K^+$ in the ICF and ECF are typically about 135 millimolar (m$M$) and 4 m$M$, respectively. For $Na^+$, however, the concentration difference between the ICF and ECF is opposite that for $K^+$; typically, $[Na^+]_{ICF} = 10$ m$M$ and $[Na^+]_{ECF} = 145$ m$M$.

The cell membrane is initially permeable to $K^+$ ions but is much less so to $Na^+$ and $Ca^{2+}$. The difference in concentration of $K^+$ ions between the ICF and ECF generates a concentration cell: Even though the same ions are present on both sides of the membrane, there is a potential difference between the two fluids that we can calculate using the Nernst equation with $E° = 0$. At physiological temperature (37 °C) the potential in millivolts for moving $K^+$ from the ECF to the ICF is

$$E = E° - \frac{2.30\,RT}{nF} \log \frac{[K^+]_{ICF}}{[K^+]_{ECF}}$$

$$= 0 - (61.5 \text{ mV}) \log\left(\frac{135 \text{ m}M}{4 \text{ m}M}\right) = -94 \text{ mV}$$

In essence, the interior of the cell and the ECF together serve as a voltaic cell. The negative sign for the potential indicates that work is required to move $K^+$ into the intracellular fluid.

Changes in the relative concentrations of the ions in the ECF and ICF lead to changes in the emf of the voltaic cell. The cells of the heart that govern the rate of heart contraction are called the *pacemaker cells*. The membranes of the cells regulate the concentrations of ions in the ICF, allowing them to change in a systematic way. The concentration changes cause the emf to change in a cyclic fashion, as shown

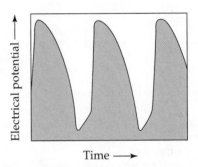

▲ **FIGURE 20.16  Changes in electrical potential in the human heart.** Variation of the electrical potential caused by changes of ion concentrations in the pacemaker cells of the heart.

in ▲ **FIGURE 20.16.** The emf cycle determines the rate at which the heart beats. If the pacemaker cells malfunction because of disease or injury, an artificial pacemaker can be surgically implanted. The artificial pacemaker contains a small battery that generates the electrical pulses needed to trigger the contractions of the heart.

During the late 1800s, scientists discovered that the electrical impulses that cause the contraction of the heart muscle are strong enough to be detected at the surface of the body. This observation formed the basis for *electrocardiography*, noninvasive monitoring of the heart by using a complex array of electrodes on the skin to measure voltage changes during heartbeats. A typical electrocardiogram is shown in ▼ **FIGURE 20.17.** It is quite striking that, although the heart's major function is the *mechanical* pumping of blood, it is most easily monitored by using the *electrical* impulses generated by tiny voltaic cells.

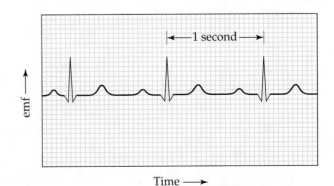

▲ **FIGURE 20.17  A typical electrocardiogram.** The printout records the electrical events monitored by electrodes attached to the body surface.

**SAMPLE EXERCISE 20.13** Determining pH Using a Concentration Cell

A voltaic cell is constructed with two hydrogen electrodes. Electrode 1 has $P_{H_2} = 1.00$ atm and an unknown concentration of $H^+(aq)$. Electrode 2 is a standard hydrogen electrode ($P_{H_2} = 1.00$ atm, $[H^+] = 1.00$ M). At 298 K the measured cell potential is 0.211 V, and the electrical current is observed to flow from electrode 1 through the external circuit to electrode 2. Calculate $[H^+]$ for the solution at electrode 1. What is the pH of the solution?

### SOLUTION

**Analyze** We are given the potential of a concentration cell and the direction in which the current flows. We also have the concentrations or partial pressures of all reactants and products except for $[H^+]$ in half-cell 1, which is our unknown.

**Plan** We can use the Nernst equation to determine $Q$ and then use $Q$ to calculate the unknown concentration. Because this is a concentration cell, $E^\circ_{cell} = 0$ V.

**Solve** Using the Nernst equation, we have

$$0.211 \text{ V} = 0 - \frac{0.0592 \text{ V}}{2} \log Q$$

$$\log Q = -(0.211 \text{ V})\left(\frac{2}{0.0592 \text{ V}}\right) = -7.13$$

$$Q = 10^{-7.13} = 7.4 \times 10^{-8}$$

Because electrons flow from electrode 1 to electrode 2, electrode 1 is the anode of the cell and electrode 2 is the cathode. The electrode reactions are therefore as follows, with the concentration of $H^+(aq)$ in electrode 1 represented with the unknown $x$:

| | | |
|---|---|---|
| *Electrode: 1* | $H_2(g, 1.00 \text{ atm}) \longrightarrow 2 H^+(aq, x M) + 2 e^-$ | $E^\circ_{red} = 0$ V |
| *Electrode: 2* | $2 H^+(aq; 1.00 M) + 2 e^- \longrightarrow H_2(g, 1.00 \text{ atm})$ | $E^\circ_{red} = 0$ V |
| *Overall:* | $2 H^+(aq; 1.00 M) \longrightarrow 2 H^+(aq, x M)$ | |

Thus,

$$Q = \frac{[H^+ (aq, x M)]^2}{[H^+ (aq, 1.00M)]^2}$$

$$= \frac{x^2}{(1.00)^2} = x^2 = 7.4 \times 10^{-8}$$

$$x = [H^+] = \sqrt{7.4 \times 10^{-8}} = 2.7 \times 10^{-4}$$

At electrode 1, therefore, the pH of the solution is

$$pH = -\log[H^+] = -\log(2.7 \times 10^{-4}) = 3.57$$

**Comment** The concentration of $H^+$ at electrode 1 is lower than that in electrode 2, which is why electrode 1 is the anode of the cell: The oxidation of $H_2$ to $H^+(aq)$ increases $[H^+]$ at electrode 1.

### PRACTICE EXERCISE

A concentration cell is constructed with two $Zn(s)-Zn^{2+}(aq)$ half-cells. In one half-cell $[Zn^{2+}] = 1.35$ M, and in the other $[Zn^{2+}] = 3.75 \times 10^{-4}$ M. **(a)** Which half-cell is the anode? **(b)** What is the emf of the cell?
**Answers:** **(a)** the half-cell in which $[Zn^{2+}] = 3.75 \times 10^{-4}$ M, **(b)** 0.105 V

1.5 V

3.0 V

1.5 V

## 20.7 | BATTERIES AND FUEL CELLS

A **battery** is a portable, self-contained electrochemical power source that consists of one or more voltaic cells. For example, the 1.5-V batteries used to power flashlights and many consumer electronic devices are single voltaic cells. Greater voltages can be achieved by using multiple cells, as in 12-V automotive batteries. When cells are connected in series (which means the cathode of one attached to the anode of another), the battery produces a voltage that is the sum of the voltages of the individual cells. Higher voltages can also be achieved by using multiple batteries in series (◄ **FIGURE 20.18**). Battery electrodes are marked following the convention of Figure 20.6—plus for cathode and minus for anode.

◄ **FIGURE 20.18 Combining batteries.** When batteries are connected in series, as in most flashlights, the total voltage is the sum of the individual voltages.

Although any spontaneous redox reaction can serve as the basis for a voltaic cell, making a commercial battery that has specific performance characteristics can require considerable ingenuity. The substances oxidized at the anode and reduced by the cathode determine the voltage, and the usable life of the battery depends on the quantities of these substances packaged in the battery. Usually a barrier analogous to the porous barrier of Figure 20.6 separates the anode and cathode half-cells.

Different applications require batteries with different properties. The battery required to start a car, for example, must be capable of delivering a large electrical current for a short time period, whereas the battery that powers a heart pacemaker must be very small and capable of delivering a small but steady current over an extended time period. Some batteries are *primary* cells, meaning they cannot be recharged and must be either discarded or recycled after the voltage drops to zero. A *secondary* cell can be recharged from an external power source after its voltage has dropped.

As we consider some common batteries, notice how the principles we have discussed so far help us understand these important sources of portable electrical energy.

## Lead-Acid Battery

A 12-V lead-acid automotive battery consists of six voltaic cells in series, each producing 2 V. The cathode of each cell is lead dioxide ($PbO_2$) packed on a lead grid (▶ **FIGURE 20.19**). The anode of each cell is lead. Both electrodes are immersed in sulfuric acid.

The reactions that occur during discharge are

*Cathode:* $PbO_2(s) + HSO_4^-(aq) + 3\,H^+(aq) + 2\,e^- \longrightarrow PbSO_4(s) + 2\,H_2O(l)$

*Anode:* $\underline{\qquad\qquad Pb(s) + HSO_4^-(aq) \longrightarrow PbSO_4(s) + H^+(aq) + 2\,e^-}$

$PbO_2(s) + Pb(s) + 2\,HSO_4^-(aq) + 2\,H^+(aq) \longrightarrow 2\,PbSO_4(s) + 2\,H_2O(l)$ $\qquad$ [20.20]

The standard cell potential can be obtained from the standard reduction potentials in Appendix E:

$E°_{cell} = E°_{red} \text{(cathode)} - E°_{red} \text{(anode)} = (+1.685\text{ V}) - (-0.356\text{ V}) = +2.041\text{V}$

The reactants Pb and $PbO_2$ are the electrodes. Because these reactants are solids, there is no need to separate the cell into half-cells; the Pb and $PbO_2$ cannot come into contact with each other unless one electrode touches another. To keep the electrodes from touching, wood or glass-fiber spacers are placed between them (Figure 20.19). Using a reaction whose reactants and products are solids has another benefit. Because solids are excluded from the reaction quotient $Q$, the relative amounts of $Pb(s)$, $PbO_2(s)$, and $PbSO_4(s)$ have no effect on the voltage of the lead storage battery, helping the battery maintain a relatively constant voltage during discharge. The voltage does vary somewhat with use because the concentration of $H_2SO_4$ varies with the extent of discharge. As Equation 20.20 indicates, $H_2SO_4$ is consumed during the discharge.

A major advantage of the lead-acid battery is that it can be recharged. During recharging, an external source of energy is used to reverse the direction of the cell reaction, regenerating $Pb(s)$ and $PbO_2(s)$:

$2\,PbSO_4(s) + 2\,H_2O(l) \longrightarrow PbO_2(s) + Pb(s) + 2\,HSO_4^-(aq) + 2\,H^+(aq)$

In an automobile the alternator provides the energy necessary for recharging the battery. Recharging is possible because $PbSO_4$ formed during discharge adheres to the electrodes. As the external source forces electrons from one electrode to the other, the $PbSO_4$ is converted to Pb at one electrode and to $PbO_2$ at the other.

## Alkaline Battery

The most common primary (nonrechargeable) battery is the alkaline battery (▶ **FIGURE 20.20**). The anode is powdered zinc metal immobilized in a gel in contact with a concentrated solution of KOH (hence, the name *alkaline* battery). The cathode is a mixture of

**GO FIGURE**

**What is the oxidation state of lead in the cathode of this battery?**

Lead grid filled with spongy lead (anode)

$H_2SO_4$ electrolyte

Lead grid filled with $PbO_2$ (cathode)

▲ **FIGURE 20.19** **A 12-V automotive lead-acid battery.** Each anode/cathode pair in this schematic cutaway produces a voltage of about 2 V. Six pairs of electrodes are connected in series, producing 12 V.

Separator

Anode (Zn plus KOH)

Cathode ($MnO_2$ plus graphite)

▲ **FIGURE 20.20** **Cutaway view of a miniature alkaline battery.**

$MnO_2(s)$ and graphite, separated from the anode by a porous fabric. The battery is sealed in a steel can to reduce the risk of any of the concentrated KOH escaping.

The cell reactions are complex but can be approximately represented as follows:

*Cathode:*      $2\ MnO_2(s) + 2\ H_2O(l) + 2\ e^- \longrightarrow 2\ MnO(OH)(s) + 2\ OH^-(aq)$

*Anode:*      $Zn(s) + 2\ OH^-(aq) \longrightarrow Zn(OH)_2(s) + 2\ e^-$

## Nickel-Cadmium, Nickel-Metal-Hydride, and Lithium-Ion Batteries

The tremendous growth in high-power-demand portable electronic devices in the last decade has increased the demand for lightweight, readily recharged batteries. One of the most common rechargeable batteries is the nickel-cadmium (nicad) battery. During discharge, cadmium metal is oxidized at the anode while nickel oxyhydroxide [$NiO(OH)(s)$] is reduced at the cathode:

*Cathode:*      $2\ NiO(OH)(s) + 2\ H_2O(l) + 2\ e^- \longrightarrow 2\ Ni(OH)_2(s) + 2\ OH^-(aq)$

*Anode:*      $Cd(s) + 2\ OH^-(aq) \longrightarrow Cd(OH)_2(s) + 2\ e^-$

As in the lead-acid battery, the solid reaction products adhere to the electrodes, which permits the electrode reactions to be reversed during charging. A single nicad voltaic cell has a voltage of 1.30 V. Nicad battery packs typically contain three or more cells in series to produce the higher voltages needed by most electronic devices.

Two drawbacks to nickel-cadmium batteries are that cadmium is both toxic and dense. Its use increases battery weight and provides an environmental hazard—roughly 1.5 billion nickel-cadmium batteries are produced annually, and these must eventually be recycled as they lose their ability to be recharged. Some of the problem has been alleviated by the development of the nickel-metal-hydride (NiMH) battery. The cathode reaction is the same as that for nickel-cadmium batteries, but the anode reaction is very different. The anode consists of a metal *alloy*, such as $ZrNi_2$, that has the ability to absorb hydrogen atoms. During oxidation at the anode, the hydrogen atoms lose electrons, and the resultant $H^+$ ions react with $OH^-$ ions to form $H_2O$, a process that is reversed during charging.

The current generation of hybrid gas–electric automobiles use NiMH batteries, which are recharged by the electric motor while braking. These batteries can last up to 8 years.

The newest rechargeable battery to receive large use in consumer devices is the lithium-ion (Li-ion) battery. You will find this battery in cell phones and laptop computers. Because lithium is a very light element, Li-ion batteries achieve a greater *energy density*—the amount of energy stored per unit mass—than nickel-based batteries. The technology of Li-ion batteries is based on the ability of $Li^+$ ions to be inserted into and removed from certain layered solids. For example, $Li^+$ ions can be inserted reversibly into layers of graphite (Figure 12.30). In most commercial cells, one electrode is graphite or some other carbon-based material, and the other is usually made of lithium cobalt oxide ($LiCoO_2$). When the cell is charged, cobalt ions are oxidized and $Li^+$ ions migrate into the graphite. During discharge, when the battery is producing electricity for use, the $Li^+$ ions spontaneously migrate from the graphite anode to the cathode, enabling electrons to flow through the external circuit. An Li-ion battery produces a maximum voltage of 3.7 V, considerably higher than typical 1.5-V alkaline batteries.

## Hydrogen Fuel Cells

The thermal energy released by burning fuels can be converted to electrical energy. The thermal energy may convert water to steam, for instance, which drives a turbine that in turn drives an electrical generator. Typically, a maximum of only 40% of the energy from combustion is converted to electricity in this manner; the remainder is lost as heat. The direct production of electricity from fuels by a voltaic cell could, in principle, yield a higher rate of conversion of chemical energy to electrical energy. Voltaic cells that perform this conversion using conventional fuels, such as $H_2$ and $CH_4$, are called **fuel cells**. Strictly speaking, fuel cells are *not* batteries because they are not self-contained systems—the fuel must be continuously supplied to generate electricity.

The most common fuel-cell systems involve the reaction of $H_2(g)$ and $O_2(g)$ to form $H_2O(l)$. These cells can generate electricity twice as efficiently as the best internal combustion engine. Under acidic conditions, the reactions are

*Cathode:* $\qquad O_2(g) + 4 H^+ + 4 e^- \longrightarrow 2 H_2O(l)$

*Anode:* $\qquad\qquad\qquad 2 H_2(g) \longrightarrow 4 H^+ + 4 e^-$

*Overall:* $\qquad 2 H_2(g) + O_2(g) \longrightarrow 2 H_2O(l)$

These cells employ hydrogen gas as the fuel and oxygen gas from air as the oxidant and generate about 1 V.

Fuel cells are often named for either the fuel or the electrolyte used. In the hydrogen-PEM fuel cell (the acronym PEM stands for either proton-exchange membrane or polymer-electrolyte membrane), the anode and cathode are separated by a membrane, which is permeable to protons but not to electrons (▶ **FIGURE 20.21**). The membrane therefore acts as a salt bridge. The electrodes are typically made from graphite.

The hydrogen-PEM cell operates at around 80 °C. At this temperature the electrochemical reactions would normally occur very slowly, and so a thin layer of platinum on each electrode catalyzes the reactions. Many fuel cells require much higher temperatures to operate.

In order to power a vehicle, multiple cells must be assembled into a fuel cell *stack*. The amount of power generated by a stack depends on the number and size of the fuel cells in the stack and on the surface area of the PEM.

Much fuel cell research today is directed toward improving electrolytes and catalysts and toward developing cells that use fuels such as hydrocarbons and alcohols, which are not as difficult to handle and distribute as hydrogen gas.

▲ **FIGURE 20.21 A hydrogen-PEM fuel cell.** The proton-exchange membrane (PEM) allows $H^+$ ions generated by $H_2$ oxidation at the anode to migrate to the cathode, where $H_2O$ is formed.

## CHEMISTRY PUT TO WORK

### Direct Methanol Fuel Cells

Even though the hydrogen fuel cell is highly developed, liquid methanol, $CH_3OH$, is a far more attractive fuel to store and transport than hydrogen gas. Furthermore, methanol is a clean-burning liquid, and its use would require only minor modifications to existing engines and to fuel-delivery infrastructure.

One of the intriguing aspects of methanol fuel is that manufacturing it could consume carbon dioxide, a source of global warming. ∞ (Section 18.2) Methanol can be made by combining $CO_2$ and $H_2$, although the process is presently costly. Imagine, though, that the synthesis can be improved and that the $CO_2$ used in the synthesis is captured from exhaust gases from power plants or even directly from the atmosphere. In such cases, the $CO_2$ released by subsequently burning the methanol would be canceled by the carbon dioxide captured to make it. Thus, the process would be

carbon neutral, meaning that it would not increase the concentration of $CO_2$ in the atmosphere. The prospect of a liquid fuel that could replace conventional fuels without contributing to the greenhouse effect has spurred considerable research to reduce the cost of methanol synthesis and to develop and improve methanol fuel cell technology.

A direct methanol fuel cell has been developed that is similar to the hydrogen-PEM fuel cell. The reactions in the cell are

*Cathode:* $\frac{3}{2} O_2(g) + 6 H^+ + 6 e^- \longrightarrow 3 H_2O(g)$

*Anode:* $\quad CH_3OH(l) + H_2O(g) \longrightarrow CO_2(g) + 6 H^+ + 6 e^-$

*Overall:* $\quad CH_3OH(g) + \frac{3}{2} O_2(g) \longrightarrow CO_2(g) + 2 H_2O(g)$

The direct methanol fuel cell is currently too expensive and too inefficient to be used in passenger cars. Nevertheless, small methanol fuel cells could appear in mobile devices such as computers or cell phones in the near future.

# 20.8 | CORROSION

In this section we examine the undesirable redox reactions that lead to **corrosion** of metals. Corrosion reactions are spontaneous redox reactions in which a metal is attacked by some substance in its environment and converted to an unwanted compound.

For nearly all metals, oxidation is thermodynamically favorable in air at room temperature. When oxidation of a metal object is not inhibited, it can destroy the object. Oxidation can form an insulating protective oxide layer, however, that prevents further reaction of the underlying metal. Based on the standard reduction potential for $Al^{3+}$, for example, we expect aluminum metal to be readily oxidized. The many aluminum soft-drink and beer cans that litter the environment are ample evidence, however, that aluminum undergoes only very slow chemical corrosion. The exceptional stability of this active metal in air is due to the formation of a thin protective coat of oxide—a hydrated form of $Al_2O_3$—on the metal surface. The oxide coat is impermeable to $O_2$ or $H_2O$ and so protects the underlying metal from further corrosion.

Magnesium metal is similarly protected, and some metal alloys, such as stainless steel, likewise form protective impervious oxide coats.

## Corrosion of Iron (Rusting)

The rusting of iron is a familiar corrosion process that carries a significant economic impact. Up to 20% of the iron produced annually in the United States is used to replace iron objects that have been discarded because of rust damage.

Rusting of iron requires both oxygen and water, and the process can be accelerated by other factors such as pH, presence of salts, contact with metals more difficult to oxidize than iron, and stress on the iron. The corrosion process involves oxidation and reduction, and the metal conducts electricity. Thus, electrons can move through the metal from a region where oxidation occurs to a region where reduction occurs, as in voltaic cells. Because the standard reduction potential for reduction of $Fe^{2+}(aq)$ is less positive than that for reduction of $O_2$, $Fe(s)$ can be oxidized by $O_2(g)$:

| | | |
|---|---|---|
| *Cathode:* | $O_2(g) + 4\,H^+(aq) + 4\,e^- \longrightarrow 2\,H_2O(l)$ | $E^\circ_{red} = 1.23\ V$ |
| *Anode:* | $Fe(s) \longrightarrow Fe^{2+}(aq) + 2\,e^-$ | $E^\circ_{red} = -0.44\ V$ |

A portion of the iron, often associated with a dent or region of strain, can serve as an anode at which Fe is oxidized to $Fe^{2+}$ (▼ **FIGURE 20.22**). The electrons produced in the oxidation migrate through the metal from this anodic region to another portion of the surface, which serves as the cathode where $O_2$ is reduced. The reduction of $O_2$ requires $H^+$, so lowering the concentration of $H^+$ (increasing the pH) makes $O_2$ reduction less favorable. Iron in contact with a solution whose pH is greater than 9 does not corrode.

The $Fe^{2+}$ formed at the anode is eventually oxidized to $Fe^{3+}$, which forms the hydrated iron(III) oxide known as rust:*

$$4\,Fe^{2+}(aq) + O_2(g) + 4\,H_2O(l) + 2\,xH_2O(l) \longrightarrow 2\,Fe_2O_3 \cdot xH_2O(s) + 8\,H^+(aq)$$

◢ **GO FIGURE**

**What is the oxidizing agent in this corrosion reaction?**

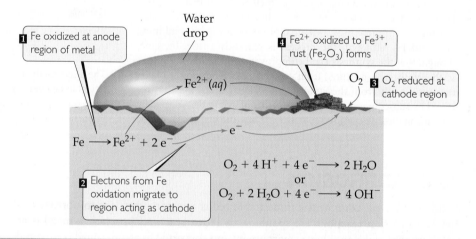

▶ **FIGURE 20.22** **Corrosion of iron in contact with water.** One region of the iron acts as the cathode and another region acts as the anode.

---

*Frequently, metal compounds obtained from aqueous solution have water associated with them. For example, copper(II) sulfate crystallizes from water with 5 mol of water per mole of $CuSO_4$. We represent this substance by the formula $CuSO_4 \cdot 5H_2O$. Such compounds are called hydrates. ∞ (Section 13.1) Rust is a hydrate of iron(III) oxide with a variable amount of water of hydration. We represent this variable water content by writing the formula $Fe_2O_3 \cdot xH_2O$.

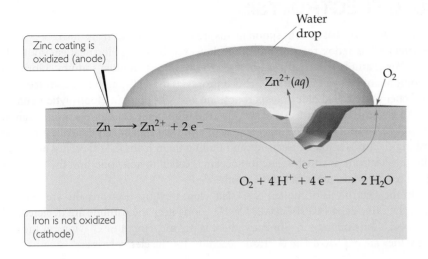

$$Zn \longrightarrow Zn^{2+} + 2\,e^-$$

$$O_2 + 4\,H^+ + 4\,e^- \longrightarrow 2\,H_2O$$

◀ **FIGURE 20.23 Cathodic protection of iron in contact with zinc.** The standard reduction potentials are $E^\circ_{red,\ Fe^{2+}} = -0.440$ V, $E^\circ_{red,\ Zn^{2+}} = -0.763$ V, making the zinc more readily oxidized.

Because the cathode is generally the area having the largest supply of $O_2$, rust often deposits there. If you look closely at a shovel after it has stood outside in the moist air with wet dirt adhered to its blade, you may notice that pitting has occurred under the dirt but that rust has formed elsewhere, where $O_2$ is more readily available. The enhanced corrosion caused by the presence of salts is usually evident on autos in areas where roads are heavily salted during winter. Like a salt bridge in a voltaic cell, the ions of the salt provide the electrolyte necessary to complete the electrical circuit.

## Preventing Corrosion of Iron

Objects made of iron are often covered with a coat of paint or another metal to protect against corrosion. Covering the surface with paint prevents oxygen and water from reaching the iron surface. If the coating is broken, however, and the iron exposed to oxygen and water, corrosion begins as the iron is oxidized.

With *galvanized iron*, which is iron coated with a thin layer of zinc, the iron is protected from corrosion even after the surface coat is broken. The standard reduction potentials are

$$Fe^{2+}(aq) + 2\,e^- \longrightarrow Fe(s) \quad E^\circ_{red} = -0.44\ V$$

$$Zn^{2+}(aq) + 2\,e^- \longrightarrow Zn(s) \quad E^\circ_{red} = -0.76\ V$$

Because $E^\circ_{red}$ for $Fe^{2+}$ is less negative (more positive) than $E^\circ_{red}$ for $Zn^{2+}$, $Zn(s)$ is more readily oxidized than $Fe(s)$. Thus, even if the zinc coating is broken and the galvanized iron is exposed to oxygen and water, as in ▲ **FIGURE 20.23**, the zinc serves as the anode and is corroded (oxidized) instead of the iron. The iron serves as the cathode at which $O_2$ is reduced.

Protecting a metal from corrosion by making it the cathode in an electrochemical cell is known as **cathodic protection**. The metal that is oxidized while protecting the cathode is called the *sacrificial anode*. Underground pipelines and storage tanks made of iron are often protected against corrosion by making the iron the cathode of a voltaic cell. For example, pieces of a metal that is more easily oxidized than iron, such as magnesium ($E^\circ_{red} = -2.37$ V), are buried near the pipe or storage tank and connected to it by wire (▶ **FIGURE 20.24**). In moist soil, where corrosion can occur, the sacrificial metal serves as the anode, and the pipe or tank experiences cathodic protection.

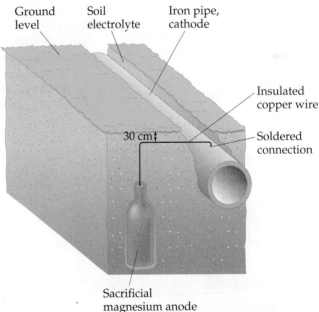

▲ **FIGURE 20.24 Cathodic protection of an iron pipe.** A mixture of gypsum, sodium sulfate, and clay surrounds the sacrificial magnesium anode to promote conductivity of ions.

> **GIVE IT SOME THOUGHT**
>
> Based on the values in Table 20.1, which of these metals could provide cathodic protection to iron: Al, Cu, Ni, Zn?

$$2\,Cl^- \longrightarrow Cl_2(g) + 2\,e^-$$

$$2\,Na^+ + 2\,e^- \longrightarrow 2\,Na(l)$$

▲ **FIGURE 20.25 Electrolysis of molten sodium chloride.** Pure NaCl melts at 801 °C.

# 20.9 | ELECTROLYSIS

Voltaic cells are based on spontaneous redox reactions. It is also possible for *nonspontaneous* redox reactions to occur, however, by using electrical energy to drive them. For example, electricity can be used to decompose molten sodium chloride into its component elements Na and $Cl_2$. Such processes driven by an outside source of electrical energy are called **electrolysis reactions** and take place in **electrolytic cells**.

An electrolytic cell consists of two electrodes immersed either in a molten salt or in a solution. A battery or some other source of electrical energy acts as an electron pump, pushing electrons into one electrode and pulling them from the other. Just as in voltaic cells, the electrode at which reduction occurs is called the cathode, and the electrode at which oxidation occurs is called the anode.

In the electrolysis of molten NaCl, $Na^+$ ions pick up electrons and are reduced to Na at the cathode ◀ **FIGURE 20.25**. As $Na^+$ ions near the cathode are depleted, additional $Na^+$ ions migrate in. Similarly, there is net movement of $Cl^-$ ions to the anode where they are oxidized. The electrode reactions for the electrolysis are

$$
\begin{array}{ll}
\textit{Cathode:} & 2\,Na^+(l) + 2\,e^- \longrightarrow 2\,Na(l) \\
\textit{Anode:} & \underline{\phantom{2\,Na^+(l) +}\ 2\,Cl^-(l) \longrightarrow Cl_2(g) + 2\,e^-} \\
& 2\,Na^+(l) + 2\,Cl^-(l) \longrightarrow 2\,Na(l) + Cl_2(g)
\end{array}
$$

Notice how the energy source is connected to the electrodes in Figure 20.25. The positive terminal is connected to the anode and the negative terminal is connected to the cathode, which forces electrons to move from the anode to the cathode.

Because of the high melting points of ionic substances, the electrolysis of molten salts requires very high temperatures. Do we obtain the same products if we electrolyze the aqueous solution of a salt instead of the molten salt? Frequently the answer is no because water itself might be oxidized to form $O_2$ or reduced to form $H_2$ rather than the ions of the salt.

In our examples of the electrolysis of NaCl, the electrodes are *inert*; they do not react but merely serve as the surface where oxidation and reduction occur. Several practical applications of electrochemistry, however, are based on *active* electrodes—electrodes that participate in the electrolysis process. *Electroplating*, for example, uses electrolysis to deposit a thin layer of one metal on another metal to improve beauty or resistance to corrosion. Examples include electroplating nickel or chromium onto steel and electroplating a precious metal like silver onto a less expensive one.

◀ **FIGURE 20.26** illustrates an electrolytic cell for electroplating nickel onto a piece of steel. The anode is a strip of nickel metal, and the cathode is the steel. The electrodes are immersed in a solution of $NiSO_4(aq)$. When an external voltage is applied, reduction occurs at the cathode. The standard reduction potential of $Ni^{2+}$ ($E^\circ_{red} = -0.28$ V) is less negative than that of $H_2O$ ($E^\circ_{red} = -0.83$ V), so $Ni^{2+}$ is preferentially reduced, depositing a layer of nickel metal on the steel cathode.

At the anode, the nickel metal is oxidized. To explain this behavior, we need to compare the substances in contact with the anode, $H_2O$ and $NiSO_4(aq)$, with the anode material, Ni. For the $NiSO_4(aq)$ solution, neither $Ni^{2+}$ nor $SO_4^{2-}$ can be oxidized (because both already have their elements in their highest possible oxidation state). The $H_2O$ solvent and the Ni atoms in the anode, however, can both undergo oxidation:

$$2\,H_2O(l) \longrightarrow O_2(g) + 4\,H^+(aq) + 4\,e^- \qquad E^\circ_{red} = +1.23\ V$$

$$Ni(s) \longrightarrow Ni^{2+}(aq) + 2\,e^- \qquad\qquad E^\circ_{red} = -0.28\ V$$

We saw in Section 20.4 that the half-reaction with the more negative $E^\circ_{red}$ undergoes oxidation more readily. (Remember Figure 20.12: The strongest reducing agents, which are the substances oxidized most readily, have the most negative $E^\circ_{red}$ values.)

| **Anode** | **Cathode** |
|---|---|
| $Ni(s) \longrightarrow Ni^{2+}(aq) + 2\,e^-$ | $Ni^{2+}(aq) + 2\,e^- \longrightarrow Ni(s)$ |

▲ **FIGURE 20.26 Electrolytic cell with an active metal electrode.** Nickel dissolves from the anode to form $Ni^{2+}(aq)$. At the cathode $Ni^{2+}(aq)$ is reduced and forms a nickel "plate" on the steel cathode.

Thus, it is the Ni(s), with its $E^\circ_{red} = -0.28$ V, that is oxidized at the anode rather than the $H_2O$. If we look at the overall reaction, it appears as if nothing has been accomplished. However, this is not true because Ni atoms are transferred from the Ni anode to the steel cathode, plating the steel with a thin layer of nickel atoms.

The standard emf for the overall reaction is

$$E^\circ_{cell} = E^\circ_{red} \text{ (cathode)} - E^\circ_{red} \text{ (anode)} = (-0.28 \text{ V}) - (-0.28 \text{ V}) = 0$$

Because the standard emf is zero, only a small emf is needed to cause the transfer of nickel atoms from one electrode to the other.

## Quantitative Aspects of Electrolysis

The stoichiometry of a half-reaction shows how many electrons are needed to achieve an electrolytic process. For example, the reduction of $Na^+$ to Na is a one-electron process:

$$Na^+ + e^- \longrightarrow Na$$

Thus, 1 mol of electrons plates out 1 mol of Na metal, 2 mol of electrons plate out 2 mol of Na metal, and so forth. Similarly, 2 mol of electrons are required to produce 1 mol of Cu from $Cu^{2+}$, and 3 mol of electrons are required to produce 1 mol of Al from $Al^{3+}$:

$$Cu^{2+} + 2 e^- \longrightarrow Cu$$
$$Al^{3+} + 3 e^- \longrightarrow Al$$

For any half-reaction, the amount of substance reduced or oxidized in an electrolytic cell is directly proportional to the number of electrons passed into the cell.

The quantity of charge passing through an electrical circuit, such as that in an electrolytic cell, is generally measured in *coulombs*. As noted in Section 20.5, the charge on 1 mol of electrons is 96,485 C. A coulomb is the quantity of charge passing a point in a circuit in 1 s when the current is 1 ampere (A). Therefore, the number of coulombs passing through a cell can be obtained by multiplying the current in amperes by the elapsed time in seconds.

$$\text{Coulombs} = \text{amperes} \times \text{seconds} \qquad [20.21]$$

▶ FIGURE 20.27 shows how the quantities of substances produced or consumed in electrolysis are related to the quantity of electrical charge used. The same relationships can also be applied to voltaic cells. In other words, electrons can be thought of as "reagents" in electrolysis reactions.

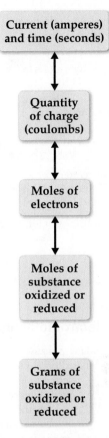

▲ FIGURE 20.27  Relationship between charge and amount of reactant and product in electrolysis reactions.

---

**SAMPLE EXERCISE 20.14**  **Relating Electrical Charge and Quantity of Electrolysis**

Calculate the number of grams of aluminum produced in 1.00 h by the electrolysis of molten $AlCl_3$ if the electrical current is 10.0 A.

**SOLUTION**

**Analyze**  We are told that $AlCl_3$ is electrolyzed to form Al and asked to calculate the number of grams of Al produced in 1.00 h with 10.0 A.

**Plan**  Figure 20.27 provides a road map for this problem. First, the product of the amperage and the time in seconds gives the number of coulombs of electrical charge being used (Equation 20.21). Second, the coulombs can be converted with Faraday's constant ($F = 96,485$ C/mol electrons) to tell us the number of moles of electrons being supplied. Third, reduction of 1 mol of $Al^{3+}$ to Al requires 3 mol of electrons. Hence, we can use the number of moles of electrons to calculate the number of moles of Al metal it produces. Finally, we convert moles of Al into grams.

**Solve**  First, we calculate the coulombs of electrical charge passed into the electrolytic cell:

$$\text{Coulombs} = \text{amperes} \times \text{seconds} = (10.0 \text{ A})(1.00 \text{ h})\left(\frac{3600 \text{ s}}{\text{h}}\right) = 3.60 \times 10^4 \text{ C}$$

Second, we calculate the number of moles of electrons that pass into the cell:

$$\text{Moles } e^- = (3.60 \times 10^4 \text{ C})\left(\frac{1 \text{ mol } e^-}{96,485 \text{ C}}\right) = 0.373 \text{ mol } e^-$$

Third, we relate number of moles of electrons to number of moles of aluminum formed, using the half-reaction for the reduction of $Al^{3+}$:

$$Al^{3+} + 3 e^- \longrightarrow Al$$

Thus, 3 mol of electrons are required to form 1 mol of Al:

$$\text{Moles Al} = (0.373 \text{ mol e}^-)\left(\frac{1 \text{ mol Al}}{3 \text{ mol e}^-}\right) = 0.124 \text{ mol Al}$$

Finally, we convert moles to grams:

$$\text{Grams Al} = (0.124 \text{ mol Al})\left(\frac{27.0 \text{ g Al}}{1 \text{ mol Al}}\right) = 3.36 \text{ g Al}$$

Because each step involves multiplication by a new factor, we can combine all the steps:

$$\text{Grams Al} = (3.60 \times 10^4 \text{ C})\left(\frac{1 \text{ mole e}^-}{96,485 \text{ C}}\right)\left(\frac{1 \text{ mol Al}}{3 \text{ mol e}^-}\right)\left(\frac{27.0 \text{ g Al}}{1 \text{ mol Al}}\right) = 3.36 \text{ g Al}$$

### PRACTICE EXERCISE

**(a)** The half-reaction for formation of magnesium metal upon electrolysis of molten $MgCl_2$ is $Mg^{2+} + 2 e^- \longrightarrow Mg$. Calculate the mass of magnesium formed upon passage of a current of 60.0 A for a period of $4.00 \times 10^3$ s. **(b)** How many seconds would be required to produce 50.0 g of Mg from $MgCl_2$ if the current is 100.0 A?

**Answers:** **(a)** 30.2 g of Mg, **(b)** $3.97 \times 10^3$ s

---

# CHEMISTRY PUT TO WORK

## Electrometallurgy of Aluminum

Many processes used to produce or refine metals are based on electrolysis. Collectively these processes are referred to as *electrometallurgy*. Electrometallurgical procedures can be broadly differentiated according to whether they involve electrolysis of a molten salt or of an aqueous solution.

Electrolytic methods using molten salts are important for obtaining the more active metals, such as sodium, magnesium, and aluminum. These metals cannot be obtained from aqueous solution because water is more easily reduced than the metal ions. The standard reduction potentials of water under both acidic ($E°_{red} = 0.00$ V) and basic ($E°_{red} = -0.83$ V) conditions are more positive than those of $Na^+$ ($E°_{red} = -2.71$ V), $Mg^{2+}$ ($E°_{red} = -2.37$ V), and $Al^{3+}$ ($E°_{red} = -1.66$ V).

Historically, obtaining aluminum metal has been a challenge. It is obtained from bauxite ore, which is chemically treated to concentrate aluminum oxide ($Al_2O_3$). The melting point of aluminum oxide is above 2000 °C, which is too high to permit its use as a molten medium for electrolysis.

The electrolytic process used commercially to produce aluminum is the *Hall-Héroult process*, named after its inventors, Charles M. Hall and Paul Héroult. Hall (▼ FIGURE 20.28) began working on the problem of reducing aluminum in about 1885 after he had learned from a professor of the difficulty of reducing ores of very active metals. Before the development of an electrolytic process, aluminum was obtained by a chemical reduction using sodium or potassium as the reducing agent, a costly procedure that made aluminum metal expensive. As late as 1852, the cost of aluminum was $545 per pound, far greater than the cost of gold. During the Paris Exposition in 1855, aluminum was exhibited as a rare metal, even though it is the third most abundant element in Earth's crust.

**Graphite anodes**

$Al_2O_3$ dissolved in molten cryolite

**Molten aluminum metal**

**Carbon-lined iron anode**

◀ **FIGURE 20.29**
**The Hall-Héroult process.** Because molten aluminum is denser than the mixture of cryolite ($Na_3AlF_6$) and $Al_2O_3$, the metal collects at the bottom of the cell.

Hall, who was 21 years old when he began his research, utilized handmade and borrowed equipment in his studies and used a woodshed near his Ohio home as his laboratory. In about a year's time he developed an electrolytic procedure using an ionic compound that melts to form a conducting medium that dissolves $Al_2O_3$ but does not interfere with the electrolysis reactions. The ionic compound he selected was the relatively rare mineral cryolite ($Na_3AlF_6$). Héroult, who was the same age as Hall, independently made the same discovery in France at about the same time. Because of the research of these two unknown young scientists, large-scale production of aluminum became commercially feasible, and aluminum became a common and familiar metal. Indeed, the factory that Hall subsequently built to produce aluminum evolved into Alcoa Corporation.

In the Hall-Héroult process, $Al_2O_3$ is dissolved in molten cryolite, which melts at 1012 °C and is an effective electrical conductor (▲ FIGURE 20.29). Graphite rods are employed as anodes and are consumed in the electrolysis:

*Anode:* $\quad C(s) + 2 O^{2-}(l) \longrightarrow CO_2(g) + 4 e^-$

*Cathode:* $\quad 3 e^- + Al^{3+}(l) \longrightarrow Al(l)$

A large amount of electrical energy is needed in the Hall-Héroult process with the result that the aluminum industry consumes about 2% of the electrical energy generated in the United States. Because recycled aluminum requires only 5% of the energy needed to produce "new" aluminum, considerable energy savings can be realized by increasing the amount of aluminum recycled. Approximately 42% of postconsumer aluminum is recycled in the United States.

◀ **FIGURE 20.28** **Charles M. Hall (1863–1914) as a young man.**

**SAMPLE INTEGRATIVE EXERCISE**  Putting Concepts Together

The $K_{sp}$ at 298 K for iron(II) fluoride is $2.4 \times 10^{-6}$. (a) Write a half-reaction that gives the likely products of the two-electron reduction of $FeF_2(s)$ in water. (b) Use the $K_{sp}$ value and the standard reduction potential of $Fe^{2+}(aq)$ to calculate the standard reduction potential for the half-reaction in part (a). (c) Rationalize the difference between the reduction potential in part (a) and the reduction potential for $Fe^{2+}(aq)$.

## SOLUTION

**Analyze** We are going to have to combine what we know about equilibrium constants and electrochemistry to obtain reduction potentials.

**Plan** For (a) we need to determine which ion, $Fe^{2+}$ or $F^-$, is more likely to be reduced by two electrons and complete the overall reaction $FeF_2 + 2 e^- \longrightarrow$ ?. For (b) we need to write the chemical equation associated with the $K_{sp}$ and see how it relates to $E°$ for the reduction half-reaction in (a). For (c) we need to compare $E°$ from (b) with the value for the reduction of $Fe^{2+}$.

**Solve**
(a) Iron(II) fluoride is an ionic substance that consists of $Fe^{2+}$ and $F^-$ ions. We are asked to predict where two electrons could be added to $FeF_2$. We cannot envision adding the electrons to the $F^-$ ions to form $F^{2-}$, so it seems likely that we could reduce the $Fe^{2+}$ ions to $Fe(s)$. We therefore predict the half-reaction

$$FeF_2(s) + 2 e^- \longrightarrow Fe(s) + 2 F^-(aq)$$

(b) The $K_{sp}$ for $FeF_2$ refers to the following equilibrium: (Section 17.4)

$$FeF_2(s) \rightleftharpoons Fe^{2+}(aq) + 2 F^-(aq) \qquad K_{sp} = [Fe^{2+}][F^-]^2 = 2.4 \times 10^{-6}$$

We were also asked to use the standard reduction potential of $Fe^{2+}$, whose half-reaction and standard reduction potentials are listed in Appendix E:

$$Fe^{2+}(aq) + 2 e^- \longrightarrow Fe(s) \qquad E = -0.440 \text{ V}$$

According to Hess's law, if we can add chemical equations to get a desired equation, then we can add their associated thermodynamic state functions, like $\Delta H$ or $\Delta G$, to determine that thermodynamic quantity for the desired reaction. ⚬⚬ (Section 5.6) So we need to consider whether the three equations we are working with can be combined in a similar fashion. Notice that if we add the $K_{sp}$ reaction to the standard reduction half-reaction for $Fe^{2+}$, we get the half-reaction we want:

1. $\qquad\qquad FeF_2(s) \longrightarrow Fe^{2+}(aq) + 2 F^-(aq)$

2. $Fe^{2+}(aq) + 2 e^- \longrightarrow Fe(s)$

*Overall:* 3. $\overline{\qquad FeF_2(s) + 2 e^- \longrightarrow Fe(s) + 2 F^-(aq)}$

Reaction 3 is still a half-reaction, so we do see the free electrons.

If we knew $\Delta G°$ for reactions 1 and 2, we could add them to get $\Delta G°$ for reaction 3. We can relate $\Delta G°$ to $E°$ by $\Delta G° = -nFE°$ (Equation 20.12) and to $K$ by $\Delta G° = -RT \ln K$ (Equation 19.20, see also Figure 20.14). Furthermore, we know that $K$ for reaction 1 is the $K_{sp}$ of $FeF_2$, and we know $E°$ for reaction 2. Therefore we can calculate $\Delta G°$ for reactions 1 and 2:

*Reaction 1:*
$$\Delta G° = -RT \ln K = -(8.314 \text{ J/K mol})(298 \text{ K}) \ln(2.4 \times 10^{-6}) = 3.21 \times 10^4 \text{ J/mol}$$

*Reaction 2:*
$$\Delta G° = -nFE° = -(2)(96{,}485 \text{ C/mol})(-0.440 \text{ J/C}) = 8.49 \times 10^4 \text{ J/mol}$$

(Recall that 1 volt is 1 joule per coulomb.)

Then $\Delta G°$ for reaction 3, the one we want, is the sum of the $\Delta G°$ values for reactions 1 and 2:

$$3.21 \times 10^4 \text{ J/mol} + 8.49 \times 10^4 \text{ J/mol} = 1.17 \times 10^5 \text{ J/mol}$$

We can convert this to $E°$ from the relationship $\Delta G° = -nFE°$:

$$1.17 \times 10^5 \text{ J/mol} = -(2)(96{,}485 \text{ C/mol}) E°$$

$$E° = \frac{1.17 \times 10^5 \text{ J/mol}}{-(2)(96{,}485 \text{ C/mol})} = -0.606 \text{ J/C} = -0.606 \text{ V}$$

(c) The standard reduction potential for $FeF_2$ (−0.606 V) is more negative than that for $Fe^{2+}$ (−0.440 V), telling us that the reduction of $FeF_2$ is the less favorable process. When $FeF_2$ is reduced, we not only reduce the $Fe^{2+}$ ions but also break up the ionic solid. Because this additional energy must be overcome, the reduction of $FeF_2$ is less favorable than the reduction of $Fe^{2+}$.

# CHAPTER SUMMARY AND KEY TERMS

**INTRODUCTION AND SECTION 20.1** In this chapter we have focused on **electrochemistry**, the branch of chemistry that relates electricity and chemical reactions. Electrochemistry involves oxidation-reduction reactions, also called redox reactions. These reactions involve a change in the oxidation state of one or more elements. In every oxidation-reduction reaction one substance is oxidized (its oxidation state, or number, increases) and one substance is reduced (its oxidation state, or number, decreases). The substance that is oxidized is referred to as a **reducing agent**, or **reductant**, because it causes the reduction of some other substance. Similarly, the substance that is reduced is referred to as an **oxidizing agent**, or **oxidant**, because it causes the oxidation of some other substance.

**SECTION 20.2** An oxidization-reduction reaction can be balanced by dividing the reaction into two **half-reactions**, one for oxidation and one for reduction. A half-reaction is a balanced chemical equation that includes electrons. In oxidation half-reactions the electrons are on the product (right) side of the equation; we can envision that these electrons are transferred from a substance when it is oxidized. In reduction half-reactions the electrons are on the reactant (left) side of the equation. Each half-reaction is balanced separately, and the two are brought together with proper coefficients to balance the electrons on each side of the equation, so the electrons cancel when the half-reactions are added.

**SECTION 20.3** A **voltaic** (or **galvanic**) **cell** uses a spontaneous oxidation-reduction reaction to generate electricity. In a voltaic cell the oxidation and reduction half-reactions often occur in separate half-cells. Each half-cell has a solid surface called an electrode, where the half-reaction occurs. The electrode where oxidation occurs is called the **anode**; reduction occurs at the **cathode**. The electrons released at the anode flow through an external circuit (where they do electrical work) to the cathode. Electrical neutrality in the solution is maintained by the migration of ions between the two half-cells through a device such as a salt bridge.

**SECTION 20.4** A voltaic cell generates an **electromotive force (emf)** that moves the electrons from the anode to the cathode through the external circuit. The origin of emf is a difference in the electrical potential energy of the two electrodes in the cell. The emf of a cell is called its **cell potential**, $E_{cell}$, and is measured in volts ($1 V = 1 J/C$). The cell potential under standard conditions is called the **standard emf**, or the **standard cell potential**, and is denoted $E_{cell}^\circ$.

A **standard reduction potential**, $E_{red}^\circ$, can be assigned for an individual half-reaction. This is achieved by comparing the potential of the half-reaction to that of the **standard hydrogen electrode** (SHE), which is defined to have $E_{red}^\circ = 0 V$ and is based on the following half-reaction:

$$2 H^+(aq, 1 M) + 2 e^- \longrightarrow H_2(g, 1 atm) \qquad E_{red}^\circ = 0 V$$

The standard cell potential of a voltaic cell is the difference between the standard reduction potentials of the half-reactions that occur at the cathode and the anode: $E_{cell}^\circ = E_{red}^\circ$ (cathode) $- E_{red}^\circ$ (anode). The value of $E_{cell}^\circ$ is positive for a voltaic cell.

For a reduction half-reaction, $E_{red}^\circ$ is a measure of the tendency of the reduction to occur; the more positive the value for $E_{red}^\circ$, the greater the tendency of the substance to be reduced. Thus, $E_{red}^\circ$ provides a measure of the oxidizing strength of a substance. Substances that are strong oxidizing agents produce products that are weak reducing agents, and vice versa.

**SECTION 20.5** The emf, $E$, is related to the change in the Gibbs free energy, $\Delta G$: $\Delta G = -nFE$, where $n$ is the number of electrons

transferred during the redox process and $F$ is **Faraday's constant**, defined as the quantity of electrical charge on one mole of electrons: $F = 96,485$ C/mol. Because $E$ is related to $\Delta G$, the sign of $E$ indicates whether a redox process is spontaneous: $E > 0$ indicates a spontaneous process, and $E < 0$ indicates a nonspontaneous one. Because $\Delta G$ is also related to the equilibrium constant for a reaction ($\Delta G = -RT \ln K$), we can relate $E$ to $K$ as well.

The maximum amount of electrical work produced by a voltaic cell is given by the product of the total charge delivered, $nF$, and the emf, $E$: $w_{max} = -nFE$. The watt is a unit of power: $1 W = 1 J/s$. Electrical work is often measured in kilowatt-hours.

**SECTION 20.6** The emf of a redox reaction varies with temperature and with the concentrations of reactants and products. The **Nernst equation** relates the emf under nonstandard conditions to the standard emf and the reaction quotient $Q$:

$$E = E^\circ - (RT/nF) \ln Q = E^\circ - (0.0592/n) \log Q$$

The factor 0.0592 is valid when $T = 298 K$. A **concentration cell** is a voltaic cell in which the same half-reaction occurs at both the anode and cathode but with different concentrations of reactants in each half-cell. At equilibrium, $Q = K$ and $E = 0$.

**SECTION 20.7** A **battery** is a self-contained electrochemical power source that contains one or more voltaic cells. Batteries are based on a variety of different redox reactions. Several common batteries were discussed. The lead-acid battery, the nickel-cadmium battery, the nickel-metal-hydride battery, and the lithium-ion battery are examples of rechargeable batteries. The common alkaline dry cell is not rechargeable. **Fuel cells** are voltaic cells that utilize redox reactions in which reactants such as $H_2$ have to be continuously supplied to the cell to generate voltage.

**SECTION 20.8** Electrochemical principles help us understand **corrosion**, undesirable redox reactions in which a metal is attacked by some substance in its environment. The corrosion of iron into rust is caused by the presence of water and oxygen, and it is accelerated by the presence of electrolytes, such as road salt. The protection of a metal by putting it in contact with another metal that more readily undergoes oxidation is called **cathodic protection**. Galvanized iron, for example, is coated with a thin layer of zinc; because zinc is oxidized more readily than iron, the zinc serves as a sacrificial anode in the redox reaction.

**SECTION 20.9** An **electrolysis reaction**, which is carried out in an **electrolytic cell**, employs an external source of electricity to drive a nonspontaneous electrochemical reaction. The current-carrying medium within an electrolytic cell may be either a molten salt or an electrolyte solution. The products of electrolysis can generally be predicted by comparing the reduction potentials associated with possible oxidation and reduction processes. The electrodes in an electrolytic cell can be active, meaning that the electrode can be involved in the electrolysis reaction. Active electrodes are important in electroplating and in metallurgical processes.

The quantity of substances formed during electrolysis can be calculated by considering the number of electrons involved in the redox reaction and the amount of electrical charge that passes into the cell. The amount of electrical charge is measured in coulombs and is related to the magnitude of the current and the time it flows ($1 C = 1 A$-s). Electrometallurgy is the use of electrolytic methods to prepare or purify a metallic element. Aluminum is obtained in the Hall-Héroult process by electrolysis of $Al_2O_3$ in molten cryolite ($Na_3AlF_6$).

# KEY SKILLS

- Identify oxidation, reduction, oxidizing agent, and reducing agent in a chemical equation. (Section 20.1)
- Complete and balance redox equations using the method of half-reactions. (Section 20.2)
- Sketch a voltaic cell and identify its cathode, anode, and the directions that electrons and ions move. (Section 20.3)
- Calculate standard emfs (cell potentials), $E^\circ_{cell}$, from standard reduction potentials. (Section 20.4)
- Use reduction potentials to predict whether a redox reaction is spontaneous. (Section 20.4)
- Relate $E^\circ_{cell}$ to $\Delta G^\circ$ and equilibrium constants. (Section 20.5)
- Calculate emf under nonstandard conditions. (Section 20.6)
- Describe the components of common batteries and fuel cells. (Section 20.7)
- Explain how corrosion occurs and how it is prevented by cathodic protection. (Section 20.8)
- Describe the reactions in electrolytic cells. (Section 20.9)
- Relate amounts of products and reactants in redox reactions to electrical charge. (Section 20.9)

# KEY EQUATIONS

- $E^\circ_{cell} = E^\circ_{red}(\text{cathode}) - E^\circ_{red}(\text{anode})$    [20.8]    Relating standard emf to standard reduction potentials of the reduction (cathode) and oxidation (anode) half-reactions

- $\Delta G = -nFE$    [20.11]    Relating free-energy change and emf

- $E = E^\circ - \dfrac{0.0592 \text{ V}}{n} \log Q$    (at 298 K)    [20.18]    The Nernst equation, expressing the effect of concentration on cell potential

# EXERCISES

## VISUALIZING CONCEPTS

**20.1** In the Brønsted-Lowry concept of acids and bases, acid–base reactions are viewed as proton-transfer reactions. The stronger the acid, the weaker is its conjugate base. In what ways are redox reactions analogous? [Sections 20.1 and 20.2]

**20.2** You may have heard that "antioxidants" are good for your health. Based on what you have learned in this chapter, what do you deduce an "antioxidant" is? [Sections 20.1 and 20.2]

**20.3** The diagram that follows represents a molecular view of a process occurring at an electrode in a voltaic cell.

**(a)** Does the process represent oxidation or reduction? **(b)** Is the electrode the anode or cathode? **(c)** Why are the atoms in the electrode represented by larger spheres than the ions in the solution? [Section 20.3]

**20.4** Assume that you want to construct a voltaic cell that uses the following half-reactions:

$$A^{2+}(aq) + 2\,e^- \longrightarrow A(s) \quad E^\circ_{red} = -0.10 \text{ V}$$
$$B^{2+}(aq) + 2\,e^- \longrightarrow B(s) \quad E^\circ_{red} = -1.10 \text{ V}$$

You begin with the incomplete cell pictured here in which the electrodes are immersed in water.

**(a)** What additions must you make to the cell for it to generate a standard emf? **(b)** Which electrode functions as the cathode? **(c)** Which direction do electrons move through the external circuit? **(d)** What voltage will the cell generate under standard conditions? [Sections 20.3 and 20.4]

**20.5** For a spontaneous reaction $A(aq) + B(aq) \longrightarrow A^-(aq) + B^+(aq)$, answer the following questions:
**(a)** If you made a voltaic cell out of this reaction, what half-reaction would be occurring at the cathode, and what half-reaction would be occurring at the anode?
**(b)** Which half-reaction from (a) is higher in potential energy?
**(c)** What is the sign of $E^\circ_{cell}$? [Section 20.3]

**20.6** Consider the following table of standard electrode potentials for a series of hypothetical reactions in aqueous solution:

| Reduction Half-Reaction | $E°(V)$ |
|---|---|
| $A^+(aq) + e^- \longrightarrow A(s)$ | 1.33 |
| $B^{2+}(aq) + 2e^- \longrightarrow B(s)$ | 0.87 |
| $C^{3+}(aq) + e^- \longrightarrow C^{2+}(aq)$ | -0.12 |
| $D^{3+}(aq) + 3e^- \longrightarrow D(s)$ | -1.59 |

(a) Which substance is the strongest oxidizing agent? Which is weakest?

(b) Which substance is the strongest reducing agent? Which is weakest?

(c) Which substance(s) can oxidize $C^{2+}$? [Sections 20.4 and 20.5]

**20.7** Consider a redox reaction for which $E°$ is a negative number.
(a) What is the sign of $\Delta G°$ for the reaction?
(b) Will the equilibrium constant for the reaction be larger or smaller than 1?
(c) Can an electrochemical cell based on this reaction accomplish work on its surroundings? [Section 20.5]

**20.8** Consider the following voltaic cell:

(a) Which electrode is the cathode?
(b) How would you determine the standard emf generated by this cell?
(c) What is the change in the cell voltage when the ion concentrations in the cathode half-cell are increased by a factor of 10?
(d) What is the change in the cell voltage when the ion concentrations in the anode half-cell are increased by a factor of 10? [Sections 20.4 and 20.6]

**20.9** Consider the half-reaction $Ag^+(aq) + e^- \longrightarrow Ag(s)$. (a) Which of the lines in the following diagram indicates how the reduction potential varies with the concentration of $Ag^+$? (b) What is the value of $E_{red}$ when $\log[Ag^+] = 0$? [Section 20.6]

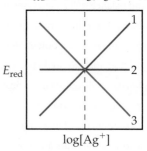

**20.10** Draw a generic picture of a fuel cell. What is the main difference between it and a battery, regardless of the redox reactions that occur inside? [Section 20.7]

**20.11** How does a zinc coating on iron protect the iron from unwanted oxidation? [Section 20.8]

**20.12** Magnesium is produced commercially by electrolysis from a molten salt using a cell similar to the one shown here. (a) What salt is used as the electrolyte? (b) Which electrode is the anode, and which one is the cathode? (c) Write the overall cell reaction and individual half-reactions. (d) What precautions would need to be taken with respect to the magnesium formed? [Section 20.9]

# OXIDATION-REDUCTION REACTIONS (section 20.1)

**20.13** (a) What is meant by the term *oxidation*? (b) On which side of an oxidation half-reaction do the electrons appear? (c) What is meant by the term *oxidant*? (d) What is meant by the term *oxidizing agent*?

**20.14** (a) What is meant by the term *reduction*? (b) On which side of a reduction half-reaction do the electrons appear? (c) What is meant by the term *reductant*? (d) What is meant by the term *reducing agent*?

**20.15** Indicate whether each of the following statements is true or false:
(a) If something is oxidized, it is formally losing electrons.

(b) For the reaction $Fe^{3+}(aq) + Co^{2+}(aq) \longrightarrow Fe^{2+}(aq) + Co^{3+}(aq)$, $Fe^{3+}(aq)$ is the reducing agent and $Co^{2+}(aq)$ is the oxidizing agent.
(c) If there are no changes in the oxidation state of the reactants or products of a particular reaction, that reaction is not a redox reaction.

**20.16** Indicate whether each of the following statements is true or false:
(a) If something is reduced, it is formally losing electrons.
(b) A reducing agent gets oxidized as it reacts.
(c) Oxidizing agents can convert CO into $CO_2$.

**20.17** In each of the following balanced oxidation-reduction equations, identify those elements that undergo changes in oxidation number and indicate the magnitude of the change in each case.

(a) $I_2O_5(s) + 5\,CO(g) \longrightarrow I_2(s) + 5\,CO_2(g)$

(b) $2\,Hg^{2+}(aq) + N_2H_4(aq) \longrightarrow$
$$2\,Hg(l) + N_2(g) + 4\,H^+(aq)$$

(c) $3\,H_2S(aq) + 2\,H^+(aq) + 2\,NO_3^-(aq) \longrightarrow$
$$3\,S(s) + 2\,NO(g) + 4\,H_2O(l)$$

(d) $Ba^{2+}(aq) + 2\,OH^-(aq) + H_2O_2(aq) + 2\,ClO_2(aq)$
$$\longrightarrow Ba(ClO_2)_2\,(s) + 2\,H_2O(l) + O_2(g)$$

**20.18** Indicate whether the following balanced equations involve oxidation-reduction. If they do, identify the elements that undergo changes in oxidation number.

(a) $PBr_3(l) + 3\,H_2O(l) \longrightarrow H_3PO_3(aq) + 3\,HBr(aq)$

(b) $NaI(aq) + 3\,HOCl(aq) \longrightarrow NaIO_3(aq) + 3\,HCl(aq)$

(c) $3\,SO_2(g) + 2\,HNO_3(aq) + 2\,H_2O(l) \longrightarrow$
$$3\,H_2SO_4(aq) + 2\,NO(g)$$

(d) $2\,H_2SO_4(aq) + 2\,NaBr(s) \longrightarrow$
$$Br_2(l) + SO_2(g) + Na_2SO_4(aq) + 2\,H_2O(l)$$

# BALANCING OXIDATION-REDUCTION REACTIONS (section 20.2)

**20.19** At 900 °C titanium tetrachloride vapor reacts with molten magnesium metal to form solid titanium metal and molten magnesium chloride. (a) Write a balanced equation for this reaction. (b) What is being oxidized, and what is being reduced? (c) Which substance is the reductant, and which is the oxidant?

**20.20** Hydrazine ($N_2H_4$) and dinitrogen tetroxide ($N_2O_4$) form a self-igniting mixture that has been used as a rocket propellant. The reaction products are $N_2$ and $H_2O$. (a) Write a balanced chemical equation for this reaction. (b) What is being oxidized, and what is being reduced? (c) Which substance serves as the reducing agent and which as the oxidizing agent?

**20.21** Complete and balance the following half-reactions. In each case indicate whether the half-reaction is an oxidation or a reduction.

(a) $Sn^{2+}(aq) \longrightarrow Sn^{4+}(aq)$ (acidic solution)

(b) $TiO_2(s) \longrightarrow Ti^{2+}(aq)$ (acidic solution)

(c) $ClO_3^-(aq) \longrightarrow Cl^-(aq)$ (acidic solution)

(d) $N_2(g) \longrightarrow NH_4^+(aq)$ (acidic solution)

(e) $OH^-(aq) \longrightarrow O_2(g)$ (basic solution)

(f) $SO_3^{2-}(aq) \longrightarrow SO_4^{2-}(aq)$ (basic solution)

(g) $N_2(g) \longrightarrow NH_3(g)$ (basic solution)

**20.22** Complete and balance the following half-reactions. In each case indicate whether the half-reaction is an oxidation or a reduction.

(a) $Mo^{3+}(aq) \longrightarrow Mo(s)$ (acidic solution)

(b) $H_2SO_3(aq) \longrightarrow SO_4^{2-}(aq)$ (acidic solution)

(c) $NO_3^-(aq) \longrightarrow NO(g)$ (acidic solution)

(d) $O_2(g) \longrightarrow H_2O(l)$ (acidic solution)

(e) $O_2(g) \longrightarrow H_2O(l)$ (basic solution)

(f) $Mn^{2+}(aq) \longrightarrow MnO_2(s)$ (basic solution)

(g) $Cr(OH)_3(s) \longrightarrow CrO_4^{2-}(aq)$ (basic solution)

**20.23** Complete and balance the following equations, and identify the oxidizing and reducing agents:

(a) $Cr_2O_7^{2-}(aq) + I^-(aq) \longrightarrow Cr^{3+}(aq) + IO_3^-(aq)$
(acidic solution)

(b) $MnO_4^-(aq) + CH_3OH(aq) \longrightarrow$
$$Mn^{2+}(aq) + HCO_2H(aq)\ \text{(acidic solution)}$$

(c) $I_2(s) + OCl^-(aq) \longrightarrow IO_3^-(aq) + Cl^-(aq)$
(acidic solution)

(d) $As_2O_3(s) + NO_3^-(aq) \longrightarrow H_3AsO_4(aq) + N_2O_3(aq)$
(acidic solution)

(e) $MnO_4^-(aq) + Br^-(aq) \longrightarrow MnO_2(s) + BrO_3^-(aq)$
(basic solution)

(f) $Pb(OH)_4^{2-}(aq) + ClO^-(aq) \longrightarrow PbO_2(s) + Cl^-(aq)$
(basic solution)

**20.24** Complete and balance the following equations, and identify the oxidizing and reducing agents. (Recall that the O atoms in hydrogen peroxide, $H_2O_2$, have an atypical oxidation state.)

(a) $NO_2^-(aq) + Cr_2O_7^{2-}(aq) \longrightarrow$
$$Cr^{3+}(aq) + NO_3^-(aq)\ \text{(acidic solution)}$$

(b) $S(s) + HNO_3(aq) \longrightarrow H_2SO_3(aq) + N_2O(g)$
(acidic solution)

(c) $Cr_2O_7^{2-}(aq) + CH_3OH(aq) \longrightarrow$
$$HCO_2H(aq) + Cr^{3+}(aq)\ \text{(acidic solution)}$$

(d) $BrO_3^-(aq) + N_2H_4(g) \longrightarrow Br^-(aq) + N_2(g)$
(acidic solution)

(e) $NO_2^-(aq) + Al(s) \longrightarrow NH_4^+(aq) + AlO_2^-(aq)$
(basic solution)

(f) $H_2O_2(aq) + ClO_2(aq) \longrightarrow ClO_2^-(aq) + O_2(g)$
(basic solution)

# VOLTAIC CELLS (section 20.3)

**20.25** (a) What are the similarities and differences between Figure 20.3 and Figure 20.4? (b) Why are $Na^+$ ions drawn into the cathode half-cell as the voltaic cell shown in Figure 20.5 operates?

**20.26** (a) What is the role of the porous glass disc shown in Figure 20.4? (b) Why do $NO_3^-$ ions migrate into the anode half-cell as the voltaic cell shown in Figure 20.5 operates?

**20.27** A voltaic cell similar to that shown in Figure 20.5 is constructed. One electrode half-cell consists of a silver strip placed in a

solution of $AgNO_3$, and the other has an iron strip placed in a solution of $FeCl_2$. The overall cell reaction is

$$Fe(s) + 2\,Ag^+(aq) \longrightarrow Fe^{2+}(aq) + 2\,Ag(s)$$

(a) What is being oxidized, and what is being reduced? (b) Write the half-reactions that occur in the two half-cells. (c) Which electrode is the anode, and which is the cathode? (d) Indicate the signs of the electrodes. (e) Do electrons flow from the silver electrode to the iron electrode or from the iron to the silver? (f) In which directions do the cations and anions migrate through the solution?

**20.28** A voltaic cell similar to that shown in Figure 20.5 is constructed. One half-cell consists of an aluminum strip placed in a solution of $Al(NO_3)_3$, and the other has a nickel strip placed in a solution of $NiSO_4$. The overall cell reaction is

$$2\, Al(s) + 3\, Ni^{2+}(aq) \longrightarrow 2\, Al^{3+}(aq) + 3\, Ni(s)$$

**(a)** What is being oxidized, and what is being reduced? **(b)** Write the half-reactions that occur in the two half-cells.

**(c)** Which electrode is the anode, and which is the cathode? **(d)** Indicate the signs of the electrodes. **(e)** Do electrons flow from the aluminum electrode to the nickel electrode or from the nickel to the aluminum? **(f)** In which directions do the cations and anions migrate through the solution? Assume the Al is not coated with its oxide.

## CELL POTENTIALS UNDER STANDARD CONDITIONS (section 20.4)

**20.29** **(a)** What does the term *electromotive force* mean? **(b)** What is the definition of the *volt*? **(c)** What does the term *cell potential* mean?

**20.30** **(a)** Which electrode of a voltaic cell, the cathode or the anode, corresponds to the higher potential energy for the electrons? **(b)** What are the units for electrical potential? How does this unit relate to energy expressed in joules? **(c)** What is special about a *standard* cell potential?

**20.31** **(a)** Write the half-reaction that occurs at a hydrogen electrode in acidic aqueous solution when it serves as the cathode of a voltaic cell. **(b)** What is *standard* about the standard hydrogen electrode? **(c)** What is the role of the platinum foil in a standard hydrogen electrode?

**20.32** **(a)** Write the half-reaction that occurs at a hydrogen electrode in acidic aqueous solution when it serves as the anode of a voltaic cell. **(b)** The platinum electrode in a standard hydrogen electrode is specially prepared to have a large surface area. Why is this important? **(c)** Sketch a standard hydrogen electrode.

**20.33** **(a)** What is a *standard reduction potential*? **(b)** What is the standard reduction potential of a standard hydrogen electrode?

**20.34** **(a)** Why is it impossible to measure the standard reduction potential of a single half-reaction? **(b)** Describe how the standard reduction potential of a half-reaction can be determined.

**20.35** A voltaic cell that uses the reaction

$$Tl^{3+}(aq) + 2\, Cr^{2+}(aq) \longrightarrow Tl^{+}(aq) + 2\, Cr^{3+}(aq)$$

has a measured standard cell potential of $+1.19$ V. **(a)** Write the two half-cell reactions. **(b)** By using data from Appendix E, determine $E^{\circ}_{red}$ for the reduction of $Tl^{3+}(aq)$ to $Tl^{+}(aq)$. **(c)** Sketch the voltaic cell, label the anode and cathode, and indicate the direction of electron flow.

**20.36** A voltaic cell that uses the reaction

$$PdCl_4{}^{2-}(aq) + Cd(s) \longrightarrow Pd(s) + 4\, Cl^{-}(aq) + Cd^{2+}(aq)$$

has a measured standard cell potential of $+1.03$ V. **(a)** Write the two half-cell reactions. **(b)** By using data from Appendix E, determine $E^{\circ}_{red}$ for the reaction involving Pd. **(c)** Sketch the voltaic cell, label the anode and cathode, and indicate the direction of electron flow.

**20.37** Using standard reduction potentials (Appendix E), calculate the standard emf for each of the following reactions:

**(a)** $Cl_2(g) + 2\, I^{-}(aq) \longrightarrow 2\, Cl^{-}(aq) + I_2(s)$

**(b)** $Ni(s) + 2\, Ce^{4+}(aq) \longrightarrow Ni^{2+}(aq) + 2\, Ce^{3+}(aq)$

**(c)** $Fe(s) + 2\, Fe^{3+}(aq) \longrightarrow 3\, Fe^{2+}(aq)$

**(d)** $2\, NO_3{}^{-}(aq) + 8\, H^{+}(aq) + 3\, Cu(s) \longrightarrow$
$$2\, NO(g) + 4\, H_2O(l) + 3\, Cu^{2+}(aq)$$

**20.38** Using data in Appendix E, calculate the standard emf for each of the following reactions:

**(a)** $H_2(g) + F_2(g) \longrightarrow 2\, H^{+}(aq) + 2\, F^{-}(aq)$

**(b)** $Cu^{2+}(aq) + Ca(s) \longrightarrow Cu(s) + Ca^{2+}(aq)$

**(c)** $3\, Fe^{2+}(aq) \longrightarrow Fe(s) + 2\, Fe^{3+}(aq)$

**(d)** $2\, ClO_3{}^{-}(aq) + 10\, Br^{-}(aq) + 12\, H^{+}(aq) \longrightarrow$
$$Cl_2(g) + 5\, Br_2(l) + 6\, H_2O(l)$$

**20.39** The standard reduction potentials of the following half-reactions are given in Appendix E:

$$Ag^{+}(aq) + e^{-} \longrightarrow Ag(s)$$
$$Cu^{2+}(aq) + 2\, e^{-} \longrightarrow Cu(s)$$
$$Ni^{2+}(aq) + 2\, e^{-} \longrightarrow Ni(s)$$
$$Cr^{3+}(aq) + 3\, e^{-} \longrightarrow Cr(s)$$

**(a)** Determine which combination of these half-cell reactions leads to the cell reaction with the largest positive cell potential and calculate the value. **(b)** Determine which combination of these half-cell reactions leads to the cell reaction with the smallest positive cell potential and calculate the value.

**20.40** Given the following half-reactions and associated standard reduction potentials:

$$AuBr_4{}^{-}(aq) + 3\, e^{-} \longrightarrow Au(s) + 4\, Br^{-}(aq)$$
$$E^{\circ}_{red} = -0.858\,V$$
$$Eu^{3+}(aq) + e^{-} \longrightarrow Eu^{2+}(aq)$$
$$E^{\circ}_{red} = -0.43\,V$$
$$IO^{-}(aq) + H_2O(l) + 2\, e^{-} \longrightarrow I^{-}(aq) + 2\, OH^{-}(aq)$$
$$E^{\circ}_{red} = +0.49\,V$$

**(a)** Write the equation for the combination of these half-cell reactions that leads to the largest positive emf and calculate the value. **(b)** Write the equation for the combination of half-cell reactions that leads to the smallest positive emf and calculate that value.

**20.41** A 1 *M* solution of $Cu(NO_3)_2$ is placed in a beaker with a strip of Cu metal. A 1 *M* solution of $SnSO_4$ is placed in a second beaker with a strip of Sn metal. A salt bridge connects the two beakers, and wires to a voltmeter link the two metal electrodes. **(a)** Which electrode serves as the anode and which as the cathode? **(b)** Which electrode gains mass and which loses mass as the cell reaction proceeds? **(c)** Write the equation for the overall cell reaction. **(d)** What is the emf generated by the cell under standard conditions?

**20.42** A voltaic cell consists of a strip of cadmium metal in a solution of $Cd(NO_3)_2$ in one beaker, and in the other beaker a platinum electrode is immersed in a NaCl solution, with $Cl_2$ gas bubbled around the electrode. A salt bridge connects the two beakers. **(a)** Which electrode serves as the anode and which as the cathode? **(b)** Does the Cd electrode gain or lose mass as the cell reaction proceeds? **(c)** Write the equation for the overall cell reaction. **(d)** What is the emf generated by the cell under standard conditions?

# STRENGTHS OF OXIDIZING AND REDUCING AGENTS (section 20.4)

**20.43** From each of the following pairs of substances, use data in Appendix E to choose the one that is the stronger reducing agent:
**(a)** Fe($s$) or Mg($s$)
**(b)** Ca($s$) or Al($s$)
**(c)** H$_2$($g$, acidic solution) or H$_2$S($g$)
**(d)** BrO$_3^-$($aq$) or IO$_3^-$($aq$)

**20.44** From each of the following pairs of substances, use data in Appendix E to choose the one that is the stronger oxidizing agent:
**(a)** Cl$_2$($g$) or Br$_2$($l$)
**(b)** Zn$^{2+}$($aq$) or Cd$^{2+}$($aq$)
**(c)** Cl$^-$($aq$) or ClO$_3^-$($aq$)
**(d)** H$_2$O$_2$($aq$) or O$_3$($g$)

**20.45** By using the data in Appendix E, determine whether each of the following substances is likely to serve as an oxidant or a reductant: **(a)** Cl$_2$($g$), **(b)** MnO$_4^-$($aq$, acidic solution), **(c)** Ba($s$), **(d)** Zn($s$).

**20.46** Is each of the following substances likely to serve as an oxidant or a reductant: **(a)** Ce$^{3+}$($aq$), **(b)** Ca($s$), **(c)** ClO$_3^-$($aq$), **(d)** N$_2$O$_5$($g$)?

**20.47** **(a)** Assuming standard conditions, arrange the following in order of increasing strength as oxidizing agents in acidic solution: Cr$_2$O$_7^{2-}$, H$_2$O$_2$, Cu$^{2+}$, Cl$_2$, O$_2$. **(b)** Arrange the following in order of increasing strength as reducing agents in acidic solution: Zn, I$^-$, Sn$^{2+}$, H$_2$O$_2$, Al.

**20.48** Based on the data in Appendix E, **(a)** which of the following is the strongest oxidizing agent and which is the weakest in acidic solution:, Br$_2$, H$_2$O$_2$, Zn, Cr$_2$O$_7^{2-}$? **(b)** Which of the following is the strongest reducing agent, and which is the weakest in acidic solution: F$^-$, Zn, N$_2$H$_5^+$, I$_2$, NO?

**20.49** The standard reduction potential for the reduction of Eu$^{3+}$($aq$) to Eu$^{2+}$($aq$) is −0.43 V. Using Appendix E, which of the following substances is capable of reducing Eu$^{3+}$($aq$) to Eu$^{2+}$($aq$) under standard conditions: Al, Co, H$_2$O$_2$, N$_2$H$_5^+$, H$_2$C$_2$O$_4$?

**20.50** The standard reduction potential for the reduction of RuO$_4^-$($aq$) to RuO$_4^{2-}$($aq$) is +0.59 V. By using Appendix E, which of the following substances can oxidize RuO$_4^{2-}$($aq$) to RuO$_4^-$($aq$) under standard conditions: Br$_2$($l$), BrO$_3^-$($aq$), Mn$^{2+}$($aq$), O$_2$($g$), Sn$^{2+}$($aq$)?

# FREE ENERGY AND REDOX REACTIONS (section 20.5)

**20.51** Given the following reduction half-reactions:

$$Fe^{3+}(aq) + e^- \longrightarrow Fe^{2+}(aq)$$
$$E_{red}^\circ = +0.77 \text{ V}$$

$$S_2O_6^{2-}(aq) + 4 H^+(aq) + 2 e^- \longrightarrow 2 H_2SO_3(aq)$$
$$E_{red}^\circ = +0.60 \text{ V}$$

$$N_2O(g) + 2 H^+(aq) + 2 e^- \longrightarrow N_2(g) + H_2O(l)$$
$$E_{red}^\circ = -1.77 \text{ V}$$

$$VO_2^+(aq) + 2 H^+(aq) + e^- \longrightarrow VO^{2+} + H_2O(l)$$
$$E_{red}^\circ = +1.00 \text{ V}$$

**(a)** Write balanced chemical equations for the oxidation of Fe$^{2+}$($aq$) by S$_2$O$_6^{2-}$($aq$), by N$_2$O($aq$), and by VO$_2^+$($aq$). **(b)** Calculate $\Delta G^\circ$ for each reaction at 298 K. **(c)** Calculate the equilibrium constant $K$ for each reaction at 298 K.

**20.52** For each of the following reactions, write a balanced equation, calculate the standard emf, calculate $\Delta G^\circ$ at 298 K, and calculate the equilibrium constant $K$ at 298 K. **(a)** Aqueous iodide ion is oxidized to I$_2$($s$) by Hg$_2^{2+}$($aq$). **(b)** In acidic solution, copper(I) ion is oxidized to copper(II) ion by nitrate ion. **(c)** In basic solution, Cr(OH)$_3$($s$) is oxidized to CrO$_4^{2-}$($aq$) by ClO$^-$($aq$).

**20.53** If the equilibrium constant for a two-electron redox reaction at 298 K is $1.5 \times 10^{-4}$, calculate the corresponding $\Delta G^\circ$ and $E_{red}^\circ$.

**20.54** If the equilibrium constant for a one-electron redox reaction at 298 K is $8.7 \times 10^4$, calculate the corresponding $\Delta G^\circ$ and $E_{red}^\circ$.

**20.55** Using the standard reduction potentials listed in Appendix E, calculate the equilibrium constant for each of the following reactions at 298 K:
**(a)** Fe($s$) + Ni$^{2+}$($aq$) $\longrightarrow$ Fe$^{2+}$($aq$) + Ni($s$)
**(b)** Co($s$) + 2 H$^+$($aq$) $\longrightarrow$ Co$^{2+}$($aq$) + H$_2$($g$)
**(c)** 10 Br$^-$($aq$) + 2 MnO$_4^-$($aq$) + 16 H$^+$($aq$) $\longrightarrow$
2 Mn$^{2+}$($aq$) + 8 H$_2$O($l$) + 5 Br$_2$($l$)

**20.56** Using the standard reduction potentials listed in Appendix E, calculate the equilibrium constant for each of the following reactions at 298 K:
**(a)** Cu($s$) + 2 Ag$^+$($aq$) $\longrightarrow$ Cu$^{2+}$($aq$) + 2 Ag($s$)
**(b)** 3 Ce$^{4+}$($aq$) + Bi($s$) + H$_2$O($l$) $\longrightarrow$
3 Ce$^{3+}$($aq$) + BiO$^+$($aq$) + 2 H$^+$($aq$)
**(c)** N$_2$H$_5^+$($aq$) + 4 Fe(CN)$_6^{3-}$($aq$) $\longrightarrow$
N$_2$($g$) + 5 H$^+$($aq$) + 4 Fe(CN)$_6^{4-}$($aq$)

**20.57** A cell has a standard cell potential of +0.177 V at 298 K. What is the value of the equilibrium constant for the reaction **(a)** if $n = 1$? **(b)** if $n = 2$? **(c)** if $n = 3$?

**20.58** At 298 K a cell reaction has a standard cell potential of +0.17 V. The equilibrium constant for the reaction is $5.5 \times 10^5$. What is the value of $n$ for the reaction?

**20.59** A voltaic cell is based on the reaction

$$Sn(s) + I_2(s) \longrightarrow Sn^{2+}(aq) + 2 I^-(aq)$$

Under standard conditions, what is the maximum electrical work, in joules, that the cell can accomplish if 75.0 g of Sn is consumed?

**20.60** Consider the voltaic cell illustrated in Figure 20.5, which is based on the cell reaction

$$Zn(s) + Cu^{2+}(aq) \longrightarrow Zn^{2+}(aq) + Cu(s)$$

Under standard conditions, what is the maximum electrical work, in joules, that the cell can accomplish if 50.0 g of copper is formed?

# CELL EMF UNDER NONSTANDARD CONDITIONS (section 20.6)

**20.61** (a) Under what circumstances is the Nernst equation applicable? (b) What is the numerical value of the reaction quotient, Q, under standard conditions? (c) What happens to the emf of a cell if the concentrations of the reactants are increased?

**20.62** (a) A voltaic cell is constructed with all reactants and products in their standard states. Will this condition hold as the cell operates? Explain. (b) Can the Nernst equation be used at temperatures other than room temperature? Explain. (c) What happens to the emf of a cell if the concentrations of the products are increased?

**20.63** What is the effect on the emf of the cell shown in Figure 20.9, which has the overall reaction $Zn(s) + 2 H^+(aq) \longrightarrow Zn^{2+}(aq) + H_2(g)$, for each of the following changes? (a) The pressure of the $H_2$ gas is increased in the cathode half-cell. (b) Zinc nitrate is added to the anode half-cell. (c) Sodium hydroxide is added to the cathode half-cell, decreasing $[H^+]$. (d) The surface area of the anode is doubled.

**20.64** A voltaic cell utilizes the following reaction:

$$Al(s) + 3 Ag^+(aq) \longrightarrow Al^{3+}(aq) + 3 Ag(s)$$

What is the effect on the cell emf of each of the following changes? (a) Water is added to the anode half-cell, diluting the solution. (b) The size of the aluminum electrode is increased. (c) A solution of $AgNO_3$ is added to the cathode half-cell, increasing the quantity of $Ag^+$ but not changing its concentration. (d) HCl is added to the $AgNO_3$ solution, precipitating some of the $Ag^+$ as AgCl.

**20.65** A voltaic cell is constructed that uses the following reaction and operates at 298 K:

$$Zn(s) + Ni^{2+}(aq) \longrightarrow Zn^{2+}(aq) + Ni(s)$$

(a) What is the emf of this cell under standard conditions? (b) What is the emf of this cell when $[Ni^{2+}] = 3.00\ M$ and $[Zn^{2+}] = 0.100\ M$? (c) What is the emf of the cell when $[Ni^{2+}] = 0.200\ M$ and $[Zn^{2+}] = 0.900\ M$?

**20.66** A voltaic cell utilizes the following reaction and operates at 298 K:

$$3 Ce^{4+}(aq) + Cr(s) \longrightarrow 3 Ce^{3+}(aq) + Cr^{3+}(aq)$$

(a) What is the emf of this cell under standard conditions? (b) What is the emf of this cell when $[Ce^{4+}] = 3.0\ M$, $[Ce^{3+}] = 0.10\ M$, and $[Cr^{3+}] = 0.010\ M$? (c) What is the emf of the cell when $[Ce^{4+}] = 0.010\ M$, $[Ce^{3+}] = 2.0\ M$, and $[Cr^{3+}] = 1.5\ M$?

**20.67** A voltaic cell utilizes the following reaction:

$$4 Fe^{2+}(aq) + O_2(g) + 4 H^+(aq) \longrightarrow 4 Fe^{3+}(aq) + 2 H_2O(l)$$

(a) What is the emf of this cell under standard conditions? (b) What is the emf of this cell when $[Fe^{2+}] = 1.3\ M$, $[Fe^{3+}] = 0.010\ M$, $P_{O_2} = 0.50$ atm, and the pH of the solution in the cathode half-cell is 3.50?

**20.68** A voltaic cell utilizes the following reaction:

$$2 Fe^{3+}(aq) + H_2(g) \longrightarrow 2 Fe^{2+}(aq) + 2 H^+(aq)$$

(a) What is the emf of this cell under standard conditions? (b) What is the emf for this cell when $[Fe^{3+}] = 3.50\ M$, $P_{H_2} = 0.95$ atm, $[Fe^{2+}] = 0.0010\ M$, and the pH in both half-cells is 4.00?

**20.69** A voltaic cell is constructed with two $Zn^{2+}$–Zn electrodes. The two half-cells have $[Zn^{2+}] = 1.8\ M$ and $[Zn^{2+}] = 1.00 \times 10^{-2}\ M$, respectively. (a) Which electrode is the anode of the cell? (b) What is the standard emf of the cell? (c) What is the cell emf for the concentrations given? (d) For each electrode, predict whether $[Zn^{2+}]$ will increase, decrease, or stay the same as the cell operates.

**20.70** A voltaic cell is constructed with two silver–silver chloride electrodes, each of which is based on the following half-reaction:

$$AgCl(s) + e^- \longrightarrow Ag(s) + Cl^-(aq)$$

The two half-cells have $[Cl^-] = 0.0150\ M$ and $[Cl^-] = 2.55\ M$, respectively. (a) Which electrode is the cathode of the cell? (b) What is the standard emf of the cell? (c) What is the cell emf for the concentrations given? (d) For each electrode, predict whether $[Cl^-]$ will increase, decrease, or stay the same as the cell operates.

**20.71** The cell in Figure 20.9 could be used to provide a measure of the pH in the cathode half-cell. Calculate the pH of the cathode half-cell solution if the cell emf at 298 K is measured to be +0.684 V when $[Zn^{2+}] = 0.30\ M$ and $P_{H_2} = 0.90$ atm.

**20.72** A voltaic cell is constructed that is based on the following reaction:

$$Sn^{2+}(aq) + Pb(s) \longrightarrow Sn(s) + Pb^{2+}(aq)$$

(a) If the concentration of $Sn^{2+}$ in the cathode half-cell is 1.00 M and the cell generates an emf of +0.22 V, what is the concentration of $Pb^{2+}$ in the anode half-cell? (b) If the anode half-cell contains $[SO_4^{2-}] = 1.00\ M$ in equilibrium with $PbSO_4(s)$, what is the $K_{sp}$ of $PbSO_4$?

# BATTERIES AND FUEL CELLS (section 20.7)

**20.73** (a) What happens to the emf of a battery as it is used? Why does this happen? (b) The AA-size and D-size alkaline batteries are both 1.5-V batteries that are based on the same electrode reactions. What is the major difference between the two batteries? What performance feature is most affected by this difference?

**20.74** (a) Suggest an explanation for why liquid water is needed in an alkaline battery. (b) What is the advantage of using highly concentrated or solid reactants in a voltaic cell?

**20.75** During a period of discharge of a lead-acid battery, 402 g of Pb from the anode is converted into $PbSO_4(s)$. (a) What mass of

$PbO_2(s)$ is reduced at the cathode during this same period? (b) How many coulombs of electrical charge are transferred from Pb to $PbO_2$?

**20.76** During the discharge of an alkaline battery, 4.50 g of Zn is consumed at the anode of the battery. (a) What mass of $MnO_2$ is reduced at the cathode during this discharge? (b) How many coulombs of electrical charge are transferred from Zn to $MnO_2$?

**20.77** Heart pacemakers are often powered by lithium–silver chromate "button" batteries. The overall cell reaction is

$$2 Li(s) + Ag_2CrO_4(s) \longrightarrow Li_2CrO_4(s) + 2 Ag(s)$$

**(a)** Lithium metal is the reactant at one of the electrodes of the battery. Is it the anode or the cathode? **(b)** Choose the two half-reactions from Appendix E that *most closely approximate* the reactions that occur in the battery. What standard emf would be generated by a voltaic cell based on these half-reactions? **(c)** The battery generates an emf of +3.5 V. How close is this value to the one calculated in part (b)? **(d)** Calculate the emf that would be generated at body temperature, 37 °C. How does this compare to the emf you calculated in part (b)?

**20.78** Mercuric oxide dry-cell batteries are often used where a high-energy density is required, such as in watches and cameras. The two half-cell reactions that occur in the battery are

$$HgO(s) + H_2O(l) + 2\,e^- \longrightarrow Hg(l) + 2\,OH^-(aq)$$
$$Zn(s) + 2\,OH^-(aq) \longrightarrow ZnO(s) + H_2O(l) + 2\,e^-$$

**(a)** Write the overall cell reaction. **(b)** The value of $E^\circ_{red}$ for the cathode reaction is +0.098 V. The overall cell potential is +1.35 V. Assuming that both half-cells operate under standard conditions, what is the standard reduction potential for the anode reaction? **(c)** Why is the potential of the anode reaction different than would be expected if the reaction occurred in an acidic medium?

**20.79** **(a)** Suppose that an alkaline battery was manufactured using cadmium metal rather than zinc. What effect would this have on the cell emf? **(b)** What environmental advantage is provided by the use of nickel-metal-hydride batteries over nickel-cadmium batteries?

**20.80** **(a)** The nonrechargeable lithium batteries used for photography use lithium metal as the anode. What advantages might be realized by using lithium rather than zinc, cadmium, lead, or nickel? **(b)** The rechargeable lithium-ion battery does not use lithium metal as an electrode material. Nevertheless, it still has a substantial advantage over nickel-based batteries. Suggest an explanation.

**20.81** The hydrogen-oxygen fuel cell has a standard emf of 1.23 V. What advantages and disadvantages there to using this device as a source of power compared to a 1.55-V alkaline battery?

**20.82** **(a)** What is the difference between a battery and a fuel cell? **(b)** Can the "fuel" of a fuel cell be a solid? Explain.

# CORROSION (section 20.8)

**20.83** **(a)** Write the anode and cathode reactions that cause the corrosion of iron metal to aqueous iron(II). **(b)** Write the balanced half-reactions involved in the air oxidation of $Fe^{2+}(aq)$ to $Fe_2O_3 \cdot 3\,H_2O$.

**20.84** **(a)** Based on standard reduction potentials, would you expect copper metal to oxidize under standard conditions in the presence of oxygen and hydrogen ions? **(b)** When the Statue of Liberty was refurbished, Teflon spacers were placed between the iron skeleton and the copper metal on the surface of the statue. What role do these spacers play?

**20.85** **(a)** Magnesium metal is used as a sacrificial anode to protect underground pipes from corrosion. Why is the magnesium referred to as a "sacrificial anode"? **(b)** Looking in Appendix E, suggest what metal the underground pipes could be made from in order for magnesium to be successful as a sacrificial anode.

**20.86** An iron object is plated with a coating of cobalt to protect against corrosion. Does the cobalt protect iron by cathodic protection? Explain.

**20.87** A plumber's handbook states that you should not connect a brass pipe directly to a galvanized steel pipe because electrochemical reactions between the two metals will cause corrosion. The handbook recommends you use instead an insulating fitting to connect them. Brass is a mixture of copper and zinc. What spontaneous redox reaction(s) might cause the corrosion? Justify your answer with standard emf calculations.

**20.88** A plumber's handbook states that you should not connect a copper pipe directly to a steel pipe because electrochemical reactions between the two metals will cause corrosion. The handbook recommends you use instead an insulating fitting to connect them. What spontaneous redox reaction(s) might cause the corrosion? Justify your answer with standard emf calculations.

# ELECTROLYSIS (section 20.9)

**20.89** **(a)** What is *electrolysis*? **(b)** Are electrolysis reactions thermodynamically spontaneous? Explain. **(c)** What process occurs at the anode in the electrolysis of molten NaCl? **(d)** Why is sodium metal not obtained when an aqueous solution of NaCl undergoes electrolysis?

**20.90** **(a)** What is an *electrolytic cell*? **(b)** The negative terminal of a voltage source is connected to an electrode of an electrolytic cell. Is the electrode the anode or the cathode of the cell? Explain. **(c)** The electrolysis of water is often done with a small amount of sulfuric acid added to the water. What is the role of the sulfuric acid? **(d)** Why are active metals such as Al obtained by electrolysis using molten salts rather than aqueous solutions?

**20.91** **(a)** A $Cr^{3+}(aq)$ solution is electrolyzed, using a current of 7.60 A. What mass of Cr(s) is plated out after 2.00 days? **(b)** What amperage is required to plate out 0.250 mol Cr from a $Cr^{3+}$ solution in a period of 8.00 h?

**20.92** Metallic magnesium can be made by the electrolysis of molten $MgCl_2$. **(a)** What mass of Mg is formed by passing a current of 4.55 A through molten $MgCl_2$, for 4.50 days? **(b)** How many minutes are needed to plate out 25.00 g Mg from molten $MgCl_2$ using 3.50 A of current?

**20.93** **(a)** Calculate the mass of Li formed by electrolysis of molten LiCl by a current of $7.5 \times 10^4$ A flowing for a period of 24 h. Assume the electrolytic cell is 85% efficient. **(b)** What is the minimum voltage required to drive the reaction?

**20.94** Elemental calcium is produced by the electrolysis of molten $CaCl_2$. **(a)** What mass of calcium can be produced by this process if a current of $7.5 \times 10^3$ A is applied for 48 h? Assume that the electrolytic cell is 68% efficient. **(b)** What is the minimum voltage needed to cause the electrolysis?

**20.95** Metallic gold is collected from below the anode when crude copper metal is refined by electrolysis. Explain this behavior.

**20.96** The crude copper that is subjected to electrorefining contains tellurium as an impurity. The standard reduction potential between tellurium and its lowest common oxidation state, $Te^{4+}$, is

$$Te^{4+}(aq) + 4\,e^- \longrightarrow Te(s) \quad E^\circ_{red} = 0.57\ V$$

Given this information, describe the probable fate of tellurium impurities during electrorefining. Do the impurities fall to the bottom of the refining bath, unchanged, as copper is oxidized, or do they go into solution? If they go into solution, do they plate out on the cathode?

# ADDITIONAL EXERCISES

**20.97** A *disproportionation* reaction is an oxidation-reduction reaction in which the same substance is oxidized and reduced. Complete and balance the following disproportionation reactions:

(a) $Ni^+(aq) \longrightarrow Ni^{2+}(aq) + Ni(s)$      (acidic solution)

(b) $MnO_4^{2-}(aq) \longrightarrow MnO_4^-(aq) + MnO_2(s)$

                                          (acidic solution)

(c) $H_2SO_3(aq) \longrightarrow S(s) + HSO_4^-(aq)$    (acidic solution)

(d) $Cl_2(aq) \longrightarrow Cl^-(aq) + ClO^-(aq)$     (basic solution)

**20.98** This oxidation-reduction reaction in acidic solution is spontaneous:

$$5\,Fe^{2+}(aq) + MnO_4^-(aq) + 8\,H^+(aq) \longrightarrow$$
$$5\,Fe^{3+}(aq) + Mn^{2+}(aq) + 4\,H_2O(l)$$

A solution containing $KMnO_4$ and $H_2SO_4$ is poured into one beaker, and a solution of $FeSO_4$ is poured into another. A salt bridge is used to join the beakers. A platinum foil is placed in each solution, and a wire that passes through a voltmeter connects the two solutions. (a) Sketch the cell, indicating the anode and the cathode, the direction of electron movement through the external circuit, and the direction of ion migrations through the solutions. (b) Sketch the process that occurs at the atomic level at the surface of the anode. (c) Calculate the emf of the cell under standard conditions. (d) Calculate the emf of the cell at 298 K when the concentrations are the following: $pH = 0.0$, $[Fe^{2+}] = 0.10\,M$, $[MnO_4^-] = 1.50\,M$, $[Fe^{3+}] = 2.5 \times 10^{-4}\,M$, $[Mn^{2+}] = 0.001\,M$.

**20.99** A common shorthand way to represent a voltaic cell is

      anode|anode solution‖cathode solution|cathode

A double vertical line represents a salt bridge or a porous barrier. A single vertical line represents a change in phase, such as from solid to solution. (a) Write the half-reactions and overall cell reaction represented by $Fe|Fe^{2+}‖Ag^+|Ag$; sketch the cell. (b) Write the half-reactions and overall cell reaction represented by $Zn|Zn^{2+}‖H^+|H_2$; sketch the cell. (c) Using the notation just described, represent a cell based on the following reaction:

$$ClO_3^-(aq) + 3\,Cu(s) + 6\,H^+(aq) \longrightarrow$$
$$Cl^-(aq) + 3\,Cu^{2+}(aq) + 3\,H_2O(l)$$

Pt is used as an inert electrode in contact with the $ClO_3^-$ and $Cl^-$. Sketch the cell.

**20.100** Predict whether the following reactions will be spontaneous in acidic solution under standard conditions: (a) oxidation of Sn to $Sn^{2+}$ by $I_2$ (to form $I^-$), (b) reduction of $Ni^{2+}$ to Ni by $I^-$ (to form $I_2$), (c) reduction of $Ce^{4+}$ to $Ce^{3+}$ by $H_2O_2$, (d) reduction of $Cu^{2+}$ to Cu by $Sn^{2+}$ (to form $Sn^{4+}$).

[**20.101**] Gold exists in two common positive oxidation states, +1 and +3. The standard reduction potentials for these oxidation states are

$$Au^+(aq) + e^- \longrightarrow Au(s) \quad E_{red}^° = +1.69\,V$$
$$Au^{3+}(aq) + 3\,e^- \longrightarrow Au(s) \quad E_{red}^° = +1.50\,V$$

(a) Can you use these data to explain why gold does not tarnish in the air? (b) Suggest several substances that should be strong enough oxidizing agents to oxidize gold metal. (c) Miners obtain gold by soaking gold-containing ores in an aqueous solution of sodium cyanide. A very soluble complex ion of gold forms in the aqueous solution because of the redox reaction

$$4\,Au(s) + 8\,NaCN(aq) + 2\,H_2O(l) + O_2(g) \longrightarrow$$
$$4\,Na[Au(CN)_2](aq) + 4\,NaOH(aq)$$

What is being oxidized and what is being reduced in this reaction? (d) Gold miners then react the basic aqueous product solution from part (c) with Zn dust to get gold metal. Write a balanced redox reaction for this process. What is being oxidized, and what is being reduced?

**20.102** A voltaic cell is constructed from an $Ni^{2+}(aq)$-$Ni(s)$ half-cell and an $Ag^+(aq)$-$Ag(s)$ half-cell. The initial concentration of $Ni^{2+}(aq)$ in the $Ni^{2+}$-Ni half-cell is $[Ni^{2+}] = 0.0100\,M$. The initial cell voltage is +1.12 V. (a) By using data in Table 20.1, calculate the standard emf of this voltaic cell. (b) Will the concentration of $Ni^{2+}(aq)$ increase or decrease as the cell operates? (c) What is the initial concentration of $Ag^+(aq)$ in the $Ag^+$-Ag half-cell?

[**20.103**] A voltaic cell is constructed that uses the following half-cell reactions:

$$Cu^+(aq) + e^- \longrightarrow Cu(s)$$
$$I_2(s) + 2\,e^- \longrightarrow 2\,I^-(aq)$$

The cell is operated at 298 K with $[Cu^+] = 0.25\,M$ and $[I^-] = 3.5\,M$. (a) Determine $E$ for the cell at these concentrations. (b) Which electrode is the anode of the cell? (c) Is the answer to part (b) the same as it would be if the cell were operated under standard conditions? (d) If $[Cu^+]$ was equal to $0.15\,M$, at what concentration of $I^-$ would the cell have zero potential?

**20.104** Using data from Appendix E, calculate the equilibrium constant for the disproportionation of the copper(I) ion at room temperature: $2\,Cu^+(aq) \longrightarrow Cu^{2+}(aq) + Cu(s)$.

**20.105** (a) Write the reactions for the discharge and charge of a nickel-cadmium (nicad) rechargeable battery. (b) Given the following reduction potentials, calculate the standard emf of the cell:

$$Cd(OH)_2(s) + 2\,e^- \longrightarrow Cd(s) + 2\,OH^-(aq)$$
$$E_{red}^° = -0.76\,V$$
$$NiO(OH)(s) + H_2O(l) + e^- \longrightarrow Ni(OH)_2(s) + OH^-(aq)$$
$$E_{red}^° = +0.49\,V$$

(c) A typical nicad voltaic cell generates an emf of +1.30 V. Why is there a difference between this value and the one you calculated in part (b)? (d) Calculate the equilibrium constant for the overall nicad reaction based on this typical emf value.

**20.106** The capacity of batteries such as the typical AA alkaline battery is expressed in units of milliamp-hours (mAh). An AA alkaline battery yields a nominal capacity of 2850 mAh. (a) What quantity of interest to the consumer is being expressed by the units of mAh? (b) The starting voltage of a fresh alkaline battery is 1.55 V. The voltage decreases during discharge and is 0.80 V when the battery has delivered its rated capacity. If we assume that the voltage declines linearly as current is withdrawn, estimate the total maximum electrical work the battery could perform during discharge.

**20.107** If you were going to apply a small potential to a steel ship resting in the water as a means of inhibiting corrosion, would you apply a negative or a positive charge? Explain.

[**20.108**] (a) How many coulombs are required to plate a layer of chromium metal 0.25 mm thick on an auto bumper with a total area of $0.32\,m^2$ from a solution containing $CrO_4^{2-}$? The density of chromium metal is $7.20\,g/cm^3$. (b) What current flow is required for this electroplating if the bumper is to be plated in 10.0 s? (c) If the external source has an emf of +6.0 V and the electrolytic cell is 65% efficient, how much electrical power is expended to electroplate the bumper?

**20.109** Magnesium is obtained by electrolysis of molten $MgCl_2$. **(a)** Why is an aqueous solution of $MgCl_2$ not used in the electrolysis? **(b)** Several cells are connected in parallel by very large copper buses that convey current to the cells. Assuming that the cells are 96% efficient in producing the desired products in electrolysis, what mass of Mg is formed by passing a current of 97,000 A for a period of 24 hr?

**20.110** Calculate the number of kilowatt-hours of electricity required to produce $1.0 \times 10^3$ kg (1 metric ton) of aluminum by electrolysis of $Al^{3+}$ if the applied voltage is 4.50 V and the process is 45% efficient.

**20.111** Some years ago a unique proposal was made to raise the *Titanic*. The plan involved placing pontoons within the ship using a surface-controlled submarine-type vessel. The pontoons would contain cathodes and would be filled with hydrogen gas formed by the electrolysis of water. It has been estimated that it would require about $7 \times 10^8$ mol of $H_2$ to provide the buoyancy to lift the ship (*J. Chem. Educ.*, 1973, Vol. 50, 61). **(a)** How many coulombs of electrical charge would be required? **(b)** What is the minimum voltage required to generate $H_2$ and $O_2$ if the pressure on the gases at the depth of the wreckage (2 mi) is 300 atm? **(c)** What is the minimum electrical energy required to raise the *Titanic* by electrolysis? **(d)** What is the minimum cost of the electrical energy required to generate the necessary $H_2$ if the electricity costs 85 cents per kilowatt-hour to generate at the site?

# INTEGRATIVE EXERCISES

**20.112** The Haber process is the principal industrial route for converting nitrogen into ammonia:

$$N_2(g) + 3 H_2(g) \longrightarrow 2 NH_3(g)$$

**(a)** What is being oxidized, and what is being reduced? **(b)** Using the thermodynamic data in Appendix C, calculate the equilibrium constant for the process at room temperature. **(c)** Calculate the standard emf of the Haber process at room temperature.

**[20.113]** In a galvanic cell the cathode is an $Ag^+$ (1.00 *M*)/Ag(*s*) half-cell. The anode is a standard hydrogen electrode immersed in a buffer solution containing 0.10 *M* benzoic acid ($C_6H_5COOH$) and 0.050 *M* sodium benzoate ($C_6H_5COO^-Na^+$). The measured cell voltage is 1.030 V. What is the p$K_a$ of benzoic acid?

**20.114** Consider the general oxidation of a species A in solution: $A \longrightarrow A^+ + e^-$. The term *oxidation potential* is sometimes used to describe the ease with which species A is oxidized—the easier a species is to oxidize, the greater its oxidation potential. **(a)** What is the relationship between the standard oxidation potential of A and the standard reduction potential of $A^+$? **(b)** Which of the metals listed in Table 4.5 has the highest standard oxidation potential? Which has the lowest? **(c)** For a series of substances, the trend in oxidation potential is often related to the trend in the first ionization energy. Explain why this relationship makes sense.

**20.115** A voltaic cell is based on $Ag^+(aq)$/Ag(*s*) and $Fe^{3+}(aq)$/$Fe^{2+}(aq)$ half-cells. **(a)** What is the standard emf of the cell? **(b)** Which reaction occurs at the cathode and which at the anode of the cell? **(c)** Use $S°$ values in Appendix C and the relationship between cell potential and free-energy change to predict whether the standard cell potential increases or decreases when the temperature is raised above 25 °C.

**20.116** Hydrogen gas has the potential as a clean fuel in reaction with oxygen. The relevant reaction is

$$2 H_2(g) + O_2(g) \longrightarrow 2 H_2O(l)$$

Consider two possible ways of utilizing this reaction as an electrical energy source: (i) Hydrogen and oxygen gases are combusted and used to drive a generator, much as coal is currently used in the electric power industry; (ii) hydrogen and oxygen gases are used to generate electricity directly by using fuel cells that operate at 85 °C. **(a)** Use data in Appendix C to calculate $\Delta H°$ and $\Delta S°$ for the reaction. We will assume that these values do not change appreciably with temperature. **(b)** Based on the values from part (a), what trend would you expect for the magnitude of $\Delta G$ for the reaction as the temperature increases? **(c)** What is the significance of the change in the magnitude of $\Delta G$ with temperature with respect to the utility of hydrogen as a fuel? **(d)** Based on the analysis here, would it be more efficient to use the combustion method or the fuel-cell method to generate electrical energy from hydrogen?

**20.117** Cytochrome, a complicated molecule that we will represent as $CyFe^{2+}$, reacts with the air we breathe to supply energy required to synthesize adenosine triphosphate (ATP). The body uses ATP as an energy source to drive other reactions. (Section 19.7) At pH 7.0 the following reduction potentials pertain to this oxidation of $CyFe^{2+}$:

$$O_2(g) + 4 H^+(aq) + 4 e^- \longrightarrow 2 H_2O(l) \qquad E°_{red} = +0.82 \text{ V}$$
$$CyFe^{3+}(aq) + e^- \longrightarrow CyFe^{2+}(aq) \qquad E°_{red} = +0.22 \text{ V}$$

**(a)** What is $\Delta G$ for the oxidation of $CyFe^{2+}$ by air? **(b)** If the synthesis of 1.00 mol of ATP from adenosine diphosphate (ADP) requires a $\Delta G$ of 37.7 kJ, how many moles of ATP are synthesized per mole of $O_2$?

**[20.118]** The standard potential for the reduction of AgSCN(*s*) is +0.0895 V.

$$AgSCN(s) + e^- \longrightarrow Ag(s) + SCN^-(aq)$$

Using this value and the electrode potential for $Ag^+(aq)$, calculate the $K_{sp}$ for AgSCN.

**[20.119]** The $K_{sp}$ value for PbS(*s*) is $8.0 \times 10^{-28}$. By using this value together with an electrode potential from Appendix E, determine the value of the standard reduction potential for the reaction

$$PbS(s) + 2 e^- \longrightarrow Pb(s) + S^{2-}(aq)$$

**[20.120]** A student designs an ammeter (a device that measures electrical current) that is based on the electrolysis of water into hydrogen and oxygen gases. When electrical current of unknown magnitude is run through the device for 2.00 min, 12.3 mL of water-saturated $H_2(g)$ is collected. The temperature of the system is 25.5 °C, and the atmospheric pressure is 768 torr. What is the magnitude of the current in amperes?

# WHAT'S AHEAD

**21.1 RADIOACTIVITY**
In this chapter we learn how to describe nuclear reactions by equations analogous to chemical equations, in which the nuclear charges and masses of reactants and products are in balance. Radioactive nuclei most commonly decay by emission of *alpha*, *beta*, or *gamma* radiation.

**21.2 PATTERNS OF NUCLEAR STABILITY**
We recognize that nuclear stability is determined largely by the *neutron-to-proton ratio*. For stable nuclei, this ratio increases with increasing atomic number. All nuclei with 84 or more protons are radioactive. Heavy nuclei gain stability by a series of nuclear disintegrations leading to stable nuclei.

**21.3 NUCLEAR TRANSMUTATIONS**
We study *nuclear transmutations*, which are nuclear reactions induced by bombardment of a nucleus by a neutron or an accelerated charged particle.

**21.4 RATES OF RADIOACTIVE DECAY**
We learn that radioisotope decays are first-order kinetic processes with characteristic half-lives. Decay rates can be used to determine the age of ancient artifacts and geological formations.

21

**THE REMNANT OF THE SUPERNOVA CASSIOPEIA A** as viewed from the Chandra X-ray Observatory.

# NUCLEAR CHEMISTRY

**ULTIMATELY THE CHEMICAL ENERGY** that fuels life on Earth comes from sunlight. Plants convert the radiant energy of the Sun into chemical energy through photosynthesis, producing oxygen and carbohydrates. Life on Earth could not exist without energy from the Sun, but where does the Sun get its energy? Stars,

including our sun, use **nuclear reactions** that involve changes in atomic nuclei to generate their energy. For example, the Sun produces energy by fusing hydrogen atoms to form helium, releasing vast amounts of energy in the process.

The fusion of hydrogen to form helium is the dominant nuclear reaction for most of a star's lifetime. Toward the end of its life, the hydrogen in the star's core is exhausted and the helium atoms fuse to form progressively heavier elements. A select few stars end their lives in dramatic supernova explosions such as the one shown in the chapter opening photograph. The nuclear reactions that occur when a star goes supernova are responsible for the existence of all naturally occurring elements heavier than nickel.

*Nuclear chemistry* is the study of nuclear reactions, with an emphasis on their uses in chemistry and their effects on biological systems. Nuclear chemistry affects our lives in many ways, particularly in energy and medical applications. In radiation therapy, for example, gamma rays from a radioactive substance such as cobalt-60 are directed to cancerous tumors to destroy them. Positron emission tomography (PET) is one example of a medical diagnostic tool that relies on decay of a radioactive element injected into the body.

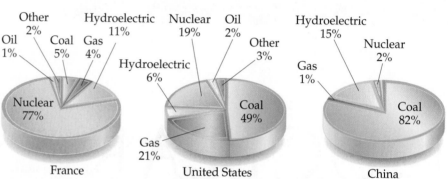

► **FIGURE 21.1** **Sources of electricity generation, worldwide and for select countries.**

Radioactivity is also used to help determine the mechanisms of chemical reactions, to trace the movement of atoms in biological systems and the environment, and to date historical artifacts.

Nuclear reactions are also used to generate electricity. Roughly 15% of the electricity generated worldwide comes from nuclear power plants, though the percentage varies from one country to the next, as ▲ **FIGURE 21.1** shows.

The use of nuclear energy for power generation and the disposal of nuclear wastes from power plants are controversial social and political issues. It is imperative, therefore, that as a citizen with a stake in these matters, you have some understanding of nuclear reactions and the uses of radioactive substances.

## 21.1 | RADIOACTIVITY

To understand nuclear reactions, we must review and develop some ideas introduced in Section 2.3. First, recall that two types of subatomic particles reside in the nucleus: *protons* and *neutrons*. We will refer to these particles as **nucleons**. Recall also that all atoms of a given element have the same number of protons; this number is the element's *atomic number*. The atoms of a given element can have different numbers of neutrons, however, so they can have different *mass numbers*; the mass number is the total number of nucleons in the nucleus. Atoms with the same atomic number but different mass numbers are known as *isotopes*.

The different isotopes of an element are distinguished by their mass numbers. For example, the three naturally occurring isotopes of uranium are uranium-234, uranium-235, and uranium-238, where the numerical suffixes represent the mass numbers. These isotopes are also written $^{234}_{92}U$, $^{235}_{92}U$, and $^{238}_{92}U$, where the superscript is the mass number and the subscript is the atomic number.

Different isotopes of an element have different natural abundances. For example, 99.3% of naturally occurring uranium is uranium-238, 0.7% is uranium-235, and only a trace is uranium-234. Different isotopes of an element also have different stabilities. Indeed, the nuclear properties of any given isotope depend on the number of protons and neutrons in its nucleus.

A *nuclide* is a nucleus containing a specified number of protons and neutrons. Nuclides that are radioactive are called **radionuclides**, and atoms containing these nuclei are called **radioisotopes**.

# Nuclear Equations

Most nuclei in nature are stable and remain intact indefinitely. Radionuclides, however, are unstable and spontaneously emit particles and electromagnetic radiation. Emission of radiation is one of the ways in which an unstable nucleus is transformed into a more stable one that has less energy. The emitted radiation is the carrier of the excess energy. Uranium-238, for example, is radioactive, undergoing a nuclear reaction emitting helium-4 nuclei. The helium-4 particles are known as **alpha ($\alpha$) particles**, and a stream of them is called *alpha radiation*. When a $^{238}_{92}U$ nucleus loses an alpha particle, the remaining fragment has an atomic number of 90 and a mass number of 234. The element with atomic number 90 is Th, thorium. Therefore, the products of uranium-238 decomposition are an alpha particle and a thorium-234 nucleus. We represent this reaction by the *nuclear equation*

$$^{238}_{92}U \longrightarrow {}^{234}_{90}Th + {}^{4}_{2}He \qquad [21.1]$$

When a nucleus spontaneously decomposes in this way, it is said either to have decayed or to have undergone *radioactive decay*. Because an alpha particle is involved in this reaction, scientists also describe the process as **alpha decay**.

> ## ⚠ GIVE IT SOME THOUGHT
>
> What change in the mass number of a nucleus occurs when the nucleus emits an alpha particle?

In Equation 21.1 the sum of the mass numbers is the same on both sides of the equation (238 = 234 + 4). Likewise, the sum of the atomic numbers on both sides of the equation is equal (92 = 90 + 2). Mass numbers and atomic numbers must be balanced in all nuclear equations.

The radioactive properties of the nucleus in an atom are independent of the chemical state of the atom. In writing nuclear equations, therefore, we are not concerned with the chemical form (element or compound) of the atom in which the nucleus resides.

---

## SAMPLE EXERCISE 21.1 | Predicting the Product of a Nuclear Reaction

What product is formed when radium-226 undergoes alpha decay?

### SOLUTION

**Analyze** We are asked to determine the nucleus that results when radium-226 loses an alpha particle.

**Plan** We can best do this by writing a balanced nuclear reaction for the process.

**Solve** The periodic table shows that radium has an atomic number of 88. The complete chemical symbol for radium-226 is therefore $^{226}_{88}Ra$. An alpha particle is a helium-4 nucleus, and so its symbol is $^{4}_{2}He$ (sometimes written as $^{4}_{2}\alpha$). The alpha particle is a product of the nuclear reaction, and so the equation is of the form

$$^{226}_{88}Ra \longrightarrow {}^{A}_{Z}X + {}^{4}_{2}He$$

where $A$ is the mass number of the product nucleus and $Z$ is its atomic number. Mass numbers and atomic numbers must balance, so

$$226 = A + 4$$

and

$$88 = Z + 2$$

Hence,

$$A = 222 \quad \text{and} \quad Z = 86$$

Again, from the periodic table, the element with $Z = 86$ is radon (Rn). The product, therefore, is $^{222}_{86}Rn$, and the nuclear equation is

$$^{226}_{88}Ra \longrightarrow {}^{222}_{86}Rn + {}^{4}_{2}He$$

### PRACTICE EXERCISE

Which element undergoes alpha decay to form lead-208?

***Answer:*** $^{212}_{84}Po$

| | Type of Radiation | | |
|---|---|---|---|
| Property | $\alpha$ | $\beta$ | $\gamma$ |
| Charge | 2+ | 1− | 0 |
| Mass | $6.64 \times 10^{-24}$ g | $9.11 \times 10^{-28}$ g | 0 |
| Relative penetrating power | 1 | 100 | 10,000 |
| Nature of radiation | $_2^4$He nuclei | Electrons | High-energy photons |

**TABLE 21.1 • Properties of Alpha, Beta, and Gamma Radiation**

## Types of Radioactive Decay

The three most common kinds of radiation given off when a radionuclide decays are alpha ($\alpha$), beta ($\beta$), and gamma ($\gamma$) radiation. ∞ (Section 2.2) ▲ **TABLE 21.1** summarizes some of the important properties of these types of radiation. As just described, alpha radiation consists of a stream of helium-4 nuclei known as alpha particles, which we denote as $_2^4$He or $_2^4\alpha$.

*Beta radiation* consists of streams of **beta ($\beta$) particles**, which are high-speed electrons emitted by an unstable nucleus. Beta particles are represented in nuclear equations by $_{-1}^0$e or sometimes by $_{-1}^0\beta$. The superscript 0 indicates that the mass of the electron is exceedingly small relative to the mass of a nucleon. The subscript −1 represents the negative charge of the beta particle, which is opposite that of the proton.

Iodine-131 is an isotope that undergoes decay by **beta emission**:

$$_{53}^{131}\text{I} \longrightarrow {}_{54}^{131}\text{Xe} + {}_{-1}^0\text{e} \qquad [21.2]$$

You can see from this equation that beta decay causes the atomic number of the reactant to increase from 53 to 54, which means a proton was created. Therefore, beta emission is equivalent to the conversion of a neutron ($_0^1$n) to a proton ($_1^0$p or $_1^1$H):

$$_0^1\text{n} \longrightarrow {}_1^1\text{p} + {}_{-1}^0\text{e} \qquad [21.3]$$

Just because an electron is emitted from a nucleus in beta decay, we should not think that the nucleus is composed of these particles any more than we consider a match to be composed of sparks simply because it gives them off when struck. The beta-particle electron comes into being only when the nucleus undergoes a nuclear reaction. Furthermore, the speed of the beta particle is sufficiently high that it does not end up in an orbital of the decaying atom.

**Gamma ($\gamma$) radiation** (or gamma rays) consists of high-energy photons (that is, electromagnetic radiation of very short wavelength). It changes neither the atomic number nor the mass number of a nucleus and is represented as either $_0^0\gamma$ or merely $\gamma$. Gamma radiation usually accompanies other radioactive emission because it represents the energy lost when the nucleons in a nuclear reaction reorganize into more stable arrangements. Generally, gamma rays are not shown when writing nuclear equations.

Two other types of radioactive decay are positron emission and electron capture. A **positron**, $_1^0$e, is a particle that has the same mass as an electron (thus, we use the letter e and superscript 0 for the mass) but the opposite charge (represented by the +1 subscript).*

The isotope carbon-11 decays by **positron emission**:

$$_6^{11}\text{C} \longrightarrow {}_5^{11}\text{B} + {}_1^0\text{e} \qquad [21.4]$$

Positron emission causes the atomic number of the reactant in this equation to decrease from 6 to 5. In general, positron emission has the effect of converting a proton to a neutron, thereby decreasing the atomic number of the nucleus by 1:

$$_1^1\text{p} \longrightarrow {}_0^1\text{n} + {}_1^0\text{e} \qquad [21.5]$$

---

*The positron has a very short life because it is annihilated when it collides with an electron, producing gamma rays: $_1^0\text{e} + {}_{-1}^0\text{e} \longrightarrow 2\,{}_0^0\gamma$.

**Electron capture** is the capture by the nucleus of an electron from the electron cloud surrounding the nucleus, as in this rubidium-81 decay:

$$^{81}_{37}Rb + {}^{0}_{-1}e \text{ (orbital electron)} \longrightarrow {}^{81}_{36}Kr \qquad [21.6]$$

Because the electron is consumed rather than formed in the process, it is shown on the reactant side of the equation. Electron capture, like positron emission, has the effect of converting a proton to a neutron:

$$^{1}_{1}p + {}^{0}_{-1}e \longrightarrow {}^{1}_{0}n \qquad [21.7]$$

▶ TABLE 21.2 summarizes the symbols used to represent the particles commonly encountered in nuclear reactions. The various types of radioactive decay are summarized in ▼ TABLE 21.3.

### TABLE 21.2 • Particles Found in Nuclear Reactions

| Particle | Symbol |
|---|---|
| Neutron | $^{1}_{0}n$ |
| Proton | $^{1}_{1}H$ or $^{1}_{1}p$ |
| Electron | $^{0}_{-1}e$ |
| Alpha particle | $^{4}_{2}He$ or $^{4}_{2}\alpha$ |
| Beta particle | $^{0}_{-1}e$ or $^{0}_{-1}\beta$ |
| Positron | $^{0}_{1}e$ |

### TABLE 21.3 • Types of Radioactive Decay

| Type | Nuclear Equation | Change in Atomic Number | Change in Mass Number |
|---|---|---|---|
| Alpha decay | $^{A}_{Z}X \longrightarrow {}^{A-4}_{Z-2}Y + {}^{4}_{2}He$ | −2 | −4 |
| Beta emission | $^{A}_{Z}X \longrightarrow {}^{A}_{Z+1}Y + {}^{0}_{-1}e$ | +1 | Unchanged |
| Positron emission | $^{A}_{Z}X \longrightarrow {}^{A}_{Z-1}Y + {}^{0}_{1}e$ | −1 | Unchanged |
| Electron capture* | $^{A}_{Z}X + {}^{0}_{-1}e \longrightarrow {}^{A}_{Z-1}Y$ | −1 | Unchanged |

*The electron captured comes from the electron cloud surrounding the nucleus.

 **GIVE IT SOME THOUGHT**

Which particles in Table 21.2 result in no change in nuclear charge when emitted in nuclear decay?

### SAMPLE EXERCISE 21.2 | Writing Nuclear Equations

Write nuclear equations for **(a)** mercury-201 undergoing electron capture; **(b)** thorium-231 decaying to protactinium-231.

#### SOLUTION

**Analyze** We must write balanced nuclear equations in which the masses and charges of reactants and products are equal.

**Plan** We can begin by writing the complete chemical symbols for the nuclei and decay particles that are given in the problem.

**Solve**
**(a)** The information given in the question can be summarized as

$$^{201}_{80}Hg + {}^{0}_{-1}e \longrightarrow {}^{A}_{Z}X$$

The mass numbers must have the same sum on both sides of the equation:

$$201 + 0 = A$$

Thus, the product nucleus must have a mass number of 201. Similarly, balancing the atomic numbers gives

$$80 - 1 = Z$$

Thus, the atomic number of the product nucleus must be 79, which identifies it as gold (Au):

$$^{201}_{80}Hg + {}^{0}_{-1}e \longrightarrow {}^{201}_{79}Au$$

**(b)** In this case we must determine what type of particle is emitted in the course of the radioactive decay:

$$^{231}_{90}Th \longrightarrow {}^{231}_{91}Pa + {}^{A}_{Z}X$$

From $231 = 231 + A$ and $90 = 91 + Z$, we deduce $A = 0$ and $Z = -1$. According to Table 21.2, the particle with these characteristics is the beta particle (electron). We therefore write

$$^{231}_{90}Th \longrightarrow {}^{231}_{91}Pa + {}^{0}_{-1}e$$

# 21.2 | PATTERNS OF NUCLEAR STABILITY

No single rule allows us to predict whether a particular nucleus is radioactive and, if it is, how it might decay. However, several empirical observations can help us predict the stability of a nucleus.

## Neutron-to-Proton Ratio

Because like charges repel each other, it may seem surprising that a large number of protons can reside within the small volume of the nucleus. At close distances, however, a strong force of attraction, called the *nuclear force*, exists between nucleons. Neutrons are intimately involved in this attractive force. All nuclei other than $^{1}_{1}H$ contain neutrons. As the number of protons in a nucleus increases, there is an ever greater need for neutrons to counteract the proton–proton repulsions. Stable nuclei with atomic numbers up to about 20 have approximately equal numbers of neutrons and protons. For nuclei with atomic number above 20, the number of neutrons exceeds the number of protons. Indeed, the number of neutrons necessary to create a stable nucleus increases more rapidly than the number of protons. Thus, the neutron-to-proton ratios of stable nuclei increase with increasing atomic number, as illustrated by the most common isotopes of carbon, $^{12}_{6}C$ (n/p = 1), manganese, $^{55}_{25}Mn$ (n/p = 1.20), and gold, $^{197}_{79}Au$ (n/p = 1.49).

The dark blue dots in ▶ FIGURE 21.2 represent stable (nonradioactive) isotopes. The region of the graph covered by these dark blue dots is known as the *belt of stability*. The belt of stability ends at element 83 (bismuth), which means that *all nuclei with 84 or more protons are radioactive*. For example, all isotopes of uranium, $Z = 92$, are radioactive.

The type of radioactive decay that a particular radionuclide undergoes depends largely on how its neutron-to-proton ratio compares with those of nearby nuclei that lie within the belt of stability. We can envision three general situations:

1. **Nuclei above the belt of stability (high neutron-to-proton ratios).** These neutron-rich nuclei can lower their ratio and thereby move toward the belt of stability by emitting a beta particle because beta emission decreases the number of neutrons and increases the number of protons (Equation 21.3).

2. **Nuclei below the belt of stability (low neutron-to-proton ratios).** These proton-rich nuclei can increase their ratio and so move closer to the belt of stability by either positron emission or electron capture because both decays increase the number of neutrons and decrease the number of protons (Equations 21.5 and 21.7). Positron emission is more common among lighter nuclei. Electron capture becomes increasingly common as the nuclear charge increases.

3. **Nuclei with atomic numbers ≥ 84.** These heavy nuclei tend to undergo alpha emission, which decreases both the number of neutrons and the number of protons by two, moving the nucleus diagonally toward the belt of stability.

**SAMPLE EXERCISE 21.3**    Predicting Modes of Nuclear Decay

Predict the mode of decay of (a) carbon-14, (b) xenon-118.

**SOLUTION**

**Analyze** We are asked to predict the modes of decay of two nuclei.

**Plan** To do this, we must locate the respective nuclei in Figure 21.2 and determine their positions with respect to the belt of stability in order to predict the most likely mode of decay.

**Solve**

**(a)** Carbon is element 6. Thus, carbon-14 has 6 protons and $14 - 6 = 8$ neutrons, giving it a neutron-to-proton ratio of 1.25. Elements with $Z < 20$ normally have stable nuclei that contain approximately equal numbers of neutrons and protons (n/p = 1). Thus, carbon-14 is located above the belt of stability and we expect it to decay by emitting a beta particle to lessen the n/p ratio:

$$^{14}_{6}\text{C} \longrightarrow \, ^{0}_{-1}\text{e} + \, ^{14}_{7}\text{N}$$

This is indeed the mode of decay observed for carbon-14, a reaction that lowers the n/p ratio from 1.25 to 1.0.

**(b)** Xenon is element 54. Thus, xenon-118 has 54 protons and $118 - 54 = 64$ neutrons, giving it an n/p ratio of 1.18. According to Figure 21.2, stable nuclei in this region of the belt of stability have higher neutron-to-proton ratios than xenon-118. The nucleus can increase this ratio by either positron emission or electron capture:

$$^{118}_{54}\text{Xe} \longrightarrow \, ^{0}_{1}\text{e} + \, ^{118}_{53}\text{I}$$

$$^{118}_{54}\text{Xe} + \, ^{0}_{-1}\text{e} \longrightarrow \, ^{118}_{53}\text{I}$$

In this case both modes of decay are observed.

**Comment** Keep in mind that our guidelines do not always work. For example, thorium-233, which we might expect to undergo alpha decay, actually undergoes beta emission. Furthermore, a few radioactive nuclei lie within the belt of stability. Both $^{146}_{60}\text{Nd}$ and $^{148}_{60}\text{Nd}$, for example, are stable and lie in the belt of stability. $^{147}_{60}\text{Nd}$, however, which lies between them, is radioactive.

**PRACTICE EXERCISE**

Predict the mode of decay of **(a)** plutonium-239, **(b)** indium-120.

**Answers:** **(a)** $\alpha$ decay, **(b)** $\beta$ emission

---

▲ **GO FIGURE**

Estimate the optimal number of neutrons for a nucleus containing 70 protons.

◀ **FIGURE 21.2  Stable and radioactive isotopes as a function of numbers of neutrons and protons in a nucleus.** The stable nuclei (dark blue dots) define a region known as the belt of stability.

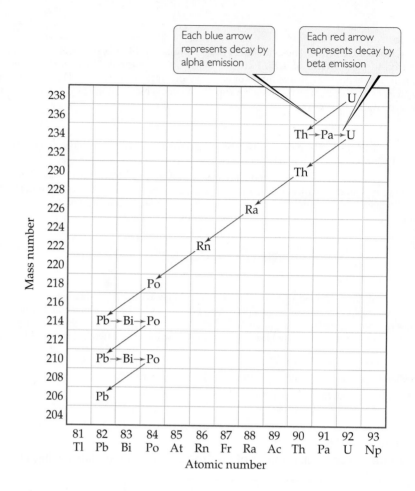

► FIGURE 21.3 **Nuclear disintegration series for uranium-238.** The decay continues until the stable nucleus $^{206}_{82}$Pb is formed.

## Radioactive Series

Some nuclei cannot gain stability by a single emission. Consequently, a series of successive emissions occurs as shown for uranium-238 in ▲ **FIGURE 21.3.** Decay continues until a stable nucleus—lead-206 in this case—is formed. A series of nuclear reactions that begins with an unstable nucleus and terminates with a stable one is known as a **radioactive series** or a **nuclear disintegration series.** Three such series occur in nature: uranium-238 to lead-206, uranium-235 to lead-207, and thorium-232 to lead-208.

## Further Observations

Two further observations can help us to predict stable nuclei:

• Nuclei with the **magic numbers** of 2, 8, 20, 28, 50, or 82 protons or 2, 8, 20, 28, 50, 82, or 126 neutrons are generally more stable than nuclei that do not contain these numbers of nucleons.

• Nuclei with even numbers of protrons, neutrons, or both are more likely to be stable than those with odd numbers of protons and/or neutrons. Approximately 60% of stable nuclei have an even number of both protons and neutrons, whereas less than 2% have odd numbers of both (◄ **TABLE 21.4**).

These observations can be understood in terms of the *shell model of the nucleus,* in which nucleons are described as residing in shells analogous to the shell structure for electrons in atoms. Just as certain numbers of electrons correspond to stable filled-shell electron configurations, so also the magic numbers of nucleons represent filled shells in nuclei.

There are several examples of the stability of nuclei with magic numbers of nucleons. For example, the radioactive series in Figure 21.3 ends with the stable $^{206}_{82}$Pb nucleus, which has a magic number of protons (82). Another example is the observation that tin, which has a magic number of protons (50), has ten stable isotopes, more than any other element.

**TABLE 21.4 • Number of Stable Isotopes with Even and Odd Numbers of Protons and Neutrons**

| Number of Stable Isotopes | Proton Number | Neutron Number |
|---|---|---|
| 157 | Even | Even |
| 53 | Even | Odd |
| 50 | Odd | Even |
| 5 | Odd | Odd |

## GO FIGURE

Among the elements shown here, how many have an even number of protons and fewer than three stable isotopes? How many have an odd number of protons and more than two stable isotopes?

| 1<br>H<br>(2) | ← Number of stable isotopes | | | | | | | | | | | | | | | | 2<br>He<br>(2) |
|---|---|---|---|---|---|---|---|---|---|---|---|---|---|---|---|---|---|

Elements with two or fewer isotopes

Elements with three or more isotopes

| 3<br>Li<br>(2) | 4<br>Be<br>(1) | | | | | | | | | | | 5<br>B<br>(2) | 6<br>C<br>(2) | 7<br>N<br>(2) | 8<br>O<br>(3) | 9<br>F<br>(1) | 10<br>Ne<br>(3) |
|---|---|---|---|---|---|---|---|---|---|---|---|---|---|---|---|---|---|
| 11<br>Na<br>(1) | 12<br>Mg<br>(3) | | | | | | | | | | | 13<br>Al<br>(1) | 14<br>Si<br>(3) | 15<br>P<br>(1) | 16<br>S<br>(4) | 17<br>Cl<br>(2) | 18<br>Ar<br>(3) |
| 19<br>K<br>(2) | 20<br>Ca<br>(5) | 21<br>Sc<br>(1) | 22<br>Ti<br>(5) | 23<br>V<br>(2) | 24<br>Cr<br>(4) | 25<br>Mn<br>(1) | 26<br>Fe<br>(4) | 27<br>Co<br>(1) | 28<br>Ni<br>(5) | 29<br>Cu<br>(2) | 30<br>Zn<br>(5) | 31<br>Ga<br>(2) | 32<br>Ge<br>(4) | 33<br>As<br>(1) | 34<br>Se<br>(5) | 35<br>Br<br>(2) | 36<br>Kr<br>(6) |
| 37<br>Rb<br>(1) | 38<br>Sr<br>(3) | 39<br>Y<br>(1) | 40<br>Zr<br>(4) | 41<br>Nb<br>(1) | 42<br>Mo<br>(6) | 43<br>Tc<br>(0) | 44<br>Ru<br>(7) | 45<br>Rh<br>(1) | 46<br>Pd<br>(6) | 47<br>Ag<br>(2) | 48<br>Cd<br>(6) | 49<br>In<br>(1) | 50<br>Sn<br>(10) | 51<br>Sb<br>(2) | 52<br>Te<br>(6) | 53<br>I<br>(1) | 54<br>Xe<br>(9) |

▲ **FIGURE 21.4  Number of stable isotopes for elements 1–54.**

Evidence also suggests that pairs of protons and pairs of neutrons have a special stability, analogous to the pairs of electrons in molecules. This evidence accounts for the second observation noted earlier, that stable nuclei with an even number of protons and/or neutrons are far more numerous than those with odd numbers. The preference for even numbers of protons is illustrated in ▲ **FIGURE 21.4**, which shows the number of stable isotopes for all elements up to Xe. Notice that once we move past nitrogen, the elements with an odd number of protons invariably have fewer stable isotopes than their neighbors with an even number of protons.

## GIVE IT SOME THOUGHT

What can you say about the number of neutrons in the stable isotopes of fluorine, sodium, aluminum, and phosphorus?

---

**SAMPLE EXERCISE 21.4  Predicting Nuclear Stability**

Predict which of these nuclei are especially stable: $^{4}_{2}\text{He}$, $^{40}_{20}\text{Ca}$, $^{98}_{43}\text{Tc}$.

### SOLUTION

**Analyze** We are asked to identify especially stable nuclei, given their mass numbers and atomic numbers.

**Plan** We look to see whether the numbers of protons and neutrons correspond to magic numbers.

**Solve** The $^{4}_{2}\text{He}$ nucleus (the alpha particle) has a magic number of both protons (2) and neutrons (2) and is very stable. The $^{40}_{20}\text{Ca}$ nucleus also has a magic number of both protons (20) and neutrons (20) and is especially stable.

The $^{98}_{43}\text{Tc}$ nucleus does not have a magic number of either protons or neutrons. In fact, it has an odd number of both protons (43) and neutrons (55). There are very few stable nuclei with odd numbers of both protons and neutrons. Indeed, technetium-98 is radioactive.

### PRACTICE EXERCISE

Which of the following nuclei would you expect to exhibit a special stability: $^{118}_{50}\text{Sn}$, $^{210}_{85}\text{At}$, $^{208}_{82}\text{Pb}$?

**Answer:** $^{118}_{50}\text{Sn}$, $^{208}_{82}\text{Pb}$

# 21.3 | NUCLEAR TRANSMUTATIONS

Thus far we have examined nuclear reactions in which a nucleus decays spontaneously. A nucleus can also change identity if it is struck by a neutron or by another nucleus. Nuclear reactions induced in this way are known as **nuclear transmutations**.

In 1919, Ernest Rutherford performed the first conversion of one nucleus into another, using alpha particles emitted by radium to convert nitrogen-14 into oxygen-17:

$$^{14}_{7}\text{N} + {}^{4}_{2}\text{He} \longrightarrow {}^{17}_{8}\text{O} + {}^{1}_{1}\text{H} \qquad [21.8]$$

Such reactions have allowed scientists to synthesize hundreds of radioisotopes in the laboratory.

Nuclear transmutations are sometimes represented by listing, in order, the target nucleus, the bombarding particle, the ejected particle, and the product nucleus. Using this condensed notation, Equation 21.8 becomes

$$^{14}_{7}\text{N} (\alpha, \text{p}) {}^{17}_{8}\text{O}$$

Target nucleus      Product nucleus

Bombarding particle      Ejected particle

---

**SAMPLE EXERCISE 21.5** | **Writing a Balanced Nuclear Equation**

Write the balanced nuclear equation for the process summarized as $^{27}_{13}\text{Al}(\text{n}, \alpha)^{24}_{11}\text{Na}$.

**SOLUTION**

**Analyze** We must go from the condensed descriptive form of the reaction to the balanced nuclear equation.

**Plan** We arrive at the balanced equation by writing n and $\alpha$, each with its associated subscripts and superscripts.

**Solve** The n is the abbreviation for a neutron ($^{1}_{0}\text{n}$) and $\alpha$ represents an alpha particle ($^{4}_{2}\text{He}$). The neutron is the bombarding particle, and the alpha particle is a product. Therefore, the nuclear equation is

$$^{27}_{13}\text{Al} + {}^{1}_{0}\text{n} \longrightarrow {}^{24}_{11}\text{Na} + {}^{4}_{2}\text{He}$$

**PRACTICE EXERCISE**

Write the condensed version of the nuclear reaction

$$^{16}_{8}\text{O} + {}^{1}_{1}\text{H} \longrightarrow {}^{13}_{7}\text{N} + {}^{4}_{2}\text{He}$$

**Answer:** $^{16}_{8}\text{O}(\text{p}, \alpha)^{13}_{7}\text{N}$

---

## Accelerating Charged Particles

Alpha particles and other positively charged particles must move very fast to overcome the electrostatic repulsion between them and the target nucleus. The higher the nuclear charge on either the bombarding particle or the target nucleus, the faster the bombarding particle must move to bring about a nuclear reaction. Many methods have been devised to accelerate charged particles, using strong magnetic and electrostatic fields. These **particle accelerators**, popularly called "atom smashers," bear such names as *cyclotron* and *synchrotron*.

A common theme in all particle accelerators is the need to create charged particles so that they can be manipulated by electrical and magnetic fields. The tubes through which the particles move must be kept at high vacuum so that the particles do not inadvertently collide with any gas-phase molecules.

▶ **FIGURE 21.5** shows the Relativistic Heavy Ion Collider (RHIC) located at Brookhaven National Laboratory. This facility and the Large Hadron Collider (LHC) at CERN (Conseil Européen pour la Recherche Nucléaire) near Geneva are two of the largest particle accelerators in the world. Both LHC and RHIC are capable of accelerating protons, as well as heavy ions such as gold and lead, to speeds approaching the speed

**4** Finally the ions are transferred to RHIC, which has a circumference of 3.8 km. Ions moving in opposite directions can collide at one of six points on the ring, marked with white rectangles

**3** The booster synchrotron and alternate gradient synchrotron (AGS) further accelerate the ions to 99.7% of the speed of light

**2** If needed, beams of $H^+$ ions can be generated in the Linac

**1** Gold atoms are ionized, creating ions that are accelerated in Tandem van de Graaff accelerator

▲ **FIGURE 21.5** **The Relativistic Heavy Ion Collider.** This particle accelerator is located at Brookhaven National Laboratory on Long Island, New York.

of light. Scientists study the outcomes of collisions involving these ultra-high-energy particles. These experiments are used to investigate the fundamental structure of matter and ultimately answer questions about the beginning of the universe.

## Reactions Involving Neutrons

Most synthetic isotopes used in medicine and scientific research are made using neutrons as the bombarding particles. Because neutrons are neutral, they are not repelled by the nucleus. Consequently, they do not need to be accelerated to cause nuclear reactions. The neutrons are produced in nuclear reactors. For example, cobalt-60, which is used in cancer radiation therapy, is produced by neutron capture. Iron-58 is placed in a nuclear reactor and bombarded by neutrons to trigger the reactions sequence

$$\ce{^{58}_{26}Fe} + \ce{^{1}_{0}n} \longrightarrow \ce{^{59}_{26}Fe} \qquad [21.9]$$

$$\ce{^{59}_{26}Fe} \longrightarrow \ce{^{59}_{27}Co} + \ce{^{0}_{-1}e} \qquad [21.10]$$

$$\ce{^{59}_{27}Co} + \ce{^{1}_{0}n} \longrightarrow \ce{^{60}_{27}Co} \qquad [21.11]$$

▲ **GIVE IT SOME THOUGHT**

Can an electrostatic or magnetic field be used to accelerate neutrons in a particle accelerator? Why or why not?

## Transuranium Elements

Nuclear transmutations have been used to produce the elements with atomic number above 92, collectively known as the **transuranium elements** because they follow uranium in the periodic table. Elements 93 (neptunium, Np) and 94 (plutonium, Pu) were produced in 1940 by bombarding uranium-238 with neutrons:

$$\ce{^{238}_{92}U + ^{1}_{0}n \longrightarrow ^{239}_{92}U \longrightarrow ^{239}_{93}Np + ^{0}_{-1}e} \qquad [21.12]$$

$$\ce{^{239}_{93}Np \longrightarrow ^{239}_{94}Pu + ^{0}_{-1}e} \qquad [21.13]$$

Elements with still larger atomic numbers are normally formed in small quantities in particle accelerators. Curium-242, for example, is formed when a plutonium-239 target is bombarded with accelerated alpha particles:

$$\ce{^{239}_{94}Pu + ^{4}_{2}He \longrightarrow ^{242}_{96}Cm + ^{1}_{0}n} \qquad [21.14]$$

In 1996 a team of European scientists based in Germany synthesized element 112, copernicium, Cn, by bombarding a lead target continuously for three weeks with a beam of zinc atoms:

$$\ce{^{208}_{82}Pb + ^{70}_{30}Zn \longrightarrow ^{277}_{112}Cn + ^{1}_{0}n} \qquad [21.15]$$

Amazingly, their discovery was based on the detection of only one atom of the new element, which decays after roughly 100 μs by alpha decay to form darmstadtium-273 (element 110). Within one minute, another five alpha decays take place producing fermium-253 (element 100). The finding has been verified in both Japan and Russia. More recently, scientists have reported the synthesis of elements 113 through 118. These results have yet to be confirmed by the International Union for Pure and Applied Chemistry, although the results look promising. Names and symbols have not yet been chosen for these new elements.

## 21.4 | RATES OF RADIOACTIVE DECAY

Some radioisotopes, such as uranium-238, are found in nature even though they are not stable. Other radioisotopes do not exist in nature but can be synthesized in nuclear reactions. To understand this distinction, we must realize that different nuclei undergo radioactive decay at different rates. Many radioisotopes decay essentially completely in a matter of seconds, so we do not find them in nature. Uranium-238, on the other hand, decays very slowly. Therefore, despite its instability, we can still observe what remains from its formation in the early history of the universe.

Radioactive decay is a first-order kinetic process. Recall that a first-order process has a characteristic **half-life**, which is the time required for half of any given quantity of a substance to react. ⟴ (Section 14.4) Nuclear decay rates are commonly expressed in terms of half-lives. Each isotope has its own characteristic half-life. For example, the half-life of strontium-90 is 28.8 yr (◄ FIGURE 21.6). If we start with 10.0 g of strontium-90, only 5.0 g of that isotope remains after 28.8 yr, 2.5 g remains after another 28.8 yr, and so on. Strontium-90 decays to yttrium-90:

$$\ce{^{90}_{38}Sr \longrightarrow ^{90}_{39}Y + ^{0}_{-1}e} \qquad [21.16]$$

Half-lives as short as millionths of a second and as long as billions of years are known. The half-lives of some radioisotopes are listed in ► TABLE 21.5. One important feature of half-lives for nuclear decay is that they are unaffected by external conditions such as temperature, pressure, or state of chemical combination. Unlike toxic chemicals, therefore, radioactive atoms cannot be rendered harmless by chemical reaction or by any other practical treatment. At this point, we can do nothing but allow these nuclei to lose radioactivity at their characteristic rates. In the meantime, we must take precautions to prevent radioisotopes, such as those produced in nuclear power plants (Section 21.7), from entering the environment because of the damage radiation can cause.

▲ **GO FIGURE**

**If we start with a 50.0-g sample, how much of it remains after three half-lives have passed?**

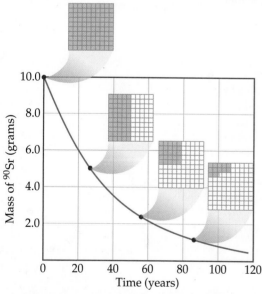

▲ **FIGURE 21.6 Decay of a 10.0-g sample of strontium-90 ($t_{1/2}$ = 28.8 yr).** The 10 × 10 grids show how much of the radioactive isotope remains after various amounts of time.

**TABLE 21.5 • The Half-Lives and Type of Decay for Several Radioisotopes**

|  | Isotope | Half-Life (yr) | Type of Decay |
|---|---|---|---|
| Natural radioisotopes | $^{238}_{92}U$ | $4.5 \times 10^9$ | Alpha |
|  | $^{235}_{92}U$ | $7.0 \times 10^8$ | Alpha |
|  | $^{232}_{90}Th$ | $1.4 \times 10^{10}$ | Alpha |
|  | $^{40}_{19}K$ | $1.3 \times 10^9$ | Beta |
|  | $^{14}_{6}C$ | 5715 | Beta |
| Synthetic radioisotopes | $^{239}_{94}Pu$ | 24,000 | Alpha |
|  | $^{137}_{55}Cs$ | 30 | Beta |
|  | $^{90}_{38}Sr$ | 28.8 | Beta |
|  | $^{131}_{53}I$ | 0.022 | Beta |

---

**SAMPLE EXERCISE 21.6** | **Calculation Involving Half-Lives**

The half-life of cobalt-60 is 5.3 yr. How much of a 1.000-mg sample of cobalt-60 is left after 15.9 yr?

**SOLUTION**

**Analyze** We are given the half-life for cobalt-60 and asked to calculate the amount of cobalt-60 remaining from an initial 1.000-mg sample after 15.9 yr.

**Plan** We will use the fact that the amount of a radioactive substance decreases by 50% for every half-life that passes.

**Solve** Because $5.3 \times 3 = 15.9$, 15.9 yr is three half-lives for cobalt-60. At the end of one half-life, 0.500 mg of cobalt-60 remains, 0.250 mg at the end of two half-lives, and 0.125 mg at the end of three half-lives.

**PRACTICE EXERCISE**

Carbon-11, used in medical imaging, has a half-life of 20.4 min. The carbon-11 nuclides are formed, and the carbon atoms are then incorporated into an appropriate compound. The resulting sample is injected into a patient, and the medical image is obtained. If the entire process takes five half-lives, what percentage of the original carbon-11 remains at this time?

*Answer:* 3.12%

---

# Radiometric Dating

Because the half-life of any particular nuclide is constant, the half-life can serve as a nuclear clock to determine the age of objects. The method of dating objects based on their isotopes and isotope abundances is called *radiometric dating*.

When carbon-14 is used in radiometric dating, the technique is known as *radiocarbon dating*. The procedure is based on the formation of carbon-14 as neutrons created by cosmic rays in the upper atmosphere convert nitrogen-14 into carbon-14 (▶ FIGURE 21.7). The $^{14}C$ reacts with oxygen to form $^{14}CO_2$ in the atmosphere, and this "labeled" $CO_2$ is taken up by plants and introduced into the food chain through photosynthesis. This process provides a small but reasonably constant source of carbon-14, which is radioactive and undergoes beta decay with a half-life of 5715 yr:

$$^{14}_{6}C \longrightarrow {}^{14}_{7}N + {}^{0}_{-1}e \qquad [21.17]$$

Because a living plant or animal has a constant intake of carbon compounds, it is able to maintain a ratio of carbon-14 to carbon-12 that is nearly identical with that of the atmosphere. Once the organism dies, however, it no longer ingests carbon compounds to replenish the carbon-14 lost through radioactive decay. The ratio of carbon-14 to carbon-12 therefore decreases. By measuring this ratio and comparing it with that of the atmosphere, we can estimate the age of an object. For example, if the ratio diminishes to half that of the atmosphere, we can conclude that the object is one half-life, or 5715 yr old.

This method cannot be used to date objects older than about 50,000 yr because after this length of time the radioactivity is too low to be measured accurately.

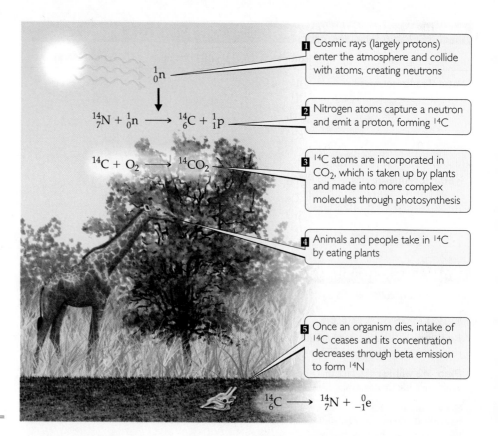

The following annotations appear in the figure:

**1** Cosmic rays (largely protons) enter the atmosphere and collide with atoms, creating neutrons

$$^{1}_{0}n$$

$$^{14}_{7}N + ^{1}_{0}n \longrightarrow ^{14}_{6}C + ^{1}_{1}P$$

**2** Nitrogen atoms capture a neutron and emit a proton, forming $^{14}C$

$$^{14}C + O_2 \longrightarrow ^{14}CO_2$$

**3** $^{14}C$ atoms are incorporated in $CO_2$, which is taken up by plants and made into more complex molecules through photosynthesis

**4** Animals and people take in $^{14}C$ by eating plants

**5** Once an organism dies, intake of $^{14}C$ ceases and its concentration decreases through beta emission to form $^{14}N$

$$^{14}_{6}C \longrightarrow ^{14}_{7}N + ^{0}_{-1}e$$

▶ **FIGURE 21.7 Creation and distribution of carbon-14.** The ratio of carbon-14 to carbon-12 in a dead animal or plant is related to the time since death occurred.

In radiocarbon dating, a reasonable assumption is that the ratio of carbon-14 to carbon-12 in the atmosphere has been relatively constant for the past 50,000 yr. However, because variations in solar activity control the amount of carbon-14 produced in the atmosphere, that ratio can fluctuate. We can correct for this effect by using other kinds of data. Recently scientists have compared carbon-14 data with data from tree rings, corals, lake sediments, ice cores, and other natural sources to correct variations in the carbon-14 "clock" back to 26,000 yr.

Other isotopes can be similarly used to date other types of objects. For example, it takes $4.5 \times 10^9$ yr for half of a sample of uranium-238 to decay to lead-206. The age of rocks containing uranium can therefore be determined by measuring the ratio of lead-206 to uranium-238. If the lead-206 had somehow become incorporated into the rock by normal chemical processes instead of by radioactive decay, the rock would also contain large amounts of the more abundant isotope lead-208. In the absence of large amounts of this "geonormal" isotope of lead, it is assumed that all of the lead-206 was at one time uranium-238.

The oldest rocks found on Earth are approximately $3 \times 10^9$ yr old. This age indicates that Earth's crust has been solid for at least this length of time. Scientists estimate that it required $1 \times 10^9$ to $1.5 \times 10^9$ yr for Earth to cool and its surface to become solid, making the age of Earth 4.0 to $4.5 \times 10^9$ yr.

## Calculations Based on Half-Life

So far, our discussion has been mainly qualitative. We now consider the topic of half-lives from a more quantitative point of view. This approach enables us to determine the half-life of a radioisotope or the age of an object.

As noted earlier, radioactive decay is a first-order kinetic process. Its rate, therefore, is proportional to the number of radioactive nuclei $N$ in a sample:

$$\text{Rate} = kN \qquad [21.18]$$

The first-order rate constant, $k$, is called the *decay constant*.

The rate at which a sample decays is called its **activity**, and it is often expressed as number of disintegrations per unit time. The **becquerel** (Bq) is the SI unit for expressing activity. A becquerel is defined as one nuclear disintegration per second. An older, but still widely used, unit of activity is the **curie** (Ci), defined as $3.7 \times 10^{10}$ disintegrations per second, which is the rate of decay of 1 g of radium. Thus, a 4.0-mCi sample of cobalt-60 undergoes

$$4.0 \times 10^{-3} \cancel{Ci} \times \frac{3.7 \times 10^{10} \text{ disintegrations/s}}{1 \cancel{Ci}} = 1.5 \times 10^8 \text{ disintegrations/s}$$

and so has an activity of $1.5 \times 10^8$ Bq.

As a radioactive sample decays, the amount of radiation emanating from the sample decays as well. For example, the half-life of cobalt-60 is 5.26 yr. The 4.0-mCi sample of cobalt-60 would, after 5.26 yr, have a radiation activity of 2.0 mCi, or $7.5 \times 10^7$ Bq.

**GIVE IT SOME THOUGHT**

Why can't spontaneous radioactive decay be a zero-order or second-order kinetic process?

As we saw in Section 14.4, a first-order rate law can be transformed into the equation

$$\ln \frac{N_t}{N_0} = -kt \qquad [21.19]$$

In this equation $t$ is the time interval of decay, $k$ is the decay constant, $N_0$ is the initial number of nuclei (at time zero), and $N_t$ is the number remaining after the time interval. Both the mass of a particular radioisotope and its activity are proportional to the number of radioactive nuclei. Thus, either the ratio of the mass at any time $t$ to the mass at time $t = 0$ or the ratio of the activities at time $t$ and $t = 0$ can be substituted for $N_t/N_0$ in Equation 21.19.

From Equation 21.19 we can obtain the relationship between the decay constant, $k$, and half-life, $t_{1/2}$: ∞ (Section 14.4)

$$k = \frac{0.693}{t_{1/2}} \qquad [21.20]$$

where we have used the value $\ln(N_t/N_0) = \ln(0.5) = -0.693$ for one half-life. Thus, if we know the value of either the decay constant or the half-life, we can calculate the value of the other.

**GIVE IT SOME THOUGHT**

a. Would doubling the mass of a radioactive sample change the activity of the sample?
b. Would doubling the mass change the half-life for the radioactive decay?

---

**SAMPLE EXERCISE 21.7** | **Calculating the Age of a Mineral**

A rock contains 0.257 mg of lead-206 for every milligram of uranium-238. The half-life for the decay of uranium-238 to lead-206 is $4.5 \times 10^9$ yr. How old is the rock?

**SOLUTION**

**Analyze** We are told that a rock sample has a certain amount of lead-206 for every unit mass of uranium-238 and asked to estimate the age of the rock.

**Plan** Lead-206 is the product of the radioactive decay of uranium-238. We will assume that the only source of lead-206 in the rock is from the decay of uranium-238, with a known half-life. To apply first-order kinetics expressions (Equations 21.19 and 21.20) to calculate the time elapsed since the rock was formed, we first need to calculate how much initial uranium-238 there was for every 1 mg that remains today.

**Solve** Let's assume that the rock currently contains 1.000 mg of uranium-238 and therefore 0.257 mg of lead-206. The amount of uranium-238 in the rock when it was first formed therefore equals 1.000 mg plus the quantity that has decayed to lead-206. Because the mass of lead atoms is not the same as the mass of uranium atoms, we cannot just add 1.000 mg and 0.257 mg. We have to multiply the present mass of lead-206 (0.257 mg) by the ratio of the mass number of uranium to that of lead, into which it has decayed. Therefore, the original mass of $^{238}_{92}U$ was

$$\text{Original } {}^{238}_{92}\text{U} = 1.000 \text{ mg} + \frac{238}{206}(0.257 \text{ mg})$$

$$= 1.297 \text{ mg}$$

Using Equation 21.20, we can calculate the decay constant for the process from its half-life:

$$k = \frac{0.693}{4.5 \times 10^9 \text{ yr}} = 1.5 \times 10^{-10} \text{ yr}^{-1}$$

Rearranging Equation 21.19 to solve for time, $t$, and substituting known quantities gives

$$t = -\frac{1}{k} \ln \frac{N_t}{N_0} = -\frac{1}{1.5 \times 10^{-10} \text{ yr}^{-1}} \ln \frac{1.000}{1.297} = 1.7 \times 10^9 \text{ yr}$$

**Comment** To check this result, you could use the fact that the decay of uranium-237 to lead-207 has a half-life of $7 \times 10^8$ yr and measure the relative amounts of uranium-237 and lead-207 in the rock.

### PRACTICE EXERCISE

A wooden object from an archeological site is subjected to radiocarbon dating. The activity due to $^{14}$C is measured to be 11.6 disintegrations per second. The activity of a carbon sample of equal mass from fresh wood is 15.2 disintegrations per second. The half-life of $^{14}$C is 5715 yr. What is the age of the archeological sample?
*Answer:* 2230 yr

We can also use measurements of radioactive activity to determine the half-life of a radioactive isotope, as the next sample exercise shows.

### SAMPLE EXERCISE 21.8 | Calculations Involving Radioactive Decay

If we start with 1.000 g of strontium-90, 0.953 g will remain after 2.00 yr. **(a)** What is the half-life of strontium-90? **(b)** How much strontium-90 will remain after 5.00 yr? **(c)** What is the initial activity of the sample in becquerels and curies?

### SOLUTION

**(a) Analyze** We are asked to calculate a half-life, $t_{1/2}$, based on data that tell us how much of a radioactive nucleus has decayed in a time interval $t = 2.00$ yr and the information $N_0 = 1.000$ g, $N_t = 0.953$ g.

**Plan** We first calculate the rate constant for the decay, $k$, and then use that to compute $t_{1/2}$.

**Solve** Equation 21.19 is solved for the decay constant, $k$, and then Equation 21.20 is used to calculate half-life, $t_{1/2}$:

$$k = -\frac{1}{t} \ln \frac{N_t}{N_0} = -\frac{1}{2.00 \text{ yr}} \ln \frac{0.953 \text{ g}}{1.000 \text{ g}}$$

$$= -\frac{1}{2.00 \text{ yr}} (-0.0481) = 0.0241 \text{ yr}^{-1}$$

$$t_{1/2} = \frac{0.693}{k} = \frac{0.693}{0.0241 \text{ yr}^{-1}} = 28.8 \text{ yr}$$

**(b) Analyze** We are asked to calculate the amount of a radionuclide remaining after a given period of time.

**Plan** We need to calculate $N_t$, the amount of strontium present at time $t$, using the initial quantity, $N_0$, and the rate constant for decay, $k$, calculated in part (a).

**Solve** Again using Equation 21.19, with $k = 0.0241 \text{ yr}^{-1}$, we have

$$\ln \frac{N_t}{N_0} = -kt = -(0.0241 \text{ yr}^{-1})(5.00 \text{ yr}) = -0.120$$

$N_t/N_0$ is calculated from $\ln(N_t/N_0) = -0.120$ using the $e^x$ or INV LN function of a calculator:

$$\frac{N_t}{N_0} = e^{-0.120} = 0.887$$

Because $N_0 = 1.000$ g, we have

$$N_t = (0.887)N_0 = (0.887)(1.000 \text{ g}) = 0.887 \text{ g}$$

**(c) Analyze** We are asked to calculate the activity of the sample in becquerels and curies.

**Plan** We must calculate the number of disintegrations per atom per second and then multiply by the number of atoms in the sample.

**Solve** The number of disintegrations per atom per second is given by the rate constant, $k$:

$$k = \left(\frac{0.0241}{yr}\right)\left(\frac{1\ yr}{365\ days}\right)\left(\frac{1\ day}{24\ h}\right)\left(\frac{1\ h}{3600\ s}\right) = 7.64 \times 10^{-10}\ s^{-1}$$

To obtain the total number of disintegrations per second, we calculate the number of atoms in the sample. We multiply this quantity by $k$, where we express $k$ as the number of disintegrations per atom per second, to obtain the number of disintegrations per second:

$$(1.000\ g\ ^{90}Sr)\left(\frac{1\ mol\ ^{90}Sr}{90\ g\ ^{90}Sr}\right)\left(\frac{6.022 \times 10^{23}\ atoms\ Sr}{1\ mol\ ^{90}Sr}\right) = 6.7 \times 10^{21}\ atoms\ ^{90}Sr$$

$$\text{Total disintegrations/s} = \left(\frac{7.64 \times 10^{-10}\ disintegrations}{atom \cdot s}\right)(6.7 \times 10^{21}\ atoms)$$

$$= 5.1 \times 10^{12}\ disintegrations/s$$

Because 1 Bq is one disintegration per second, the activity is $5.1 \times 10^{12}$ Bq. The activity in curies is given by

$$(5.1 \times 10^{12}\ disintegrations/s)\left(\frac{1\ Ci}{3.7 \times 10^{10}\ disintegrations/s}\right) = 1.4 \times 10^{2}\ Ci$$

We have used only two significant figures in products of these calculations because we do not know the atomic weight of $^{90}Sr$ to more than two significant figures without looking it up in a special source.

**PRACTICE EXERCISE**

A sample to be used for medical imaging is labeled with $^{18}F$, which has a half-life of 110 min. What percentage of the original activity in the sample remains after 300 min?

***Answer:*** 15.1%

# 21.5 | DETECTION OF RADIOACTIVITY

A variety of methods have been devised to detect emissions from radioactive substances. Henri Becquerel discovered radioactivity because radiation caused fogging of photographic plates, and since that time photographic plates and film have been used to detect radioactivity. The radiation affects photographic film in much the same way as X-rays do. The greater the extent of exposure to radiation, the darker the area of the developed negative. People who work with radioactive substances carry film badges to record the extent of their exposure to radiation (▼ **FIGURE 21.8**).

Radioactivity can also be detected and measured by a Geiger counter. The operation of this device is based on the fact that radiation is able to ionize matter. The ions and electrons produced by the ionizing radiation permit conduction of an electrical current. The basic design of a Geiger counter is shown in ▶ **FIGURE 21.9**. A current pulse between the anode and the metal cylinder occurs whenever entering radiation produces ions. Each pulse is counted in order to estimate the amount of radiation.

The film strip is white before exposure to radiation

The film strip is darkened on exposure to radiation

◀ FIGURE 21.8   **Badge dosimeters monitor the extent to which the individual has been exposed to high-energy radiation.** The radiation dose is determined from the extent of darkening of the film in the dosimeter.

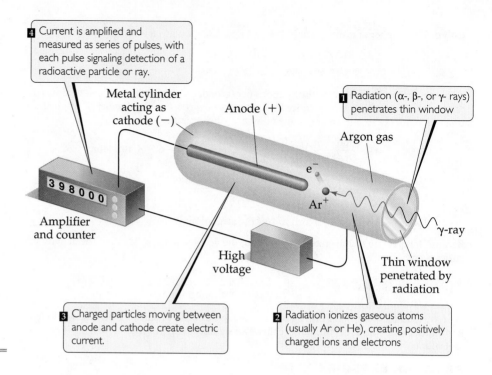

Current is amplified and measured as series of pulses, with each pulse signaling detection of a radioactive particle or ray.

Metal cylinder acting as cathode (−)

Anode (+)

Radiation (α-, β-, or γ- rays) penetrates thin window

Argon gas

e⁻

3 9 8 0 0 0

Ar⁺

γ-ray

Amplifier and counter

High voltage

Thin window penetrated by radiation

Charged particles moving between anode and cathode create electric current.

Radiation ionizes gaseous atoms (usually Ar or He), creating positively charged ions and electrons

▶ **FIGURE 21.9** **Schematic drawing of a Geiger counter.**

▲ **GIVE IT SOME THOUGHT**

Will alpha, beta, and gamma rays pass through the window of a Geiger counter with equal efficiency?

Substances that are electronically excited by radiation can also be used to detect and measure radiation. For example, some substances excited by radiation give off light as electrons return to their lower-energy states. These substances are called *phosphors*. Different substances respond to different particles. Zinc sulfide, for example, responds to alpha particles. An instrument called a scintillation counter is used to detect and measure radiation, based on the tiny flashes of light produced when radiation strikes a suitable phosphor. The flashes of light are magnified electronically and counted to measure the amount of radiation.

## Radiotracers

Because radioisotopes can be detected readily, they can be used to follow an element through its chemical reactions. The incorporation of carbon atoms from $CO_2$ into glucose during photosynthesis, for example, has been studied using $CO_2$ enriched in carbon-14:

$$6\,{}^{14}CO_2 + 6\,H_2O \xrightarrow[\text{Chlorophyll}]{\text{Sunlight}} {}^{14}C_6H_{12}O_6 + 6\,O_2 \qquad [21.21]$$

The use of the carbon-14 label provides direct experimental evidence that carbon dioxide in the environment is chemically converted to glucose in plants. Analogous labeling experiments using oxygen-18 show that the $O_2$ produced during photosynthesis comes from water, not carbon dioxide. When it is possible to isolate and purify intermediates and products from reactions, detection devices such as scintillation counters can be used to "follow" the radioisotope as it moves from starting material through intermediates to final product. These types of experiments are useful for identifying elementary steps in a reaction mechanism. ∞ (Section 14.6)

The use of radioisotopes is possible because all isotopes of an element have essentially identical chemical properties. When a small quantity of a radioisotope is mixed with the naturally occurring stable isotopes of the same element, all the isotopes go through the same reactions together. The element's path is revealed by the radioactivity of the radioisotope. Because the radioisotope can be used to trace the path of the element, it is called a **radiotracer**.

# CHEMISTRY AND LIFE

## MEDICAL APPLICATIONS OF RADIOTRACERS

Radiotracers have found wide use as diagnostic tools in medicine. ▼ TABLE 21.6 lists some radiotracers and their uses. These radioisotopes are incorporated into a compound that is administered to the patient, usually intravenously. The diagnostic use of these isotopes is based on the ability of the radioactive compound to localize and concentrate in the organ or tissue under investigation. Iodine-131, for example, has been used to test the activity of the thyroid gland. This gland is the only important user of iodine in the body. The patient drinks a solution of NaI containing iodine-131. Only a very small amount is used so that the patient does not receive a harmful dose of radioactivity. A Geiger counter placed close to the thyroid, in the neck region, determines the ability of the thyroid to take up the iodine. A normal thyroid will absorb about 12% of the iodine within a few hours.

The medical applications of radiotracers are further illustrated by positron emission tomography (PET). PET is used for clinical diagnosis of many diseases. In this method, compounds containing radionuclides that decay by positron emission are injected into a patient. These compounds are chosen to enable researchers to monitor blood flow, oxygen and glucose metabolic rates, and other biological functions. Some of the most interesting work involves the study of the brain, which depends on glucose for most of its energy. Changes in how this sugar is metabolized or used by the brain may signal a disease such as cancer, epilepsy, Parkinson's disease, or schizophrenia.

The compound to be detected in the patient must be labeled with a radionuclide that is a positron emitter. The most widely used nuclides are carbon-11 ($t_{1/2}$ = 20.4 min), fluorine-18 ($t_{1/2}$ = 110 min), oxygen-15 ($t_{1/2}$ = 2 min), and nitrogen-13 ($t_{1/2}$ = 10 min). Glucose, for example, can be labeled with carbon-11. Because the half-lives of positron emitters are so short, the chemist must quickly incorporate the radionuclide into the sugar (or other appropriate) molecule and inject the compound immediately. The patient is placed in an instrument that measures the positron emission and constructs a computer-based image of the organ in which the emitting compound is localized. When the element decays, the emitted positron quickly collides with an electron. The positron and electron are annihilated in the collision, producing two gamma rays that move in opposite directions. The gamma rays are detected by an encircling ring of scintillation counters (◄ FIGURE 21.10). Because the rays move in opposite directions but were created in the same place at the same time, it is possible to accurately locate the point in the body where the radioactive isotope decayed. The nature of this image provides clues to the presence of disease or other abnormality and helps medical researchers understand how a particular disease affects the functioning of the brain. For example, the images shown in ◄ FIGURE 21.11 reveal that levels of activity in brains of patients with Alzheimer's disease are different from the levels in those without the disease.

*RELATED EXERCISES:* 21.53, 21.54

**TABLE 21.6 • Some Radionuclides Used as Radiotracers**

| Nuclide | Half-Life | Area of the Body Studied |
| --- | --- | --- |
| Iodine-131 | 8.04 days | Thyroid |
| Iron-59 | 44.5 days | Red blood cells |
| Phosphorus-32 | 14.3 days | Eyes, liver, tumors |
| Technetium-99 | 6.0 hours | Heart, bones, liver, and lungs |
| Thallium-201 | 73 hours | Heart, arteries |
| Sodium-24 | 14.8 hours | Circulatory system |

Scintillation counters detect gamma rays

Gamma rays moving in opposite directions are created when a positron and an electron collide, annihilating each other

Radioactive isotope decays emitting a positron

▲ FIGURE 21.10 Schematic representation of a positron emission tomography (PET) scanner.

Normal

Mild cognitive impairment

Alzheimer's disease

◄ FIGURE 21.11 **Positron emission tomography (PET) scans showing glucose metabolism levels in the brain.** Red and yellow colors show higher levels of glucose metabolism.

## 21.6 | ENERGY CHANGES IN NUCLEAR REACTIONS

The energies associated with nuclear reactions can be considered with the aid of Einstein's celebrated equation relating mass and energy:

$$E = mc^2 \qquad [21.22]$$

In this equation $E$ stands for energy, $m$ for mass, and $c$ for the speed of light, $2.9979 \times 10^8$ m/s. This equation states that the mass and energy of an object are proportional. If a system loses mass, it loses energy (exothermic); if it gains mass, it gains energy (endothermic). Because the proportionality constant in the equation, $c^2$, is such a large number, even small changes in mass are accompanied by large changes in energy.

The mass changes in chemical reactions are too small to detect. For example, the mass change associated with the combustion of 1 mol of $CH_4$ (an exothermic process) is $-9.9 \times 10^{-9}$ g. Because the mass change is so small, it is possible to treat chemical reactions as though mass is conserved.

The mass changes and the associated energy changes in nuclear reactions are much greater than those in chemical reactions. The mass change accompanying the radioactive decay of 1 mol of uranium-238, for example, is 50,000 times greater than that for the combustion of 1 mol of $CH_4$. Let's examine the energy change for the nuclear reaction

$$^{238}_{92}U \longrightarrow {}^{234}_{90}Th + {}^4_2He$$

The masses of the nuclei are $^{238}_{92}U$, 238.0003 amu; $^{234}_{90}Th$, 233.9942 amu; and $^4_2He$, 4.0015 amu. The mass change, $\Delta m$, is the total mass of the products minus the total mass of the reactants. The mass change for the decay of 1 mol of uranium-238 can then be expressed in grams:

$$233.9942 \text{ g} + 4.0015 \text{ g} - 238.0003 \text{ g} = -0.0046 \text{ g}$$

The fact that the system has lost mass indicates that the process is exothermic. All spontaneous nuclear reactions are exothermic.

The energy change per mole associated with this reaction is

$$\Delta E = \Delta(mc^2) = c^2 \Delta m$$

$$= (2.9979 \times 10^8 \text{ m/s})^2(-0.0046 \text{ g})\left(\frac{1 \text{ kg}}{1000 \text{ g}}\right)$$

$$= -4.1 \times 10^{11} \frac{\text{kg-m}^2}{\text{s}^2} = -4.1 \times 10^{11} \text{ J}$$

Notice that $\Delta m$ must be converted to kilograms, the SI unit of mass, to obtain $\Delta E$ in joules, the SI unit of energy. The negative sign for the energy change indicates that energy is released in the reaction—in this case, over 400 billion joules per mole of uranium!

---

**SAMPLE EXERCISE 21.9** Calculating Mass Change in a Nuclear Reaction

How much energy is lost or gained when 1 mol of cobalt-60 undergoes beta decay, $^{60}_{27}Co \longrightarrow {}^0_{-1}e + {}^{60}_{28}Ni$? The mass of a $^{60}_{27}Co$ atom is 59.933819 amu, and that of a $^{60}_{28}Ni$ atom is 59.930788 amu.

**SOLUTION**

**Analyze** We are asked to calculate the energy change in a nuclear reaction.

**Plan** We must first calculate the mass change in the process. We are given atomic masses, but we need the masses of the nuclei in the reaction. We calculate these by taking account of the masses of the electrons that contribute to the atomic masses.

**Solve** A $^{60}_{27}Co$ atom has 27 electrons. The mass of an electron is $5.4858 \times 10^{-4}$ amu. (See the list of fundamental constants in the back inside cover.) We subtract the mass of the 27 electrons from the mass of the $^{60}_{27}Co$ atom to find the mass of the $^{60}_{27}Co$ nucleus:

$$59.933819 \text{ amu} - (27)(5.4858 \times 10^{-4} \text{ amu}) = 59.919007 \text{ amu (or 59.919007 g/mol)}$$

Likewise, for $^{60}_{28}$Ni, the mass of the nucleus is

59.930788 amu $-$ (28)(5.4858 $\times$ 10$^{-4}$ amu) = 59.915428 amu (or 59.915428 g/mol)

The mass change in the nuclear reaction is the total mass of the products minus the mass of the reactant:

$$\Delta m = \text{mass of electron} + \text{mass } ^{60}_{28}\text{Ni nucleus} - \text{mass of } ^{60}_{27}\text{Co nucleus}$$

$$= 0.00054858 \text{ amu} + 59.915428 \text{ amu} - 59.919007 \text{ amu}$$

$$= -0.003030 \text{ amu}$$

Thus, when a mole of cobalt-60 decays,

$$\Delta m = -0.003030 \text{ g}$$

Because the mass decreases ($\Delta m < 0$), energy is released ($\Delta E < 0$). The quantity of energy released *per mole* of cobalt-60 is calculated using Equation 21.22:

$$\Delta E = c^2 \, \Delta m$$

$$= (2.9979 \times 10^8 \text{ m/s})^2 (-0.003030 \text{ g}) \left( \frac{1 \text{ kg}}{1000 \text{ g}} \right)$$

$$= -2.723 \times 10^{11} \frac{\text{kg-m}^2}{\text{s}^2} = -2.723 \times 10^{11} \text{J}$$

**PRACTICE EXERCISE**

Positron emission from $^{11}$C, $^{11}_{6}$C $\longrightarrow$ $^{11}_{5}$B + $^{0}_{1}$e, occurs with release of 2.87 $\times$ 10$^{11}$ J per mole of $^{11}$C. What is the mass change per mole of $^{11}$C in this nuclear reaction? The masses of $^{11}$B and $^{11}$C are 11.009305 and 11.011434 amu, respectively.

**Answer:** $-3.19 \times 10^{-3}$ g

## Nuclear Binding Energies

Scientists discovered in the 1930s that the masses of nuclei are always less than the masses of the individual nucleons of which they are composed. For example, the helium-4 nucleus has a mass of 4.00150 amu. The mass of a proton is 1.00728 amu and that of a neutron is 1.00866 amu. Consequently, two protons and two neutrons have a total mass of 4.03188 amu:

$$\text{Mass of two protons} = 2(1.00728 \text{ amu}) = 2.01456 \text{ amu}$$

$$\text{Mass of two neutrons} = 2(1.00866 \text{ amu}) = \underline{2.01732 \text{ amu}}$$

$$\text{Total mass} = 4.03188 \text{ amu}$$

The mass of the individual nucleons is 0.03038 amu greater than that of the helium-4 nucleus:

$$\text{Mass of two protons and two neutrons} = 4.03188 \text{ amu}$$

$$\text{Mass of } ^{4}_{2}\text{He nucleus} = \underline{4.00150 \text{ amu}}$$

$$\text{Mass difference } \Delta m = 0.03038 \text{ amu}$$

The mass difference between a nucleus and its constituent nucleons is called the **mass defect**. The origin of the mass defect is readily understood if we consider that energy must be added to a nucleus to break it into separated protons and neutrons:

$$\text{Energy} + ^{4}_{2}\text{He} \longrightarrow 2\,^{1}_{1}\text{p} + 2\,^{1}_{0}\text{n} \qquad [21.23]$$

The addition of energy to a system must be accompanied by a proportional increase in mass. The mass change we just calculated for the conversion of helium-4 into separated nucleons is $\Delta m = 0.03038$ amu. Therefore, the energy required for this process is

$$\Delta E = c^2 \, \Delta m$$

$$= (2.9979 \times 10^8 \text{ m/s})^2 (0.03038 \text{ amu}) \left( \frac{1 \text{ g}}{6.022 \times 10^{23} \text{ amu}} \right) \left( \frac{1 \text{ kg}}{1000 \text{ g}} \right)$$

$$= 4.534 \times 10^{-12} \text{ J}$$

The energy required to separate a nucleus into its individual nucleons is called the **nuclear binding energy**. The mass defect and nuclear binding energy for three elements are compared in ▶ TABLE 21.7.

**TABLE 21.7 • Mass Defects and Binding Energies for Three Nuclei**

| Nucleus | Mass of Nucleus (amu) | Mass of Individual Nucleons (amu) | Mass Defect (amu) | Binding Energy (J) | Binding Energy per Nucleon (J) |
|---|---|---|---|---|---|
| $^{4}_{2}\text{He}$ | 4.00150 | 4.03188 | 0.03038 | $4.53 \times 10^{-12}$ | $1.13 \times 10^{-12}$ |
| $^{56}_{26}\text{Fe}$ | 55.92068 | 56.44914 | 0.52846 | $7.90 \times 10^{-11}$ | $1.41 \times 10^{-12}$ |
| $^{238}_{92}\text{U}$ | 238.00031 | 239.93451 | 1.93420 | $2.89 \times 10^{-10}$ | $1.21 \times 10^{-12}$ |

△ **GIVE IT SOME THOUGHT**

The atomic mass of iron-56 is 55.93494 amu. Why is this number different from the mass of the nucleus given in Table 21.7?

▲ **FIGURE 21.12  Nuclear binding energies.** The average binding energy per nucleon increases initially as the mass number increases and then decreases slowly. Because of these trends, fusion of light nuclei and fission of heavy nuclei are exothermic processes.

Values of binding energies per nucleon can be used to compare the stabilities of different combinations of nucleons (such as two protons and two neutrons arranged either as $^{4}_{2}\text{He}$ or as $2\,^{2}_{1}\text{H}$). ◀ **FIGURE 21.12** shows average binding energy per nucleon plotted against mass number. Binding energy per nucleon at first increases in magnitude as mass number increases, reaching about $1.4 \times 10^{-12}$ J for nuclei whose mass numbers are in the vicinity of iron-56. It then decreases slowly to about $1.2 \times 10^{-12}$ J for very heavy nuclei. This trend indicates that nuclei of intermediate mass numbers are more tightly bound (and therefore more stable) than those with either smaller or larger mass numbers.

This trend has two significant consequences: First, heavy nuclei gain stability and therefore give off energy if they are fragmented into two midsized nuclei. This process, known as **fission**, is used to generate energy in nuclear power plants. Second, even greater amounts of energy are released if very light nuclei are combined, or fused together, to give more massive nuclei. This **fusion** process is the essential energy-producing process in the Sun.

△ **GIVE IT SOME THOUGHT**

Could fusing two stable nuclei that have mass numbers in the vicinity of 100 be an energy-releasing process?

# 21.7 | NUCLEAR POWER: FISSION

Commercial nuclear power plants and most forms of nuclear weaponry depend on nuclear fission for their operation. The first nuclear fission reaction to be discovered was that of uranium-235. This nucleus, as well as those of uranium-233 and plutonium-239, undergoes fission when struck by a slow-moving neutron (▼ **FIGURE 21.13**).*

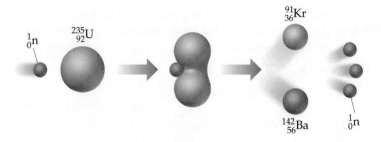

▶ **FIGURE 21.13  Uranium-235 fission.** This is just one of many fission patterns. In this reaction, $3.5 \times 10^{-11}$ J of energy is produced per $^{235}$U nucleus.

*Other heavy nuclei can be induced to undergo fission. However, these three are the only ones of practical importance.

A heavy nucleus can split in many ways. Two ways that the uranium-235 nucleus splits, for instance, are

$$\begin{array}{ll} & ^{137}_{52}\text{Te} + ^{97}_{40}\text{Zr} + 2\,^1_0\text{n} & [21.24] \\ \\ ^1_0\text{n} + ^{235}_{92}\text{U} & \\ \\ & ^{142}_{56}\text{Ba} + ^{91}_{36}\text{Kr} + 3\,^1_0\text{n} & [21.25] \end{array}$$

More than 200 isotopes of 35 elements have been found among the fission products of uranium-235. Most of them are radioactive.

Slow-moving neutrons are required in fission because the process involves initial absorption of the neutron by the nucleus. The resulting more massive nucleus is often unstable and spontaneously undergoes fission. Fast neutrons tend to bounce off the nucleus, and little fission occurs.

Note that the coefficients of the product neutrons in Equations 21.24 and 21.25 are 2 and 3. On average, 2.4 neutrons are produced by every fission of a uranium-235 nucleus. If one fission produces two neutrons, the two neutrons can cause two additional fissions, each producing two neutrons. The four neutrons thereby released can produce four fissions, and so forth, as shown in ▶ FIGURE 21.14. The number of fissions and the energy released quickly escalate, and if the process is unchecked, the result is a violent explosion. Reactions that multiply in this fashion are called **chain reactions**.

For a fission chain reaction to occur, the sample of fissionable material must have a certain minimum mass. Otherwise, neutrons escape from the sample before they have the opportunity to strike other nuclei and cause additional fission. The amount of fissionable material large enough to maintain a chain reaction with a constant rate of fission is called the **critical mass**. When a critical mass of material is present, one neutron on average from each fission is subsequently effective in producing another fission and the fission continues at a constant, controllable rate. The critical mass of uranium-235 is about 50 kg for a bare sphere of the metal.\*

If more than a critical mass of fissionable material is present, very few neutrons escape. The chain reaction thus multiplies the number of fissions, which can lead to a nuclear explosion. A mass in excess of a critical mass is referred to as a **supercritical mass**. The effect of mass on a fission reaction is illustrated in ▼ FIGURE 21.15.

▶ FIGURE 21.16 shows a schematic diagram of the first atomic bomb used in warfare, the bomb dropped on Hiroshima, Japan, on August 6, 1945. To trigger a fission

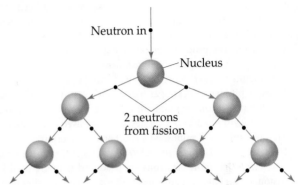

▲ FIGURE 21.14    **Fission chain reaction.**

Neutron in

Nucleus

2 neutrons from fission

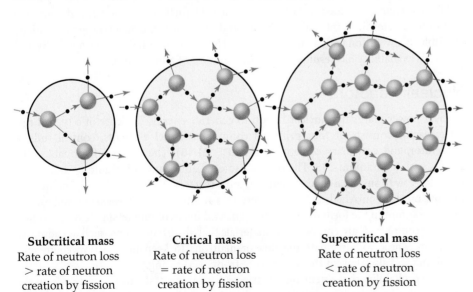

**Subcritical mass**
Rate of neutron loss > rate of neutron creation by fission

**Critical mass**
Rate of neutron loss = rate of neutron creation by fission

**Supercritical mass**
Rate of neutron loss < rate of neutron creation by fission

▲ FIGURE 21.15    **Subcritical, critical, and supercritical fission.**

Subcritical uranium-235 target

Subcritical uranium-235 wedge

Chemical explosive

▲ FIGURE 21.16    **An atomic bomb design.** A conventional explosive is used to bring two subcritical masses together to form a supercritical mass.

\*The exact value of the critical mass depends on the shape of the radioactive substance. The critical mass can be reduced if the radioisotope is surrounded by a material that reflects some neutrons.

# A CLOSER LOOK

## THE DAWNING OF THE NUCLEAR AGE

Uranium-235 fission was first achieved during the late 1930s by Enrico Fermi and coworkers in Rome and shortly thereafter by Otto Hahn and coworkers in Berlin. Both groups were trying to produce transuranium elements. In 1938, Hahn identified barium among his reaction products. He was puzzled by this observation and questioned the identification because the presence of barium was so unexpected. He sent a letter describing his experiments to Lise Meitner, a former coworker who had been forced to leave Germany because of the anti-Semitism of the Third Reich and had settled in Sweden. She surmised that Hahn's experiment indicated a nuclear process was occurring in which the uranium-235 split. She called this process *nuclear fission*.

Meitner passed word of this discovery to her nephew, Otto Frisch, a physicist working at Niels Bohr's institute in Copenhagen. Frisch repeated the experiment, verifying Hahn's observations, and found that tremendous energies were involved. In January 1939, Meitner and Frisch published a short article describing the reaction. In March 1939, Leo Szilard and Walter Zinn at Columbia University discovered that more neutrons are produced than are used in each fission. As we have seen, this result allows a chain reaction to occur.

News of these discoveries and an awareness of their potential use in explosive devices spread rapidly within the scientific community. Several scientists finally persuaded Albert Einstein, the most famous physicist of the time, to write a letter to President Franklin D. Roosevelt explaining the implications of these discoveries. Einstein's letter, written in August 1939, outlined the possible military applica-

tions of nuclear fission and emphasized the danger that weapons based on fission would pose if they were developed by the Nazis. Roosevelt judged it imperative that the United States investigate the possibility of such weapons. Late in 1941, the decision was made to build a bomb based on the fission reaction. An enormous research project, known as the Manhattan Project, began.

On December 2, 1942, the first artificial self-sustaining nuclear fission chain reaction was achieved in an abandoned squash court at the University of Chicago. This accomplishment led to the development of the first atomic bomb, at Los Alamos National Laboratory in New Mexico in July 1945 (▼ FIGURE 21.17). In August 1945 the United States dropped atomic bombs on two Japanese cities, Hiroshima and Nagasaki. The nuclear age had arrived.

▲ FIGURE 21.17 **The Trinity test for the atom bomb developed during World War II.** The first human-made nuclear explosion took place on July 16, 1945, on the Alamogordo test range in New Mexico.

reaction, two subcritical masses of uranium-235 are slammed together using chemical explosives. The combined masses of the uranium form a supercritical mass, which leads to a rapid, uncontrolled chain reaction and, ultimately, a nuclear explosion. The energy released by the bomb dropped on Hiroshima was equivalent to that of 20,000 tons of TNT (it therefore is called a *20-kiloton* bomb). Unfortunately, the basic design of a fission-based atomic bomb is quite simple, and the fissionable materials are potentially available to any nation with a nuclear reactor. The combination of design simplicity and materials availability has resulted in the proliferation of atomic weapons.

## Nuclear Reactors

Nuclear power plants use nuclear fission to generate energy. The core of a typical nuclear reactor consists of four principal components: fuel elements, control rods, a moderator, and a primary coolant (◄ FIGURE 21.18). The fuel is a fissionable substance, such as uranium-235. The natural isotopic abundance of uranium-235 is only 0.7%, too low to sustain a chain reaction in most reactors. Therefore, the $^{235}$U content of the fuel must be enriched to 3–5% for use in a reactor. The *fuel elements* contain enriched uranium in the form of $UO_2$ pellets encased in zirconium or stainless steel tubes.

The *control rods* are composed of materials that absorb neutrons, such as cadmium or boron. These rods regulate the flux of neutrons to keep the reaction chain self-sustaining and also prevent the reactor core from overheating.*

The probability that a neutron will trigger fission of a $^{235}$U nucleus depends on the speed of the neutron. The neutrons produced by fission have high speeds (typically

Control-rod drive

Control rods

Fuel elements

Water acts as both moderator and coolant

▲ FIGURE 21.18 **Diagram of a pressurized water reactor core.**

*The reactor core cannot reach supercritical levels and explode with the violence of an atomic bomb because the concentration of uranium-235 is too low. However, if the core overheats, sufficient damage can lead to release of radioactive materials into the environment.

▲ **GO FIGURE**

Why are nuclear power plants usually located near a large body of water?

▲ **FIGURE 21.19    Basic design of a pressurized water reactor nuclear power plant.**

in excess of 10,000 km/s). The function of the *moderator* is to slow down the neutrons (to speeds of a few kilometers per second) so that they can be captured more readily by the fissionable nuclei. The moderator is typically either water or graphite.

The *primary coolant* is a substance that transports the heat generated by the nuclear chain reaction away from the reactor core. In a *pressurized water reactor*, which is the most common commercial reactor design, water acts as both the moderator and the primary coolant.

The design of a nuclear power plant is basically the same as that of a power plant that burns fossil fuel (except that the burner is replaced by a reactor core). The nuclear power plant design shown in ▲ **FIGURE 21.19**, a pressurized water reactor, is currently the most popular. The primary coolant passes through the core in a closed system, which lessens the chance that radioactive products could escape the core. As an added safety precaution, the reactor is surrounded by a reinforced concrete *containment shell* to shield personnel and nearby residents from radiation and to protect the reactor from external forces. After passing through the reactor core, the very hot primary coolant passes through a heat exchanger where much of its heat is transferred to a *secondary coolant*, converting the latter to high-pressure steam that is used to drive a turbine. The secondary coolant is then condensed by transferring heat to an external source of water, such as a river or lake.

Approximately two-thirds of all commercial reactors are pressurized water reactors, but there are several variations on this basic design, each with advantages and disadvantages. A *boiling water reactor* generates steam by boiling the primary coolant; thus, no secondary coolant is needed. Pressurized water reactors and boiling water reactors are collectively referred to as *light water reactors* because they use $H_2O$ as moderator and primary coolant. A *heavy water reactor* uses $D_2O$ (D = deuterium, $^2H$) as moderator and primary coolant, and a *gas-cooled reactor* uses a gas, typically $CO_2$, as primary coolant and graphite as the moderator. Use of either $D_2O$ or graphite as the moderator has the advantage that both substances absorb fewer neutrons than $H_2O$. Consequently, the uranium fuel does not need to be enriched (though the reactor can also be run with enriched fuel).

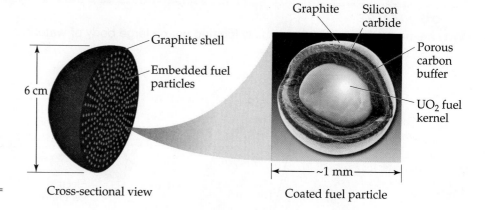

▶ **FIGURE 21.20 Fuel spheres used in a high-temperature pebble-bed reactor.** The image on the right is an optical microscope image of a fuel particle.

In a *high-temperature pebble-bed reactor*, the fuel elements are spheres ("pebbles") roughly the size of an orange (▲ **FIGURE 21.20**). The spheres are made of graphite, which acts as the moderator, and thousands of tiny fuel particles are embedded in the interior of each sphere. Each fuel particle is a kernel of fissionable material, typically $^{235}U$ in the form of $UO_2$, surrounded by carbon and a coating of a ceramic material, such as SiC. Hundreds of thousands of these spheres are loosely packed in the reactor core, and helium gas, which acts as the primary coolant, flows up through the packed spheres. The reactor core operates at temperatures considerably higher than those in a light water reactor, approaching 950 °C. A pebble-bed reactor is not subject to steam explosions and does not need to be shut down to refuel. Engineers can remove spent spheres from the bottom of the reactor core and add fresh ones to the top. This design is relatively new and is not yet in commercial use.

## Nuclear Waste

The fission products that accumulate as a reactor operates decrease the efficiency of the reactor by capturing neutrons. For this reason, commercial reactors must be stopped periodically to either replace or reprocess the nuclear fuel. When the fuel elements are removed from the reactor, they are initially very radioactive. It was originally intended that they be stored for several months in pools at the reactor site to allow decay of short-lived radioactive nuclei. They were then to be transported in shielded containers to reprocessing plants where the fuel would be separated from the fission products. Reprocessing plants have been plagued with operational difficulties, however, and there is intense opposition in the United States to the transport of nuclear wastes on the nation's roads.

Even if the transportation difficulties could be overcome, the high level of radioactivity of the spent fuel makes reprocessing a hazardous operation. At present in the United States spent fuel elements are kept in storage at reactor sites. Spent fuel is reprocessed, however, in France, Russia, the United Kingdom, India, and Japan.

Storage of spent nuclear fuel poses a major problem because the fission products are extremely radioactive. It is estimated that 20 half-lives are required for their radioactivity to reach levels acceptable for biological exposure. Based on the 28.8-yr half-life of strontium-90, one of the longer-lived and most dangerous of the products, the wastes must be stored for 600 years. Plutonium-239 is one of the by-products present in spent fuel elements. It is formed by absorption of a neutron by uranium-238, followed by two successive beta emissions. (Remember that most of the uranium in the fuel elements is uranium-238.) If the elements are reprocessed, the plutonium-239 is largely recovered because it can be used as a nuclear fuel. However, if the plutonium is not removed, spent elements must be stored for a very long time because plutonium-239 has a half-life of 24,000 yr.

One approach to getting more power out of existing uranium sources and potentially reducing radioactive waste is a *fast breeder reactor.* This type of reactor is so named because it creates ("breeds") more fissionable material than it consumes. The reactor operates without a moderator, which means the neutrons used are not slowed down. In order to capture the fast neutrons, the fuel must be highly enriched with both uranium-235 and plutonium-239. Water cannot be used as a primary coolant because it would moderate the neutrons, and so a liquid metal, usually sodium, is used. The core is surrounded by a blanket of uranium-238 that captures neutrons that escape the core, producing plutonium-239 in the process. The plutonium can later be separated by reprocessing and used as fuel in a future cycle.

Because fast neutrons are more effective at decaying many radioactive nuclides, the material separated from the uranium and plutonium during reprocessing is less radioactive than waste from other reactors. However, generation of relatively high levels of plutonium coupled with the need for reprocessing is problematic in terms of nuclear nonproliferation. Thus, political factors coupled with increased safety concerns and higher operational costs make fast breeder reactors quite rare.

A considerable amount of research is being devoted to disposal of radioactive wastes. At present, the most attractive possibilities appear to be formation of glass, ceramic, or synthetic rock from the wastes, as a means of immobilizing them. These solid materials would then be placed in containers of high corrosion resistance and durability and buried deep underground. The U.S. Department of Energy (DOE) had designated Yucca Mountain in Nevada as a disposal site, and extensive construction has been done there. However, as of the writing of this book, the DOE has publicly stated that the Yucca Mountain site will not be used for storage, although some members of Congress are fighting this decision. The long-term solution to nuclear waste storage in the United States remains unclear. Whatever the solution finally decided on, there must be assurances that the solids and their containers will not crack from the heat generated by nuclear decay, allowing radioactivity to find its way into underground water supplies.

In spite of all these difficulties, nuclear power is making a modest comeback as an energy source. The threat of global warming has moved some organizations to propose nuclear power as a major energy source in the future. Increasing demand for power in developing Asian countries has sparked a rise in construction of new nuclear power plants in that part of the world (▼ **FIGURE 21.21**).

## GO FIGURE

**Which country has the most reactors in operation? Which country has the most reactors under construction? Which country generates the highest percentage of its electricity from nuclear power?**

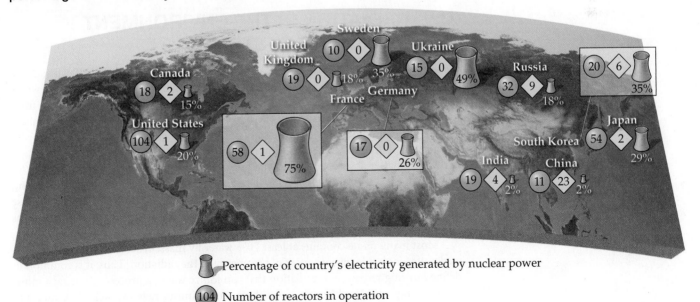

Percentage of country's electricity generated by nuclear power

Number of reactors in operation

Number of reactors under construction

▲ **FIGURE 21.21**   **Number of reactors in operation and under construction for the countries with the largest nuclear power generation capabilities.**

# 21.8 | NUCLEAR POWER: FUSION

Energy is produced when light nuclei fuse into heavier ones. Reactions of this type are responsible for the energy produced by the Sun. Spectroscopic studies indicate that the mass composition of the Sun is 73% H, 26% He, and only 1% all other elements. The following reactions are among the numerous fusion processes believed to occur in the Sun:

$$\text{}_1^1\text{H} + \text{}_1^1\text{H} \longrightarrow \text{}_1^2\text{H} + \text{}_1^0\text{e} \qquad [21.26]$$

$$\text{}_1^1\text{H} + \text{}_1^2\text{H} \longrightarrow \text{}_2^3\text{He} \qquad [21.27]$$

$$\text{}_2^3\text{He} + \text{}_2^3\text{He} \longrightarrow \text{}_2^4\text{He} + 2\,\text{}_1^1\text{H} \qquad [21.28]$$

$$\text{}_2^3\text{He} + \text{}_1^1\text{H} \longrightarrow \text{}_2^4\text{He} + \text{}_1^0\text{e} \qquad [21.29]$$

Fusion is appealing as an energy source because of the availability of light isotopes on Earth and because fusion products are generally not radioactive. Despite this fact, fusion is not presently used to generate energy. The problem is that, in order for two nuclei to fuse, high temperatures and pressures are needed to overcome the electrostatic repulsion between them. Fusion reactions are therefore also known as **thermonuclear reactions**. The lowest temperature required for any fusion is about 40,000,000 K, the temperature needed to fuse deuterium and tritium:

$$\text{}_1^2\text{H} + \text{}_1^3\text{H} \longrightarrow \text{}_2^4\text{He} + \text{}_0^1\text{n} \qquad [21.30]$$

Such high temperatures have been achieved by using an atomic bomb to initiate fusion. This is the operating principle behind a thermonuclear, or hydrogen, bomb. This approach is obviously unacceptable, however, for a power generation plant.*

Numerous problems must be overcome before fusion becomes a practical energy source. In addition to the high temperatures necessary to initiate the reaction, there is the problem of confining the reaction. No known structural material is able to withstand the enormous temperatures necessary for fusion. Research has centered on the use of an apparatus called a *tokamak*, which uses strong magnetic fields to contain and to heat the reaction. Temperatures of over 100,000,000 K have been achieved in a tokamak. Unfortunately, scientists have not yet been able to generate more power than is consumed over a sustained period of time.

# 21.9 | RADIATION IN THE ENVIRONMENT AND LIVING SYSTEMS

We are continuously bombarded by radiation from both natural and artificial sources. We are exposed to infrared, ultraviolet, and visible radiation from the Sun; radio waves from radio and television stations; microwaves from microwave ovens; X-rays from medical procedures; and radioactivity from natural materials (▶ TABLE 21.8). Understanding the different energies of these various kinds of radiation is necessary in order to understand their different effects on matter.

When matter absorbs radiation, the radiation energy can cause atoms in the matter to be either excited or ionized. In general, radiation that causes ionization, called **ionizing radiation**, is far more harmful to biological systems than radiation that does not cause ionization. The latter, called **nonionizing radiation**, is generally of lower energy, such as radiofrequency electromagnetic radiation ∞ (Section 6.7) or slow-moving neutrons.

Most living tissue contains at least 70% water by mass. When living tissue is irradiated, water molecules absorb most of the energy of the radiation. Thus, it is common to define ionizing radiation as radiation that can ionize water, a process requiring a minimum energy of 1216 kJ/mol. Alpha, beta, and gamma rays (as well as X-rays and higher-energy ultraviolet radiation) possess energies in excess of this quantity and are therefore forms of ionizing radiation.

---

*Historically a nuclear weapon that relies solely on a fission process to release energy is called an atomic bomb, whereas one that also releases energy via a fusion reaction is called a hydrogen bomb.

# A CLOSER LOOK

## NUCLEAR SYNTHESIS OF THE ELEMENTS

The lightest elements—hydrogen and helium along with very small amounts of lithium and beryllium—were formed as the universe expanded in the moments following the Big Bang. All the heavier elements owe their existence to nuclear reactions that occur in stars. These heavier elements are not all created equally, however. Carbon and oxygen are a million times more abundant than lithium and boron, for instance, and over 100 million times more abundant that beryllium (▼ FIGURE 21.22)! In fact, of the elements heavier than helium, carbon and oxygen are the most abundant. This is more than an academic curiosity given the fact that these elements, together with hydrogen, are the most important elements for life on Earth. Let's look at the factors responsible for the relatively high abundance of carbon and oxygen in the universe.

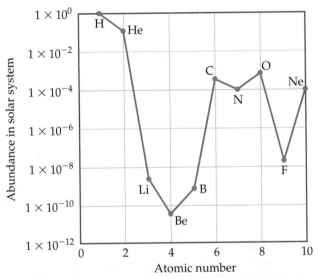

▲ **FIGURE 21.22  Abundances of elements 1–10 in the solar system.** Note the logarithmic scale used for the *y*-axis.

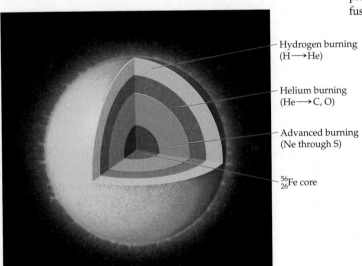

- Hydrogen burning (H ⟶ He)
- Helium burning (He ⟶ C, O)
- Advanced burning (Ne through S)
- $^{56}_{26}$Fe core

A star is born from a cloud of gas and dust called a *nebula*. When conditions are right, gravitational forces collapse the cloud, and its core density and temperature rise until nuclear fusion commences. Hydrogen nuclei fuse to form deuterium, $^2$H, and eventually $^4$He through the reactions shown in Equations 21.26 through 21.29. Because $^4$He has a larger binding energy than any of its immediate neighbors (Figure 21.12), these reactions release an enormous amount of energy. This process, called *hydrogen burning*, is the dominant process for most of a star's lifetime.

Once a star's supply of hydrogen is nearly exhausted, several important changes occur as the star enters the red giant phase of its life. The decrease in nuclear fusion causes the core to contract, triggering an increase in core temperature and pressure. At the same time, the outer regions expand and cool enough to make the star emit red light (thus, the name *red giant*). The star now must use $^4_2$He nuclei as its fuel. The simplest reaction that can occur in the He-rich core, fusion of two alpha particles to form a $^8_4$Be nucleus, does occur. However, this nucleus is highly unstable (half-life of $7 \times 10^{-17}$ s) and so falls apart almost immediately. In a tiny fraction of cases, however, a third $^4_2$He collides with a $^8_4$Be nucleus before it decays, forming carbon-12 through the triple-alpha process:

$$^4_2\text{He} + {}^4_2\text{He} \longrightarrow {}^8_4\text{Be}$$

$$^8_4\text{Be} + {}^4_2\text{He} \longrightarrow {}^{12}_6\text{C}$$

Some of the $^{12}_6$C nuclei go on to react with alpha particles to form oxygen-16:

$$^{12}_6\text{C} + {}^4_2\text{He} \longrightarrow {}^{16}_8\text{O}$$

This stage of nuclear fusion is called *helium burning*. Notice that carbon, element 6, is formed without prior formation of elements 3, 4, and 5, explaining in part their unusually low abundance. Nitrogen is relatively abundant because it can be produced from carbon through a series of reactions involving proton capture and positron emission.

Most stars gradually cool and dim as the helium is converted to carbon and oxygen, ending their lives as *white dwarfs*. In stars that are 10 or more times more massive than our Sun, however, a more dramatic fate awaits. The extreme mass of these stars leads to much higher temperatures and pressures at the core, where a variety of fusion processes lead to synthesis of the elements from neon to sulfur. These fusion reactions are collectively called *advanced burning*.

Eventually progressively heavier elements form at the core until it becomes predominantly $^{56}$Fe as shown in ◀ **FIGURE 21.23.** Because this is such a stable nucleus, further fusion to heavier nuclei consumes energy rather than releasing it. When this happens, the fusion reactions that power the star diminish, and immense gravitational forces lead to a dramatic collapse called a *supernova explosion*. Neutron capture coupled with subsequent radioactive decays in the dying moments of such a star are responsible for the presence of all elements heavier than iron and nickel.

Without these dramatic supernova events, heavier elements that are so familiar to us, such as silver, gold, iodine, lead, and uranium, would not exist.

*RELATED EXERCISES:* 21.70, 21.72

◀ **FIGURE 21.23  Fusion processes going on in a red giant just prior to a supernova explosion.**

**TABLE 21.8 • Average Abundances and Activities of Natural Radionuclides***

|  | Potassium-40 | Rubidium-87 | Thorium-232 | Uranium-238 |
|---|---|---|---|---|
| Land elemental abundance (ppm) | 28,000 | 112 | 10.7 | 2.8 |
| Land activity (Bq/kg) | 870 | 102 | 43 | 35 |
| Ocean elemental concentration (mg/L) | 339 | 0.12 | $1 \times 10^{-7}$ | 0.0032 |
| Ocean activity (Bq/L) | 12 | 0.11 | $4 \times 10^{-7}$ | 0.040 |
| Ocean sediments elemental abundance (ppm) | 17,000 | — | 5.0 | 1.0 |
| Ocean sediments activity (Bq/kg) | 500 | — | 20 | 12 |
| Human body activity (Bq) | 4000 | 600 | 0.08 | 0.4** |

*Data from "Ionizing Radiation Exposure of the Population of the United States," Report 93, 1987, National Council on Radiation Protection.

**Includes lead-210 and polonium-210, daughter nuclei of uranium-238.

When ionizing radiation passes through living tissue, electrons are removed from water molecules, forming highly reactive $H_2O^+$ ions. An $H_2O^+$ ion can react with another water molecule to form an $H_3O^+$ ion and a neutral OH molecule:

$$H_2O^+ + H_2O \longrightarrow H_3O^+ + OH \qquad [21.31]$$

The unstable and highly reactive OH molecule is a **free radical**, a substance with one or more unpaired electrons, as seen in the Lewis structure $\cdot\ddot{O}\!-\!H$. The OH molecule is also called the *hydroxyl radical*, and the presence of the unpaired electron is often emphasized by writing the species with a single dot, $\cdot OH$. In cells and tissues, hydroxyl radicals can attack biomolecules to produce new free radicals, which in turn attack yet other biomolecules. Thus, the formation of a single hydroxyl radical via Equation 21.31 can initiate a large number of chemical reactions that are ultimately able to disrupt the normal operations of cells.

The damage produced by radiation depends on the activity and energy of the radiation, the length of exposure, and whether the source is inside or outside the body. Gamma rays are particularly harmful outside the body because they penetrate human tissue very effectively, just as X-rays do. Consequently, their damage is not limited to the skin. In contrast, most alpha rays are stopped by skin, and beta rays are able to penetrate only about 1 cm beyond the skin surface (◄ FIGURE 21.24). Neither alpha rays nor beta rays are as dangerous as gamma rays, therefore, *unless* the radiation source somehow enters the body. Within the body, alpha rays are particularly dangerous because they transfer their energy efficiently to the surrounding tissue, causing considerable damage.

In general, the tissues damaged most by radiation are those that reproduce rapidly, such as bone marrow, blood-forming tissues, and lymph nodes. The principal effect of extended exposure to low doses of radiation is to cause cancer. Cancer is caused by damage to the growth-regulation mechanism of cells, inducing the cells to reproduce uncontrollably. Leukemia, which is characterized by excessive growth of white blood cells, is probably the major type of radiation-caused cancer.

In light of the biological effects of radiation, it is important to determine whether any levels of exposure are safe. Unfortunately, we are hampered in our attempts to set realistic standards because we do not fully understand the effects of long-term exposure. Scientists concerned with setting health standards have used the hypothesis that the effects of radiation are proportional to exposure. *Any* amount of radiation is assumed to cause some finite risk of injury, and the effects of high dosage rates are extrapolated to those of lower ones. Other scientists believe, however, that there is a threshold below which there are no radiation risks. Until scientific evidence enables us to settle the matter with some confidence, it is safer to assume that even low levels of radiation present some danger.

**GO FIGURE**

Why are alpha rays much more dangerous when the source of radiation is located inside the body?

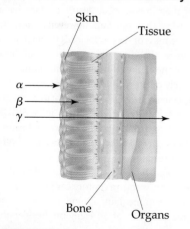

Skin
Tissue
$\alpha$
$\beta$
$\gamma$
Bone
Organs

▲ FIGURE 21.24 **Relative penetrating abilities of alpha, beta, and gamma radiation.**

## Radiation Doses

Two units are commonly used to measure exposure to radiation. The **gray** (Gy), the SI unit of absorbed dose, corresponds to the absorption of 1 J of energy per kilogram of tissue. The **rad** (radiation *a*bsorbed *d*ose) corresponds to the absorption of $1 \times 10^{-2}$ J of energy per kilogram of tissue. Thus, 1 Gy = 100 rad. The rad is the unit most often used in medicine.

Not all forms of radiation harm biological materials with the same efficiency. For example, 1 rad of alpha radiation can produce more damage than 1 rad of beta radiation. To correct for these differences, the radiation dose is multiplied by a factor that measures the relative damage caused by the radiation. This multiplication factor is known as the *relative biological effectiveness, RBE*. The RBE is approximately 1 for gamma and beta radiation, and 10 for alpha radiation.

The exact value of the RBE varies with dose rate, total dose, and type of tissue affected. The product of the radiation dose in rads and the RBE of the radiation give the *effective dosage* in **rem** (roentgen equivalent for *man*):

$$\text{Number of rem} = (\text{number of rad})(\text{RBE}) \qquad [21.32]$$

The SI unit for effective dose is the *sievert* (Sv), obtained by multiplying the RBE times the SI unit for radiation dose, the gray; because a gray is 100 times larger than a rad, 1 Sv = 100 rem. The rem is the unit of radiation damage usually used in medicine.

 GIVE IT SOME THOUGHT

If a 50-kg person is uniformly irradiated by 0.10-J alpha radiation, what is the absorbed dosage in rad and the effective dosage in rem?

The effects of short-term exposure to radiation appear in ▼ TABLE 21.9. An exposure of 600 rem is fatal to most humans. To put this number in perspective, a typical dental X-ray entails an exposure of about 0.5 mrem. The average exposure for a person in 1 year due to all natural sources of ionizing radiation (called *background radiation*) is about 360 mrem (▼ FIGURE 21.25).

**TABLE 21.9 • Effects of Short-Term Exposures to Radiation**

| Dose (rem) | Effect |
| --- | --- |
| 0–25 | No detectable clinical effects |
| 25–50 | Slight, temporary decrease in white blood cell counts |
| 100–200 | Nausea; marked decrease in white blood cell counts |
| 500 | Death of half the exposed population within 30 days |

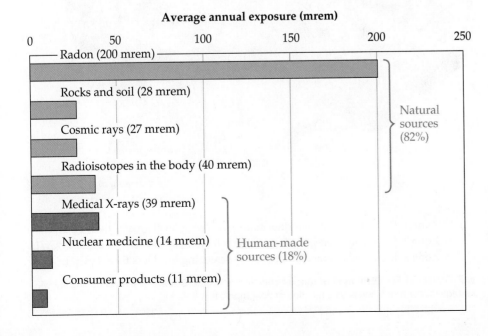

▲ FIGURE 21.25  **Sources of U.S. average annual exposure to high-energy radiation.** The total average annual exposure is 360 mrem.
*Data from "Ionizing Radiation Exposure of the Population of the United States," Report 93, 1987, National Council on Radiation Protection.*

# Radon

Radon-222 is a product of the nuclear disintegration series of uranium-238 (Figure 21.3) and is continuously generated as uranium in rocks and soil decays. As Figure 21.25 indicates, radon exposure is estimated to account for more than half the 360-mrem average annual exposure to ionizing radiation.

The interplay between the chemical and nuclear properties of radon makes it a health hazard. Because radon is a noble gas, it is extremely unreactive and is therefore free to escape from the ground without chemically reacting along the way. It is readily inhaled and exhaled with no direct chemical effects. Its half-life, however, is only 3.82 days. It decays, by losing an alpha particle, into a radioisotope of polonium:

$$^{222}_{86}\text{Rn} \longrightarrow {}^{218}_{84}\text{Po} + {}^{4}_{2}\text{He} \qquad [21.33]$$

Because radon has such a short half-life and because alpha particles have a high RBE, inhaled radon is considered a probable cause of lung cancer. Even worse than the radon, however, is the decay product because polonium-218 is an alpha-emitting chemically active element that has an even shorter half-life (3.11 min) than radon-222:

$$^{218}_{84}\text{Po} \longrightarrow {}^{214}_{82}\text{Pb} + {}^{4}_{2}\text{He} \qquad [21.34]$$

When a person inhales radon, therefore, atoms of polonium-218 can become trapped in the lungs, where they bathe the delicate tissue with harmful alpha radiation. The resulting damage is estimated to contribute to 10% of all lung cancer deaths in the United States.

The U.S. Environmental Protection Agency (EPA) has recommended that radon-222 levels not exceed 4 pCi per liter of air in homes. Homes located in areas where the natural uranium content of the soil is high often have levels much greater than that (▼ **FIGURE 21.26**). Because of public awareness, radon-testing kits are readily available in many parts of the country.

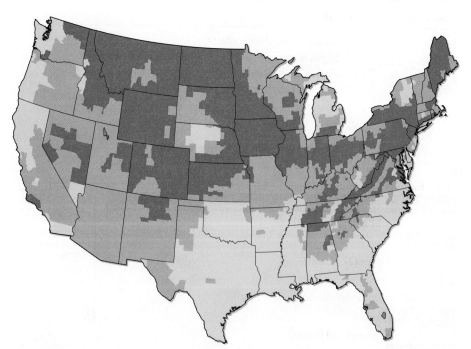

■ **Zone 1** Predicted average indoor radon screening level greater than 4 pCi/L
■ **Zone 2** Predicted average indoor radon screening level between 2 and 4 pCi/L
■ **Zone 3** Predicted average indoor radon screening level less than 2 pCi/L

▲ **FIGURE 21.26  EPA map of radon zones in the United States.**  The color coding shows average indoor radon levels as a function of geographic location.

# CHEMISTRY AND LIFE

## RADIATION THERAPY

Healthy cells are either destroyed or damaged by high-energy radiation, leading to physiological disorders. This radiation can also destroy *unhealthy* cells, however, including cancerous cells. All cancers are characterized by runaway cell growth that can produce *malignant tumors*. These tumors can be caused by the exposure of healthy cells to high-energy radiation. Paradoxically, however, they can be destroyed by the same radiation that caused them because the rapidly reproducing cells of the tumors are very susceptible to radiation damage. Thus, cancerous cells are more susceptible to destruction by radiation than healthy ones, allowing radiation to be used effectively in the treatment of cancer. As early as 1904, physicians used the radiation emitted by radioactive substances to treat tumors by destroying the mass of unhealthy tissue. The treatment of disease by high-energy radiation is called *radiation therapy*.

Many radionuclides are currently used in radiation therapy. Most of them have short half-lives, meaning that they emit a great deal of radiation in a short period of time (▶ TABLE 21.10).

The radiation source used in radiation therapy may be inside or outside the body. In almost all cases, radiation therapy uses gamma radiation emitted by radioisotopes. Any alpha or beta radiation that is emitted concurrently can be blocked by appropriate packaging. For example, $^{192}$Ir is often administered as "seeds" consisting of a core of radioactive isotope coated with 0.1 mm of platinum metal. The platinum coating stops the alpha and beta rays, but the gamma rays penetrate it readily. The radioactive seeds can be surgically implanted in a tumor.

In some cases, human physiology allows a radioisotope to be ingested. For example, most of the iodine in the human body ends up in the thyroid gland, so thyroid cancer can be treated by using large doses of $^{131}$I. Radiation therapy on deep organs, where a surgical implant is impractical, often uses a $^{60}$Co "gun" outside the body to shoot a beam of gamma rays at the tumor. Particle accelerators are also used as an external source of high-energy radiation for radiation therapy.

Because gamma radiation is so strongly penetrating, it is nearly impossible to avoid damaging healthy cells during radiation therapy. Many cancer patients undergoing radiation treatment experience unpleasant and dangerous side effects such as fatigue, nausea, hair loss, a weakened immune system, and occasionally even death. However, if other treatments such as *chemotherapy* (the use of drugs to combat cancer) fail, radiation therapy can be a good option.

**TABLE 21.10 • Some Radioisotopes Used in Radiation Therapy**

| Isotope | Half-Life | Isotope | Half-Life |
|---------|-----------|---------|-----------|
| $^{32}$P | 14.3 days | $^{137}$Cs | 30 yr |
| $^{60}$Co | 5.27 yr | $^{192}$Ir | 74.2 days |
| $^{90}$Sr | 28.8 yr | $^{198}$Au | 2.7 days |
| $^{125}$I | 60.25 days | $^{222}$Rn | 3.82 days |
| $^{131}$I | 8.04 days | $^{226}$Ra | 1600 yr |

---

## SAMPLE INTEGRATIVE EXERCISE | Putting Concepts Together

Potassium ion is present in foods and is an essential nutrient in the human body. One of the naturally occurring isotopes of potassium, potassium-40, is radioactive. Potassium-40 has a natural abundance of 0.0117% and a half-life $t_{1/2} = 1.28 \times 10^9$ yr. It undergoes radioactive decay in three ways: 98.2% is by electron capture, 1.35% is by beta emission, and 0.49% is by positron emission. (a) Why should we expect $^{40}$K to be radioactive? (b) Write the nuclear equations for the three modes by which $^{40}$K decays. (c) How many $^{40}$K$^+$ ions are present in 1.00 g of KCl? (d) How long does it take for 1.00% of the $^{40}$K in a sample to undergo radioactive decay?

### SOLUTION

(a) The $^{40}$K nucleus contains 19 protons and 21 neutrons. There are very few stable nuclei with odd numbers of both protons and neutrons (Section 21.2).

(b) Electron capture is capture of an inner-shell electron by the nucleus:

$$^{40}_{19}\text{K} + {}^{0}_{-1}\text{e} \longrightarrow {}^{40}_{18}\text{Ar}$$

Beta emission is loss of a beta particle ($^{0}_{-1}$e) by the nucleus:

$$^{40}_{19}\text{K} \longrightarrow {}^{40}_{20}\text{Ca} + {}^{0}_{-1}\text{e}$$

Positron emission is loss of a positron ($^{0}_{1}$e) by the nucleus:

$$^{40}_{19}\text{K} \longrightarrow {}^{40}_{18}\text{Ar} + {}^{0}_{1}\text{e}$$

(c) The total number of K$^+$ ions in the sample is

$$(1.00 \text{ g KCl})\left(\frac{1 \text{ mol KCl}}{74.55 \text{ g KCl}}\right)\left(\frac{1 \text{ mol K}^+}{1 \text{ mol KCl}}\right)\left(\frac{6.022 \times 10^{23} \text{ K}^+}{1 \text{ mol K}^+}\right) = 8.08 \times 10^{21} \text{ K}^+ \text{ ions}$$

Of these, 0.0117% are $^{40}\text{K}^+$ ions:

$$(8.08 \times 10^{21}\,\text{K}^+\,\text{ions})\left(\frac{0.0117\ ^{40}\text{K}^+\,\text{ions}}{100^+\,\text{ions}}\right) = 9.45 \times 10^{17}\,\text{potassium-40 ions}$$

**(d)** The decay constant (the rate constant) for the radioactive decay can be calculated from the half-life, using Equation 21.20:

$$k = \frac{0.693}{t_{1/2}} = \frac{0.693}{1.28 \times 10^9\,\text{yr}} = (5.41 \times 10^{-10})/\text{yr}$$

The rate equation, Equation 21.19, then allows us to calculate the time required:

$$\ln\frac{N_t}{N_0} = -kt$$

$$\ln\frac{99}{100} = -[(5.41 \times 10^{-10})/\text{yr}]t$$

$$-0.01005 = -[(5.41 \times 10^{-10})/\text{yr}]t$$

$$t = \frac{-0.01005}{(-5.41 \times 10^{-10})/\text{yr}} = 1.86 \times 10^7\,\text{yr}$$

That is, it would take 18.6 million years for just 1.00% of the $^{40}\text{K}$ in a sample to decay.

# CHAPTER SUMMARY AND KEY TERMS

**INTRODUCTION AND SECTION 21.1**  The nucleus of an atom contains protons and neutrons, both of which are called **nucleons**. Reactions that involve changes in atomic nuclei are called **nuclear reactions**. Nuclei that spontaneously change by emitting radiation are said to be radioactive. Radioactive nuclei are called **radionuclides,** and the atoms containing them are called **radioisotopes.** Radionuclides spontaneously change through a process called radioactive decay. The three most important types of radiation given off as a result of radioactive decay are **alpha ($\alpha$) particles** ($^4_2\text{He}$), **beta ($\beta$) particles** ($^0_{-1}\text{e}$), and **gamma ($\gamma$) radiation** ($^0_0\gamma$). **Positrons** ($^0_1\text{e}$), which are particles with the same mass as an electron but the opposite charge, can also be produced when a radioisotope decays.

In nuclear equations, reactant and product nuclei are represented by giving their mass numbers and atomic numbers, as well as their chemical symbol. The totals of the mass numbers on both sides of the equation are equal; the totals of the atomic numbers on both sides are also equal. There are four common modes of radioactive decay: **alpha decay**, which reduces the atomic number by 2 and the mass number by 4, **beta emission**, which increases the atomic number by 1 and leaves the mass number unchanged, **positron emission** and **electron capture**, both of which reduce the atomic number by 1 and leave the mass number unchanged.

**SECTION 21.2**  The neutron-to-proton ratio is an important factor determining nuclear stability. By comparing a nuclide's neutron-to-proton ratio with those in the band of stability, we can predict the mode of radioactive decay. In general, neutron-rich nuclei tend to emit beta particles; proton-rich nuclei tend to either emit positrons or undergo electron capture; and heavy nuclei tend to emit alpha particles. The presence of **magic numbers** of nucleons and an even number of protons and neutrons also help determine the stability of a nucleus. A nuclide may undergo a series of decay steps before a stable nuclide forms. This series of steps is called a **radioactive series** or a **nuclear disintegration series.**

**SECTION 21.3  Nuclear transmutations**, induced conversions of one nucleus into another, can be brought about by bombarding nuclei with either charged particles or neutrons. **Particle accelerators** increase the kinetic energies of positively charged particles, allowing these particles to overcome their electrostatic repulsion by the nucleus. Nuclear transmutations are used to produce the **transuranium elements**, those elements with atomic numbers greater than that of uranium.

**SECTIONS 21.4 AND 21.5**  The SI unit for the activity of a radioactive source is the **becquerel** (Bq), defined as one nuclear disintegration per second. A related unit, the **curie** (Ci), corresponds to $3.7 \times 10^{10}$ disintegrations per second. Nuclear decay is a first-order process. The decay rate (**activity**) is therefore proportional to the number of radioactive nuclei. The **half-life** of a radionuclide, which is a constant, is the time needed for one-half of the nuclei to decay. Some radioisotopes can be used to date objects; $^{14}\text{C}$, for example, is used to date organic objects. Geiger counters and scintillation counters count the emissions from radioactive samples. The ease of detection of radioisotopes also permits their use as **radiotracers** to follow elements through reactions.

**SECTION 21.6**  The energy produced in nuclear reactions is accompanied by measurable changes of mass in accordance with Einstein's relationship, $\Delta E = c^2\,\Delta m$. The difference in mass between nuclei and the nucleons of which they are composed is known as the **mass defect**. The mass defect of a nuclide makes it possible to calculate its **nuclear binding energy**, the energy required to separate the nucleus into individual nucleons. Energy is produced when heavy nuclei split (**fission**) and when light nuclei fuse (**fusion**).

**SECTIONS 21.7 AND 21.8**  Uranium-235, uranium-233, and plutonium-239 undergo fission when they capture a neutron, splitting into lighter nuclei and releasing more neutrons. The neutrons produced in one fission can cause further fission reactions, which can lead to a nuclear **chain reaction**. A reaction that maintains a constant rate is said to be critical, and the mass necessary to maintain this constant rate is called a **critical mass**. A mass in excess of the critical mass is termed a **supercritical mass**.

In nuclear reactors the fission rate is controlled to generate a constant power. The reactor core consists of fuel elements containing fissionable nuclei, control rods, a moderator, and a primary coolant. A nuclear power plant resembles a conventional power plant except that the reactor core replaces the fuel burner. There is concern about the disposal of highly radioactive nuclear wastes that are generated in nuclear power plants.

Nuclear fusion requires high temperatures because nuclei must have large kinetic energies to overcome their mutual repulsions. Fusion reactions are therefore called **thermonuclear reactions**. It is not yet possible to generate power on Earth through a controlled fusion process.

**SECTION 21.9 Ionizing radiation** is energetic enough to remove an electron from a water molecule; radiation with less energy is called **nonionizing radiation**. Ionizing radiation generates **free radicals**, reactive substances with one or more unpaired electrons. The effects of long-term exposure to low levels of radiation are not completely understood, but it is usually assumed that the extent of biological damage varies in direct proportion to the level of exposure.

The amount of energy deposited in biological tissue by radiation is called the radiation dose and is measured in units of gray or rad. One **gray** (Gy) corresponds to a dose of 1 J/kg of tissue. The **rad** is a smaller unit; 100 rad = 1 Gy. The effective dose, which measures the biological damage created by the deposited energy, is measured in units of rem or sievert (Sv). The **rem** is obtained by multiplying the number of rad by the relative biological effectiveness (RBE); 100 rem = 1 Sv.

## KEY SKILLS

- Write balanced nuclear equations. (Section 21.1)
- Predict nuclear stability and expected type of nuclear decay from the neutron-to-proton ratio of an isotope. (Section 21.2)
- Write balanced nuclear equations for nuclear transmutations. (Section 21.3)
- Calculate ages of objects and/or the amount of a radionuclide remaining after a given period of time using the half-life of the radionuclide in question. (Section 21.4)
- Calculate mass and energy changes for nuclear reactions. (Section 21.6)
- Calculate the binding energies for nuclei. (Section 21.6)
- Describe the difference between fission and fusion. (Sections 21.7 and 21.8)
- Understand how a nuclear power plant operates and know the differences among various types of nuclear power plants. (Section 21.7)
- Understand the meaning of radiation dosage terms. (Section 21.9)
- Understand the biological effects of different kinds of radiation. (Section 21.9)

## KEY EQUATIONS

- $\ln \dfrac{N_t}{N_0} = -kt$  [21.19]  First-order rate law for nuclear decay

- $k = \dfrac{0.693}{t_{1/2}}$  [21.20]  Relationship between nuclear decay constant and half-life; this is derived from the previous equation at $N_t = \frac{1}{2}N_0$

- $E = mc^2$  [21.22]  Einstein's equation that relates mass and energy

# EXERCISES

## VISUALIZING CONCEPTS

**21.1** Indicate whether each of the following nuclides lies within the belt of stability in Figure 21.2: **(a)** neon-24, **(b)** chlorine-32, **(c)** tin-108, **(d)** polonium-216. For any that do not, describe a nuclear decay process that would alter the neutron-to-proton ratio in the direction of increased stability. [Section 21.2]

**21.2** Write the balanced nuclear equation for the reaction represented by the diagram shown here. [Section 21.2]

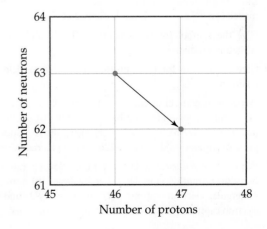

**21.3** Draw a diagram similar to that shown in Exercise 21.2 that illustrates the nuclear reaction $^{211}_{83}\text{Bi} \longrightarrow {}^{4}_{2}\text{He} + {}^{207}_{81}\text{Tl}$. [Section 21.2]

**21.4** The accompanying graph illustrates the decay of $^{88}_{42}\text{Mo}$, which decays via positron emission. **(a)** What is the half-life of the decay? **(b)** What is the rate constant for the decay? **(c)** What fraction of the original sample of $^{88}_{42}\text{Mo}$ remains after 12 min? **(d)** What is the product of the decay process? [Section 21.4]

**21.5** All the stable isotopes of boron, carbon, nitrogen, oxygen, and fluorine are shown in the chart in the right hand column (in red), along with their radioactive isotopes with $t_{1/2} > 1$ min (in blue). **(a)** Write the chemical symbols, including mass and atomic numbers, for all of the stable isotopes. **(b)** Which radioactive isotopes are most likely to decay by beta emission? **(c)** Some of the isotopes shown are used in positron emission tomography. Which ones would you expect to be most useful for this application? **(d)** Which isotope would decay to 12.5%

of its original concentration after 1 hour? [Sections 21.2, 21.4, and 21.5]

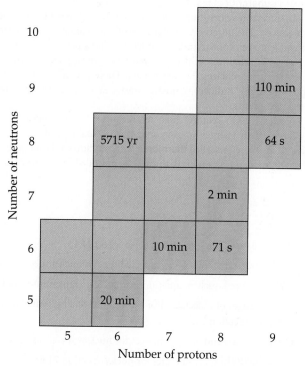

**21.6** The diagram shown here illustrates a fission process. **(a)** What is the unidentified product of the fission? **(b)** Use Figure 21.2 to predict whether the nuclear products of this fission reaction are stable. [Section 21.7]

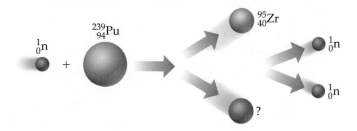

# RADIOACTIVITY (section 21.1)

**21.7** Indicate the number of protons and neutrons in the following nuclei: **(a)** $^{55}_{22}\text{Mn}$, **(b)** $^{201}\text{Hg}$, **(c)** potassium-39.

**21.8** Indicate the number of protons and neutrons in the following nuclei: **(a)** $^{124}_{52}\text{Te}$, **(b)** $^{37}\text{Cl}$, **(c)** thorium-232.

**21.9** Give the symbol for **(a)** a neutron, **(b)** an alpha particle, **(c)** gamma radiation.

**21.10** Give the symbol for **(a)** a proton, **(b)** a beta particle, **(c)** a positron.

**21.11** Write balanced nuclear equations for the following processes: **(a)** rubidium-90 undergoes beta emission; **(b)** selenium-72 undergoes electron capture; **(c)** krypton-76 undergoes positron emission; **(d)** radium-226 emits alpha radiation.

**21.12** Write balanced nuclear equations for the following transformations: **(a)** bismuth-213 undergoes alpha decay; **(b)** nitrogen-13 undergoes electron capture; **(c)** technicium-98 undergoes electron capture; **(d)** gold-188 decays by positron emission.

**21.13** Decay of which nucleus will lead to the following products: **(a)** bismuth-211 by beta decay; **(b)** chromium-50 by positron emission; **(c)** tantalum-179 by electron capture; **(d)** radium-226 by alpha decay?

**21.14** What particle is produced during the following decay processes: **(a)** sodium-24 decays to magnesium-24; **(b)** mercury-188 decays to gold-188; **(c)** iodine-122 decays to xenon-122; **(d)** plutonium-242 decays to uranium-238?

**21.15** The naturally occurring radioactive decay series that begins with $^{235}_{92}\text{U}$ stops with formation of the stable $^{207}_{82}\text{Pb}$ nucleus. The decays proceed through a series of alpha-particle and beta-particle emissions. How many of each type of emission are involved in this series?

**21.16** A radioactive decay series that begins with $^{232}_{90}\text{Th}$ ends with formation of the stable nuclide $^{208}_{82}\text{Pb}$. How many alpha-particle emissions and how many beta-particle emissions are involved in the sequence of radioactive decays?

# NUCLEAR STABILITY (section 21.2)

**21.17** Predict the type of radioactive decay process for the following radionuclides: (a) $^{8}_{5}B$, (b) $^{68}_{29}Cu$, (c) phosphorus-32, (d) chlorine-39.

**21.18** Each of the following nuclei undergoes either beta decay or positron emission. Predict the type of emission for each: (a) tritium, $^{3}_{1}H$, (b) $^{89}_{38}Sr$, (c) iodine-120, (d) silver-102.

**21.19** One of the nuclides in each of the following pairs is radioactive. Predict which is radioactive and which is stable: (a) $^{39}_{19}K$ and $^{40}_{19}K$, (b) $^{209}Bi$ and $^{208}Bi$, (c) nickel-58 and nickel-65. Explain.

**21.20** One nuclide in each of these pairs is radioactive. Predict which is radioactive and which is stable: (a) $^{40}_{20}Ca$ and $^{45}_{20}Ca$, (b) $^{12}C$ and $^{14}C$, (c) lead-206 and thorium-230. Explain your choice in each case.

**21.21** Which of the following nuclides have magic numbers of both protons and neutrons: (a) helium-4, (b) oxygen-18, (c) calcium-40, (d) zinc-66, (e) lead-208?

**21.22** Despite the similarities in the chemical reactivity of elements in the lanthanide series, their abundances in Earth's crust vary by two orders of magnitude. This graph shows the relative abundance as a function of atomic number. How do you explain the sawtooth variation across the series?

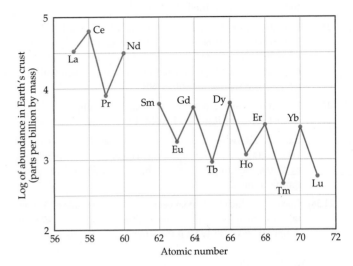

**21.23** Using the concept of magic numbers, explain why alpha emission is relatively common, but proton emission is nonexistent.

**21.24** Which of the following nuclides would you expect to be radioactive: $^{62}_{28}Ni$, $^{58}_{29}Cu$, $^{108}_{47}Ag$, tungsten-184, polonium-206? Justify your choices.

# NUCLEAR TRANSMUTATIONS (section 21.3)

**21.25** Why are nuclear transmutations involving neutrons generally easier to accomplish than those involving protons or alpha particles?

**21.26** In 1930 the American physicist Ernest Lawrence designed the first cyclotron in Berkeley, California. In 1937 Lawrence bombarded a molybdenum target with deuterium ions, producing for the first time an element not found in nature. What was this element? Starting with molybdenum-96 as your reactant, write a nuclear equation to represent this process.

**21.27** Complete and balance the following nuclear equations by supplying the missing particle:
(a) $^{252}_{98}Cf + ^{10}_{5}B \longrightarrow 3 ^{1}_{0}n + ?$
(b) $^{2}_{1}H + ^{3}_{2}He \longrightarrow ^{4}_{2}He + ?$
(c) $^{1}_{1}H + ^{11}_{5}B \longrightarrow 3?$

(d) $^{122}_{53}I \longrightarrow ^{122}_{54}Xe + ?$
(e) $^{59}_{26}Fe \longrightarrow ^{0}_{-1}e + ?$

**21.28** Complete and balance the following nuclear equations by supplying the missing particle:
(a) $^{14}_{7}N + ^{4}_{2}He \longrightarrow ? + ^{1}_{1}H$
(b) $^{40}_{19}K + ^{0}_{-1}e$ (orbital electron) $\longrightarrow ?$
(c) $? + ^{4}_{2}He \longrightarrow ^{30}_{14}Si + ^{1}_{1}H$
(d) $^{58}_{26}Fe + 2 ^{1}_{0}n \longrightarrow ^{60}_{27}Co + ?$
(e) $^{235}_{92}U + ^{1}_{0}n \longrightarrow ^{135}_{54}Xe + 2 ^{1}_{0}n + ?$

**21.29** Write balanced equations for (a) $^{238}_{92}U(\alpha, n)^{241}_{94}Pu$, (b) $^{14}_{7}N(\alpha, p)^{17}_{8}O$, (c) $^{56}_{26}Fe(\alpha, \beta)^{60}_{29}Cu$.

**21.30** Write balanced equations for each of the following nuclear reactions: (a) $^{238}_{92}U(n, \gamma)^{239}_{92}U$, (b) $^{14}_{7}N(p, \alpha)^{11}_{6}C$, (c) $^{18}_{8}O(n, \beta)^{19}_{9}F$.

# RATES OF RADIOACTIVE DECAY (section 21.4)

**21.31** Each statement that follows refers to a comparison between two radioisotopes, A and X. Indicate whether each of the following statements is true or false, and why.
(a) If the half-life for A is shorter than the half-life for X, A has a larger decay rate constant.
(b) If X is "not radioactive," its half-life is essentially zero.
(c) If A has a half-life of 10 years, and X has a half-life of 10,000 years, A would be a more suitable radioisotope to measure processes occurring on the 40-year time scale.

**21.32** It has been suggested that strontium-90 (generated by nuclear testing) deposited in the hot desert will undergo radioactive decay more rapidly because it will be exposed to much higher average temperatures. (a) Is this a reasonable suggestion? (b) Does the process of radioactive decay have an activation energy, like the Arrhenius behavior of many chemical reactions (Section 14.5)? Discuss.

**21.33** Some watch dials are coated with a phosphor, like ZnS, and a polymer in which some of the $^{1}H$ atoms have been replaced by $^{3}H$ atoms, tritium. The phosphor emits light when struck by the beta particle from the tritium decay, causing the dials to glow in the dark. The half-life of tritium is 12.3 yr. If the light given off is assumed to be directly proportional to the amount of tritium, by how much will a dial be dimmed in a watch that is 50 years old?

**21.34** It takes 5.2 min for a 1.000-g sample of $^{210}$Fr to decay to 0.250 g. What is the half-life of $^{210}$Fr?

**21.35** Cobalt-60 is a strong gamma emitter that has a half-life of 5.26 yr. The cobalt-60 in a radiotherapy unit must be replaced when its radioactivity falls to 75% of the original sample. If an original sample was purchased in June 2010, when will it be necessary to replace the cobalt-60?

**21.36** How much time is required for a 6.25-mg sample of $^{51}$Cr to decay to 0.75 mg if it has a half-life of 27.8 days?

**[21.37]** Radium-226, which undergoes alpha decay, has a half-life of 1600 yr. (a) How many alpha particles are emitted in 5.0 min by a 10.0-mg sample of $^{226}$Ra? (b) What is the activity of the sample in mCi?

**[21.38]** Cobalt-60, which undergoes beta decay, has a half-life of 5.26 yr. (a) How many beta particles are emitted in 600 s by a 3.75-mg sample of $^{60}$Co? (b) What is the activity of the sample in Bq?

**21.39** The cloth shroud from around a mummy is found to have a $^{14}$C activity of 9.7 disintegrations per minute per gram of carbon as compared with living organisms that undergo 16.3 disintegrations per minute per gram of carbon. From the half-life for $^{14}$C decay, 5715 yr, calculate the age of the shroud.

**21.40** A wooden artifact from a Chinese temple has a $^{14}$C activity of 38.0 counts per minute as compared with an activity of 58.2 counts per minute for a standard of zero age. From the half-life for $^{14}$C decay, 5715 yr, determine the age of the artifact.

**21.41** Potassium-40 decays to argon-40 with a half-life of $1.27 \times 10^9$ yr. What is the age of a rock in which the mass ratio of $^{40}$Ar to $^{40}$K is 4.2?

**21.42** The half-life for the process $^{238}$U $\longrightarrow$ $^{206}$Pb is $4.5 \times 10^9$ yr. A mineral sample contains 75.0 mg of $^{238}$U and 18.0 mg of $^{206}$Pb. What is the age of the mineral?

# ENERGY CHANGES (section 21.6)

**21.43** The thermite reaction, $Fe_2O_3(s) + 2 Al(s) \longrightarrow 2 Fe(s) + Al_2O_3(s)$, $\Delta H° = -851.5$ kJ/mol, is one of the most exothermic reactions known. Because the heat released is sufficient to melt the iron product, the reaction is used to weld metal under the ocean. How much heat is released per mole of $Fe_2O_3$ produced? How does this amount of thermal energy compare with the energy released when 2 mol of protons and 2 mol of neutrons combine to form 1 mol of alpha particles?

**21.44** An analytical laboratory balance typically measures mass to the nearest 0.1 mg. What energy change would accompany the loss of 0.1 mg in mass?

**21.45** How much energy must be supplied to break a single aluminum-27 nucleus into separated protons and neutrons if an aluminum-27 atom has a mass of 26.9815386 amu? How much energy is required for 100.0 grams of aluminum-27? (The mass of an electron is given on the inside back cover.)

**21.46** How much energy must be supplied to break a single $^{21}$Ne nucleus into separated protons and neutrons if the nucleus has a mass of 20.98846 amu? What is the nuclear binding energy for 1 mol of $^{21}$Ne?

**21.47** The atomic masses of hydrogen-2 (deuterium), helium-4, and lithium-6 are 2.014102 amu, 4.002602 amu, and 6.0151228 amu, respectively. For each isotope, calculate (a) the nuclear mass, (b) the nuclear binding energy, (c) the nuclear binding energy per nucleon. (d) Which of these three isotopes has the largest nuclear binding energy per nucleon? Does this agree with the trends plotted in Figure 21.12?

**21.48** The atomic masses of nitrogen-14, titanium-48, and xenon-129 are 13.999234 amu, 47.935878 amu, and 128.904779 amu, respectively. For each isotope, calculate (a) the nuclear mass,

(b) the nuclear binding energy, (c) the nuclear binding energy per nucleon.

**21.49** The energy from solar radiation falling on Earth is $1.07 \times 10^{16}$ kJ/min. (a) How much loss of mass from the Sun occurs in one day from just the energy falling on Earth? (b) If the energy released in the reaction

$$^{235}U + {}^1_0n \longrightarrow {}^{141}_{56}Ba + {}^{92}_{36}Kr + 3{}^1_0n$$

($^{235}$U nuclear mass, 234.9935 amu; $^{141}$Ba nuclear mass, 140.8833 amu; $^{92}$Kr nuclear mass, 91.9021 amu) is taken as typical of that occurring in a nuclear reactor, what mass of uranium-235 is required to equal 0.10% of the solar energy that falls on Earth in 1.0 day?

**21.50** Based on the following atomic mass values—$^1$H, 1.00782 amu; $^2$H, 2.01410 amu; $^3$H, 3.01605 amu; $^3$He, 3.01603 amu; $^4$He, 4.00260 amu—and the mass of the neutron given in the text, calculate the energy released per mole in each of the following nuclear reactions, all of which are possibilities for a controlled fusion process:

(a) ${}^2_1H + {}^3_1H \longrightarrow {}^4_2He + {}^1_0n$

(b) ${}^2_1H + {}^2_1H \longrightarrow {}^3_2He + {}^1_0n$

(c) ${}^2_1H + {}^3_2He \longrightarrow {}^4_2He + {}^1_1H$

**21.51** Which of the following nuclei is likely to have the largest mass defect per nucleon: (a) $^{59}$Co, (b) $^{11}$B, (c) $^{118}$Sn, (d) $^{243}$Cm? Explain your answer.

**21.52** The isotope ${}^{62}_{28}$Ni has the largest binding energy per nucleon of any isotope. Calculate this value from the atomic mass of nickel-62 (61.928345 amu) and compare it with the value given for iron-56 in Table 21.7.

# EFFECTS AND USES OF RADIOISOTOPES (sections 21.7–21.9)

**21.53** Iodine-131 is a convenient radioisotope to monitor thyroid activity in humans. It is a beta emitter with a half-life of 8.02 days. The thyroid is the only gland in the body that uses iodine. A person undergoing a test of thyroid activity drinks a solution of NaI, in which only a small fraction of the iodide is radioactive. (a) Why is NaI a good choice for the source of iodine? (b) If a Geiger counter

is placed near the person's thyroid (which is near the neck) right after the sodium iodide solution is taken, what will the data look like as a function of time? (c) A normal thyroid will take up about 12% of the ingested iodide in a few hours. How long will it take for the radioactive iodide taken up and held by the thyroid to decay to 0.01% of the original amount?

**21.54** Why is it important that radioisotopes used as diagnostic tools in nuclear medicine produce gamma radiation when they decay? Why are alpha emitters not used as diagnostic tools?

**21.55** What is the most common fissionable isotope in a commercial nuclear power reactor?

**21.56** What is meant by enriched uranium? How is enriched uranium different from natural uranium?

**21.57** What is the function of the control rods in a nuclear reactor? What substances are used to construct control rods? Why are these substances chosen?

**21.58** (a) What is the function of the moderator in a nuclear reactor? (b) What substance acts as the moderator in a pressurized water generator? (c) What other substances are used as a moderator in nuclear reactor designs?

**21.59** Complete and balance the nuclear equations for the following fission or fusion reactions:
(a) $^{2}_{1}H + ^{2}_{1}H \longrightarrow ^{3}_{2}He + \_\_$
(b) $^{239}_{92}U + ^{1}_{0}n \longrightarrow ^{133}_{51}Sb + ^{98}_{41}Nb + \_\_ ^{1}_{0}n$

**21.60** Complete and balance the nuclear equations for the following fission reactions:
(a) $^{235}_{92}U + ^{1}_{0}n \longrightarrow ^{160}_{62}Sm + ^{72}_{30}Zn + \_\_ ^{1}_{0}n$
(b) $^{239}_{94}Pu + ^{1}_{0}n \longrightarrow ^{144}_{58}Ce + \_\_ + 2^{1}_{0}n$

**21.61** A portion of the Sun's energy comes from the reaction
$$4^{1}_{1}H \longrightarrow ^{4}_{2}He + 2^{0}_{1}e$$
which requires a temperature of $10^6$ to $10^7$ K. (a) Use the mass of the helium-4 nucleus given in Table 21.7 to determine how much energy is released when the reaction is run with 1 mol of hydrogen atoms. (b) Why is such a high temperature required?

**21.62** The spent fuel elements from a fission reactor are much more intensely radioactive than the original fuel elements. (a) What does this tell you about the products of the fission process in relationship to the belt of stability, Figure 21.2? (b) Given that only two or three neutrons are released per fission event and knowing that the nucleus undergoing fission has a neutron-to-proton ratio characteristic of a heavy nucleus, what sorts of decay would you expect to be dominant among the fission products?

# ADDITIONAL EXERCISES

**21.69** Radon-222 decays to a stable nucleus by a series of three alpha emissions and two beta emissions. What is the stable nucleus that is formed?

**21.70** Equation 21.28 is the nuclear reaction responsible for much of the helium-4 production in our Sun. How much energy is released in this reaction?

**21.71** Chlorine has two stable nuclides, $^{35}Cl$ and $^{37}Cl$. In contrast, $^{36}Cl$ is a radioactive nuclide that decays by beta emission. (a) What is the product of decay of $^{36}Cl$? (b) Based on the empirical rules about nuclear stability, explain why the nucleus of $^{36}Cl$ is less stable than either $^{35}Cl$ or $^{37}Cl$.

**21.72** When two protons fuse in a star, the product is $^{2}H$ plus a positron (Equation 21.26). Why do you think the more obvious product of the reaction, $^{2}He$, is unstable?

**21.73** Nuclear scientists have synthesized approximately 1600 nuclei not known in nature. More might be discovered with heavy-ion bombardment using high-energy particle accelerators. Complete and balance the following reactions, which involve heavy-ion bombardments:

**21.63** Which type or types of nuclear reactors have these characteristics?
(a) Does not use a secondary coolant
(b) Creates more fissionable material than it consumes
(c) Uses a gas, such as He or $CO_2$, as the primary coolant

**21.64** Which type or types of nuclear reactors have these characteristics?
(a) Can use natural uranium as a fuel
(b) Does not use a moderator
(s) Can be refueled without shutting down

**21.65** Hydroxyl radicals can pluck hydrogen atoms from molecules ("hydrogen abstraction"), and hydroxide ions can pluck protons from molecules ("deprotonation"). Write the reaction equations and Lewis dot structures for the hydrogen abstraction and deprotonation reactions for the generic carboxylic acid R–COOH with hydroxyl radical and hydroxide ion, respectively. Why is hydroxyl radical more toxic to living systems than hydroxide ion?

**21.66** Which are classified as ionizing radiation: X-rays, alpha particles, microwaves from a cell phone, and gamma rays?

**21.67** A laboratory rat is exposed to an alpha-radiation source whose activity is 14.3 mCi. (a) What is the activity of the radiation in disintegrations per second? In becquerels? (b) The rat has a mass of 385 g and is exposed to the radiation for 14.0 s, absorbing 35% of the emitted alpha particles, each having an energy of $9.12 \times 10^{-13}$ J. Calculate the absorbed dose in millirads and grays. (c) If the RBE of the radiation is 9.5, calculate the effective absorbed dose in mrem and Sv.

**21.68** A 65-kg person is accidentally exposed for 240 s to a 15-mCi source of beta radiation coming from a sample of $^{90}Sr$. (a) What is the activity of the radiation source in disintegrations per second? In becquerels? (b) Each beta particle has an energy of $8.75 \times 10^{-14}$ J, and 7.5% of the radiation is absorbed by the person. Assuming that the absorbed radiation is spread over the person's entire body, calculate the absorbed dose in rads and in grays. (c) If the RBE of the beta particles is 1.0, what is the effective dose in mrem and in sieverts? (d) How does the magnitude of this dose of radiation compare with that of a mammogram (300 mrem)?

(a) $^{6}_{3}Li + ^{56}_{28}Ni \longrightarrow ?$
(b) $^{40}_{20}Ca + ^{248}_{96}Cm \longrightarrow ^{147}_{62}Sm + ?$
(c) $^{88}_{38}Sr + ^{84}_{36}Kr \longrightarrow ^{116}_{46}Pd + ?$
(d) $^{40}_{20}Ca + ^{238}_{92}U \longrightarrow ^{70}_{30}Zn + 4^{1}_{0}n + 2?$

**[21.74]** The synthetic radioisotope technetium-99, which decays by beta emission, is the most widely used isotope in nuclear medicine. The following data were collected on a sample of $^{99}Tc$:

| Disintegrations per Minute | Time (h) |
| --- | --- |
| 180 | 0 |
| 130 | 2.5 |
| 104 | 5.0 |
| 77 | 7.5 |
| 59 | 10.0 |
| 46 | 12.5 |
| 24 | 17.5 |

Using these data, make an appropriate graph and curve fit to determine the half-life.

[**21.75**] According to current regulations, the maximum permissible dose of strontium-90 in the body of an adult is $1 \mu Ci$ ($1 \times 10^{-6}$ Ci). Using the relationship rate = $kN$, calculate the number of atoms of strontium-90 to which this dose corresponds. To what mass of strontium-90 does this correspond? The half-life for strontium-90 is 28.8 yr.

[**21.76**] Suppose you had a detection device that could count every decay event from a radioactive sample of plutonium-239 ($t_{1/2}$ is 24,000 yr). How many counts per second would you obtain from a sample containing 0.385 g of plutonium-239?

**21.77** Methyl acetate ($CH_3COOCH_3$) is formed by the reaction of acetic acid with methyl alcohol. If the methyl alcohol is labeled with oxygen-18, the oxygen-18 ends up in the methyl acetate:

$$CH_3\overset{O}{\overset{\|}{C}}OH + H^{18}OCH_3 \longrightarrow CH_3\overset{O}{\overset{\|}{C}}{}^{18}OCH_3 + H_2O$$

Do the C—OH bond of the acid and the O—H bond of the alcohol break in the reaction, or do the O—H bond of the acid and the C—OH bond of the alcohol break? Explain.

**21.78** An experiment was designed to determine whether an aquatic plant absorbed iodide ion from water. Iodine-131 ($t_{1/2} = 8.02$ days) was added as a tracer, in the form of iodide ion, to a tank containing the plants. The initial activity of a 1.00-$\mu$L sample of the water was 214 counts per minute. After 30 days the level of activity in a 1.00-$\mu$L sample was 15.7 counts per minute. Did the plants absorb iodide from the water? Explain.

**21.79** The nuclear masses of $^7Be$, $^9Be$, and $^{10}Be$ are 7.0147, 9.0100, and 10.0113 amu, respectively. Which of these nuclei has the largest binding energy per nucleon?

[**21.80**] A 26.00-g sample of water containing tritium, $^3_1H$, emits $1.50 \times 10^3$ beta particles per second. Tritium is a weak beta emitter with a half-life of 12.3 yr. What fraction of all the hydrogen in the water sample is tritium?

**21.81** The Sun radiates energy into space at the rate of $3.9 \times 10^{26}$ J/s. **(a)** Calculate the rate of mass loss from the Sun in kg/s. **(b)** How does this mass loss arise? **(c)** It is estimated that the Sun contains $9 \times 10^{56}$ free protons. How many protons per second are consumed in nuclear reactions in the Sun?

[**21.82**] The average energy released in the fission of a single uranium-235 nucleus is about $3 \times 10^{-11}$ J. If the conversion of this energy to electricity in a nuclear power plant is 40% efficient, what mass of uranium-235 undergoes fission in a year in a plant that produces 1000 megawatts? Recall that a watt is 1 J/s.

**21.83** Tests on human subjects in Boston in 1965 and 1966, following the era of atomic bomb testing, revealed average quantities of about 2 pCi of plutonium radioactivity in the average person. How many disintegrations per second does this level of activity imply? If each alpha particle deposits $8 \times 10^{-13}$ J of energy and if the average person weighs 75 kg, calculate the number of rads and rems of radiation in 1 yr from such a level of plutonium.

# INTEGRATIVE EXERCISES

**21.84** A 53.8-mg sample of sodium perchlorate contains radioactive chlorine-36 (whose atomic mass is 36.0 amu). If 29.6% of the chlorine atoms in the sample are chlorine-36 and the remainder are naturally occurring nonradioactive chlorine atoms, how many disintegrations per second are produced by this sample? The half-life of chlorine-36 is $3.0 \times 10^5$ yr.

**21.85** Calculate the mass of octane, $C_8H_{18}(l)$, that must be burned in air to evolve the same quantity of energy as produced by the fusion of 1.0 g of hydrogen in the following fusion reaction:

$$4{}^1_1H \longrightarrow {}^4_2He + 2{}^0_1e$$

Assume that all the products of the combustion of octane are in their gas phases. Use data from Exercise 21.50, Appendix C, and the inside covers of the text. The standard enthalpy of formation of octane is $-250.1$ kJ/mol.

**21.86** A sample of an alpha emitter having an activity of 0.18i is stored in a 25.0-mL sealed container at 22 °C for 245 days. **(a)** How many alpha particles are formed during this time? **(b)** Assuming that each alpha particle is converted to a helium atom, what is the partial pressure of helium gas in the container after this 245-day period?

**[21.87]** Charcoal samples from Stonehenge in England were burned in $O_2$, and the resultant $CO_2$ gas bubbled into a solution of $Ca(OH)_2$ (limewater), resulting in the precipitation of $CaCO_3$. The $CaCO_3$ was removed by filtration and dried. A 788-mg sample of the $CaCO_3$ had a radioactivity of $1.5 \times 10^{-2}$ Bq due to carbon-14. By comparison, living organisms undergo 15.3 disintegrations per minute per gram of carbon. Using the half-life of carbon-14, 5715 yr, calculate the age of the charcoal sample.

**21.88** A 25.0-mL sample of 0.050 $M$ barium nitrate solution was mixed with 25.0 mL of 0.050 $M$ sodium sulfate solution labeled with radioactive sulfur-35. The activity of the initial sodium sulfate solution was $1.22 \times 10^6$ Bq/mL. After the resultant precipitate was removed by filtration, the remaining filtrate was found to have an activity of 250 Bq/mL. **(a)** Write a balanced chemical equation for the reaction that occurred. **(b)** Calculate the $K_{sp}$ for the precipitate under the conditions of the experiment.

# WHAT'S AHEAD

# CHEMISTRY OF THE NONMETALS

**THE CHAPTER-OPENING PHOTOGRAPH** shows the sun setting over the ocean, viewed through a window. Everything we see there comes from nonmetallic elements. The heat and light of the Sun result from the nuclear reactions of hydrogen. We know that water is $H_2O$; glass, too, is nonmetallic, being based on silicon dioxide, $SiO_2$.

In this chapter we take a panoramic view of the descriptive chemistry of the nonmetallic elements, starting with hydrogen and progressing group by group across the periodic table. We will consider how the elements occur in nature, how they are isolated from their sources, and how they are used. We will emphasize hydrogen, oxygen, nitrogen, and carbon because these four nonmetals form many commercially important compounds and account for 99% of the atoms required by living cells.

As you study this *descriptive chemistry*, it is important to look for trends rather than trying to memorize all the facts presented. The periodic table is your most valuable tool in this task.

# 22.1 | PERIODIC TRENDS AND CHEMICAL REACTIONS

☐ Metals ☐ Metalloids ☐ Nonmetals

Increasing ionization energy
Decreasing atomic radius
Increasing electronegativity
Decreasing metallic character

Decreasing ionization energy
Increasing atomic radius
Decreasing electronegativity
Increasing metallic character

▲ **FIGURE 22.1** Trends in elemental properties.

Recall that we can classify elements as metals, metalloids, and non-metals. ∞ (Section 7.6) Except for hydrogen, which is a special case, the nonmetals occupy the upper right portion of the periodic table. This division of elements relates nicely to trends in the properties of the elements as summarized in ◄ **FIGURE 22.1**. Electronegativity, for example, increases as we move left to right across a period and decreases as we move down a group. The nonmetals thus have higher electronegativities than the metals. This difference leads to the formation of ionic solids in reactions between metals and nonmetals. ∞ (Sections 7.6, 8.2, 8.4) In contrast, compounds formed between two or more nonmetals are usually molecular substances. ∞ (Sections 7.8 and 8.4)

The chemistry exhibited by the first member of a nonmetal group can differ from that of subsequent members. For example, nonmetals in period 3 and below can accommodate a larger number of bonded neighbors. ∞ (Section 8.7) Another important difference is that the first element in any group can more readily form $\pi$ bonds. This trend is due, in part, to size because small atoms are able to approach each other more closely. As a result, the overlap of $p$ orbitals, which results in the formation of $\pi$ bonds, is more effective for the first element in each group (▼ **FIGURE 22.2**). More effective overlap means stronger $\pi$ bonds, reflected in bond enthalpies. ∞ (Section 8.8) For example, the difference between the enthalpies of the C—C bond and the C=C bond is about 270 kJ/mol; ∞ (Table 8.4) this value reflects the "strength" of a carbon–carbon $\pi$ bond, and the difference between Si—Si and Si=Si bonds is only about 100 kJ/mol, significantly lower than that for carbon.

As we shall see, $\pi$ bonds are particularly important in the chemistry of carbon, nitrogen, and oxygen, each the first member in its group. The heavier elements in these groups have a tendency to form only single bonds.

C–C

Smaller nucleus-to-nucleus distance, more orbital overlap, stronger $\pi$ bond

Si—Si

Larger nucleus-to-nucleus distance, less orbital overlap, weaker $\pi$ bond

▲ **FIGURE 22.2** $\pi$ bonds in period 2 and period 3 elements.

---

**SAMPLE EXERCISE 22.1** | Identifying Elemental Properties

Of the elements Li, K, N, P, and Ne, which (a) is the most electronegative, (b) has the greatest metallic character, (c) can bond to more than four atoms in a molecule, (d) forms $\pi$ bonds most readily?

**SOLUTION**

**Analyze** We are given a list of elements and asked to predict several properties that can be related to periodic trends.

**Plan** We can use Figures 22.1 and 22.2 to guide us to the answers.

**Solve**
(a) Electronegativity increases as we proceed toward the upper right portion of the periodic table, excluding the noble gases. Thus, N is the most electronegative element of our choices.

(b) Metallic character correlates inversely with electronegativity—the less electronegative an element, the greater its metallic character. The element with the greatest metallic character is therefore K, which is closest to the lower left corner of the periodic table.

(c) Nonmetals tend to form molecular compounds, so we can narrow our choice to the three nonmetals on the list: N, P, and Ne. To form more than four bonds, an element must be able to expand its valence shell to allow more than an octet of electrons around it. Valence-shell expansion occurs for period 3 elements and below; N and Ne are both in period 2 and do not undergo valence-shell expansion. Thus, the answer is P.

(d) Period 2 nonmetals form $\pi$ bonds more readily than elements in period 3 and below. There are no compounds known that contain covalent bonds to Ne. Thus, N is the element from the list that forms $\pi$ bonds most readily.

The ready ability of period 2 elements to form $\pi$ bonds is an important factor in determining the structures of these elements and their compounds. Compare, for example, the elemental forms of carbon and silicon. Carbon has five major crystalline allotropes: diamond, graphite, buckminsterfullerene, graphene, and carbon nanotubes.  (Sections 12.7, 12.9) Diamond is a covalent-network solid that has C—C $\sigma$ bonds but no $\pi$ bonds. Graphite, buckminsterfullerene, graphene, and carbon nanotubes have $\pi$ bonds that result from the sideways overlap of $p$ orbitals. Elemental silicon, however, exists only as a diamondlike covalent-network solid with $\sigma$ bonds; it has no forms analogous to graphite, buckminsterfullerene, graphene, or carbon nanotubes, apparently because Si—Si $\pi$ bonds are weak.

### GIVE IT SOME THOUGHT
Can silicon–silicon double bonds form in elemental silicon?

We likewise see significant differences in the dioxides of carbon and silicon (▶ FIGURE 22.3). $CO_2$ is a molecular substance containing C=O double bonds, whereas $SiO_2$ is a covalent-network solid in which four oxygen atoms are bonded to each silicon atom by single bonds, forming an extended structure that has the empirical formula $SiO_2$.

### GIVE IT SOME THOUGHT
Nitrogen is found in nature as $N_2(g)$. Would you expect phosphorus to be found in nature as $P_2(g)$? Explain.

## Chemical Reactions

Because $O_2$ and $H_2O$ are abundant in our environment, it is particularly important to consider how these substances react with other compounds. About one-third of the reactions discussed in this chapter involve either $O_2$ (oxidation or combustion reactions) or $H_2O$ (especially proton-transfer reactions).

In combustion reactions,  (Section 3.2) hydrogen-containing compounds produce $H_2O$. Carbon-containing ones produce $CO_2$ (unless the amount of $O_2$ is insufficient, in which case CO or even C can form). Nitrogen-containing compounds tend to form $N_2$, although NO can form in special cases or in small amounts. A reaction illustrating these points is:

$$4\,CH_3NH_2(g) + 9\,O_2(g) \longrightarrow 4\,CO_2(g) + 10\,H_2O(g) + 2\,N_2(g) \qquad [22.1]$$

The formation of $H_2O$, $CO_2$, and $N_2$ reflects the high thermodynamic stability of these substances, indicated by the large bond energies for the O—H, C=O, and N≡N bonds (463, 799, and 941 kJ/mol, respectively).  (Section 8.8)

When dealing with proton-transfer reactions, remember that the weaker a Brønsted–Lowry acid, the stronger its conjugate base.  (Section 16.2) For example, $H_2$, $OH^-$, $NH_3$, and $CH_4$ are exceedingly weak proton donors that have *no* tendency to act as acids in water. Thus, the species formed by removing one or more protons from them are extremely strong bases. All react readily with water, removing protons from $H_2O$ to form $OH^-$. Two representative reactions are:

$$CH_3^-(aq) + H_2O(l) \longrightarrow CH_4(g) + OH^-(aq) \qquad [22.2]$$

$$N^{3-}(aq) + 3\,H_2O(l) \longrightarrow NH_3(aq) + 3\,OH^-(aq) \qquad [22.3]$$

Fragment of extended $SiO_2$ lattice; Si forms only single bonds

$CO_2$; C forms double bonds

▲ **FIGURE 22.3   Comparison of the bonds in $SiO_2$ and $CO_2$.**

**SAMPLE EXERCISE 22.2** | **Predicting the Products of Chemical Reactions**

Predict the products formed in each of the following reactions, and write a balanced equation:

**(a)** $CH_3NHNH_2(g) + O_2(g) \longrightarrow$

**(b)** $Mg_3P_2(s) + H_2O(l) \longrightarrow$

**SOLUTION**

**Analyze:** We are given the reactants for two chemical equations and asked to predict the products and then balance the equations.

**Plan** We need to examine the reactants to see if we might recognize a reaction type. In **(a)** the carbon compound is reacting with $O_2$, which suggests a combustion reaction. In **(b)** water reacts with an ionic compound. The anion, $P^{3-}$, is a strong base and $H_2O$ is able to act as an acid, so the reactants suggest an acid–base (proton-transfer) reaction.

**Solve**

**(a)** Based on the elemental composition of the carbon compound, this combustion reaction should produce $CO_2$, $H_2O$, and $N_2$:

$$2\,CH_3NHNH_2(g) + 5\,O_2(g) \longrightarrow 2\,CO_2(g) + 6\,H_2O(g) + 2\,N_2(g)$$

**(b)** $Mg_3P_2$ is ionic, consisting of $Mg^{2+}$ and $P^{3-}$ ions. The $P^{3-}$ ion, like $N^{3-}$, has a strong affinity for protons and reacts with $H_2O$ to form $OH^-$ and $PH_3$ ($PH_2^{2-}$, $PH_2^-$, and $PH_3$ are all exceedingly weak proton donors).

$$Mg_3P_2(s) + 6\,H_2O(l) \longrightarrow 2\,PH_3(g) + 3\,Mg(OH)_2(s)$$

$Mg(OH)_2$ has low solubility in water and will precipitate.

**PRACTICE EXERCISE**

Write a balanced equation for the reaction of solid sodium hydride with water.

**Answer:** $NaH(s) + H_2O(l) \longrightarrow NaOH(aq) + H_2(g)$

## 22.2 | HYDROGEN

The English chemist Henry Cavendish (1731–1810) was the first to isolate hydrogen. Because the element produces water when burned in air, the French chemist Antoine Lavoisier ∞ (Figure 3.1) gave it the name *hydrogen*, which means "water producer" (Greek: *hydro*, water; *gennao*, to produce).

Hydrogen is the most abundant element in the universe. It is the nuclear fuel consumed by our Sun and other stars to produce energy. ∞ (Section 21.8) Although about 75% of the known mass of the universe is hydrogen, it constitutes only 0.87% of Earth's mass. Most of the hydrogen on our planet is found associated with oxygen. Water, which is 11% hydrogen by mass, is the most abundant hydrogen compound.

### Isotopes of Hydrogen

The most common isotope of hydrogen, $^1_1H$, has a nucleus consisting of a single proton. This isotope, sometimes referred to as **protium**,* makes up 99.9844% of naturally occurring hydrogen.

Two other isotopes are known: $^2_1H$, whose nucleus contains a proton and a neutron, and $^3_1H$, whose nucleus contains a proton and two neutrons. The $^2_1H$ isotope, **deuterium**, makes up 0.0156% of naturally occurring hydrogen. It is not radioactive and is often given the symbol D in chemical formulas, as in $D_2O$ (deuterium oxide), which is known as *heavy water*.

Because an atom of deuterium is about twice as massive as an atom of protium, the properties of deuterium-containing substances vary somewhat from those of the protium-containing analogs. For example, the normal melting and boiling points of $D_2O$ are 3.81 °C and 101.42 °C, respectively, versus 0.00 °C and 100.00 °C for $H_2O$. Not surprisingly, the

---

*Giving unique names to isotopes is limited to hydrogen. Because of the proportionally large differences in their masses, the isotopes of H show appreciably more differences in their properties than isotopes of heavier elements.

density of $D_2O$ at 25 °C (1.104 g/mL) is greater than that of $H_2O$ (0.997 g/mL). Replacing protium with deuterium (a process called *deuteration*) can also have a profound effect on reaction rates, a phenomenon called a *kinetic-isotope effect*. For example, heavy water can be obtained from the electrolysis $[2 \, H_2O(l) \longrightarrow 2 \, H_2(g) + O_2(g)]$ of ordinary water because the small amount of naturally occurring $D_2O$ in the sample undergoes electrolysis more slowly than $H_2O$ and, therefore, becomes concentrated during the reaction.

The third isotope, $^3_1H$, **tritium**, is radioactive, with a half-life of 12.3 yr:

$$^3_1H \longrightarrow \, ^3_2He + \, ^0_{-1}e \qquad t_{1/2} = 12.3 \text{ yr} \qquad [22.4]$$

Because of its short half-life, only trace quantities of tritium exist naturally. The isotope can be synthesized in nuclear reactors by neutron bombardment of lithium-6:

$$^6_3Li + \, ^1_0n \longrightarrow \, ^3_1H + \, ^4_2He \qquad [22.5]$$

Deuterium and tritium are useful in studying reactions of compounds containing hydrogen. A compound is "labeled" by replacing one or more ordinary hydrogen atoms with deuterium or tritium at specific locations in a molecule. By comparing the locations of the label atoms in reactants and products, the reaction mechanism can often be inferred. When methyl alcohol ($CH_3OH$) is placed in $D_2O$, for example, the H atom of the O—H bond exchanges rapidly with the D atoms, forming $CH_3OD$. The H atoms of the $CH_3$ group do not exchange. This experiment demonstrates the kinetic stability of C—H bonds and reveals the speed at which the O—H bond in the molecule breaks and re-forms.

## Properties of Hydrogen

Hydrogen is the only element that is not a member of any family in the periodic table. Because of its $1s^1$ electron configuration, it is generally placed above lithium in the table. However, it is definitely *not* an alkali metal. It forms a positive ion much less readily than any alkali metal. The ionization energy of the hydrogen atom is 1312 kJ/mol, whereas that of lithium is 520 kJ/mol.

Hydrogen is sometimes placed above the halogens in the periodic table because the hydrogen atom can pick up one electron to form the *hydride ion, $H^-$*, which has the same electron configuration as helium. However, the electron affinity of hydrogen, $E = -73$ kJ/mol, is not as large as that of any halogen. In general, hydrogen shows no closer resemblance to the halogens than it does to the alkali metals.

Elemental hydrogen exists at room temperature as a colorless, odorless, tasteless gas composed of diatomic molecules. We can call $H_2$ *dihydrogen*, but it is more commonly referred to as either *molecular hydrogen* or simply hydrogen. Because $H_2$ is nonpolar and has only two electrons, attractive forces between molecules are extremely weak. As a result, its melting point ($-259$ °C) and boiling point ($-253$ °C) are very low.

The H—H bond enthalpy (436 kJ/mol) is high for a single bond. ∞ (Table 8.4) By comparison, the Cl—Cl bond enthalpy is only 242 kJ/mol. Because $H_2$ has a strong bond, most reactions involving $H_2$ are slow at room temperature. However, the molecule is readily activated by heat, irradiation, or catalysis. The activation generally produces hydrogen atoms, which are very reactive. Once $H_2$ is activated, it reacts rapidly and exothermically with a wide variety of substances.

> ⚠ GIVE IT SOME THOUGHT
> If $H_2$ is activated to produce $H^+$, what must the other product be?

Hydrogen forms strong covalent bonds with many other elements, including oxygen; the O—H bond enthalpy is 463 kJ/mol. The formation of the strong O—H bond makes hydrogen an effective reducing agent for many metal oxides. When $H_2$ is passed over heated CuO, for example, copper is produced:

$$CuO(s) + H_2(g) \longrightarrow Cu(s) + H_2O(g) \qquad [22.6]$$

When $H_2$ is ignited in air, a vigorous reaction occurs, forming $H_2O$. Air containing as little as 4% $H_2$ by volume is potentially explosive. Combustion of hydrogen-oxygen mixtures is used in liquid-fuel rocket engines such as those of the Space Shuttle. The hydrogen and oxygen are stored at low temperatures in liquid form.

## Production of Hydrogen

When a small quantity of $H_2$ is needed in the laboratory, it is usually obtained by the reaction between an active metal such as zinc and a dilute strong acid such as HCl or $H_2SO_4$:

$$Zn(s) + 2\,H^+(aq) \longrightarrow Zn^{2+}(aq) + H_2(g) \qquad [22.7]$$

Large quantities of $H_2$ are produced by reacting methane with steam at 1100 °C. We can view this process as involving two reactions:

$$CH_4(g) + H_2O(g) \longrightarrow CO(g) + 3\,H_2(g) \qquad [22.8]$$

$$CO(g) + H_2O(g) \longrightarrow CO_2(g) + H_2(g) \qquad [22.9]$$

Carbon heated with water to about 1000 °C is another source of $H_2$:

$$C(s) + H_2O(g) \longrightarrow H_2(g) + CO(g) \qquad [22.10]$$

This mixture, known as *water gas*, is used as an industrial fuel.

## A CLOSER LOOK

### THE HYDROGEN ECONOMY

The reaction of hydrogen with oxygen is highly exothermic:

$$2\,H_2(g) + O_2(g) \longrightarrow 2\,H_2O(g)$$
$$\Delta H = -483.6\ \text{kJ} \qquad [22.11]$$

Because the only product of the reaction is water vapor, the prospect of using hydrogen as a fuel in fuel cells is attractive. ∞ (Section 20.7) Alternatively, hydrogen could be combusted directly with oxygen from the atmosphere in an internal combustion engine. In either case, it would be necessary to generate elemental hydrogen on a large scale and arrange for its transport and storage.

▼ **FIGURE 22.4** illustrates various sources and uses of $H_2$ fuel. The generation of $H_2$ through electrolysis of water is in principle the cleanest route, because this process—the reverse of Equation 22.11— produces only hydrogen and oxygen. ∞ (Figure 1.7 and Section 20.9) However, the energy required to electrolyze water must come from somewhere. If we burn fossil fuels to generate this energy, we have not advanced very far toward a true hydrogen economy. If the energy for electrolysis came instead from a hydroelectric or nuclear power plant, solar cells, or wind generators, consumption of nonrenewable energy sources and undesired production of $CO_2$ could be avoided.

*RELATED EXERCISES:* 22.29, 22.30, 22.91

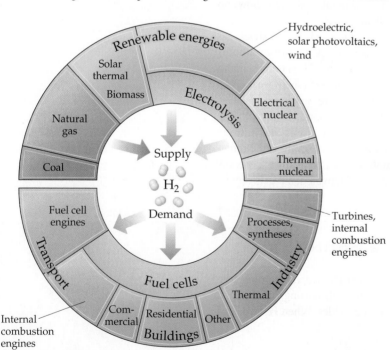

◄ **FIGURE 22.4** The "hydrogen economy" would require hydrogen to be produced from various sources and would use hydrogen in energy-related applications.

Electrolysis of water consumes too much energy and is consequently too costly to be used commercially to produce $H_2$. However, $H_2$ is produced as a by-product in the electrolysis of brine (NaCl) solutions in the course of commercial $Cl_2$ and NaOH manufacture:

$$2\,NaCl(aq) + 2\,H_2O(l) \xrightarrow{\text{electrolysis}} H_2(g) + Cl_2(g) + 2\,NaOH(aq) \quad [22.12]$$

▲ GIVE IT SOME THOUGHT

What are the oxidation states of the H atoms in Equations 22.7–22.12?

## Uses of Hydrogen

Hydrogen is commercially important. About $5.0 \times 10^{10}$ kg (50 million metric tons) is produced annually across the world. About half of the $H_2$ produced is used to synthesize ammonia by the Haber process. ∞ (Section 15.2) Much of the remaining hydrogen is used to convert high-molecular-weight hydrocarbons from petroleum into lower-molecular-weight hydrocarbons suitable for fuel (gasoline, diesel, and others) in a process known as *cracking*. Hydrogen is also used to manufacture methanol via the catalytic reaction of CO and $H_2$ at high pressure and temperature:

$$CO(g) + 2\,H_2(g) \longrightarrow CH_3OH(g) \quad [22.13]$$

## Binary Hydrogen Compounds

Hydrogen reacts with other elements to form three types of compounds: (1) ionic hydrides, (2) metallic hydrides, and (3) molecular hydrides.

The **ionic hydrides** are formed by the alkali metals and by the heavier alkaline earths (Ca, Sr, and Ba). These active metals are much less electronegative than hydrogen. Consequently, hydrogen acquires electrons from them to form hydride ions ($H^-$):

$$Ca(s) + H_2(g) \longrightarrow CaH_2(s) \quad [22.14]$$

The hydride ion is very basic and reacts readily with compounds having even weakly acidic protons to form $H_2$:

$$H^-(aq) + H_2O(l) \longrightarrow H_2(g) + OH^-(aq) \quad [22.15]$$

Ionic hydrides can therefore be used as convenient (although expensive) sources of $H_2$.

Calcium hydride ($CaH_2$) is used to inflate life rafts, weather balloons, and the like where a simple, compact means of generating $H_2$ is desired (▼ **FIGURE 22.5**).

▲ GO FIGURE

**This reaction is exothermic. Is the beaker on the right warmer or colder than the beaker on the left?**

CaH₂

H₂O with pH indicator

H₂ gas

Color change indicates presence of OH⁻

◀ **FIGURE 22.5  The reaction of CaH₂ with water.**

The reaction between $H^-$ and $H_2O$ (Equation 22.15) is an acid–base reaction *and* a redox reaction. The $H^-$ ion, therefore, is a good base *and* a good reducing agent. In fact, hydrides are able to reduce $O_2$ to $OH^-$:

$$2\,NaH(s) + O_2(g) \longrightarrow 2\,NaOH(s) \qquad [22.16]$$

For this reason, hydrides are normally stored in an environment that is free of both moisture and air.

**Metallic hydrides** are formed when hydrogen reacts with transition metals. These compounds are so named because they retain their metallic properties. They are not molecular substances, just as metals are not. In many metallic hydrides, the ratio of metal atoms to hydrogen atoms is not fixed or in small whole numbers. The composition can vary within a range, depending on reaction conditions. $TiH_2$ can be produced, for example, but preparations usually yield $TiH_{1.8}$. These nonstoichiometric metallic hydrides are sometimes called *interstitial hydrides*. Because hydrogen atoms are small enough to fit between the sites occupied by the metal atoms, many metal hydrides behave like interstitial alloys. ∞ (Section 12.3)

The most interesting interstitial metallic hydride is that of palladium. Palladium can take up nearly 900 times its volume of hydrogen, making it very attractive for hydrogen storage in any possible future "hydrogen economy." However, to be practical, any hydrogen-storage compound will have to contain 75% or more hydrogen by mass and be able to charge and discharge hydrogen quickly and safely near room temperature.

**GIVE IT SOME THOUGHT**

Palladium has a density of $12.023\ g/cm^3$. Can a sample of Pd that has a volume of $1\ cm^3$ increase its mass to over 900 g by adsorbing hydrogen?

The **molecular hydrides,** formed by nonmetals and metalloids, are either gases or liquids under standard conditions. The simple molecular hydrides are listed in ◀ FIGURE 22.6, together with their standard free energies of formation, $\Delta G_f^\circ$. ∞ (Section 19.5) In each family the thermal stability (measured as $\Delta G_f^\circ$) decreases as we move down the family. (Recall that the more stable a compound is with respect to its elements under standard conditions, the more negative $\Delta G_f^\circ$ is.)

**GO FIGURE**

Which is the most thermodynamically stable hydride? Which is the least thermodynamically stable?

| 4A | 5A | 6A | 7A |
|---|---|---|---|
| $CH_4(g)$ −50.8 | $NH_3(g)$ −16.7 | $H_2O(l)$ −237 | $HF(g)$ −271 |
| $SiH_4(g)$ +56.9 | $PH_3(g)$ +18.2 | $H_2S(g)$ −33.0 | $HCl(g)$ −95.3 |
| $GeH_4(g)$ +117 | $AsH_3(g)$ +111 | $H_2Se(g)$ +71 | $HBr(g)$ −53.2 |
| | $SbH_3(g)$ +187 | $H_2Te(g)$ +138 | $HI(g)$ +1.30 |

▲ **FIGURE 22.6 Standard free energies of formation of molecular hydrides.** All values are kilojoules per mole of hydride.

## 22.3 | GROUP 8A: THE NOBLE GASES

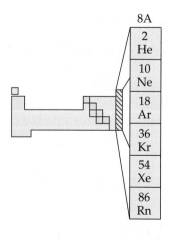

The elements of group 8A are chemically unreactive. Indeed, most of our references to these elements have been in relation to their physical properties, as when we discussed intermolecular forces. ∞ (Section 11.2) The relative inertness of these elements is due to the presence of a completed octet of valence-shell electrons (except He, which only has a filled $1s$ shell). The stability of such an arrangement is reflected in the high ionization energies of the group 8A elements. ∞ (Section 7.4)

The group 8A elements are all gases at room temperature. They are components of Earth's atmosphere, except for radon, which exists only as a short-lived radioisotope. ∞ (Section 21.9) Only argon is relatively abundant. ∞ (Table 18.1) Neon, argon, krypton, and xenon are recovered from liquid air by distillation. All four of these noble gases are used in lighting, display, and laser applications in which the atoms are excited electrically and electrons that are in a higher energy state emit light as they fall to the ground state. ∞ (Section 6.2) Argon is used as a blanketing atmosphere in electric lightbulbs. The gas conducts heat away from the filament but does not react with it. Argon is also used as a protective atmosphere to prevent oxidation in welding and certain high-temperature metallurgical processes.

Helium is in many ways the most important noble gas. Liquid helium is used as a coolant to conduct experiments at very low temperatures. Helium boils at 4.2 K and 1 atm, the lowest boiling point of any substance. It is found in relatively high concentrations in many natural-gas wells and can be obtained from them.

# Noble-Gas Compounds

Because the noble gases are exceedingly stable, they react only under rigorous conditions. We expect the heavier ones to be most likely to form compounds because their ionization energies are lower. ∞ (Figure 7.9) A lower ionization energy suggests the possibility of sharing an electron with another atom, leading to a chemical bond. In addition, because the group 8A elements (except helium) already contain eight electrons in their valence shell, formation of covalent bonds will require an expanded valence shell. Valence-shell expansion occurs most readily with larger atoms. ∞ (Section 8.7)

The first noble-gas compound was reported in 1962. This discovery caused a sensation because it undercut the belief that the noble-gas elements were inert. The initial study involved xenon in combination with fluorine, the element we would expect to be most reactive in pulling electron density from another atom. Since that time chemists have prepared several xenon compounds of fluorine and oxygen (▼ TABLE 22.1). The fluorides $XeF_2$, $XeF_4$, and $XeF_6$ are made by direct reaction of the elements. By varying the ratio of reactants and altering reaction conditions, one of the three compounds can be obtained. The oxygen-containing compounds are formed when the fluorides react with water as, for example,

$$XeF_6(s) + 3\ H_2O(l) \longrightarrow XeO_3(aq) + 6\ HF(aq) \qquad [22.17]$$

---

**SAMPLE EXERCISE 22.3** **Predicting a Molecular Structure**

Use the VSEPR model to predict the structure of $XeF_4$.

**SOLUTION**

**Analyze** We must predict the geometrical structure given only the molecular formula.

**Plan** We must first write the Lewis structure for the molecule. We then count the number of electron pairs (domains) around the Xe atom and use that number and the number of bonds to predict the geometry.

**Solve** There are 36 valence-shell electrons (8 from xenon and 7 from each fluorine). If we make four single Xe—F bonds, each fluorine has its octet satisfied. Xe then has 12 electrons in its valence shell, so we expect an octahedral arrangement of six electron pairs. Two of these are nonbonded pairs. Because nonbonded pairs require more volume than bonded pairs ∞ (Section 9.2), it is reasonable to expect these nonbonded pairs to be opposite each other. The expected structure is square planar, as shown in ▶ FIGURE 22.7.

**Comment** The experimentally determined structure agrees with this prediction.

**PRACTICE EXERCISE**

Describe the electron-domain geometry and molecular geometry of $XeF_2$.
**Answer:** trigonal bipyramidal, linear

▲ FIGURE 22.7    Xenon tetrafluoride.

---

The other noble-gas elements form compounds much less readily than xenon. For many years, only one binary krypton compound, $KrF_2$, was known with certainty, and it decomposes to its elements at $-10\ °C$. Other compounds of krypton have been isolated at very low temperatures (40 K).

**TABLE 22.1 • Properties of Xenon Compounds**

| Compound | Oxidation State of Xe | Melting Point (°C) | $\Delta H_f^\circ$ (kJ/mol)[a] |
|---|---|---|---|
| $XeF_2$ | +2 | 129 | $-109(g)$ |
| $XeF_4$ | +4 | 117 | $-218(g)$ |
| $XeF_6$ | +6 | 49 | $-298(g)$ |
| $XeOF_4$ | +6 | $-41$ to $-28$ | $+146(l)$ |
| $XeO_3$ | +6 | $-$[b] | $+402(s)$ |
| $XeO_2F_2$ | +6 | 31 | $+145(s)$ |
| $XeO_4$ | +8 | $-$[c] | $-$ |

[a] At 25 °C, for the compound in the state indicated.
[b] A solid; decomposes at 40 °C.
[c] A solid; decomposes at $-40$ °C.

## 22.4 | GROUP 7A: THE HALOGENS

The elements of group 7A, the halogens, have the outer-electron configuration $ns^2np^5$, where $n$ ranges from 2 through 6. The halogens have large negative electron affinities ∞ (Section 7.5), and they most often achieve a noble-gas configuration by gaining an electron, which results in a $-1$ oxidation state. Fluorine, being the most electronegative element, exists in compounds only in the $-1$ state. The other halogens exhibit positive oxidation states up to $+7$ in combination with more electronegative atoms such as O. In the positive oxidation states, the halogens tend to be good oxidizing agents, readily accepting electrons.

Chlorine, bromine, and iodine are found as the halides in seawater and in salt deposits. Fluorine occurs in the minerals fluorspar ($CaF_2$), cryolite ($Na_3AlF_6$), and fluorapatite [$Ca_5(PO_4)_3F$].* Only fluorspar is an important commercial source of fluorine.

All isotopes of astatine are radioactive. The longest-lived isotope is astatine-210, which has a half-life of 8.1 hr and decays mainly by electron capture. Because astatine is so unstable, very little is known about its chemistry.

### Properties and Production of the Halogens

Most properties of the halogens vary in a regular fashion as we go from fluorine to iodine (▼ TABLE 22.2).

Under ordinary conditions the halogens exist as diatomic molecules. The molecules are held together in the solid and liquid states by dispersion forces. ∞ (Section 11.2) Because $I_2$ is the largest and most polarizable halogen molecule, the intermolecular forces between $I_2$ molecules are the strongest. Thus, $I_2$ has the highest melting point and boiling point. At room temperature and 1 atm, $I_2$ is a purple solid, $Br_2$ is a red-brown liquid, and $Cl_2$ and $F_2$ are gases. ∞ (Figure 7.27) Chlorine readily liquefies upon compression at room temperature and is normally stored and handled in liquid form under pressure in steel containers.

The comparatively low bond enthalpy of $F_2$ (155 kJ/mol) accounts in part for the extreme reactivity of elemental fluorine. Because of its high reactivity, $F_2$ is difficult to work with. Certain metals, such as copper and nickel, can be used to contain $F_2$ because their surfaces form a protective coating of metal fluoride. Chlorine and the heavier halogens are also reactive, although less so than fluorine.

Because of their high electronegativities, the halogens tend to gain electrons from other substances and thereby serve as oxidizing agents. The oxidizing ability of the halogens, indicated by their standard reduction potentials, decreases going down the group. As a result, a given halogen is able to oxidize the halide anions below it. For example, $Cl_2$ oxidizes $Br^-$ and $I^-$ but not $F^-$, as seen in ◄ FIGURE 22.8.

**7A**

| 9 F |
|:---:|
| 17 Cl |
| 35 Br |
| 53 I |
| 85 At |

### GO FIGURE

Do $Br_2$ and $I_2$ appear to be more or less soluble in $CCl_4$ than in $H_2O$?

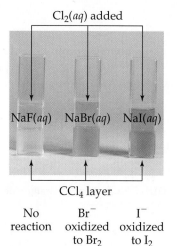

$Cl_2(aq)$ added

NaF($aq$)    NaBr($aq$)    NaI($aq$)

$CCl_4$ layer

| No reaction | $Br^-$ oxidized to $Br_2$ | $I^-$ oxidized to $I_2$ |

▲ **FIGURE 22.8 Reaction of $Cl_2$ with aqueous solutions of NaF, NaBr, and NaI.** The top liquid layer is water; the bottom liquid layer is carbon tetrachloride.

| TABLE 22.2 • Some Properties of the Halogens | | | | |
|---|---|---|---|---|
| **Property** | **F** | **Cl** | **Br** | **I** |
| Atomic radius (Å) | 0.71 | 0.99 | 1.14 | 1.33 |
| Ionic radius, $X^-$ (Å) | 1.33 | 1.81 | 1.96 | 2.20 |
| First ionization energy (kJ/mol) | 1681 | 1251 | 1140 | 1008 |
| Electron affinity (kJ/mol) | −328 | −349 | −325 | −295 |
| Electronegativity | 4.0 | 3.0 | 2.8 | 2.5 |
| X—X single-bond enthalpy (kJ/mol) | 155 | 242 | 193 | 151 |
| Reduction potential (V): $\frac{1}{2}X_2(aq) + e^- \longrightarrow X^-(aq)$ | 2.87 | 1.36 | 1.07 | 0.54 |

*Minerals are solid substances that occur in nature. They are usually known by their common names rather than by their chemical names. What we know as rock is merely an aggregate of different minerals.

| SAMPLE EXERCISE 22.4 | Predicting Chemical Reactions among the Halogens |
|---|---|

Write the balanced equation for the reaction, if any, between (**a**) $I^-(aq)$ and $Br_2(l)$, (**b**) $Cl^-(aq)$ and $I_2(s)$.

### SOLUTION

**Analyze** We are asked to determine whether a reaction occurs when a particular halide and halogen are combined.

**Plan** A given halogen is able to oxidize anions of the halogens below it in the periodic table. Thus, in each pair the halogen having the smaller atomic number ends up as the halide ion. If the halogen with the smaller atomic number is already the halide, there is no reaction. Thus, the key to determining whether a reaction occurs is locating the elements in the periodic table.

**Solve**
(**a**) $Br_2$ can oxidize (remove electrons from) the anions of the halogens below it in the periodic table. Thus, it oxidizes $I^-$:

$$2\, I^-(aq) + Br_2(aq) \longrightarrow I_2(s) + 2\, Br^-(aq)$$

(**b**) $Cl^-$ is the anion of a halogen above iodine in the periodic table. Thus, $I_2$ cannot oxidize $Cl^-$; there is no reaction.

### PRACTICE EXERCISE
Write the balanced chemical equation for the reaction between $Br^-(aq)$ and $Cl_2(aq)$.
**Answer:** $2\, Br^-(aq) + Cl_2(aq) \longrightarrow Br_2(aq) + 2\, Cl^-(aq)$

Notice in Table 22.2 that the standard reduction potential of $F_2$ is exceptionally high. Fluorine gas readily oxidizes water:

$$F_2(aq) + H_2O(l) \longrightarrow 2\, HF(aq) + \tfrac{1}{2} O_2(g) \qquad E° = 1.80\ \text{V} \qquad [22.18]$$

Fluorine cannot be prepared by electrolytic oxidation of aqueous solutions of fluoride salts because water is oxidized more readily than $F^-$. ∞ (Section 20.9) In practice, the element is formed by electrolytic oxidation of a solution of KF in anhydrous HF.

Chlorine is produced mainly by electrolysis of either molten or aqueous sodium chloride. Both bromine and iodine are obtained commercially from brines containing the halide ions; the reaction used is oxidation with $Cl_2$.

## Uses of the Halogens

Fluorine is used to prepare fluorocarbons—very stable carbon–fluorine compounds used as refrigerants, lubricants, and plastics. Teflon® (▶ **FIGURE 22.9**) is a polymeric fluorocarbon noted for its high thermal stability and lack of chemical reactivity.

Chlorine is by far the most commercially important halogen. About $1 \times 10^{10}$ kg (10 million tons) of $Cl_2$ is produced annually in the United States. In addition, hydrogen chloride production is about $4.0 \times 10^9$ kg (4.4 million tons) annually. About half of this chlorine finds its way eventually into the manufacture of chlorine-containing organic compounds, such as the vinyl chloride ($C_2H_3Cl$) used in making polyvinyl chloride (PVC) plastics. ∞ (Section 12.8) Much of the remainder is used as a bleaching agent in the paper and textile industries. When $Cl_2$ dissolves in cold dilute base, it converts into $Cl^-$ and hypochlorite, $ClO^-$:

$$Cl_2(aq) + 2\, OH^-(aq) \rightleftharpoons Cl^-(aq) + ClO^-(aq) + H_2O(l) \qquad [22.19]$$

 **GIVE IT SOME THOUGHT**

What is the oxidation state of Cl in each Cl species in Equation 22.19?

Sodium hypochlorite (NaClO) is the active ingredient in many liquid bleaches. Chlorine is also used in water treatment to oxidize and thereby destroy bacteria. ∞ (Section 18.4)

△ **GO FIGURE**

**What is the repeating unit in this polymer?**

▲ **FIGURE 22.9  Structure of Teflon®, a fluorocarbon polymer.**

A common use of iodine is as KI in table salt. Iodized salt provides the small amount of iodine necessary in our diets; it is essential for the formation of thyroxin, a hormone secreted by the thyroid gland. Lack of iodine in the diet results in an enlarged thyroid gland, a condition called *goiter*.

## The Hydrogen Halides

All the halogens form stable diatomic molecules with hydrogen. Aqueous solutions of HCl, HBr, and HI are strong acids. The hydrogen halides can be formed by direct reaction of the elements. The most important means of preparing HF and HCl, however, is by reacting a salt of the halide with a strong nonvolatile acid, as in the reaction

$$CaF_2(s) + H_2SO_4(l) \xrightarrow{\Delta} 2\,HF(g) + CaSO_4(s) \qquad [22.20]$$

Neither HBr nor HI can be prepared in this way, however, because $H_2SO_4$ oxidizes $Br^-$ and $I^-$ (▼ FIGURE 22.10). This difference in reactivity reflects the greater ease of oxidation of $Br^-$ and $I^-$ relative to $F^-$ and $Cl^-$. These undesirable oxidations are avoided by using a nonvolatile acid, such as $H_3PO_4$, that is a weaker oxidizing agent than $H_2SO_4$.

---

**SAMPLE EXERCISE 22.5**  **Writing a Balanced Chemical Equation**

Write a balanced equation for the formation of hydrogen bromide gas from the reaction of solid sodium bromide with phosphoric acid.

### SOLUTION

**Analyze** We are asked to write a balanced equation for the reaction between NaBr and $H_3PO_4$ to form HBr and another product.

**Plan** As in Equation 22.20, a metathesis reaction takes place. ∞ (Section 4.2) Let's assume that only one H in $H_3PO_4$ reacts. (The actual number depends on the reaction conditions.) The $H_2PO_4^-$ and $Na^+$ will form $NaH_2PO_4$ as one product.

**Solve** The balanced equation is

$$NaBr(s) + H_3PO_4(l) \longrightarrow NaH_2PO_4(s) + HBr(g)$$

### PRACTICE EXERCISE

Write the balanced equation for the preparation of HI from NaI and $H_3PO_4$.

**Answer:** $NaI(s) + H_3PO_4(l) \longrightarrow NaH_2PO_4(s) + HI(g)$

---

⚠ GO FIGURE

**Are these reactions acid–base reactions or oxidation-reduction reactions?**

▶ FIGURE 22.10  **Reaction of $H_2SO_4$ with NaI and NaBr.**

**TABLE 22.3 • The Stable Oxyacids of the Halogens**

| Oxidation State of Halogen | Formula of Acid | | | Acid Name |
|---|---|---|---|---|
| | Cl | Br | I | |
| +1 | HClO | HBrO | HIO | *Hypohalous* acid |
| +3 | $HClO_2$ | — | — | Hal*ous* acid |
| +5 | $HClO_3$ | $HBrO_3$ | $HIO_3$ | Hal*ic* acid |
| +7 | $HClO_4$ | $HBrO_4$ | $HIO_4$ | *Perhalic* acid |

The hydrogen halides form hydrohalic acid solutions when dissolved in water. These solutions have the characteristic properties of acids, such as reactions with active metals to produce hydrogen gas. ∞ (Section 4.4) Hydrofluoric acid also reacts readily with **silica** ($SiO_2$) and with silicates to form hexafluorosilicic acid ($H_2SiF_6$):

$$SiO_2(s) + 6\ HF(aq) \longrightarrow H_2SiF_6(aq) + 2\ H_2O(l) \qquad [22.21]$$

## Interhalogen Compounds

Because the halogens exist as diatomic molecules, diatomic molecules made up of two different halogen atoms exist. These compounds are the simplest examples of **interhalogens**, compounds, such as ClF and $IF_5$, formed between two halogen elements.

With one exception, the higher interhalogen compounds have a central Cl, Br, or I atom surrounded by 3, 5, or 7 fluorine atoms. The large size of the iodine atom allows the formation of $IF_3$, $IF_5$, and $IF_7$, in which the oxidation state of I is +3, +5, and +7, respectively. With the smaller bromine and chorine atoms, only compounds with 3 or 5 fluorines form. The only higher interhalogen compounds that do not have outer F atoms are $ICl_3$ and $ICl_5$; the large size of the I atom can accommodate 5 Cl atoms, whereas Br is not large enough to allow even $BrCl_3$ to form. All of the interhalogen compounds are powerful oxidizing agents.

## Oxyacids and Oxyanions

▲ **TABLE 22.3** summarizes the formulas of the known oxyacids of the halogens and the way they are named.* ∞ (Section 2.8) The acid strengths of the oxyacids increase with increasing oxidation state of the central halogen atom. ∞ (Section 16.10) All the oxyacids are strong oxidizing agents. The oxyanions, formed on removal of $H^+$ from the oxyacids, are generally more stable than the oxyacids. Hypochlorite salts are used as bleaches and disinfectants because of the powerful oxidizing capabilities of the $ClO^-$ ion. Sodium hypochlorite is used as a bleaching agent. Chlorate salts are similarly very reactive. For example, potassium chlorate is used to make matches and fireworks.

> ⚠ **GIVE IT SOME THOUGHT**
> Which do you expect to be the stronger oxidizing agent, $NaBrO_3$ or $NaClO_3$?

Perchloric acid and its salts are the most stable oxyacids and oxyanions. Dilute solutions of perchloric acid are quite safe, and many perchlorate salts are stable except when heated with organic materials. When heated, however, perchlorates can become vigorous, even violent, oxidizers. Considerable caution should be exercised, therefore, when handling these substances, and it is crucial to avoid contact between perchlorates and readily oxidized material. The use of ammonium perchlorate ($NH_4ClO_4$) as the oxidizer in the solid booster rockets for the Space Shuttle demonstrates the oxidizing power of perchlorates. The solid propellant contains a mixture of $NH_4ClO_4$ and powdered aluminum, the reducing agent. Each shuttle launch requires about $6 \times 10^5$ kg (700 tons) of $NH_4ClO_4$ (▶ **FIGURE 22.11**).

*Fluorine forms one oxyacid, HOF. Because the electronegativity of fluorine is greater than that of oxygen, we must consider fluorine to be in a −1 oxidation state and oxygen to be in the 0 oxidation state in this compound.

$$10\ Al(s) + 6\ NH_4ClO_4(s) \longrightarrow$$
$$4\ Al_2O_3(s) + 2\ AlCl_3(s)$$
$$+ 12\ H_2O(g) + 3\ N_2(g)$$

The large volume of gases produced provides thrust for the booster rockets

▲ **FIGURE 22.11** **Launch of the Space Shuttle *Columbia* from the Kennedy Space Center.**

## CHEMISTRY AND LIFE

### HOW MUCH PERCHLORATE IS TOO MUCH?

Since the 1950s both NASA and the Pentagon have used ammonium perchlorate, $NH_4ClO_4$, as a rocket fuel. The result is that traces of perchlorate ion are found in groundwater in many regions of the United States, with levels ranging from about 4 to 100 ppb.

Perchlorate is known to suppress thyroid hormone levels in humans. However, it is disputed whether the amounts found in drinking water are sufficiently high to cause health problems. The Environmental Protection Agency currently states that a dose of 0.007 mg per kilogram of body mass per day is not expected to cause adverse health effects in humans. For a 70-kg (154-lb.) person drinking 2 L of water per day, that amounts to a concentration of 25 ppb. California has proposed a standard of 6 ppb.

Removal of perchlorate ion from water supplies is not easy. Although perchlorate is an oxidizing agent, the $ClO_4^-$ ion is quite stable in aqueous solution. One promising avenue is reduction by microorganisms. While research continues on the best means of decreasing perchlorate levels in drinking water, federal agencies continue to explore what level constitutes a safe upper limit.

*RELATED EXERCISE: 22.93*

# 22.5 | OXYGEN

By the middle of the seventeenth century, scientists recognized that air contained a component associated with burning and breathing. That component was not isolated until 1774, however, when English scientist Joseph Priestley discovered oxygen. Lavoisier subsequently named the element *oxygen*, meaning "acid former." There is some historical debate about who "really" discovered oxygen, and the debate is the subject of a play written by the chemist-authors Carl Djerassi and Roald Hoffmann (◀ FIGURE 22.12).

Oxygen is found in combination with other elements in a great variety of compounds—water ($H_2O$), silica ($SiO_2$), alumina ($Al_2O_3$), and the iron oxides ($Fe_2O_3$, $Fe_3O_4$) are obvious examples. Indeed, oxygen is the most abundant element by mass both in Earth's crust and in the human body. ∞ (Section 1.2) It is the oxidizing agent for the metabolism of our foods and is crucial to human life.

▲ **FIGURE 22.12   *Oxygen* is the name of a play by the chemists Carl Djerassi (Stanford University) and Roald Hoffmann (Cornell University).** Its subject is the controversy over who discovered oxygen.

## Properties of Oxygen

Oxygen has two allotropes, $O_2$ and $O_3$. When we speak of molecular oxygen or simply oxygen, it is usually understood that we are speaking of *dioxygen* ($O_2$), the normal form of the element; $O_3$ is ozone.

At room temperature, dioxygen is a colorless, odorless gas. It condenses to a liquid at $-183\,°C$ and freezes at $-218\,°C$. It is only slightly soluble in water (0.04 g/L, or 0.001 $M$ at 25 °C), but its presence in water is essential to marine life.

The electron configuration of the oxygen atom is $[He]2s^2 2p^4$. Thus, oxygen can complete its octet of valence electrons either by picking up two electrons to form the oxide ion ($O^{2-}$) or by sharing two electrons. In its covalent compounds, it tends to form either two single bonds, as in $H_2O$, or a double bond, as in formaldehyde ($H_2C=O$). The $O_2$ molecule contains a double bond. The bond in $O_2$ is very strong (bond enthalpy 495 kJ/mol). Oxygen also forms strong bonds with many other elements. Consequently, many oxygen-containing compounds are thermodynamically more stable than $O_2$. In the absence of a catalyst, however, most reactions of $O_2$ have high activation energies and thus require high temperatures to proceed at a suitable rate. Once a sufficiently exothermic reaction begins, it may accelerate rapidly, producing a reaction of explosive violence.

## Production of Oxygen

Nearly all commercial oxygen is obtained from air. The normal boiling point of $O_2$ is $-183\,°C$, whereas that of $N_2$, the other principal component of air, is $-196\,°C$. Thus, when air is liquefied and then allowed to warm, the $N_2$ boils off, leaving liquid $O_2$ contaminated mainly by small amounts of $N_2$ and Ar.

In the laboratory, $O_2$ can be obtained by heating either aqueous hydrogen peroxide or solid potassium chlorate ($KClO_3$):

$$2\, KClO_3(s) \longrightarrow 2\, KCl(s) + 3\, O_2(g) \qquad [22.22]$$

Manganese dioxide ($MnO_2$) catalyzes both reactions.

Much of the $O_2$ in the atmosphere is replenished through photosynthesis, in which green plants use the energy of sunlight to generate $O_2$ (along with glucose, $C_6H_{12}O_6$) from atmospheric $CO_2$:

$$6\, CO_2(g) + 6\, H_2O(l) \longrightarrow C_6H_{12}O_6(aq) + 6\, O_2(g)$$

## Uses of Oxygen

In industrial use, oxygen ranks behind only sulfuric acid ($H_2SO_4$) and nitrogen ($N_2$). About $3 \times 10^{10}$ kg (30 million tons) of $O_2$ is used annually in the United States. It is shipped and stored either as a liquid or in steel containers as a compressed gas. About 70% of the $O_2$ output, however, is generated where it is needed.

Oxygen is by far the most widely used oxidizing agent in industry. Over half of the $O_2$ produced is used in the steel industry, mainly to remove impurities from steel. It is also used to bleach pulp and paper. (Oxidation of colored compounds often gives colorless products.) Oxygen is used together with acetylene ($C_2H_2$) in oxyacetylene welding (▶ FIGURE 22.13). The reaction between $C_2H_2$ and $O_2$ is highly exothermic, producing temperatures in excess of 3000 °C.

$$2\, C_2H_2(g) + 5\, O_2(g) \longrightarrow$$
$$4\, CO_2(g) + 2\, H_2O(g);$$
$$\Delta H° = -2510\ kJ$$

▲ **FIGURE 22.13  Welding with an oxyacetylene torch.**

## Ozone

Ozone is a pale blue, poisonous gas with a sharp, irritating odor. Most people can detect about 0.01 ppm in air. Exposure to 0.1 to 1 ppm produces headaches, burning eyes, and irritation to the respiratory passages.

The $O_3$ molecule possesses a $\pi$ bond that is delocalized over the three oxygen atoms. ∞ (Section 8.6) The molecule dissociates readily, forming reactive oxygen atoms:

$$O_3(g) \longrightarrow O_2(g) + O(g) \qquad \Delta H° = 105\ kJ \qquad [22.23]$$

**GIVE IT SOME THOUGHT**

What wavelength of light is needed to break an O—O bond in ozone?

Ozone is a stronger oxidizing agent than dioxygen. Ozone forms oxides with many elements under conditions where $O_2$ will not react; indeed, it oxidizes all the common metals except gold and platinum.

Ozone can be prepared by passing electricity through dry $O_2$ in a flow-through apparatus. The electrical discharge causes the $O_2$ bond to break, resulting in reactions like those described in Section 18.1. During thunderstorms, ozone is generated (and can be smelled, if you are too close) from lightning strikes:

$$3\, O_2(g) \xrightarrow{\text{electricity}} 2\, O_3(g) \qquad \Delta H° = 285\ kJ \qquad [22.24]$$

Ozone cannot be stored for long, except at low temperature, because it readily decomposes to $O_2$. The decomposition is catalyzed by Ag, Pt, and Pd and by many transition-metal oxides.

---

**SAMPLE EXERCISE 22.6 | Calculating an Equilibrium Constant**

Using $\Delta G_f°$ for ozone from Appendix C, calculate the equilibrium constant for Equation 22.24 at 298.0 K, assuming no electrical input.

### SOLUTION

**Analyze** We are asked to calculate the equilibrium constant for the formation of $O_3$ from $O_2$, given the temperature and $\Delta G_f°$.

**Plan** The relationship between the standard free-energy change, $\Delta G_f°$, for a reaction and the equilibrium constant for the reaction is given in Equation 19.20.

**Solve** From Appendix C we have       $\Delta G_f°(O_3) = 163.4\ \text{kJ/mol}$

Thus, for Equation 22.24,       $\Delta G° = (2\ \text{mol}\ O_3)(163.4\ \text{kJ/mol}\ O_3) = 326.8\ \text{kJ}$

From Equation 19.20 we have       $\Delta G° = -RT \ln K$

Thus,       $\ln K = \dfrac{-\Delta G°}{RT} = \dfrac{-326.8 \times 10^3\ \text{J}}{(8.314\ \text{J/K-mol})(298.0\ \text{K})} = -131.9$

$$K = e^{-131.9} = 5.207 \times 10^{-58}$$

Ozone is sometimes used to treat drinking water. Like $Cl_2$, ozone kills bacteria and oxidizes organic compounds. The largest use of ozone, however, is in the preparation of pharmaceuticals, synthetic lubricants, and other commercially useful organic compounds, where $O_3$ is used to sever carbon–carbon double bonds.

Ozone is an important component of the upper atmosphere, where it screens out ultraviolet radiation and so protects us from the effects of these high-energy rays. For this reason, depletion of stratospheric ozone is a major scientific concern. ∞ (Section 18.2) In the lower atmosphere, ozone is considered an air pollutant and is a major constituent of smog. ∞ (Section 18.2) Because of its oxidizing power, ozone damages living systems and structural materials, especially rubber.

## Oxides

The electronegativity of oxygen is second only to that of fluorine. As a result, oxygen has negative oxidation states in all compounds except $OF_2$ and $O_2F_2$. The $-2$ oxidation state is by far the most common. Compounds in this oxidation state are called *oxides*.

Nonmetals form covalent oxides, most of which are simple molecules with low melting and boiling points. $SiO_2$ and $B_2O_3$, however, have extended structures. Most nonmetal oxides combine with water to give oxyacids. Sulfur dioxide ($SO_2$), for example, dissolves in water to give sulfurous acid ($H_2SO_3$):

$$SO_2(g) + H_2O(l) \longrightarrow H_2SO_3(aq) \qquad [22.25]$$

This reaction and that of $SO_3$ with $H_2O$ to form $H_2SO_4$ are largely responsible for acid rain. ∞ (Section 18.2) The analogous reaction of $CO_2$ with $H_2O$ to form carbonic acid ($H_2CO_3$) causes the acidity of carbonated water.

Oxides that form acids when they react with water are called either **acidic anhydrides** (anhydride means "without water") or **acidic oxides**. A few nonmetal oxides, especially ones with the nonmetal in a low oxidation state—such as $N_2O$, $NO$, and $CO$—do not react with water and are not acidic anhydrides.

⚠ **GIVE IT SOME THOUGHT**
What acid is produced by the reaction of $I_2O_5$ with water?

Most metal oxides are ionic compounds. The ionic oxides that dissolve in water form hydroxides and, consequently, are called either **basic anhydrides** or **basic oxides**. Barium oxide, for example, reacts with water to form barium hydroxide (▶ **FIGURE 22.14**). These kinds of reactions are due to the high basicity of the $O^{2-}$ ion and its virtually complete hydrolysis in water:

$$O^{2-}(aq) + H_2O(l) \longrightarrow 2\ OH^-(aq) \qquad [22.26]$$

Even those ionic oxides that are insoluble in water tend to dissolve in strong acids. Iron(III) oxide, for example, dissolves in acids:

$$Fe_2O_3(s) + 6\ H^+(aq) \longrightarrow 2\ Fe^{3+}(aq) + 3\ H_2O(l) \qquad [22.27]$$

This reaction is used to remove rust ($Fe_2O_3 \cdot nH_2O$) from iron or steel before a protective coat of zinc or tin is applied.

Oxides that can exhibit both acidic and basic character are said to be *amphoteric*. ∞ (Section 17.5) If a metal forms more than one oxide, the basic character of the oxide decreases as the oxidation state of the metal increases (◀ **TABLE 22.4**).

**TABLE 22.4 · Acid–Base Character of Chromium Oxides**

| Oxide | Oxidation State of Cr | Nature of Oxide |
|---|---|---|
| CrO | +2 | Basic |
| $Cr_2O_3$ | +3 | Amphoteric |
| $CrO_3$ | +6 | Acidic |

**Is this reaction a redox reaction?**

$$BaO(s) \quad + \quad H_2O(l) \quad \longrightarrow \quad Ba(OH)_2(aq)$$

▲ **FIGURE 22.14** **Reaction of a basic oxide with water.**

## Peroxides and Superoxides

Compounds containing O—O bonds and oxygen in the −1 oxidation state are *peroxides*. Oxygen has an oxidation state of $-\frac{1}{2}$ in $O_2^-$, which is called the *superoxide* ion. The most active (easily oxidized) metals (K, Rb, and Cs) react with $O_2$ to give superoxides ($KO_2$, $RbO_2$, and $CsO_2$). Their active neighbors in the periodic table (Na, Ca, Sr, and Ba) react with $O_2$, producing peroxides ($Na_2O_2$, $CaO_2$, $SrO_2$, and $BaO_2$). Less active metals and nonmetals produce normal oxides. ∞ (Section 7.6)

When superoxides dissolve in water, $O_2$ is produced:

$$4\,KO_2(s) + 2\,H_2O(l) \longrightarrow 4\,K^+(aq) + 4\,OH^-(aq) + 3\,O_2(g) \qquad [22.28]$$

Because of this reaction, potassium superoxide is used as an oxygen source in masks worn by rescue workers (▶ **FIGURE 22.15**). For proper breathing in toxic environments, oxygen must be generated in the mask and exhaled carbon dioxide in the mask must be eliminated. Moisture in the breath causes the $KO_2$ to decompose to $O_2$ and KOH, and the KOH removes $CO_2$ from the exhaled breath:

$$2\,OH^-(aq) + CO_2(g) \longrightarrow H_2O(l) + CO_3^{2-}(aq) \qquad [22.29]$$

Hydrogen peroxide (▶ **FIGURE 22.16**) is the most familiar and commercially important peroxide. Pure hydrogen peroxide is a clear, syrupy liquid that melts at −0.4 °C. Concentrated hydrogen peroxide is dangerously reactive because the decomposition to water and oxygen is very exothermic:

$$2\,H_2O_2(l) \longrightarrow 2\,H_2O(l) + O_2(g) \qquad \Delta H° = -196.1 \text{ kJ} \qquad [22.30]$$

This is another example of a **disproportionation** reaction, in which an element is simultaneously oxidized and reduced. The oxidation number of oxygen changes from −1 to −2 and 0.

Hydrogen peroxide is marketed as a chemical reagent in aqueous solutions of up to about 30% by mass. A solution containing about 3% $H_2O_2$ by mass is sold in drugstores and used as a mild antiseptic. Somewhat more concentrated solutions are used to bleach fabrics.

The peroxide ion is a by-product of metabolism that results from the reduction of $O_2$. The body disposes of this reactive ion with enzymes such as peroxidase and catalase.

$$4\,KO_2(s) + 2\,H_2O(l, \text{from breath}) \longrightarrow$$
$$4\,K^+(aq) + 4\,OH^-(aq) + 3\,O_2(g)$$

$$2\,OH^-(aq) + CO_2(g, \text{from breath}) \longrightarrow$$
$$H_2O(l) + CO_3^{2-}(aq)$$

▲ **FIGURE 22.15** **A self-contained breathing apparatus.**

**Does $H_2O_2$ have a dipole moment?**

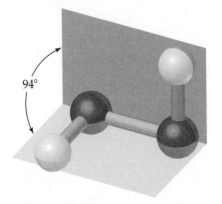

94°

▲ **FIGURE 22.16** **Molecular structure of hydrogen peroxide.**

## 22.6 | THE OTHER GROUP 6A ELEMENTS: S, Se, Te, AND Po

| 6A |
|---|
| 8 O |
| 16 S |
| 34 Se |
| 52 Te |
| 84 Po |

The other group 6A elements are sulfur, selenium, tellurium, and polonium. In this section we will survey the properties of the group as a whole and then examine the chemistry of sulfur, selenium, and tellurium. We will not say much about polonium, which has no stable isotopes and is found only in minute quantities in radium-containing minerals.

### General Characteristics of the Group 6A Elements

The group 6A elements possess the general outer-electron configuration $ns^2np^4$ with $n$ ranging from 2 to 6. Thus, these elements attain a noble-gas electron configuration by adding two electrons, which results in a $-2$ oxidation state. Except for oxygen, the group 6A elements are also commonly found in positive oxidation states up to $+6$, and they can have expanded valence shells. Thus, we have such compounds as $SF_6$, $SeF_6$, and $TeF_6$ with the central atom in the $+6$ oxidation state.

▼ TABLE 22.5 summarizes some properties of the group 6A elements.

### Occurrence and Production of S, Se, and Te

Sulfur, selenium, and tellurium can all be mined from the earth. Large underground deposits are the principal source of elemental sulfur (◄ FIGURE 22.17). Sulfur also occurs widely as sulfide ($S^{2-}$) and sulfate ($SO_4^{2-}$) minerals. Its presence as a minor component of coal and petroleum poses a major problem. Combustion of these "unclean" fuels leads to serious pollution by sulfur oxides. ∞ (Section 18.2) Much effort has been directed at removing this sulfur, and these efforts have increased the availability of sulfur. The sale of this sulfur helps to partially offset the costs of the desulfurizing processes and equipment.

Selenium and tellurium occur in rare minerals, such as $Cu_2Se$, $PbSe$, $Cu_2Te$, and $PbTe$, and as minor constituents in sulfide ores of copper, iron, nickel, and lead.

▲ FIGURE 22.17 Massive amounts of sulfur are extracted every year from the earth.

### Properties and Uses of Sulfur, Selenium, and Tellurium

Elemental sulfur is yellow, tasteless, and nearly odorless. It is insoluble in water and exists in several allotropic forms. The thermodynamically stable form at room temperature is rhombic sulfur, which consists of puckered $S_8$ rings. ∞ (Figure 7.26) When heated above its melting point (113 °C), molten sulfur first contains $S_8$ molecules and is fluid because the rings slip over one another. Further heating causes the rings to break; the fragments then join to form long molecules that can become entangled. In this polymeric form, sulfur becomes highly viscous. Further heating breaks the chains, and the viscosity again decreases.

Most of the approximately $1 \times 10^{10}$ kg (10 million tons) of sulfur produced in the United States each year is used to manufacture sulfuric acid. Sulfur is also used to vulcanize rubber, a process that toughens rubber by introducing cross-linking between polymer chains. ∞ (Section 12.8)

### TABLE 22.5 • Some Properties of the Group 6A Elements

| Property | O | S | Se | Te |
|---|---|---|---|---|
| Atomic radius (Å) | 0.73 | 1.04 | 1.17 | 1.43 |
| $X^{2-}$ ionic radius (Å) | 1.40 | 1.84 | 1.98 | 2.21 |
| First ionization energy (kJ/mol) | 1314 | 1000 | 941 | 869 |
| Electron affinity (kJ/mol) | $-141$ | $-200$ | $-195$ | $-190$ |
| Electronegativity | 3.5 | 2.5 | 2.4 | 2.1 |
| X—X single-bond enthalpy (kJ/mol) | 146* | 266 | 172 | 126 |
| Reduction potential to $H_2X$ in acidic solution (V) | 1.23 | 0.14 | $-0.40$ | $-0.72$ |

*Based on O—O bond energy in $H_2O_2$.

Selenium and tellurium do not form eight-membered rings in their elemental forms. ∞ (Section 7.8) The most stable allotropes of these elements are crystalline substances containing helical chains of atoms (▶ **FIGURE 22.18**). Each atom is close to atoms in adjacent chains, and it appears that some sharing of electron pairs between these atoms occurs.

The electrical conductivity of elemental selenium is low in the dark but increases greatly upon exposure to light. This property is exploited in photoelectric cells and light meters. Photocopiers also depend on the photoconductivity of selenium. Photocopy machines contain a belt or drum coated with a film of selenium. This drum is electrostatically charged and then exposed to light reflected from the image being photocopied. The charge drains from the regions where the selenium film has been made conductive by exposure to light. A black powder (the toner) sticks only to the areas that remain charged. The photocopy is made when the toner is transferred to a sheet of plain paper.

▲ **FIGURE 22.18  Portion of helical chains making up the structure of crystalline selenium.**

## Sulfides

When an element is less electronegative than sulfur, *sulfides* that contain $S^{2-}$ form. Many metallic elements are found in the form of sulfide ores, such as PbS (galena) and HgS (cinnabar). A series of related ores containing the disulfide ion, $S_2^{2-}$ (analogous to the peroxide ion), are known as *pyrites*. Iron pyrite, $FeS_2$, occurs as golden yellow cubic crystals (▶ **FIGURE 22.19**). Because it has been occasionally mistaken for gold by miners, iron pyrite is often called fool's gold.

One of the most important sulfides is hydrogen sulfide ($H_2S$). This substance is not normally produced by direct union of the elements because it decomposes at elevated temperatures. It is normally prepared by action of dilute acid on iron(II) sulfide:

$$FeS(s) + 2\,H^+(aq) \longrightarrow H_2S(aq) + Fe^{2+}(aq) \qquad [22.31]$$

One of hydrogen sulfide's most readily recognized properties is its odor, which is most frequently encountered as the offensive odor of rotten eggs. Hydrogen sulfide is toxic but our noses can detect $H_2S$ in extremely low, nontoxic concentrations. A sulfur-containing organic molecule, such as dimethyl sulfide, $(CH_3)_2S$, which is similarly odoriferous and can be detected by smell at a level of one part per trillion, is added to natural gas as a safety factor to give it a detectable odor.

▲ **FIGURE 22.19  Iron pyrite (FeS₂, on the right) with gold for comparison.**

## Oxides, Oxyacids, and Oxyanions of Sulfur

Sulfur dioxide, formed when sulfur burns in air, has a choking odor and is poisonous. The gas is particularly toxic to lower organisms, such as fungi, so it is used to sterilize dried fruit and wine. At 1 atm and room temperature, $SO_2$ dissolves in water to produce a 1.6 *M* solution. The $SO_2$ solution is acidic, and we describe it as sulfurous acid ($H_2SO_3$).

Salts of $SO_3^{2-}$ (sulfites) and $HSO_3^-$ (hydrogen sulfites or bisulfites) are well known. Small quantities of $Na_2SO_3$ or $NaHSO_3$ are used as food additives to prevent bacterial spoilage. Because some people are extremely allergic to sulfites, all food products with sulfites must now carry a warning label disclosing their presence.

Although combustion of sulfur in air produces mainly $SO_2$, small amounts of $SO_3$ are also formed. The reaction produces chiefly $SO_2$ because the activation-energy barrier for oxidation to $SO_3$ is very high unless the reaction is catalyzed. Interestingly, the $SO_3$ by-product is used industrially to make $H_2SO_4$, which is the ultimate product of the reaction between $SO_3$ and water. In the manufacture of sulfuric acid, $SO_2$ is obtained by burning sulfur and then oxidized to $SO_3$, using a catalyst such as $V_2O_5$ or platinum. The $SO_3$ is dissolved in $H_2SO_4$ because it does not dissolve quickly in water, and then the $H_2S_2O_7$ formed in this reaction, called pyrosulfuric acid, is added to water to form $H_2SO_4$:

$$SO_3(g) + H_2SO_4(l) \longrightarrow H_2S_2O_7(l) \qquad [22.32]$$

$$H_2S_2O_7(l) + H_2O(l) \longrightarrow 2\,H_2SO_4(l) \qquad [22.33]$$

GO FIGURE

In this reaction, what has happened to the H and O atoms in the sucrose?

► FIGURE 22.20 Sulfuric acid dehydrates table sugar to produce elemental carbon.

▲ GIVE IT SOME THOUGHT

What is the net reaction of Equations 22.32 and 22.33?

Commercial sulfuric acid is 98% $H_2SO_4$. It is a dense, colorless, oily liquid that boils at 340 °C. It is a strong acid, a good dehydrating agent (▲ FIGURE 22.20), and a moderately good oxidizing agent.

Year after year, the production of sulfuric acid is the largest of any chemical produced in the United States. About $4 \times 10^{10}$ kg (40 million tons) is produced annually in this country. Sulfuric acid is employed in some way in almost all manufacturing. Consequently, its consumption is considered a measure of industrial activity.

Sulfuric acid is a strong acid, but only the first hydrogen is completely ionized in aqueous solution:

$$H_2SO_4(aq) \longrightarrow H^+(aq) + HSO_4^-(aq) \qquad [22.34]$$

$$HSO_4^-(aq) \rightleftharpoons H^+(aq) + SO_4^{2-}(aq) \quad K_a = 1.1 \times 10^{-2} \qquad [22.35]$$

Consequently, sulfuric acid forms both sulfates ($SO_4^{2-}$ salts) and bisulfates (or hydrogen sulfates, $HSO_4^-$ salts). Bisulfate salts are common components of the "dry acids" used for adjusting the pH of swimming pools and hot tubs; they are also components of many toilet bowl cleaners.

The term *thio* indicates substitution of sulfur for oxygen, and the thiosulfate ion ($S_2O_3^{2-}$) is formed by boiling an alkaline solution of $SO_3^{2-}$ with elemental sulfur:

$$8\,SO_3^{2-}(aq) + S_8(s) \longrightarrow 8\,S_2O_3^{2-}(aq) \qquad [22.36]$$

The structures of the sulfate and thiosulfate ions are compared in ◄ FIGURE 22.21. Thiosulfate salts are used industrially in the paper-making and textile industries and are the "fixer" solutions in the development of photographic film.

▲ GO FIGURE

What are the oxidation states of the sulfur atoms in the $S_2O_3^{2-}$ ion?

▲ FIGURE 22.21 Structures of the sulfate (left) and thiosulfate (right) ions.

# 22.7 | NITROGEN

In 1772 the Scottish botanist Daniel Rutherford found that a mouse enclosed in a sealed jar quickly consumed the life-sustaining component of air (oxygen) and died. When the "fixed air" ($CO_2$) in the container was removed, a "noxious air" remained that would not sustain combustion or life. We now know that gas as *nitrogen*.

Nitrogen constitutes 78% by volume of Earth's atmosphere, where it occurs as $N_2$ molecules. Although nitrogen is a key element in living organisms, compounds of nitrogen are not abundant in Earth's crust. The major natural deposits of nitrogen compounds are those of $KNO_3$ (saltpeter) in India and $NaNO_3$ (Chile saltpeter) in Chile and other desert regions of South America.

## Properties of Nitrogen

Nitrogen is a colorless, odorless, tasteless gas composed of $N_2$ molecules. Its melting point is $-210\,°C$, and its normal boiling point is $-196\,°C$.

The $N_2$ molecule is very unreactive because of the strong triple bond between nitrogen atoms (the $N\equiv N$ bond enthalpy is 941 kJ/mol, nearly twice that for the bond in $O_2$; ∞ Table 8.4). When substances burn in air, they normally react with $O_2$ but not with $N_2$. When magnesium burns in air, however, it reacts with $N_2$ to form magnesium nitride ($Mg_3N_2$):

$$3\,Mg(s) + N_2(g) \longrightarrow Mg_3N_2(s) \qquad [22.37]$$

A similar reaction occurs with lithium, forming $Li_3N$.

The nitride ion is a strong Brønsted–Lowry base and reacts with water to form ammonia:

$$Mg_3N_2(s) + 6\,H_2O(l) \longrightarrow 2\,NH_3(aq) + 3\,Mg(OH)_2(s) \qquad [22.38]$$

The electron configuration of the nitrogen atom is $[He]2s^2 2p^3$. The element exhibits all formal oxidation states from +5 to −3 (▶ TABLE 22.6). The +5, 0, and −3 oxidation states are the most common and generally the most stable of these. Because nitrogen is more electronegative than all other elements except fluorine, oxygen, and chlorine, it exhibits positive oxidation states only in combination with these three elements.

| TABLE 22.6 • Oxidation States of Nitrogen | |
|---|---|
| **Oxidation State** | **Examples** |
| +5 | $N_2O_5$, $HNO_3$, $NO_3^-$ |
| +4 | $NO_2$, $N_2O_4$ |
| +3 | $HNO_2$, $NO_2^-$, $NF_3$ |
| +2 | $NO$ |
| +1 | $N_2O$, $H_2N_2O_2$, $N_2O_2^{2-}$, $HNF_2$ |
| 0 | $N_2$ |
| −1 | $NH_2OH$, $NH_2F$ |
| −2 | $N_2H_4$ |
| −3 | $NH_3$, $NH_4^+$, $NH_2^-$ |

## Production and Uses of Nitrogen

Elemental nitrogen is obtained in commercial quantities by fractional distillation of liquid air. About $4 \times 10^{10}$ kg (40 million tons) of $N_2$ is produced annually in the United States.

Because of its low reactivity, large quantities of $N_2$ are used as an inert gaseous blanket to exclude $O_2$ in food processing, manufacture of chemicals, metal fabrication, and production of electronic devices. Liquid $N_2$ is employed as a coolant to freeze foods rapidly.

The largest use of $N_2$ is in the manufacture of nitrogen-containing fertilizers, which provide a source of *fixed* nitrogen. We have previously discussed nitrogen fixation in the "Chemistry and Life" box in Section 14.7 and in the "Chemistry Put to Work" box in Section 15.2. Our starting point in fixing nitrogen is the manufacture of ammonia via the Haber process. ∞ (Section 15.2) The ammonia can then be converted into a variety of useful, simple nitrogen-containing species (▶ FIGURE 22.22).

## Hydrogen Compounds of Nitrogen

*Ammonia* is one of the most important compounds of nitrogen. It is a colorless, toxic gas that has a characteristic irritating odor. As noted in previous discussions, the $NH_3$ molecule is basic ($K_b = 1.8 \times 10^{-5}$). ∞ (Section 16.7)

In which of these species is the oxidation number of nitrogen +3?

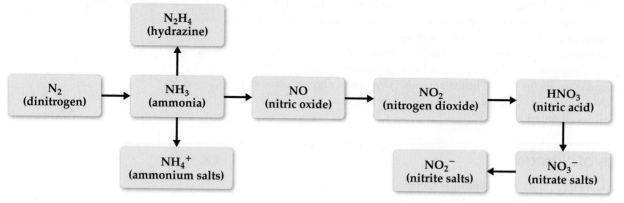

▲ **FIGURE 22.22** Sequence of conversion of $N_2$ into common nitrogen compounds.

Is the N—N bond length in these molecules shorter or longer than the N—N bond length in $N_2$?

▲ **FIGURE 22.23** Hydrazine (top, $N_2H_4$) and methylhydrazine (bottom, $CH_3NHNH_2$).

In the laboratory, $NH_3$ can be prepared by the action of NaOH on an ammonium salt. The $NH_4^+$ ion, which is the conjugate acid of $NH_3$, transfers a proton to $OH^-$. The resultant $NH_3$ is volatile and is driven from the solution by mild heating:

$$NH_4Cl(aq) + NaOH(aq) \longrightarrow NH_3(g) + H_2O(l) + NaCl(aq) \qquad [22.39]$$

Commercial production of $NH_3$ is achieved by the Haber process:

$$N_2(g) + 3\,H_2(g) \longrightarrow 2\,NH_3(g) \qquad [22.40]$$

About $1 \times 10^{10}$ kg (10 million tons) of ammonia is produced annually in the United States. About 75% is used for fertilizer.

*Hydrazine* ($N_2H_4$) is another important hydride of nitrogen. The hydrazine molecule contains an N—N single bond (◄ **FIGURE 22.23**). Hydrazine is quite poisonous. It can be prepared by the reaction of ammonia with hypochlorite ion ($OCl^-$) in aqueous solution:

$$2\,NH_3(aq) + OCl^-(aq) \longrightarrow N_2H_4(aq) + Cl^-(aq) + H_2O(l) \qquad [22.41]$$

The reaction involves several intermediates, including chloramine ($NH_2Cl$). The poisonous $NH_2Cl$ bubbles out of solution when household ammonia and chlorine bleach (which contains $OCl^-$) are mixed. This reaction is one reason for the frequently cited warning not to mix bleach and household ammonia.

Pure hydrazine is a strong and versatile reducing agent. The major use of hydrazine and compounds related to it, such as methylhydrazine (Figure 22.23), is as rocket fuel.

---

**SAMPLE EXERCISE 22.7**  | **Writing a Balanced Equation**

Hydroxylamine ($NH_2OH$) reduces copper(II) to the free metal in acid solutions. Write a balanced equation for the reaction, assuming that $N_2$ is the oxidation product.

**SOLUTION**

**Analyze** We are asked to write a balanced oxidation-reduction equation in which $NH_2OH$ is converted to $N_2$ and $Cu^{2+}$ is converted to Cu.

**Plan** Because this is a redox reaction, the equation can be balanced by the method of half-reactions discussed in Section 20.2. Thus, we begin with two half-reactions, one involving the $NH_2OH$ and $N_2$ and the other involving $Cu^{2+}$ and Cu.

**Solve** The unbalanced and incomplete half-reactions are

$$Cu^{2+}(aq) \longrightarrow Cu(s)$$
$$NH_2OH(aq) \longrightarrow N_2(g)$$

Balancing these equations as described in Section 20.2 gives

$$Cu^{2+}(aq) + 2\,e^- \longrightarrow Cu(s)$$

$$2\,NH_2OH(aq) \longrightarrow N_2(g) + 2\,H_2O(l) + 2\,H^+(aq) + 2\,e^-$$

Adding these half-reactions gives the balanced equation:

$$Cu^{2+}(aq) + 2\,NH_2OH(aq) \longrightarrow Cu(s) + N_2(g) + 2\,H_2O(l) + 2\,H^+(aq)$$

**PRACTICE EXERCISE**

(**a**) In power plants, hydrazine is used to prevent corrosion of the metal parts of steam boilers by the $O_2$ dissolved in the water. The hydrazine reacts with $O_2$ in water to give $N_2$ and $H_2O$. Write a balanced equation for this reaction. (**b**) Methylhydrazine, $N_2H_3CH_3(l)$, is used with the oxidizer dinitrogen tetroxide, $N_2O_4(l)$, to power the steering rockets of the Space Shuttle orbiter. The reaction of these two substances produces $N_2$, $CO_2$, and $H_2O$. Write a balanced equation for this reaction.

*Answers:* (**a**) $N_2H_4(aq) + O_2(aq) \longrightarrow N_2(g) + 2\,H_2O(l)$;
(**b**) $5\,N_2O_4(l) + 4\,N_2H_3CH_3(l) \longrightarrow 9\,N_2(g) + 4\,CO_2(g) + 12\,H_2O(g)$

# Oxides and Oxyacids of Nitrogen

Nitrogen forms three common oxides: $N_2O$ (nitrous oxide), $NO$ (nitric oxide), and $NO_2$ (nitrogen dioxide). It also forms two unstable oxides that we will not discuss, $N_2O_3$ (dinitrogen trioxide) and $N_2O_5$ (dinitrogen pentoxide).

*Nitrous oxide* ($N_2O$) is also known as laughing gas because a person becomes giddy after inhaling a small amount. This colorless gas was the first substance used as a general anesthetic. It is used as the compressed gas propellant in several aerosols and foams, such as in whipped cream. It can be prepared in the laboratory by carefully heating ammonium nitrate to about 200 °C:

$$NH_4NO_3(s) \xrightarrow{\Delta} N_2O(g) + 2\,H_2O(g) \qquad [22.42]$$

*Nitric oxide* ($NO$) is also a colorless gas but, unlike $N_2O$, it is slightly toxic. It can be prepared in the laboratory by reduction of dilute nitric acid, using copper or iron as a reducing agent (▼ **FIGURE 22.24**):

$$3\,Cu(s) + 2\,NO_3^-(aq) + 8\,H^+(aq) \longrightarrow 3\,Cu^{2+}(aq) + 2\,NO(g) + 4\,H_2O(l) \qquad [22.43]$$

Nitric oxide is also produced by direct reaction of $N_2$ and $O_2$ at high temperatures. This reaction is a significant source of nitrogen oxide air pollutants. ∞ (Section 18.2) The direct combination of $N_2$ and $O_2$ is not used for commercial production of $NO$, however, because the yield is low, the equilibrium constant $K_p$ at 2400 K being only 0.05. ∞ (Section 15.7, "Chemistry Put to Work: Controlling Nitric Oxide Emissions")

The commercial route to $NO$ (and hence to other oxygen-containing compounds of nitrogen) is via the catalytic oxidation of $NH_3$:

$$4\,NH_3(g) + 5\,O_2(g) \xrightarrow[850\,°C]{Pt\ catalyst} 4\,NO(g) + 6\,H_2O(g) \qquad [22.44]$$

This reaction is the first step in the **Ostwald process**, by which $NH_3$ is converted commercially into nitric acid ($HNO_3$).

◀ **FIGURE 22.24 Copper metal reacts with nitric acid to produce blue $Cu^{2+}$(*aq*) and NO(*g*).**

▲ **FIGURE 22.25** Formation of $NO_2(g)$ as $NO(g)$ combines with $O_2(g)$ in the air.

When exposed to air, nitric oxide reacts readily with $O_2$ (▲ **FIGURE 22.25**):

$$2 NO(g) + O_2(g) \longrightarrow 2 NO_2(g) \qquad [22.45]$$

When dissolved in water, $NO_2$ forms nitric acid:

$$3 NO_2(g) + H_2O(l) \longrightarrow 2 H^+(aq) + 2 NO_3^-(aq) + NO(g) \qquad [22.46]$$

Nitrogen is both oxidized and reduced in this reaction, which means it disproportionates. The NO can be converted back into $NO_2$ by exposure to air (Equation 22.45) and thereafter dissolved in water to prepare more $HNO_3$.

NO is an important neurotransmitter in the human body. It causes the muscles that line blood vessels to relax, thus allowing an increased passage of blood (see the "Chemistry and Life" box on page 941).

*Nitrogen dioxide* ($NO_2$) is a yellow-brown gas (Figure 22.25). Like NO, it is a major constituent of smog. ∞ (Section 18.2) It is poisonous and has a choking odor. As discussed in Section 15.1, $NO_2$ and $N_2O_4$ exist in equilibrium:

$$2 NO_2(g) \rightleftharpoons N_2O_4(g) \quad \Delta H° = -58 \text{ kJ} \qquad [22.47]$$

The two common oxyacids of nitrogen are nitric acid ($HNO_3$) and nitrous acid ($HNO_2$) (◄ **FIGURE 22.26**). *Nitric acid* is a strong acid. It is also a powerful oxidizing agent, as indicated by the standard reduction potential in the reaction

$$NO_3^-(aq) + 4 H^+(aq) + 3 e^- \longrightarrow NO(g) + 2 H_2O(l) \qquad E° = +0.96 \text{ V} \quad [22.48]$$

Concentrated nitric acid attacks and oxidizes most metals except Au, Pt, Rh, and Ir.

About $7 \times 10^9$ kg (8 million tons) of nitric acid is produced annually in the United States. Its largest use is in the manufacture of $NH_4NO_3$ for fertilizers. It is also used in the production of plastics, drugs, and explosives. Among the explosives made from nitric acid are nitroglycerin, trinitrotoluene (TNT), and nitrocellulose. The following reaction occurs when nitroglycerin explodes:

$$4 C_3H_5N_3O_9(l) \longrightarrow 6 N_2(g) + 12 CO_2(g) + 10 H_2O(g) + O_2(g) \quad [22.49]$$

All the products of this reaction contain very strong bonds and are gases. As a result, the reaction is very exothermic, and the volume of the products is far larger than the volume occupied by the reactant. Thus, the expansion resulting from the heat generated by the reaction produces the explosion. ∞ (Section 8.8: "Chemistry Put to Work: Explosives and Alfred Nobel")

*Nitrous acid* is considerably less stable than $HNO_3$ and tends to disproportionate into NO and $HNO_3$. It is normally made by action of a strong acid, such as $H_2SO_4$, on a cold solution of a nitrite salt, such as $NaNO_2$. Nitrous acid is a weak acid ($K_a = 4.5 \times 10^{-4}$).

▲ **GO FIGURE**

**Which is the shortest NO bond in these two molecules?**

▲ **FIGURE 22.26** Structures of nitric acid (top) and nitrous acid (bottom).

▲ **GIVE IT SOME THOUGHT**

What are the oxidation numbers of the nitrogen atoms in
**a.** nitric acid;
**b.** nitrous acid?

## CHEMISTRY AND LIFE

### NITROGLYCERIN AND HEART DISEASE

During the 1870s an interesting observation was made in Alfred Nobel's dynamite factories. Workers who suffered from heart disease that caused chest pains when they exerted themselves found relief from the pains during the workweek. It quickly became apparent that nitroglycerin, present in the air of the factory, acted to enlarge blood vessels. Thus, this powerfully explosive chemical became a standard treatment for angina pectoris, the chest pains accompanying heart failure. It took more than 100 years to discover that nitroglycerin was converted in the vascular smooth muscle into NO, which is the chemical agent actually causing dilation of the blood vessels. In 1998 the Nobel Prize in Physiology or Medicine was awarded to Robert F. Furchgott, Louis J. Ignarro, and Ferid Murad for their discoveries of the detailed pathways by which NO acts in the cardiovascular system. It was a sensation that this simple, common air pollutant could exert important functions in mammals, including humans.

As useful as nitroglycerin is to this day in treating angina pectoris, it has a limitation in that prolonged administration results in development of tolerance, or desensitization, of the vascular muscle to further vasorelaxation by nitroglycerin. The bioactivation of nitroglycerin is the subject of active research in the hope that a means of circumventing desensitization can be found.

## 22.8 | THE OTHER GROUP 5A ELEMENTS: P, As, Sb, AND Bi

Of the other group 5A elements—phosphorus, arsenic, antimony, and bismuth—phosphorus has a central role in several aspects of biochemistry and environmental chemistry.

### General Characteristics of the Group 5A Elements

The group 5A elements have the outer-shell electron configuration $ns^2np^3$, with $n$ ranging from 2 to 6. A noble-gas configuration is achieved by adding three electrons to form the $-3$ oxidation state. Ionic compounds containing $X^{3-}$ ions are not common, however. More commonly, the group 5A element acquires an octet of electrons via covalent bonding and oxidation numbers ranging from $-3$ to $+5$.

Because of its lower electronegativity, phosphorus is found more frequently in positive oxidation states than is nitrogen. Furthermore, compounds in which phosphorus has the $+5$ oxidation state are not as strongly oxidizing as the corresponding compounds of nitrogen. Compounds in which phosphorus has a $-3$ oxidation state are much stronger reducing agents than are the corresponding nitrogen compounds.

Some properties of the group 5A elements are listed in ▼ TABLE 22.7. The general pattern is similar to what we saw with other groups: Size and metallic character increase as atomic number increases in the group.

The variation in properties among group 5A elements is more striking than that seen in groups 6A and 7A. Nitrogen at the one extreme exists as a gaseous diatomic molecule, clearly nonmetallic. At the other extreme, bismuth is a reddish white, metallic-looking substance that has most of the characteristics of a metal.

The values listed for X—X single-bond enthalpies are not reliable because it is difficult to obtain such data from thermochemical experiments. However, there is no doubt

| 5A |
|----|
| 7 N |
| 15 P |
| 33 As |
| 51 Sb |
| 83 Bi |

| TABLE 22.7 • Properties of the Group 5A Elements | | | | | |
|---|---|---|---|---|---|
| Property | N | P | As | Sb | Bi |
| Atomic radius (Å) | 0.75 | 1.10 | 1.21 | 1.41 | 1.55 |
| First ionization energy (kJ/mol) | 1402 | 1012 | 947 | 834 | 703 |
| Electron affinity (kJ/mol) | > 0 | −72 | −78 | −103 | −91 |
| Electronegativity | 3.0 | 2.1 | 2.0 | 1.9 | 1.9 |
| X—X single-bond enthalpy (kJ/mol)* | 163 | 200 | 150 | 120 | — |
| X≡X triple-bond enthalpy (kJ/mol) | 941 | 490 | 380 | 295 | 192 |

*Approximate values only.

about the general trend: a low value for the N—N single bond, an increase at phosphorus, and then a gradual decline to arsenic and antimony. From observations of the elements in the gas phase, it is possible to estimate the X≡X triple-bond enthalpies. Here we see a trend that is different from that for the X—X single bond. Nitrogen forms a much stronger triple bond than the other elements, and there is a steady decline in the triple-bond enthalpy down through the group. These data help us to appreciate why nitrogen alone of the group 5A elements exists as a diatomic molecule in its stable state at 25 °C. All the other elements exist in structural forms with single bonds between the atoms.

## Occurrence, Isolation, and Properties of Phosphorus

Phosphorus occurs mainly in the form of phosphate minerals. The principal source of phosphorus is phosphate rock, which contains phosphate principally as $Ca_3(PO_4)_2$. The element is produced commercially by reduction of calcium phosphate with carbon in the presence of $SiO_2$:

$$2\,Ca_3(PO_4)_2(s) + 6\,SiO_2(s) + 10\,C(s) \xrightarrow{1500\,°C} P_4(g) + 6\,CaSiO_3(l) + 10\,CO(g)$$
[22.50]

The phosphorus produced in this fashion is the allotrope known as white phosphorus. This form distills from the reaction mixture as the reaction proceeds.

Phosphorus exists in several allotropic forms. White phosphorus consists of $P_4$ tetrahedra (◀ **FIGURE 22.27**). The bond angles in this molecule, 60°, are unusually small, so there is much strain in the bonding, which is consistent with the high reactivity of white phosphorus. This allotrope bursts spontaneously into flames if exposed to air. When heated in the absence of air to about 400 °C, white phosphorus is converted to a more stable allotrope known as red phosphorus, which does not ignite on contact with air. Red phosphorus is also considerably less poisonous than the white form. We will denote elemental phosphorus as simply P(s).

White phosphorus

Red phosphorus

▲ **FIGURE 22.27** **White and red phosphorus.** Despite the fact that both contain nothing but phosphorus atoms, these two forms of phosphorus differ greatly in reactivity. The white allotrope, which reacts violently with oxygen, must be stored under water so that it is not exposed to air. The much less reactive red form does not need to be stored this way.

## Phosphorus Halides

Phosphorus forms a wide range of compounds with the halogens, the most important of which are the trihalides and pentahalides. Phosphorus trichloride ($PCl_3$) is commercially the most significant of these compounds and is used to prepare a wide variety of products, including soaps, detergents, plastics, and insecticides.

Phosphorus chlorides, bromides, and iodides can be made by direct oxidation of elemental phosphorus with the elemental halogen. $PCl_3$, for example, which is a liquid at room temperature, is made by passing a stream of dry chlorine gas over white or red phosphorus:

$$2\,P(s) + 3\,Cl_2(g) \longrightarrow 2\,PCl_3(l)$$
[22.51]

If excess chlorine gas is present, an equilibrium is established between $PCl_3$ and $PCl_5$.

$$PCl_3(l) + Cl_2(g) \rightleftharpoons PCl_5(s)$$
[22.52]

The phosphorus halides hydrolyze on contact with water. The reactions occur readily, and most of the phosphorus halides fume in air because of reaction with water vapor. In the presence of excess water the products are the corresponding phosphorus oxyacid and hydrogen halide:

$$PBr_3(l) + 3\,H_2O(l) \longrightarrow H_3PO_3(aq) + 3\,HBr(aq)$$
[22.53]

$$PCl_5(l) + 4\,H_2O(l) \longrightarrow H_3PO_4(aq) + 5\,HCl(aq)$$
[22.54]

## Oxy Compounds of Phosphorus

Probably the most significant phosphorus compounds are those in which the element is combined with oxygen. Phosphorus(III) oxide ($P_4O_6$) is obtained by allowing white phosphorus to oxidize in a limited supply of oxygen. When oxidation takes place in the presence of excess oxygen, phosphorus(V) oxide ($P_4O_{10}$) forms. This compound is also readily formed by oxidation of $P_4O_6$. These two oxides represent the two most common oxidation states for phosphorus, +3 and +5. The structural relationship between $P_4O_6$ and $P_4O_{10}$ is shown in ▶ **FIGURE 22.28**. Notice the resemblance these molecules have to the $P_4$ molecule (Figure 22.27); all three substances have a $P_4$ core.

**GO FIGURE**

How do the electron domains about P in $P_4O_6$ differ from those about P in $P_4O_{10}$?

▲ **FIGURE 22.28** Structures of $P_4O_6$ (top) and $P_4O_{10}$ (bottom).

---

### SAMPLE EXERCISE 22.8 | Calculating a Standard Enthalpy Change

The reactive chemicals on the tip of a "strike anywhere" match are usually $P_4S_3$ and an oxidizing agent such as $KClO_3$. When the match is struck on a rough surface, the heat generated by the friction ignites the $P_4S_3$, and the oxidizing agent brings about rapid combustion. The products of the combustion of $P_4S_3$ are $P_4O_{10}$ and $SO_2$. Calculate the standard enthalpy change for the combustion of $P_4S_3$ in air, given the following standard enthalpies of formation: $P_4S_3$ (−154.4 kJ/mol), $P_4O_{10}$ (−2940.1 kJ/mol), $SO_2$ (−296.9 kJ/mol).

#### SOLUTION

**Analyze** We are given the reactants ($P_4S_3$ and $O_2$ from air) and the products ($P_4O_{10}$ and $SO_2$) for a reaction, together with their standard enthalpies of formation, and asked to calculate the standard enthalpy change for the reaction.

**Plan** We first need a balanced chemical equation for the reaction. The enthalpy change for the reaction is then equal to the enthalpies of formation of products minus those of reactants (Equation 5.31). We also need to recall that the standard enthalpy of formation of any element in its standard state is zero. Thus, $\Delta H_f^\circ(O_2) = 0$.

**Solve** The balanced chemical equation for the combustion is

$$P_4S_3(s) + 8\ O_2(g) \longrightarrow P_4O_{10}(s) + 3\ SO_2(g)$$

Thus, we can write

$$\Delta H^\circ = \Delta H_f^\circ(P_4O_{10}) + 3\ \Delta H_f^\circ(SO_2) - \Delta H_f^\circ(P_4S_3) - 8\ \Delta H_f^\circ(O_2)$$

$$= -2940.1\ kJ + 3(-296.9)\ kJ - (-154.4\ kJ) - 8(0)$$

$$= -3676.4\ kJ$$

**Comment** The reaction is strongly exothermic, making it evident why $P_4S_3$ is used on match tips.

#### PRACTICE EXERCISE

Write the balanced equation for the reaction of $P_4O_{10}$ with water, and calculate $\Delta H^\circ$ for this reaction using data from Appendix C.

**Answer:** $P_4O_{10}(s) + 6\ H_2O(l) \longrightarrow 4\ H_3PO_4(aq)$; −498.1 kJ

---

Phosphorus(V) oxide is the anhydride of phosphoric acid ($H_3PO_4$), a weak triprotic acid. In fact, $P_4O_{10}$ has a very high affinity for water and is consequently used as a drying agent. Phosphorus(III) oxide is the anhydride of phosphorous acid ($H_3PO_3$), a weak diprotic acid (▶ **FIGURE 22.29**).*

One characteristic of phosphoric and phosphorous acids is their tendency to undergo condensation reactions when heated. ∞ (Section 12.8) For example, two $H_3PO_4$ molecules are joined by the elimination of one $H_2O$ molecule to form $H_4P_2O_7$:

$$\underset{\underset{OH}{|}}{\overset{\overset{O}{\|}}{HO-P}}-OH \ + \ \underset{\underset{OH}{|}}{\overset{\overset{O}{\|}}{HO-P}}-OH \longrightarrow \underset{\underset{OH}{|}}{\overset{\overset{O}{\|}}{HO-P}}-O-\underset{\underset{OH}{|}}{\overset{\overset{O}{\|}}{P}}-OH \ + \ H_2O$$

These atoms are eliminated as $H_2O$

[22.55]

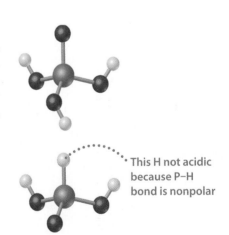

This H not acidic because P–H bond is nonpolar

▲ **FIGURE 22.29** Structures of $H_3PO_4$ (top) and $H_3PO_3$ (bottom).

Phosphoric acid and its salts find their most important uses in detergents and fertilizers. The phosphates in detergents are often in the form of sodium tripolyphosphate ($Na_5P_3O_{10}$).

*Note that the element phosphorus (*FOS·for·us*) has a *-us* suffix, whereas the first word in the name phosphorous (*fos·FOR·us*) acid has an *-ous* suffix.

The phosphate ions "soften" water by binding their oxygen groups to the metal ions that contribute to the hardness of water. This keeps the metal ions from interfering with the action of the detergent. The phosphates also keep the pH above 7 and thus prevent the detergent molecules from becoming protonated.

Most mined phosphate rock is converted to fertilizers. The $Ca_3(PO_4)_2$ in phosphate rock is insoluble ($K_{sp} = 2.0 \times 10^{-29}$). It is converted to a soluble form for use in fertilizers by treatment with sulfuric or phosphoric acid. The reaction with phosphoric acid yields $Ca(H_2PO_4)_2$:

$$Ca_3(PO_4)_2(s) + 4\,H_3PO_4(aq) \longrightarrow 3\,Ca^{2+}(aq) + 6\,H_2PO_4^-(aq) \quad [22.56]$$

Although the solubility of $Ca(H_2PO_4)_2$ allows it to be assimilated by plants, it also allows it to be washed from the soil and into bodies of water, thereby contributing to water pollution. ∞ (Section 18.4)

Phosphorus compounds are important in biological systems. The element occurs in phosphate groups in RNA and DNA, the molecules responsible for the control of protein biosynthesis and transmission of genetic information. It also occurs in adenosine triphosphate (ATP), which stores energy in biological cells and has the structure

The P—O—P bond of the end phosphate group is broken by hydrolysis with water, forming adenosine diphosphate (ADP):

[22.57]

This reaction releases 33 kJ of energy under standard conditions, but in the living cell, the Gibbs free energy change for the reaction is closer to −57 kJ/mol. The concentration of ATP inside a living cell is in the range of 1–10 m$M$, which means a typical human metabolizes her or his body mass of ATP in one day! ATP is continually made from ADP and continually converted back to ADP, releasing energy that can be harnessed by other cellular reactions.

# CHEMISTRY AND LIFE

### ARSENIC IN DRINKING WATER

"Arsenic," meaning its oxides, has been known as a poison for centuries. The current Environmental Protection Agency (EPA) standard for arsenic in public water supplies is 10 ppb (equivalent to 10 $\mu$g/L). Most regions of the United States tend to have low to moderate (2–10 ppb) groundwater arsenic levels (▼ FIGURE 22.30). The western region tends to have higher levels, coming mainly from natural geological sources in the area. Estimates, for example, indicate that 35% of water-supply wells in Arizona have arsenic concentrations above 10 ppb.

The problem of arsenic in drinking water in the United States is dwarfed by the problem in other parts of the world—especially in Bangladesh, where the problem is tragic. Historically, surface water

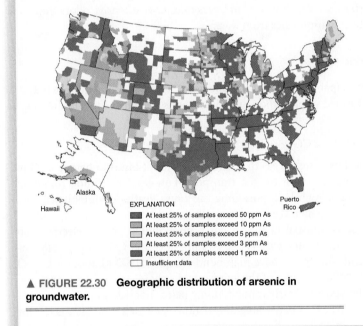

EXPLANATION
- At least 25% of samples exceed 50 ppm As
- At least 25% of samples exceed 10 ppm As
- At least 25% of samples exceed 5 ppm As
- At least 25% of samples exceed 3 ppm As
- At least 25% of samples exceed 1 ppm As
- Insufficient data

▲ **FIGURE 22.30  Geographic distribution of arsenic in groundwater.**

sources in that country have been contaminated with microorganisms, causing significant health problems, including one of the highest infant mortality rates in the world. During the 1970s, international agencies, headed by the United Nations Children's Fund (UNICEF), began investing millions of dollars of aid money in Bangladesh for wells to provide "clean" drinking water. Unfortunately, no one tested the well water for the presence of arsenic; the problem was not discovered until the 1980s. The result has been the biggest outbreak of mass poisoning in history. Up to half of the country's estimated 10 million wells have arsenic concentrations above 50 ppb.

In water the most common forms of arsenic are the arsenate ion and its protonated hydrogen anions ($AsO_4^{3-}$, $HAsO_4^{2-}$, and $H_2AsO_4^-$) and the arsenite ion and its protonated forms ($AsO_3^{3-}$, $HAsO_3^{2-}$, $H_2AsO_3^-$, and $H_3AsO_3$). These species are collectively referred to by the oxidation number of the arsenic as arsenic(V) and arsenic(III), respectively. Arsenic(V) is more prevalent in oxygen-rich (aerobic) surface waters, whereas arsenic(III) is more likely to occur in oxygen-poor (anaerobic) groundwaters. In the pH range from 4 to 10, the arsenic(V) is present primarily as $HAsO_4^{2-}$ and $H_2AsO_4^-$, and the arsenic(III) is present primarily as the neutral acid $H_3AsO_3$.

One of the challenges in determining the health effects of arsenic in drinking waters is the different chemistry of arsenic(V) and arsenic(III), as well as the different concentrations required for physiological responses in different individuals. In Bangladesh, skin lesions were the first sign of the arsenic problem. Statistical studies correlating arsenic levels with the occurrence of disease indicate a lung and bladder cancer risk arising from even low levels of arsenic.

The current technologies for removing arsenic perform most effectively when treating arsenic in the form of arsenic(V), so water treatment strategies require preoxidation of the drinking water. Once in the form of arsenic(V), there are a number of possible removal strategies. For example, $Fe_2(SO_4)_3$ could be added to precipitate $FeAsO_4$, which is then removed by filtration.

*RELATED EXERCISE: 22.104.*

---

# 22.9 | CARBON

Carbon constitutes only 0.027% of Earth's crust. Although some carbon occurs in elemental form as graphite and diamond, most is found in combined form. Over half occurs in carbonate compounds, and carbon is also found in coal, petroleum, and natural gas. The importance of the element stems in large part from its occurrence in all living organisms: Life as we know it is based on carbon compounds.

## Elemental Forms of Carbon

We have seen that carbon exists in several allotropic crystalline forms: graphite, diamond, fullerenes, carbon nanotubes, and graphene. Fullerenes, nanotubes, and graphene are discussed in Chapter 12; here we focus on graphite and diamond.

*Graphite* is a soft, black, slippery solid that has a metallic luster and conducts electricity. It consists of parallel sheets of $sp^2$-hybridized carbon atoms held together by dispersion forces. ∞ (Section 12.7) *Diamond* is a clear, hard solid in which the carbon atoms form an $sp^3$-hybridized covalent network. ∞ (Section 12.7) Diamond is denser than graphite ($d$ = 2.25 g/cm$^3$ for graphite; $d$ = 3.51 g/cm$^3$ for diamond). At approximately 100,000 atm at 3000 °C, graphite converts to diamond. In fact, almost any carbon-containing substance, if put under sufficiently high pressure, forms diamonds; scientists at General Electric in the 1950s used peanut butter to make diamonds. About $3 \times 10^4$ kg of industrial-grade diamonds are synthesized each year, mainly for use in cutting, grinding, and polishing tools.

Graphite has a well-defined crystalline structure, but it also exists in two common amorphous forms: **carbon black** and **charcoal**. Carbon black is formed when hydrocarbons are heated in a very limited supply of oxygen, such as in this methane reaction:

$$CH_4(g) + O_2(g) \longrightarrow C(s) + 2\,H_2O(g) \qquad [22.58]$$

Carbon black is used as a pigment in black inks; large amounts are also used in making automobile tires.

Charcoal is formed when wood is heated strongly in the absence of air. Charcoal has an open structure, giving it an enormous surface area per unit mass. "Activated charcoal," a pulverized form of charcoal whose surface is cleaned by heating with steam, is widely used to adsorb molecules. It is used in filters to remove offensive odors from air and colored or bad-tasting impurities from water.

## Oxides of Carbon

Carbon forms two principal oxides: carbon monoxide (CO) and carbon dioxide ($CO_2$). *Carbon monoxide* is formed when carbon or hydrocarbons are burned in a limited supply of oxygen:

$$2\,C(s) + O_2(g) \longrightarrow 2\,CO(g) \qquad [22.59]$$

CO is a colorless, odorless, tasteless gas that is toxic because it binds to hemoglobin in the blood and thus interfere with oxygen transport. Low-level poisoning results in headaches and drowsiness; high-level poisoning can cause death. Automobile engines produce carbon monoxide, which is a major air pollutant.

Carbon monoxide is unusual in that it has a nonbonding pair of electrons on carbon: $:C \equiv O:$. It is isoelectronic with $N_2$, so you might expect CO to be equally unreactive. Moreover, both substances have high bond energies (1072 kJ/mol for $C \equiv O$ and 941 kJ/mol for $N \equiv N$). Because of the lower nuclear charge on carbon (compared with either N or O), however, the carbon nonbonding pair is not held as strongly as that on N or O. Consequently, CO is better able to function as a Lewis base than is $N_2$; for example, CO can coordinate its nonbonding pair to the iron of hemoglobin, displacing $O_2$, but $N_2$ cannot. In addition, CO forms a variety of covalent compounds, known as metal carbonyls, with transition metals. $Ni(CO)_4$, for example, is a volatile, toxic compound formed by warming metallic nickel in the presence of CO. The formation of metal carbonyls is the first step in the transition-metal catalysis of a variety of reactions of CO.

Carbon monoxide has several commercial uses. Because it burns readily, forming $CO_2$, it is employed as a fuel:

$$2\,CO(g) + O_2(g) \longrightarrow 2\,CO_2(g) \qquad \Delta H° = -566\ \text{kJ} \qquad [22.60]$$

Carbon monoxide is an important reducing agent, widely used in metallurgical operations to reduce metal oxides, such as the iron oxides:

$$Fe_3O_4(s) + 4\,CO(g) \longrightarrow 3\,Fe(s) + 4\,CO_2(g) \qquad [22.61]$$

*Carbon dioxide* is produced when carbon-containing substances are burned in excess oxygen, such as in this reaction involving ethanol:

$$C_2H_5OH(l) + 3\,O_2(g) \longrightarrow 2\,CO_2(g) + 3\,H_2O(g) \qquad [22.62]$$

# CHEMISTRY PUT TO WORK

## Carbon Fibers and Composites

The properties of graphite are anisotropic; that is, they differ in different directions through the solid. Along the carbon planes, graphite possesses great strength because of the number and strength of the carbon–carbon bonds in this direction. The bonds between planes are relatively weak, however, making graphite weak in that direction.

Fibers of graphite can be prepared in which the carbon planes are aligned to varying extents parallel to the fiber axis. These fibers are lightweight (density of about $2 \text{ g/cm}^3$) and chemically quite unreactive. The oriented fibers are made by first slowly pyrolyzing (decomposing by action of heat) organic fibers at about 150 °C to 300 °C. These fibers are then heated to about 2500 °C to graphitize them (convert amorphous carbon to graphite). Stretching the fiber during pyrolysis helps orient the graphite planes parallel to the fiber axis. More amorphous carbon fibers are formed by pyrolysis of organic fibers at lower temperatures (1200 °C to 400 °C). These amorphous materials, commonly called *carbon fibers*, are the type most often used in commercial materials.

Composite materials that take advantage of the strength, stability, and low density of carbon fibers are widely used. Composites are combinations of two or more materials. These materials are present as separate phases and are combined to form structures that take advantage of certain desirable properties of each component. In carbon composites the graphite fibers are often woven into a fabric that is embedded in a matrix that binds them into a solid structure. The fibers transmit loads evenly throughout the matrix. The finished composite is thus stronger than any one of its components.

Carbon composite materials are used widely in a number of applications, including high-performance graphite sports equipment such as tennis racquets, golf clubs, and bicycle wheels (▼ FIGURE 22.31). Heat-resistant composites are required for many aerospace applications, where carbon composites now find wide use.

▲ **FIGURE 22.31  Carbon composites in commercial products.**

It is also produced when many carbonates are heated:

$$CaCO_3(s) \xrightarrow{\Delta} CaO(s) + CO_2(g) \qquad [22.63]$$

Large quantities of $CO_2$ are obtained as a by-product of the fermentation of sugar during the production of ethanol:

$$\underset{\text{Glucose}}{C_6H_{12}O_6(aq)} \xrightarrow{\text{yeast}} 2\,\underset{\text{Ethanol}}{C_2H_5OH(aq)} + 2\,CO_2(g) \qquad [22.64]$$

In the laboratory, $CO_2$ can be produced by the action of acids on carbonates (▶ FIGURE 22.32):

$$CO_3{}^{2-}(aq) + 2\,H^+(aq) \longrightarrow CO_2(g) + H_2O(l) \qquad [22.65]$$

▲ **FIGURE 22.32  $CO_2$ formation from the reaction between an acid and calcium carbonate in rock.**

Carbon dioxide is a colorless, odorless gas. It is a minor component of Earth's atmosphere but a major contributor to the greenhouse effect. ∞ (Section 18.2) Although it is not toxic, high concentrations of $CO_2$ increase respiration rate and can cause suffocation. It is readily liquefied by compression. When cooled at atmospheric pressure, however, $CO_2$ forms a solid rather than liquefying. The solid sublimes at atmospheric pressure at −78 °C. This property makes solid $CO_2$, known as dry ice, valuable as a refrigerant. About half of the $CO_2$ consumed annually is used for refrigeration. The other major use of $CO_2$ is in the production of carbonated beverages. Large quantities are also used to manufacture *washing soda* ($Na_2CO_3 \cdot 10\,H_2O$), used to precipitate metal ions that interfere with the cleansing action of soap, and *baking soda* ($NaHCO_3$). Baking soda is so named because this reaction occurs during baking:

$$NaHCO_3(s) + H^+(aq) \longrightarrow Na^+(aq) + CO_2(g) + H_2O(l) \qquad [22.66]$$

The $H^+(aq)$ is provided by vinegar, sour milk, or the hydrolysis of certain salts. The bubbles of $CO_2$ that form are trapped in the baking dough, causing it to rise.

 **GIVE IT SOME THOUGHT**

Yeast are living organisms that make bread rise in the absence of baking soda and acid. What must the yeast be producing to make bread rise?

## Carbonic Acid and Carbonates

Carbon dioxide is moderately soluble in $H_2O$ at atmospheric pressure. The resulting solution is moderately acidic because of the formation of carbonic acid ($H_2CO_3$):

$$CO_2(aq) + H_2O(l) \rightleftharpoons H_2CO_3(aq) \qquad [22.67]$$

Carbonic acid is a weak diprotic acid. Its acidic character causes carbonated beverages to have a sharp, slightly acidic taste.

Although carbonic acid cannot be isolated, hydrogen carbonates (bicarbonates) and carbonates can be obtained by neutralizing carbonic acid solutions. Partial neutralization produces $HCO_3^-$, and complete neutralization gives $CO_3^{2-}$. The $HCO_3^-$ ion is a stronger base than acid ($K_b = 2.3 \times 10^{-8}$; $K_a = 5.6 \times 10^{-11}$). The carbonate ion is much more strongly basic ($K_b = 1.8 \times 10^{-4}$).

The principal carbonate minerals are calcite ($CaCO_3$), magnesite ($MgCO_3$), dolomite [$MgCa(CO_3)_2$], and siderite ($FeCO_3$). Calcite is the principal mineral in limestone and the main constituent of marble, chalk, pearls, coral reefs, and the shells of marine animals such as clams and oysters. Although $CaCO_3$ has low solubility in pure water, it dissolves readily in acidic solutions with evolution of $CO_2$:

$$CaCO_3(s) + 2\,H^+(aq) \rightleftharpoons Ca^{2+}(aq) + H_2O(l) + CO_2(g) \qquad [22.68]$$

Because water containing $CO_2$ is slightly acidic (Equation 22.67), $CaCO_3$ dissolves slowly in this medium:

$$CaCO_3(s) + H_2O(l) + CO_2(g) \longrightarrow Ca^{2+}(aq) + 2\,HCO_3^-(aq) \qquad [22.69]$$

This reaction occurs when surface waters move underground through limestone deposits. It is the principal way $Ca^{2+}$ enters groundwater, producing "hard water." If the limestone deposit is deep enough underground, dissolution of the limestone produces a cave.

One of the most important reactions of $CaCO_3$ is its decomposition into $CaO$ and $CO_2$ at elevated temperatures (Equation 22.63). About $2 \times 10^{10}$ kg (20 million tons) of calcium oxide, known as lime or quicklime, is produced in the United States annually. Because calcium oxide reacts with water to form $Ca(OH)_2$, it is an important commercial base. It is also important in making mortar, the mixture of sand, water, and $CaO$ used to bind bricks, blocks, or rocks together. Calcium oxide reacts with water and $CO_2$ to form $CaCO_3$, which binds the sand in the mortar:

$$CaO(s) + H_2O(l) \rightleftharpoons Ca^{2+}(aq) + 2\,OH^-(aq) \qquad [22.70]$$

$$Ca^{2+}(aq) + 2\,OH^-(aq) + CO_2(aq) \longrightarrow CaCO_3(s) + H_2O(l) \qquad [22.71]$$

## Carbides

The binary compounds of carbon with metals, metalloids, and certain nonmetals are called **carbides**. The more active metals form *ionic carbides*, and the most common of these contain the *acetylide* ion ($C_2^{2-}$). This ion is isoelectronic with $N_2$, and its Lewis structure, $[:C\equiv C:]^{2-}$, has a carbon–carbon triple bond. The most important ionic carbide is calcium carbide ($CaC_2$), produced by the reduction of $CaO$ with carbon at high temperature:

$$2\,CaO(s) + 5\,C(s) \longrightarrow 2\,CaC_2(s) + CO_2(g) \qquad [22.72]$$

The carbide ion is a very strong base that reacts with water to form acetylene ($H$—$C$≡$C$—$H$):

$$CaC_2(s) + 2\,H_2O(l) \longrightarrow Ca(OH)_2(aq) + C_2H_2(g) \qquad [22.73]$$

Calcium carbide is therefore a convenient solid source of acetylene, which is used in welding (Figure 22.13).

*Interstitial carbides* are formed by many transition metals. The carbon atoms occupy open spaces (interstices) between the metal atoms in a manner analogous to the interstitial hydrides (Section 22.2). This process generally makes the metal harder. Tungsten carbide, for example, is very hard and very heat-resistant and, thus, used to make cutting tools.

*Covalent carbides* are formed by boron and silicon. Silicon carbide ($SiC$), known as Carborundum®, is used as an abrasive and in cutting tools. Almost as hard as diamond, $SiC$ has a diamondlike structure with alternating Si and C atoms.

## Other Inorganic Compounds of Carbon

Hydrogen cyanide, $HCN$, is an extremely toxic gas that famously has the odor of bitter almonds. It is produced by the reaction of a cyanide salt, such as NaCN, with an acid. Aqueous solutions of $HCN$ are known as hydrocyanic acid. Neutralization with a base produces cyanide salts, which are used in the manufacture of several plastics, including nylon and Orlon®. The $CN^-$ ion forms stable complexes with most transition metals. ∞ (Section 17.5)

Carbon disulfide, $CS_2$, is an important industrial solvent for waxes, greases, celluloses, and other nonpolar substances. It is a colorless, volatile liquid (bp 46.3 °C). The vapor is very poisonous and highly flammable.

 **GIVE IT SOME THOUGHT**

Based on what you know of their physical properties, does $CS_2$ have stronger intermolecular forces than $CO_2$? Explain.

---

# 22.10 | THE OTHER GROUP 4A ELEMENTS: Si, Ge, Sn, AND Pb

The trend from nonmetallic to metallic character as we go down a family is strikingly evident in group 4A. Carbon is a nonmetal; silicon and germanium are metalloids; tin and lead are metals. In this section we consider a few general characteristics of group 4A and then look more thoroughly at silicon.

## General Characteristics of the Group 4A Elements

The group 4A elements possess the outer-shell electron configuration $ns^2np^2$. The electronegativities of the elements are generally low (▼ TABLE 22.8); carbides that formally contain $C^{4-}$ ions are observed only in the case of a few compounds of carbon with very active metals. Formation of 4+ ions by electron loss is not observed for any of these elements; the ionization energies are too high. The +2 oxidation state is found in the

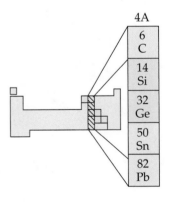

**TABLE 22.8 • Some Properties of the Group 4A Elements**

| Property | C | Si | Ge | Sn | Pb |
|---|---|---|---|---|---|
| Atomic radius (Å) | 0.77 | 1.17 | 1.22 | 1.40 | 1.46 |
| First ionization energy (kJ/mol) | 1086 | 786 | 762 | 709 | 716 |
| Electronegativity | 2.5 | 1.8 | 1.8 | 1.8 | 1.9 |
| X—X single-bond enthalpy (kJ/mol) | 348 | 226 | 188 | 151 | — |

chemistry of germanium, tin, and lead, however, and it is the principal oxidation state for lead. The vast majority of the compounds of the group 4A elements are covalently bonded. Carbon, except in highly unusual examples, forms a maximum of four bonds. The other members of the family are able to form more than four bonds. ∞ (Section 8.7)

Table 22.8 shows that the strength of a bond between two atoms of a given element decreases as we go down group 4A. Carbon–carbon bonds are quite strong. Carbon, therefore, has a striking ability to form compounds in which carbon atoms are bonded to one another in extended chains and rings, which accounts for the large number of organic compounds that exist. Other elements can form chains and rings, but these bonds are far less important in the chemistries of these other elements. The Si—Si bond strength (226 kJ/mol), for example, is much lower than the Si—O bond strength (386 kJ/mol). As a result, the chemistry of silicon is dominated by the formation of Si—O bonds, and Si—Si bonds play a minor role in silicon chemistry.

## Occurrence and Preparation of Silicon

Silicon is the second most abundant element, after oxygen, in Earth's crust. It occurs in $SiO_2$ and in an enormous variety of silicate minerals. The element is obtained by the reduction of molten silicon dioxide with carbon at high temperature:

$$SiO_2(l) + 2\,C(s) \longrightarrow Si(l) + 2\,CO(g) \qquad [22.74]$$

Elemental silicon has a diamond-type structure. Crystalline silicon is a gray metallic-looking solid that melts at 1410 °C. The element is a semiconductor, as we saw in Chapters 7 and 12, and is used to make solar cells and transistors for computer chips. To be used as a semiconductor, it must be extremely pure, possessing less than $10^{-7}\%$ (1 ppb) impurities. One method of purification is to treat the element with $Cl_2$ to form $SiCl_4$, a volatile liquid that is purified by fractional distillation and then converted back to elemental silicon by reduction with $H_2$:

$$SiCl_4(g) + 2\,H_2(g) \longrightarrow Si(s) + 4\,HCl(g) \qquad [22.75]$$

The process known as *zone refining* can further purify the element (◀ FIGURE 22.33). As a heated coil is passed slowly along a silicon rod, a narrow band of the element is melted. As the molten section is swept slowly along the length of the rod, the impurities concentrate in this section, following it to the end of the rod. The purified top portion of the rod crystallizes as 99.999999999% pure silicon.

## Silicates

Silicon dioxide and other compounds that contain silicon and oxygen make up over 90% of Earth's crust. In **silicates**, a silicon atom is surrounded by four oxygens and silicon is found in its most common oxidation state, +4. The orthosilicate ion, $SiO_4{}^{4-}$, is found in very few silicate minerals, but we can view it as the "building block" for many mineral structures. As ▶ FIGURE 22.34 shows, adjacent tetrahedra are linked by a common oxygen atom. Two tetrahedra joined in this way, called the *disilicate* ion, contain two Si atoms and seven O atoms. Silicon and oxygen are in the +4 and −2 oxidation states, respectively, in all silicates, so the overall charge of any silicate ion must be consistent with these oxidation states. Thus, the charge on $Si_2O_7$ is $(2)(+4) + (7)(-2) = -6$; it is the $Si_2O_7{}^{6-}$ ion.

In most silicate minerals, silicate tetrahedra are linked together to form chains, sheets, or three-dimensional structures. We can connect two vertices of each tetrahedron to two other tetrahedra, for example, leading to an infinite chain with an $\cdots O—Si—O—Si\cdots$ backbone. As Figure 22.34(b) shows, this chain can be viewed as repeating units of the $Si_2O_6{}^{4-}$ ion or, in terms of its simplest formula, $SiO_3{}^{2-}$. The mineral *enstatite* ($MgSiO_3$) consists of rows of single-strand silicate chains with $Mg^{2+}$ ions between the strands to balance charge.

In Figure 22.34(c) each silicate tetrahedron is linked to three others, forming an infinite sheet structure. The simplest formula of this sheet is $Si_2O_5{}^{2-}$. The mineral *talc*, also known as talcum powder, has the formula $Mg_3(Si_2O_5)_2(OH)_2$ and is based on this sheet structure. The $Mg^{2+}$ and $OH^-$ ions lie between the silicate sheets. The slippery feel of talcum powder is due to the silicate sheets sliding relative to one another.

---

**What limits the range of temperatures you can use for zone refining of silicon?**

Molten section

As heating coil slowly moves down, impurities concentrate in molten section, leaving behind ultrapure Si

Silicon rod

Inert atmosphere

▲ **FIGURE 22.33   Zone-refining apparatus for production of ultrapure silicon.**

▲ **FIGURE 22.34   Silicate chains and sheets.**

Many minerals are based on silicates, and many are useful as clays, ceramics, and other materials. Some silicates, however, have harmful effects on human health, the best-known example being *asbestos*, a general term applied to a group of fibrous silicate minerals. The structure of these minerals is either chains of silicate tetrahedra or sheets formed into rolls. The result is that the minerals have a fibrous character (▶ **FIGURE 22.35**). Asbestos minerals were once widely used as thermal insulation, especially in high-temperature applications, because of the great chemical stability of the silicate structure. In addition, the fibers can be woven into asbestos cloth, which was used for fireproof curtains and other applications. However, the fibrous structure of asbestos minerals poses a health risk because the fibers readily penetrate soft tissues, such as the lungs, where they can cause diseases, including cancer. The use of asbestos as a common building material has therefore been discontinued.

When all four vertices of each $SiO_4$ tetrahedron are linked to other tetrahedra, the structure extends in three dimensions. This linking of the tetrahedra forms quartz ($SiO_2$). Because the structure is locked together in a three-dimensional array much like diamond ∞ (Section 12.7) quartz is harder than strand- or sheet-type silicates.

▲ **FIGURE 22.35   Serpentine asbestos.**

---

**SAMPLE EXERCISE 22.9**   **Determining an Empirical Formula**

The mineral *chrysotile* is a noncarcinogenic asbestos mineral that is based on the sheet structure shown in Figure 22.34(c). In addition to silicate tetrahedra, the mineral contains $Mg^{2+}$ and $OH^-$ ions. Analysis of the mineral shows that there are 1.5 Mg atoms per Si atom. What is the empirical formula for chrysotile?

**SOLUTION**

**Analyze**  A mineral is described that has a sheet silicate structure with $Mg^{2+}$ and $OH^-$ ions to balance charge and 1.5 Mg for each 1 Si. We are asked to write the empirical formula for the mineral.

**Plan**  As shown in Figure 22.34(c), the silicate sheet structure is based on the $Si_2O_5{}^{2-}$ ion. We first add $Mg^{2+}$ to give the proper Mg : Si ratio. We then add $OH^-$ ions to obtain a neutral compound.

**Solve**  The observation that the Mg : Si ratio equals 1.5 is consistent with three $Mg^{2+}$ ions per $Si_2O_5{}^{2-}$ ion. The addition of three $Mg^{2+}$ ions would make $Mg_3(Si_2O_5)^{4+}$. In order to achieve charge balance in the mineral, there must be four $OH^-$ ions per $Si_2O_5{}^{2-}$ ion. Thus, the formula of chrysotile is $Mg_3(Si_2O_5)(OH)_4$. Since this is not reducible to a simpler formula, this is the empirical formula.

## Glass

Quartz melts at approximately 1600 °C, forming a tacky liquid. In the course of melting, many silicon–oxygen bonds are broken. When the liquid cools rapidly, silicon–oxygen bonds are re-formed before the atoms are able to arrange themselves in a regular fashion. An amorphous solid, known as quartz glass or silica glass, results. Many substances can be added to $SiO_2$ to cause it to melt at a lower temperature. The common **glass** used in windows and bottles, known as soda-lime glass, contains $CaO$ and $Na_2O$ in addition to $SiO_2$ from sand. The $CaO$ and $Na_2O$ are produced by heating two inexpensive chemicals, limestone ($CaCO_3$) and soda ash ($Na_2CO_3$), which decompose at high temperatures:

$$CaCO_3(s) \longrightarrow CaO(s) + CO_2(g) \qquad [22.76]$$

$$Na_2CO_3(s) \longrightarrow Na_2O(s) + CO_2(g) \qquad [22.77]$$

Other substances can be added to soda-lime glass to produce color or to change the properties of the glass in various ways. The addition of CoO, for example, produces the deep blue color of "cobalt glass." Replacing $Na_2O$ with $K_2O$ results in a harder glass that has a higher melting point. Replacing CaO with PbO results in a denser "lead crystal" glass with a higher refractive index. Lead crystal is used for decorative glassware; the higher refractive index gives this glass a particularly sparkling appearance. Addition of nonmetal oxides, such as $B_2O_3$ and $P_4O_{10}$, which form network structures related to the silicates, also changes the properties of the glass. Adding $B_2O_3$ creates a "borosilicate" glass with a higher melting point and a greater ability to withstand temperature changes. Such glasses, sold commercially under trade names such as Pyrex® and Kimax®, are used where resistance to thermal shock is important, such as in laboratory glassware or coffeemakers.

## Silicones

Silicones consist of O—Si—O chains in which the remaining bonding positions on each silicon are occupied by organic groups such as $CH_3$:

Depending on chain length and degree of cross-linking, silicones can be either oils or rubber-like materials. Silicones are nontoxic and have good stability toward heat, light, oxygen, and water. They are used commercially in a wide variety of products, including lubricants, car polishes, sealants, and gaskets. They are also used for waterproofing fabrics. When applied to a fabric, the oxygen atoms form hydrogen bonds with the molecules on the surface of the fabric. The hydrophobic (water-repelling) organic groups of the silicone are then left pointing away from the surface as a barrier.

⚠ **GIVE IT SOME THOUGHT**
Distinguish among the substances silicon, silica, and silicone.

# 22.11 | BORON

Boron is the only group 3A element that can be considered nonmetallic and thus is our final element in this chapter. The element has an extended network structure with a melting point (2300 °C) that is intermediate between the melting points of carbon (3550 °C) and silicon (1410 °C). The electron configuration of boron is $[He]2s^2 2p^1$.

In the family of compounds called **boranes,** the molecules contain only boron and hydrogen. The simplest borane is $BH_3$. This molecule contains only six valence electrons and is therefore an exception to the octet rule. As a result, $BH_3$ reacts with itself to form *diborane* ($B_2H_6$). This reaction can be viewed as a Lewis acid–base reaction in which one B—H bonding pair of electrons in each $BH_3$ molecule is donated to the other. As a result, diborane is an unusual molecule in which hydrogen atoms form a bridge between two B atoms (▶ **FIGURE 22.36**). Such hydrogens, called *bridging hydrogens*, exhibit interesting chemical reactivity, which you may learn about in a more advanced chemistry course.

Sharing hydrogen atoms between the two boron atoms compensates somewhat for the deficiency in valence electrons around each boron. Nevertheless, diborane is an extremely reactive molecule, spontaneously flammable in air in a highly exothermic reaction:

$$B_2H_6(g) + 3\,O_2(g) \longrightarrow B_2O_3(s) + 3\,H_2O(g) \qquad \Delta H° = -2030\ kJ \quad [22.78]$$

Boron and hydrogen form a series of anions called *borane anions*. Salts of the borohydride ion ($BH_4^-$) are widely used as reducing agents. For example, sodium borohydride ($NaBH_4$) is a commonly used reducing agent for certain organic compounds.

▲ **FIGURE 22.36** **The structure of diborane ($B_2H_6$).**

### ◢ GIVE IT SOME THOUGHT

Recall that the hydride ion is $H^-$. What is the oxidation state of boron in sodium borohydride?

The only important oxide of boron is boric oxide ($B_2O_3$). This substance is the anhydride of boric acid, which we may write as $H_3BO_3$ or $B(OH)_3$. Boric acid is so weak an acid ($K_a = 5.8 \times 10^{-10}$) that solutions of $H_3BO_3$ are used as an eyewash. Upon heating, boric acid loses water by a condensation reaction similar to that described for phosphorus in Section 22.8:

$$4\,H_3BO_3(s) \longrightarrow H_2B_4O_7(s) + 5\,H_2O(g) \qquad [22.79]$$

The diprotic acid $H_2B_4O_7$ is tetraboric acid. The hydrated sodium salt $Na_2B_4O_7 \cdot 10\,H_2O$, called borax, occurs in dry lake deposits in California and can also be prepared from other borate minerals. Solutions of borax are alkaline, and the substance is used in various laundry and cleaning products.

---

**SAMPLE INTEGRATIVE EXERCISE** **Putting Concepts Together**

The interhalogen compound $BrF_3$ is a volatile, straw-colored liquid. The compound exhibits appreciable electrical conductivity because of autoionization ("solv" refers to $BrF_3$ as the solvent):

$$2\,BrF_3(l) \rightleftharpoons BrF_2^+(solv) + BrF_4^-(solv)$$

**(a)** What are the molecular structures of the $BrF_2^+$ and $BrF_4^-$ ions? **(b)** The electrical conductivity of $BrF_3$ decreases with increasing temperature. Is the autoionization process exothermic or endothermic? **(c)** One chemical characteristic of $BrF_3$ is that it acts as a Lewis acid toward fluoride ions. What do we expect will happen when KBr is dissolved in $BrF_3$?

**SOLUTION**

**(a)** The $BrF_2^+$ ion has $7 + 2(7) - 1 = 20$ valence-shell electrons. The Lewis structure for the ion is

$$\left[ :\ddot{F} - \ddot{Br} - \ddot{F}: \right]^+$$

Because there are four electron domains around the central Br atom, the resulting electron domain geometry is tetrahedral. ∞ (Section 9.2) Because bonding pairs of electrons occupy two of these domains, the molecular geometry is nonlinear:

The $BrF_4^-$ ion has $7 + 4(7) + 1 = 36$ electrons, leading to the Lewis structure

$$\left[ \begin{array}{c} :\ddot{F}: \\ :\ddot{F}-\ddot{Br}-\ddot{F}: \\ :\ddot{F}: \end{array} \right]^-$$

Because there are six electron domains around the central Br atom in this ion, the geometry is octahedral. The two nonbonding pairs of electrons are located opposite each other on the octahedron, leading to a square-planar molecular geometry:

**(b)** The observation that conductivity decreases as temperature increases indicates that there are fewer ions present in the solution at the higher temperature. Thus, increasing the temperature causes the equilibrium to shift to the left. According to Le Châtelier's principle, this shift indicates that the reaction is exothermic as it proceeds from left to right. ∞ (Section 15.7)

**(c)** A Lewis acid is an electron-pair acceptor. ∞ (Section 16.11) The fluoride ion has four valence-shell electron pairs and can act as a Lewis base (an electron-pair donor). Thus, we can envision the following reaction occurring:

$$:\ddot{F}:^- \;+\; \underset{\underset{F}{|}}{\overset{}{Br}}\!\!-\!F \quad\longrightarrow\quad \left[ \underset{\underset{F}{|}}{\overset{F}{|}} F\!-\!Br\!-\!F \right]^-$$

$$F^- \;+\; BrF_3 \longrightarrow BrF_4^-$$

# CHAPTER SUMMARY AND KEY TERMS

**INTRODUCTION AND SECTION 22.1** The periodic table is useful for organizing and remembering the descriptive chemistry of the elements. Among elements of a given group, size increases with increasing atomic number, and electronegativity and ionization energy decrease. Nonmetallic character parallels electronegativity, so the most nonmetallic elements are found in the upper right portion of the periodic table.

Among the nonmetallic elements, the first member of each group differs dramatically from the other members; it forms a maximum of four bonds to other atoms and exhibits a much greater tendency to form $\pi$ bonds than the heavier elements in its group.

Because $O_2$ and $H_2O$ are abundant in our world, we focus on two important and general reaction types as we discuss the nonmetals: oxidation by $O_2$ and proton-transfer reactions involving $H_2O$ or aqueous solutions.

**SECTION 22.2** Hydrogen has three isotopes: **protium** ($^1_1H$), **deuterium** ($^2_1H$), and **tritium** ($^3_1H$). Hydrogen is not a member of any particular periodic group, although it is usually placed above lithium. The hydrogen atom can either lose an electron, forming $H^+$, or gain one, forming $H^-$ (the hydride ion). Because the H—H bond is relatively strong, $H_2$ is fairly unreactive unless activated by heat or a catalyst. Hydrogen forms a very strong bond to oxygen, so the reactions of $H_2$ with oxygen-containing compounds usually lead to the formation of $H_2O$. Because the bonds in CO and $CO_2$ are even stronger than the O—H bond, the reaction of $H_2O$ with carbon or certain organic compounds leads to the formation of $H_2$. The $H^+(aq)$ ion is able to oxidize many metals, forming $H_2(g)$. The electrolysis of water also forms $H_2(g)$.

The binary compounds of hydrogen are of three general types: **ionic hydrides** (formed by active metals), **metallic hydrides** (formed by transition metals), and **molecular hydrides** (formed by non-metals). The ionic hydrides contain the $H^-$ ion; because this ion is extremely basic, ionic hydrides react with $H_2O$ to form $H_2$ and $OH^-$.

**SECTIONS 22.3 AND 22.4** The noble gases (group 8A) exhibit a very limited chemical reactivity because of the exceptional stability of their electron configurations. The xenon fluorides and oxides and $KrF_2$ are the best-established compounds of the noble gases.

The halogens (group 7A) occur as diatomic molecules. All except fluorine exhibit oxidation states varying from $-1$ to $+7$. Fluorine is the most electronegative element, so it is restricted to the oxidation states 0 and $-1$. The oxidizing power of the element (the tendency to form the $-1$ oxidation state) decreases as we proceed down the group. The hydrogen halides are among the most useful compounds of these elements; these gases dissolve in water to form the hydrohalic acids, such as $HCl(aq)$. Hydrofluoric acid reacts with **silica**. The **interhalogens** are compounds formed between two different halogen elements. Chlorine, bromine, and iodine form a series of oxyacids, in which the halogen atom is in a positive oxidation state. These compounds and their associated oxyanions are strong oxidizing agents.

**SECTIONS 22.5 AND 22.6** Oxygen has two allotropes, $O_2$ and $O_3$ (ozone). Ozone is unstable compared to $O_2$, and it is a stronger oxidizing agent than $O_2$. Most reactions of $O_2$ lead to oxides, compounds in which oxygen is in the $-2$ oxidation state. The soluble oxides of nonmetals generally produce acidic aqueous solutions; they are called **acidic anhydrides** or **acidic oxides**. In contrast, soluble metal oxides produce basic solutions and are called **basic anhydrides** or **basic oxides**. Many metal oxides that are insoluble in water dissolve in acid, accompanied by the formation of $H_2O$. Peroxides contain $O-O$ bonds and oxygen in the $-1$ oxidation state. Peroxides are unstable, decomposing to $O_2$ and oxides. In such reactions peroxides are simultaneously oxidized and reduced, a process called **disproportionation**. Superoxides contain the $O_2^-$ ion in which oxygen is in the $-\frac{1}{2}$ oxidation state.

Sulfur is the most important of the other group 6A elements. It has several allotropic forms; the most stable one at room temperature consists of $S_8$ rings. Sulfur forms two oxides, $SO_2$ and $SO_3$, and both are important atmospheric pollutants. Sulfur trioxide is the anhydride of sulfuric acid, the most important sulfur compound and the most-produced industrial chemical. Sulfuric acid is a strong acid and a good dehydrating agent. Sulfur forms several oxyanions as well, including the $SO_3^{2-}$ (sulfite), $SO_4^{2-}$ (sulfate), and $S_2O_3^{2-}$ (thiosulfate) ions. Sulfur is found combined with many metals as a sulfide, in which sulfur is in the $-2$ oxidation state. These compounds often react with acids to form hydrogen sulfide ($H_2S$), which smells like rotten eggs.

**SECTIONS 22.7 AND 22.8** Nitrogen is found in the atmosphere as $N_2$ molecules. Molecular nitrogen is chemically very stable because of the strong $N \equiv N$ bond. Molecular nitrogen can be converted into ammonia via the Haber process. Once the ammonia is made, it can be converted into a variety of different compounds that exhibit nitrogen oxidation states ranging from $-3$ to $+5$. The most important industrial conversion of ammonia is the **Ostwald process**, in which ammonia is oxidized to nitric acid ($HNO_3$). Nitrogen has three important oxides: nitrous oxide ($N_2O$), nitric oxide (NO), and nitrogen dioxide ($NO_2$). Nitrous acid ($HNO_2$) is a weak acid; its conjugate base is the nitrite ion ($NO_2^-$). Another important nitrogen compound is hydrazine ($N_2H_4$).

Phosphorus is the most important of the remaining group 5A elements. It occurs in nature as phosphate minerals. Phosphorus has several allotropes, including white phosphorus, which consists of $P_4$ tetrahedra. In reaction with the halogens, phosphorus forms trihalides $PX_3$ and pentahalides $PX_5$. These compounds undergo hydrolysis to produce an oxyacid of phosphorus and HX. Phosphorus forms two oxides, $P_4O_6$ and $P_4O_{10}$. Their corresponding acids, phosphorous acid and phosphoric acid, undergo condensation reactions when heated. Phosphorus compounds are important in biochemistry and as fertilizers.

**SECTIONS 22.9 AND 22.10** The allotropes of carbon include diamond, graphite, fullerenes, carbon nanotubes, and graphene. Amorphous forms of graphite include **charcoal** and **carbon black**. Carbon forms two common oxides, CO and $CO_2$. Aqueous solutions of $CO_2$ produce the weak diprotic acid carbonic acid ($H_2CO_3$), which is the parent acid of hydrogen carbonate and carbonate salts. Binary compounds of carbon are called **carbides**. Carbides may be ionic, interstitial, or covalent. Calcium carbide ($CaC_2$) contains the strongly basic acetylide ion ($C_2^{2-}$), which reacts with water to form acetylene. Other important inorganic carbon compounds include hydrogen cyanide (HCN) and carbon disulfide ($CS_2$).

The other group 4A elements show great diversity in physical and chemical properties. Silicon, the second most abundant element, is a semiconductor. It reacts with $Cl_2$ to form $SiCl_4$, a liquid at room temperature, a reaction that is used to help purify silicon from its native minerals. Silicon forms strong $Si-O$ bonds and therefore occurs in a variety of silicate minerals. Silica is $SiO_2$; **silicates** consist of $SiO_4$ tetrahedra, linked together at their vertices to form chains, sheets, or three-dimensional structures. The most common three-dimensional silicate is quartz ($SiO_2$). **Glass** is an amorphous (noncrystalline) form of $SiO_2$. Silicones contain $O-Si-O$ chains with organic groups bonded to the Si atoms. Like silicon, germanium is a metalloid; tin and lead are metallic.

**SECTION 22.11** Boron is the only group 3A element that is a nonmetal. It forms a variety of compounds with hydrogen called boron hydrides, or **boranes**. Diborane ($B_2H_6$) has an unusual structure with two hydrogen atoms that bridge between the two boron atoms. Boranes react with oxygen to form boric oxide ($B_2O_3$), in which boron is in the $+3$ oxidation state. Boric oxide is the anhydride of boric acid ($H_3BO_3$). Boric acid readily undergoes condensation reactions.

# KEY SKILLS

- Be able to use periodic trends to explain the basic differences between the elements of a group or period (Section 22.1).

- Explain the ways in which the first element in a group differs from subsequent elements in the group (Section 22.1).

- Be able to determine electron configurations, oxidation numbers, and molecular shapes of elements and compounds (Sections 22.2–22.11).

- Know the sources of the common nonmetals, how they are obtained, and how they are used (Sections 22.2–22.11).

- Understand how phosphoric and phosphorous acids undergo condensation reactions (Section 22.8).

- Explain how the bonding and structures of silicates relate to their chemical formulas and properties (Section 22.10).

# EXERCISES

## VISUALIZING CONCEPTS

**22.1** **(a)** One of these structures is a stable compound; the other is not. Identify the stable compound, and explain why it is stable. Explain why the other compound is not stable. **(b)** What is the geometry around the central atoms of the stable compound? [Section 22.1]

**22.2** **(a)** Identify the *type* of chemical reaction represented by the following diagram. **(b)** Place appropriate charges on the species on both sides of the equation. **(c)** Write the chemical equation for the reaction. [Section 22.1]

**22.3** Which of the following species (there may be more than one) is/are likely to have the structure shown here: **(a)** $XeF_4$, **(b)** $BrF_4^+$, **(c)** $SiF_4$, **(d)** $TeCl_4$, **(e)** $HClO_4$? (The colors do not reflect atom identities.) [Sections 22.3, 22.4, 22.6, and 22.10]

**22.4** You have two glass bottles, one containing oxygen and one filled with ozone. How could you determine which one is which? [Section 22.5]

**22.5** Write the molecular formula and Lewis structure for each of the following oxides of nitrogen: [Section 22.7]

**22.6** Which property of the group 6A elements might be the one depicted in the graph shown here: **(a)** electronegativity, **(b)** first ionization energy, **(c)** density, **(d)** X—X single-bond enthalpy, **(e)** electron affinity? Explain your answer. [Sections 22.5 and 22.6]

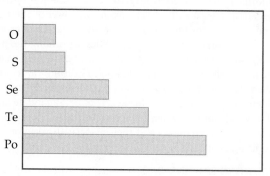

**22.7** The atomic and ionic radii of the first three group 6A elements are

| Atomic radius (Å) | Ionic radius (Å) |
|---|---|
| O | $O^{2-}$ |
| 0.73 | 1.40 |
| S | $S^{2-}$ |
| 1.03 | 1.84 |
| Se | $Se^{2-}$ |
| 1.17 | 1.98 |

**(a)** Explain why the atomic radius increases in moving downward in the group. **(b)** Explain why the ionic radii are larger than the atomic radii. **(c)** Which of the three anions would you expect to be the strongest base in water? Explain. [Sections 22.5 and 22.6]

**22.8** Which property of the third-row nonmetallic elements might be the one depicted in the graph on the next page: **(a)** first ionization energy, **(b)** atomic radius, **(c)** electronegativity, **(d)** melting point, **(e)** X—X single-bond enthalpy? Explain both your choice and why the other choices would not be correct. [Sections 22.3, 22.4, 22.6, 22.8, and 22.10]

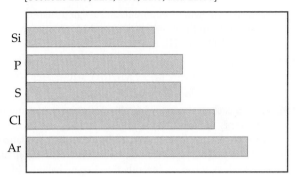

**22.9** Which of the following compounds would you expect to be the most generally reactive, and why? [Section 22.8]

**22.10** (a) Draw the Lewis structures for at least four species that have the general formula

$$\left[:X\equiv Y:\right]^{n}$$

where X and Y may be the same or different, and $n$ may have a value from $+1$ to $-2$. (b) Which of the compounds is likely to be the strongest Brønsted base? Explain. [Sections 22.1, 22.7, and 22.9]

# PERIODIC TRENDS AND CHEMICAL REACTIONS (section 22.1)

**22.11** Identify each of the following elements as a metal, nonmetal, or metalloid: (a) phosphorus, (b) strontium, (c) manganese, (d) selenium, (e) sodium, (f) krypton.

**22.12** Identify each of the following elements as a metal, nonmetal, or metalloid: (a) gallium, (b) molybdenum, (c) tellurium, (d) arsenic, (e) xenon, (f) ruthenium.

**22.13** Consider the elements O, Ba, Co, Be, Br, and Se. From this list select the element that (a) is most electronegative, (b) exhibits a maximum oxidation state of $+7$, (c) loses an electron most readily, (d) forms $\pi$ bonds most readily, (e) is a transition metal, (f) is a liquid at room temperature and pressure.

**22.14** Consider the elements Li, K, Cl, C, Ne, and Ar. From this list select the element that (a) is most electronegative, (b) has the greatest metallic character, (c) most readily forms a positive ion, (d) has the smallest atomic radius, (e) forms $\pi$ bonds most readily, (f) has multiple allotropes.

**22.15** Explain the following observations: (a) The highest fluoride compound formed by nitrogen is $NF_3$, whereas phosphorus readily forms $PF_5$. (b) Although CO is a well-known compound, SiO does not exist under ordinary conditions. (c) $AsH_3$ is a stronger reducing agent than $NH_3$.

**22.16** Explain the following observations: (a) $HNO_3$ is a stronger oxidizing agent than $H_3PO_4$. (b) Silicon can form an ion with six fluorine atoms, $SiF_6{}^{2-}$, whereas carbon is able to bond to a maximum of four, $CF_4$. (c) There are three compounds formed by carbon and hydrogen that contain two carbon atoms each ($C_2H_2$, $C_2H_4$, and $C_2H_6$), whereas silicon forms only one analogous compound ($Si_2H_6$).

**22.17** Complete and balance the following equations:
(a) $NaOCH_3(s) + H_2O(l) \longrightarrow$
(b) $CuO(s) + HNO_3(aq) \longrightarrow$
(c) $WO_3(s) + H_2(g) \overset{\Delta}{\longrightarrow}$
(d) $NH_2OH(l) + O_2(g) \longrightarrow$
(e) $Al_4C_3(s) + H_2O(l) \longrightarrow$

**22.18** Complete and balance the following equations:
(a) $Mg_3N_2(s) + H_2O(l) \longrightarrow$
(b) $C_3H_7OH(l) + O_2(g) \longrightarrow$
(c) $MnO_2(s) + C(s) \overset{\Delta}{\longrightarrow}$
(d) $AlP(s) + H_2O(l) \longrightarrow$
(e) $Na_2S(s) + HCl(aq) \longrightarrow$

# HYDROGEN, THE NOBLE GASES, AND THE HALOGENS (sections 22.2, 22.3, 22.4)

**22.19** (a) Give the names and chemical symbols for the three isotopes of hydrogen. (b) List the isotopes in order of decreasing natural abundance. (c) Which hydrogen isotope is radioactive? (d) Write the nuclear equation for the radioactive decay of this isotope.

**22.20** Are the physical properties of $H_2O$ different from $D_2O$? Explain.

**22.21** Give a reason why hydrogen might be placed along with the group 1A elements of the periodic table.

**22.22** What does hydrogen have in common with the halogens? Explain.

**22.23** Write a balanced equation for the preparation of $H_2$ using (a) Mg and an acid, (b) carbon and steam, (c) methane and steam.

**22.24** List (a) three commercial means of producing $H_2$, (b) three industrial uses of $H_2$.

**22.25** Complete and balance the following equations:
(a) $NaH(s) + H_2O(l) \longrightarrow$
(b) $Fe(s) + H_2SO_4(aq) \longrightarrow$
(c) $H_2(g) + Br_2(g) \longrightarrow$
(d) $Na(l) + H_2(g) \longrightarrow$
(e) $PbO(s) + H_2(g) \longrightarrow$

**22.26** Write balanced equations for each of the following reactions (some of these are analogous to reactions shown in the chapter). (a) Aluminum metal reacts with acids to form hydrogen gas. (b) Steam reacts with magnesium metal to give magnesium oxide and hydrogen. (c) Manganese(IV) oxide is reduced to manganese(II) oxide by hydrogen gas. (d) Calcium hydride reacts with water to generate hydrogen gas.

**22.27** Identify the following hydrides as ionic, metallic, or molecular: (a) $BaH_2$, (b) $H_2Te$, (c) $TiH_{1.7}$.

**22.28** Identify the following hydrides as ionic, metallic, or molecular: (a) $B_2H_6$, (b) RbH, (c) $Th_4H_{1.5}$.

**22.29** Describe two characteristics of hydrogen that are favorable for its use as a general energy source in vehicles.

**22.30** The $H_2/O_2$ fuel cell converts elemental hydrogen and oxygen into water, producing, theoretically, 1.23 V of energy. What is the most sustainable way to obtain hydrogen to run a large number of fuel cells? Explain.

**22.31** Why does xenon form stable compounds with fluorine, whereas argon does not?

**22.32** A friend tells you that the "neon" in neon signs is a compound of neon and aluminum. Can your friend be correct? Explain.

**22.33** Write the chemical formula for each of the following, and indicate the oxidation state of the halogen or noble-gas atom in each: (a) calcium hypobromite, (b) bromic acid, (c) xenon trioxide, (d) perchlorate ion, (e) iodous acid, (f) iodine pentafluoride.

**22.34** Write the chemical formula for each of the following compounds, and indicate the oxidation state of the halogen or noble-gas atom in each: (a) chlorate ion, (b) hydroiodic acid, (c) iodine trichloride, (d) sodium hypochlorite, (e) perchloric acid, (f) xenon tetrafluoride.

**22.35** Name the following compounds and assign oxidation states to the halogens in them: (a) $Fe(ClO_3)_3$, (b) $HClO_2$, (c) $XeF_6$, (d) $BrF_5$, (e) $XeOF_4$, (f) $HIO_3$.

**22.36** Name the following compounds and assign oxidation states to the halogens in them: (a) $KClO_3$, (b) $Ca(IO_3)_2$, (c) $AlCl_3$, (d) $HBrO_3$, (e) $H_5IO_6$, (f) $XeF_4$.

**22.37** Explain each of the following observations: (a) At room temperature $I_2$ is a solid, $Br_2$ is a liquid, and $Cl_2$ and $F_2$ are both gases. (b) $F_2$ cannot be prepared by electrolytic oxidation of aqueous $F^-$ solutions. (c) The boiling point of HF is much higher than those of the other hydrogen halides. (d) The halogens decrease in oxidizing power in the order $F_2 > Cl_2 > Br_2 > I_2$.

**22.38** Explain the following observations: (a) For a given oxidation state, the acid strength of the oxyacid in aqueous solution decreases in the order chlorine > bromine > iodine. (b) Hydrofluoric acid cannot be stored in glass bottles. (c) HI cannot be prepared by treating NaI with sulfuric acid. (d) The interhalogen $ICl_3$ is known, but $BrCl_3$ is not.

## OXYGEN AND THE OTHER GROUP 6A ELEMENTS (sections 22.5 and 22.6)

**22.39** Write balanced equations for each of the following reactions. (a) When mercury(II) oxide is heated, it decomposes to form $O_2$ and mercury metal. (b) When copper(II) nitrate is heated strongly, it decomposes to form copper(II) oxide, nitrogen dioxide, and oxygen. (c) Lead(II) sulfide, PbS($s$), reacts with ozone to form $PbSO_4(s)$ and $O_2(g)$. (d) When heated in air, ZnS($s$) is converted to ZnO. (e) Potassium peroxide reacts with $CO_2(g)$ to give potassium carbonate and $O_2$. (f) Oxygen is converted to ozone in the upper atmosphere.

**22.40** Complete and balance the following equations:
(a) $CaO(s) + H_2O(l) \longrightarrow$
(b) $Al_2O_3(s) + H^+(aq) \longrightarrow$
(c) $Na_2O_2(s) + H_2O(l) \longrightarrow$
(d) $N_2O_3(g) + H_2O(l) \longrightarrow$
(e) $KO_2(s) + H_2O(l) \longrightarrow$
(f) $NO(g) + O_3(g) \longrightarrow$

**22.41** Predict whether each of the following oxides is acidic, basic, amphoteric, or neutral: (a) $NO_2$, (b) $CO_2$, (c) $Al_2O_3$, (d) CaO.

**22.42** Select the more acidic member of each of the following pairs: (a) $Mn_2O_7$ and $MnO_2$, (b) SnO and $SnO_2$, (c) $SO_2$ and $SO_3$, (d) $SiO_2$ and $SO_2$, (e) $Ga_2O_3$ and $In_2O_3$, (f) $SO_2$ and $SeO_2$.

**22.43** Write the chemical formula for each of the following compounds, and indicate the oxidation state of the group 6A element in each: (a) selenous acid, (b) potassium hydrogen sulfite, (c) hydrogen telluride, (d) carbon disulfide, (e) calcium sulfate, (f) cadmium sulfide, (g) zinc telluride.

**22.44** Write the chemical formula for each of the following compounds, and indicate the oxidation state of the group 6A element in each: (a) sulfur tetrachloride, (b) selenium trioxide, (c) sodium thiosulfate, (d) hydrogen sulfide, (e) sulfuric acid, (f) sulfur dioxide, (g) mercury telluride.

**22.45** In aqueous solution, hydrogen sulfide reduces (a) $Fe^{3+}$ to $Fe^{2+}$, (b) $Br_2$ to $Br^-$, (c) $MnO_4^-$ to $Mn^{2+}$, (d) $HNO_3$ to $NO_2$. In all cases, under appropriate conditions, the product is elemental sulfur. Write a balanced net ionic equation for each reaction.

**22.46** An aqueous solution of $SO_2$ reduces (a) aqueous $KMnO_4$ to $MnSO_4(aq)$, (b) acidic aqueous $K_2Cr_2O_7$ to aqueous $Cr^{3+}$, (c) aqueous $Hg_2(NO_3)_2$ to mercury metal. Write balanced equations for these reactions.

**22.47** Write the Lewis structure for each of the following species, and indicate the structure of each: (a) $SeO_3^{2-}$; (b) $S_2Cl_2$; (c) chlorosulfonic acid, $HSO_3Cl$ (chlorine is bonded to sulfur).

**22.48** The $SF_5^-$ ion is formed when $SF_4(g)$ reacts with fluoride salts containing large cations, such as CsF($s$). Draw the Lewis structures for $SF_4$ and $SF_5^-$, and predict the molecular structure of each.

**22.49** Write a balanced equation for each of the following reactions: (a) Sulfur dioxide reacts with water. (b) Solid zinc sulfide reacts with hydrochloric acid. (c) Elemental sulfur reacts with sulfite ion to form thiosulfate. (d) Sulfur trioxide is dissolved in sulfuric acid.

**22.50** Write a balanced equation for each of the following reactions. (You may have to guess at one or more of the reaction products, but you should be able to make a reasonable guess, based on your study of this chapter.) (a) Hydrogen selenide can be prepared by reaction of an aqueous acid solution on aluminum selenide. (b) Sodium thiosulfate is used to remove excess $Cl_2$ from chlorine-bleached fabrics. The thiosulfate ion forms $SO_4^{2-}$ and elemental sulfur, while $Cl_2$ is reduced to $Cl^-$.

## NITROGEN AND THE OTHER GROUP 5A ELEMENTS (sections 22.7 and 22.8)

**22.51** Write the chemical formula for each of the following compounds, and indicate the oxidation state of nitrogen in each: (a) sodium nitrite, (b) ammonia, (c) nitrous oxide, (d) sodium cyanide, (e) nitric acid, (f) nitrogen dioxide, (g) nitrogen, (h) boron nitride.

**22.52** Write the chemical formula for each of the following compounds, and indicate the oxidation state of nitrogen in each: (a) nitric oxide, (b) hydrazine, (c) potassium cyanide, (d) sodium nitrite, (e) ammonium chloride, (f) lithium nitride.

22.53 Write the Lewis structure for each of the following species, describe its geometry, and indicate the oxidation state of the nitrogen: (a) $HNO_2$, (b) $N_3^-$, (c) $N_2H_5^+$, (d) $NO_3^-$.

22.54 Write the Lewis structure for each of the following species, describe its geometry, and indicate the oxidation state of the nitrogen: (a) $NH_4^+$, (b) $NO_2^-$, (c) $N_2O$, (d) $NO_2$.

22.55 Complete and balance the following equations:
   (a) $Mg_3N_2(s) + H_2O(l) \longrightarrow$
   (b) $NO(g) + O_2(g) \longrightarrow$
   (c) $N_2O_5(g) + H_2O(l) \longrightarrow$
   (d) $NH_3(aq) + H^+(aq) \longrightarrow$
   (e) $N_2H_4(l) + O_2(g) \longrightarrow$

   Which ones of these are redox reactions?

22.56 Write a balanced net ionic equation for each of the following reactions: (a) Dilute nitric acid reacts with zinc metal with formation of nitrous oxide. (b) Concentrated nitric acid reacts with sulfur with formation of nitrogen dioxide. (c) Concentrated nitric acid oxidizes sulfur dioxide with formation of nitric oxide. (d) Hydrazine is burned in excess fluorine gas, forming $NF_3$. (e) Hydrazine reduces $CrO_4^{2-}$ to $Cr(OH)_4^-$ in base (hydrazine is oxidized to $N_2$).

22.57 Write complete balanced half-reactions for (a) oxidation of nitrous acid to nitrate ion in acidic solution, (b) oxidation of $N_2$ to $N_2O$ in acidic solution.

22.58 Write complete balanced half-reactions for (a) reduction of nitrate ion to NO in acidic solution, (b) oxidation of $HNO_2$ to $NO_2^-$ in acidic solution.

22.59 Write a molecular formula for each compound, and indicate the oxidation state of the group 5A element in each formula:

(a) phosphorous acid, (b) pyrophosphoric acid, (c) antimony trichloride, (d) magnesium arsenide, (e) diphosphorus pentoxide, (f) sodium phosphate.

22.60 Write a chemical formula for each compound or ion, and indicate the oxidation state of the group 5A element in each formula: (a) phosphate ion, (b) arsenous acid, (c) antimony(III) sulfide, (d) calcium dihydrogen phosphate, (e) potassium phosphide, (f) gallium arsenide.

22.61 Account for the following observations: (a) Phosphorus forms a pentachloride, but nitrogen does not. (b) $H_3PO_2$ is a monoprotic acid. (c) Phosphonium salts, such as $PH_4Cl$, can be formed under anhydrous conditions, but they can't be made in aqueous solution. (d) White phosphorus is more reactive than red phosphorus.

22.62 Account for the following observations: (a) $H_3PO_3$ is a diprotic acid. (b) Nitric acid is a strong acid, whereas phosphoric acid is weak. (c) Phosphate rock is ineffective as a phosphate fertilizer. (d) Phosphorus does not exist at room temperature as diatomic molecules, but nitrogen does. (e) Solutions of $Na_3PO_4$ are quite basic.

22.63 Write a balanced equation for each of the following reactions: (a) preparation of white phosphorus from calcium phosphate, (b) hydrolysis of $PBr_3$, (c) reduction of $PBr_3$ to $P_4$ in the gas phase, using $H_2$.

22.64 Write a balanced equation for each of the following reactions: (a) hydrolysis of $PCl_5$, (b) dehydration of phosphoric acid (also called orthophosphoric acid) to form pyrophosphoric acid, (c) reaction of $P_4O_{10}$ with water.

# CARBON, THE OTHER GROUP 4A ELEMENTS, AND BORON (sections 22.9, 22.10, 22.11)

22.65 Give the chemical formula for (a) hydrocyanic acid, (b) nickel tetracarbonyl, (c) barium bicarbonate, (d) calcium acetylide (e) potassium carbonate.

22.66 Give the chemical formula for (a) carbonic acid, (b) sodium cyanide, (c) potassium hydrogen carbonate, (d) acetylene, (e) iron pentacarbonyl.

22.67 Complete and balance the following equations:
   (a) $ZnCO_3(s) \xrightarrow{\Delta}$
   (b) $BaC_2(s) + H_2O(l) \longrightarrow$
   (c) $C_2H_2(g) + O_2(g) \longrightarrow$
   (d) $CS_2(g) + O_2(g) \longrightarrow$
   (e) $Ca(CN)_2(s) + HBr(aq) \longrightarrow$

22.68 Complete and balance the following equations:
   (a) $CO_2(g) + OH^-(aq) \longrightarrow$
   (b) $NaHCO_3(s) + H^+(aq) \longrightarrow$
   (c) $CaO(s) + C(s) \xrightarrow{\Delta}$
   (d) $C(s) + H_2O(g) \xrightarrow{\Delta}$
   (e) $CuO(s) + CO(g) \longrightarrow$

22.69 Write a balanced equation for each of the following reactions: (a) Hydrogen cyanide is formed commercially by passing a mixture of methane, ammonia, and air over a catalyst at 800 °C. Water is a by-product of the reaction. (b) Baking soda reacts with acids to produce carbon dioxide gas. (c) When barium carbonate reacts in air with sulfur dioxide, barium sulfate and carbon dioxide form.

22.70 Write a balanced equation for each of the following reactions: (a) Burning magnesium metal in a carbon dioxide atmosphere reduces the $CO_2$ to carbon. (b) In photosynthesis, solar energy is used to produce glucose ($C_6H_{12}O_6$) and $O_2$ from carbon dioxide and water. (c) When carbonate salts dissolve in water, they produce basic solutions.

22.71 Write the formulas for the following compounds, and indicate the oxidation state of the group 4A element or of boron in each: (a) boric acid, (b) silicon tetrabromide, (c) lead(II) chloride, (d) sodium tetraborate decahydrate (borax), (e) boric oxide, (f) germanium dioxide.

22.72 Write the formulas for the following compounds, and indicate the oxidation state of the group 4A element or of boron in each: (a) silicon dioxide, (b) germanium tetrachloride, (c) sodium borohydride, (d) stannous chloride, (e) diborane, (f) boron trichloride.

22.73 Select the member of group 4A that best fits each description: (a) has the lowest first ionization energy, (b) is found in oxidation states ranging from −4 to +4, (c) is most abundant in Earth's crust.

22.74 Select the member of group 4A that best fits each description: (a) forms chains to the greatest extent, (b) forms the most basic oxide, (c) is a metalloid that can form 2+ ions.

22.75 (a) What is the characteristic geometry about silicon in all silicate minerals? (b) Metasilicic acid has the empirical formula $H_2SiO_3$. Which of the structures shown in Figure 22.34 would you expect metasilicic acid to have?

**22.76** Speculate as to why carbon forms carbonate rather than silicate analogs.

**22.77** (a) How does the structure of diborane ($B_2H_6$) differ from that of ethane ($C_2H_6$)? (b) Explain why diborane adopts the geometry that it does. (c) What is the significance of the statement that the hydrogen atoms in diborane are described as "hydridic"?

# ADDITIONAL EXERCISES

**22.79** In your own words, define the following terms: (a) allotrope, (b) disproportionation, (c) interhalogen, (d) acidic anhydride, (e) condensation reaction, (f) protium.

**22.80** Although the $ClO_4^-$ and $IO_4^-$ ions have been known for a long time, $BrO_4^-$ was not synthesized until 1965. The ion was synthesized by oxidizing the bromate ion with xenon difluoride, producing xenon, hydrofluoric acid, and the perbromate ion. (a) Write the balanced equation for this reaction. (b) What are the oxidation states of Br in the Br-containing species in this reaction?

**22.81** Write a balanced equation for the reaction of each of the following compounds with water: (a) $SO_2(g)$, (b) $Cl_2O_7(g)$, (c) $Na_2O_2(s)$, (d) $BaC_2(s)$, (e) $RbO_2(s)$, (f) $Mg_3N_2(s)$, (g) $NaH(s)$.

**22.82** What is the anhydride for each of the following acids: (a) $H_2SO_4$, (b) $HClO_3$, (c) $HNO_2$, (d) $H_2CO_3$, (e) $H_3PO_4$?

**22.83** Explain why $SO_2$ can be used as a reducing agent but $SO_3$ cannot.

**22.84** A sulfuric acid plant produces a considerable amount of heat. This heat is used to generate electricity, which helps reduce operating costs. The synthesis of $H_2SO_4$ consists of three main chemical processes: (1) oxidation of S to $SO_2$, (2) oxidation of $SO_2$ to $SO_3$, (3) the dissolving of $SO_3$ in $H_2SO_4$ and its reaction with water to form $H_2SO_4$. If the third process produces 130 kJ/mol, how much heat is produced in preparing a mole of $H_2SO_4$ from a mole of S? How much heat is produced in preparing 5000 pounds of $H_2SO_4$?

**22.78** Write a balanced equation for each of the following reactions: (a) Diborane reacts with water to form boric acid and molecular hydrogen. (b) Upon heating, boric acid undergoes a condensation reaction to form tetraboric acid. (c) Boron oxide dissolves in water to give a solution of boric acid.

**22.85** (a) What is the oxidation state of P in $PO_4^{3-}$ and of N in $NO_3^-$? (b) Why doesn't N form a stable $NO_4^{3-}$ ion analogous to P?

**22.86** (a) The $P_4$, $P_4O_6$, and $P_4O_{10}$ molecules have a common structural feature of four P atoms arranged in a tetrahedron (Figures 22.27 and 22.28). Does this mean that the bonding between the P atoms is the same in all these cases? Explain. (b) Sodium trimetaphosphate ($Na_3P_3O_9$) and sodium tetrametaphosphate ($Na_4P_4O_{12}$) are used as water-softening agents. They contain cyclic $P_3O_9^{3-}$ and $P_4O_{12}^{4-}$ ions, respectively. Propose reasonable structures for these ions.

**22.87** Ultrapure germanium, like silicon, is used in semiconductors. Germanium of "ordinary" purity is prepared by the high-temperature reduction of $GeO_2$ with carbon. The Ge is converted to $GeCl_4$ by treatment with $Cl_2$ and then purified by distillation; $GeCl_4$ is then hydrolyzed in water to $GeO_2$ and reduced to the elemental form with $H_2$. The element is then zone refined. Write a balanced chemical equation for each of the chemical transformations in the course of forming ultrapure Ge from $GeO_2$.

**22.88** Hydrogen peroxide is capable of oxidizing (a) hydrazine to $N_2$ and $H_2O$, (b) $SO_2$ to $SO_4^{2-}$, (c) $NO_2^-$ to $NO_3^-$, (d) $H_2S(g)$ to S(s), (e) $Fe^{2+}$ to $Fe^{3+}$. Write a balanced net ionic equation for each of these redox reactions.

# INTEGRATIVE EXERCISES

**[22.89]** (a) How many grams of $H_2$ can be stored in 100.0 kg of the alloy FeTi if the hydride $FeTiH_2$ is formed? (b) What volume does this quantity of $H_2$ occupy at STP? (c) If this quantity of hydrogen was combusted in air to produce liquid water, how much energy could be produced?

**[22.90]** Using the thermochemical data in Table 22.1 and Appendix C, calculate the average Xe—F bond enthalpies in $XeF_2$, $XeF_4$, and $XeF_6$, respectively. What is the significance of the trend in these quantities?

**22.91** Hydrogen gas has a higher fuel value than natural gas on a mass basis but not on a volume basis. Thus, hydrogen is not competitive with natural gas as a fuel transported long distances through pipelines. Calculate the heats of combustion of $H_2$ and $CH_4$ (the principal component of natural gas) (a) per mole of each, (b) per gram of each, (c) per cubic meter of each at STP. Assume $H_2O(l)$ as a product.

**22.92** The solubility of $Cl_2$ in 100 g of water at STP is 310 $cm^3$. Assume that this quantity of $Cl_2$ is dissolved and equilibrated as follows:

$$Cl_2(aq) + H_2O \rightleftharpoons Cl^-(aq) + HClO(aq) + H^+(aq)$$

(a) If the equilibrium constant for this reaction is $4.7 \times 10^{-4}$, calculate the equilibrium concentration of HClO formed. (b) What is the pH of the final solution?

**[22.93]** When ammonium perchlorate decomposes thermally, the products of the reaction are $N_2(g)$, $O_2(g)$, $H_2O(g)$, and HCl(g). (a) Write a balanced equation for the reaction. [*Hint:* You might find it easier to use fractional coefficients for the products.] (b) Calculate the enthalpy change in the reaction per mole of $NH_4ClO_4$. The standard enthalpy of formation of $NH_4ClO_4(s)$ is −295.8 kJ. (c) When $NH_4ClO_4(s)$ is employed in solid-fuel booster rockets, it is packed with powdered aluminum. Given the high temperature needed for $NH_4ClO_4(s)$ decomposition and what the products of the reaction are, what role does the aluminum play? (d) Calculate the volume of all the gases that would be produced at STP, assuming complete reaction of one pound of ammonium perchlorate.

**22.94** The dissolved oxygen present in any highly pressurized, high-temperature steam boiler can be extremely corrosive to its metal parts. Hydrazine, which is completely miscible with water, can be added to remove oxygen by reacting with it to form nitrogen and water. (a) Write the balanced equation for the reaction between gaseous hydrazine and oxygen. **(b)** Calculate the enthalpy change accompanying this reaction. **(c)** Oxygen in air dissolves in water to the extent of 9.1 ppm at 20 °C at sea level. How many grams of hydrazine are required to react with all the oxygen in $3.0 \times 10^4$ L (the volume of a small swimming pool) under these conditions?

**22.95** One method proposed for removing $SO_2$ from the flue gases of power plants involves reaction with aqueous $H_2S$. Elemental sulfur is the product. **(a)** Write a balanced chemical equation for the reaction. **(b)** What volume of $H_2S$ at 27 °C and 760 torr would be required to remove the $SO_2$ formed by burning 2.0 tons of coal containing 3.5% S by mass? **(c)** What mass of elemental sulfur is produced? Assume that all reactions are 100% efficient.

**22.96** The maximum allowable concentration of $H_2S(g)$ in air is 20 mg per kilogram of air (20 ppm by mass). How many grams of FeS would be required to react with hydrochloric acid to produce this concentration at 1.00 atm and 25 °C in an average room measuring 12 ft × 20 ft × 8 ft? (Under these conditions, the average molar mass of air is 29.0 g/mol.)

**22.97** The standard heats of formation of $H_2O(g)$, $H_2S(g)$, $H_2Se(g)$, and $H_2Te(g)$ are −241.8, −20.17, +29.7, and +99.6 kJ/mol, respectively. The enthalpies necessary to convert the elements in their standard states to one mole of gaseous atoms are 248, 277, 227, and 197 kJ/mol of atoms for O, S, Se, and Te, respectively. The enthalpy for dissociation of $H_2$ is 436 kJ/mol. Calculate the average H—O, H—S, H—Se, and H—Te bond enthalpies, and comment on their trend.

**22.98** Manganese silicide has the empirical formula MnSi and melts at 1280 °C. It is insoluble in water but does dissolve in aqueous HF. **(a)** What type of compound do you expect MnSi to be: metallic, molecular, covalent-network, or ionic? **(b)** Write a likely balanced chemical equation for the reaction of MnSi with concentrated aqueous HF.

**[22.99]** Chemists tried for a long time to make molecular compounds containing silicon–silicon double bonds; they finally succeed in 1981. The trick is having large, bulky R groups on the silicon atoms to make $R_2Si$=$SiR_2$ compounds. What experiments could you do to prove that a new compound has a silicon–silicon double bond rather than a silicon–silicon single bond?

**22.100** Hydrazine has been employed as a reducing agent for metals. Using standard reduction potentials, predict whether the following metals can be reduced to the metallic state by hydrazine under standard conditions in acidic solution: **(a)** $Fe^{2+}$, **(b)** $Sn^{2+}$, **(c)** $Cu^{2+}$, **(d)** $Ag^+$, **(e)** $Cr^{3+}$, **(f)** $Co^{3+}$.

**22.101** Both dimethylhydrazine, $(CH_3)_2NNH_2$, and methylhydrazine, $CH_3NHNH_2$, have been used as rocket fuels. When dinitrogen tetroxide ($N_2O_4$) is used as the oxidizer, the products are $H_2O$, $CO_2$, and $N_2$. If the thrust of the rocket depends on the volume of the products produced, which of the substituted hydrazines produces a greater thrust per gram total mass of oxidizer plus fuel? [Assume that both fuels generate the same temperature and that $H_2O(g)$ is formed.]

**22.102** Carbon forms an unusual unstable oxide of formula $C_3O_2$, called carbon suboxide. Carbon suboxide is made by using $P_2O_5$ to dehydrate the dicarboxylic acid called malonic acid, which has the formula $HOOC$—$CH_2$—$COOH$. **(a)** Write a balanced reaction for the production of carbon suboxide from malonic acid. **(b)** How many grams of carbon suboxide could be made from 20.00 g of malonic acid? **(c)** Suggest a Lewis structure for $C_3O_2$. (*Hint:* The Lewis structure of malonic acid suggests which atoms are connected to which.) **(d)** By using the information in Table 8.5, predict the C—C and C—O bond lengths in $C_3O_2$. **(e)** Sketch the Lewis structure of a product that could result by the addition of 2 mol of $H_2$ to 1 mol of $C_3O_2$.

**22.103** Borazine, $(BH)_3(NH)_3$, is an analog of $C_6H_6$, benzene. It can be prepared from the reaction of diborane with ammonia, with hydrogen as another product; or from lithium borohydride and ammonium chloride, with lithium chloride and hydrogen as the other products. **(a)** Write balanced chemical equations for the production of borazine using both synthetic methods. **(b)** Draw the Lewis dot structure of borazine. **(c)** How many grams of borazine can be prepared from 2.00 L of ammonia at STP, assuming diborane is in excess?

**22.104** Throughout history, arsenic(III) oxide, known simply to the general public as "arsenic," has been a poison favored by murderers: It is tasteless, colorless, can be easily added to food or drink, produces symptoms that are similar to several diseases, and until the mid-1800s, was undetectable in the body. James Marsh developed the famous "Marsh test" for arsenic that was instrumental in convicting the murderer in a famous poisoning case in France in 1840. The Marsh test relies on the reaction of arsenic(III) oxide in a sample with elemental zinc and sulfuric acid to produce arsine (an analog of ammonia), zinc sulfate, and water. Upon igniting the final mixture, arsine is oxidized to elemental arsenic, and if captured on a ceramic bowl, a characteristic silvery-black powder would appear. **(a)** Write the balanced chemical equations of the Marsh test. **(b)** Antimony is the only potential interferent, as it reacts similarly to arsenic and produces a similar silvery-black film; however, antimony does not dissolve in a solution of sodium hypochlorite, but arsenic does. Therefore, the completion of the Marsh test is to add a solution of sodium hypochlorite to the elemental arsenic and see if the silvery-black film dissolves. Write the balanced chemical equation for this final reaction. **(c)** Today, commercial kits for arsenic testing rely on a different reaction. The sample is reacted with hydrogen sulfide in the presence of hydrochloric acid; if arsenic is present, $As_2S_3$, which is a bright yellow precipitate, forms. Write the balanced equation for this reaction.

**THIS STAINED GLASS WINDOW,** representing chemistry, is in the Kalamazoo Public Library, Kalamazoo, Michigan.

# TRANSITION METALS AND COORDINATION CHEMISTRY

**THE COLORS OF OUR WORLD ARE** beautiful, but to a chemist they are also informative—providing insights into the structure and bonding of matter. Compounds of the transition metals constitute an important group of colored substances. Some of them are used in paint pigments; others produce the colors in glass and precious gems. For example, the colors in the stained-glass artwork shown in the chapter-opening photograph are due mainly to transition-metal compounds. Why do these compounds have color, and why do the colors change as the ions or molecules bonded to the metal change? The chemistry we explore in this chapter will help us to answer these questions.

In earlier chapters we saw that metal ions can function as Lewis acids, forming covalent bonds with molecules and ions functioning as Lewis bases. ∞ (Section 16.11) We have encountered many ions and compounds that result from such interactions, such as $[Fe(H_2O)_6]^{3+}$ and $[Ag(NH_3)_2]^+$ in Sections 16.11 and 17.5 and hemoglobin in

963

Section 13.6. In this chapter, we focus on the rich and important chemistry associated with such complex assemblies of metal ions surrounded by molecules and ions. Metal compounds of this kind are called *coordination compounds*, and the branch of chemistry that focuses on them is called *coordination chemistry*.

# 23.1 | THE TRANSITION METALS

The part of the periodic table in which the *d* orbitals are being filled as we move left to right across a row is the home of the transition metals (◀ **FIGURE 23.1**). ∞ (Section 6.8)

With some exceptions (e.g., platinum, gold), metallic elements are found in nature as solid inorganic compounds called **minerals**. Notice from ▼ **TABLE 23.1** that minerals are identified by common names rather than chemical names. These common names are usually based on the location where a mineral was discovered, the person who discovered it, or some physical characteristic such as color.

Most transition metals in minerals have oxidation states of +1, +2, or +3. To obtain a pure metal from its mineral, various chemical processes must be performed to reduce the metal to the 0 oxidation state. **Metallurgy** is the science and technology of extracting metals from their natural sources and preparing them for practical use. It usually involves several steps: (1) mining, that is, removing the relevant *ore* (a mixture of minerals) from the ground, (2) concentrating the ore or otherwise preparing it for further treatment, (3) reducing the ore to obtain the free metal, (4) purifying the metal, and (5) mixing it with other elements to modify its properties. This last process produces an *alloy*, a metallic material composed of two or more elements. ∞ (Section 12.3)

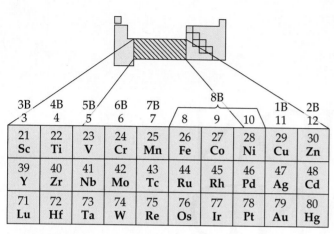

▲ **FIGURE 23.1** **The position of the transition metals in the periodic table.** They are the B groups in periods 4, 5, and 6.

## Physical Properties

Some physical properties of the period 4 (also known as "first-row") transition metals are listed in ▶ **TABLE 23.2**. The properties of the heavier transition metals vary similarly across periods 5 and 6.

▶ **FIGURE 23.2** shows the atomic radius observed in close-packed metallic structures as a function of group number.* The trends seen in the graph are a result of two competing forces. On the one hand, increasing effective nuclear charge favors a decrease

| TABLE 23.1 • Principal Mineral Sources of Some Transition Metals | | |
|---|---|---|
| **Metal** | **Mineral** | **Mineral Composition** |
| Chromium | Chromite | $FeCr_2O_4$ |
| Copper | Chalcocite | $Cu_2S$ |
| | Chalcopyrite | $CuFeS_2$ |
| | Malachite | $Cu_2CO_3(OH)_2$ |
| Iron | Hematite | $Fe_2O_3$ |
| | Magnetite | $Fe_3O_4$ |
| Manganese | Pyrolusite | $MnO_2$ |
| Mercury | Cinnabar | $HgS$ |
| Molybdenum | Molybdenite | $MoS_2$ |
| Titanium | Rutile | $TiO_2$ |
| | Ilmenite | $FeTiO_3$ |
| Zinc | Sphalerite | $ZnS$ |

*Note that the radii defined in this way, often referred to as metallic radii, differ somewhat from the bonding atomic radii defined in Section 7.3.

**TABLE 23.2 • Properties of the Period 4 Transition Metals**

| Group | 3B | 4B | 5B | 6B | 7B | 8B | | | 1B | 2B |
|---|---|---|---|---|---|---|---|---|---|---|
| Element: | Sc | Ti | V | Cr | Mn | Fe | Co | Ni | Cu | Zn |
| Ground state electron configuration | $3d^14s^2$ | $3d^24s^2$ | $3d^34s^2$ | $3d^54s^1$ | $3d^54s^2$ | $3d^64s^2$ | $3d^74s^2$ | $3d^84s^2$ | $3d^{10}4s^1$ | $3d^{10}4s^2$ |
| First ionization energy (kJ/mol) | 631 | 658 | 650 | 653 | 717 | 759 | 758 | 737 | 745 | 906 |
| Radius in metallic substances (Å) | 1.64 | 1.47 | 1.35 | 1.29 | 1.37 | 1.26 | 1.25 | 1.25 | 1.28 | 1.37 |
| Density (g/cm³) | 3.0 | 4.5 | 6.1 | 7.9 | 7.2 | 7.9 | 8.7 | 8.9 | 8.9 | 7.1 |
| Melting point (°C) | 1541 | 1660 | 1917 | 1857 | 1244 | 1537 | 1494 | 1455 | 1084 | 420 |

in radius as we move left to right across each period. ∞(Section 7.2) On the other hand, the metallic bonding strength increases until we reach the middle of each period and then decreases as we fill antibonding orbitals. ∞(Section 12.4) As a general rule, a bond shortens as it becomes stronger. ∞(Section 8.8) For groups 3B through 6B, these two effects work cooperatively and the result is a marked decrease in radius. In elements to the right of group 6B, the two effects counteract each other, reducing the decrease and eventually leading to an increase in radius.

▲ **GIVE IT SOME THOUGHT**

Which element has the largest bonding atomic radius: Sc, Fe, or Au?

In general, atomic radii increase as we move down in a family in the periodic table because of the increasing principal quantum number of the outer-shell electrons. ∞ (Section 7.3) Note in Figure 23.2, however, that once we move beyond the group 3B elements, the period 5 and period 6 transition elements in a given family have virtually the same radii. In group 5B, for example, tantalum in period 6 has virtually the same radius as niobium in period 5. This interesting and important effect has its origin in the lanthanide series, elements 57 through 70. The filling of 4*f* orbitals through the lanthanide elements ∞ (Figure 6.31) causes a steady increase in the effective nuclear charge, producing a size decrease, called the **lanthanide contraction**, that just offsets the increase we expect as we go from period 5 transition metals to period 6. Thus, the period 5 and period 6 transition metals in each group have about the same radii all the way across the periodic table. Consequently, the period 5 and period 6 transition metals in a given group have similar chemical properties. For example, the chemical properties of the group 4B metals zirconium (period 5) and hafnium (period 6) are remarkably similar. These two metals always occur together in nature, and they are very difficult to separate.

▲ **FIGURE 23.2  Radii of transition metals as a function of group number.**

## Electron Configurations and Oxidation States

Transition metals owe their location in the periodic table to the filling of the *d* subshells, as you saw in Figure 6.31. Many of the chemical and physical properties of transition metals result from the unique characteristics of the *d* orbitals. For a given transition-metal atom, the valence $(n-1)d$ orbitals are smaller than the corresponding valence *ns* and *np* orbitals. In quantum mechanical terms, the $(n-1)d$ orbital wave functions drop off more rapidly as we move away from the nucleus than do the *ns* and *np* orbital wave functions. This characteristic feature of the *d* orbitals limits their interaction with orbitals on neighboring atoms, but not so much that they are insensitive to

**GO FIGURE**

In which transition-metal ion of this group are the 3*d* orbitals completely filled?

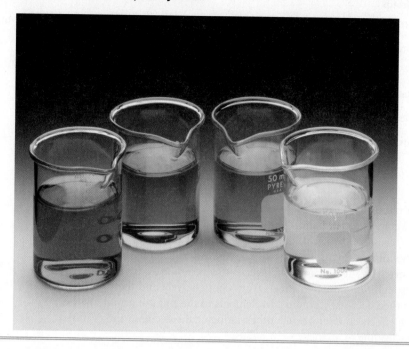

► **FIGURE 23.3  Aqueous solutions of transition metal ions.** Left to right: $Co^{2+}$, $Ni^{2+}$, $Cu^{2+}$, and $Zn^{2+}$. The counterion is nitrate in all cases.

surrounding atoms. As a result, electrons in these orbitals behave sometimes like valence electrons and sometimes like core electrons. The details depend on location in the periodic table and the atom's environment.

When transition metals are oxidized, they lose their outer *s* electrons before they lose electrons from the *d* subshell. ∞ (Section 7.4) The electron configuration of Fe is $[Ar]3d^64s^2$, for example, whereas that of $Fe^{2+}$ is $[Ar]3d^6$. Formation of $Fe^{3+}$ requires loss of one 3*d* electron, giving $[Ar]3d^5$. Most transition-metal ions contain partially occupied *d* subshells, which are responsible in large part for three characteristics:

**1.** Transition metals often have more than one stable oxidation state.

**2.** Many transition-metal compounds are colored, as shown in ▲ **FIGURE 23.3**.

**3.** Transition metals and their compounds often exhibit magnetic properties.

**GO FIGURE**

Why does the maximum oxidation state increase linearly from Sc through Mn?

▲ **FIGURE 23.4  Nonzero oxidation states of the period 4 transition metals.**

◄ **FIGURE 23.4** shows the common nonzero oxidation states for the period 4 transition metals. The +2 oxidation state, which is common for most transition metals, is due to the loss of the two outer 4*s* electrons. This oxidation state is found for all these elements except Sc, where the 3+ ion with an [Ar] configuration is particularly stable.

Oxidation states above +2 are due to successive losses of 3*d* electrons. From Sc through Mn the maximum oxidation state increases from +3 to +7, equaling in each case the total number of 4*s* plus 3*d* electrons in the atom. Thus, manganese has a maximum oxidation state of 2 + 5 = +7. As we move to the right beyond Mn in Figure 23.4, the maximum oxidation state decreases. This decrease is due in part to the attraction of *d* orbital electrons to the nucleus, which increases faster than the attraction of the *s* orbital electrons to the nucleus as we move left to right across the periodic table. In other words, in each period the *d* electrons become more corelike as the atomic number increases. By the time we get to zinc, it is not possible to remove electrons from the 3*d* orbitals through chemical oxidation.

In the transition metals of periods 5 and 6, the increased size of the $4d$ and $5d$ orbitals makes it possible to attain maximum oxidation states as high as +8, which is achieved in $RuO_4$ and $OsO_4$. In general, the maximum oxidation states are found only when the metals are combined with the most electronegative elements, especially O, F, and in some cases Cl.

## GIVE IT SOME THOUGHT

Why doesn't $Ti^{5+}$ exist?

## Magnetism

The spin an electron possesses gives the electron a *magnetic moment*, a property that causes the electron to behave like a tiny magnet. In a *diamagnetic* solid, defined as one in which all the electrons in the solid are paired, the spin-up and spin-down electrons cancel one another. ∞ (Section 9.8) Diamagnetic substances are generally described as being nonmagnetic, but when a diamagnetic substance is placed in a magnetic field, the motions of the electrons cause the substance to be very weakly repelled by the magnet. In other words, these supposedly nonmagnetic substances do show some very faint magnetic character in the presence of a magnetic field.

A substance in which the atoms or ions have one or more unpaired electrons is *paramagnetic*. ∞ (Section 9.8) In a paramagnetic solid, the electrons on one atom or ion do not influence the unpaired electrons on neighboring atoms or ions. As a result, the magnetic moments on the atoms or ions are randomly oriented, as shown in ▶ **FIGURE 23.5**(a). When a paramagnetic substance is placed in a magnetic field, however, the magnetic moments tend to align parallel to one another, producing a net attractive interaction with the magnet. Thus, unlike a diamagnetic substance, which is weakly repulsed by a magnetic field, a paramagnetic substance is attracted to a magnetic field.

When you think of a magnet, you probably picture a simple iron magnet. Iron exhibits **ferromagnetism**, a form of magnetism much stronger than paramagnetism. Ferromagnetism arises when the unpaired electrons of the atoms or ions in a solid are influenced by the orientations of the electrons in neighboring atoms or ions. The most stable (lowest-energy) arrangement is when the spins of electrons on adjacent atoms or ions are aligned in the same direction, as in Figure 23.5(b). When a ferromagnetic solid is placed in a magnetic field, the electrons tend to align strongly in a direction parallel to the magnetic field. The attraction to the magnetic field that results may be as much as one million times stronger than that for a paramagnetic substance.

When a ferromagnet is removed from an external magnetic field, the interactions between the electrons cause the ferromagnetic substance to maintain a magnetic moment. We then refer to it as a *permanent magnet* (▶ **FIGURE 23.6**).

The only ferromagnetic transition metals are Fe, Co, and Ni, but many alloys also exhibit ferromagnetism, which is in some cases stronger than the ferromagnetism of the pure metals. Particularly powerful ferromagnetism is found in compounds containing both transition metals and lanthanide metals. Two of the most important examples are $SmCo_5$ and $Nd_2Fe_{14}B$.

Two additional types of magnetism involving ordered arrangements of unpaired electrons are depicted in Figure 23.5. In materials that exhibit **antiferromagnetism** [Figure 23.5(c)], the unpaired electrons on a given atom or ion align so that their spins are oriented in the direction opposite the spin direction on neighboring atoms.

## GO FIGURE

Describe how the representation shown for the paramagnetic material would have to be changed if the material were placed in a magnetic field.

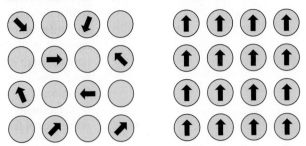

(a) Paramagnetic; spins random; spins do align if in magnetic field

(b) Ferromagnetic; spins aligned; spins become random at high temperature

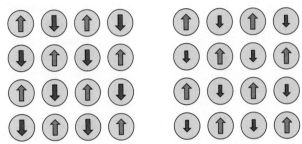

(c) Antiferromagnetic; spins opposed and cancel; spins become random at high temperature

(d) Ferrimagnetic; unequal spins opposed but do not cancel; spins become random at high temperature

▲ **FIGURE 23.5** The relative orientation of electron spins in various types of magnetic substances.

▲ **FIGURE 23.6** **A permanent magnet.** Permanent magnets are made from ferromagnetic and ferrimagnetic materials.

This means that the spin-up and spin-down electrons cancel each other. Examples of antiferromagnetic substances are chromium metal, FeMn alloys, and such transition-metal oxides as $Fe_2O_3$, $LaFeO_3$, and MnO.

A substance that exhibits **ferrimagnetism** [Figure 23.5(d)] has both ferromagnetic and antiferromagnetic properties. Like an antiferromagnet, the unpaired electrons align so that the spins in adjacent atoms or ions point in opposite directions. However, unlike an antiferromagnet, the net magnetic moments of the spin-up electrons are not fully canceled by the spin-down electrons. This can happen because the magnetic centers have different numbers of unpaired electrons ($NiMnO_3$), because the number of magnetic sites aligned in one direction is larger than the number aligned in the other direction ($Y_3Fe_5O_{12}$), or because both these conditions apply ($Fe_3O_4$). Because the magnetic moments do not cancel, the properties of ferrimagnetic materials are similar to the properties of ferromagnetic materials.

### GIVE IT SOME THOUGHT

How do you think spin-spin interactions of unpaired electrons on adjacent atoms in a substance are affected by the interatomic distance?

Ferromagnets, ferrimagnets, and antiferromagnets all become paramagnetic when heated above a critical temperature. This happens when the thermal energy is sufficient to overcome the forces determining the spin directions of the electrons. This temperature is called the *Curie temperature*, $T_C$, for ferromagnets and ferrimagnets and the *Néel temperature*, $T_N$, for antiferromagnets.

## 23.2 | TRANSITION-METAL COMPLEXES

The transition metals occur in many interesting and important molecular forms. Species that are assemblies of a central transition-metal ion bonded to a group of surrounding molecules or ions, such as $[Ag(NH_3)_2]^+$ and $[Fe(H_2O)_6]^{3+}$, are called **metal complexes**, or merely *complexes*.* If the complex carries a net charge, it is generally called a *complex ion*. ∞ (Section 17.5) Compounds that contain complexes are known as **coordination compounds**.

The molecules or ions that bond to the metal ion in a complex are known as **ligands** (from the Latin word *ligare*, "to bind"). There are two $NH_3$ ligands bonded to $Ag^+$ in the complex ion $[Ag(NH_3)_2]^+$, for instance, and six $H_2O$ ligands bonded to $Fe^{3+}$ in $[Fe(H_2O)_6]^{3+}$. Each ligand functions as a Lewis base and so donates a pair of electrons to form the ligand–metal bond. ∞ (Section 16.11) Thus, every ligand has at least one unshared pair of valence electrons. Four of the most frequently encountered ligands,

illustrate that most ligands are either polar molecules or anions. In forming a complex, the ligands are said to *coordinate* to the metal.

### GIVE IT SOME THOUGHT

Is the interaction between an ammonia ligand and a metal cation a Lewis acid–base interaction? If so, which species acts as the Lewis acid?

*Most of the coordination compounds we examine in this chapter contain transition-metal ions, although ions of other metals can also form complexes.

**TABLE 23.3 • Properties of Some Ammonia Complexes of Cobalt(III)**

| Original Formulation | Color | Ions per Formula Unit | "Free" Cl⁻ Ions per Formula Unit | Modern Formulation |
|---|---|---|---|---|
| $CoCl_3 \cdot 6\,NH_3$ | Orange | 4 | 3 | $[Co(NH_3)_6]Cl_3$ |
| $CoCl_3 \cdot 5\,NH_3$ | Purple | 3 | 2 | $[Co(NH_3)_5Cl]Cl_2$ |
| $CoCl_3 \cdot 4\,NH_3$ | Green | 2 | 1 | $trans\text{-}[Co(NH_3)_4Cl_2]Cl$ |
| $CoCl_3 \cdot 4\,NH_3$ | Violet | 2 | 1 | $cis\text{-}[Co(NH_3)_4Cl_2]Cl$ |

## The Development of Coordination Chemistry: Werner's Theory

Because compounds of the transition metals are beautifully colored, the chemistry of these elements fascinated chemists even before the periodic table was introduced. During the late 1700s through the 1800s, the many coordination compounds that were isolated and studied had properties that were puzzling in light of the bonding theories prevailing at the time. ▲ TABLE 23.3, for example, lists a series of $CoCl_3$-$NH_3$ compounds that have strikingly different colors. Note that the third and fourth species have different colors even though the originally assigned formula was the same for both, $CoCl_3 \cdot 4\,NH_3$.

The modern formulations of the compounds in Table 23.3 are based on various lines of experimental evidence. For example, all four compounds are strong electrolytes ∞ (Section 4.1) but yield different numbers of ions when dissolved in water. Dissolving $CoCl_3 \cdot 6\,NH_3$ in water yields four ions per formula unit ($[Co(NH_3)_6]^{3+}$ plus three $Cl^-$ ions), whereas $CoCl_3 \cdot 5\,NH_3$ yields only three ions per formula unit ($[Co(NH_3)_5Cl]^{2+}$ and two $Cl^-$ ions). Furthermore, the reaction of the compounds with excess aqueous silver nitrate leads to the precipitation of different amounts of $AgCl(s)$. When $CoCl_3 \cdot 6\,NH_3$ is treated with excess $AgNO_3(aq)$, 3 mol of $AgCl(s)$ are produced per mole of complex, which means all three $Cl^-$ ions in the complex can react to form $AgCl(s)$. By contrast, when $CoCl_3 \cdot 5\,NH_3$ is treated with excess $AgNO_3(aq)$, only 2 mol of $AgCl(s)$ precipitate per mole of complex, telling us that one of the $Cl^-$ ions in the complex does not react. These results are summarized in Table 23.3.

In 1893 the Swiss chemist Alfred Werner (1866–1919) proposed a theory that successfully explained the observations in Table 23.3. In a theory that became the basis for understanding coordination chemistry, Werner proposed that any metal ion exhibits both a primary valence and a secondary valence. The *primary valence* is the oxidation state of the metal, which is +3 for the complexes in Table 23.3. ∞ (Section 4.4) The *secondary valence* is the number of atoms bonded to the metal ion, which is also called the **coordination number**. For these cobalt complexes, Werner deduced a coordination number of 6 with the ligands in an octahedral arrangement around the $Co^{3+}$ ion.

Werner's theory provided a beautiful explanation for the results in Table 23.3. The $NH_3$ molecules are ligands bonded to the $Co^{3+}$ ion; if there are fewer than six $NH_3$ molecules, the remaining ligands are $Cl^-$ ions. The central metal and the ligands bound to it constitute the **coordination sphere** of the complex.

In writing the chemical formula for a coordination compound, Werner suggested using square brackets to signify the makeup of the coordination sphere in any given compound. He therefore proposed that $CoCl_3 \cdot 6\,NH_3$ and $CoCl_3 \cdot 5\,NH_3$ are better written as $[Co(NH_3)_6]Cl_3$ and $[Co(NH_3)_5Cl]Cl_2$, respectively. He further proposed that the chloride ions that are part of the coordination sphere are bound so tightly that they do not dissociate when the complex is dissolved in water. Thus, dissolving $[Co(NH_3)_5Cl]Cl_2$ in water produces a $[Co(NH_3)_5Cl]^{2+}$ ion and two $Cl^-$ ions.

Werner's ideas also explained why there are two forms of $CoCl_3 \cdot 4\,NH_3$. Using Werner's postulates, we write the formula as $[Co(NH_3)_4Cl_2]Cl$. As shown in ▶ FIGURE 23.7, there are two ways to arrange the ligands in the $[Co(NH_3)_4Cl_2]^+$ complex, called the cis and trans forms. In the *cis* form, the two chloride ligands occupy adjacent vertices

► **FIGURE 23.7 Isomers of [Co(NH₃)₄Cl₂]⁺.** The cis isomer is violet, and the trans isomer is green.

of the octahedral arrangement. In *trans*-$[Co(NH_3)_4Cl_2]^+$ the two chlorides are opposite each other. It is this difference in positions of the Cl ligands that leads to two compounds, one violet and one green.

The insight Werner provided into the bonding in coordination compounds is even more remarkable when we realize that his theory predated Lewis's ideas of covalent bonding by more than 20 years! Because of his tremendous contributions to coordination chemistry, Werner was awarded the 1913 Nobel Prize in Chemistry.

---

**SAMPLE EXERCISE 23.1** **Identifying the Coordination Sphere of a Complex**

Palladium(II) tends to form complexes with coordination number 4. A compound has the composition $PdCl_2 \cdot 3\, NH_3$. **(a)** Write the formula for this compound that best shows the coordination structure. **(b)** When an aqueous solution of the compound is treated with excess $AgNO_3(aq)$, how many moles of $AgCl(s)$ are formed per mole of $PdCl_2 \cdot 3\, NH_3$?

**SOLUTION**

**Analyze** We are given the coordination number of Pd(II) and a chemical formula indicating that the complex contains $NH_3$ and $Cl^-$. We are asked to determine **(a)** which ligands are attached to Pd(II) in the compound and **(b)** how the compound behaves toward $AgNO_3$ in aqueous solution.

**Plan** **(a)** Because of their charge, the $Cl^-$ ions can be either in the coordination sphere, where they are bonded directly to the metal, or outside the coordination sphere, where they are bonded ionically to the complex. The electrically neutral $NH_3$ ligands must be in the coordination sphere, if we assume four ligands bonded to the Pd(II) ion. **(b)** Any chlorides in the coordination sphere do not precipitate as AgCl.

**Solve**

**(a)** By analogy to the ammonia complexes of cobalt(III) shown in Figure 23.7, we predict that the three $NH_3$ are ligands attached to the Pd(II) ion. The fourth ligand around Pd(II) is one chloride ion. The second chloride ion is not a ligand; it serves only as a *counterion* (a noncoordinating ion that balances charge) in the compound. We conclude that the formula showing the structure best is $[Pd(NH_3)_3Cl]Cl$.

**(b)** Because only the non-ligand $Cl^-$ can react, we expect to produce 1 mol of $AgCl(s)$ per mole of complex. The balanced equation is

$$[Pd(NH_3)_3Cl]Cl(aq) + AgNO_3(aq) \longrightarrow [Pd(NH_3)_3Cl]NO_3(aq) + AgCl(s)$$

This is a metathesis reaction ∞ (Section 4.2) in which one of the cations is the $[Pd(NH_3)_3Cl]^+$ complex ion.

### PRACTICE EXERCISE

Predict the number of ions produced per formula unit in an aqueous solution of $CoCl_2 \cdot 6\,H_2O$.

***Answer:*** three: $[Co(H_2O)_6]^{2+}$ and two $Cl^-$

## The Metal–Ligand Bond

The bond between a ligand and a metal ion is a Lewis acid–base interaction. Because the ligands have available pairs of electrons, they can function as Lewis bases (electron-pair donors). Metal ions (particularly transition-metal ions) have empty valence orbitals, so they can act as Lewis acids (electron-pair acceptors). We can picture the bond between the metal ion and ligand as the result of their sharing a pair of electrons initially on the ligand:

$$Ag^+(aq) + 2\ :\!\!\underset{\underset{H}{|}}{\overset{\overset{H}{|}}{N}}\!\!-\!\!H(aq) \longrightarrow \left[ H\!-\!\underset{\underset{H}{|}}{\overset{\overset{H}{|}}{N}}\!:\!Ag\!:\!\underset{\underset{H}{|}}{\overset{\overset{H}{|}}{N}}\!-\!H \right]^+ (aq) \qquad [23.1]$$

The formation of metal–ligand bonds can markedly alter the properties we observe for the metal ion. A metal complex is a distinct chemical species that has physical and chemical properties different from those of the metal ion and ligands from which it is formed. As one example, ▼ FIGURE 23.8 shows the color change that occurs when aqueous solutions of $NCS^-$ (colorless) and $Fe^{3+}$ (yellow) are mixed, forming $[Fe(H_2O)_5NCS]^{2+}$.

Complex formation can also significantly change other properties of metal ions, such as their ease of oxidation or reduction. Silver ion, for example, is readily reduced in water,

$$Ag^+(aq) + e^- \longrightarrow Ag(s) \qquad E° = +0.799\ V \qquad [23.2]$$

but the $[Ag(CN)_2]^-$ ion is not so easily reduced because complexation by $CN^-$ ions stabilizes silver in the $+1$ oxidation state:

$$[Ag(CN)_2]^-(aq) + e^- \longrightarrow Ag(s) + 2\ CN^-(aq) \qquad E° = -0.31\ V \qquad [23.3]$$

Hydrated metal ions are complexes in which the ligand is water. Thus, $Fe^{3+}(aq)$ consists largely of $[Fe(H_2O)_6]^{3+}$. ∞ (Section 16.11) It is important to realize that

NH₄NCS(aq) solution

[Fe(H₂O)₆]³⁺(aq) solution

Red [Fe(H₂O)₅NCS]²⁺ forms

◀ **FIGURE 23.8  Reaction of $Fe^{3+}(aq)$ and $NCS^-(aq)$.**

ligands can undergo reaction. For example, we saw in Figure 16.16 that a water molecule in $[Fe(H_2O)_6]^{3+}(aq)$ can be deprotonated to yield $[Fe(H_2O)_5OH]^{2+}(aq)$ and $H^+(aq)$. The iron ion retains its oxidation state; the coordinated hydroxide ligand, with a 1− charge, reduces the complex charge to 2+. Ligands can also be displaced from the coordination sphere by other ligands, if the incoming ligands bind more strongly to the metal ion than the original ones. For example, ligands such as $NH_3$, $NCS^-$, and $CN^-$ can replace $H_2O$ in the coordination sphere of metal ions.

### ▲ GIVE IT SOME THOUGHT

Write a balanced chemical equation for the reaction that causes the color change in Figure 23.8.

## Charges, Coordination Numbers, and Geometries

The charge of a complex is the sum of the charges on the metal and on the ligands. In $[Cu(NH_3)_4]SO_4$ we can deduce the charge on the complex ion because we know that the charge of the sulfate ion is 2−. Because the compound is electrically neutral, the complex ion must have a 2+ charge, $[Cu(NH_3)_4]^{2+}$. We can then use the charge of the complex ion to deduce the oxidation number of copper. Because the $NH_3$ ligands are uncharged molecules, the oxidation number of copper must be +2:

$$+2 + 4(0) = +2$$
$$[Cu(NH_3)_4]^{2+}$$

---

**SAMPLE EXERCISE 23.2** | **Determining the Oxidation Number of a Metal in a Complex**

What is the oxidation number of the metal in $[Rh(NH_3)_5Cl](NO_3)_2$?

### SOLUTION

**Analyze** We are given the chemical formula of a coordination compound and asked to determine the oxidation number of its metal atom.

**Plan** To determine the oxidation number of Rh, we need to figure out what charges are contributed by the other groups. The overall charge is zero, so the oxidation number of the metal must balance the charge due to the rest of the compound.

**Solve** The $NO_3$ group is the nitrate anion, which has a 1− charge. The $NH_3$ ligands carry zero charge, and the Cl is a coordinated chloride ion, which has a 1− charge. The sum of all the charges must be zero:

$$x + 5(0) + (-1) + 2(-1) = 0$$
$$[Rh(NH_3)_5Cl](NO_3)_2$$

The oxidation number of rhodium, $x$, must therefore be +3.

### PRACTICE EXERCISE

What is the charge of the complex formed by a platinum(II) metal ion surrounded by two ammonia molecules and two bromide ions?

**Answer:** zero

---

**SAMPLE EXERCISE 23.3** | **Determining the Formula of a Complex Ion**

A complex ion contains a chromium(III) bound to four water molecules and to two chloride ions. What is the formula and charge of this ion?

### SOLUTION

**Analyze** We are given a metal, its oxidation number, and the number of ligands of each kind in a complex ion containing the metal, and we are asked to write the chemical formula and charge of the ion.

**Plan** We write the metal first, then the ligands. We can use the charges of the metal ion and ligands to determine the charge of the complex ion. The oxidation state of the metal is +3, water has no charge, and chloride has a 1− charge.

**Solve**

$$+3 + 4(0) + 2(-1) = +1$$
$$Cr(H_2O)_4Cl_2$$

The charge on the ion is 1+, $[Cr(H_2O)_4Cl_2]^+$.

**PRACTICE EXERCISE**

Write the formula for the complex described in the Practice Exercise accompanying Sample Exercise 23.2.

**Answer:** $[Pt(NH_3)_2Br_2]$

Recall that the number of atoms directly bonded to the metal atom in a complex is the *coordination number* of the complex. Thus, the silver ion in $[Ag(NH_3)_2]^+$ has a coordination number of 2, and the cobalt ion has a coordination number of 6 in all four complexes in Table 23.3.

Some metal ions have only one observed coordination number. The coordination number of chromium(III) and cobalt(III) is invariably 6, for example, and that of platinum(II) is always 4. For most metals, however, the coordination number is different for different ligands. In these complexes, the most common coordination numbers are 4 and 6.

The coordination number of a metal ion is often influenced by the relative sizes of the metal ion and the ligands. As the ligand gets larger, fewer of them can coordinate to the metal ion. Thus, iron(III) is able to coordinate to six fluorides in $[FeF_6]^{3-}$ but to only four chlorides in $[FeCl_4]^-$.

Ligands that transfer substantial negative charge to the metal also produce reduced coordination numbers. For example, six ammonia molecules can coordinate to nickel(II), forming $[Ni(NH_3)_6]^{2+}$, but only four cyanide ions can coordinate to this ion, forming $[Ni(CN)_4]^{2-}$.

Complexes in which the coordination number is 4 have two common geometries—tetrahedral and square planar (▶ **FIGURE 23.9**). The tetrahedral geometry is the more common of the two and is especially common among nontransition metals. The square-planar geometry is characteristic of transition-metal ions with eight *d* electrons in the valence shell, such as platinum(II) and gold(III).

The vast majority of complexes in which the coordination number is 6 have an octahedral geometry. The octahedron, which has eight faces and six vertices, is often represented as a square with ligands above and below the plane, as in ▼ **FIGURE 23.10**. Recall, however, that all six vertices on an octahedron are geometrically equivalent.

**GO FIGURE**

**What is the size of the NH$_3$-Zn-NH$_3$ bond angle? Of the NH$_3$-Pt-NH$_3$ bond angle?**

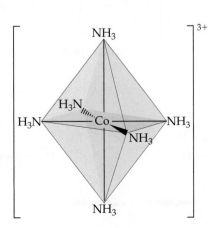

tetrahedral        square planar

▲ **FIGURE 23.9   In complexes having coordination number 4, the molecular geometry can be tetrahedral or square planar.**

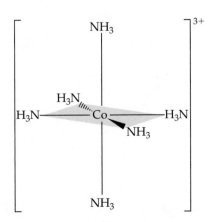

◀ **FIGURE 23.10   In complexes having coordination number 6, the molecular geometry is almost always octahedral.** Two ways to draw octahedral geometry are shown.

(Section 9.2) The octahedron can also be thought of as two square pyramids that share the same square base.

### ▲ GIVE IT SOME THOUGHT

What are the geometries most commonly associated with
**a.** coordination number 4,
**b.** coordination number 6?

## 23.3 | COMMON LIGANDS IN COORDINATION CHEMISTRY

The ligand atom that binds to the central metal ion in a coordination complex is called the **donor atom** of the ligand. Ligands having only one donor atom are called **monodentate ligands** (from the Latin, meaning "one-toothed"). These ligands are able to occupy only one site in a coordination sphere. Ligands having two donor atoms are **bidentate ligands** ("two-toothed"), and those having three or more donor atoms are **polydentate ligands** ("many-toothed"). In both bidentate and polydentate species, the multiple donor atoms can simultaneously bond to the metal ion, thereby occupying two or more sites in a coordination sphere. ▼ TABLE 23.4 gives examples of all three types of ligands.

Because they appear to grasp the metal between two or more donor atoms, bidentate and polydentate ligands are also known as **chelating agents** (pronounced "KEE-lay-ting"; from the Greek *chele*, "claw").

**TABLE 23.4 • Some Common Ligands**

| Ligand Type | Examples |
|---|---|
| Monodentate | $H_2\overset{..}{O}:$ Water    $:\overset{..}{\underset{..}{F}}:^-$ Fluoride ion    $[:C\equiv N:]^-$ Cyanide ion    $[:\overset{..}{\underset{..}{O}}-H]^-$ Hydroxide ion |
|  | $:NH_3$ Ammonia    $:\overset{..}{\underset{..}{Cl}}:^-$ Chloride ion    $[:\overset{..}{\underset{..}{S}}=C=\overset{..}{N}:]^-$ Thiocyanate ion    $[:\overset{..}{\underset{..}{O}}-N=\overset{..}{O}:]^-$ Nitrite ion |

Bidentate:

$$H_2C-CH_2$$
$$H_2N \qquad NH_2$$
Ethylenediamine (en)

Bipyridine (bipy or bpy) — N, N

*Ortho*-phenanthroline (*o*-phen) — N, N

Oxalate ion $\left[\begin{array}{c}:\overset{..}{O}: \quad :\overset{..}{O}: \\ C-C \\ :\overset{..}{O}: \quad :\overset{..}{O}:\end{array}\right]^{2-}$

Carbonate ion $\left[\begin{array}{c}:O: \\ C \\ :\overset{..}{O}: \quad :\overset{..}{O}:\end{array}\right]^{2-}$

Polydentate:

$$H_2C-CH_2 \quad CH_2-CH_2$$
$$H_2N \qquad NH \qquad NH_2$$
Diethylenetriamine

Triphosphate ion
$$\left[:\overset{..}{\underset{..}{O}}-\overset{\overset{:O:}{\|}}{P}-\overset{..}{\underset{..}{O}}-\overset{\overset{:O:}{\|}}{P}-\overset{..}{\underset{..}{O}}-\overset{\overset{:O:}{\|}}{P}-\overset{..}{\underset{..}{O}}:\right]^{5-}$$

Ethylenediaminetetraacetate ion (EDTA$^{4-}$)
$$\left[\begin{array}{c} :\overset{..}{\underset{..}{O}}-\overset{\overset{:O:}{\|}}{C}-CH_2 \qquad\qquad CH_2-\overset{\overset{:O:}{\|}}{C}-\overset{..}{\underset{..}{O}}: \\ \overset{..}{N}-CH_2-CH_2-\overset{..}{N} \\ :\overset{..}{\underset{..}{O}}-\overset{\underset{\|}{C}}{\underset{:O:}{C}}-CH_2 \qquad\qquad CH_2-\overset{\underset{\|}{C}}{\underset{:O:}{C}}-\overset{..}{\underset{..}{O}}: \end{array}\right]^{4-}$$

$$[Co(en)_3]^{3+}$$

◀ **FIGURE 23.11 The [Co(en)₃]³⁺ ion.** The ligand is ethylenediamine.

One common chelating agent is the bidentate ligand *ethylenediamine,* en:

$$\underset{H_2\ddot{N}}{\overset{CH_2{-}CH_2}{}}\overset{}{\ddot{N}H_2}$$

in which each donor nitrogen atom has one nonbonding electron pair. These donor atoms are sufficiently far apart to allow both of them to bond to the metal ion in adjacent positions. The $[Co(en)_3]^{3+}$ complex ion, which contains three ethylenediamine ligands in the octahedral coordination sphere of cobalt(III), is shown in ▲ **FIGURE 23.11.** Notice that in the image on the right the en is written in a shorthand notation as two nitrogen atoms connected by an arc.

The ethylenediaminetetraacetate ion, $[EDTA]^{4-}$, is an important polydentate ligand that has six donor atoms. It can wrap around a metal ion using all six donor atoms, as shown in ▶ **FIGURE 23.12,** although it sometimes binds to a metal using only five of its donor atoms.

In general, the complexes formed by chelating ligands (that is, bidentate and polydentate ligands) are more stable than the complexes formed by related monodentate ligands. The equilibrium formation constants for $[Ni(NH_3)_6]^{2+}$ and $[Ni(en)_3]^{2+}$ illustrate this observation:

$$[Ni(H_2O)_6]^{2+}(aq) + 6\,NH_3(aq) \rightleftharpoons [Ni(NH_3)_6]^{2+}(aq) + 6\,H_2O(l)$$
$$K_f = 1.2 \times 10^9 \qquad [23.4]$$

$$[Ni(H_2O)_6]^{2+}(aq) + 3\,en(aq) \rightleftharpoons [Ni(en)_3]^{2+}(aq) + 6\,H_2O(l)$$
$$K_f = 6.8 \times 10^{17} \qquad [23.5]$$

Although the donor atom is nitrogen in both instances, $[Ni(en)_3]^{2+}$ has a formation constant that is more than $10^8$ times larger than that of $[Ni(NH_3)_6]^{2+}$. This trend of generally larger formation constants for bidentate and polydentate ligands, known as the **chelate effect,** is examined in the "A Closer Look" essay on page 977.

Chelating agents are often used to prevent one or more of the customary reactions of a metal ion without removing the ion from solution. For example, a metal ion that interferes with a chemical analysis can often be complexed and its interference thereby removed. In a sense, the chelating agent hides the metal ion. For this reason, scientists sometimes refer to these ligands as *sequestering agents.*

Phosphate ligands, such as sodium tripolyphosphate, $Na_5[OPO_2OPO_2OPO_3]$, are used to sequester $Ca^{2+}$ and $Mg^{2+}$ ions in hard water so that these ions cannot interfere with the action of soap or detergents.

Chelating agents are used in many prepared foods, such as salad dressings and frozen desserts, to complex trace metal ions that catalyze decomposition reactions. Chelating agents are used in medicine to remove toxic heavy metal ions that have been ingested, such as $Hg^{2+}$, $Pb^{2+}$, and $Cd^{2+}$. One method of treating lead poisoning, for example, is to administer $Na_2[Ca(EDTA)]$. The EDTA chelates the lead, allowing it to be removed from the body via urine.

$$[EDTA]^{4-}$$

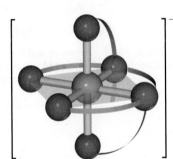

▲ **FIGURE 23.12 The EDTA⁴⁻ ligand (top) and the complex ion [Co(EDTA)]⁻ (bottom).** The ligand is the polydentate ethylenediaminetetraacetate ion, which has six donor atoms, two N and four O.

GO FIGURE

**What is the coordination number of the metal ion in heme b? In chlorophyll a?**

Porphine

Heme b

Chlorophyll a

▲ FIGURE 23.13 **Porphine and two porphyrins, heme b and chlorophyll a.** Fe(II) and Mg(II) ions replace the two blue H atoms in porphine and bond with all four nitrogens in heme b and chlorophyll a, respectively.

▲ GIVE IT SOME THOUGHT

Cobalt(III) has a coordination number of 6 in all its complexes. Is the carbonate ion a monodentate or bidentate ligand in the $[Co(NH_3)_4CO_3]^+$ ion?

## Metals and Chelates in Living Systems

Ten of the 29 elements known to be necessary for human life are transition metals. ∞ (Section 2.7, "Chemistry and Life: Elements Required by Living Organisms") These ten elements—V, Cr, Mn, Fe, Co, Ni, Cu, Zn, Mo, and Cd—form complexes with a variety of groups present in biological systems.

Although our bodies require only small quantities of metals, deficiencies can lead to serious illness. A deficiency of manganese, for example, can lead to convulsive disorders. Some epilepsy patients have been helped by the addition of manganese to their diets.

Among the most important chelating agents in nature are those derived from the *porphine* molecule (◀ FIGURE 23.13). This molecule can coordinate to a metal via its four nitrogen donor atoms. Once porphine bonds to a metal ion, the two H atoms on the nitrogens are displaced to form complexes called **porphyrins**. Two important porphyrins are *hemes*, in which the metal ion is Fe(II), and *chlorophylls*, with a Mg(II) central ion.

▼ FIGURE 23.14 shows a schematic structure of myoglobin, a protein that contains one heme group. Myoglobin is a *globular protein*, one that folds into a compact, roughly spherical shape. Myoglobin is found in the cells of skeletal muscle, particularly in seals, whales, and porpoises. It stores oxygen in cells, one molecule of $O_2$ per myoglobin, until it is needed for metabolic activities. Hemoglobin, the protein that transports oxygen in human blood, is made up of four heme-containing subunits, each of which is very similar to myoglobin. One hemoglobin can bind up to four $O_2$ molecules.

In both myoglobin and hemoglobin, the iron is coordinated to the four nitrogen atoms of a porphyrin and to a nitrogen atom from the protein chain (▶ FIGURE 23.15). In hemoglobin, the sixth position around the iron is occupied either by $O_2$ (in oxyhemoglobin, the

Heme

▲ FIGURE 23.14 **Myoglobin.** This ribbon diagram does not show most of the atoms.

bright red form) or by water (in deoxyhemoglobin, the purplish red form). (The oxy form is the one shown in Figure 23.15.)

Carbon monoxide is poisonous because the equilibrium binding constant of human hemoglobin for CO is about 210 times greater than that for $O_2$. As a result, a relatively small quantity of CO can inactivate a substantial fraction of the hemoglobin in the blood. For example, a person breathing air that contains only 0.1% CO takes in enough CO after a few hours to convert up to 60% of the hemoglobin (Hb) into COHb, thereby reducing the blood's normal oxygen-carrying capacity by 60%.

Under normal conditions, a nonsmoker breathing unpolluted air has about 0.3 to 0.5% COHb in her or his blood. This amount arises mainly from the production of small quantities of CO in the course of normal body chemistry and from the small amount of CO present in clean air. Exposure to higher concentrations of CO causes the COHb level to increase, which in turn leaves fewer Hb sites to which $O_2$ can bind. If the level of COHb becomes too high, oxygen transport is effectively shut down and death occurs. Because CO is colorless and odorless, CO poisoning occurs with very little warning. Improperly ventilated combustion devices, such as kerosene lanterns and stoves, thus pose a potential health hazard.

## GO FIGURE

**Where would CO bind in this molecule?**

▲ **FIGURE 23.15 Coordination sphere of the hemes in oxymyoglobin and oxyhemoglobin.**

## A CLOSER LOOK

### ENTROPY AND THE CHELATE EFFECT

We learned in Section 19.5 that chemical processes are favored by positive entropy changes and by negative enthalpy changes. The special stability associated with the formation of chelates, called the *chelate effect*, can be explained by comparing the entropy changes that occur with monodentate ligands with the entropy changes that occur with polydentate ligands.

We begin with the reaction in which two $H_2O$ ligands of the square-planar Cu(II) complex $[Cu(H_2O)_4]^{2+}$ are replaced by monodentate $NH_3$ ligands at 27 °C:

$$[Cu(H_2O)_4]^{2+}(aq) + 2 NH_3(aq) \rightleftharpoons$$
$$[Cu(H_2O)_2(NH_3)_2]^{2+}(aq) + 2 H_2O(l)$$
$$\Delta H° = -46 \text{ kJ}; \quad \Delta S° = -8.4 \text{ J/K}; \quad \Delta G° = -43 \text{ kJ}$$

The thermodynamic data tell us about the relative abilities of $H_2O$ and $NH_3$ to serve as ligands in this reaction. In general, $NH_3$ binds more tightly to metal ions than does $H_2O$, so this substitution reaction is exothermic ($\Delta H < 0$). The stronger bonding of the $NH_3$ ligands also causes the $[Cu(H_2O)_2(NH_3)_2]^{2+}$ ion to be more rigid, which is probably the reason $\Delta S°$ is slightly negative.

We can use Equation 19.20, $\Delta G° = -RT \ln K$, to calculate the equilibrium constant of the reaction at 27 °C. The result, $K = 3.1 \times 10^7$, tells us that the equilibrium lies far to the right, favoring replacement of $H_2O$ by $NH_3$. For this equilibrium, therefore, the enthalpy change, $\Delta H° = -46$ kJ, is large enough and negative enough to overcome the entropy change, $\Delta S° = -8.4$ J/K.

Now let's use a single bidentate ethylenediamine ligand in our substitution reaction:

$$[Cu(H_2O)_4]^{2+}(aq) + en(aq) \rightleftharpoons$$
$$[Cu(H_2O)_2(en)]^{2+}(aq) + 2 H_2O(l)$$
$$\Delta H° = -54 \text{ kJ}; \Delta S° = +23 \text{ J/K}; \Delta G° = -61 \text{ kJ}$$

The en ligand binds slightly more strongly to the $Cu^{2+}$ ion than two $NH_3$ ligands, so the enthalpy change here ($-54$ kJ) is slightly more

negative than for $[Cu(H_2O)_2(NH_3)_2]^{2+}$ ($-46$ kJ). There is a big difference in the entropy change, however: $\Delta S°$ is $-8.4$ J/K for the $NH_3$ reaction but $+23$ J/K for the en reaction. We can explain the positive $\Delta S°$ value by using concepts discussed in Section 19.3. Because a single en ligand occupies two coordination sites, two molecules of $H_2O$ are released when one en ligand bonds. Thus, there are three product molecules in the reaction but only two reactant molecules. The greater number of product molecules leads to the positive entropy change for the equilibrium.

The slightly more negative value of $\Delta H°$ for the en reaction ($-54$ kJ versus $-46$ kJ) coupled with the positive entropy change leads to a much more negative value of $\Delta G°$ ($-61$ kJ for en, $-43$ for $NH_3$) and a correspondingly larger equilibrium constant: $K = 4.2 \times 10^{10}$.

We can combine our two equations using Hess's law ∞ (Section 5.6) to calculate the enthalpy, entropy, and free-energy changes that occur for en to replace ammonia as ligands on Cu(II):

$$[Cu(H_2O)_2(NH_3)_2]^{2+}(aq) + en(aq) \rightleftharpoons$$
$$[Cu(H_2O)_2(en)]^{2+}(aq) + 2 NH_3(aq)$$
$$\Delta H° = (-54 \text{ kJ}) - (-46 \text{ kJ}) = -8 \text{ kJ}$$
$$\Delta S° = (+23 \text{ J/K}) - (-8.4 \text{ J/K}) = +31 \text{ J/K}$$
$$\Delta G° = (-61 \text{ kJ}) - (-43 \text{ kJ}) = -18 \text{ kJ}$$

Notice that at 27 °C, the entropic contribution ($-T\Delta S°$) to the free-energy change, $\Delta G° = \Delta H° - T\Delta S°$ (Equation 19.12), is negative and greater in magnitude than the enthalpic contribution ($\Delta H°$). The equilibrium constant for the $NH_3$–en reaction, $1.4 \times 10^3$, shows that the replacement of $NH_3$ by en is thermodynamically favorable.

The chelate effect is important in biochemistry and molecular biology. The additional thermodynamic stabilization provided by entropy effects helps stabilize biological metal–chelate complexes, such as porphyrins, and can allow changes in the oxidation state of the metal ion while retaining the structural integrity of the complex.

*RELATED EXERCISES:* 23.31, 23.32, 23.33, 23.98

**Which peak in this curve corresponds to the lowest-energy transition by an electron in a chlorophyll molecule?**

▲ **FIGURE 23.16** **The absorption of sunlight by chlorophyll.**

The **chlorophylls**, which are porphyrins that contain Mg(II) (Figure 23.13), are the key components in the conversion of solar energy into forms that can be used by living organisms. This process, called **photosynthesis**, occurs in the leaves of green plants:

$$6 \, CO_2(g) + 6 \, H_2O(l) \longrightarrow C_6H_{12}O_6(aq) + 6 \, O_2(g) \qquad [23.6]$$

The formation of 1 mol of glucose, $C_6H_{12}O_6$, requires the absorption of 48 mol of photons from sunlight or other sources of light. Chlorophyll-containing pigments in the leaves of plants absorb the photons. Figure 23.13 shows that the chlorophyll molecule has a series of alternating, or *conjugated*, double bonds in the ring surrounding the metal ion. This system of conjugated double bonds makes it possible for chlorophyll to absorb light strongly in the visible region of the spectrum. As ◀ **FIGURE 23.16** shows, chlorophyll is green because it absorbs red light (maximum absorption at 655 nm) and blue light (maximum absorption at 430 nm) and transmits green light.

Photosynthesis is nature's solar-energy–conversion machine, and thus all living systems on Earth depend on photosynthesis for continued existence.

What property of the porphine ligand makes it possible for chlorophyll to play a role in plant photosynthesis?

## CHEMISTRY AND LIFE

### THE BATTLE FOR IRON IN LIVING SYSTEMS

Because living systems have difficulty assimilating enough iron to satisfy their nutritional needs, iron-deficiency anemia is a common problem in humans. Chlorosis, an iron deficiency in plants that makes leaves turn yellow, is also commonplace.

Living systems have difficulty assimilating iron because most iron compounds found in nature are not very soluble in water. Microorganisms have adapted to this problem by secreting an iron-binding compound, called a *siderophore*, that forms an extremely stable water-soluble complex with iron(III). One such complex is *ferrichrome* (▶ FIGURE 23.17). The iron-binding strength of a siderophore is so great that it can extract iron from glass cooking pots and the iron in iron oxides.

When ferrichrome enters a living cell, the iron it carries is removed through an enzyme-catalyzed reaction that reduces the strongly bonding iron(III) to iron(II), which is only weakly complexed by the siderophore (▶ FIGURE 23.18). Microorganisms thus acquire iron by excreting a siderophore into their immediate environment and then taking the resulting iron complex into the cell.

In humans, iron is assimilated from food in the intestine. A protein called *transferrin* binds iron and transports it across the intestinal wall to distribute it to other tissues in the body. The normal adult body contains about 4 g of iron. At any one time, about 3 g of this iron is in the blood, mostly in the form of hemoglobin. Most of the remainder is carried by transferrin.

A bacterium that infects the blood requires a source of iron if it is to grow and reproduce. The bacterium excretes a siderophore into the blood to compete with transferrin for iron. The equilibrium con-

▲ **FIGURE 23.17** **Ferrichrome.**

stants for forming the iron complex are about the same for transferrin and siderophores. The more iron available to the bacterium, the more rapidly it can reproduce and thus the more harm it can do.

Several years ago, New Zealand clinics regularly gave iron supplements to infants soon after birth. However, the incidence of certain bacterial infections was eight times higher in treated than in

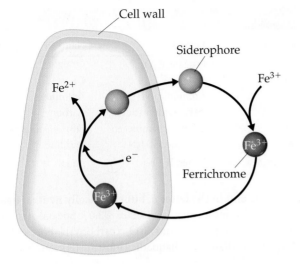

**▲ FIGURE 23.18 The iron-transport system of a bacterial cell.**

untreated infants. Presumably, the presence of more iron in the blood than absolutely necessary makes it easier for bacteria to obtain the iron needed for growth and reproduction.

In the United States it is common medical practice to supplement infant formula with iron sometime during the first year of life. However, iron supplements are not necessary for infants who breast-feed because breast milk contains two specialized proteins, lactoferrin and transferrin, which provide sufficient iron while denying its availability to bacteria. Even for infants fed with infant formulas, supplementing with iron during the first several months of life may be ill-advised.

For bacteria to continue to multiply in the blood, they must synthesize new supplies of siderophores. Synthesis of siderophores in bacteria slows, however, as the temperature is increased above the normal body temperature of 37 °C and stops completely at 40 °C. This suggests that fever in the presence of an invading microbe is a mechanism used by the body to deprive bacteria of iron.

*RELATED EXERCISE: 23.74*

# 23.4 | NOMENCLATURE AND ISOMERISM IN COORDINATION CHEMISTRY

When complexes were first discovered, they were named after the chemist who originally prepared them. A few of these names persist, as, for example, with the dark red substance $NH_4[Cr(NH_3)_2(NCS)_4]$, which is still known as Reinecke's salt. Once the structures of complexes were more fully understood, it became possible to name them in a more systematic manner. Let's use two substances to illustrate how coordination compounds are named:

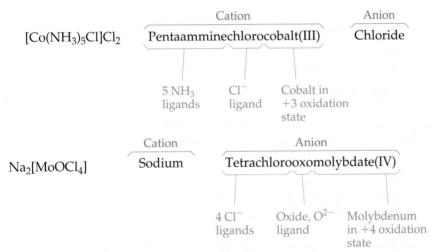

1. **In naming complexes that are salts, the name of the cation is given before the name of the anion.** Thus, in $[Co(NH_3)_5Cl]Cl_2$ we name the $[Co(NH_3)_5Cl]^{2+}$ cation and then the $Cl^-$.

2. **In naming complex ions or molecules, the ligands are named before the metal. Ligands are listed in alphabetical order, regardless of their charges. Prefixes that give the number of ligands are not considered part of the ligand name in determining alphabetical order.** Thus, the $[Co(NH_3)_5Cl]^{2+}$ ion is pentaamminechlorocobalt(III). (Be careful to note, however, that the metal is written first in the chemical formula.)

**TABLE 23.5 • Some Common Ligands and Their Names**

| Ligand | Name in Complexes | Ligand | Name in Complexes |
|---|---|---|---|
| Azide, $N_3^-$ | Azido | Oxalate, $C_2O_4^{2-}$ | Oxalato |
| Bromide, $Br^-$ | Bromo | Oxide, $O^{2-}$ | Oxo |
| Chloride, $Cl^-$ | Chloro | Ammonia, $NH_3$ | Ammine |
| Cyanide, $CN^-$ | Cyano | Carbon monoxide, CO | Carbonyl |
| Fluoride, $F^-$ | Fluoro | Ethylenediamine, en | Ethylenediamine |
| Hydroxide, $OH^-$ | Hydroxo | Pyridine, $C_5H_5N$ | Pyridine |
| Carbonate, $CO_3^{2-}$ | Carbonato | Water, $H_2O$ | Aqua |

3. **The names of anionic ligands end in the letter *o*, but electrically neutral ligands ordinarily bear the name of the molecules** (▲ TABLE 23.5). Special names are used for $H_2O$ (aqua), $NH_3$ (ammine), and CO (carbonyl). For example, $[Fe(CN)_2(NH_3)_2(H_2O)_2]^+$ is the diamminediaquadicyanoiron(III) ion.

4. **Greek prefixes (*di-, tri-, tetra-, penta-, hexa-*) are used to indicate the number of each kind of ligand when more than one is present. If the ligand contains a Greek prefix (*for example, ethylenediamine*) or is polydentate, the alternate prefixes *bis-, tris-, tetrakis-, pentakis-,* and *hexakis-* are used and the ligand name is placed in parentheses.** For example, the name for $[Co(en)_3]Br_3$ is tris(ethylenediamine)-cobalt(III) bromide.

5. **If the complex is an anion, its name ends in *-ate*.** The compound $K_4[Fe(CN)_6]$ is potassium hexacyanoferrate(II), for example, and the ion $[CoCl_4]^{2-}$ is tetrachloro-cobaltate(II) ion.

6. **The oxidation number of the metal is given in parentheses in Roman numerals following the name of the metal.**

Three examples for applying these rules are

| | |
|---|---|
| $[Ni(NH_3)_6]Br_2$ | Hexaamminenickel(II) bromide |
| $[Co(en)_2(H_2O)(CN)]Cl_2$ | Aquacyanobis(ethylenediamine)cobalt(III) chloride |
| $Na_2[MoOCl_4]$ | Sodium tetrachlorooxomolybdate(IV) |

---

**SAMPLE EXERCISE 23.4** | **Naming Coordination Compounds**

Name the compounds (a) $[Cr(H_2O)_4Cl_2]Cl$, (b) $K_4[Ni(CN)_4]$.

**SOLUTION**

**Analyze** We are given the chemical formulas for two coordination compounds and assigned the task of naming them.

**Plan** To name the complexes, we need to determine the ligands in the complexes, the names of the ligands, and the oxidation state of the metal ion. We then put the information together following the rules listed in the text.

**Solve**

(a) The ligands are four water molecules—tetraaqua—and two chloride ions—dichloro. By assigning all the oxidation numbers we know for this molecule, we see that the oxidation number of Cr is +3:

$$+3 + 4(0) + 2(-1) + (-1) = 0$$
$$[Cr(H_2O)_4Cl_2]Cl$$

Thus, we have chromium(III). Finally, the anion is chloride. The name of the compound is

tetraaquadichlorochromium(III) chloride

(b) The complex has four cyanide ion ligands, $CN^-$, which means tetra-cyano, and the oxidation state of the nickel is zero:

$$4(+1) + 0 + 4(-1) = 0$$
$$K_4[Ni(CN)_4]$$

Because the complex is an anion, the metal is indicated as nickelate(0). Putting these parts together and naming the cation first, we have

potassium tetracyanonickelate(0)

**PRACTICE EXERCISE**

Name the compounds (a) $[Mo(NH_3)_3Br_3]NO_3$, (b) $(NH_4)_2[CuBr_4]$. (c) Write the formula for sodium diaquabis(oxalato)ruthenate(III).

*Answers:* (a) triamminetribromomolybdenum(IV) nitrate, (b) ammonium tetrabromocuprate(II) (c) $Na[Ru(H_2O)_2(C_2O_4)_2]$

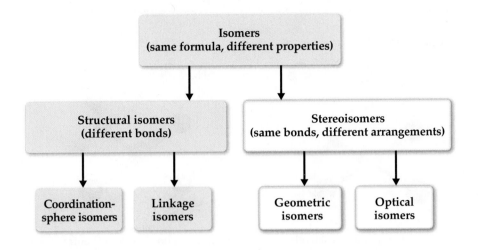

## Isomerism

When two or more compounds have the same composition but a different arrangement of atoms, we call them **isomers**. ∞ (Section 2.9) Here we consider two main kinds of isomers in coordination compounds: **structural isomers** (which have different bonds) and **stereoisomers** (which have the same bonds but different ways in which the ligands occupy the space around the metal center). Each of these classes also has subclasses, as shown in ▲ **FIGURE 23.19**.

## Structural Isomerism

Many types of structural isomerism are known in coordination chemistry, including the two named in Figure 23.19: linkage isomerism and coordination-sphere isomerism. **Linkage isomerism** is a relatively rare but interesting type that arises when a particular ligand is capable of coordinating to a metal in two ways. The nitrite ion, $NO_2^-$, for example, can coordinate to a metal ion through either its nitrogen or one of its oxygens (▶ **FIGURE 23.20**). When it coordinates through the nitrogen atom, the $NO_2^-$ ligand is called *nitro*; when it coordinates through the oxygen atom, it is called *nitrito* and is generally written $ONO^-$. The isomers shown in Figure 23.20 have different properties. The nitro isomer is yellow, for example, whereas the nitrito isomer is red.

Another ligand capable of coordinating through either of two donor atoms is thiocyanate, $SCN^-$, whose potential donor atoms are N and S.

**Coordination-sphere isomers** are isomers that differ in which species in the complex are ligands and which are outside the coordination sphere in the solid lattice. For example, three isomers have the formula $CrCl_3(H_2O)_6$. When the ligands are six $H_2O$ and the chloride ions are in the crystal lattice (as counterions), we have the violet compound $[Cr(H_2O)_6]Cl_3$. When the ligands are five $H_2O$ and one $Cl^-$, with the sixth $H_2O$ and the two $Cl^-$ out in the lattice, we have the green compound $[Cr(H_2O)_5Cl]Cl_2 \cdot H_2O$. The third isomer, $[Cr(H_2O)_4Cl_2]Cl \cdot 2\ H_2O$, is also a green compound. In the two green compounds, either one or two water molecules have been displaced from the coordination sphere by chloride ions and occupy a site in the crystal lattice.

⚠ **GIVE IT SOME THOUGHT**

Can the ammonia ligand engage in linkage isomerism? Explain.

Nitro isomer
Bonding via ligand N atom

Nitrito isomer
Bonding via ligand O atom

▲ **FIGURE 23.20** Linkage isomerism.

▲ GO FIGURE

**Which of these isomers has a nonzero dipole moment?**

| ● = N | ● = Cl | ○ = H | ○ = Pt |

*cis*
Cl ligands adjacent to each other
NH₃ ligands adjacent to each other

*trans*
Cl ligands on opposite sides of central atom
NH₃ ligands on opposite sides of central atom

▶ **FIGURE 23.21** **Geometric isomerism.**

## Stereoisomerism

Stereoisomers have the same chemical bonds but different spatial arrangements. In the square-planar complex $[Pt(NH_3)_2Cl_2]$, for example, the chloro ligands can be either adjacent to or opposite each other (▲ **FIGURE 23.21**). (We saw an earlier example of this type of isomerism in the cobalt complex of Figure 23.7, and we'll return to that complex in a moment.) This form of stereoisomerism, in which the arrangement of the atoms is different but the same bonds are present, is called **geometric isomerism**. The isomer on the left in Figure 23.21, with like ligands in adjacent positions, is the *cis* isomer, and the isomer on the right, with like ligands across from one another, is the *trans* isomer.

Geometric isomers generally have different physical properties and may also have markedly different chemical reactivities. For example, *cis*-$[Pt(NH_3)_2Cl_2]$, also called *cisplatin*, is effective in the treatment of testicular, ovarian, and certain other cancers, whereas the *trans* isomer is ineffective. This is because cisplatin forms a chelate with two nitrogens of DNA, displacing the chloride ligands. The chloride ligands of the *trans* isomer are too far apart to form the N-Pt-N chelate with DNA nitrogens.

Geometric isomerism is also possible in octahedral complexes when two or more different ligands are present, as in the *cis* and *trans* tetraamminedichlorocobalt(III) ion in Figure 23.7. Because all the corners of a tetrahedron are adjacent to one another, *cis-trans* isomerism is not observed in tetrahedral complexes.

---

**SAMPLE EXERCISE 23.5** | **Determining the Number of Geometric Isomers**

The Lewis structure :C≡O: indicates that the CO molecule has two lone pairs of electrons. When CO binds to a transition-metal atom, it nearly always does so by using the C lone pair. How many geometric isomers are there for tetracarbonyldichloroiron(II)?

**SOLUTION**

**Analyze** We are given the name of a complex containing only monodentate ligands, and we must determine the number of isomers the complex can form.

**Plan** We can count the number of ligands to determine the coordination number of the Fe and then use the coordination number to predict the geometry. We can then either make a series of drawings with ligands in different positions to determine the number of isomers or deduce the number of isomers by analogy to cases we have discussed.

**Solve** The name indicates that the complex has four carbonyl (CO) ligands and two chloro (Cl⁻) ligands, so its formula is $Fe(CO)_4Cl_2$. The complex therefore has a coordination number of 6, and we can assume an octahedral geometry. Like $[Co(NH_3)_4Cl_2]^+$ (Figure 23.7), it has four ligands of one type and two of another. Consequently, there are two isomers possible: one with the Cl⁻ ligands across the metal from each other, *trans*-$[Fe(CO)_4Cl_2]$, and one with the Cl⁻ ligands adjacent to each other, *cis*-$[Fe(CO)_4Cl_2]$.

**Comment**  It is easy to overestimate the number of geometric isomers. Sometimes different orientations of a single isomer are incorrectly thought to be different isomers. If two structures can be rotated so that they are equivalent, they are not isomers of each other. The problem of identifying isomers is compounded by the difficulty we often have in visualizing three-dimensional molecules from their two-dimensional representations. It is sometimes easier to determine the number of isomers if we use three-dimensional models.

**PRACTICE EXERCISE**

How many isomers exist for the square-planar molecule $[Pt(NH_3)_2ClBr]$?

**Answer:** two

The second type of stereoisomerism listed in Figure 23.19 is **optical isomerism**. Optical isomers, called **enantiomers**, are mirror images that cannot be superimposed on each other. They bear the same resemblance to each other that your left hand bears to your right hand. If you look at your left hand in a mirror, the image is identical to your right hand (▼ **FIGURE 23.22**). No matter how hard you try, however, you cannot superimpose your two hands on each other. An example of a complex that exhibits this type of isomerism is the $[Co(en)_3]^{3+}$ ion. Figure 23.22 shows the two enantiomers of this complex and their mirror-image relationship. Just as there is no way that we can twist or turn our right hand to make it look identical to our left, so also there is no way to rotate one of these enantiomers to make it identical to the other. Molecules or ions that are not superimposable on their mirror image are said to be **chiral** (pronounced KY-rul).

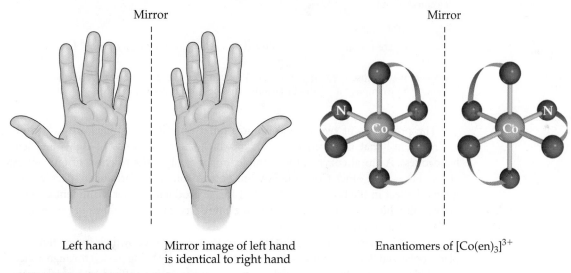

Mirror                                                    Mirror

Left hand        Mirror image of left hand          Enantiomers of $[Co(en)_3]^{3+}$
                 is identical to right hand

▲ **FIGURE 23.22    Optical isomerism.**

**SAMPLE EXERCISE 23.6    Predicting Whether a Complex Has Optical Isomers**

Does either $cis\text{-}[Co(en)_2Cl_2]^+$ or $trans\text{-}[Co(en)_2Cl_2]^-$ have optical isomers?

**SOLUTION**

**Analyze**  We are given the chemical formula for two geometric isomers and asked to determine whether either one has optical isomers. Because en is a bidentate ligand, we know that both complexes are octahedral and both have coordination number 6.

**Plan**  We need to sketch the structures of the cis and trans isomers and their mirror images. We can draw the en ligand as two N atoms connected by an arc. If the mirror image cannot be superimposed on the original structure, the complex and its mirror image are optical isomers.

**Solve** The trans isomer of $[Co(en)_2Cl_2]^+$ and its mirror image are:

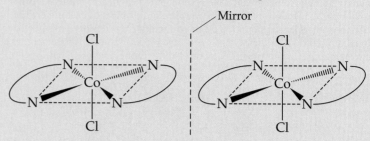

Notice that the mirror image of the isomer is identical to the original. Consequently *trans*-$[Co(en)_2Cl_2]^+$ does not exhibit optical isomerism.

The mirror image of the cis isomer cannot be superimposed on the original:

Thus, the two cis structures are optical isomers (enantiomers). We say that *cis*-$[Co(en)_2Cl_2]^+$ is a chiral complex.

### PRACTICE EXERCISE

Does the square-planar complex ion $[Pt(NH_3)(N_3)ClBr]^-$ have optical isomers? Explain your answer.

**Answer:** no, because the complex is flat. This complex ion does, however, have geometric isomers (for example, the Cl and Br ligands could be cis or trans).

The properties of two optical isomers differ only if the isomers are in a chiral environment—that is, an environment in which there is a sense of right- and left-handedness. A chiral enzyme, for example, might catalyze the reaction of one optical isomer but not the other. Consequently, one optical isomer may produce a specific physiological effect in the body, with its mirror image producing either a different effect or none at all. Chiral reactions are also extremely important in the synthesis of pharmaceuticals and other industrially important chemicals.

Optical isomers are usually distinguished from each other by their interaction with plane-polarized light. If light is polarized—for example, by being passed through a sheet of polarizing film—the electric-field vector of the light is confined to a single plane (▼ **FIGURE 23.23**). If the polarized light is then passed through a solution containing one optical isomer, the plane of polarization is rotated either to the right or to the left. The isomer that rotates the plane of polarization to the right is **dextrorotatory**; it is the

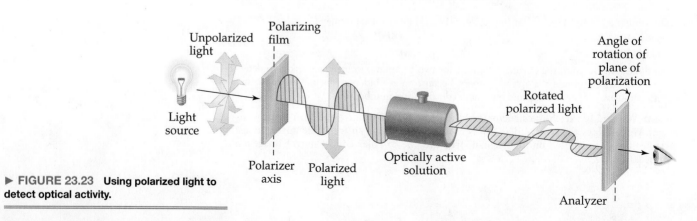

▶ **FIGURE 23.23** **Using polarized light to detect optical activity.**

dextro, or *d*, isomer (Latin *dexter*, "right"). Its mirror image rotates the plane of polarization to the left; it is **levorotatory** and is the levo, or *l*, isomer (Latin *laevus*, "left"). The $[Co(en)_3]^{3+}$ isomer on the right in Figure 23.22 is found experimentally to be the *l* isomer of this ion. Its mirror image is the *d* isomer. Because of their effect on plane-polarized light, chiral molecules are said to be **optically active**.

 GIVE IT SOME THOUGHT

What is the similarity and what is the difference between the *d* and *l* isomers of a compound?

When a substance with optical isomers is prepared in the laboratory, the chemical environment during the synthesis is not usually chiral. Consequently, equal amounts of the two isomers are obtained, and the mixture is said to be **racemic**. A racemic mixture does not rotate polarized light because the rotatory effects of the two isomers cancel each other.

# 23.5 | COLOR AND MAGNETISM IN COORDINATION CHEMISTRY

Studies of the colors and magnetic properties of transition-metal complexes have played an important role in the development of modern models for metal–ligand bonding. We discussed the various types of magnetic behavior of the transition metals in Section 23.1, and we discussed the interaction of radiant energy with matter in Section 6.3. Let's briefly examine the significance of these two properties for transition-metal complexes before we develop a model for metal–ligand bonding.

## Color

In Figure 23.3 we saw the diverse range of colors seen in salts of transition-metal ions and their aqueous solutions. In general, the color of a complex depends on the identity of the metal ion, on its oxidation state, and on the ligands bound to it. ▼ **FIGURE 23.24**, for instance, shows how the pale blue color characteristic of $[Cu(H_2O)_4]^{2+}$ changes to deep blue as $NH_3$ ligands replace the $H_2O$ ligands to form $[Cu(NH_3)_4]^{2+}$.

 GO FIGURE

 Is the equilibrium binding constant of ammonia for Cu(II) likely to be larger or smaller than that of water for Cu(II)?

$[Cu(H_2O)_4]^{2+}(aq)$          $NH_3(aq)$          $[Cu(NH_3)_4]^{2+}(aq)$

◀ **FIGURE 23.24    The color of a coordination complex changes when the ligand changes.**

Eye perceives orange since only orange light reflected

Only blue light absorbed; eye perceives orange, blue's complementary color

▲ **FIGURE 23.25** **Two ways of perceiving the color orange.** An object appears orange either when it reflects orange light to the eye (left), or when it transmits to the eye all colors except blue, the complement of orange (middle). Complementary colors lie opposite to each other on an artist's color wheel (right).

For a substance to have color we can see, it must absorb some portion of the spectrum of visible light. ∞ (Section 6.1) Absorption happens, however, only if the energy needed to move an electron in the substance from its ground state to an excited state corresponds to the energy of some portion of the visible spectrum. ∞ (Section 6.3) Thus, the particular energies of radiation a substance absorbs dictate the color we see for the substance.

When an object absorbs some portion of the visible spectrum, the color we perceive is the sum of the unabsorbed portions, which are either reflected or transmitted by the object and strike our eyes. (Opaque objects *reflect* light, and transparent ones *transmit* it.) If an object absorbs all wavelengths of visible light, none reaches our eyes and the object appears black. If it absorbs no visible light, it is white if it is a solid or colorless if it is a liquid. If it absorbs all but orange light, the orange light is what reaches our eye and therefore the color we see.

An interesting phenomenon of vision is that we also perceive an orange color when an object absorbs only the blue portion of the visible spectrum and all the other colors strike our eyes. This is because orange and blue are **complementary colors**, which means that the removal of blue from white light makes the light look orange (and the removal of orange makes the light look blue).

Complementary colors can be determined with an artist's color wheel, which shows complementary colors on opposite sides (▲ **FIGURE 23.25**).

---

**SAMPLE EXERCISE 23.7** | **Relating Color Absorbed to Color Observed**

The complex ion *trans*-$[Co(NH_3)_4Cl_2]^+$ absorbs light primarily in the red region of the visible spectrum (the most intense absorption is at 680 nm). What is the color of the complex?

**SOLUTION**

**Analyze** We need to relate the color absorbed by a complex (red) to the color observed for the complex.

**Plan** For an object that absorbs only one color from the visible spectrum, the color we see is complementary to the color absorbed. We can use the color wheel of Figure 23.25 to determine the complementary color.

**Solve** From Figure 23.25, we see that green is complementary to red, so the complex appears green.

**Comment** As noted in Section 23.2, this green complex was one of those that helped Werner establish his theory of coordination (Table 23.3). The other geometric isomer of this complex, *cis*-$[Co(NH_3)_4Cl_2]^+$, absorbs yellow light and therefore appears violet.

**PRACTICE EXERCISE**

A certain transition-metal complex ion absorbs at 630 nm. Which color is this ion most likely to be—blue, yellow, green, or orange?

*Answer:* blue

The amount of light absorbed by a sample as a function of wavelength is known as the sample's **absorption spectrum**. The visible absorption spectrum of a transparent sample can be determined using a spectrometer, as described in the "A Closer Look" box on page 564. The absorption spectrum of the ion $[Ti(H_2O)_6]^{3+}$ is shown in ▶ **FIGURE 23.26**. The absorption maximum is at 500 nm, but the graph shows that much of the yellow, green, and blue light is also absorbed. Because the sample absorbs all of these colors, what we see is the unabsorbed red and violet light, which we perceive as red-violet.

## Magnetism of Coordination Compounds

Many transition-metal complexes exhibit paramagnetism, as described in Sections 9.8 and 23.1. In such compounds the metal ions possess some number of unpaired electrons. It is possible to experimentally determine the number of unpaired electrons per metal ion from the measured degree of paramagnetism, and experiments reveal some interesting comparisons.

Compounds of the complex ion $[Co(CN)_6]^{3-}$ have no unpaired electrons, for example, but compounds of the $[CoF_6]^{3-}$ ion have four unpaired electrons per metal ion. Both complexes contain Co(III) with a $3d^6$ electron configuration. ∞ (Section 7.4) Clearly, there is a major difference in the ways in which the electrons are arranged in these two cases. Any successful bonding theory must explain this difference, and we present such a theory in the next section.

 **GIVE IT SOME THOUGHT**

What is the electron configuration for
a. the Co atom and
b. the $Co^{3+}$ ion? How many unpaired electrons does each possess? (See Section 7.4 to review electron configurations of ions.)

# 23.6 | CRYSTAL-FIELD THEORY

Scientists have long recognized that many of the magnetic properties and colors of transition-metal complexes are related to the presence of $d$ electrons in the metal cation. In this section we consider a model for bonding in transition-metal complexes, **crystal-field theory**, that accounts for many of the observed properties of these substances.* Because the predictions of crystal-field theory are essentially the same as those obtained with more advanced molecular-orbital theories, crystal-field theory is an excellent place to start in considering the electronic structure of coordination compounds.

The ability of a metal ion to attract ligands is a Lewis acid–base interaction, in which the base—that is, the ligand—donates a pair of electrons to an empty orbital on the metal ion (▶ **FIGURE 23.27**). Much of the attractive interaction between the metal ion and the ligands is due, however, to the electrostatic forces between the positive charge on the metal ion and negative charges on the ligands. If the ligand is ionic, as in the case of $Cl^-$ or $SCN^-$, the electrostatic interaction is the usual cation–anion attraction. When the ligand is a neutral molecule, as in the case of $H_2O$ or $NH_3$, the negative ends of these polar molecules, which contain an unshared electron pair, are directed toward the metal ion. In this case, the attractive interaction is of the ion–dipole type. ∞ (Section 11.2) In either case, the ligands are attracted strongly toward the metal ion. Because of the metal–ligand electrostatic attraction, the energy of the complex is lower than the combined energy of the separated metal ion and ligands.

Although the metal ion is attracted to the ligand electrons, the metal ion's $d$ electrons are repulsed by the ligands. Let's examine this effect more closely, specifically the case in which the ligands form an octahedral array around a metal ion that has coordination number 6.

*The name *crystal field* arose because the theory was first developed to explain the properties of solid crystalline materials. The theory applies equally well to complexes in solution, however.

**GO FIGURE**

How would this absorbance spectrum change if you decreased the concentration of the $[Ti(H_2O)_6]^{3+}$ in solution?

Blue, green, yellow absorbed; violet and red light travel to eye, solution appears red-violet

▲ **FIGURE 23.26  The color of $[Ti(H_2O)_6]^{3+}$.** A solution containing the $[Ti(H_2O)_6]^{3+}$ ion appears red-violet because, as its visible absorption spectrum shows, the solution does not absorb light from the violet and red ends of the spectrum. That unabsorbed light is what reaches our eyes.

▲ **FIGURE 23.27  Metal–ligand bond formation.** The ligand acts as a Lewis base by donating its nonbonding electron pair to a hybrid orbital on the metal ion. The bond that results is strongly polar with some covalent character.

△ GO FIGURE

**Which *d* orbitals have lobes that point directly toward the ligands in an octahedral crystal field?**

▲ FIGURE 23.28 **Energies of *d* orbitals in a free metal ion, a spherically symmetric crystal field, and an octahedral crystal field.**

In crystal-field theory, we consider the ligands to be negative points of charge that repel the electrons in the *d* orbitals of the metal ion. The energy diagram in ▲ FIGURE 23.28 shows how these ligand point charges affect the energies of the *d* orbitals. First we imagine the complex as having all the ligand point charges uniformly distributed on the surface of a sphere centered on the metal ion. The *average* energy of the metal ion's *d* orbitals is raised by the presence of this uniformly charged sphere. Hence, the energies of all five *d* orbitals are raised by the same amount.

This energy picture is only a first approximation, however, because the ligands are not distributed uniformly on a spherical surface and, therefore, do not approach the metal ion equally from every direction. Instead, we envision the six ligands approaching along *x*-, *y*-, and *z*-axes, as shown on the right in Figure 23.28. This arrangement of ligands is called an *octahedral crystal field*. Because the metal ion's *d* orbitals have different orientations and shapes, they do not all experience the same repulsion from the ligands and, therefore, do not all have the same energy under the influence of the octahedral crystal field. To see why, we must consider the shapes of the *d* orbitals and how their lobes are oriented relative to the ligands.

Figure 23.28 shows that the lobes of the $d_{z^2}$ and $d_{x^2-y^2}$ orbitals are directed *along* the *x*-, *y*-, and *z*-axes and so point directly toward the ligand point charges. In the $d_{xy}$, $d_{xz}$, and $d_{yz}$ orbitals, however, the lobes are directed *between* the axes and so do not point directly toward the charges. The result of this difference in orientation—$d_{x^2-y^2}$ and $d_{z^2}$ lobes point directly toward the ligand charges; $d_{xy}$, $d_{xz}$, and $d_{yz}$ lobes do not—is that the energy of the $d_{x^2-y^2}$ and $d_{z^2}$ orbitals is higher than the energy of the $d_{xy}$, $d_{xz}$, and $d_{yz}$ orbitals. This difference in energy is represented by the red boxes in the energy diagram of Figure 23.28.

It might seem like the energy of the $d_{x^2-y^2}$ orbital should be different from that of the $d_{z^2}$ orbital because the $d_{x^2-y^2}$ has four lobes pointing at ligands and the $d_{z^2}$ has only two lobes pointing at ligands. However, the $d_{z^2}$ orbital does have electron density in the *xy* plane, represented by the ring encircling the point where the two lobes meet. More advanced calculations show that two orbitals do indeed have the same energy in the presence of the octahedral crystal field.

Because their lobes point directly at the negative ligand charges, electrons in the metal ion's $d_{z^2}$ and $d_{x^2-y^2}$ orbitals experience stronger repulsions than those in the $d_{xy}$, $d_{xz}$, and $d_{yz}$ orbitals. As a result, the energy splitting shown in Figure 23.28 occurs. The three lower-energy *d* orbitals are called the $t_2$ set of orbitals, and the two higher-energy ones are called the *e* set.* The energy gap Δ between the two sets is often called the *crystal-field splitting energy*.

*The labels $t_2$ for the $d_{xy}$, $d_{xz}$, and $d_{yz}$ orbitals and *e* for the $d_{z^2}$ and $d_{x^2-y^2}$ orbitals come from the application of a branch of mathematics called *group theory* to crystal-field theory. Group theory can be used to analyze the effects of symmetry on molecular properties.

Crystal-field theory helps us account for the colors observed in transition-metal complexes. The energy gap $\Delta$ between the $e$ and $t_2$ sets of $d$ orbitals is of the same order of magnitude as the energy of a photon of visible light. It is therefore possible for a transition-metal complex to absorb visible light that excites an electron from a lower-energy ($t_2$) $d$ orbital into a higher-energy ($e$) one. In $[\text{Ti}(\text{H}_2\text{O})_6]^{3+}$, for example, the Ti(III) ion has an $[\text{Ar}]3d^1$ electron configuration. (Recall from Section 7.4 that when determining the electron configurations of transition-metal ions, we remove the $s$ electrons first.) Ti(III) is thus called a $d^1$ *ion*. In the ground state of $[\text{Ti}(\text{H}_2\text{O})_6]^{3+}$, the single $3d$ electron resides in an orbital in the $t_2$ set ($\blacktriangleright$ **FIGURE 23.29**). Absorption of 495-nm light excites this electron up to an orbital in the $e$ set, generating the absorption spectrum shown in Figure 23.26. Because this transition involves exciting an electron from one set of $d$ orbitals to the other, we call it a *d-d* **transition**. As noted earlier, the absorption of visible radiation that produces this $d$-$d$ transition causes the $[\text{Ti}(\text{H}_2\text{O})_6]^{3+}$ ion to appear red-violet.

**GIVE IT SOME THOUGHT**
Why are compounds of Ti(IV) colorless?

The magnitude of the crystal-field splitting energy and, consequently, the color of a complex depend on both the metal and the ligands. For example, $[\text{Fe}(\text{H}_2\text{O})_6]^{3+}$ is light violet, $[\text{Cr}(\text{H}_2\text{O})_6]^{3+}$ is a deeper violet, and $[\text{Cr}(\text{NH}_3)_6]^{3+}$ is yellow. In a ranking called the **spectrochemical series**, ligands are arranged in order of their abilities to increase splitting energy, as in this abbreviated list:

$$\text{----Increasing } \Delta \longrightarrow$$
$$\text{Cl}^- < \text{F}^- < \text{H}_2\text{O} < \text{NH}_3 < \text{en} < \text{NO}_2^- \text{ (N-bonded)} < \text{CN}^-$$

The magnitude of $\Delta$ increases by roughly a factor of 2 from the far left to the far right of the spectrochemical series. Ligands at the low-$\Delta$ end of the spectrochemical series are termed *weak-field ligands*; those at the high-$\Delta$ end are termed *strong-field ligands*.

$\blacktriangledown$ **FIGURE 23.30** shows what happens to crystal-field splitting when the ligand is varied in a series of chromium(III) complexes. Because the Cr atom has an $[\text{Ar}]3d^54s^1$ electron configuration, $\text{Cr}^{3+}$ has the configuration $[\text{Ar}]3d^3$ and therefore is a $d^3$ ion. Consistent with Hund's rule, the three $3d$ electrons occupy the $t_2$ set of orbitals, with one electron in each orbital and all the spins the same. $\infty$ (Section 6.8) As the crystal field exerted by the six ligands increases, $\Delta$ increases. Because the absorption spectrum is related to this energy separation, these complexes vary in color.

**GO FIGURE**
If you were told to add a colorless Cr(III) complex to this diagram, what would you draw and where would you place it?

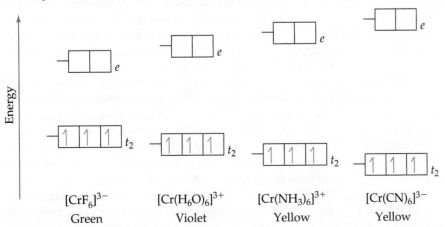

$\blacktriangle$ **FIGURE 23.30  Effect of ligand on crystal-field splitting.** The greater the crystal-field strength of the ligand, the greater the energy gap $\Delta$ it causes between the $t_2$ and $e$ sets of the metal ion's $d$ orbitals.

**GO FIGURE**
How would you calculate the energy gap between the $t_2$ and $e$ orbitals from this diagram?

$\blacktriangle$ **FIGURE 23.29  The** *d-d* **transition in** $[\text{Ti}(\text{H}_2\text{O})_6]^{3+}$ **is produced by the absorption of 495-nm light.**

$[Ti(H_2O)_6]^{3+}$, $[Ti(en)_3]^{3+}$, and $[TiCl_6]^{3-}$ all absorb visible light. Which one absorbs at the shortest wavelength?

**SOLUTION**

**Analyze** We are given three octahedral complexes, each containing Ti in the +3 oxidation state. We need to predict which complex absorbs the shortest wavelength of visible light.

**Plan** Ti(III) is a $d^1$ ion, so we anticipate that the absorption is due to a $d$-$d$ transition in which the $3d$ electron is excited from a $t_2$ orbital to an $e$ orbital. The wavelength of the light absorbed is determined by the magnitude of the crystal-field splitting energy, $\Delta$. Thus, we use the position of the ligands in the spectrochemical series to predict the relative values of $\Delta$. The larger the splitting energy, the shorter the wavelength.

**Solve** Of these three ligands, ethylenediamine (en) is highest in the spectrochemical series and therefore causes the largest split between the $t_2$ and $e$ orbitals. The larger the split, the shorter the wavelength of the light absorbed. Thus, the complex that absorbs the shortest-wavelength light is $[Ti(en)_3]^{3+}$.

**PRACTICE EXERCISE**

The absorption spectrum of a Ti(III) complex containing the ligand L, $[TiL_6]^{3-}$, shows a peak maximum at a wavelength intermediate between the wavelengths of the absorption maxima for $[TiCl_6]^{3-}$ and $[TiF_6]^{3-}$. What can we conclude about the place of L in the spectrochemical series?

**Answer:** It lies between $Cl^-$ and $F^-$.

## Electron Configurations in Octahedral Complexes

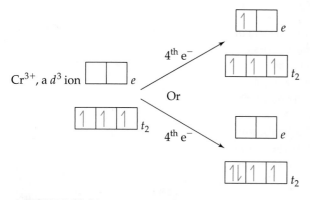

$Cr^{3+}$, a $d^3$ ion

$4^{th}$ $e^-$

Or

$4^{th}$ $e^-$

▲ **FIGURE 23.31 Two possibilities for adding a fourth electron to a $d^3$ octahedral complex.** Whether the fourth electron goes into a $t_2$ orbital or into an $e$ orbital depends on the relative energies of the crystal-field splitting energy and the spin-pairing energy.

Crystal-field theory helps us understand the magnetic properties and some important chemical properties of transition-metal ions. From Hund's rule, we expect electrons to always occupy the lowest-energy vacant orbitals first and to occupy a set of degenerate (same-energy) orbitals one at a time with their spins parallel. ∞ (Section 6.8) Thus, if we have a $d^1$, $d^2$, or $d^3$ octahedral complex, the electrons go into the lower-energy $t_2$ orbitals, with their spins parallel. When a fourth electron must be added, we have the two choices shown in ◄ **FIGURE 23.31**: The electron can either go into an $e$ orbital, where it will be the sole electron in the orbital, or become the second electron in a $t_2$ orbital. Because the energy difference between the $t_2$ and $e$ sets is the splitting energy $\Delta$, the energy cost of going into an $e$ orbital rather than a $t_2$ orbital is also $\Delta$. Thus, the goal of filling lowest-energy available orbitals first is met by putting the electron in a $t_2$ orbital.

There is a penalty for doing this, however, because the electron must now be paired with the electron already occupying the orbital. The difference between the energy required to pair an electron in an occupied orbital and the energy required to place that electron in an empty orbital is called the **spin-pairing energy**. The spin-pairing energy arises from the fact that the electrostatic repulsion between two electrons that share an orbital (and so must have opposite spins) is greater than the repulsion between two electrons that are in different orbitals and have parallel spins.

In coordination complexes, the nature of the ligands and the charge on the metal ion often play major roles in determining which of the two electron arrangements shown in Figure 23.31 is used. In $[CoF_6]^{3-}$ and $[Co(CN)_6]^{3-}$, both ligands have a 1− charge. The $F^-$ ion, however, is on the low end of the spectrochemical series, so it is a weak-field ligand. The $CN^-$ ion is on the high end and so is a strong-field ligand, which means it produces a larger energy gap $\Delta$ than the $F^-$ ion. The splittings of the $d$-orbital energies in these two complexes are compared in ► **FIGURE 23.32**.

Cobalt(III) has an $[Ar]3d^6$ electron configuration, so both complexes in Figure 23.32 are $d^6$ complexes. Let's imagine that we add these six electrons one at a time to the $d$ orbitals of the $[CoF_6]^{3-}$ ion. The first three go into the $t_2$ orbitals with their spins parallel. The fourth electron could pair up in one of the $t_2$ orbitals. The $F^-$ ion is a weak-field ligand, however, and so the energy gap $\Delta$ between the $t_2$ set and the $e$ set is small. In this case, the more stable arrangement is the fourth electron in one of the $e$ orbitals. By the same energy argument, the fifth electron goes into the other *e* orbital. With all five *d* orbitals containing one electron, the sixth must pair up, and the energy needed to pair with a $t_2$ electron is less than that needed to pair with an *e* electron. We end up with four $t_2$ electrons and two *e* electrons.

Figure 23.32 shows that the crystal-field splitting energy $\Delta$ is much larger in the $[Co(CN)_6]^{3-}$ complex. In this case, the spin-pairing energy is smaller than $\Delta$, so the lowest-energy arrangement is the six electrons paired in the $t_2$ orbitals.

The $[CoF_6]^{3-}$ complex is a **high-spin complex**; that is, the electrons are arranged so that they remain unpaired as much as possible. The $[Co(CN)_6]^{3-}$ ion is a **low-spin complex**; that is, the electrons are arranged so that they remain paired as much as possible while still following Hund's rule. These two electronic arrangements can be readily distinguished by measuring the magnetic properties of the complex. Experiments show that $[CoF_6]^{3-}$ has four unpaired electrons and $[Co(CN)_6]^{3-}$ has none. The absorption spectrum also shows peaks corresponding to the different values of $\Delta$ in these two complexes.

 GIVE IT SOME THOUGHT

Are strong-field ligands more likely to lead to a high-spin complex or a low-spin complex?

In the transition metal ions of periods 5 and 6 (which have $4d$ and $5d$ valence electrons), the *d* orbitals are larger than in the period 4 ions (which have only $3d$ electrons). Thus, ions from periods 5 and 6 interact more strongly with ligands, resulting in a larger crystal-field splitting. Consequently, metal ions in periods 5 and 6 are invariably low spin in an octahedral crystal field.

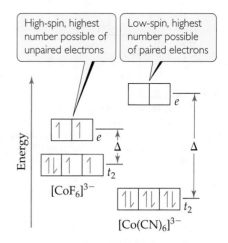

▲ **FIGURE 23.32  High-spin and low-spin complexes.** The high-spin $[CoF_6]^{3-}$ ion has a weak-field ligand and so a small $\Delta$ value. The spin-pairing energy required to pair electrons in the $t_2$ orbitals is greater than the $e$-$t_2$ gap energy $\Delta$. Therefore, filling $e$ orbitals before any electrons are paired in $t_2$ orbitals is the lower-energy state. The low-spin $[Co(CN)_6]^{3-}$ ion has a strong-field ligand and so a large $\Delta$ value. Here the spin-pairing energy is less than $\Delta$, making three sets of $t_2$-paired electrons the lower-energy state.

---

**SAMPLE EXERCISE 23.9**  **Predicting the Number of Unpaired Electrons in an Octahedral Complex**

Predict the number of unpaired electrons in high-spin and low-spin $Fe^{3+}$ complexes that have a coordination number of 6.

**SOLUTION**

**Analyze** We must determine how many unpaired electrons there are in the high-spin and low-spin complexes of $Fe^{3+}$.

**Plan** We need to consider how the electrons populate the *d* orbitals in $Fe^{3+}$ when the metal is in an octahedral complex. There are two possibilities: one giving a high-spin complex and the other giving a low-spin complex. The electron configuration of $Fe^{3+}$ gives us the number of *d* electrons. We then determine how these electrons populate the $t_2$ and *e* sets of *d* orbitals. In the high-spin case, the energy difference between the $t_2$ and *e* orbitals is small, and the complex has the maximum number of unpaired electrons. In the low-spin case, the energy difference between the $t_2$ and *e* orbitals is large, causing the $t_2$ orbitals to be filled before any electrons occupy the *e* orbitals.

**Solve** $Fe^{3+}$ is a $d^5$ ion. In a high-spin complex, all five electrons are unpaired, with three in the $t_2$ orbitals and two in the *e* orbitals. In a low-spin complex, all five electrons reside in the $t_2$ set, so there is one unpaired electron:

**PRACTICE EXERCISE**

In octahedral complexes, for which *d* electron configurations is it possible to distinguish between high-spin and low-spin arrangements?

**Answer:** $d^4, d^5, d^6, d^7$

---

## Tetrahedral and Square-Planar Complexes

Thus far we have considered crystal-field theory only for complexes having an octahedral geometry. When there are only four ligands in a complex, the geometry is generally tetrahedral, except for the special case of $d^8$ metal ions, which we will discuss in a moment.

▲ **FIGURE 23.33 Energies of the $d$ orbitals in a tetrahedral crystal field.** The $t_2$ set is the higher-energy set. Compare the relative $e$ and $t_2$ energy levels here with those in Figure 23.28 for an octahedral crystal field.

GO FIGURE

**Why is the $d_{x^2-y^2}$ orbital the highest-energy orbital in the square-planar crystal field?**

Square planar

▲ **FIGURE 23.34 Energies of the $d$ orbitals in a square-planar crystal field.**

The crystal-field splitting of $d$ orbitals in tetrahedral complexes differs from that in octahedral complexes. Four equivalent ligands can interact with a central metal ion most effectively by approaching along the vertices of a tetrahedron. It turns out—and this is not easy to explain in just a few sentences—that when $d$ orbitals split in a tetrahedral crystal, the three $t_2$ orbitals are raised in energy above the two $e$ orbitals( ◀ **FIGURE 23.33**). Because there are only four ligands instead of six, as in the octahedral case, the crystal-field splitting energy Δ is much smaller for tetrahedral complexes. Calculations show that for the same metal ion and ligand set, Δ for the tetrahedral complex is only four-ninths as large as for the octahedral complex. For this reason, all tetrahedral complexes are high spin; the crystal-field splitting energy is never large enough to overcome the spin-pairing energies.

In a square-planar complex, four ligands are arranged about the metal ion such that all five species are in the $xy$ plane. The resulting energy levels of the $d$ orbitals are illustrated in ◀ **FIGURE 23.34**. Note in particular that the $d_{z^2}$ orbital is considerably lower in energy than the $d_{x^2-y^2}$ orbital. To understand why this is so, recall from Figure 23.28 that in an octahedral field the $d_{z^2}$ orbital of the metal ion interacts with the ligands positioned above and below the $xy$ plane. There are no ligands in these two positions in a square-planar complex, which means that the $d_{z^2}$ orbital experiences no repulsive force and so remains in a lower-energy, more stable state.

Square-planar complexes are characteristic of metal ions with a $d^8$ electron configuration. They are nearly always low spin, with the eight $d$ electrons spin-paired to form a diamagnetic complex. This pairing leaves the $d_{x^2-y^2}$ orbital empty. Such an electronic arrangement is particularly common among the ions of heavier metals, such as $Pd^{2+}$, $Pt^{2+}$, $Ir^+$, and $Au^{3+}$.

GIVE IT SOME THOUGHT

Why is the energy of the $d_{xz}$ and $d_{yz}$ orbitals in a square-planar complex lower than that of the $d_{xy}$ orbital?

---

**SAMPLE EXERCISE 23.10** | **Populating $d$ Orbitals in Tetrahedral and Square-Planar Complexes**

Nickel(II) complexes in which the metal coordination number is 4 can have either square-planar or tetrahedral geometry. $[NiCl_4]^{2-}$ is paramagnetic, and $[Ni(CN)_4]^{2-}$ is diamagnetic. One of these complexes is square planar, and the other is tetrahedral. Use the relevant crystal-field splitting diagrams in the text to determine which complex has which geometry.

**SOLUTION**

**Analyze** We are given two complexes containing $Ni^{2+}$ and their magnetic properties. We are given two molecular geometry choices and asked to use crystal-field splitting diagrams from the text to determine which complex has which geometry.

**Plan** We need to determine the number of $d$ electrons in $Ni^{2+}$ and then use Figure 23.33 for the tetrahedral complex and Figure 23.34 for the square-planar complex.

**Solve** Nickel(II) has the electron configuration $[Ar]3d^8$. Tetrahedral complexes are always high spin, and square-planar complexes are almost always low spin. Therefore, the population of the $d$ electrons in the two geometries is

Tetrahedral          Square planar

The tetrahedral complex has two unpaired electrons, and the square-planar complex has none. We know from Section 23.1 that the tetrahedral complex must be paramagnetic and the square planar must be diamagnetic. Therefore, $[NiCl_4]^{2-}$ is tetrahedral, and $[Ni(CN)_4]^{2-}$ is square planar.

**Comment** Nickel(II) forms octahedral complexes more frequently than square-planar ones, whereas heavier $d^8$ metals tend to favor square-planar coordination.

### PRACTICE EXERCISE
How many unpaired electrons do you predict for the tetrahedral $[CoCl_4]^{2-}$ ion?
**Answer:** three

Crystal-field theory can be used to explain many observations in addition to those we have discussed. The theory is based on electrostatic interactions between ions and atoms, which essentially means ionic bonds. Many lines of evidence show, however, that

## A CLOSER LOOK

### CHARGE-TRANSFER COLOR

In the laboratory portion of your course, you have probably seen many colorful transition-metal compounds, including those shown in ▼ **FIGURE 23.35**. Many of these compounds are colored because of *d-d* transitions. Some colored complexes, however, including the violet permanganate ion, $MnO_4^-$, and the yellow chromate ion, $CrO_4^{2-}$, derive their color from a different type of excitation involving the *d* orbitals.

The permanganate ion strongly absorbs visible light, with a maximum absorption at 565 nm. Because violet is complementary to yellow, this strong absorption in the yellow portion of the visible spectrum is responsible for the violet color of salts and solutions of the ion. What is happening during this absorption of light? The $MnO_4^-$ ion is a complex of Mn(VII). Because Mn(VII) has a $d^0$ electron configuration, the absorption cannot be due to a *d-d* transition because there are no *d* electrons to excite! That does not mean, however, that the *d* orbitals are not involved in the transition. The excitation in the $MnO_4^-$ ion is due to a *charge-transfer transition*, in which an electron on one oxygen ligand is excited into a vacant *d* orbital on the Mn ion (▶ **FIGURE 23.36**). In essence, an electron is transferred from a ligand to the metal, so this transition is called a *ligand-to-metal charge-transfer (LMCT) transition*.

An LMCT transition is also responsible for the color of the $CrO_4^{2-}$, which is a $d^0$ Cr(VI) complex.

Also shown in Figure 23.35 is a salt of the perchlorate ion $(ClO_4^-)$. Like $MnO_4^-$, $ClO_4^-$ is tetrahedral and has its central atom

in the +7 oxidation state. However, because the Cl atom does not have low-lying *d* orbitals, exciting a Cl electron requires a more energetic photon than does $MnO_4^-$. The first absorption for $ClO_4^-$ is in the ultraviolet portion of the spectrum, so all the visible light is transmitted and the salt appears white.

Other complexes exhibit charge-transfer excitations in which an electron from the metal atom is excited to an empty orbital on a ligand. Such an excitation is called a *metal-to-ligand charge-transfer (MLCT) transition*.

Charge-transfer transitions are generally more intense than *d-d* transitions. Many metal-containing pigments used for oil painting, such as cadmium yellow (CdS), chrome yellow ($PbCrO_4$), and red ochre ($Fe_2O_3$), have intense colors because of charge-transfer transitions.

*RELATED EXERCISES: 23.82, 23.83*

◀ **FIGURE 23.36 Ligand-to-metal charge-transfer transition in $MnO_4^-$.** As shown by the blue arrow, an electron is excited from a nonbonding pair on O into one of the empty *d* orbitals on Mn.

KMnO₄

K₂CrO₄

KClO₄

▲ **FIGURE 23.35 The colors of compounds can arise from charge-transfer transitions.** KMnO₄ and K₂CrO₄ are colored due to ligand-to-metal charge-transfer transitions in their anions. KClO₄'s anion has no occupied *d* orbitals and its charge-transfer transition is at higher energy, corresponding to ultraviolet absorption; therefore it appears white.

the bonding in complexes must have some covalent character. Therefore, molecular-orbital theory ∞ (Sections 9.7 and 9.8) can also be used to describe the bonding in complexes, although the application of molecular-orbital theory to coordination compounds is beyond the scope of our discussion. Crystal-field theory, although not entirely accurate in all details, provides an adequate and useful first description of the electronic structure of complexes.

---

### SAMPLE INTEGRATIVE EXERCISE | Putting Concepts Together

The oxalate ion has the Lewis structure shown in Table 23.4. **(a)** Show the geometry of the complex formed when this ion complexes with cobalt(II) to form $[Co(C_2O_4)(H_2O)_4]$. **(b)** Write the formula for the salt formed when three oxalate ions complex with Co(II), assuming that the charge-balancing cation is $Na^+$. **(c)** Sketch all the possible geometric isomers for the cobalt complex formed in part (b). Are any of these isomers chiral? Explain. **(d)** The equilibrium constant for the formation of the cobalt(II) complex produced by coordination of three oxalate anions, as in part (b), is $5.0 \times 10^9$, and the equilibrium constant for formation of the cobalt(II) complex with three molecules of *ortho*-phenanthroline (Table 23.4) is $9 \times 10^{19}$. From these results, what conclusions can you draw regarding the relative Lewis base properties of the two ligands toward cobalt(II)? **(e)** Using the approach described in Sample Exercise 17.14, calculate the concentration of free aqueous Co(II) ion in a solution initially containing 0.040 M oxalate (*aq*) and 0.0010 M $Co^{2+}$(*aq*).

### SOLUTION

**(a)** The complex formed by coordination of one oxalate ion is octahedral:

**(b)** Because the oxalate ion has a charge of 2−, the net charge of a complex with three oxalate anions and one $Co^{2+}$ ion is 4−. Therefore, the coordination compound has the formula $Na_4[Co(C_2O_4)_3]$.

**(c)** There is only one geometric isomer. The complex is chiral, however, in the same way the $[Co(en)_3]^{3+}$ complex is chiral (Figure 23.22). The two mirror images are not superimposable, so there are two enantiomers:

**(d)** The *ortho*-phenanthroline ligand is bidentate, like the oxalate ligand, so they both exhibit the chelate effect. Thus, we conclude that *ortho*-phenanthroline is a stronger Lewis base toward $Co^{2+}$ than oxalate. This conclusion is consistent with what we learned about bases in Section 16.7, that nitrogen bases are generally stronger than oxygen bases. (Recall, for example, that $NH_3$ is a stronger base than $H_2O$.)

**(e)** The equilibrium we must consider involves 3 mol of oxalate ion (represented as $Ox^{2-}$).

$$Co^{2+}(aq) + 3\,Ox^{2-}(aq) \rightleftharpoons [Co(Ox)_3]^{4-}(aq)$$

The formation-constant expression is

$$K_f = \frac{[[Co(Ox)_3]^{4-}]}{[Co^{2+}][Ox^{2-}]^3}$$

Because $K_f$ is so large, we can assume that essentially all the $Co^{2+}$ is converted to the oxalato complex. Under that assumption, the final concentration of $[Co(Ox)_3]^{4-}$ is 0.0010 $M$ and that of oxalate ion is $[Ox^{2-}] = (0.040) - 3(0.0010) = 0.037\ M$ (three $Ox^{2-}$ ions react with each $Co^{2+}$ ion). We then have

$$[Co^{2+}] = xM,\ [Ox^{2-}] \cong 0.037\ M,\ [[Co(Ox)_3]^{4-}] \cong 0.0010\ M$$

Inserting these values into the equilibrium-constant expression, we have

$$K_f = \frac{(0.0010)}{x(0.037)^3} = 5 \times 10^9$$

Solving for $x$, we obtain $4 \times 10^{-9}\ M$. From this, we see that the oxalate has complexed all but a tiny fraction of the $Co^{2+}$ in solution.

# CHAPTER SUMMARY AND KEY TERMS

**SECTION 23.1.** Metallic elements occur in nature in **minerals,** which are solid inorganic compounds found in nature. **Metallurgy** is the science and technology of extracting metals from the earth and processing them for further use. Transition metals are characterized by incomplete filling of the $d$ orbitals. The presence of $d$ electrons in transition elements leads to multiple oxidation states. As we proceed through the transition metals in a given row of the periodic table, the attraction between the nucleus and the valence electrons increases more markedly for $d$ electrons than for $s$ electrons. As a result, the later transition elements in a period tend to have lower oxidation states.

The atomic and ionic radii of period 5 transition metals are larger than those of period 4 metals. The transition metals of periods 5 and 6 have comparable atomic and ionic radii and are also similar in other properties. This similarity is due to the **lanthanide contraction.**

The presence of unpaired electrons in valence orbitals leads to magnetic behavior in transition metals and their compounds. In **ferromagnetic, ferrimagnetic,** and **antiferromagnetic** substances the unpaired electron spins on atoms in a solid are affected by spins on neighboring atoms. In a ferromagnetic substance the spins all point in the same direction. In an antiferromagnetic substance the spins point in opposite directions and cancel one another. In a ferrimagnetic substance the spins point in opposite directions but do not fully cancel. Ferromagnetic and ferrimagnetic substances are used to make permanent magnets.

**SECTION 23.2** **Coordination compounds** are substances that contain **metal complexes.** Metal complexes contain metal ions bonded to several surrounding anions or molecules known as **ligands.** The metal ion and its ligands make up the **coordination sphere** of the complex. The number of atoms attached to the metal ion is the **coordination number** of the metal ion. The most common coordination numbers are 4 and 6; the most common coordination geometries are tetrahedral, square planar, and octahedral.

**SECTION 23.3** Ligands that occupy only one site in a coordination sphere are called **monodentate ligands.** The atom of the ligand that bonds to the metal ion is the **donor atom.** Ligands that have two donor atoms are **bidentate ligands. Polydentate ligands** have three or more

donor atoms. Bidentate and polydendate ligands are also called **chelating agents.** In general, chelating agents form more stable complexes than do related monodentate ligands, an observation known as the **chelate effect.** Many biologically important molecules, such as the **porphyrins,** are complexes of chelating agents. A related group of plant pigments known as **chlorophylls** is important in **photosynthesis,** the process by which plants use solar energy to convert $CO_2$ and $H_2O$ into carbohydrates.

**SECTION 23.4** In naming coordination compounds, the number and type of ligands attached to the metal ion are specified, as is the oxidation state of the metal ion. **Isomers** are compounds with the same composition but different arrangements of atoms and therefore different properties. **Structural isomers** differ in the bonding arrangements of the ligands. **Linkage isomerism** occurs when a ligand can coordinate to a metal ion through either of two donor atoms. **Coordination-sphere isomers** contain different ligands in the coordination sphere. **Stereoisomers** are isomers with the same chemical bonding arrangements but different spatial arrangements of ligands. The most common forms of stereoisomerism are **geometric isomerism** and **optical isomerism.** Geometric isomers differ from one another in the relative locations of donor atoms in the coordination sphere; the most common are *cis-trans* isomers. Optical isomers are nonsuperimposable mirror images of each other. Geometric isomers differ from one another in their chemical and physical properties; optical isomers, or **enantiomers,** are **chiral,** however, meaning that they have a specific "handedness" and differ only in the presence of a chiral environment. Optical isomers can be distinguished from one another by their interactions with plane-polarized light; solutions of one isomer rotate the plane of polarization to the right (**dextrorotatory**), and solutions of its mirror image rotate the plane to the left (**levorotatory**). Chiral molecules, therefore, are **optically active.** A 50–50 mixture of two optical isomers does not rotate plane-polarized light and is said to be **racemic.**

**SECTION 23.5** A substance has a particular color because it either reflects or transmits light of that color or absorbs light of the **complementary color.** The amount of light absorbed by a sample as a function of wavelength is known as its **absorption spectrum**. The light absorbed provides the energy to excite electrons to higher-energy states.

It is possible to determine the number of unpaired electrons in a complex from its degree of paramagnetism. Compounds with no unpaired electrons are diamagnetic.

**SECTION 23.6** **Crystal-field theory** successfully accounts for many properties of coordination compounds, including their color and magnetism. In crystal-field theory, the interaction between metal ion and ligand is viewed as electrostatic. Because some $d$ orbitals point right at the ligands whereas others point between them, the ligands split the energies of the metal $d$ orbitals. For an octahedral complex, the $d$ orbitals are split into a lower-energy set of three degenerate orbitals (the $t_2$ set) and a higher-energy set of two degenerate orbitals (the $e$ set). Visible light can cause a ***d-d* transition**, in which an electron is excited from a lower-energy $d$ orbital to a higher-energy $d$ orbital. The

**spectrochemical series** lists ligands in order of their ability to increase the split in $d$-orbital energies in octahedral complexes.

Strong-field ligands create a splitting of $d$-orbital energies that is large enough to overcome the **spin-pairing energy**. The $d$ electrons then preferentially pair up in the lower-energy orbitals, producing a **low-spin complex**. When the ligands exert a weak crystal field, the splitting of the $d$ orbitals is small. The electrons then occupy the higher-energy $d$ orbitals in preference to pairing up in the lower-energy set, producing a **high-spin complex**.

Crystal-field theory also applies to tetrahedral and square-planar complexes, which leads to different $d$-orbital splitting patterns. In a tetrahedral crystal field, the splitting of the $d$ orbitals results in a higher-energy $t_2$ set and a lower-energy $e$ set, the opposite of the octahedral case. The splitting by a tetrahedral crystal field is much smaller than that by an octahedral crystal field, so tetrahedral complexes are always high-spin complexes.

# KEY SKILLS

• Describe the periodic trends in radii and oxidation states of the transition-metal ions, including the origin and effect of the lanthanide contraction. (Section 23.1)

• Determine the oxidation number and number of $d$ electrons for metal ions in complexes. (Section 23.2)

• Distinguish between chelating and nonchelating ligands. (Section 23.3)

• Name coordination compounds given their formula and write their formula given their name. (Section 23.4)

• Recognize and draw the geometric isomers of a complex. (Section 23.4)

• Recognize and draw the optical isomers of a complex. (Section 23.4)

• Use crystal-field theory to explain the colors and to determine the number of unpaired electrons in a complex. (Sections 23.5 and 23.6)

# EXERCISES

## VISUALIZING CONCEPTS

**23.1** This chart shows the variation in an important property of the metals from K through Ge. Is the property atomic radius, electronegativity, or first ionization energy? Explain your choice. [Section 23.1]

**23.2** **(a)** Draw the structure for $Pt(en)Cl_2$. **(b)** What is the coordination number for platinum in this complex, and what is the coordination geometry? **(c)** What is the oxidation state of the platinum? [Section 23.2]

**23.3** Draw the Lewis structure for the ligand shown in the next column. **(a)** Which atoms can serve as donor atoms? Classify this ligand as monodentate, bidentate, or tridentate. **(b)** How many of these ligands are needed to fill the coordination sphere in an octahedral complex? [Section 23.2]

$$NH_2CH_2CH_2NHCH_2CO_2^-$$

**23.4** The complex ion shown here has a $1-$ charge. Name the complex ion. [Section 23.4]

○ = N
○ = Cl
○ = H
○ = Pt

**23.5** There are two geometric isomers of octahedral complexes of the type MA₃X₃, where M is a metal and A and X are monodentate ligands. Of the complexes shown here, which are identical to (1) and which are the geometric isomers of (1)? [Section 23.4]

(1)      (2)      (3)      (4)      (5)

**23.6** Which of the complexes shown here are chiral? Explain. [Section 23.4]

● = Cr     ◗◖ = NH₂CH₂CH₂NH₂     ● = Cl     ● = NH₃

(1)        (2)        (3)        (4)

**23.7** The solutions shown here each have an absorption spectrum with a single absorption peak like that shown in Figure 23.26. What color does each solution absorb most strongly? [Section 23.5]

**23.8** Which of these crystal-field splitting diagrams represents: **(a)** a weak-field octahedral complex of $Fe^{3+}$, **(b)** a strong-field octahedral complex of $Fe^{3+}$, **(c)** a tetrahedral complex of $Fe^{3+}$, **(d)** a tetrahedral complex of $Ni^{2+}$? (The diagrams do not indicate the relative magnitudes of $\Delta$.) [Section 23.6]

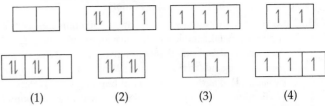

(1)        (2)        (3)        (4)

**23.9** In the linear crystal field shown here, the negative charges are on the $z$-axis. Using Figure 23.28 as a guide, predict which $d$ orbital has lobes closest to the charges. Which two have lobes farthest from the charges? Predict the crystal-field splitting of the $d$ orbitals in linear complexes. [Section 23.6]

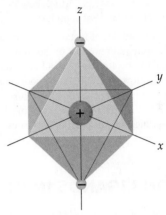

**23.10** Two Fe(II) complexes are both low spin but have different ligands. A solution of one is green and a solution of the other is red. Which solution is likely to contain the complex that has the stronger-field ligand? [Section 23.6]

# THE TRANSITION METALS (section 23.1)

**23.11** Explain the lanthanide contraction, and describe how it affects the properties of the transition-metal elements.

**23.12** Sketch a plot of atomic radius versus number of valence $d$ electrons for the period 5 transition metals, and explain the trend.

**23.13** The +2 oxidation state is common for almost all the transition metals. Suggest an explanation.

**23.14** No compounds are known in which scandium is in the +2 oxidation state. Suggest an explanation.

**23.15** Write out the ground-state electron configurations of **(a)** $Ti^{3+}$, **(b)** $Ru^{2+}$, **(c)** $Au^{3+}$, **(d)** $Mn^{4+}$.

**23.16** How many electrons are in the valence $d$ orbitals in these transition-metal ions? **(a)** $Co^{3+}$, **(b)** $Cu^{+}$, **(c)** $Cd^{2+}$, **(d)** $Os^{3+}$.

**23.17** Explain the difference between a diamagnetic substance and a paramagnetic substance.

**23.18** Distinguish among a ferromagnetic substance, an antiferromagnetic substance, and a ferrimagnetic substance.

**23.19** What kind of magnetism is exhibited by this diagram:

Put in vertical magnetic field          Magnetic field

**23.20** The most important oxides of iron are magnetite, $Fe_3O_4$, and hematite, $Fe_2O_3$. **(a)** What are the oxidation states of iron in these compounds? **(b)** One of these iron oxides is ferrimagnetic, and the other is antiferromagnetic. Which iron oxide is likely to show which type of magnetism? Explain.

# TRANSITION-METAL COMPLEXES (section 23.2)

**23.21** (a) What is the difference between Werner's concepts of *primary valence* and *secondary valence*? What terms do we now use for these concepts? (b) Why can the $NH_3$ molecule serve as a ligand but the $BH_3$ molecule cannot?

**23.22** (a) What is the meaning of the term *coordination number* as it applies to metal complexes? (b) Give an example of a ligand that is neutral and one that is negatively charged. (c) Would you expect ligands that are positively charged to be common? Explain. (d) What type of chemical bonding is characteristic of coordination compounds? Illustrate with the compound $Co(NH_3)_6Cl_3$. (e) What are the most common coordination numbers for metal complexes?

**23.23** A complex is written as $NiBr_2 \cdot 6\,NH_3$. (a) What is the oxidation state of the Ni atom in this complex? (b) What is the likely coordination number for the complex? (c) If the complex is treated with excess $AgNO_3(aq)$, how many moles of AgBr will precipitate per mole of complex?

**23.24** A certain complex of metal M is formulated as $MCl_3 \cdot 3\,H_2O$. The coordination number of the complex is not known but is expected to be 4 or 6. (a) Would conductivity measurements provide information about the coordination number? (b) In using conductivity measurements to test which ligands are bound to the metal ion, what assumption is made about the rate at which ligands enter or leave the coordination sphere of the metal? (c) Suppose you experimentally determine that this complex exists in aqueous solution as a single species. Suggest a likely coordination number and the number and type of each ligand.

**23.25** Indicate the coordination number of the metal and the oxidation number of the metal as well as the number and type of each donor atom of the ligands for each of the following complexes:
(a) $Na_2[CdCl_4]$
(b) $K_2[MoOCl_4]$
(c) $[Co(NH_3)_4Cl_2]Cl$
(d) $[Ni(CN)_5]^{3-}$
(e) $K_3[V(C_2O_4)_3]$
(f) $[Zn(en)_2]Br_2$

**23.26** Indicate the coordination number of the metal and the oxidation number of the metal as well as the number and type of each donor atom of the ligands for each of the following complexes:
(a) $K_3[Co(CN)_6]$
(b) $Na_2[CdBr_4]$
(c) $[Pt(en)_3](ClO_4)_4$
(d) $[Co(en)_2(C_2O_4)]^+$
(e) $NH_4[Cr(NH_3)_2(NCS)_4]$
(f) $[Cu(bipy)_2I]I$

# COMMON LIGANDS IN COORDINATION CHEMISTRY (section 23.3)

**23.27** (a) What is the difference between a monodentate ligand and a bidentate ligand? (b) How many bidentate ligands are necessary to fill the coordination sphere of a six-coordinate complex? (c) You are told that a certain molecule can serve as a tridentate ligand. Based on this statement, what do you know about the molecule?

**23.28** For each of the following polydentate ligands, determine (i) the maximum number of coordination sites that the ligand can occupy on a single metal ion and (ii) the number and type of donor atoms in the ligand: (a) ethylenediamine (en), (b) bipyridine (bipy), (c) the oxalate anion ($C_2O_4^{2-}$), (d) the $2-$ ion of the porphine molecule (Figure 23.13); (e) $[EDTA]^{4-}$.

**23.29** Polydentate ligands can vary in the number of coordination positions they occupy. In each of the following, identify the polydentate ligand present and indicate the probable number of coordination positions it occupies:
(a) $[Co(NH_3)_4(o\text{-phen})]Cl_3$
(b) $[Cr(C_2O_4)(H_2O)_4]Br$
(c) $[Cr(EDTA)(H_2O)]^-$
(d) $[Zn(en)_2](ClO_4)_2$

**23.30** Indicate the likely coordination number of the metal in each of the following complexes:
(a) $[Rh(bipy)_3](NO_3)_3$
(b) $Na_3[Co(C_2O_4)_2Cl_2]$
(c) $[Cr(o\text{-phen})_3](CH_3COO)_3$
(d) $Na_2[Co(EDTA)Br]$

**23.31** (a) What is meant by the term *chelate effect*? (b) What thermodynamic factor is generally responsible for the chelate effect? (c) Why are polydentate ligands often called *sequestering agents*?

**23.32** *Pyridine* ($C_5H_5N$), abbreviated py, is the molecule

(a) Why is pyridine referred to as a monodentate ligand? (b) For the equilibrium reaction

$$[Ru(py)_4(bipy)]^{2+} + 2\,py \rightleftharpoons [Ru(py)_6]^{2+} + bipy$$

what would you predict for the magnitude of the equilibrium constant? Explain your answer.

**23.33** Is the following ligand a chelating one? Explain.

**23.34** What is the geometry about the metal center in this complex? Would you expect this complex to have counterions? Explain.

# NOMENCLATURE AND ISOMERISM IN COORDINATION CHEMISTRY (section 23.4)

**23.35** Write the formula for each of the following compounds, being sure to use brackets to indicate the coordination sphere:
  **(a)** hexaamminechromium(III) nitrate
  **(b)** tetraamminecarbonatocobalt(III) sulfate
  **(c)** dichlorobis(ethylenediamine)platinum(IV) bromide
  **(d)** potassium diaquatetrabromovanadate(III)
  **(e)** bis(ethylenediamine)zinc(II) tetraiodomercurate(II)

**23.36** Write the formula for each of the following compounds, being sure to use brackets to indicate the coordination sphere:
  **(a)** tetraaquadibromomanganese(III) perchlorate
  **(b)** bis(bipyridyl)cadmium(II) chloride
  **(c)** potassium tetrabromo(*ortho*-phenanthroline)-cobaltate (III)
  **(d)** cesium diamminetetracyanochromate(III)
  **(e)** tris(ethylenediamine)rhodium(III) tris(oxalato)-cobaltate(III)

**23.37** Write the names of the following compounds, using the standard nomenclature rules for coordination complexes:
  **(a)** $[Rh(NH_3)_4Cl_2]Cl$
  **(b)** $K_2[TiCl_6]$
  **(c)** $MoOCl_4$
  **(d)** $[Pt(H_2O)_4(C_2O_4)]Br_2$

**23.38** Write names for the following coordination compounds:
  **(a)** $[Cd(en)Cl_2]$
  **(b)** $K_4[Mn(CN)_6]$
  **(c)** $[Cr(NH_3)_5CO_3]Cl$
  **(d)** $[Ir(NH_3)_4(H_2O)_2](NO_3)_3$

**23.39** By writing formulas or drawing structures related to any one of these three complexes,
  $[Co(NH_3)_4Br_2]Cl$
  $[Pd(NH_3)_2(ONO)_2]$
  *cis*-$[V(en)_2Cl_2]^+$,
  illustrate **(a)** geometric isomerism, **(b)** linkage isomerism, **(c)** optical isomerism, **(d)** coordination-sphere isomerism.

**23.40** **(a)** Draw the two linkage isomers of $[Co(NH_3)_5SCN]^{2+}$.
  **(b)** Draw the two geometric isomers of $[Co(NH_3)_3Cl_3]^{2+}$.
  **(c)** Two compounds with the formula $Co(NH_3)_5ClBr$ can be prepared. Use structural formulas to show how they differ. What kind of isomerism does this illustrate?

**23.41** A four-coordinate complex $MA_2B_2$ is prepared and found to have two different isomers. Is it possible to determine from this information whether the complex is square planar or tetrahedral? If so, which is it?

**23.42** Consider an octahedral complex $MA_3B_3$. How many geometric isomers are expected for this compound? Will any of the isomers be optically active? If so, which ones?

**23.43** Sketch all the possible stereoisomers of **(a)** tetrahedral $[Cd(H_2O)_2Cl_2]$, **(b)** square-planar $[IrCl_2(PH_3)_2]^-$, **(c)** octahedral $[Fe(o\text{-}phen)_2Cl_2]^+$.

**23.44** Sketch all the possible stereoisomers of **(a)** $[Rh(bipy)(o\text{-}phen)_2]^{3+}$, **(b)** $[Co(NH_3)_3(bipy)Br]^{2+}$, **(c)** square-planar $[Pd(en)(CN)_2]$.

# COLOR AND MAGNETISM IN COORDINATION CHEMISTRY; CRYSTAL-FIELD THEORY (sections 23.5 and 23.6)

**23.45** **(a)** Can we see light that is 300 nm in wavelength? 500 nm in wavelength? **(b)** What is meant by the term *complementary color*? **(c)** What is the significance of complementary colors in understanding the colors of metal complexes? **(d)** If a complex absorbs light at 610 nm, what is the energy of this absorption in kJ/mol?

**23.46** **(a)** A complex absorbs light in the range of 200–300 nm. Do you expect it to have visible color? **(b)** A solution of a compound appears green. Does this observation necessarily mean that all colors of visible light other than green are absorbed by the solution? Explain. **(c)** What information is usually presented in a *visible absorption spectrum* of a compound? **(d)** What energy is associated with an absorption at 440 nm in kJ/mol?

**23.47** Is it possible for a low-spin octahedral Fe(II) complex to be paramagnetic? Explain.

**23.48** If a transition-metal complex has an even number of valence $d$ electrons, does it necessarily mean that the complex is diamagnetic? Explain.

**23.49** In crystal-field theory, ligands are modeled as if they are point negative charges. What is the basis of this assumption, and how does it relate to the nature of metal–ligand bonds?

**23.50** Explain why the $d_{xy}$, $d_{xz}$, and $d_{yz}$ orbitals lie lower in energy than the $d_{z^2}$ and $d_{x^2-y^2}$ orbitals in the presence of an octahedral arrangement of ligands about the central metal ion.

**23.51** **(a)** Sketch a diagram that shows the definition of the *crystal-field splitting energy* ($\Delta$) for an octahedral crystal field. **(b)** What is the relationship between the magnitude of $\Delta$ and the energy of the *d-d* transition for a $d^1$ complex? **(c)** Calculate $\Delta$ in kJ/mol if a $d^1$ complex has an absorption maximum at 545 nm.

**23.52** As shown in Figure 23.26, the *d-d* transition of $[Ti(H_2O)_6]^{3+}$ produces an absorption maximum at a wavelength of about 500 nm. **(a)** What is the magnitude of $\Delta$ for $[Ti(H_2O)_6]^{3+}$ in kJ/mol? **(b)** What is the *spectrochemical series*? How would the magnitude of $\Delta$ change if the $H_2O$ ligands in $[Ti(H_2O)_6]^{3+}$ were replaced with $NH_3$ ligands?

**23.53** Explain why many cyano complexes of divalent transition-metal ions are yellow, whereas many aqua complexes of these ions are blue or green.

**23.54** The $[Ni(H_2O)_6]^{2+}$ ion has an absorption maximum at about 725 nm, whereas the $[Ni(NH_3)_6]^{2+}$ ion absorbs at about 570 nm. Predict the color of a solution of each ion. **(b)** The $[Ni(en)_3]^{2+}$ ion absorption maximum occurs at about 545 nm, and that of the $[Ni(bipy)_3]^{2+}$ ion occurs at about 520 nm. From these data, indicate the relative strengths of the ligand fields created by the four ligands involved.

**23.55** Give the number of (valence) $d$ electrons associated with the central metal ion in each of the following complexes: **(a)** $K_3[TiCl_6]$, **(b)** $Na_3[Co(NO_2)_6]$, **(c)** $[Ru(en)_3]Br_3$, **(d)** $[Mo(EDTA)]ClO_4$, **(e)** $K_3[ReCl_6]$.

**23.56** Give the number of (valence) $d$ electrons associated with the central metal ion in each of the following complexes: (a) $K_3[Fe(CN)_6]$, (b) $[Mn(H_2O)_6](NO_3)_2$, (c) $Na[Ag(CN)_2]$, (d) $[Cr(NH_3)_4Br_2]ClO_4$, (e) $[Sr(EDTA)]^{2-}$.

**23.57** A classmate says, "A weak-field ligand usually means the complex is high spin." Is your classmate correct? Explain.

**23.58** A classmate says, "A strong-field ligand means that the ligand binds strongly to the metal ion." Is your classmate correct? Explain.

**23.59** For each of the following metals, write the electronic configuration of the atom and its 2+ ion: (a) Mn, (b) Ru, (c) Rh. Draw the crystal-field energy-level diagram for the $d$ orbitals of an octahedral complex, and show the placement of the $d$ electrons for each 2+ ion, assuming a strong-field complex. How many unpaired electrons are there in each case?

**23.60** For each of the following metals, write the electronic configuration of the atom and its 3+ ion: (a) Ru, (b) Mo, (c) Co. Draw the crystal-field energy-level diagram for the $d$ orbitals of an octahedral complex, and show the placement of the $d$ electrons for each 3+ ion, assuming a weak-field complex. How many unpaired electrons are there in each case?

**23.61** Draw the crystal-field energy-level diagrams and show the placement of $d$ electrons for each of the following: (a) $[Cr(H_2O)_6]^{2+}$ (four unpaired electrons), (b) $[Mn(H_2O)_6]^{2+}$ (high spin), (c) $[Ru(NH_3)_5H_2O]^{2+}$ (low spin), (d) $[IrCl_6]^{2-}$ (low spin), (e) $[Cr(en)_3]^{3+}$, (f) $[NiF_6]^{4-}$.

**23.62** Draw the crystal-field energy-level diagrams and show the placement of electrons for the following complexes: (a) $[VCl_6]^{3-}$, (b) $[FeF_6]^{3-}$ (a high-spin complex), (c) $[Ru(bipy)_3]^{3+}$ (a low-spin complex), (d) $[NiCl_4]^{2-}$ (tetrahedral), (e) $[PtBr_6]^{2-}$, (f) $[Ti(en)_3]^{2+}$.

**23.63** The complex $[Mn(NH_3)_6]^{2+}$ contains five unpaired electrons. Sketch the energy-level diagram for the $d$ orbitals, and indicate the placement of electrons for this complex ion. Is the ion a high-spin or a low-spin complex?

**23.64** The ion $[Fe(CN)_6]^{3-}$ has one unpaired electron, whereas $[Fe(NCS)_6]^{3-}$ has five unpaired electrons. From these results, what can you conclude about whether each complex is high spin or low spin? What can you say about the placement of $NCS^-$ in the spectrochemical series?

## ADDITIONAL EXERCISES

**23.65** The *Curie temperature* is the temperature at which a ferromagnetic solid switches from ferromagnetic to paramagnetic, and for nickel, the Curie temperature is 354 °C. Knowing this, you tie a string to two paper clips made of nickel and hold the paper clips near a permanent magnet. The magnet attracts the paper clips, as shown in the photograph on the left. Now you heat one of the paper clips with a cigarette lighter, and the clip drops (right photograph). Explain what happened.

**23.66** Explain why the transition metals in periods 5 and 6 have nearly identical radii in each group.

**23.67** Based on the molar conductance values listed here for the series of platinum(IV) complexes, write the formula for each complex so as to show which ligands are in the coordination sphere of the metal. By way of example, the molar conductances of 0.050 $M$ NaCl and BaCl$_2$ are 107 ohm$^{-1}$ and 197 ohm$^{-1}$, respectively.

| Complex | Molar Conductance (ohm$^{-1}$)* of 0.050 $M$ Solution |
|---|---|
| $Pt(NH_3)_6Cl_4$ | 523 |
| $Pt(NH_3)_4Cl_4$ | 228 |
| $Pt(NH_3)_3Cl_4$ | 97 |
| $Pt(NH_3)_2Cl_4$ | 0 |
| $KPt(NH_3)Cl_5$ | 108 |

*The ohm is a unit of resistance; conductance is the inverse of resistance.

**23.68** (a) A compound with formula $RuCl_3 \cdot 5 H_2O$ is dissolved in water, forming a solution that is approximately the same color as the solid. Immediately after forming the solution, the addition of excess $AgNO_3(aq)$ forms 2 mol of solid AgCl per mole of complex. Write the formula for the compound, showing which ligands are likely to be present in the coordination sphere. (b) After a solution of $RuCl_3 \cdot 5 H_2O$ has stood for about a year, addition of $AgNO_3(aq)$ precipitates 3 mol of AgCl per mole of complex. What has happened in the ensuing time?

**23.69** Sketch the structure of the complex in each of the following compounds and give the full compound name:
(a) *cis*-$[Co(NH_3)_4(H_2O)_2](NO_3)_2$
(b) $Na_2[Ru(H_2O)Cl_5]$
(c) *trans*-$NH_4[Co(C_2O_4)_2(H_2O)_2]$
(d) *cis*-$[Ru(en)_2Cl_2]$

**23.70** (a) Which complex ions in Exercise 23.69 have a mirror plane? (b) Will any of the complexes be optically active? Explain.

**23.71** The molecule *dimethylphosphinoethane* $[(CH_3)_2PCH_2-CH_2P(CH_3)_2$, which is abbreviated dmpe] is used as a ligand for some complexes that serve as catalysts. A complex that contains this ligand is $Mo(CO)_4(dmpe)$. (a) Draw the Lewis structure for dmpe, and compare it with ethylenediamine as a coordinating ligand. (b) What is the oxidation state of Mo in $Na_2[Mo(CN)_2(CO)_2(dmpe)]$? (c) Sketch the structure of the $[Mo(CN)_2(CO)_2(dmpe)]^{2-}$ ion, including all the possible isomers.

**23.72** Although the *cis* configuration is known for [Pt(en)Cl₂], no *trans* form is known. **(a)** Explain why the *trans* compound is not possible. **(b)** Would NH₂CH₂CH₂CH₂CH₂NH₂ be more likely than en (NH₂CH₂CH₂NH₂) to form the *trans* compound? Explain.

**23.73** The acetylacetone ion forms very stable complexes with many metallic ions. It acts as a bidentate ligand, coordinating to the metal at two adjacent positions. Suppose that one of the CH₃ groups of the ligand is replaced by a CF₃ group, as shown here,

Trifluoromethyl
acetylacetonate
(tfac)

$$\left[ \begin{array}{c} H \\ \\ CF_3-C \\ \\ :O: \end{array} \begin{array}{c} C \\ \\ C-CH_3 \\ \\ :O: \end{array} \right]^-$$

Sketch all possible isomers for the complex with three tfac ligands on cobalt(III). (You can use the symbol ●○ to represent the ligand.)

**23.74** Give brief statements about the relevance of the following complexes in living systems: **(a)** hemoglobin, **(b)** chlorophylls, **(c)** siderophores.

**23.75** Write balanced chemical equations to represent the following observations. (In some instances the complex involved has been discussed previously in the text.) **(a)** Solid silver chloride dissolves in an excess of aqueous ammonia. **(b)** The green complex [Cr(en)₂Cl₂]Cl, on treatment with water over a long time, converts to a brown-orange complex. Reaction of AgNO₃ with a solution of the product precipitates 3 mol of AgCl per mole of Cr present. (Write two chemical equations.) **(c)** When an NaOH solution is added to a solution of Zn(NO₃)₂, a precipitate forms. Addition of excess NaOH solution causes the precipitate to dissolve. (Write two chemical equations.) **(d)** A pink solution of Co(NO₃)₂ turns deep blue on addition of concentrated hydrochloric acid.

**23.76** Some metal complexes have a coordination number of 5. One such complex is Fe(CO)₅, which adopts a *trigonal bipyramidal* geometry (see Figure 9.8). **(a)** Write the name for Fe(CO)₅, using the nomenclature rules for coordination compounds. **(b)** What is the oxidation state of Fe in this compound? **(c)** Suppose one of the CO ligands is replaced with a CN⁻ ligand, forming [Fe(CO)₄(CN)]⁻. How many geometric isomers would you predict this complex could have?

**23.77** Which of the following objects is chiral: **(a)** a left shoe, **(b)** a slice of bread, **(c)** a wood screw, **(d)** a molecular model of Zn(en)Cl₂, **(e)** a typical golf club?

**23.78** The complexes [V(H₂O)₆]³⁺ and [VF₆]³⁻ are both known. **(a)** Draw the d-orbital energy-level diagram for V(III) octahedral complexes. **(b)** What gives rise to the colors of these complexes? **(c)** Which of the two complexes would you expect to absorb light of higher energy? Explain.

**[23.79]** One of the more famous species in coordination chemistry is the Creutz–Taube complex,

$$\left[ (NH_3)_5RuN \bigcirc NRu(NH_3)_5 \right]^{5+}$$

It is named for the two scientists who discovered it and initially studied its properties. The central ligand is pyrazine, a planar six-membered ring with nitrogens at opposite sides. **(a)** How can you account for the fact that the complex, which has only neutral ligands, has an odd overall charge? **(b)** The metal is in a low-spin configuration in both cases. Assuming octahedral coordination, draw the d-orbital energy-level diagram for each metal. **(c)** In many experiments the two metal ions appear to be in exactly equivalent states. Can you think of a reason that this might appear to be so, recognizing that electrons move very rapidly compared to nuclei?

**23.80** Solutions of [Co(NH₃)₆]²⁺, [Co(H₂O)₆]²⁺ (both octahedral), and [CoCl₄]²⁻ (tetrahedral) are colored. One is pink, one is blue, and one is yellow. Based on the spectrochemical series and remembering that the energy splitting in tetrahedral complexes is normally much less than that in octahedral ones, assign a color to each complex.

**23.81** Oxyhemoglobin, with an O₂ bound to iron, is a low-spin Fe(II) complex; deoxyhemoglobin, without the O₂ molecule, is a high-spin complex. **(a)** Assuming that the coordination environment about the metal is octahedral, how many unpaired electrons are centered on the metal ion in each case? **(b)** What ligand is coordinated to the iron in place of O₂ in deoxyhemoglobin? **(c)** Explain in a general way why the two forms of hemoglobin have different colors (hemoglobin is red, whereas deoxyhemoglobin has a bluish cast). **(d)** A 15-minute exposure to air containing 400 ppm of CO causes about 10% of the hemoglobin in the blood to be converted into the carbon monoxide complex, called carboxyhemoglobin. What does this suggest about the relative equilibrium constants for binding of carbon monoxide and O₂ to hemoglobin? **(e)** CO is a strong-field ligand. What color might you expect carboxyhemoglobin to be?

**[23.82]** Consider the tetrahedral anions VO₄³⁻ (orthovanadate ion), CrO₄²⁻ (chromate ion), and MnO₄⁻ (permanganate ion). **(a)** These anions are *isoelectronic*. What does this statement mean? **(b)** Would you expect these anions to exhibit d-d transitions? Explain. **(c)** As mentioned in "A Closer Look" on charge-transfer color, the violet color of MnO₄⁻ is due to a *ligand-to-metal charge transfer* (LMCT) transition. What is meant by this term? **(d)** The LMCT transition in MnO₄⁻ occurs at a wavelength of 565 nm. The CrO₄²⁻ ion is yellow. Is the wavelength of the LMCT transition for chromate larger or smaller than that for MnO₄⁻? Explain. **(e)** The VO₄³⁻ ion is colorless. Do you expect the light absorbed by the LMCT to fall in the UV or the IR region of the electromagnetic spectrum? Explain your reasoning.

**[23.83]** Given the colors observed for VO₄³⁻ (orthovanadate ion), CrO₄²⁻ (chromate ion), and MnO₄⁻ (permanganate ion) (see Exercise 23.82), what can you say about how the energy separation between the ligand orbitals and the empty d orbitals changes as a function of the oxidation state of the transition metal at the center of the tetrahedral anion?

**[23.84]** The red color of ruby is due to the presence of Cr(III) ions at octahedral sites in the close-packed oxide lattice of Al₂O₃. Draw the crystal-field splitting diagram for Cr(III) in this environment. Suppose that the ruby crystal is subjected to high pressure. What do you predict for the variation in the wavelength of absorption of the ruby as a function of pressure? Explain.

**23.85** In 2001, chemists at SUNY-Stony Brook succeeded in synthesizing the complex *trans*-$[Fe(CN)_4(CO)_2]^{2-}$, which could be a model of complexes that may have played a role in the origin of life. **(a)** Sketch the structure of the complex. **(b)** The complex is isolated as a sodium salt. Write the complete name of this salt. **(c)** What is the oxidation state of Fe in this complex? How many *d* electrons are associated with the Fe in this complex? **(d)** Would you expect this complex to be high spin or low spin? Explain.

**[23.86]** When Alfred Werner was developing the field of coordination chemistry, it was argued by some that the optical activity he observed in the chiral complexes he had prepared was because of the presence of carbon atoms in the molecule. To disprove this argument, Werner synthesized a chiral complex of cobalt that had no carbon atoms in it, and he was able to resolve it into its enantiomers. Design a cobalt(III) complex that would be chiral if it could be synthesized and that contains no carbon atoms. (It may not be possible to synthesize the complex you design, but we won't worry about that for now.)

**23.87** Generally speaking, for a given metal and ligand, the stability of a coordination compound is greater for the metal in the +3 rather than in the +2 oxidation state (for metals that

form stable +3 ions in the first place). Suggest an explanation, keeping in mind the Lewis acid–base nature of the metal–ligand bond.

**23.88** Many trace metal ions exist in the blood complexed with amino acids or small peptides. The anion of the amino acid glycine (gly),

$$H_2NCH_2\overset{\overset{\displaystyle O}{\|}}{C}—O^-$$

can act as a bidentate ligand, coordinating to the metal through nitrogen and oxygen atoms. How many isomers are possible for **(a)** $[Zn(gly)_2]$ (tetrahedral), **(b)** $[Pt(gly)_2]$ (square planar), **(c)** $[Co(gly)_3]$ (octahedral)? Sketch all possible isomers. Use the symbol N͜O to represent the ligand.

**[23.89]** Suppose that a transition-metal ion was in a lattice in which it was in contact with just two nearby anions, located on opposite sides of the metal. Diagram the splitting of the metal *d* orbitals that would result from such a crystal field. Assuming a strong field, how many unpaired electrons would you expect for a metal ion with six *d* electrons? (*Hint:* Consider the linear axis to be the *z*-axis)

# INTEGRATIVE EXERCISES

**[23.90]** Metallic elements are essential components of many important enzymes operating within our bodies. *Carbonic anhydrase*, which contains $Zn^{2+}$ in its active site, is responsible for rapidly interconverting dissolved $CO_2$ and bicarbonate ion, $HCO_3^-$. The zinc in carbonic anhydrase is tetrahedrally coordinated by three neutral nitrogen-containing groups and a water molecule. The coordinated water molecule has a $pK_a$ of 7.5, which is crucial for the enzyme's activity. **(a)** Draw the active site geometry for the Zn(II) center in carbonic anhydrase, just writing "N" for the three neutral nitrogen ligands from the protein. **(b)** Compare the $pK_a$ of carbonic anhydrase's active site with that of pure water; which species is more acidic? **(c)** When the coordinated water to the Zn(II) center in carbonic anhydrase is deprotonated, what ligands are bound to the Zn(II) center? Assume the three nitrogen ligands are unaffected. **(d)** The $pK_a$ of $[Zn(H_2O)_6]^{2+}$ is 10. Suggest an explanation for the difference between this $pK_a$ and that of carbonic anhydrase. **(e)** Would you expect carbonic anhydrase to have a deep color, like hemoglobin and other metal-ion containing proteins do? Explain.

**23.91** Two different compounds have the formulation $CoBr(SO_4) \cdot 5\ NH_3$. Compound A is dark violet, and compound B is red-violet. When compound A is treated with $AgNO_3(aq)$, no reaction occurs, whereas compound B reacts with $AgNO_3(aq)$ to form a white precipitate. When compound A is treated with $BaCl_2(aq)$, a white precipitate is formed, whereas compound B has no reaction with $BaCl_2(aq)$. **(a)** Is Co in the same oxidation state in these complexes? **(b)** Explain the reactivity of compounds A and B with $AgNO_3(aq)$ and $BaCl_2(aq)$. **(c)** Are compounds A and B isomers of one another? If so, which category from Figure 23.19 best describes the isomerism observed for these complexes? **(d)** Would compounds A and B be expected to be strong electrolytes, weak electrolytes, or nonelectrolytes?

**23.92** A manganese complex formed from a solution containing potassium bromide and oxalate ion is purified and analyzed. It contains 10.0% Mn, 28.6% potassium, 8.8% carbon, and 29.2% bromine by mass. The remainder of the compound is oxygen. An aqueous solution of the complex has about the same electrical conductivity as an equimolar solution of $K_4[Fe(CN)_6]$. Write the formula of the compound, using brackets to denote the manganese and its coordination sphere.

**23.93** The $E°$ values for two low-spin iron complexes in acidic solution are as follows:

$$[Fe(\textit{o}\text{-phen})_3]^{3+}(aq) + e^- \rightleftharpoons [Fe(\textit{o}\text{-phen})_3]^{2+}(aq) \quad E° = 1.12\ V$$

$$[Fe(CN)_6]^{3-}(aq) + e^- \rightleftharpoons [Fe(CN)_6]^{4-}(aq) \quad E° = 0.36\ V$$

**(a)** Is it thermodynamically favorable to reduce both Fe(III) complexes to their Fe(II) analogs? Explain. **(b)** Which complex, $[Fe(\textit{o}\text{-phen})_3]^{3+}$ or $[Fe(CN)_6]^{3-}$, is more difficult to reduce? **(c)** Suggest an explanation for your answer to (b).

**23.94** A palladium complex formed from a solution containing bromide ion and pyridine, $C_5H_5N$ (a good electron-pair donor), is found on elemental analysis to contain 37.6% bromine, 28.3% carbon, 6.60% nitrogen, and 2.37% hydrogen by mass. The compound is slightly soluble in several organic solvents; its solutions in water or alcohol do not conduct electricity. It is found experimentally to have a zero dipole moment. Write the chemical formula, and indicate its probable structure.

**23.95** **(a)** In early studies it was observed that when the complex $[Co(NH_3)_4Br_2]Br$ was placed in water, the electrical conductivity of a 0.05 M solution changed from an initial value of 191 $ohm^{-1}$ to a final value of 374 $ohm^{-1}$ over a period of an hour or so. Suggest an explanation for the observed results. (See Exercise 23.67 for relevant comparison data.) **(b)** Write a balanced chemical equation to describe the reaction. **(c)** A 500-mL solution is made up by dissolving 3.87 g of the complex. As soon as the solution is formed, and before any change in conductivity has occurred, a 25.00-mL portion of the solution is titrated with 0.0100 $M$ AgNO$_3$ solution. What volume of AgNO$_3$ solution do you expect to be required to precipitate the free Br$^-$(aq)? **(d)** Based on the response you gave to part (b), what volume of AgNO$_3$ solution would be required to titrate a fresh 25.00-mL sample of [Co(NH$_3$)$_4$Br$_2$]Br after all conductivity changes have occurred?

**23.96** The total concentration of Ca$^{2+}$ and Mg$^{2+}$ in a sample of hard water was determined by titrating a 0.100-L sample of the water with a solution of EDTA$^{4-}$. The EDTA$^{4-}$ chelates the two cations:

$$Mg^{2+} + [EDTA]^{4-} \longrightarrow [Mg(EDTA)]^{2-}$$

$$Ca^{2+} + [EDTA]^{4-} \longrightarrow [Ca(EDTA)]^{2-}$$

It requires 31.5 mL of 0.0104 $M$ [EDTA]$^{4-}$ solution to reach the end point in the titration. A second 0.100-L sample was then treated with sulfate ion to precipitate Ca$^{2+}$ as calcium sulfate. The Mg$^{2+}$ was then titrated with 18.7 mL of 0.0104 $M$ [EDTA]$^{4-}$. Calculate the concentrations of Mg$^{2+}$ and Ca$^{2+}$ in the hard water in mg/L.

**23.97** Carbon monoxide is toxic because it binds more strongly to the iron in hemoglobin (Hb) than does O$_2$, as indicated by these approximate standard free-energy changes in blood:

$$Hb + O_2 \longrightarrow HbO_2 \qquad \Delta G° = -70 \text{ kJ}$$
$$Hb + CO \longrightarrow HbCO \qquad \Delta G° = -80 \text{ kJ}$$

Using these data, estimate the equilibrium constant at 298 K for the equilibrium

$$HbO_2 + CO \rightleftharpoons HbCO + O_2$$

**[23.98]** The molecule *methylamine* (CH$_3$NH$_2$) can act as a monodentate ligand. The following are equilibrium reactions and the thermochemical data at 298 K for reactions of methylamine and en with Cd$^{2+}$(aq):

$$Cd^{2+}(aq) + 4 CH_3NH_2(aq) \rightleftharpoons [Cd(CH_3NH_2)_4]^{2+}(aq)$$
$$\Delta H° = -57.3 \text{ kJ}; \quad \Delta S° = -67.3 \text{ J/K}; \quad \Delta G° = -37.2 \text{ kJ}$$
$$Cd^{2+}(aq) + 2 en(aq) \rightleftharpoons [Cd(en)_2]^{2+}(aq)$$
$$\Delta H° = -56.5 \text{ kJ}; \quad \Delta S° = +14.1 \text{ J/K}; \quad \Delta G° = -60.7 \text{ kJ}$$

**(a)** Calculate $\Delta G°$ and the equilibrium constant $K$ for the following *ligand exchange* reaction:

$$[Cd(CH_3NH_2)_4]^{2+}(aq) + 2 en(aq) \rightleftharpoons$$
$$[Cd(en)_2]^{2+}(aq) + 4 CH_3NH_2(aq)$$

Based on the value of $K$ in part (a), what would you conclude about this reaction? What concept is demonstrated? **(b)** Determine the magnitudes of the enthalpic ($\Delta H°$) and the entropic ($-T\Delta S°$) contributions to $\Delta G°$ for the ligand exchange reaction. Explain the relative magnitudes. **(c)** Based on information in this exercise and in the "A Closer Look" box on the chelate effect, predict the sign of $\Delta H°$ for the following hypothetical reaction:

$$[Cd(CH_3NH_2)_4]^{2+}(aq) + 4 NH_3(aq) \rightleftharpoons$$
$$[Cd(NH_3)_4]^{2+}(aq) + 4 CH_3NH_2(aq)$$

**23.99** The value of $\Delta$ for the [CrF$_6$]$^{3-}$ complex is 182 kJ/mol. Calculate the expected wavelength of the absorption corresponding to promotion of an electron from the lower-energy to the higher-energy $d$-orbital set in this complex. Should the complex absorb in the visible range?

**[23.100]** A Cu electrode is immersed in a solution that is 1.00 $M$ in [Cu(NH$_3$)$_4$]$^{2+}$ and 1.00 $M$ in NH$_3$. When the cathode is a standard hydrogen electrode, the emf of the cell is found to be +0.08 V. What is the formation constant for [Cu(NH$_3$)$_4$]$^{2+}$?

**[23.101]** The complex [Ru(EDTA)(H$_2$O)]$^-$ undergoes substitution reactions with several ligands, replacing the water molecule with the ligand. In all cases the ruthenium stays in the +3 oxidation state and the ligands use a nitrogen donor atom to bind to the metal.

$$[Ru(EDTA)(H_2O)]^- + L \longrightarrow [Ru(EDTA)L]^- + H_2O$$

The rate constants for several ligands are as follows:

| Ligand, L | $k$ $(M^{-1}s^{-1})$ |
|---|---|
| Pyridine | $6.3 \times 10^3$ |
| SCN$^-$ | $2.7 \times 10^2$ |
| CH$_3$CN | $3.0 \times 10$ |

**(a)** One possible mechanism for this substitution reaction is that the water molecule dissociates from the Ru(III) in the rate-determining step, and then the ligand L binds to Ru(III) in a rapid second step. A second possible mechanism is that L approaches the complex, begins to form a new bond to the Ru(III), and displaces the water molecule, all in a single concerted step. Which of these two mechanisms is more consistent with the data? Explain. **(b)** What do the results suggest about the relative donor ability of the nitrogens of the three ligands toward Ru(III)? **(c)** Assuming that the complexes are all low spin, how many unpaired electrons are in each?

# MATHEMATICAL OPERATIONS

## A.1 | EXPONENTIAL NOTATION

The numbers used in chemistry are often either extremely large or extremely small. Such numbers are conveniently expressed in the form

$$N \times 10^n$$

where $N$ is a number between 1 and 10, and $n$ is the exponent. Some examples of this *exponential notation*, which is also called *scientific notation*, follow.

1,200,000 is $1.2 \times 10^6$      (read "one point two times ten to the sixth power")

0.000604 is $6.04 \times 10^{-4}$      (read "six point zero four times ten to the negative fourth power")

A positive exponent, as in the first example, tells us how many times a number must be multiplied by 10 to give the long form of the number:

$$1.2 \times 10^6 = 1.2 \times 10 \times 10 \times 10 \times 10 \times 10 \times 10 \quad \text{(six tens)}$$
$$= 1,200,000$$

It is also convenient to think of the *positive exponent* as the number of places the decimal point must be moved to the *left* to obtain a number greater than 1 and less than 10. For example, if we begin with 3450 and move the decimal point three places to the left, we end up with $3.45 \times 10^3$.

In a related fashion, a negative exponent tells us how many times we must divide a number by 10 to give the long form of the number.

$$6.04 \times 10^{-4} = \frac{6.04}{10 \times 10 \times 10 \times 10} = 0.000604$$

It is convenient to think of the *negative exponent* as the number of places the decimal point must be moved to the *right* to obtain a number greater than 1 but less than 10. For example, if we begin with 0.0048 and move the decimal point three places to the right, we end up with $4.8 \times 10^{-3}$.

In the system of exponential notation, with each shift of the decimal point one place to the right, the exponent *decreases* by 1:

$$4.8 \times 10^{-3} = 48 \times 10^{-4}$$

Similarly, with each shift of the decimal point one place to the left, the exponent *increases* by 1:

$$4.8 \times 10^{-3} = 0.48 \times 10^{-2}$$

Many scientific calculators have a key labeled EXP or EE, which is used to enter numbers in exponential notation. To enter the number $5.8 \times 10^3$ on such a calculator, the key sequence is

$$\boxed{5}\ \boxed{\cdot}\ \boxed{8}\ \boxed{\text{EXP}}\ (\text{or}\ \boxed{\text{EE}}\ )\ \boxed{3}$$

On some calculators the display will show 5.8, then a space, followed by 03, the exponent. On other calculators, a small 10 is shown with an exponent 3.

To enter a negative exponent, use the key labeled $+/-$. For example, to enter the number $8.6 \times 10^{-5}$, the key sequence is

$$\boxed{8}\ \boxed{\cdot}\ \boxed{6}\ \boxed{\text{EXP}}\ \boxed{+/-}\ \boxed{5}$$

*When entering a number in exponential notation, do not key in the 10 if you use the EXP or EE button.*

In working with exponents, it is important to recall that $10^0 = 1$. The following rules are useful for carrying exponents through calculations.

1. **Addition and Subtraction** In order to add or subtract numbers expressed in exponential notation, the powers of 10 must be the same.

$$(5.22 \times 10^4) + (3.21 \times 10^2) = (522 \times 10^2) + (3.21 \times 10^2)$$
$$= 525 \times 10^2 \quad (3 \text{ significant figures})$$
$$= 5.25 \times 10^4$$
$$(6.25 \times 10^{-2}) - (5.77 \times 10^{-3}) = (6.25 \times 10^{-2}) - (0.577 \times 10^{-2})$$
$$= 5.67 \times 10^{-2} \quad (3 \text{ significant figures})$$

When you use a calculator to add or subtract, you need not be concerned with having numbers with the same exponents because the calculator automatically takes care of this matter.

2. **Multiplication and Division** When numbers expressed in exponential notation are multiplied, the exponents are added; when numbers expressed in exponential notation are divided, the exponent of the denominator is subtracted from the exponent of the numerator.

$$(5.4 \times 10^2)(2.1 \times 10^3) = (5.4)(2.1) \times 10^{2+3}$$
$$= 11 \times 10^5$$
$$= 1.1 \times 10^6$$
$$(1.2 \times 10^5)(3.22 \times 10^{-3}) = (1.2)(3.22) \times 10^{5+(-3)} = 3.9 \times 10^2$$
$$\frac{3.2 \times 10^5}{6.5 \times 10^2} = \frac{3.2}{6.5} \times 10^{5-2} = 0.49 \times 10^3 = 4.9 \times 10^2$$
$$\frac{5.7 \times 10^7}{8.5 \times 10^{-2}} = \frac{5.7}{8.5} \times 10^{7-(-2)} = 0.67 \times 10^9 = 6.7 \times 10^8$$

3. **Powers and Roots** When numbers expressed in exponential notation are raised to a power, the exponents are multiplied by the power. When the roots of numbers expressed in exponential notation are taken, the exponents are divided by the root.

$$(1.2 \times 10^5)^3 = (1.2)^3 \times 10^{5\times3}$$
$$= 1.7 \times 10^{15}$$
$$\sqrt[3]{2.5 \times 10^6} = \sqrt[3]{2.5} \times 10^{6/3}$$
$$= 1.3 \times 10^2$$

Scientific calculators usually have keys labeled $x^2$ and $\sqrt{x}$ for squaring and taking the square root of a number, respectively. To take higher powers or roots, many calculators have $y^x$ and $\sqrt[x]{y}$ (or INV $y^x$) keys. For example, to perform the operation $\sqrt[3]{7.5 \times 10^{-4}}$ on such a calculator, you would key in $7.5 \times 10^{-4}$, press the $\sqrt[x]{y}$ key (or the INV and then the $y^x$ keys), enter the root, 3, and finally press $=$. The result is $9.1 \times 10^{-2}$.

**SAMPLE EXERCISE 1**   **Using Exponential Notation**

Perform each of the following operations, using your calculator where possible:

(a)  Write the number 0.0054 in standard exponential notation.
(b)  $(5.0 \times 10^{-2}) + (4.7 \times 10^{-3})$
(c)  $(5.98 \times 10^{12})(2.77 \times 10^{-5})$
(d)  $\sqrt[4]{1.75 \times 10^{-12}}$

**SOLUTION**

(a)  Because we move the decimal point three places to the right to convert 0.0054 to 5.4, the exponent is −3:

$$5.4 \times 10^{-3}$$

Scientific calculators are generally able to convert numbers to exponential notation using one or two keystrokes; frequently "SCI" for "scientific notation" will convert a number into exponential notation. Consult your instruction manual to see how this operation is accomplished on your calculator.

(b)  To add these numbers longhand, we must convert them to the same exponent.

$$(5.0 \times 10^{-2}) + (0.47 \times 10^{-2}) = (5.0 + 0.47) \times 10^{-2} = 5.5 \times 10^{-2}$$

(Note that the result has only two significant figures.) To perform this operation on a calculator, we enter the first number, strike the $+$ key, then enter the second number and strike the $=$ key.

(c)  Performing this operation longhand, we have

$$(5.98 \times 2.77) \times 10^{12-5} = 16.6 \times 10^{7} = 1.66 \times 10^{8}$$

On a scientific calculator, we enter $5.98 \times 10^{12}$, press the $\times$ key, enter $2.77 \times 10^{-5}$, and press the $=$ key.

(d)  To perform this operation on a calculator, we enter the number, press the $\sqrt[x]{y}$ key (or the INV and $y^x$ keys), enter 4, and press the $=$ key. The result is $1.15 \times 10^{-3}$.

**PRACTICE EXERCISE**

Perform the following operations:

(a)  Write 67,000 in exponential notation, showing two significant figures.
(b)  $(3.378 \times 10^{-3}) - (4.97 \times 10^{-5})$
(c)  $(1.84 \times 10^{15})(7.45 \times 10^{-2})$
(d)  $(6.67 \times 10^{-8})^3$

*Answers:*  (a) $6.7 \times 10^4$, (b) $3.328 \times 10^{-3}$, (c) $2.47 \times 10^{16}$, (d) $2.97 \times 10^{-22}$

# A.2  LOGARITHMS

## Common Logarithms

The common, or base-10, logarithm (abbreviated log) of any number is the power to which 10 must be raised to equal the number. For example, the common logarithm of 1000 (written log 1000) is 3 because raising 10 to the third power gives 1000.

$$10^3 = 1000, \text{ therefore, } \log 1000 = 3$$

Further examples are

$$\log 10^5 = 5$$
$$\log 1 = 0 \qquad \text{Remember that } 10^0 = 1$$
$$\log 10^{-2} = -2$$

In these examples the common logarithm can be obtained by inspection. However, it is not possible to obtain the logarithm of a number such as 31.25 by inspection. The logarithm of 31.25 is the number $x$ that satisfies the following relationship:

$$10^x = 31.25$$

Most electronic calculators have a key labeled LOG that can be used to obtain logarithms. For example, on many calculators we obtain the value of log 31.25 by entering 31.25 and pressing the LOG key. We obtain the following result:

$$\log 31.25 = 1.4949$$

Notice that 31.25 is greater than 10 ($10^1$) and less than 100 ($10^2$). The value for log 31.25 is accordingly between log 10 and log 100, that is, between 1 and 2.

## Significant Figures and Common Logarithms

For the common logarithm of a measured quantity, the number of digits after the decimal point equals the number of significant figures in the original number. For example, if 23.5 is a measured quantity (three significant figures), then log 23.5 = 1.371 (three significant figures after the decimal point).

## Antilogarithms

The process of determining the number that corresponds to a certain logarithm is known as obtaining an *antilogarithm*. It is the reverse of taking a logarithm. For example, we saw previously that log 23.5 = 1.371. This means that the antilogarithm of 1.371 equals 23.5.

$$\log 23.5 = 1.371$$
$$\text{antilog } 1.371 = 23.5$$

The process of taking the antilog of a number is the same as raising 10 to a power equal to that number.

$$\text{antilog } 1.371 = 10^{1.371} = 23.5$$

Many calculators have a key labeled $10^x$ that allows you to obtain antilogs directly. On others, it will be necessary to press a key labeled INV (for *inverse*), followed by the LOG key.

## Natural Logarithms

Logarithms based on the number $e$ are called natural, or base $e$, logarithms (abbreviated ln). The natural log of a number is the power to which $e$ (which has the value 2.71828...) must be raised to equal the number. For example, the natural log of 10 equals 2.303.

$$e^{2.303} = 10, \text{ therefore } \ln 10 = 2.303$$

Your calculator probably has a key labeled LN that allows you to obtain natural logarithms. For example, to obtain the natural log of 46.8, you enter 46.8 and press the LN key.

$$\ln 46.8 = 3.846$$

The natural antilog of a number is $e$ raised to a power equal to that number. If your calculator can calculate natural logs, it will also be able to calculate natural antilogs. On some calculators there is a key labeled $e^x$ that allows you to calculate natural antilogs directly; on others, it will be necessary to first press the INV key followed by the LN key. For example, the natural antilog of 1.679 is given by

$$\text{Natural antilog } 1.679 = e^{1.679} = 5.36$$

The relation between common and natural logarithms is as follows:

$$\ln a = 2.303 \log a$$

Notice that the factor relating the two, 2.303, is the natural log of 10, which we calculated earlier.

# Mathematical Operations Using Logarithms

Because logarithms are exponents, mathematical operations involving logarithms follow the rules for the use of exponents. For example, the product of $z^a$ and $z^b$ (where $z$ is any number) is given by

$$z^a \cdot z^b = z^{(a+b)}$$

Similarly, the logarithm (either common or natural) of a product equals the *sum* of the logs of the individual numbers.

$$\log ab = \log a + \log b \qquad \ln ab = \ln a + \ln b$$

For the log of a quotient,

$$\log(a/b) = \log a - \log b \qquad \ln(a/b) = \ln a - \ln b$$

Using the properties of exponents, we can also derive the rules for the logarithm of a number raised to a certain power.

$$\log a^n = n \log a \qquad \ln a^n = n \ln a$$

$$\log a^{1/n} = (1/n) \log a \qquad \ln a^{1/n} = (1/n) \ln a$$

## pH Problems

One of the most frequent uses for common logarithms in general chemistry is in working pH problems. The pH is defined as $-\log[H^+]$, where $[H^+]$ is the hydrogen ion concentration of a solution. ∞ (Section 16.4) The following sample exercise illustrates this application.

---

**SAMPLE EXERCISE 2**   **Using Logarithms**

(a) What is the pH of a solution whose hydrogen ion concentration is 0.015 $M$?

(b) If the pH of a solution is 3.80, what is its hydrogen ion concentration?

**SOLUTION**

1. We are given the value of $[H^+]$. We use the LOG key of our calculator to calculate the value of $\log[H^+]$. The pH is obtained by changing the sign of the value obtained. (Be sure to change the sign *after* taking the logarithm.)

$$[H^+] = 0.015$$
$$\log[H^+] = -1.82 \qquad \text{(2 significant figures)}$$
$$pH = -(-1.82) = 1.82$$

2. To obtain the hydrogen ion concentration when given the pH, we must take the antilog of $-pH$.

$$pH = -\log[H^+] = 3.80$$
$$\log[H^+] = -3.80$$
$$[H^+] = \text{antilog}(-3.80) = 10^{-3.80} = 1.6 \times 10^{-4}\ M$$

**PRACTICE EXERCISE**

Perform the following operations: (a) $\log(2.5 \times 10^{-5})$, (b) $\ln 32.7$, (c) antilog $-3.47$, (d) $e^{-1.89}$.
*Answers:*  (a) $-4.60$, (b) $3.487$, (c) $3.4 \times 10^{-4}$, (d) $1.5 \times 10^{-1}$

---

# A.3 | QUADRATIC EQUATIONS

An algebraic equation of the form $ax^2 + bx + c = 0$ is called a *quadratic equation*. The two solutions to such an equation are given by the quadratic formula:

$$x = \frac{-b \pm \sqrt{b^2 - 4ac}}{2a}$$

Many calculators today can calculate the solutions to a quadratic equation with one or two keystrokes. Most of the time, $x$ corresponds to the concentration of a chemical species in solution. Only one of the solutions will be a positive number, and that is the one you should use; a "negative concentration" has no physical meaning.

---

**SAMPLE EXERCISE 3**    **Using the Quadratic Formula**

Find the values of $x$ that satisfy the equation $2x^2 + 4x = 1$.

**SOLUTION**

To solve the given equation for $x$, we must first put it in the form

$$ax^2 + bx + c = 0$$

and then use the quadratic formula. If

$$2x^2 + 4x = 1$$

then

$$2x^2 + 4x - 1 = 0$$

Using the quadratic formula, where $a = 2$, $b = 4$, and $c = -1$, we have

$$x = \frac{-4 \pm \sqrt{(4)(4) - 4(2)(-1)}}{2(2)}$$

$$= \frac{-4 \pm \sqrt{16 + 8}}{4} = \frac{-4 \pm \sqrt{24}}{4} = \frac{-4 \pm 4.899}{4}$$

The two solutions are

$$x = \frac{0.899}{4} = 0.225 \quad \text{and} \quad x = \frac{-8.899}{4} = -2.225$$

If this was a problem in which $x$ represented a concentration, we would say $x = 0.225$ (in the appropriate units), since a negative number for concentration has no physical meaning.

---

**TABLE A.1** • **Interrelation between Pressure and Temperature**

| Temperature (°C) | Pressure (atm) |
|---|---|
| 20.0 | 0.120 |
| 30.0 | 0.124 |
| 40.0 | 0.128 |
| 50.0 | 0.132 |

▲ **FIGURE A.1** A graph of pressure versus temperature yields a straight line for the data.

## A.4 | GRAPHS

Often the clearest way to represent the interrelationship between two variables is to graph them. Usually, the variable that is being experimentally varied, called the *independent variable*, is shown along the horizontal axis ($x$-axis). The variable that responds to the change in the independent variable, called the *dependent variable*, is then shown along the vertical axis ($y$-axis). For example, consider an experiment in which we vary the temperature of an enclosed gas and measure its pressure. The independent variable is temperature, and the dependent variable is pressure. The data shown in ◀ TABLE A.1 can be obtained by means of this experiment. These data are shown graphically in ◀ FIGURE A.1. The relationship between temperature and pressure is linear. The equation for any straight-line graph has the form

$$y = mx + b$$

where $m$ is the slope of the line and $b$ is the intercept with the $y$-axis. In the case of Figure A.1, we could say that the relationship between temperature and pressure takes the form

$$P = mT + b$$

where $P$ is pressure in atm and $T$ is temperature in °C. As shown in Figure A.1, the slope is $4.10 \times 10^{-4}$ atm/°C, and the intercept—the point where the line crosses the $y$-axis—is 0.112 atm. Therefore, the equation for the line is

$$P = \left(4.10 \times 10^{-4} \frac{\text{atm}}{\text{°C}}\right)T + 0.112 \text{ atm}$$

# A.5 | STANDARD DEVIATION

The standard deviation from the mean, $s$, is a common method for describing precision in experimentally determined data. We define the standard deviation as

$$s = \sqrt{\frac{\sum_{i=1}^{N}(x_i - \bar{x})^2}{N - 1}}$$

where $N$ is the number of measurements, $\bar{x}$ is the average (also called the mean) of the measurements, and $x_i$ represents the individual measurements. Electronic calculators with built-in statistical functions can calculate $s$ directly by inputting the individual measurements.

A smaller value of $s$ indicates a higher precision, meaning that the data are more closely clustered around the average. The standard deviation has statistical significance. If a large number of measurements is made, 68% of the measured values is expected to be within one standard deviation of the average, assuming only random errors are associated with the measurements.

## SAMPLE EXERCISE 4 | Calculating an Average and Standard Deviation

The percent carbon in a sugar is measured four times: 42.01%, 42.28%, 41.79%, and 42.25%. Calculate (a) the average and (b) the standard deviation for these measurements.

### SOLUTION

(a) The average is found by adding the quantities and dividing by the number of measurements:

$$\bar{x} = \frac{42.01 + 42.28 + 41.79 + 42.25}{4} = \frac{168.33}{4} = 42.08$$

(b) The standard deviation is found using the preceding equation:

$$s = \sqrt{\frac{\sum_{i=1}^{N}(x_i - \bar{x})^2}{N - 1}}$$

Let's tabulate the data so the calculation of $\sum_{i=1}^{N}(x_i - \bar{x})^2$ can be seen clearly.

| Percent C | Difference between Measurement and Average, $(x_i - \bar{x})$ | Square of Difference, $(x_i - \bar{x})^2$ |
|---|---|---|
| 42.01 | $42.01 - 42.08 = -0.07$ | $(-0.07)^2 = 0.005$ |
| 42.28 | $42.28 - 42.08 = 0.20$ | $(0.20)^2 = 0.040$ |
| 41.79 | $41.79 - 42.08 = -0.29$ | $(-0.29)^2 = 0.084$ |
| 42.25 | $42.25 - 42.08 = 0.17$ | $(0.17)^2 = 0.029$ |

The sum of the quantities in the last column is

$$\sum_{i=1}^{N}(x_i - \bar{x})^2 = 0.005 + 0.040 + 0.084 + 0.029 = 0.16$$

Thus, the standard deviation is

$$s = \sqrt{\frac{\sum_{i=1}^{N}(x_i - \bar{x})^2}{N - 1}} = \sqrt{\frac{0.16}{4 - 1}} = \sqrt{\frac{0.16}{3}} = \sqrt{0.053} = 0.23$$

Based on these measurements, it would be appropriate to represent the measured percent carbon as $42.08 \pm 0.23$.

# PROPERTIES OF WATER

|  |  |
|---|---|
| Density: | 0.99987 g/mL at 0 °C |
|  | 1.00000 g/mL at 4 °C |
|  | 0.99707 g/mL at 25 °C |
|  | 0.95838 g/mL at 100 °C |
| Heat (enthalpy) of fusion: | 6.008 kJ/mol at 0 °C |
| Heat (enthalpy) of vaporization: | 44.94 kJ/mol at 0 °C |
|  | 44.02 kJ/mol at 25 °C |
|  | 40.67 kJ/mol at 100 °C |
| Ion-product constant, $K_w$: | $1.14 \times 10^{-15}$ at 0 °C |
|  | $1.01 \times 10^{-14}$ at 25 °C |
|  | $5.47 \times 10^{-14}$ at 50 °C |
| Specific heat: | 2.092 J/g-K = 2.092 J/g $\cdot$ °C for ice at $-3$ °C |
|  | 4.184 J/g-K = 4.184 J/g $\cdot$ °C for water at 25 °C |
|  | 1.841 J/g-K = 1.841 J/g $\cdot$ °C for steam at 100 °C |

## Vapor Pressure (torr) at Different Temperatures

| $T$(°C) | P | $T$(°C) | P | $T$(°C) | P | $T$(°C) | P |
|---|---|---|---|---|---|---|---|
| 0 | 4.58 | 21 | 18.65 | 35 | 42.2 | 92 | 567.0 |
| 5 | 6.54 | 22 | 19.83 | 40 | 55.3 | 94 | 610.9 |
| 10 | 9.21 | 23 | 21.07 | 45 | 71.9 | 96 | 657.6 |
| 12 | 10.52 | 24 | 22.38 | 50 | 92.5 | 98 | 707.3 |
| 14 | 11.99 | 25 | 23.76 | 55 | 118.0 | 100 | 760.0 |
| 16 | 13.63 | 26 | 25.21 | 60 | 149.4 | 102 | 815.9 |
| 17 | 14.53 | 27 | 26.74 | 65 | 187.5 | 104 | 875.1 |
| 18 | 15.48 | 28 | 28.35 | 70 | 233.7 | 106 | 937.9 |
| 19 | 16.48 | 29 | 30.04 | 80 | 355.1 | 108 | 1004.4 |
| 20 | 17.54 | 30 | 31.82 | 90 | 525.8 | 110 | 1074.6 |

# THERMODYNAMIC QUANTITIES FOR SELECTED SUBSTANCES AT 298.15 K (25 °C)

| Substance | $\Delta H_f^\circ$ (kJ/mol) | $\Delta G_f^\circ$ (kJ/mol) | $S^\circ$ (J/mol-K) | Substance | $\Delta H_f^\circ$ (kJ/mol) | $\Delta G_f^\circ$ (kJ/mol) | $S^\circ$ (J/mol-K) |
|---|---|---|---|---|---|---|---|
| Aluminum | | | | $C_2H_4(g)$ | 52.30 | 68.11 | 219.4 |
| Al(s) | 0 | 0 | 28.32 | $C_2H_6(g)$ | −84.68 | −32.89 | 229.5 |
| $AlCl_3(s)$ | −705.6 | −630.0 | 109.3 | $C_3H_8(g)$ | −103.85 | −23.47 | 269.9 |
| $Al_2O_3(s)$ | −1669.8 | −1576.5 | 51.00 | $C_4H_{10}(g)$ | −124.73 | −15.71 | 310.0 |
| | | | | $C_4H_{10}(l)$ | −147.6 | −15.0 | 231.0 |
| Barium | | | | $C_6H_6(g)$ | 82.9 | 129.7 | 269.2 |
| Ba(s) | 0 | 0 | 63.2 | $C_6H_6(l)$ | 49.0 | 124.5 | 172.8 |
| $BaCO_3(s)$ | −1216.3 | −1137.6 | 112.1 | $CH_3OH(g)$ | −201.2 | −161.9 | 237.6 |
| BaO(s) | −553.5 | −525.1 | 70.42 | $CH_3OH(l)$ | −238.6 | −166.23 | 126.8 |
| | | | | $C_2H_5OH(g)$ | −235.1 | −168.5 | 282.7 |
| Beryllium | | | | $C_2H_5OH(l)$ | −277.7 | −174.76 | 160.7 |
| Be(s) | 0 | 0 | 9.44 | $C_6H_{12}O_6(s)$ | −1273.02 | −910.4 | 212.1 |
| BeO(s) | −608.4 | −579.1 | 13.77 | CO(g) | −110.5 | −137.2 | 197.9 |
| $Be(OH)_2(s)$ | −905.8 | −817.9 | 50.21 | $CO_2(g)$ | −393.5 | −394.4 | 213.6 |
| | | | | $CH_3COOH(l)$ | −487.0 | −392.4 | 159.8 |
| Bromine | | | | | | | |
| Br(g) | 111.8 | 82.38 | 174.9 | Cesium | | | |
| $Br^-(aq)$ | −120.9 | −102.8 | 80.71 | Cs(g) | 76.50 | 49.53 | 175.6 |
| $Br_2(g)$ | 30.71 | 3.14 | 245.3 | Cs(l) | 2.09 | 0.03 | 92.07 |
| $Br_2(l)$ | 0 | 0 | 152.3 | Cs(s) | 0 | 0 | 85.15 |
| HBr(g) | −36.23 | −53.22 | 198.49 | CsCl(s) | −442.8 | −414.4 | 101.2 |
| | | | | | | | |
| Calcium | | | | Chlorine | | | |
| Ca(g) | 179.3 | 145.5 | 154.8 | Cl(g) | 121.7 | 105.7 | 165.2 |
| Ca(s) | 0 | 0 | 41.4 | Cl(aq) | −167.2 | −131.2 | 56.5 |
| $CaCO_3$(s, calcite) | −1207.1 | −1128.76 | 92.88 | $Cl_2(g)$ | 0 | 0 | 222.96 |
| $CaCl_2(s)$ | −795.8 | −748.1 | 104.6 | HCl(aq) | −167.2 | −131.2 | 56.5 |
| $CaF_2(s)$ | −1219.6 | −1167.3 | 68.87 | HCl(g) | −92.30 | −95.27 | 186.69 |
| CaO(s) | −635.5 | −604.17 | 39.75 | | | | |
| $Ca(OH)_2(s)$ | −986.2 | −898.5 | 83.4 | Chromium | | | |
| $CaSO_4(s)$ | −1434.0 | −1321.8 | 106.7 | Cr(g) | 397.5 | 352.6 | 174.2 |
| | | | | Cr(s) | 0 | 0 | 23.6 |
| Carbon | | | | $Cr_2O_3(s)$ | −1139.7 | −1058.1 | 81.2 |
| C(g) | 718.4 | 672.9 | 158.0 | | | | |
| C(s, diamond) | 1.88 | 2.84 | 2.43 | Cobalt | | | |
| C(s, graphite) | 0 | 0 | 5.69 | Co(g) | 439 | 393 | 179 |
| $CCl_4(g)$ | −106.7 | −64.0 | 309.4 | Co(s) | 0 | 0 | 28.4 |
| $CCl_4(l)$ | −139.3 | −68.6 | 214.4 | | | | |
| $CF_4(g)$ | −679.9 | −635.1 | 262.3 | Copper | | | |
| $CH_4(g)$ | −74.8 | −50.8 | 186.3 | Cu(g) | 338.4 | 298.6 | 166.3 |
| $C_2H_2(g)$ | 226.77 | 209.2 | 200.8 | Cu(s) | 0 | 0 | 33.30 |

| Substance | $\Delta H_f^\circ$ (kJ/mol) | $\Delta G_f^\circ$ (kJ/mol) | $S^\circ$ (J/mol-K) | Substance | $\Delta H_f^\circ$ (kJ/mol) | $\Delta G_f^\circ$ (kJ/mol) | $S^\circ$ (J/mol-K) |
|---|---|---|---|---|---|---|---|
| $CuCl_2(s)$ | −205.9 | −161.7 | 108.1 | $MgO(s)$ | −601.8 | −569.6 | 26.8 |
| $CuO(s)$ | −156.1 | −128.3 | 42.59 | $Mg(OH)_2(s)$ | −924.7 | −833.7 | 63.24 |
| $Cu_2O(s)$ | −170.7 | −147.9 | 92.36 | **Manganese** | | | |
| **Fluorine** | | | | $Mn(g)$ | 280.7 | 238.5 | 173.6 |
| $F(g)$ | 80.0 | 61.9 | 158.7 | $Mn(s)$ | 0 | 0 | 32.0 |
| $F(aq)$ | −332.6 | −278.8 | −13.8 | $MnO(s)$ | −385.2 | −362.9 | 59.7 |
| $F_2(g)$ | 0 | 0 | 202.7 | $MnO_2(s)$ | −519.6 | −464.8 | 53.14 |
| $HF(g)$ | −268.61 | −270.70 | 173.51 | $MnO_4^-(aq)$ | −541.4 | −447.2 | 191.2 |
| **Hydrogen** | | | | **Mercury** | | | |
| $H(g)$ | 217.94 | 203.26 | 114.60 | $Hg(g)$ | 60.83 | 31.76 | 174.89 |
| $H^+(aq)$ | 0 | 0 | 0 | $Hg(l)$ | 0 | 0 | 77.40 |
| $H^+(g)$ | 1536.2 | 1517.0 | 108.9 | $HgCl_2(s)$ | −230.1 | −184.0 | 144.5 |
| $H_2(g)$ | 0 | 0 | 130.58 | $Hg_2Cl_2(s)$ | −264.9 | −210.5 | 192.5 |
| **Iodine** | | | | **Nickel** | | | |
| $I(g)$ | 106.60 | 70.16 | 180.66 | $Ni(g)$ | 429.7 | 384.5 | 182.1 |
| $I^-(aq)$ | −55.19 | −51.57 | 111.3 | $Ni(s)$ | 0 | 0 | 29.9 |
| $I_2(g)$ | 62.25 | 19.37 | 260.57 | $NiCl_2(s)$ | −305.3 | −259.0 | 97.65 |
| $I_2(s)$ | 0 | 0 | 116.73 | $NiO(s)$ | −239.7 | −211.7 | 37.99 |
| $HI(g)$ | 25.94 | 1.30 | 206.3 | **Nitrogen** | | | |
| **Iron** | | | | $N(g)$ | 472.7 | 455.5 | 153.3 |
| $Fe(g)$ | 415.5 | 369.8 | 180.5 | $N_2(g)$ | 0 | 0 | 191.50 |
| $Fe(s)$ | 0 | 0 | 27.15 | $NH_3(aq)$ | −80.29 | −26.50 | 111.3 |
| $Fe^{2+}(aq)$ | −87.86 | −84.93 | 113.4 | $NH_3(g)$ | −46.19 | −16.66 | 192.5 |
| $Fe^{3+}(aq)$ | −47.69 | −10.54 | 293.3 | $NH_4^+(aq)$ | −132.5 | −79.31 | 113.4 |
| $FeCl_2(s)$ | −341.8 | −302.3 | 117.9 | $N_2H_4(g)$ | 95.40 | 159.4 | 238.5 |
| $FeCl_3(s)$ | −400 | −334 | 142.3 | $NH_4CN(s)$ | 0.0 | — | — |
| $FeO(s)$ | −271.9 | −255.2 | 60.75 | $NH_4Cl(s)$ | −314.4 | −203.0 | 94.6 |
| $Fe_2O_3(s)$ | −822.16 | −740.98 | 89.96 | $NH_4NO_3(s)$ | −365.6 | −184.0 | 151 |
| $Fe_3O_4(s)$ | −1117.1 | −1014.2 | 146.4 | $NO(g)$ | 90.37 | 86.71 | 210.62 |
| $FeS_2(s)$ | −171.5 | −160.1 | 52.92 | $NO_2(g)$ | 33.84 | 51.84 | 240.45 |
| **Lead** | | | | $N_2O(g)$ | 81.6 | 103.59 | 220.0 |
| $Pb(s)$ | 0 | 0 | 68.85 | $N_2O_4(g)$ | 9.66 | 98.28 | 304.3 |
| $PbBr_2(s)$ | −277.4 | −260.7 | 161 | $NOCl(g)$ | 52.6 | 66.3 | 264 |
| $PbCO_3(s)$ | −699.1 | −625.5 | 131.0 | $HNO_3(aq)$ | −206.6 | −110.5 | 146 |
| $Pb(NO_3)_2(aq)$ | −421.3 | −246.9 | 303.3 | $HNO_3(g)$ | −134.3 | −73.94 | 266.4 |
| $Pb(NO_3)_2(s)$ | −451.9 | — | — | **Oxygen** | | | |
| $PbO(s)$ | −217.3 | −187.9 | 68.70 | $O(g)$ | 247.5 | 230.1 | 161.0 |
| **Lithium** | | | | $O_2(g)$ | 0 | 0 | 205.0 |
| $Li(g)$ | 159.3 | 126.6 | 138.8 | $O_3(g)$ | 142.3 | 163.4 | 237.6 |
| $Li(s)$ | 0 | 0 | 29.09 | $OH^-(aq)$ | −230.0 | −157.3 | −10.7 |
| $Li^+(aq)$ | −278.5 | −273.4 | 12.2 | $H_2O(g)$ | −241.82 | −228.57 | 188.83 |
| $Li^+(g)$ | 685.7 | 648.5 | 133.0 | $H_2O(l)$ | −285.83 | −237.13 | 69.91 |
| $LiCl(s)$ | −408.3 | −384.0 | 59.30 | $H_2O_2(g)$ | −136.10 | −105.48 | 232.9 |
| **Magnesium** | | | | $H_2O_2(l)$ | −187.8 | −120.4 | 109.6 |
| $Mg(g)$ | 147.1 | 112.5 | 148.6 | **Phosphorus** | | | |
| $Mg(s)$ | 0 | 0 | 32.51 | $P(g)$ | 316.4 | 280.0 | 163.2 |
| $MgCl_2(s)$ | −641.6 | −592.1 | 89.6 | $P_2(g)$ | 144.3 | 103.7 | 218.1 |

| Substance | $\Delta H_f^\circ$ (kJ/mol) | $\Delta G_f^\circ$ (kJ/mol) | $S^\circ$ (J/mol-K) | Substance | $\Delta H_f^\circ$ (kJ/mol) | $\Delta G_f^\circ$ (kJ/mol) | $S^\circ$ (J/mol-K) |
|---|---|---|---|---|---|---|---|
| $P_4(g)$ | 58.9 | 24.4 | 280 | $AgNO_3(s)$ | −124.4 | −33.41 | 140.9 |
| $P_4(s, \text{red})$ | −17.46 | −12.03 | 22.85 | **Sodium** | | | |
| $P_4(s, \text{white})$ | 0 | 0 | 41.08 | $Na(g)$ | 107.7 | 77.3 | 153.7 |
| $PCl_3(g)$ | −288.07 | −269.6 | 311.7 | $Na(s)$ | 0 | 0 | 51.45 |
| $PCl_3(l)$ | −319.6 | −272.4 | 217 | $Na^+(aq)$ | −240.1 | −261.9 | 59.0 |
| $PF_5(g)$ | −1594.4 | −1520.7 | 300.8 | $Na^+(g)$ | 609.3 | 574.3 | 148.0 |
| $PH_3(g)$ | 5.4 | 13.4 | 210.2 | $NaBr(aq)$ | −360.6 | −364.7 | 141.00 |
| $P_4O_6(s)$ | −1640.1 | — | — | $NaBr(s)$ | −361.4 | −349.3 | 86.82 |
| $P_4O_{10}(s)$ | −2940.1 | −2675.2 | 228.9 | $Na_2CO_3(s)$ | −1130.9 | −1047.7 | 136.0 |
| $POCl_3(g)$ | −542.2 | −502.5 | 325 | $NaCl(aq)$ | −407.1 | −393.0 | 115.5 |
| $POCl_3(l)$ | −597.0 | −520.9 | 222 | $NaCl(g)$ | −181.4 | −201.3 | 229.8 |
| $H_3PO_4(aq)$ | −1288.3 | −1142.6 | 158.2 | $NaCl(s)$ | −410.9 | −384.0 | 72.33 |
| | | | | $NaHCO_3(s)$ | −947.7 | −851.8 | 102.1 |
| **Potassium** | | | | $NaNO_3(aq)$ | −446.2 | −372.4 | 207 |
| $K(g)$ | 89.99 | 61.17 | 160.2 | $NaNO_3(s)$ | −467.9 | −367.0 | 116.5 |
| $K(s)$ | 0 | 0 | 64.67 | $NaOH(aq)$ | −469.6 | −419.2 | 49.8 |
| $KCl(s)$ | −435.9 | −408.3 | 82.7 | $NaOH(s)$ | −425.6 | −379.5 | 64.46 |
| $KClO_3(s)$ | −391.2 | −289.9 | 143.0 | $Na_2SO_4(s)$ | −1387.1 | −1270.2 | 149.6 |
| $KClO_3(aq)$ | −349.5 | −284.9 | 265.7 | | | | |
| $K_2CO_3(s)$ | −1150.18 | −1064.58 | 155.44 | **Strontium** | | | |
| $KNO_3(s)$ | −492.70 | −393.13 | 132.9 | $SrO(s)$ | −592.0 | −561.9 | 54.9 |
| $K_2O(s)$ | −363.2 | −322.1 | 94.14 | $Sr(g)$ | 164.4 | 110.0 | 164.6 |
| $KO_2(s)$ | −284.5 | −240.6 | 122.5 | | | | |
| $K_2O_2(s)$ | −495.8 | −429.8 | 113.0 | **Sulfur** | | | |
| $KOH(s)$ | −424.7 | −378.9 | 78.91 | $S(s, \text{rhombic})$ | 0 | 0 | 31.88 |
| $KOH(aq)$ | −482.4 | −440.5 | 91.6 | $S_8(g)$ | 102.3 | 49.7 | 430.9 |
| | | | | $SO_2(g)$ | −296.9 | −300.4 | 248.5 |
| **Rubidium** | | | | $SO_3(g)$ | −395.2 | −370.4 | 256.2 |
| $Rb(g)$ | 85.8 | 55.8 | 170.0 | $SO_4^{2-}(aq)$ | −909.3 | −744.5 | 20.1 |
| $Rb(s)$ | 0 | 0 | 76.78 | $SOCl_2(l)$ | −245.6 | — | — |
| $RbCl(s)$ | −430.5 | −412.0 | 92 | $H_2S(g)$ | −20.17 | −33.01 | 205.6 |
| $RbClO_3(s)$ | −392.4 | −292.0 | 152 | $H_2SO_4(aq)$ | −909.3 | −744.5 | 20.1 |
| | | | | $H_2SO_4(l)$ | −814.0 | −689.9 | 156.1 |
| **Scandium** | | | | | | | |
| $Sc(g)$ | 377.8 | 336.1 | 174.7 | **Titanium** | | | |
| $Sc(s)$ | 0 | 0 | 34.6 | $Ti(g)$ | 468 | 422 | 180.3 |
| | | | | $Ti(s)$ | 0 | 0 | 30.76 |
| **Selenium** | | | | $TiCl_4(g)$ | −763.2 | −726.8 | 354.9 |
| $H_2Se(g)$ | 29.7 | 15.9 | 219.0 | $TiCl_4(l)$ | −804.2 | −728.1 | 221.9 |
| | | | | $TiO_2(s)$ | −944.7 | −889.4 | 50.29 |
| **Silicon** | | | | | | | |
| $Si(g)$ | 368.2 | 323.9 | 167.8 | **Vanadium** | | | |
| $Si(s)$ | 0 | 0 | 18.7 | $V(g)$ | 514.2 | 453.1 | 182.2 |
| $SiC(s)$ | −73.22 | −70.85 | 16.61 | $V(s)$ | 0 | 0 | 28.9 |
| $SiCl_4(l)$ | −640.1 | −572.8 | 239.3 | | | | |
| $SiO_2(s, \text{quartz})$ | −910.9 | −856.5 | 41.84 | **Zinc** | | | |
| | | | | $Zn(g)$ | 130.7 | 95.2 | 160.9 |
| **Silver** | | | | $Zn(s)$ | 0 | 0 | 41.63 |
| $Ag(s)$ | 0 | 0 | 42.55 | $ZnCl_2(s)$ | −415.1 | −369.4 | 111.5 |
| $Ag^+(aq)$ | 105.90 | 77.11 | 73.93 | $ZnO(s)$ | −348.0 | −318.2 | 43.9 |
| $AgCl(s)$ | −127.0 | −109.70 | 96.11 | | | | |
| $Ag_2O(s)$ | −31.05 | −11.20 | 121.3 | | | | |

# AQUEOUS EQUILIBRIUM CONSTANTS

**TABLE D.1** • Dissociation Constants for Acids at 25 °C

| Name | Formula | $K_{a1}$ | $K_{a2}$ | $K_{a3}$ |
|---|---|---|---|---|
| Acetic acid | $CH_3COOH$ (or $HC_2H_3O_2$) | $1.8 \times 10^{-5}$ | | |
| Arsenic acid | $H_3AsO_4$ | $5.6 \times 10^{-3}$ | $1.0 \times 10^{-7}$ | $3.0 \times 10^{-12}$ |
| Arsenous acid | $H_3AsO_3$ | $5.1 \times 10^{-10}$ | | |
| Ascorbic acid | $H_2C_6H_6O_6$ | $8.0 \times 10^{-5}$ | $1.6 \times 10^{-12}$ | |
| Benzoic acid | $C_6H_5COOH$ (or $HC_7H_5O_2$) | $6.3 \times 10^{-5}$ | | |
| Boric acid | $H_3BO_3$ | $5.8 \times 10^{-10}$ | | |
| Butanoic acid | $C_3H_7COOH$ (or $HC_4H_7O_2$) | $1.5 \times 10^{-5}$ | | |
| Carbonic acid | $H_2CO_3$ | $4.3 \times 10^{-7}$ | $5.6 \times 10^{-11}$ | |
| Chloroacetic acid | $CH_2ClCOOH$ (or $HC_2H_2O_2Cl$) | $1.4 \times 10^{-3}$ | | |
| Chlorous acid | $HClO_2$ | $1.1 \times 10^{-2}$ | | |
| Citric acid | $HOOCC(OH)(CH_2COOH)_2$ (or $H_3C_6H_5O_7$) | $7.4 \times 10^{-4}$ | $1.7 \times 10^{-5}$ | $4.0 \times 10^{-7}$ |
| Cyanic acid | $HCNO$ | $3.5 \times 10^{-4}$ | | |
| Formic acid | $HCOOH$ (or $HCHO_2$) | $1.8 \times 10^{-4}$ | | |
| Hydroazoic acid | $HN_3$ | $1.9 \times 10^{-5}$ | | |
| Hydrocyanic acid | $HCN$ | $4.9 \times 10^{-10}$ | | |
| Hydrofluoric acid | $HF$ | $6.8 \times 10^{-4}$ | | |
| Hydrogen chromate ion | $HCrO_4^-$ | $3.0 \times 10^{-7}$ | | |
| Hydrogen peroxide | $H_2O_2$ | $2.4 \times 10^{-12}$ | | |
| Hydrogen selenate ion | $HSeO_4^-$ | $2.2 \times 10^{-2}$ | | |
| Hydrogen sulfide | $H_2S$ | $9.5 \times 10^{-8}$ | $1 \times 10^{-19}$ | |
| Hypobromous acid | $HBrO$ | $2.5 \times 10^{-9}$ | | |
| Hypochlorous acid | $HClO$ | $3.0 \times 10^{-8}$ | | |
| Hypoiodous acid | $HIO$ | $2.3 \times 10^{-11}$ | | |
| Iodic acid | $HIO_3$ | $1.7 \times 10^{-1}$ | | |
| Lactic acid | $CH_3CH(OH)COOH$ (or $HC_3H_5O_3$) | $1.4 \times 10^{-4}$ | | |
| Malonic acid | $CH_2(COOH)_2$ (or $H_2C_3H_2O_4$) | $1.5 \times 10^{-3}$ | $2.0 \times 10^{-6}$ | |
| Nitrous acid | $HNO_2$ | $4.5 \times 10^{-4}$ | | |
| Oxalic acid | $(COOH)_2$ (or $H_2C_2O_4$) | $5.9 \times 10^{-2}$ | $6.4 \times 10^{-5}$ | |
| Paraperiodic acid | $H_5IO_6$ | $2.8 \times 10^{-2}$ | $5.3 \times 10^{-9}$ | |
| Phenol | $C_6H_5OH$ (or $HC_6H_5O$) | $1.3 \times 10^{-10}$ | | |
| Phosphoric acid | $H_3PO_4$ | $7.5 \times 10^{-3}$ | $6.2 \times 10^{-8}$ | $4.2 \times 10^{-13}$ |
| Propionic acid | $C_2H_5COOH$ (or $HC_3H_5O_2$) | $1.3 \times 10^{-5}$ | | |
| Pyrophosphoric acid | $H_4P_2O_7$ | $3.0 \times 10^{-2}$ | $4.4 \times 10^{-3}$ | $2.1 \times 10^{-7}$ |
| Selenous acid | $H_2SeO_3$ | $2.3 \times 10^{-3}$ | $5.3 \times 10^{-9}$ | |
| Sulfuric acid | $H_2SO_4$ | Strong acid | $1.2 \times 10^{-2}$ | |
| Sulfurous acid | $H_2SO_3$ | $1.7 \times 10^{-2}$ | $6.4 \times 10^{-8}$ | |
| Tartaric acid | $HOOC(CHOH)_2COOH$ (or $H_2C_4H_4O_6$) | $1.0 \times 10^{-3}$ | | |

## TABLE D.2 • Dissociation Constants for Bases at 25 °C

| Name | Formula | $K_b$ |
|---|---|---|
| Ammonia | $NH_3$ | $1.8 \times 10^{-5}$ |
| Aniline | $C_6H_5NH_2$ | $4.3 \times 10^{-10}$ |
| Dimethylamine | $(CH_3)_2NH$ | $5.4 \times 10^{-4}$ |
| Ethylamine | $C_2H_5NH_2$ | $6.4 \times 10^{-4}$ |
| Hydrazine | $H_2NNH_2$ | $1.3 \times 10^{-6}$ |
| Hydroxylamine | $HONH_2$ | $1.1 \times 10^{-8}$ |
| Methylamine | $CH_3NH_2$ | $4.4 \times 10^{-4}$ |
| Pyridine | $C_5H_5N$ | $1.7 \times 10^{-9}$ |
| Trimethylamine | $(CH_3)_3N$ | $6.4 \times 10^{-5}$ |

## TABLE D.3 • Solubility-Product Constants for Compounds at 25 °C

| Name | Formula | $K_{sp}$ | Name | Formula | $K_{sp}$ |
|---|---|---|---|---|---|
| Barium carbonate | $BaCO_3$ | $5.0 \times 10^{-9}$ | Lead(II) fluoride | $PbF_2$ | $3.6 \times 10^{-8}$ |
| Barium chromate | $BaCrO_4$ | $2.1 \times 10^{-10}$ | Lead(II) sulfate | $PbSO_4$ | $6.3 \times 10^{-7}$ |
| Barium fluoride | $BaF_2$ | $1.7 \times 10^{-6}$ | Lead(II) sulfide* | $PbS$ | $3 \times 10^{-28}$ |
| Barium oxalate | $BaC_2O_4$ | $1.6 \times 10^{-6}$ | Magnesium hydroxide | $Mg(OH)_2$ | $1.8 \times 10^{-11}$ |
| Barium sulfate | $BaSO_4$ | $1.1 \times 10^{-10}$ | Magnesium carbonate | $MgCO_3$ | $3.5 \times 10^{-8}$ |
| Cadmium carbonate | $CdCO_3$ | $1.8 \times 10^{-14}$ | Magnesium oxalate | $MgC_2O_4$ | $8.6 \times 10^{-5}$ |
| Cadmium hydroxide | $Cd(OH)_2$ | $2.5 \times 10^{-14}$ | Manganese(II) carbonate | $MnCO_3$ | $5.0 \times 10^{-10}$ |
| Cadmium sulfide* | $CdS$ | $8 \times 10^{-28}$ | Manganese(II) hydroxide | $Mn(OH)_2$ | $1.6 \times 10^{-13}$ |
| Calcium carbonate (calcite) | $CaCO_3$ | $4.5 \times 10^{-9}$ | Manganese(II) sulfide* | $MnS$ | $2 \times 10^{-53}$ |
| Calcium chromate | $CaCrO_4$ | $4.5 \times 10^{-9}$ | Mercury(I) chloride | $Hg_2Cl_2$ | $1.2 \times 10^{-18}$ |
| Calcium fluoride | $CaF_2$ | $3.9 \times 10^{-11}$ | Mercury(I) iodide | $Hg_2I_2$ | $1.1 \times 10^{-1.1}$ |
| Calcium hydroxide | $Ca(OH)_2$ | $6.5 \times 10^{-6}$ | Mercury(II) sulfide* | $HgS$ | $2 \times 10^{-53}$ |
| Calcium phosphate | $Ca_3(PO_4)_2$ | $2.0 \times 10^{-29}$ | Nickel(II) carbonate | $NiCO_3$ | $1.3 \times 10^{-7}$ |
| Calcium sulfate | $CaSO_4$ | $2.4 \times 10^{-5}$ | Nickel(II) hydroxide | $Ni(OH)_2$ | $6.0 \times 10^{-16}$ |
| Chromium(III) hydroxide | $Cr(OH)_3$ | $1.6 \times 10^{-30}$ | Nickel(II) sulfide* | $NiS$ | $3 \times 10^{-20}$ |
| Cobalt(II) carbonate | $CoCO_3$ | $1.0 \times 10^{-10}$ | Silver bromate | $AgBrO_3$ | $5.5 \times 10^{-13}$ |
| Cobalt(II) hydroxide | $Co(OH)_2$ | $1.3 \times 10^{-15}$ | Silver bromide | $AgBr$ | $5.0 \times 10^{-13}$ |
| Cobalt(II) sulfide* | $CoS$ | $5 \times 10^{-22}$ | Silver carbonate | $Ag_2CO_3$ | $8.1 \times 10^{-12}$ |
| Copper(I) bromide | $CuBr$ | $5.3 \times 10^{-9}$ | Silver chloride | $AgCl$ | $1.8 \times 10^{-10}$ |
| Copper(II) carbonate | $CuCO_3$ | $2.3 \times 10^{-10}$ | Silver chromate | $Ag_2CrO_4$ | $1.2 \times 10^{-12}$ |
| Copper(II) hydroxide | $Cu(OH)_2$ | $4.8 \times 10^{-20}$ | Silver iodide | $AgI$ | $8.3 \times 10^{-17}$ |
| Copper(II) sulfide* | $CuS$ | $6 \times 10^{-37}$ | Silver sulfate | $Ag_2SO_4$ | $1.5 \times 10^{-5}$ |
| Iron(II) carbonate | $FeCO_3$ | $2.1 \times 10^{-11}$ | Silver sulfide* | $Ag_2S$ | $6 \times 10^{-51}$ |
| Iron(II) hydroxide | $Fe(OH)_2$ | $7.9 \times 10^{-16}$ | Strontium carbonate | $SrCO_3$ | $9.3 \times 10^{-10}$ |
| Lanthanum fluoride | $LaF_3$ | $2 \times 10^{-19}$ | Tin(II) sulfide* | $SnS$ | $1 \times 10^{-26}$ |
| Lanthanum iodate | $La(IO_3)_3$ | $7.4 \times 10^{-14}$ | Zinc carbonate | $ZnCO_3$ | $1.0 \times 10^{-10}$ |
| Lead(II) carbonate | $PbCO_3$ | $7.4 \times 10^{-14}$ | Zinc hydroxide | $Zn(OH)_2$ | $3.0 \times 10^{-16}$ |
| Lead(II) chloride | $PbCl_2$ | $1.7 \times 10^{-5}$ | Zinc oxalate | $ZnC_2O_4$ | $2.7 \times 10^{-8}$ |
| Lead(II) chromate | $PbCrO_4$ | $2.8 \times 10^{-13}$ | Zinc sulfide* | $ZnS$ | $2 \times 10^{-25}$ |

*For a solubility equilibrium of the type $MS(s) + H_2O(l) \rightleftharpoons M^{2+}(aq) + HS^-(aq) + OH^-(aq)$

# STANDARD REDUCTION POTENTIALS AT 25 °C

| Half-Reaction | $E°(V)$ | Half-Reaction | $E°(V)$ |
|---|---|---|---|
| $Ag^+(aq) + e^- \longrightarrow Ag(s)$ | +0.799 | $2\,H_2O(l) + 2\,e^- \longrightarrow H_2(g) + 2\,OH^-(aq)$ | −0.83 |
| $AgBr(s) + e^- \longrightarrow Ag(s) + Br^-(aq)$ | +0.095 | $HO_2^-(aq) + H_2O(l) + 2\,e^- \longrightarrow 3\,OH^-(aq)$ | +0.88 |
| $AgCl(s) + e^- \longrightarrow Ag(s) + Cl^-(aq)$ | +0.222 | $H_2O_2(aq) + 2\,H^+(aq) + 2\,e^- \longrightarrow 2\,H_2O(l)$ | +1.776 |
| $Ag(CN)_2^-(aq) + e^- \longrightarrow Ag(s) + 2\,CN^-(aq)$ | −0.31 | $Hg_2^{2+}(aq) + 2\,e^- \longrightarrow 2\,Hg(l)$ | +0.789 |
| $Ag_2CrO_4(s) + 2\,e^- \longrightarrow 2\,Ag(s) + CrO_4^{2-}(aq)$ | +0.446 | $2\,Hg^{2+}(aq) + 2\,e^- \longrightarrow Hg_2^{2+}(aq)$ | +0.920 |
| $AgI(s) + e^- \longrightarrow Ag(s) + I^-(aq)$ | −0.151 | $Hg^{2+}(aq) + 2\,e^- \longrightarrow Hg(l)$ | +0.854 |
| $Ag(S_2O_3)_2^{3-}(aq) + e^- \longrightarrow Ag(s) + 2\,S_2O_3^{2-}(aq)$ | +0.01 | $I_2(s) + 2\,e^- \longrightarrow 2\,I^-(aq)$ | +0.536 |
| $Al^{3+}(aq) + 3\,e^- \longrightarrow Al(s)$ | −1.66 | $2\,IO_3^-(aq) + 12\,H^+(aq) + 10\,e^- \longrightarrow$ $I_2(s) + 6\,H_2O(l)$ | +1.195 |
| $H_3AsO_4(aq) + 2\,H^+(aq) + 2\,e^- \longrightarrow$ $H_3AsO_3(aq) + H_2O(l)$ | +0.559 | | |
| $Ba^{2+}(aq) + 2\,e^- \longrightarrow Ba(s)$ | −2.90 | $K^+(aq) + e^- \longrightarrow K(s)$ | −2.925 |
| $BiO^+(aq) + 2\,H^+(aq) + 3\,e^- \longrightarrow Bi(s) + H_2O(l)$ | +0.32 | $Li^+(aq) + e^- \longrightarrow Li(s)$ | −3.05 |
| $Br_2(l) + 2\,e^- \longrightarrow 2\,Br^-(aq)$ | +1.065 | $Mg^{2+}(aq) + 2\,e^- \longrightarrow Mg(s)$ | −2.37 |
| $2\,BrO_3^-(aq) + 12\,H^+(aq) + 10\,e^- \longrightarrow$ $Br_2(l) + 6\,H_2O(l)$ | +1.52 | $Mn^{2+}(aq) + 2\,e^- \longrightarrow Mn(s)$ | −1.18 |
| | | $MnO_2(s) + 4\,H^+(aq) + 2\,e^- \longrightarrow$ $Mn^{2+}(aq) + 2\,H_2O(l)$ | +1.23 |
| $2\,CO_2(g) + 2\,H^+(aq) + 2\,e^- \longrightarrow H_2C_2O_4(aq)$ | −0.49 | | |
| $Ca^{2+}(aq) + 2\,e^- \longrightarrow Ca(s)$ | −2.87 | $MnO_4^-(aq) + 8\,H^+(aq) + 5\,e^- \longrightarrow$ $Mn^{2+}(aq) + 4\,H_2O(l)$ | +1.51 |
| $Cd^{2+}(aq) + 2\,e^- \longrightarrow Cd(s)$ | −0.403 | | |
| $Ce^{4+}(aq) + e^- \longrightarrow Ce^{3+}(aq)$ | +1.61 | $MnO_4^-(aq) + 2\,H_2O(l) + 3\,e^- \longrightarrow$ $MnO_2(s) + 4\,OH^-(aq)$ | +0.59 |
| $Cl_2(g) + 2\,e^- \longrightarrow 2\,Cl^-(aq)$ | +1.359 | | |
| $2\,HClO(aq) + 2\,H^+(aq) + 2\,e^- \longrightarrow$ $Cl_2(g) + 2\,H_2O(l)$ | +1.63 | $HNO_2(aq) + H^+(aq) + e^- \longrightarrow NO(g) + H_2O(l)$ | +1.00 |
| | | $N_2(g) + 4\,H_2O(l) + 4\,e^- \longrightarrow 4\,OH^-(aq) + N_2H_4(aq)$ | −1.16 |
| $ClO^-(aq) + H_2O(l) + 2\,e^- \longrightarrow$ $Cl^-(aq) + 2\,OH^-(aq)$ | +0.89 | $N_2(g) + 5\,H^+(aq) + 4\,e^- \longrightarrow N_2H_5^+(aq)$ | −0.23 |
| | | $NO_3^-(aq) + 4\,H^+(aq) + 3\,e^- \longrightarrow NO(g) + 2\,H_2O(l)$ | +0.96 |
| $2\,ClO_3^-(aq) + 12\,H^+(aq) + 10\,e^- \longrightarrow$ $Cl_2(g) + 6\,H_2O(l)$ | +1.47 | $Na^+(aq) + e^- \longrightarrow Na(s)$ | −2.71 |
| | | $Ni^{2+}(aq) + 2\,e^- \longrightarrow Ni(s)$ | −0.28 |
| $Co^{2+}(aq) + 2\,e^- \longrightarrow Co(s)$ | −0.277 | $O_2(g) + 4\,H^+(aq) + 4\,e^- \longrightarrow 2\,H_2O(l)$ | +1.23 |
| $Co^{3+}(aq) + e^- \longrightarrow Co^{2+}(aq)$ | +1.842 | $O_2(g) + 2\,H_2O(l) + 4\,e^- \longrightarrow 4\,OH^-(aq)$ | +0.40 |
| $Cr^{3+}(aq) + 3\,e^- \longrightarrow Cr(s)$ | −0.74 | $O_2(g) + 2\,H^+(aq) + 2\,e^- \longrightarrow H_2O_2(aq)$ | +0.68 |
| $Cr^{3+}(aq) + e^- \longrightarrow Cr^{2+}(aq)$ | −0.41 | $O_3(g) + 2\,H^+(aq) + 2\,e^- \longrightarrow O_2(g) + H_2O(l)$ | +2.07 |
| $CrO_7^{2-}(aq) + 14\,H^+(aq) + 6\,e^- \longrightarrow$ $2\,Cr^{3+}(aq) + 7\,H_2O(l)$ | +1.33 | $Pb^{2+}(aq) + 2\,e^- \longrightarrow Pb(s)$ | −0.126 |
| | | $PbO_2(s) + HSO_4^-(aq) + 3\,H^+(aq) + 2\,e^- \longrightarrow$ $PbSO_4(s) + 2\,H_2O(l)$ | +1.685 |
| $CrO_4^{2-}(aq) + 4\,H_2O(l) + 3\,e^- \longrightarrow$ $Cr(OH)_3(s) + 5\,OH^-(aq)$ | −0.13 | | |
| | | $PbSO_4(s) + H^+(aq) + 2\,e^- \longrightarrow Pb(s) + HSO_4^-(aq)$ | −0.356 |
| $Cu^{2+}(aq) + 2\,e^- \longrightarrow Cu(s)$ | +0.337 | $PtCl_4^{2-}(aq) + 2\,e^- \longrightarrow Pt(s) + 4\,Cl^-(aq)$ | +0.73 |
| $Cu^{2+}(aq) + e^- \longrightarrow Cu^+(aq)$ | +0.153 | $S(s) + 2\,H^+(aq) + 2\,e^- \longrightarrow H_2S(g)$ | +0.141 |
| $Cu^+(aq) + e^- \longrightarrow Cu(s)$ | +0.521 | $H_2SO_3(aq) + 4\,H^+(aq) + 4\,e^- \longrightarrow S(s) + 3\,H_2O(l)$ | +0.45 |
| $CuI(s) + e^- \longrightarrow Cu(s) + I^-(aq)$ | −0.185 | $HSO_4^-(aq) + 3\,H^+(aq) + 2\,e^- \longrightarrow$ $H_2SO_3(aq) + H_2O(l)$ | +0.17 |
| $F_2(g) + 2\,e^- \longrightarrow 2\,F^-(aq)$ | +2.87 | | |
| $Fe^{2+}(aq) + 2\,e^- \longrightarrow Fe(s)$ | −0.440 | $Sn^{2+}(aq) + 2\,e^- \longrightarrow Sn(s)$ | −0.136 |
| $Fe^{3+}(aq) + e^- \longrightarrow Fe^{2+}(aq)$ | +0.771 | $Sn^{4+}(aq) + 2\,e^- \longrightarrow Sn^{2+}(aq)$ | +0.154 |
| $Fe(CN)_6^{3-}(aq) + e^- \longrightarrow Fe(CN)_6^{4-}(aq)$ | +0.36 | $VO_2^+(aq) + 2\,H^+(aq) + e^- \longrightarrow VO^{2+}(aq) + H_2O(l)$ | +1.00 |
| $2\,H^+(aq) + 2\,e^- \longrightarrow H_2(g)$ | 0.000 | $Zn^{2+}(aq) + 2\,e^- \longrightarrow Zn(s)$ | −0.763 |

# UNIVERSITY OF NEVADA AT RENO CHEMISTRY MINOR REQUIREMENTS

Students majoring in another field may obtain a minor in chemistry by completing one of the following two course sequence options:

## 1 | ANALYTICAL-ORGANIC OPTION

- CHEM 121 – General Chemistry I or CHEM 201 (4 credits)
- CHEM 122 – General Chemistry II or CHEM 202 (4 credits)
- CHEM 330 – Analytical Chemistry (4 credits)
- CHEM 341 – Organic Chemistry for Scientists and Professionals I (3 credits)
- CHEM 342 – Organic Chemistry for Scientists and Professionals II (3 credits)
- CHEM 345 – Organic Chemistry Laboratory (2 credits)

**Total: 20 credits**

## 2 | BIOPHYSICAL-ORGANIC OPTION

- CHEM 121 – General Chemistry I or CHEM 201 (4 credits)
- CHEM 122 – General Chemistry II or CHEM 202 (4 credits)
- CHEM 341 – Organic Chemistry for Scientists and Professionals I (3 credits)
- CHEM 342 – Organic Chemistry for Scientists and Professionals II (3 credits)
- CHEM 345 – Organic Chemistry Laboratory (2 credits)
- CHEM 425 – Biophysical Chemistry (3 credits)
- CHEM 443 – Organic Spectroscopy and Structure (2 credits)

**Total: 21 credits**

## Note:

Deviations from these sequences are possible with approval of a chemistry advisor. Minimum requirements are a total of 20 chemistry credits, including nine upper-division credits and a two-credit organic chemistry laboratory course. A maximum of two credits of CHEM 392 and 490 may be applied to comprise the nine upper-division credits, with departmental approval.

To apply for the minor, complete the minor application form (available from the Chemistry Department Office or website) and submit it to the Chemistry Department Office in CB 213.

# ANSWERS TO SELECTED EXERCISES

## CHAPTER 1

**1.1** (a) Pure element: i (b) mixture of elements: v, vi (c) pure compound: iv (d) mixture of an element and a compound: ii, iii **1.3** This kind of separation based on solubility differences is called *extraction*. The insoluble grounds are then separated from the coffee solution by *filtration*. **1.5** (a) The aluminum sphere is lightest, then nickel, then silver. (b) The platinum sphere is largest, then gold, then lead. **1.7** (a) 7.5 cm; two significant figures (sig figs) (b) 72 mi/hr (inner scale, two significant figures) or 115 km/hr (outer scale, three significant figures) **1.9** Arrange the conversion factor so that the given unit cancels and the desired unit is in the correct position. **1.11** (a) Heterogeneous mixture (b) homogeneous mixture (heterogeneous if there are undissolved particles) (c) pure substance (d) pure substance. **1.13** (a) S (b) Au (c) K (d) Cl (e) Cu (f) uranium (g) nickel (h) sodium (i) aluminum (j) silicon **1.15** C is a compound; it contains both carbon and oxygen. A is a compound; it contains at least carbon and oxygen. B is not defined by the data given; it is probably also a compound because few elements exist as white solids. **1.17** Physical properties: silvery white; lustrous; melting point = 649 °C; boiling point = 1105 °C; density at 20 °C = 1.738 g/cm$^3$; pounded into sheets; drawn into wires; good conductor. Chemical properties: burns in air; reacts with $Cl_2$. **1.19** (a) Chemical (b) physical (c) physical (d) chemical (e) chemical **1.21** (a) Add water to dissolve the sugar; filter this mixture, collecting the sand on the filter paper and the sugar water in the flask. Evaporate water from the flask to recover solid sugar. (b) Allow the mixture to settle so that there are two distinct layers. Carefully pour off most of the top oil layer. After the layers reform, use a dropper to remove any remaining oil. Vinegar is in the original vessel and oil is in a second container. **1.23** (a) $1 \times 10^{-1}$ (b) $1 \times 10^{-2}$ (c) $1 \times 10^{-15}$ (d) $1 \times 10^{-6}$ (e) $1 \times 10^{6}$ (f) $1 \times 10^{3}$ (g) $1 \times 10^{-9}$ (h) $1 \times 10^{-3}$ (i) $1 \times 10^{-12}$ **1.25** (a) 22 °C (b) 422.1 °F (c) 506 K (d) 107 °C (e) 1644 K (f) −459.67 °F **1.27** (a) 1.62 g/mL. Tetrachloroethylene, 1.62 g/mL, is more dense than water, 1.00 g/mL; tetrachloroethylene will sink rather than float on water. (b) 11.7 g **1.29** (a) Calculated density = 0.86 g/mL. The substance is probably toluene, density = 0.866 g/mL. (b) 40.4 mL ethylene glycol (c) $1.11 \times 10^{3}$ g nickel **1.31** 28 Pg **1.33** Exact: (c), (d), and (f) **1.35** (a) 3 (b) 2 (c) 5 (d) 3 (e) 5 (f) 1 **1.37** (a) $1.025 \times 10^{2}$ (b) $6.570 \times 10^{5}$ (c) $8.543 \times 10^{-3}$ (d) $2.579 \times 10^{-4}$ (e) $-3.572 \times 10^{-2}$ **1.39** (a) 17.00 (b) 812.0 (c) $8.23 \times 10^{3}$ (d) $8.69 \times 10^{-2}$ **1.41** 5 significant figures

**1.43** (a) $\dfrac{1 \times 10^{-3}\,\text{m}}{1\,\text{mm}} \times \dfrac{1\,\text{nm}}{1 \times 10^{-9}\,\text{m}}$ (b) $\dfrac{1 \times 10^{-3}\,\text{g}}{1\,\text{mg}} \times \dfrac{1\,\text{kg}}{1000\,\text{g}}$

(c) $\dfrac{1000\,\text{m}}{1\,\text{km}} \times \dfrac{1\,\text{cm}}{1 \times 10^{-2}\,\text{m}} \times \dfrac{1\,\text{in.}}{2.54\,\text{cm}} \times \dfrac{1\,\text{ft}}{12\,\text{in.}}$ (d) $\dfrac{(2.54)^3\,\text{cm}^3}{1^3\,\text{in.}^3}$

**1.45** (a) 54.7 km/hr (b) $1.3 \times 10^{3}$ gal (c) 46.0 m (d) 0.984 in/hr **1.47** (a) $4.32 \times 10^{5}$ s (b) 88.5 m (c) $0.499/L (d) 46.6 km/hr (e) 1.420 L/s (f) 707.9 cm$^3$ **1.49** (a) $1.2 \times 10^{2}$ L (b) $5 \times 10^{2}$ mg (c) 19.9 mi/gal ($2 \times 10^{1}$ mi/gal for 1 significant figure) (d) 26 mL/g ($3 \times 10^{1}$ mL/g for 1 significant figure) **1.51** 64 kg air **1.53** 14-in. shoe < 57-cm string < 1.1-m pipe **1.55** $6 \times 10^{4}$ **1.59** 8.47 g O; the *law of constant composition* **1.62** (a) Volume (b) area (c) volume (d) density (e) time (f) length (g) temperature **1.65** (a) $1.13 \times 10^{5}$ quarters (b) $6.41 \times 10^{5}$ g (c) $2.83 \times 10^{4}$ (d) $4.13 \times 10^{8}$ stacks **1.68** The most dense liquid, Hg, will sink; the least dense, cyclohexane, will float; $H_2O$ will be in the middle. **1.71** density of solid = 1.63 g/mL **1.74** (a) Density of peat = 0.13 g/cm$^3$, density of soil = 2.5 g/cm$^3$. It is not correct to say that peat is "lighter" than topsoil. Volumes must be specified in order to compare masses. (b) Buy 16 bags of peat (more than 15 are needed). (Results to 1 significant figure are not meaningful.) **1.77** The inner diameter of the tube is 1.13 cm. **1.79** The separation

is successful if two distinct spots are seen on the paper. To quantify the characteristics of the separation, calculate a reference value for each spot: distance traveled by spot/distance traveled by solvent. If the values for the two spots are fairly different, the separation is successful.

## CHAPTER 2

**2.1** (a) The path of the charged particle bends because the particle is repelled by the negatively charged plate and attracted to the positively charged plate. (b) (−) (c) increase (d) decrease **2.4** The particle is an ion. $^{32}_{16}S^{2-}$ **2.6** Formula: $IF_5$; name: iodine pentafluoride; the compound is molecular. **2.9** Postulate 4 of the atomic theory states that the relative number and kinds of atoms in a compound are constant, regardless of the source. Therefore, 1.0 g of pure water should always contain the same relative amounts of hydrogen and oxygen, no matter where or how the sample is obtained. **2.11** (a) 0.5711 g O/1 g N; 1.142 g O/1 g N; 2.284 g O/1 g N; 2.855 g O/1 g N (b) The numbers in part (a) obey the *law of multiple proportions*. Multiple proportions arise because atoms are the indivisible entities combining, as stated in Dalton's atomic theory. **2.13** (1) Electric and magnetic fields deflected the rays in the same way they would deflect negatively charged particles. (2) A metal plate exposed to cathode rays acquired a negative charge. **2.15** (a) Most of the volume of an atom is empty space in which electrons move. Most alpha particles passed through this space. (b) The few alpha particles that hit the massive, positively charged gold nuclei were strongly repelled and deflected back in the direction they came from. (c) Because the Be nuclei have a smaller volume and a smaller positive charge than the Au nuclei, fewer alpha particles will be scattered and fewer will be strongly back scattered. **2.17** (a) 0.135 nm; $1.35 \times 10^{2}$ or 135 pm (b) $3.70 \times 10^{6}$ Au atoms (c) $1.03 \times 10^{-23}$ cm$^3$ **2.19** (a) Proton, neutron, electron (b) proton = 1+, neutron = 0, electron = 1− (c) The neutron is most massive. (The neutron and proton have very similar masses.) (d) The electron is least massive. **2.21** (a) Atomic number is the number of protons in the nucleus of an atom. Mass number is the total number of nuclear particles, protons plus neutrons, in an atom. (b) mass number **2.23** (a) $^{40}$Ar: 18 p, 22 n, 18 e (b) $^{65}$Zn: 30 p, 35 n, 30 e (c) $^{70}$Ga: 31 p, 39 n, 31 e (d) $^{80}$Br: 35 p, 45 n, 35 e (e) $^{184}$W: 74 p, 110 n, 74 e (f) $^{243}$Am: 95 p, 148 n, 95e

**2.25**

| Symbol | $^{52}$Cr | $^{55}$Mn | $^{112}$Cd | $^{222}$Rn | $^{207}$Pb |
|---|---|---|---|---|---|
| Protons | 24 | 25 | 48 | 86 | 82 |
| Neutrons | 28 | 30 | 64 | 136 | 125 |
| Electrons | 24 | 25 | 48 | 86 | 82 |
| Mass no. | 52 | 55 | 112 | 222 | 207 |

**2.27** (a) $^{196}_{78}$Pt (b) $^{84}_{36}$Kr (c) $^{75}_{33}$As (d) $^{24}_{12}$Mg **2.29** (a) $^{12}_{6}$C (b) Atomic weights are average atomic masses, the sum of the mass of each naturally occurring isotope of an element times its fractional abundance. Each B atom will have the mass of one of the naturally occurring isotopes, while the "atomic weight" is an average value. **2.31** 63.55 amu **2.33** (a) In Thomson's cathode-ray experiments and in mass spectrometry, a stream of charged particles is passed through the poles of a magnet. The charged particles are deflected by the magnetic field according to their mass and charge. (b) The *x*-axis label is atomic weight, and the *y*-axis label is signal intensity. (c) Uncharged particles are not deflected in a magnetic field. The effect of the magnetic field on charged moving particles is the basis of their separation by mass. **2.35** (a) average atomic mass = 24.31 amu

(b)

**2.37** (a) Cr, 24 (metal) (b) He, 2 (nonmetal) (c) P, 15 (nonmetal) (d) Zn, 30 (metal) (e) Mg, 12 (metal) (f) Br, 35 (nonmetal) (g) As, 33 (metalloid) **2.39** (a) K, alkali metals (metal) (b) I, halogens (nonmetal) (c) Mg, alkaline earth metals (metal) (d) Ar, noble gases (nonmetal) (e) S, chalcogens (nonmetal) **2.41** An empirical formula shows the simplest mole ratio of elements in a compound. A molecular formula shows the exact number and kinds of atoms in a molecule. A structural formula shows which atoms are attached to which. **2.43** (a) $AlBr_3$ (b) $C_4H_5$ (c) $C_2H_4O$ (d) $P_2O_5$ (e) $C_3H_2Cl$ (f) $BNH_2$ **2.45** (a) 6 (b) 6 (c) 12

**2.47**

(a) $C_2H_6O$,

$$H-\overset{\overset{\displaystyle H}{|}}{\underset{\underset{\displaystyle H}{|}}{C}}-O-\overset{\overset{\displaystyle H}{|}}{\underset{\underset{\displaystyle H}{|}}{C}}-H$$

(b) $C_2H_6O$,

$$H-\overset{\overset{\displaystyle H}{|}}{\underset{\underset{\displaystyle H}{|}}{C}}-\overset{\overset{\displaystyle H}{|}}{\underset{\underset{\displaystyle H}{|}}{C}}-O-H$$

(c) $CH_4O$,

$$H-\overset{\overset{\displaystyle H}{|}}{\underset{\underset{\displaystyle H}{|}}{C}}-O-H$$

(d) $PF_3$,

$$F-\overset{}{\underset{\underset{\displaystyle F}{|}}{P}}-F$$

**2.49**

| Symbol | $^{59}Co^{3+}$ | $^{80}Se^{2-}$ | $^{192}Os^{2+}$ | $^{200}Hg^{2+}$ |
|---|---|---|---|---|
| Protons | 27 | 34 | 76 | 80 |
| Neutrons | 32 | 46 | 116 | 120 |
| Electrons | 24 | 36 | 74 | 78 |
| Net Charge | 3+ | 2− | 2+ | 2+ |

**2.51** (a) $Mg^{2+}$ (b) $Al^{3+}$ (c) $K^+$ (d) $S^{2-}$ (e) $F^-$ **2.53** (a) $GaF_3$, gallium(III) fluoride (b) LiH, lithium hydride (c) $AlI_3$, aluminum iodide (d) $K_2S$, potassium sulfide **2.55** (a) $CaBr_2$ (b) $K_2CO_3$ (c) $Al(CH_3COO)_3$ (d) $(NH_4)_2SO_4$ (e) $Mg_3(PO_4)_2$

**2.57**

| Ion | $K^+$ | $NH_4^+$ | $Mg^{2+}$ | $Fe^{3+}$ |
|---|---|---|---|---|
| $Cl^-$ | KCl | $NH_4Cl$ | $MgCl_2$ | $FeCl_3$ |
| $OH^-$ | KOH | $NH_4OH$ | $Mg(OH)_2$ | $Fe(OH)_3$ |
| $CO_3^{2-}$ | $K_2CO_3$ | $(NH_4)_2CO_3$ | $MgCO_3$ | $Fe_2(CO_3)_3$ |
| $PO_4^{3-}$ | $K_3PO_4$ | $(NH_4)_3PO_4$ | $Mg_3(PO_4)_2$ | $FePO_4$ |

**2.59** Molecular: (a) $B_2H_6$ (b) $CH_3OH$ (f) NOCl (g) $NF_3$. Ionic: (c) $LiNO_3$ (d) $Sc_2O_3$ (e) CsBr (h) $Ag_2SO_4$ **2.61** (a) $ClO_2^-$ (b) $Cl^-$ (c) $ClO_3^-$ (d) $ClO_4^-$ (e) $ClO^-$ **2.63** (a) calcium, 2+; oxide, 2− (b) sodium, 1+; sulfate, 2− (c) potassium, 1+; nitrate, 1− (d) iron, 2+, nitrate, 1− (e) chromium, 3+; hydroxide, 1− **2.65** (a) lithium oxide (b) iron(III) chloride (ferric chloride) (c) sodium hypochlorite (d) calcium sulfite (e) copper(II) hydroxide (cupric hydroxide) (f) iron(II) nitrate (ferrous nitrate) (g) calcium acetate (h) chromium(III) carbonate (chromic carbonate) (i) potassium chromate (j) ammonium sulfate **2.67** (a) $Al(OH)_3$ (b) $K_2SO_4$ (c) $Cu_2O$ (d) $Zn(NO_3)_2$ (e) $HgBr_2$ (f) $Fe_2(CO_3)_3$ (g) NaBrO **2.69** (a) Bromic acid (b) hydrobromic acid (c) phosphoric acid (d) HClO (e) $HIO_3$ (f) $H_2SO_3$ **2.71** (a) Sulfur hexafluoride (b) iodine pentafluoride (c) xenon trioxide (d) $N_2O_4$ (e) HCN (f) $P_4S_6$ **2.73** (a) $ZnCO_3$, ZnO, $CO_2$ (b) HF, $SiO_2$, $SiF_4$, $H_2O$ (c) $SO_2$, $H_2O$, $H_2SO_3$ (d) $PH_3$ (e) $HClO_4$, Cd, $Cd(ClO_4)_2$ (f) $VBr_3$ **2.75** (a) A hydrocarbon is a compound composed of the elements hydrogen and carbon only.

(b)

$$H-\overset{\overset{\displaystyle H}{|}}{\underset{\underset{\displaystyle H}{|}}{C}}-\overset{\overset{\displaystyle H}{|}}{\underset{\underset{\displaystyle H}{|}}{C}}-\overset{\overset{\displaystyle H}{|}}{\underset{\underset{\displaystyle H}{|}}{C}}-\overset{\overset{\displaystyle H}{|}}{\underset{\underset{\displaystyle H}{|}}{C}}-H$$

Molecular: $C_4H_{10}$
Empirical: $C_2H_5$

**2.77** (a) Functional groups are groups of specific atoms that are constant from one molecule to the next. (b) —OH

(c)

$$H-\overset{\overset{\displaystyle H}{|}}{\underset{\underset{\displaystyle H}{|}}{C}}-\overset{\overset{\displaystyle H}{|}}{\underset{\underset{\displaystyle H}{|}}{C}}-\overset{\overset{\displaystyle H}{|}}{\underset{\underset{\displaystyle H}{|}}{C}}-\overset{\overset{\displaystyle H}{|}}{\underset{\underset{\displaystyle H}{|}}{C}}-OH$$

**2.79**
(a, b)

$$H-\overset{\overset{\displaystyle H}{|}}{\underset{\underset{\displaystyle H}{|}}{C}}-\overset{\overset{\displaystyle H}{|}}{\underset{\underset{\displaystyle H}{|}}{C}}-\overset{\overset{\displaystyle H}{|}}{\underset{\underset{\displaystyle H}{|}}{C}}-Cl$$

1-chloropropane

$$H-\overset{\overset{\displaystyle H}{|}}{\underset{\underset{\displaystyle H}{|}}{C}}-\overset{\overset{\displaystyle Cl}{|}}{\underset{\underset{\displaystyle H}{|}}{C}}-\overset{\overset{\displaystyle H}{|}}{\underset{\underset{\displaystyle H}{|}}{C}}-H$$

2-chloropropane

**2.82** (a) 2 protons, 1 neutron, 2 electrons (b) tritium, $^3H$, is more massive. (c) A precision of $1 \times 10^{-27}$ g would be required to differentiate between $^3H^+$ and $^3He^+$. **2.84** Arrangement A, $4.1 \times 10^{14}$ atoms/cm$^2$ (b) Arrangement B, $4.7 \times 10^{14}$ atoms/cm$^2$ (c) The ratio of atoms going from arrangement B to arrangement A is 1.2 to 1. In three dimensions, arrangement B leads to a greater density for Rb metal. **2.87** (a) $^{16}_8O$, $^{17}_8O$, $^{18}_8O$ (b) All isotopes are atoms of the same element, oxygen, with the same atomic number, 8 protons in the nucleus and 8 electrons. We expect their electron arrangements to be the same and their chemical properties to be very similar. Each has a different number of neutrons, a different mass number, and a different atomic mass. **2.90** (a) $^{69}_{31}Ga$, 31 protons, 38 neutrons; $^{71}_{31}Ga$, 31 protons, 40 neutrons (b) $^{69}_{31}Ga$, 60.3%, $^{71}_{31}Ga$, 39.7%. **2.93** (a) 5 significant figures (b) An electron is 0.05444% of the mass of an $^1H$ atom. **2.96** Strontium is an alkaline earth metal, similar in chemical properties to calcium and magnesium. Harmful strontium closely mimics essential calcium and magnesium, then behaves badly when the body tries to use it as it uses calcium and magnesium. **2.98** (a) Nickel(II) oxide, 2+ (b) manganese(IV) oxide, 4+ (c) chromium(III) oxide, 3+ (d) molybdenum(VI) oxide, 6+ **2.101** (a) Perbromate ion (b) selenite ion (c) $AsO_4^{3-}$ (d) $HTeO_4^-$ **2.104** (a) Potassium nitrate (b) sodium carbonate (c) calcium oxide (d) hydrochloric acid (e) magnesium sulfate (f) magnesium hydroxide

## CHAPTER 3

**3.1** Equation (a) best fits the diagram. **3.3** (a) $NO_2$ (b) No, because we have no way of knowing whether the empirical and molecular formulas are the same. $NO_2$ represents the simplest ratio of atoms in a molecule but not the only possible molecular formula. **3.5** (a) $C_2H_5NO_2$ (b) 75.0 g/mol (c) 225 g glycine (d) Mass %N in glycine is 18.7%.

**3.7**

$N_2 + 3 H_2 \longrightarrow 2 NH_3$. Eight N atoms (4 $N_2$ molecules) require 24 H atoms (12 $H_2$ molecules) for complete reaction. Only 9 $H_2$ molecules are available, so $H_2$ is the limiting reactant. Nine $H_2$ molecules (18 H atoms) determine that 6 $NH_3$ molecules are produced. One $N_2$ molecule is in excess. **3.9** (a) Conservation of mass (b) Subscripts in chemical formulas should not be changed when balancing equations, because changing the subscript changes the identity of the compound (*law of constant composition*). (c) $H_2O(l)$, $H_2O(g)$, $NaCl(aq)$, $NaCl(s)$

**3.11** (a) $2 CO(g) + O_2(g) \longrightarrow 2 CO_2(g)$

(b) $N_2O_5(g) + H_2O(l) \longrightarrow 2 HNO_3(aq)$

(c) $CH_4(g) + 4 Cl_2(g) \longrightarrow CCl_4(l) + 4 HCl(g)$

(d) $Al_4C_3(s) + 12 H_2O(l) \longrightarrow 4 Al(OH)_3(s) + 3 CH_4(g)$

(e) $2 C_5H_{10}O_2(l) + 13 O_2(g) \longrightarrow 10 CO_2(g) + 10 H_2O(l)$

(f) $2 Fe(OH)_3(s) + 3 H_2SO_4(aq) \longrightarrow Fe_2(SO_4)_3(aq) + 6 H_2O(l)$

(g) $Mg_3N_2(s) + 4 H_2SO_4(aq) \longrightarrow 3 MgSO_4(aq) + (NH_4)_2SO_4(aq)$

**3.13** (a) $CaC_2(s) + 2 H_2O(l) \longrightarrow Ca(OH)_2(aq) + C_2H_2(g)$

(b) $2 KClO_3(s) \xrightarrow{\Delta} 2 KCl(s) + 3 O_2(g)$

(c) $Zn(s) + H_2SO_4(aq) \longrightarrow ZnSO_4(aq) + H_2(g)$

(d) $PCl_3(l) + 3 H_2O(l) \longrightarrow H_3PO_3(aq) + 3 HCl(aq)$

(e) $3 H_2S(g) + 2 Fe(OH)_3(s) \longrightarrow Fe_2S_3(s) + 6 H_2O(l)$

**3.15** (a) Determine the formula by balancing the positive and negative charges in the ionic product. All ionic compounds are solids. $2 Na(s) + Br_2(l) \longrightarrow 2 NaBr(s)$ (b) The second reactant is $O_2(g)$. The products are $CO_2(g)$ and $H_2O(l)$. $2 C_6H_6(l) + 15 O_2(g) \longrightarrow 12 CO_2(g) + 6 H_2O(l)$

**3.17** (a) $Mg(s) + Cl_2(g) \longrightarrow MgCl_2(s)$

(b) $BaCO_3(s) \xrightarrow{\Delta} BaO(s) + CO_2(g)$

(c) $C_8H_8(l) + 10 O_2(g) \longrightarrow 8 CO_2(g) + 4 H_2O(l)$

(d) $C_2H_6O(g) + 3 O_2(g) \longrightarrow 2 CO_2(g) + 3 H_2O(l)$

**3.19** (a) $2 C_3H_6(g) + 9 O_2(g) \longrightarrow 6 CO_2(g) + 6 H_2O(g)$ combustion

(b) $NH_4NO_3(s) \longrightarrow N_2O(g) + 2 H_2O(g)$ decomposition

(c) $C_5H_6O(l) + 6 O_2(g) \longrightarrow 5 CO_2(g) + 3 H_2O(g)$ combustion

(d) $N_2(g) + 3 H_2(g) \longrightarrow 2 NH_3(g)$ combination

(e) $K_2O(s) + H_2O(l) \longrightarrow 2 KOH(aq)$ combination

**3.21** (a) 63.0 amu (b) 158.0 amu (c) 310.3 amu (d) 60.1 amu (e) 235.7 amu (f) 392.3 amu (g) 137.5 amu **3.23** (a) 16.8% (b) 16.1% (c) 21.1% (d) 28.8% (e) 27.2% (f) 26.5% **3.25** (a) 79.2% (b) 63.2%

(c) 64.6% **3.27** (a) $6.022 \times 10^{23}$ (b) The formula weight of a substance in amu has the same numerical value as the molar mass expressed in grams. **3.29** 23 g Na contains 1 mol of atoms; 0.5 mol $H_2O$ contains 1.5 mol atoms; $6.0 \times 10^{23}$ $N_2$ molecules contain 2 mol of atoms. **3.31** $4.37 \times 10^{25}$ kg (assuming 160 lb has 3 significant figures). One mole of people weighs 7.31 times as much as Earth. **3.33** (a) 35.9 g $C_{12}H_{22}O_{11}$ (b) 0.75766 mol $Zn(NO_3)_2$ (c) $6.0 \times 10^{17}$ $CH_3CH_2OH$ molecules (d) $2.47 \times 10^{23}$ N atoms **3.35** (a) 0.373 g $(NH_4)_3PO_4$ (b) $5.737 \times 10^{-3}$ mol $Cl^-$ (c) 0.248 g $C_8H_{10}N_4O_2$ (d) 387 g cholesterol/mol **3.37** (a) Molar mass = 162.3 g (b) $3.08 \times 10^{-5}$ mol allicin (c) $1.86 \times 10^{19}$ allicin molecules (d) $3.71 \times 10^{19}$ S atoms **3.39** (a) $2.500 \times 10^{21}$ H atoms (b) $2.083 \times 10^{20}$ $C_6H_{12}O_6$ molecules (c) $3.460 \times 10^{-4}$ mol $C_6H_{12}O_6$ (d) 0.06227 g $C_6H_{12}O_6$ **3.41** $3.2 \times 10^{-8}$ mol $C_2H_3Cl/L$; $1.9 \times 10^{16}$ molecules/L **3.43** (a) $C_2H_6O$ (b) $Fe_2O_3$ (c) $CH_2O$ **3.45** (a) $CSCl_2$ (b) $C_3OF_6$ (c) $Na_3AlF_6$ **3.47** 31 g/mol **3.49** (a) $C_6H_{12}$ (b) $NH_2Cl$ **3.51** (a) Empirical formula, CH; molecular formula, $C_8H_8$ (b) empirical formula, $C_4H_5N_2O$; molecular formula, $C_8H_{10}N_4O_2$ (c) empirical formula and molecular formula, $NaC_5H_8O_4N$ **3.53** (a) $C_7H_8$ (b) The empirical and molecular formulas are $C_{10}H_{20}O$. **3.55** The molecular formula from the model is $C_8H_{16}O_2$, which corresponds to an empirical formula of $C_4H_8O$. The results from combustion analysis are consistent with this empirical formula. **3.57** $x = 10$; $Na_2CO_3 \cdot 10 H_2O$ **3.59** If the equation is not balanced, the mole ratios derived from the coefficients will be incorrect and lead to erroneous calculated amounts of products. **3.61** (a) 2.40 mol HF (b) 5.25 g NaF (c) 0.610 g $Na_2SiO_3$ **3.63** (a) $Al(OH)_3(s) + 3 HCl(aq) \longrightarrow AlCl_3(aq) + 3 H_2O(l)$ (b) 0.701 g HCl (c) 0.855 g $AlCl_3$; 0.347 g $H_2O$ (d) Mass of reactants = 0.500 g + 0.701 g = 1.201 g; mass of products = 0.855 g + 0.347 g = 1.202 g. Mass is conserved, within the precision of the data. **3.65** (a) $Al_2S_3(s) + 6 H_2O(l) \longrightarrow 2 Al(OH)_3(s) + 3 H_2S(g)$ (b) 14.7 g $Al(OH)_3$ **3.67** (a) 2.25 mol $N_2$ (b) 15.5 g $NaN_3$ (c) 548 g $NaN_3$ **3.69** (a) $5.50 \times 10^{-3}$ mol Al (b) 1.47 g $AlBr_3$ **3.71** (a) The *limiting reactant* determines the maximum number of product moles resulting from a chemical reaction; any other reactant is an *excess reactant*. (b) The limiting reactant regulates the amount of products because it is completely used up during the reaction; no more product can be made when one of the reactants is unavailable. (c) Combining ratios are molecule and mole ratios. Since different molecules have different masses, comparing initial masses of reactants will not provide a comparison of numbers of molecules or moles. **3.73** (a) 2255 bicycles (b) 50 frames left over, 305 wheels left over (c) the handlebars **3.75** NaOH is the limiting reactant; 0.925 mol $Na_2CO_3$ can be produced; 0.075 mol $CO_2$ remains. **3.77** (a) $NaHCO_3$ is the limiting reactant. (b) 0.524 g $CO_2$ (c) 0.238 g citric acid remains **3.79** 0.00 g $AgNO_3$ (limiting reactant), 1.94 g $Na_2CO_3$, 4.06 g $Ag_2CO_3$, 2.50 g $NaNO_3$ **3.81** (a) The theoretical yield is 60.3 g $C_6H_5Br$. (b) 70.1% yield **3.83** 28 g $S_8$ actual yield **3.85** (a) $C_2H_4O_2(l) + 2 O_2(g) \longrightarrow 2 CO_2(g) + 2 H_2O(l)$ (b) $Ca(OH)_2(s) \longrightarrow CaO(s) + H_2O(g)$ (c) $Ni(s) + Cl_2(g) \longrightarrow NiCl_2(s)$ **3.89** (a) $8 \times 10^{-20}$ g Si (b) $2 \times 10^3$ Si atoms (with 2 significant figures, 1700 Si atoms) (c) $1 \times 10^3$ Ge atoms (with 2 significant figures, 1500 Ge atoms) **3.93** $C_8H_8O_3$ **3.97** (a) $1.19 \times 10^{-5}$ mol NaI (b) $8.1 \times 10^{-3}$ g NaI **3.101** 7.5 mol $H_2$ and 4.5 mol $N_2$ present initially **3.105** $6.46 \times 10^{24}$ O atoms **3.107** (a) 88 kg $CO_2$ (b) $4 \times 10^2$ (400) kg $CO_2$ **3.109** (a) $S(s) + O_2(g) \longrightarrow SO_2(g)$; $SO_2(g) + CaO(s) \longrightarrow CaSO_3(s)$ (b) $7.9 \times 10^7$ g CaO (c) $1.7 \times 10^8$ g $CaSO_3$

## CHAPTER 4

**4.1** Diagram (c) represents $Li_2SO_4$ **4.3** (a) HCOOH is a weak electrolyte. (b) $HNO_3$ is a strong electrolyte. (c) $CH_3CH_2OH$ is a nonelectrolyte. **4.5** $BaCl_2$ **4.7** (b) $NO_3^-$ and (c) $NH_4^+$ will always be spectator ions. **4.9** In a redox reaction, electrons are transferred from the oxidized substance to the reduced substance. In an acid–base reaction, protons are transferred from an acid to a base. **4.11** No. Electrolyte solutions conduct electricity because the dissolved ions carry charge through the solution from one electrode to the other. **4.13** Although $H_2O$ molecules are electrically neutral, there is an unequal distribution of electrons throughout the molecule. The partially

positive ends of $H_2O$ molecules are attracted to anions in the solid, while the partially negative ends are attracted to cations. Thus, both cations and anions in an ionic solid are surrounded and separated (dissolved) by $H_2O$. We do not expect ionic compounds to be soluble in molecular liquids such as $Br_2(l)$ or $Hg(l)$. There is a symmetrical charge distribution in Hg atoms and $Br_2$ molecules, so there are no attractive forces to stabilize the separated ions of an ionic solid. **4.15** (a) $ZnCl_2(aq) \longrightarrow Zn^{2+}(aq) + 2\ Cl^-(aq)$ (b) $HNO_3(aq) \longrightarrow H^+(aq) + NO_3^-(aq)$ (c) $(NH_4)_2SO_4(aq) \longrightarrow 2\ NH_4^+(aq) + SO_4^{2-}(aq)$ (d) $Ca(OH)_2(aq) \longrightarrow Ca^{2+}(aq) + 2\ OH^-(aq)$ **4.17** HCOOH molecules, $H^+$ ions, and $HCOO^-$ ions; $HCOOH(aq) \rightleftharpoons H^+(aq) + HCOO^-(aq)$ **4.19** (a) Soluble (b) insoluble (c) soluble (d) soluble (e) soluble **4.21** (a) $Na_2CO_3(aq) + 2\ AgNO_3(aq) \longrightarrow Ag_2CO_3(s) + 2\ NaNO_3(aq)$ (b) No precipitate (c) $FeSO_4(aq) + Pb(NO_3)_2(aq) \longrightarrow PbSO_4(s) + Fe(NO_3)_2(aq)$ **4.23** (a) $Na^+$, $SO_4^{2-}$ (b) $Na^+$, $NO_3^-$ (c) $NH_4^+$, $Cl^-$ **4.25** The solution contains $Pb^{2+}$ .
**4.27**

| Compound | Ba(NO₃)₂ Result | NaCl Result |
|---|---|---|
| $AgNO_3(aq)$ | No ppt | AgCl ppt |
| $CaCl_2(aq)$ | No ppt | No ppt |
| $Al_2(SO_4)_3(aq)$ | $BaSO_4$ ppt | No ppt |

This sequence of tests would definitely identify the bottle contents. **4.29** LiOH is a strong base, HI is a strong acid, and $CH_3OH$ is a molecular compound and nonelectrolyte. The strong acid HI will have the greatest concentration of solvated protons. **4.31** (a) A monoprotic acid has one ionizable (acidic) H, whereas a diprotic acid has two. (b) A strong acid is completely ionized in aqueous solution, whereas only a fraction of weak acid molecules are ionized. (c) An acid is an $H^+$ donor, and a base is an $H^+$ acceptor. **4.33** When each of the strong acids in Table 4.2 dissociates, the anions formed are the same ones that normally form soluble ionic compounds (Table 4.1). The one exception is acetate, $CH_3COO^-$, the anion of a weak acid. **4.35** (a) Acid, mixture of ions and molecules (weak electrolyte) (b) none of the above, entirely molecules (nonelectrolyte) (c) salt, entirely ions (strong electrolyte) (d) base, entirely ions (strong electrolyte) **4.37** (a) $H_2SO_3$, weak electrolyte (b) $C_2H_5OH$, nonelectrolyte (c) $NH_3$, weak electrolyte (d) $KClO_3$, strong electrolyte (e) $Cu(NO_3)_2$, strong electrolyte **4.39** (a) $2\ HBr(aq) + Ca(OH)_2(aq) \longrightarrow CaBr_2(aq) + 2\ H_2O(l)$; $H^+(aq) + OH^-(aq) \longrightarrow H_2O(l)$ (b) $Cu(OH)_2(s) + 2\ HClO_4(aq) \longrightarrow Cu(ClO_4)_2(aq) + 2\ H_2O(l)$; $Cu(OH)_2(s) + 2\ H^+(aq) \longrightarrow 2\ H_2O(l) + Cu^{2+}(aq)$ (c) $Al(OH)_3(s) + 3\ HNO_3(aq) \longrightarrow Al(NO_3)_3(aq) + 3\ H_2O(l)$; $Al(OH)_3(s) + 3\ H^+(aq) \longrightarrow 3\ H_2O(l) + Al^{3+}(aq)$ **4.41** (a) $CdS(s) + H_2SO_4(aq) \longrightarrow CdSO_4(aq) + H_2S(g)$; $CdS(s) + 2\ H^+(aq) \longrightarrow H_2S(g) + Cd^{2+}(aq)$ (b) $MgCO_3(s) + 2\ HClO_4(aq) \longrightarrow Mg(ClO_4)_2(aq) + H_2O(l) + CO_2(g)$; $MgCO_3(s) + 2\ H^+(aq) \longrightarrow H_2O(l) + CO_2(g) + Mg^{2+}(aq)$ **4.43** (a) $MgCO_3(s) + 2\ HCl(aq) \longrightarrow MgCl_2(aq) + H_2O(l) + CO_2(g)$; $MgCO_3(s) + 2\ H^+(aq) \longrightarrow Mg^{2+}(aq) + H_2O(l) + CO_2(g)$; $MgO(s) + 2\ HCl(aq) \longrightarrow MgCl_2(aq) + H_2O(l)$; $MgO(s) + 2\ H^+(aq) \longrightarrow Mg^{2+}(aq) + H_2O(l)$; $Mg(OH)_2(s) + 2\ HCl(aq) \longrightarrow MgCl_2(aq) + 2\ H_2O(l)$; $Mg(OH)_2(s) + 2\ H^+(aq) \longrightarrow Mg^{2+}(aq) + 2\ H_2O(l)$ (b) Yes. The reaction involving magnesium carbonate, $MgCO_3(s)$, produces $CO_2(g)$, which appears as bubbles. The other two reactions are calm. (c) If excess $HCl(aq)$ is added in each case, the identity of the ions in the clear product solution is the same. The ions are $Mg^{2+}(aq)$; $Cl^-(aq)$; and $H^+(aq)$. **4.45** (a) In terms of electron transfer, oxidation is the loss of electrons by a substance and reduction is the gain of electrons (LEO says GER). (b) Relative to oxidation numbers, when a substance is oxidized, its oxidation number increases. When a substance is reduced, its oxidation number decreases. **4.47** Metals in region A are most easily oxidized. Nonmetals in region D are least easily oxidized.

**4.49** (a) +4 (b) +4 (c) +7 (d) +1 (e) 0 (f) −1 **4.51** (a) $N_2 \longrightarrow 2\ NH_3$, N is reduced; $3\ H_2 \longrightarrow 2\ NH_3$, H is oxidized (b) $Fe^{2+} \longrightarrow Fe$, Fe is reduced; $Al \longrightarrow Al^{3+}$, Al is oxidized (c) $Cl_2 \longrightarrow 2\ Cl^-$, Cl is reduced; $2\ I^- \longrightarrow I_2$ I is oxidized (d) $S^{2-} \longrightarrow SO_4^{2-}$, S is oxidized; $H_2O_2 \longrightarrow H_2O$, O is reduced **4.53** (a) $Mn(s) + H_2SO_4(aq) \longrightarrow MnSO_4(aq) + H_2(g)$; $Mn(s) + 2\ H^+(aq) \longrightarrow Mn^{2+}(aq) + H_2(g)$ (b) $2\ Cr(s) + 6\ HBr(aq) \longrightarrow 2\ CrBr_3(aq) + 3\ H_2(g)$; $2\ Cr(s) + 6\ H^+(aq) \longrightarrow 2\ Cr^{3+}(aq) + 3\ H_2(g)$ (c) $Sn(s) + 2\ HCl(aq) \longrightarrow SnCl_2(aq) + H_2(g)$; $Sn(s) + 2\ H^+(aq) \longrightarrow Sn^{2+}(aq) + H_2(g)$ (d) $2\ Al(s) + 6\ HCOOH(aq) \longrightarrow 2\ Al(HCOO)_3(aq) + 3\ H_2(g)$; $2\ Al(s) + 6\ HCOOH(aq) \longrightarrow 2\ Al^{3+}(aq) + 6\ HCOO^-(aq) + 3\ H_2(g)$ **4.55** (a) $Fe(s) + Cu(NO_3)_2(aq) \longrightarrow Fe(NO_3)_2(aq) + Cu(s)$ (b) NR (c) $Sn(s) + 2\ HBr(aq) \longrightarrow SnBr_2(aq) + H_2(g)$ (d) NR (e) $2\ Al(s) + 3\ CoSO_4(aq) \longrightarrow Al_2(SO_4)_3(aq) + 3\ Co(s)$ **4.57** (a) i. $Zn(s) + Cd^{2+}(aq) \longrightarrow Cd(s) + Zn^{2+}(aq)$; ii. $Cd(s) + Ni^{2+}(aq) \longrightarrow Ni(s) + Cd^{2+}(aq)$ (b) Cd is between Zn and Ni on the activity series. (c) Place an iron strip in $CdCl_2(aq)$. If $Cd(s)$ is deposited, Cd is less active than Fe; if there is no reaction, Cd is more active than Fe. Do the same test with Co if Cd is less active than Fe or with Cr if Cd is more active than Fe. **4.59** (a) Intensive; the ratio of amount of solute to total amount of solution is the same, regardless of how much solution is present. (b) The term 0.50 mol HCl defines an amount ($\sim$18 g) of the pure substance HCl. The term 0.50 $M$ HCl is a ratio; it indicates that there is 0.50 mol of HCl solute in 1.0 liter of solution. **4.61** (a) 1.17 $M$ $ZnCl_2$ (b) 0.158 mol $HNO_3$ (c) 54.2 mL of 6.00 $M$ NaOH **4.63** 16 g $Na^+(aq)$ **4.65** BAC of $0.08 = 0.02\ M$ $CH_3CH_2OH$ (alcohol) **4.67** (a) 5.21 g KBr (b) 0.06537 $M$ $Ca(NO_3)_2$ (c) 10.2 mL of 1.50 $M$ $Na_3PO_4$ **4.69** (a) 0.15 $M$ $K_2CrO_4$ has the highest $K^+$ concentration. (b) 30.0 mL of 0.15 $M$ $K_2CrO_4$ has more $K^+$ ions. **4.71** (a) 0.25 $M$ $Na^+$, 0.25 $M$ $NO_3^-$ (b) $1.3 \times 10^{-2}\ M$ $Mg^{2+}$, $1.3 \times 10^{-2}\ M$ $SO_4^{2-}$ (c) 0.0150 $M$ $C_6H_{12}O_6$ (d) 0.111 $M$ $Na^+$, 0.111 $M$ $Cl^-$, 0.0292 $M$ $NH_4^+$, 0.0146 $M$ $CO_3^{2-}$ **4.73** (a) 16.9 mL 14.8 $M$ $NH_3$ (b) 0.296 $M$ $NH_3$ **4.75** (a) Add 21.4 g $C_{12}H_{22}O_{11}$ to a 250-mL volumetric flask, dissolve in a small volume of water, and add water to the mark on the neck of the flask. Agitate thoroughly to ensure total mixing. (b) Thoroughly rinse, clean, and fill a 50-mL buret with the 1.50 $M$ $C_{12}H_{22}O_{11}$. Dispense 23.3 mL of this solution into a 350-mL volumetric container, add water to the mark, and mix thoroughly. **4.77** 1.398 $M$ $CH_3COOH$ **4.79** 0.227 g KCl **4.81** (a) 38.0 mL of 0.115 $M$ $HClO_4$ (b) 769 mL of 0.128 $M$ HCl (c) 0.408 $M$ $AgNO_3$ (d) 0.275 g KOH **4.83** 27 g $NaHCO_3$ **4.85** (a) Molar mass of metal hydroxide is 103 g/mol. (b) $Rb^+$ **4.87** (a) $NiSO_4(aq) + 2\ KOH(aq) \longrightarrow Ni(OH)_2(s) + K_2SO_4(aq)$ (b) $Ni(OH)_2$ (c) KOH is the limiting reactant. (d) 0.927 g $Ni(OH)_2$ (e) 0.0667 $M$ $Ni^{2+}(aq)$, 0.0667 $M$ $K^+(aq)$, 0.100 $M$ $SO_4^{2-}(aq)$ **4.89** 91.40% $Mg(OH)_2$ **4.92** The precipitate is $CdS(s)$. $Na^+(aq)$ and $NO_3^-(aq)$ remain in solution, along with any excess reactant ions. The net ionic equation is $Cd^{2+}(aq) + S^{2-}(aq) \longrightarrow CdS(s)$. **4.94** (a, b) Expt. 1: NR; Expt. 2: $2\ Ag^+(aq) + CrO_4^{2-}(aq) \longrightarrow Ag_2CrO_4(s)$ red precipitate; Expt. 3: $2\ Ca^{2+}(aq) + CrO_4^{2-}(aq) \longrightarrow CaCrO_4(s)$ yellow precipitate; Expt. 4: $2\ Ag^+(aq) + C_2O_4^{2-}(aq) \longrightarrow Ag_2C_2O_4(s)$ white precipitate; Expt. 5: $Ca^{2+}(aq) + C_2O_4^{2-}(aq) \longrightarrow CaC_2O_4(s)$ white precipitate; Expt. 6: $Ag^+(aq) + Cl^-(aq) \longrightarrow AgCl(s)$ white precipitate. **4.96** $4\ NH_3(g) + 5\ O_2(g) \longrightarrow 4\ NO(g) + 6\ H_2O(g)$. (a) redox reaction (b) N is oxidized, O is reduced. $2\ NO(g) + O_2(g) \longrightarrow 2\ NO_2(g)$. (a) redox reaction (b) N is oxidized, O is reduced. $3\ NO_2(g) + H_2O(l) \longrightarrow HNO_3(aq) + NO(g)$. (a) redox reaction (b) N is both oxidized and reduced. **4.99** 1.42 $M$ KBr **4.100** (a) $2.2 \times 10^{-9}\ M$ $Na^+$ (b) $1.3 \times 10^{12}$ $Na^+$ ions **4.103** (a) 1.718 $M$ $Sr(OH)_2$ (b) $2\ HNO_3(aq) + Sr(OH)_2(s) \longrightarrow Sr(NO_3)_2(aq) + 2\ H_2O(l)$ (c) 2.61 $M$ $HNO_3$ **4.106** (a) The molar mass of the acid is 136 g/mol. (b) The molecular formula is $C_8H_8O_2$. **4.109** (a) $Mg(OH)_2(s) + 2\ HNO_3(aq) \longrightarrow Mg(NO_3)_2(aq) + 2\ H_2O(l)$ (b) $HNO_3$ is the limiting reactant. (c) 0.0923 mol $Mg(OH)_2$, 0 mol $HNO_3$, and 0.00250 mol $Mg(NO_3)_2$ are present. **4.112** 1.766% $Cl^-$ by mass **4.114** $1.5 \times 10^{-5}$ g $Na_3AsO_4$ in 1.00 L $H_2O$

# CHAPTER 5

**5.1** (a) As the book falls, potential energy decreases and kinetic energy increases. (b) 71 J, assuming no transfer of energy as heat (c) A heavier book falling from the same shelf has greater kinetic energy when it hits the floor.  **5.5** (a) No. The distance traveled to the top of a mountain depends on the path taken by the hiker. Distance is a path function, not a state function. (b) Yes. Change in elevation depends only on the location of the base camp and the height of the mountain, not on the path to the top. Change in elevation is a state function, not a path function. **5.8** (a) The sign of $w$ is (+). (b) The internal energy of the system increases during the change; the sign of $\Delta E$ is (+). **5.11** (a) $\Delta H_A = \Delta H_B + \Delta H_C$. The diagram and equation both show that the net enthalpy change for a process is independent of path, that $\Delta H$ is a state function. (b) $\Delta H_Z = \Delta H_X + \Delta H_Y$. (c) Hess's law states that the enthalpy change for net reaction $Z$ is the sum of the enthalpy changes for steps $X$ and $Y$, regardless of whether the reaction actually occurs via this path. The diagrams are a visual statement of Hess's law. **5.13** An object can possess energy by virtue of its motion or position. Kinetic energy depends on the mass of the object and its velocity. Potential energy depends on the position of the object relative to the body with which it interacts.  **5.15** (a) $1.9 \times 10^5$ J (b) $4.6 \times 10^4$ cal (c) As the automobile brakes to a stop, its speed (and hence its kinetic energy) drops to zero. The kinetic energy of the automobile is primarily transferred to friction between brakes and wheels and somewhat to deformation of the tire and friction between the tire and road. **5.17** 1 Btu = 1054 J  **5.19** (a) The *system* is the well-defined part of the universe whose energy changes are being studied. (b) A *closed system* can exchange heat but not mass with its surroundings. (c) Any part of the universe not part of the system is called the surroundings. **5.21** (a) Work is a force applied over a distance. (b) The amount of work done is the magnitude of the force times the distance over which it is applied. $w = F \times d$.  **5.23** (a) Gravity; work is done because the force of gravity is opposed and the pencil is lifted. (b) Mechanical force; work is done because the force of the coiled spring is opposed as the spring is compressed over a distance.  **5.25** (a) In any chemical or physical change, energy can be neither created nor destroyed; energy is conserved. (b) The *internal energy (E)* of a system is the sum of all the kinetic and potential energies of the system components. (c) Internal energy of a closed system increases when work is done on the system and when heat is transferred to the system. **5.27** (a) $\Delta E = -0.077$ kJ, endothermic (b) $\Delta E = -22.1$ kJ, exothermic (c) $\Delta E = 7.25$ kJ, endothermic  **5.29** (a) Since no work is done by the system in case (2), the gas will absorb most of the energy as heat; the case (2) gas will have the higher temperature. (b) In case (2) $w = 0$ and $q = 100$ J. In case (1) energy will be used to do work on the surroundings ($-w$), but some will be absorbed as heat ($+q$). (c) $\Delta E$ is greater for case (2) because the entire 100 J increases the internal energy of the system rather than a part of the energy doing work on the surroundings.  **5.31** (a) A *state function* is a property that depends only on the physical state (pressure, temperature, etc.) of the system, not on the route used to get to the current state. (b) Internal energy is a state function; heat is not a state function. (c) Volume is a state function. The volume of a system depends only on conditions (pressure, temperature, amount of substance), not the route or method used to establish that volume.  **5.33** (a) $\Delta H$ is usually easier to measure than $\Delta E$ because at constant pressure, $\Delta H = q_p$. The heat flow associated with a process at constant pressure can easily be measured as a change in temperature, while measuring $\Delta E$ requires a means to measure both $q$ and $w$. (b) $H$ is a static quantity that depends only on the specific conditions of the system. $q$ is an energy *change* that, in the general case, does depend on how the change occurs. We can equate change in enthalpy, $\Delta H$, with heat, $q_p$, only for the specific conditions of constant pressure and exclusively $P$-$V$ work. (c) The process is endothermic. **5.35** At constant pressure, $\Delta E = \Delta H - P\,\Delta V$. The values of either $P$ and $\Delta V$ or $T$ and $\Delta n$ must be known to calculate $\Delta E$ from $\Delta H$. **5.37** $\Delta E = 1.47$ kJ; $\Delta H = 0.824$ kJ  **5.39** (a) $C_2H_5OH(l) + 3\,O_2(g) \longrightarrow$ $3\,H_2O + 2\,CO_2(g)$, $\Delta H = -1235$ kJ

(b) $C_2H_5OH(l) + 3\,O_2(g)$

$\Delta H = -1235$ kJ

$3\,H_2O(g) + 2\,CO_2(g)$

**5.41** (a) $\Delta H = -142.3$ kJ/mol $O_3(g)$ (b) $2\,O_3(g)$ has the higher enthalpy.  **5.43** (a) Exothermic (b) $-87.9$ kJ heat transferred (c) 15.7 g MgO produced (d) 602 kJ heat absorbed  **5.45** (a) $-29.5$ kJ (b) $-4.11$ kJ (c) 60.6 J  **5.47** (a) $\Delta H = 726.5$ kJ (b) $\Delta H = -1453$ kJ (c) The exothermic forward reaction is more likely to be thermodynamically favored. (d) Vaporization is endothermic. If the product were $H_2O(g)$, the reaction would be more endothermic and would have a less negative $\Delta H$.  **5.49** (a) J/mol-°C or J/mol-K (b) J/g-°C or J/g-K (c) To calculate heat capacity from specific heat, the mass of the particular piece of copper pipe must be known.  **5.51** (a) 4.184 J/g-K (b) 75.40 J/mol-°C (c) 774 J/°C (d) 904 kJ  **5.53** (a) $2.66 \times 10^3$ J (b) It will require more heat to increase the temperature of one mole of octane, $C_8H_{18}(l)$, by a certain amount than to increase the temperature of one mole of water, $H_2O(l)$, by the same amount. **5.55** $\Delta H = -44.4$ kJ/mol NaOH  **5.57** $\Delta H_{rxn} = -25.5$ kJ/g $C_6H_4O_2$ or $-2.75 \times 10^3$ kJ/mol $C_6H_4O_2$  **5.59** (a) Heat capacity of the complete calorimeter = 14.4 kJ/°C (b) 7.56 °C  **5.61** Hess's law is a consequence of the fact that enthalpy is a state function. Since $\Delta H$ is independent of path, we can describe a process by any series of steps that adds up to the overall process. $\Delta H$ for the process is the sum of $\Delta H$ values for the steps.  **5.63** $\Delta H = -1300.0$ kJ **5.65** $\Delta H = -2.49 \times 10^3$ kJ  **5.67** (a) *Standard conditions* for enthalpy changes are $P = 1$ atm and some common temperature, usually 298 K. (b) *Enthalpy of formation* is the enthalpy change that occurs when a compound is formed from its component elements. (c) *Standard enthalpy of formation* $\Delta H_f^\circ$ is the enthalpy change that accompanies formation of one mole of a substance from elements in their standard states.  **5.69** (a) $\frac{1}{2} N_2(g) + O_2(g) \longrightarrow NO_2(g)$, $\Delta H_f^\circ = 33.84$ kJ (b) $S(s) + 3/2\,O_2(g) \longrightarrow SO_3(g)$, $\Delta H_f^\circ = -395.2$ kJ (c) $Na(s) + \frac{1}{2} Br_2(l) \longrightarrow NaBr(s)$, $\Delta H_f^\circ = -361.4$ kJ (d) $Pb(s) + N_2(g) + 3\,O_2(g) \longrightarrow Pb(NO_3)_2(s)$, $\Delta H_f^\circ = -451.9$ kJ  **5.71** $\Delta H_{rxn}^\circ = -847.6$ kJ  **5.73** (a) $\Delta H_{rxn}^\circ = -196.6$ kJ (b) $\Delta H_{rxn}^\circ = 37.1$ kJ (c) $\Delta H_{rxn}^\circ = -976.94$ kJ (d) $\Delta H_{rxn}^\circ = -68.3$ kJ  **5.75** $\Delta H_f^\circ = -248$ kJ **5.77** (a) $C_8H_{18}(l) + \frac{25}{2} O_2(g) \longrightarrow 8\,CO_2(g) + 9\,H_2O(g)$, $\Delta H = -5064.9$ kJ (b) $8\,C(s, \text{graphite}) + 9\,H_2(g) \longrightarrow C_8H_{18}(l)$ (c) $\Delta H_f^\circ = -259.5$ kJ  **5.79** (a) $C_2H_5OH(l) + 3\,O_2(g) \longrightarrow 2\,CO_2(g) + 3\,H_2O(g)$ (b) $\Delta H_{rxn}^\circ = -1234.8$ kJ (c) $2.11 \times 10^4$ kJ/L heat produced (d) 0.071284 g $CO_2$/kJ heat emitted  **5.81** (a) *Fuel value* is the amount of energy produced when 1 g of a substance (fuel) is combusted. (b) 5 g of fat (c) These products of metabolism are expelled as waste via the alimentary tract, $H_2O(l)$ primarily in urine and feces, and $CO_2(g)$ as gas.  **5.83** 108 or $1 \times 10^2$ Cal/serving (b) Sodium does not contribute to the calorie content of the food because it is not metabolized by the body.  **5.85** 59.7 Cal  **5.87** (a) $\Delta H_{comb} = -1850$ kJ/mol $C_3H_4$, $-1926$ kJ/mol $C_3H_6$, $-2044$ kJ/mol $C_3H_8$ (b) $\Delta H_{comb} = -4.616 \times 10^4$ kJ/kg $C_3H_4$, $-4.578 \times 10^4$ kJ/kg $C_3H_6$, $-4.635 \times 10^4$ kJ/kg $C_3H_8$ (c) These three substances yield nearly identical quantities of heat per unit mass, but propane is marginally higher than the other two.  **5.89** $1 \times 10^{12}$ kg $C_6H_{12}O_6$/yr **5.91** (a) 469.4 m/s (b) $5.124 \times 10^{-21}$ J (c) 3.086 kJ/mol  **5.93** The spontaneous air bag reaction is probably exothermic, with $-\Delta H$ and thus $-q$. When the bag inflates, work is done by the system, so the sign of $w$ is also negative.  **5.97** $\Delta H = 38.95$ kJ; $\Delta E = 36.48$ kJ **5.102** (a) $\Delta H_{rxn}^\circ = -353.0$ kJ (b) 1.2 g Mg needed  **5.106** (a) $\Delta H^\circ = -631.3$ kJ (b) 3 mol of acetylene gas has greater enthalpy. (c) Fuel values are 50 kJ/g $C_2H_2(g)$, 42 kJ/g $C_6H_6(l)$.  **5.109** If all work is used to increase the man's potential energy, the stair climbing uses 58 Cal and will not compensate for the extra order of 245 Cal fries. (More than 58 Cal will be required to climb the stairs because some energy is used to move limbs and some will be lost as heat.)

**5.112** (a) $1.479 \times 10^{-18}$ J/molecule (b) $1 \times 10^{-15}$ J/photon. The X-ray has approximately 1000 times more energy than is produced by the combustion of 1 molecule of $CH_4(g)$. **5.114** (a) $\Delta H°$ for neutralization of the acids is $HNO_3$, $-55.8$ kJ; HCl, $-56.1$ kJ; $NH_4^+$, $-4.1$ kJ. (b) $H^+(aq) + OH^-(aq) \longrightarrow H_2O(l)$ is the net ionic equation for the first two reactions. $NH_4^+(aq) + OH^-(aq) \longrightarrow NH_3(aq) + H_2O(l)$ (c) The $\Delta H°$ values for the first two reactions are nearly identical, $-55.8$ kJ and $-56.1$ kJ. Since spectator ions do not change during a reaction and these two reactions have the same net ionic equation, it is not surprising that they have the same $\Delta H°$. (d) Strong acids are more likely than weak acids to donate $H^+$. Neutralization of the two strong acids is energetically favorable, while the third reaction is barely so. $NH_4^+$ is likely a weak acid. **5.116** (a) $\Delta H° = -65.7$ kJ (b) $\Delta H°$ for the complete molecular equation will be the same as $\Delta H°$ for the net ionic equation. Since the overall enthalpy change is the enthalpy of products minus the enthalpy of reactants, the contributions of spectator ions cancel. (c) $\Delta H_f°$ for $AgNO_3(aq)$ is $-100.4$ kJ/mol.

## CHAPTER 6

**6.2** (a) 0.1 m or 10 cm (b) No. Visible radiation has wavelengths much shorter than 0.1 m. (c) Energy and wavelength are inversely proportional. Photons of the longer 0.1-m radiation have less energy than visible photons. (d) Radiation with $\lambda = 0.1$ m is in the low-energy portion of the microwave region. The appliance is probably a microwave oven. **6.5** (a) Increase (b) decrease (c) the light from the hydrogen discharge tube is a line spectrum, so not all visible wavelengths will be in our "hydrogen discharge rainbow." Starting on the inside, the rainbow will be violet, then blue and blue-green. After a gap, the final band will be red. **6.8** (a) 1 (b) $p$ (c) For the $n = 4$ shell, the lobes in the contour representation would extend farther along the $y$-axis. **6.11** (a) Meters (b) 1/second (c) meters/second **6.13** (a) True (b) False. Ultraviolet light has shorter wavelengths than visible light. (c) False. X-rays travel at the same speed as microwaves. (d) False. Electromagnetic radiation and sound waves travel at different speeds. **6.15** Wavelength of X-rays < ultraviolet < green light < red light < infrared < radio waves **6.17** (a) $3.0 \times 10^{13}$ s$^{-1}$ (b) $5.45 \times 10^{-7}$ m = 545 nm (c) The radiation in (b) is visible; the radiation in (a) is not. (d) $1.50 \times 10^4$ m **6.19** $5.64 \times 10^{14}$ s$^{-1}$; green. **6.21** Quantization means that energy changes can happen only in certain allowed increments. If the human growth quantum is one foot, growth occurs instantaneously in one-foot increments. The child experiences growth spurts of one foot; her height can change only by one-foot increments. **6.23** (a) $4.47 \times 10^{-21}$ J (b) $6.17 \times 10^{-19}$ J (c) 69.2 nm **6.25** (a) $\lambda = 3.3$ $\mu$m, $E = 6.0 \times 10^{-20}$ J; $\lambda = 0.154$ nm, $E = 1.29 \times 10^{-15}$ J (b) The 3.3-$\mu$m photon is in the infrared region and the 0.154-nm photon is in the X-ray region; the X-ray photon has the greater energy. **6.27** (a) $6.11 \times 10^{-19}$ J/photon (b) 368 kJ/mol (c) $1.64 \times 10^{15}$ photons (d) 368 kJ/mol **6.29** (a) The $\sim 1 \times 10^{-6}$ m radiation is in the infrared portion of the spectrum. (b) $8.1 \times 10^{16}$ photons/s **6.31** (a) $E_{min} = 7.22 \times 10^{-19}$ J (b) $\lambda = 275$ nm (c) $E_{120} = 1.66 \times 10^{-18}$ J. The excess energy of the 120-nm photon is converted into the kinetic energy of the emitted electron. $E_k = 9.3 \times 10^{-19}$ J/electron. **6.33** When applied to atoms, the notion of quantized energies means that only certain values of $\Delta E$ are allowed. These are represented by the lines in the emission spectra of excited atoms. **6.35** (a) Emitted (b) absorbed (c) emitted **6.37** (a) $E_2 = -5.45 \times 10^{-19}$ J; $E_6 = -0.606 \times 10^{-19}$ J; $\Delta E = 4.84 \times 10^{-19}$ J; $\lambda = 410$ nm (b) visible, violet **6.39** (a) Only lines with $n_f = 2$ represent $\Delta E$ values and wavelengths that lie in the visible portion of the spectrum. Lines with $n_f = 1$ have shorter wavelengths and lines with $n_f > 2$ have longer wavelengths than visible radiation. (b) $n_i = 3, n_f = 2; \lambda = 6.56 \times 10^{-7}$ m; this is the red line at 656 nm. $n_i = 4, n_f = 2; \lambda = 4.86 \times 10^{-7}$ m; this is the blue-green line at 486 nm. $n_i = 5, n_f = 2; \lambda = 4.34 \times 10^{-7}$ m; this is the blue-violet line at 434 nm. **6.41** (a) Ultraviolet region (b) $n_i = 6, n_f = 1$ **6.43** (a) $\lambda = 5.6 \times 10^{-37}$ m (b) $\lambda = 2.65 \times 10^{-34}$ m (c) $\lambda = 2.3 \times 10^{-13}$ m (d) $\lambda = 1.51 \times 10^{-11}$ m **6.45** $4.14 \times 10^3$ m/s **6.47** (a) $\Delta x \geq 4 \times 10^{-27}$ m (b) $\Delta x \geq 3 \times 10^{-10}$ m **6.49** (a) The uncertainty principle states that there is a limit to how precisely we can simultaneously

know the position and momentum (a quantity related to energy) of an electron. The Bohr model states that electrons move about the nucleus in precisely circular orbits of known radius and energy. This violates the uncertainty principle. (b) De Broglie stated that electrons demonstrate the properties of both particles and waves and that each moving particle has a wave associated with it. A wave function is the mathematical description of the matter wave of an electron. (c) Although we cannot predict the exact location of an electron in an allowed energy state, we can determine the probability of finding an electron at a particular position. This statistical knowledge of electron location is the *probability density* and is a function of $\Psi^2$, the square of the wave function $\Psi$. **6.51** (a) $n = 4, l = 3, 2, 1, 0$ (b) $l = 2, m_l = -2, -1, 0, 1, 2$ (c) $m_l = 2, l \geq 2$ or $l = 2, 3$ or $4$ **6.53** (a) $3p$: $n = 3, l = 1$ (b) $2s$: $n = 2, l = 0$ (c) $4f$: $n = 4, l = 3$ (d) $5d$: $n = 5, l = 2$ **6.55** (a) impossible, $1p$ (b) possible (c) possible (d) impossible, $2d$

**6.57** (a)        (b)        (c)

**6.59** (a) The hydrogen atom $1s$ and $2s$ orbitals have the same overall spherical shape, but the $2s$ orbital has a larger radial extension and one more node than the $1s$ orbital. (b) A single $2p$ orbital is directional in that its electron density is concentrated along one of the three Cartesian axes of the atom. The $d_{x^2-y^2}$ orbital has electron density along both the $x$- and $y$-axes, while the $p_x$ orbital has density only along the $x$-axis. (c) The average distance of an electron from the nucleus in a $3s$ orbital is greater than for an electron in a $2s$ orbital. (d) $1s < 2p < 3d < 4f < 6s$ **6.61** (a) In the hydrogen atom, orbitals with the same principal quantum number, $n$, have the same energy. (b) In a many-electron atom, for a given $n$ value, orbital energy increases with increasing $l$ value: $s < p < d < f$. **6.63** (a) There are two main pieces of experimental evidence for electron "spin." The Stern-Gerlach experiment shows that atoms with a single unpaired electron interact differently with an inhomogeneous magnetic field. Examination of the fine details of emission line spectra of multi-electron atoms reveals that each line is really a close pair of lines. Both observations can be rationalized if electrons have the property of spin.

(b)                    (c)

**6.65** (a) 6 (b) 10 (c) 2 (d) 14 **6.67** (a) "Valence electrons" are those involved in chemical bonding. They are part or all of the outer-shell electrons listed after the core. (b) "Core electrons" are inner-shell electrons that have the electron configuration of the nearest noble-gas element. (c) Each box represents an orbital. (d) Each half-arrow in an orbital diagram represents an electron. The direction of the half-arrow represents electron spin. **6.69** (a) Cs, [Xe]$6s^1$ (b) Ni, [Ar]$4s^23d^8$ (c) Se, [Ar]$4s^23d^{10}4p^4$ (d) Cd, [Kr]$5s^24d^{10}$ (e) U, [Rn]$5f^36d^17s^2$ (f) Pb, [Xe]$6s^24f^{14}5d^{10}6p^2$ **6.71** (a) Be, 0 unpaired electrons (b) O, 2 unpaired electrons (c) Cr, 6 unpaired electrons (d) Te, 2 unpaired electrons **6.73** (a) The fifth electron would fill the $2p$ subshell before the $3s$. (b) Either the core is [He], or the outer electron configuration should be $3s^23p^3$. (c) The $3p$ subshell would fill before the $3d$. **6.75** (a) $\lambda_A = 3.6 \times 10^{-8}$ m, $\lambda_B = 8.0 \times 10^{-8}$ m (b) $\nu_A = 8.4 \times 10^{15}$ s$^{-1}$, $\nu_B = 3.7 \times 10^{15}$ s$^{-1}$ (c) A, ultraviolet; B, ultraviolet **6.78** 66.7 min **6.82** $1.6 \times 10^7$ photons/s, $5.1 \times 10^{-12}$ J/s **6.85** (a) The Paschen series lies in the infrared. (b) $n_i = 4, \lambda = 1.87 \times 10^{-6}$ m; $n_i = 5, \lambda = 1.28 \times 10^{-6}$ m; $n_i = 6, \lambda = 1.09 \times 10^{-6}$ m **6.90** (a) $l$ (b) $n$ and $l$ (c) $m_s$ (d) $m_l$ **6.92** (a) The nodal plane of the $p_z$ orbital is the $xy$-plane. (b) The two nodal planes of the $d_{xy}$ orbital are the ones where

$x = 0$ and $y = 0$. These are the $yz$- and $xz$-planes. (c) The two nodal planes of the $d_{x^2-y^2}$ orbital are the ones that bisect the $x$- and $y$-axes and contain the $z$-axis.   **6.94** If $m_s$ had three allowed values instead of two, each orbital would hold three electrons instead of two. Assuming that there is no change in the $n$, $l$, and $m_l$ values, the number of elements in each of the first four rows would be 1st row, 3 elements; 2nd row, 12 elements; 3rd row, 12 elements; 4th row, 27 elements   **6.97** (a) $1.7 \times 10^{28}$ photons (b) 34 s   **6.101** (a) Bohr's theory was based on the Rutherford nuclear model of the atom: a dense positive charge at the center and a diffuse negative charge surrounding it. Bohr's theory then specified the nature of the diffuse negative charge. The prevailing theory before the nuclear model was Thomson's plum pudding model: discrete electrons scattered about a diffuse positive charge cloud. Bohr's theory could not have been based on the Thomson model of the atom. (b) De Broglie's hypothesis is that electrons exhibit both particle and wave properties. Thomson's conclusion that electrons have mass is a particle property, while the nature of cathode rays is a wave property. De Broglie's hypothesis actually rationalizes these two seemingly contradictory observations about the properties of electrons.

## CHAPTER 7

**7.3** (a) The bonding atomic radius of A, $r_A$, is $d_1/2$; $r_x = d_2 - (d_1/2)$. (b) The length of the X—X bond is $2r_x$ or $2d_2 - d_1$. **7.6** (a) X + $2F_2 \longrightarrow XF_4$ (b) X in the diagram has about the same bonding radius as F, so it is likely to be a nonmetal.   **7.7** The number of columns in the various blocks of the periodic chart corresponds to the maximum number of electrons that can occupy the various kinds of atomic orbitals: 2 columns on the left for 2 electrons in $s$ orbitals, 10 columns in the transition metals for 10 electrons in $d$ orbitals, 6 columns on the right for 6 electrons in $p$ orbitals, 14-member rows below for 14 electrons in $f$ orbitals. The order of blocks corresponds to the filling order of atomic orbitals, and the row number corresponds to the principal quantum number of the valence electrons of elements in that row, $ns$, $np$, $(n - 1)d$, $(n - 2)f$.   **7.9** In general, elements are discovered according to their ease of isolation in elemental form.   **7.11** (a) *Effective nuclear charge*, $Z_{eff}$, is a representation of the average electrical field experienced by a single electron. It is the average environment created by the nucleus and the other electrons in the molecule, expressed as a net positive charge at the nucleus. (b) Going from left to right across a period, effective nuclear charge increases.   **7.13** (a) For both Na and K, $Z_{eff} = 1$. (b) For both Na and K, $Z_{eff} = 2.2$. (c) Slater's rules give values closer to the detailed calculations: Na, 2.51; K, 3.49. (d) Both approximations give the same value of $Z_{eff}$ for Na and K; neither accounts for the gradual increase in $Z_{eff}$ moving down a group. (e) Following the trend from detailed calculations, we predict a $Z_{eff}$ value of approximately 4.5.   **7.15** The $n = 3$ electrons in Kr experience a greater effective nuclear charge and thus have a greater probability of being closer to the nucleus.   **7.17** (a) Atomic radii are determined by measuring distances between atoms in various situations. (b) Bonding radii are calculated from the internuclear separation of two atoms joined by a covalent chemical bond. Nonbonding radii are calculated from the internuclear separation between two gaseous atoms that collide and move apart but do not bond. (c) For a given element, the nonbonding radius is always larger than the bonding radius. (d) If a free atom reacts to become part of a covalent molecule, its radius changes from nonbonding to bonding and the atom gets smaller.   **7.19** (a) 1.37 Å (b) The distance between W atoms will decrease.   **7.21** From the sum of the atomic radii, As—I = 2.52 Å. This is very close to the experimental value of 2.55 Å.   **7.23** (a) Decrease (b) increase (c) O < Si < Ge < I   **7.25** (a) Cs > K > Li (b) Pb > Sn > Si (c) N > O > F   **7.27** (a) False (b) true (c) false   **7.29** The red sphere is a metal; its size decreases on reaction, characteristic of the change in radius when a metal atom forms a cation. The blue sphere is a nonmetal; its size increases on reaction, characteristic of the change in radius when a nonmetal atom forms an anion.   **7.31** (a) An isoelectronic series is a group of atoms or ions that have the same number of electrons and the same electron configuration. (b) $Ga^{3+}$: Ar; $Zr^{4+}$: Kr; $Mn^{7+}$: Ar; $I^-$: Xe; $Pb^{2+}$: Hg   **7.33** (a) Ar (b) Ar (c) There is no neutral atom isoelectronic with $Fe^{2+}$. Because transition metals fill the $s$ subshell first but

also lose $s$ electrons first when they form ions, many transition metal ions do not have isolectronic neutral atoms. (d) No isoelectronic neutral atom; same reason as part (c). (e) No isoelectronic neutral atom; same reason as part (c).   **7.35** (a) $K^+$ is smaller. (b) $Cl^-$, $Z_{eff} = 7$; $K^+$, $Z_{eff} = 9$ (c) $Cl^-$: $Z_{eff} = 5.75$; $K^+$, $Z_{eff} = 7.75$ (d) For isoelectronic ions, as nuclear charge ($Z$) increases, effective nuclear charge ($Z_{eff}$) increases and ionic radius decreases.   **7.37** (a) Se < $Se^{2-}$ < $Te^{2-}$ (b) $Co^{3+}$ < $Fe^{3+}$ < $Fe^{2+}$ (c) $Ti^{4+}$ < $Sc^{3+}$ < Ca (d) $Be^{2+}$ < $Na^+$ < Ne   **7.39** $Al(g) \longrightarrow Al^+(g) + 1e^-$; $Al^+(g) \longrightarrow Al^{2+}(g) + 1e^-$; $Al^{2+}(g) \longrightarrow Al^{3+}(g) + 1e^-$. The process for the first ionization energy requires the least amount of energy.   **7.41** (a) False. Ionization energies are always positive quantities. (b) False. F has a greater first ionization energy than O. (c) True.   **7.43** (a) The smaller the atom, the larger its first ionization energy. (b) Of the nonradioactive elements, He has the largest and Cs the smallest first ionization energy.   **7.45** (a) Cl (b) Ca (c) K (d) Ge (e) Sn   **7.47** (a) $Fe^{2+}$, $[Ar]3d^6$ (b) $Hg^{2+}$, $[Xe]4f^{14}5d^{10}$ (c) $Mn^{2+}$, $[Ar]3d^5$ (d) $Pt^{2+}$, $[Xe]4f^{14}5d^8$ (e) $P^{3-}$, $[Ne]3s^23p^6$   **7.49** $Ni^{2+}$, $[Ar]3d^8$; $Pd^{2+}$, $[Kr]4d^8$; $Pt^{2+}$, $[Xe]4f^{14}5d^8$   **7.51** (a) Positive, endothermic, values for ionization energy and electron affinity mean that energy is required to either remove or add electrons. Valence electrons in Ar experience the largest $Z_{eff}$ of any element in the third row, resulting in a large, positive ionization energy. When an electron is added to Ar, the $n = 3$ electrons become core electrons that screen the extra electron so effectively that $Ar^-$ has a higher energy than an Ar atom and a free electron. This results in a large positive electron affinity. (b) kJ/mol   **7.53** Electron affinity of Br: $Br(g) + 1e^- \longrightarrow Br^-(g)$; $[Ar]4s^23d^{10}4p^5 \longrightarrow [Ar]4s^23d^{10}4p^6$; electron affinity of Kr: $Kr(g) + 1e^- \longrightarrow Kr^-(g)$; $[Ar]4s^23d^{10}4p^6 \longrightarrow [Ar]4s^23d^{10}4p^65s^1$. $Br^-$ adopts the stable electron configuration of Kr; the added electron experiences essentially the same $Z_{eff}$ and stabilization as the other valence electrons and electron affinity is negative. In $Kr^-$ ion, the added electron occupies the higher energy $5s$ orbital. A $5s$ electron is farther from the nucleus, effectively shielded by the spherical Kr core and not stabilized by the nucleus; electron affinity is positive.   **7.55** (a) Ionization energy ($I_1$) of Ne: $Ne(g) \longrightarrow Ne^+(g) + 1e^-$; $[He]2s^22p^6 \longrightarrow [He]2s^22p^5$; electron affinity ($E_1$) of F: $F(g) + 1e^- \longrightarrow F^-(g)$; $[He]2s^22p^5 \longrightarrow [He]2s^22p^6$. (b) $I_1$ of Ne is positive; $E_1$ of F is negative. (c) One process is apparently the reverse of the other, with one important difference. Ne has a greater $Z$ and $Z_{eff}$, so we expect $I_1$ for Ne to be somewhat greater in magnitude and opposite in sign to $E_1$ for F.   **7.57** The smaller the first ionization energy of an element, the greater the metallic character of that element.   **7.59** Agree. When forming ions, all metals form cations. The only nonmetallic element that forms cations is the metalloid Sb, which is likely to have significant metallic character.   **7.61** Ionic: $SnO_2$, $Al_2O_3$, $Li_2O$, $Fe_2O_3$; molecular: $CO_2$, $H_2O$. Ionic compounds are formed by combining a metal and a nonmetal; molecular compounds are formed by two or more nonmetals.   **7.63** (a) An *acidic oxide* dissolved in water produces an acidic solution; a *basic oxide* dissolved in water produces a basic solution. (b) Oxides of nonmetals, such as $SO_3$, are acidic; oxides of metals, such as CaO, are basic.   **7.65** (a) Dichlorineheptoxide (b) $2 Cl_2(g) + 7 O_2(g) \longrightarrow 2 Cl_2O_7(l)$ (c) While most nonmetal oxides we have seen, such as $CO_2$ or $SO_2$, are gases, a boiling point of 81 °C is expected for a large molecule like $Cl_2O_7$. (d) $Cl_2O_7$ is an acidic oxide, so it will be more reactive to base, $OH^-$. (e) The oxidation state of Cl in $Cl_2O_7$ is +7; the corresponding electron configuration for Cl is $[He]2s^22p^6$ or [Ne].   **7.67** (a) $BaO(s) + H_2O(l) \longrightarrow Ba(OH)_2(aq)$ (b) $FeO(s) + 2 HClO_4(aq) \longrightarrow Fe(ClO_4)_2(aq) + H_2O(l)$ (c) $SO_3(g) + H_2O(l) \longrightarrow H_2SO_4(aq)$ (d) $CO_2(g) + 2 NaOH(aq) \longrightarrow Na_2CO_3(aq) + H_2O(l)$   **7.69** Yes, the reactivity of a metal correlates with its first ionization energy. Since metals lose electrons when they form ions, the less energy required for this process, the more reactive the metal. However, we usually observe reactivity of metals in the solid state and ionization energy is a gas phase property, so there are differences between the two properties.   **7.71** (a) Ca is more reactive because it has a lower ionization energy than Mg. (b) K is more reactive because it has a lower ionization energy than Ca.   **7.73** (a) $2 K(s) + Cl_2(g) \longrightarrow 2 KCl(s)$ (b) $SrO(s) + H_2O(l) \longrightarrow Sr(OH)_2(aq)$ (c) $4 Li(s) + O_2(g) \longrightarrow 2 Li_2O(s)$ (d) $2 Na(s) + S(l) \longrightarrow Na_2S(s)$   **7.75** (a) Both classes of reaction are redox reactions where either hydrogen or the halogen gains electrons and is reduced. The product is an ionic solid, where either hydride ion, $H^-$, or a halide ion, $X^-$, is the anion. (b) $Ca(s) + F_2(g) \longrightarrow CaF_2(s)$; $Ca(s) + H_2(g) \longrightarrow CaH_2(s)$. Both products are ionic solids containing $Ca^{2+}$ and the corresponding anion in a 1:2 ratio. **7.77** (a) Br, $[Ar]4s^2 4p^5$; Cl, $[Ne]3s^2 3p^5$ (b) Br and Cl are in the same group, and both adopt a $1-$ ionic charge. (c) The ionization energy of Br is smaller than that of Cl, because the $4p$ valence electrons in Br are farther from to the nucleus and less tightly held than the $3p$ electrons of Cl. (d) Both react slowly with water to form $HX + HOX$. (e) The electron affinity of Br is less negative than that of Cl, because the electron added to the $4p$ orbital in Br is farther from the nucleus and less tightly held than the electron added to the $3p$ orbital of Cl. (f) The atomic radius of Br is larger than that of Cl, because the $4p$ valence electrons in Br are farther from the nucleus and less tightly held than the $3p$ electrons of Cl. **7.79** (a) The term *inert* was dropped because it no longer described all the Group 8A elements. (b) In the 1960s, scientists discovered that Xe would react with substances having a strong tendency to remove electrons, such as $F_2$. Thus, Xe could not be categorized as an "inert" gas. (c) The group is now called the noble gases. **7.81** (a) $2O_3(g) \longrightarrow 3O_2(g)$ (b) $Xe(g) + F_2(g) \longrightarrow XeF_2(g)$; $Xe(g) + 2F_2(g) \longrightarrow XeF_4(s)$; $Xe(g) + 3F_2(g) \longrightarrow XeF_6(s)$ (c) $S(s) +$ (d) $2F_2(g) + 2H_2O(l) \longrightarrow 4HF(aq) + O_2(g)$ **7.83** Up to $Z = 82$, there are three instances where atomic weights are reversed relative to atomic numbers: Ar and K; Co and Ni; Te and I. In each case the most abundant isotope of the element with the larger atomic number has one more proton but fewer neutrons than the element with the smaller atomic number. The smaller number of neutrons causes the element with the larger $Z$ to have a smaller than expected atomic weight. **7.85** (a) $5+$ (b) $4.8+$ (c) Shielding is greater for $3p$ electrons, owing to penetration by $3s$ electrons, so $Z_{eff}$ for $3p$ electrons is less than that for $3s$ electrons. (d) The first electron lost is a $3p$ electron because it has a smaller $Z_{eff}$ and experiences less attraction for the nucleus than a $3s$ electron does. **7.88** (a) The estimated distances are a bit longer than the measured distances. This probably shows a systematic bias in either the estimated radii or in the method of obtaining the measured values. (b) The principal quantum number of the outer electrons and thus the average distance of these electrons from the nucleus increase from $P(n = 3)$ to $As(n = 4)$ to $Sb(n = 5)$. This causes the systematic increase in M – H distance. **7.92** (a) $2Sr(s) + O_2(g) \longrightarrow 2SrO(s)$ (b) Based on ionic radii, the length of the side of the cube is 5.16 Å. (c) There are four SrO units in the cube.

**7.95** (a) O, $[He]2s^2 2p^4$

| ⇅ | ⇅ | ↑ | ↑ |
|---|---|---|---|
| $2s$ | $2p$ | | |

$O^{2-}$, $[He]2s^2 2p^6 = [Ne]$

| ⇅ | ⇅ | ⇅ | ⇅ |
|---|---|---|---|
| $2s$ | $2p$ | | |

(b) $O^{3-}$, $[Ne]3s^1$. The third electron would be added to the $3s$ orbital, which is farther from the nucleus and more strongly shielded by the [Ne] core. The overall attraction of this $3s$ electron for the oxygen nucleus is not large enough for $O^{3-}$ to be a stable particle. **7.98** (a) For both H and the alkali metals, the added electron will complete an $ns$ subshell, so shielding and repulsion effects will be similar. For the halogens, the electron is added to an $np$ subshell, so the energy change is likely to be quite different. (b) True. The electron configuration of H is $1s^1$. The single $1s$ electron experiences no repulsion from other electrons and feels the full unshielded nuclear charge. The outer electrons of all other elements that form compounds are shielded by a spherical inner core of electrons and are less strongly attracted to the nucleus, resulting in larger bonding atomic radii. (c) Both H and the halogens have large ionization energies. The relatively large effective nuclear charge experienced by $np$ electrons of the halogens is similar to the unshielded nuclear charge experienced by the H $1s$ electron. For the alkali metals, the $ns$ electron being removed is effectively shielded by the core electrons, so ionization energies are low. (d) ionization energy of hydride, $H^-(g) \longrightarrow H(g) + 1e^-$ (e) electron affinity of hydrogen, $H(g) + 1e^- \longrightarrow H^-(g)$. The value for the ionization energy of hydride is equal in magnitude but opposite in sign to the electron affinity of hydrogen. **7.103** Electron configuration, $[Rn]7s^2 5f^{14} 6d^{10} 7p^5$; first

ionization energy, 805 kJ/mol; electron affinity, $-235$ kJ/mol; atomic size, 1.65 Å; common oxidation state, $-1$ **7.106** (a) Li, $[He]2s^1$; $Z_{eff} \approx 1+$ (b) $I_1 \approx 5.45 \times 10^{-19}$ J/mol $\approx 328$ kJ/mol (c) The estimated value of 328 kJ/mol is less than the Table 7.4 value of 520 kJ/mol. Our estimate for $Z_{eff}$ was a lower limit; the [He] core electrons do not perfectly shield the $2s$ electron from the nuclear charge. (d) Based on the experimental ionization energy, $Z_{eff} = 1.26$. This value is greater than the estimate from part (a) but agrees well with the "Slater" value of 1.3 and is consistent with the explanation in part (c). **7.108** (a) 9.8902 Å. (b) For Hg, the first ionization energy is 1007 kJ/mol, while the XPS energy of the $4f$ electron is 10,100 kJ/mol. The energy required to remove a $4f$ core electron is 10 times the energy required to remove a $6s$ valence electron. For O, the first ionization energy is 1314 kJ/mol, while the XPS energy of a $1s$ electron is 51,200 kJ/mol. The energy required to remove a $1s$ core electron is 40 times that required to remove a $2p$ valence electron. (c) $Hg^{2+}$, $[Xe]4f^{14} 5d^{10}$; valence electrons are $5d$. $O^{2-}$, $[He]2s^2 2p^6$ or $[Ne]$; valence electrons are $2p$ (d) $Hg^{2+} 5d$, $Z_{eff} = 18.85$; $Hg^{2+} 4f$, $Z_{eff} = 43.85$; $O^{2-} 4f$, $Z_{eff} = 3.85$. **7.110** (a) $Mg_3N_2$ (b) $Mg_3N_2(s) + 3H_2O(l) \longrightarrow 3MgO(s) + 2NH_3(g)$; the driving force is the production of $NH_3(g)$. (c) 17% $Mg_3N_2$ (d) $3Mg(s) + 2NH_3(g) \longrightarrow Mg_3N_2(s) + 3H_2(g)$. $NH_3$ is the limiting reactant and 0.46 g $H_2$ is formed. (e) $\Delta H^\circ_{rxn} = -368.70$ kJ

# CHAPTER 8

**8.1** (a) Group 4A or 14 (b) Group 2A or 2 (c) Group 5A or 15 **8.4** (a) Ru (b) $[Kr]5s^2 4d^6$. **8.7** (a) Moving from left to right along the molecule, the first C needs 2 H atoms, the second needs 1, the third needs none, and the fourth needs 1. (b) In order of increasing bond length: $3 < 1 < 2$ (c) In order of increasing bond enthalpy: $2 < 1 < 3$ **8.9** (a) Valence electrons are those that take part in chemical bonding. This usually means the electrons beyond the core noble-gas configuration of the atom, although it is sometimes only the outer-shell electrons. (b) A nitrogen atom has 5 valence electrons. (c) The atom (Si) has 4 valence electrons. **8.11** Si, $1s^2 2s^2 2p^6 3s^2 3p^2$. The $n = 3$ electrons are valence electrons; the others are nonvalence electrons. Valence electrons participate in chemical bonding; the others do not.

**8.13** (a) $\cdot \dot{Al} \cdot$ (b) $:\ddot{Br}:$ (c) $:\ddot{Ar}:$ (d) $\cdot \dot{Sr}$

**8.15** $\overset{\frown}{Mg} + :\ddot{O}: \longrightarrow Mg^{2+} + \left[:\ddot{O}:\right]^{2-}$

**8.17** (a) $AlF_3$ (b) $K_2S$ (c) $Y_2O_3$ (d) $Mg_3N_2$ **8.19** (a) $Sr^{2+}$, $[Ar]4s^2 3d^{10} 4p^6 = [Kr]$, noble-gas configuration (b) $Ti^{2+}$, $[Ar]3d^2$ (c) $Se^{2-}$, $[Ar]4s^2 3d^{10} 4p^6 = [Kr]$, noble-gas configuration (d) $Ni^{2+}$, $[Ar]3d^8$ (e) $Br^-$, $[Ar]4s^2 3d^{10} 4p^6 = [Kr]$, noble-gas configuration (f) $Mn^{3+}$, $[Ar]3d^4$ **8.21** (a) *Lattice energy* is the energy required to totally separate one mole of solid ionic compound into its gaseous ions. (b) The magnitude of the lattice energy depends on the magnitudes of the charges of the two ions, their radii, and the arrangement of ions in the lattice. **8.23** KF, 808 kJ/mol; CaO, 3414 kJ/mol; ScN, 7547 kJ/mol. The interionic distances in the three compounds are similar. For compounds with similar ionic separations, the lattice energies should be related as the product of the charges of the ions. The lattice energies above are approximately related as $1 : 4 : 9$. Slight variations are due to the small differences in ionic separations. **8.25** Since the ionic charges are the same in the two compounds, the K—Br and Cs—Cl separations must be approximately equal. **8.27** The large attractive energy between oppositely charged $Ca^{2+}$ and $O^{2-}$ more than compensates for the energy required to form $Ca^{2+}$ and $O^{2-}$ from the neutral atoms. **8.29** The lattice energy of $RbCl(s)$ is $+692$ kJ/mol. This value is smaller than the lattice energy for NaCl because $Rb^+$ has a larger ionic radius than $Na^+$ and therefore cannot approach $Cl^-$ as closely as $Na^+$ can. **8.31** (a) A *covalent bond* is the bond formed when two atoms share one or more pairs of electrons. (b) Any simple compound whose component atoms are nonmetals, such as $H_2$, $SO_2$, and $CCl_4$, are molecular and have covalent bonds between atoms. (c) Covalent, because it is a gas at room temperature and below.

**8.33**

:Cl· + :Cl· + :Cl· + :Cl· + ·Si· → :Cl—Si—Cl:
with :Cl: above and :Cl: below

**8.35** (a) :Ö=Ö: (b) A double bond is required because there are not enough electrons to satisfy the octet rule with single bonds and unshared pairs. (c) The greater the number of shared electron pairs between two atoms, the shorter the distance between the atoms. An O=O double bond is shorter than an O—O single bond. **8.37** (a) *Electronegativity* is the ability of an atom in a molecule to attract electrons to itself. (b) The range of electronegativities on the Pauling scale is 0.7–4.0. (c) Fluorine is the most electronegative element. (d) Cesium is the least electronegative element that is not radioactive. **8.39** (a) Mg (b) S (c) C (d) As **8.41** The bonds in (a), (c), and (d) are polar. The more electronegative element in each polar bond is (a) F (c) O (d) I. **8.43** (a) The calculated charge on H and Br is $0.12e$. (b) From Sample Exercise 8.5, the calculated charge on H and Cl in HCl is $0.178e$. HBr has a smaller dipole moment and longer bond length than HCl; these properties both contribute to the smaller charge separation in HBr. **8.45** (a) $SiCl_4$, molecular, silicon tetrachloride; $LaF_3$, ionic, lanthanum(III) fluoride (b) $FeCl_2$, ionic, iron(II) chloride; $ReCl_6$, molecular (metal in high oxidation state), rhenium hexachloride. (c) $PbCl_4$, molecular (by contrast to the distinctly ionic $RbCl$), lead tetrachloride; $RbCl$, ionic, rubidium chloride

**8.47** (a) H—Si—H with H above and H below (b) :C≡O:

(c) :F̈—S̈—F̈: (d) :Ö—S—Ö—H with :O: above and :O: below, H below

(e) [:Ö—C̈l—Ö:]⁻ (f) H—N̈—Ö—H with H below N

**8.49** (a) *Formal charge* is the charge on each atom in a molecule, assuming all atoms have the same electronegativity. (b) Formal charges are not actual charges. They are a bookkeeping system that assumes perfect covalency, one extreme for the possible electron distribution in a molecule. (c) Oxidation numbers are a bookkeeping system that assumes the more electronegative element holds all electrons in a bond. The true electron distribution is some composite of the two extremes. **8.51** Formal charges are shown on the Lewis structures; oxidation numbers are listed below each structure.

(a) Ö=C=S̈
0   0   0
O, −2; C, +4; S, −2

(b) 0 :C̈l—S—C̈l: 0 with :O:⁻¹ above, +1 on S
S, +4; Cl, −1; O, −2

(c) [−1 :Ö—Br—Ö: −1]¹⁻ with :O:⁻¹ above, +2 on Br
Br, +5; O, −2

(d) 0 H—Ö—C̈l—Ö: −1 with 0 and +1 below
Cl, +3; H, +1; O, −2

**8.53** (a) [Ö=N̈—Ö:]⁻ ⟷ [:Ö—N̈=Ö]⁻
(b) $O_3$ is isoelectronic with $NO_2^-$; both have 18 valence electrons. (c) Since each N—O bond has partial double-bond character, the N—O bond length in $NO_2^-$ should be shorter than an N—O single bond. **8.55** The more electron pairs shared by two atoms, the shorter

the bond. Thus, the C—O bond lengths vary in the order $CO < CO_2 < CO_3^{2-}$. **8.57** (a) Two equally valid Lewis structures can be drawn for benzene.

[benzene resonance structures with H atoms on hexagonal ring]

The concept of resonance dictates that the true description of bonding is some hybrid or blend of these two Lewis structures. The most obvious blend of these two resonance structures is a molecule with six equivalent C—C bonds with equal lengths. (b) This model predicts a uniform C—C bond length that is shorter than a single bond but longer than a double bond. **8.59** (a) The octet rule states that atoms will gain, lose, or share electrons until they are surrounded by eight valence electrons. (b) The octet rule applies to atoms in a covalent compound and the individual ions in an ionic compound. In the covalent compound $CCl_4$, the atoms share electrons in order to surround themselves with an octet. In the ionic compound $MgCl_2$, Mg loses $2 e^-$ to become $Mg^{2+}$ with the electron configuration of Ne. Each Cl atom gains one electron to form $Cl^-$ with the electron configuration of Ar. **8.61** No chlorine oxide will obey the octet rule. Chlorine has seven valence electrons, and oxygen has six. For neutral chlorine oxides, regardless of the number of oxygen atoms in the molecule, the total number of valence electrons will be an (odd + even) sum, which is always an odd number. **8.63**

(a) [:Ö—S̈—Ö: with :O: below]²⁻

Other resonance structures that minimize formal charges but violate the octet rule can be drawn. The octet rule versus formal charge debate is ongoing.

(b) H—Al—H with H below
6 electrons around Al

(c) [:N≡N—N̈:]⁻ ⟷ [:N̈—N≡N:]⁻ ⟷ [:N̈=N=N̈:]⁻

(d) :C̈l—C—H with :Cl: above and H below

(e) :F̈—Sb with :F: above, :F: and :F: to right, :F: below
10 electrons around Sb

**8.65** (a) :C̈l—Be—C̈l:
0    0    0
This structure violates the octet rule.
(b) C̈l=Be=C̈l ⟷ :C̈l—Be≡Cl ⟷ Cl≡Be—C̈l:
+1  −2  +1      0   −2  +2      +2  −2   0
(c) Formal charges are minimized on the structure that violates the octet rule; this form is probably dominant. **8.67** Three resonance structures for $HSO_3^-$ are shown here. Because the ion has a 1− charge, the sum of the formal charges of the atoms is −1.

[H—Ö—S̈—Ö: with :O: below, charges 0, +1, −1, −1]¹⁻  ⟷  [H—Ö—S=Ö with :O: below, charges 0, 0, 0, −1]¹⁻

[H—Ö—S=Ö with :O: below, charges 0, −1, 0, 0]¹⁻

The structure with no double bonds obeys the octet rule for all atoms, but does not lead to minimized formal charges. The structures with one and two double bonds both minimize formal charge but do not obey the octet rule. Of these two, the structure with one double bond is preferred because the formal charge is localized on the more electronegative oxygen atom. **8.69** (a) $\Delta H = -304$ kJ (b) $\Delta H = -82$ kJ (c) $\Delta H = -467$ kJ **8.71** (a) $\Delta H = -321$ kJ (b) $\Delta H = -103$ kJ (c) $\Delta H = -203$ kJ **8.73** (a) $-97$ kJ; exothermic (b) The $\Delta H$ calculated from bond enthalpies ($-97$ kJ) is slightly more exothermic (more negative) than that obtained using $\Delta H_f^\circ$ values ($-92.38$ kJ). **8.75** The average Ti—Cl bond enthalpy is 430 kJ/mol. **8.77** (a) Six (nonradioactive) elements. Yes, they are in the same family, assuming H is placed with the alkali metals. The Lewis symbol represents the number of valence electrons of an element, and all elements in the same family have the same number of valence electrons. By definition of a family, all elements with the same Lewis symbol must be in the same family. **8.81** The charge on M is likely to be 3+. The range of lattice energies for ionic compounds with the general formula MX and a charge of 2+ on the metal is 3-4 $\times 10^3$ kJ/mol. The lattice energy of $6 \times 10^3$ kJ/mol indicates that the charge on M must be greater than 2+. **8.85** (a) B—O. The most polar bond will be formed by the two elements with the greatest difference in electronegativity. (b) Te—I. These elements have the two largest covalent radii among this group. (c) $TeI_2$. The octet rule is be satisfied for all three atoms. (d) $P_2O_3$. Each P atom needs to share $3e^-$ and each O atom $2e^-$ to achieve an octet. And $B_2O_3$. Although this is not a purely ionic compound, it can be understood in terms of gaining and losing electrons to achieve a noble-gas configuration. If each B atom were to lose $3e^-$ and each O atom were to gain $2e^-$, charge balance and the octet rule would be satisfied. **8.90** (a) +1 (b) −1 (c) +1 (assuming the odd electron is on N) (d) 0 (e) +3 **8.95** An experimentally determined molecular structure will reveal bond lengths and angles of the B—A≡B molecule. If resonance structures are important, the two B—A bond lengths will be identical. If the molecule features one single and one double bond, the lengths will be significantly different. **8.98** (a) $\Delta H = 7.85$ kJ/g nitroglycerine (b) $4C_7H_5N_3O_6(s) \longrightarrow 6N_2(g) + 7CO_2(g) + 10H_2O(g) + 21C(s)$ **8.101** (a) $Ti^{2+}$, $[Ar]3d^2$; Ca, $[Ar]4s^2$. Yes. The 2 valence electrons in $Ti^{2+}$ and Ca are in different principal quantum levels and different subshells. (b) In Ca the 4s is lower in energy than the 3d, while in $Ti^{2+}$ the 3d is lower in energy than the 4s. (c) No. There is only one 4s orbital, so the 2 valence electrons in Ca are paired; there are 5 degenerate 3d orbitals, so the 2 valence electrons in $Ti^{2+}$ are unpaired. **8.107** (a) Azide ion is $N_3^-$. (b) Resonance structures with formal charges are shown.

$$\left[ :\ddot{N}=N=\ddot{N}: \right]^- \longleftrightarrow \left[ :N\equiv N-\ddot{N}: \right]^- \longleftrightarrow$$
$$\quad{-1}\quad{+1}\quad{-1} \qquad\qquad {0}\quad{+1}\quad{-2}$$

$$\left[ :\ddot{N}-N\equiv N: \right]^-$$
$$\quad{-2}\quad{+1}\quad{0}$$

(c) The structure with two double bonds minimizes formal charges and is probably the main contributor. (d) The N—N distances will be equal and have the approximate length of a N—N double bond, 1.24 Å. **8.112** (a) $D(Br—Br)(l) = 223.6$ kJ; $D(Br—Br)(g) = 193$ kJ (b) $D(C—Cl)(l) = 336.1$ kJ; $D(C—Cl)(g) = 328$ kJ (c) $D(O—O)(l) = 192.7$ kJ; $D(O—O)(g) = 146$ kJ (d) Breaking bonds in the liquid requires more energy than breaking bonds in the gas phase. Bond dissociation in the liquid phase can be thought of in two steps, vaporization of the liquid followed by bond dissociation in the gas phase. The greater bond dissociation enthalpy in the liquid phase is due to the contribution from the enthalpy of vaporization.

# CHAPTER 9

**9.1** Removing an atom from the equatorial plane of the trigonal bipyramid in Figure 9.3 creates a seesaw shape. **9.3** (a) 2 electron-domain geometries, linear and trigonal bipyramidal (b) 1 electron-domain geometry, trigonal bipyramidal (c) 1 electron-domain geometry, octahedral (c) 1 electron-domain geometry, octahedral (d) 1 electron domain geometry, octahedral (e) 1 electron domain geometry, octahedral (f) 1 electron-domain geometry, trigonal bipyramidal (This triangular pyramid is an unusual molecular geometry not listed in Table 9.3. It could occur if the equatorial substituents on the trigonal bipyramid were extremely bulky, causing the nonbonding electron pair to occupy an axial position.) **9.5** (a) Zero energy corresponds to two separate, noninteracting Cl atoms. This infinite Cl—Cl distance is beyond the right extreme of the horizontal axis on the diagram. (b) According to the valence bond model, valence orbitals on the approaching atoms overlap, allowing two electrons to mutually occupy space between the two nuclei and be stabilized by two nuclei rather than one. (c) The Cl—Cl distance at the energy minimum on the plot is the Cl—Cl bond length. (d) At interatomic separations shorter than the bond distance, the two nuclei begin to repel each other, increasing the overall energy of the system. (e) The $y$-coordinate of the minimum point on the plot is a good estimate of the Cl—Cl bond energy or bond strength. **9.6** $SiCl_4$, 109°; $PF_3$, 107°; $SF_2$, 105°. Each molecule has tetrahedral electron domain geometry, but the number of nonbonding electron pairs increases from 0 to 2, respectively. Because nonbonding electron pairs occupy more space than bonding pairs, we expect the bond angles to decrease in the series. **9.9** (a) i, Two $s$ atomic orbitals; ii, two $p$ atomic orbitals overlapping end to end; iii, two $p$ atomic orbitals overlapping side to side (b) i, $\sigma$-type MO; ii, $\sigma$-type MO; iii, $\pi$-type MO (c) i, antibonding; ii, bonding; iii, antibonding (d) i, the nodal plane is between the atom centers, perpendicular to the interatomic axis and equidistant from each atom. ii, there are two nodal planes; both are perpendicular to the interatomic axis. One is left of the left atom and the second is right of the right atom. iii, there are two nodal planes; one is between the atom centers, perpendicular to the interatomic axis and equidistant from each atom. The second contains the interatomic axis and is perpendicular to the first. **9.11** (a) Yes. The stated shape defines the bond angle and the bond length tells the size. (b) No. Atom A could have 2, 3, or 4 nonbonding electron pairs. **9.13** A molecule with tetrahedral molecular geometry has an atom at each vertex of the tetrahedron. A trigonal-pyramidal molecule has one vertex of the tetrahedron occupied by a nonbonding electron pair rather than an atom. **9.15** (a) An *electron domain* is a region in a molecule where electrons are most likely to be found. (b) Like the balloons in Figure 9.5, each electron domain occupies a finite volume of space, so they also adopt an arrangement where repulsions are minimized. **9.17** (a) The number of electron domains in a molecule or ion is the number of bonds (double and triple bonds count as one domain) plus the number of nonbonding electron pairs. (b) A *bonding electron domain* is a region between two bonded atoms that contains one or more pairs of bonding electrons. A *nonbonding electron domain* is localized on a single atom and contains one pair of nonbonding electrons. **9.19** (a) No effect on molecular shape (b) 1 nonbonding pair on P influences molecular shape (c) no effect (d) no effect (e) 1 nonbonding pair on S influences molecular shape **9.21** (a) 2 (b) 1 (c) none (d) 3 **9.23** The electron-domain geometry indicated by VSEPR describes the arrangement of all bonding and nonbonding electron domains. The molecular geometry describes just the atomic positions. In $H_2O$ there are 4 electron domains around oxygen, so the electron-domain geometry is tetrahedral. Because there are 2 bonding and 2 nonbonding domains, the molecular geometry is bent. We make this distinction because all electron domains must be considered when describing the atomic arrangement and bond angles in a molecule but the molecular geometry or shape is a description of just the atom positions. **9.25** (a) Tetrahedral, tetrahedral (b) trigonal bipyramidal, T-shaped (c) octahedral, square pyramidal (d) octahedral, square planar **9.27** (a) Linear, linear (b) tetrahedral, trigonal pyramidal (c) trigonal bipyramidal, seesaw (d) octahedral, octahedral (e) tetrahedral, tetrahedral (f) linear, linear **9.29** (a) i, trigonal planar; ii, tetrahedral; iii, trigonal bipyramidal (b) i, 0; ii, 1; iii, 2 (c) N and P (d) Cl (or Br or I). This T-shaped molecular geometry arises from a trigonal-bipyramidal electron-domain geometry with 2 nonbonding domains. Assuming each F atom has 3 nonbonding domains and forms only single bonds with A, A must have 7 valence electrons and be in or below the third row of the periodic table to produce these electron-domain and molecular geometries. **9.31** (a) 1−109°, 2−109° (b) 3−109°, 4−109° (c) 5−180° (d) 6−120°, 7−109°, 8−109° **9.33** The two molecules with trigonal-bipyramidal electron-domain geometry, $PF_5$ and $SF_4$, have more than one F—A—F bond angle. **9.35** (a) Although both ions have 4 bonding electron domains, the 6 total domains around Br require octahedral domain geometry and square-planar molecular geometry, while the 4 total domains about B lead to tetrahedral domain and molecular geometry. (b) The less electronegative the central atom, the larger the non-bonding electron domain, and the greater the effect of repulsive forces on adjacent bonding domains. The less electronegative the central atom, the greater the deviation from ideal tetrahedral angles. The angles will vary as $H_2O > H_2S > H_2Se$. **9.37** A bond dipole is the asymmetric charge distribution between two bonded atoms with unequal electronegativities. A molecular dipole moment is the three-dimensional sum of all the bond dipoles in a molecule. **9.39** (a) Yes. The net dipole moment vector points along the Cl—S—Cl angle bisector. (b) No, $BeCl_2$ does not have a dipole moment. **9.41** (a) In Exercise 9.29, molecules (ii) and (iii) will have nonzero dipole moments. Molecule (i) has no nonbonding electron pairs on A, and the 3 A—F bond dipoles are oriented so that they cancel. Molecules (ii) and (iii) have nonbonding electron pairs on A and their bond dipoles do not cancel. (b) In Exercise 9.30, molecules (i) and (ii) have a zero dipole moment. **9.43** (a) IF (d) $PCl_3$ and (f) $IF_5$ are polar.

**9.45** (a) Lewis structures

(image of Lewis structures)

Molecular geometries

Polar     Nonpolar     Polar

(b) The middle isomer has a zero net dipole moment. (c) $C_2H_3Cl$ has only one isomer, and it has a dipole moment. **9.47** (a) *Orbital overlap* occurs when valence atomic orbitals on two adjacent atoms share the same region of space. (b) A chemical bond is a concentration of electron density between the nuclei of two atoms. This concentration can take place because orbitals on the two atoms overlap. **9.49** (a) H—Mg—H, linear electron domain and molecular geometry (b) The linear electron-domain geometry in $MgH_2$ requires $sp$ hybridization.

(c) (H) Mg

**9.51**

| Molecule | Electron-Domain Geometry | Hybridization of Central Atom | Dipole Moment? Yes or No |
|---|---|---|---|
| $CO_2$ | Linear | $sp$ | No |
| $NH_3$ | Tetrahedral | $sp^3$ | Yes |
| $CH_4$ | Tetrahedral | $sp^3$ | No |
| $BH_3$ | Trigonal planar | $sp^2$ | No |
| $SF_4$ | Trigonal bipyramidal | Not applicable | Yes |
| $SF_6$ | Octahedral | Not applicable | No |
| $H_2CO$ | Trigonal planar | $sp^2$ | Yes |
| $PF_5$ | Trigonal bipyramidal | Not applicable | No |
| $XeF_2$ | Trigonal bipyramidal | Not applicable | No |

**9.53** (a) B, $[He]2s^22p^1$. One 2s electron is "promoted" to an empty 2p orbital. The 2s and two 2p orbitals that each contain one electron are hybridized to form three equivalent hybrid orbitals in a trigonal-planar arrangement. (b) $sp^2$ (d) A single 2p orbital is unhybridized. It lies perpendicular to the trigonal plane of the $sp^2$ hybrid orbitals. **9.55** (a) $sp^2$ (b) $sp^3$ (c) $sp$ (d) $sp^3$ **9.57** No hybrid orbitals discussed in this chapter form angles of 90° with each other; p atomic orbitals are perpendicular to each other. 109.5°, $sp^3$; 120°, $sp^2$

**9.59** (a)  (b)

(c) A $\sigma$ bond is generally stronger than a $\pi$ bond because there is more extensive orbital overlap. (d) No. Overlap of two s orbitals results in electron density along the internuclear axis, while a $\pi$ bond has none.

**9.61** (a)

(image of H—C—C—H, C=C, and H—C≡C—H structures)

(b) $sp^3$, $sp^2$, $sp$ (c) nonplanar, planar, planar (d) 7 $\sigma$, 0 $\pi$; 5 $\sigma$, 1 $\pi$; 3 $\sigma$, 2 $\pi$ (e) The Si analogs would have the same hybridization as the C compounds given in part (b). That Si is in the row below C means it has a larger bonding atomic radius and atomic orbitals than C. The close approach of Si atoms required to form strong, stable $\pi$ bonds in $Si_2H_4$ and $Si_2H_2$ is not possible and these Si analogs do not readily form. **9.63** (a) 18 valence electrons (b) 16 valence electrons form $\sigma$ bonds. (c) 2 valence electrons form $\pi$ bonds. (d) No valence electrons are nonbonding. (e) The left and central C atoms are $sp^2$ hybridized; the right C atom is $sp^3$ hybridized. **9.65** (a) ~109° about the leftmost C, $sp^3$; ~120° about the right-hand C, $sp^2$ (b) The doubly bonded O can be viewed as $sp^2$, and the other as $sp^3$; the nitrogen is $sp^3$ with approximately 109° bond angles. (c) nine $\sigma$ bonds, one $\pi$ bond **9.67** (a) In a localized $\pi$ bond, the electron density is concentrated between the two atoms forming the bond. In a delocalized $\pi$ bond, the electron density is spread over all the atoms that contribute p orbitals to the network. (b) The existence of more than one resonance form is a good indication that a molecule will have delocalized $\pi$ bonding. (c) delocalized **9.69** (a) Linear (b) The two central C atoms each have trigonal planar geometry with ~120° bond angles about them. The C and O atoms lie in a plane with the H atoms free to rotate in and out of this plane. (c) The molecule is planar with ~120° bond angles about the two N atoms. **9.71** (a) Hybrid orbitals are mixtures of atomic orbitals from a single atom and remain localized on that atom. Molecular orbitals are combinations of atomic orbitals from two or more atoms and are delocalized over at least two atoms. (b) Each MO can hold a maximum of two electrons. (c) Antibonding molecular orbitals can have electrons in them.

**9.73** (a)

$H_2^+$

(b) There is one electron in $H_2^+$. (c) $\sigma_{1s}^1$ (d) BO $= \frac{1}{2}$ (e) Fall apart. If the single electron in $H_2^+$ is excited to the $\sigma_{1s}^*$ orbital, its energy is higher than the energy of an H 1s atomic orbital and $H_2^+$ will decompose into a hydrogen atom and a hydrogen ion.

**9.75**

(a) 1 $\sigma$ bond (b) 2 $\pi$ bonds (c) 1 $\sigma^*$ and 2 $\pi^*$ **9.77** (a) When comparing the same two bonded atoms, bond order and bond energy are directly related, while bond order and bond length are inversely related. When comparing different bonded nuclei, there are no simple relationships. (b) $Be_2$ is not expected to exist; it has a bond order of zero and is not energetically favored over isolated Be atoms. $Be_2^+$ has a bond order of 0.5 and is slightly lower in energy than isolated Be atoms. It will probably exist under special experimental conditions. **9.79** (a, b) Substances with no unpaired electrons are weakly repelled by a magnetic field. This property is called *diamagnetism*. (c) $O_2^{2-}$, $Be_2^{2+}$ **9.81** (a) $B_2^+$, $\sigma_{2s}^2\sigma_{2s}^{*2}\pi_{2p}^1$, increase (b) $Li_2^+$, $\sigma_{1s}^2\sigma_{1s}^{*2}\sigma_{2s}^1$, increase (c) $N_2^+$, $\sigma_{2s}^2\sigma_{2s}^{*2}\pi_{2p}^4\sigma_{2p}^1$, increase (d) $Ne_2^{2+}$, $\sigma_{2s}^2\sigma_{2s}^{*2}\sigma_{2p}^2\pi_{2p}^4\pi_{2p}^{*4}$, decrease **9.83** CN, $\sigma_{2s}^2\sigma_{2s}^{*2}\sigma_{2p}^2\pi_{2p}^3$, bond order = 2.5; $CN^+$, $\sigma_{2s}^2\sigma_{2s}^{*2}\sigma_{2p}^2\pi_{2p}^2$, bond order = 2.0; $CN^-$, $\sigma_{2s}^2\sigma_{2s}^{*2}\sigma_{2p}^2\pi_{2p}^4$, bond order = 3.0. (a) $CN^-$ (b) CN, $CN^+$ **9.85** (a) $3s$, $3p_x$, $3p_y$, $3p_z$ (b) $\pi_{3p}$ (c) 2 (d) If the MO diagram for $P_2$ is similar to that of $N_2$, $P_2$ will have no unpaired electrons and be diamagnetic. **9.89** $SiF_4$ is tetrahedral, $SF_4$ is seesaw, $XeF_4$ is square planar. The shapes are different because the number of nonbonding electron domains is different in each molecule, even though all have four bonding electron domains. Bond angles and thus molecular shape are determined by the total number of electron domains. **9.92** (a) 2 $\sigma$ bonds, 2 $\pi$ bonds (b) 3 $\sigma$ bonds, 4 $\pi$ bonds (c) 3 $\sigma$ bonds, 1 $\pi$ bond (d) 4 $\sigma$ bonds, 1 $\pi$ bond **9.94** $BF_3$ is trigonal planar, the B—F bond dipoles cancel and the molecule is nonpolar. $PF_3$ has a tetrahedral electron-domain geometry with one position occupied by a nonbonding electron pair. The nonbonding electron pair ensures an asymmetrical electron distribution and the molecule is polar. **9.99**

(a) The molecule is nonplanar. (b) Allene has no dipole moment. (c) The bonding in allene would not be described as delocalized. The $\pi$ electron clouds of the two adjacent C=C are mutually perpendicular, so there is no overlap and no delocalization of $\pi$ electrons. **9.101** (a) All O atoms have $sp^2$ hybridization. (b) The two $\sigma$ bonds are formed by overlap of $sp^2$ hybrid orbitals, the $\pi$ bond is formed by overlap of atomic $p$ orbitals, one nonbonded pair is in a $p$ atomic orbital and the other five nonbonded pairs are in $sp^2$ hybrid orbitals. (c) unhybridized $p$ atomic orbitals (d) four, two from the $\pi$ bond and two from the nonbonded pair in the $p$ atomic orbital **9.104** $\sigma_{2s}^2\sigma_{2s}^{*2}\pi_{2p}^4\sigma_{2p}^1\pi_{2p}^{*1}$ (a) Paramagnetic (b) The bond order of $N_2$ in the ground state is 3; in the first excited state it has a bond order of 2. Owing to the reduction in bond order, $N_2$ in the first excited state has a weaker N—N bond. **9.110** (a) $2 SF_4(g) + O_2(g) \longrightarrow 2 OSF_4(g)$

(b)

(c) $\Delta H = -551$ kJ, exothermic (d) The electron-domain geometry is trigonal bipyramidal. The O atom can be either equatorial or axial. (e) Since F is more electronegative than O, the structure that minimizes 90° F—S—F angles, the one with O axial, is preferred.

# CHAPTER 10

**10.1** It would be much easier to drink from a straw on Mars. When a straw is placed in a glass of liquid, the atmosphere exerts equal pressure inside and outside the straw. When we drink through a straw, we withdraw air, thereby reducing the pressure on the liquid inside. If only 0.007 atm is exerted on the liquid in the glass, a very small reduction in pressure inside the straw will cause the liquid to rise. **10.4** (a) As the reaction proceeds at constant temperature and pressure, the number of particles decreases and the container volume decreases. (b) As the reaction proceeds at constant volume and temperature, the number of particles decreases and pressure decreases. **10.7** (a) $P_{red} < P_{yellow} < P_{blue}$

(b) $P_{red} = 0.28$ atm; $P_{yellow} = 0.42$ atm; $P_{blue} = 0.70$ atm **10.10** (a) $P(ii) < P(i) = P(iii)$ (b) $P_{He}(iii) < P_{He}(ii) < P_{He}(i)$ (c) $d(ii) < d(i) < d(iii)$ (d) The average kinetic energies of the particles in the three containers are equal. **10.13** (a) A gas is much less dense than a liquid. (b) A gas is much more compressible than a liquid. (c) All mixtures of gases are homogenous. Similar liquid molecules form homogeneous mixtures, while very dissimilar molecules form heterogeneous mixtures. (d) Both gases and liquids conform to the shape of their container. A gas also adopts the volume of its container, while a liquid maintains its own volume. **10.15** (a) $1.8 \times 10^3$ kPa (b) 18 atm (c) $2.6 \times 10^2$ lb/in.$^2$ **10.17** (a) 10.3 m (b) 2.1 atm **10.19** (a) The tube can have any cross-sectional area. (b) At equilibrium the force of gravity per unit area acting on the mercury column is not equal to the force of gravity per unit area acting on the atmosphere. (c) The column of mercury is held up by the pressure of the atmosphere applied to the exterior pool of mercury. (d) If you took the mercury barometer with you on a trip from the beach to high mountains, the height of the mercury column would decrease with elevation. **10.21** (a) 0.349 atm (b) 265 mm Hg (c) $3.53 \times 10^4$ Pa (d) 0.353 bar (e) 5.13 psi **10.23** (a) $P = 773.4$ torr (b) $P = 1.018$ atm (c) The pressure in Chicago is greater than standard atmospheric pressure, and so it makes sense to classify this weather system as a "high-pressure system." **10.25** (i) 0.31 atm (ii) 1.88 atm (iii) 0.136 atm **10.27** (a) If $V$ decreases by a factor of 4, $P$ increases by a factor of 4. (b) If $T$ decreases by a factor of 2, $P$ decreases by a factor of 2. (c) If $n$ decreases by a factor of 4, $P$ decreases by a factor of 4. **10.29** (a) If equal volumes of gases at the same temperature and pressure contain equal numbers of molecules and molecules react in the ratios of small whole numbers, it follows that the volumes of reacting gases are in the ratios of small whole numbers. (b) Since the two gases are at the same temperature and pressure, the ratio of the numbers of atoms is the same as the ratio of volumes. There are 1.5 times as many Xe atoms as Ne atoms. (c) Yes. By definition, one mole of an ideal gas contains Avogadro's number of particles. At a given temperature and pressure, equal numbers of particles occupy the same volume, so one mole of an ideal gas will always occupy the same volume at the given temperature and pressure. **10.31** (a) An ideal gas exhibits pressure, volume, and temperature relationships described by the equation $PV = nRT$. (b) Boyle's law, $V = \text{constant}/P$; Charles's law, $V = \text{constant} \times T$; Avogadro's law, $V = \text{constant} \times n$. Collect all the equalities: $V = (\text{constant} \times T \times n)/P$. Call the constant $R$ and multiply both sides of the equation by $P$, $PV = nRT$. (c) $PV = nRT$; $P$ in atmospheres, $V$ in liters, $n$ in moles, $T$ in kelvins. (d) $R = 0.08315$ L-bar/mol-K. **10.33** Flask A contains the gas with $\mathcal{M} = 30$ g/mol, and flask B contains the gas with $\mathcal{M} = 60$ g/mol. **10.35**

| P | V | n | T |
|---|---|---|---|
| 2.00 atm | 1.00 L | 0.500 mol | 48.7 K |
| 0.300 atm | 0.250 L | $3.05 \times 10^{-3}$ mol | 27 °C |
| 650 torr | 11.2 L | 0.333 mol | 350 K |
| 10.3 atm | 585 mL | 0.250 mol | 295 K |

**10.37** $8.2 \times 10^2$ kg He **10.39** (a) $5.15 \times 10^{22}$ molecules (b) 6.5 kg air **10.41** (a) 91 atm (b) $2.3 \times 10^2$ L **10.43** (a) 29.8 g $Cl_2$ (b) 9.42 L (c) 501 K (d) 2.28 atm **10.45** (a) $n = 2 \times 10^{-4}$ mol $O_2$ (b) The roach needs $8 \times 10^{-3}$ mol $O_2$ in 48 h, approximately 100% of the $O_2$ in the jar. **10.47** (a) $1.32 \times 10^7$ L (b) $5.1 \times 10^8$ mol Hg **10.49** For gas samples at the same conditions, molar mass determines density. Of the three gases listed, (c) $Cl_2$ has the largest molar mass. **10.51** (c) Because the helium atoms are of lower mass than the average air molecule, the helium gas is less dense than air. The balloon thus weighs less than the air displaced by its volume. **10.53** (a) $d = 1.77$ g/L (b) $\mathcal{M} = 80.1$ g/mol **10.55** $\mathcal{M} = 89.4$ g/mol **10.57** $4.1 \times 10^{-9}$ g Mg **10.59** (a) 21.4 L $CO_2$ (b) 40.7 L $O_2$ **10.61** 0.402 g Zn **10.63** (a) When the stopcock is opened, the volume occupied by $N_2(g)$ increases from 2.0 L to 5.0 L. $P_{N_2} = 0.40$ atm (b) When the gases mix, the volume of $O_2(g)$ increases from 3.0 L to 5.0 L. $P_{O_2} = 1.2$ atm (c) $P_t = 1.6$ atm

**10.65** (a) $P_{He} = 1.87\,atm$, $P_{Ne} = 0.807\,atm$, $P_{Ar} = 0.269\,atm$, (b) $P_t = 2.95\,atm$ **10.67** $\chi_{CO_2} = 0.00039$ **10.69** $P_{CO_2} = 0.305\,atm$, $P_t = 1.232\,atm$ **10.71** $P_{N_2} = 1.3\,atm$, $P_{O_2} = 0.54\,atm$, $P_{CO_2} = 0.27\,atm$ **10.73** 2.5 mole % $O_2$ **10.75** $P_t = 2.47\,atm$ **10.77** (a) Increase in temperature at constant volume or decrease in volume or increase in pressure (b) decrease in temperature (c) increase in volume, decrease in pressure (d) increase in temperature **10.79** The fact that gases are readily compressible supports the assumption that most of the volume of a gas sample is empty space. **10.81** Average speed is the sum of the speeds of all particles divided by the total number of particles. The root mean square speed is the speed of a molecule with the same kinetic energy as the average kinetic energy of the sample. The root mean square speed is larger for a given gas sample at a fixed temperature, but the difference between the two is small. **10.83** (a) Average kinetic energy of the molecules increases. (b) Root mean square speed of the molecules increases. (c) Strength of an average impact with the container walls increases. (d) Total collisions of molecules with walls per second increases. **10.85** (a) In order of increasing speed and decreasing molar mass: $HBr < NF_3 < SO_2 < CO < Ne$ (b) $u_{NF_3} = 324\ m/s$ (c) The most probable speed of an ozone molecule in the stratosphere is 306 m/s. **10.87** Effusion is the escape of gas molecules through a tiny hole. Diffusion is the distribution of a gas throughout space or throughout another substance. **10.89** The order of increasing rate of effusion is $^2H^{37}Cl < {}^1H^{37}Cl < {}^2H^{35}Cl < {}^1H^{35}Cl$. **10.91** $As_4S_6$ **10.93** (a) Non-ideal-gas behavior is observed at very high pressures and low temperatures. (b) The real volumes of gas molecules and attractive intermolecular forces between molecules cause gases to behave nonideally. (c) According to the ideal-gas law, the ratio $PV/RT$ should be constant for a given gas sample at all combinations of pressure, volume, and temperature. If this ratio changes with increasing pressure, the gas sample is not behaving ideally. **10.95** Ar ($a = 1.34$, $b = 0.0322$) will behave more like an ideal gas than $CO_2$ ($a = 3.59$, $b = 0.427$) at high pressures. **10.97** (a) $P = 4.89\,atm$ (b) $P = 4.69\,atm$ (c) Qualitatively, molecular attractions are more important as the amount of free space decreases and the number of molecular collisions increases. Molecular volume is a larger part of the total volume as the container volume decreases. **10.99** From the value of $b$ for Xe, the nonbonding radius is 2.72 Å. From Figure 7.6, the bonding atomic radius of Xe is 1.30 Å. We expect the bonding radius of an atom to be smaller than its nonbonding radius, but this difference is quite large. **10.101** $V = 3.1\,mm^3$ **10.105** (a) 13.4 mol $C_3H_8(g)$ (b) $1.47 \times 10^3$ mol $C_3H_8(l)$ (c) The ratio of moles liquid to moles gas is 110. Many more molecules and moles of liquid fit in a container of fixed volume because there is much less space between molecules in the liquid phase. **10.108** $P_t = 5.3 \times 10^2\,torr$ **10.111** 42.2 g $O_2$ **10.115** $T_2 = 687\,°C$ **10.120** (a) $P(ideal) = 177\,atm$ (b) $P(\text{van der Waals}) = 187.4\,atm$ (c) Under the conditions of this problem (large number of moles of gas), the correction for the real volume of molecules dominates. **10.123** (a) 44.58% C, 6.596% H, 16.44% Cl, 32.38% N (b) $C_8H_{14}N_5Cl$ (c) Molar mass of the compound is required in order to determine molecular formula when the empirical formula is known. **10.128** (a) $5.02 \times 10^8$ L $CH_3OH(l)$ (b) $CH_4(g) + 2\,O_2(g) \longrightarrow CO_2(g) + 2\,H_2O(l)$, $\Delta H° = -890.4$ kJ; $\Delta H$ for combustion of the methane is $-1.10 \times 10^{13}$ kJ. $CH_3OH(l) + 3/2\,O_2(g) \longrightarrow CO_2(g) + 2\,H_2O(l)$, $\Delta H° = -726.6$ kJ; $\Delta H$ for combustion of the methanol is $-9.00 \times 10^{12}$ kJ. (c) The enthalpy change upon combustion of 1.00 L of $CH_4(l)$ is $-2.59 \times 10^4$ kJ and for 1.00 L of $CH_3OH(l)$, $-1.79 \times 10^4$ kJ. Clearly $CH_4(l)$ has the higher enthalpy of combustion per unit volume.

## CHAPTER 11

**11.1** The diagram best describes a liquid. The particles are close together, mostly touching, but there is no regular arrangement or order. This rules out a gaseous sample, where the particles are far apart, and a crystalline solid, which has a regular repeating structure in all three directions. **11.4** (a) In its final state, methane is a gas at 185 °C. **11.5** (a) 385 mm Hg (b) 22 °C (c) 47 °C **11.6** The stronger the inter-

molecular forces, the higher the boiling point of a liquid. Propanol, $CH_3CH_2CH_2OH$, has hydrogen bonding and the higher boiling point. **11.7** (a) Normal boiling point, 360 K; normal freezing point, 260 K (b) (i) gas (ii) solid (iii) liquid (c) The triple point is approximately 185 K at 0.45 atm. **11.9** (a) Solid < liquid < gas (b) gas < liquid < solid (c) Matter in the gaseous state is most easily compressed because particles are far apart and there is much empty space. **11.11** $Ar < CCl_4 < Si$ **11.13** (a) The molar volumes of $Cl_2$ and $NH_3$ are nearly the same because they are both gases. (b) On cooling to 160 K, both compounds condense from the gas phase to the solid-state, so we expect a significant decrease in the molar volume. (c) The molar volumes are 0.0351 L/mol $Cl_2$ and 0.0203 L/mol $NH_3$ (d) Solid-state molar volumes are not as similar as those in the gaseous state, because most of the empty space is gone and molecular characteristics determine properties. $Cl_2(s)$ is heavier, has a longer bond distance and weaker intermolecular forces, so it has a significantly larger molar volume than $NH_3(s)$. (e) There is little empty space between molecules in the liquid state, so we expect their molar volumes to be closer to those in the solid state than those in the gaseous state. **11.15** (a) London dispersion forces (b) dipole–dipole and London dispersion forces (c) dipole–dipole forces and in certain cases hydrogen bonding **11.17** (a) $SO_2$, dipole–dipole and London dispersion forces (b) $CH_3COOH$, London dispersion, dipole–dipole, and hydrogen bonding (c) $H_2Se$, dipole–dipole and London dispersion forces (but not hydrogen bonding) **11.19** (a) *Polarizability* is the ease with which the charge distribution in a molecule can be distorted to produce a transient dipole. (b) Sb is most polarizable because its valence electrons are farthest from the nucleus and least tightly held. (c) in order of increasing polarizability: $CH_4 < SiH_4 < SiCl_4 < GeCl_4 < GeBr_4$ (d) The magnitudes of London dispersion forces and thus the boiling points of molecules increase as polarizability increases. The order of increasing boiling points is the order of increasing polarizability given in (c). **11.21** (a) $H_2S$ (b) $CO_2$ (c) $GeH_4$ **11.23** Both rodlike butane molecules and spherical 2-methylpropane molecules experience dispersion forces. The larger contact surface between butane molecules facilitates stronger forces and produces a higher boiling point. **11.25** (a) A molecule must contain H atoms, bound to either N, O, or F atoms, in order to participate in hydrogen bonding with like molecules. (b) $CH_3NH_2$ and $CH_3OH$ **11.27** (a) Replacing a hydroxyl hydrogen with a $CH_3$ group eliminates hydrogen bonding in that part of the molecule. This reduces the strength of intermolecular forces and leads to a lower boiling point. (b) $CH_3OCH_2CH_2OCH_3$ is a larger, more polarizable molecule with stronger London dispersion forces and thus a higher boiling point.

**11.29**

| Physical Property | H₂O | H₂S |
|---|---|---|
| Normal boiling point, °C | 100.00 | −60.7 |
| Normal melting point, °C | 0.00 | −85.5 |

(a) Based on its much higher normal melting point and boiling point, $H_2O$ has much stronger intermolecular forces. $H_2O$ has hydrogen bonding, while $H_2S$ has dipole–dipole forces. (b) $H_2S$ is probably a typical compound with less empty space in the ordered solid than the liquid, so that the solid is denser than the liquid. For $H_2O$, maximizing the number of hydrogen bonds to each molecule in the solid requires more empty space than in the liquid, and the solid is less dense. (c) Specific heat is the energy required to raise the temperature of one gram of the substance one degree Celsius. Hydrogen bonding in water is such a strong attractive interaction that the energy required to disrupt it and increase molecular motion is large. **11.31** $SO_4^{2-}$ has a greater negative charge than $BF_4^-$, so ion–ion electrostatic attractions are greater in sulfate salts and they are less likely to form liquids. **11.33** (a) As temperature increases, the number of molecules with sufficient kinetic energy to overcome intermolecular attractive forces increases, and viscosity and surface tension decrease. (b) The same attractive forces that cause surface molecules to be difficult to separate (high surface tension) cause molecules elsewhere in the sample to resist movement relative to each other (high viscosity).   **11.35** (a) $CHBr_3$ has a higher molar mass, is more polarizable, and has stronger dispersion forces, so the surface tension is greater. (b) As temperature increases, the viscosity of the oil decreases because the average kinetic energy of the molecules increases. (c) Adhesive forces between polar water and nonpolar car wax are weak, so the large surface tension of water draws the liquid into the shape with the smallest surface area, a sphere. (d) Adhesive forces between nonpolar oil and nonpolar car wax are similar to cohesive forces in oil, so the oil drops spread out on the waxed car hood.   **11.37** (a) The three molecules have similar structures and experience the same types of intermolecular forces. As molar mass increases, the strength of dispersion forces increases and the boiling points, surface tension, and viscosities all increase. (b) Ethylene glycol has an —OH group at both ends of the molecule. This greatly increases the possibilities for hydrogen bonding; the overall intermolecular attractive forces are greater and the viscosity of ethylene glycol is much greater. (c) Water has the highest surface tension but lowest viscosity because it is the smallest molecule in the series. There is no hydrocarbon chain to inhibit their strong attraction to molecules in the interior of the drop, resulting in high surface tension. The absence of an alkyl chain also means the molecules can move around each other easily, resulting in the low viscosity.   **11.39** (a) Melting, endothermic (b) evaporation, endothermic (c) deposition, exothermic (d) condensation, exothermic   **11.41** Melting does not require separation of molecules, so the energy requirement is smaller than for vaporization, where molecules must be separated.   **11.43** $2.3 \times 10^3$ g $H_2O$   **11.45** (a) 39.3 kJ (b) 60 kJ   **11.47** (a) The critical pressure is the pressure required to cause liquefaction at the critical temperature. (b) As the force of attraction between molecules increases, the critical temperature of the compound increases. (c) All the gases in Table 11.5 can be liquefied at the temperature of liquid nitrogen, given sufficient pressure.   **11.49** (a) No effect (b) no effect (c) Vapor pressure decreases with increasing intermolecular attractive forces because fewer molecules have sufficient kinetic energy to overcome attractive forces and escape to the vapor phase. (d) Vapor pressure increases with increasing temperature because average kinetic energies of molecules increase. (e) Vapor pressure decreases with increasing density because attractive intermolecular forces increase.   **11.51** (a) $CBr_4 < CHBr_3 < CH_2Br_2 < CH_2Cl_2 < CH_3Cl < CH_4$. The trend is dominated by dispersion forces even though four of the molecules are polar. The order of increasing volatility is the order of increasing vapor pressure, decreasing molar mass, and decreasing strength of dispersion forces. (b) Boiling point increases as the strength of intermolecular forces increases; this is the order of decreasing volatility and the reverse of the order in part (a).   $CH_4 < CH_3Cl < CH_2Cl_2 < CH_2Br_2 < CHBr_3 < CBr_4$   **11.53** (a) The temperature of the water in the two pans is the same. (b) Vapor pressure does not depend on either volume or surface area of the liquid. At the same temperature, the vapor pressures of water in the two containers are the same.   **11.55** (a) Approximately 48 °C (b) approximately 340 torr (c) approximately 17 °C (d) approximately 1000 torr   **11.57** (a) The critical point is the temperature and pressure beyond which the gas and liquid phases are indistinguishable. (b) The line that separates the gas and liquid phases ends at the critical point because at conditions beyond the critical temperature and pressure, there is no distinction between gas and liquid. In experimental terms a gas cannot be liquefied at temperatures higher than the critical temperature, regardless of pressure.   **11.59** (a) $H_2O(g)$ will condense to $H_2O(s)$ at approximately 4 torr; at a higher pressure, perhaps 5 atm or so, $H_2O(s)$ will melt to form $H_2O(l)$. (b) At 100 °C and 0.50 atm, water is in the vapor phase. As it cools, water vapor condenses to the liquid at approximately 82 °C, the temperature where the vapor pressure of liquid water is 0.50 atm. Further cooling results in freezing at approximately 0 °C. The freezing point of water increases with decreasing pressure, so at 0.50 atm the freezing temperature is very slightly above 0 °C.   **11.61** (a) 24 K (b) Neon sublimes at pressures less than the triple point pressure, 0.43 atm. (c) No   **11.63** (a) Methane on the surface of Titan is likely to exist in both solid and liquid forms. (b) As

pressure decreases upon moving away from the surface of Titan, $CH_4(l)$ (at −178 °C) will vaporize to $CH_4(g)$, and $CH_4(s)$ (at temperatures below −180 °C) will sublime to $CH_4(g)$.   **11.65** In a nematic liquid crystalline phase, molecules are aligned along their long axes, but the molecular ends are not aligned. Molecules are free to translate in all dimensions, but they cannot tumble or rotate out of the molecular plane, or the order of the nematic phase is lost and the sample becomes an ordinary liquid. In an ordinary liquid, molecules are randomly oriented and free to move in any direction.   **11.67** The presence of polar groups or nonbonded electron pairs leads to relatively strong dipole–dipole interactions between molecules. These are a significant part of the orienting forces necessary for liquid crystal formation.   **11.69** Because order is maintained in at least one dimension, the molecules in a liquid-crystalline phase are not totally free to change orientation. This makes the liquid-crystalline phase more resistant to flow, more viscous, than the isotropic liquid.   **11.71** Melting provides kinetic energy sufficient to disrupt molecular alignment in one dimension in the solid, producing a smectic phase with ordering in two dimensions. Additional heating of the smectic phase provides kinetic energy sufficient to disrupt alignment in another dimension, producing a nematic phase with one-dimensional order.   **11.73** (a) Decrease (b) increase (c) increase (d) increase (e) increase (f) increase (g) increase   **11.77** When a halogen is substituted for H in benzene, molar mass, polarizability and strength of dispersion forces increase; the order of increasing molar mass is the order of increasing boiling points for the first three compounds. $C_6H_5OH$ experiences hydrogen bonding, the strongest force between neutral molecules, so it has the highest boiling point.   **11.82** (a) Evaporation is an endothermic process. The heat required to vaporize sweat is absorbed from your body, helping to keep it cool. (b) The vacuum pump reduces the pressure of the atmosphere above the water until atmospheric pressure equals the vapor pressure of water and the water boils. Boiling is an endothermic process, and the temperature drops if the system is not able to absorb heat from the surroundings fast enough. As the temperature of the water decreases, the water freezes.   **11.86** At low Antarctic temperatures, molecules in the liquid crystalline phase have less kinetic energy due to temperature, and the applied voltage may not be sufficient to overcome orienting forces among the ends of molecules. If some or all of the molecules do not rotate when the voltage is applied, the display will not function properly.   **11.90**

(i) $\mathcal{M} = 44$   (ii) $\mathcal{M} = 72$   (iii) $\mathcal{M} = 123$

(iv) $\mathcal{M} = 58$   (v) $\mathcal{M} = 123$   (vi) $\mathcal{M} = 60$

(a) Molar mass: Compounds (i) and (ii) have similar rodlike structures. The longer chain in (ii) leads to greater molar mass, stronger London dispersion forces, and higher heat of vaporization. (b) Molecular shape: Compounds (iii) and (v) have the same chemical formula and molar mass but different molecular shapes. The more rodlike shape of (v) leads to more contact between molecules, stronger dispersion forces, and higher heat of vaporization. (c) Molecular polarity: Compound (iv) has a smaller molar mass than (ii) but a larger heat of vaporization, which must be due to the presence of dipole–dipole forces. (d) Hydrogen bonding interactions: Molecules (v) and (vi) have similar structures. Even though (v) has larger molar mass and dispersion forces, hydrogen bonding causes (vi) to have the higher heat of vaporization.   **11.93** $P$(benzene vapor) = 98.7 torr

# CHAPTER 12

### 12.1

| Two-dimensional structure | (i) | (ii) |
|---|---|---|
| (a) unit cell | 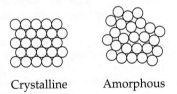 | |
| (b) lattice | square | square |
| (c) cell contents | one black, one white | one black |

**12.3** (a) 1 Re and 3 O atoms per unit cell (b) 3.92 Å (c) 6.46 g/cm³ **12.5** We expect linear polymer (a), with ordered regions, to be denser and have a higher melting point than branched polymer (b). **12.7** In molecular solids, relatively weak intermolecular forces bind the molecules in the lattice, so relatively little energy is required to disrupt these forces. In covalent-network solids, covalent bonds join atoms into an extended network. Melting or deforming a covalent-network solid means breaking covalent bonds, which requires a large amount of energy. **12.9** (a) Hydrogen bonding, dipole-dipole forces, London dispersion forces (b) covalent chemical bonds (c) ionic bonds (d) metallic bonds **12.11** (a) Ionic (b) metallic (c) covalent-network (It could also be characterized as ionic with some covalent character to the bonds.) (d) molecular (e) molecular (f) molecular **12.13** Because of its relatively high melting point and properties as a conducting solution, the solid must be ionic.

### 12.15

Crystalline     Amorphous

### 12.17

| Two-dimensional structure | (i) | (ii) |
|---|---|---|
| (a) unit cell | | |
| (b) γ, a, b | λ = 90°, a = b | λ = 120°, a = b |
| (c) lattice type | square | hexagonal |

**12.19** (a) Orthorhombic (d) tetragonal **12.21** Triclinic, rhombohedral **12.23** There is a minimum of two (metal) atoms in a body-centered cubic unit cell. **12.25** (a) Primitive hexagonal unit cell (b) NiAs **12.27** Moving left to right in the period, atomic mass and $Z_{eff}$ increase. The increase in $Z_{eff}$ leads to smaller bonding atomic radii and atomic volume. Mass increases, volume decreases, and density increases in the series. The variation in densities reflects shorter metal–metal bond distances and an increase in the extent of metal–metal bonding. The strength of metal–metal bonds in the series

is probably the most important factor influencing the increase in density. **12.29** (a) Structure types A and C have equally dense packing and are more densely packed than structure type B. (b) Structure type B is least densely packed. **12.31** (a) The radius of an Ir atom is 1.355 Å. (b) The density of Ir is 22.67 g/cm³ **12.33** (a) 4 Al atoms per unit cell (b) coordination number = 12 (c) a = 4.04 Å or 4.04 × 10⁻⁸ cm (d) density = 2.71 g/cm³ **12.35** An *alloy* contains atoms of more than one element and has the properties of a metal. In a *solution alloy* the components are randomly dispersed. In a *heterogeneous alloy* the components are not evenly dispersed and can be distinguished at a macroscopic level. In an *intermetallic compound* the components have interacted to form a compound substance, as in Cu₃As. **12.37** (a) Interstitial alloy (b) substitutional alloy (c) intermetallic compound **12.39** (a) True (b) false (c) false **12.41** (a) Nickel or palladium, substitutional alloy (b) copper, substitutional alloy (c) indium, intermetallic compound (d) silver, substitutional alloy **12.43** In the electron-sea model, valence electrons move about the metallic lattice, while metal atoms remain more or less fixed in position. Under the influence of an applied potential, the electrons are free to move throughout the structure, giving rise to thermal and electrical conductivity.

### 12.45

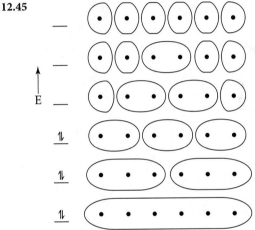

(a) Six AOs require six MOs (b) zero nodes in the lowest energy orbital (c) five nodes in highest energy orbital (d) two nodes in the HOMO (e) three nodes in the LUMO. **12.47** (a) Ag (b) Zn. Ductility decreases as the strength of metal–metal bonding increases, producing a stiffer lattice, less susceptible to distortion. **12.49** Moving from Y to Mo, the number of valence electrons, occupancy of the bonding band, and strength of metallic bonding increase. Stronger metallic bonding requires more energy to break bonds and mobilize atoms, resulting in higher melting points. **12.51** (a) SrTiO₃ (b) Each Sr atom is coordinated to twelve O atoms in eight unit cells that contain the Sr atom. **12.53** (a) a = 4.70 Å (b) 2.69 g/cm³ **12.55** (a) 7.711 g/cm³ (b) We expect Se²⁻ to have a larger ionic radius than S²⁻, so HgSe will occupy a larger volume and the unit cell edge will be longer. (c) The density of HgSe is 8.241 g/cm³. The greater mass of Se accounts for the greater density of HgSe. **12.57** (a) Cs⁺ and I⁻ have the most similar radii and will adopt the CsCl-type structure. The radii of Na⁺ and I⁻ are somewhat different; NaI will adopt the NaCl-type structure. The radii of Cu⁺ and I⁻ are very different; CuI has the ZnS-type structure. (b) CsI, 8; NaI, 6; CuI, 4 **12.59** (a) 6 (b) 3 (c) 6 **12.61** (a) False (b) true **12.63** (a) Ionic solids are much more likely to dissolve in water. (b) Covalent-network solids can become electrical conductors via chemical substitution. **12.65** (a) CdS (b) GaN (c) GaAs **12.67** Ge or Si (Ge is closer to Ga in bonding atomic radius.) **12.69** (a) A 1.1 eV photon corresponds to a wavelength of 1.1 × 10⁻⁶ m. (b) According to the figure, Si can absorb a portion of the visible light that comes from the sun. **12.71** λ = 560 nm **12.73** The band gap is approximately 1.85 eV, which corresponds to a wavelength of 672 nm. **12.75** Monomers are small molecules with low molecular mass that are joined together to form polymers. Three monomers mentioned in this chapter are

Propylene
(propene)
    Styrene
(phenyl ethene)
    Isoprene
(2-methyl-1,3-butadiene)

**12.77**

Acetic acid     Ethanol

Ethyl acetate

If a dicarboxylic acid and a dialcohol are combined, there is the potential for propagation of the polymer chain at both ends of both monomers.

**12.79** (a)

(b)

(c)

**12.81**

and

**12.83** Flexibility of molecular chains causes flexibility of the bulk polymer. Flexibility is enhanced by molecular features that inhibit order, such as branching, and diminished by features that encourage order, such as cross-linking or delocalized $\pi$ electron density. Cross-linking, the formation of chemical bonds between polymer chains, reduces flexibility of the molecular chains, increases the hardness of the material, and decreases the chemical reactivity of the polymer. **12.85** No. The function of the polymer determines whether high molecular mass and high degree of crystallinity are desirable properties. If the polymer will be used as a flexible wrapping or fiber, rigidity that is due to high molecular mass is an undesirable property. **12.87** If a solid has nanoscale dimensions of 1–10 nm, there may not be enough atoms contributing atomic orbitals to produce continuous energy bands of molecular orbitals. **12.89** (a) False. As particle size decreases, the band gap increases. (b) False. As particle size decreases, wavelength decreases. **12.91** $2.47 \times 10^5$ Au atoms **12.94** The face-centered structure will have the greater density. **12.98** (a) CsCl, primitive cubic lattice (b) Au, face-centered cubic lattice (c) NaCl, face-centered cubic lattice (d) Po, primitive cubic lattice, rare for metals (e) ZnS, face-centered cubic lattice **12.99** White tin has a structure characteristic of a metal, while gray tin has the diamond structure characteristic of group 4A semiconductors. Metallic white tin has the

longer bond distance because the valence electrons are shared with twelve nearest neighbors rather than being localized in four bonds as in gray tin.

**12.103**

Teflon™ is formed by addition polymerization. **12.105** Diffraction, the phenomenon that enables us to measure interatomic distances in crystals, is most efficient when the wavelength of light is similar to or smaller than the size of the object doing the diffracting. Atom sizes are on the order of 1–10 Å, and the wavelengths of X-rays are also in this range. Visible light, 400–700 nm or 4000–7000 Å, is too long to be diffracted effectively by atoms (electrons) in crystals. **12.107** In a diffraction experiment, we expect a Ge crystal to diffract X-rays at a smaller $\theta$ angle than a Si crystal, assuming the X-rays have the same wavelength. **12.109** (a) The bonds in a semiconductor will be weakened by $n$-type doping. (b) The bonds in a semiconductor will also be weakened by $p$-type doping. **12.112** (a) 109° (b) 120° **12.113** (a) $\Delta H = -82$ kJ/mol (b) $\Delta H = -14$ kJ/mol (of either reactant) (c) $\Delta H = 0$ kJ

## CHAPTER 13

**13.1** (a) < (b) < (c) **13.3** The greater the lattice energy of an ionic solid, the more endothermic the dissolving process and the less soluble the salt in water. **13.7** Vitamin B$_6$ is largely water soluble because of its small size and capacity for extensive hydrogen-bonding interactions. Vitamin E is largely fat soluble. The long, rodlike hydrocarbon chain will lead to strong dispersion forces among vitamin E and mostly nonpolar fats. **13.9** (a) Yes, the *molarity* changes with a change in temperature. Molarity is defined as moles solute per unit volume of solution. A change of temperature changes solution volume and molarity. (b) No, *molality* does not change with change in temperature. Molality is defined as moles solute per kilogram of solvent. Temperature affects neither mass nor moles. **13.13** If the magnitude of $\Delta H_{mix}$ is small relative to the magnitude of $\Delta H_{solute}$, $\Delta H_{soln}$ will be large and endothermic (energetically unfavorable) and not much solute will dissolve. **13.15** (a) Dispersion (b) hydrogen bonding (c) ion–dipole (d) dipole–dipole **13.17** Very soluble. In order for $\Delta H_{soln}$ to be negative, $\Delta H_{mix}$ must have a greater magnitude than ($\Delta H_{solute} + \Delta H_{solvent}$). The entropy of mixing always encourages solubility. In this case, the enthalpy of the system decreases and the entropy increases, so the ionic compound dissolves. **13.19** (a) $\Delta H_{solute}$ (b) $\Delta H_{mix}$ **13.21** (a) Since the solute and solvent experience very similar London dispersion forces, the energy required to separate them individually and the energy released when they are mixed are approximately equal. $\Delta H_{solute} + \Delta H_{solvent} \approx -\Delta H_{mix}$. Thus, $\Delta H_{soln}$ is nearly zero. (b) Since no strong intermolecular forces prevent the molecules from mixing, they do so spontaneously because of the increase in randomness. **13.23** (a) Supersaturated (b) Add a seed crystal. A seed crystal provides a nucleus of prealigned molecules, so that ordering of the dissolved particles (crystallization) is more facile. **13.25** (a) Unsaturated (b) saturated (c) saturated (d) unsaturated **13.27** The liquids water and glycerol form homogenous mixtures (solutions) regardless of the relative amounts of the two components. The —OH groups of glycerol facilitate strong hydrogen bonding similar to that in water; like dissolves like. **13.29** Toluene, C$_6$H$_5$CH$_3$, is the best solvent for nonpolar solutes. Without polar groups or nonbonding electron pairs, it forms only dispersion interactions with itself and other molecules. **13.31** (a) Dispersion interactions among nonpolar CH$_3$(CH$_2$)$_{16}$— chains dominate the properties of stearic acid, causing it to be more soluble in nonpolar $CCl_4$. (b) Dioxane can act as a hydrogen bond acceptor, so it will be more soluble than cyclohexane in water. **13.33** (a) $CCl_4$ is more soluble because dispersion forces among nonpolar $CCl_4$ molecules are similar to dispersion forces in hexane. (b) $C_6H_6$ is a nonpolar hydrocarbon and will be more soluble in the similarly nonpolar hexane. (c) The long, rodlike hydrocarbon chain of octanoic acid forms strong dispersion interactions and causes it to be more soluble in hexane. **13.35** (a) A sealed container is required to maintain a partial pressure of $CO_2(g)$ greater than 1 atm above the beverage. (b) Since the solubility of gases increases with decreasing temperature, more $CO_2(g)$ will remain dissolved in the beverage if it is kept cool. **13.37** $S_{He} = 5.6 \times 10^{-4}\,M$, $S_{N_2} = 9.0 \times 10^{-4}\,M$ **13.39** (a) 2.15% $Na_2SO_4$ by mass (b) 3.15 ppm Ag **13.41** (a) $X_{CH_3OH} = 0.0427$ (b) 7.35% $CH_3OH$ by mass (c) 2.48 $m$ $CH_3OH$ **13.43** (a) $1.46 \times 10^{-2}\,M$ $Mg(NO_3)_2$ (b) 1.12 $M$ $LiClO_4 \cdot 3\,H_2O$ (c) 0.350 $M$ $HNO_3$ **13.45** (a) 4.70 $m$ $C_6H_6$ (b) 0.235 $m$ NaCl **13.47** (a) 43.01% $H_2SO_4$ by mass (b) $X_{H_2SO_4} = 0.122$ (c) 7.69 $m$ $H_2SO_4$ (d) 5.827 $M$ $H_2SO_4$ **13.49** (a) $X_{CH_3OH} = 0.227$ (b) 7.16 $m$ $CH_3OH$ (c) 4.58 $M$ $CH_3OH$ **13.51** (a) 0.150 mol $SrBr_2$ (b) $1.56 \times 10^{-2}$ mol KCl (c) $4.44 \times 10^{-2}$ mol $C_6H_{12}O_6$ **13.53** (a) Weigh out 1.3 g KBr, dissolve in water, dilute with stirring to 0.75 L. (b) Weigh out 2.62 g KBr, dissolve it in 122.38 g $H_2O$ to make exactly 125 g of 0.180 $m$ solution. (c) Dissolve 244 g KBr in water, dilute with stirring to 1.85 L. (d) Weigh 10.1 g KBr, dissolve in a small amount of water, and dilute to 0.568 L. **13.55** 71% $HNO_3$ by mass **13.57** (a) 3.82 $m$ Zn (b) 26.8 $M$ Zn **13.59** $1.8 \times 10^{-3}\,M\,CO_2$ **13.61** Freezing point depression, $\Delta T_f = K_f(m)$; boiling-point elevation, $\Delta T_b = K_b(m)$; osmotic pressure, $\Pi = MRT$; vapor pressure lowering, $P_A = X_A P_A^\circ$ **13.63** (a) Sucrose has a greater molar mass than glucose, so the sucrose solution will contain fewer particles and have a higher vapor pressure. **13.65** (a) $P_{H_2O} = 186.4$ torr (b) 78.9 g $C_3H_8O_2$ **13.67** (a) $X_{Eth} = 0.2812$ (b) $P_{soln} = 238$ torr (c) $X_{Eth}$ in vapor $= 0.472$ **13.69** (a) Because NaCl is a strong electrolyte, one mole of NaCl produces twice as many dissolved particles as one mole of the molecular solute $C_6H_{12}O_6$. Boiling-point elevation is directly related to total moles of dissolved particles, so 0.10 $m$ NaCl has the higher boiling point. (b) 0.10 $m$ NaCl: $\Delta T_b = 0.101\,°C$, $T_b = 100.1\,°C$; 0.10 $m$ $C_6H_{12}O_6$: $\Delta T_b = 0.051\,°C$, $T_b = 100.1\,°C$ (c) Interactions between ions in solution result in nonideal behavior. **13.71** 0.050 $m$ LiBr < 0.120 $m$ glucose < 0.050 $m$ $Zn(NO_3)_2$ **13.73** (a) $T_f = -115.0\,°C$, $T_b = 78.7\,°C$ (b) $T_f = -67.3\,°C$, $T_b = 64.2\,°C$ (c) $T_f = -0.4\,°C$, $T_b = 100.1\,°C$ (c) $T_f = -0.6\,°C$, $T_b = 100.2\,°C$ **13.75** 167 g $C_2H_6O_2$ **13.77** $\Pi = 0.0168$ atm $= 12.7$ torr **13.79** Experimental molar mass of adrenaline is $1.8 \times 10^2$ g. The structure shows a molecular formula of $C_9H_{13}NO_3$, with a molar mass of 183 g. The two values agree to two significant figures, the precision of the experiment. **13.81** Molar mass of lysozyme $= 1.39 \times 10^4$ g **13.83** (a) $i = 2.8$ (b) The more concentrated the solution, the greater the ion pairing and the smaller the measured value of $i$. **13.85** (a) In the gaseous state, particles are far apart and intermolecular attractive forces are small. When two gases combine, all terms in Equation 13.1 are essentially zero and the mixture is always homogeneous. (b) To determine whether Faraday's dispersion is a true solution or a colloid, shine a beam of light on it. If light is scattered, the dispersion is a colloid. **13.87** (a) Hydrophobic (b) hydrophilic (c) hydrophobic (d) hydrophobic (but stabilized by adsorbed charges). **13.89** When electrolytes are added to a suspension of proteins, dissolved ions form ion pairs with the protein surface charges, effectively neutralizing them. The protein's capacity for ion–dipole interactions with water is diminished and the colloid separates into a protein layer and a water layer. **13.91** The periphery of the BHT molecule is mostly hydrocarbon-like groups, such as $-CH_3$. The one $-OH$ group is rather buried inside and probably does little to enhance solubility in water. Thus, BHT is more likely to be soluble in the nonpolar hydrocarbon hexane, $C_6H_{14}$, than in polar water. **13.94** (a) $k_{Rn} = 7.27 \times 10^{-3}$ mol/L-atm (b) $P_{Rn} = 1.1 \times 10^{-4}$ atm; $S_{Rn} = 8.1 \times 10^{-7}\,M$ **13.98** (a) 2.69 $m$ LiBr (b) $X_{LiBr} = 0.0994$ (c) 81.1% LiBr by mass **13.100** $X_{H_2O} = 0.808$; 0.0273 mol ions; 0.0136 mol NaCl **13.103** (a) $-0.6\,°C$ (b) $-0.4\,°C$ **13.106** (a) $CF_4$, $1.7 \times 10^{-4}\,m$; $CClF_3$, $9 \times 10^{-4}\,m$; $CCl_2F_2$, $2.3 \times 10^{-2}\,m$; $CHClF_2$,

$3.5 \times 10^{-2}\,m$ (b) Molality and molarity are numerically similar when kilograms solvent and liters solution are nearly equal. This is true when solutions are dilute and when the density of the solvent is nearly 1 g/mL, as in this exercise. (c) Water is a polar solvent; the solubility of solutes increases as their polarity increases. Nonpolar $CF_4$ has the lowest solubility and the most polar fluorocarbon, $CHClF_2$, has the greatest solubility in $H_2O$. (d) The Henry's law constant for $CHClF_2$ is $3.5 \times 10^{-2}$ mol/L-atm. This value is greater than the Henry's law constant for $N_2(g)$ because $N_2(g)$ is nonpolar and of lower molecular mass than $CHClF_2$.

**13.109**

(a) cation $(g)$ + anion $(g)$ + solvent

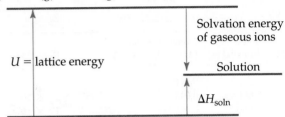

(b) Lattice energy $(U)$ is inversely related to the distance between ions, so salts with large cations like $(CH_3)_4N^+$ have smaller lattice energies than salts with simple cations like $Na^+$. Also the $-CH_3$ groups in the large cation are capable of dispersion interactions with nonpolar groups of the solvent molecules, resulting in a more negative solvation energy of the gaseous ions. Overall, for salts with larger cations, lattice energy is smaller (less positive), the solvation energy of the gaseous ions is more negative, and $\Delta H_{soln}$ is less endothermic. These salts are more soluble in polar nonaqueous solvents. **13.112** The freezing point of the $LiOH(aq)$ solution is essentially zero, $T_f = -0.00058\,°C$.

# CHAPTER 14

**14.1** Vessel 2 **14.3** Equation (d) **14.9** (1) Total potential energy of the reactants (2) $E_a$, activation energy of the reaction (3) $\Delta E$, net energy change for the reaction (4) total potential energy of the products **14.12** (a) $NO_2 + F_2 \longrightarrow NO_2F + F$; $NO_2 + F \longrightarrow NO_2F$ (b) $2\,NO_2 + F_2 \longrightarrow 2\,NO_2F$ (c) F (atomic fluorine) is the intermediate (d) rate $= k[NO_2][F_2]$)
**14.16**

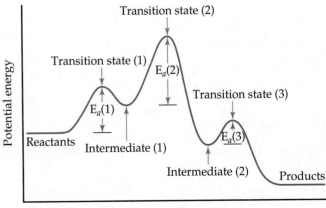

**14.17** (a) *Reaction rate* is the change in the amount of products or reactants in a given amount of time. (b) Rates depend on concentration of reactants, surface area of reactants, temperature, and presence of catalyst. (c) The stoichiometry of the reaction (mole ratios of reactants and products) must be known to relate rate of disappearance of reactants to rate of appearance of products.

**14.19**

| Time (min) | (a) Mol A | (a) Mol B | [A] (mol/L) | Δ[A] (mol/L) | (b) Rate (M/s) |
|---|---|---|---|---|---|
| 0 | 0.065 | 0.000 | 0.65 | | |
| 10 | 0.051 | 0.014 | 0.51 | −0.14 | $2.3 \times 10^{-4}$ |
| 20 | 0.042 | 0.023 | 0.42 | −0.09 | $1.5 \times 10^{-4}$ |
| 30 | 0.036 | 0.029 | 0.36 | −0.06 | $1.0 \times 10^{-4}$ |
| 40 | 0.031 | 0.034 | 0.31 | −0.05 | $0.8 \times 10^{-4}$ |

(c) $\Delta[B]_{avg}/\Delta t = 1.3 \times 10^{-4}\,M/s$
**14.21** (a)

| Time (s) | Time Interval (s) | Concentration (M) | ΔM | Rate (M/s) |
|---|---|---|---|---|
| 0 | | 0.0165 | | |
| 2,000 | 2,000 | 0.0110 | −0.0055 | $28 \times 10^{-7}$ |
| 5,000 | 3,000 | 0.00591 | −0.0051 | $17 \times 10^{-7}$ |
| 8,000 | 3,000 | 0.00314 | −0.00277 | $9.23 \times 10^{-7}$ |
| 12,000 | 4,000 | 0.00137 | −0.00177 | $4.43 \times 10^{-7}$ |
| 15,000 | 3,000 | 0.00074 | −0.00063 | $2.1 \times 10^{-7}$ |

(b) The average rate of reaction is $1.05 \times 10^{-6}\,M/s$. (c) From the slopes of the tangents to the graph, the rates are $12 \times 10^{-7}\,M/s$ at 5000 s, $5.8 \times 10^{-7}\,M/s$ at 8000 s.
**14.23**
(a) $-\Delta[H_2O_2]/\Delta t = \Delta[H_2]/\Delta t = \Delta[O_2]/\Delta t$
(b) $-\frac{1}{2}\Delta[N_2O]/\Delta t = \frac{1}{2}\Delta[N_2]/\Delta t = \Delta[O_2]/\Delta t$
(c) $-\Delta[N_2]/\Delta t = -1/3\Delta[H_2]/\Delta t = -1/2\Delta[NH_3]/2\Delta t$
(d) $-\Delta[C_2H_5NH_2]/\Delta t = \Delta[C_2H_4]/\Delta t = \Delta[NH_3]/\Delta t$
**14.25** (a) $-\Delta[O_2]/\Delta t = 0.24$ mol/s; $\Delta[H_2O]/\Delta t = 0.48$ mol/s (b) $P_{total}$ decreases by 28 torr/min. **14.27** (a) If [A] doubles, there is no change in the rate or the rate constant. The overall rate is unchanged because [A] does not appear in the rate law; the rate constant changes only with a change in temperature. (b) The reaction is zero order in A, second order in B, and second order overall. (c) units of $k = M^{-1}s^{-1}$ **14.29** (a) Rate $= k[N_2O_5]$ (b) Rate $= 1.16 \times 10^{-4}\,M/s$ (c) When the concentration of $N_2O_5$ doubles, the rate doubles. (d) When the concentration of $N_2O_5$ is halved, the rate doubles. **14.31** (a, b) $k = 1.7 \times 10^2\,M^{-1}s^{-1}$ (c) If $[OH^-]$ is tripled, the rate triples. (d) If $[OH^-]$ and $[CH_3Br]$ both triple, the rate increases by a factor of 9. **14.33** (a) Rate $= k[OCl^-][I^-]$ (b) $k = 60\,M^{-1}s^{-1}$ (c) Rate $= 6.0 \times 10^{-5}\,M/s$ **14.35** (a) Rate $= k[BF_3][NH_3]$ (b) The reaction is second order overall. (c) $k_{avg} = 3.41\,M^{-1}s^{-1}$ **14.37** (a) Rate $= k[NO]^2[Br_2]$ (b) $k_{avg} = 1.2 \times 10^4\,M^{-2}s^{-1}$ (c) $\frac{1}{2}\Delta[NOBr]/\Delta t = -\Delta[Br_2]/\Delta t$ (d) $-\Delta[Br_2]/\Delta t = 8.4\,M/s$ **14.39** (a) $[A]_0$ is the molar concentration of reactant A at time zero. $[A]_t$ is the molar concentration of reactant A at time $t$. $t_{1/2}$ is the time required to reduce $[A]_0$ by a factor of 2. $k$ is the rate constant for a particular reaction. (b) A graph of $\ln[A]$ versus time yields a straight line for a first-order reaction. (c) On a graph of $\ln[A]$ versus time, the rate constant is the (−slope) of the straight line. **14.41** Plot [A] versus time. **14.43** (a) $k = 3.0 \times 10^{-6}\,s^{-1}$ (b) $t_{1/2} = 3.2 \times 10^4\,s$ **14.45** (a) $P = 30$ torr (b) $t = 51$ s **14.47** Plot $(\ln P_{SO_2Cl_2})$ versus time, $k = -$slope $= 2.19 \times 10^{-5}\,s^{-1}$ **14.49** (a) The plot of $1/[A]$ versus time is linear, so the reaction is second order in [A]. (b) $k = 0.040\,M^{-1}min^{-1}$ (c) $t_{1/2} = 38$ min **14.51** (a) The plot of $1/[NO_2]$ versus time is linear, so the reaction is second order in $NO_2$. (b) $k = $ slope $= 10\,M^{-1}s^{-1}$ (c) rate at $0.200\,M = 0.400\,M/s$; rate at $0.100\,M = 0.100\,M/s$; rate at $0.050\,M = 0.025\,M/s$ **14.53** (a) The energy of the collision and the orientation of the molecules when they collide determine whether a reaction will occur. (b) At a higher temperature, there are more total collisions and each collision is more

energetic. (c) The rate constant usually increases with an increase in reaction temperature. **14.55** $f = 4.94 \times 10^{-2}$. At 400 K approximately 1 out of 20 molecules has this kinetic energy.
**14.57** (a)

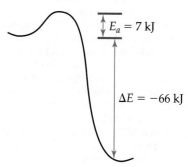

$E_a = 7$ kJ

$\Delta E = -66$ kJ

(b) $E_a$ (reverse) $= 73$ kJ **14.59** (a) False. If you compare two reactions with similar collision factors, the one with the larger activation energy will be slower. (b) False. A reaction that has a small rate constant will have either a small frequency factor, a large activation energy, or both. (c) True. **14.61** Reaction (b) is fastest and reaction (c) is slowest. **14.63** (a) $k = 1.1\,s^{-1}$ (b) $k = 13\,s^{-1}$ (c) The method in parts (a) and (b) assumes that the collision model and thus the Arrhenious equation describe the kinetics of the reactions. That is, activation energy is constant over the temperature range under consideration. **14.65** A plot of $\ln k$ versus $1/T$ has a slope of $-5.71 \times 10^3$; $E_a = -R(\text{slope}) = 47.5\,kJ/mol$. **14.67** The reaction will occur 88 times faster at 50 °C, assuming equal initial concentrations. **14.69** (a) An *elementary reaction* is a process that occurs in a single event; the order is given by the coefficients in the balanced equation for the reaction. (b) A *unimolecular* elementary reaction involves only one reactant molecule; a *bimolecular* elementary reaction involves two reactant molecules. (c) A *reaction mechanism* is a series of elementary reactions that describes how an overall reaction occurs and explains the experimentally determined rate law. **14.71** A transition state is a high-energy complex formed when one or more reactants collide and distort in a way that can lead to formation of product(s). An intermediate is the product of an early elementary reaction in a multistep reaction mechanism. **14.73** (a) Unimolecular, rate $= k[Cl_2]$ (b) bimo-lecular, rate $= k[OCl^-][H_2O]$ (c) bimolecular, rate $= k[NO][Cl_2]$ **14.75** (a) Two intermediates, B and C. (b) three transition states (c) C $\longrightarrow$ D is fastest. (d) endothermic **14.77** (a) $H_2(g) + 2\,ICl(g) \longrightarrow I_2(g) + 2\,HCl(g)$ (b) HI is the intermediate. (c) If the first step is slow, the observed rate law is rate $= k[H_2][ICl]$. **14.79** The graph of $1/[NO]$ versus time is linear with positive slope, indicating that the reaction is second order in [NO]. The rate law obtained by assuming the second step is rate determining is rate $= [NO]^2[Cl_2]$. The two-step mechanism is consistent with the data. **14.81** (a) A catalyst is a substance that changes (usually increases) the speed of a chemical reaction without undergoing a permanent chemical change itself. (b) A homogeneous catalyst is in the same phase as the reactants, while a heterogeneous catalyst is in a different phase. (c) A catalyst has no effect on the overall enthalpy change for a reaction, but it does affect activation energy. It can also affect the frequency factor. **14.83** (a) 270 Pt atoms in a 2.0-nm sphere (b) 200 Pt atoms on the surface of a 2.0-nm sphere (c) 74% Pt atoms on the surface (d) 4300 Pt atoms in a 5.0-nm sphere; 1300 Pt atoms on the surface; 30% Pt atoms on the surface (e) The 2-nm sphere will definitely be more catalytically active because it has a much greater percentage of its atoms on the surface where they can participate in the chemical reaction. **14.85** (a) Multiply the coefficients in the first reaction by 2 and sum. (b) $NO_2(g)$ is a catalyst because it is consumed and then reproduced in the reaction sequence. (c) This is a homogeneous catalysis. **14.87** (a) Use of chemically stable supports makes it possible to obtain very large surface areas per unit mass of the precious metal catalyst because the metal can be deposited in a very thin, even monomolecular, layer on the surface of the support. (b) The greater the surface area of the catalyst, the more reaction sites, the greater the rate of the catalyzed reaction. **14.89** To put two D atoms on a single carbon, it is necessary that one of the already existing C—H bonds in ethylene be broken while the molecule is adsorbed, so that the H atom moves off as an adsorbed atom and is replaced by a D atom. This requires a larger activation energy than simply adsorbing $C_2H_4$ and adding one D atom to each carbon. **14.91** (a) Living organisms operate efficiently in a very narrow temperature range; the role of enzymes as homogeneous catalysts that speed up desirable reactions, without heating and undesirable side effects, is crucial for biological systems. (b) catalase: $2 H_2O_2 \longrightarrow 2 H_2O + O_2$; nitrogenase: $N_2 \longrightarrow 2 NH_3$ (nitrogen fixation) (c) This model assumes that the rate of the bound substrate being chemically transformed into bound product is slow and rate determining. **14.93** Carbonic anyhdrase lowers the activation energy of the reaction by 42 kJ. **14.95** (a) The catalyzed reaction is approximately 10,000,000 times faster at 25 °C. (b) The catalyzed reaction is 180,000 times faster at 125 °C. **14.99** (a) Rate $= 4.7 \times 10^{-5} M/s$ (b, c) $k = 0.84 M^{-2} s^{-1}$ (d) If the [NO] is increased by a factor of 1.8, the rate would increase by a factor of 3.2. **14.101** The reaction is second order in $NO_2$. If $[NO_2]_0 = 0.100 M$ and $[NO_2]_t = 0.025 M$, use the integrated form of the second-order rate equation to solve for $t$. $t = 48 s$ **14.105** (a) The half-life of $^{241}Am$ is $4.3 \times 10^2$ yr, that of $^{125}I$ is 63 days (b) $^{125}I$ decays at a much faster rate. (c) 0.13 mg of each isotope remains after 3 half-lives. (d) The amount of $^{241}Am$ remaining after 4 days is 1.00 mg. The amount of $^{125}I$ remaining after 4 days is 0.957 grams. **14.109** The plot of $1/[C_5H_6]$ versus time is linear and the reaction is second order. $k = 0.167 M^{-1} s^{-1}$ **14.112** (a) When the two elementary reactions are added, $N_2O_2(g)$ appears on both sides and cancels, resulting in the overall reaction. $2NO(g) + H_2(g) \longrightarrow N_2O(g) + H_2O(g)$ (b) First reaction, $-[NO]/\Delta t = k[NO]^2$; second reaction, $-[H_2]/\Delta t = k[H_2][N_2O_2]$ (c) $N_2O_2$ is the intermediate. (d) Since $[H_2]$ appears in the rate law, the second step must be slow relative to the first. **14.115** (a) $Cl_2(g) + CHCl_3(g) \longrightarrow HCl(g) + CCl_4(g)$ (b) $Cl(g)$, $CCl_3(g)$ (c) reaction 1, unimolecular; reaction 2, bimolecular; reaction 3, bimolecular (d) Reaction 2 is rate determining. (e) Rate $= k[CHCl_3][Cl_2]^{1/2}$. **14.122** (a) $k = 8 \times 10^7 M^{-1} s^{-1}$

(b) :N≡Ö:

:Ö=N—F̈:  ⟷  (:Ö̈—N=F̈)

(c) NOF is bent with a bond angle of approximately 120°.

(d) [ O=N
        ↘
        F⌣F ]

(e) The electron-deficient NO molecule is attracted to electron-rich $F_2$, so the driving force for formation of the transition state is greater than simple random collisions.

## CHAPTER 15

**15.1** $k_f > k_r$ (b) The equilibrium constant is greater than 1. **15.7** From the smallest to the largest equilibrium constant, (c) < (b) < (a). **15.11** $K_c$ decreases as $T$ increases, so the reaction is exothermic. **15.13** (a) $K_p = K_c = 8.1 \times 10^{-3}$. (b) Since $k_f < k_r$, in order for the two rates to be equal, [A] must be greater than [B], and the partial pressure of A is greater than the partial pressure of B. **15.15** (a) $K_c = [N_2O][NO_2]/[NO]^3$; homogeneous (b) $K_c = [CS_2][H_2]^4/[CH_4][H_2S]^2$; homogeneous (c) $K_c = [CO]^4/[Ni(CO)_4]$; heterogeneous (d) $K_c = [H^+][F^-]/[HF]$; homogeneous (e) $K_c = [Ag^+]^2/[Zn^{2+}]$; heterogeneous (f) $K_c = [H^+][OH^-]$; homogeneous (g) $K_c = [H^+][OH^-]$; homogeneous **15.17** (a) Mostly reactants (b) mostly products **15.19** No, the equilibrium constant can never be a negative number. The equilibrium constant is a ratio of rate constants (or a ratio of concentrations), which are never negative. **15.21** $K_p = 1.0 \times 10^{-3}$ **15.23** (a) The equilibrium favors NO and $Br_2$ at this temperature. (b) $K_c = 77$ (c) $K_c = 8.8$ **15.25** (a) $K_p = 0.541$ (b) $K_p = 3.42$ (c) $K_c = 281$ **15.27** $K_c = 0.14$ **15.29** Pure solids

and liquids are normally excluded from equilibrium-constant expressions because their concentrations, the ratio of moles of a substance to volume occupied by the substance, are constant. **15.31** (a) $K_p = P_{O_2}$ (b) $K_c = [Hg(solv)]^4[O_2(solv)]$ **15.33** $K_c = 10.5$ **15.35** (a) $K_p = 51$ (b) $K_c = 2.1 \times 10^3$ **15.37** (a) $[H_2] = 0.012 M$, $[N_2] = 0.019 M$, $[H_2O] = 0.138 M$ (b) $K_c = 653.7 = 7 \times 10^2$ **15.39** (a) $P_{CO_2} = 4.10$ atm, $P_{H_2} = 2.05$ atm, $P_{H_2O} = 3.28$ atm (b) $P_{CO_2} = 3.87$ atm, $P_{H_2} = 1.82$ atm, $P_{CO} = 0.23$ atm (c) $K_p = 0.11$ **15.41** $K_c = 2.0 \times 10^4$ **15.43** (a) A reaction quotient is the result of a general set of concentrations whereas the equilibrium constant requires equilibrium concentrations. (b) to the right (c) The concentrations used to calculate $Q$ must be equilibrium concentrations. **15.45** (a) $Q = 1.1 \times 10^{-8}$, the reaction will proceed to the left. (b) $Q = 5.5 \times 10^{-12}$, the reaction will proceed to the right. (c) $Q = 2.19 \times 10^{-10}$, the mixture is at equilibrium. **15.47** $P_{Cl_2} = 5.0$ atm **15.49** (a) $[Br_2] = 0.00767 M$, $[Br] = 0.00282 M$, 0.0451 g Br(g) (b) $[H_2] = 0.014 M$, $[I_2] = 0.00859 M$, $[HI] = 0.081 M$, 21 g HI **15.51** $[NO] = 0.002 M$, $[N_2] = [O_2] = 0.087 M$ **15.53** The equilibrium pressure of $Br_2(g)$ is 0.416 atm. **15.55** (a) $[Ca^{2+}] = [SO_4^{2-}] = 4.9 \times 10^{-3} M$ (b) A bit more than 1.0 g $CaSO_4$ is needed in order to have some undissolved $CaSO_4(s)$ in equilibrium with 1.4 L of saturated solution. **15.57** $[IBr] = 0.223 M$, $[I_2] = [Br_2] = 0.0133 M$ **15.59** (a) $P_{CH_3I} = P_{HI} = 0.422$ torr, $P_{CH_4} = 104.7$ torr, $P_{I_2} = 7.54$ torr **15.61** (a) Shift equilibrium to the right (b) decrease the value of $K$ (c) shift equilibrium to the left (d) no effect (e) no effect (f) shift equilibrium to the right **15.63** (a) No effect (b) no effect (c) no effect (d) increase equilibrium constant (e) no effect **15.65** (a) $\Delta H° = -155.7$ kJ (b) The reaction is exothermic, so the equilibrium constant will decrease with increasing temperature. (c) $\Delta n$ does not equal zero, so a change in volume at constant temperature will affect the fraction of products in the equilibrium mixture. **15.67** An increase in pressure favors formation of ozone. **15.71** $K_p = 24.7$; $K_c = 3.67 \times 10^{-3}$ **15.74** (a) $P_{Br_2} = 1.61$ atm, $P_{NO} = 0.628$ atm, $P_{NOBr} = 0.179$ atm; $K_c = 0.0643$ (b) $P_t = 0.968$ atm (c) 10.49 g NOBr **15.77** At equilibrium, $P_{IBr} = 0.21$ atm, $P_{I_2} = P_{Br_2} = 1.9 \times 10^{-3}$ atm **15.80** $K_p = 4.33$, $K_c = 0.0480$ **15.83** $[CO_2] = [H_2] = 0.264 M$, $[CO] = [H_2O] = 0.236 M$ **15.87** (a) 26% of the $CCl_4$ is converted to C and $Cl_2$. (b) $P_{CCl_4} = 1.47$ atm, $P_{Cl_2} = 1.06$ atm **15.91** $Q = 8 \times 10^{-6}$. $Q > K_p$, so the system is not at equilibrium; it will shift left to attain equilibrium. A catalyst that speeds up the reaction and thereby promotes the attainment of equilibrium would decrease the CO concentration in the exhaust. **15.93** At equilibrium, $[H_6IO_4^-] = 0.0015 M$ **15.97** At 850 °C, $K_p = 14.1$; at 950 °C, $K_p = 73.8$; at 1050 °C, $K_p = 2.7 \times 10^2$; at 1200 °C, $K_p = 1.7 \times 10^3$. Because $K$ increases with increasing temperature, the reaction is endothermic.

## CHAPTER 16

**16.1** (a) HX, the $H^+$ donor, is the Brønsted–Lowry acid. $NH_3$, the $H^+$ acceptor, is the Brønsted–Lowry base. (b) HX, the electron pair acceptor, is the Lewis acid. $NH_3$, the electron pair donor, is the Lewis base. **16.3** (a) HY is a strong acid. There are no neutral HY molecules in solution, only $H^+$ cations and $Y^-$ anions. (b) HX has the smallest $K_a$ value. It has most neutral acid molecules and fewest ions. (c) HX has fewest $H^+$ and highest pH. **16.5** (a) True. (b) False. Methyl orange turns yellow at a pH slightly greater than 4, so solution B could be at any pH greater than 4. (c) True. **16.7** (a) Molecule A, $NH_2OH$ (hydroxyl amine), acts as a base. Molecule A is an $H^+$ acceptor because of the nonbonded electron pair on the N atom of the amine (—$NH_2$) group, not because it contains an —OH group. (b) Molecule B, HCOOH (formic acid), acts as an acid. The molecule contains a —COOH group where the H atom bonded to O is ionizable and HCOOH is an $H^+$ donor. (c) Molecule C, $CH_3OH$ (methanol), is an organic alcohol. The H atom bonded to O is not ionizable, and the —OH group does not dissociate in aqueous solution; it is neither an acid nor a base. **16.9** (a) Molecule (b) is more acidic because its conjugate base is resonance-stabilized and the ionization equilibrium favors the more stable products. (b) Increasing the electronegativity of X increases the strength of both acids. As X becomes more electronegative and attracts more electron density, the O—H bond becomes weaker, more polar, and more likely to be ionized. An electronegative X group also stabilizes the anionic conjugate base, causing the ionization equilibrium to favor products and the value of $K_a$ to increase. **16.11** Solutions of HCl and $H_2SO_4$ conduct electricity, taste sour, turn litmus paper red (are acidic), neutralize solutions of bases, and react with active metals to form $H_2(g)$. HCl and $H_2SO_4$ solutions have these properties in common because both compounds are strong acids. That is, they both ionize completely in $H_2O$ to form $H^+(aq)$ and an anion. ($HSO_4^-$ is not completely ionized, but the first ionization step for $H_2SO_4$ is complete.) The presence of ions enables the solutions to conduct electricity; the presence of $H^+(aq)$ in excess of $1 \times 10^{-7} M$ accounts for all other properties listed. **16.13** (a) The Arrhenius definition of an acid is confined to aqueous solution; the Brønsted–Lowry definition applies to any physical state. (b) HCl is the Brønsted–Lowry acid; $NH_3$ is the Brønsted–Lowry base. **16.15** (a) (i) $IO_3^-$ (ii) $NH_3$ (b) (i) $OH^-$ (ii) $H_3PO_4$

**16.17**

| Acid | + | Base | $\rightleftharpoons$ | Conjugate Acid | + | Conjugate Base |
|------|---|------|------|-----------------|---|-----------------|
| (a) $NH_4^+(aq)$ | | $CN^-(aq)$ | | $HCN(aq)$ | | $NH_3(aq)$ |
| (b) $H_2O(l)$ | | $(CH_3)_3 N(aq)$ | | $(CH_3)_3NH^+(aq)$ | | $OH^-(aq)$ |
| (c) $HCOOH(aq)$ | | $PO_4^{3-}(aq)$ | | $HPO_4^{2-}(aq)$ | | $HCOO^-(aq)$ |

**16.19** (a) Acid:
$HC_2O_4^-(aq) + H_2O(l) \rightleftharpoons C_2O_4^{2-}(aq) + H_3O^+(aq)$;
Base: $HC_2O_4^-(aq) + H_2O(l) \rightleftharpoons H_2C_2O_4(aq) + OH^-(aq)$.
(b) $H_2C_2O_4$ is the conjugate acid of $HC_2O_4^-$. $C_2O_4^{2-}$ is the conjugate base of $HC_2O_4^-$. **16.21** (a) $CH_3COO^-$, weak base; $CH_3COOH$, weak acid (b) $HCO_3^-$, weak base; $H_2CO_3$, weak acid (c) $O_2^-$, strong base; $OH^-$, strong base (d) $Cl^-$, negligible base; HCl, strong acid (e) $NH_3$, weak base; $NH_4^+$, weak acid **16.23** (a) HBr. It is one of the seven strong acids. (b) $F^-$. HCl is a stronger acid than HF, so $F^-$ is the stronger conjugate base. **16.25** (a) $OH^-(aq) + OH^-(aq)$, the equilibrium lies to the right. (b) $H_2S(aq) + CH_3COO^-(aq)$, the equilibrium lies to the right. (c) $HNO_3(aq) + OH^-(aq)$, the equilibrium lies to the left. **16.27** (a) No. In pure water, the only source of $H^+$ is the autoionization reaction, which produces equal concentrations of $H^+$ and $OH^-$. As the temperature of water changes, the value of $K_w$ changes, and the pH at which $[H^+] = [OH^-]$ changes. **16.29** (a) $[H^+] = 2.2 \times 10^{-11} M$, basic (b) $[H^+] = 1.1 \times 10^{-6} M$, acidic (c) $[H^+] = 1.0 \times 10^{-8} M$, basic **16.31** $[H^+] = [OH^-] = 3.5 \times 10^{-8} M$ **16.33** (a) $[H^+]$ changes by a factor of 100. (b) $[H^+]$ changes by a factor of 3.2. **16.35** (a) $[H^+]$ decreases, pH increases (b) The pH is between 3 and 4. By calculation, pH = 3.2; the solution is acidic. (c) pH = 5.2 is between pH 5 and pH 6, closer to pH = 5. A good estimate is $7 \times 10^{-6} M H^+$ and $3 \times 10^{-9} M OH^-$. By calculation, $[H^+] = 6 \times 10^{-6} M$ and $[OH^-] = 2 \times 10^{-9} M$.

**16.37**

| $[H^+]$ | $[OH^-]$ | pH | pOH | Acidic or Basic |
|---------|----------|-----|-----|-----------------|
| $7.5 \times 10^{-3} M$ | $1.3 \times 10^{-12} M$ | 2.12 | 11.88 | acidic |
| $2.8 \times 10^{-5} M$ | $3.6 \times 10^{-10} M$ | 4.56 | 9.44 | acidic |
| $5.6 \times 10^{-9} M$ | $1.8 \times 10^{-6} M$ | 8.25 | 5.75 | basic |
| $5.0 \times 10^{-9} M$ | $2.0 \times 10^{-6} M$ | 8.30 | 5.70 | basic |

**16.39** $[H^+] = 4.0 \times 10^{-8} M$, $[OH^-] = 6.0 \times 10^{-7} M$, pOH = 6.22 **16.41** (a) A strong acid is completely ionized in aqueous solution. (b) $[H^+] = 0.500 M$ (c) HCl, HBr, HI **16.43** (a) $[H^+] = 8.5 \times 10^{-3} M$, pH = 2.07 (b) $[H^+] = 0.0419 M$, pH = 1.377 (c) $[H^+] = 0.0250 M$, pH = 1.602 (d) $[H^+] = 0.167 M$, pH = 0.778 **16.45** (a) $[OH^-] = 3.0 \times 10^{-3} M$, pH = 11.48 (b) $[OH^-] = 0.3758 M$, pH = 13.5750 (c) $[OH^-] = 8.75 \times 10^{-5} M$, pH = 9.942 (d) $[OH^-] = 0.17 M$, pH = 13.23 **16.47** $3.2 \times 10^{-3} M$ NaOH **16.49** (a) $HBrO_2(aq) \rightleftharpoons H^+(aq) + BrO_2^-(aq)$, $K_a = [H^+][BrO_2^-]/[HBrO_2]$; $HBrO_2(aq) + H_2O(l) \rightleftharpoons H_3O^+(aq) + BrO_2^-(aq)$, $K_a = [H_3O^+][BrO_2^-]/[HBrO_2]$ (b) $C_2H_5COOH(aq) \rightleftharpoons H^+(aq) + C_2H_5COO^-(aq)$, $K_a = [H^+][C_2H_5COO^-]/[C_2H_5COOH]$; $C_2H_5COOH(aq) + H_2O(l) \rightleftharpoons H_3O^+(aq) + C_2H_5COO^-(aq)$, $K_a = [H_3O^+][C_2H_5COO^-]/[C_2H_5COOH]$ **16.51** $K_a = 1.4 \times 10^{-4}$ **16.53** $[H^+] = [ClCH_2COO^-] = 0.0110 M$, $[ClCH_2COOH] = 0.089 M$, $K_a = 1.4 \times 10^{-3}$ **16.55** 0.089 $M$ $CH_3COOH$ **16.57** $[H^+] = [C_6H_5COO^-] = 1.8 \times 10^{-3} M$, $[C_6H_5COOH] = 0.048 M$ **16.59** (a) $[H^+] = 1.1 \times 10^{-3} M$, pH = 2.95 (b) $[H^+] = 1.7 \times 10^{-4} M$, pH = 3.76 (c) $[OH^-] = 1.4 \times 10^{-5} M$, pH = 9.15 **16.61** $[H^+] = 2.0 \times 10^{-2} M$, pH = 1.71 **16.63** (a) $[H^+] = 2.8 \times 10^{-3} M$, 0.69% ionization (b) $[H^+] = 1.4 \times 10^{-3} M$, 1.4% ionization (c) $[H^+] = 8.7 \times 10^{-4} M$, 2.2% ionization **16.65** $HX(aq) \rightleftharpoons H^+(aq) + X^-(aq)$; $K_a = [H^+][X^-]/[HX]$. Assume that the percent of acid that ionizes is small. Let $[H^+] = [X^-] = y$, $K_a = y^2/[HX]$; $y = K_a^{1/2}[HX]^{1/2}$. Percent ionization = $y/[HX] \times 100$. Substituting for $y$, percent ionization = $100 K_a^{1/2}[HX]^{1/2}/[HX]$ or $100 K_a^{1/2}/[HX]^{1/2}$. That is, percent ionization varies inversely as the square root of the concentration of HX. **16.67** $[H^+] = 5.1 \times 10^{-3} M$, pH = 2.29, $[C_6H_5O_7^{3-}] = 1.3 \times 10^{-9} M$. The approximation that the first ionization is less than 5% of the total acid concentration is not valid; the quadratic equation must be solved. The $[H^+]$ produced from the second and third ionizations is small with respect to that present from the first step; the second and third ionizations can be neglected when calculating the $[H^+]$ and pH. $[C_6H_5O_7^{3-}]$ is much less than $[H^+]$. **16.69** (a) $HONH_3^+$ (b) When hydroxylamine acts as a base, the nitrogen atom accepts a proton. (c) In hydroxylamine, O and N are the atoms with nonbonding electron pairs; in the neutral molecule both have zero formal charges. Nitrogen is less electronegative than oxygen and more likely to share a lone pair of electrons with an incoming (and electron-deficient) $H^+$. The resulting cation with the +1 formal charge on N is more stable than the one with the +1 formal charge on O. **16.71** (a) $(CH_3)_2NH(aq) + H_2O(l) \rightleftharpoons (CH_3)_2NH_2^+(aq) + OH^-(aq)$; $K_b = [(CH_3)_2NH_2^+][OH^-]/[(CH_3)_2NH]$ (b) $CO_3^{2-}(aq) + H_2O(l) \rightleftharpoons HCO_3^-(aq) + OH^-(aq)$; $K_b = [HCO_3^-][OH^-]/[(CO_3^{2-})]$ (c) $HCOO^-(aq) + H_2O(l) \rightleftharpoons HCOOH(aq) + OH^-(aq)$ $K_b = [HCOOH][OH^-]/[HCOO^-]$ **16.73** From the quadratic formula, $[OH^-] = 6.6 \times 10^{-3} M$, pH = 11.82. **16.75** (a) $[C_{10}H_{15}ON] = 0.033 M$, $[C_{10}H_{15}ONH^+] = [OH^-] = 2.1 \times 10^{-3} M$ (b) $K_b = 1.4 \times 10^{-4}$ **16.77** (a) For a conjugate acid/conjugate base pair such as $C_6H_5OH/C_6H_5O^-$, $K_b$ for the conjugate base can always be calculated from $K_a$ for the conjugate acid, so a separate list of $K_b$ values is not necessary. (b) $K_b = 7.7 \times 10^{-5}$ (c) Phenolate is a stronger base than $NH_3$. **16.79** (a) Acetic acid is stronger. (b) Hypochlorite ion is the stronger base. (c) For $CH_3COO^-$, $K_b = 5.6 \times 10^{-10}$; for $ClO^-$, $K_b = 3.3 \times 10^{-7}$. **16.81** (a) $[OH^-] = 6.3 \times 10^{-4} M$, pH = 10.80 (b) $[OH^-] = 9.2 \times 10^{-5} M$, pH = 9.96 (c) $[OH^-] = 3.3 \times 10^{-6} M$, pH = 8.52 **16.83** (a) Acidic (b) acidic (c) basic (d) neutral (e) acidic **16.85** $K_b$ for the anion of the unknown salt is $1.4 \times 10^{-11}$; $K_a$ for the conjugate acid is $7.1 \times 10^{-4}$. The conjugate acid is HF and the salt is NaF. **16.87** (a) As the electronegativity of the central atom (X) increases, the strength of the oxyacid increases. (b) As the number of nonprotonated oxygen atoms in the molecule increases, the strength of the oxyacid increases. **16.89** (a) $HNO_3$ is a stronger acid because it has one more nonprotonated oxygen atom and thus a higher oxidation number on N. (b) For binary hydrides, acid strength increases going down a family, so $H_2S$ is a stronger acid than $H_2O$. (c) $H_2SO_4$ is a stronger acid because $H^+$ is much more tightly held by the anion $HSO_4^-$. (d) For oxyacids, the greater the electronegativity of the central atom, the stronger the acid, so $H_2SO_4$ is the stronger acid. (e) $CCl_3COOH$ is stronger because the electronegative Cl atoms withdraw electron density from other parts of the molecule, which weakens the O—H bond and stabilizes the anionic conjugate base. Both effects favor increased ionization and acid strength. **16.91** (a) $BrO^-$ (b) $BrO^-$ (c) $HPO_4^{2-}$ **16.93** (a) True (b) False. In a series of acids that have the same central atom, acid strength increases with the number of nonprotonated oxygen atoms bonded to the central atom. (c) False. $H_2Te$ is a stronger acid than $H_2S$ because the H—Te bond is longer, weaker, and more easily ionized than the H—S bond. **16.95** Yes. The Arrhenius definition of a base, an $OH^-(aq)$ donor, is most restrictive; the Brønsted definition, an $H^+$ acceptor, is more general; and the Lewis definition, an electron-pair donor, is most general. Any substance that fits the narrow Arrhenius definition will fit the broader Brønsted and Lewis definitions. **16.97** (a) Acid, $Fe(ClO_4)_3$ or $Fe^{3+}$; base, $H_2O$ (b) Acid, $H_2O$; base, $CN^-$ (c) Acid, $BF_3$; base, $(CH_3)_3N$ (d) Acid, HIO; base, $NH_2^-$ **16.99** (a) $Cu^{2+}$, higher cation charge (b) $Fe^{3+}$, higher cation charge (c) $Al^{3+}$, smaller cation radius, same charge **16.101** $(C_2H_5)_3N$ is a stronger base than $NH_3$ by virtue of its smaller $pK_b$. **16.104** $K = 3.3 \times 10^7$ **16.107** (a) For solutions with equal concentrations, the weaker acid will have a lower $[H^+]$ and higher pH. (b) The acid with $K_a = 8 \times 10^{-5}$ is the weaker acid, so it has the higher pH. (c) The base with $pK_b = 4.5$ is the stronger base, has the greater $[OH^-]$ and smaller $[H^+]$, so higher pH. **16.109** $K_a = 1.4 \times 10^{-5}$ **16.115** $6.0 \times 10^{13}$ $H^+$ ions **16.118** (a) To the precision of the reported data, the pH of rainwater 40 years ago was 5.4, no different from the pH today. With extra significant figures, $[H^+] = 3.61 \times 10^{-6}$ $M$, pH = 5.443 (b) A 20.0-L bucket of today's rainwater contains 0.02 L (with extra significant figures, 0.0200 L) of dissolved $CO_2$.

**16.119** (a)

:Cl̈—Al—C̈l:
     |
    :Cl̈:

The electron-domain geometry and molecular structure are trigonal planar. (b) The Al atom is electron deficient. It acts like a Lewis acid in order to complete its octet.

(c)

:C̈l:   :C̈l:           Cl      H
  Al← +:NH₃ ⟶ Cl⋯Al—N⋯H
:C̈l:                Cl      H

(d) The Lewis theory is most appropriate. $H^+$ and $AlCl_3$ are both electron pair acceptors. **16.121** Rx 1, $\Delta H = 104$ kJ; Rx 2, $\Delta H = -32$ kJ. Reaction 2 is exothermic while reaction 1 is endothermic. For binary acids with heavy atoms (X) in the same family, the longer and weaker the H—X bond, the stronger the acid (and the more exothermic the ionization reaction). **16.124** (a) $K(i) = 5.6 \times 10^3$, $K(ii) = 10$ (b) Both (i) and (ii) have $K > 1$, so both could be written with a single arrow.

# CHAPTER 17

**17.1** The middle box has the highest pH. For equal amounts of acid HX, the greater the amount of conjugate base $X^-$, the smaller the amount of $H^+$ and the higher the pH. **17.4** (a) Drawing 3 (b) Drawing 1 (c) Drawing 2 **17.7** (a) The red curve corresponds to the more concentrated acid solution. (b) On the titration curve of a weak acid,

pH = $pK_a$ at the volume halfway to the equivalence point. At this volume, the red curve has the smaller $pK_a$ and the larger $K_a$. **17.10** (a) $Q = 4.67 \times 10^{-6}$; $Q < K_{sp}$ and the solution is not saturated. (b) $Ca(OH)_2$ precipitate forms in beaker (iii). **17.13** (a) The extent of ionization of a weak electrolyte is decreased when a strong electrolyte containing an ion in common with the weak electrolyte is added to it. (b) $NaNO_2$ **17.15** (a) $[H^+] = 1.8 \times 10^{-5}$ $M$, pH = 4.73 (b) $[OH^-] = 4.8 \times 10^{-5}$ $M$, pH = 9.68 (c) $[H^+] = 1.4 \times 10^{-5}$ $M$, pH = 4.87 **17.17** (a) 4.5% ionization (b) 0.018% ionization **17.19** In a mixture of $CH_3COOH$ and $CH_3COONa$, $CH_3COOH$ reacts with added base and $CH_3COO^-$ combines with added acid, leaving $[H^+]$ relatively unchanged. Although HCl and $Cl^-$ are a conjugate acid–base pair, $Cl^-$ has no tendency to combine with added acid to form undissociated HCl. Any added acid simply increases $[H^+]$ in an $HCl$—NaCl mixture. **17.21** (a) pH = 3.82 (b) pH = 3.96 **17.23** (a) pH = 5.26 (b) $Na^+(aq) + CH_3COO^-(aq) + H^+(aq) + Cl^-(aq) \longrightarrow$
$$CH_3COOH(aq) + Na^+(aq) + Cl^-(aq)$$
(c) $CH_3COOH(aq) + Na^+(aq) + OH^-(aq) \longrightarrow$
$$CH_3COO^-(aq) + H_2O(l) + Na^+(aq)$$
**17.25** (a) pH = 1.58 (b) 36 g NaF **17.27** (a) pH = 4.86 (b) pH = 5.0 (c) pH = 4.71 **17.29** (a) $[HCO_3^-]/[H_2CO_3] = 11$ (b) $[HCO_3^-]/[H_2CO_3] = 5.4$ **17.31** 360 mL of 0.10 $M$ HCOONa, 640 mL of 0.10 $M$ HCOOH **17.33** (a) Curve B (b) pH at the approximate equivalence point of curve A = 8.0, pH at the approximate equivalence point of curve B = 7.0 (c) For equal volumes of A and B, the concentration of acid B is greater, since it requires a larger volume of base to reach the equivalence point. **17.35** (a) False (b) true (c) true **17.37** (a) Above pH 7 (b) below pH 7 (c) at pH 7 **17.39** The second color change of Thymol blue is in the correct pH range to show the equivalence point of the titration of a weak acid with a strong base. **17.41** (a) 42.4 mL NaOH soln (b) 35.0 mL NaOH soln (c) 29.8 mL NaOH soln **17.43** (a) pH = 1.54 (b) pH = 3.30 (c) pH = 7.00 (d) pH = 10.69 (e) pH = 12.74 **17.45** (a) pH = 2.78 (b) pH = 4.74 (c) pH = 6.58 (d) pH = 8.81 (e) pH = 11.03 (f) pH = 12.42 **17.47** (a) pH = 7.00 (b) $[HONH_3^+] = 0.100\,M$, pH = 3.52 (c) $[C_6H_5\,NH_3^+] = 0.100\,M$, pH = 2.82 **17.49** (a) The concentration of undissolved solid does not appear in the solubility product expression because it is constant. (b) $K_{sp} = [Ag^+][I^-]$; $K_{sp} = [Sr^{2+}][SO_4^{2-}]$; $K_{sp} = [Fe^{2+}][OH^-]^2$; $K_{sp} = [Hg_2^{2+}][Br^-]^2$ **17.51** (a) $K_{sp} = 7.63 \times 10^{-9}$ (b) $K_{sp} = 2.7 \times 10^{-9}$ (c) $5.3 \times 10^{-4}$ mol $Ba(IO_3)_2$/L **17.53** $K_{sp} = 2.3 \times 10^{-9}$ **17.55** (a) $7.1 \times 10^{-7}$ mol AgBr/L (b) $1.7 \times 10^{-11}$ mol AgBr/L (c) $5.0 \times 10^{-12}$ mol AgBr/L **17.57** (a) The amount of $CaF_2(s)$ on the bottom of the beaker increases. (b) The $[Ca^{2+}]$ in solution increases. (c) The $[F^-]$ in solution decreases. **17.59** (a) $1.4 \times 10^3$ g $Mn(OH)_2$/L (b) 0.014 g/L (c) $3.6 \times 10^{-7}$ g/L **17.61** More soluble in acid: (a) $ZnCO_3$ (b) ZnS (d) AgCN (e) $Ba_3(PO_4)_2$ **17.63** $[Ni^{2+}] = 1 \times 10^{-8}\,M$ **17.65** (a) $9.1 \times 10^{-9}$ mol AgI/L pure water (b) $K = K_{sp} \times K_f = 8 \times 10^4$ (c) 0.0500 mol AgI/L 0.100 $M$ NaCN **17.67** (a) $Q < K_{sp}$; no $Ca(OH)_2$ precipitates (b) $Q < K_{sp}$; no $Ag_2SO_4$ precipitates **17.69** pH = 11.5 **17.71** AgI will precipitate first, at $[I^-] = 4.2 \times 10^{-13}\,M$. **17.73** AgCl will precipitate first. **17.75** The first two experiments eliminate group 1 and 2 ions (Figure 17.23). The absence of insoluble phosphate precipitates in the filtrate from the third experiment rules out group 4 ions. The ions that might be in the sample are those from group 3, $Al^{3+}$, $Fe^{3+}$, $Cr^{3+}$, $Zn^{2+}$, $Ni^{2+}$, $Mn^{2+}$, or $Co^{2+}$, and from group 5, $NH_4^+$, $Na^+$, or $K^+$. **17.77** (a) Make the solution acidic with 0.2 $M$ HCl; saturate with $H_2S$. CdS will precipitate; ZnS will not. (b) Add excess base; $Fe(OH)_3(s)$ precipitates, but $Cr^{3+}$ forms the soluble complex $Cr(OH)_4^-$. (c) Add $(NH_4)_2HPO_4$; $Mg^{2+}$ precipitates as $MgNH_4PO_4$; $K^+$ remains soluble. (d) Add 6 $M$ HCl; precipitate $Ag^+$ as $AgCl(s)$; $Mn^{2+}$ remains soluble. **17.79** (a) Base is required to increase $[PO_4^{3-}]$ so that the solubility product of the metal phosphates of interest is exceeded and the phosphate salts precipitate. (b) $K_{sp}$ for the cations in group 3 is much larger, and so to exceed $K_{sp}$, a higher $[S^{2-}]$ is required. (c) They should all redissolve in strongly acidic solution.

**17.81** $pOH = pK_b + \log\{|BH^-|/|B|\}$  **17.83** (a) pH = 3.171
(b) pH = 2.938 (c) pH = 12.862  **17.86** (a) pH of buffer A = pH of
buffer B = 3.74. For buffers containing the same conjugate acid and
base components, the pH is determined by the ratio of concentrations
of conjugate acid and base. Buffers A and B have the same ratio of concentrations, so their pH values are equal. (b) Buffer capacity is determined by the absolute amount of buffer components available to
absorb strong acid or strong base. Buffer A has the greater capacity because it contains the greater absolute concentrations of HCOOH and
$HCOO^-$. (c) Buffer A: pH = 3.74, $\Delta$pH = 0.00; buffer B: pH = 3.66,
$\Delta$pH = −0.12 (d) Buffer A: pH = 3.74, $\Delta$pH = 0.00; buffer B:
pH = 2.74, $\Delta$pH = −1.00 (e) The results of parts (c) and (d) are
quantitative confirmation that buffer A has a significantly greater
capacity than buffer B.  **17.88** (a) molar mass = 82.2 g/mol
(b) $K_a = 3.8 \times 10^{-7}$  **17.90** At the halfway point, mol HA = mol $A^-$
and $[HA] = [A^-]$.

$$pH = pK_a + \log\frac{[\text{conj. base}]}{[\text{conj. acid}]} = pK_a + \log\frac{[A^-]}{[HA^-]}. \text{ If } [A^-]/[HA] = 1,$$

$\log(1) = 0$ and $pH = pK_a$ of the weak acid being titrated.  **17.92**
pH = 7.75  **17.93** 1.6 L of 1.0 M NaOH  **17.96** (a) CdS (b) $BaCrO_4$
(c) $NiCO_3$ (d) $Ag_2SO_4$  **17.100** The solubility of $Mg(OH)_2$ in 0.50 M
$NH_4Cl$ is 0.11 mol/L  **17.101** $[KMnO_4] = [MnO_4^-] = 0.11 M$
**17.104** $[OH^-] = 1.7 \times 10^{-11} M$, pH of the buffer = 3.22
**17.107** (a) The molar solubility of $Cd(OH)_2$ is $1.8 \times 10^{-5}$ mol/L.
(b) The initial concentration of NaBr required to increase the molar
solubility of $Cd(OH)_2$ to $1.0 \times 10^{-3}$ mol/L is 2 M.  **17.108**
(a) $H^+(aq) + HCOO^-(aq) \longrightarrow HCOOH(aq)$ (b) $K = 5.6 \times 10^3$
(c) $[Na^+] = [Cl^-] = 0.075 M$, $[H^+] = [HCOO^-] = 3.7 \times 10^{-3} M$,
$[HCOOH] = 0.071 M$  **17.114** $[Sr^{2+}] = [SO_4^{2-}] = 5.7 \times 10^{-4} M$,
$K_{sp} = 3.2 \times 10^{-7}$

# CHAPTER 18

**18.1** (a) A greater volume than 22.4 L (b) The gas will occupy more volume at 85 km than at 50 km. (c) We expect gases to behave most ideally
in the thermosphere, around the stratopause and in the troposphere at
low altitude.  **18.6** *Salt water* contains high concentrations of dissolved
salts and solids. It includes the world ocean (97.2% of all water, approximately 35,000 ppm of dissolved salts) and brackish or salty water (0.1%
of all water). *Freshwater* (0.6% of all water on earth) refers to natural waters that have low concentrations (less than 500 ppm) of dissolved salts
and solids. It includes the waters of lakes, rivers, ponds, and streams.
*Groundwater* is freshwater that is under the soil. It resides in aquifers,
porous rock that holds water, and composes 20% of the world's freshwater.  **18.9** The basic goals of green chemistry are to minimize or eliminate solvents and waste, generate nontoxic waste, be energy efficient,
employ renewable starting materials, and take advantage of catalysts that
enable the use of safe and common reagents.  **18.11** (a) Its temperature
profile (b) troposphere, 0 to 12 km; stratosphere, 12 to 50 km; mesosphere, 50 to 85 km; thermosphere, 85 to 110 km  **18.13** (a) The partial
pressure of $O_3$ is $3.0 \times 10^{-7}$ atm ($2.2 \times 10^{-4}$ torr). (b) $7.3 \times 10^{15}$ $O_3$
molecules/1.0 L air  **18.15** $8.6 \times 10^{16}$ CO molecules/1.0 L air
**18.17** (a) 570 nm (b) visible electromagnetic radiation  **18.19** (a) *Photodissociation* is cleavage of a bond such that two neutral species are produced. *Photoionization* is absorption of a photon with sufficient energy to
eject an electron, producing an ion and the ejected electron. (b) Photoionization of $O_2$ requires 1205 kJ/mol. Photodissociation requires only
495 kJ/mol. At lower elevations, high-energy short-wavelength solar radiation has already been absorbed. Below 90 km, the increased concentration of $O_2$ and the availability of longer-wavelength radiation cause the
photodissociation process to dominate.  **18.21** Ozone depletion reactions, which involve only $O_3$, $O_2$, or O (oxidation state = 0), do not involve a change in oxidation state for oxygen atoms. Reactions involving
ClO and one of the oxygen species with a zero oxidation state do involve
a change in the oxidation state of oxygen atoms.  **18.23** (a) A chlorofluorocarbon is a compound that contains chlorine, fluorine, and

carbon, while a hydrofluorocarbon is a compound that contains hydrogen,
fluorine, and carbon. An HFC contains hydrogen in place of the chlorine
present in a CFC. (b) HFCs are potentially less harmful than CFCs because
their photodissociation does not produce Cl atoms, which catalyze the destruction of ozone.  **18.25** (a) The C—F bond requires more energy than
dissociation than the C—Cl bond and is not readily cleaved by the available
wavelengths of UV light. (b) Chlorine is present as chlorine atoms and chlorine oxide molecules, Cl and ClO, respectively.  **18.27** (a) Methane, $CH_4$,
arises from decomposition of organic matter by certain microorganisms;
it also escapes from underground gas deposits. (b) $SO_2$ is released in volcanic gases and also is produced by bacterial action on decomposing
vegetable and animal matter. (c) Nitric oxide, NO, results from oxidation
of decomposing organic matter and is formed in lightning flashes.
**18.29** (a) $H_2SO_4(aq) + CaCO_3(s) \longrightarrow CaSO_4(s) + H_2O(l) + CO_2(g)$
(b) The $CaSO_4(s)$ would be much less reactive with acidic solution,
since it would require a strongly acidic solution to shift the relevant
equilibrium to the right: $CaSO_4(s) + 2H^+(aq) \rightleftharpoons Ca^{2+}(aq) +$
$2HSO_4^-(aq)$. $CaSO_4$ would protect $CaCO_3$ from attack by acid rain,
but it would not provide the structural strength of limestone.
**18.31** (a) Ultraviolet (b) 357 kJ/mol (c) The average C—H bond energy from Table 8.4 is 413 kJ/mol. The C—H bond energy in $CH_2O$,
357 kJ/mol, is less than the "average" C—H bond energy.
(d)

$$\overset{\displaystyle :\!O\!:}{\underset{\displaystyle H-C-H}{\|}} + h\nu \longrightarrow \overset{\displaystyle :\!O\!:}{\underset{\displaystyle H-C\cdot}{\|}} + H\cdot$$

**18.33** Incoming and outgoing energies are in different regions of the
electromagnetic spectrum. $CO_2$ is transparent to incoming visible radiation but absorbs outgoing infrared radiation.  **18.35** 0.099 M $Na^+$
**18.37** (a) $3.22 \times 10^3$ g $H_2O$ (b) The final temperature is 43.4°C.
**18.39** $4.361 \times 10^5$ g CaO  **18.41** (a) *Groundwater* is freshwater (less
than 500 ppm total salt content) that is under the soil; it composes 20%
of the world's freshwater. (b) An *aquifer* is a layer of porous rock that
holds groundwater.  **18.43** The minimum pressure required to initiate
reverse osmosis is greater than 5.1 atm.  **18.45** (a) $CO_2(g)$, $HCO_3^-$,
$H_2O(l)$, $SO_4^{2-}$, $NO_3^-$, $HPO_4^{2-}$, $H_2PO_4^-$ (b) $CH_4(g)$, $H_2S(g)$, $NH_3(g)$,
$PH_3(g)$  **18.47** 25.1 g $O_2$  **18.49** $Mg^{2+}(aq) + Ca(OH)_2(s) \longrightarrow$
$Mg(OH)_2(s) + Ca^{2+}(aq)$  **18.51** 0.42 mol $Ca(OH)_2$, 0.18 mol
$Na_2CO_3$  **18.53** $4FeSO_4(aq) + O_2(aq) + 2H_2O(l) \longrightarrow$
$4Fe^{3+}(aq) + 4OH^-(aq) + 4SO_4^{2-}(aq)$; $Fe^{3+}(aq) + 3HCO_3^-(aq) \longrightarrow$
$Fe(OH)_3(s) + 3CO_2(g)$  **18.55** (a) *Trihalomethanes* are the by-
products of water chlorination; they contain one central carbon atom
bound to one hydrogen and three halogen atoms.
(b)

$$\underset{\displaystyle Cl}{\overset{\displaystyle H}{Cl-C-Cl}} \qquad \underset{\displaystyle Cl}{\overset{\displaystyle H}{Cl-C-Br}}$$

**18.57** The fewer steps in a process, the less waste is generated.
Processes with fewer steps require less energy at the site of the process
and for subsequent cleanup or disposal of waste.  **18.59** (a) $H_2O$
(b) It is better to prevent waste than to treat it. Atom economy. Less
hazardous chemical synthesis and inherently safer for accident prevention. Catalysis and design for energy efficiency. Raw materials should
be renewable.  **18.61** (a) Water as a solvent, by criteria 5, 7, and 12.
(b) Reaction temperature of 500 K, by criteria 6, 12, and 1. (c) Sodium
chloride as a by-product, according to criteria 1, 3, and 12.
**18.66** Multiply Equation 18.7 by a factor of 2; then add it to Equation
18.9. 2 Cl(g) and 2 ClO(g) cancel from each side of the resulting equation to produce Equation 18.10.  **18.69** Although HFCs have long
lifetimes in the stratosphere, it is infrequent that light with energy sufficient to dissociate a C—F bond will reach an HFC molecule. F atoms,
the bad actors in ozone destruction, are much less likely than Cl atoms
to be produced by photodissociation in the stratosphere.  **18.71** The
formation of NO(g) is endothermic, so K increases with increasing

temperature. The oxidation of $NO(g)$ to $NO_2(g)$ is exothermic, so the value of $K$ decreases with increasing temperature. **18.75** $7.1 \times 10^8 \, m^2$ **18.77** (a)$CO_3^{2-}$ is a relatively strong Brønsted–Lowry base and produces $OH^-$ in aqueous solution. If $[OH^-(aq)]$ is sufficient for the reaction quotient to exceed $K_{sp}$ for $Mg(OH)_2$, the solid will precipitate. (b) At these ion concentrations, $Q > K_{sp}$ and $Mg(OH)_2$ will precipitate. **18.81** (a) $2.5 \times 10^7$ ton $CO_2$, $4.2 \times 10^5$ ton $SO_2$ (b) $4.3 \times 10^5$ ton $CaSO_3$ **18.84** (a)

$$H—\ddot{O}—H \longrightarrow H\cdot + \cdot\ddot{O}—H$$

(b) 258 nm (c) The overall reaction is $O_3(g) + O(g) \longrightarrow 2\,O_2(g)$. $OH(g)$ is the catalyst in the overall reaction because it is consumed and then reproduced. **18.86** The enthalpy change for the first step is $-141$ kJ, for the second step, $-249$ kJ, for the overall reaction, $-390$ kJ. **18.90** (a) Rate $= k[O_3][H]$ (b) $k_{avg} = 1.13 \times 10^{44}\,M^{-1}\,s^{-1}$ **18.95** (a) Process (i) is greener because it involves neither the toxic reactant phosgene nor the by-product HCl. (b) Reaction (i): C in $CO_2$ is linear with $sp$ hybridization; C in $R—N=C=O$ is linear with $sp$ hybridization; C in the urethane monomer is trigonal planar with $sp^2$ hybridization. Reaction (ii): C in $COCl_2$ is linear with $sp^2$ hybridization; C in $R—N=C=O$ is linear with $sp$ hybridization; C in the urethane monomer is trigonal planar with $sp^2$ hybridization. (c) The greenest way to promote formation of the isocyanate is to remove by-product, either water or HCl, from the reaction mixture.

# CHAPTER 19

**19.1** (a)

(b) $\Delta H = 0$ for mixing ideal gases. $\Delta S$ is positive because the disorder of the system increases. (c) The process is spontaneous and therefore irreversible. (d) Since $\Delta H = 0$, the process does not affect the entropy of the surroundings. **19.4** $\Delta S$ is positive. **19.7** (a) At 300 K, $\Delta G = 0$, and the system is at equilibrium. (b) The reaction is spontaneous at temperatures above 300 K. **19.10** (a) The minimum in the plot is the equilibrium position of the reaction. (b) The quantity $x$ is $\Delta G°$. **19.11** Spontaneous: a, b, c, d; nonspontaneous: e **19.13** (a) $NH_4NO_3(s)$ dissolves in water, as in a chemical cold pack. Naphthalene (moth balls) sublimes at room temperature. (b) Melting of a solid is spontaneous above its melting point but nonspontaneous below its melting point. **19.15** (a) Endothermic (b) above 100 °C (c) below 100 °C (d) at 100 °C **19.17** (a) For a *reversible* process, the forward and reverse changes occur by the same path. In a reversible process, both the system and the surroundings are restored to their original condition by exactly reversing the change. A reversible change produces the maximum amount of work. (b) There is no net change in the surroundings. (c) The vaporization of water to steam is reversible if it occurs at the boiling temperature of water for a specified external (atmospheric) pressure and if the required heat is added infinitely slowly. (d) No. Natural processes are spontaneous in the direction they occur and nonspontaneous in the opposite direction. By definition they are irreversible. **19.19** (a) If the ideal gas is contained in a closed system at constant volume, a decrease in external temperature leads to a decrease in both temperature and pressure of the gas. (b) If the ideal gas is contained in a closed system at constant pressure, a decrease in external temperature leads to a decrease in both temperature and volume of the gas. (c) No. $\Delta E$ is a state function. $\Delta E = q + w$; $q$ and $w$ are not state functions. Their values do depend on path, but their sum, $\Delta E$, does not. **19.21** (a) An ice cube can melt reversibly at the conditions of temperature and pressure where the solid and liquid are in equilibrium. (b) We know that melting is a process that increases the energy of the system even though there is no change in temper-

ature. $\Delta E$ is not zero for the process. **19.23** (a) At constant temperature, $\Delta S = q_{rev}/T$, where $q_{rev}$ is the heat that would be transferred if the process were reversible. (b) No. $\Delta S$ is a state function, so it is independent of path. **19.25** (a) Entropy increases. (b) 89.2 J/K **19.27** (a) For a spontaneous process, the entropy of the universe increases; for a reversible process, the entropy of the universe does not change. (b) For a reversible process, if the entropy of the system increases, the entropy of the surroundings must decrease by the same amount. (c) For a spontaneous process, the entropy of the universe must increase, so the entropy of the surroundings must decrease by less than 42 J/K. **19.29** (a) Positive $\Delta S$ (b) $\Delta S = 1.02$ J/K (c) Temperature need not be specified to calculate $\Delta S$, as long as the expansion is isothermal. **19.31** (a) Yes, the expansion is spontaneous. (b) As the ideal gas expands into the vacuum, there is nothing for it to "push back," so no work is done. Mathematically, $w = -P_{ext}\Delta V$. Since the gas expands into a vacuum, $P_{ext} = 0$ and $w = 0$. (c) The "driving force" for the expansion of the gas is the increase in entropy. **19.33** (a) An increase in temperature produces more available microstates for a system. (b) A decrease in volume produces fewer available microstates for a system. (c) Going from liquid to gas, the number of available microstates increases. **19.35** (a) $\Delta S$ is positive. (b) $S$ of the system clearly increases in 19.11 (b) and (e); it clearly decreases in 19.9 (c). The entropy change is difficult to judge in 19.9 (a) and definition of the system in (d) is problematic. **19.37** $S$ increases in (a) and (c); $S$ decreases in (b). **19.39** (a) The entropy of a pure crystalline substance at absolute zero is zero. (b) In translational motion the entire molecule moves in a single direction; in rotational motion the molecule rotates or spins around a fixed axis. In vibrational motion the bonds within a molecule stretch and bend, but the average position of the atoms does not change.

(c) H—Cl $\xrightarrow{\text{translational}}$ H—Cl

H—Cl     H—Cl $\longleftrightarrow$ H——Cl $\longleftrightarrow$ H—Cl
rotational                              vibrational

**19.41** (a) $Ar(g)$ (b) $He(g)$ at 1.5 atm (c) 1 mol of $Ne(g)$ in 15.0 L (d) $CO_2(g)$ **19.43** (a) $\Delta S < 0$ (b) $\Delta S > 0$ (c) $\Delta S < 0$ (d) $\Delta S \approx 0$ **19.45** (a)

(b) Boiling water, at 100 °C, has a much larger entropy change than melting ice at 0 °C. **19.47** (a) $C_2H_6(g)$ (b) $CO_2(g)$ **19.49** (a) $Sc(s)$, 34.6 J/mol-K; $Sc(g)$, 174.7 J/mol-K. In general, the gas phase of a substance has a larger $S°$ than the solid phase because of the greater volume and motional freedom of the molecules. (b) $NH_3(g)$, 192.5 J/mol-K; $NH_3(aq)$, 111.3 J/mol-K. Molecules in the gas phase have more motional freedom than molecules in solution. (c) 1 mol of

$P_4(g)$, 280 J/K; 2 mol of $P_2(g)$, 2(218.1) = 436.2 J/K. More particles have a greater motional energy (more available microstates). (d) C (diamond), 2.43 J/mol-K; C (graphite), 5.69 J/mol-K. The internal entropy in graphite is greater because there is translational freedom among planar sheets of C atoms, while there is very little freedom within the covalent-network diamond lattice. **19.51** For elements with similar structures, the heavier the atoms, the lower the vibrational frequencies at a given temperature. This means that more vibrations can be accessed at a particular temperature, resulting in greater absolute entropy for the heavier elements. **19.53** (a) $\Delta S° = -120.5$ J/K. $\Delta S°$ is negative because there are fewer moles of gas in the products. (b) $\Delta S° = +176.6$ J/K. $\Delta S°$ is positive because there are more moles of gas in the products. (c) $\Delta S° = +152.39$ J/K. $\Delta S°$ is positive because the product contains more total particles and more moles of gas. (d) $\Delta S° = +92.3$ J/K. $\Delta S°$ is positive because there are more moles of gas in the products. **19.55** (a) $\Delta G = \Delta H - T\Delta S$ (b) If $\Delta G$ is positive, the process is nonspontaneous, but the reverse process is spontaneous. (c) There is no relationship between $\Delta G$ and rate of reaction. **19.57** (a) Exothermic (b) $\Delta S°$ is negative; the reaction leads to a decrease in disorder. (c) $\Delta G° = -9.9$ kJ (d) If all reactants and products are present in their standard states, the reaction is spontaneous in the forward direction at this temperature. **19.59** (a) $\Delta H° = -537.22$ kJ, $\Delta S° = 13.7$ J/K, $\Delta G° = -541.40$ kJ, $\Delta G° = \Delta H° - T\Delta S° = -541.31$ kJ (b) $\Delta H° = -106.7$ kJ, $\Delta S° = -142.2$ kJ, $\Delta G° = -64.0$ kJ, $\Delta G° = \Delta H° - T\Delta S° = -64.3$ kJ (c) $\Delta H° = -508.3$ kJ, $\Delta S° = -178$ kJ, $\Delta G° = -465.8$ kJ, $\Delta G° = \Delta H° - T\Delta S° = -455.1$ kJ. The discrepancy in $\Delta G°$ values is due to experimental uncertainties in the tabulated thermodynamic data. (d) $\Delta H° = -165.9$ kJ, $\Delta S° = 1.4$ kJ, $\Delta G° = -166.2$ kJ, $\Delta G° = \Delta H° - T\Delta S° = -166.3$ kJ **19.61** (a) $\Delta G° = -140.0$ kJ, spontaneous (b) $\Delta G° = +104.70$ kJ, nonspontaneous (c) $\Delta G° = +146$ kJ, nonspontaneous (d) $\Delta G° = -156.7$ kJ, spontaneous **19.63** (a) $2 C_8H_{18}(l) + 25 O_2(g) \longrightarrow 16 CO_2(g) + 18 H_2O(l)$ (b) Because $\Delta S°$ is positive, $\Delta G°$ is more negative than $\Delta H°$. **19.65** (a) The forward reaction is spontaneous at low temperatures but becomes nonspontaneous at higher temperatures. (b) The reaction is nonspontaneous in the forward direction at all temperatures. (c) The forward reaction is nonspontaneous at low temperatures but becomes spontaneous at higher temperatures. **19.67** $\Delta S > 60.8$ J/K **19.69** (a) $T = 330$ K (b) nonspontaneous **19.71** (a) $\Delta H° = 155.7$ kJ, $\Delta S° = 171.4$ kJ. Since $\Delta S°$ is positive, $\Delta G°$ becomes more negative with increasing temperature. (b) $\Delta G° = 19$ kJ. The reaction is not spontaneous under standard conditions at 800 K (c) $\Delta G° = -15.7$ kJ. The reaction is spontaneous under standard conditions at 1000 K. **19.73** (a) $T_b = 79$ °C (b) From the *Handbook of Chemistry and Physics*, 74th Edition, $T_b = 80.1$ °C. The values are remarkably close; the small difference is due to deviation from ideal behavior by $C_6H_6(g)$ and experimental uncertainty in the boiling point measurement and the thermodynamic data. **19.75** (a) $C_2H_2(g) + \frac{5}{2} O_2(g) \longrightarrow 2 CO_2(g) + H_2O(l)$ (b) $-1299.5$ kJ of heat produced/mol $C_2H_2$ burned (c) $w_{max} = -1235.1$ kJ/mol $C_2H_2$ **19.77** (a) $\Delta G$ becomes more negative. (b) $\Delta G$ becomes more positive. (c) $\Delta G$ becomes more positive. **19.79** (a) $\Delta G° = -5.40$ kJ (b) $\Delta G = 0.30$ kJ **19.81** (a) $\Delta G° = -16.77$ kJ, $K = 870$ (b) $\Delta G° = 8.0$ kJ, $K = 0.039$ (c) $\Delta G° = -497.9$ kJ, $K = 2 \times 10^{87}$ **19.83** $\Delta H° = 269.3$ kJ, $\Delta S° = 0.1719$ kJ/K (a) $P_{CO_2} = 6.0 \times 10^{-39}$ atm (b) $P_{CO_2} = 1.6 \times 10^{-4}$ atm **19.85** (a) $HNO_2(aq) \rightleftharpoons H^+(aq) + NO_2^-(aq)$ (b) $\Delta G° = 19.1$ kJ (c) $\Delta G = 0$ at equilibrium (d) $\Delta G = -2.7$ kJ **19.87** (a) The thermodynamic quantities $T$, $E$, and $S$ are state functions. (b) The quantities $q$ and $w$ depend on the path taken. (c) There is only one *reversible* path between states. (d) $\Delta E = q_{rev} + w_{max}$, $\Delta S = q_{rev} / T$. **19.91** (a) 16 arrangements (b) 1 arrangement (c) The gas will spontaneously adopt the state with the most possible arrangements for the molecules, the state with maximum disorder. **19.96** (a) For all three compounds listed, there are fewer moles of gaseous products than reactants in the formation reaction, so we expect $\Delta S_f°$ to be negative. If $\Delta G_f° = \Delta H_f° - T\Delta S_f°$ and $\Delta S_f°$ is negative, $-T\Delta S_f°$ is positive and $\Delta G_f°$ is more positive than

$\Delta H_f°$. (b) In this reaction, there are more moles of gas in products, $\Delta S_f°$ is positive, $-T\Delta S_f°$ is negative and $\Delta G_f°$ is more negative than $\Delta H_f°$. **19.100** (a) $K = 4 \times 10^{15}$ (b) An increase in temperature will decrease the mole fraction of $CH_3COOH$ at equilibrium. Elevated temperatures must be used to increase the speed of the reaction. (c) $K = 1$ at 836 K or 563 °C. **19.104** (a) $\Delta G = 8.77$ kJ (b) $w_{min} = 8.77$ kJ. In practice, a larger than minimum amount of work is required. **19.108** (a) Acetone, $\Delta S°_{vap} = 88.4$ J/mol-K; dimethyl ether, $\Delta S°_{vap} = 86.6$ J/mol-K; ethanol, $\Delta S°_{vap} = 110$ J/mol-K; octane, $\Delta S°_{vap} = 86.3$ J/mol-K; pyridine, $\Delta S°_{vap} = 90.4$ J/mol-K. Ethanol does not obey Trouton's rule. (b) Hydrogen bonding (in ethanol and other liquids) leads to more ordering in the liquid state and a greater than usual increase in entropy upon vaporization. Liquids that experience hydrogen bonding are probably exceptions to Trouton's rule. (c) Owing to strong hydrogen bonding interactions, water probably does not obey Trouton's rule. $\Delta S°_{vap} = 109.0$ J/mol-K. (d) $\Delta H_{vap}$ for $C_6H_5Cl \approx 36$ kJ/mol **19.113** (a) For any given total pressure, the condition of equal moles of the two gases can be achieved at some temperature. For individual gas pressures of 1 atm and a total pressure of 2 atm, the mixture is at equilibrium at 328.5 K or 55.5 °C. (b) 333.0 K or 60 °C (c) 374.2 K or 101.2 °C (d) The reaction is endothermic, so an increase in the value of $K$ as calculated in parts (a)–(c) should be accompanied by an increase in $T$.

## CHAPTER 20

**20.1** In a Brønsted–Lowry acid–base reaction, $H^+$ is transferred from the acid to the base. In a redox reaction, one or more electrons are transferred from the reductant to the oxidant. The greater the tendency of an acid to donate $H^+$, the lesser the tendency of its conjugate base to accept $H^+$. The stronger the acid, the weaker its conjugate base. Similarly, the greater the tendency of a reduced species to donate electrons, the lesser the tendency of the corresponding oxidized species to accept electrons. The stronger the reducing agent, the weaker the corresponding oxidizing agent. **20.4** (a) Add 1 $M$ $A^{2+}(aq)$ to the beaker with the A(s) electrode. Add 1 $M$ $B^{2+}(aq)$ to the beaker with the B(s) electrode. Add a salt bridge to enable the flow of ions from one compartment to the other. (b) The A electrode functions as the cathode. (c) Electrons flow through the external circuit from the anode to the cathode, from B to A in this cell. (d) $E°_{cell} = 1.00$ V. **20.7** (a) The sign of $\Delta G°$ is positive. (b) The equilibrium constant is less than one. (c) No. An electrochemical cell based on this reaction cannot accomplish work on its surroundings. **20.9** (a) Line 1 (b) $E_{red} = E°_{red} = 0.799$ V. **20.13** (a) *Oxidation* is the loss of electrons. (b) Electrons appear on the products' side (right side). (c) The *oxidant* is the reactant that is reduced. (d) An *oxidizing agent* is the substance that promotes oxidation; it is the oxidant. **20.15** (a) True (b) false (c) true **20.17** (a) I, +5 to 0; C, +2 to +4 (b) Hg, +2 to 0; N, −2 to 0 (c) N, +5 to +2; S, −2 to 0 (d) Cl, +4 to +3; O, −1 to 0 **20.19** (a) $TiCl_4(g) + 2 Mg(l) \longrightarrow Ti(s) + 2 MgCl_2(l)$ (b) Mg(l) is oxidized; $TiCl_4(g)$ is reduced. (c) Mg(l) is the reductant; $TiCl_4(g)$ is the oxidant. **20.21** (a) $Sn^{2+}(aq) \longrightarrow Sn^{4+}(aq) + 2e^-$, oxidation (b) $TiO_2(s) + 4 H^+(aq) + 2e^- \longrightarrow Ti^{2+}(aq) + 2 H_2O(l)$, reduction (c) $ClO_3^-(aq) + 6 H^+(aq) + 6e^- \longrightarrow Cl^-(aq) + 3 H_2O(l)$, reduction (d) $N_2(g) + 8 H^+(aq) + 6e^- \longrightarrow 2 NH_4^+(aq)$, reduction (e) $4 OH^-(aq) \longrightarrow O_2(g) + 2 H_2O(l) + 4e^-$, oxidation (f) $SO_3^{2-}(aq) + 2 OH^-(aq) \longrightarrow SO_4^{2-}(aq) + H_2O(l) + 2e^-$, oxidation (g) $N_2(g) + 6 H_2O(l) + 6e^- \longrightarrow 2 NH_3(g) + 6 OH^-(aq)$, reduction **20.23** (a) $Cr_2O_7^{2-}(aq) + I^-(aq) + 8 H^+(aq) \longrightarrow 2 Cr^{3+}(aq) + IO_3^-(aq) + 4 H_2O(l)$; oxidizing agent, $Cr_2O_7^{2-}$; reducing agent, $I^-$ (b) $4 MnO_4^-(aq) + 5 CH_3OH(aq) + 12 H^+(aq) \longrightarrow 4 Mn^{2+}(aq) + 5 HCO_2H(aq) + 12 H_2O(aq)$; oxidizing agent, $MnO_4^-$; reducing agent, $CH_3OH$ (c) $I_2(s) + 5 OCl^-(aq) + H_2O(l) \longrightarrow 2 IO_3^-(aq) + 5 Cl^-(aq) + 2 H^+(aq)$; oxidizing agent, $OCl^-$; reducing agent, $I_2$ (d) $As_2O_3(s) +$

$2\,NO_3^-(aq) + 2\,H_2O(l) + 2\,H^+(aq) \longrightarrow 2\,H_3AsO_4(aq) +$ $N_2O_3(aq)$; oxidizing agent, $NO_3^-$; reducing agent, $As_2O_3$ (e) $2\,MnO_4^-(aq) + Br^-(aq) + H_2O(l) \longrightarrow 2\,MnO_2(s) + BrO_3^-(aq) +$ $2\,OH^-(aq)$; oxidizing agent, $MnO_4^-$; reducing agent, $Br^-$ (f) $Pb(OH)_4^{2-}(aq) + ClO^-(aq) \longrightarrow PbO_2(s) + Cl^-(aq) + 2\,OH^-(aq) +$ $H_2O(l)$; oxidizing agent, $ClO^-$; reducing agent, $Pb(OH)_4^{2-}$ **20.25** (a) The reaction $Cu^{2+}(aq) + Zn(s) \longrightarrow Cu(s) + Zn^{2+}(aq)$ is occurring in both figures. In Figure 20.3 the reactants are in contact, while in Figure 20.4 the oxidation half-reaction and reduction half-reaction are occurring in separate compartments. In Figure 20.3 the flow of electrons cannot be isolated or utilized; in Figure 20.4 electrical current is isolated and flows through the voltmeter. (b) $Na^+$ cations are drawn into the cathode compartment to maintain charge balance as $Cu^{2+}$ ions are removed. **20.27** (a) $Fe(s)$ is oxidized, $Ag^+(aq)$ is reduced. (b) $Ag^+(aq) + e^- \longrightarrow Ag(s)$; $Fe(s) \longrightarrow Fe^{2+}(aq) + 2e^-$ (c) $Fe(s)$ is the anode, $Ag(s)$ is the cathode. (d) $Fe(s)$ is negative; $Ag(s)$ is positive. (e) Electrons flow from the Fe electrode $(-)$ toward the Ag electrode $(+)$. (f) Cations migrate toward the $Ag(s)$ cathode; anions migrate toward the $Fe(s)$ anode. **20.29** *Electromotive force*, emf, is the potential energy difference between an electron at the anode and an electron at the cathode of a voltaic cell. (b) One *volt* is the potential energy difference required to impart 1 J of energy to a charge of 1 coulomb. (c) *Cell potential*, $E_{cell}$, is the emf of an electrochemical cell. **20.31** (a) $2\,H^+(aq) + 2e^- \longrightarrow H_2(g)$ (b) A *standard* hydrogen electrode, SHE, has components that are at standard conditions, 1 $M$ $H^+(aq)$ and $H_2(g)$ at 1 atm. (c) The platinum foil in a SHE serves as an inert electron carrier and a solid reaction surface. **20.33** (a) A *standard reduction potential* is the relative potential of a reduction half-reaction measured at standard conditions. (b) $E_{red}^\circ = 0\,V$ **20.35** (a) $Cr^{2+}(aq) \longrightarrow Cr^{3+}(aq) + e^-$; $Tl^{3+}(aq) + 2e^- \longrightarrow Tl^+(aq)$ (b) $E_{red}^\circ = 0.78\,V$ (c)

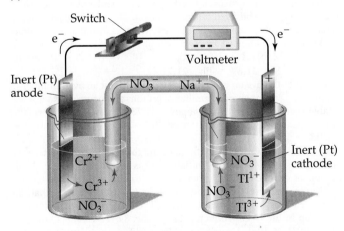

Movement of cations →

← Movement of anions

**20.37** (a) $E^\circ = 0.823\,V$ (b) $E^\circ = 1.89\,V$ (c) $E^\circ = 1.211\,V$ (d) $E^\circ = 0.62\,V$ **20.39** (a) $3\,Ag^+(aq) + Cr(s) \longrightarrow 3\,Ag(s) + Cr^{3+}(aq)$, $E^\circ = 1.54\,V$ (b) Two of the combinations have essentially equal $E^\circ$ values: $2\,Ag^+(aq) + Cu(s) \longrightarrow 2\,Ag(s) + Cu^{2+}(aq)$, $E^\circ = 0.462\,V$; $3\,Ni^{2+}(aq) + 2\,Cr(s) \longrightarrow 3\,Ni(s) + 2\,Cr^{3+}(aq)$, $E^\circ = 0.46\,V$ **20.41** (a) Anode, $Sn(s)$; cathode, $Cu(s)$. (b) The copper electrode gains mass as Cu is plated out, and the tin electrode loses mass as Sn is oxidized. (c) $Cu^{2+}(aq) + Sn(s) \longrightarrow Cu(s) + Sn^{2+}(aq)$. (d) $E^\circ = 0.473\,V$. **20.43** (a) $Mg(s)$ (b) $Ca(s)$ (c) $H_2(g)$ (d) $BrO_3^-(aq)$ **20.45** (a) $Cl_2(aq)$, strong oxidant (b) $MnO_4^-(aq)$, acidic, strong oxidant (c) $Ba(s)$ strong reductant (d) $Zn(s)$, reductant **20.47** (a) $Cu^{2+}(aq) < O_2(g) < Cr_2O_7^{2-}(aq) < Cl_2(g) < H_2O_2(aq)$

(b) $H_2O_2(aq) < I^-(aq) < Sn^{2+}(aq) < Zn(s) < Al(s)$ **20.49** Al and $H_2C_2O_4$ **20.51** (a) $2\,Fe^{2+}(aq) + S_2O_6^{2-}(aq) + 4\,H^+(aq) \longrightarrow$ $2\,Fe^{3+}(aq) + 2\,H_2SO_3(aq)$; $2\,Fe^{2+}(aq) + N_2O(aq) + 2\,H^+(aq) \longrightarrow$ $2\,Fe^{3+}(aq) + N_2(g) + H_2O(l)$; $Fe^{2+}(aq) + VO_2^+(aq) + 2\,H^+(aq) \longrightarrow$ $Fe^{3+}(aq) + VO^{2+}(aq) + H_2O(l)$ (b) $E^\circ = -0.17\,V$, $\Delta G^\circ = 33\,kJ$; $E^\circ = -2.54\,V$, $\Delta G^\circ = 4.90 \times 10^2\,kJ$; $E^\circ = 0.23\,V$, $\Delta G^\circ = -22\,kJ$ (c) $K = 1.8 \times 10^{-6} = 10^{-6}$; $K = 1.2 \times 10^{-86} = 10^{-86}$; $K = 7.8 \times 10^3 = 8 \times 10^3$ **20.53** $\Delta G^\circ = 21.8\,kJ$, $E_{cell}^\circ = -0.113\,V$ **20.55** (a) $E^\circ = 0.16\,V$, $K = 2.54 \times 10^5 = 3 \times 10^5$ (b) $E^\circ = 0.277\,V$, $K = 2.3 \times 10^9$ (c) $E^\circ = 0.45\,V$, $K = 1.5 \times 10^{75} = 10^{75}$ **20.57** (a) $K = 9.8 \times 10^2$ (b) $K = 9.5 \times 10^5$ (c) $K = 9.3 \times 10^8$ **20.59** (a) $w_{max} = -130\,kJ/mol$ Sn **20.61** (a) The Nernst equation is applicable when the components of an electrochemical cell are at nonstandard conditions. (b) $Q = 1$ (c) $Q$ decreases and $E$ increases **20.63** (a) $E$ decreases (b) $E$ decreases (c) $E$ decreases (d) no effect **20.65** (a) $E^\circ = 0.48\,V$ (b) $E = 0.53\,V$ (c) $E = 0.46\,V$ **20.67** (a) $E^\circ = 0.46\,V$ (b) $E = 0.37\,V$ **20.69** (a) The compartment with $[Zn^{2+}] = 1.00 \times 10^{-2}\,M$ is the anode. (b) $E^\circ = 0$ (c) $E = 0.0668\,V$ (d) In the anode compartment $[Zn^{2+}]$ increases; in the cathode compartment $[Zn^{2+}]$ decreases **20.71** $E^\circ = 0.763\,V$, pH = 1.6 **20.73** (a) The emf of a battery decreases as it is used. The concentrations of products increase and the concentrations of reactants decrease, causing $Q$ to increase and $E_{cell}$ to decrease. (b) A D-size battery contains more reactants than a AA, enabling the D to provide power for a longer time. **20.75** (a) $464\,g\,PbO_2$ (b) $3.74 \times 10^5\,C$ of charge transferred **20.77** (a) The anode (b) $E^\circ = 0.50\,V$ (c) The emf of the battery, 3.5 V, is exactly the standard cell potential calculated in part (b). (d) At ambient conditions, $E \approx E^\circ$, so log $Q \approx 1$. Assuming that the value of $E^\circ$ is relatively constant with temperature, the value of the second term in the Nernst equation is approximately zero at 37 °C, and $E \approx 3.5\,V$. **20.79** (a) The cell emf will have a smaller value. (b) NiMH batteries use an alloy such as $ZrNi_2$ as the anode material. This eliminates the use and disposal problems associated with Cd, a toxic heavy metal. **20.81** The main advantage of a fuel cell is that fuel is continuously supplied, so that it can produce electrical current for a time limited only by the amount of available fuel. For the hydrogen-oxygen fuel cell, this is also a disadvantage because volatile and explosive hydrogen must be acquired and stored. Alkaline batteries are convenient, but they have a short lifetime, and the disposal of their zinc and manganese solids is more problematic than disposal of water produced by the hydrogen-oxygen fuel cell. **20.83** (a) anode: $Fe(s) \longrightarrow Fe^{2+}(aq) + 2e^-$; cathode: $O_2(g) + 4\,H^+(aq) + 4e^- \longrightarrow 2\,H_2O(l)$ (b) $2\,Fe^{2+}(aq) +$ $3\,H_2O(l) + 3\,H_2O(l) \longrightarrow Fe_2O_3 \cdot 3\,H_2O(s) + 6\,H^+(aq) + 2e^-$; $O_2(g) + 4\,H^+(aq) + 4e^- \longrightarrow 2\,H_2O(l)$ **20.85** (a) Mg is called a "sacrificial anode" because it has a more negative $E_{red}^\circ$ than the pipe metal and is preferentially oxidized when the two are coupled. It is sacrificed to preserve the pipe. (b) $E_{red}^\circ$ for $Mg^{2+}$ is $-2.37$ V, more negative than most metals present in pipes, including Fe and Zn. **20.87** Under acidic conditions, air ($O_2$) oxidation of $Zn(s)$, 1.99 V; $Fe(s)$, 1.67 V; and $Cu(s)$, 0.893 V are all spontaneous. When the three metals are in contact, Zn will act as a sacrificial anode for both Fe and Cu, but after the Zn is depleted, Fe will be oxidized (corroded). **20.89** (a) *Electrolysis* is an electrochemical process driven by an outside energy source. (b) By definition, electrolysis reactions are nonspontaneous. (c) $2\,Cl^-(l) \longrightarrow Cl_2(g) + 2e^-$ (d) When an aqueous solution of NaCl undergoes electrolysis, sodium metal is not formed because $H_2O$ is preferentially reduced to form $H_2(g)$. **20.91** (a) $236\,g\,Cr(s)$ (b) 2.51 A **20.93** (a) $4.0 \times 10^5\,g$ Li (b) The minimum voltage required to drive the electrolysis is $+4.41\,V$. **20.95** Gold is less active than copper and thus more difficult to oxidize. When crude copper is refined by electrolysis, Cu is oxidized from the crude anode, but any metallic gold present in the crude copper is not oxidized, so it accumulates near the anode, available for collection. **20.97** (a) $2\,Ni^+(aq) \longrightarrow Ni(s) + Ni^{2+}(aq)$ (b) $3\,MnO_4^{2-}(aq) +$ $4\,H^+(aq) \longrightarrow 2\,MnO_4^-(aq) + MnO_2(s) + 2\,H_2O(l)$

(c) $3 H_2SO_3(aq) \longrightarrow S(s) + 2 HSO_4^-(aq) + 2 H^+(aq) + H_2O(l)$
(d) $Cl_2(aq) + 2 OH^-(aq) \longrightarrow Cl^-(aq) + ClO^-(aq) + H_2O(l)$
**20.100** (a) $E° = 0.627 V$, spontaneous (b) $E° = -0.82 V$, nonspontaneous (c) $E° = 0.93 V$, spontaneous (d) $E° = 0.183 V$, spontaneous **20.104** $K = 1.6 \times 10^6$ **20.107** The ship's hull should be made negative. The ship, as a negatively charged "electrode," becomes the site of reduction, rather than oxidation, in an electrolytic process. **20.110** $3.0 \times 10^4$ kWh required **20.112** (a) $H_2$ is being oxidized and $N_2$ is being reduced. (b) $K = 6.9 \times 10^5$ (c) $E° = 0.05755 V$ **20.115** (a) $E° = 0.028 V$ (b) cathode: $Ag^+(aq) + e^- \longrightarrow Ag(s)$; anode: $Fe^{2+}(aq) \longrightarrow Fe^{3+}(aq) + e^-$ (c) $\Delta S° = 148.5 J$. Since $\Delta S°$ is positive, $\Delta G°$ will become more negative and $E°$ will become more positive as temperature is increased. **20.118** $K_{sp}$ for AgSCN is $1.0 \times 10^{-12}$.

# CHAPTER 21

**21.1** (a) $^{24}Ne$; outside; reduce neutron-to-proton ratio via $\beta$ decay (b) $^{32}Cl$; outside; increase neutron-to-proton ratio via positron emission or orbital electron capture (c) $^{108}Sn$; outside; increase neutron-to-proton ratio via positron emission or orbital electron capture (d) $^{216}Po$; outside; nuclei with $Z \geq 84$ usually decay via $\alpha$ emission. **21.4** (a) 7 min (b) $0.1 min^{-1}$ (c) 30% (3/10) of the sample remains after 12 min. (d) $^{88}_{41}Nb$ **21.5** (a) $^{10}_5B$, $^{11}_5B$; $^{12}_6C$, $^{13}_6C$; $^{14}_7N$, $^{15}_7N$; $^{16}_8O$, $^{17}_8O$, $^{18}_8O$; $^{19}_9F$ (b) $^{14}_6C$ (c) $^{11}_6C$, $^{13}_7N$, $^{15}_8O$, $^{18}_9F$ (d) $^{11}_6C$ **21.7** (a) 25 protons, 30 neutrons (b) 80 protons, 121 neutrons (c) 19 protons, 20 neutrons **21.9** (a) $^1_0n$ (b) $^4_2He$ or $\alpha$ (c) $^0_0\gamma$ or $\gamma$ **21.11** (a) $^{90}_{37}Rb \longrightarrow ^{90}_{38}Sr + ^0_{-1}e$ (b) $^{72}_{34}Se + ^0_{-1}e$ (orbital electron) $\longrightarrow ^{72}_{33}As$ (c) $^{76}_{36}Kr \longrightarrow ^{76}_{35}Br + ^0_{1}e$ (d) $^{226}_{88}Ra \longrightarrow ^{222}_{86}Rn + ^4_2He$ **21.13** (a) $^{211}_{82}Pb \longrightarrow ^{211}_{83}Bi + ^0_{-1}\beta$ (b) $^{50}_{25}Mn \longrightarrow ^{50}_{24}Cr + ^0_{1}e$ (c) $^{179}_{74}W + ^0_{-1}e \longrightarrow ^{179}_{73}Ta$ (d) $^{230}_{90}Th \longrightarrow ^{266}_{88}Ra + ^4_2He$ **21.15** 7 alpha emissions, 4 beta emissions **21.17** (a) Positron emission (for low atomic numbers, positron emission is more common than electron capture) (b) beta emission (c) beta emission (d) beta emission **21.19** (a) Stable; $^{39}_{19}K$, 20 neutrons is a magic number (b) stable: $^{209}_{83}Bi$, 126 neutrons is a magic number (c) stable: $^{58}_{28}Ni$ even proton, even neutron more likely to be stable; $^{65}_{28}Ni$ has high neutron-to-proton ratio **21.21** (a) $^4_2He$ (c) $^{40}_{20}Ca$ (e) $^{126}_{82}Pb$ **21.23** The alpha particle, $^4_2He$, has a magic number of both protons and neutrons, while the proton is an odd proton, even neutron particle. Alpha is a very stable emitted particle, which makes alpha emission a favorable process. The proton is not a stable emitted particle, and its formation does not encourage proton emission as a process. **21.25** Protons and alpha particles are positively charged and must be moving very fast to overcome electrostatic forces that would repel them from the target nucleus. Neutrons are electrically neutral and not repelled by the nucleus. **21.27** (a) $^{252}_{98}Cf + ^{10}_5B \longrightarrow 3 ^1_0n + ^{259}_{103}Lr$ (b) $^2_1H + ^3_2He \longrightarrow ^4_2He + ^1_1H$ (c) $^1_1H + ^{11}_5B \longrightarrow 3 ^4_2He$ (d) $^{122}_{53}I \longrightarrow ^{122}_{54}Xe + ^0_{-1}e$ (e) $^{59}_{26}Fe \longrightarrow ^0_{-1}e + ^{59}_{27}Co$ **21.29** (a) $^{238}_{92}U + ^4_2He \longrightarrow ^{241}_{94}Pu + ^1_0n$ (b) $^{14}_7N + ^4_2He \longrightarrow ^{17}_8O + ^1_1H$ (c) $^{56}_{26}Fe + ^4_2He \longrightarrow ^{60}_{29}Cu + ^0_{-1}e$ **21.31** (a) True. The decay rate constant and half-life are inversely related. (b) False. If X is not radioactive, its half-life is essentially infinity. (c) True. Changes in the amount of A would be substantial and measurable over the 40-year time frame, while changes in the amount of X would be very small and difficult to detect. **21.33** When the watch is 50 years old, only 6% of the tritium remains. The dial will be dimmed by 94%. **21.35** The source must be replaced after 2.18 yr or 26.2 months; this corresponds to August 2012. **21.37** (a) $1.1 \times 10^{11}$ alpha particles emitted in 5.0 min (b) 9.9 mCi **21.39** $k = 1.21 \times 10^{-4} yr^{-1}$; $t = 4.3 \times 10^3$ yr **21.41** $k = 5.46 \times 10^{-10} yr^{-1}$; $t = 3.0 \times 10^9$ yr **21.43** The energy released when one mole of $Fe_2O_3$ reacts is $8.515 \times 10^3 J$. The energy released when one mole of $^4_2He$ is formed from protons and neutrons is

$2.73 \times 10^{12} J$. This is $3 \times 10^8$ or 300 million times as much energy as the thermite reaction. **21.45** $\Delta m = 0.2414960$ amu, $\Delta E = 3.604129 \times 10^{-11} J/^{27}Al$ nucleus required, $8.044234 \times 10^{13} J/100 g ^{27}Al$ **21.47** (a) Nuclear mass: $^2H$, 2.013553 amu; $^4He$, 4.001505 amu; $^6Li$, 6.0134771 amu (b) nuclear binding energy: $^2H$, $3.564 \times 10^{-13} J$; $^4He$, $4.5336 \times 10^{-12} J$; $^6Li$, $5.12602 \times 10^{-12} J$ (c) binding energy/nucleon: $^2H$, $1.782 \times 10^{-13}$ J/nucleon; $^4He$, $1.1334 \times 10^{-12}$ J/nucleon; $^6Li$, $8.54337 \times 10^{-13}$ J/nucleon. This trend in binding energy/nucleon agrees with the curve in Figure 21.12. The anomalously high calculated value for $^4He$ is also apparent on the figure. **21.49** (a) $1.71 \times 10^5$ kg/d (b) $2.1 \times 10^8$ g $^{235}U$ **21.51** (a) $^{59}Co$; it has the largest binding energy per nucleon, and binding energy gives rise to mass defect. **21.53** (a) NaI is a good source of iodine because iodine is a large percentage of its mass; it is completely dissociated into ions in aqueous solution, and iodine in the form of $I^-(aq)$ is mobile and immediately available for biouptake. (b) A Geiger counter placed near the thyroid immediately after ingestion will register background, then gradually increase in signal until the concentration of iodine in the thyroid reaches a maximum. Over time, iodine-131 decays, and the signal decreases. (c) The radioactive iodine will decay to 0.01% of the original amount in approximately 82 days. **21.55** $^{235}U$ **21.57** The *control rods* in a nuclear reactor regulate the flux of neutrons to keep the reaction chain self-sustaining and also prevent the reactor core from overheating. They are composed of materials such as boron or cadmium that absorb neutrons. **21.59** (a) $^2_1H + ^2_1H \longrightarrow ^3_2He + ^1_0n$ (b) $^{239}_{92}U + ^1_0n \longrightarrow ^{133}_{51}Sb + ^{98}_{41}Nb + 9 ^1_0n$ **21.61** (a) $\Delta m = 0.006627 g/mol$; $\Delta E = 5.956 \times 10^{11} J = 5.956 \times 10^8 kJ/mol ^1_1H$ (b) The extremely high temperature is required to overcome electrostatic charge repulsions between the nuclei so that they can come together to react. **21.63** (a) Boiling water reactor (b) fast breeder reactor (c) gas-cooled reactor **21.65** Hydrogen abstraction: $RCOOH + \cdot OH \longrightarrow RCOO \cdot + H_2O$; deprotonation: $RCOOH + OH^- \longrightarrow RCOO^- + H_2O$. Hydroxyl radical is more toxic to living systems because it produces other radicals when it reacts with molecules in the organism. Hydroxide ion, $OH^-$, on the other hand, will be readily neutralized in the buffered cell environment. The acid–base reactions of $OH^-$ are usually much less disruptive to the organism than the chain of redox reactions initiated by $\cdot OH$ radical. **21.67** (a) $5.3 \times 10^8$ dis/s, $5.3 \times 10^8$ Bq (b) $6.1 \times 10^2$ mrad, $6.1 \times 10^{-3}$ Gy (c) $5.8 \times 10^3$ mrem, $5.8 \times 10^{-2}$ Sv **21.69** $^{210}_{82}Pb$ **21.71** (a) $^{36}_{17}Cl \rightarrow ^{36}_{18}Ar + ^0_{-1}e$ (b) $^{35}Cl$ and $^{37}Cl$ both have an odd number of protons but an even number of neutrons. $^{36}Cl$ has an odd number of protons and neutrons, so it is less stable than the other two isotopes. **21.73** (a) $^6_3Li + ^{56}_{28}Ni \longrightarrow ^{62}_{31}Ga$ (b) $^{40}_{20}Ca + ^{248}_{96}Cm \longrightarrow ^{147}_{62}Sm + ^{141}_{54}Xe$ (c) $^{88}_{38}Sr + ^{84}_{36}Kr \longrightarrow ^{116}_{46}Pd + ^{56}_{28}Ni$ (d) $^{40}_{20}Ca + ^{238}_{92}U \longrightarrow ^{70}_{30}Zn + 4 ^1_0n + 2 ^{102}_{41}Nb$ **21.77** The C—OH bond of the acid and the O—H bond of the alcohol break in this reaction. Initially, $^{18}O$ is present in the $C—^{18}OH$ group of the alcohol. In order for $^{18}O$ to end up in the ester, the $^{18}O—H$ bond of the alcohol must break. This requires that the C—OH bond in the acid also breaks. The unlabeled O from the acid ends up in the $H_2O$ product. **21.79** $^7Be$, $8.612 \times 10^{-13}$ J/nucleon; $^9Be$, $1.035 \times 10^{-12}$ J/nucleon; $^{10}Be$: $1.042 \times 10^{-12}$ J/nucleon. The binding energies/nucleon for $^9Be$ and $^{10}Be$ are very similar; that for $^{10}Be$ is slightly higher. **21.85** $1.4 \times 10^4$ kg $C_8H_{18}$

# CHAPTER 22

**22.1** (a) $C_2H_4$, the structure on the left, is the stable compound. Carbon can form strong multiple bonds to satisfy the octet rule, while silicon cannot. (b) The geometry about the central atoms in $C_2H_4$ is trigonal planar. **22.3** Molecules (b) and (d) will have the seesaw structure shown in the figure. **22.6** (c) Density, the ratio of mass to volume, increases going down the family; only this trend is consistent with the data in the figure. Other properties do not match the trend because (a) electronegativity and (b) first ionization energy both decrease rather than increase going down the family. Trends for both (d) X—X single bond enthalpy and (e) electron affinity are

somewhat erratic, with the trends decreasing from S to Po, and anomalous values for the properties of O, probably owing to its small covalent radius. **22.9** The compound on the left, with the strained three-membered ring, will be the most generally reactive. The larger the deviation from ideal bond angles, the more strain in the molecule and the more generally reactive it is. **22.11** Metals: (b) Sr, (c) Mn, (e) Na; nonmetals: (a) P, (d) Se, (f) Kr; metalloids: none. **22.13** (a) O (b) Br (c) Ba (d) O (e) Co (f) Br **22.15** (a) N is too small a central atom to fit five fluorine atoms, and it does not have available $d$ orbitals, which can help accommodate more than eight electrons. (b) Si does not readily form $\pi$ bonds, which are necessary to satisfy the octet rule for both atoms in the molecule. (c) As has a lower electronegativity than N; that is, it more readily gives up electrons to an acceptor and is more easily oxidized. **22.17** (a) $NaOCH_3(s) + H_2O(l) \longrightarrow NaOH(aq) + CH_3OH(aq)$
(b) $CuO(s) + 2HNO_3(aq) \longrightarrow Cu(NO_3)_2(aq) + H_2O(l)$
(c) $WO_3(s) + 3H_2(g) \longrightarrow W(s) + 3H_2O(g)$
(d) $4NH_2OH(l) + O_2(g) \longrightarrow 6H_2O(l) + 2N_2(g)$
(e) $Al_4C_3(s) + 12H_2O(l) \longrightarrow 4Al(OH)_3(s) + 3CH_4(g)$
**22.19** (a) $^1_1H$, protium; $^2_1H$, deuterium; $^3_1H$, tritium (b) in order of decreasing natural abundance: protium > deuterium > tritium (c) Tritium is radioactive. (d) $^3_1H \longrightarrow {}^3_2He + {}^0_{-1}e$ **22.21** Like other elements in group 1A, hydrogen has only one valence electron and its most common oxidation number is +1.
**22.23** (a) $Mg(s) + 2H^+(aq) \longrightarrow Mg^{2+}(aq) + H_2(g)$
(b) $C(s) + H_2O(g) \xrightarrow{1100\,°C} CO(g) + 3H_2(g)$
(c) $CH_4(g) + H_2O(g) \xrightarrow{1100\,°C} CO(g) + 3H_2(g)$
**22.25** (a) $NaH(s) + H_2O(l) \longrightarrow NaOH(aq) + H_2(g)$
(b) $Fe(s) + H_2SO_4(aq) \longrightarrow Fe^{2+}(aq) + H_2(g) + SO_4^{2-}(aq)$
(c) $H_2(g) + Br_2(g) \longrightarrow 2HBr(g)$
(d) $2Na(l) + H_2(g) \longrightarrow 2NaH(s)$
(e) $PbO(s) + H_2(g) \xrightarrow{\Delta} Pb(s) + H_2O(g)$ **22.27** (a) Ionic (b) molecular (c) metallic **22.29** Vehicle fuels produce energy via combustion reactions. The combustion of hydrogen is very exothermic and its only product, $H_2O$, is a nonpollutant. **22.31** Xenon has a lower ionization energy than argon; because the valence electrons are not as strongly attracted to the nucleus, they are more readily promoted to a state in which the atom can form bonds with fluorine. Also, Xe is larger and can more easily accommodate an expanded octet of electrons. **22.33** (a) $Ca(OBr)_2$, Br, +1 (b) $HBrO_3$, Br, +5 (c) $XeO_3$, Xe, +6 (d) $ClO_4^-$, Cl, +7 (e) $HIO_2$, I, +3 (f) $IF_5$; I, +5; F, −1 **22.35** (a) iron(III) chlorate, Cl, +5 (b) chlorous acid, Cl, +3 (c) xenon hexafluoride, F, −1 (d) bromine pentafluoride; Br, +5; F, −1 (e) xenon oxide tetrafluoride, F, −1 (f) iodic acid, I, +5 **22.37** (a) van der Waals intermolecular attractive forces increase with increasing number of electrons in the atoms. (b) $F_2$ reacts with water: $F_2(g) + H_2O(l) \longrightarrow 2HF(g) + O_2(g)$. That is, fluorine is too strong an oxidizing agent to exist in water. (c) HF has extensive hydrogen bonding. (d) Oxidizing power is related to electronegativity. Electronegativity and oxidizing power decrease in the order given. **22.39** (a) $2HgO(s) \xrightarrow{\Delta} 2Hg(l) + O_2(g)$
(b) $2Cu(NO_3)_2(s) \xrightarrow{\Delta} 2CuO(s) + 4NO_2(g) + O_2(g)$
(c) $PbS(s) + 4O_3(g) \longrightarrow PbSO_4(s) + 4O_2(g)$
(d) $2ZnS(s) + 3O_2(g) \longrightarrow 2ZnO(s) + 2SO_2(g)$
(e) $2K_2O_2(s) + 2CO_2(g) \longrightarrow 2K_2CO_3(s) + O_2(g)$
(f) $3O_2(g) \xrightarrow{hv} 2O_3(g)$ **22.41** (a) acidic (b) acidic (c) amphoteric (d) basic **22.43** (a) $H_2SeO_3$, Se, +4 (b) $KHSO_3$, S, +4 (c) $H_2Te$, Te, −2 (d) $CS_2$, S, −2 (e) $CaSO_4$, S, +6 (f) CdS, S, −2 (g) ZnTe, Te, −2
**22.45** (a) $2Fe^{3+}(aq) + H_2S(aq) \longrightarrow 2Fe^{2+}(aq) + S(s) + 2H^+(aq)$
(b) $Br_2(l) + H_2S(aq) \longrightarrow 2Br^-(aq) + S(s) + 2H^+(aq)$
(c) $2MnO_4^-(aq) + 6H^+(aq) + 5H_2S(aq) \longrightarrow$
$\qquad 2Mn^{2+}(aq) + 5S(s) + 8H_2O(l)$
(d) $2NO_3^-(aq) + H_2S(aq) + 2H^+(aq) \longrightarrow$
$\qquad 2NO_2(aq) + S(s) + 2H_2O(l)$

**22.47**
(a)

Trigonal pyramidal

(b)

Bent (free rotation around S–S bond)

(c)

Tetrahedral (around S)

**22.49** (a) $SO_2(s) + H_2O(l) \rightleftharpoons H_2SO_3(aq) \rightleftharpoons H^+(aq) + HSO_3^-(aq)$
(b) $ZnS(s) + 2HCl(aq) \longrightarrow ZnCl_2(aq) + H_2S(g)$
(c) $8SO_3^{2-}(aq) + S_8(s) \longrightarrow 8S_2O_3^{2-}(aq)$
(d) $SO_3(aq) + H_2SO_4(l) \longrightarrow H_2S_2O_7(l)$
**22.51** (a) $NaNO_2$, +3 (b) $NH_3$, −3 (c) $N_2O$, +1 (d) NaCN, −3 (e) $HNO_3$, +5 (f) $NO_2$, +4 (g) $N_2$, 0 (h) BN, −3
**22.53** (a)

The molecule is bent around the central oxygen and nitrogen atoms; the four atoms need not be coplanar. The right-most form does not minimize formal charges and is less important in the actual bonding model. The oxidation state of N is +3.
(b)

The molecule is linear. The oxidation state of N is −1/3.
(c)

The geometry is tetrahedral around the left nitrogen, trigonal pyramidal around the right. The oxidation state of N is −2.
(d)

The ion is trigonal planar; it has three equivalent resonance forms. The oxidation state of N is +5.
**22.55** (a) $Mg_3N_2(s) + 6H_2O(l) \longrightarrow 3Mg(OH)_2(s) + 2NH_3(aq)$
(b) $2NO(g) + O_2(g) \longrightarrow 2NO_2(g)$, redox reaction
(c) $N_2O_5(g) + H_2O(l) \longrightarrow 2H^+(aq) + 2NO_3^-(aq)$
(d) $NH_3(aq) + H^+(aq) \longrightarrow NH_4^+(aq)$
(e) $N_2H_4(l) + O_2(g) \longrightarrow N_2(g) + 2H_2O(g)$, redox reaction
**22.57** (a) $HNO_2(aq) + H_2O(l) \longrightarrow NO_3^-(aq) + 2e^-$
(b) $N_2(g) + H_2O(l) \longrightarrow N_2O(aq) + 2H^+(aq) + 2e^-$
**22.59** (a) $H_3PO_3$, +3 (b) $H_4P_2O_7$, +5 (c) $SbCl_3$, +3 (d) $Mg_3As_2$, +5 (e) $P_2O_5$, +5 (f) $Na_3PO_4$, +5 **22.61** (a) Phosphorus is a larger atom than nitrogen, and P has energetically available $3d$ orbitals, which participate in the bonding, but nitrogen does not. (b) Only one of the three hydrogens in $H_3PO_2$ is bonded to oxygen. The other two are bonded directly to phosphorus and are not easily ionized. (c) $PH_3$ is a weaker base

than $H_2O$ so any attempt to add $H^+$ to $PH_3$ in the presence of $H_2O$ causes protonation of $H_2O$. (d) The $P_4$ molecules in white phosphorus have more severely strained bond angles than the chains in red phosphorus, causing white phosphorus to be more reactive.

**22.63** (a)
$2\,Ca_3PO_4(s) + 6\,SiO_2(s) + 10\,C(s) \longrightarrow P_4(g) + 6\,CaSiO_3(l) + 10\,CO(g)$
(b) $PBr_3(l) + 3\,H_2O(l) \longrightarrow H_3PO_3(aq) + 3\,HBr(aq)$
(c) $4\,PBr_3(g) + 6\,H_2(g) \longrightarrow P_4(g) + 12\,HBr(g)$
**22.65** (a) HCN (b) $Ni(CO)_4$ (c) $Ba(HCO_3)_2$ (d) $CaC_2$ (e) $K_2CO_3$
**22.67** (a) $ZnCO_3(s) \xrightarrow{\Delta} ZnO(s) + CO_2(g)$
(b) $BaC_2(s) + 2\,H_2O(l) \longrightarrow Ba^{2+}(aq) + 2\,OH^-(aq) + C_2H_2(g)$
(c) $2\,C_2H_2(g) + 5\,O_2(g) \longrightarrow 4\,CO_2(g) + 2\,H_2O(g)$
(d) $CS_2(g) + 3\,O_2(g) \longrightarrow CO_2(g) + 2\,SO_2(g)$
(e) $Ca(CN)_2(s) + 2\,HBr(aq) \longrightarrow CaBr_2(aq) + 2\,HCN(aq)$
**22.69**
(a) $2\,CH_4(g) + 2\,NH_3(g) + 3\,O_2(g) \xrightarrow{800\,°C} 2\,HCN(g) + 6\,H_2O(g)$
(b) $NaHCO_3(s) + H^+(aq) \longrightarrow CO_2(g) + H_2O(l) + Na^+(aq)$
(c) $2\,BaCO_3(s) + O_2(g) + 2\,SO_2(g) \longrightarrow 2\,BaSO_4(s) + 2\,CO_2(g)$
**22.71** (a) $H_3BO_3$, $+3$ (b) $SiBr_4$, $+4$ (c) $PbCl_2$, $+2$
(d) $Na_2B_4O_7 \cdot 10\,H_2O$, $+3$ (e) $B_2O_3$, $+3$ (f) $GeO_2$, $+4$ **22.73** (a) Tin (b) carbon, silicon, and germanium (c) silicon **22.75** (a) Tetrahedral (b) Metasilicic acid will probably adopt the single-strand silicate chain structure shown in Figure 22.34 (b). The Si to O ratio is correct and there are two terminal O atoms per Si that can accommodate the two H atoms associated with each Si atom of the acid. **22.77** (a) Diborane has bridging H atoms linking the two B atoms. The structure of ethane has the C atoms bound directly, with no bridging atoms. (b) $B_2H_6$ is an electron-deficient molecule. The 6 valence electron pairs are all involved in B—H sigma bonding, so the only way to satisfy the octet rule at B is to have the bridging H atoms shown in Figure 22.36. (c) The term *hydridic* indicates that the H atoms in $B_2H_6$ have more than the usual amount of electron density for a covalently bound H atom.
**22.81** (a) $SO_2(g) + H_2O(l) \rightleftharpoons H_2SO_3(aq)$
(b) $Cl_2O_7(g) + H_2O(l) \rightleftharpoons 2\,HClO_4(aq)$
(c) $Na_2O_2(s) + 2\,H_2O(l) \longrightarrow H_2O_2(aq) + 2\,NaOH(aq)$
(d) $BaC_2(s) + 2\,H_2O(l) \longrightarrow Ba^{2+}(aq) + 2\,OH^-(aq) + C_2H_2(g)$
(e) $2\,RbO_2(s) + 2\,H_2O(l) \longrightarrow$
$\qquad 2\,Rb^+(aq) + 2\,OH^-(aq) + O_2(g) + H_2O_2(aq)$
(f) $Mg_3N_2(s) + 6\,H_2O(l) \longrightarrow 3\,Mg(OH)_2(s) + 2\,NH_3(g)$
(g) $NaH(s) + H_2O(l) \longrightarrow NaOH(aq) + H_2(g)$ **22.85** (a) $PO_4^{3-}$, $+5$; $NO_3^-$, $+5$, (b) The Lewis structure for $NO_4^{3-}$ would be:

$$\left[\begin{array}{c} \ddot{\text{O}}: \\ | \\ :\ddot{\text{O}}-\text{N}-\ddot{\text{O}}: \\ | \\ :\ddot{\text{O}}: \end{array}\right]^{3-}$$

The formal charge on N is $+1$ and on each O atom is $-1$. The four electronegative oxygen atoms withdraw electron density, leaving the nitrogen deficient. Since N can form a maximum of four bonds, it cannot form a $\pi$ bond with one or more of the O atoms to regain electron density, as the P atom in $PO_4^{3-}$ does. Also, the short N—O distance would lead to a tight tetrahedron of O atoms subject to steric repulsion. **22.89** (a) $1.94 \times 10^3\,g\,H_2$ (b) $2.16 \times 10^4\,L\,H_2$ (c) $2.76 \times 10^5\,kJ$ **22.91** (a) $-285.83\,kJ/mol\,H_2$; $-890.4\,kJ/mol\,CH_4$ (b) $-141.79\,kJ/g\,H_2$; $-55.50\,kJ/g\,CH_4$ (c) $1.276 \times 10^4\,kJ/m^3\,H_2$; $3.975 \times 10^4\,kJ/m^3\,CH_4$ **22.95** (a) $SO_2(g) + 2\,H_2S(aq) \longrightarrow 3\,S(s) + 2\,H_2O(l)$ or $8\,SO_2(g) + 16\,H_2S(aq) \longrightarrow 3\,S_8(s) + 16\,H_2O(l)$ (b) $4.0 \times 10^3\,mol = 9.7 \times 10^4\,L\,H_2S$ (c) $1.9 \times 10^5\,g\,S$ produced **22.97** The average bond enthalpies are H—O, 463 kJ; H—S, 367 kJ; H—Se, 316 kJ; H—Te, 266 kJ. The H—X bond enthalpy decreases steadily in the series. The origin of this effect is probably the increasing size of the orbital from X with which the hydrogen 1s orbital must overlap. **22.101** Dimethylhydrazine produces 0.0369 mol gas per gram of reactants, while methylhydrazine produces 0.0388 mol gas per gram of reactants. Methylhydrazine has marginally greater thrust.

**22.103** (a) $3\,B_2H_6(g) + 6\,NH_3(g) \longrightarrow 2\,(BH)_3(NH)_3(l) + 12\,H_2(g)$;
$3\,LiBH_4(s) + 3\,NH_4Cl(s) \longrightarrow 2\,(BH)_3(NH)_3(l) + 9\,H_2(g) + 3\,LiCl(s)$
(b)

(c) $2.40\,g\,(BH)_3(NH)_3$

## CHAPTER 23

**23.2** (a)

(b) Coordination number = 4, coordination geometry = square planar (c) oxidation state = $+2$ **23.4** aminotrichloroplatinate(II) **23.6** Molecules (1), (3), and (4) are chiral because their mirror images are not superimposible on the original molecules. **23.8** (a) diagram (4) (b) diagram (1) (c) diagram (3) (d) diagram (2) **23.11** The lanthanide contraction is the name given to the decrease in atomic size due to the build-up in effective nuclear charge as we move through the lanthanides (elements 58–71) and beyond them. This effect offsets the expected increase in atomic size, decrease in ionization energy, and increase in electron affinity going from period 5 to period 6 transition elements. This causes the chemical properties of period 5 and period 6 elements in the same family to be even more similar than we would expect. **23.13** (a) All transition metal atoms have two s-electrons in their valence shell. Loss of these s-electrons leads to the $+2$ oxidation state common for most of the transition metals. **23.15** (a) $Ti^{3+}$, $[Ar]3d^1$ (b) $Ru^{2+}$, $[Kr]4d^6$ (c) $Au^{3+}$, $[Xe]4f^{14}5d^8$ (d) $Mn^{4+}$, $[Ar]3d^3$ **23.17** (a) The unpaired electrons in a paramagnetic material cause it to be weakly attracted into a magnetic field. A diamagnetic material, where all electrons are paired, is very weakly repelled by a magnetic field. **23.19** The diagram shows a material with misaligned spins that become aligned in the direction of an applied magnetic field. This is a paramagnetic material. **23.21** (a) In Werner's theory, *primary valence* is the charge of the metal cation at the center of the complex. *Secondary valence* is the number of atoms bound or coordinated to the central metal ion. The modern terms for these concepts are *oxidation state* and *coordination number*, respectively. (b) Ligands are the Lewis base in metal–ligand interactions. As such, they must possess at least one unshared electron pair. $NH_3$ has an unshared electron pair but $BH_3$, with less than 8 electrons about B, has no unshared electron pair and cannot act as a ligand. **23.23** (a) $+2$ (b) 6 (c) 2 mol $AgBr(s)$ will precipitate per mole of complex. **23.25** (a) Coordination number = 4, oxidation number = $+2$; 4 $Cl^-$ (b) 5, $+4$; 4 $Cl^-$, 1 $O^{2-}$ (c) 6, $+3$; 4 N, 2 $Cl^-$ (d) 5, $+2$; 5 C (e) 6, $+3$; 6 O (f) 4, $+2$; 4 N **23.27** (a) A monodentate ligand binds to a metal via one atom, a bidentate ligand binds through two atoms. (b) Three bidentate ligands fill the coordination sphere of a six-coordinate complex. (c) A tridentate ligand has at least three atoms with unshared electron pairs in the correct orientation to simultaneously bind one or more metal ions. **23.29** (a) *Ortho*-phenanthroline, o-phen, is bidentate (b) oxalate, $C_2O_4^{2-}$, is bidentate (c) ethylenediaminetetraacetate, EDTA, is pentadentate (d) ethylenediamine, en, is bidentate. **23.31** (a) The term *chelate effect* refers to the special stability associated with formation of a metal complex containing a polydentate (chelate) ligand relative to a complex containing only monodentate ligands. (b) The increase in entropy, $+\Delta S$, associated with the substitution of a chelating ligand for two or more monodentate ligands generally gives rise to the *chelate effect*. Chemical reactions with $+\Delta S$ tend to be spontaneous, have negative $\Delta G$ and large values of $K$. (c) Polydentate ligands are used as *sequestering agents* to bind metal ions and prevent them from undergoing unwanted chemical reactions without removing them from solution.  **23.33** The ligand is not typically a chelate. The entire molecule is planar and the benzene rings on either side of the two N atoms inhibit their approach in the correct orientation for chelation.  **23.35** (a) $[Cr(NH_3)_6](NO_3)_3$ (b) $[Co(NH_3)_4CO_3]_2SO_4$ (c)  $[Pt(en)_2Cl_2]Br_2$ (d) $K[V(H_2O)_2Br_4]$ (e) $[Zn(en)_2][HgI_4]$ **23.37** (a) tetraamminedichlororhodium(III) chloride (b) potassium hexachlorotitanate(IV)  (c)  tetrachlorooxomolybdenum(VI)  (d) tetraaqua(oxalato)platinum (IV) bromide

**23.39**

(b) $[Pd(NH_3)_2(ONO)_2]$, $[Pd(NH_3)_2(NO_2)_2]$

(c)

(d) $[Co(NH_3)_4Br_2]Cl$, $[Co(NH_3)_4BrCl]Br$  **23.41** Yes. No structural or stereoisomers are possible for a tetrahedral complex of the form $MA_2B_2$. The complex must be square planar with cis and trans geometric isomers.  **23.43** (a) One isomer (b) trans and cis isomers with 180° and 90° Cl—Ir—Cl angles, respectively (c) trans and cis isomers with 180° and 90° Cl—Fe—Cl angles, respectively. The cis isomer is optically active.  **23.45** (a) We cannot see the light with 300 nm wavelength, but we can see the 500 nm light. (b) *Complementary* colors are opposite each other on an artist's color wheel. (c) A colored metal complex absorbs visible light of its complementary color. (d) 196 kJ/mol  **23.47** No. All 6 $d$-electrons in a low-spin octahedral Fe(II) complex will pair and occupy the low-energy $d_{xy}$, $d_{xz}$, and $d_{yz}$ orbitals. With no unpaired electrons, the complex cannot be paramagnetic.  **23.49** Most of the attraction between a metal ion and a ligand is electrostatic. Whether the interaction is ion–ion or ion–dipole, the ligand is strongly attracted to the metal center and can be modeled as a point negative charge.

**23.51** (a)

(b) The magnitude of $\Delta$ and the energy of the $d$-$d$ transition for a $d^1$ complex are equal. (c) $\Delta = 220\,kJ/mol$  **23.53** A yellow color is due to absorption of light around 400 to 430 nm, a blue color to absorption near 620 nm. The shorter wavelength corresponds to a higher-energy electron transition and larger $\Delta$ value. Cyanide is a stronger-field ligand, and its complexes are expected to have larger $\Delta$ values than aqua complexes.  **23.55** (a) $Ti^{3+}$, $d^1$ (b) $Co^{3+}$, $d^6$ (c) $Ru^{3+}$, $d^5$ (d) $Mo^{5+}$, $d^1$, (e) $Re^{3+}$, $d^4$  **23.57** Yes. A weak-field ligand leads to a small $\Delta$ value and a small $d$-orbital splitting energy. If the splitting energy of a complex is smaller than the energy required to pair electrons in an orbital, the complex is high spin.  **23.59** (a) Mn, $[Ar]4s^23d^5$; $Mn^{2+}$, $[Ar]3d^5$; 1 unpaired electron (b) Ru, $[Kr]5s^14d^7$; $Ru^{2+}$, $[Kr]4d^6$; 0 unpaired electrons (c) Rh, $[Kr]5s^14d^8$; $Rh^{2+}$, $[Kr]4d^7$; 1 unpaired electron  **23.61** All complexes in this exercise are six-coordinate octahedral.

(a) [transcribed: 1 | (blank); 1 | 1 | 1]  $d^4$, high spin
(b) [1 | 1; 1 | 1 | 1]  $d^5$, high spin
(c) [(blank) | (blank); ⇅ | ⇅ | ⇅]  $d^6$, low spin

(d) [(blank) | (blank); ⇅ | ⇅ | 1]  $d^5$, low spin
(e) [(blank) | (blank); 1 | 1 | 1]  $d^3$
(f) [1 | 1; ⇅ | ⇅ | ⇅]  $d^8$

**23.63**

[1 | 1]
[1 | 1 | 1]

high spin

**23.67** $[Pt(NH_3)_6]Cl_4$; $[Pt(NH_3)_4Cl_2]Cl_2$; $[Pt(NH_3)_3Cl_3]Cl$; $[Pt(NH_3)_2Cl_4]$; $K[Pt(NH_3)Cl_5]$

**23.71** (a)

Both dmpe and en are bidentate ligands, binding through P and N, respectively. Because phosphorus is less electronegative than N, dmpe is a stronger electron pair donor and Lewis base than en. Dmpe creates a stronger ligand field and is higher on the spectrochemical series. Structurally, dmpe occupies a larger volume than en. M–P bonds are longer than M—N bonds and the two —CH$_3$ groups on each P atom in dmpe create more steric hindrance than the H atoms on N in en. (b) The oxidation state of Mo is zero. (c)The symbol P̄P̄ represents the bidentate dmpe ligand.

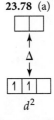

optical isomers

**23.74** (a) Hemoglobin is the iron-containing protein that transports O$_2$ in human blood. (b) Chlorophylls are magnesium-containing porphyrins in plants. They are the key components in the conversion of solar energy into chemical energy that can be used by living organisms. (c) Siderophores are iron-binding compounds or ligands produced by a microorganism. They compete on a molecular level for iron in the medium outside the organism and carry needed iron into the cells of the organism.  **23.76** (a) Pentacarbonyliron(0) (b) The oxidation state of iron must be zero. (c) Two. One isomer has CN in an axial position and the other has it in an equatorial position.

**23.78** (a)

[(blank) | (blank); 1 | 1 | (blank)]  $d^2$

(b) Visible light with $\lambda = hc/\Delta$ is absorbed by the complex, promoting one of the $d$ electrons into a higher-energy $d$-orbital. The remaining wavelengths are reflected or transmitted; the combination of these wavelengths is the color we see. (c) $[V(H_2O)_6]^{3+}$ will absorb light with

higher energy because it has a larger $\Delta$ than $[VF_6]^{3-}$. $H_2O$ is in the middle of the spectrochemical series and causes a larger $\Delta$ than $F^-$, a weak-field ligand. **23.80** $[Co(NH_3)_6]^{3+}$, yellow; $[Co(H_2O)_6]^{2+}$, pink; $[CoCl_4]^{2-}$, blue
**23.85**

(a)

(b) sodium dicarbonyltetracyanoferrate(II) (c) +2, 6 $d$-electrons (d) We expect the complex to be low spin. Cyanide (and carbonyl) are high on the spectrochemical series, which means the complex will have a large $\Delta$ splitting, characteristic of low-spin complexes. **23.91** (a) Yes, the oxidation state of Co is +3 in both complexes. (b) Compound A has $SO_4^{2-}$ outside the coordination sphere and coordinated $Br^-$, so it forms a precipitate with $BaCl_2(aq)$ but not $AgNO_3(aq)$. Compound B has $Br^-$ outside the coordination sphere and coordinated $SO_4^{2-}$, so it forms a precipitate with $AgNO_3(aq)$ but not $BaCl_2(aq)$. (c) Compounds A and B are coordination sphere isomers. (d) Both compounds are strong electrolytes. **23.94** The chemical formula is $[Pd(NC_5H_5)_2Br_2]$. This is an electrically neutral square-planar complex of Pd(II), a nonelectrolyte whose solutions do not conduct electricity. Because the dipole moment is zero, it must be the trans isomer. **23.96** 47.3 mg $Mg^{2+}$/L, 53.4 mg $Ca^{2+}$/L **23.99** $\Delta E = 3.02 \times 10^{-19}$ J/photon, $\lambda = 657$ nm. The complex will absorb in the visible around 660 nm and appear blue-green.

## CHAPTER 1

**page 5** (a) 100 (b) atoms

**page 10** Water is composed of two types of atoms: hydrogen and oxygen. Hydrogen is composed only of hydrogen atoms, and oxygen is composed only of oxygen atoms. Therefore, hydrogen and oxygen are elements and water is a compound.

**page 13** (a) Chemical change: Carbon dioxide and water are different compounds than sugar. (b) Physical change: Water in the gas phase becomes water in the solid phase (frost). (c) Physical change: Gold in the solid state becomes liquid and then resolidifies.

**page 16** pg, picogram ($10^{-12}$ g)

**page 19** $2.5 \times 10^2$ m$^3$ is, because it has units of length to the third power.

**page 21** (b) Mass of a penny

**page 27** Use all digits given in the conversion factor. Conversion factors may be exact and then have "infinite" significant digits (for example, 2.54 cm = 1 inch exactly). Usually, your answer will have its number of significant digits limited by those of the quantities given in the problem.

## CHAPTER 2

**page 41** (a) The law of multiple proportions. (b) The second compound must contain two oxygen atoms for each carbon atom (that is, twice as many carbon atoms as the first compound).

**page 44** Most $\alpha$ particles pass through the foil without being deflected because most of the volume of the atoms that comprise the foil is empty space.

**page 45** (a) The atom has 15 electrons because atoms have equal numbers of electrons and protons. (b) The protons reside in the nucleus of the atom.

**page 48** Any single atom of chromium must be one of the isotopes of that element. The isotope mentioned has a mass of 52.94 amu and is probably $^{53}$Cr. The atomic weight differs from the mass of any particular atom because it is the average atomic mass of the naturally occurring isotopes of the element.

**page 51** (a) Cl, (b) third period and group 7A, (c) 17, (d) nonmetal

**page 54** (a) $C_2H_6$, (b) $CH_3$, (c) Probably the ball-and-stick model because the angles between the sticks indicate the angles between the atoms

**page 57** We write the empirical formulas for ionic compounds. Thus, the formula is CaO.

**page 60** (a) The transition metals can form more than one type of cation, and the charges of these ions are therefore indicated explicitly with Roman numerals: Chromium(II) ion is $Cr^{2+}$. Calcium, on the other hand, always forms the $Ca^{2+}$ ion, so there is no need to distinguish it from other calcium ions with different charges. (b) The –*ium* ending indicates that the ion is formed from nonmetals.

**page 61** An -*ide* ending usually means a monatomic anion, although there are some anions with two atoms that are also named this way. An -*ate* ending indicates an oxyanion. The most common oxyanions have the -*ate* ending. An -*ite* ending also indicates an oxyanion, but one having less O than the anion whose name ends in -*ate*.

**page 62** $BO_3^{3-}$ and $SiO_4^{4-}$. The borate has three O atoms, like the other oxyanions of the second period in Figure 2.27, and its charge is 3−, following the trend of increasing negative charge as you move to the left in the period. The silicate has four O atoms, as do the other oxyanions in the third period in Figure 2.25, and its charge is 4−, also following the trend of increasing charge moving to the left.

**page 65** Iodic acid, by analogy to the relationship between the chlorate ion and chloric acid

**page 67**

## CHAPTER 3

**page 78** Each $Mg(OH)_2$ has 1 Mg, 2 O, and 2 H; thus, 3 $Mg(OH)_2$ represents 3 Mg, 6 O, and 6 H.

**page 83** The product is an ionic compound involving $Na^+$ and $S^{2-}$, and its chemical formula is therefore $Na_2S$.

**page 88** (a) A mole of glucose. By inspecting their chemical formulas we find that glucose has more atoms of H and O than water and in addition it also has C atoms. Thus, a molecule of glucose has a greater mass than a molecule of water. (b) They both contain the same number of molecules because a mole of each substance contains $6.02 \times 10^{23}$ molecules.

**page 93** The N:H ratio is 2:4 = 1:2.

**page 96** There are experimental uncertainties in the measurements.

**page 97** 3.14 mol because 2 mol $H_2 \hat{=} 1$ mol $O_2$ based on the coefficients in the balanced equation.

**page 98** The number of grams of product formed is the sum of the masses of the two reactants, 50 g. When two substances react in a combination reaction, only one substance is formed as a product. According to the law of conservation of mass, the mass of the product must equal the masses of the two reactants.

## CHAPTER 4

**page 118** (a) $K^+(aq)$ and $CN^-(aq)$, (b) $Na^+(aq)$ and $ClO_4^-(aq)$

**page 119** NaOH because it is the only solute that is a strong electrolyte

**page 123** $Na^+(aq)$ and $NO_3^-(aq)$

**page 125** Three. Each COOH group will partially ionize in water to form $H^+(aq)$.

**page 126** Only soluble metal hydroxides are classified as strong bases and $Al(OH)_3$ is insoluble.

**page 130** $SO_2(g)$

**page 133** (a) −3, (b) +5

**page 136** (a) Yes, nickel is below zinc in the activity series so $Ni^{2+}(aq)$ will oxidize $Zn(s)$ to form $Ni(s)$ and $Zn^{2+}(aq)$. (b) No reaction will occur because the $Zn^{2+}(aq)$ ions cannot be further oxidized.

**page 139** The second solution is more concentrated, 2.50 *M*, than the first solution, which has a concentration of 1.00 *M*.

**page 142** The concentration is halved to 0.25 *M*.

## CHAPTER 5

**page 162** No. The potential energy is lower at the bottom of the hill. (b) Once the bike comes to a stop, its kinetic energy is zero, just as it was at the top of the hill.

**page 163** Open system. Humans exchange matter and energy with their surroundings.

**page 167** Endothermic

**page 169** The balance (current state) does not depend on the ways the money may have been transferred into the account or on the particular expenditures made in withdrawing money from the account. It depends only on the net total of all the transactions.

**page 169** Because $E$, $P$, and $V$ are state functions that don't depend on path, $H = E + PV$ must also be a state function.

**page 170** No. If $\Delta V$ is zero, then the expression $w = -P\Delta V$ is also zero.

**page 171** A thermometer to measure temperature changes

**page 173** No. Because only half as much matter is involved, the value of $\Delta H$ would be $\frac{1}{2}(-483.6 \text{ kJ}) = -241.8 \text{ kJ}$.

**page 176** Hg($l$). Rearranging Equation 5.22 gives $\Delta T = \dfrac{q}{C_s \times m}$. When $q$ and $m$ are constant for a series of substances, then $\Delta T = \dfrac{\text{constant}}{C_s}$. Therefore, the element with the smallest $C_s$ in Table 5.2 has the largest $\Delta T$, Hg($l$).

**page 181** (a) The sign of $\Delta H$ changes. (b) The magnitude of $\Delta H$ doubles.

**page 184** No. Because $O_3(g)$ is not the most stable form of oxygen at 25 °C, 1 atm [$O_2(g)$ is], $\Delta H_f^\circ$ for $O_3(g)$ is not necessarily zero. In Appendix C we see that it is 142.3 kJ/mol.

**page 189** Fats, because they have the largest fuel value of the three

**page 191** Combustion of $H_2(g)$ produces only $H_2O(g)$. No $CO_2(g)$ or other gases that might contribute to climate change issues are produced.

## CHAPTER 6

**page 210** No. Both visible light and X-rays are forms of electromagnetic radiation. They therefore both travel at the speed of light, $c$. Their differing ability to penetrate skin is due to their different energies, which we will discuss in the next section.

**page 211** $E = h\nu = (6.63 \times 10^{-34} \text{ J-s})(5 \times 10^{-3} \text{ s}^{-1}) = 3 \times 10^{-30} \text{ J}$; this radiation cannot produce a burst of $5 \times 10^{-36}$ J because it can only produce energy in multiples of $3 \times 10^{-30}$ J.

**page 212** Ultraviolet. Figure 6.4 shows that a photon in the ultraviolet region of the electromagnetic spectrum has a higher frequency and therefore a greater energy than a photon in the infrared region.

**page 214** According to the third postulate, photons of only certain allowed frequencies can be absorbed or emitted as the electron changes energy state. The lines in the spectrum correspond to the allowed frequencies.

**page 215** Absorb, because it is moving from a lower-energy state ($n = 3$) to a higher-energy state ($n = 7$)

**page 217** Yes, all moving objects produce matter waves, but the wavelengths associated with macroscopic objects, such as the baseball, are too small to allow for any way of observing them.

**page 219** The small size and mass of subatomic particles. The term $h/4\pi$ in the uncertainty principle is a very small number that becomes important only when considering extremely small objects, such as electrons.

**page 220** Bohr proposed that the electron in the hydrogen atom moves in a well-defined circular path around the nucleus (an orbit). In the quantum-mechanical model, no effort is made to describe the motion of the electron. An orbital is a wave function related to the probability of finding the electron at any point in space.

**page 221** The energy of an electron in the hydrogen atom is proportional to $-1/n^2$, as seen in Equation 6.5. The difference between $-1/(2)^2$ and $-1/(1)^2$ is much greater than the difference between $-1/(3)^2$ and $-1/(2)^2$.

**page 226** (a) There is one 3$s$ orbital, three 3$p$ orbitals, and ten 3$d$ orbitals, for a total of 14 orbitals. (b) 3$s$ < 3$p$ < 3$d$.

**page 232** The 6$s$ orbital, which starts to hold electrons at element 55, Cs

**page 237** We can't conclude anything! Each of the three elements has a different valence electron configuration for its $(n-1)d$ and $ns$ subshells: For Ni, $3d^8 4s^2$; for Pd, $4d^{10}$; and for Pt, $5d^9 6s^1$.

## CHAPTER 7

**page 251** Atomic number is governed by the number of protons in the nucleus, but atomic weight is governed by both the number of protons and neutrons in the nucleus (electrons are too light to worry about). Co/Ni, Cu/Zn, and Te/I are other pairs of elements whose atomic weights are "off" compared to their atomic numbers.

**page 254** The 2$p$ electron in a Ne atom would experience a larger $Z_{\text{eff}}$ than the 3$s$ electron in Na, due to the better shielding by all the 2$s$ and 2$p$ electrons for Na's 3$s$ electron.

**page 256** These trends work against each other: $Z_{\text{eff}}$ increasing would imply that the valence electrons are pulled tighter in to make the atom smaller, while orbital size "increasing" would imply that atomic size would also increase. The orbital size effect is larger: As you go down a column in the periodic table, atomic size generally increases.

**page 259** It is harder to remove another electron from $Na^+$, so the process in Equation 7.3 would require more energy and, hence, shorter-wavelength light (see Sections 6.1 and 6.2).

**page 260** Since $Z_{\text{eff}}$ increases as you go from boron to carbon, we would expect that the first ionization energy would be larger for carbon. Therefore, $I_2$ for C is even greater.

**page 262** The same

**page 264** The numbers are the same; the signs are opposite.

**page 265** Increasing metallic character is correlated with decreasing ionization energy.

**page 268** Since the melting point is so low, we would expect a molecular rather than ionic compound. Thus, so $PCl_3$ is more likely than $ScCl_3$.

**page 270** Its low ionization energy

**page 272** In the acidic environment of the stomach, carbonate can react to give carbonic acid, which decomposes to water and carbon dioxide gas.

**page 274** The longest wavelength of visible light is about 750 nm (Section 6.1). We can assume that this corresponds to the lowest energy of light (since $E = hc/\lambda$) needed to break bonds in hydrogen peroxide. If we plug in 750 nm for $\lambda$, we can calculate the energy to break one OO bond in one molecule of hydrogen peroxide, in joules. If we multiple by Avogadro's number, we can calculate how many joules it would take to break a mole of OO bonds in hydrogen peroxide (which is the number one normally finds).

**page 275** The halogens all have ground-state electron configurations that are $ns^2 np^5$; sharing an electron with only one other atom makes stable compounds.

**page 276** We can estimate the radius to be 1.5 Å, and the first ionization energy to be 900 kJ/mol. In fact, its bonding radius is indeed 1.5 Å, and the experimental ionization energy is 920 kJ/mol.

## CHAPTER 8

**page 290** No. Cl has seven valence electrons. The first and second Lewis symbols are both correct—they both show seven valence electrons, and it doesn't matter which of the four sides has the single electron. The third symbol shows only five electrons and is incorrect.

**page 292** $CaF_2$ is an ionic compound consisting of $Ca^{2+}$ and $F^-$ ions. When Ca and $F_2$ react to form $CaF_2$, each Ca atom loses two electrons to form a $Ca^{2+}$ ion and each fluorine atom in $F_2$ takes up an electron, forming two $F^-$ ions. Thus, we can say that each Ca atom transfers one electron to each of two fluorine atoms.

*page 292* No. Figure 7.9 shows that the alkali metal with the smallest first ionization energy is Cs with a value of $+376$ kJ/mol. Figure 7.11 shows that the halogen with the largest electron affinity is Cl with a value of $-349$ kJ/mol. The sum of the two energies gives a positive energy (endothermic). Therefore, all other combinations of alkali metals with halogens will also have positive values.

*page 296* Rhodium, Rh

*page 297* Weaker. In both $H_2$ and $H_2^+$ the two H atoms are principally held together by the electrostatic attractions between the nuclei and the electron(s) concentrated between them. $H_2^+$ has only one electron between the nuclei whereas $H_2$ has two and this results in the H—H bond in $H_2$ being stronger.

*page 298* Triple bond. $CO_2$ has two C—O double bonds. Because the C—O bond in carbon monoxide is shorter, it is likely to be a triple bond.

*page 299* Electron affinity measures the energy released when an isolated atom gains an electron to form a $1-$ ion. The electronegativity measures the ability of the atom to hold on to its own electrons and attract electrons from other atoms in compounds.

*page 300* Polar covalent. The difference in electronegativity between S and O is $3.5 - 2.5 = 1.0$. Based on the examples of $F_2$, HF, and LiF, the difference in electronegativity is great enough to introduce some polarity to the bond but not sufficient to cause a complete electron transfer from one atom to the other.

*page 302* IF. Because the difference in electronegativity between I and F is greater than that between Cl and F, the magnitude of $Q$ should be greater for IF. In addition, because I has a larger atomic radius than Cl, the bond length in IF is longer than that in ClF. Thus, both $Q$ and $r$ are larger for IF and, therefore, $\mu = Qr$ will be larger for IF.

*page 303* Smaller dipole moment for C—H. The magnitude of $Q$ should be similar for C—H and H—I bonds because the difference in electronegativity for each bond is 0.4. The C—H bond length is 1.1 Å and the H—I bond length is 1.6 Å. Therefore $\mu = Qr$ will be greater for H—I because it has a longer bond (larger $r$).

*page 304* $OsO_4$. The data suggest that the yellow substance is a molecular species with its low melting and boiling points. Os in $OsO_4$ has an oxidation number of $+8$ and Cr in $Cr_2O_3$ has an oxidation number of $+3$. In Section 8.4, we learn that a compound with a metal in a high oxidation state should show a high degree of covalence and $OsO_4$ fits this situation.

*page 308* There is probably a better choice of Lewis structure than the one chosen. Because the formal charges must add up to 0 and the formal charge on the F atom is $+1$, there must be an atom that has a formal charge of $-1$. Because F is the most electronegative element, we don't expect it to carry a positive formal charge.

*page 310* Yes. There are two resonance structures for ozone that each contribute equally to the overall description of the molecule. Each O—O bond is therefore an average of a single bond and a double bond, which is a "one-and-a-half" bond.

*page 310* As "one-and-a-third" bonds. There are three resonance structures, and each of the three N—O bonds is single in two of those structures and double in the third. Each bond in the actual ion is an average of these: $(1 + 1 + 2)/3 = 1\frac{1}{3}$.

*page 312* No, it will not have multiple resonance structures. We can't "move" the double bonds, as we did in benzene, because the positions of the hydrogen atoms dictate specific positions for the double bonds. We can't write any other reasonable Lewis structures for the molecule.

*page 312* The formal charge of each atom is shown here:

$$\ddot{N}{=}\ddot{O} \qquad \ddot{N}{=}\ddot{O}$$
F.C.   0    0      $-1$   $+1$

The first structure shows each atom with a zero formal charge and therefore it is the dominant Lewis structure. The second one shows a positive formal charge for an oxygen atom, which is a highly electronegative atom, and this is not a favorable situation.

*page 315* The atomization of ethane produces $2\,C(g) + 6\,H(g)$. In this process, six C—H bonds and one C—C bond are broken. We can use $6D(C—H)$ to estimate the amount of enthalpy needed to break the six C—H bonds. The difference between that number and the enthalpy of atomization is an estimate of the bond enthalpy of the C—C bond, $D(C—C)$.

*page 315* $H_2O_2$. From Table 8.4, the bond enthalpy of the O—O single bond in $H_2O_2$ (146 kJ/mol) is much lower than that of the O=O bond in $O_2$ (495 kJ/mol). The weaker bond in $H_2O_2$ is expected to make it more reactive than $O_2$.

# CHAPTER 9

*page 334* Octahedral. Removing two atoms that are opposite each other leads to a square-planar geometry.

*page 335* The molecule does not follow the octet rule because it has ten electrons around the central A atom. There are four electron domains around A: two single bonds, one double bond, and one nonbonding pair.

*page 336* Each of the three represents a single electron domain in the VSEPR model.

*page 339* Yes. Based on one resonance structure, we might expect the electron domain that is due to the double bond to "push" the domains that are due to the single bonds, leading to angles slightly different from 120°. However, we must remember that there are two other equivalent resonance structures—each of the three O atoms has a double bond to N in one of the three resonance structures (Section 8.6). Because of resonance, all three O atoms are equivalent, and they will experience the same amount of repulsion, which leads to bond angles equal to 120°.

*page 339* A tetrahedral arrangement of electron domains is preferred because the bond angles are 109.5° compared to 90°. bond angles in a square-planar arrangement of electron domains. The larger bond angles result in smaller repulsions among electron domains and a more stable structure.

*page 343* Yes. The C—O and C—S bond dipoles exactly oppose each other, like in $CO_2$, but because O and S have different electronegativities, the magnitudes of the bond dipoles will be different. As a consequence, the bond dipoles will not cancel each other and the OCS molecule has a nonzero dipole moment.

*page 348* Both $p$ orbitals are perpendicular to the Be—F bond axes.

*page 348* (bottom) The unhybridized $p$ orbital is oriented perpendicular to the plane defined by the three $sp^2$ hybrids (trigonal-planar array of lobes) with one lobe on each side of the plane.

*page 353* The molecule should not be linear. Because there are three electron domains around each N atom, we expect $sp^2$ hybridization and H—N—N angles of approximately 120°. The molecule is expected to be planar; the unhybridized $2p$ orbitals on the N atoms can form a $\pi$ bond only if all four atoms lie in the same plane. You might notice that there are two ways in which the H atoms can be arranged: They can be both on the same side of the N=N bond or on opposite sides of the N=N bond.

*page 358* The $\sigma$ bond component is formed from $sp$ hybrid orbitals.

*page 360* The molecule would fall apart. With one electron in the bonding MO and one in the antibonding MO, there is no net stabilization of the electrons relative to two separate H atoms.

*page 362* Yes. In $Be_2^+$ there would be two electrons in the $\sigma_{2s}$ MO but only one electron in the $\sigma_{2s}^*$ MO; therefore, the ion is predicted to have a bond order of $\frac{1}{2}$. It should (and does) exist.

*page 366* No. If the $\sigma_{2p}$ MO were lower in energy than the $\pi_{2p}$ MOs, we would expect the $\sigma_{2p}$ MO to hold two electrons and the $\pi_{2p}$ MOs to hold one electron each, with the same spin. The molecule would therefore be paramagnetic.

## CHAPTER 10

*page 384* Small

*page 385* 1470 lb

*page 389* It would be halved.

*page 390* No—you have to convert $T$ to Kelvin to calculate this properly.

*page 392* Avogadro's number, $6.022 \times 10^{23}$

*page 396* Less dense

*page 399* The pressure due to $N_2$ would be the same, but the total pressure would increase.

*page 404* HCl (slowest) $< O_2 < H_2$ (fastest)

*page 406* 3/2

*page 409* (a) Decrease, (b) No change

*page 410* (b) 100 K and 5 atm

*page 411* They do have intermolecular attractions for each other, and they do take up space.

## CHAPTER 11

*page 430* $CH_4 < CCl_4 < CBr_4$. Because all three molecules are nonpolar, the strength of dispersion forces determines the relative boiling points. Polarizability increases in order of increasing molecular size and molecular weight, $CH_4 < CCl_4 < CBr_4$; hence, the dispersion forces and boiling points increase in the same order.

*page 434* $Ca(NO_3)_2$ in water, because calcium nitrate is a strong electrolyte that forms ions and water is a polar molecule with a dipole moment. Ion–dipole forces cannot be present in a $CH_3OH/H_2O$ mixture because $CH_3OH$ does not form ions.

*page 438* (a) Both viscosity and surface tension decrease with increasing temperature because of the increased molecular motion. (b) Both properties increase as the strength of intermolecular forces increases.

*page 440* Melting (or fusion), endothermic

*page 443* $CCl_4$. Both compounds are nonpolar; therefore, only dispersion forces exist between the molecules. Because dispersion forces are stronger for the larger, heavier $CBr_4$, it has a lower vapor pressure than $CCl_4$. The substance with the larger vapor pressure at a given temperature is more volatile.

## CHAPTER 12

*page 466* Tetragonal. There are two three-dimensional lattices that have a square base with a third vector perpendicular to the base, tetragonal and cubic, but in a cubic lattice the $a$, $b$, and $c$ lattice vectors are all of the same length.

*page 473* The packing efficiency decreases as the number of nearest neighbors decreases. The structures with the highest packing efficiency, hexagonal and cubic close packing, both have atoms with a coordination number of 12. Body-centered cubic packing, where the coordination number is 8, has a lower packing efficiency, and primitive cubic packing, where the coordination number is 6, has a lower packing efficiency still.

*page 474* Interstitial, because boron is a small nonmetal atom that can fit in the voids between the larger palladium atoms

*page 481* (a) Gold, Au. Tungsten, W, lies near the middle of the transition metal series where the bands arising from the $d$ orbitals and the $s$ orbital are approximately half-filled. This electron count should fill the bonding orbitals and leave the antibonding orbitals mostly empty. (b) Because both elements have similar numbers of electrons in the bonding orbitals but tungsten has fewer electrons in antibonding orbitals, it will have a higher melting point.

*page 482* No. In a crystal the lattice points must be identical. Therefore, if an atom lies on top of a lattice point, then the same type of atom must lie on all lattice points. In an ionic compound there are at least two different types of atoms, and only one can lie on the lattice points.

*page 484* Four. The empirical formula of potassium oxide is $K_2O$. Rearranging Equation 12.1 we can determine the potassium coordination number to be anion coordination number × (number of anions per formula unit/number of cations per formula unit) $= 8(1/2) = 4$.

*page 494* A condensation polymer. The presence of both —COOH and —NH₂ groups allow molecules to react with one another forming C—N bonds and splitting out $H_2O$.

*page 495* As the vinyl acetate content increases more side chain branching occurs which inhibits the formation of crystalline regions thereby lowering the melting point.

*page 498* No. The emitted photons have energies that are similar in energy to the band gap of the semiconductor. If the size of the crystals is reduced into the nanometer range, the band gap will increase. However, because 340-nm light falls in the UV region of the electromagnetic spectrum, increasing the energy of the band gap will only shift the light deeper into the UV.

## CHAPTER 13

*page 514* Energy (or enthalpy) and entropy

*page 515* The lattice energy of $NaCl(s)$ must be overcome to separate $Na^+$ and $Cl^-$ ions and disperse them into a solvent. $C_6H_{14}$ is nonpolar. Interactions between ions and nonpolar molecules tend to be very weak. Thus, the energy required to separate the ions in NaCl is not recovered in the form of ion–$C_6H_{14}$ interactions.

*page 517* (a) Separating solvent molecules from each other requires energy and is therefore endothermic. (b) Forming the solute–solvent interactions is exothermic.

*page 519* The added solute provides a template for the solid to begin to crystallize from solution, and the excess dissolved solute comes out of solution leaving a saturated solution.

*page 522* The solubility in water would be considerably lower because there would no longer be hydrogen bonding with water, which promotes solubility.

*page 526* Dissolved gases become less soluble as temperature increases, and they come out of solution, forming bubbles below the boiling point of water.

*page 526* 230 ppm (1 ppm is 1 part in $10^6$); $2.30 \times 10^5$ ppb (1 ppb is 1 part in $10^9$).

*page 528* For dilute aqueous solutions the molality will be nearly equal to the molarity. Molality is the number of moles of solute per kilogram of solvent, whereas molarity is the number moles of solute per liter of solution. Because the solution is dilute, the mass of solvent is essentially equal to the mass of the solution. Furthermore, a dilute aqueous solution will have a density of 1.0 kg/L. Thus, the number of liters of solution and the number of kilograms of solvent will be essentially equal.

*page 531* The lowering of the vapor pressure depends on the total solute concentration (Equation 13.11). One mole of NaCl (a strong electrolyte) provides 2 mol of particles (1 mol of $Na^+$ and 1 mol of Cl), whereas one mole of (a nonelectrolyte) provides only 1 mol particles.

*page 534* Not necessarily; if the solute is a strong or weak electrolyte, it could have a lower molality and still cause an increase of 0.51 °C. The total molality of all the particles in the solution is 1 m.

*page 537* The 0.20-m solution is hypotonic with respect to the 0.5-m solution. (A hypotonic solution will have a lower concentration and hence a lower osmotic pressure.)

*page 539* They would have the same osmotic pressure because they have the same concentration of particles. (Both are strong electrolytes that are 0.20 $M$ in total ions.)

*page 543* The smaller droplets carry negative charges because of the embedded stearate ions and thus repel one another.

# CHAPTER 14

*page 559* The rate will increase.

*page 562* Average rate is for a large time interval; instantaneous rate is for an "instant" in time. Yes, they can have the same numeric value, especially if a plot of concentration versus time is linear.

*page 565* (top) Reaction rate is what we measure as a reaction proceeds—change in concentration in time for one or more of the components in the mixture. Reaction rate always has units of concentration per time, usually $M/s$. A rate constant is what we calculate from reaction rate data, and its magnitude is proportional to the reaction rate, but its units depend on the reaction order. The rate law of a reaction is an equation that relates reaction rate to the rate constant: Rate = $k[A]^m[B]^n$, for components A and B in the reaction.

*page 565* No. Rate is always change in concentration per time; rate constant has units that depend on the form of the rate law.

*page 566* (a) The reaction is second order in NO, first order in $H_2$, and third order overall. (b) No. Doubling NO concentration will quadruple the rate, but doubling $H_2$ concentration will merely double the rate.

*page 567* No reaction will take place.

*page 573* 1.25 g

*page 575* The half-life will increase.

*page 578* No—transition states are by definition not stable.

*page 578* The collision may not have occurred with enough energy for reaction to occur, and/or the collision may not have occurred with the proper orientation of reactant molecules to favor product formation.

*page 581* Bimolecular

*page 585* Most reactions occur in elementary steps; the rate law is governed by the elementary steps, not by their sum (which is the overall balanced equation).

*page 587* The odds of three molecules colliding with each other properly to react is very low.

*page 590* By lowering the activation energy for the reaction or by increasing the frequency factor

*page 591* A homogeneous catalyst will be harder to separate from the reaction mixture than a heterogeneous one.

*page 593* People do say this, but we have to be careful. An enzyme-catalyzed reaction will have a lower transition state energy than the uncatalyzed reaction, but the nature of the transition state is probably different than the uncatalyzed version.

# CHAPTER 15

*page 614* (a) The rates of the forward and reverse reactions. (b) Greater than 1

*page 614* When the concentrations of reactants and products are no longer changing

*page 617* It does not depend on starting concentrations.

*page 617* Units of moles/L are used to calculate $K_c$; units of partial pressure are used to calculate $K_p$.

*page 618* 0.00140

*page 621* It is cubed.

*page 623* $K_p = P_{H_2O}$

*page 625* $K_c = [NH_4^+][OH^-]/[NH_3]$

*page 633* (a) It shifts to the right. (b) It shifts to the left.

*page 633* (bottom) It will shift to the left, the side with a larger number of moles of gas.

*page 636* As the temperature increases, a larger fraction of molecules in the liquid phase have enough energy to overcome their inter-molecular attractions and go into the vapor; the evaporation process is endothermic.

*page 638* No

# CHAPTER 16

*page 652* The $H^+$ ion for acids and the $OH^-$ ion for bases

*page 654* $CH_3NH_2$ is the base because it accepts a $H^+$ from $H_2S$ as the reaction moves from the left-hand to the right-hand side of the equation.

*page 657* As the conjugate base of a strong acid, we would classify $ClO_4^-$ as having negligible basicity.

*page 661* pH is defined as $-\log[H^+]$. This quantity will become negative if the $H^+$ concentration exceeds 1 $M$, which is possible. Such a solution would be highly acidic.

*page 662* pH = $14.00 - 3.00 = 11.00$. This solution is basic because pH > 7.0.

*page 665* Both NaOH and $Ba(OH)_2$ are soluble hydroxides. Therefore, the hydroxide concentrations will be 0.001 $M$ for NaOH and 0.002 $M$ for $Ba(OH)_2$. Because the $Ba(OH)_2$ solution has a higher $[OH^-]$, it is more basic and has a higher pH.

*page 666* Because $CH_3^-$ is the conjugate base of a substance that has negligible acidity, $CH_3^-$ must be a strong base. Bases stronger than $OH^-$ abstract $H^+$ from water molecules:
$$CH_3^- + H_2O \longrightarrow CH_4 + OH^-.$$

*page 668* Oxygen

*page 671* Because weak acids typically undergo very little ionization, often less than 1%. Normally we make this assumption and then check its validity based on the concentration of conjugate base formed in the calculation. If it is ≤5% of the initial concentration of the weak acid, we can generally use this assumption. If not, we must do an exact calculation.

*page 674* This is the acid-dissociation constant for the loss of the third and final proton from $H_3PO_4$, corresponding to the equilibrium $HPO_4^{2-} \rightleftharpoons H^+ + PO_4^{3-}$.

*page 680* The $pK_a$ value is $-\log K_a = -\log(6.8 \times 10^{-4}) = 3.17$. The $pK_b$ value is $14.00 - pK_a = 14.00 - 3.17 = 10.83$.

*page 682* Nitrate is the conjugate base of nitric acid, $HNO_3$. The conjugate base of a strong acid does not act as a base, so $NO_3^-$ ions will not affect the pH. Carbonate is the conjugate base of hydrogen carbonate, $HCO_3^-$, which is a weak acid. The conjugate base of a weak acid acts as a weak base, so $CO_3^{2-}$ ions will increase the pH.

*page 686* The increasing acidity going down a group is due mainly to decreasing H—X bond strength. The trend going across a period is due mainly to the increasing electronegativity of X, which weakens the H—X bond.

*page 687* $HBrO_3$. For an oxyacid, acidity increases as the electronegativity of the central ion increases, which would make $HBrO_2$ more acidic than $HIO_2$. Acidity also increases as the number of oxygens bound to the central atom increases, which would make $HBrO_3$ more acidic than $HBrO_2$. Combining these two relationships we can order these acids in terms of increasing acid-dissociation constant, $HIO_2 < HBrO_2 < HBrO_3$.

*page 689* The carboxyl group, —COOH

*page 690* It must have an unshared pair of electrons that can be shared with another atom.

# CHAPTER 17

*page 707* (top) The $Cl^-$ ion is the only spectator ion. The pH is determined by the equilibrium $NH_3(aq) + H_2O(l) \rightleftharpoons OH^-(aq) + NH_4^+(aq)$.

*page 707* (bottom) $HNO_3$ and $NO_3^-$. To form a buffer we need comparable concentrations of a weak acid and its conjugate base.

HNO$_3$ and NO$_3^-$ will not form a buffer because HNO$_3$ is a strong acid and the NO$_3^-$ ion is merely a spectator ion.

***page 708*** (a) The OH$^-$ of NaOH (a strong base) reacts with the acid member of the buffer (CH$_3$COOH), abstracting a proton. Thus, [CH$_3$COOH] decreases and [CH$_3$COO$^-$] increases. (b) The H$^+$ of HCl (a strong acid) reacts with the base member of the buffer [CH$_3$COOH$^-$]. Thus, [CH$_3$COO$^-$] decreases and [CH$_3$COOH] increases.

***page 711*** A buffer will be most resistant to changes in pH when the concentrations of the weak acid and its conjugate base are equal. When the two are exactly equal the Henderson–Hasselbach equation tells us that the pH of the buffer will be equal to the p$K_a$ of the weak acid. The p$K_a$ values of nitrous acid and hypochlorous acid are 3.35 and 7.52, respectively. Thus, HClO would be more suitable for a pH = 7.0 buffer solution. To make a buffer we would also need a salt containing ClO$^-$, such as NaClO.

***page 716*** The pH = 7. The neutralization of a strong base with a strong acid gives a salt solution at the equivalence point. The salt contains ions that do not change the pH of water.

***page 721*** The following titration curve shows the titration of 25 mL of Na$_2$CO$_3$ with HCl, both with 0.1 $M$ concentrations. The overall reaction between the two is

$$Na_2CO_3(aq) + HCl(aq) \longrightarrow 2\,NaCl(aq) + CO_2(g) + H_2O(l)$$

The initial pH (sodium carbonate in water only) is near 11 because CO$_3^{2-}$ is a weak base in water. The graph shows two equivalence points, **A** and **B**. The first point, **A**, is reached at a pH of about 9:

$$Na_2CO_3(aq) + HCl(aq) \longrightarrow NaCl(aq) + NaHCO_3(aq)$$

HCO$_3^-$ is weakly basic in water and is a weaker base than the carbonate ion. The second point, **B**, is reached at a pH of about 4:

$$NaHCO_3(aq) + HCl(aq) \longrightarrow NaCl(aq) + CO_2(g) + H_2O(l)$$

H$_2$CO$_3$, a weak acid, forms and decomposes to carbon dioxide and water.

***page 722*** The nearly vertical portion of the titration curve at the equivalence point is smaller for a weak acid–strong base titration; as a result fewer indicators undergo their color change within this narrow range.

***page 724*** AgCl. Because all three compounds produce the same number of ions, their relative stabilities correspond directly to the $K_{sp}$ values, with the compound with the largest $K_{sp}$ value being the most soluble.

***page 734*** Amphoteric substances are insoluble in water but dissolve in the presence of sufficient acid or base. Amphiprotic substances can both donate and accept protons.

***page 738*** The solution must contain one or more of the cations in group 1 of the qualitative analysis scheme, Ag$^+$, Pb$^{2+}$ or Hg$_2^{2+}$.

# CHAPTER 18

***page 754*** Photoionization is a process in which a molecule breaks into ions upon illumination with light; photodissociation is a process in which molecules break up upon illumination with light but the products bear no charge.

***page 755*** Because those molecules do not absorb light at those wavelengths

***page 757*** Yes—Cl is neither a product nor a reactant in the overall reaction, and its presence does speed the reaction up.

***page 760*** SO$_2$ in the atmosphere reacts with oxygen to form SO$_3$. SO$_3$ in the atmosphere reacts with water in the atmosphere to form H$_2$SO$_4$, sulfuric acid. The sulfuric acid dissolves in water droplets that fall to Earth, causing "acid rain" that has a pH of 4 or so.

***page 761*** NO$_2$ photodissociates to NO and O; the O atoms react with O$_2$ in the atmosphere to form ozone, which is a key ingredient in photochemical smog.

***page 763*** Higher humidity means there is more water in the air. Water absorbs infrared light, which we feel as heat. After sundown, the ground that has been warmed earlier in the day reradiates heat out. In locations with higher humidity, this energy is absorbed somewhat by the water and in turn is reradiated to some extent back to the Earth, resulting in warmer temperatures compared to a low-humidity location.

***page 764*** We need to be below water's critical point. Therefore, to sublime water we need to be below 0.006 atm. A wide range of temperatures will work for sublimation at this pressure—the most environmentally relevant ones are −50 °C to 100 °C.

***page 768*** The pollutants are capable of being oxidized (either directly by reaction with dissolved oxygen or indirectly by the action of organisms such as bacteria).

***page 772*** With a catalyst, the reaction is always faster, therefore costing less energy to run. In addition, with a catalyst the reaction may occur readily at a lower temperature, also costing less energy.

***page 773*** Fossil fuel combustion puts a great deal more CO$_2$ in the atmosphere right now than any supercritical use of CO$_2$. Compared to other (halogenated organic) solvents, supercritical CO$_2$ is far less toxic to life. Therefore, at present, using CO$_2$ as a solvent or a reactant in industrial processes is a reasonable choice for environmental sustainability.

***page 774*** Use room temperature and room pressure; use water as a solvent if possible; use O$_2$ as the oxidizing agent instead of hydrogen peroxide if possible.

***page 775*** $sp$ before reaction; $sp^2$ after reaction

# CHAPTER 19

***page 787*** No, nonspontaneous processes can occur so long as they receive some continuous outside assistance. Examples of nonspontaneous processes with which we may be familiar include the building of a brick wall and the electrolysis of water to form hydrogen gas and oxygen gas.

***page 789*** No. Just because the system is restored to its original condition doesn't mean that the surroundings have likewise been restored to their original condition, so it is not necessarily reversible.

***page 791*** $\Delta S$ depends not merely on $q$ but on $q_{rev}$. Although there are many possible paths that could take a system from its initial to final state, there is always only one reversible isothermal path between two states. Thus, $\Delta S$ has only one particular value regardless of the path taken between states.

***page 793*** Because rusting is a spontaneous process, $\Delta S_{univ}$ must be positive. Therefore, the entropy of the surroundings must increase, and that increase must be larger than the entropy decrease of the system.

***page 795*** $S = 0$, based on Equation 19.5 and the fact that ln 1 = 0.

*page* 796 A molecule can vibrate (atoms moving relative to one another) and rotate (tumble), whereas a single atom cannot undergo these motions.

*page* 799 It must be a perfect crystal at 0 K (third law of thermodynamics), which means it has only a single accessible microstate.

*page* 803 $\Delta S_{surr}$ always increases. For simplicity, assume that the process is isothermal. The change in entropy of the surroundings in an isothermal process is $\Delta S_{surr} = \dfrac{-q_{sys}}{T}$. Because the reaction is exothermic, $-q_{sys}$ is a positive number. Thus, $\Delta S_{surr}$ is a positive number and the entropy of the surroundings increases.

*page* 805 (a) In any spontaneous process the entropy of the universe increases. (b) In any spontaneous process operating at constant temperature, the free energy of the system decreases.

*page* 806 It indicates that the process to which the thermodynamic quantity refers has taken place under standard conditions, as summarized in Table 19.2.

*page* 810 Above the boiling point, vaporization is spontaneous, and $\Delta G < 0$. Therefore, $\Delta H - T\Delta S < 0$, and $\Delta H < T\Delta S$.

## CHAPTER 20

*page* 829 Oxygen is first assigned an oxidation number of $-2$. Nitrogen must then have a $+3$ oxidation number for the sum of oxidation numbers to equal $-1$, the charge of the ion.

*page* 832 No. Electrons should appear in the two half-reactions but cancel when the half-reactions are added properly.

*page* 839 Yes. A redox reaction with a positive standard cell potential is spontaneous under standard conditions.

*page* 840 1 atm pressure of $Cl_2(g)$ and 1 $M$ concentration of $Cl^-(aq)$

*page* 846 Using data from Appendix E, we have $E^\circ_{red} = -0.126\,V$ for $Pb^{2+}(aq) \rightarrow Pb(s)$ and $E^\circ_{red} = 0.854\,V$ for $Hg^{2+}(aq) \rightarrow Hg(l)$. Because $Pb(s)$ has the most negative value for $E^\circ_{red}$, it is the stronger reducing agent. (See Figure 20.12.) The comparison can also be made by reference to the activity series where Pb lies also above Hg, indicating that Pb is oxidized more readily than Hg. The more readily a substance is oxidized, the stronger it is as a reducing agent.

*page* 859 Al, Zn. Both are easier to oxidize than Fe.

## CHAPTER 21

*page* 877 The mass number decreases by 4.

*page* 879 Only the neutron, as it is the only neutral particle listed.

*page* 883 From Figure 21.4 we can see that each of these four elements has only one stable isotope, and from their atomic numbers we see that they each have an odd number of protons. Given the rarity of stable isotopes with odd numbers of neutrons and protons, we expect that each isotope will possess an even number of neutrons. From their atomic weights we see that this is the case: F (10 neutrons), Na (12 neutrons), Al (14 neutrons), and P (16 neutrons).

*page* 885 No. Electric and magnetic fields are only effective at accelerating charged particles and a neutron is not charged.

*page* 889 top Spontaneous radioactive decay is a unimolecular process: A $\rightarrow$ Products. The rate law that fits this observation is a first-order kinetic rate law, rate $= k[A]$. A second-order kinetic process has rate $= k[A]^2$ and the elementary reaction is bimolecular: A + A $\rightarrow$ Products. A zero-order kinetic process has rate $= k$, and the rate does not change until the limiting reactant is entirely consumed. The latter two rate laws do not fit a unimolecular process.

*page* 889 (bottom) (a) Yes; doubling the mass would double the amount of radioactivity of the sample as shown in Equation 21.18. (b) No; changing the mass would not change the half-life as shown in Equation 21.20.

*page* 892 No. Alpha particles are more readily absorbed by matter than beta or gamma rays. Geiger counters must be calibrated for the radiation they are being used to detect.

*page* 896 (top) The values in Table 21.7 only reflect the mass of the nucleus, while the atomic mass is the sum of the mass of the nucleus and the electrons. So the atomic mass of iron-56 is $26 \times m_e$ larger than the nuclear mass.

*page* 896 (bottom) No. Stable nuclei having mass numbers around 100 are the most stable nuclei. They could not form a still more stable nucleus with an accompanying release of energy.

*page* 905 The absorbed dose is equal to $0.10\,J \times (1\,rad/1 \times 10^{-2}\,J) = 10$ rads. The effective dosage is calculated by multiplying the absorbed dose by the relative biological effectiveness (RBE) factor, which is 10 for alpha radiation. Thus, the effective dosage is 100 rems.

## CHAPTER 22

*page* 919 (top) No.

*page* 919 No. N can form triple bonds but P cannot, as it would have to form $P_2$.

*page* 921 $H^-$, hydride.

*page* 923 $+1$ for everything except $H_2$, for which the oxidation state of H is 0.

*page* 924 No—it is the volume of Pd that can increase to accommodate hydrogen, not its mass.

*page* 927 0 for $Cl_2$; $-1$ for $Cl^-$; $+1$ for $ClO^-$

*page* 929 They should both be strong, since the central halogen is in the $+5$ oxidation state for both of them. We need to look up the redox potentials to see which ion, $BrO_3^-$ or $ClO_3^-$, has the larger reduction potential. The ion with the larger reduction potential is the stronger oxidizing agent. $BrO_3^-$ is the stronger oxidizing agent on this basis ($+1.52$ V standard reduction potential in acid compared to $+1.47$ V for $ClO_3^-$).

*page* 931 The standard energy to dissociate one mole of oxygen atoms from one mole of ozone was given as 105 kJ. If we assume, as usual, that one photon will dissociate one molecule, that means the energy of the photons should be 105 kJ per mole (of photons). Using Avogadro's number, we can calculate that one photon would then have $1.744 \times 10^{-19}$ J of energy. Using equations from Chapter 6, $c = \lambda\nu$ and $E = h\nu$, we can find that a photon with $1.744 \times 10^{-19}$ J of energy will have a wavelength $\lambda$ of 1140 nm, or $1.14 \times 10^6$ m, which is in the infrared part of the spectrum.

*page* 932 $HIO_3$

*page* 936 $SO_3(g) + H_2O(l) \longrightarrow H_2SO_4(l)$

*page* 940 (a) $+5$ (b) $+3$

*page* 948 $CO_2(g)$

*page* 949 Yes, it must, since $CS_2$ is a liquid at room temperature and pressure, and $CO_2$ is a gas.

*page* 952 Silicon is the element, Si. Silica is $SiO_2$. Silicones are polymers that have an $O-Si-O$ backbone and hydrocarbon groups on the Si.

*page* 953 $+3$

## CHAPTER 23

*page* 965 Sc is the biggest.

*page* 967 You would have to remove core electrons.

*page* 968 (top) The larger the distance, the weaker the spin–spin interactions.

*page* 968 (bottom) Yes, it is a Lewis acid–base interaction; the metal ion is the Lewis acid (electron pair acceptor).

*page* 972 $[Fe(H_2O)_6]^{3+}(aq) + SCN^-(aq) \longrightarrow$
$$[Fe(H_2O)_5SCN]^{2+}(aq) + H_2O(l)$$

*page 974* (a) tetrahedral (b) octahedral

*page 976* Bidentate

*page 978* Its conjugation (alternating single and double CC bonds)

*page 981* No, ammonia cannot engage in linkage isomerism—the only atom that can coordinate to a metal is the nitrogen.

*page 985* Both isomers have the same chemical formulas and the same donor atoms on the ligands bonding to the metal ion. The difference is that the *d* isomer has a right-handed "twist" and the *l* isomer has a "left-handed" twist.

*page 987* Co is $1s^2 2s^2 2p^6 3s^2 3p^6 4s^2 3d^7$. $Co^{3+}$ is $1s^2 2s^2 2p^6 3s^2 3p^6 3d^6$. Co has 3 unpaired electrons; $Co^{3+}$ has 4 unpaired electrons, assuming all 5 *d* orbitals have the same energy.

*page 989* It has lost all of the Ti valence electrons; only core electrons remain, and the energy gap between filled and empty orbitals is large, corresponding to light in the ultraviolet, which we cannot perceive as colored.

*page 991* Low spin

*page 992* The ligands are in the *xy* plane. The $d_{xy}$ orbital has its lobes mostly in that plane, so its energy is higher than $d_{xz}$ and $d_{yz}$.

# CHAPTER 1

*Figure 1.1* 9

*Figure 1.4* Vapor (gas)

*Figure 1.5* Molecules of a compound are composed of more than one type of atom, and molecules of an element are composed of only one type of atom.

*Figure 1.6* Earth is rich in silicon and aluminum; the human body is rich in carbon and hydrogen

*Figure 1.7* They are the same; there are twice as many hydrogen molecules as oxygen molecules, and the hydrogen gas takes up twice the volume of the oxygen gas.

*Figure 1.17* True

*Figure 1.18* 1000

*Figure 1.23* The darts would be scattered widely (poor precision) but their average position would be at the center (good accuracy).

# CHAPTER 2

*Figure 2.3* We know the rays travel from the cathode because of the way the magnetic field diverts the path (b).

*Figure 2.4* The electron beam would be deflected downward because of repulsion by the negative plate and attraction toward the positive plate.

*Figure 2.8* The beta rays, whose path is diverted away from the negative plate and toward the positive plate, consist of electrons. Because the electrons are much less massive than the alpha particles, their motion is affected more strongly by the electric field.

*Figure 2.10* The beam consists of alpha particles, which carry a +2 charge.

*Figure 2.14* Based on the periodic trend, we expect that elements that precede a nonreactive gas, as F does, will also be reactive nonmetals. The elements fitting this pattern are H and Cl.

*Figure 2.19* The ball-and-stick model more clearly shows the connections between atoms, so we can see the angles at which the atoms are attached in the molecule.

*Figure 2.20* The elements are in the following groups: $Ag^+$ is 1B, $Zn^{2+}$ is 2B, and $Sc^{3+}$ is 3B. $Sc^{3+}$ has the same number of electrons as Ar (element 18).

*Figure 2.24* Removing one O atom from the perbromate ion gives the bromate ion, $BrO_3^-$.

# CHAPTER 3

*Figure 3.3* The formula $CO_2$ represents one molecule containing one C and two O atoms, whereas 2 CO represents two molecules, each containing one C atom and one O atom for a total of two C and two O atoms.

*Figure 3.8* Both figures show combustion reactions in which the fuel is a hydrocarbon ($CH_4$ in Figure 3.4 and $C_3H_8$ in Figure 3.8). In both cases the reactants are the hydrocarbon and $O_2$, and the products are $CO_2$ and $H_2O$.

*Figure 3.9* As shown, 18.0 g $H_2O$ = 1 mol $H_2O$ = $6.02 \times 10^{23}$ molecules $H_2O$. Thus, 9.00 g $H_2O$ = 0.500 mol $H_2O$ = $3.01 \times 10^{23}$ molecules $H_2O$.

*Figure 3.12* (a) The molar mass of $CH_4$, 16.0 g $CH_4$/1 mol $CH_4$. (b) Avogadro's number, 1 mol $CH_4$/$6.02 \times 10^{23}$ formula units $CH_4$, where a formula unit in this case is a molecule.

*Figure 3.13* The mole ratio is obtained by dividing the molecular weight by the empirical formula weight, Equation 3.11.

*Figure 3.17* There are 7 mol $O_2$, and each mol $O_2$ yields 2 mol $H_2O$. Thus, 14 mol $H_2O$ would have formed.

# CHAPTER 4

*Figure 4.3* NaCl(*aq*)

*Figure 4.4* $K^+$ and $NO_3^-$

*Figure 4.9* Two moles of hydrochloric acid are needed to react with each mole of $Mg(OH)_2$.

*Figure 4.19* The volume needed to reach the end point if $Ba(OH)_2(aq)$ were used would be one-half the volume needed for titration with NaOH(*aq*).

# CHAPTER 5

*Figure 5.1* In the act of throwing, the pitcher transfers energy to the ball, which then becomes kinetic energy of the ball. For a given amount of energy $E$ transferred to the ball, Equation 5.1 tells us that the speed of the ball is $v = \sqrt{2E/m}$ where $m$ is the mass of the ball. Because a baseball has less mass than a bowling bowl, it will have a higher speed for a given amount of energy transferred.

*Figure 5.2* When she starts going uphill, kinetic energy is converted to potential energy and her speed decreases.

*Figure 5.3* The electrostatic potential energy of two oppositely charged particles is negative (Equation 5.2). As the particles become closer, the electrostatic potential energy becomes even more negative—that is, it decreases.

*Figure 5.4* Yes, the system is still closed—matter can't escape the system to the surroundings unless the piston is pulled completely out of the cylinder.

*Figure 5.5* If $E_{final} = E_{initial}$, then $\Delta E = 0$.

*Figure 5.6*

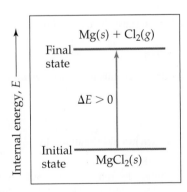

*Figure 5.7* No. The sign on $w$ is positive and the sign on $q$ is negative. We need to know the magnitudes of $q$ and $w$ to determine whether $\Delta E = q + w$ is positive or negative.

*Figure 5.10* The battery is doing work on the surroundings, so $w < 0$.

*Figure 5.11* We need to know whether Zn(*s*) or HCl(*aq*) is the limiting reagent of the reaction. If it is Zn(*s*), then the addition of more Zn will lead to the generation of more $H_2(g)$ and more work will be done.

*Figure 5.17* Endothermic—heat is being added to the system to raise the temperature of the water.

*Figure 5.18* Two cups provide more thermal insulation so less heat will escape the system.

*Figure 5.19* The stirrer ensures that all of the water in the bomb is at the same temperature.

**Figure 5.21** The condensation of 2 $H_2O(g)$ to 2 $H_2O(l)$

**Figure 5.22** Yes, $\Delta H_3$ would remain the same as it is the enthalpy change for the process $CO(g) + \frac{1}{2}O_2(g) \longrightarrow CO_2(g)$.

**Figure 5.24** Grams of fat

## CHAPTER 6

**Figure 6.3** The wavelength of (a) is twice that of (b) and the frequency of (a) is consequently half that of (b). Thus, the wavelength of (b) is 0.50 m and its frequency is $6.0 \times 10^8$ cycles/s.

**Figure 6.4** The X-ray has a shorter wavelength and, consequently, higher frequency than the red light.

**Figure 6.5** The hottest area is the white or yellowish white area in the center.

**Figure 6.7** If the tube is not evacuated, the electrons that are freed from the metal surface will strike gas molecules near that surface. As a result, they will become attached to the gas molecules and never arrive at the positive terminal.

**Figure 6.12** The $n = 2$ to $n = 1$ transition involves a larger energy change than the $n = 3$ to $n = 2$ transition. (Compare the space differences between the states in the figure.) If the $n = 2$ to $n = 1$ transition produces visible light, the $n = 3$ to $n = 2$ transition must produce radiation of lower energy. The infrared radiation has lower frequency and, hence, lower energy than visible light, whereas the ultraviolet has greater frequency and greater energy. Thus, the $n = 2$ to $n = 1$ transition will produce ultraviolet radiation.

**Figure 6.16** The region of highest electron density is where the density of dots is highest, which is near the nucleus.

**Figure 6.17** The fourth shell ($n = 4$) would contain four subshells, labeled 4s, 4p, 4d, and 4f.

**Figure 6.18** There would be four maxima and three nodes.

**Figure 6.22** (a) The intensity of the color indicates that the probability of finding the electron is greater at the interior of the lobes than on the edges. (b) $2p_x$.

**Figure 6.24** The 4d and 4f subshells are not shown.

## CHAPTER 7

**Figure 7.1** Row 7—these elements are generally radioactive and not stable.

**Figure 7.3** 2s

**Figure 7.6** Bottom and left

**Figure 7.7** They get larger, just like the atoms do.

**Figure 7.9** Ar; it has a larger $Z_{eff}$.

**Figure 7.10** There is more electron–electron repulsion in the case of oxygen because two electrons have to occupy the same orbital.

**Figure 7.11** The halogens (group 7A); it does make sense because we know that they are very stable as anions.

**Figure 7.12** Ionization energy—lower ionization energy is correlated with increasing metallic character.

**Figure 7.14** Anions are above the lines; cations are below the line.

**Figure 7.22** Lilac

## CHAPTER 8

**Figure 8.1** Covalent

**Figure 8.2** Yes, the same sort of reaction should occur between any of the alkali metals and any of the elemental halogens.

**Figure 8.3** Cations have a smaller radius than their neutral atoms and anions have a larger radius. Because Na and Cl are in the same row of the periodic table, we would expect $Na^+$ to have a smaller radius than $Cl^-$, so we would guess that the larger green spheres represent $Cl^-$.

**Figure 8.4** The distance between ions in KF should be larger than that in NaF and smaller than that in KCl. We would thus expect the lattice energy of KF to be between 701 and 910 kJ/mol.

**Figure 8.6** The repulsions between the nuclei would decrease, the attractions between the nuclei and the electrons would decrease, and the repulsions between the electrons would be unaffected.

**Figure 8.7** The electronegativity decreases with increasing atomic number.

**Figure 8.9** $\mu$ will decrease

**Figure 8.10** The bonds are not polar enough to cause enough excess electron density on the halogen atom to lead to a red shading.

**Figure 8.12** The lengths of the bonds of the outer O atoms to the inner O atom are the same.

**Figure 8.13** Yes. The electron densities on the left and right parts of the molecule are the same, indicating that resonance has made the two O—O bonds equivalent to one another.

**Figure 8.14** The dashed bonds represent the "half bonds" that result when the two resonance structures are averaged.

**Figure 8.15** Exothermic

**Figure 8.17** As the bond gets longer, it gets weaker. We would therefore expect a plot of bond enthalpy versus bond length to have a negative slope.

## CHAPTER 9

**Figure 9.1** The atomic radii (Figure 7.7)

**Figure 9.3** Octahedral

**Figure 9.7** The electron pair in the bonding domain is attracted toward two nuclear centers, whereas the nonbonding pair is attracted toward just one.

**Figure 9.8** 90°

**Figure 9.9** The nonbonding electron pairs exert a greater repulsive force than the bonding electron pairs.

**Figure 9.10** The heads of the arrows point toward regions of highest electron density, as indicated by the red color.

**Figure 9.14** As the internuclear distance decreases, nucleus–nucleus repulsion becomes a dominant component of the potential energy.

**Figure 9.16** The small lobes of the sp hybrid orbitals are very much smaller in spatial extent and, therefore, provide very little overlap with the F orbitals.

**Figure 9.17** Three: one s and two p orbitals

**Figure 9.23** The two p orbitals that form the $\pi$ bond must align, and each of them is perpendicular to the plane of the $sp^2$ hybrid orbitals.

**Figure 9.24** Acetylene, because it has two C—C $\pi$ bonds, whereas ethylene has one $\pi$ bond

**Figure 9.26** C—H and C—C

**Figure 9.33** The $\sigma^*_{1s}$

**Figure 9.34** The two electrons in the $\sigma_{1s}$ MO

**Figure 9.35** The 1s orbitals of Li are small in spatial extent because they experience a strong nuclear attraction. In addition, both the bonding and antibonding MOs formed from them are occupied, so that there is no significant net bonding.

**Figure 9.36** Nodal planes between the atoms are found in antibonding MOs.

**Figure 9.42** The $\sigma_{2p}$ and $\pi_{2p}$ orbitals. Because the $\sigma_{2p}$ orbital mixes with the $\sigma_{2s}$, it is pushed to higher energy and the $\sigma_{2s}$ is moved to lower energy. The $\sigma_{2p}$ orbital thus rises above the $\pi_{2p}$ in energy.

**Figure 9.43** $F_2$ contains four more electrons than $N_2$. These electrons go into the antibonding $\pi^*_{2p}$ orbitals, thus lowering the bond order.

*Figure 9.45* Because $N_2$ has no unpaired electrons, it is diamagnetic. Therefore, it would simply flow down with no tendency to remain in the magnetic field.

*Figure 9.46* 11. All the electrons in the $n = 2$ level are valence-shell electrons.

## CHAPTER 10

*Figure 10.2* It will increase.

*Figure 10.5* Decrease

*Figure 10.6* 1520 torr

*Figure 10.7* Linear

*Figure 10.10* one

*Figure 10.11* It is small and inert.

*Figure 10.17* About a third

*Figure 10.18* Higher speeds are correlated with smaller molar masses (assuming constant $T$).

*Figure 10.20* $n$, moles of gas

*Figure 10.22* Not really—$CO_2$ is least ideal and does have the largest molar mass, but $H_2$, the lightest gas, deviates more from the ideal line than the heavier $N_2$.

*Figure 10.23* True

*Figure 10.25* It would increase.

## CHAPTER 11

*Figure 11.2* The density in a liquid is much closer to a solid than it is to a gas.

*Figure 11.9* Both compounds are nonpolar and incapable of forming hydrogen bonds. Therefore, the boiling point is determined by the dispersion forces, which are stronger for the larger, heavier $SnH_4$.

*Figure 11.10* The non-hydrogen atom must possess a nonbonding electron pair.

*Figure 11.11* There are four electron pairs surrounding oxygen in a water molecule. Two of the electron pairs are used to make covalent bonds to hydrogen within the $H_2O$ molecule, while the other two are available to make hydrogen bonds to neighboring molecules. Because the electron-pair geometry is tetrahedral (four electron domains around the central atom), the $H$—$O \cdots H$ bond angle is approximately 109°.

*Figure 11.19* Wax is a hydrocarbon that cannot form hydrogen bonds. Therefore, coating the inside of tube with wax will dramatically decrease the adhesive forces between water and the tube and change the shape of the water meniscus to an inverted U-shape. Neither wax nor glass can form metallic bonds with mercury so the shape of the mercury meniscus will be qualitatively the same, an inverted U-shape.

*Figure 11.21* Because we are dealing with a state function, the energy of going straight from a solid to a gas must be the same as going from a solid to a gas through an intermediate liquid state. Therefore, the heat of sublimation must be equal to the sum of the heat of fusion and the heat of vaporization: $\Delta H_{sub} = \Delta H_{fus} + \Delta H_{vap}$.

*Figure 11.24* Increases, because the molecules have more kinetic energy as the temperature increases and can escape more easily

*Figure 11.25* All liquids including ethylene glycol reach their normal boiling point when their vapor pressure is equal to atmospheric pressure, 760 torr.

*Figure 11.27* Freezing, because for most substances the solid phase is denser than the liquid phase and increasing the pressure will eventually drive a phase transition from the liquid to the solid state (provided the temperature is below the critical temperature)

## CHAPTER 12

*Figure 12.13* A hexagonal lattice

*Figure 12.15* The solvent is the majority component and the solute the minority component. Therefore, there will be more solvent atoms than solute atoms.

*Figure 12.17* The samarium atoms sit on the corners of the unit cell so there is only $8 \times (1/8) = 1$ Sm atom per unit cell. Eight of the nine cobalt atoms sit on faces of the unit cell, and the other sits in the middle of the unit cell so there are $8 \times (1/2) + 1 = 5$ Co atoms per unit cell.

*Figure 12.19* The atoms are randomly arranged in red gold, which is a substitutional alloy. Purple gold is an intermetallic compound in which the atoms are arranged in a specific ordered pattern.

*Figure 12.20* By drawing Lewis structures you can show that there are three (chlorine), two (sulfur), one (phosphorus), and zero (silicon) nonbonding electron pairs per atom.

*Figure 12.22* In the fourth period, vanadium and chromium have very similar melting points. Molybdenum and tungsten have the highest melting points in the fifth and sixth periods, respectively. All of these elements are located near the middle of the period where the bonding orbitals are mostly filled and the antibonding orbitals mostly empty.

*Figure 12.23* The molecular orbitals become more closely spaced in energy.

*Figure 12.24* Potassium has only one valence electron per atom. If we fill the 4s band halfway probably a small amount of electron density will leak over and start to fill the 3d orbitals as well. The 4p orbitals should be empty.

*Figure 12.25* Ionic substances cleave because the nearest neighbor interactions switch from attractive to repulsive if the atoms slide so that ions of like charge (cation–cation and anion–anion) touch each other. Metals don't cleave because the atoms are attracted to all other atoms in the crystal through metallic bonding.

*Figure 12.26* No, ions of like charge do not touch in an ionic compound because they are repelled from one another. In an ionic compound the cations touch the anions.

*Figure 12.28* In NaF there are four $Na^+$ ions $(12 \times 1/4)$ and four $F^-$ ions $(8 \times 1/8 + 6 \times 1/2)$ per unit cell. In $MgF_2$ there are two $Mg^{2+}$ ions $(8 \times 1/8 + 1)$ and four $F^-$ ions $(4 \times 1/2 + 2)$ per unit cell. In $ScF_3$ there is one $Sc^{3+}$ ion $(8 \times 1/8)$ and three $F^-$ ions $(12 \times 1/4)$ per unit cell.

*Figure 12.29* The intermolecular forces are stronger in toluene, as shown by its higher boiling point. The molecules pack more efficiently in benzene, which explains its higher melting point, even though the intermolecular forces are weaker.

*Figure 12.44* Decrease. As the quantum dots get smaller, the band gap increases and the emitted light shifts to shorter wavelength.

*Figure 12.47* Each carbon atom in $C_{60}$ is bonded to three neighboring carbon atoms through covalent bonds. Thus, the bonding is more like graphite, where carbon atoms also bond to three neighbors, than diamond, where carbon atoms bond to four neighbors.

## CHAPTER 13

*Figure 13.2* Opposite charges attract. The electron-rich O atom of the $H_2O$ molecule, which is the negative end of the dipole, is attracted to the positive $Na^+$ ion.

*Figure 13.3* The negative end of the water dipole (the O) is attracted to the positive $Na^+$ ion, whereas the positive end of the dipole (the H) is attracted to the negative $Cl^-$ ion.

*Figure 13.4* For exothermic solution processes the magnitude of $\Delta H_{mix}$ will be larger than the magnitude of $\Delta H_{solute} + \Delta H_{solvent}$

*Figure 13.8* The dissolving of the crystal and the crystallization by which ions in solution become reattached to the solid

*Figure 13.9* If the solution wasn't supersaturated, solute would not crystallize from it.

*Figure 13.14* If the partial pressure of a gas over a solution is doubled, the concentration of gas in the solution would double.

*Figure 13.15* The slopes increase as the molecular weight increases. The larger the molecular weight, the greater the polarizability of the gas molecules, leading to greater intermolecular attractive forces between gas molecules and water molecules.

*Figure 13.18* Looking at where the solubility curves for KCl and NaCl intersect the 80 °C line, we see that the solubility of KCl is about 51 g/100 g $H_2O$, whereas NaCl has a solubility of about 39 g/100 g $H_2O$. Thus, KCl is more soluble than NaCl at this temperature.

*Figure 13.19* $N_2$ has the same molecular weight as CO but is nonpolar, so we can predict that its curve will be just below that of CO.

*Figure 13.25* The water will move through the semipermeable membrane toward the more concentrated solution. Thus, the liquid level in the left arm will increase.

*Figure 13.26* Water will move toward the more concentrated solute solution, which is inside the red blood cells, causing them to undergo hemolysis.

*Figure 13.30* The two negatively charged groups both have the composition $-CO_2^-$.

*Figure 13.32* Recall the rule that likes dissolve likes. The oil drop is composed of nonpolar molecules, which interact with the nonpolar part of the stearate ion with dispersion forces.

## CHAPTER 14

*Figure 14.3* B

*Figure 14.4* It decreases.

*Figure 14.8* The reaction is first order in $CH_3NC$.

*Figure 14.10* At early times in the reaction; both graphs look linear close to $t = 0$.

*Figure 14.17* The energy needed to overcome the energy barrier (the activation energy) looks about twice as large as the overall energy change for the reaction.

*Figure 14.23* For the blue curve: The transition states are at the top of the peaks (2) and the intermediate is in the "valley" between the two peaks. For the red curve: The top of the peak is the transition state; no intermediates are shown.

*Figure 14.27* Substrate; if products bound tightly, they would not leave and the active site would not be free.

## CHAPTER 15

*Figure 15.1* The color in the tube stops changing.

*Figure 15.2* No

*Figure 15.6* The boxes would be approximately the same size.

*Figure 15.7* It will be lower; some $CO_2$ has to react with CaO to make some $CaCO_3$.

*Figure 15.9* 500 atm and 400 °C

*Figure 15.10* Nitrogen (and some of the added hydrogen) is converted into ammonia.

*Figure 15.14* About two to three times faster, based on the graph

*Figure 15.15* About $5 \times 10^{-4}$

## CHAPTER 16

*Figure 16.2* Hydrogen bonds

*Figure 16.3* $O^{2-}(aq) + H_2O(l) \longrightarrow 2\,OH^-(aq)$

*Figure 16.7* Phenolphthalein changes from colorless, for pH values less than 8, to pink for pH values greater than 10. A pink color indicates pH > 10.

*Figure 16.8* Bromothymol blue would be most suitable because it changes pH over a range that brackets pH = 7. Methyl red is not sensitive to pH changes when pH > 6, while phenolphthalein is not sensitive to pH changes when pH < 8, so neither changes color at pH = 7.

*Figure 16.11* Yes. The equilibrium of interest is $H_3CCOOH \rightleftharpoons H^+ + H_3CCOO^-$. If the percent dissociation remained constant as the acid concentration increased, the concentration of all three species would increase at the same rate. However, because there are two products and only one reactant, the total concentration of products would increase faster than the concentration of reactants. To offset this effect the percent dissociation decreases as the acid concentration increases.

*Figure 16.12* The acidic hydrogens belong to carboxylate ($-COOH$) groups, whereas the fourth proton bound to oxygen is part of a hydroxyl ($-OH$) group. In organic acids, like citric acid, the acidic protons are almost always part of a carboxylate group.

*Figure 16.13* The nitrogen atom in hydroxylamine accepts a proton to form $NH_3OH^+$. As a general rule, nonbonding electron pairs on nitrogen atoms are more basic than nonbonding electron pairs on oxygen atoms.

## CHAPTER 17

*Figure 17.6* The pH will increase on addition of the base.

*Figure 17.7* 25.00 mL. The number of moles of added base needed to reach the equivalence point remains the same. Therefore, by doubling the concentration of added base the volume needed to reach the equivalence point is halved.

*Figure 17.9* The volume of base needed to reach the equivalence point would not change because this quantity does not depend on the strength of the acid. However, the pH at the equivalence point, which is greater than 7 for a weak acid–strong base titration, would decrease to 7 because hydrochloric acid is a strong acid.

*Figure 17.11* The pH at the equivalence point increases (becomes more basic) as the acid becomes weaker. The volume of added base needed to reach the equivalence point remains unchanged.

*Figure 17.13* Yes. Any indicator that changes color between pH = 3 and pH = 11 could be used for a strong acid–strong base titration. Methyl red changes color between pH values of approximately 4 and 6.

*Figure 17.22* ZnS and CuS would both precipitate on addition of $H_2S$, preventing separation of the two ions.

*Figure 17.23* Yes. CuS would precipitate in step 2 on addition of $H_2S$ to an acidic solution, while the $Zn^{2+}$ ions remained in solution.

## CHAPTER 18

*Figure 18.1* About 85 km

*Figure 18.3* The atmosphere absorbs a significant fraction of solar radiation.

*Figure 18.4* The peak value is about $5 \times 10^{12}$ molecules per $cm^3$. If we use Avogadro's number to convert molecules to moles, and the conversion factor of $1000\ cm^3 = 1000\ mL = 1\ L$, we find that the concentration of ozone at the peak is $8 \times 10^{-9}$ mole/L.

*Figure 18.16* This is ambiguous; both temperature and salinity vary with density in similar ways; but temperature seems to parallel density better. Temperature decreases down to 1000 m, then remains relatively constant; density increases down to 1000 m, and then remains relatively constant.

*Figure 18.17* The depth of the aquifer; the nature of the intervening layers (how porous or dense they are)

*Figure 18.19* Water is the chemical species that is crossing the membrane, not the ions.

## CHAPTER 19

*Figure 19.1* Yes, the potential energy of the eggs decreases as they fall.

*Figure 19.2* Because the final volume would be less than twice the volume of Flask A, the final pressure would be greater than 0.5 atm.

*Figure 19.3*  The freezing of liquid water to ice is exothermic.

*Figure 19.4*  To be truly reversible, the temperature change $\delta T$ must be infinitesimally small.

*Figure 19.8*  There are two other independent rotational motions of the $H_2O$ molecule:

*Figure 19.9*  Ice, because it is the phase in which the molecules are held most rigidly

*Figure 19.11*  The decrease in the number of molecules due to the formation of new bonds.

*Figure 19.13*  During a phase change, the temperature remains constant but the entropy change can be large.

*Figure 19.14*  Based on the three molecules shown, the addition of each C increases $S°$ by 40–45 J/mol-K. Based on this observation, we would predict that $S°(C_4H_{10})$ would 310–315 J/mol-K. Appendix C confirms that this is a good prediction: $S°(C_4H_{10})$ = 310.0 J/mol-K.

*Figure 19.16*  Spontaneous

*Figure 19.17*  If we plot progress of the reaction versus free energy, equilibrium is at a minimum point in free energy, as shown in the figure. In that sense, the reaction runs "downhill" until it reaches that minimum point.

## CHAPTER 20

*Figure 20.1*  (a) The bubbling is caused by the hydrogen gas formed in the reaction. (b) The reaction is exothermic, and the heat causes the formation of steam.

*Figure 20.2*  The permanganate, $MnO_4^-$, is reduced, as the half-reactions in the text show.

*Figure 20.3*  The blue color is due to $Cu^{2+}(aq)$. As this ion is reduced, forming $Cu(s)$, the blue color fades.

*Figure 20.4*  The Zn is oxidized and, therefore, serves as the anode of the cell.

*Figure 20.5*  The electrical balance is maintained in two ways: Anions migrate into the half-cell, and cations migrate out.

*Figure 20.9*  As the cell operates, $H^+$ is reduced to $H_2$ in the cathode half-cell. As $H^+$ is depleted, the positive $Na^+$ ions are drawn into the half-cell to maintain electrical balance in the solution.

*Figure 20.10*  The reduction reaction occurs at the cathode. The substance that is reduced most easily is the one with the larger standard reduction potential, $E_{red}°$.

*Figure 20.12*  Oxidation is the loss of electrons. An oxidizing agent causes another substance to lose electrons by gaining them itself. A strong oxidizing agent readily gains electrons, meaning that it is easily reduced.

*Figure 20.14*  The variable $n$ is the number of moles of electrons transferred in the process.

*Figure 20.15*  The $Ni^{2+}(aq)$ and the cations in the salt bridge migrate toward the cathode. The $NO_3^-(aq)$ and the anions in the salt bridge migrate toward the anode.

*Figure 20.19*  The cathode consists of $PbO_2(s)$. Because each oxygen has an oxidation state of $-2$, lead must have an oxidation state of $+4$ in this compound.

*Figure 20.22*  The oxidizing agent of $O_2(g)$ from the air

## CHAPTER 21

*Figure 21.2*  From Figure 21.2 we see that the belt of stability for a nucleus containing 70 protons lies at approximately 102 neutrons.

*Figure 21.4*  Only three of the elements with an even number of protons have fewer than three isotopes: He, Be, and C. Note that these three elements are the lightest elements that have an even atomic number. Because they are so light, any change in the number of neutrons will change the neutron/proton ratio significantly. This helps to explain why they do not have more stable isotopes. None of the elements in Figure 21.4 that have an odd number of protons have more than two stable isotopes.

*Figure 21.6*  6.25 g. After one half-life, the amount of the radioactive material will have dropped to 25.0 g. After two half-lives, it will have dropped to 12.5 g. After three half-lives, it will have dropped to 6.25 g.

*Figure 21.19*  Because large quantities of water are needed to condense the secondary coolant once it passes through the turbine

*Figure 21.21*  The United States has the most reactors in operation. China has the most reactors under construction. France generates the largest percentage of its electricity from nuclear power.

*Figure 21.24*  Alpha rays are less dangerous when outside the body because they cannot penetrate the skin. However, once inside the body they can do great harm to any cells they come in contact with.

## CHAPTER 22

*Figure 22.5*  Beaker on the right is warmer.

*Figure 22.6*  HF is the most stable, $SbH_3$ the least stable.

*Figure 22.8*  More soluble in $CCl_4$—the colors are deeper.

*Figure 22.9*  $CF_2$

*Figure 22.10*  Redox reactions: The halides are being oxidized.

*Figure 22.14*  No

*Figure 22.16*  Based on this structure—yes, it would have a dipole moment. In fact, if you look it up, hydrogen peroxide's dipole moment is larger than water's!

*Figure 22.20*  They have been converted into water.

*Figure 22.21*  Formally they could both be $+2$. If we consider that the central sulfur is like $SO_4^{2-}$, however, then the central sulfur would be $+6$, like $SO_4^{2-}$, and then the terminal sulfur would be $-2$.

*Figure 22.22*  Nitrite

*Figure 22.23*  Longer

*Figure 22.26*  The NO double bond

*Figure 22.28*  In $P_4O_6$ the electron domains about the P atoms are trigonal pyramidal; in $P_4O_{10}$ the electron domains about the P atoms are tetrahedral.

*Figure 22.33*  The minimum temperature should be the melting point of silicon; the temperature of the heating coil should not be so high that the silicon rod starts to melt outside the zone of the heating coil.

## CHAPTER 23

*Figure 23.3*  Zn (it is colorless)

*Figure 23.4*  The increase parallels the linear increase in valence electron count.

*Figure 23.5*  All the electron spins would align with the direction of the magnetic field.

*Figure 23.9*  109.5 degrees for the tetrahedral Zn complex; 90 degrees for the square-planar Pt complex

*Figure 23.13*  4 for both (assuming no other ligands come in to bind)

*Figure 23.15*  In the same place as $O_2$

*Figure 23.16*  The peak with a maximum at 650 nm, the longest wavelength and lowest energy

*Figure 23.21*  The *cis* one

*Figure 23.24*  Larger, since ammonia can displace water

*Figure 23.26*  The peak would stay in the same position in terms of wavelength, but its absorbance would decrease.

**Figure 23.28** $d_{x^2-y^2}$ and $d_{z^2}$

**Figure 23.29** Convert the wavelength of light, 495 nm, into energy in joules using $E = hc/\lambda$.

**Figure 23.30** It would be to the right of the "yellow" member of the series, but the energy gap between filled and empty $d$ orbitals would be even larger than that of the "yellow" one.

**Figure 23.34** That orbital has the lobes that point directly at the ligands.

**absolute zero** The lowest attainable temperature; 0 K on the Kelvin scale and $-273.15\ °C$ on the Celsius scale. (Section 1.4)

**absorption spectrum** A pattern of variation in the amount of light absorbed by a sample as a function of wavelength. (Section 23.5)

**accuracy** A measure of how closely individual measurements agree with the correct value. (Section 1.5)

**acid** A substance that is able to donate a $H^+$ ion (a proton) and, hence, increases the concentration of $H^+(aq)$ when it dissolves in water. (Section 4.3)

**acid-dissociation constant ($K_a$)** An equilibrium constant that expresses the extent to which an acid transfers a proton to solvent water. (Section 16.6)

**acidic anhydride (acidic oxide)** An oxide that forms an acid when added to water; soluble nonmetal oxides are acidic anhydrides. (Section 22.5)

**acidic oxide (acidic anhydride)** An oxide that either reacts with a base to form a salt or with water to form an acid. (Section 22.5)

**acid rain** Rainwater that has become excessively acidic because of absorption of pollutant oxides, notably $SO_3$, produced by human activities. (Section 18.2)

**actinide element** Element in which the $5f$ orbitals are only partially occupied. (Section 6.8)

**activated complex (transition state)** The particular arrangement of atoms found at the top of the potential-energy barrier as a reaction proceeds from reactants to products. (Section 14.5)

**activation energy ($E_a$)** The minimum energy needed for reaction; the height of the energy barrier to formation of products. (Section 14.5)

**active site** Specific site on a heterogeneous catalyst or an enzyme where catalysis occurs. (Section 14.7)

**activity** The decay rate of a radioactive material, generally expressed as the number of disintegrations per unit time. (Section 21.4)

**activity series** A list of metals in order of decreasing ease of oxidation. (Section 4.4)

**addition polymerization** Polymerization that occurs through coupling of monomers with one another, with no other products formed in the reaction. (Section 12.8)

**addition reaction** A reaction in which a reagent adds to the two carbon atoms of a carbon–carbon multiple bond. (Section 24.3)

**adsorption** The binding of molecules to a surface. (Section 14.7)

**alcohol** An organic compound obtained by substituting a hydroxyl group (—OH) for a hydrogen on a hydrocarbon. (Sections 2.9 and 24.4)

**aldehyde** An organic compound that contains a carbonyl group (C=O) to which at least one hydrogen atom is attached. (Section 24.4)

**alkali metals** Members of group 1A in the periodic table. (Section 7.7)

**alkaline earth metals** Members of group 2A in the periodic table. (Section 7.7)

**alkanes** Compounds of carbon and hydrogen containing only carbon–carbon single bonds. (Sections 2.9 and 24.2)

**alkenes** Hydrocarbons containing one or more carbon–carbon double bonds. (Section 24.2)

**alkyl group** A group that is formed by removing a hydrogen atom from an alkane. (Section 25.3)

**alkynes** Hydrocarbons containing one or more carbon–carbon triple bonds. (Section 24.2)

**alloy** A substance that has the characteristic properties of a metal and contains more than one element. Often there is one principal metallic component, with other elements present in smaller amounts. Alloys may be homogeneous or heterogeneous. (Section 12.3)

**alpha decay** A type of radioactive decay in which an atomic nucleus emits an alpha particle and thereby transforms (or "decays") into an atom with a mass number 4 less and atomic number 2 less. (Section 21.1)

**alpha ($\alpha$) helix** A protein structure in which the protein is coiled in the form of a helix with hydrogen bonds between C=O and N—H groups on adjacent turns. (Section 24.7)

**alpha particles** Particles that are identical to helium-4 nuclei, consisting of two protons and two neutrons, symbol ${}_{2}^{4}He$ or ${}_{2}^{4}\alpha$. (Section 21.1)

**amide** An organic compound that has an $NR_2$ group attached to a carbonyl. (Section 24.4)

**amine** A compound that has the general formula $R_3N$, where R may be H or a hydrocarbon group. (Section 16.7)

**amino acid** A carboxylic acid that contains an amino (—$NH_2$) group attached to the carbon atom adjacent to the carboxylic acid (—COOH) functional group. (Section 24.7)

**amorphous solid** A solid whose molecular arrangement lacks the regularly repeating long-range pattern of a crystal. (Section 12.2)

**amphiprotic** Refers to the capacity of a substance to either add or lose a proton ($H^+$). (Section 16.2)

**amphoteric oxides and hydroxides** Oxides and hydroxides that are only slightly soluble in water but that dissolve in either acidic or basic solutions. (Section 17.5)

**angstrom** A common non-SI unit of length, denoted Å, that is used to measure atomic dimensions: $1\ \text{Å} = 10^{-10}\ m$. (Section 2.3)

**anion** A negatively charged ion. (Section 2.7)

**anode** An electrode at which oxidation occurs. (Section 20.3)

**antibonding molecular orbital** A molecular orbital in which electron density is concentrated outside the region between the two nuclei of bonded atoms. Such orbitals, designated as $\sigma^*$ or $\pi^*$, are less stable (of higher energy) than bonding molecular orbitals. (Section 9.7)

**antiferromagnetism** A form of magnetism in which unpaired electron spins on adjacent sites point in opposite directions and cancel each other's effects. (Section 23.1)

**aqueous solution** A solution in which water is the solvent. (Chapter 4: Introduction)

**aromatic hydrocarbons** Hydrocarbon compounds that contain a planar, cyclic arrangement of carbon atoms linked by both $\sigma$ and delocalized $\pi$ bonds. (Section 24.2)

**Arrhenius equation** An equation that relates the rate constant for a reaction to the frequency factor, $A$, the activation energy, $E_a$, and the temperature, $T$: $k = Ae^{-E_a/RT}$. In its logarithmic form it is written $\ln k = -E_a/RT + \ln A$. (Section 14.5)

**atmosphere (atm)** A unit of pressure equal to 760 torr; 1 atm = 101.325 kPa. (Section 10.2)

**atom** The smallest representative particle of an element. (Sections 1.1 and 2.1)

**atomic mass unit (amu)** A unit based on the value of exactly 12 amu for the mass of the isotope of carbon that has six protons and six neutrons in the nucleus. (Sections 2.3 and 3.3)

**atomic number** The number of protons in the nucleus of an atom of an element. (Section 2.3)

**atomic radius** An estimate of the size of an atom. See **bonding atomic radius**. (Section 7.3)

**atomic weight** The average mass of the atoms of an element in atomic mass units (amu); it is numerically equal to the mass in grams of one mole of the element. (Section 2.4)

**autoionization** The process whereby water spontaneously forms low concentrations of $H^+(aq)$ and $OH^-(aq)$ ions by proton transfer from one water molecule to another. (Section 16.3)

**Avogadro's hypothesis** A statement that equal volumes of gases at the same temperature and pressure contain equal numbers of molecules. (Section 10.3)

**Avogadro's law** A statement that the volume of a gas maintained at constant temperature and pressure is directly proportional to the number of moles of the gas. (Section 10.3)

**Avogadro's number ($N_A$)** The number of $^{12}C$ atoms in exactly 12 g of $^{12}C$; it equals $6.022 \times 10^{23}$ $mol^{-1}$. (Section 3.4)

**band** An array of closely spaced molecular orbitals occupying a discrete range of energy. (Section 12.4)

**band gap** The energy gap between a fully occupied band called a valence band and an empty band called the conduction band. (Section 12.7)

**band structure** The electronic structure of a solid, defining the allowed ranges of energy for electrons in a solid. (Section 12.7)

**bar** A unit of pressure equal to $10^5$ Pa. (Section 10.2)

**base** A substance that is an $H^+$ acceptor; a base produces an excess of $OH^-(aq)$ ions when it dissolves in water. (Section 4.3)

**base-dissociation constant ($K_b$)** An equilibrium constant that expresses the extent to which a base reacts with solvent water, accepting a proton and forming $OH^-(aq)$. (Section 16.7)

**basic anhydride (basic oxide)** An oxide that forms a base when added to water; soluble metal oxides are basic anhydrides. (Section 22.5)

**basic oxide (basic anhydride)** An oxide that either reacts with water to form a base or reacts with an acid to form a salt and water. (Section 22.5)

**battery** A self-contained electrochemical power source that contains one or more voltaic cells. (Section 20.7)

**becquerel** The SI unit of radioactivity. It corresponds to one nuclear disintegration per second. (Section 21.4)

**Beer's law** The light absorbed by a substance ($A$) equals the product of its extinction coefficient ($\varepsilon$), the path length through which the light passes ($b$), and the molar concentration of the substance ($c$): $A = \varepsilon bc$. (Section 14.2)

**beta emission** A nuclear decay process where a beta particle is emitted from the nucleus; also called beta decay. (Section 21.1)

**beta particles** Energetic electrons emitted from the nucleus, symbol $_{-1}^{0}e$. (Section 21.1)

**beta sheet** A structural form of protein in which two strands of amino acids are hydrogen-bonded together in a zipperlike configuration. (Section 24.7)

**bidentate ligand** A ligand in which two linked coordinating atoms are bound to a metal. (Section 23.3)

**bimolecular reaction** An elementary reaction that involves two molecules. (Section 14.6)

**biochemistry** The study of the chemistry of living systems. (Chapter 24: Introduction)

**biodegradable** Organic material that bacteria are able to oxidize. (Section 18.4)

**body-centered lattice** A crystal lattice in which the lattice points are located at the center and corners of each unit cell. (Section 12.2)

**bomb calorimeter** A device for measuring the heat evolved in the combustion of a substance under constant-volume conditions. (Section 5.5)

**bond angles** The angles made by the lines joining the nuclei of the atoms in a molecule. (Section 9.1)

**bond dipole** The dipole moment that is due to unequal electron sharing between two atoms in a covalent bond. (Section 9.3)

**bond enthalpy** The enthalpy change, $\Delta H$, required to break a particular bond when the substance is in the gas phase. (Section 8.8)

**bonding atomic radius** The radius of an atom as defined by the distances separating it from other atoms to which it is chemically bonded. (Section 7.3)

**bonding molecular orbital** A molecular orbital in which the electron density is concentrated in the internuclear region. The energy of a bonding molecular orbital is lower than the energy of the separate atomic orbitals from which it forms. (Section 9.7)

**bonding pair** In a Lewis structure a pair of electrons that is shared by two atoms. (Section 9.2)

**bond length** The distance between the centers of two bonded atoms. (Section 8.3)

**bond order** The number of bonding electron pairs shared between two atoms, minus the number

of antibonding electron pairs: bond order = (number of bonding electrons − number of antibonding electrons)/2. (Section 9.7)

**bond polarity** A measure of the degree to which the electrons are shared unequally between two atoms in a chemical bond. (Section 8.4)

**boranes** Covalent hydrides of boron. (Section 22.11)

**Born–Haber cycle** A thermodynamic cycle based on Hess's law that relates the lattice energy of an ionic substance to its enthalpy of formation and to other measurable quantities. (Section 8.2)

**Boyle's law** A law stating that at constant temperature, the product of the volume and pressure of a given amount of gas is a constant. (Section 10.3)

**Brønsted–Lowry acid** A substance (molecule or ion) that acts as a proton donor. (Section 16.2)

**Brønsted–Lowry base** A substance (molecule or ion) that acts as a proton acceptor. (Section 16.2)

**buffer capacity** The amount of acid or base a buffer can neutralize before the pH begins to change appreciably. (Section 17.2)

**buffered solution (buffer)** A solution that undergoes a limited change in pH upon addition of a small amount of acid or base. (Section 17.2)

**calcination** The heating of an ore to bring about its decomposition and the elimination of a volatile product. For example, a carbonate ore might be calcined to drive off $CO_2$. (Section 23.2)

**calorie** A unit of energy, it is the amount of energy needed to raise the temperature of 1 g of water by 1 °C from 14.5 °C to 15.5 °C. A related unit is the joule: 1 cal = 4.184 J. (Section 5.1)

**calorimeter** An apparatus that measures the heat released or absorbed in a chemical or physical process. (Section 5.5)

**calorimetry** The experimental measurement of heat produced in chemical and physical processes. (Section 5.5)

**capillary action** The process by which a liquid rises in a tube because of a combination of adhesion to the walls of the tube and cohesion between liquid particles. (Section 11.3)

**carbide** A binary compound of carbon with a metal or metalloid. (Section 22.9)

**carbohydrates** A class of substances formed from polyhydroxy aldehydes or ketones. (Section 24.8)

**carbon black** A microcrystalline form of carbon. (Section 22.9)

**carbonyl group** The $C=O$ double bond, a characteristic feature of several organic functional groups, such as ketones and aldehydes. (Section 24.4)

**carboxylic acid** A compound that contains the —COOH functional group. (Sections 16.10 and 24.4)

**catalyst** A substance that changes the speed of a chemical reaction without itself undergoing a permanent chemical change in the process. (Section 14.7)

**cathode** An electrode at which reduction occurs. (Section 20.3)

**cathode rays** Streams of electrons that are produced when a high voltage is applied to electrodes in an evacuated tube. (Section 2.2)

**cathodic protection** A means of protecting a metal against corrosion by making it the cathode in

a voltaic cell. This can be achieved by attaching a more easily oxidized metal, which serves as an anode, to the metal to be protected. (Section 20.8)

**cation** A positively charged ion. (Section 2.7)

**cell potential** The potential difference between the cathode and anode in an electrochemical cell; it is measured in volts: 1 V = 1 J/C. Also called electromotive force. (Section 20.4)

**cellulose** A polysaccharide of glucose; it is the major structural element in plant matter. (Section 24.8)

**Celsius scale** A temperature scale on which water freezes at 0° and boils at 100° at sea level. (Section 1.4)

**chain reaction** A series of reactions in which one reaction initiates the next. (Section 21.7)

**changes of state** Transformations of matter from one state to a different one, for example, from a gas to a liquid. (Section 1.3)

**charcoal** A form of carbon produced when wood is heated strongly in a deficiency of air. (Section 22.9)

**Charles's law** A law stating that at constant pressure, the volume of a given quantity of gas is proportional to absolute temperature. (Section 10.3)

**chelate effect** The generally larger formation constants for polydentate ligands as compared with the corresponding *monodentate* ligands. (Section 23.3)

**chelating agent** A polydentate ligand that is capable of occupying two or more sites in the coordination sphere. (Section 23.3)

**chemical bond** A strong attractive force that exists between atoms in a molecule. (Section 8.1)

**chemical changes** Processes in which one or more substances are converted into other substances; also called **chemical reactions**. (Section 1.3)

**chemical equation** A representation of a chemical reaction using the chemical formulas of the reactants and products; a balanced chemical equation contains equal numbers of atoms of each element on both sides of the equation. (Section 3.1)

**chemical equilibrium** A state of dynamic balance in which the rate of formation of the products of a reaction from the reactants equals the rate of formation of the reactants from the products; at equilibrium the concentrations of the reactants and products remain constant. (Section 4.1; Chapter 15: Introduction)

**chemical formula** A notation that uses chemical symbols with numerical subscripts to convey the relative proportions of atoms of the different elements in a substance. (Section 2.6)

**chemical kinetics** The area of chemistry concerned with the speeds, or rates, at which chemical reactions occur. (Chapter 14: Introduction)

**chemical nomenclature** The rules used in naming substances. (Section 2.8)

**chemical properties** Properties that describe a substance's composition and its reactivity; how the substance reacts or changes into other substances. (Section 1.3)

**chemical reactions** Processes in which one or more substances are converted into other substances; also called **chemical changes**. (Section 1.3)

**chemistry** The scientific discipline that studies the composition, properties, and transformations of matter. (Chapter 1: Introduction)

**chiral** A term describing a molecule or an ion that cannot be superimposed on its mirror image. (Sections 23.4 and 24.5)

**chlorofluorocarbons** Compounds composed entirely of chlorine, fluorine, and carbon. (Section 18.3)

**chlorophyll** A plant pigment that plays a major role in conversion of solar energy to chemical energy in photosynthesis. (Section 23.3)

**cholesteric liquid crystalline phase** A liquid crystal formed from flat, disc-shaped molecules that align through a stacking of the molecular discs. (Section 11.7)

**coal** A naturally occurring solid containing hydrocarbons of high molecular weight, as well as compounds containing sulfur, oxygen, and nitrogen. (Section 5.8)

**colligative property** A property of a solvent (vapor-pressure lowering, freezing-point lowering, boiling-point elevation, osmotic pressure) that depends on the total concentration of solute particles present. (Section 13.5)

**collision model** A model of reaction rates based on the idea that molecules must collide to react; it explains the factors influencing reaction rates in terms of the frequency of collisions, the number of collisions with energies exceeding the activation energy, and the probability that the collisions occur with suitable orientations. (Section 14.5)

**colloids (colloidal dispersions)** Mixtures containing particles larger than normal solutes but small enough to remain suspended in the dispersing medium. (Section 13.6)

**combination reaction** A chemical reaction in which two or more substances combine to form a single product. (Section 3.2)

**combustion reaction** A chemical reaction that proceeds with evolution of heat and usually also a flame; most combustion involves reaction with oxygen, as in the burning of a match. (Section 3.2)

**common-ion effect** A shift of an equilibrium induced by an ion common to the equilibrium. For example, added $Na_2SO_4$ decreases the solubility of the slightly soluble salt $BaSO_4$, or added NaF decreases the percent ionization of HF. (Section 17.1)

**complementary colors** Colors that, when mixed in proper proportions, appear white or colorless. (Section 23.5)

**complete ionic equation** A chemical equation in which dissolved strong electrolytes (such as dissolved ionic compounds) are written as separate ions. (Section 4.2)

**complex ion (complex)** An assembly of a metal ion and the Lewis bases (ligands) bonded to it. (Section 17.5)

**compound** A substance composed of two or more elements united chemically in definite proportions. (Section 1.2)

**compound semiconductor** A semiconducting material formed from two or more elements. (Section 12.7)

**concentration** The quantity of solute present in a given quantity of solvent or solution. (Section 4.5)

**concentration cell** A voltaic cell containing the same electrolyte and the same electrode materials in both the anode and cathode compartments. The emf of the cell is derived from a difference in the concentrations of the same electrolyte solutions in the compartments. (Section 20.6)

**condensation polymerization** Polymerization in which molecules are joined together through condensation reactions. (Section 12.8)

**condensation reaction** A chemical reaction in which a small molecule (such as a molecule of water) is split out from between two reacting molecules. (Sections 12.6 and 22.8)

**conduction band** A band of molecular orbitals lying higher in energy than the occupied valence band and distinctly separated from it. (Section 12.7)

**conjugate acid** A substance formed by addition of a proton to a Brønsted–Lowry base. (Section 16.2)

**conjugate acid–base pair** An acid and a base, such as $H_2O$ and $OH^-$, that differ only in the presence or absence of a proton. (Section 16.2)

**conjugate base** A substance formed by the loss of a proton from a Brønsted–Lowry acid. (Section 16.2)

**continuous spectrum** A spectrum that contains radiation distributed over all wavelengths. (Section 6.3)

**conversion factor** A ratio relating the same quantity in two systems of units that is used to convert the units of measurement. (Section 1.6)

**coordination compound** A compound containing a metal ion bonded to a group of surrounding molecules or ions that act as ligands. (Section 23.2)

**coordination number** The number of adjacent atoms to which an atom is directly bonded. In a complex the coordination number of the metal ion is the number of donor atoms to which it is bonded. (Sections 12.37 and 24.2)

**coordination sphere** The metal ion and its surrounding ligands. (Section 23.2)

**coordination-sphere isomers** Structural isomers of coordination compounds in which the ligands within the coordination sphere differ. (Section 23.4)

**copolymer** A complex polymer resulting from the polymerization of two or more chemically different monomers. (Section 12.8)

**core electrons** The electrons that are not in the outermost shell of an atom. (Section 6.8)

**corrosion** The process by which a metal is oxidized by substances in its environment. (Section 20.8)

**covalent bond** A bond formed between two or more atoms by a sharing of electrons. (Section 8.1)

**covalent-network solids** Solids in which the units that make up the three-dimensional network are joined by covalent bonds. (Section 12.1)

**critical mass** The amount of fissionable material necessary to maintain a nuclear chain reaction. (Section 21.7)

**critical pressure** The pressure at which a gas at its critical temperature is converted to a liquid state. (Section 11.4)

**critical temperature** The highest temperature at which it is possible to convert the gaseous form of a substance to a liquid. The critical temperature increases with an increase in the magnitude of intermolecular forces. (Section 11.4)

**crystal-field theory** A theory that accounts for the colors and the magnetic and other properties of transition-metal complexes in terms of the splitting of the energies of metal ion $d$ orbitals by the electrostatic interaction with the ligands. (Section 23.6)

**crystal lattice** An imaginary network of points on which the repeating motif of a solid may be imagined to be laid down so that the structure of the crystal is obtained. The motif may be a single atom or a group of atoms. Each lattice point represents an identical environment in the crystal. (Section 12.2)

**crystalline solid (crystal)** A solid whose internal arrangement of atoms, molecules, or ions possesses a regularly repeating pattern in any direction through the solid. (Section 12.2)

**crystallization** The process in which molecules, ions, or atoms come together to form a crystalline solid. (Section 13.2)

**cubic close packing** A crystal structure where the atoms are packed together as close as possible, and the close-packed layers of atoms adopt a three-layer repeating pattern that leads to a face-centered cubic unit cell. (Section 12.3)

**curie** A measure of radioactivity: 1 curie = $3.7 \times 10^{10}$ nuclear disintegrations per second. (Section 21.4)

**cycloalkanes** Saturated hydrocarbons of general formula $C_nH_{2n}$ in which the carbon atoms form a closed ring. (Section 24.2)

**Dalton's law of partial pressures** A law stating that the total pressure of a mixture of gases is the sum of the pressures that each gas would exert if it were present alone. (Section 10.6)

**d-d transition** The transition of an electron in a transition-metal compound from a lower-energy $d$ orbital to a higher-energy $d$ orbital. (Section 23.6)

**decomposition reaction** A chemical reaction in which a single compound reacts to give two or more products. (Section 3.2)

**degenerate** A situation in which two or more orbitals have the same energy. (Section 6.7)

**delocalized electrons** Electrons that are spread over a number of atoms in a molecule or a crystal rather than localized on a single atom or a pair of atoms. (Section 9.6)

**density** The ratio of an object's mass to its volume. (Section 1.4)

**deoxyribonucleic acid (DNA)** A polynucleotide in which the sugar component is deoxyribose. (Section 24.10)

**desalination** The removal of salts from seawater, brine, or brackish water to make it fit for human consumption. (Section 18.4)

**deuterium** The isotope of hydrogen whose nucleus contains a proton and a neutron: $^2_1H$. (Section 22.2)

**dextrorotatory, or merely dextro or d** A term used to label a chiral molecule that rotates the plane of polarization of plane-polarized light to the right (clockwise). (Section 23.4)

**diamagnetism** A type of magnetism that causes a substance with no unpaired electrons to be weakly repelled from a magnetic field. (Section 9.8)

**diatomic molecule** A molecule composed of only two atoms. (Section 2.6)

**diffusion** The spreading of one substance through a space occupied by one or more other substances. (Section 10.8)

**dilution** The process of preparing a less concentrated solution from a more concentrated one by adding solvent. (Section 4.5)

**dimensional analysis** A method of problem solving in which units are carried through all calculations. Dimensional analysis ensures that the final answer of a calculation has the desired units. (Section 1.6)

**dipole** A molecule with one end having a partial negative charge and the other end having a partial positive charge; a polar molecule. (Section 8.4)

**dipole–dipole force** A force that becomes significant when polar molecules come in close contact with one another. The force is attractive when the positive end of one polar molecule approaches the negative end of another. (Section 11.2)

**dipole moment** A measure of the separation and magnitude of the positive and negative charges in polar molecules. (Section 8.4)

**dispersion forces** Intermolecular forces resulting from attractions between induced dipoles. Also called London dispersion forces. (Section 11.2)

**displacement reaction** A reaction in which an element reacts with a compound, displacing an element from it. (Section 4.4)

**donor atom** The atom of a ligand that bonds to the metal. (Section 23.2)

**doping** Incorporation of a hetero atom into a solid to change its electrical properties. For example, incorporation of P into Si. (Section 12.7)

**double bond** A covalent bond involving two electron pairs. (Section 8.3)

**double helix** The structure for DNA that involves the winding of two DNA polynucleotide chains together in a helical arrangement. The two strands of the double helix are complementary in that the organic bases on the two strands are paired for optimal hydrogen bond interaction. (Section 24.10)

**dynamic equilibrium** A state of balance in which opposing processes occur at the same rate. (Section 11.5)

**effective nuclear charge** The net positive charge experienced by an electron in a many-electron atom; this charge is not the full nuclear charge because there is some shielding of the nucleus by the other electrons in the atom. (Section 7.2)

**effusion** The escape of a gas through an orifice or hole. (Section 10.8)

**elastomer** A material that can undergo a substantial change in shape via stretching, bending, or compression and return to its original shape upon release of the distorting force. (Section 12.6)

**electrochemistry** The branch of chemistry that deals with the relationships between electricity and chemical reactions. (Chapter 20: Introduction)

**electrolysis reaction** A reaction in which a nonspontaneous redox reaction is brought about by the passage of current under a sufficient external electrical potential. The devices in which electrolysis reactions occur are called electrolytic cells. (Section 20.9)

**electrolyte** A solute that produces ions in solution; an electrolytic solution conducts an electric current. (Section 4.1)

**electrolytic cell** A device in which a nonspontaneous oxidation-reduction reaction is caused to occur by passage of current under a sufficient external electrical potential. (Section 20.9)

**electromagnetic radiation (radiant energy)** A form of energy that has wave characteristics and that propagates through a vacuum at the characteristic speed of $3.00 \times 10^8$ m/s. (Section 6.1)

**electrometallurgy** The use of electrolysis to reduce or refine metals. (Section 20.9)

**electromotive force (emf)** A measure of the driving force, or *electrical pressure*, for the completion of an electrochemical reaction. Electromotive force is measured in volts: $1 \text{ V} = 1 \text{ J/C}$. Also called the cell potential. (Section 20.4)

**electron** A negatively charged subatomic particle found outside the atomic nucleus; it is a part of all atoms. An electron has a mass 1/1836 times that of a proton. (Section 2.3)

**electron affinity** The energy change that occurs when an electron is added to a gaseous atom or ion. (Section 7.5)

**electron capture** A mode of radioactive decay in which an inner-shell orbital electron is captured by the nucleus. (Section 21.1)

**electron configuration** The arrangement of electrons in the orbitals of an atom or molecule (Section 6.8)

**electron density** The probability of finding an electron at any particular point in an atom; this probability is equal to $\psi^2$, the square of the wave function. Also called the probability density. (Section 6.5)

**electron domain** In the VSEPR model, a region about a central atom in which an electron pair is concentrated. (Section 9.2)

**electron-domain geometry** The three-dimensional arrangement of the electron domains around an atom according to the VSEPR model. (Section 9.2)

**electronegativity** A measure of the ability of an atom that is bonded to another atom to attract electrons to itself. (Section 8.4)

**electronic charge** The negative charge carried by an electron; it has a magnitude of $1.602 \times 10^{-19}$ C. (Section 2.3)

**electronic structure** The arrangement of electrons in an atom or molecule. (Chapter 6: Introduction)

**electron-sea model** A model for the behavior of electrons in metals. (Section 12.4)

**electron shell** A collection of orbitals that have the same value of $n$. For example, the orbitals with $n = 3$ (the $3s$, $3p$, and $3d$ orbitals) comprise the third shell. (Section 6.5)

**electron spin** A property of the electron that makes it behave as though it were a tiny magnet. The electron behaves as if it were spinning on its axis; electron spin is quantized. (Section 6.7)

**element** A substance consisting of atoms of the same atomic number. Historically defined as a substance that cannot be separated into simpler substances by chemical means. (Sections 1.1 and 1.2)

**elemental semiconductor** A semiconducting material composed of just one element. (Section 12.7)

**elementary reaction** A process in a chemical reaction that occurs in a single event or step. An overall chemical reaction consists of one or more elementary reactions or steps. (Section 14.6)

**empirical formula** A chemical formula that shows the kinds of atoms and their relative numbers in a substance in the smallest possible whole-number ratios. (Section 2.6)

**enantiomers** Two mirror-image molecules of a chiral substance. The enantiomers are nonsuperimposable. (Section 23.4)

**endothermic process** A process in which a system absorbs heat from its surroundings. (Section 5.2)

**energy** The capacity to do work or to transfer heat. (Section 5.1)

**energy-level diagram** A diagram that shows the energies of molecular orbitals relative to the atomic orbitals from which they are derived. Also called a **molecular-orbital diagram**. (Section 9.7)

**enthalpy** A quantity defined by the relationship $H = E + PV$; the enthalpy change, $\Delta H$, for a reaction that occurs at constant pressure is the heat evolved or absorbed in the reaction: $\Delta H = q_p$. (Section 5.3)

**enthalpy of formation** The enthalpy change that accompanies the formation of a substance from the most stable forms of its component elements. (Section 5.7)

**enthalpy of reaction** The enthalpy change associated with a chemical reaction. (Section 5.4)

**entropy** A thermodynamic function associated with the number of different equivalent energy states or spatial arrangements in which a system may be found. It is a thermodynamic state function, which means that once we specify the conditions for a system—that is, the temperature, pressure, and so on—the entropy is defined. (Section 19.2)

**enzyme** A protein molecule that acts to catalyze specific biochemical reactions. (Section 14.7)

**equilibrium constant** The numerical value of the equilibrium-constant expression for a system at equilibrium. The equilibrium constant is most usually denoted by $K_p$ for gas-phase systems or $K_c$ for solution-phase systems. (Section 15.2)

**equilibrium-constant expression** The expression that describes the relationship among the concentrations (or partial pressures) of the substances present in a system at equilibrium. The numerator is obtained by multiplying the concentrations of the substances on the product side of the equation, each raised to a power equal to its coefficient in the chemical equation. The denominator similarly contains the concentrations of the substances on the reactant side of the equation. (Section 15.2)

**equivalence point** The point in a titration at which the added solute reacts completely with the solute present in the solution. (Section 4.6)

**ester** An organic compound that has an OR group attached to a carbonyl; it is the product of a reaction between a carboxylic acid and an alcohol. (Section 24.4)

**ether** A compound in which two hydrocarbon groups are bonded to one oxygen. (Section 24.4)

**exchange (metathesis) reaction** A reaction between compounds that when written as a molecular equation appears to involve the exchange of ions between the two reactants. (Section 4.2)

**excited state** A higher energy state than the ground state. (Section 6.3)

**exothermic process** A process in which a system releases heat to its surroundings. (Section 5.2)

**extensive property** A property that depends on the amount of material considered; for example, mass or volume. (Section 1.3)

**face-centered lattice** A crystal lattice in which the lattice points are located at the faces and corners of each unit cell. (Section 12.2)

**Faraday's constant (F)** The magnitude of charge of one mole of electrons: 96,500 C/mol. (Section 20.5)

**f-block metals** Lanthanide and actinide elements in which the 4f or 5f orbitals are partially occupied. (Section 6.9)

**ferrimagnetism** A form of magnetism in which unpaired electron spins on different-type ions point in opposite directions but do not fully cancel out. (Section 23.1)

**ferromagnetism** A form of magnetism in which unpaired electron spins align parallel to one another. (Section 23.1)

**first law of thermodynamics** A statement that energy is conserved in any process. One way to express the law is that the change in internal energy, $\Delta E$, of a system in any process is equal to the heat, $q$, added to the system, plus the work, $w$, done on the system by its surroundings: $\Delta E = q + w$. (Section 5.2)

**first-order reaction** A reaction in which the reaction rate is proportional to the concentration of a single reactant, raised to the first power. (Section 14.4)

**fission** The splitting of a large nucleus into two smaller ones. (Section 21.6)

**folding** The process by which a protein adopts its biologically active shape. (Section 24.7)

**force** A push or a pull. (Section 5.1)

**formal charge** The number of valence electrons in an isolated atom minus the number of electrons assigned to the atom in the Lewis structure. (Section 8.5)

**formation constant** For a metal ion complex, the equilibrium constant for formation of the complex from the metal ion and base species present in solution. It is a measure of the tendency of the complex to form. (Section 17.5)

**formula weight** The mass of the collection of atoms represented by a chemical formula. For example, the formula weight of $NO_2$ (46.0 amu) is the sum of the masses of one nitrogen atom and two oxygen atoms. (Section 3.3)

**fossil fuels** Coal, oil, and natural gas, which are presently our major sources of energy. (Section 5.8)

**free energy (Gibbs free energy, G)** A thermodynamic state function that gives a criterion for spontaneous change in terms of enthalpy and entropy: $G = H - TS$. (Section 19.5)

**free radical** A substance with one or more unpaired electrons. (Section 21.9)

**frequency** The number of times per second that one complete wavelength passes a given point. (Section 6.1)

**frequency factor (A)** A term in the Arrhenius equation that is related to the frequency of collision and the probability that the collisions are favorably oriented for reaction. (Section 14.5)

**fuel cell** A voltaic cell that utilizes the oxidation of a conventional fuel, such as $H_2$ or $CH_4$, in the cell reaction. (Section 20.7)

**fuel value** The energy released when 1 g of a substance is combusted. (Section 5.8)

**functional group** An atom or group of atoms that imparts characteristic chemical properties to an organic compound. (Section 24.1)

**fusion** The joining of two light nuclei to form a more massive one. (Section 21.6)

**galvanic cell** See **voltaic cell**. (Section 20.3)

**gamma radiation** Energetic electromagnetic radiation emanating from the nucleus of a radioactive atom. (Section 21.1)

**gas** Matter that has no fixed volume or shape; it conforms to the volume and shape of its container. (Section 1.2)

**gas constant (R)** The constant of proportionality in the ideal-gas equation. (Section 10.4)

**geometric isomerism** A form of isomerism in which compounds with the same type and number of atoms and the same chemical bonds have different spatial arrangements of these atoms and bonds. (Sections 23.4 and 24.4)

**Gibbs free energy** A thermodynamic state function that combines enthalpy and entropy, in the form $G = H - TS$. For a change occurring at constant temperature and pressure, the change in free energy is $\Delta G = \Delta H - T\Delta S$. (Section 19.5)

**glass** An amorphous solid formed by fusion of $SiO_2$, $CaO$, and $Na_2O$. Other oxides may also be used to form glasses with differing characteristics. (Section 22.10)

**glucose** A polyhydroxy aldehyde whose formula is $CH_2OH(CHOH)_4CHO$; it is the most important of the monosaccharides. (Section 24.8)

**glycogen** The general name given to a group of polysaccharides of glucose that are synthesized in mammals and used to store energy from carbohydrates. (Section 24.7)

**Graham's law** A law stating that the rate of effusion of a gas is inversely proportional to the square root of its molecular weight. (Section 10.8)

**gray (Gy)** The SI unit for radiation dose corresponding to the absorption of 1 J of energy per kilogram of biological material; 1 Gy = 100 rads. (Section 21.9)

**green chemistry** Chemistry that promotes the design and application of chemical products and processes that are compatible with human health and that preserve the environment. (Section 18.5)

**greenhouse gases** Gases in an atmosphere that absorb and emit infrared radiation (radiant heat), "trapping" heat in the atmosphere. (Section 18.2)

**ground state** The lowest-energy, or most stable, state. (Section 6.3)

**group** Elements that are in the same column of the periodic table; elements within the same group or family exhibit similarities in their chemical behavior. (Section 2.5)

**Haber process** The catalyst system and conditions of temperature and pressure developed by Fritz Haber and coworkers for the formation of $NH_3$ from $H_2$ and $N_2$. (Section 15.2)

**half-life** The time required for the concentration of a reactant substance to decrease to half its initial value; the time required for half of a sample of a particular radioisotope to decay. (Sections 14.4 and 21.4)

**half-reaction** An equation for either an oxidation or a reduction that explicitly shows the electrons

involved, for example, $Zn^{2+}(aq) + 2\,e^{-} \longrightarrow Zn(s)$. (Section 20.2)

**Hall–Héroult process** A process used to obtain aluminum by electrolysis of $Al_2O_3$ dissolved in molten cryolite, $Na_3AlF_6$. (Section 20.9)

**halogens** Members of group 7A in the periodic table. (Section 7.8)

**hard water** Water that contains appreciable concentrations of $Ca^{2+}$ and $Mg^{2+}$; these ions react with soaps to form an insoluble material. (Section 18.4)

**heat** The flow of energy from a body at higher temperature to one at lower temperature when they are placed in thermal contact. (Section 5.1)

**heat capacity** The quantity of heat required to raise the temperature of a sample of matter by 1 °C (or 1 K). (Section 5.5)

**heat of fusion** The enthalpy change, $\Delta H$, for melting a solid. (Section 11.4)

**heat of sublimation** The enthalpy change, $\Delta H$, for vaporization of a solid. (Section 11.4)

**heat of vaporization** The enthalpy change, $\Delta H$, for vaporization of a liquid. (Section 11.4)

**Henderson–Hasselbalch equation** The relationship among the pH, $pK_a$, and the concentrations of acid and conjugate base in an aqueous solution: $pH = pK_a + \log \dfrac{[\text{base}]}{[\text{acid}]}$. (Section 17.2)

**Henry's law** A law stating that the concentration of a gas in a solution, $S_g$, is proportional to the pressure of gas over the solution: $S_g = kP_g$. (Section 13.3)

**Hess's law** The heat evolved in a given process can be expressed as the sum of the heats of several processes that, when added, yield the process of interest. (Section 5.6)

**heterogeneous alloy** An alloy in which the components are not distributed uniformly; instead, two or more distinct phases with characteristic compositions are present. (Section 12.3)

**heterogeneous catalyst** A catalyst that is in a different phase from that of the reactant substances. (Section 14.7)

**heterogeneous equilibrium** The equilibrium established between substances in two or more different phases, for example, between a gas and a solid or between a solid and a liquid. (Section 15.4)

**hexagonal close packing** A crystal structure where the atoms are packed together as closely as possible. The close-packed layers adopt a two-layer repeating pattern, which leads to a primitive hexagonal unit cell. (Section 12.3)

**high-spin complex** A complex whose electrons populate the $d$ orbitals to give the maximum number of unpaired electrons. (Section 23.6)

**hole** A vacancy in the valence band of a semiconductor, created by doping. (Section 12.7)

**homogeneous catalyst** A catalyst that is in the same phase as the reactant substances. (Section 14.7)

**homogeneous equilibrium** The equilibrium established between reactant and product substances that are all in the same phase. (Section 15.4)

**Hund's rule** A rule stating that electrons occupy degenerate orbitals in such a way as to maximize the number of electrons with the same spin. In other words, each orbital has one electron placed in it before pairing of electrons in orbitals occurs. (Section 6.8)

**hybridization** The mixing of different types of atomic orbitals to produce a set of equivalent hybrid orbitals. (Section 9.5)

**hybrid orbital** An orbital that results from the mixing of different kinds of atomic orbitals on the same atom. For example, an $sp^3$ hybrid results from the mixing, or hybridizing, of one $s$ orbital and three $p$ orbitals. (Section 9.5)

**hydration** Solvation when the solvent is water. (Section 13.1)

**hydride ion** An ion formed by the addition of an electron to a hydrogen atom: $H^-$. (Section 7.7)

**hydrocarbons** Compounds composed of only carbon and hydrogen. (Section 2.9)

**hydrogen bonding** Bonding that results from intermolecular attractions between molecules containing hydrogen bonded to an electronegative element. The most important examples involve OH, NH, and HF. (Section 11.2)

**hydrolysis** A reaction with water. When a cation or anion reacts with water, it changes the pH. (Sections 16.9 and 24.4)

**hydronium ion ($H_3O^+$)** The predominant form of the proton in aqueous solution. (Section 16.2)

**hydrophilic** Water attracting. The term is often used to describe a type of colloid. (Section 13.6)

**hydrophobic** Water repelling. The term is often used to describe a type of colloid. (Section 13.6)

**hypothesis** A tentative explanation of a series of observations or of a natural law. (Section 1.3)

**ideal gas** A hypothetical gas whose pressure, volume, and temperature behavior is completely described by the ideal-gas equation. (Section 10.4)

**ideal-gas equation** An equation of state for gases that embodies Boyle's law, Charles's law, and Avogadro's hypothesis in the form $PV = nRT$. (Section 10.4)

**ideal solution** A solution that obeys Raoult's law. (Section 13.5)

**immiscible liquids** Liquids that do not dissolve in one another to a significant extent. (Section 13.3)

**indicator** A substance added to a solution that changes color when the added solute has reacted with all the solute present in solution. The most common type of indicator is an acid–base indicator whose color changes as a function of pH. (Section 4.6)

**instantaneous rate** The reaction rate at a particular time as opposed to the average rate over an interval of time. (Section 14.2)

**intensive property** A property that is independent of the amount of material considered, for example, density. (Section 1.3)

**interhalogens** Compounds formed between two different halogen elements. Examples include IBr and $BrF_3$. (Section 22.4)

**intermediate** A substance formed in one elementary step of a multistep mechanism and consumed in another; it is neither a reactant nor an ultimate product of the overall reaction. (Section 14.6)

**intermetallic compound** A homogeneous alloy with definite properties and a fixed composition. Intermetallic compounds are stoichiometric

compounds that form between metallic elements. (Section 12.3)

**intermolecular forces** The short-range attractive forces operating between the particles that make up the units of a liquid or solid substance. These same forces also cause gases to liquefy or solidify at low temperatures and high pressures. (Chapter 11: Introduction)

**internal energy** The total energy possessed by a system. When a system undergoes a change, the change in internal energy, $\Delta E$, is defined as the heat, $q$, added to the system, plus the work, $w$, done on the system by its surroundings: $\Delta E = q + w$. (Section 5.2)

**interstitial alloy** An alloy in which smaller atoms fit into spaces between larger atoms. The larger atoms are metallic elements and the smaller atoms are typically nonmetallic elements. (Section 12.3)

**ion** Electrically charged atom or group of atoms (polyatomic ion); ions can be positively or negatively charged, depending on whether electrons are lost (positive) or gained (negative) by the atoms. (Section 2.7)

**ion–dipole force** The force that exists between an ion and a neutral polar molecule that possesses a permanent dipole moment. (Section 11.2)

**ion exchange** A process by which ions in solution are exchanged for other ions held on the surface of an ion-exchange resin; the exchange of a hard-water cation such as $Ca^{2+}$ for a soft-water cation such as $Na^+$ is used to soften water. (Section 18.4)

**ionic bond** A bond between oppositely charged ions. The ions are formed from atoms by transfer of one or more electrons. (Section 8.1)

**ionic compound** A compound composed of cations and anions. (Section 2.7)

**ionic hydrides** Compounds formed when hydrogen reacts with alkali metals and also the heavier alkaline earths (Ca, Sr, and Ba); these compounds contain the hydride ion, $H^-$. (Section 22.2)

**ionic solids** Solids that are composed of ions. (Section 12.1)

**ionization energy** The energy required to remove an electron from a gaseous atom when the atom is in its ground state. (Section 7.4)

**ionizing radiation** Radiation that has sufficient energy to remove an electron from a molecule, thereby ionizing it. (Section 21.9)

**ion-product constant** For water, $K_w$ is the product of the aquated hydrogen ion and hydroxide ion concentrations: $[H^+][OH^-] = K_w = 1.0 \times 10^{-14}$ at 25 °C. (Section 16.3)

**irreversible process** A process that cannot be reversed to restore both the system and its surroundings to their original states. Any spontaneous process is irreversible. (Section 19.1)

**isoelectronic series** A series of atoms, ions, or molecules having the same number of electrons. (Section 7.3)

**isomers** Compounds whose molecules have the same overall composition but different structures. (Sections 2.9 and 23.4)

**isothermal process** One that occurs at constant temperature. (Section 19.1)

**isotopes** Atoms of the same element containing different numbers of neutrons and therefore having different masses. (Section 2.3)

**joule (J)** The SI unit of energy, $1 \text{ kg-m}^2/s^2$. A related unit is the calorie: 4.184 J = 1 cal. (Section 5.1)

**Kelvin scale** The absolute temperature scale; the SI unit for temperature is the kelvin. Zero on the Kelvin scale corresponds to $-273.15$ °C. (Section 1.4)

**ketone** A compound in which the carbonyl group (C=O) occurs at the interior of a carbon chain and is therefore flanked by carbon atoms. (Section 24.4)

**kinetic energy** The energy that an object possesses by virtue of its motion. (Section 5.1)

**kinetic-molecular theory** A set of assumptions about the nature of gases. These assumptions, when translated into mathematical form, yield the ideal-gas equation. (Section 10.7)

**lanthanide contraction** The gradual decrease in atomic and ionic radii with increasing atomic number among the lanthanide elements, atomic numbers 57 through 70. The decrease arises because of a gradual increase in effective nuclear charge through the lanthanide series. (Section 23.1)

**lanthanide (rare earth) element** Element in which the $4f$ subshell is only partially occupied. (Sections 6.8 and 6.9)

**lattice energy** The energy required to separate completely the ions in an ionic solid. (Section 8.2)

**lattice points** Points in a crystal all of which have identical environments. (Section 12.2)

**lattice vectors** The vectors $a$, $b$, and $c$ that define a crystal lattice. The position of any lattice point in a crystal can be represented by summing integer multiples of the lattice vectors. (Section 12.2)

**law of constant composition** A law that states that the elemental composition of a pure compound is always the same, regardless of its source; also called the **law of definite proportions**. (Section 1.2)

**law of definite proportions** A law that states that the elemental composition of a pure substance is always the same, regardless of its source; also called the **law of constant composition**. (Section 1.2)

**law of mass action** The rules by which the equilibrium constant is expressed in terms of the concentrations of reactants and products, in accordance with the balanced chemical equation for the reaction. (Section 15.2)

**Le Châtelier's principle** A principle stating that when we disturb a system at chemical equilibrium, the relative concentrations of reactants and products shift so as to partially undo the effects of the disturbance. (Section 15.7)

**levorotatory, or merely levo or *l*** A term used to label a chiral molecule that rotates the plane of polarization of plane-polarized light to the left (counterclockwise). (Section 24.4)

**Lewis acid** An electron-pair acceptor. (Section 16.11)

**Lewis base** An electron-pair donor. (Section 16.11)

**Lewis structure** A representation of covalent bonding in a molecule that is drawn using Lewis symbols. Shared electron pairs are shown as lines, and unshared electron pairs are shown as pairs of dots. Only the valence-shell electrons are shown. (Section 8.3)

**Lewis symbol** (electron-dot symbol) The chemical symbol for an element, with a dot for each valence electron. (Section 8.1)

**ligand** An ion or molecule that coordinates to a metal atom or to a metal ion to form a complex. (Section 23.2)

**lime-soda process** A method used in large-scale water treatment to reduce water hardness by removing $Mg^{2+}$ and $Ca^{2+}$. The substances added to the water are lime, $CaO$ [or slaked lime, $Ca(OH)_2$], and soda ash, $Na_2CO_3$, in amounts determined by the concentrations of the undesired ions. (Section 18.4)

**limiting reactant** (limiting reagent) The reactant present in the smallest stoichiometric quantity in a mixture of reactants; the amount of product that can form is limited by the complete consumption of the limiting reactant. (Section 3.7)

**line spectrum** A spectrum that contains radiation at only certain specific wavelengths. (Section 6.3)

**linkage isomers** Structural isomers of coordination compounds in which a ligand differs in its mode of attachment to a metal ion. (Section 23.4)

**lipid** A nonpolar molecule derived from glycerol and fatty acids that is used by organisms for long-term energy storage. (Section 24.9)

**liquid** Matter that has a distinct volume but no specific shape. (Section 1.2)

**liquid crystal** A substance that exhibits one or more partially ordered liquid phases above the melting point of the solid form. By contrast, in nonliquid crystalline substances the liquid phase that forms upon melting is completely unordered. (Section 11.7)

**lock-and-key model** A model of enzyme action in which the substrate molecule is pictured as fitting rather specifically into the active site on the enzyme. It is assumed that in being bound to the active site, the substrate is somehow activated for reaction. (Section 14.7)

**low-spin complex** A metal complex in which the electrons are paired in lower-energy orbitals. (Section 23.6)

**magic numbers** Numbers of protons and neutrons that result in very stable nuclei. (Section 21.2)

**main-group elements** Elements in the $s$ and $p$ blocks of the periodic table. (Section 6.9)

**mass** A measure of the amount of material in an object. It measures the resistance of an object to being moved. In SI units, mass is measured in kilograms. (Section 1.4)

**mass defect** The difference between the mass of a nucleus and the total masses of the individual nucleons that it contains. (Section 21.6)

**mass number** The sum of the number of protons and neutrons in the nucleus of a particular atom. (Section 2.3)

**mass percentage** The number of grams of solute in each 100 g of solution. (Section 13.4)

**mass spectrometer** An instrument used to measure the precise masses and relative amounts of atomic and molecular ions. (Section 2.4)

**matter** Anything that occupies space and has mass; the physical material of the universe. (Section 1.1)

**matter waves** The term used to describe the wave characteristics of a moving particle. (Section 6.4)

**mean free path** The average distance traveled by a gas molecule between collisions. (Section 10.8)

**metal complex** An assembly of a metal ion and the Lewis bases bonded to it. (Section 23.2)

**metallic bond** Bonding, usually in solid metals, in which the bonding electrons are relatively free to move throughout the three-dimensional structure. (Section 8.1)

**metallic character** The extent to which an element exhibits the physical and chemical properties characteristic of metals, for example, luster, malleability, ductility, and good thermal and electrical conductivity. (Section 7.6)

**metallic elements (metals)** Elements that are usually solids at room temperature, exhibit high electrical and heat conductivity, and appear lustrous. Most of the elements in the periodic table are metals. (Sections 2.5 and 12.1)

**metallic hydrides** Compounds formed when hydrogen reacts with transition metals; these compounds contain the hydride ion, $H^-$. (Section 22.2)

**metallic solids** Solids that are composed of metal atoms. (Section 12.1)

**metalloids** Elements that lie along the diagonal line separating the metals from the nonmetals in the periodic table; the properties of metalloids are intermediate between those of metals and nonmetals. (Section 2.5)

**metallurgy** The science of extracting metals from their natural sources by a combination of chemical and physical processes. It is also concerned with the properties and structures of metals and alloys. (Section 23.1)

**metathesis (exchange) reaction** A reaction in which two substances react through an exchange of their component ions: $AX + BY \longrightarrow AY + BX$. Precipitation and acid–base neutralization reactions are examples of metathesis reactions. (Section 4.2)

**metric system** A system of measurement used in science and in most countries. The meter and the gram are examples of metric units. (Section 1.4)

**microstate** The state of a system at a particular instant; one of many possible energetically equivalent ways to arrange the components of a system to achieve a particular state. (Section 19.3)

**mineral** A solid, inorganic substance occurring in nature, such as calcium carbonate, which occurs as calcite. (Section 23.1)

**miscible liquids** Liquids that mix in all proportions. (Section 13.3)

**mixture** A combination of two or more substances in which each substance retains its own chemical identity. (Section 1.2)

**molal boiling-point-elevation constant ($K_b$)** A constant characteristic of a particular solvent that gives the increase in boiling point as a function of solution molality: $\Delta T_b = K_b m$. (Section 13.5)

**molal freezing-point-depression constant ($K_f$)** A constant characteristic of a particular solvent that gives the decrease in freezing point as a function of solution molality: $\Delta T_f = K_f m$. (Section 13.5)

**molality** The concentration of a solution expressed as moles of solute per kilogram of solvent; abbreviated $m$. (Section 13.4)

**molar heat capacity** The heat required to raise the temperature of one mole of a substance by 1 °C. (Section 5.5)

**molarity** The concentration of a solution expressed as moles of solute per liter of solution; abbreviated $M$. (Section 4.5)

**molar mass** The mass of one mole of a substance in grams; it is numerically equal to the formula weight in atomic mass units. (Section 3.4)

**mole** A collection of Avogadro's number ($6.022 \times 10^{23}$) of objects; for example, a mole of $H_2O$ is $6.022 \times 10^{23}$ $H_2O$ molecules. (Section 3.4)

**molecular compound** A compound that consists of molecules. (Section 2.6)

**molecular equation** A chemical equation in which the formula for each substance is written without regard for whether it is an electrolyte or a nonelectrolyte. (Section 4.2)

**molecular formula** A chemical formula that indicates the actual number of atoms of each element in one molecule of a substance. (Section 2.6)

**molecular geometry** The arrangement in space of the atoms of a molecule. (Section 9.2)

**molecular hydrides** Compounds formed when hydrogen reacts with nonmetals and metalloids. (Section 22.2)

**molecularity** The number of molecules that participate as reactants in an elementary reaction. (Section 14.6)

**molecular orbital (MO)** An allowed state for an electron in a molecule. According to molecular-orbital theory, a molecular orbital is entirely analogous to an atomic orbital, which is an allowed state for an electron in an atom. Most bonding molecular orbitals can be classified as $\sigma$ or $\pi$, depending on the disposition of electron density with respect to the internuclear axis. (Section 9.7)

**molecular-orbital diagram** A diagram that shows the energies of molecular orbitals relative to the atomic orbitals from which they are derived; also called an **energy-level diagram**. (Section 9.7)

**molecular-orbital theory** A theory that accounts for the allowed states for electrons in molecules. (Section 9.7)

**molecular solids** Solids that are composed of molecules. (Sections 12.1 and 12.6)

**molecular weight** The mass of the collection of atoms represented by the chemical formula for a molecule. (Section 3.3)

**molecule** A chemical combination of two or more atoms. (Sections 1.1 and 2.6)

**mole fraction** The ratio of the number of moles of one component of a mixture to the total moles of all components; abbreviated $X$, with a subscript to identify the component. (Section 10.6)

**momentum** The product of the mass, $m$, and velocity, $v$, of an object. (Section 6.4)

**monodentate ligand** A ligand that binds to the metal ion via a single donor atom. It occupies one position in the coordination sphere. (Section 23.3)

**monomers** Molecules with low molecular weights, which can be joined together (polymerized) to form a polymer. (Section 12.8)

**monosaccharide** A simple sugar, most commonly containing six carbon atoms. The joining together of monosaccharide units by condensation reactions results in formation of polysaccharides. (Section 24.8)

**nanomaterial** A solid whose dimensions range from 1 to 100 nm and whose properties differ from those of a bulk material with the same composition. (Section 12.1)

**natural gas** A naturally occurring mixture of gaseous hydrocarbon compounds composed of hydrogen and carbon. (Section 5.8)

**nematic liquid crystalline phase** A liquid crystal in which the molecules are aligned in the same general direction, along their long axes, but in which the ends of the molecules are not aligned. (Section 11.7)

**Nernst equation** An equation that relates the cell emf, $E$, to the standard emf, $E°$, and the reaction quotient, $Q: E = E° - (RT/nF) \ln Q$. (Section 20.6)

**net ionic equation** A chemical equation for a solution reaction in which soluble strong electrolytes are written as ions and spectator ions are omitted. (Section 4.2)

**neutralization reaction** A reaction in which an acid and a base react in stoichiometrically equivalent amounts; the neutralization reaction between an acid and a metal hydroxide produces water and a salt. (Section 4.3)

**neutron** An electrically neutral particle found in the nucleus of an atom; it has approximately the same mass as a proton. (Section 2.3)

**noble gases** Members of group 8A in the periodic table. (Section 7.8)

**node** Points in an atom at which the electron density is zero. For example, the node in a $2s$ orbital is a spherical surface. (Section 6.6)

**nonbonding pair** In a Lewis structure a pair of electrons assigned completely to one atom; also called a lone pair. (Section 9.2)

**nonelectrolyte** A substance that does not ionize in water and consequently gives a nonconducting solution. (Section 4.1)

**nonionizing radiation** Radiation that does not have sufficient energy to remove an electron from a molecule. (Section 21.9)

**nonmetallic elements (nonmetals)** Elements in the upper right corner of the periodic table; nonmetals differ from metals in their physical and chemical properties. (Section 2.5)

**nonpolar covalent bond** A covalent bond in which the electrons are shared equally. (Section 8.4)

**normal boiling point** The boiling point at 1 atm pressure. (Section 11.5)

**normal melting point** The melting point at 1 atm pressure. (Section 11.6)

**nuclear binding energy** The energy required to decompose an atomic nucleus into its component protons and neutrons. (Section 21.6)

**nuclear disintegration series** A series of nuclear reactions that begins with an unstable nucleus and terminates with a stable one; also called a **radioactive series**. (Section 21.2)

**nuclear model** Model of the atom with a nucleus containing protons and neutrons and with electrons in the space outside the nucleus. (Section 2.2)

**nuclear transmutation** A conversion of one kind of nucleus to another. (Section 21.3)

**nucleic acids** Polymers of high molecular weight that carry genetic information and control protein synthesis. (Section 24.10)

**nucleon** A particle found in the nucleus of an atom. (Section 21.1)

**nucleotide** Compounds formed from a molecule of phosphoric acid, a sugar molecule, and an organic nitrogen base. Nucleotides form linear polymers called DNA and RNA, which are involved in protein synthesis and cell reproduction. (Section 24.10)

**nucleus** The very small, very dense, positively charged portion of an atom; it is composed of protons and neutrons. (Section 2.2)

**octet rule** A rule stating that bonded atoms tend to possess or share a total of eight valence-shell electrons. (Section 8.1)

**optical isomerism** A form of isomerism in which the two forms of a compound (stereoisomers) are nonsuperimposable mirror images. (Section 23.4)

**optically active** Possessing the ability to rotate the plane of polarized light. (Section 23.4)

**orbital** An allowed energy state of an electron in the quantum mechanical model of the atom; the term *orbital* is also used to describe the spatial distribution of the electron. An orbital is defined by the values of three quantum numbers: $n$, $l$, and $m_l$ (Section 6.5)

**organic chemistry** The study of carbon-containing compounds, typically containing carbon–carbon bonds. (Section 2.9; Chapter 24: Introduction)

**osmosis** The net movement of solvent through a semipermeable membrane toward the solution with greater solute concentration. (Section 13.5)

**osmotic pressure** The pressure that must be applied to a solution to stop osmosis from pure solvent into the solution. (Section 13.5)

**Ostwald process** An industrial process used to make nitric acid from ammonia. The $NH_3$ is catalytically oxidized by $O_2$ to form NO; NO in air is oxidized to $NO_2$; $HNO_3$ is formed in a disproportionation reaction when $NO_2$ dissolves in water. (Section 22.7)

**overall reaction order** The sum of the reaction orders of all the reactants appearing in the rate expression when the rate can be expressed as rate $= k[A]^a[B]^b \ldots$ (Section 14.3)

**overlap** The extent to which atomic orbitals on different atoms share the same region of space. When the overlap between two orbitals is large, a strong bond may be formed. (Section 9.4)

**oxidation** A process in which a substance loses one or more electrons. (Section 4.4)

**oxidation number (oxidation state)** A positive or negative whole number assigned to an element in a molecule or ion on the basis of a set of formal rules; to some degree it reflects the positive or negative character of that atom. (Section 4.4)

**oxidation-reduction (redox) reaction** A chemical reaction in which the oxidation states of certain atoms change. (Section 4.4; Chapter 20: Introduction)

**oxidizing agent, or oxidant** The substance that is reduced and thereby causes the oxidation of some other substance in an oxidation-reduction reaction. (Section 20.1)

**oxyacid** A compound in which one or more OH groups, and possibly additional oxygen atoms, are bonded to a central atom. (Section 16.10)

**oxyanion** A polyatomic anion that contains one or more oxygen atoms. (Section 2.8)

**ozone** The name given to $O_3$, an allotrope of oxygen. (Section 7.8)

**paramagnetism** A property that a substance possesses if it contains one or more unpaired electrons. A paramagnetic substance is drawn into a magnetic field. (Section 9.8)

**partial pressure** The pressure exerted by a particular gas in a mixture. (Section 10.6)

**particle accelerator** A device that uses strong magnetic and electrostatic fields to accelerate charged particles. (Section 21.3)

**parts per billion (ppb)** The concentration of a solution in grams of solute per $10^9$ (billion) grams of solution; equals micrograms of solute per liter of solution for aqueous solutions. (Section 13.4)

**parts per million (ppm)** The concentration of a solution in grams of solute per $10^6$ (million) grams of solution; equals milligrams of solute per liter of solution for aqueous solutions. (Section 13.4)

**pascal (Pa)** The SI unit of pressure: 1 Pa $= 1 N/m^2$. (Section 10.2)

**Pauli exclusion principle** A rule stating that no two electrons in an atom may have the same four quantum numbers ($n$, $l$, $m_l$, and $m_s$). As a reflection of this principle, there can be no more than two electrons in any one atomic orbital. (Section 6.7)

**peptide bond** A bond formed between two amino acids. (Section 24.7)

**percent ionization** The percent of a substance that undergoes ionization on dissolution in water. The term applies to solutions of weak acids and bases. (Section 16.6)

**percent yield** The ratio of the actual (experimental) yield of a product to its theoretical (calculated) yield, multiplied by 100. (Section 3.7)

**period** The row of elements that lie in a horizontal row in the periodic table. (Section 2.5)

**periodic table** The arrangement of elements in order of increasing atomic number, with elements having similar properties placed in vertical columns. (Section 2.5)

**petroleum** A naturally occurring combustible liquid composed of hundreds of hydrocarbons and other organic compounds. (Section 5.8)

**pH** The negative log in base 10 of the aquated hydrogen ion concentration: pH $= -\log[H^+]$. (Section 16.4)

**pH titration curve** A graph of pH as a function of added titrant. (Section 17.3)

**phase change** The conversion of a substance from one state of matter to another. The phase changes we consider are melting and freezing (solid $\rightleftharpoons$ liquid), sublimation and deposition, and vaporization and condensation (liquid $\rightleftharpoons$ gas). (Section 11.4)

**phase diagram** A graphic representation of the equilibria among the solid, liquid, and gaseous phases of a substance as a function of temperature and pressure. (Section 11.6)

**phospholipid** A form of lipid molecule that contains charged phosphate groups. (Section 24.9)

**photochemical smog** A complex mixture of undesirable substances produced by the action of sunlight on an urban atmosphere polluted with automobile emissions. The major starting ingredients are nitrogen oxides and organic substances, notably olefins and aldehydes. (Section 18.2)

**photodissociation** The breaking of a molecule into two or more neutral fragments as a result of absorption of light. (Section 18.2)

**photoelectric effect** The emission of electrons from a metal surface induced by light. (Section 6.2)

**photoionization** The removal of an electron from an atom or molecule by absorption of light. (Section 18.2)

**photon** The smallest increment (a quantum) of radiant energy; a photon of light with frequency $\nu$ has an energy equal to $h\nu$. (Section 6.2)

**photosynthesis** The process that occurs in plant leaves by which light energy is used to convert carbon dioxide and water to carbohydrates and oxygen. (Section 23.3)

**physical changes** Changes (such as a phase change) that occur with no change in chemical composition. (Section 1.3)

**physical properties** Properties that can be measured without changing the composition of a substance, for example, color and freezing point. (Section 1.3)

**pi (π) bond** A covalent bond in which electron density is concentrated above and below the internuclear axis. (Section 9.6)

**pi (π) molecular orbital** A molecular orbital that concentrates the electron density on opposite sides of an imaginary line that passes through the nuclei. (Section 9.8)

**Planck's constant (h)** The constant that relates the energy and frequency of a photon, $E = h\nu$. Its value is $6.626 \times 10^{-34}$ J-s. (Section 6.2)

**plastic** A material that can be formed into particular shapes by application of heat and pressure. (Section 12.8)

**polar covalent bond** A covalent bond in which the electrons are not shared equally. (Section 8.4)

**polarizability** The ease with which the electron cloud of an atom or a molecule is distorted by an outside influence, thereby inducing a dipole moment. (Section 11.2)

**polar molecule** A molecule that possesses a nonzero dipole moment. (Section 8.4)

**polyatomic ion** An electrically charged group of two or more atoms. (Section 2.7)

**polydentate ligand** A ligand in which two or more donor atoms can coordinate to the same metal ion. (Section 23.3)

**polymer** A large molecule of high molecular mass, formed by the joining together, or polymerization, of a large number of molecules of low molecular mass. The individual molecules forming the polymer are called monomers. (Sections 12.1 and 12.8)

**polypeptide** A polymer of amino acids that has a molecular weight of less than 10,000. (Section 24.7)

**polyprotic acid** A substance capable of dissociating more than one proton in water; $H_2SO_4$ is an example. (Section 16.6)

**polysaccharide** A substance made up of many monosaccharide units joined together. (Section 24.8)

**porphyrin** A complex derived from the porphine molecule. (Section 23.3)

**positron emission** A nuclear decay process where a positron, a particle with the same mass as an electron but with a positive charge, symbol $^{0}_{1}e$, is emitted from the nucleus. (Section 21.1)

**potential energy** The energy that an object possesses as a result of its composition or its position with respect to another object. (Section 5.1)

**precipitate** An insoluble substance that forms in, and separates from, a solution. (Section 4.2)

**precipitation reaction** A reaction that occurs between substances in solution in which one of the products is insoluble. (Section 4.2)

**precision** The closeness of agreement among several measurements of the same quantity; the reproducibility of a measurement. (Section 1.5)

**pressure** A measure of the force exerted on a unit area. In chemistry, pressure is often expressed in units of atmospheres (atm) or torr: 760 torr = 1 atm; in SI units pressure is expressed in pascals (Pa). (Section 10.2)

**pressure–volume (PV) work** Work performed by expansion of a gas against a resisting pressure. (Section 5.3)

**primary structure** The sequence of amino acids along a protein chain. (Section 24.7)

**primitive lattice** A crystal lattice in which the lattice points are located only at the corners of each unit cell. (Section 12.2)

**probability density (ψ²)** A value that represents the probability that an electron will be found at a given point in space. Also called **electron density**. (Section 6.5)

**product** A substance produced in a chemical reaction; it appears to the right of the arrow in a chemical equation. (Section 3.1)

**property** A characteristic that gives a sample of matter its unique identity. (Section 1.1)

**protein** A biopolymer formed from amino acids. (Section 24.7)

**protium** The most common isotope of hydrogen. (Section 22.2)

**proton** A positively charged subatomic particle found in the nucleus of an atom. (Section 2.3)

**pure substance** Matter that has a fixed composition and distinct properties. (Section 1.2)

**pyrometallurgy** A process in which heat converts a mineral in an ore from one chemical form to another and eventually to the free metal. (Section 23.2)

**qualitative analysis** The determination of the presence or absence of a particular substance in a mixture. (Section 17.7)

**quantitative analysis** The determination of the amount of a given substance that is present in a sample. (Section 17.7)

**quantum** The smallest increment of radiant energy that may be absorbed or emitted; the magnitude of radiant energy is $h\nu$. (Section 6.2)

**quaternary structure** The structure of a protein resulting from the clustering of several individual protein chains into a final specific shape. (Section 24.7)

**racemic mixture** A mixture of equal amounts of the dextrorotatory and levorotatory forms of a chiral molecule. A racemic mixture will not rotate the plane of polarized light. (Section 23.4)

**rad** A measure of the energy absorbed from radiation by tissue or other biological material; 1 rad = transfer of $1 \times 10^{-2}$ J of energy per kilogram of material. (Section 21.9)

**radial probability function** The probability that the electron will be found at a certain distance from the nucleus. (Section 6.6)

**radioactive** Possessing **radioactivity**, the spontaneous disintegration of an unstable atomic nucleus with accompanying emission of radiation. (Section 2.2; Chapter 21: Introduction)

**radioactive series** A series of nuclear reactions that begins with an unstable nucleus and terminates with a stable one. Also called **nuclear disintegration series**. (Section 21.2)

**radioisotope** An isotope that is radioactive; that is, it is undergoing nuclear changes with emission of radiation. (Section 21.1)

**radionuclide** A radioactive nuclide. (Section 21.1)

**radiotracer** A radioisotope that can be used to trace the path of an element in a chemical system. (Section 21.5)

**Raoult's law** A law stating that the partial pressure of a solvent over a solution, $P_{solution}$, is given by the vapor pressure of the pure solvent, $P^{\circ}_{solvent}$, times the mole fraction of a solvent in the solution, $X_{solvent}$: $P_{solution} = X_{solvent}P^{\circ}_{solvent}$. (Section 13.5)

**rare earth element** See **lanthanide element**. (Sections 6.8 and 6.9)

**rate constant** A constant of proportionality between the reaction rate and the concentrations of reactants that appear in the rate law. (Section 14.3)

**rate-determining step** The slowest elementary step in a reaction mechanism. (Section 14.6)

**rate law** An equation that relates the reaction rate to the concentrations of reactants (and sometimes of products also). (Section 14.3)

**reactant** A starting substance in a chemical reaction; it appears to the left of the arrow in a chemical equation. (Section 3.1)

**reaction mechanism** A detailed picture, or model, of how the reaction occurs; that is, the order in which bonds are broken and formed and the changes in relative positions of the atoms as the reaction proceeds. (Section 14.6)

**reaction order** The power to which the concentration of a reactant is raised in a rate law. (Section 14.3)

**reaction quotient (Q)** The value that is obtained when concentrations of reactants and products are inserted into the equilibrium expression. If the concentrations are equilibrium concentrations, $Q = K$; otherwise, $Q \neq K$. (Section 15.6)

**reaction rate** A measure of the decrease in concentration of a reactant or the increase in concentration of a product with time. (Section 14.2)

**redox (oxidation-reduction) reaction** A reaction in which certain atoms undergo changes in oxidation states. The substance increasing in oxidation state is oxidized; the substance decreasing in oxidation state is reduced. (Section 4.4; Chapter 20: Introduction)

**reducing agent, or reductant** The substance that is oxidized and thereby causes the reduction of some other substance in an oxidation-reduction reaction. (Section 20.1)

**reduction**   A process in which a substance gains one or more electrons. (Section 4.4)

**rem**   A measure of the biological damage caused by radiation; rems = rads × RBE. (Section 21.9)

**renewable energy sources**   Energy such as solar energy, wind energy, and hydroelectric energy derived from essentially inexhaustible sources. (Section 5.8)

**representative (main-group) element**   An element from within the $s$ and $p$ blocks of the periodic table (Figure 6.29). (Section 6.9)

**resonance structures (resonance forms)**   Individual Lewis structures in cases where two or more Lewis structures are equally good descriptions of a single molecule. The resonance structures in such an instance are "averaged" to give a more accurate description of the real molecule. (Section 8.6)

**reverse osmosis**   The process by which water molecules move under high pressure through a semipermeable membrane from the more concentrated to the less concentrated solution. (Section 18.4)

**reversible process**   A process that can go back and forth between states along exactly the same path; a system at equilibrium is reversible if equilibrium can be shifted by an infinitesimal modification of a variable such as temperature. (Section 19.1)

**ribonucleic acid (RNA)**   A polynucleotide in which ribose is the sugar component. (Section 24.10)

**root-mean-square (rms) speed ($\mu$)**   The square root of the average of the squared speeds of the gas molecules in a gas sample. (Section 10.7)

**rotational motion**   Movement of a molecule as though it is spinning like a top. (Section 19.3)

**salinity**   A measure of the salt content of seawater, brine, or brackish water. It is equal to the mass in grams of dissolved salts present in 1 kg of seawater. (Section 18.3)

**salt**   An ionic compound formed by replacing one or more hydrogens of an acid by other cations. (Section 4.3)

**saponification**   Hydrolysis of an ester in the presence of a base. (Section 24.4)

**saturated solution**   A solution in which undissolved solute and dissolved solute are in equilibrium. (Section 13.2)

**scientific law**   A concise verbal statement or a mathematical equation that summarizes a wide range of observations and experiences. (Section 1.3)

**scientific method**   The general process of advancing scientific knowledge by making experimental observations and by formulating hypotheses, theories, and laws. (Section 1.3)

**secondary structure**   The manner in which a protein is coiled or stretched. (Section 24.7)

**second law of thermodynamics**   A statement of our experience that there is a direction to the way events occur in nature. When a process occurs spontaneously in one direction, it is nonspontaneous in the reverse direction. It is possible to state the second law in many different forms, but they all relate back to the same idea about spontaneity. One of the most common statements found in chemical contexts is that in any spontaneous process the entropy of the universe increases. (Section 19.2)

**second-order reaction**   A reaction in which the overall reaction order (the sum of the concentration-term exponents) in the rate law is 2. (Section 14.4)

**sigma ($\sigma$) bond**   A covalent bond in which electron density is concentrated along the internuclear axis. (Section 9.6)

**sigma ($\sigma$) molecular orbital**   A molecular orbital that centers the electron density about an imaginary line passing through two nuclei. (Section 9.7)

**significant figures**   The digits that indicate the precision with which a measurement is made; all digits of a measured quantity are significant, including the last digit, which is uncertain. (Section 1.5)

**silica**   Common name for silicon dioxide. (Section 22.4)

**silicates**   Compounds containing silicon and oxygen, structurally based on $SiO_4$ tetrahedra. (Section 22.10)

**single bond**   A covalent bond involving one electron pair. (Section 8.3)

**SI units**   The preferred metric units for use in science. (Section 1.4)

**smectic liquid crystalline phase**   A liquid crystal in which the molecules are aligned along their long axes and arranged in sheets, with the ends of the molecules aligned. There are several different kinds of smectic phases. (Section 12.8)

**solid**   Matter that has both a definite shape and a definite volume. (Section 1.2)

**solubility**   The amount of a substance that dissolves in a given quantity of solvent at a given temperature to form a saturated solution. (Sections 4.2 and 13.2)

**solubility-product constant (solubility product) ($K_{sp}$)**   An equilibrium constant related to the equilibrium between a solid salt and its ions in solution. It provides a quantitative measure of the solubility of a slightly soluble salt. (Section 17.4)

**solute**   A substance dissolved in a solvent to form a solution; it is normally the component of a solution present in the smaller amount. (Section 4.1)

**solution**   A mixture of substances that has a uniform composition; a homogeneous mixture. (Section 1.2)

**solution alloy**   A homogeneous alloy, where two or more elements are distributed randomly and uniformly throughout the solid. (Section 12.3)

**solvation**   The clustering of solvent molecules around a solute particle. (Section 13.1)

**solvent**   The dissolving medium of a solution; it is normally the component of a solution present in the greater amount. (Section 4.1)

**specific heat ($C_s$)**   The heat capacity of 1 g of a substance; the heat required to raise the temperature of 1 g of a substance by 1 °C. (Section 5.5)

**spectator ions**   Ions that go through a reaction unchanged and that appear on both sides of the complete ionic equation. (Section 4.2)

**spectrochemical series**   A list of ligands arranged in order of their abilities to split the $d$-orbital energies (using the terminology of the crystal-field model). (Section 23.6)

**spectrum**   The distribution among various wavelengths of the radiant energy emitted or absorbed by an object. (Section 6.3)

**spin magnetic quantum number ($m_s$)**   A quantum number associated with the electron spin; it may have values of $+\frac{1}{2}$ or $-\frac{1}{2}$. (Section 6.7)

**spin-pairing energy**   The energy required to pair an electron with another electron occupying an orbital. (Section 23.6)

**spontaneous process**   A process that is capable of proceeding in a given direction, as written or described, without needing to be driven by an outside source of energy. A process may be spontaneous even though it is very slow. (Section 19.1)

**standard atmospheric pressure**   Defined as 760 torr or, in SI units, 101.325 kPa. (Section 10.2)

**standard emf, also called the standard cell potential ($E°$)**   The emf of a cell when all reagents are at standard conditions. (Section 20.4)

**standard enthalpy change ($\Delta H°$)**   The change in enthalpy in a process when all reactants and products are in their stable forms at 1 atm pressure and a specified temperature, commonly 25 °C. (Section 5.7)

**standard enthalpy of formation ($\Delta H_f°$)**   The change in enthalpy that accompanies the formation of one mole of a substance from its elements, with all substances in their standard states. (Section 5.7)

**standard free energy of formation ($\Delta G_f°$)**   The change in free energy associated with the formation of a substance from its elements under standard conditions. (Section 19.5)

**standard hydrogen electrode (SHE)**   An electrode based on the half-reaction $2 H^+(1 M) + 2 e^- \longrightarrow H_2(1 atm)$. The standard electrode potential of the standard hydrogen electrode is defined as 0 V. (Section 20.4)

**standard molar entropy ($S°$)**   The entropy value for a mole of a substance in its standard state. (Section 19.4)

**standard reduction potential ($E°_{red}$)**   The potential of a reduction half-reaction under standard conditions, measured relative to the standard hydrogen electrode. A standard reduction potential is also called a **standard electrode potential**. (Section 20.4)

**standard solution**   A solution of known concentration. (Section 4.6)

**standard temperature and pressure (STP)**   Defined as 0 °C and 1 atm pressure; frequently used as reference conditions for a gas. (Section 10.4)

**starch**   The general name given to a group of polysaccharides that acts as energy-storage substances in plants. (Section 24.8)

**state function**   A property of a system that is determined by its state or condition and not by how it got to that state; its value is fixed when temperature, pressure, composition, and physical form are specified; $P$, $V$, $T$, $E$, and $H$ are state functions. (Section 5.2)

**states of matter**   The three forms that matter can assume: solid, liquid, and gas. (Section 1.2)

**stereoisomers**   Compounds possessing the same formula and bonding arrangement but differing in the spatial arrangements of the atoms. (Section 23.4)

**stoichiometry**   The relationships among the quantities of reactants and products involved in chemical reactions. (Chapter 3: Introduction)

**stratosphere**   The region of the atmosphere directly above the troposphere. (Section 18.1)

**strong acid**   An acid that ionizes completely in water. (Section 4.3)

**strong base**   A base that ionizes completely in water. (Section 4.3)

**strong electrolyte**   A substance (strong acids, strong bases, and most salts) that is completely ionized in solution. (Section 4.1)

**structural formula**   A formula that shows not only the number and kinds of atoms in the molecule but also the arrangement (connections) of the atoms. (Section 2.6)

**structural isomers**   Compounds possessing the same formula but differing in the bonding arrangements of the atoms. (Sections 23.4 and 24.2)

**subatomic particles**   Particles such as protons, neutrons, and electrons that are smaller than an atom. (Section 2.2)

**subshell**   One or more orbitals with the same set of quantum numbers $n$ and $l$. For example, we speak of the $2p$ subshell ($n = 2$, $l = 1$), which is composed of three orbitals ($2p_x$, $2p_y$, and $2p_z$). (Section 6.5)

**substitutional alloy**   A homogeneous (solution) alloy in which atoms of different elements randomly occupy sites in the lattice. (Section 23.6)

**substitution reactions**   Reactions in which one atom (or group of atoms) replaces another atom (or group) within a molecule; substitution reactions are typical for alkanes and aromatic hydrocarbons. (Section 24.3)

**substrate**   A substance that undergoes a reaction at the active site in an enzyme. (Section 14.7)

**supercritical mass**   An amount of fissionable material larger than the critical mass. (Section 21.7)

**supersaturated solution**   A solution containing more solute than an equivalent saturated solution. (Section 13.2)

**surface tension**   The intermolecular, cohesive attraction that causes a liquid to minimize its surface area. (Section 11.3)

**surroundings**   In thermodynamics, everything that lies outside the system that we study. (Section 5.1)

**system**   In thermodynamics, the portion of the universe that we single out for study. We must be careful to state exactly what the system contains and what transfers of energy it may have with its surroundings. (Section 5.1)

**termolecular reaction**   An elementary reaction that involves three molecules. Termolecular reactions are rare. (Section 14.6)

**tertiary structure**   The overall shape of a large protein, specifically, the manner in which sections of the protein fold back upon themselves or intertwine. (Section 24.7)

**theoretical yield**   The quantity of product that is calculated to form when all of the limiting reagent reacts. (Section 3.7)

**theory**   A tested model or explanation that satisfactorily accounts for a certain set of phenomena. (Section 1.3)

**thermochemistry**   The relationship between chemical reactions and energy changes. (Chapter 5: Introduction)

**thermodynamics**   The study of energy and its transformation. (Chapter 5: Introduction)

**thermonuclear reaction**   Another name for fusion reactions; reactions in which two light nuclei are joined to form a more massive one. (Section 21.8)

**thermoplastic**   A polymeric material that can be readily reshaped by application of heat and pressure. (Section 12.8)

**thermosetting plastic**   A plastic that, once formed in a particular mold, is not readily reshaped by application of heat and pressure. (Section 12.8)

**third law of thermodynamics**   A law stating that the entropy of a pure, crystalline solid at absolute zero temperature is zero: $S(0 \text{ K}) = 0$. (Section 19.3)

**titration**   The process of reacting a solution of unknown concentration with one of known concentration (a standard solution). (Section 4.6)

**torr**   A unit of pressure (1 torr = 1 mm Hg). (Section 10.2)

**transition elements (transition metals)**   Elements in which the $d$ orbitals are partially occupied. (Section 6.8)

**transition state (activated complex)**   The particular arrangement of reactant and product molecules at the point of maximum energy in the rate-determining step of a reaction. (Section 14.5)

**translational motion**   Movement in which an entire molecule moves in a definite direction. (Section 19.3)

**transuranium elements**   Elements that follow uranium in the periodic table. (Section 21.3)

**triple bond**   A covalent bond involving three electron pairs. (Section 8.3)

**triple point**   The temperature at which solid, liquid, and gas phases coexist in equilibrium. (Section 11.6)

**tritium**   The isotope of hydrogen whose nucleus contains a proton and two neutrons. (Section 22.2)

**troposphere**   The region of Earth's atmosphere extending from the surface to about 12 km altitude. (Section 18.1)

**Tyndall effect**   The scattering of a beam of visible light by the particles in a colloidal dispersion. (Section 13.6)

**uncertainty principle**   A principle stating there is an inherent uncertainty in the precision with which we can simultaneously specify the position and momentum of a particle. This uncertainty is significant only for particles of extremely small mass, such as electrons. (Section 6.4)

**unimolecular reaction**   An elementary reaction that involves a single molecule. (Section 14.6)

**unit cell**   The smallest portion of a crystal that reproduces the structure of the entire crystal when repeated in different directions in space. It is the repeating unit or building block of the crystal lattice. (Section 12.2)

**unsaturated solution**   A solution containing less solute than a saturated solution. (Section 13.2)

**valence band**   A band of closely spaced molecular orbitals that is essentially fully occupied by electrons. (Section 12.7)

**valence-bond theory**   A model of chemical bonding in which an electron-pair bond is formed between two atoms by the overlap of orbitals on the two atoms. (Section 9.4)

**valence electrons**   The outermost electrons of an atom; those that occupy orbitals not occupied in the nearest noble-gas element of lower atomic number. The valence electrons are the ones the atom uses in bonding. (Section 6.8)

**valence orbitals**   Orbitals that contain the outer-shell electrons of an atom. (Chapter 7: Introduction)

**valence-shell electron-pair repulsion (VSEPR) model**   A model that accounts for the geometric arrangements of shared and unshared electron pairs around a central atom in terms of the repulsions between electron pairs. (Section 9.2)

**van der Waals equation**   An equation of state for nonideal gases that is based on adding corrections to the ideal-gas equation. The correction terms account for intermolecular forces of attraction and for the volumes occupied by the gas molecules themselves. (Section 10.9)

**vapor**   Gaseous state of any substance that normally exists as a liquid or solid. (Section 10.1)

**vapor pressure**   The pressure exerted by a vapor in equilibrium with its liquid or solid phase. (Section 11.5)

**vibrational motion**   Movement of the atoms within a molecule in which they move periodically toward and away from one another. (Section 19.3)

**viscosity**   A measure of the resistance of fluids to flow. (Section 11.3)

**volatile**   Tending to evaporate readily. (Section 11.5)

**voltaic (galvanic) cell**   A device in which a spontaneous oxidation-reduction reaction occurs with the passage of electrons through an external circuit. (Section 20.3)

**vulcanization**   The process of cross-linking polymer chains in rubber. (Section 12.6)

**watt**   A unit of power; 1 W = 1 J/s. (Section 20.5)

**wave function**   A mathematical description of an allowed energy state (an orbital) for an electron in the quantum mechanical model of the atom; it is usually symbolized by the Greek letter $\psi$. (Section 6.5)

**wavelength**   The distance between identical points on successive waves. (Section 6.1)

**weak acid**   An acid that only partly ionizes in water. (Section 4.3)

**weak base**   A base that only partly ionizes in water. (Section 4.3)

**weak electrolyte**   A substance that only partly ionizes in solution. (Section 4.1)

**work**   The movement of an object against some force. (Section 5.1)

**CHAPTER 1: CO01** J. Hester/NASA **1.2a** iStockphoto **1.2b** Francis G. Mayer/Corbis **1.2c** Shutterstock **1.3** Eric Schrader - Pearson Science **1.7** Charles D. Winters/Photo Researchers, Inc. **1.8a** Sergej Petrakov/iStockphoto **1.8b** Richard Megna/Fundamental Photographs **1.11a** Pearson Education **1.11b-c** Richard Megna/Fundamental Photographs **1.12a-b** Richard Megna/Fundamental Photographs **1.14a-c** Richard Megna/Fundamental Photographs **1.15** Eric Schrader - Pearson Science **1.20** AP Photo/Paul Sancya **1.22** Dwight Cendrowski/Cree, Inc. **p. 23** Sidney Harris **p. 34 (top)** sciencephotos/Alamy **p. 34 (middle)** Shutterstock

**CHAPTER 2: CO02** Charles D. Winters/Photo Researchers, Inc. **2.1** Corbis/Bettmann **2.2** Wilson Ho/University of California Irvine **2.3a-b** Richard Megna/Fundamental Photographs **2.6** Radium Institute/Emilio Segre Archives **2.7** Reserve Bank of New Zealand **2.16a-b** Richard Megna/Fundamental Photographs **2.17** University of California Berkeley/Emilio Segre Archives **2.21** iStockphoto **2.23** Eric Schrader - Pearson Science

**CHAPTER 3: CO03** Shutterstock **3.1** Jean-Loup Charmet/SPL/Photo Researchers, Inc. **3.4** Shutterstock **3.6a-c** Richard Megna/Fundamental Photographs **3.7** Donald Johnston/Getty Images **3.8** Richard Megna/Fundamental Photographs **3.10** Richard Megna/Fundamental Photographs **3.11** iStockphoto **p. 109** AP Photo/Damian Dovarganes **p. 110** Richard Megna/Fundamental Photographs **p. 111** iStockphoto

**CHAPTER 4: CO04** Macduff Everton/Getty Images **4.2a-c** Eric Schrader - Pearson Science **4.4a-c** Richard Megna/Fundamental Photographs **4.5** Eric Schrader - Pearson Education **4.8** Eric Schrader - Pearson Science **4.9a-c** Richard Megna/Fundamental Photographs **4.10** Eric Schrader - Pearson Science **4.11a-c** iStockphoto **4.12a-b** Richard Megna/Fundamental Photographs **4.13a-c** Eric Schrader - Pearson Science **4.14a-c** Richard Megna/Fundamental Photographs **4.15** AP Photo/Jim Cole **4.16a-c** Pearson Education **4.17a-c** Richard Megna/Fundamental Photographs **4.19a-d** Richard Megna/Fundamental Photographs **p. 154** Richard Megna/Fundamental Photographs

**CHAPTER 5: CO05** Paulo Fridman/Bloomberg via Getty Images **5.1a** REUTERS/Adam Hunger **5.1b** iStockphoto **5.8a-b** Richard Megna/Fundamental Photographs **5.14a-b** Charles D. Winters/Photo Researchers, Inc. **5.15** Corbis/Bettmann **5.20** iStockphoto **5.24** Eric Schrader - Pearson Science **5.26** iStockphoto **p. 196** James Urbach/Photolibrary

**CHAPTER 6: CO06** Gary Corbett/AGE Photostock **6.1** Pal Hermansen/Getty Images **6.5** Peter Arnold/AGE Fotostock **6.8** Emilio Segre Archives **6.10a-b** Richard Megna/Fundamental Photographs **6.13** Dr. Nicola Pinna **6.14** Emilio Segre Archives **6.28** Medical Body Scans/Photo Researchers, Inc. **p. 240 (top left)** iStockphoto **p. 240 (bottom)** Getty Images **p. 240 (right)** iStockphoto

**CHAPTER 7: CO07** Steven Puetzer/Getty Images **7.13** iStockphoto **7.15b** Richard Megna/Fundamental Photographs **7.16** SPL/Photo Researchers, Inc. **7.17a-b** Richard Megna/Fundamental Photographs **7.18** Andrew Lambert Photography/Photo Researchers, Inc. **7.19** Charles D. Winters/Photo Researchers, Inc. **7.20a-c** Richard Megna/Fundamental Photographs **7.21a-b** David Taylor/Photo Researchers, Inc. **7.21c** Andrew Lambert Photography/Photo Researchers, Inc. **7.22** iStockphoto **7.23** Write Stuff Syndicate **7.24** Richard Megna/Fundamental Photographs **7.25** Eric Schrader - Pearson Science **7.27** Richard Megna/Fundamental Photographs

**CHAPTER 8: CO08** Barry O'Neill **8.1** Shutterstock **8.16** Bettmann/Corbis

**CHAPTER 9: CO09** Richard Megna/Fundamental Photographs **9.5a-c** Kristen Brochmann/Fundamental Photographs **9.29** Science Photo Library RF/Photolibrary **9.45** Richard Megna/Fundamental Photographs **9.47** Michael Graetzel

**CHAPTER 10: CO10** NASA **10.4** Pearson Education **10.12** Andrew Putler/Redferns/Getty Images **10.20b** Richard Megna/Fundamental Photographs

**CHAPTER 11: CO11** Tongro Image Stock/AGE Fotostock **11.1** Bharat Bhushan/Ohio State University **11.2a** Leslie Garland Picture Library/Alamy **11.2b** Dorling Kindersley **11.2c** Dennis "S.K" used under a Creative Commons license. http://creativecommons.org/licenses/by/3.0/ **p. 433** Bill Waterson/Universal Press Syndicate **11.11** Ted Kinsman/Photo Researchers, Inc. **11.12** Eric Schrader - Pearson Science **11.17** Kristen Brochmann/Fundamental Photographs **11.18** Hermann Eisenbeiss/Photo Researchers, Inc. **11.19** Richard Megna/Fundamental Photographs **11.31a-b** Richard Megna/Fundamental Photographs **11.35** REUTERS/Yuriko Nakao **p. 458** Richard Megna/Fundamental Photographs

**CHAPTER 12: CO12** iStockphoto **12.2a** iStockphoto **12.2b** Dorling Kindersley Media Library **12.10** Eric Schrader - Pearson Science **12.16** DoITPoMS Micrograph Library, University of Cambridge **12.19a** Katharine "GoldenRuby" **12.19b** Anne Hänsel **12.25** iStockphoto **12.34** Grace Harbor Industries **12.36** Richard Megna/Fundamental Photographs **12.43** Horst Weller **12.44** Horst Weller **12.45** Photo by Vassil. (666vassil@orange.fr) **12.46** The Royal Institution of Great Britain/Bridgeman **p. 504 (middle)** iStockphoto **p. 504 (bottom)** Jinghong Li

**CHAPTER 13: CO13** Clark Little Photography **13.5** Tom Bochsler - Pearson Education **13.6a-c** Richard Megna/Fundamental Photographs **13.7** Richard Megna/Fundamental Photographs **13.9a-c** Richard Megna/Fundamental Photographs **13.10** Richard Megna/Fundamental Photographs **13.16** Charles D. Winters/Photo Researchers, Inc. **13.17** iStockphoto **13.22** iStockphoto **13.28** Richard Megna/Fundamental Photographs **13.29a** iStockphoto **13.29b** Shutterstock **13.33** Oliver Meckes & Nicole Ottawa/Photo Researchers, Inc.

**CHAPTER 14: CO14** Philippe Plailly/SPL/Photo Researchers, Inc. **14.1a** Michael S. Yamashita/Corbis **14.1b-c** Shutterstock **14.2a** Michael Dalton/Fundamental Photographs **14.2b** Richard Megna/Fundamental Photographs **14.13** Richard Megna/Fundamental Photographs **14.22a-c** Richard Megna/Fundamental Photographs **14.26** Richard Megna/Fundamental Photographs **14.30** Science Photo Library/Photo Researchers, Inc.

**CHAPTER 15: CO15** Bruno Perousse/AGE Fotostock **15.1a-c** Richard Megna/Fundamental Photographs **15.4** iStockphoto **p. 631** Public Domain **15.13a-c** Richard Megna/Fundamental Photographs

**CHAPTER 16: CO16** Charles Mann **16.6** Richard Megna/Fundamental Photographs **16.8a-c** Richard Megna/Fundamental Photographs **16.10a-d** Eric Schrader - Pearson Science **16.14** Eric Schrader - Pearson Science **16.15** Richard Megna/Fundamental Photographs **p. 694** Eric Schrader - Pearson Science

**CHAPTER 17: CO17** Corbis/Photolibrary **17.1** EMD Chemicals **17.5** P. Motta and S. Corer/SPL/Photo Researchers, Inc. **17.18** Pacific Stock/Photolibrary **17.20a-c** Eric Schrader - Pearson Science **17.21a-c** Richard Megna/Fundamental Photographs **17.22a-c** Richard Megna/Fundamental Photographs **p. 740** Richard Megna/Fundamental Photographs

**CHAPTER 18: CO18** Shutterstock **18.2** iStockphoto **18.5** Karin Jackson/U.S. Air Force/USGS **18.6** NASA **18.7** National Atmospheric Deposition Program **18.8a** Hulton Archive/Getty Images **18.8b** Dan Breckwoldt/iStockphoto **18.10** iStockphoto **18.14** Astralia Picture Library/Corbis **18.18** iStockphoto **18.19** E. I. Dupont de Nemours & Co. **18.21** Vestergaard Frandsen **18.22** Sheila Terry/SPL/Photo Researchers, Inc. **18.23** Los Angeles Department of Water and Power

**CHAPTER 19: CO19** iStockphoto **19.1a-b** Kristen Brochmann/Fundamental Photographs **19.3a-b** Michael Dalton/Fundamental Photographs **19.7** Osterreichische Zentralbibliothek fur Physik **19.12a** GM Pictures/Alamy **19.12b** Ben Levy - RapidRepair.com **19.15** Manuscripts & Archives - Yale University Library **19.18** iStockphoto

**CHAPTER 20: CO20** Shutterstock **20.1a-b** Richard Megna/Fundamental Photographs **20.2a-b** Richard Megna/Fundamental Photographs **20.3a-b** Richard Megna/Fundamental Photographs **20.4** Richard Megna/Fundamental Photographs **20.7** iStockphoto **20.13** Michael Faraday, oil, by Thomas Phillips **20.28** Oberlin College Archives

**CHAPTER 21: CO21** JPL/NASA **21.5** Brookhaven National Laboratory **21.8** Don Murray/Getty Images **21.11** Drs. Suzanne Baker, William Jagust, and Susan Landau **21.17** Los Alamos National Laboratory **21.20** Idaho National Laboratory **21.26** Environmental Protection Agency

**CHAPTER 22: CO22** Feng Yu/Fotolia **22.5a-b** Richard Megna/Fundamental Photographs **22.8** Pearson Education **22.10a-b** Richard Megna/Fundamental Photographs **22.11** NASA/Johnson Space Center **22.12** Prof. Carl Djerassi **22.13** Shutterstock **22.14a-b** Richard Megna/Fundamental Photographs **22.15** Maksym Gorpenyuk/Fotolia **22.17** Corbis RF/Alamy **22.19** Paul Silverman/Fundamental Photographs **22.20a-b** Kristen Brochmann/Fundamental Photographs **22.24a-b** Richard Megna/Fundamental Photographs **22.25a-b** Pearson Education **22.27** Richard Megna/Fundamental Photographs **22.30** United States Geological Service **22.31** Shutterstock **22.32** Eric Schrader - Pearson Science **22.35** National Institute for Occupational Safety and Health

# Common Ions

**Positive Ions (Cations)**

**1+**

ammonium ($NH_4^+$)
cesium ($Cs^+$)
copper(I) or cuprous ($Cu^+$)
hydrogen ($H^+$)
lithium ($Li^+$)
potassium ($K^+$)
silver ($Ag^+$)
sodium ($Na^+$)

**2+**

barium ($Ba^{2+}$)
cadmium ($Cd^{2+}$)
calcium ($Ca^{2+}$)
chromium(II) or chromous ($Cr^{2+}$)
cobalt(II) or cobaltous ($Co^{2+}$)
copper(II) or cupric ($Cu^{2+}$)
iron(II) or ferrous ($Fe^{2+}$)
lead(II) or plumbous ($Pb^{2+}$)
magnesium ($Mg^{2+}$)
manganese(II) or manganous ($Mn^{2+}$)
mercury(I) or mercurous ($Hg_2^{2+}$)

mercury(II) or mercuric ($Hg^{2+}$)
strontium ($Sr^{2+}$)
nickel(II) ($Ni^{2+}$)
tin(II) or stannous ($Sn^{2+}$)
zinc ($Zn^{2+}$)

**3+**

aluminum ($Al^{3+}$)
chromium(III) or chromic ($Cr^{3+}$)
iron(III) or ferric ($Fe^{3+}$)

**Negative Ions (Anions)**

**1−**

acetate ($CH_3COO^-$ or $C_2H_3O_2^-$)
bromide ($Br^-$)
chlorate ($ClO_3^-$)
chloride ($Cl^-$)
cyanide ($CN^-$)
dihydrogen phosphate ($H_2PO_4^-$)
fluoride ($F^-$)
hydride ($H^-$)
hydrogen carbonate or
  bicarbonate ($HCO_3^-$)

hydrogen sulfite or bisulfite ($HSO_3^-$)
hydroxide ($OH^-$)
iodide ($I^-$)
nitrate ($NO_3^-$)
nitrite ($NO_2^-$)
perchlorate ($ClO_4^-$)
permanganate ($MnO_4^-$)
thiocyanate ($SCN^-$)

**2−**

carbonate ($CO_3^{2-}$)
chromate ($CrO_4^{2-}$)
dichromate ($Cr_2O_7^{2-}$)
hydrogen phosphate ($HPO_4^{2-}$)
oxide ($O^{2-}$)
peroxide ($O_2^{2-}$)
sulfate ($SO_4^{2-}$)
sulfide ($S^{2-}$)
sulfite ($SO_3^{2-}$)

**3−**

arsenate ($AsO_4^{3-}$)
phosphate ($PO_4^{3-}$)

# Fundamental Constants*

| | | |
|---|---|---|
| Atomic mass unit | 1 amu | $= 1.660538782 \times 10^{-27}$ kg |
| | 1 g | $= 6.02214179 \times 10^{23}$ amu |
| Avogadro's number | $N_A$ | $= 6.02214179 \times 10^{23}$/mol |
| Boltzmann's constant | $k$ | $= 1.3806504 \times 10^{-23}$ J/K |
| Electron charge | $e$ | $= 1.602176487 \times 10^{-19}$ C |
| Faraday's constant | $F$ | $= 9.64853399 \times 10^4$ C/mol |
| Gas constant | $R$ | $= 0.082058205$ L-atm/mol-K |
| | | $= 8.314472$ J/mol-K |
| Mass of electron | $m_e$ | $= 5.48579909 \times 10^{-4}$ amu |
| | | $= 9.10938215 \times 10^{-31}$ kg |
| Mass of neutron | $m_n$ | $= 1.008664916$ amu |
| | | $= 1.674927211 \times 10^{-27}$ kg |
| Mass of proton | $m_p$ | $= 1.007276467$ amu |
| | | $= 1.672621637 \times 10^{-27}$ kg |
| Pi | $\pi$ | $= 3.1415927$ |
| Planck's constant | $h$ | $= 6.62606896 \times 10^{-34}$ J-s |
| Speed of light in vacuum | $c$ | $= 2.99792458 \times 10^8$ m/s |

*Fundamental constants are listed at the National Institute of Standards and Technology Web site:
http://www.nist.gov/physlab/data/physicalconst.cfm